# Glencoe Science

# CHEMISTRY
## MATTER AND CHANGE

## FEATURES AND BENEFITS

| Feature | Benefit | Sample Pages |
|---|---|---|
| **Dynamic Instructional Strategies** | **...accommodate students of all ability levels.** | |
| | ■ *Differentiated Instruction* strategies help meet the needs of all learning disabled students | **54D** |
| | ■ *Gifted* activities provide opportunities for gifted students to use more complex thinking skills | **61** |
| | ■ *Cultural Diversity* connections allow teachers show successful scientists from diverse ethnic backgrounds, allowing students to understand how people from different cultures approach and solve problems | **581** |
| **Integrated Math Support** | **...reinforces students' math and problem-solving skills.** | |
| | ■ *Example Problems, Practice Problems,* and *Mastering Problems* provide problem-solving practice | **42, 104, 346** |
| | ■ *Supplemental Problems* provide additional practice for students | **871-886** |
| | ■ *Math in Chemistry* reviews important math concepts at point of use | **576** |
| | ■ The *Math Handbook* reinforces the math skills needed to solve chemistry problems | **887-911** |
| **Variety of Labs and Demos** | **...get students excited about being involved in chemistry.** | |
| | ■ Each chapter in the Student Edition includes a *Discovery Lab,* a *Problem-Solving Lab,* a *MiniLab,* a *ChemLab,* and a *Try at Home Lab.* | **117, 390, 539, 654, 952-965** |
| | ■ The Teacher Wraparound Edition provides more hands-on activities such as *Demonstrations* and *Quick Demos* | **136-137, 459** |
| | ■ The *Laboratory Manual, ChemLab and MiniLab Worksheets, Small-Scale Lab Manual,* and *Forensics Lab Manual* provide additional opportunities to practice laboratory techniques | **18T-19T** |
| **Teacher Resources** | **...provide innovative strategies to help new and experienced teachers.** | |
| | ■ *Resource Manager* helps teachers reduce preparation time and add variety and interest to the classroom presentation | **295, 425** |
| | ■ *Assessment Planner* summarizes assessment options for each chapter and provides techniques teachers can use to evaluate students' understanding | |
| | ■ *Standardized Test Practice* includes test-taking tips, strategies, and practice | |
| **Online Resources** | **...enrich the learning experience with the click of a mouse.** | |
| | ■ Link to chemistrymc.com for the *Problem of the Week, Teacher Forum, Safety Links,* and *Chemistry in the News* | **25T** |
| | ■ Students can build vocabulary through word scrambles, word jumbles, and crosswords at chemistrymc.com/vocabulary_puzzlemaker | **TK** |
| **Meeting the Needs of all Students** | **...facilitates understanding of chemistry concepts for students of all learning levels.** | |
| | ■ *Identifying Misconceptions* helps teachers identify student misconceptions and provides strategies to replace the misconceptions with correct information | **703** |
| | ■ The *English/Spanish glossary,* also in the Student Edition, helps English-language learners comprehend chemistry terms | **965–988** |
| | ■ Engaging narrative relates chemistry to students' lives and the world around them | |
| **Technology** | **...provides time-saving products to help teachers creatively engage their students.** | |
| | ■ Easy-to-edit *Interactive Chalkboard* Microsoft® PowerPoint® CD-ROM presentations include step-by-step lessons, an image bank, transparencies, animations, video, and audio | **25T** |
| | ■ *ExamView® Pro Testmaker* CD-ROM allows teachers to quickly create tests for the desired difficulty level | **TK** |
| | ■ *TeacherWorks™* CD-ROM is a teacher's all-in-one resource center that helps plan and organize lessons | |

SO-BRR-296

# SAFETY SYMBOLS

| SAFETY SYMBOLS | HAZARD | EXAMPLES | PRECAUTION | REMEDY |
|---|---|---|---|---|
| DISPOSAL | Special disposal procedures need to be followed. | certain chemicals, living organisms | Do not dispose of these materials in the sink or trash can. | Dispose of wastes as directed by your teacher. |
| BIOLOGICAL | Organisms or other biological materials that might be harmful to humans | bacteria, fungi, blood, unpreserved tissues, plant materials | Avoid skin contact with these materials. Wear mask or gloves. | Notify your teacher if you suspect contact with material. Wash hands thoroughly. |
| EXTREME TEMPERATURE | Objects that can burn skin by being too cold or too hot | boiling liquids, hot plates, dry ice, liquid nitrogen | Use proper protection when handling. | Go to your teacher for first aid. |
| SHARP OBJECT | Use of tools or glassware that can easily puncture or slice skin | razor blades, pins, scalpels, pointed tools, dissecting probes, broken glass | Practice common-sense behavior and follow guidelines for use of the tool. | Go to your teacher for first aid. |
| FUME | Possible danger to respiratory tract from fumes | ammonia, acetone, nail polish remover, heated sulfur, moth balls | Make sure there is good ventilation. Never smell fumes directly. Wear a mask. | Leave foul area and notify your teacher immediately. |
| ELECTRICAL | Possible danger from electrical shock or burn | improper grounding, liquid spills, short circuits, exposed wires | Double-check setup with teacher. Check condition of wires and apparatus. | Do not attempt to fix electrical problems. Notify your teacher immediately. |
| IRRITANT | Substances that can irritate the skin or mucous membranes of the respiratory tract | pollen, moth balls, steel wool, fiberglass, potassium permanganate | Wear dust mask and gloves. Practice extra care when handling these materials. | Go to your teacher for first aid. |
| CHEMICAL | Chemicals that can react with and destroy tissue and other materials | bleaches such as hydrogen peroxide; acids such as sulfuric acid, hydrochloric acid; bases such as ammonia, sodium hydroxide | Wear goggles, gloves, and an apron. | Immediately flush the affected area with water and notify your teacher. |
| TOXIC | Substance may be poisonous if touched, inhaled, or swallowed | mercury, many metal compounds, iodine, poinsettia plant parts | Follow your teacher's instructions. | Always wash hands thoroughly after use. Go to your teacher for first aid. |
| OPEN FLAME | Open flame may ignite flammable chemicals, loose clothing, or hair | alcohol, kerosene, potassium permanganate, hair, clothing | Tie back hair. Avoid wearing loose clothing. Avoid open flames when using flammable chemicals. Be aware of locations of fire safety equipment. | Notify your teacher immediately. Use fire safety equipment if applicable. |

**Eye Safety** Proper eye protection should be worn at all times by anyone performing or observing science activities.

**Clothing Protection** This symbol appears when substances could stain or burn clothing.

**Radioactivity** This symbol appears when radioactive materials are used.

**Handwashing** After the lab, wash hands with soap and water before removing goggles.

Glencoe Science · **Indiana**

# CHEMISTRY
## MATTER AND CHANGE

Indiana Dunes State Park

Mc Graw Hill **Glencoe**

New York, New York    Columbus, Ohio    Chicago, Illinois    Peoria, Illinois    Woodland Hills, California

ISBN: 0-07-866420-9 *(Indiana Teacher Wraparound Edition)*

## Contents

Cox Ford covered bridge in Turkey Run State Park

# Indiana Teacher Advisory Board

The Indiana Teacher Advisory Board gave the editorial staff feedback on the content of the Student Edition. They provided valuable input in the development of the 2005 edition of *Chemistry: Matter and Change.*

# The Glencoe Formula

**for successfully mastering Indiana's Academic Standards for Chemistry.**

## Learning + Practicing = *Success!*

**Learning**

### Chapter Opener

- Each chapter opener lists the concepts that students will learn in that chapter.

### Section Opener

- Each section opener lists the objectives that students will learn in that section.

**What You'll Learn**

▶ You will write mole ratios from balanced chemical equations.

▶ You will calculate the number of moles and the mass of a reactant or product when given the

**Why It's Important**

The cost of the things you buy is lower because chemists use stoichiometric calculations to increase efficiency in laboratories, decrease waste in manufacturing, and prod

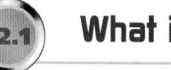

**Section** 12.1

## What is stoichiometry?

### Objectives

- **Identify** the quantitative relationships in a balanced chemical equation.

- **Determine** the mole ratios from a balanced chemical equation.

### Vocabulary

stoichiometry
mole ratio

Were you surprised when, in doing the **DISCOVERY LAB,** you saw the purple color of potassium permanganate disappear as you added sodium hydrogen sulfite? If you concluded that the potassium permanganate had been used up and the reaction had stopped, you are right. The photo on the opposite page shows the combustion of a candle using the oxygen in the surrounding air. What would happen if a bell jar was lowered over the burning candle blocking off the supply of oxygen? You know that oxygen is needed for the combustion of candle wax, so when the oxygen inside the bell jar is used up, the candle will go out.

Chemical reactions, such as the reaction of potassium permanganate with sodium hydrogen sulfite and the combustion of a candle, stop when one of the reactants is used up. Thus, in pl___ing the ___ on of ___

Indiana State Capitol Building

**Standardized Test Practice**

A full page of questions in each chapter helps students prepare for the Core 40 End-of-Course Assessment for Chemistry.

# Test–Taking Tips

✓ Go to bed early the night before the test. You will think more clearly after a good night's rest.

✓ Read each problem carefully, underline key words, and think about ways to solve the problem before answering the question.

✓ Relax. It's natural to be nervous when taking a test. Just do your best.

✓ Try to answer each question in order. If you are unsure of an answer, mark your best guess and then mark the question in your test booklet. This will be a reminder to come back to the question at the end of the test.

✓ Think positively. Some problems may seem hard to you, but you may be able to figure out what to do if you read each question carefully.

✓ If no figure is provided, draw one. If one is furnished, mark it up to help you solve the problem.

✓ When you have finished each problem, reread it to make sure your answer is complete and reasonable.

✓ Make sure that the number of the question on the answer sheet matches the number of the question on which you are working in your test booklet.

# Indiana's Academic Standards Overview

*Indiana's Academic Standards for Chemistry contain two Standards, The Principles of Chemistry and Historical Perspectives of Chemistry. Ideas listed underneath each Standard build the framework for the Chemistry course.*

*In addition, ideas from the following four supporting themes will enable students to understand that science, mathematics, and technology are interdependent human enterprises, and that scientific knowledge and scientific thinking serve both individual and community purposes.*

## Standard 1 THE NATURE OF SCIENCE AND TECHNOLOGY

It is the union of science and technology that forms the scientific endeavor and that makes it so successful. Although each of these human enterprises has a character and history of its own, each is dependent on and reinforces the other. This first theme draws portraits of science and technology that emphasize their roles in the scientific endeavor and reveal some of the similarities and connections between them. In order for students to truly understand the nature of science and technology, they must model the process of scientific investigation through inquiries, fieldwork, lab work, etc. Through these experiences, students will practice designing investigations and experiments, making observations, and formulating theories based on evidence.

## Standard 2 SCIENTIFIC THINKING

There are certain thinking skills associated with science, mathematics, and technology that young people need to develop during their school years. These are mostly, but not exclusively, mathematical and logical skills that are essential tools for both formal and informal learning and for a lifetime of participation in society as a whole. Good communication is also essential in order to both receive and disseminate information and to understand others' ideas as well as have one's own ideas understood. Writing, in the form of journals, essays, lab reports, procedural summaries, etc., should be an integral component of students' experiences in Chemistry I.

## Standard 3 THE MATHEMATICAL WORLD

Mathematics is essentially a process of thinking that involves building and applying abstract, logically connected networks of ideas. These ideas often arise from the need to solve problems in science, technology, and everyday life—problems ranging from how to model certain aspects of a complex scientific problem to how to balance a checkbook. Students should apply mathematics in scientific contexts and understand that mathematics is a tool used in science to help solve problems, make decisions, and understand the world around them.

## Standard 4 COMMON THEMES

Some important themes, such as systems, models, constancy, and change, pervade science, mathematics, and technology and appear over and over again, whether we are looking at ancient civilization, the human body, or a comet. These ideas transcend disciplinary boundaries and prove fruitful in explanation, in theory, in observation, and in design. These themes provide students with opportunities to engage in long-term and on-going laboratory and fieldwork and to understand the role of change over time in studying concepts in Chemistry I.

# Indiana's Academic Standards Expanded and Correlated to *Chemistry: Matter and Change*

This correlation "expands," or breaks down, each standard into its components. The page numbers of text, activities, and assessment that address each component are listed. Some standards do not require expanding.

under teaching: T—instructive illustration, diagram, or table,
under activities: R—feature of interest that may extend the curriculum, P—solved problem, L—laboratory activity, PL—problem-solving lab

| Academic Standards | Student Edition Pages |
|---|---|

## Standard 1    PRINCIPLES OF CHEMISTRY

*Students begin to conceptualize the general structure of the atom and the roles played by the main parts of the atom in determining the properties of materials. They investigate, through such methods as laboratory work, the nature of chemical changes and the role of energy in those changes.*

### Properties of Matter

| | | Text | Activities | Assessment |
|---|---|---|---|---|
| C.1.1 | Differentiate between pure substances and mixtures based on physical properties such as density, melting point, boiling point, and solubility. | 27–29, 54–69, 151, 155, 158, 292–294, 303, 386–387, 399–400, 404–406, 408–409, 454, 455, 457, 472, 476–479, 578, 620–621 | 15L, 25L, 28L, 29L, 46–47L, 55L, 60R, 68L, 170–171L, 241L, 268–269L, 294P, 386–387L, 396L, 410–411L, 476–477L, 480–481L | 60, 69, 82–85, 409, 479, 484–487 |
| expanded standard | Density | 27–28, 49, 54–57, 66–69, 151, 155, 158, 386–387, 399–400 | 25L, 28L, 29P, 46–47L, 48R, 385L | 60, 69, 82 |
| | Melting point | 54–57, 404–405, 408–409 | | 60, 69, 82–85, 409 |
| | Boiling point | 54–57, 405–406, 408–409 | 410–411L | 60, 69, 82–85, 409 |
| | Solubility | 54–57, 66–69, 292–294, 303, 577–585, 620–621 | 68L, 241L, 268–269L, 294P, 295L | 23, 60, 69, 82–85, 294 |
| C.1.2 | Determine the properties and quantities of matter such as mass, volume, temperature, density, melting point, boiling point, conductivity, solubility, color, numbers of moles, and pH (calculate pH from the hydrogen-ion concentration), and designate these properties as either extensive or intensive. | 27–29, 54–69, 151, 155, 158, 173, 292, 303, 386–387, 396–413, 454, 455, 457, 472, 578, 619T, 619–621 | 15L, 18–19L, 25L, 28L, 29L, 46–47L, 55L, 60R, 68L, 170–171L, 234R, 241L, 386–387L, 396L, 401L, 410–411, 412R | 60, 82–85, 174–177, 304, 306–307, 403, 409, 414–417 |
| expanded standard | Mass | 8 | 18–19L | 60, 82 |
| | Volume | 27 | | 60, 82 |
| | Temperature | 386, 413 | 18–19L | 414 |
| | Density | 27–28, 49, 54–57, 151, 155, 158, 386–387, 399–400 | 25L, 28L, 29P, 46–47L, 48R, 385L | 29, 30, 50–52, 60, 82 |
| | Melting point | 54–57, 151, 155, 158, 404–405, 408–409, 413 | 155PL | 60, 82, 158, 174 |
| | Boiling point | 54–57, 151, 155, 158, 405–406, 408–409, 413 | 155PL | 60, 82, 158, 174, 415 |
| | Conductivity | 155, 158 | | 158, 174 |
| | Solubility | 292, 303, 457, 577–585 | 241L | 23, 60, 82, 306–307 |
| | Color | 54–58, 572, 619–621 | 15L, 170–171L, 234R, 480–481L | 60, 82, 630 |
| | Number of moles | 308–327, 345 | 309L, 312P, 314PL, 315P, 316P, 321P, 323P, 324P, 325P | 311, 312, 316, 321, 323, 326, 327, 346–349 |

| Academic Standards | | Student Edition Pages | | |
|---|---|---|---|---|
| | | Text | Activities | Assessment |
| expanded standard | pH | 608–625, 629 | 609P, 610P, 612P, 613P, 615P | 609, 611, 612, 614, 616, 630–633 |
| | Extensive/intensive | 56 | | 82 |
| C.1.3 | Recognize indicators of chemical changes such as temperature change, the production of a gas, the production of a precipitate, or a color change. | 62–65, 276–283, 285, 287, 292–294, 296–299, 303, 577–585 | 170–171L, 277L, 294P, 295L, 299P, 300–301L, 302R, 353L, 583R | 65, 283, 294, 299, 304–307, 583, 585, 590–593 |
| expanded standard | Temperature change | 62–63, 277, 279 | | 65, 283 |
| | Production of gas | 278, 296–299 | 299P, 300–301L | 283, 299 |
| | Production of precipitate | 278, 287, 292–294, 303, 577–585 | 294P, 295L, 579P, 580P, 583R | 283, 299, 580, 581, 583, 585 |
| | Color change | 62–63, 276, 278, 287 | 277L, 353L | 60, 283 |
| C.1.4 | Describe solutions in terms of their degree of saturation. | 458–459, 483 | | 461, 463, 464, 465, 466, 468, 469, 470, 484–487 |
| C.1.5 | Describe solutions in appropriate concentration units (be able to calculate these units) such as molarity, percent by mass or volume, parts per million (ppm), or parts per billion (ppb). | 462–470, 462T, 483 | 463P, 464P, 468P, 469P, 480–481L, 465P | 463, 464, 465, 466, 468, 469, 470, 484–487, 866, 867 |
| expanded standard | Molarity | 464–468, 483 | 465P, 468P | 465, 466, 468, 470, 484–487, 866 |
| | Percent by mass | 463, 483 | 463P | 463, 470, 484–487, 867 |
| | Percent by volume | 464, 483 | 464, 470, 484–487 | |
| C.1.6 | Predict formulas of stable ionic compounds based on charge balance of stable ions. | 210–225, 235 | 217P, 219P, 223P, 225P, 232–233L | 214, 217, 224, 225, 226, 227, 236–239 |
| C.1.7 | Use appropriate nomenclature when naming compounds. | 225–227, 248–251, 603T, 605T, 221–227, 248–251, 603T, 605T, 700T, 701–705, 702T, 706–708, 711T, 712–713, 715T, 724, 731, 738T, 739, 744–752, 754–758, 763T, 769 | 223P, 225P, 248P, 704P 707P, 713P | 224, 225, 226, 227, 249, 250, 251, 272–275, 704, 705, 708, 710, 714, 716, 732–735, 740, 742, 746, 760, 765, 770–773, 874 |
| C.1.8 | Use formulas and laboratory investigations to classify substances as metal or nonmetal, ionic or molecular, acid or base, and organic or inorganic. | 154–158, 156–157T, 159–162(spdf), 173, 178–205 (ch7 goes in-depth on this objective), 211–232, 235, 240–249, (ionic/molec), 594–601, 697–698, 731 | 155PL, 162P(spdf), 170–171L, 595L | 82–83, 158, 162(spdf), 174–177, 206–209, 214, 217, 220, 236–239, 247, 249, 272–275, 599, 601, 630–633, 705, 732, 780 |
| expanded standard | Metal or nonmetal | 154–162, 173 | 162P, 170–171L | 158, 162, 174–177 |
| | Ionic or molecular | 211–232, 235, 240–249, 271 | 217P, 248–249P | 214, 217, 220, 236–239, 247, 249, 272–275 |
| | Acid or base | 250, 594–601, 629 | 595L | 250, 251, 601, 630–633 |
| | Organic or inorganic | 697–698, 731 | | 705, 732, 780 |
| **The Nature of Chemical Change** | | | | |
| C.1.9 | Describe chemical reactions with balanced chemical equations. | 63–65, 81, 276–299, 278T, 290T, 291T, 303, 352–373, 377, 354T, 440–443, 447, 498–501, 506–516, 532, 534–536, 548–549, 555–557, 559–585, 590–593, 596–604, 605–608, 614–615, 617–618, 620–625, 629, 635–640, 643–649, 654–655, 658–661, 663–664, 666–678, 667T, 680, 684–687, 742, 752, 754–760, 776, 785, 793, 808–809, 811–816, 820, 822, 826, 828, 843–845, 847–849, 854, 861 | 64P, 282P, 289P, 294P, 295L, 296P, 299P, 300–301L, 353L, 355P, 359P, 374–375L, 361P, 362L, 367P, 371P, 376R, 441P, 442P, 504P, 586–587L, 604L, 624L, 626L, 628R, 670P, 688–689L, 728–729L, 796–797L, 813P, 816P | 65, 82–85, 279, 282, 283, 285, 286, 289, 291, 294, 296, 299, 304–307, 378–383, 356, 357, 359, 362, 363, 368, 369, 373, 441, 443, 468, 505, 617, 622, 625, 630–632, 671, 672, 693–694, 772, 787, 814, 837–839, 849, 795, 802–803, 836–839, 867–869 |

| Academic Standards | | Student Edition Pages | | |
|---|---|---|---|---|
| | | Text | Activities | Assessment |
| C.1.10 | Recognize and classify reactions of various types such as oxidation-reduction. | 235, 284–299, 657T, 741, 742, 750, 752–760, 762–764, 776, 785, 792, 794, 795, 808, 811, 812, 815, 835, 847, 849 | 288L, 289P, 786L, 805L | 285, 286, 289, 291, 753, 760, 765, 802, 809, 836 |
| C.1.11 | Predict products of simple reaction types including acid/base, electron transfer, and precipitation. | 215–217, 235, 284–299, 657T, 741, 742, 750, 752–760, 762–764, 776, 785, 792, 794, 795, 808, 811, 812, 815, 835, 847, 849 | 78–79L, 202–203L, 217P, 223P, 225P, 232–233L, 288L, 289P, 294P, 295L, 586–587L, 786L, 805L | 217, 224, 225, 236–239, 285, 286, 289, 291, 299, 304–307, 753, 760(org), 765, 787(org), 802, 809, 836, 837–839(nuc) |
| expanded standard | Acid/base | 295 | 296P | 296 |
| | Electron transfer | 215–217, 235, 284–291, 296–299 | 217P, 223P, 225P, 232–233L, 289P | 217, 224, 225, 236–239, 285, 286, 289, 291 |
| | Precipitation | 292–294 | 294P, 295L | 294 |
| C.1.12 | Demonstrate the principle of conservation of mass through laboratory investigations. | 63–65 | 232–233L, 355P, 362L, 728–729L | 65, 356 |
| C.1.13 | Use the principle of conservation of mass to make calculations related to chemical reactions. Calculate the masses of reactants and products in a chemical reaction from the mass of one of the reactants or products and the relevant atomic masses. | 63–65, 81, 352–373, 377, 354T, 363T, 440–443 | 64P, 355P, 359P, 360P, 361P, 362L, 367P, 371P, 374–375L | 65, 82–83, 356, 357, 359, 362, 363, 368, 369, 373, 378–383, 441, 443 |
| expanded standard | Calculate the masses of reactants and products in a chemical reaction from the mass of one of the reactants or products and the relevant atomic masses. | 352–373, 377, 440–443 | 355P, 359P, 360P, 361P, 362L, 367P, 374–375L, 441P, 442 | 356, 357, 359, 362, 363, 368, 369, 373, 378–383, 441, 443 |
| C.1.14 | Use Avogadro's law to make mass-volume calculations for simple chemical reactions. | 428–433 | 429P, 431P, 432P | 430, 432, 433, 448–451 |
| C.1.15 | Given a chemical equation, calculate the mass, gas volume, and/or number of moles needed to produce a given gas volume, mass, and/or number of moles of product. | 63–65, 81, 352–373, 377, 354T, 363T, 440–443, 447, 498–501, 605–608, 614–615, 617–618, 620–625, 629 | 64P, 353L, 355P, 359P, 360P, 361P, 362L, 367P, 371P, 374–375L, 376R, 441P, 442P, 444–445L, 504P, 604L, 624L, 626–627L, 628R, 728–729L | 65, 82–83, 378–383, 356, 357, 359, 362, 363, 368, 369, 373, 441, 443, 468, 630–632, 795, 802–803, 867–879 |
| C.1.16 | Calculate the percent composition by mass of a compound or mixture when given the formula. | 328–337, 339–341, 345 | 329R, 336P, 340P, 329L, 330P, 332P, 334P, 342–343L, 344R | 83, 331, 333, 335, 337, 341, 340, 346–351 |
| C.1.17 | Perform calculations that demonstrate an understanding of the relationship between molarity, volume, and number of moles of a solute in a solution. | 464–470, 466T, 467T, 483, 620–621, 620T | 465P, 468P, 469P, 480–481L | 465, 466, 468, 469, 470, 484–487, 616, 621 |
| C.1.18 | Prepare a specified volume of a solution of given molarity. | 464–479, 466T, 467T, 483, 620–621, 620T | 465P, 468P, 469P, 480–481L | 465, 466, 468, 469, 470, 484–487, 621 |
| C.1.19 | Use titration data to calculate the concentration of an unknown solution. | 618–625, 624T, 629 | 604L, 609P, 610P, 624L, 626–627L, 628R | 601, 605, 606, 607, 609, 611, 616, 621, 622, 625, 630–633 |
| C.1.20 | Predict how a reaction rate will be quantitatively affected by changes of conc. | 528–531, 553 | 473L freezing point depression, 531P | 531, 535, 541, 554–557 |
| C.1.21 | Predict how changes in temperature, surface area, and the use of catalysts will qualitatively affect the rate of a reaction. | 532–535(theory), 536–541, 538T, 553 | 533PL, 539L, 550–551L, 552R | 535, 541, 554–557 |

| Academic Standards | | Student Edition Pages | | |
|---|---|---|---|---|
| | | **Text** | **Activities** | **Assessment** |
| expanded standard | Temperature | 538, 553 | 533PL, 539L | 541, 554–555 |
| | Surface area | 537–538, 553 | | 541, 554–555, 557 |
| | Catalysts | 539–541, 553 | | 541, 554–555, 557 |
| C.1.22 | Use oxidation states to recognize electron transfer reactions and identify the substance(s) losing and gaining electrons in an electron transfer reaction. | 634–653, 644T, 651T, 657, 663, 666–678, 667T, 680, 684–687 | 217P, 640P, 642P, 645P, 647PL, 648P, 652P, 654–655L, 688–689L | 640, 642, 643, 646, 649, 653, 658–661, 692–695 |
| C.1.23 | Write a rate law for a chemical equation using experimental data. | 529–531, 542–545, instantaneous rates 546–547, 553 | 531P, 547P, 550–551L | 531, 535, 545, 547, 549, 554–557 |
| C.1.24 | Recognize and describe nuclear changes. | 105–107, 111, 180, 804–831, 805T, 807T, 811T, 812T, 825T, 835 | 805L, 813P, 816P, 818P, 819L, 830PL, 832–833L, 834R | 107, 112–115, 809, 814, 816, 819, 820, 826, 831, 836–839 |
| C.1.25 | Recognize the importance of chemical processes in industrial and laboratory settings, e.g., electroplating, electrolysis, the operation of voltaic cells, and such important applications as the refining of aluminum. | 4–15, 17, 20–21, 56–57, 60, 62–65, 80, 91, 110, 121–123, 129, 155, 159, 160, 162, 172, 178–180, 182–196, 199–201, 204–205, 210, 226, 240, 247, 253, 255, 262, 264–267, 278, 281, 282, 285–286, 289, 294, 296, 289, 299, 312, 315, 317–318, 321, 323–324, 328–330, 333, 335, 336, 338, 352, 355, 366, 384, 386, 389, 390–403, 407, 408, 418, 423, 426–428, 430, 432–435, 441, 442, 452, 454, 456–457, 459–460, 462–465, 475, 477, 490–495, 498–499, 501–503, 507, 508, 510, 511, 513, 517, 528, 535, 541, 558, 559, 564, 566, 569, 574–575, 577–580, 582, 594, 597, 599–600, 605, 610, 612–613, 615, 622–625, 634, 637, 639, 642, 645, 652, 662, 670, 673, 673–691, 696–698, 700, 700–703, 707, 709, 714, 716, 723–727, 731, 736–737, 741–746, 748–752, 754–755, 758–759, 761–765, 769, 794–795, 804, 808, 809, 815, 818, 820, 824–831, 835, 840, 846–849, 851–854, 857, 865 | 412R, 424R, 446R, 473L, 478PL, 482R, 522R, 552R, 583PL, 588R, 595L, 609P, 624PL, 628R, 638L, 647PL, 656R, 663L, 681L, 688–689L, 690R, 697L, 728–729L, 730R, 768R, 786L, 798R, 805R, 830PL, 834R, 841L, 848L, 862–863L, 864R | 414, 416, 427, 433, 448–451, 470, 485, 486, 495, 519, 526, 541, 556, 592, 632, 649, 660, 682, 687, 692–695, 727, 732–734, 746, 765, 770–772, 795, 802, 826, 831, 836–839, 849, 854, 866–869 |
| expanded standard | Electroplating | 687, 691 | | 687, 692–695 |
| | Electrolysis | 683–687, 691 | | 687, 692–695 |
| | Voltaic cells | 662–672, 691 | 663L, 670P, 688–689L | 671, 672, 687, 692–695 |
| | Aluminum refining | 685–687 | | 687 |
| **The Structure of Matter** | | | | |
| C.1.26 | Describe physical changes and properties of matter through sketches and descriptions of the involved materials. | 8, 54–60, 66–69, 72–73T, 94–97, 100, 103, 106, 119, 120, 123, 128, 131–133, 137, 151, 155, 158, 163, 166, 188, 199, 213–214, 216, 217, 228–229, 242–246, 252–262, 260T, 265, 267, 270, 287, 292–293, 310, 313, 314, 319, 320, 325, 327, 363, 364, 386–389, 391–409, 420–421, 423, 430, 436, 440, 455–460, 467, 471–472, 476–479, 478, 515, 516, 561–562, 565, 571, 603, 615, 708–709, 725, 807–808, 817, 825, 827, 829, 844–846, 849, 850, 852, 854, 858, 860, 861, 914–916, 920, 921, 959 | 25L, 46–47L, 55L, 60PL, 68L, 108–109L, 110R, 144R, 170–170L, 172R, 204R, 257P, 268–269L, 401L, 476–477L, 480–481L, 522R, 552R, 768R | 60, 65, 69, 82–85, 97, 112, 146–149, 174–176, 236–239, 247, 258, 262, 267, 392, 395, 403, 409, 414, 461, 479, 484–487, 837–838 |

| Academic Standards | | Student Edition Pages | | |
|---|---|---|---|---|
| | | **Text** | **Activities** | **Assessment** |
| C.1.27 | Describe chemical changes and reactions using sketches and descriptions of the reactants and products. | 5, 13, 62–63, 90, 243, 276–285, 287, 292–293, 295–299, 303, 365, 532–534, 561, 571, 581–582, 599–601, 603, 608, 618, 628, 636, 650, 664–666, 668, 678, 680, 682, 698–701, 704, 708, 713–725, 727, 737–765, 776–793, 812, 815, 822–823, 844–845, 849 | 78–79L, 376R, 552R, 583PL, 864R | 82, 660, 705, 716, 721, 732–735, 742, 746, 753, 770–773, 780, 783, 787, 791, 800–802, 836–838 |
| C.1.28 | Explain that chemical bonds between atoms in molecules such as $H_2$, $CH_4$, $NH_3$, $C_2H_4$, $N_2$, $Cl_2$, and many large biological molecules are covalent. | 240–247, 391, 392, 393, 394, 774–793, 799 | 241L, 244P | 244, 247, 414, 800–801 |
| C.1.29 | Describe dynamic equilibrium. | 558–589, 567T, 578T, 581T, 585T, 595–616(acid-base), 603T, 605T, 606T, 607T, 618–625, 624T, 629 | 559L, 564P, 566P, 568P, 573L, 576P, 579P, 580P, 582P, 583L, 586–587L, 588R, 604L, 609P, 610P, 624L, 626–627L, 628R | 565, 567, 568, 574, 576, 580, 581, 583, 585, 590–593, 601, 605, 606, 607, 609, 611, 616, 621, 622, 625, 630–633 |
| C.1.30 | Perform calculations that demonstrate an understanding of the gas laws. Apply the gas laws to relations between pressure, temperature, and volume of any amount of an ideal gas or any mixture of ideal gases. | 384–392, 413, 418–439, 447 | 388P, 390PL, 391P, 419L, 422P, 424R, 425P, 426P, 429P, 431P, 432P, 436P, 438P, 439L, 441P, 442P, 444–445L, 446R | 388, 392, 395, 414–417, 422, 425, 427, 430, 432, 433, 437, 438, 439, 441, 442, 448–451, 867, 878, 879 |
| expanded standard | Ideal gas | 384–392, 418–439, 447 | 388P, 390PL, 422P, 424R, 425P, 426P, 429P, 431P, 432P, 436P, 438P, 439L | 388, 414–417, 422, 425, 427, 430, 432, 433, 437, 438, 439, 441, 442, 448–451 |
| | Mixture of ideal gases | 384–392, 418–429, 447 | 388P, 391P, 422P, 424R, 425P, 426P, 429P | 388, 392, 414–417, 422, 425, 427, 448–451 |
| C.1.31 | Use kinetic molecular theory to explain changes in gas volumes, pressure, and temperature (Solve problems using $pV = nRT$). | 384–392, 413, 418–443, 421T, 435T, 447 | 390PL, 419L, 422P, 425P, 429P, 431P, 432P, 436P, 438P, 444–445L | 388, 392, 414–417, 422, 425, 427, 430, 433, 437, 438, 443, 448–451, 867, 878, 879 |
| expanded standard | Change in volume | 421–425, 428–439 | 422P, 425P, 429P, 431P, 432P, 437P, 438P, 439L, 444–445L | 422, 425, 427, 430, 433, 437, 438, 439, 448–449, 451 |
| | Change in pressure | 421–422, 426–439 | 390PL, 422P, 426P, 429P, 431P, 432P, 437P, 438P, 439L, 444–445L | 422, 427, 430, 433, 437, 438, 439, 448–449, 451 |
| | Change in temperature | 423–439 | 425P, 426P, 429P, 431P, 432P, 437P, 438P, 439L, 444–445L | 425, 427, 430, 433, 437, 438, 439, 448–449, 451 |
| C.1.32 | Describe the possible subatomic particles within an atom or ion. | 92–97, 97T, 98–107, 111, 117–145 (electrons) 810–814, 812T | 96PL, 99P, 103P, 108–109L, 110R, 117–L, 142–143–L, 144–R | 97, 99, 104, 112–115, 146–149, 814, 836–839 |
| expanded standard | Atom | 92–107, 117–145, 810–814, 812T | 96PL, 99P, 108–109L, 110R | 97, 99, 104, 112–115, 146–149, 814, 836–839 |
| | Ion | 212–220 | 217P, 219P | 214, 217, 220, 236–239 |
| C.1.33 | Use an element's location in the Periodic Table to determine its number of valence electrons, and predict what stable ion or ions an element is likely to form in reacting with other specified elements. | 159–162, 210–227, 221T, 222T | 162P, 217P, 219R, 223P, 232–233L | 162, 214, 217, 220, 224, 225, 227 |
| expanded standard | Number of valence electrons | 159–162, 173 | | 162, 174–177 |
| | Predict what stable ion or ions an element is likely to form in reacting with other specified elements. | 210–227 | 217P, 219R, 223P, 225P | 214, 217, 220, 224, 225, 226, 227 |

| Academic Standards | | Student Edition Pages | | |
|---|---|---|---|---|
| | | **Text** | **Activities** | **Assessment** |
| C.1.34 | Use the Periodic Table to compare attractions that atoms have for their electrons and explain periodic properties, such as atomic size, based on these attractions. | 154T, 154–158, 156–157T, 163–169, 173, 393T | 155PL, 164L, 165P, 170–171L | 158, 162, 165, 169, 174–177 |
| expanded standard | Use the Periodic Table to compare attractions that atoms have for their electrons. | 168–169, 173 | | 169, 174–177 |
| | Explain periodic properties, such as atomic size, based on these attractions. | 163–169, 173 | 164L, 165P | 165, 169, 174–177 |
| C.1.35 | Infer and explain physical properties of substances, such as melting points, boiling points, and solubility, based on the strength of molecular attractions. | 266, 393–409, 413, 708–709, 740–741 | 401L, 410–411L, 412R, 268–269L, 267PL, 768R | 395, 403, 409, 414–417 |
| expanded standard | Melting point | 266, 402–405, 408–409, 413, 708–709, 740–741 | | 409, 414–417 |
| | Boiling point | 266, 405–406, 408–409, 413, 708–709, 740–741 | 267PL, 410–411L | 409, 414–417 |
| | Solubility | 266, 456, 413 | 268–269L | 409, 414–417 |
| C.1.36 | Describe the nature of ionic, covalent, and hydrogen bonds and give examples of how they contribute to the formation of various types of compounds. | 215–220, 240–247, 252– 268, 271, 393–403 | 401L, 244P, 261L | 220, 244, 247, 258, 262, 266, 267, 304–307, 403, 414–417 |
| expanded standard | Ionic—nature of bonds | 215–220 | | 220 |
| | Covalent—nature of bonds | 240–247, 271 | | 244 |
| | Hydrogen—nature of bonds | 395, 413 | | 395, 414 |
| | Contribute to formation of compounds | 215–220, 243–247, 252–258, 259–268, 271 | 217P, 244P, 253P, 254P, 255P, 257P, 261L, 267PL | 244, 247, 255, 256, 258, 262, 267 |
| C.1.37 | Describe that spectral lines are the result of transitions of electrons between energy levels and that these lines correspond to photons with a frequency related to the energy spacing between levels by using Planck's relationship ($E=hv$). | 116–138, 127T, 128T, 133T, 135T, 137T, 138T, 145 | 121P, 124P, 125L, 130PL, 142–143L, 144R | 121, 124, 126, 134, 146–149 |
| expanded standard | Describe that spectral lines are the result of transitions of electrons between energy levels. | 116–120, 125–126, 145 | 125L, 142–143L, 144R | 126, 134 |
| | These lines correspond to photons with a frequency related to the energy spacing between levels by using Planck's relationship ($E=hv$). | 122–124, 127–130, 145 | 124P, 130PL | 124, 126, 134 |

## The Nature of Energy and Change

| | | | | |
|---|---|---|---|---|
| C.1.38 | Distinguish between the concepts of temperature and heat. | 490–491 | 302R | |
| C.1.39 | Solve problems involving heat flow and temperature changes, using known values of specific heat and latent heat of phase change. | 489–512, 513–519(spontaneity), 523 | 302R, 491P, 494P, 497P, 503PL, 504P, 505L, 508P, 511P, 518P(spont), 520–521L, 522R | 492, 495, 498, 500, 504, 505, 508, 512, 516(entropy), 519(entropy), 524–527, 556 |

| Academic Standards | | Student Edition Pages | | |
|---|---|---|---|---|
| | | **Text** | **Activities** | **Assessment** |
| expanded standard | Solve problems using specific heat | 492–500, 523 | 494P, 497P | 495, 498, 500 |
| | Solve problems using latent heat of phase change | 501–505, 523 | 503PL, 504P, 505L, 520–521L | 505 |
| C.1.40 | Classify chemical reactions and/or phase changes as exothermic or endothermic. | 247, 498–505, 523 | 302R, 503PL, 504P, 505L, 520–521L | 500, 505, 524–527 |
| expanded standard | Chemical reactions | 247, 498–500, 506–519, 523 | 520–521L | 519 |
| | Phase changes | 501–505, 523 | 503PL, 504P, 505L | 505 |
| C.1.41 | Describe the role of light, heat, and electrical energies in physical, chemical, and nuclear changes. | 2, 4–6, 247, 488–519, 523, 662–679, 683–687, 691, 804–809, 821–826, 829–831, 835, 850–854, 858–861, 865 | 3L, 302R, 491P, 494P, 497P, 503PL, 504P, 505L, 508P, 511P, 520–521L, 522R, 663L, 670P, 688–689L, 690R, 730R, 813P, 832–833L, 834R, 862–863L | 492, 495, 498, 500, 504, 505, 508, 512, 516(entropy), 519(entropy), 524–527, 556, 671, 672, 682, 687, 692–695, 809, 826, 836–839, 866–869 |
| expanded standard | Physical | 501–505, 523 | 503PL, 504P, 505L, 862–863L | 504, 505, 524–527 |
| | Chemical | 2, 4–6, 247, 488–500, 506–519, 523, 662–679, 683–687, 691, 850–854, 858–861 | 3L, 302R, 491P, 663L, 670P, 688–689L, 690R | 492, 495, 498, 508, 512, 671, 672, 682, 687, 692–695, 866–869 |
| | Nuclear | 2, 804–809, 821–826, 829–831, 835 | 813P, 832–833L, 834R | 809, 826, 836–839, |
| C.1.42 | Describe that the energy release per gram of material is much larger in nuclear fusion or fission reactions than in chemical reactions. The change in mass (calculated by E=$mc^2$) is small but significant in nuclear reactions. | 105–107, 111, 804–805, 805T, 821–831, 835 | 805L, 834R | 107, 112–115, 809, 826, 836–839 |
| expanded standard | Describe that the energy release per gram of material is much larger in nuclear fusion or fission reactions than in chemical reactions. | 105–107, 111, 804–805, 835 | 805L | 107, 112–115, 809, 836–839 |
| | The change in mass (calculated by E=$mc^2$) is small but significant in nuclear reactions. | 821–826, 835 | | 826, 836–839 |
| C.1.43 | Calculate the amount of radioactive substance remaining after an integral number of half-lives have passed. | 815–820, 817T, 818T, 835 | 816P, 818P, 819L, 834R | 816, 819, 820, 836–839 |
| **The Basic Structures and Reactions of Organic Chemicals** | | | | |
| C.1.44 | Convert between formulas and names of common organic compounds. | 698–705, 700T, 702T, 706–708, 711T, 712–13, 715T, 724, 731, 738T, 739, 740T, 744–52, 754–58, 763T, 769, 776–795 | 704P, 707P, 713P | 704, 705, 708, 710, 714, 716, 732–735, 740, 742, 746, 760, 765, 770–773, 780, 783, 787, 791, 800–803 |
| C.1.45 | Recognize common functional groups and polymers when given chemical formulas and names. | 702T, 700–727, 731, 737–765, 738T, 740T, 763T, 774–778, 781–782, 784–791, 793, 799 | 704P, 707P, 713P, 737L, 757PL, 766–767L, 786L, 790PL | 705, 708, 710, 714, 716, 721, 732–735, 742, 746, 753, 760, 765, 770–773, 780, 783, 787, 791, 800–803 |
| expanded standard | Functional groups | 700–727, 731, 737–760, 769, 774–795, 799 | 704P, 707P, 713P, 751L, 757PL, 766–767L, 786L, 798R | 705, 708, 710, 714, 716, 721, 727, 732–735, 742, 746, 753, 760, 770–773, 780, 787, 791 |
| | Polymers | 761–765, 769, 774–795, 799 | 737L, 790PL | 765, 770–773, 780, 787, 791 |

| Academic Standards | Student Edition Pages |
|---|---|

## Standard 2  HISTORICAL PERSPECTIVES OF CHEMISTRY

*Students gain understanding of how the scientific enterprise operates through examples of historical events. Through the study of these events, they understand that new ideas are limited by the context in which they are conceived, are often rejected by the scientific establishment, sometimes spring from unexpected findings, and grow or transform slowly through the contributions of many different investigators.*

| | | |
|---|---|---|
| C.2.1 | Explain that Antoine Lavoisier invented a whole new field of science based on a theory of materials, physical laws, and quantitative methods, with the conservation of matter at its core. Recognize that he persuaded a generation of scientists that his approach accounted for the experimental results better than other chemical systems. | 63–64, 75 |
| C.2.2 | Describe how Lavoisier's system for naming substances and describing their reactions to the rapid growth of chemistry by enabling scientists everywhere to share their findings about chemical reactions with one another without ambiguity. | 151–152, 180 |
| C.2.3 | Explain that John Dalton's modernization of the ancient Greek ideas of element, atom, compound, and molecule strengthened the new chemistry by providing physical explanations for reactions that could be expressed in quantitative terms. | 87–90, 391–392 |
| C.2.4 | Explain how Frederich Wohler's synthesis of the simple organic compound urea from inorganic substances made it clear that living organisms carry out chemical processes not fundamentally different from inorganic chemical processes. Describe how this discovery led to the development of the huge field of organic chemistry, the industries based on it, and eventually to the field of biochemistry. | 698 |
| C.2.5 | Explain how Arrhenius' discovery of the nature of ionic solutions contributed to the understanding of a broad class of chemical reactions. | 597–598 |
| C.2.6 | Explain that the appreciation of the laws of quantum mechanics to chemistry by Linus Pauling and others made possible an understanding of chemical reactions on the atomic level. | 127, 129–132, 169 |
| C.2.7 | Describe how the discovery of the structure of DNA by James D. Watson and Francis Crick made it possible to interpret the genetic code on the basis of a sequence of "letters." | 789 |

# TEACHER WRAPAROUND EDITION

Glencoe Science

# CHEMISTRY
## MATTER AND CHANGE

chemistrymc.com

Glencoe

New York, New York    Columbus, Ohio    Chicago, Illinois    Peoria, Illinois    Woodland Hills, California

**A Glencoe Program**

# Chemistry:
## Matter and Change

## Visit the Chemistry Web site at
### chemistrymc.com

**You'll find:**

Online Student Edition, Online Study
Tools, Interactive Tutor, Online Quizzes,
WebQuests, Teacher Forum, Problem of
the Week, Safety Links, Math Handbook,
Chemistry in the News, Science Fair Ideas,
Periodic Table Links

**and much more!**

Joanne Bowers, M.S. Safety Consultant
David R. McCleary, Inclusion Consultant
Lois Veath, Ph.D Misconceptions Consultant

Send all inquiries to:
Glencoe/McGraw-Hill
8787 Orion Place
Columbus, OH 43240-4027

ISBN 0-07-866420-9
Printed in the United States of America.
1 2 3 4 5 6 027/043 09 08 07 06 05 04

# CONTENTS IN BRIEF

## TEACHER WRAPAROUND EDITION

## STUDENT EDITION

# NATIONAL SCIENCE EDUCATION STANDARDS

The *National Science Education Standards,* published by the National Research Council and representing the contribution of thousands of educators and scientists, offer a comprehensive vision of a scientifically literate society. The standards not only describe what students should know but also offer guidelines for science teaching and assessment. If you are using, or plan to use, the standards to guide changes in your curriculum, you can be assured that *Chemistry: Matter and Change* aligns with the *National Science Education Standards.*

*Chemistry: Matter and Change* is an example of how Glencoe's commitment to effective science education is changing the materials used in classrooms today. More than just a collection of facts in a textbook, *Chemistry: Matter and Change* is a program that provides numerous opportunities for students, teachers, and school districts to meet the *National Science Education Standards.*

## National Science Content Standards

Correlations by numbered sections in each chapter Resource Manager and at point of use on the pages of the *Teacher Wraparound Edition* show the close alignment between *Chemistry: Matter and Change* and the content standards. Correlations are designated according to the numbering system in the table of science content standards shown on the opposite page. The approach of *Chemistry: Matter and Change* allows students to discover concepts within each of the content standards, giving them opportunities to make connections between chemistry concepts and the real world. Hands-on labs and inquiry-based lessons reinforce the science processes emphasized in the standards.

## Teaching Standards

Alignment with the *National Science Education Standards* requires much more than alignment with the outcomes in the content standards. The way in which concepts are presented is critical to effective learning. The teaching standards within the *National Science Education*

*Standards* recommend an inquiry-based program facilitated and guided by teachers. *Chemistry: Matter and Change* provides such opportunities through activities and discussions that allow students to discover critical concepts by inquiry and apply the knowledge they've gained to their own lives. Throughout the program, students are building critical skills that will be available to them for lifelong learning. The *Teacher Wraparound Edition* helps you make the most of every instructional moment. It offers an abundance of effective strategies and suggestions for guiding students as they explore chemistry.

## Assessment Standards

The assessment standards are supported by many of the components that make up the *Chemistry: Matter and Change* program. The *Teacher Wraparound Edition* and *Teacher Classroom Resources* provide multiple chances to assess students' understanding of important concepts as well as their abilities to perform a wide range of skills. Ideas for portfolios, performance assessment, written reports, and other assessment activities accompany every lesson. For more suggestions about assessment ideas and resources, see pages 30T-32T of the Teacher Guide.

## Philosophy and Themes

In *Chemistry: Matter and Change,* there is an emphasis on five themes, as adapted from the Unifying Concepts and Processes of the National Science Content Standards. These themes are: Systems, order, and organization; Evidence, models, and explanation; Change, constancy, and measurement; Evolution and equilibrium; and Form and function. Emphasis on themes contributes to the big picture by focusing learning on connections among major ideas and concepts. The thematic approach contributes to students' comprehension of fundamental chemistry processes, ability to integrate facts with concepts, and appreciation of how scientists work.

# NATIONAL SCIENCE CONTENT STANDARDS

## Unifying Concepts and Processes

**UCP.1** Systems, order, and organization
**UCP.2** Evidence, models, and explanation
**UCP.3** Change, constancy, and measurement
**UCP.4** Evolution and equilibrium
**UCP.5** Form and function

## Science as Inquiry

**A.1** Abilities necessary to do scientific inquiry
**A.2** Understandings about scientific inquiry

## Physical Science

**B.1** Structure of atoms
**B.2** Structure and properties of matter
**B.3** Chemical reactions
**B.4** Motions and forces
**B.5** Conservation of energy and increase in disorder
**B.6** Interactions of energy and matter

## Life Science

**C.1** The cell
**C.2** Molecular basis of heredity
**C.3** Biological evolution
**C.4** Interdependence of organisms
**C.5** Matter, energy, and organization in living systems
**C.6** Behavior of organisms

## Earth and Space Science

**D.1** Energy in the earth system
**D.2** Geochemical cycles
**D.3** Origin and evolution of the earth system
**D.4** Origin and evolution of the universe

## Science and Technology

**E.1** Abilities of technological design
**E.2** Understandings about science and technology

## Science in Personal and Social Perspectives

**F.1** Personal and community health
**F.2** Population growth
**F.3** Natural resources
**F.4** Environmental quality
**F.5** Natural and human-induced hazards
**F.6** Science and technology in local, national, and global challenges

## History and Nature of Science

**G.1** Science as a human endeavor
**G.2** Nature of scientific knowledge
**G.3** Historical perspectives

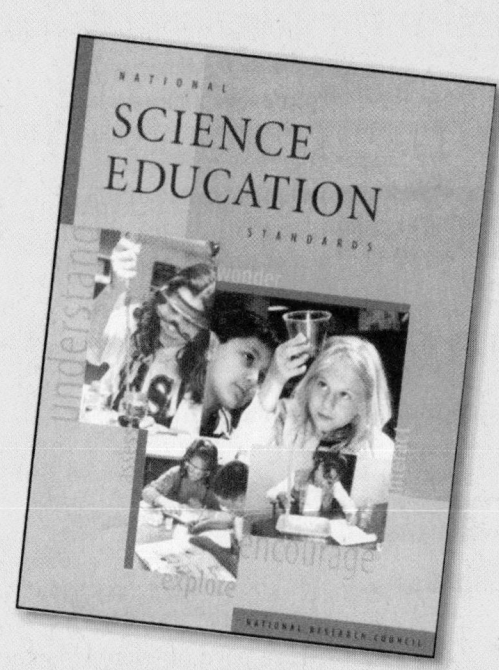

# PROGRAM RESOURCES

## PROGRAM TOUR

### STUDENT EDITION

| FEATURE | LOCATION | SUGGESTIONS FOR USE |
|---|---|---|
| ChemLab | At the end of every chapter | Assign to groups in a lab setting. Use to strengthen lab skills and understanding of scientific methods |
| miniLAB | In every chapter at the point where concept is taught | Assign to groups in a lab setting |
| Discovery Lab | At the beginning of every chapter | Introduce students to chapter concepts. Get attention with initial activity |
| problem-solving LAB | In every chapter at the point where concept is taught | Reinforce scientific methods. Allow students to evaluate data |
| Try at Home Labs | Appendix E | Expand chapter material to daily life. |
| Example Problems | At point in chapter where math skills are needed | Use to strengthen students' math skills |
| Practice Problems | With Example Problems or as independent sets of problems | Assign as homework or use in class |
| Connections | At least one in every chapter | Connects chemistry to other disciplines |
| Careers Using Chemistry | In every chapter | Use to encourage students to pursue careers in science |
| How It Works | At the end of chapter | Use to illustrate how scientific concepts make things work |
| Chemistry and Technology | At the end of chapter | Involves students in cutting-edge technological advances |
| Chemistry and Society | At the end of chapter | Helps students realize that chemistry impacts society as a whole |
| Everyday Chemistry | At the end of chapter | Expand chapter material to daily life |
| Test-Taking Tips | In the Chapter Assessment | Prepare students for taking standardized tests |
| Standardized Test Practice | Last page of every Chapter Assessment | Use as practice for standardized tests |

# GETTING STUDENTS INVOLVED

## What You'll Learn
Introduces the main concepts of the chapter before students begin to study the material.

## Why It's Important
Provides an answer to the "Why do we have to learn this?" question that students ask.

## Chemistry Online
Connects students to the resources available at chemistrymc.com. Encourages individual Internet research on science topics at home, or in class for those who finish the lesson early. Assign a different site to each student group for group reports, and use to enrich text information.

**CHAPTER 17**

# Reaction Rates

### What You'll Learn
▶ You will investigate a model describing how chemical reactions occur as a result of collisions.
▶ You will compare the rates of chemical reactions under varying conditions.
▶ You will calculate the rates of chemical reactions.

### Why It's Important
Perhaps someday you'll be involved with the space program. Rockets, along with their crews and cargo, are propelled into space by the result of a chemical reaction. An understanding of reaction rates is the tool that allows us to control chemical reactions and use them effectively.

Visit the Chemistry Web site at chemistrymc.com to find links about reaction rates.

# HANDS-ON EXPERIENCES

Working in the lab is often the most enjoyable part of chemistry. A *Discovery Lab* introduces the chapter with a quick activity. When students feel inquisitive but there's a shortage of time, assign a *MiniLab. ChemLabs* give your students an opportunity to use scientific methods that chemists use, develop their lab skills while studying a question or problem, and share their data with others. As they follow well-tested procedures, they'll have fun doing these lab activities.

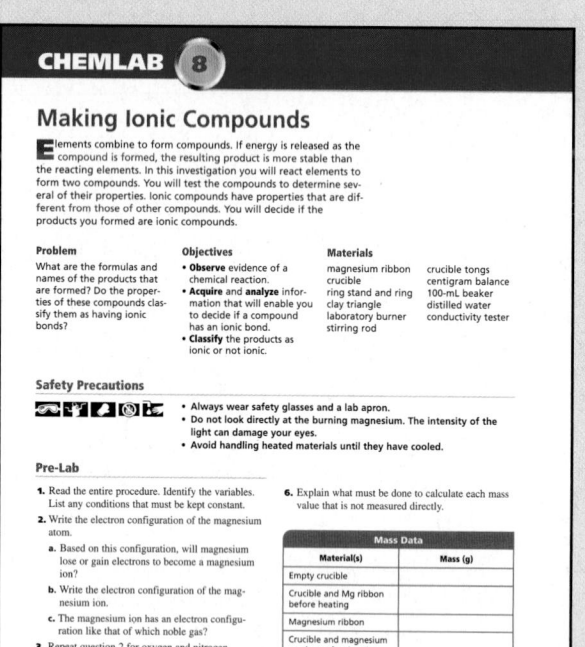

## CHEMLAB 8

### Making Ionic Compounds

**E**lements combine to form compounds. If energy is released as the compound is formed, the resulting product is more stable than the reacting elements. In this investigation you will react elements to form two compounds. You will test the compounds to determine several of their properties. Ionic compounds have properties that are different from those of other compounds. You will decide if the products you formed are ionic compounds.

**Problem**

What are the formulas and names of the products that are formed? Do the properties of these compounds classify them as having ionic bonds?

**Objectives**

• **Observe** evidence of a chemical reaction.
• **Acquire** and **analyze** information that will enable you to decide if a compound has an ionic bond.
• **Classify** the products as ionic or not ionic.

**Materials**

magnesium ribbon
crucible
ring stand and ring
clay triangle
laboratory burner
stirring rod
crucible tongs
centigram balance
100-mL beaker
distilled water
conductivity tester

**Safety Precautions**

• Always wear safety glasses and a lab apron.
• Do not look directly at the burning magnesium. The intensity of the light can damage your eyes.
• Avoid handling heated materials until they have cooled.

**Pre-Lab**

1. Read the entire procedure. Identify the variables. List any conditions that must be kept constant.
2. Write the electron configuration of the magnesium atom.
   a. Based on this configuration, will magnesium lose or gain electrons to become a magnesium ion?
   b. Write the electron configuration of the magnesium ion.
   c. The magnesium ion has an electron configuration like that of which noble gas?
3. Repeat question 2 for oxygen and nitrogen.
4. Prepare your data table.
5. In your data table, which mass values will be measured directly? Which mass values will be calculated?

6. Explain what must be done to calculate each mass value that is not measured directly.

| Mass Data | |
|---|---|
| **Material(s)** | **Mass (g)** |
| Empty crucible | |
| Crucible and Mg ribbon before heating | |
| Magnesium ribbon | |
| Crucible and magnesium products after heating | |
| Magnesium products | |

232    Chap

## ChemLab

Guide students in following the procedure steps to arrive at the answer to the lab problem. Labs can also be set up as teacher demos if time or materials are short.

### miniLAB

**Examining Reaction Rate and Temperature**

**Recognizing Cause and Effect** Several factors affect the rate of a chemical reaction. This lab allows you to examine the effect of temperature on a common chemical reaction.

**Materials** small beaker, thermometer, hot plate, 250-mL beaker, balance, water, effervescent (bicarbonate) tablet, stopwatch or clock with second hand

**Procedure**

1. Take a single effervescent tablet and break it into four roughly equal pieces.
2. Measure the mass of one piece of the tablet. Measure 50 mL of room-temperature water (approximately 20°C) into a small cup or beaker. Measure the temperature of the water.
3. With a stopwatch ready, add the piece of tablet to the water. Record the amount of time elapsed between when the tablet hits the water and when you see that all of the piece of tablet has dissolved in the water.
4. Repeat steps 2 and 3 twice more, except use water temperatures of about 50°C and 65°C. Be sure to raise the temperature gradually and maintain the desired temperature (equilibrate) throughout the run.

**Analysis**

1. Calculate the reaction rate by finding the mass/time for each run.
2. Graph the reaction rate (mass/time) versus temperature for the runs.
3. What is the relationship between reaction rate and temperature for this reaction?
4. Using your graphed data, predict the reaction rate for the reaction carried out at 40°C. Heat and equilibrate the water to 40°C and use the last piece of tablet to test your prediction.
5. How did your prediction for the reaction rate at 40°C compare to the actual reaction rate?

**Catalysts**

You've seen that increasing the temperature and/or the concentration of reactants can dramatically increase the rate of a reaction. However, an increase in temperature is not always the best (or most practical) thing to do. For example, suppose that you want to increase the rate of a reaction such as the decomposition of glucose in a living cell. Increasing the temperature and/or the concentration of reactants is not a viable alternative because it might ...uld not ...it were ...a sub- ...ing con- ...es in a ...includ- ...d in the ...he next ...The red ...ay with ...athway.

2 Factors Affecting Reaction Rates    **539**

## MiniLabs

Answers the how, what, and why about the chemical world in just a few minutes. Assign to individuals or to student pairs or groups in a lab setting. Can be used as a class demonstration.

### DISCOVERY LAB

**Speeding Reactions**

**M**any chemical reactions occur so slowly that you don't even know they are happening. For some reactions, it is possible to alter the reaction speed using another substance.

**Safety Precautions**

Always use safety goggles and an apron in the lab.

**Materials**

hydrogen peroxide
beaker or cup
baker's yeast
toothpicks

**Procedure**

1. Create a "before and after" table and record your observations.
2. Pour about 10 mL of hydrogen peroxide into a small beaker or cup. Observe the hydrogen peroxide.
3. Add a "pinch" (1/8 tsp) of yeast to the hydrogen peroxide. Stir gently with a toothpick and observe the mixture again.

**Analysis**

Into what two products does hydrogen peroxide decompose? Why aren't bubbles produced in step 1? What is the function of the yeast?

### Section 17.1 — A Model for Reaction Rates

**Objectives**

• **Calculate** average rates of chemical reactions from experimental data.
• **Relate** rates of chemical reactions to collisions between reacting particles.

**Vocabulary**

reaction rate
collision theory
activated complex
transition state
activation energy

One of the most spectacular chemical reactions, the one between liquid hydrogen and liquid oxygen, provides the energy to launch rockets into space as shown on the opposite page. This reaction is fast and exothermic. Yet other reactions and processes you're familiar with, such as the hardening of concrete or the formation of fossil fuels, occur at considerably slower rates. The DISCOVERY LAB for this chapter emphasized that the speed at which a reaction occurs can vary if other substances are introduced into the reaction. In this section, you'll learn about a model that scientists use to describe and calculate the rates at which chemical reactions occur.

**Expressing Reaction Rates**

As you know, some chemical reactions are fast and others are slow; however, *fast* and *slow* are inexact, relative terms. Chemists, engineers, medical researchers, and others often need to be more specific.

Think about how you express speed or rate in the situations shown in **Figure 17-1** on the next page. The speed of the sprinter on the track team may be expressed as meters per second. The speed at which the hiker moves might be expressed differently, perhaps as meters per minute. We generally define the average rate of an action or process to be the change in a given quantity during a specific period of time. Recall from your study of math that the Greek letter delta ($\Delta$) before a quantity indicates a change in the quantity. In equation form, average rate or speed is written as

$$\text{Average rate} = \frac{\Delta\text{quantity}}{\Delta t}$$

17.1 A Model for Reaction Rates    **529**

## Discovery Lab

Easy-to-perform activities provide an inquiry approach to introducing the chapter and get students involved right from the first page.

# VISUAL LEARNING

## How It Works

Use the *How It Works* features to give students an understanding of how scientific concepts make things work. Struggling readers or English Language Learners can use these graphic features instead of full-text information.

### How It Works
#### Catalytic Converter

Concerns for our environment have made a huge impact in the products and processes we use every day. The catalytic converter is one of those impacts.

When a combustion engine converts fuel into energy, the reactions of the combustion process are incomplete. Incomplete combustion results in the production of poisonous carbon monoxide and undesirable nitrogen oxides. Since 1975, catalytic converters have reduced the exhaust emissions that contribute to air pollution by approximately 90%.

❶ Gases from the engine and the air pass through the exhaust system to the catalytic converter. Oxygen intake into the engine at this point is critical for the reactions of the catalysts.

❷ Inside the catalytic converter is a porous ceramic structure with a surface coating of platinum and rhodium particles.

❸ In many models of catalytic converters, this inner structure resembles tubes in a honeycomb arrangement, which provides significant surface area to accommodate the catalysts.

Rhodium

Platinum

❺ At the rhodium catalyst surface, nitric oxide is converted to nitrogen and oxygen.

Nitric oxide    Nitrogen gas    Oxygen gas    Nitric oxide

Hot (500°C) rhodium particle
$2 NO \rightarrow N_2 + O_2$

Carbon monoxide    Carbon dioxide    Water    Hydrocarbon    Oxygen

Hot (500°C) platinum particle
$2 CO + O_2 \rightarrow 2 CO_2$
$C_xH_y + O_2 \rightarrow CO_2 + H_2O$

❹ At high temperatures (300–500°C) on the platinum catalyst surface, the dangerous carbon monoxide and hydrocarbons react with oxygen to form the compounds carbon dioxide and water.

Hypothesizing A catalytic converter is not effective when cold. Use the concept of activation energy to explain why.

## Figure References

Each figure and table is referenced in the text, fully integrating the text with all graphics—the ideal visual learning strategy.

Containment structure

Steam turbine (high-energy steam spins turbines and generates electricity)

Hot coolant

Steam

Control rods

Fuel elements

Carbon moderators

Reactor

Steam generator

Condenser (low-energy steam from turbines is condensed back to liquid water)

Cool coolant

Pump

Pumps

Large body of water

Cool water    Warm water

a

b

c

the reactor. The main purpose of the containment structure is to shield personnel and nearby residents from harmful radiation. The major components of a nuclear power plant are illustrated in **Figure 25-21**.

As the reactor operates, the fuel rods are gradually depleted and products from the fission reaction accumulate. Because of this, the reactor must be serviced periodically. Spent fuel rods can be reprocessed and repackaged to make new fuel rods. Some fission products, however, are extremely radioactive and cannot be used again. These products must be stored as nuclear waste. The storage of highly radioactive nuclear waste is one of the major issues surrounding the debate over the use of nuclear power. Approximately 20 half-lives are required for the radioactivity of nuclear waste materials to reach levels acceptable for biological exposure. For some types of nuclear fuels, the wastes remain substantially radioactive for thousands of years. A considerable amount of scientific research has been devoted to the disposal of radioactive wastes. How does improper disposal or storage of nuclear wastes affect the environment? Is this a short-term effect? Why?

Another issue is the limited supply of the uranium-235 used in the fuel rods. One option is to build reactors that produce new quantities of fissionable fuels. Reactors able to produce more fuel than they use are called **breeder reactors**. Although the design of breeder reactors poses many difficult technical problems, breeder reactors are in operation in several countries.

**Figure 25-21**

ⓐ The diagram illustrates the major parts of a nuclear power plant. The photos show ⓑ the submerged reactor and ⓒ the steam-driven turbines.

How does this containment structure protect the environment? What would be the effect on the environment if this structure leaked radiation?

25.4 Fission and Fusion of Atomic Nuclei    825

## Art

Visually exciting pages help students to conceptualize chemical structures and processes. The use of photographs and diagrams ensures that your students will learn and remember important chemistry concepts and their applications. Use the step-by-step diagrams to help students understand more challenging chemical processes.

# SKILL DEVELOPMENT

## Math Handbook

The labs in *Chemistry: Matter and Change* require students to collect a variety of data and display it graphically. Example Problems and Practice Problems require students to use math skills. Questions in the Section Assessment and in the Chapter Assessment provide students with another opportunity to practice the math skills relevant to the material they are studying. The *Math Handbook* provides students with review of the math skills they need to practice during these activities.

## Problem-Solving Lab

*Problem-Solving Labs* offer a unique opportunity for students to evaluate another scientist's experiments and data. These labs can be assigned as homework or class work. Use them to reinforce the steps of scientific methods.

---

**APPENDIX B Math Handbook**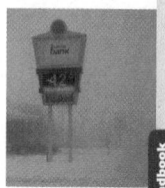

*Mathematics is a language used in science to express and solve problems. Use this handbook to review basic math skills and to reinforce some math skills presented in the chapters in more depth.*

### Arithmetic Operations

Calculations you perform during your study of chemistry require arithmetic operations, such as addition, subtraction, multiplication, and division, using numbers. Numbers can be positive or negative, as you can see in **Figure 1**. Examine the number line below. Numbers that are positive are greater than zero. A plus sign ($+$) or no sign at all indicates a positive number. Numbers that are less than zero are negative. A minus sign ($-$) indicates a negative number. Zero (the origin) is neither positive nor negative.

#### 1. Addition and subtraction

Addition is an arithmetic operation. As you can see in **Table 1**, the result of addition is called a sum. When the signs of the numbers you are adding are alike, add the numbers and keep the same sign. Use the number line below to solve for the sum $5 + 2$ in which both numbers are positive. To represent the first number, draw an arrow that starts at the origin. The arrow that represents the second number starts at the arrowhead of the first arrow. The sum is at the head of the second arrow. In this case, the sum equals the positive number seven.

$$5 + 2 = 7$$

The process of adding two negative numbers is similar to adding two positive numbers. The negative sign indicates that you must move in the direction opposite to the direction that you moved to add two positive numbers. Use the number line below to verify that the sum below equals $-7$. Notice that the sign of the resulting number when you add two negative numbers is always negative.

$$-2 - 5 = -7$$
$$-2 + (-5) = -7$$

**Figure 1**
Water freezes at 32°F and 0°C. What temperature scale do you think was used on this sign? Explain.

**Table 1**

| Arithmetic Operations | | |
|---|---|---|
| Operation | Sign | Result |
| Addition | + | Sum |
| Subtraction | − | Difference |
| Multiplication | × | Product |
| Division | ÷ | Quotient |

Math Handbook **887**

---

**Energy and the ionic bond** During any ~~...~~ absorbed or released. When energy is ab~~...~~ the reaction is endothermic. If energy is re~~...~~ see in the **CHEMLAB** at the end of this ch~~...~~ nesium reacts with oxygen.

Energy changes also occur during the ~~...~~ ions formed during a chemical reaction. ~~...~~ from positive and negative ions is always ~~...~~ positive ion for the negative ions close to ~~...~~ is lower in energy than the individual ions. If the amount of energy released during bond formation is added to an ionic compound, the bonds that hold the positive and negative ions together break.

You just learned that the ions in an ionic compound are arranged in a pattern in a crystal lattice. The energy required to separate one mole of the ions of an ionic compound is referred to as the **lattice energy.** The strength of the forces holding ions in place is reflected by the lattice energy. The more negative the lattice energy, the stronger the force of attraction.

### problem-solving LAB

**How is color related to a transferred electron?**

| Factors that Affect Color of an Ionic Compound | | | |
|---|---|---|---|
| Compound | Color | Anion radius (Å) | Visible absorption band |
| AgF | Yellow | 1.36 | Blue-violet |
| AgCl | White | 1.81 | None |
| AgBr | Cream | 1.95 | Violet |
| AgI | Yellow | 2.16 | Blue-violet |
| Ag₂S | Black | 1.84 | All |
| Al₂O₃ | White | 1.40 | None |
| Sb₂O₃ | White | 1.40 | None |
| Bi₂O₃ | ? | 1.40 | Violet |

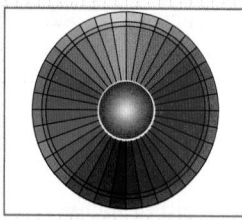

**Predicting** Once an ionic bond is formed, the cation has a tendency to pull the transferred electron toward the nucleus. The appearance of color is directly related to the strength of the pull, which depends upon the size of the ions involved and their oxidation numbers. If visible light of a certain color can send the electron back to the cation momentarily, then the light reflected from a crystal of the compound will be missing this color from its spectrum. The resulting color of the crystal will be the complement of this color of light and can be predicted using the color wheel that is shown here. Complementary colors are across from each other on the color wheel.

**Analysis**
The information in the table can be used to make some general conclusions about a compound's color and the strength of the cation's pull on the transferred electron. Using this information, the color of a compound can be predicted.

**Thinking Critically**
1. A larger anion radius results in a more pronounced color. What reason can you give for this fact?
2. Which do you think produces a more pronounced color, a high oxidation state for the anions or a low one? Explain.
3. Use the color wheel to predict the color of Bi₂O₃, the last compound on the list.

8.2 The Formation and Nature of Ionic Bonds **219**

---

**d.** $3.81 \times 10^{-6}$ mol/(L·s)

### TEST-TAKING TIP

**Watch the Little Words** Underline words like *least, not,* and *except* when you see them in test questions. They change the meaning of the question!

## Test-Taking Tips

*Test-Taking Tips* help prepare students for taking the tests that are an integral part of their school experience. Found in every Chapter Assessment, these tips can be collected in a journal by students and reviewed before they take end-of-course, PSAT, or state exams.

# ENRICHMENT AND APPLICATION

## Careers Using Chemistry

### Radiation Therapist

*Would you like to work with a team of medical specialists that help people battle and recover from cancer? If so, consider a career as a radiation therapist.*

Radiation therapists, working under the direction of physicians, administer doses of radiation to cancer patients in order to kill invasive cancer cells. Computers are used to help plan the course of treatment. The therapists also prepare the patients for treatment

## Careers Using Chemistry

What careers involve the knowledge of chemistry? Use the *Careers Using Chemistry* features to emphasize that chemical applications can be used in many careers.

## How It Works
### Catalytic Converter

Concerns for our environment have made a huge impact in the products and processes we use every day. The catalytic converter is one of those impacts.

When a combustion engine converts fuel into energy, the reactions of the combustion process are incomplete. Incomplete combustion results in the production of poisonous carbon monoxide and undesirable nitrogen oxides. Since 1975, catalytic converters have reduced the exhaust emissions that contribute to air pollution by approximately 90%.

❶ Gases from the engine and the air pass through the exhaust system to the catalytic converter. Oxygen intake into the engine at this point is critical for the reactions of the catalysts.

❷ Inside porous surface rhod

❸ At the rhodium catalyst surface, nitric oxide is converted to nitrogen and oxygen.

Nitrogen Oxygen gas

Nitric oxide

Hot (500°C) rhod
2 NO →

## CHEMISTRY and Society
### The Realities of Radon

In the late 1800s, doctors identified lung cancer as a prevalent cause of mine worker deaths out the world. It became clear that something in the air of underground mines was related to the culprit. The heaviest known gas was the nine times greater than air, radon is naturally ring and highly radioactive. Regardless location, radon, a gas you cannot see taste, is an ever-present part of the air y

### Why be concerned?

Radon is produced when uranium-238 present in many rock layers and soils. Because buildings are built on top sometimes constructed of stone and gas often accumulates inside.

Radon exposure is the second le lung cancer in the United States, 14 000 deaths annually. Because of posed by radon, Congress man Environmental Protection Agency reduction of indoor radon gas level

Although radon is an inert ga duces highly radioactive heavy me one of the radioactive decay pro radon-containing air results in polonium in the tissues of the lungs, the polonium decays fur particles and gamma radiation, ages the cells of the lungs.

### How much is too much

The average outdoor radiation 0.04 pCi/L (picocuries per li mum level considered to be

### What is your risk fac

Examine the map showing area of the United States. area? Fortunately, only believed to have radon le Homes at highest risk in nium-rich rock and thos However, even buildings

## CHEMISTRY and Technology
### Giving a Lift to Cargo

Have you ever been caught in a traffic by a truck carrying an over efficien

## Everyday Chemistry
### Colors of Gems

Have you ever wondered what produces the gorgeous colors in a stained-glass window or in the rubies, emeralds, and sapphires mounted on a ring? Compounds of transition elements are responsible for creating the entire spectrum of colors.

**Transition elements color gems and glass**
Transition elements have many important uses, but one that is often overlooked is their role in giving colors to gemstones and glass. Although not all compounds of transition elements are colored, most inorganic colored compounds contain a transition element such as chromium, iron, cobalt, copper, manganese, nickel, cadmium, titanium, gold, or vanadium. The color of a compound is determined by the identity of the metal, its oxidation number, and the negative ion combined with it.

**Impurities give gems-**

present in the $Al_2O_3$, the resulting gem is a red ruby. A second kind of gemstone is one composed entirely of a colored compound. Most are transition element compounds, such as rose-red rhodochrosite ($MnCO_3$), black-grey hematite ($Fe_2O_3$), or green malachite ($CuCO_3·Cu(OH)_2$).

**How metal ions interact with light to produce color**
Why does the presence of $Cr_2O_3$ in $Al_2O_3$ make a ruby red? The $Cr^{3+}$ ion absorbs yellow-green colors from white light striking the ruby, and the remaining red-blue light is transmitted, resulting in a deep red color. This same process occurs in all gems. Trace impurities absorb certain colors of light from white light striking or passing through the stone. The remaining colors of light that are reflected or transmitted produce the color of the gem.

**Adding transition elements to molten glass for**

## Chemistry and Technology, Chemistry and Society, Everyday Chemistry, How It Works

Help students to realize that chemistry impacts their lives and society as a whole. These features cover topics that students hear about from the media. *Chemistry and Society* gives students the opportunity to understand the many different sides of issues, and—as future decision-makers and voters—develop their own viewpoints. Use these features as topics for debate or persuasive writing. *Chemistry and Technology* features show students how technology may affect their lives. Encourages students to take other science courses. *Everyday Chemistry* and *How It Works* show students the world of chemistry around them.

## Biology
### CONNECTION

The venom of poisonous snakes contains a class of enzymes known as phospholipases. These enzymes catalyze the breakdown of phospholipids, triglycerides in which one fatty acid has been replaced by a phosphate group. The venom of the [dia]mondback rattles[nake] phospholipase tha[t] the ester bond at carbon of phosph[olipids] larger of the two products of this re[action] the bloodstream, membranes of red[ blood cells] causing them to r[upture] from the eastern diamondback can lead to death if not treated immediately.

## Connections

Show students that even if they don't major in chemistry, they will use chemical concepts in other areas, both science and non-science. Share these features with other teachers for cross-disciplinary instruction.

**Energy and the ionic bond** During any chemical reaction, energy is either absorbed or released. When energy is absorbed during a chemical reaction, the reaction is endothermic. If energy is released, it is exothermic. As you will see in the **CHEMLAB** at the end of this chapter, energy is released when magnesium reacts with oxygen.

Energy changes also occur during the formation of ionic bonds from the ions formed during a chemical reaction. The formation of ionic compounds from positive and negative ions is always exothermic. The attraction of the positive ion for the negative ions close to it forms a more stable system that is lower in energy than the individual ions. If the amount of energy released during bond formation is added to an ionic compound, the bonds that hold the positive and negative ions together break.

You just learned that the ions in an ionic compound are arranged in a pattern in a crystal lattice. The energy required to separate one mole of the ions of an ionic compound is referred to as the **lattice energy**. The strength of the forces holding ions in place is reflected by the lattice energy. The more negative the lattice energy, the stronger the force of attraction.

## In-text references to labs and features

In-text references call out all labs and features in the chapter and show how they are integrated into the chapter.

## problem-solving LAB

### How is color related to a transferred electron?

| Factors that Affect Color of an Ionic Compound | | | |
|---|---|---|---|
| Compound | Color | Anion radius (Å) | Visible absorption band |
| AgF | Yellow | 1.36 | Blue-violet |
| AgCl | White | 1.81 | None |

## TEACHER WRAPAROUND EDITION

| FEATURE | LOCATION | SUGGESTIONS FOR USE |
|---|---|---|
| Resource Manager | At the beginning of each chapter | Preview chapter content. Correlate all activities, and features, and resources |
| Materials List | At the beginning of each chapter | Summarize the materials needed for the activities and demonstration in the chapter |
| Preparation of Solutions | At the beginning of each chapter | Use to prepare all reagents needed for chapter activities and demonstration |
| Key to Teaching Strategies | At the beginning of each chapter | Correlate activities to learning levels and strategies |
| Multiple Learning Styles | At the beginning of each chapter | Use to develop teaching strategies for varied learning styles |
| ✓ Assessment Planner | At the beginning of each chapter | Use to plan varied assessment strategies |
| Glencoe Technology Summary | At the beginning of each chapter | Use to plan which technology segments to use in daily lessons |
| Section Focus | At the beginning of each section | Focus students' attention with section focus transparency |
| Demonstration | At the point where concept is taught | Help students visualize chemistry concepts that may be too costly or dangerous for student performance |
| CULTURAL DIVERSITY | One per chapter | Introduce diversity into chemistry topics |
| Glencoe Technology | At point of use | Plan to use technology segments in your daily lessons |
| Differentiated Instruction | At least one per section | Use to develop teaching strategies for special needs students |
| CHEMISTRY JOURNAL | At least one per section | Use to develop students' writing skills |
| ✓ Assessment | At point of use and in all activities | Use to assess students' understanding of material |
| Resource Manager | At point of use | Correlate subject matter to Teacher Classroom Resources |

# RESOURCE MANAGER

Each chapter is preceded by a *Resource Manager,* a complete planning guide that lists the objectives, text features, and laboratory activities for each numbered section. Correlated to each section are all the components of the Teacher Classroom Resources. National Science Education Content Standards correlated to each numbered section ensure that your lessons align well with the guidelines.

## Glencoe Technology
Summarizes what CD-ROM, DVD and videotape materials are available for the chapter from Glencoe. Look for more detailed information about these technology materials at point of use in the margins of the *Teacher Wraparound Edition*.

## Materials List
This list of all the materials you will need for all the labs and demonstration in the chapter is conveniently located at the point where you plan your lessons.

## Preparation of Solutions
Want to know how to prepare the solution needed for a particular lab? This listing tells you how—and lets you know if any special precautions are needed during its preparation.

## Multiple Learning Styles
Summarizes the teaching strategies in the chapter by learning modality so you can plan your lessons for all students.

## ✔ Assessment and Additional Resources
These Teacher Classroom Resources that accompany the chapter can be used for review, assessment, or lesson-planning.

## Key to Teaching Strategies
The activities in the *Teacher Wraparound Edition* are broken down into three levels to accommodate all student ability levels. In addition, certain teaching strategies are designated as suitable for English Language Learners or cooperative learning groups. Finally, strategies that produce work suitable for placement in student portfolios and strategies that are useful in a block scheduling format are called out with easy-to-find icons. Use this coding to select strategies and reproducible masters or transparencies for different learners.

## ✔ Assessment Planner
Summarizes the assessment strategies you can use to check students' progress. Performance, Knowledge, Skill, and Portfolio assessments offer a wide range of options.

# CLASSROOM MANAGEMENT

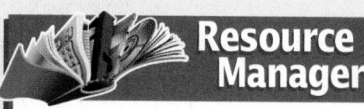

## Resource Manager

Study Guide for Content
  Mastery, p. 100 **L2**
Solving Problems: A Chemistry
  Handbook, Section 17.3 **L2**
Section Focus Transparency 66
  and Master **L1** **ELL**

## Resource Manager boxes

*Resource Manager* boxes located at point of use show you where to integrate the many *Teacher Classroom Resources* materials into your lessons.

## Section Focus

The first step to teaching any set of concepts or skills is to focus the students' attention. Each numbered section begins with a suggestion for using a *Section Focus Transparency* to focus the class on a key topic of the text section. A reduced transparency in the teacher margin lets you preview the transparency.

---

### Section 17.3

## 1 Focus

**Focus Transparency**

Before presenting the lesson, display **Section Focus Transparency 66** on the overhead projector. Have students answer the accompanying questions using **Section Focus Transparency Master 66.** **L1** **ELL**

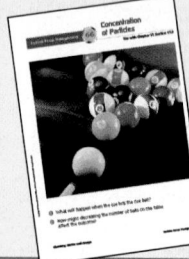

## 2 Teach

**✓ Assessment**

**Performance**

**Have students** design and carry out an experiment in which they evaluate the effect of vinegar concentration on the rate of the reaction between vinegar, $CH_3COOH(aq)$, and baking soda, $NaHCO_3(s)$. Student experiments may involve diluting vinegar and comparing the rates at which $CO_2(g)$ is produced from given concentrations of vinegar for a given mass of baking soda. Use the Performance Task Assessment List for Designing an Experiment in PASC, p. 23. 

542

---

### Section 17.3

## Reaction Rate Laws

### Objectives

• **Express** the relationship between reaction rate and concentration.

• **Determine** reaction orders using the method of initial rates.

### Vocabulary

rate law
specific rate constant
reaction order
method of initial rates

In Section 17.1, you learned how to calculate the average rate of a reaction given the initial and final times and concentrations. The average is important because we need chemical reactions slow down as reactants are consumed. To understand why most reaction rates slow down, recall that the collision theory states that chemical reactions can occur only if the reacting particles collide and that reaction rate depends on concentration. As reactants are consumed, fewer particles collide and the reaction slows. Chemists use the concept of rate laws to quantify the collision theory in terms of a mathematical relationship between the rate of a chemical reaction and the reactant concentration.

### Reaction Rate Laws

The equation that expresses the mathematical relationship between the rate of a chemical reaction and the concentration of reactants is called the rate law. For example, the reaction $A \rightarrow B$, which is a one-step reaction with an activated complex between reactants and products. The rate law for this reaction is expressed as

$$Rate = k[A]$$

where $k$ is the **specific rate constant**, or a numerical value that relates reaction rate and concentration of reactants at a given temperature. Units of the rate constant include $L/(mol \cdot s)$, $1/(mol \cdot s)$, and $s^{-1}$. Depending on reaction conditions, especially temperature, $k$ is unique for every reaction.

The rate law means that the reaction rate is directly proportional to the concentration of A. Thus, doubling the concentration of A will double the reaction rate. Increasing the concentration of A by a factor of 5 will increase the reaction rate by a factor of 5. The specific rate constant, $k$, does not change with concentration; however, $k$ does change with temperature. A large value of $k$ means that A reacts rapidly to form B. What does a small value of

**Figure 17-14**

Specific rate constants are determined experimentally. Scientists have a number of methods at their disposal that can be used to establish $k$ for a given reaction.

A spectrophotometer measures the absorption of specific wavelengths of light by a reactant or product as a reaction progresses to determine the specific rate constant for the reaction.

542    Chapter 17 Reaction Rates

### Internet Address Book

**Chemistry Online**  Note Internet addresses that you find useful in the space below for quick reference.

_____
_____
_____
_____

---

### Section 17.4

## 1 Focus

**Focus Transparency**

Before presenting the lesson, display **Section Focus Transparency 67** on the overhead projector. Have students answer the accompanying questions using **Section Focus Transparency Master 67.** **L1** **ELL**

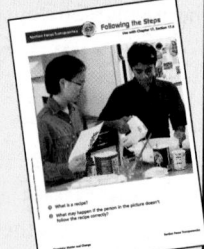

## Objectives

• **Calculate** instantaneous rates of chemical reactions.

• **Understand** that chemical reactions occur in steps.

• **Relate** the instantaneous rate of a complex reaction to its reaction mechanism.

## Vocabulary

instantaneous rate
complex reaction
reaction mechanism
intermediate
rate-determining step

## 2 Teach

**Visual Learning**

**Figure 17-15** Review with students how to determine the slope of a straight line, which is constant. That is, $\Delta x/\Delta y$ (in the case of reaction rate, $\Delta[A]/\Delta t$) is the same for any line segment. However, the plot of concentration of a reactant or product over an appreciable time interval will be a curve. Point out that, because the slope of the curve varies, the reaction rate varies. Students can determine the instantaneous reaction rate at any point on the curve by drawing a straight line tangent to the curve at that point and determining the slope of the line.

546

---

### Section 17.4

### Instantaneous Reaction Rates

The decomposition of hydrogen peroxide ($H_2O_2$) is represented as follows.

$$2H_2O_2(aq) \rightarrow 2H_2O(l) + O_2(g)$$

For this reaction, the decrease in $H_2O_2$ concentration over time is shown in **Figure 17-15**. The curved line shows the average reaction rate and how the reaction rate decreases as the reaction proceeds. The **instantaneous rate**, or the rate of decomposition at a specific time, can be determined by finding the slope of the straight line tangent to the curve at that instant. This is because the slope of the tangent to the curve at a particular point is $\Delta A/\Delta t$, which is the definition of the rate law. In other words, the concentration and rate relate to one specific point (or instant) on the graph.

Another way to determine the instantaneous rate for a chemical reaction is to use the rate law, Rate $= k[A]$, given the reactant concentrations and the specific rate constant for the temperature at which the reaction occurs. For example, the decomposition of dinitrogen pentoxide ($N_2O_5$) into nitrogen dioxide ($NO_2$) and oxygen ($O_2$) is given by the following equation.

$$2N_2O_5(g) \rightarrow 4NO_2(g) + O_2(g)$$

Change in $[H_2O_2]$ with Time

Instantaneous rate $= \dfrac{\Delta [H_2O_2]}{\Delta t}$

**Figure 17-15**

The instantaneous rate for a specific point in the reaction progress can be determined from the tangent to the curve that passes through that point. The equation for the slope of the line ($\Delta y/\Delta x$) is the equation for instantaneous rate in terms of $\Delta[A]$ and $\Delta t$.

instantaneous rate $= \dfrac{\Delta[A]}{\Delta t}$

546    Chapter 17 Reaction Rates

---

### **CHEMISTRY JOURNAL**

**Reaction Rates—How Poetic**

**Linguistic** Have a contest in which students write creative, multistanza poems that incorporate several facets of reaction rates. For example, you could require that the first stanza begin with the line: Reaction rates, reaction rate... . Have students include the poems in their chemistry journals. Ask a colleague to help you judge the poems and choose winners. After awarding prizes, read the best poems to the class. **L2**

---

## Internet Address Book

Do you jot down interesting web sites on little scraps of paper, only to lose them before you can use them? Each chapter in the *Teacher Wraparound Edition* provides several *Chemistry Online* boxes at the bottom of the teacher margin where you can write down those URLs you want to investigate.

# HANDS-ON EXPERIENCES

## Demonstrations

Some reactions or experiments are just too costly for students to perform or are better performed by teachers. These are presented as demonstrations. To involve students, each demo includes an assessment strategy.

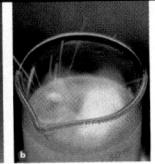

---

gen generator, you may have noticed a sign cautioning against smoking or using open flames. Can you now explain the reason for the caution notice? The high concentration of oxygen could cause a combustion reaction to speed at an explosive rate. The CHEMLAB at the end of this chapter gives you an opportunity to further investigate the effect of concentration on reaction rates.

### Surface Area

Now suppose you were to lower a red-hot chunk of steel instead of steel wool into a flask of oxygen gas. The oxygen would react with the steel much more slowly than it would with the steel wool. Using what you know about the collision theory, can you explain why? You are correct if you said that, for the same mass of iron, steel wool has much more surface area than the chunk of steel. The greater surface area of the steel wool allows the oxygen molecules to collide with many more iron atoms per unit of time.

gases—helium, neon, nitrogen.

**Resource Manager**
Study Guide for Content Mastery, p. 99 L2
Challenge Problems, p. 17 L3
Solving Problems: A Chemistry Handbook, Section 17.2 L2
Section Focus Transparency 65 and Master L1 ELL
Teaching Transparency 50 and Master L2 ELL

### Demonstration

#### Surface Area and Reaction Rate

**Purpose**
To demonstrate that increasing the surface area of a reactant increases the rate of a chemical reaction

**Materials**
lycopodium powder (2 g); ceramic pad; laboratory burner or butane lighter

National Science Content Standards
Pages 536–537
UCP2, UCP3; B.2, B.3, B.6

**536**

**Safety Precautions**
**Disposal** Throw the product in the trash.

**Procedure**
Dim the room lights. Using a burner or lighter, attempt to ignite about 2 g of lycopodium powder placed in a small pile on a ceramic pad. Have students observe that there is no reaction. Then lift the pad containing the powder about 40 cm above the burner flame and turn the pad over. **CAUTION:** *The falling dust will produce a roaring flame.* Have students discuss the effect of increased surface area on reaction rate. Relate this to dust explosions in grain elevators.

**Results**
The lycopodium powder does not ignite until dispersed above the flame. The falling dust ignites explosively.

**Analysis**
1. Write a summary statement describing

this demonstration. Reaction rate increases when surface area increases.
2. Predict which would dissolve first, a sugar cube or the same mass of granulated sugar, the granulated sugar
3. What do you believe happens to the concentration of oxygen gas reacting with each dust particle as the surface area increases? The concentration of oxygen effectively increases as surface area increases.

**Assessment**
**Portfolio** Have interested students photograph the demonstration. They can add the developed photographs to their portfolios with a written summary of the demonstration. L2 ELL P

17.2 Factors Affecting Reaction Rates    **537**

**537**

---

As you may recall, isotopes are atoms of the same element that have different numbers of neutrons. Isotopes of atoms with unstable nuclei are called **radioisotopes**. These unstable nuclei emit radiation to attain more stable atomic configurations in a process called radioactive decay. During radioactive decay, unstable atoms lose energy by emitting one of several types of radiation. The three most common types of radiation are alpha (α), beta (β), and gamma (γ). **Table 25-2** summarizes some of their important properties. Later in this chapter you'll learn about other types of radiation that may be emitted in a nuclear reaction.

**TRY AT HOME — LAB**
See page 964 in Appendix E for Modeling Radiation Penetration.

**Table 25-2**

#### Properties of Alpha, Beta, and Gamma Radiation

| Property | Alpha (α) | Beta (β) | Gamma (γ) |
|---|---|---|---|
| Composition | Alpha particles | Beta particles | High-energy electromagnetic radiation |
| Description of radiation | Helium nuclei $^4_2He$ | Electrons $^0_{-1}\beta$ | photons $^0_0\gamma$ |
| Charge | 2+ | 1− | 0 |
| Mass | $6.64 \times 10^{-24}$ kg | $9.11 \times 10^{-28}$ kg | 0 |
| Approximate energy* | 5 MeV | 0.05 to 1 MeV | 1 MeV |
| Relative penetrating power | Blocked by paper | Blocked by metal foil | Not completely blocked by lead or concrete |

*(1 MeV = $1.60 \times 10^{-13}$ J)

Ernest Rutherford (1871–1937), whom you know of because of his famous gold foil experiment that helped define modern atomic structure, identified alpha, beta, and gamma radiation when studying the effects of an electric field on the emissions from a radioactive source. As you can see in **Figure 25-3**, alpha particles carry a 2+ charge and are deflected toward the negatively charged plate. Beta particles carry a 1− charge and are deflected toward the positively charged plate. In contrast, gamma rays carry no charge and are not affected by the electric field.

**Figure 25-3**
The effect of an electric field on three types of radiation is shown here. Positively charged alpha particles are deflected toward the negatively charged plate. Negatively charged beta particles are deflected toward the positively charged plate. Beta particles undergo greater deflection because they have considerably less mass than alpha particles. Gamma rays, which have no electrical charge, are not deflected.

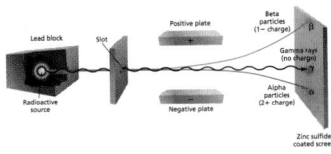

Lead block    Slot    Positive plate
Beta particles (1− charge) β
Gamma rays (no charge) γ
Alpha particles (2+ charge) α
Radioactive source
Negative plate
Zinc sulfide coated screen

25.1 Nuclear Radiation    **807**

**Assessment**
**Knowledge** Ask students what is the difference between the following symbols: $^{14}_6C$, $^{13}_6C$, and $^{12}_6C$? These are three different isotopes of carbon: the first has six neutrons, the second has seven neutrons, and the third has 1... neutrons. L2

### Quick Demo

**Kinesthetic** Students can simulate the effect of Becquerel's experiment by arranging small items such as jewelry, hardware, or leaves on top of blueprint paper inside a notebook in semidarkness, then taking their arrangement outside for exposure to the Sun for several minutes. After exposure, students should bring the blueprint paper back inside to semi-darkness and place it inside a dome or large inverted beaker filled with ammonia vapor. The vapor will "develop" the blueprint paper and show the rough shapes of the objects placed on it. Blueprint paper can be obtained from technical drawing supply stores or from architect offices. L2 ELL

### Reinforcement

Ask students to describe the similarities and differences between an alpha particle and a helium atom; between a beta particle and an electron. The alpha particle and the helium atom both contain two protons and two neutrons. A helium atom is neutral, whereas an alpha particle has had two electrons removed and, therefore, has an overall charge of +2. A beta particle is exactly like an electron except for the fact that its point of origin comes from the nucleus. Beta particles are ejected from the nucleus during the decay of a neutron into a proton.

### Quick Demos

Sometimes, the easiest way to teach students a concept is to show them. Many *Quick Demos* are provided in the teacher margin for your use in helping students visualize chemistry concepts.

**DIFFERENTIATED INSTRUCTION**

**Learning Disabled**
**Visual-Spatial** Use two different colors of magnetic marbles or gumdrops (with small toothpick pieces) to assemble a nucleus of any given atom. Have students demonstrate an alpha decay by removing two protons of one color and two neutrons of another color. A beta decay can be demonstrated by removing a neutron and substituting a proton in its place. L1 ELL

---

**Table 25-6**

#### Effects of Short-term Radiation Exposure

| Dose (rem) | Effects on humans |
|---|---|
| 0–25 | No detectable effects |
| 25–50 | Temporary decrease in white blood cell population |
| 100–200 | Nausea, substantial decrease in white blood cell population |
| 500 | 50% chance of death within 30 days of exposure |

is a measure of the amount of radiation that results in the absorption of 0.01 J of energy per kilogram of tissue. The dose in rads, however, does not account for the energy of the radiation, the type of living tissue absorbing the radiation, or the time of the exposure. To account for these factors, the dose in rads is multiplied by a numerical factor that is related to the radiation's effect on the tissue involved. The result of this multiplication is a unit called the rem. The rem, which stands for roentgen equivalent for man, is named after Wilhelm Roentgen, who, as you learned in Section 25.1, discovered X rays in 1895.

So how does radiation exposure affect you? You may be surprised to learn that you are exposed to radiation on a regular basis. A variety of sources—some naturally occurring, others not—constantly bombard your body with radiation. Read the **Chemistry and Society** at the end of this chapter to learn about one of the most common sources of exposure. Your exposure to these sources results in an average annual radiation exposure of 100–300 millirems of high-energy radiation. Remembering that the SI prefix *milli*- stands for one-thousandth, this dose of radiation is equivalent to 0.10 to 0.30 rem. To help you put this in perspective, a typical dental X ray exposes you to the virtually harmless dose of 0.0005 rem. However, both short exposures to high doses of radiation and long exposures to lower doses of radiation can be harmful. As you can see from the data in **Table 25-4**, short-term radiation exposures in excess of 500 rem can be fatal. **Table 25-7** shows your annual exposure to common radiation sources. You can perform the CHEMLAB at the end of this chapter to examine radiation emitted by a common substance.

**Table 25-7**

#### Average Annual Radiation exposure

| Source | Average exposure (mrem/yr) |
|---|---|
| Cosmic Radiation | 20–50 |
| Radiation from ground | 25–170 |
| Radiation from buildings | 10–160 |
| Radiation from air | 20–260 |
| Human body (internal) | ~20 |
| Medical and dental X rays | 50–75 |
| Nuclear weapon testing | <1 |
| Air travel | 5 |
| Total average | 100–300 |

**3 Assess**
**Check for Understanding**
Ask students to compare the functioning of a Geiger counter and a smoke detector. Both systems depend on the ionization of a gas (air in a smoke detector and argon [usually] in a Geiger counter).

**Reteach**
Ask students what factors determine the extent of radiation damage to an individual? Dosage, exposure time, nature of radiation, area exposed, and type of tissue are all factors to be considered.

**Extension**
Radiation is more destructive to rapidly dividing cells. How can this be an advantage? because cancer cells divide rapidly How can this be a disadvantage? Healthy, noncancerous cells could be damaged.

**Assessment**
**Performance** Set up a "Jeopardy" style game with categories such as nuclear medicine, detecting radiation, nuclear power, fission or fusion. Have teams of students compete for points. Use the Performance Task Assessment List for Group Work in PASC, p. 97. L2 COOP LEARN

## ChemLab placement icon

The ChemLab for each chapter is located at the end of each chapter so as not to disrupt the flow of text. How do you know where to teach the ChemLab? Look for the *ChemLab placement icon* in the teacher margin for the best place to teach the lab.

### Section 25.5 Assessment

30. Describe several methods used to detect and measure radiation.
31. Explain one way in which nuclear chemistry is used to diagnose or treat disease.
32. Compare and contrast somatic and genetic biological damage.
33. **Thinking Critically** Using what you know about the biological effects of radiation, explain why it is safe to use radioisotopes for the diagnosis of medical problems.
34. **Hypothesizing** The average person is exposed to 100–300 millirems of radiation per year. Airline crewmembers, however, are exposed to almost twice the average amount of radiation per year. Suggest a possible reason for their increased exposure to radiation.

25.5 Applications and Effects of Nuclear Reactions    **831**

### Section 25.5 Assessment

30. Geiger counters, scintillation counters, and film badges may be described.
31. Explanations will vary, but might include radiotracers, PET scans, or radiation treatment to kill cancer cells.
32. Somatic damage affects the body cells of the organism and will have effects only on that organism in its lifetime. Genetic damage affects the DNA of the organism, and could be transferred to later generations.
33. Radioisotopes used in medical diagnosis have short half-lives, thereby minimizing the patient's exposure.
34. Airline crews experience greater exposure because they travel at altitudes where solar and cosmic radiation levels are higher.

**CHEMLAB**

ChemLab 25, located at the end of this chapter, can be used at this point in the lesson.

National Science Content Standards
Pages 830–831
UCP1, UCP3; B.6; E.2; F.1, F.5

**831**

# DIVERSITY IN THE CLASSROOM

In an effort to provide all students with a positive science experience, *Chemistry: Matter and Change Teacher Wraparound Edition* offers a variety of ways for students to interact with materials so that they utilize their preferred method of learning.

## Multiple Learning Styles

The *Teacher Wraparound Edition* provides a number of strategies for encouraging students with diverse learning styles. Look for the various learning style icons that identify strategies suitable for each style of learning. Strategies in each chapter are summarized in the *Multiple Learning Styles* box on page D of each Resource Manager.

## ✓ Portfolio

### Naming Ionic Compounds

*Visual-Spatial* Have students design flow charts to be used to name ionic compounds or to determine the formula unit of ionic compounds. Have them explain their flow charts to the class. **L2** **P**

## Differentiated Instruction

Use these teaching strategies and student activities to structure the learning environment in your classroom to meet students' special needs.

## DIFFERENTIATED INSTRUCTION

### Learning Disabled

*Kinesthetic* Students might have trouble determining formula units from the ions involved. Use puzzlelike pieces to represent ions. Pieces representing positive ions have one wedge-shaped tab for each positive charge, and negative ions will have a matching notch for each negative charge. Allow students to manipulate the pieces to discover that, for example, two 1+ ions are needed for each 2− ion. Have students write the correct formula units for the ionic compounds formed. **L1** **ELL**

## Cultural Diversity

Respond to diversity by sharing with students the *Cultural Diversity* connections found at the bottom of the page in every chapter of the *Teacher Wraparound Edition*.

## Tech Prep

Look for the *Tech Prep icon* on Careers Using Chemistry and Applying Chemistry, features that will interest your tech prep students.

## CULTURAL DIVERSITY

### Pottery

One of the most ancient arts is the making of pottery. The oldest known pottery dates back to 400 B.C. in Japan. Chinese, Middle Eastern, and Native American potters also produced a variety of pottery. Basically, the chemical composition of pottery is that of clay or clay blends, $Al_2O_3 \cdot 2SiO_2 \cdot 2H_2O$. When formed to the desired shape, the clay piece is baked hard and the intensity of the heat determines the degree of hardness. Pottery is often coated with glaze to render it waterproof and add decoration. Pottery glaze has a composition similar to that of pottery clay, as well as a mixture of ionically bonded metal oxides. The addition of metal oxides to the glaze results in many properties, including hardness, color, surface character, crystal development, and chemical stability. Adding $Fe_2O_3$ produces a rich red color, while $CuO$ produces a clear green color. The addition of $Al_2O_3$ adds hardness and durability to the pottery.

# ASSESSMENT

## Assessment

Every ChemLab, MiniLab, Problem-Solving Lab, and Demonstration includes an ✔ Assessment strategy in the teacher margin. In addition, you will find many more ✔ Assessment strategies within a section. Finally, each chapter contains ✔ Portfolio suggestions that can be used as assessments.

### ✔ Assessment Planner

**GLENCOE'S ASSESSMENT ADVANTAGE**

**Portfolio Assessment**
Assessment, TWE, p. 541
Demonstration, TWE, p. 537
Portfolio, TWE, pp. 538, 553

**Performance Assessment**
Assessment, TWE, pp. 534, 542, 549
Discovery Lab, SE, p. 528
MiniLab, SE, p. 539
ChemLab, SE, pp. 550–551

**Knowledge Assessment**
Assessment, TWE, pp. 531, 532, 535, 537, 545

Section Assessment, SE, pp. 535, 541, 545, 549
Chapter Assessment, SE, pp. 554–557

**Skill Assessment**
MiniLab
ChemLab
Problem-
p. 533

## ✔ Assessment Planner

All the assessments in a chapter are summarized in the *Assessment Planner* located on the D page of each chapter Resource Manager. A variety of Skill, Knowledge, Performance, and Portfolio assessment strategies provide a variety of assessments for you to know exactly how much of the lesson each student understands.

---

$t_2 = 4.00$ s
$[C_4H_9Cl]$ at $t_1 = 0.220M$
$[C_4H_9Cl]$ at $t_2 = 0.100M$

**2** **Solve for the Unknown**
Write the equation for the average reaction rate, insert the known quantities, and perform the calculation.

$$\text{ion rate} = -\frac{[C_4H_9Cl] \text{ at time } t_2 - [C_4H_9Cl] \text{ at time } t_1}{t_2 - t_1}$$

$$= -\frac{0.100M - 0.220M}{}$$

e units) $= -\frac{0.100 \text{ mol/L} - 0.220 \text{ mol/L}}{}$

$= -\frac{-0.120 \text{ mol/L}}{4.00 \text{ s}}$

$= 0.0300 \text{ mol/(L·s)}$

**e Answer**
reaction rate of 0.0300 moles $C_4H_9Cl$ consumed per liter
rms reasonable based on start and end amounts. The
ctly expressed in three significant figures.

**ROBLEMS**
following table to calculate the average reaction rates.

**Experimental Data for $H_2 + Cl_2 \rightarrow 2HCl$**

| | $[H_2]$ (M) | $[Cl_2]$ (M) | $[HCl]$ (M) |
|---|---|---|---|
| | 0.030 | 0.050 | 0.000 |
| | 0.020 | 0.040 | 0.020 |

erage reaction rate expressed in moles $H_2$ consumed
ond.

erage reaction rate expressed in moles $Cl_2$ consumed
ond.

erage reaction rate expressed in moles HCl produced
ond.

17.1 A Model for Reaction Rates **531**

---

### ✔ Assessment
**Knowledge** For the reaction $A + 2B \rightarrow 3C$ at time = 0, $[A] = 2.00$ mol/L, $[B] = 4.00$ mol/L, and $[C] = 0.00$ mol/L. At time = 3.00 minutes, $[A]$ has dropped to 0.50 mol/L. Have students calculate and express the rate of the reaction over the 3.00-minute time interval in mol A consumed/(L·min), mol B consumed/(L·min), and mol C produced/(L·min). Rate = 0.500 mol A/(L·min); Rate = 1.00 mol B/(L·min); Rate = 1.50 mol C/(L·min) **L2**

### Practice **PROBLEMS**
Have students refer to Appendix D for complete solutions to Practice Problems.
1. 0.0025 mol/(L·s)
2. 0.0025 mol/(L·s)
3. 0.0050 mol/(L·s)

---

**CHEMISTRY JOURNAL**

**Miles per Gallon and Miles per Dollar**

*Logical-Mathematical* To give students experience in stating the change of one quantity in proportion to the change of another, ask them to keep track of the miles driven, gallons of gasoline consumed, and cost of gasoline for an automobile for one week. Then, have them calculate the automobile's mileage in miles driven per gallon consumed and cost to drive in miles driven per dollar spent (gasoline only). If a student's family has more then one automobile, ask them to keep records for all the vehicles and compare their mileage and cost to drive figures. Data and calculations may be placed in students' portfolios. **L2** **P**

National Science Content Standards
**Pages 530–531**
UCP.2, UCP.3; B.3

**531**

---

**CHAPTER 17 ASSESSMENT**

**Concept Mapping**
**32.** 1. reaction rates; 2. collision theory; 3–7. surface area, temperature, concentration, reactivity, catalyst

**Mastering Concepts**
**33.** Although this information tells you the reaction is spontaneous under the specified conditions, it tells you nothing about the reaction rate.
**34.** The rate may be expressed as the decrease in $[A]$ per unit time: Rate = $\frac{\Delta[A]}{\Delta t}$. Numerically, the two rates would be equal; however, $\frac{\Delta[A]}{\Delta t}$ would be negative and $\frac{\Delta[B]}{\Delta t}$ would be positive.
**35.** Activation energy represents the minimum amount of energy that reacting particles must have to form the activated complex.
**36.** The activated complex is a transition state between reactants and products.
**37.** The molecules do not react if they collide with insufficient energy or lack favorable orientations at the instant of impact.
**38.** The activation energy defines the minimum energy particles must have in order to result in the formation of the activated complex.
**39.** Reactant bonds are being broken and product bonds are being formed.
**40.** The activation energy for the forward reaction is less than the activation energy for the reverse reaction.
**41.** Generally, the greater the reactivity of the reactants, the faster the reaction.
**42.** The finely divided solid presents a larger surface area than the large chunk.
**43.** a catalyst

**44.** Increasing the concentration increases the rate, and decreasing the concentration decreases the rate.

**554**

---

**CHAPTER 17 ASSESSMENT**

**Chemistry** Online
Go to the Chemistry Web site at chemistrymc.com f
Chapter 17 Assess

**Concept M**
**32.** Complete the f
ing terms: surf
reaction rates,

**Mastering**
**33.** For a specific c
in free energy
mation tell you
**34.** How would you
tion A → B ba
How would the
based on the pr
**35.** What does the
tion represent?
**36.** What is the rol
cal reaction? (1
**37.** Suppose two
what circumsta
react? (17.1)
**38.** How is the acti
related to whet
cules initiates a
**39.** In the activated
bonds are broken and bonds are formed (17.1)
**40.** If A → B is exothermic, how does the activation energy for the forward reaction compare with the activation energy for the reverse reaction (A → B)? (17.1)

**41.** What role does the reactivity of the reactants play in determining the rate of a chemical reaction? (17.2)
**42.** Explain why a crushed solid reacts with a gas more quickly than a large chunk of the same solid. (17.2)

**59.** Distinguish between an elementary step, a complex reaction, and a reaction mechanism. (17.4)
**60.** Under what circumstances is the rate law for the reaction $2A + 3B \rightarrow$ products correctly written as Rate = $k[A]^2[B]^3$? (17.3)

**554** Chapter 17 Reaction Rates
chemistrymc.com/chapter_test

**Resource Manager**
Chapter Assessment, pp. 97–102 **L2**
Supplemental Problems, Ch. 17
ExamView® Pro CD-ROM
MindJogger Videoquizzes DVD/VHS
Solutions Manual, Ch. 17
Chemistry Interactive CD-ROM, Ch. 17 quiz

## Chapter Assessment

All Chapter Assessment questions and answers have been validated for accuracy and suitability. All Chapter Assessment questions have been checked against the chapter's objectives to ensure that the objectives are adequately tested. You can be sure when you assign a Chapter Assessment question that it reflects the content of the chapter in an accurate and suitable way for your class.

## National Science Education Content Standards

Correlations to the National Science Education Content Standards have been placed on each two-page spread of the *Teacher Wraparound Edition* so you can be sure that the concepts on those pages meet the national guidelines. In addition, these correlations appear by section on page B of each chapter Resource Manager.

National Science Content Standards
**Pages 528–529**
UCP.2, UCP.3; A.1; B.3; E.2

**17T**

## HANDS-ON LEARNING

### Resources For All Your Needs

In addition to the wide array of instructional options provided in the student and teacher editions, *Chemistry: Matter and Change* offers an extensive list of support materials and program resources. Some of these materials offer alternative ways of presenting your chemistry program, others provide tools for reinforcing core concepts and evaluating student learning, and still others will help you extend and enrich your course. You won't have time to use them all, but the ones you use will help you make the best use of the time you have.

**Laboratory Manual Teacher Edition**

Glencoe **CHEMISTRY** MATTER AND CHANGE

Contents and Features
- 52 traditional labs
- Students record data and conclusions directly on lab worksheets
- Lab safety and chemical storage and disposal guidelines

Includes Math Handbook

**Laboratory Manual**

Glencoe **CHEMISTRY** MATTER AND CHANGE

### Lab Manual, Student Edition and Teacher Edition

If you want more hands-on options, the *Laboratory Manual* offers you two more labs for each chapter, which provide students with a variety of laboratory experiences that reinforce the chemistry principles in the text.

**CBL Laboratory Manual**

**Small-Scale Laboratory Manual**

**Forensics Laboratory Manual**

Glencoe CHEMISTRY MATTER AND CHANGE

Includes Math Handbook

**ChemLab and MiniLab Worksheets**

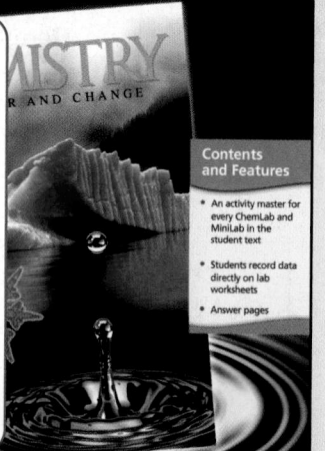

Contents and Features
- An activity master for every ChemLab and MiniLab in the student text
- Students record data directly on lab worksheets
- Answer pages

### ChemLab and MiniLab Worksheets

Each of the ChemLabs and MiniLabs in the student text is also available in copymaster form in *ChemLab and MiniLab Worksheets.* As students proceed with a lab, have them copy their observations and data on the expanded data tables provided in these worksheets.

### Additional Lab Manuals

If you want even more hands-on options, the *Small-Scale Lab Manual, CBL Lab Manual,* and *Forensics Lab Manual* offer still more laboratory experiences for your students.

# APPLICATIONS AND ENRICHMENTS

## Challenge Problems

### Challenge Problems
Challenge students to solve the more advanced problems in the *Challenge Problems* book. They are especially suited to average and above-average ability students.

Glencoe
CHEMISTRY
MATTER AND CHANGE

**Contents and Features**
- One-page activity per chapter
- Application and extension of concepts in the student text
- Answer pages

Includes Math Handbook

## Supplemental Problems

Glencoe
CHEMISTRY
MATTER AND CHANGE

**Contents and Features**
- Additional problems not found in the textbook
- Extra practice in solving chemistry problems
- Complete solutions to all problems

Includes Math Handbook

### Supplemental Problems
For further review and reinforcement, the *Supplemental Problems* book provides you with additional practice problems.

# TEACHER CLASSROOM RESOURCES

## ✔ ASSESSMENT

Chapter Assessment

### Chapter Assessment

*Chapter Assessment* includes a four-part assessment tool containing questions of various levels for every chapter, which helps you assess process as well as content objectives. Unique simulations require students to analyze experimental designs and interpret data.

**Contents and Features**

- Six pages of objectives-based assessment for each chapter
- Questions for all ability levels
- Answer pages

### Performance Assessment in the Science Classroom

Use the performance assessment lists and rubrics in *Performance Assessment in the Science Classroom* to assess students' work. Every performance assessment in the text is correlated to an assessment list in this book.

### Alternate Assessment in the Science Classroom

*Alternate Assessment in the Science Classroom* provides practical strategies for using alternate forms of assessment such as performance-based methods and portfolios. In addition, there are report forms and scoring rubrics.

### Multimedia Assessment Options (MindJogger DVD/VHS, ExamView® Pro CD-ROM, Vocabulary Puzzlemaker CD-ROM)

Multimedia offers you assessment options for every chapter in the form of MindJogger videotape and DVD quizzes, ExamView® Pro Testmaker, and puzzles on the Vocabulary Puzzlemaker CD-ROM. You will never have to write another test question with the options you have.

# REVIEW AND REINFORCEMENT

### Study Guide for Content Mastery, Student and Teacher Editions

Use section-by-section masters from the *Study Guide for Content Mastery* book to reinforce the core concepts presented in the student text. These worksheets are ideal for students of average and below-average ability. A consumable student edition of the guide also is available.

Study Guide for Content Mastery
Teacher Edition

**Contents and Features**

- Six pages of activities per chapter
- Developed for students with special learning needs
- Answer pages

Study Guide for Content Mastery

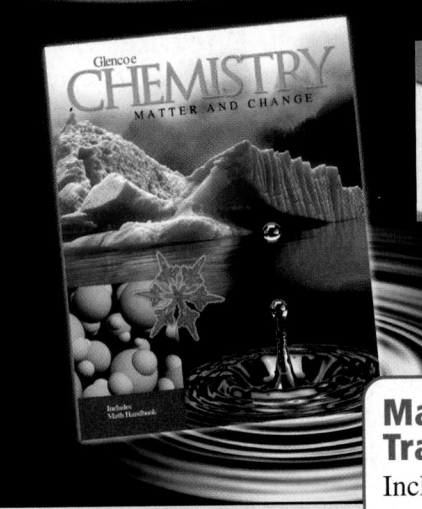

### Math Skills Transparency Package

**Contents and Features**

- 45 full-color transparencies that teach quantitative problem-solving skills
- Blackline copy master of each transparency
- Student worksheet for each transparency
- Teaching strategies

### Math Skills Transparency Package

Includes transparencies designed to help students solve problems, write formulas, or balance equations. A blackline master and worksheet accompany each transparency.

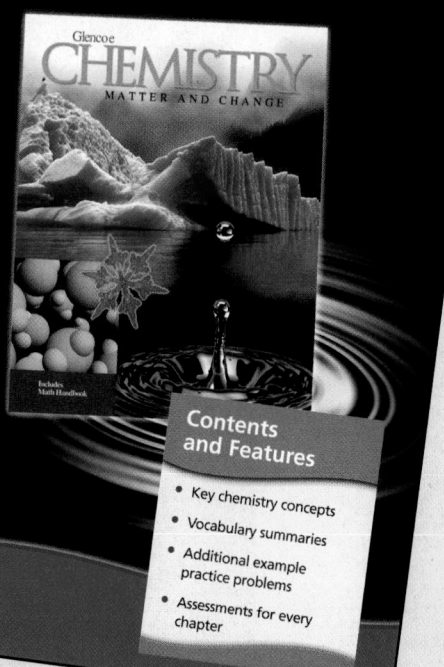

### Solving Problems: A Chemistry Handbook

**Contents and Features**

- Key chemistry concepts
- Vocabulary summaries
- Additional example practice problems
- Assessments for every chapter

### Solving Problems: A Chemistry Handbook

This handbook provides brief summaries of key concepts in each section of the textbook. Additional example problems and practice problems help to reinforce students' problem-solving skills.

## TEACHER RESOURCES

**Solutions Manual**

**Lesson Plans**

**Block Scheduling Lesson Plans**

### Solutions Manual
The *Solutions Manual* contains solutions and answers to all Practice Problems, Section Assessment questions, Chapter Assessment questions, Math Handbook questions, and the Supplemental Practice Problems from Appendix A.

### Lesson Plans and Block Scheduling Lesson Plans
The *Lesson Plans* book offers you a complete planning resource by correlating objectives, activities, and program resources for every lesson. Each plan is geared to the teaching cycle employed in the *Teacher Wraparound Edition* and contains a complete list of all the resources available for that numbered section. If you use block scheduling, the *Block Scheduling Lesson Plans* book offers the same resources for your schedule.

**Spanish Resources**

**Section Focus Transparency Package**

### Section Focus Transparency Package
The 104 full-color transparencies in the *Section Focus Transparency Package* provide a way for you to begin each lesson by capturing the attention of your students with simple activities. Each numbered section begins with a Section Focus strategy that shows a photo of the Section Focus Transparency for that section. The package also contains a booklet of blackline masters and teaching strategies for all transparencies.

### Spanish Resources
Help your Spanish-speaking students get more out of their science lessons by reproducing pages from the *Spanish Resources* book. In addition to the complete English/Spanish glossary, the book contains translations of all objectives, vocabulary, and What You'll Learn for each chapter of the student text.

**Teaching Transparency Package**

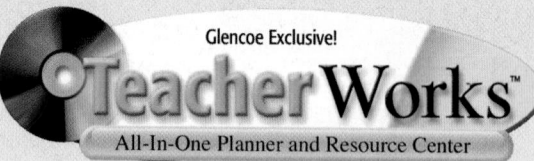

Glencoe Exclusive!

**TeacherWorks™**
All-In-One Planner and Resource Center

### TeacherWorks™
The TeacherWorks™ CD-ROM provides instant access to all classroom resources, allowing you to quickly and efficiently preview chapters and plan lessons.

### Teaching Transparency Package
These full-color teaching transparencies reinforce concepts taught in the student text. Each transparency is accompanied by a worksheet and blackline master.

Glencoe's *Chemistry: Matter and Change* offers a broad array of technology products to enhance your students' chemistry experience.

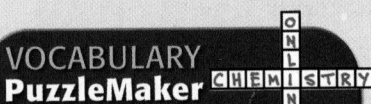

For additional help with vocabulary, have students access the Vocabulary PuzzleMaker online.

**chemistrymc.com/ vocabulary_puzzlemaker**

## Vocabulary PuzzleMaker

The Glencoe **Vocabulary** *PuzzleMaker* is an easy-to-use program that lets you create crossword puzzles, word search puzzles, and jumble puzzles to review chapter content. Puzzles can be completed online or printed.

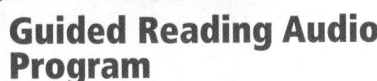

## Guided Reading Audio Program

The **Guided Reading Audio Program** provides comprehensive content in English and Spanish. These audio CDs are another way for auditory learners, students with reading difficulties, and ELL students to learn chapter material. Students can listen individually during class or check out audio CDs and use them at home. Point-of-use references to the pages in the **Study Guide for Content Mastery** also are indicated on the audio CDs.

## MindJogger Videoquizzes

The interactive quiz-show format of **Chemistry: Matter and Change MindJogger Videoquizzes** provides fun for your students while reviewing core concepts for every chapter. The quizzes are available in VHS and DVD formats.

# TECHNOLOGY

## EXAMVIEW® PRO

### Use Exam*View*® Pro Testmaker CD-ROM to:

- Create **multiple versions** of tests.
- Create **modified** tests with one mouse click for struggling students.
- **Edit** existing questions and add your own questions.
- **Build** tests based on national curriculum standards.

## ExamView Pro CD-ROM

Design and create your own test instruments from our *ExamView® Pro CD-ROM* for Windows and Macintosh. Select your own test items by objective from two different levels of difficulty, or write and edit your own.

## Chemistry Interactive CD-ROM

A creative combination of sound, video, and animation makes the *Chemistry Interactive CD-ROM* an exciting addition to your chemistry program. A large array of interactive simulations that engage and help students to learn is also offered. Full-motion videos, animations, explorations, demonstrations, and lab simulations let students explore chemistry concepts safely, all at the computer. Interactive quizzes allow students to self-assess understanding of chapter content.

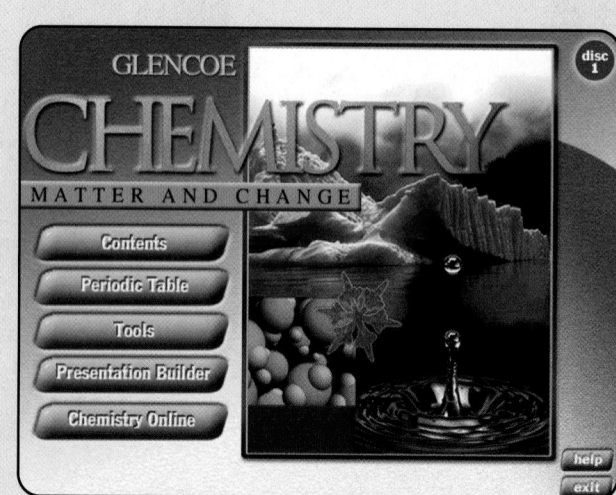

GLENCOE

disc 1

# CHEMISTRY
## MATTER AND CHANGE

- Contents
- Periodic Table
- Tools
- Presentation Builder
- Chemistry Online

help

exit

# CHEMISTRY WEB SITE

The *Chemistry Web site* at **chemistrymc.com** provides students and teachers with a wide range of materials. On the student site, links to other web sites provide more information on the topics being studied. Projects give students an opportunity to research and share data with other students. The teacher site contains professional development resources for teaching chemistry.

**Chemistry Online**

In-text *Chemistry Online* boxes at point of use in the student chapter direct students to use Web curriculum as part of an integrated study of chapter content.

TECHNOLOGY

## Chapter-by-Chapter Links

bring a world of relevant chemistry resources to enrich and extend classroom learning.

## Interactive Activities

provide lab simulations and activities that foster critical thinking. Students will have options to post and share data with classrooms worldwide.

## Self-Check Quizzes

help students review, reinforce and prepare for chapter assessment. Online feedback is provided.

## Our Pledge to You

Glencoe is committed to providing textbooks that are as error-free and as accurate as possible. As part of this commitment, we will be updating critical time-sensitive data such as charts, graphs, and statistics along with the latest information in the field of chemistry on our Web site. In this way, you and your students will always have access to the most accurate information possible. Glencoe monitors all links and updates them to maintain chapter relevancy.

## Glencoe Teaching Today Web site

Glencoe now has a professional development Web site designed just for secondary teachers. The *Glencoe Teaching Today Web site* provides teachers with a wide range of materials. Features include daily teaching tips, free pdf downloads, annotated Web resources, educational news, and more. The site contains a wealth of information on topics from high stakes testing to classroom management. Access the Teaching Today Web site by clicking on **www.chemistrymc.com**

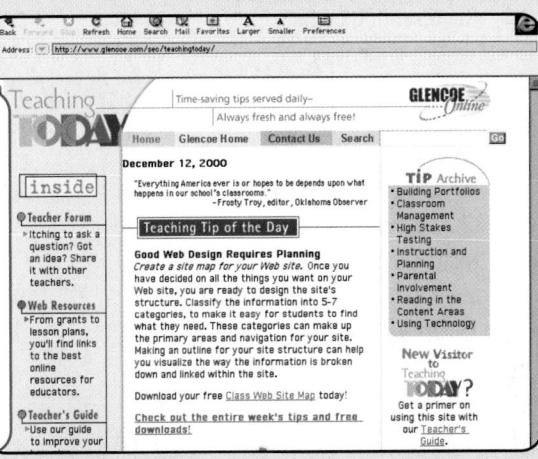

# COURSE PLANNING GUIDE

*Chemistry: Matter and Change* provides a complete selection of core concepts that are presented in a way to meet the needs of all your students. As the teacher, you are in the best position to design a chemistry course that meets the needs of individual students and classes, sets the pace at which the content is covered, and determines what material should be given the most emphasis. To assist you in planning the course, the following Course Planning Guide is provided.

*Chemistry: Matter and Change* may be used in a full-year, two-semester program that is comprised of 165 periods of approximately 45 minutes each. This type of schedule is represented in the table under the heading of Single-Class Scheduling. This table also outlines a plan under the heading Block Scheduling for schools that use a block scheduling system. With block scheduling, it is assumed that the course will be taught for 90 class periods of approximately 90 minutes each.

Please remember that the planning guide is provided as an aid in planning the best course for your students. Use this guide in relation to your curriculum and the ability levels of the classes you teach.

## COURSE PLANNING GUIDE FOR CHEMISTRY: MATTER AND CHANGE

| Chapter/Section | Single-Class Scheduling (165 days) | Block Scheduling (90 days) |
|---|---|---|
| **1 Introduction to Chemistry** | 3 | 1 |
| 1.1 The Stories of Two Chemicals | 1/2 | -- |
| 1.2 Chemistry and Matter | 1/2 | 1/4 |
| 1.3 Scientific Methods | 1 | 1/4 |
| 1.4 Scientific Research | 1/2 | -- |
| Chapter Assessment | 1/2 | 1/2 |
| | | |
| **2 Data Analysis** | 6 | 3 |
| 2.1 Units of Measurement | 1/2 | 1/2 |
| 2.2 Scientific Notation and Dimensional Analysis | 2 | 1 |
| 2.3 How reliable are measurements? | 1 | 1/2 |
| 2.4 Representing Data | 1 1/2 | 1/2 |
| Chapter Assessment | 1 | 1/2 |
| | | |
| **3 Matter—Properties and Changes** | 6 | 3 |
| 3.1 Properties of Matter | 1 | 1/2 |
| 3.2 Changes in Matter | 1 | 1/2 |
| 3.3 Mixtures of Matter | 2 | 1 |
| 3.4 Elements and Compounds | 1 | 1/2 |
| Chapter Assessment | 1 | 1/2 |

| Chapter/Section | Single-Class Scheduling (165 days) | Block Scheduling (90 days) |
|---|---|---|
| **4 The Structure of the Atom** | 6 | 3 |
| 4.1 Early Theories of Matter | 1 | 1/2 |
| 4.2 Subatomic Particles and the Nuclear Atom | 1 | 1/2 |
| 4.3 How Atoms Differ | 2 | 1 |
| 4.4 Unstable Nuclei and Radioactive Decay | 1 | 1/2 |
| Chapter Assessment | 1 | 1/2 |
| | | |
| **5 Electrons in Atoms** | 6 | 3 |
| 5.1 Light and Quantized Energy | 1 1/2 | 1/2 |
| 5.2 Quantum Theory and the Atom | 1 1/2 | 1 |
| 5.3 Electron Configurations | 2 | 1 |
| Chapter Assessment | 1 | 1/2 |
| | | |
| **6 The Periodic Table and Periodic Law** | 6 | 3 |
| 6.1 Development of the Modern Periodic Table | 1 | 1/2 |
| 6.2 Classification of the Elements | 2 | 1 |
| 6.3 Periodic Trends | 2 | 1 |
| Chapter Assessment | 1 | 1/2 |

| Chapter/Section | Single-Class Scheduling (165 days) | Block Scheduling (90 days) |
|---|---|---|
| **7 The Elements** | 5 | 2 |
| 7.1 Properties of s-Block Elements | 1 | 1/2 |
| 7.2 Properties of p-Block Elements | 1 1/2 | 1/2 |
| 7.3 Properties of d-Block and f-Block Elements | 1 1/2 | 1/2 |
| Chapter Assessment | 1 | 1/2 |
| **8 Ionic Compounds** | 6 | 3 1/2 |
| 8.1 Forming Chemical Bonds | 1 | 1/2 |
| 8.2 The Formation and Nature of Ionic Bonds | 1 1/2 | 1 |
| 8.3 Names and Formulas for Ionic Compounds | 1 1/2 | 1 |
| 8.4 Metallic Bonds and Properties of Metals | 1 | 1/2 |
| Chapter Assessment | 1 | 1/2 |
| **9 Covalent Bonding** | 8 | 4 |
| 9.1 The Covalent Bond | 1 | 1/2 |
| 9.2 Naming Molecules | 1 | 1/2 |
| 9.3 Molecular Structures | 2 | 1 |
| 9.4 Molecular Shape | 2 | 1 |
| 9.5 Electronegativity and Polarity | 1 | 1/2 |
| Chapter Assessment | 1 | 1/2 |
| **10 Chemical Reactions** | 6 | 3 |
| 10.1 Reactions and Equations | 2 | 1 |
| 10.2 Classifying Chemical Reactions | 1 | 1/2 |
| 10.3 Reactions in Aqueous Solutions | 2 | 1 |
| Chapter Assessment | 1 | 1/2 |
| **11 The Mole** | 9 | 5 1/2 |
| 11.1 Measuring Matter | 1 1/2 | 1 |
| 11.2 Mass and the Mole | 1 1/2 | 1 |
| 11.3 Moles of Compounds | 1 1/2 | 1 |
| 11.4 Empirical and Molecular Formulas | 2 | 1 |

| Chapter/Section | Single-Class Scheduling (165 days) | Block Scheduling (90 days) |
|---|---|---|
| 11.5 The Formula for a Hydrate | 1 1/2 | 1 |
| Chapter Assessment | 1 | 1/2 |
| **12 Stoichiometry** | 9 | 6 |
| 12.1 What is stoichiometry? | 1 | 1/2 |
| 12.2 Stoichiometric Calculations | 3 | 3 |
| 12.3 Limiting Reactants | 2 | 1 |
| 12.4 Percent Yield | 2 | 1 |
| Chapter Assessment | 1 | 1/2 |
| **13 States of Matter** | 6 | 3 1/2 |
| 13.1 Gases | 1 | 1/2 |
| 13.2 Forces of Attraction | 1 1/2 | 1 |
| 13.3 Liquids and Solids | 1 | 1/2 |
| 13.4 Phase Changes | 1 1/2 | 1 |
| Chapter Assessment | 1 | 1/2 |
| **14 Gases** | 7 | 4 1/2 |
| 14.1 The Gas Laws | 1 1/2 | 1 |
| 14.2 The Combined Gas Law and Avogadro's Principle | 1 1/2 | 1 |
| 14.3 The Ideal Gas Law | 1 | 1/2 |
| 14.4 Gas Stoichiometry | 2 | 1 1/2 |
| Chapter Assessment | 1 | 1/2 |
| **15 Solutions** | 7 | 3 1/2 |
| 15.1 What are solutions? | 1 | 1/2 |
| 15.2 Solution Concentration | 2 | 1 |
| 15.3 Colligative Properties of Solutions | 2 | 1 |
| 15.4 Heterogeneous Mixtures | 1 | 1/2 |
| Chapter Assessment | 1 | 1/2 |
| **16 Energy and Chemical Change** | 8 | 5 |
| 16.1 Energy | 1 | 1/2 |
| 16.2 Heat in Chemical Reactions and Processes | 1 | 1/2 |
| 16.3 Thermochemical Equations | 2 | 1 1/2 |
| 16.4 Calculating Enthalpy Change | 2 | 1 1/2 |
| 16.5 Reaction Spontaneity | 1 | 1/2 |
| Chapter Assessment | 1 | 1/2 |

# COURSE PLANNING GUIDE

| Chapter/Section | Single-Class Scheduling (165 days) | Block Scheduling (90 days) |
|---|---|---|
| **17 Reaction Rates** | **7** | **4** |
| 17.1 A Model for Reaction Rates | 1 | 1/2 |
| 17.2 Factors Affecting Reaction Rates | 1 | 1/2 |
| 17.3 Reaction Rate Laws | 2 | 1 1/2 |
| 17.4 Instantaneous Reaction Rates and Reaction Mechanisms | 2 | 1 |
| Chapter Assessment | 1 | 1/2 |
| | | |
| **18 Chemical Equilibrium** | **6** | **3** |
| 18.1 Equilibrium: A State of Dynamic Balance | 1 1/2 | 1/2 |
| 18.2 Factors Affecting Chemical Equilibrium | 1 1/2 | 1/2 |
| 18.3 Using Equilibrium Constants | 2 | 1 1/2 |
| Chapter Assessment | 1 | 1/2 |
| | | |
| **19 Acids and Bases** | **7** | **4 1/2** |
| 19.1 Acids and Bases: An Introduction | 1 | 1/2 |
| 19.2 Strengths of Acids and Bases | 1 1/2 | 1 |
| 19.3 What is pH? | 1 1/2 | 1 |
| 19.4 Neutralization | 2 | 1 1/2 |
| Chapter Assessment | 1 | 1/2 |
| | | |
| **20 Redox Reactions** | **5** | **3** |
| 20.1 Oxidation and Reduction | 1 | 1/2 |
| 20.2 Balancing Redox Equations | 1 1/2 | 1 |
| 20.3 Half-Reactions | 1 1/2 | 1 |
| Chapter Assessment | 1 | 1/2 |
| | | |
| **21 Electrochemistry** | **5** | **3** |
| 21.1 Voltaic Cells | 2 | 1 |
| 21.2 Types of Batteries | 1 | 1/2 |
| 21.3 Electrolysis | 1 | 1 |
| Chapter Assessment | 1 | 1/2 |
| | | |
| **22 Hydrocarbons** | **7** | **4 1/2** |
| 22.1 Alkanes | 1 | 1 |
| 22.2 Cyclic Alkanes and Alkane Properties | 1 | 1/2 |

| Chapter/Section | Single-Class Scheduling (165 days) | Block Scheduling (90 days) |
|---|---|---|
| 22.3 Alkenes and Alkynes | 1 1/2 | 1 |
| 22.4 Isomers | 1 1/2 | 1 |
| 22.5 Aromatic Hydrocarbons and Petroleum | 1 | 1/2 |
| Chapter Assessment | 1 | 1/2 |
| | | |
| **23 Substituted Hydrocarbons and Their Reactions** | **8** | **5** |
| 23.1 Functional Groups | 1 | 1/2 |
| 23.2 Alcohols, Ethers, and Amines | 1 1/2 | 1 |
| 23.3 Carbonyl Compounds | 1 1/2 | 1 |
| 23.4 Other Reactions of Organic Compounds | 1 1/2 | 1 |
| 23.5 Polymers | 1 1/2 | 1 |
| Chapter Assessment | 1 | 1/2 |
| | | |
| **24 The Chemistry of Life** | **6** | **3** |
| 24.1 Proteins | 1 | 1/2 |
| 24.2 Carbohydrates | 1 | 1/2 |
| 24.3 Lipids | 1 | 1/2 |
| 24.4 Nucleic Acids | 1 | 1/2 |
| 24.5 Metabolism | 1 | 1/2 |
| Chapter Assessment | 1 | 1/2 |
| | | |
| **25 Nuclear Chemistry** | **6** | **3 1/2** |
| 25.1 Nuclear Radiation | 1 | 1/2 |
| 25.2 Radioactive Decay | 1 | 1/2 |
| 25.3 Transmutation | 1 | 1 |
| 25.4 Fission and Fusion of Atomic Nuclei | 1 | 1/2 |
| 25.5 Applications and Effects of Nuclear Reactions | 1 | 1/2 |
| Chapter Assessment | 1 | 1/2 |
| | | |
| **26 Chemistry in the Environment** | **4** | **—** |
| 26.1 Earth's Atmosphere | 1 1/2 | — |
| 26.2 Earth's Water | 1/2 | — |
| 26.3 Earth's Crust | 1/2 | — |
| 26.4 Cycles in the Environment | 1/2 | — |
| Chapter Assessment | 1 | — |
| | | |
| **Total Sessions** | **165** | **90** |

# IDENTIFYING MISCONCEPTIONS

*Chemistry: Matter and Change* contains many opportunities to find, explore, and correct misconceptions about chemistry that students may have.
Each chapter in the *Teacher Wraparound Edition* contains at least one four-part *Identifying Misconceptions* feature.

> The **introductory paragraph** explains the misconception that students may have concerning the chapter topic.

---

### CHEMLAB

ChemLab 17, located at the end of the chapter, can be used at this point in the lesson.

### Identifying Misconceptions

Students often confuse catalysts and intermediates in reaction mechanisms.

**Uncover the Misconception**
Have students examine the three elementary reactions that comprise the mechanism for the complex reaction shown on this page. Ask if $N_2O_2$ and $N_2O$ are catalysts or intermediates. Both are intermediates because they are produced in one elementary step and consumed in a subsequent step.

**Demonstrate the Concept**
Have students examine the following general reaction mechanism and identify catalysts and intermediates.
$A + B + C \rightarrow X$
$X + D \rightarrow Y + A$
$Y \rightarrow E$
X and Y are intermediates. A is a catalyst.

**Assess New Knowledge**
Have students write the overall reaction for the previous reaction. $B + C + D \rightarrow E$. Ask students to explain why A is a catalyst whereas B and C are reactants. A is a catalyst because it reacts in step 1 of the reaction mechanism and is reformed in step 2. However, B and C are also reactants because they are rearranged into different molecules in the first elementary step and are not reformed.

**Figure 17-9**
Increasing the surface area of reactants provides more opportunity for collisions with other reactants, thereby increasing the reaction rate.

**Figure 17-10**

**a** Increasing the temperature of a reaction increases the frequency of collisions and therefore the rate of reaction.
**b** Increasing the temperature also raises the kinetic energy of the particles, thus more of the collisions at high temperatures have enough energy to overcome the activation energy barrier and react.

Pulverizing (or grinding) a substance is one way to increase its rate of reaction. This is because, for the same mass, many small particles have more total surface area than one large particle. So, a spoonful of sugar placed in a cup of water dissolves faster than the same mass in a single chunk, which has less surface area, as shown in **Figure**. example illustrates that increasing the surface area of a reactant change its concentration, but it does increase the rate of reaction ing the collision rate between reacting particles.

### Temperature

Generally, increasing the temperature at which a reaction occurs the reaction rate. For example, you know that the reactions that to spoil occur much faster at room temperature than when refrigerated. The graph in **Figure 17-10a** illustrates that increasing perature by 10 K can approximately double the rate of a reaction a small increase in temperature have such a significant effect?

As you learned in Chapter 13, increasing the temperature of increases the average kinetic energy of the particles that make stance. For that reason, reacting particles collide more frequent temperatures than at lower temperatures. However, that fact account for the increase in reaction rate with increasing temperature understand how reaction rate varies with temperature, exam shown in **Figure 17-10b**. This graph compares the numbers of ing sufficient energy to react at temperatures $T_1$ and $T_2$, where than $T_1$. The shaded area under each curve represents the number of collisions having energy equal to or greater than the activation energy. The dotted line indicates the activation energy ($E_a$) for the reaction. How do the shaded areas compare? The number of high-energy collisions temperature, $T_2$, is much greater than at the lower temperature, as the temperature increases more collisions result in a reaction.

As you can see, increasing the temperature of the reactants reaction rate because raising the kinetic energy of the reacting es both the collision frequency and the collision energy. You ca the relationship between reaction rate and temperature by pe **miniLAB** for this chapter.

> **Uncover the Misconception** helps you to explore the origin of students' misconception.

> **Demonstrate the Concept** provides new information in an interactive strategy that corrects the current misconception and replaces it with sound, scientific knowledge.

> **Assess New Knowledge** has students demonstrate their grasp of the correct information in an interactive activity. You can assess students' understanding of this knowledge to make sure their misconception has been corrected.

**Reaction Rate and Temperature**
(330K, 32)
(320K, 16)
(310K, 8)
(290K, 2)

**Particle Energy and Temperature**
$T_2 > T_1$
$T_1$
$T_2$
Activation energy

538 Chapter 17 Reaction Rates

---

### GLENCOE TECHNOLOGY

**CD-ROM**
**Chemistry: Matter and Change**
Demonstration: *Surface Area Affects Reactions*

538

### CHEMISTRY JOURNAL
**Kitchen Reaction Rates**
*Linguistic* Ask students to keep notes while they watch or assist in the preparation of at least five meals. Their notes should describe ways in which conditions in their kitchens are varied or controlled to influence the rates of reactions during food storage and preparation. Have them include their notes in their chemistry journals. L2 ELL

### Portfolio
**Reaction Pathways**
*Visual-Spatial* Have students make general energy diagrams for one of each of the following types of chemical reactions: exothermic, endothermic, and thermoneutral (neither exothermic nor endothermic). The diagrams should show both uncatalyzed and catalyzed reaction pathways. Have students include the diagrams in their portfolios. L2 P

## ✓ Assessment

**W**hat criteria do you use to assess your students as they progress through a course? Do you rely on formal tests and quizzes? To assess students' achievement in science, you need to measure not only their knowledge of the subject matter, but also their ability to handle scientific apparatus; to organize, predict, record, and interpret data; to design experiments; and to communicate orally and in writing. *Chemistry: Matter and Change* has been designed to provide you with a variety of assessment tools, both formal and informal, to help you develop a clearer picture of your students' progress.

## ASSESSMENT IN CHEMISTRY: MATTER AND CHANGE

*Chemistry: Matter and Change* provides numerous opportunities to observe student behavior in both informal and formal settings. Each *ChemLab, MiniLab, Problem-Solving Lab,* and *Demonstration* contains an assessment suggestion. In addition, each numbered section contains at least one, and sometimes many, additional assessment strategies. Each assessment strategy is classified as Performance, Portfolio, Knowledge, or Skill.

### PERFORMANCE ASSESSMENT

Performance assessments are becoming more common in today's schools. Science curricula are being revised to prepare students to cope with change and with futures that will depend on their abilities to think, learn, and solve problems. Although learning core concepts will always be important in the chemistry curriculum, the concepts alone are no longer sufficient in a student's scientific education.

### Defining Performance Assessment

Performance assessment is based on judging the quality of a student's response to a performance task. A performance task is constructed to require the use of important concepts with supporting information, work habits important to science, and one or more of the elements of scientific literacy. The performance task attempts to put the student in a real-world context so that the class learning can be put to authentic use later on.

### Performance Assessment Is a Learning Activity

Performance assessment is designed to improve the student. Whereas a traditional test is designed to take a snapshot of what the student knows, the performance task involves the student in work that makes the learning more meaningful and builds on the student's knowledge and skills. As a student is engaged in a performance task with performance assessment lists and examples of excellent work, both learning and assessment are occurring.

### Performance Task Assessment Lists

A performance task can be assessed according to many different criteria. These criteria, which may include observing, data collecting, or modeling, are then divided up into a number of well-defined categories that are assigned points. These categories can then be scored separately by both teacher and student. The teacher scores not only the quality of the product, but also the quality of the student's self-assessment. Examples of performance assessment lists can be found in the *Glencoe Professional Development Series* booklet *Performance Assessment in the Science Classroom.* Each performance assessment in

*Chemistry: Matter and Change* is correlated to a specific assessment list in this booklet.

In addition to using the performance task assessment list to help guide his or her work and then to self-assess it, the student needs to study examples of excellent work. These examples could come from published sources, or they could be other students' work. These examples include the same type of product for different topics, but they should all be rated excellent using the assessment list for that product type.

## Assessing Student Work with Rubrics

A rubric is a set of descriptions of the quality of a process and/or a product. The set of descriptions includes a continuum of quality from excellent to poor. Rubrics for various types of assessment products can be found in *Performance Assessment in the Science Classroom.*

## Group Performance Assessment

Recent research has shown that a cooperative learning environment improves student learning outcomes for students of all ability levels. *Chemistry: Matter and Change* provides many opportunities for cooperative learning and, as a result, many opportunities to observe group work processes and products. Glencoe's *Cooperative Learning in the Science Classroom* provides strategies and

resources for implementing and evaluating various group activities.

In cooperative group assessment, all members of the group contribute to the work process and its products. For example, if a mixed-ability, four-member laboratory work group conducts an activity, you can use a rating scale or checklist to assess the quality of both group interactions and work skills. All four members of the group are expected to review and agree on the data sheet produced by the group. You can require each member to certify the group's results by signing the data sheet or lab report. In this approach, all members of the group receive the same grade on the work product. Research shows that cooperative group assessment is as valid as individual assessment. Additionally, it reduces the marking and grading workload of the teacher.

## PORTFOLIOS: PUTTING IT ALL TOGETHER

The purpose of a student or cooperative group portfolio is to present examples of the individual's or group's work in a non-testing environment. A portfolio is simply a method for assembling and presenting selected examples of work products. It should help the student see the big picture of how he or she is performing in gaining knowledge and skills and how effective his or her work habits are. The portfolio is a way for students to see how the individual performance tasks done during the year fit into a pattern that reveals the overall quality of their learning. The process of assembling the portfolio should be both integrative (of process and content) and reflective. The portfolio is not a complete collection of all worksheets and other assignments for a grading period. At its best, it should include integrated performance products that show growth in concept attainment and skill development.

You can structure the portfolio development process by establishing categories and other limiting specifications. An essential component in portfolio development is the composition of a submission letter or reflective paper that lists the contents of the portfolio and discusses growth in knowledge, attitudes, and skills.

*Chemistry: Matter and Change* presents a wealth of opportunities for portfolio development. Each chapter contains ideas for portfolio activities, enrichment activities, laboratory investigations, skill reviews, library research, writing activities, and features with critical-thinking opportunities. Each of these student activities results in a product. A mixture of these products can be used to document student growth during the grading period.

In addition, *Chemistry: Matter and Change* strongly suggests the use of student journals. Students are encouraged to write observations, descriptions, and reflections in their journals. They are also encouraged to include diagrams and drawings. Excerpts from the student journal can be included in an individual or group portfolio. Additionally, as many writers have discovered, the journal will be an excellent resource for developing the reflective submission letter or paper.

## KNOWLEDGE ASSESSMENT

Although new and exciting performance skill assessments are emerging, paper-and-pencil tests are still a mainstay of student evaluation. Students must learn to conceptualize scientific processes and prepare for traditional content assessments. Presently, and in the foreseeable future, students will be required to pass written tests to exit high school and to enter college, trade schools, and other training programs.

The *Chemistry: Matter and Change* program contains numerous strategies and an assortment of traditional aids for evaluating student progress toward mastery of chemistry concepts. Concluding each numbered section in the *Student Edition, Section Assessment* questions are presented. This spaced review process helps to build learning bridges that allow all students to progress confidently from one lesson to the next.

When instruction for the chapter has been completed, a summation of the major concepts is presented in a *Study Guide*. Small groups of students can research the major concepts in the chapter and present restatements of their meaning in writing and as oral reports to the class.

After the main idea presentations, the formal review process for the written content assessment can begin. *Chemistry: Matter and Change* presents a two- to six-page *Chapter Assessment* at the end of each chapter. By evaluating the student responses to this extensive review, which also includes *Cumulative Review* questions, you can determine whether any substantial reteaching is needed. Throughout the text, wherever *Example Problems* are presented, they are always followed by *Practice Problems*. Additional practice problem sets are placed wherever students would benefit by practicing problem-solving skills. For further assessment, additional practice problems are provided in *Appendix A* and in the *Supplemental Problems* booklet of *the Teacher Classroom Resources.*

For the formal content assessment, a six-page test for each chapter is provided in the *Chapter Assessment* booklet. If your individual assessment plan requires a test that differs from this test in the resource package, customized tests can be easily produced using the *ExamView® Pro CD-ROM.*

## SKILL ASSESSMENT

The *Chemistry: Matter and Change* program contains many assessment strategies that require students to use graphing and computational skills. The *Math Handbook,* located in Appendix B at the back of the *Student Edition,* can help students master these skills.

## CHAPTER ASSESSMENT

All *Chapter Assessment* questions and answers have been validated for accuracy and suitability. In addition, each *Chapter Assessment* contains a test-taking tip that will aid students in preparing for and taking tests.

# STANDARDIZED TESTS

Glencoe has worked to align our texts with state and national standardized tests. Alignment ensures that students are prepared for these tests without the need for extensive "cram sessions" or expensive tutoring at the end of the year. Preparation is built in, not added on, to the instructional process. The textbook's end-of-chapter assessments are written to the same standards as those of the standardized tests themselves. In addition, the last page of the *Chapter Assessment—Standardized Test Practice*—gives students practice with the type of questions usually found in these standardized tests.

- Standardized Test Practice workbooks give students practice drills tied to state and national tests.
- Without sacrificing your instructional objectives, you can guide your students toward state goals.
- Textbook alignment ensures that the skills and concepts students learn are the skills and concepts that are tested.
- Integrated, cumulative test preparation throughout the year reduces test anxiety and improves student performance.

This workbook includes two pages of questions per chapter that reflect the major concepts and themes of the text. Each question has been correlated to the National Science Content Standards. Not only are answers given, but the book also explains why each answer is the correct one, thus providing feedback and remediation.

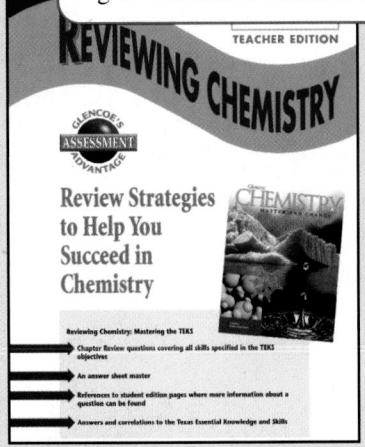

All *Chapter Assessment* questions and answers have been validated for accuracy and suitability.

Standardized Test Practices are consistent with standardized tests and proficiency exams on state and national levels.

Test-Taking Tips prepare students for exams in other disciplines, as well as in chemistry.

# TEACHING STRATEGIES

## DIFFERENTIATED INSTRUCTION

| | DESCRIPTION | SOURCES OF HELP/INFORMATION |
|---|---|---|
| **Learning Disabled** | All learning disabled students have an academic problem in one or more areas, such as academic learning, language, perception, social-emotional adjustment, memory, or attention. | *Journal of Learning Disabilities*<br>*Learning Disability Quarterly* |
| **Behaviorally Disordered** | Children with behavior disorders deviate from standards or expectations of behavior and impair the functioning of others and themselves. These children may also be gifted or learning disabled. | *Exceptional Children*<br>*Journal of Special Education* |
| **Physically Challenged** | Children who are physically disabled fall into two categories—those with orthopedic impairments and those with other health impairments. Orthopedically impaired children have the use of one or more limbs severely restricted, so the use of wheelchairs, crutches, or braces may be necessary. Children with other health impairments may require the use of respirators or other medical equipment. | Batshaw, M.L. and M.Y. Perset. *Children with Handicaps: A Medical Primer.* Baltimore: Paul H. Brooks, 1981.<br>Hale, G. (Ed.). *The Source Book for the Disabled.* New York: Holt, Rinehart & Winston, 1982.<br>*Teaching Exceptional Children* |
| **Visually Impaired** | Children who are visually disabled have partial or total loss of sight. Individuals with visual impairments are not significantly different from their sighted peers in ability range or personality. However, blindness may affect cognitive, motor, and social development, especially if early intervention is lacking. | *Journal of Visual Impairment and Blindness*<br>*Education of Visually Handicapped*<br>*American Foundation for the Blind* |
| **Hearing Impaired** | Children who are hearing impaired have partial or total loss of hearing. Individuals with hearing impairments are not significantly different from their hearing peers in ability range or personality. However, the chronic condition of deafness may affect cognitive, motor, and social development if early intervention is lacking. Speech development also is often affected. | *American Annals of the Deaf*<br>*Journal of Speech and Hearing Research*<br>*Sign Language Studies* |
| **English Language Learners** | Multicultural and/or bilingual children often speak English as a second language or not at all. The customs and behavior of people in the majority culture may be confusing for some of these students. Cultural values may inhibit some of these students from full participation. | *Teaching English as a Second Language Reporter*<br>R.L. Jones (Ed.). *Mainstreaming and the Minority Child.* Reston, VA: Council for Exceptional Children, 1976. |
| **Gifted** | Although no formal definition exists, these students can be described as having above-average ability, task commitment, and creativity. Gifted students rank in the top 5% of their class. They usually finish work more quickly than other students, and are capable of divergent thinking. | *Journal for the Education of the Gifted*<br>*Gifted Child Quarterly*<br>*Gifted Creative/Talented* |

## TIPS FOR INSTRUCTION

1. Provide support and structure; clearly specify rules, assignments, and duties.
2. Practice skills frequently. Use games and drills to help maintain student interest.
3. Allow students to record answers on tape and allow extra time to complete tests and assignments.
4. Provide outlines or tape lecture material.
5. Pair students with peer helpers, and provide class time for pair interaction.

1. Provide a clearly structured environment with regard to scheduling, rules, room arrangement, and safety.
2. Clearly outline objectives and how you will help students obtain objectives. Seek input from them about their strengths, weaknesses, and goals.
3. Reinforce appropriate behavior and model it for students.
4. Do not expect immediate success. Instead, work for long-term improvement.
5. Balance individual needs with group requirements.

1. Openly discuss with the student any uncertainties you have about when to offer aid.
2. Ask parents or therapists and students what special devices or procedures are needed, and whether any special safety precautions need to be taken.
3. Allow physically disabled students to do everything their peers do, including participating in field trips, special events, and projects.
4. Help nondisabled students and adults understand physically disabled students.

1. As with all students, help the student become independent. Some assignments may need to be modified.
2. Teach classmates how to serve as guides.
3. Limit unnecessary noise in the classroom.
4. Encourage students to use their sense of touch. Provide tactile models whenever possible.
5. Describe people and events as they occur in the classroom.
6. Provide taped lectures and reading assignments.
7. Team the student with a sighted peer for laboratory work.

1. Seat students where they can see your lip movements easily, and avoid visual distractions.
2. Avoid standing with your back to the window or light source.
3. Using an overhead projector allows you to maintain eye contact while writing.
4. Seat students where they can see speakers.
5. Write all assignments on the board, or hand out written instructions.
6. If the student has a manual interpreter, allow both student and interpreter to select the most favorable seating arrangements.

1. Remember that students' ability to speak English does not reflect their academic ability.
2. Try to incorporate the student's cultural experience into your instruction. The help of a bilingual aide may be effective.
3. Include information about different cultures in your curriculum to help build students' self-image. Avoid cultural stereotypes.
4. Encourage students to share their cultures in the classroom.

1. Make arrangements for students to take selected subjects early and to work on independent projects.
2. Let students express themselves in art forms such as drawing, creative writing, or acting.
3. Make public services available through a catalog of resources, such as agencies providing free and inexpensive materials, community services and programs, and people in the community with specific expertise.
4. Ask "what if" questions to develop high-level thinking skills. Establish an environment safe for risk taking.
5. Emphasize concepts, theories, ideas, relationships, and generalizations.

The *Student Edition* and *Teacher Wraparound Edition* contain a variety of strategies for addressing the individual needs of students:

- **Differentiated Instruction** strategies
- Traditional, CBL, and Small-Scale **ChemLabs**
- Introductory **Discovery Labs**
- Hands-on **MiniLabs**
- **Demonstrations**
- **Visual Learning** strategies

The following Glencoe products also can help you tailor your instruction to meet the individual needs of your students:

- **Study Guide for Content Mastery**
- **Challenge Problems**
- **Section Focus Transparencies**
- **MindJogger Videoquizzes**
- **Guided Reading Audio Program**

# CULTURAL DIVERSITY

"Multicultural education is an idea stating that all students, regardless of the groups to which they belong, such as those related to gender, ethnicity, race, culture, social class, religion, or exceptionality, should experience education equality in the schools"

—James Banks

## Diverse Cultural Heritages

American classrooms reflect the rich and diverse cultural heritages of the American people. Students come from different ethnic backgrounds and different cultural experiences into a common classroom that must assist all of them in learning. The diversity itself is an important focus of the learning experience. Diversity can be repressed, creating a hostile environment; ignored, creating an indifferent environment; or appreciated, creating a receptive and productive environment.

## Cultural Diversity in *Chemistry: Matter and Change*

Responding to diversity and approaching it as a part of every curriculum may be challenging to a teacher, experienced or not. The goal of science is understanding. The goal of multicultural education is to promote an understanding of how people from different cultures approach and solve the basic problems all humans have in living and learning. Students should understand that all people, regardless of their cultural background or ethnic origin, have made and continue to make contributions to science. *Chemistry: Matter and Change* addresses this issue by including numerous *Cultural Diversity* connections in the *Teacher Wraparound Edition*, by showing successful scientists from diverse ethnic backgrounds, and by showing chemistry topics reflected in other cultures and historical settings. The intent is to build awareness and appreciation for the global community in which we all live.

These features offer opportunities to integrate multicultural materials that relate to the topics presented in each chapter into the curriculum. By providing these opportunities, *Chemistry: Matter and Change* is helping to meet the four major goals of multicultural education.

1. Promoting the strength and value of cultural diversity
2. Promoting the human rights of and respect for those who are different from oneself
3. Promoting social justice and equal opportunity for all people
4. Promoting equity in the distribution of power among groups

These goals are accomplished when students see others like themselves in positive settings in their textbooks. They also are accomplished when students realize that major contributions in science are the result of the work of hundreds of individuals from diverse backgrounds. The philosophy and design of *Chemistry: Matter and Change* attempts to help you with these goals by showing students of diverse ethnic origins taking part in the scientific endeavor.

Additional information on multicultural education can be found in the following references.

Atwater, Mary, et al. *Multicultural Education: Inclusion of All.* Athens, Georgia: University of Georgia Press, 1994.

Banks, James A. and Cherry A. McGee Banks. *Multicultural Education: Issues and Perspectives.* Boston: Allyn and Bacon, 1989.

Banks, James A. *Curriculum Guidelines for Multiethnic Education.* Washington, DC: National Council for the Social Studies, 1977.

Selin, Helaine. *Science Across Cultures: An Annotated Bibliography of Books on Non-Western Science, Technology and Medicine.* New York: Garland, 1992.

# SAFETY SYMBOLS

The *Chemistry: Matter and Change* program uses safety symbols to alert you and your students to possible laboratory hazards. These symbols are provided in the student text inside the front cover and are explained below. Be sure your students understand each symbol before they begin an activity that displays a symbol.

| | HAZARD | EXAMPLES | PRECAUTION | REMEDY |
|---|---|---|---|---|
| DISPOSAL | Special disposal procedures need to be followed. | certain chemicals, living organisms | Do not dispose of these materials in the sink or trash can. | Dispose of wastes as directed by your teacher. |
| BIOLOGICAL | Organisms or other biological materials that might be harmful to humans | bacteria, fungi, blood, unpreserved tissues, plant materials | Avoid skin contact with these materials. Wear mask or gloves. | Notify your teacher if you suspect contact with material. Wash hands thoroughly. |
| EXTREME TEMPERATURE | Objects that can burn skin by being too cold or too hot | boiling liquids, hot plates, dry ice, liquid nitrogen | Use proper protection when handling. | Go to your teacher for first aid. |
| SHARP OBJECT | Use of tools or glassware that can easily puncture or slice skin | razor blades, pins, scalpels, pointed tools, dissecting probes, broken glass | Practice common-sense behavior and follow guidelines for use of the tool. | Go to your teacher for first aid. |
| FUME | Possible danger to respiratory tract from fumes | ammonia, acetone, nail polish remover, heated sulfur, moth balls | Make sure there is good ventilation. Never smell fumes directly. Wear a mask. | Leave foul area and notify your teacher immediately. |
| ELECTRICAL | Possible danger from electrical shock or burn | improper grounding, liquid spills, short circuits, exposed wires | Double-check setup with teacher. Check condition of wires and apparatus. | Do not attempt to fix electrical problems. Notify your teacher immediately. |
| IRRITANT | Substances that can irritate the skin or mucous membranes of the respiratory tract | pollen, moth balls, steel wool, fiber glass, potassium permanganate | Wear dust mask and gloves. Practice extra care when handling these materials. | Go to your teacher for first aid. |
| CHEMICAL | Chemicals that can react with and destroy tissue and other materials | bleaches such as hydrogen peroxide; acids such as sulfuric acid, hydrochloric acid; bases such as ammonia, sodium hydroxide | Wear goggles, gloves, and an apron. | Immediately flush the affected area with water and notify your teacher. |
| TOXIC | Substance may be poisonous if touched, inhaled, or swallowed | mercury, many metal compounds, iodine, poinsettia plant parts | Follow your teacher's instructions. | Always wash hands thoroughly after use. Go to your teacher for first aid. |
| OPEN FLAME | Open flame may ignite flammable chemicals, loose clothing, or hair | alcohol, kerosene, potassium permanganate, hair, clothing | Tie back hair. Avoid wearing loose clothing. Avoid open flames when using flammable chemicals. Be aware of locations of fire safety equipment. | Notify your teacher immediately. Use fire safety equipment if applicable. |

 **Eye Safety** Proper eye protection should be worn at all times by anyone performing or observing science activities.

 **Clothing Protection** This symbol appears when substances could stain or burn clothing.

 **Animal Safety** This symbol appears when safety of animals and students must be ensured.

 **Handwashing** After the lab, wash hands with soap and water before removing goggles.

# SAFETY IN THE LABORATORY

The activities in *Chemistry: Matter and Change* are designed to minimize dangers in the laboratory. Careful planning and preparation as well as being aware of hazards can keep accidents to a minimum. Practice good laboratory housekeeping and management by observing these guidelines.

## Personal Protection

The use of personal protection equipment is required when potentially hazardous material is present. Personal protection equipment includes eyewear, protective gloves, and laboratory aprons and coats.

### Eyewear

Safety goggles are required for science laboratory and field activities involving any hazardous chemical, which could damage the eye if splashed or rubbed into the eye. Goggles provide eye protection from fine dusts, liquids, splashes, mists, and sprays. They also prevent splashes and sprays from body fluids or dangerous chemicals.

Safety goggles should be large enough to protect and form a seal around the eyes. If not able to seal, goggles should contain side shields to prevent contamination to the eyes.

Eyewear should meet the ANSI Standard Z87.1-*Practice for Occupational and Educational Eye and Face Protection.* Eyewear meeting this standard will bear markings such as "Z87.1" on the frames, and the lens will be marked with the manufacturer's trademark.

Eye protection may also be provided with safety glasses. Safety glasses with side shields will not provide adequate protection from chemical splashes. They are designed primarily to protect the eyes from flying objects.

### Protective Gloves

Gloves protect hands from heat, absorb perspiration, provide a shield from corrosive chemicals and body fluids, and prevent the transmission of microorganisms from person to person. Always check gloves to be sure that there are no tears, punctures, or holes. When removing gloves, peel the gloves off your hand, starting at the wrists and working toward the fingers. Keep the working surface of the gloves from contact with the skin during removal.

### PROTECTIVE GLOVES AND THEIR FUNCTION

| GLOVE TYPE | FUNCTION |
|---|---|
| Plastic | Protects against light corrosives and irritants. |
| Latex | Provides protection against biological materials. Should be changed as soon as they are soiled. *Note: Some people may have an allergic reaction to latex, which can lead to serious medical problems.* |
| Natural Rubber | Protects against electric shock and light corrosive material. |
| Neoprene | Use when working with solvents, oils, or light corrosive material. |
| Cotton | Absorbs perspiration. Wear under latex gloves. |
| Asbestos | Insulates against heat. *Note: Asbestos gloves are labeled with a warning about the danger of cancer. Asbestos is a known carcinogen.* |

## Laboratory Aprons and Coats

Laboratory aprons and coats are designed to protect clothing and skin from splashed and spilled chemicals and biological materials. They should fit the wearer properly to provide maximum protection. A laboratory coat or apron should be worn at all times in the laboratory.

Aprons are usually listed as "bib type," which are suitable for laboratory use. Aprons should be worn over clothing that covers the arms and body. Laboratory coats are usually fire retardant and made of cotton or paper. They are good for protection against flying objects, sharp or rough edges, splashes and spills, and fire.

## Fire Protection

Fire is one of the most frequent mishaps in the science laboratory. The first line of defense from a fire is fire prevention. Effective fire prevention centers on thorough understanding of combustion and the required ingredients. As long as air is present, oxygen will be available for combustion to take place. The areas where prevention measures are best exercised are the fuel and ignition sources.

Fires are classified by the chemical properties of the fuel. The basic classifications are grouped as follows.

- Class A – Ordinary combustible (i.e., paper, wood)
- Class B – Organic solvents (i.e., acetone, alcohols, ethers)
- Class C – Electrical wiring or static charges
- Class D – Active metals (i.e., sodium, potassium, magnesium)

These symbols are accepted for the different classifications of fire. They are applied to fire extinguishers and extinguisher locations to indicate their suitability in extinguishing the different types of fires.

The following precautions should be taken to prevent fires from occurring in the science classroom, laboratory, storage, and preparation area.

- Be aware of ignition sources in your laboratory area (open flames, heat, and electrical equipment).
- Purchase and store flammable reagents in the smallest quantities possible.
- Do not store flammable liquids in standard refrigerators (an explosion-proof refrigerator should be used).
- Store flammable liquids in appropriate safety cabinets and/or safety cans.
- Do not store incompatible reagents together (e.g., acids with flammables).
- Do not store ethers for extended periods of time as explosive peroxides can form.
- Make sure that all electrical cords are in good condition. All electrical outlets should be grounded and should accommodate a 3-pronged plug.

Each science classroom, laboratory, storage and preparation area should have a fire blanket and an appropriate fire extinguisher.

## Fire Extinguishers

In most school environments, hand-held, portable fire extinguishers are the first fire-extinguishing agent used. Therefore, a multipurpose ABC fire extinguisher must be located in each science classroom, laboratory, storage room, and preparation area. Extinguishers must be

- located to be easily seen and the area around them kept clear.
- inspected on a regular basis.
- used by well-trained teachers and students.

Fire extinguishers are labeled in accordance with NFPA standards.

## Fire Blankets

Actual fire control revolves around proper types of control devices such as a fire blanket. Fire blankets are made of specially treated fabric and should be located at strategic areas for all science laboratories where hazardous chemicals are stored and used. Fire blankets can be used if one is unable to reach the safety shower.

## Electrical Protection

Electrical safety needs must be considered for all new, old, and renovated science classrooms, laboratories, storage rooms, and preparation areas. The emphasis of electrical safety should be on prevention. Minimum considerations for electrical safety include the following.

- Ground-fault interrupters (GFI) should be installed to protect against major shock and electrical fires by preventing short circuits.
- All outlets must be grounded to prevent electrical accidents, Sufficient outlets should be provided to eliminate the need for extension cords. If floor boxes are used, they should not be located near water sources or areas where water is used.
- Surge protectors should be used to protect computers and other electronic devices from power surges.
- Emergency shut-off controls (electricity, gas, and water) should be located in an area that is not easily accessible to students.
- Circuits should not be overloaded.
- Use only spark-free refrigeration in laboratories, storage rooms, and preparation areas for storage of flammable chemicals.
- Avoid the use of extension cords.
- Wiring should not have frayed or bare areas.

In developing the school's safety program, include provisions for handling electrical emergencies. All teachers of science should know where the master electrical cutoff switch and the control box are located, and how to operate both of these. Before an activity is conducted that requires the use of an electrical device, the teacher and students must be familiar with its operation and safety features.

*Safety in the Laboratory material used with permission from Texas Safety Standards, produced by the Texas Education Agency.*

# CHEMICAL SAFETY AND DISPOSAL

The teaching of chemistry requires the use of certain supplies and safety equipment if a safe classroom is to be maintained.

## Safety Equipment

As a chemistry teacher, you should be familiar with the use and maintenance of the following equipment.

### Fume Hoods

Each laboratory facility and preparation room where chemicals are used should be equipped with a fume hood. No open face fume hood with a low face velocity can provide complete safety against events that take place in the hood. However, a properly designed hood in a properly ventilated room can provide adequate protection. To provide proper protections, follow these recommended guidelines.

- Keep the interior light on so that the working area is properly illuminated.
- Check the exhaust system—air movement is inward and upward in the hood.
- Conduct all portions of the experiment that cause contaminants to form inside the hood.
- Large objects should not be placed directly on the hood's working surface. Use blocks under the large object to allow proper airflow under the object.
- Move the vertical sash to the lowest position that allows access so that manipulation is possible. The sash should protect the head and upper body in case of an explosion. (Safety goggles are required.)
- Do not place your head in the hood when contaminants are being generated.
- Do not use the fume hood as a waste disposal unit except for very small amounts of volatile chemicals.
- Do not store chemicals or apparatuses in the hood.
- Keep the slots in the hood baffle (air intake) free from obstructions.
- Keep the laboratory door closed unless indicated from the manufacturer.
- Remove the sash or panels only when necessary for apparatus setup. Do not operate until sash has been replaced.

- Do not place electrical receptacles or other sources that may produce a spark in the fume hood when using flammable chemicals or when gases may be present.
- The hood's sash should be marked for appropriate closure point when it is necessary to partially close the sash during an operation.
- The sash should be closed when the hood's exhaust system is not operating.
- Provide regular maintenance on the hood's exhaust system. Use static pressure gauges on the hood throat and across filters in the exhaust system to ensure proper exhaust flow.

### Eyewashes

The first response prior to medical treatment, for a student or teacher who has hazardous material in the eye, is flushing with water to dilute chemicals, wash out debris, or irrigate the eyes. It is very important that the eyelids are held open and the eyeballs rolled so water can flow on all surfaces and in the folds surrounding the eyeballs. **Note:** Squeeze bottles are not sufficient and should not be used as eyewashes in any science laboratory.

An eyewash that can wash both eyes simultaneously should be located in every science laboratory, classroom, and preparation room where hazardous chemicals are used. To ensure that the eyewash station in your science facility will meet safety requirements, it should

- be located no more than 10 seconds (25 feet) from any student work station.
- comply (one eyewash) with ADA regulations on accessibility.
- be provided sufficient water pressure to operate correctly.
- wash both eyes simultaneously.
- supply an instant flow of recirculated tempered water continuously for at least 15 minutes.
- have a water control valve that remains on, allowing the user to use both hands.
- be clearly marked and unobstructed for immediate use.

**Note:** Eyewashes should be flushed for 5 minutes once a week to remove any harmful contaminant that may form or grow in the eyewash.

## Safety Showers

A safety shower should be found in any laboratory where hazardous chemicals are used. Safety showers

- must meet the standards for height, spray pattern, tepid water temperature, and water flow of 20 gallons per minute at 30 PSI.
- should have a control valve that can remain on without requiring the use of the operator's hands.
- should be located no more than 50 feet or 10 seconds away from any student work station.
- should be marked with a highly visible sign for each safety shower.
- should be large enough to accommodate the injured person and a teacher assisting with the emergency.
- should have a fixed valve handle or a chain with a large ring that can be pulled down to start the flow of water.
- must have sufficient water flow and pressure to function properly for immediate use.
- should be flushed once a week to eliminate contamination and check for proper working conditions.

Tepid water should not exceed the temperature of a person's eyeball (approximately 85°F) on combination eyewash/shower systems. Mixing valves for tepid water to eyewashes or eyewash/shower systems should have a minimum flow of 2 gallons per minute and a maximum flow of 60 gallons per minute.

## Ventilation

A well-maintained ventilation system is an important contributor to a healthy environment in science classroom and laboratories. According to the *NSTA Guide to School Science Facilities,* "Forced ventilation at a minimum rate of four changes of air per hour should be provided for science laboratories, and continuous ventilation at six changes per hour for chemical storage rooms. Assuming that there is a fume hood in each preparation room, four changes per hour is adequate. All exhausts should be

vented to the outside of the building, not recirculated in the building's ventilation system.

Chemical storage rooms need systems that vent directly outside, usually to the roof, and away from fresh-air intake pipes. Stage cabinets for flammables should not be ventilated to the outside.

Every science room should be equipped with exhaust fans designed for rapid venting of smoke or bad odors created by an investigation."

## Material Safety Data Sheets

Every chemical manufacturer is required by law to supply a recent Material Safety Data Sheet (MSDS) with each chemical it produces. These should be sent with each chemical that is purchased by a school or school district. If MSDS forms are not available, request them from the chemical manufacturer. Every teacher needs to know and understand the information on a MSDS. The following information should be listed on MSDS forms for science teachers.

- Product identification
- Hazardous components
- Physical data
- Fire and explosion hazards
- Health hazards
- Fire and explosion data
- Spill and disposal procedures
- Protective equipment
- Storage and handling procedures
- Transportation data and additional information

## Chemical Storage

Safe chemical storage is based on the chemical properties of the substances that are to be stored. The hazards of the chemicals are closely associated with their chemical and physical properties. Proper storage of chemicals should follow these guidelines.

1. The chemicals must be properly labeled with the identity of the contents, hazards, and manufacturer's name and address.
2. The chemicals must be stored in compatible families.
3. The chemical storage room should be located so that people in the building or damage to the building will be minimal if an explosion or fire was to occur.
4. The chemical storeroom must have two exits and doors that lock.
5. The doors should be labeled "Authorized Personnel Only" or "Hazardous Materials".
6. The storage room must have continuous forced air ventilation that is vented to the outside away from air intakes.
7. Storage cabinets and shelves must be resistant to corrosion.
8. Chemicals must be stored in upright position and no more than two or three containers deep.
9. Shelves may be equipped with a lip to prevent chemicals from being jarred off the shelf.
10. Corrosives (acids and bases) should be stored in an approved corrosive cabinet.
11. Flammables should be stored in an approved flammable cabinet.
12. Chemicals should not be stored above eye level and never stored on the floor.
13. Water-reactive chemicals (metals) should be stored where they will remain dry.
14. Proper safety equipment must be clearly marked inside the storeroom.
    - ABC fire extinguisher
    - Safety goggles
    - Fire blanket
    - Spill kit
    - First aid kit
15. The room must be adequately lighted.
16. Smoke detectors should be present.
17. An on-going chemical inventory should be maintained.

## Chemical Disposal

There are several important steps that should be taken prior to proceeding with chemical disposal. First, determine how many chemicals are designated for disposal. Remove
- out-of-date or contaminated chemicals.
- chemicals without legible labels.
- chemicals that are too hazardous for student use.

Then, make arrangements with an appropriate disposal company.

### Options for Proper Chemical Disposal

Contact commercial chemical disposal companies in your area. Many waste disposal companies recycle chemicals and resell them. Other options may be available by contacting
- other schools in your area and combine quantities for disposal.
- industries in the area for assistance in disposal.
- institutions of higher education. They may allow you to use their system of disposal.
- the Natural Resources Conservation Commission in your state.

### Disposal of Liquid Waste

A frequent question from chemistry teachers is about which liquids may safely be disposed of in the sanitary drains. First, the teacher must be certain that the sewer flows to a wastewater treatment plant and not to a stream or other natural waterway. Second, any substance from a laboratory should be flushed with at least 100 times its own volume of tap water. Third, disposal methods should be checked with local authorities because local regulations are often more stringent than federal requirements. The book, *Prudent Practices in the Laboratory,* published by the National Research Council, Washington, DC: National Academy Press, 1995, lists many substances that can be disposed of in the sanitary drain.

Some positive and negative ions from the *Prudent Practices* lists are given in the table shown on the opposite page. Note that it is important that both the positive and negative ion of a salt be listed in order for its drain disposal to be considered safe. Also note that although hydrogen and hydroxide ions are listed, acids and bases should be neutralized before disposal. A good rule of thumb is that nothing of pH less than 3 or greater than 8 should be discarded without neutralizing it first.

| Positive Ions | Negative Ions |
|---|---|
| aluminum | borate |
| ammonium | bromide |
| bismuth | carbonate |
| calcium | chloride |
| copper | hydrogen sulfate |
| hydrogen | hydroxide |
| iron | iodide |
| lithium | nitrate |
| magnesium | phosphate |
| potassium | sulfate |
| sodium | sulfite |
| strontium | tetraborate |
| tin | thiocyanate |
| titanium | |
| zinc | |

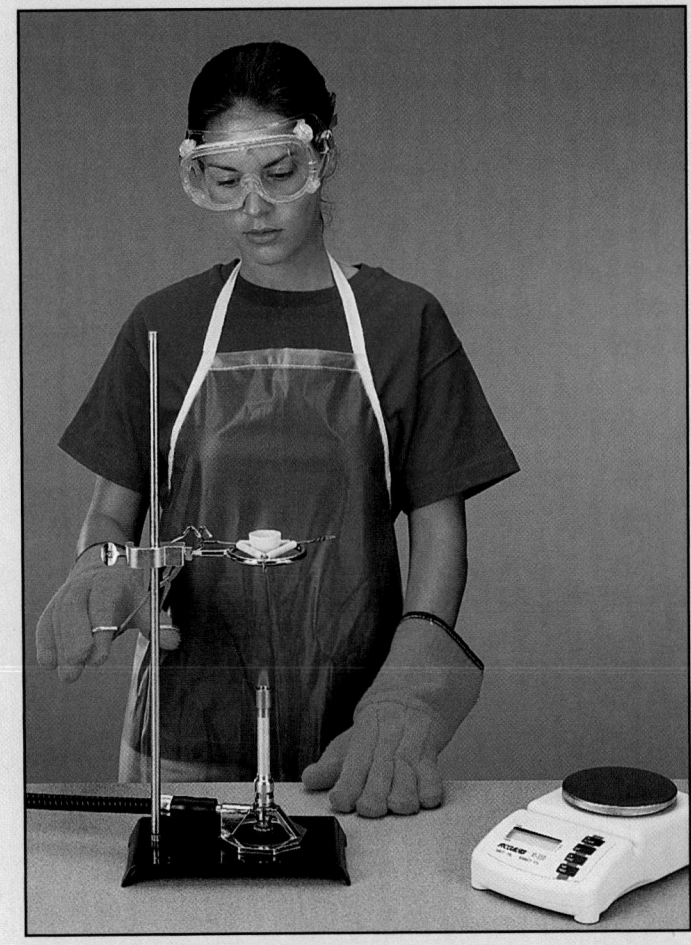

## Disposal of Organic Waste

Of the organic compounds most often found in high school laboratories, the following can be disposed of in the drain: methanol, ethanol, propanols, butanols, pentanols, ethylene, glycol, glycerol, sugars, formaldehyde, formic acid, acetic acid, oxalic acid, sodium and potassium salts of carboxylic acids, esters with fewer than five carbon atoms, and acetone. More extensive lists can be found in *Prudent Practices*.

## Disposal of Other Waste

Other chemicals can be properly treated and disposed of in one of the following ways.

- Treat waste chemically to convert it to a form that is drain-disposable. A good example is the iodate ion, which is too strong an oxidizing agent to be disposed of untreated. However, it is readily reduced to iodide (disposable) by acidified sodium hydrogen sulfite. Many procedures for processing laboratory waste to a discardable form can be found in *Prudent Practices*.

- Recycle waste. A good example is the recovery of valuable metals such as mercury and silver. Solvents can be recycled through distillation.
- If a waste cannot be recycled or processed to disposable form, then it must be packed and shipped by a Department of Transportation-approved shipper to a landfill designated to receive chemical and hazardous waste.

Numerous processes are described in *Prudent Practices* for reducing both the bulk and hazard of wastes. An example is the reduction of chromate and dichromate waste solutions to chromium(III) solutions, which are then made basic. The chromium(III) oxide precipitate is filtered off, dried, and crushed, resulting in significant savings. As hazardous wastes are accumulated awaiting shipment, it is important to observe the proper storage procedures for separating incompatible substances.

## Microscale Chemistry

Microscale science techniques may appear out of place in a discussion of laboratory safety. Quite the contrary, microscale techniques offer a pedagogically sound approach to science laboratory investigations and provide simple solutions to many safety issues.

Major concepts emphasized in laboratory instruction have shifted from a simple reduction in amounts of chemicals used to a re-education approach. The primary construct put forth by advocates of microscale chemistry is to instill in educators and students "If you don't need that much, then don't use it." The purpose is to move away from the throwaway mentality in our society. One way to express to students that the prevention of environmental pollution begins at the source is to reduce the amount of materials being "wasted" while teaching them basic science concepts.

Hazardous waste management is a problem confronting all educational institutions. Schools are finding it increasingly difficult to fund the disposal of hazardous waste while attempting to maintain a hands-on chemical learning environment. Microscale experiments make it possible to promote critical thinking skills while addressing major safety issues for a safe learning environment. Advantages of incorporating microscale/small scale chemistry into the learning environment include the

- reduction in the cost of chemicals.
- reduction of possible fire and explosion danger.
- reduction of chemical waste disposal costs.
- introduction of experiments where chemicals once thought to be too expensive or hazardous can be made available with the reduced amounts.
- recycling products for future experiments (plan ahead and use it again).
- introduction of less expensive glassware.
- reduction of exposure to toxic materials.

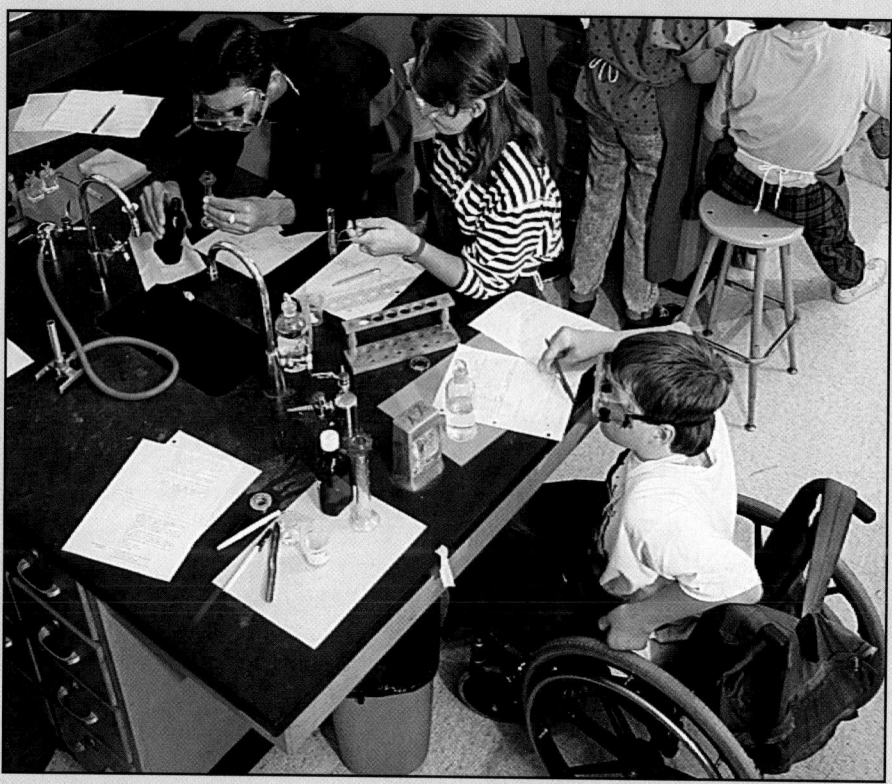

## Safety Advantages

Using microscale techniques means that dispensing liquids from plastic dropper bottles greatly reduces many spills. Accidental glass container breakage and fire hazards are eliminated, and air quality is improved due to smaller amounts of escaping vapor. Although some liquid is lost due to vaporization during both techniques, the microscale technique reduces hazardous organic chemicals that must be recovered and disposed of properly. In addition, this technique represents a responsible step in reducing environmental pollutants. In the science storeroom, chemicals in smaller containers (approximately 10% of the size used in macroscale) reduce the need for storage space.

## Chemical Spills

If a chemical spill occurs in the laboratory or preparatory room, quick action by the teacher can reduce the possibility of injury to a student or themselves. A chemical spill such as a liter bottle of hydrochloric acid breaking in the laboratory is considered a major spill. The teacher should

- immediately evacuate all students through the exits farthest from the spill. Fumes from a chemical spill can cause severe damage to the body.
- immediately assist any person splashed with the chemical to the safety shower.
- turn on emergency exhaust fan.
- contain the spill wearing proper protective clothing. Do not allow the spill to trap you.
- call for help. The school safety plan should contain agencies or departments in your community that will assist in containment and removal of the chemical.

## Spill-Control Materials

There are many types of commercial materials that have been developed for containment and removal of chemical spills. They range from absorbent pads that quickly absorb chemicals in a liquid state, porous bags filled with an amorphous silicate, to materials that neutralize an acid or a caustic spill.

What is typically found in public schools is a plastic 5-gallon bucket filled with dry sand, vermiculite, or dry clay materials. These do nothing to neutralize an acid or base, but they absorb the liquid or contain it in a small area. The disadvantage of using sand is that it is heavy and difficult to transport.

Once the chemical has been contained and neutralized, use clean-up equipment that is made of plastic or polypropylene so that the equipment doesn't react with any of the chemical that remains. The contaminated material is to be placed in plastic bags or containers and marked appropriately. The custodial staff should be informed of the material so that it can be disposed of properly.

### Disclaimer

# PREPARATION OF SOLUTIONS

Many of the chemical reactions you will demonstrate—as well as many that your students will perform in *ChemLabs, MiniLabs, and Discovery Labs*—take place in solution. Fortunately, you can prepare these solutions quickly and safely. **CAUTION: *Read the HAZARD ALERT label on every chemical and follow all recommended safety precautions when using the chemical. When preparing solutions, wear chemical-resistant gloves, a chemical-resistant apron, and chemical safety goggles or a full-face shield. In addition, toxic fumes given off by some chemicals, particularly concentrated acids, require that you open and use them only in a fume hood or in a room with excellent ventilation.***

The following equipment will enable you to prepare solutions in a correct, safe, and time-efficient manner: balance; Pyrex glass beakers (1000 mL, 600 mL, 400 mL, 250 mL, 150 mL, 100 mL); glass graduated cylinders (1000 mL, 500 mL, 100 mL, 50 mL); Pyrex glass volumetric flasks (1000 mL, 500 mL, 250 mL, 100 mL); standard-stem glass funnels; polypropylene powder funnels;

glass stirring rods; polyethylene wash bottle (for distilled or demineralized water). Additional equipment that can further reduce your time and effort include a magnetic stirrer, magnetic stirring bars, and a stirring-bar retriever.

Because tap water contains minerals and dissolved gases that can lead to unwanted reactions, you should prepare most solutions using only distilled or demineralized (deionized) water. Distilled water is free of inorganic materials, suspended impurities, and most organic contaminants. Demineralized water, which is less expensive than distilled water, is free of inorganic materials and most suspended contaminants and is suitable for most solutions. Many laboratory supply companies carry demineralizer cartridges that enable you to demineralize tap water in your school laboratory.

You will find that the solutions needed for the demonstrations and activities in *Chemistry: Matter and Change* are specified by amount and solute concentration. Concentration units include molarity ($M$), mass percent, and volume percent.

## Molarity

### Procedure for preparing a solution by dissolving a solid chemical in water

**Example:** Prepare 100.0 mL aqueous 0.0500$M$ $CuSO_4$ solution using solid $CuSO_4 \cdot 5H_2O$.

1. Calculate moles of $CuSO_4 \cdot 5H_2O$ required.

$$M = \frac{\text{moles of solute}}{\text{liters of solution}}$$

moles of solute = $M \times$ liters of solution

moles of solute = 0.0500 moles/L × 0.100 L = 0.00500 mol

2. Calculate mass of $CuSO_4 \cdot 5H_2O$ needed.

$$0.00500 \text{ mol } CuSO_4 \cdot 5H_2O \times \frac{249.68 \text{ g } CuSO_4 \cdot 5H_2O}{\text{mol } CuSO_4 \cdot 5H_2O} = 1.25 \text{ g } CuSO_4 \cdot 5H_2O$$

3. Weigh out 1.25 g $CuSO_4 \cdot 5H_2O$. Use a powder funnel to add the solid to a 100-mL volumetric flask. Add approximately 75 mL distilled or demineralized water. Swirl or stir until all the solid dissolves. If you used a magnetic stirrer, retrieve the stirring bar and use a wash bottle to rinse the bar and retriever, being sure the rinse water goes into the flask. Add water up to the 100-mL mark on the flask. If the dissolution of a solute is highly exothermic or highly endothermic, wait until the solution returns to room temperature before adding water up to the mark.

# Procedure for preparing a solution by diluting a concentrated, or stock, solution

**Example:** Prepare 500.0 mL aqueous 3.0$M$ $H_2SO_4$ by diluting concentrated (18.0$M$) $H_2SO_4$.

1. Let $M_1$ and $V_1$ represent the molarity and volume of the starting, more concentrated solution. Let $M_2$ and $V_2$ represent the molarity and volume of the final, more dilute solution. Substitute $M_1$, $M_2$, and $V_2$ into the equation $M_1V_1 = M_2V_2$ and solve for $V_1$.

   $(18.0M)(V_1) = (3.0M)(500.0\ mL)$

   $V_1 = 83\ mL$

2. Fill a 500-mL volumetric flask approximately one-half full with distilled or demineralized water. Slowly and carefully add 83 mL 18$M$ $H_2SO_4$ to the water in the flask. Swirl or stir to mix the two liquids. **CAUTION: *Always add a concentrated acid to water, never the reverse.*** After the solution has cooled to room temperature, add water up to the 500-mL mark on the flask.

The molarities of other commonly used, concentrated acids and bases are given below.

ammonium hydroxide ($NH_4OH$), 14.8$M$

hydrochloric acid (HCl), 12$M$

nitric acid ($HNO_3$), 15.8$M$

# Mass Percent

Mass percent solutions are determined by the grams of solute per 100 grams of solution.

## Procedure for preparing a solution of a given mass percent solute

**Example:** Prepare 300.0 g of aqueous sodium chloride solution that is 10.0 % NaCl by mass.

1. Calculate the mass of NaCl required.

   $$\frac{10.0\ g\ NaCl}{100\ g\ solution} \times 300.0\ grams\ solution = 30.0\ g\ NaCl$$

2. Calculate the mass of water required.

   300.0 grams solution – 30.0 g NaCl = 270.0 g water

3. Prepare the solution by dissolving 30.0 grams NaCl in 270.0 g water. Note: Because water's density equals 1.00 g/mL at 4°C, and is quite close to 1.00 g/mL at room temperature, you can measure 270.0 mL of water in a graduated cylinder rather than weigh 270.0 g on a balance.

# Volume Percent

Volume percent solutions are determined by milliliters of solute per 100 mL of solution.

## Procedure for preparing a solution of a given volume percent solute

**Example:** Prepare 75.0 mL of aqueous ethanol solution that is 50.0 % $C_2H_5OH$ by volume.

1. Calculate the volume of $C_2H_5OH$ required.

   $$\frac{50.0\ mL\ C_2H_5OH}{100\ mL\ solution} \times 75.0\ mL\ solution = 37.5\ mL\ C_2H_5OH$$

2. Prepare the solution by mixing 37.5 mL $C_2H_5OH$ with sufficient water to make 75.0 mL of solution.

# EQUIPMENT AND MATERIALS LIST

These easy-to-use tables of materials can help you prepare for your chemistry classes for the year. All quantities are for one lab setup of each *Discovery Lab, MiniLab,* or *ChemLab* for the entire course. Before placing your order for supplies, determine how many classes you will be teaching and how many students you expect in each class. The amounts listed for *Demonstrations* are for one performance of the demonstration. Therefore, if you have seven classes, you will need to multiply the quantities of materials for *Demonstrations* by seven. However, if you have ten groups of students in each of your seven classes, multiply the quantities of materials for *Discovery Labs, ChemLabs,* and *MiniLabs* by 70 to arrive at your total course requirements.

The standard list of equipment is made up of a set of equipment that is generally recommended for each lab bench station in the chemistry laboratory. For all lab activities in this program, it is assumed that your classroom is equipped with these items for each setup of a *Discovery Lab, MiniLab,* or *ChemLab*. Additional equipment required for the course is listed under **Nonconsumables**. The listed amounts of **Chemicals** and **Other Consumables** for Demonstrations, *Discovery Labs, MiniLabs,* and *ChemLabs* are sufficient for one demonstration or one lab setup per student or group of students.

## STANDARD EQUIPMENT LIST (FOR EACH STATION)

apron, 1 per student
goggles, 1 pair per student
beakers, 100-mL, 2
beakers, 250-mL, 2
beakers, 400-mL, 2
beaker tongs
Bunsen burner and tubing
clay triangle
crucible and cover
crucible tongs

droppers, 2
Erlenmeyer flask, 125 mL
Erlenmeyer flask, 250 mL
evaporating dish
forceps
funnel
graduated cylinder, 10-mL
graduated cylinder, 50-mL or 100-mL
microplate, 24-well
microplate, 96-well

scissors
spatula, stainless steel
stirring rods, 2
test-tube holder
test-tube rack
test tubes, 6 large
test tubes, 6 small
wash bottle
watch glass
wire gauze

## CLASSROOM EQUIPMENT (FOR GENERAL USE)

balance
beakers, assorted small 50-mL, 150-mL
beakers, assorted large 600-mL, 800-mL, 1-L, 2-L
CBL system, including sensors and cables
ChemBio software
clamps, assorted including buret clamps
conductivity tester
dishpan, plastic
Erlenmeyer flasks, 500-mL, 1-L
hot plate

iron rings, assorted
iron tripod
lighter for burner
mortar and pestle
ring stands, 2
rubber or Tygon tubing
rubber stoppers, assorted
thermometer, −10°C to 150°C
thermometer clamp

These easy-to-use tables of equipment and consumable materials can help you prepare for your chemistry classes for the year. Quantities listed for *ChemLabs, Discovery Labs,* and *MiniLabs* are the maximum quantities you will need for one student group for the year. Quantities listed for *Demonstrations* are for one performance of the demonstration. The pages on which each item is used are listed in parentheses after the quantities. Refer to the *Resource Manager* in front of each chapter for a list of equipment and materials used for each laboratory activity in the chapter.

# NON-CONSUMABLES

| ITEM | CHEMLAB | DISCOVERY LAB | MINILAB | DEMONSTRATION |
|---|---|---|---|---|
| alpha source | | | | 1 (p. 810) |
| barometer | 1 (pp. 444, 728) | | 1 (p. 439) | |
| basting bulb | 1 (p. 796) | | | |
| battery | | 1 (p. 151) | | |
| beaker, 50-mL | 1 (p. 78) | | 1 (p. 604) | |
| beaker, 150-mL | 1 (p. 374) | | 4 (pp. 295, 681, 715) | 1 (p. 670, 702) |
| beaker, 600-mL | 1 (p. 796) | 1 (pp. 385, 841) | 1 (p. 786) | 3 (pp. 166, 636) |
| beaker, 600-mL with graduations | 1 (p. 444) | | | |
| beaker, 1-L | | | 1 (p. 439) | 3 (p. 28) |
| boiling chip | | 1 (p. 775) | | |
| bottle, widemouth glass with stopper | | | | 1 (p. 280) |
| bucket, 4-L | 1 (p. 444) | | | |
| bucket, 5-gallon | | 1 (p. 419) | | |
| bucket, 8-L metal | | | | 1 (p. 492) |
| buret, 50-mL | 1 (p. 626) | | | 2 (p. 366) |
| can, large metal | | | | 1 (p. 248) |
| ceramic pad | | | | 1 (p. 536) |
| clothespin, spring-type | | | | 10 (p. 762) |
| cloud chamber | | | | 1 (p. 810) |
| coins, copper | | 2 (p. 151) | | |
| comb, plastic | | 1 (p. 87) | | |
| connecting leads with alligator clips each end | | | | 2 (p. 670) |
| connecting wires | | 3 (p. 151) | | |
| Crooke's tube | | | | 1 (p. 92) |
| cuvette | 1 (p. 480) | | | |
| deflagrating spoon | | | | 1 (p. 248) |
| diffraction grating | 1 (p. 142) | | | 1 (p. 136) |
| dominoes | | 28 (p. 805) | | |
| dropper | 5 (pp. 108, 202, 410, 626) | 1 (p. 385) | 3 (pp. 573, 848) | 1 (pp. 280, 420, 622, 636) |
| explosion shield | | | | 1 (pp. 166, 492) |
| flask, 275-mL polystyrene culture | 4 (p. 142) | | | |
| flask, 500-mL Florence | 1 (p. 626) | | | |
| flood lamp, 150-watt | | | | 1 (p. 846) |
| forceps, long | | 1 (p. 697) | 2 (p. 230) | |
| funnel, powder | | | | 1 (p. 222) |
| graduated cylinder, 25-mL | 1 (p. 202) | 1 (pp. 277, 489) | 1 (pp. 15, 28, 786) | 1 (p. 366) |

# LABORATORY/ACTIVITIES

## NON-CONSUMABLES (CONTINUED)

| ITEM | CHEMLAB | DISCOVERY LAB | MINILAB | DEMONSTRATION |
|---|---|---|---|---|
| graduated cylinder, 50-mL | 1 (pp. 78, 480) | 1 (pp. 25, 453) | | |
| graduated cylinder, 250-mL | 1 (p. 862) | | | 1 (pp. 222, 636) |
| hair dryer | 1 (p. 18) | | | |
| hammer | 1 (p. 170) | | | 1 (pp. 192, 492) |
| hole punch | | 1 (p. 87) | | |
| jar, 1-pint canning with ring lid | | | | 1 (p. 398) |
| jar, wide-mouth with lid | | 3 (p. 697) | | |
| lead weight, identical small | | 3 (p. 697) | | |
| light bulb, 40-watt tubular with socket and power cord | 1 (p. 142) | | | |
| light bulb, 150-watt with socket and clamp | 1 (p. 862) | | | |
| light bulb, low-voltage with socket | | 1 (p. 151) | | |
| light source, high-intensity | | | | 1 (p. 810) |
| magnet, bar type | | 1 (p. 179) | | 1 (pp. 92, 492) |
| mass, 500 g | 1 (p. 18) | | | |
| metal object, identical small | | 6 (p. 697) | | |
| meterstick | 1 (p. 18) | | | 1 (p. 702) |
| overhead projector | | | | 1 (p. 166) |
| pennies, pre- and post-1982 | | | 100 (pp. 102, 819) | 3 (p. 62) |
| petri dish with lid | 1 (pp. 78, 832) | | 2 (pp. 15, 751, 848) | 1 (p. 846) |
| pin | | 1 (p. 385) | | |
| pipet, Beral-type | 5 (pp. 688, 766) | 1 (p. 241) | 1 (p. 751) | |
| pipet, thin-stem | 3 (p. 586) | | | |
| pipette | 4 (pp. 300, 480, 796) | 2 (p. 277) | | |
| pipette filler (bulb) | 1 (pp. 480, 550) | | | |
| pipette, dropping | 1 (p. 654) | | 1 (p. 604) | |
| pipette, graduated | 1 (p. 550) | | | |
| pipette, plastic microtip | 1 (p. 444) | | | |
| pneumatic trough | 1 (p. 728) | | | |
| power supply, high voltage | | | | 1 (p. 92) |
| power supply, spectrum tube | 2 (p. 142) | | | 1 (p. 136) |
| rubber stopper assembly, #5 | 1 (p. 796) | | | |
| ruler | 1 (pp. 46, 202, 268, 550) | 1 (pp. 87, 309) | 1 (pp. 438, 715) | 1 (p. 366) |
| sand, dry | | | | 10 kg (p. 492) |
| scupula | | | | 1 (p. 332) |
| spectrum tubes (hydrogen, mercury, and neon) | 1 ea. (p. 142) | | | 1 ea. (p. 136) |
| spoon | 1 (p. 654) | 3 (pp. 626, 841) | 1 (p. 638) | |
| stopwatch (timer, clock) | 1 (pp. 410, 550, 766) | 1 (pp. 3, 489, 697, 805) | 1 (pp. 329, 539, 848) | 1 (p. 28) |
| test tube, large | 3 (p. 202) | 2 (p. 489) | | 3 (pp. 332, 622, 776) |
| test tube, small | 6 (pp. 170, 480, 550, 796) | 2 (pp. 635, 775) | 2 (pp. 184, 573, 751) | 8 (pp. 10, 55, 192, 280, 366) |
| towel, cloth | 1 (p. 766) | | | 1 (p. 192) |
| tubing, glass | 20 cm (p. 444) | 50 cm (p. 559) | | 100 cm (p. 332) |
| voltmeter with leads | | 1 (p. 663) | | |
| washer, metal | | | 1 (p. 28) | |

# NON-CONSUMABLES (CONTINUED)

| ITEM | CHEMLAB | DISCOVERY LAB | MINILAB | DEMONSTRATION |
|---|---|---|---|---|
| weighing bottle | 1 (p. 626) | | | |
| wire cutters | 1 (p. 300) | | | 1 (p. 846) |
| wire screen | | | 10 cm x 10 cm (p. 329) | 9 cm x 9 cm (p. 398) 10 cm x 10 cm (p. 166) |
| CBL-DIN cable | 1 (pp. 480, 796) | | | |
| CBL link cable | 1 (pp. 796, 832, 862) | | | |
| CBL-P adapter | 1 (p. 832) | | | |
| CBL temperature probe | 2 (p. 862) | | | |
| CBL vernier colorimeter | 1 (p. 480) | | | |
| CBL vernier pressure sensor | 1 (p. 796) | | | |
| CBL voltage probe | 1 (p. 688) | | | |
| RADIATIN software program | 1 (p. 832) | | | |
| student radiation monitor | 1 (p. 832) | | | |
| TI-Graphlink cable | 1 (pp. 480, 832, 862) | | | |

# CHEMICALS

| ITEM | CHEMLAB | DISCOVERY LAB | MINILAB | DEMONSTRATION |
|---|---|---|---|---|
| 2-propanol, 91% (isopropanol) | 1 mL (p. 410) | | | |
| 2-propanol, 99% (isopropanol) | 2 mL (p. 766) | | | |
| acetic acid, glacial | | | 12 mL (pp. 439, 604) | 1 mL (p. 622) |
| acetone | 300 mL (pp. 268, 410) | | | 60 mL (p. 570) |
| aluminum nitrate | 42 g (pp. 300, 688) | | | |
| aluminum powder (100 mesh) | | | | 50 g (p. 492) |
| aluminum strip | 1 (p. 688) | | | |
| aluminum wire | 10 cm (p. 300) | | | |
| ammonia (aq) 15M | | 1 mL (p. 277) | | 5 mL (p. 636) |
| ammonium chloride | | 10 g (p. 453) | | |
| ammonium metavanadate | | | | 0.7 g (p. 222) |
| barium chloride dihydrate | | | | 1 g (p. 10) |
| Benedict's solution | | 15 mL (p. 775) | | |
| bromocresol green indicator | | | 2 mL (p. 848) | |
| calcium acetate | | | | 20 g (p. 458) |
| calcium carbide | | | 1 g (p. 715) | |
| calcium chloride | | 10 g (p. 453) | 0.1 g (p. 125) | |
| cobalt chloride test paper | | | | 1 strip (p. 776) |
| cobalt(II) chloride dihydrate | | | | 1.4 g (p. 570) |
| cobalt(II) chloride hexahydrate | | | 0.25 g (p. 573) | |
| copper metal | 1 g (p. 654) | | | |
| copper shot | 40 g (p. 46) | 1 g (p. 151) | | |
| copper strip | 1 (p. 688) | 3 (pp. 151, 663) | 10 cm (p. 681) | |
| copper(II) nitrate | 28 g (pp. 300, 688) | | | |

## CHEMICALS (CONTINUED)

| ITEM | CHEMLAB | DISCOVERY LAB | MINILAB | DEMONSTRATION |
|---|---|---|---|---|
| copper(II) oxide | | | | 10 g (p. 332) |
| copper(II) sulfate pentahydrate | 12 g (p. 374) | 3 g (p. 635) | | 2.5 g (p.366) |
| dextrose | | | | 3 g (p. 636) |
| dry ice | | | | 500 g (p. 810) |
| ethanol, 95% | 3 mL (pp. 410, 766) | 5 mL (p. 25) | 12 mL (p. 786) | 50 mL (p. 810) |
| glucose | | 2 mL (p. 775) | | |
| glycerol (glycerin) | | 5 mL (p. 25) | | 5 mL (p. 702) |
| hydrochloric acid, 12$M$ | 30 mL (pp. 170, 550) | 102 mL (pp. 55, 489) | 15 mL (pp. 184, 573) | 50 mL (p. 670) |
| hydrogen peroxide, 30% | | 3 mL (p. 529) | | |
| iodine crystals | | | | 3 g (p. 280) |
| iron(III) oxide | | | | 125 g (p. 492) |
| iron filings (20 mesh) | 2 g (p. 374) | | | |
| lead acetate test paper | | | | 1 strip (p. 776) |
| lithium | | | | 0.1 g (p. 166) |
| lithium chloride | | | 0.1 g (p.125) | |
| litmus paper, blue | | 8 strips (p. 595) | | |
| litmus paper, red | | 8 strips (p. 595) | | 1 strip (p. 776) |
| lycopodium powder | | | | 2 g (p. 536) |
| magnesium nitrate | 40 g (pp. 300, 688) | | | |
| magnesium ribbon | 42 cm (pp. 232, 550 688) | | 13 cm (pp. 184, 681) | 33 cm (pp. 248, 492, 670) |
| magnesium sulfate heptahydrate, (Epsom salts) | 6 g (pp. 202, 342) | | 6 g (p. 295) | |
| magnesium sulfate, anhydrous | 1 g (p. 202) | | | |
| methanol | 2 mL (p. 766) | | 3 mL (p. 751) | |
| nitric acid, 16$M$ | 38 mL (p. 654) | | | 50 mL (p. 636) |
| Onion's Fusible Alloy | | 5 g (p. 211) | | |
| phenolphthalein | 0.1 g (p. 626) | 0.1 g (p. 595) | 0.1 g (p. 715) | 0.1 g (p. 166) |
| polyvinyl alcohol powder | | 4 g (p. 737) | | |
| potassium | | | | 0.1 g (p. 166) |
| potassium chlorate | | | | 10 g (p. 492) |
| potassium chloride | 10 g (p. 832) | | 0.1 g (p. 125) | |
| potassium hydrogen phthalate | 0.5 g (p. 626) | | | |
| potassium hydroxide | | | | 6 g (pp. 366, 636) |
| potassium nitrate | 1 g (p. 688) | | | 20 g (p. 458) |
| potassium nitrite | | | 0.5 g (p. 848) | |
| potassium permanganate | | 0.3 g (p. 353) | | 0.05g (p. 10) |
| powdered lime | | 5 g (p. 841) | | |
| rock salt | | | 100 g (p. 473) | |
| salicylic acid | | | 1.5 g (p. 751) | |
| silver nitrate | 9.5 g (pp. 78, 586) | | | 13 g (p. 636) |
| sodium | | | | 0.1 g (p. 166) |
| sodium acetate | | | | 4 g (p. 622) |

# CHEMICALS (CONTINUED)

| ITEM | CHEMLAB | DISCOVERY LAB | MINILAB | DEMONSTRATION |
|------|---------|---------------|---------|---------------|
| sodium chloride (table salt) | 50 g (pp. 586, 862) | | 70 g (pp. 125, 573, 638, 681, 786) | |
| sodium hydrogen carbonate (baking soda) | | | 38 g (pp. 362, 438, 638) | |
| sodium hydrogen sulfite | | 0.2 g (p. 353) | | 1 g (p. 10) |
| sodium hydroxide | 4 g (p. 626) | 1 g (p. 489) | 9 g (pp. 295, 786) | 2 g (pp. 62, 622) |
| sodium sulfide | 0.2 g (p. 586) | | | |
| sodium tetraborate decahydrate | | 1 g (p. 737) | | |
| starch, soluble | | 2 g (p. 775) | | |
| strontium chloride | | | 0.1 g (p. 125) | |
| sucrose (table sugar) | 1 g (p. 796) | | | 5 g (p. 702) |
| sulfur, roll | | | | 22 g (pp. 192, 248) |
| sulfuric acid, 18$M$ | | | 2 mL (pp. 751, 848) | |
| thermite mixture | | | | 100 g (p.492) |
| thermite starter | | | | 10 g (p. 492) |
| universal indicator | | 0.5 mL (p. 277) | | 0.5 mL (p. 622) |
| washing soda | 0.2 g (p. 202) | | | |
| zinc dust | | | | 1 g (p. 280) |
| zinc metal | | 1 g (p. 55) | | 2 g (p. 62) |
| zinc nitrate | 33 g (pp. 300, 688) | | | |
| zinc strip | 5 (pp. 300, 688) | 1 (p. 663) | | |
| zinc-mercury(II) chloride (aq) amalgam, granular | | | | 63 g (p. 222) |

# OTHER CONSUMABLES

| ITEM | CHEMLAB | DISCOVERY LAB | MINILAB | DEMONSTRATION |
|------|---------|---------------|---------|---------------|
| aluminum foil | 12 cm x 12 cm (p. 268) | 30 cm x 30 cm (p. 179) | 30 cm x 30 cm (p. 438) 5 cm x 5 cm (p. 638) | |
| ammonia, household | 11 mL (pp. 410, 654) | | | |
| bag, 1-gallon plastic zip-close | | | 1 (p. 848) | 1 (p. 846) |
| balloon, 9-inch latex | 2 (p. 108) | 1 (p. 419) | | |
| bottle, 1-L plastic soft drink with cap | 1 (p. 728) | | | |
| bottle, 2-L plastic soft drink with cap | 1 (p. 268) | | | 1 (p. 420) |
| can, empty soup | | 2 (p. 179) | | |
| can, soda | | 1 (p. 179) | | |
| candle | | | 1 (p. 438) | 1 (p. 702) |
| card stock | | | | 9 cm x 9 cm (p. 398) |
| cardboard | 10 cm x 10 cm (p. 766) | | 2 cm x 2 cm (p. 184) | |
| cheesecloth | | | 20 cm x 20 cm (p. 786) | |

# LABORATORY/ACTIVITIES

## OTHER CONSUMABLES (CONTINUED)

| ITEM | CHEMLAB | DISCOVERY LAB | MINILAB | DEMONSTRATION |
|---|---|---|---|---|
| chewing gum | | | 2 pieces (p. 329) | |
| chromatography paper | 3 (p. 268) | | | |
| | | | | |
| coat hanger, wire | | | | 1 (p. 846) |
| coin | | 2 (p. 179) | | |
| container, small plastic | | 4 (p. 25) | | |
| cooking oil | 2 mL (p. 796) | 5 mL (p. 241) | 1 mL (p. 15) | |
| corn oil | | 5 mL (p. 25) | | |
| cotton ball | | | 1 (p. 751) | |
| cup, 5-oz. plastic | 5 (pp. 46, 410) | 1 (p. 737) | 1 (p. 819) | |
| cup, 9-oz. plastic | | | 2 (p. 68) | |
| cup, foam | | | 1 (p. 505) | |
| detergent, liquid dish | 1 mL (p. 202) | 1 mL (p. 385) | 6 mL (pp. 15, 715) | 25 mL (p. 702) |
| dish, black plastic frozen dinner | 1 (p. 862) | | | |
| drain cleaner, crystal Drano | 10 g (p. 654) | | | |
| duster, aerosol can | 1 (p. 444) | | | |
| effervescent antacid tablet | | 1 (p. 277) | 1 (p. 539) | |
| filter paper | 3 (pp. 78, 202, 688) | 1 (p. 841) | 2 (p. 68) | 1 (p. 492) |
| flashbulb or flashcube | | | | 1 (p. 670) |
| food coloring (red, blue, green, yellow) | 0.1 mL ea. (p. 142) | | 1 mL ea. (p. 15) | |
| food coloring, blue | 0.5 mL (p. 480) | 0.5 mL (p. 25) | | 2 mL (pp. 398, 846) |
| food coloring, red | | 0.5 mL (p. 25) | | 1 mL (p. 420) |
| gelatin | | 2 g (p. 775) | | |
| gumdrops, small | | | 3 (p. 261) | |
| hairpin | | 1 (p. 179) | 3 (p. 230) | |
| honey | | 1 mL (p. 775) | | |
| household products, food or cleaning products | | 8 (p. 595) | | |
| label | 4 (p. 550) | | | |
| leaf samples from deciduous trees or plants, fresh | 3 (p. 268) | | | |
| lemon | | 1 (p. 663) | | |
| marker, water-soluble black | | | 1 (p. 68) | |
| marshmallows, mini-sized | | | 9 (p. 261) | |
| marshmallows, regular-sized | | | 3 (p. 261) | |
| matches | 1 (p. 520) | | 6 (pp. 184, 438, 715) | 1 (p. 702) |
| matches, large kitchen | | 2 (p. 3) | | |
| metal items, assorted | | 5 (p. 179) | | |
| milk, whole | | | 50 mL (p.15) | |
| motor oil, 10W-30 | | 150 mL (p. 697) | | |
| motor oil, 20W-50 | | 150 mL (p. 697) | | |
| nail, iron | | 1 (p. 635) | 4 (p. 681) | |
| nail, large iron | | | 1 (p. 68) | |
| newspaper | | | | 1 (p. 702) |
| paper clip | 1 (p. 78) | 3 (pp. 179, 309) | | 1 box (p. 762) |
| paper towel | 12 (pp. 410, 728) | 10 (p. 697) | 3 (p. 329) | 11 (pp. 28, 62) |
| paper, black construction | | | | 1 sheet (p. 846) |

# OTHER CONSUMABLES (CONTINUED)

| ITEM | CHEMLAB | DISCOVERY LAB | MINILAB | DEMONSTRATION |
|------|---------|---------------|---------|---------------|
| paper, graph | 1 sheet (p. 46) | | 2 sheet (pp. 164, 819) | |
| paper, white | | 1 sheet (p. 87) | 1 sheet (p. 848) | |
| peanut | | | | 3 (p. 776) |
| pen, marking | 1 (p. 410) | | | |
| pencil | 3 (pp. 46, 268) | | | |
| pencil, glass-marking | 1 (p. 170) | | | |
| pencil, grease | 1 (pp. 202, 410) | | | |
| pencils, colored, assorted | 1 set (p. 142) | | | 1 set (p. 136) |
| potato chip, large | 1 (p. 520) | | | |
| rubber band, large | 1 (p. 18) | | 1 (p. 715) | |
| sandpaper, fine (10 cm x 10 cm) | 1 (pp. 300, 550) | 1 (p. 635) | 2 (pp. 184, 681) | |
| silver object, small tarnished | | | 1 (p. 638) | |
| soil | | 15 g (p. 841) | | |
| steel wool, pad | 1 (p. 688) | 1 (p. 635) | 1 (p. 638) | 1 (p. 670) |
| straw, plastic soda | | | 12 (p. 401) | |
| string | | 10 cm (p. 419) | | |
| swab, cotton | 6 (p. 480) | | 6 (p. 125) | |
| tape, clear plastic | 12 cm (p. 268) | 40 cm (p. 87) | | |
| tape, electrical | 20 cm (p. 444) | | | |
| tape, masking | 10 cm (p. 410) | 10 cm (p. 151) | 30 cm (p. 438) | 20 cm (p. 702) |
| tissue, facial | 11 (pp. 480, 766) | | | |
| toothpick | | 1 (p. 529) | 22 (pp. 15, 261) | |
| twist tie | 1 (p. 766) | | | |
| vanilla extract | 6 mL (p. 108) | | | |
| vegetable shortening, solid | | | 25 g (p. 786) | |
| vinegar, household | | 5 mL (p. 241) | | |
| waxed paper | 30 cm x 30 cm (p. 410) | | | |
| weighing paper | 1 (p. 374) | | 4 (pp. 295, 329, 751) | |
| wire, 12-ga copper | 0.5 m (p. 46) | | | |
| wire, 14-ga copper | | | | 15 cm (p. 670) |
| wire, 18-ga copper | 0.5 m (p. 46) | | | |
| wire, 22- or 26- gauge copper | | | 2 m (p. 401) | |
| wire, aluminum | 10 cm (p. 300) | | | |
| wire, copper | 18 cm (pp. 78, 300) | 10 cm (p. 151) | | |
| wood splint | | 1 (p. 55) | 4 (pp. 184, 638, 715) | |
| wrap, clear plastic | | | | 30 cm x 30 cm (p. 166) |
| yeast, active dry | 1 pkg. (p. 796) | 1 pkg. (p. 529) | | |

# SUPPLIERS

## Equipment Suppliers

**American Science & Surplus**
P.O. Box 1030
Skokie, IL 60076
(847) 647-0011
www.sciplus.com

**Bio-Rad Laboratories**
Life Science Group
2000 Alfred Nobel Dr.
Hercules, CA 94547
(800) 424-6723
www.bio-rad.com

**Carolina Biological
   Supply Co.**
2700 York Rd.
Burlington, NC 27215
(800) 334-5551
www.carolina.com

**Edmund Scientific Company**
60 Pearce Ave.
Tonawanda, NY 14150-6711
(800) 728-6999
www.scientificsonline.com

**Fisher Science Education**
Educational Materials Division
4500 Turnberry Dr.
Hanover Park, IL 60133
(800) 955-1177
www.fisheredu.com

**Nasco Science**
901 Janesville Avenue,
P.O. Box 901
Fort Atkinson, WI 53538-0901
(800) 558-9595
www.enasco.com

**Nebraska Scientific**
3823 Leavenworth St.
Omaha, NE 68105-1180
(800) 228-7117
www.nebraskascientific.com

**PASCO Scientific**
10101 Foothills Blvd.
P.O. Box 619011
Roseville, CA 95747
(800) 772-8700
www.pasco.com

**Sargent-Welch/VWR Scientific
   Products**
P.O. Box 5229
Buffalo Grove, IL 60089-5229
(800) SAR-GENT 727-4368
www.SargentWelch.com

**Science Kit and Boreal
   Laboratories**
777 East Park Dr.
Tonawanda, NY 14150
(800) 828-7777
www.sciencekit.com

**Vernier Software & Technology**
13979 SW Millikan Way
Beaverton, OR 97005-2886
(503) 277-2299
www.vernier.com

**WARD's Natural Science Est.**
5100 W. Henrietta Road,
P.O. Box 92912
Rochester, NY 14692-9012
(800) 962-2660
www.wardsci.com

## Audiovisual Distributors

**Bullfrog Films**
P.O. Box 149
Oley, PA 19547
(800) 543-FROG
www.bullfrogfilms.com

**Coronet/MTI Film & Video**
2349 Chaffee Dr.
St Louis, MO 63146
(800) 221-1274
www.phoenixcoronet.com

**Discovery Channel School**
MD 20910
(240) 662-2000
www.discoveryschool.com

**Films for the Humanities and
   Sciences**
P.O. Box 2053
Princeton, NJ 08543
(800) 257-5126
www.film.com

**Flinn Scientific**
P.O. Box 219
770 N. Raddant Rd.
Batavia, IL 60510
(800) 452-1261
www.flinnsci.com

**Frey Scientific**
P.O. Box 8101
100 Paragon Parkway
Mansfield, OH 44903
(800) 225-FREY
www.freyscientific.com

**Media Design Associates**
P.O. Box 3189
Boulder, CO 80307-3189
(800) 228-8854
www.indra.com/mediades

**National Geographic Society
   Educational Services**
1145 17th Street, N.W.
Washington, DC 20036
(800) 368-2728
www.nationalgeographic.com

**Optical Data/SRA/McGraw-
   Hill**
12600 Deerfield Parkway
Alpharetta, GA 30004
(800) 201-7103
www.opticaldata.com

**Scholastic, Inc.**
555 Broadway
New York, NY 10012-3999
(800) 325-6149
www.scholastic.com

**Videodiscovery, Inc.**
920 N. 34th Street
Suite 300
Seattle, WA 98103
(800) 548-3472
www.videodiscovery.com

## Software Distributors

**Boreal Laboratories, Ltd.**
399 Vansickle Rd.
St. Catherines, Ontario
L25 3T4 CANADA
(800) 387-9393
www.boreal.com

**Educational Activities, Inc.**
1937 Grand Avenue
Baldwin, NY 11510
(800) 645-3739
www.edact.com

**IBM Education**
www.solutions.ibm.com/K12

**J. Weston Walch, Publisher**
321 Valley St.
P.O. Box 658
Portland, ME 04104-0658
(800) 341-6094
www.walch.com

**Scholastic, Inc.**
555 Broadway
New York, NY 10012-3999
(800) 325-6149
www.scholastic.com

**SciCity**
8100 Shaffer Parkway
Suite 130
Littleton, CO 80127
(303) 792-5615

**Sunburst Technology**
1550 Executive Drive
Eglin, IL 60123
(800) 321-7511
www.SUNBURST.com

Glencoe Science

# CHEMISTRY

## MATTER AND CHANGE

chemistrymc.com

**Glencoe**

New York, New York    Columbus, Ohio    Chicago, Illinois    Peoria, Illinois    Woodland Hills, California

**A Glencoe Program**

# Chemistry:
## Matter and Change

### Visit the Chemistry Web site at
### chemistrymc.com

**You'll find:**

Online Student Edition, Online Study
Tools, Interactive Tutor, Online Quizzes,
WebQuests, Teacher Forum, Problem of
the Week, Safety Links, Math Handbook,
Chemistry in the News, Science Fair Ideas,
Periodic Table Links

**and much more!**

Send all inquiries to:
Glencoe/McGraw-Hill
8787 Orion Place
Columbus, OH 43240-4027

ISBN 0-07-866418-7
Printed in the United States of America.
1 2 3 4 5 6 027/043 09 08 07 06 05 04

# About the Authors

**Laurel Dingrando** teaches chemistry at North Garland Math, Science and Technology High School in Garland, Texas. Ms. Dingrando has a B.S. in Microbiology with a minor in Chemistry from Texas Tech University and an M.A.T. in Science from University of Texas at Dallas. She has taught Chemistry for 25 years and currently serves as the Secondary Science Coordinator for the Garland Independent School District. She is a member of the American Chemical Society, National Science Teachers Association, Science Teachers Association of Texas, Texas Science Educators Leadership Association, and T3 (Teacher Teaching with Technology). She has also received two grants to study the chemistry of both fresh and salt water ecosystems.

**Kathleen (Gregg) Tallman** is an Assistant Professor in the Biology Department at Doane College in Crete, Nebraska. She has taught science at the college level for seven years. She has a B.A in Biology/ Chemistry from Point Loma Nazarene College, and a Ph.D. from the Ohio State University, where she studied neuropeptides in cerebellar circuits. As a BRIN Associate, she is part of an NIH-funded grant to increase research quality and opportunities for undergr aduates and faculty at small colleges in Nebraska. She is also a member of the Society for Neuroscience and is a Nationally Registered EMT-Basic.

**Nicholas Hainen** taught chemistry and physics at Worthington City Schools, Worthington, Ohio, for 31 years. Mr. Hainen has a B.S. and M.A. in Science Education from The Ohio State University with majors in chemistry and physics. He is a member of the American Chemical Society and the ACS Division of Chemical Education. He coordinated the Central Ohio Chemistry Olympiad competition for many years, and he was named the American Chemical Society's Outstanding Central Ohio High School Educator in Chemical Science in 1991. In 1985, Mr. Hainen was elected to The Ohio State University's Honor Roll of Outstanding High School Teachers, and received the Ashland Oil Company Golden Apple Award in 1990. He was named to Who's Who Among America's Teachers in 1992.

**Cheryl Wistrom** is an associate professor of chemistry at Saint Joseph's College in Rensselaer, Indiana. She has taught chemistry and chemical education at the college level for several years. She earned her B.S. degree at Northern Michigan University and her M.S. and Ph.D. at the University of Michigan, where she carried out research on gene expression during aging of human cells. She has participated in summer institutes for educators at Pennsylvania State University and Miami University of Ohio. She is a member of the Indiana Academy of Science and the National Science Teachers Association.

## Contributing Writers

Linda Barr, Westerville, OH
Christine Caputo, Jacksonville, FL
Robert Davisson, Delaware, OH
Gary W. Harris, Delaware, OH
Pamela E. Hirschfeld, Briarcliff Manor, NY

Nancy Kerr, Winnipeg, Manitoba, Canada
Thomas K. McCarthy, Concord, NH
Jack Minot, Columbus, OH
Richard G. Smith, Columbus, OH
Matthew C. Walker, Portland, OR
Jenipher Willoughby, Forest, VA

# Consultants & Reviewers

## Content Consultants

Alton J. Banks, Ph.D.
Department of Chemistry
North Carolina State University
Raleigh, NC

Peter C. Chen, Ph.D.
Department of Chemistry
Spelman College
Atlanta, GA

Howard Drossman, Ph.D.
Department of Chemistry
Colorado College
Colorado Springs, CO

Kristen Kulinowski, Ph.D.
Department of Chemistry
Rice University
Houston, TX

## Safety Consultants

Joanne Bowers
Plainview, TX

Anne Davidson
Madison, AL

John Longo
Philadelphia, PA

## Teacher Reviewers

George G. Allen
Daphne High School
Daphne, AL

Edward L. Barry
El Camino High School
Sacramento, CA

Sonja Crowell
Lubbock High School
Lubbock, TX

Carolyn Ericson
W. P. Clements High School
Sugar Land, TX

Whit Hames
Division Leader--Science
Southeast Raleigh High School
Raleigh, NC

Cathy Jelovich Haywood
Science Department Chair
Southeast Raleigh High School
Raleigh, NC

Bernard J. Kenyon
Mt. St. Joseph High School
Baltimore, MD

Bill Lees
Science Department Chair
Monterey High School
Lubbock, TX

Pam Lehrman
Columbia River High School
Vancouver, WA

Jane Davis Mahon
Hoover High School
Hoover, AL

Charles E. Matthews
Science Department Head
Mergenthaler Vocational
Technical High School
Baltimore, MD

Steve Pike
Madison West High School
Madison, WI

Kathy Brannum Prislovsky
Stuttgart High School
Stuttgart, AR

Alice Veyvoda
Half Hollow Hills High School
West
Dix Hills, NY

Greg Wilson
Beloit Memorial High School
Beloit, WI

# Contents In Brief

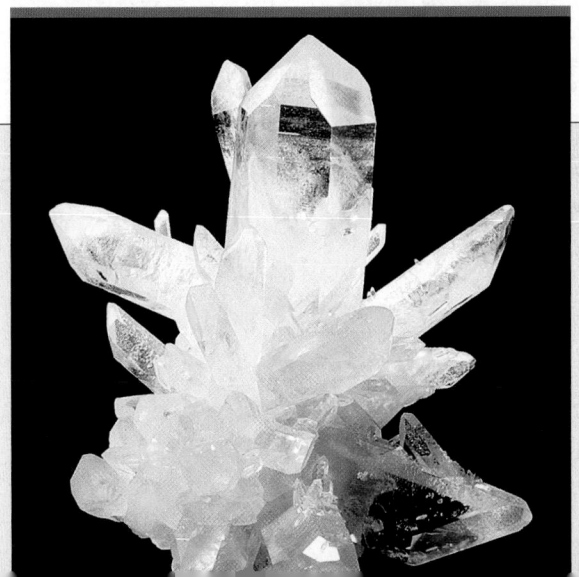

**Chemistry: Matter and Change**    **v**

# Table of Contents

# Table of Contents

# Table of Contents

# CHEMLAB

# mini LAB

# problem-solving LAB

# DISCOVERY LAB

# Features

## How It Works

Expansion valve

Compressor

## Everyday Chemistry

# Features

# CONNECTIONS

# Resource Manager

| Section | Objectives | Activities/Features |
|---|---|---|
| **Section 1.1**<br>**The Stories of Two Chemicals**<br>$1/2$ session<br>0 block | 1. **Explain** the formation and importance of ozone.<br>2. **Describe** the development of chlorofluorocarbons. | **Discovery Lab:** Where is it? p. 3 |
| **Section 1.2**<br>**Chemistry and Matter**<br>$1/2$ session<br>$1/4$ block | 3. **Define** chemistry and matter.<br>4. **Compare** and **contrast** mass and weight.<br>5. **Explain** why chemists are interested in a submicroscopic description of matter. | **Problem-Solving Lab:** Chemical Models, p. 8<br>**Careers Using Chemistry:** Chemistry Teacher, p. 9 |
| **Section 1.3**<br>**Scientific Methods**<br>1 session<br>$1/4$ block | 6. **Identify** the common steps of scientific methods.<br>7. **Compare** and **contrast** types of data.<br>8. **Compare** and **contrast** types of variables.<br>9. **Describe** the difference between a theory and a scientific law. | **ChemLab:** The Rubber Band Stretch, pp. 18–19 |
| **Section 1.4**<br>**Scientific Research**<br>1 session<br>$1/2$ block | 10. **Compare** and **contrast** pure research, applied research, and technology.<br>11. **Apply** knowledge of laboratory safety. | **MiniLab:** Developing Observation Skills, p. 15<br>**Chemistry and Society:** The Human Genome Project, p. 20 |

| National Science Content Standards | State/Local Standards | Reproducible Masters | Transparencies |
|---|---|---|---|
| UCP.1, UCP.2; A.1, A.2; B.3, B.6; E.2; F.4, F.5, F.6; G.2, G.3 | | **Study Guide for Content Mastery,** p. 1 L2<br>**Challenge Problems,** p. 1 L3 | **Section Focus**<br>Transparency 1 L1 ELL<br>**Teaching**<br>Transparency 1 L2 ELL |
| UCP.1, UCP.2; A.1; B.2; G.1, G.2 | | **Study Guide for Content Mastery,** pp. 2–3 L2 | **Section Focus**<br>Transparency 2 L1 ELL |
| UCP.1, UCP.2; A.2; G.1, G.2 | | **Study Guide for Content Mastery,** pp. 4–5 L2<br>**ChemLab and MiniLab Worksheets,** pp. 2–4 L2<br>**CBL Laboratory Manual,** pp. 1–4 L2 | **Section Focus**<br>Transparency 3 L1 ELL<br>**Teaching**<br>Transparency 2 L2 ELL |
| UCP.1, UCP.2; A.1, A.2; B.2, B.6; E.2; F.1, F.4, F.6; G.1, G.2, G.3 | | **Study Guide for Content Mastery,** p. 6 L2<br>**ChemLab and MiniLab Worksheets,** p. 1 L2<br>**Laboratory Manual,** pp. 1-4, 5–8 L2 | **Section Focus**<br>Transparency 4 L1 ELL<br>**Teaching**<br>Transparency 3 L2 ELL |

**Key to National Science Content Standards:** UCP = Unifying Concepts and Processes, A = Science as Inquiry, B = Physical Science, C = Life Science, D = Earth and Space Sciences, E = Science and Technology, F = Science in Personal and Social Perspectives, G = History and Nature of Science

Refer to pages 4T–5T of the Teacher Guide for an explanation of the National Science Content Standards correlations.

# Resource Manager

## Materials List

### ChemLab (pages 18–19)
large rubber band, 500-g mass, ring stand, clamp, hair dryer, meterstick

### Discovery Lab (page 3)
large kitchen matches, laboratory balance, stopwatch or clock

### MiniLab (page 15)
petri dish (2), 25-mL graduated cylinder, whole milk, water, vegetable oil, food coloring (4 different colors), toothpicks (2), dishwashing detergent

### Demonstration (pages 10–11)
0.05 g potassium permanganate ($KMnO_4$), 1 g sodium hydrogen sulfite ($NaHSO_3$), 1 g barium chloride dihydrate ($BaCl_2 \cdot 2H_2O$), 400-mL beakers (3), small test tubes (2), water

## Preparation of Solutions

For a review of solution preparation, see page 46T of the Teacher Guide.

Quantities are for a class of 30 students.

### Demonstration (pages 10–11)
**potassium permanganate solution** Dissolve 3 or 4 small crystals, about 0.05 gram, of potassium permanganate ($KMnO_4$) in 250 mL water. **CAUTION:** The solution is toxic.
**barium chloride solution** Add 1 gram of barium chloride dihydrate ($BaCl_2 \cdot 2H_2O$) to 1 mL water in a small test tube. **CAUTION:** The solution is toxic.
**sodium hydrogen sulfite solution** Add 1 gram sodium hydrogen sulfite ($NaHSO_3$) to 1 mL water in a small test tube. **CAUTION:** The solution is toxic.

## Assessment Resources

**Chapter Assessment,** pp. 1–6
**MindJogger Videoquizzes DVD/VHS**
**Alternate Assessment in the Science Classroom**
**Examview® Pro CD-ROM**
**Solutions Manual,** Chapter 1
**Supplemental Problems,** Chapter 1
**Performance Assessment in the Science Classroom**

## Additional Resources

**Spanish Resources** ELL
**Guided Reading Audio Program,** Chapter 1 ELL
**Cooperative Learning in the Science Classroom**
**Lab and Safety Skills in the Science Classroom**
**Lesson Plans**
**Block Scheduling Lesson Plans**
**Chemistrymc.com**

## Glencoe Technology

The following multimedia for this chapter are available from Glencoe.

 **VIDEOTAPE/DVD**
MindJogger Videoquizzes

 **CD-ROM**
**Interactive Chalkboard**

 **CD-ROM**
**ExamView® Pro**
**Testmaker**

 **CD-ROM**
**TeacherWorks™**

## Multiple Learning Styles

Look for the following icons for strategies that emphasize different learning modalities.

**Kinesthetic**
Meeting Individual Needs, pp. 5, 7

**Visual-Spatial**
Reteach, pp. 5, 9; Portfolio, p. 16

**Interpersonal**
Meeting Individual Needs, p. 15; Reinforcement, p. 16

**Intrapersonal**
Chemistry Journal, pp. 5, 12, 14; Extension, p. 11; Differentiated Instruction, p. 12

**Linguistic**
Chemistry Journal, p. 8

**Logical-Mathematical**
Quick Demo, p. 10

## Key to Teaching Strategies

 **L1** Level 1 activities should be appropriate for students with learning difficulties.

 **L2** Level 2 activities should be within the ability range of all students.

 **L3** Level 3 activities are designed for above-average students.

**ELL** ELL activities should be within the ability range of English Language Learners.

**COOP LEARN** Cooperative Learning activities are designed for small group work.

**P** These strategies represent student products that can be placed into a best-work portfolio.

These strategies are useful in a block scheduling format.

## Assessment Planner

**Portfolio Assessment**
Portfolio, TWE, p. 16
Assessment, TWE, pp. 4, 17

**Performance Assessment**
Assessment, TWE, p. 13
Problem-Solving Lab, TWE, p. 8
ChemLab, TWE, p. 19
MiniLab, SE, p. 15
MiniLab, TWE, p. 15
Demonstration, TWE, p. 11
ChemLab, SE, pp. 18–19
Discovery Lab, SE, p. 3

**Knowledge Assessment**
Assessment, TWE, pp. 6, 9
Section Assessment, SE, pp. 6, 9, 13, 17
Chapter Assessment, SE, pp. 22–23

**Skill Assessment**
Assessment, TWE, p. 11

## Using the Photo

Ask students what is involved when a star explodes. Lead them to understand that the event involves matter and energy and how they interact. Tell them that this interaction is what chemistry is all about—matter and energy and how they relate to each other.

## Chapter Themes

The following themes from the National Science Education Standards are covered in this chapter. Refer to page 4T of the Teacher Guide for an explanation of the correlations.

Systems, order, and organization (UCP.1)

Evidence, models, and explanation (UCP.2)

Change, constancy, and measurement (UCP.3)

**PowerPoint® Presentations**
This CD-ROM is an editable Microsoft® PowerPoint® presentation that includes:
• Section presentations
• Section checks
• Image bank
• Links to Chemistry Online
• All transparencies
• Animations
• Audio

# Introduction to Chemistry

### What You'll Learn

▶ You will describe the relationship between chemistry and matter.

▶ You will recognize how scientific methods can be used to solve problems.

▶ You will distinguish between scientific research and technology.

### Why It's Important

▶ You, and all the objects around you, are composed of matter. By studying matter and the way it changes, you will gain an understanding of your body and all the "stuff" you see and interact with in your everyday life.

Visit the Chemistry Web site at chemistrymc.com to find links about chemistry and matter.

The four nebulae shown here contain a stew of elements. The red color in two of the nebulae is emitted by hydrogen atoms. The Horsehead Nebula can be seen on the right. The fourth nebula is the bluish structure below the horse's head. The round, bright object on the left is the star Zeta Orionis.

2    Chapter 1

## DISCOVERY LAB

### Purpose
Students will observe a chemical reaction and relate their observations to definitions of matter and chemistry.

### Safety and Disposal
Caution students to use care around an open flame. Have them place used matches in a flameproof container or in a container of water.

### Teaching Strategies
• Ask students what evidence they observe that a change in matter is taking place. Answers might include change in appearance or odor or a gas and energy are given off.
• Use the odor produced by this experiment to introduce a discussion of air pollution. This lab can be used to introduce the ozone problem discussed in this chapter.

### Expected Results
The match loses mass in each trial. The data from trial 1 should agree closely with the data from trial 2.

### Analysis
The change in mass occurs because solids are changed into the gases that are released during the reaction.

## DISCOVERY LAB

### Where is it?

When an object burns, the quantity of ashes that remain is smaller than the original object that was burned. What happened to the rest of the object?

### Safety Precautions

 Do not place matches in the sink. Use caution around flames.

### Procedure

1. Measure the mass of a large kitchen match. Record this measurement and detailed observations about the match.

2. Carefully strike the match and allow it to burn for five seconds. Then, blow it out. CAUTION: *Keep hair and loose clothing away from the flame.* Record observations about the match as it burns and after the flame is extinguished.

3. Allow the match to cool. Measure and record the mass of the burned match.

4. Place the burned match in a container designated by your instructor.

5. Repeat this procedure. Compare your data from the two trials.

### Analysis

How do you account for the change in mass? Where is the matter that appears to have been lost?

### Materials

large kitchen matches
laboratory balance
lab notebook
pen
stopwatch or clock

---

## Section 1.1

# The Stories of Two Chemicals

### Objectives

- **Explain** the formation and importance of ozone.
- **Describe** the development of chlorofluorocarbons.

Take a moment to look around you. Where did all the "stuff" you see come from? All the stuff in the universe is made from building blocks formed in stars such as the ones shown in the photo on the opposite page. And, as you learned in the **DISCOVERY LAB,** this stuff changes form.

Scientists are naturally curious. They continually ask questions about and seek answers to all that they observe in the universe. One of the areas in which scientists work is the branch of science called chemistry. Your introduction to chemistry will begin with two unrelated discoveries that now form the basis of one of the most important environmental issues of our time.

### The Ozone Layer

You are probably aware of some of the damaging effects of ultraviolet radiation from the Sun if you have ever suffered from a sunburn. Overexposure to ultraviolet radiation also is harmful to plants and animals, lowering crop yields and disrupting food chains. Living things can exist on Earth because ozone, a chemical in Earth's atmosphere, absorbs most of this radiation before it reaches Earth's surface. A chemical is any substance that has a definite composition. Ozone is a substance that consists of three particles of oxygen.

1.1 The Stories of Two Chemicals    **3**

 Resource Manager

**Study Guide for Content Mastery,**
p. 1 **L2**
**Solving Problems: A Chemistry Handbook,** Section 1.1 **L2**
**Section Focus Transparency 1 and Master L1 ELL**

National Science Content Standards

**Pages 2–3**
UCP.1, UCP.2; A.1, A.2; B.3; E.2

---

## Section 1.1

# 1 Focus

## Focus Transparency

Before presenting the lesson, display **Section Focus Transparency 1** on the overhead projector and have students answer the accompanying questions using **Section Focus Transparency Master 1. L1 ELL**

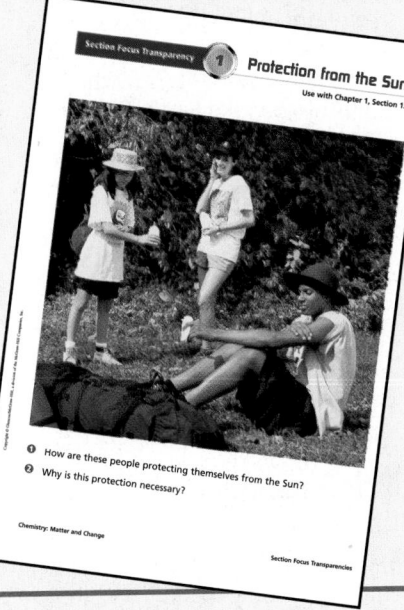

# 2 Teach

## Quick Demo

Demonstrate that chemicals are everywhere. Burn a candle in the front of the classroom. Explain that the wax in the candle is a chemical, as is the oxygen in the air needed to burn the wax. If you hold your hand too close to the flame, the flame will burn the chemicals that form your skin. UV light from the sun can also burn your skin. Sunscreen contains chemicals that absorb UV light before it reaches your skin. Ozone is a chemical in the air that absorbs UV light before it reaches Earth's surface.

3

Figure 1-1

Earth's atmosphere consists of several layers. The layer nearest Earth is the troposphere. The stratosphere is above the troposphere.

**Figure 1-2**

The troposphere extends to a height of about 15 km. Cumulonimbus clouds, or thunderheads, produce thunder, lightning, and rain.

**Earth's atmosphere** As you can see in **Figure 1-1,** Earth's atmosphere consists of layers. The lowest layer is called the troposphere and contains the air we breathe. The troposphere is where the clouds shown in **Figure 1-2** occur and where airplanes fly. All of Earth's weather occurs in the troposphere.

The stratosphere is the layer above the troposphere. It extends from about 15 to 50 kilometers (km) above Earth's surface. The ozone that protects Earth is located in the stratosphere. About 90% of Earth's ozone is spread out in a layer that surrounds and protects our planet.

**Ozone formation** How does ozone enter the stratosphere? Ozone ($O_3$) is formed when oxygen gas is exposed to ultraviolet radiation in the upper regions of the stratosphere. Particles of oxygen gas are made of two smaller oxygen particles. The energy of the radiation breaks the gas particles into oxygen particles, which then interact with oxygen gas to form ozone. **Figure 1-3** illustrates this process. Ozone also can absorb radiation and break apart to reform oxygen gas. Thus, there tends to be a balance between oxygen gas and ozone levels in the stratosphere.

Ozone was first identified and measured in the late 1800s, so its presence has been studied for a long time. It was of interest to scientists because air currents in the stratosphere move ozone around Earth. Ozone forms over the equator where the rays of sunlight are the strongest and then flows toward the poles. Thus, ozone makes a convenient marker to follow the flow of air in the stratosphere.

In the 1920s, G.M.B. Dobson began measuring the amount of ozone in the atmosphere. Although ozone is formed in the higher regions of the stratosphere, most of it is stored in the lower stratosphere, where it can be measured by instruments on the ground or in balloons, satellites, and rockets. Dobson measured levels of stratospheric ozone of more than 300 Dobson units (DU). His measurements serve as a basis for comparison with recent measurements.

During 1981–1983, a research group from the British Antarctic Survey was monitoring the atmosphere above Antarctica. They measured surprisingly low levels of ozone, readings as low as 160 DU, especially during the Antarctic spring in October. They checked their instruments and repeated their measurements. In October 1985, they reported a confirmed decrease in the amount of ozone in the stratosphere and concluded that the ozone layer was thinning.

**4**     **Chapter 1** Introduction to Chemistry

---

## CULTURAL DIVERSITY

### Skin Tones

Darker skin tones offer more protection from harmful UV rays in sunlight. Therefore, where rays from the sun are strong near the equator, skin tones have evolved to be darker. UV rays are less intense in areas farther from the equator, so skin tones are lighter there.

Although the Inuit people live far north of the equator, their skin tones are darker than would be expected because snow reflects UV light. The Inuit need darker skin to protect them from the increased levels of UV light they receive from reflection.

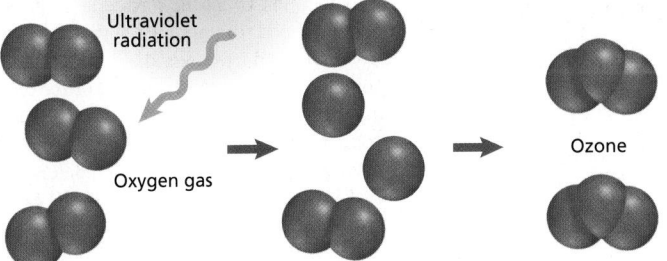

Formation of ozone

**Figure 1-3**

This model of the formation of ozone shows that ultraviolet radiation from the Sun causes oxygen gas to break down into two individual particles of oxygen. These individual particles combine with oxygen gas to form ozone, which consists of three oxygen particles.

Although the thinning of the ozone layer is often called the ozone hole, it is not actually a hole. You can think of it as being similar to the old sock in **Figure 1-4a** in which the material of the heel is wearing thin. You might be able to see your skin through the thinning sock. So although the ozone is still present in the atmosphere, the protective layer is much thinner than normal. This fact has alarmed scientists who never expected to find such low levels. Measurements made from balloons, high-altitude planes, and satellites have supported the measurements made from the ground, as the satellite map in **Figure 1-4b** shows. What could be causing the ozone hole?

## Chlorofluorocarbons

The story of the second chemical in this chapter begins in the 1920s. Refrigerators, which used toxic gases such as ammonia as coolants, were just beginning to be produced large scale. Because ammonia fumes could escape from the refrigerator and harm the members of a household, chemists began to search for safer coolants. Thomas Midgley, Jr. synthesized the first chlorofluorocarbons in 1928. A chlorofluorocarbon (CFC) is a chemical that consists of chlorine, fluorine, and carbon. There are several different chemicals that are classified as CFCs. They are all made in the laboratory and do not occur naturally. CFCs are nontoxic and stable. They do not readily react with other chemicals. At the time, they seemed to be ideal coolants for refrigerators. By 1935, the first self-contained home air-conditioning units and eight million new refrigerators in the United States used CFCs as coolants. In addition to their use as refrigerants, CFCs also were used in plastic foams and as propellants in spray cans.

**Figure 1-4**

(a) The thinning heel of this sock models the thinning of the ozone layer in the stratosphere.
(b) This colored satellite map of stratospheric ozone over Antarctica was taken on September 15, 1999. The lowest amount of ozone (light purple) appears over Antarctica (dark purple). Blue, green, orange, and yellow show increasing amounts of ozone.

1.1  The Stories of Two Chemicals     **5**

---

### Concept Development

Have a local mechanic or air conditioning specialist speak to the class on the safeguards that currently exist to keep harmful chemicals from affecting the atmosphere. Ask him or her to clarify that chemicals that are shown to be harmful to the environment can be either eliminated or replaced with a chemical that is less harmful.

### Discussion

Ask students what comes to mind when the term *chemical* is used. Often, the term has a negative connotation. Emphasize that chemicals are all around them and that they could not exist without them. Some chemicals can be harmful, but others are not only helpful, but essential.

## 3 Assess
### Check for Understanding

What is the normal level of ozone in the stratosphere? 300 DU What was the lowest level that scientists found over the Antarctic in the early 1980s? 160 DU Have students explain why scientists were alarmed at these findings. **L2**

### Reteach

*Visual-Spatial* Bring in a thin sock or item of clothing. Demonstrate that the material is still present, but it is thinner than normal and allows more light to pass through. Have students explain how this model is similar to the ozone hole. **L1 ELL**

**Resource Manager**

Challenge Problems, p. 1 **L3**
Teaching Transparency 1 and Master **L2 ELL**

---

**CHEMISTRY JOURNAL**

**Thomas Midgely**

*Intrapersonal* Have students research for information on Thomas Midgely, Jr. Then, have them write a short summary on why he created CFCs. **L2**

**DIFFERENTIATED INSTRUCTION**

**Visually Impaired**

*Kinesthetic* Have sighted students work with visually impaired students to create a three-dimensional, tactile model of layers of the atmosphere. Have the sighted student explain the location of the troposphere and stratosphere and ozone formation and storage. **L2 ELL**

**National Science Content Standards**

Pages 4–5
UCP.1, UCP.2; A.2; B.6; E.2; F.4; G.2

Discuss with students how the processes used to manufacture products change over time. Include in the discussion the role chemistry has in these changes. Mention the evolution of refrigerants as discussed in the text. Bring to class a cardboard milk container and a plastic milk jug. Ask students to describe the benefits and disadvantages of each type of container. The cardboard will decompose over time; the plastic will not. Both can be recycled. Milk will stay fresher in the plastic.

✓ **Assessment**

**Knowledge** Provide students with two lists. One list contains the layers of the atmosphere, listed in random order. The other list contains one characteristic of each layer. The characteristics should relate to the chemistry of the layer. Ask students to match each layer to its characteristic. **L2**

**Concentration of CFCs in the Atmosphere**

*(y-axis: CFC-11 (ppt); values 120, 160, 200, 240, 280; x-axis: Year 1977, 1979, 1981, 1983, 1985, 1987, 1989, 1991, 1993, 1995)*

**Figure 1-5**

Quantities of CFCs in the atmosphere continued to rise until a ban on products containing them went into effect in many countries.

Now think of all the refrigerators in your neighborhood, in your city, across the country, and around the world. Think of the air conditioners in homes, schools, office buildings, and cars that also used CFCs. Add to your mental list all of the aerosol cans and plastic foam cups and food containers used each day throughout the world. If all of these products contained or were made with CFCs, imagine the quantities of these chemicals that could be released into the environment in a single day.

Scientists first began to notice the presence of CFCs in the atmosphere in the 1970s. They decided to measure the amount of CFCs in the stratosphere and found that quantities in the stratosphere increased year after year. This increase is shown in **Figure 1-5.** But, it was thought that CFCs did not pose a threat to the environment because they are so stable.

Two separate occurrences had been noticed and measured: the protective ozone layer in the atmosphere was thinning, and increasingly large quantities of useful CFCs were drifting into the atmosphere. Could there be a connection between the two occurrences? Before you learn the answer to this question, you need to understand some of the basic ideas of chemistry and know how chemists—and most scientists, for that matter—solve problems.

## Section 1.1 Assessment

1. Why is ozone important in the atmosphere?

2. Where is ozone formed and stored?

3. What are CFCs? How are they used?

4. **Thinking Critically** Why do you think ozone is formed over the equator? What is the connection between sunlight and ozone formation?

5. **Comparing and Contrasting** What general trend in ozone concentration is shown in the graph at the right? How does the data for the years 1977–1987 on this graph compare to the same time span on the graph in **Figure 1-5?** What do you notice?

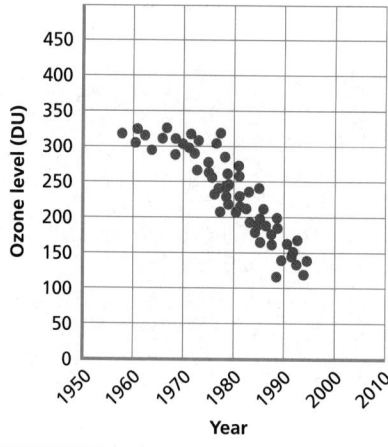

**October Ozone Concentrations**

*(y-axis: Ozone level (DU); values 0, 50, 100, 150, 200, 250, 300, 350, 400, 450; x-axis: Year 1950, 1960, 1970, 1980, 1990, 2000, 2010)*

chemistrymc.com/self_check_quiz

## Section 1.1 Assessment

1. Ozone absorbs harmful UV light from the sun, preventing it from reaching Earth's surface where it could damage living organisms.

2. in the stratosphere

3. chlorofluorocarbons; refrigerants, in foams, propellants in spray cans

4. Sunlight provides energy needed for ozone formation. Sunlight is more intense at the equator, so more ozone forms.

5. Ozone levels are decreasing. As CFCs increase, ozone concentration decreases.

**National Science Content Standards**

**Pages 6–7**
UCP.1, UCP.2; F.5, F.6; G.1, G.2, G.3

Matter, the stuff of the universe, has many different forms. You are made of matter. There is matter in the bed, blankets, and sheets on which you sleep as well as in the clothes you wear. There is matter in the food you eat, and in medications and vitamins you may take. You have learned that ozone is a chemical that occurs naturally in the environment, whereas CFCs do not. Although both chemicals are invisible gases, they, too, are matter.

## Chemistry: The Central Science

**Chemistry** is the study of matter and the changes that it undergoes. A basic understanding of chemistry is central to all sciences—biology, physics, Earth science, ecology, and others. Chemistry also is central to our everyday lives, as **Figure 1-6** illustrates. It will continue to be central to discoveries made in science and technology in the twenty-first century.

### Objectives

- **Define** chemistry and matter.
- **Compare** and **contrast** mass and weight.
- **Explain** why chemists are interested in a submicroscopic description of matter.

### Vocabulary

chemistry
matter
mass
weight

**Figure 1-6**

High-tech fabrics that don't hinder athletic performance, water, fertilizers, pesticides, food, grocery items, clothing, building materials, hair care products, plastics, and even the human body are made of chemicals.

1.2 Chemistry and Matter **7**

# 1 Focus

## Focus Transparency

Before presenting the lesson, display **Section Focus Transparency 2** on the overhead projector and have students answer the accompanying questions using **Section Focus Transparency Master 2.** L1 ELL

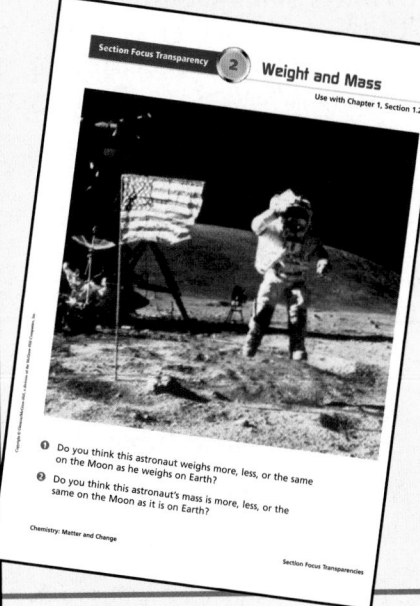

Section Focus Transparency 2 **Weight and Mass**

Use with Chapter 1, Section 1.2

❶ Do you think this astronaut weighs more, less, or the same on the Moon as he weighs on Earth?

❷ Do you think this astronaut's mass is more, less, or the same on the Moon as it is on Earth?

Chemistry: Matter and Change

Section Focus Transparencies

# 2 Teach

## Quick Demo

Light the candle used in the Quick Demo on page 3. Discuss the burning of the candle in terms of matter. Chemistry involves the study of the composition of matter, such as the wax in the candle and the oxygen in the air, and changes in matter, such as the changes that occur in the wax as it burns.

## DIFFERENTIATED INSTRUCTION

### Visually Impaired

*Kinesthetic* Have visually impaired students choose several objects, such as their textbooks, and describe them. Characteristics may include that they have weight and shape. Help students see these properties as mass and volume. Blow up a balloon. Have students touch it to "feel" the mass and volume of air contained in the balloon. L1 ELL

## Resource Manager

**Study Guide for Content Mastery,** pp. 2–3 L2

**Solving Problems: A Chemistry Handbook,** Section 1.2 L2

**Section Focus Transparency 2 and Master** L1 ELL

8

## In-Text Question

**Page 8** What else can you name that is not made of matter? Answers might include feelings, emotions, microwaves, and sound.

## 3 Assess

### Check for Understanding

Ask students to define chemical and chemistry. A chemical is any substance that has a definite composition. Chemicals make up matter. Chemistry is the study of matter and the changes it undergoes.

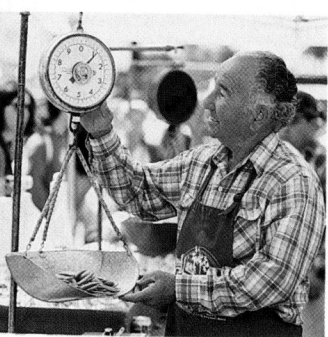

**Figure 1-7**

A scale measures the downward pull of gravity on an object. If this scale were used on the Moon, the reading would be less than on Earth.

## Matter and its Characteristics

You recognize matter in the everyday objects you are familiar with, such as those shown in **Figure 1-6**. But, how do you define matter? **Matter** is anything that has mass and takes up space. **Mass** is a measurement that reflects the amount of matter. It is easy to see that your textbook has mass and takes up space. Is air matter? You can't see it and you can't always feel it. However, when you inflate a balloon, it expands to make room for the air. The balloon gets heavier. Thus, air must be matter. Is everything made of matter? The thoughts and ideas that "fill" your head are not matter; neither are heat, light, radio waves, nor magnetic fields. What else can you name that is not matter?

**Mass and weight** When you go to the supermarket to buy a pound of vegetables, you place them on a scale like the one shown in **Figure 1-7** to find their weight. **Weight** is a measure not only of the amount of matter but also of the effect of Earth's gravitational pull on that matter. This force is not exactly the same everywhere on Earth and actually becomes less as you move away from Earth's surface at sea level. You may not notice a difference in the weight of a pound of vegetables from one place to another, but subtle differences do exist.

It might seem more convenient for scientists to simply use weight instead of mass. You might wonder why it is so important to think of matter in terms of mass. Scientists need to be able to compare the measurements that they make in different parts of the world. They could identify the gravitational force every time they weigh something but that is not practical or convenient. This is why they use mass as a way to measure matter independent of gravitational force.

**What you see and what you don't** What can you observe about the outside of your school building or a skyscraper downtown? You know that there is more than meets the eye to such a building. There are beams inside the walls that give the building structure, stability, and function. Consider another

## problem-solving LAB

### Chemical Models

**Making Models** Until the mid-1980s, scientists thought there were only two forms of carbon, each with a unique structure: diamond and graphite. As with many scientific discoveries, another form of carbon came as a surprise.

Buckminsterfullerene, also called the buckyball, was found while researching interstellar matter. Scientists worked with various models of carbon structures until they determined that 60 carbons were most stable when joined together in a shape that resembles a soccer ball.

### Analysis

Examine the structure in the diagram. Where are the carbon atoms? How many carbons is each carbon connected to? Identify the pentagons and hexagons on the faces on the buckyball.

### Thinking Critically

Go back to **Figure 1-3** to see an example of another model that chemists use. What process does the figure show? Explain why this information could not be shown in a photograph. What do the colored particles represent? Use **Table C-1** in Appendix C to help you in your identification.

**Table 1-1**

| Branches of Chemistry | | |
|---|---|---|
| **Branch** | **Area of emphasis** | **Examples** |
| Organic chemistry | Most carbon-containing chemicals | Pharmaceuticals, plastics |
| Inorganic chemistry | In general, matter that does not contain carbon | Minerals, metals and nonmetals, semi-conductors |
| Physical chemistry | The behavior and changes of matter and the related energy changes | Reaction rates, reaction mechanisms |
| Analytical chemistry | Components and composition of substances | Food nutrients, quality control |
| Biochemistry | Matter and processes of living organisms | Metabolism, fermentation |

example. When you bend your arm at the elbow, you observe that your hand comes toward your shoulder. Muscles that you cannot see under the skin contract and relax to move your arm.

Much of matter and its behavior is macroscopic; that is, you do not need a microscope to see it. You will learn in Chapter 3 that the tremendous variety of stuff around you can be broken down into more than 100 types of matter called elements, and that elements are made up of particles called atoms. Atoms are so tiny that they cannot be seen even with optical microscopes. Thus, atoms are *sub*microscopic. They are so small that 1 million million atoms could fit onto the period at the end of this sentence.

The structure, composition, and behavior of all matter can be explained on a submicroscopic level. All that we observe about matter depends on atoms and the changes they undergo. Chemistry seeks to explain the submicroscopic events that lead to macroscopic observations. One way this can be done is by making a model, a visual representation of a submicroscopic event. **Figure 1-3** is such a model. The **problem-solving Lab** on the opposite page gives you practice interpreting a simple chemical model.

**Branches in the field of chemistry** Because there are so many types of matter, there are many areas of study in the field of chemistry. Chemistry is traditionally broken down into the five branches listed in **Table 1-1.**

Additional areas of chemisty include theoretical chemistry, which focuses on why and how chemicals interact, and environmental chemistry, which deals with the role chemicals play in the environment.

## Section 1.2 Assessment

6. Define matter.

7. Compare and contrast mass and weight.

8. Why does chemistry involve the study of the changes in the world at a submicroscopic level?

9. **Thinking Critically** Explain why a scientist must be cautious when a new chemical that has many potential uses is synthesized.

10. **Using Numbers** If your weight is 120 pounds and your mass is 54 kilograms, how would those values change if you were on the moon? The gravitational force on the moon is 1/6 the gravitational force on Earth.

## Section 1.2 Assessment

6. anything that has mass and volume
7. Mass is a measure of the amount of matter. It is independent of gravity. Weight is the effect of gravity on matter.
8. The changes you see with your eyes all begin with changes at the submicroscopic level.
9. Scientists might not be able to predict how a chemical may react with substances in its environment.
10. Your mass will still be 54 kg, but your weight will be 1/6 your weight on Earth (120 lb/6 = 20 lb).

# 1 Focus

## Focus Transparency

Before presenting the lesson, display **Section Focus Transparency 3** on the overhead projector and have students answer the accompanying questions using **Section Focus Transparency Master 3.** L1 ELL

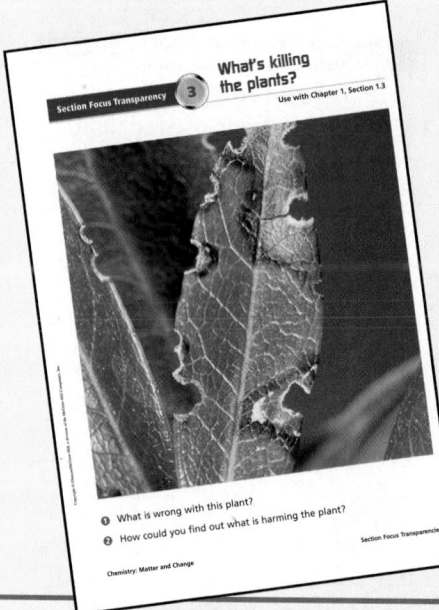

Section Focus Transparency 3

**What's killing the plants?**

Use with Chapter 1, Section 1.3

❶ What is wrong with this plant?

❷ How could you find out what is harming the plant?

Chemistry: Matter and Change
Section Focus Transparencies

# 2 Teach

## Quick Demo

*Logical-Mathematical* Ask groups of four students each to develop a list of the steps they would use to make a peanut butter and jelly sandwich. Then, have each group list their steps on the chalkboard, and have the class compare lists. Even though each group ends up with the same product, the methods used may vary. Have students relate this analogy to the development and use of scientific methods. L2

**National Science Content Standards**

**Pages 10–11**
UCP.1, UCP.2; A.2; G.1, G.2

**10**

---

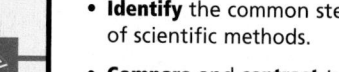

# Scientific Methods

## Objectives

• **Identify** the common steps of scientific methods.

• **Compare** and **contrast** types of data.

• **Compare** and **contrast** types of variables.

• **Describe** the difference between a theory and a scientific law.

## Vocabulary

scientific method
qualitative data
quantitative data
hypothesis
experiment
independent variable
dependent variable
control
conclusion
model
theory
scientific law

**Figure 1-8** shows students working together on an experiment in the laboratory. You know that each person in the group probably has a different idea about how to do the project and a different part of the project that interests him or her the most. Having many different ideas about how to solve a problem is one of the benefits of many people working together. Communicating ideas effectively to one another and combining individual contributions to form a solution can be difficulties encountered in group work.

## A Systematic Approach

Scientists approach their work in a similar way. Each scientist tries to understand his or her world based on a personal point of view and individual creativity. Often, the work of many scientists is combined in order to gain new insight. It is helpful if all scientists use common procedures as they conduct their experiments.

A **scientific method** is a systematic approach used in scientific study, whether it is chemistry, biology, physics, or other sciences. It is an organized process used by scientists to do research, and it provides a method for scientists to verify the work of others. An overview of the typical steps of a scientific method is shown in **Figure 1-9.** The steps are not used as a checklist to be done in the same order each time. Therefore, all scientists must describe their methods when they publish their results. If other scientists cannot confirm the results after repeating the method, then doubt arises over the validity of the reported results.

**Observation** You make observations throughout your day in order to make decisions. Scientific study usually begins with simple observation. An observation is the act of gathering information. Quite often, the types of observations scientists first make are **qualitative data**—information that describes color, odor, shape, or some other physical characteristic. In general, anything that relates to the five senses is qualitative: how something looks, feels, sounds, tastes, or smells.

**Figure 1-8**

During your chemistry course, you will have opportunities to use scientific methods to perform investigations and solve problems.

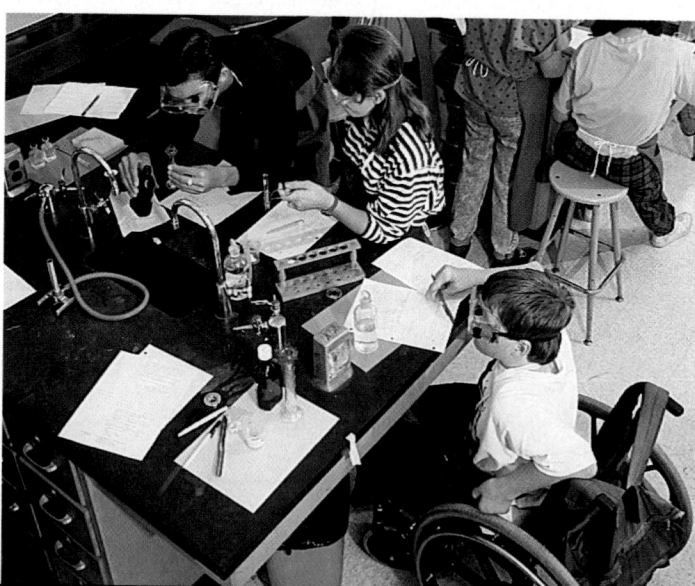

**10** Chapter 1

---

## Demonstration

### The Magic of Chemistry

#### Purpose

Students observe that one substance can be changed into another substance having different properties.

#### Materials

$KMnO_4$ (0.05 g); $NaHSO_3$ (1 g); $BaCl_2 \cdot 2H_2O$ (1 g); 400–mL beakers (3); small test tubes (2)

#### Safety Precautions

**Disposal** Filter the solution through filter paper. Dispose of the solid in a landfill approved to receive chemical waste.

#### Procedure

Before the demo, dissolve three or four small crystals of $KMnO_4$ in 250 mL of water in a beaker. In a test tube, add 1 g $NaHSO_3$ to 1 mL of water. In a second test tube, add 1 g $BaCl_2 \cdot 2H_2O$ to 1 mL of water. See page 2C for prepa-

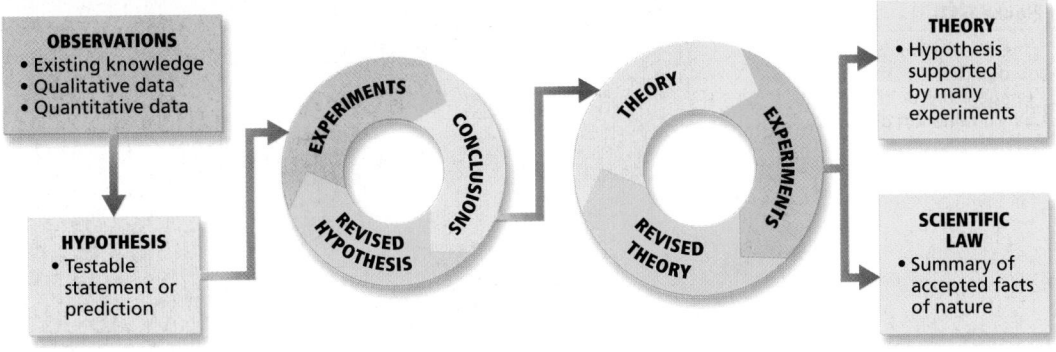

OBSERVATIONS
• Existing knowledge
• Qualitative data
• Quantitative data

HYPOTHESIS
• Testable statement or prediction

EXPERIMENTS — CONCLUSIONS — REVISED HYPOTHESIS

THEORY — EXPERIMENTS — REVISED THEORY

THEORY
• Hypothesis supported by many experiments

SCIENTIFIC LAW
• Summary of accepted facts of nature

Chemists frequently gather another type of data. For example, they can measure temperature, pressure, volume, the quantity of a chemical formed, or how much of a chemical is used up in a reaction. This numerical information is called **quantitative data.** It tells you how much, how little, how big, how tall, or how fast. What kind of qualitative and quantitative data can you gather from **Figure 1-10?**

**Hypothesis** Let's return to the stories of two chemicals that you read about earlier. Even before quantitative data showed that ozone levels were decreasing in the stratosphere, scientists observed that CFCs were found there. Chemists Mario Molina and F. Sherwood Rowland were curious about how long CFCs could exist in the atmosphere.

Molina and Rowland examined the interactions that can occur among various chemicals in the troposphere. They determined that CFCs were stable there for long periods of time. But they also knew that CFCs drift up into the stratosphere. They formed a hypothesis that CFCs break down in the stratosphere due to interactions with ultraviolet light from the Sun. In addition, the calculations they made led them to hypothesize that a chlorine particle produced by this interaction would break down ozone.

A **hypothesis** is a tentative explanation for what has been observed. Molina and Rowland's hypothesis stated what they believed to be happening, even though there was no formal evidence at that point to support the statement.

**Experiments** A hypothesis means nothing unless there are data to support it. Thus, forming a hypothesis helps the scientist focus on the next step in a scientific method, the experiment. An **experiment** is a set of controlled observations that test the hypothesis. The scientist must carefully plan and set up one or more laboratory experiments in order to change and test one variable at a time. A variable is a quantity or condition that can have more than one value.

Suppose your chemistry teacher asks your class to use the materials shown in **Figure 1-11** to design an experiment in which to test the hypothesis that table salt dissolves faster in hot water than in water at room temperature (20°C).

**Figure 1-9**

The steps in a scientific method are repeated until a hypothesis has been supported or discarded.

Try at Home **LAB**

See page 952 in Appendix E for **Testing Predictions**

**Figure 1-10**

Compare the qualitative and quantitative observations you can make from this photo with your classmates. Did you observe the same things?

**Assessment**

**Skill** Ask students to draw the steps of a scientific method as a flow chart. Under each heading, have them write a one-sentence description of that step. L2 ELL

## Extension

**Intrapersonal** Using the example of dissolving salt in water, ask students to design an experiment to determine how much salt dissolves at various temperatures. Have them identify constants, such as the amount of water. Have them identify an independent variable, such as the water temperature, and state how they want to vary it. Then have them identify the dependent variable, such as the amount of salt dissolved. If time is available, have students perform the experiment and analyze the data. L2

## In-Text Question

**Page 11** What kind of qualitative and quantitative data can you gather from Figure 1–10? Qualitative data might include colors and texture differences. Quantitative data might include relative masses and lengths.

**Resource Manager**

**Study Guide for Content Mastery,** pp. 4–5 L2
**Solving Problems: A Chemistry Handbook,** Section 1.3 L2
**Section Focus Transparency 3 and Master** L1 ELL

ration of solutions. **CAUTION:** *The solutions are toxic.* Place the $NaHSO_3$ solution in a beaker labeled 1 and the $BaCl_2$ solution in a beaker labeled 2. To start the demonstration, show students the "wine" ($KMnO_4$ solution). Pour the "wine" into beaker 1. Pour the "water" that results into beaker 2.

**Results**
The "wine" turns into "water," and the "water" is then changed into "milk."

Discussing the chemistry of this demo will be of little value at this time. Explain that a chemist learns how to change one substance into another substance having different properties.

**Analysis**
**1.** Were your observations of these changes qualitative or quantitative data? Qualitative data; students' sense of sight was used to observe color changes.

**Assessment**

**Performance** Have students make a poster showing three chemicals that they have used in the past week. Use the Performance Task Assessment List for Poster in **PASC,** p. 73. L1 ELL

## Identifying Misconceptions

Students often don't understand what a scientific theory is. Many people use the term *theory* to explain something in the world around them or human behavior. What they call a theory might be a hypothesis.

**Uncover the Misconception**
Have students work in groups to distinguish between a fact and a prediction. Conclusions should include that a fact has been tested and found to be reliable. A prediction might be based on information, but is yet to be supported. Relate these terms to *theory* and *hypothesis*.

**Demonstrate the Concept**
With students, develop an events chain concept map that shows the hierarchy of the terms *theory, hypothesis, experiments, observations.* Concept maps should show that a theory requires numerous hypotheses, which are supported by experiments that include observations.

**Assess New Knowledge**
Ask students to describe a common "theory." Help them see that simple statements based on observations are often really hypotheses. 🔲

## In-Text Question

**Page 12** Does either one contain acid? no

## Resource Manager

Teaching Transparency 2 and Master **L2** **ELL**
CBL Lab Manual, pp. 1–4 **L2**

**12**

**Figure 1-11**
These materials can be used to determine the effect of temperature on the rate at which table salt dissolves.

**Figure 1-12**
The control test tube in the middle lets you make a visual comparison.

Because temperature is the variable that you plan to change, it is an **independent variable.** Your group determines that a given quantity of salt completely dissolves within 1 minute at 40°C but that the same quantity of salt dissolves only after 3 minutes at 20°C. Thus, temperature affects the rate at which the salt dissolves. This rate is called a **dependent variable** because its value changes in response to a change in the independent variable. Although your group can determine the way the independent variable changes, it has no control over the way the dependent variable changes.

What other factors could you vary in your experiment? Would the amount of salt you try to dissolve make a difference? The amount of water you use? Would stirring the mixture affect your results? The answer can be yes to all of these questions. You must plan your experiment so that these variables are the same at each temperature, or you will not be able to tell clearly what caused your results. In a well-planned experiment, the independent variable should be the only condition that affects the experiment's outcome. A constant is a factor that is not allowed to change during the experiment. The amount of salt, water, and stirring must be constant at each temperature.

In many experiments, it is valuable to have a **control,** that is, a standard for comparison. In the above experiment, the room-temperature water is the control. The rate of dissolving at 40°C is compared to the rate at 20°C. **Figure 1-12** shows a different type of control. A chemical indicator has been added to each of three test tubes. Acid is added to the middle test tube, and the indicator turns yellow. This test tube can be used as a control. Compare the other two test tubes with the control. Does either one contain acid?

The interactions described between CFCs and ozone in Molina and Rowland's hypothesis take place high overhead. Many variables are involved. For example, there are different gases present in the stratosphere. Thus, it would be difficult to determine which gases, or possibly if all gases, are decreasing ozone levels. Winds, variations in ultraviolet light, and other factors could change the outcome of any experiment on any given day making comparisons difficult. Sometimes it is easier to simulate conditions in a laboratory where the variables can be more easily controlled.

An experiment may generate a large amount of data. These data must be carefully and systematically analyzed. Because the concept of data analysis is so important, you will learn more about it in the next chapter.

**Conclusion** Scientists take the data that have been analyzed and apply them to the hypothesis to form a conclusion. A **conclusion** is a judgment based on the information obtained. A hypothesis can never be proven. Therefore, to say that the data support a hypothesis is to give only a tentative "thumbs up" to the idea that the hypothesis may be true. If further evidence does not support it, then the hypothesis must be discarded or modified. The majority of hypotheses are not supported, but the data may still yield new information.

Molina and Rowland formed a hypothesis about the stability of CFCs in the stratosphere. They gathered data that supported their hypothesis and developed a model in which the chlorine formed by the breakdown of CFCs would react over and over again with ozone. You must realize by now a **model** is a visual, verbal, and/or mathematical explanation of experimental data.

A model can be tested and used to make predictions. Molina and Rowland's model predicted the formation of chlorine and the depletion of ozone, as shown in **Figure 1-13.** Another research group found evidence of interactions between ozone and chlorine when taking measurements in the stratosphere, but they did not know the source of the chlorine. Molina and Rowland's model predicted a source of the chlorine. They came to the conclusion that ozone in the stratosphere could be destroyed by CFCs and that they had enough support for their hypothesis to publish their discovery.

**Theory** A **theory** is an explanation that has been supported by many, many experiments. You may have heard of Einstein's theory of relativity or the atomic theory. A theory states a broad principle of nature that has been supported over time. All theories are still subject to new experimental data and can be modified. Also, theories often lead to new conclusions.

A theory is considered successful if it can be used to make predictions that are true. In 1985, the announcement by the British Antarctic Survey that the amount of ozone in the stratosphere was decreasing lent Molina and Rowland's hypothesis—that chlorine from CFCs could destroy ozone—further support.

**Scientific law** Sometimes, many scientists come over and over again to the same conclusion about certain relationships in nature. They find no exceptions. For example, you know that no matter how many times skydivers leap from a plane, they always wind up back on Earth's surface. Sir Isaac Newton was so certain that an attractive force exists between all objects that he proposed his law of universal gravitation.

Newton's law is a **scientific law** and, as such, a relationship in nature that is supported by many experiments. It is up to scientists to develop further hypotheses and experimentation to explain why these relationships exist.

**Figure 1-13**

ⓐ Molina and Rowland's model predicted that ultraviolet radiation causes a chlorine particle to split off from a CFC.
ⓑ The chlorine particle then destroys the ozone by combining with it to form oxygen gas and chlorine monoxide.

## 3 Assess

### Check for Understanding

Ask students to explain the difference between a hypothesis and a theory. A hypothesis is a statement about what is believed to be happening, without evidence. A theory is formed over time and is confirmed by verification of many hypotheses by experiments. **L2**

### Reteach

Have students clarify the difference between a theory and a scientific law. A theory is a statement that provides an explanation based on supported hypotheses. A scientific law describes something known to happen without error, such as gravity, but doesn't explain how it happens. **L2**

### Extension

Bring in a newspaper or journal article about a development in environmental chemistry. Have students identify the steps of a scientific method used as well as any controls and variables used. **L2**

### ✓ Assessment

**Performance** Cut out large pieces of paper and write a vocabulary word from this section on each. Have students place these papers in the order they are used in a scientific method. Some words may be subsets of specific steps. Accept any order that students can justify. Use the Performance Task Assessment List for Events Chain in **PASC,** p. 91. **L2**

## Section 1.3 Assessment

**11.** What is a scientific method? What are its steps?

**12.** You are asked to study the effect of temperature on the volume of a balloon. The balloon's size increases as it is warmed. What is the independent variable? Dependent variable? What factor is held constant? How would you construct a control?

**13.** Critique Molina and Rowland's hypothesis of ozone depletion as to its strengths and weaknesses.

**14.** Jacques Charles described the direct relationship between temperature and volume of all gases at constant pressure. Should this be called Charles's law or Charles's theory? Explain.

**15. Thinking Critically** Why must Molina and Rowland's data in the laboratory be supported by measurements taken in the stratosphere?

**16. Interpreting Data** A report in the media states that a specific diet will protect individuals from cancer. However, no data are reported to support this statement. Is this statement a hypothesis or a conclusion?

chemistrymc.com/self_check_quiz

1.3 Scientific Methods    **13**

## Section 1.3 Assessment

**11.** a systematic approach used in scientific study; observation, hypothesis, experiment, data analysis, conclusion

**12.** the temperature; the size of the balloon; the amount of air in the balloon; an identical balloon kept at room temperature

**13.** Answers might include that scientific evidence supports the hypothesis, but the hypothesis must be tested using models instead of actually observing the reaction.

**14.** It is called Charles's law because it describes a phenomenon that consistently takes place.

**15.** In the lab, conditions are carefully controlled. In the stratosphere, conditions vary widely. Data must show that the same phenomena occur in an unstructured environment.

**16.** It is only a hypothesis unless data supports it.

# 1 Focus

## Focus Transparency

Before presenting the lesson, display **Section Focus Transparency 4** on the overhead projector and have students answer the accompanying questions using **Section Focus Transparency Master 4.** **L1** **ELL**

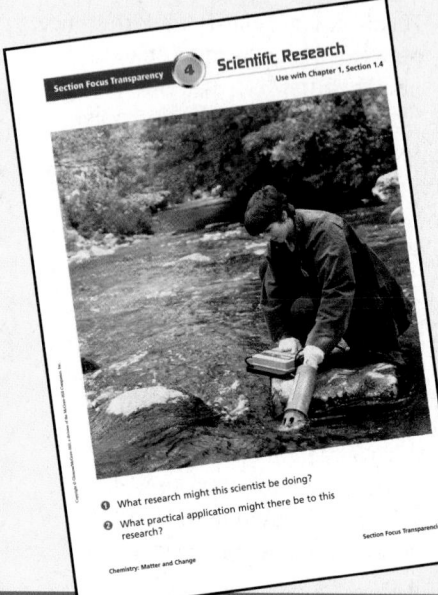

# 2 Teach

## Quick Demo

Bring in samples of nylon cloth and nylon cord. Nylon is a good example of a synthetic compound that has many uses. Explain that many such applications are chance discoveries that are byproducts of pure science.

## In-Text Questions

**Page 14** What type of research does it describe? both pure and applied

**Page 15** Which safety rules in Table 1-2 apply to the ChemLab and MiniLab? MiniLab: 1 through 9, 21, 24; ChemLab: 1 through 9, 24; student answers might vary slightly.

**14**

---

## Objectives
- **Compare** and **contrast** pure research, applied research, and technology.
- **Apply** knowledge of laboratory safety.

## Vocabulary
pure research
applied research
technology

## Biology
### CONNECTION

Many discoveries in science are made quite unexpectedly. Alexander Fleming is famous for making two such discoveries. The first occurred in 1922, when nasal mucus accidentally dripped onto bacteria that he had been growing for research. Rather than throwing the culture plate away, he decided to observe it over the next several days. He found that the bacteria died. As a result, he discovered that lysozyme, a chemical in mucus and tears, helps protect the body from bacteria.

Six years later, in 1928, Fleming found that one of his plates of *Staphylococcus* bacteria had been contaminated by a greenish mold, later identified as *Penicillium*. He observed it carefully and saw a clear area around the mold where the bacteria had died. In this case, a chemical in the mold—penicillin—was responsible for killing the bacteria.

---

Every day in the media, whether it's TV, newspapers, magazines, or the Internet, you are bombarded with the results of scientific investigations. Many deal with the environment, medicine, or health. As a consumer, you are asked to evaluate the results of scientific research and development. How do scientists use qualitative and quantitative data to solve different types of scientific problems?

## Types of Scientific Investigations

**Pure research** seeks to gain knowledge for the sake of knowledge itself. Molina and Rowland conducted research on CFCs and their interactions with ozone as pure research, motivated by curiosity. No environmental evidence at the time indicated that there was a correlation to their model in the stratosphere. Their research only showed that CFCs could speed the breakdown of ozone in a laboratory setting.

When the ozone hole was reported in 1985, scientists had made measurements of CFC levels in the stratosphere that supported the hypothesis that CFCs could be responsible for the depletion of ozone. The pure research done only for the sake of knowledge became applied research. **Applied research** is research undertaken to solve a specific problem. Scientists continue to monitor the amount of CFCs in the atmosphere and the annual changes in the amount of ozone in the stratosphere. Applied research also is being done to find replacement chemicals for the CFCs that are now banned. Read the **Chemistry and Society** feature at the end of this chapter to learn about research into the human genome. What type of research does it describe?

**Chance discoveries** Sometimes, when a scientist plans research with a specific goal in mind, he or she will conduct experiments and reach a conclusion that is expected. Sometimes, however, the conclusion reached is far different from what was expected. Some truly wonderful discoveries in science have been made unexpectedly.

The discovery of nylon is one example. In 1928, E.I. DuPont de Nemours and Company appointed a young, 32-year-old chemist from Harvard, Wallace Carothers, as the director of its new research center. The goal was to create artificial fibers similar to cellulose and silk. In 1930, Julian Hill, a member of Carothers' team, dipped a hot glass rod in a mixture of solutions and unexpectedly pulled out long fibers such as the one shown in **Figure 1-14.** Carothers pursued the development of these fibers as a synthetic silk that could withstand high temperatures and eventually developed nylon in 1934. Nylon's first use was in a toothbrush with nylon bristles. During World War II, nylon was used as a replacement for silk in parachutes. Nylon is used extensively today in textiles and some kinds of plastics.

## Students in the Laboratory

In your study of chemistry, you will learn many facts about matter. You also will do experiments in which you will be able to form and test hypotheses, gather and analyze data, and draw conclusions.

When you work in the chemistry laboratory, you are responsible for your safety and the safety of the people working nearby. **Table 1-2** on page 16 lists some safety rules that you must use as a guide each time you enter the lab.

---

## CHEMISTRY JOURNAL

### Research or Discovery

*Intrapersonal* Have students clip a newspaper article describing a scientific study. Ask them to discuss whether this example is pure research, applied research, or a chance discovery. **L2**

## Resource Manager

**Study Guide for Content Mastery,** p. 6 **L2**
**Solving Problems: A Chemistry Handbook,** Section 1.4 **L2**
**Section Focus Transparency 4 and Master** **L1** **ELL**

Chemists and all other scientists use these safety rules. Before you do the **miniLAB** at the bottom of this page or the **CHEMLAB** at the end of this chapter, read the procedures carefully. Which safety rules in **Table 1-2** apply?

**Figure 1-14**

Strands of nylon can be pulled from the top layer of solutions. After its discovery, nylon was used mainly for war materials and was unavailable for home use until after World War II.

## miniLAB

### Developing Observation Skills

**Observing and Inferring** A chemist's ability to make careful and accurate observations is developed early. The observations often are used to make inferences. An inference is an explanation or interpretation of observations.

**Materials** petri dish (2), graduated cylinder, whole milk, water, vegetable oil, four different food colorings, toothpick (2), dishwashing detergent

**Procedure**

1. Add water to a petri dish to a height of 0.5 cm. Add 1 mL of vegetable oil.
2. Dip the end of a toothpick in liquid dishwashing detergent.
3. Touch the tip of the toothpick to the water at the center of the petri dish. Record your detailed observations.
4. Add whole milk to a second petri dish to a height of 0.5 cm.
5. Place one drop each of four different food colorings in four different locations on the surface of the milk, as shown in the photo. Do not put a drop of food coloring in the center.

6. Repeat steps 2 and 3.

**Analysis**

1. What did you observe in step 3?
2. What did you observe in step 6?
3. Oil, the fat in milk, and grease belong to a class of chemicals called lipids. What can you infer about the addition of detergent to dishwater?

1.4 Scientific Research  **15**

### CHEMLAB

ChemLab 1, located at the end of the chapter, can be used at this point in the lesson.

## miniLAB

**Purpose**
Students will develop a hypothesis based on careful observations.

**Process Skills**
Observing and inferring, drawing a conclusion, hypothesizing, designing an experiment

**Disposal**
Flush the contents of the dish down the sink drain with plenty of water.

**Teaching Strategies**
- As a pre-lab activity, have students do Internet or library research on the composition of milk. Visit **science.glencoe.com.**
- Students can float pepper on the milk to trace movement if food coloring isn't available.

**Expected Results**
When the toothpick touches the milk, the detergent temporarily destroys the surface tension. The colors move to the outside of the dish. The detergent emulsifies any fat in the milk. Convectionlike currents are established, causing the colors to move from the outside toward the center.

**Analysis**
1. The oil moved away from the detergent.
2. The colors moved to the outside of the dish.
3. It helps remove grease and oil from items being washed.

### ✔ Assessment

**Performance** Have different lab groups test milk samples that have different fat content and then compare their observations. Use the Performance Task Assessment List for Carrying Out a Strategy and Collecting Data in **PASC**, p. 25. **L2** **ELL** **COOP LEARN**

## Applying Chemistry

Ask students if the discovery of CFCs was pure research, applied research, or chance discovery. It was applied research to find another source of refrigerants.

## Reinforcement

**Interpersonal** Divide students into groups of four. Give each group several safety tips from Table 1-2. Have them create a quick skit to demonstrate potential dangers and lab safety. **L2**
**COOP LEARN**

## Concept Development

As the instructor, walk into the lab demonstrating poor lab safety, such as wearing loose clothing and chewing gum. Have students identify as many rules you are breaking as they can. Have a prize, such as a special pair of lab goggles, for the student or group who identifies the greatest number of broken rules. Emphasize that although this example can be humorous, lab safety is a serious issue.

**National Science Content Standards**

**Pages 14–17**
UCP.1, UCP.2; A.1, A.2; E.2; F.6; G1, G2, G3

**16**

---

**Table 1-2**

### Safety in the Laboratory

1. Study your lab assignment **before** you come to the lab. If you have any questions, be sure to ask your teacher for help.

2. Do not perform experiments without your teacher's permission. **Never** work alone in the laboratory.

3. Use the table on the inside front cover of this textbook to understand the safety symbols. Read all **CAUTION** statements.

4. Safety goggles and a laboratory apron must be worn whenever you are in the lab. Gloves should be worn whenever you use chemicals that cause irritations or can be absorbed through the skin. Long hair must be tied back. See the photo below.

5. Do not wear contact lenses in the lab, even under goggles. Lenses can absorb vapors and are difficult to remove in case of an emergency.

6. Avoid wearing loose, draping clothing and dangling jewelry. Bare feet and sandals are not permitted in the lab.

7. Eating, drinking, and chewing gum are not allowed in the lab.

8. Know where to find and how to use the fire extinguisher, safety shower, fire blanket, and first-aid kit.

9. Report any accident, injury, incorrect procedure, or damaged equipment to your teacher.

10. If chemicals come in contact with your eyes or skin, flush the area immediately with large quantities of water. Immediately inform your teacher of the nature of the spill.

11. Handle all chemicals carefully. Check the labels of all bottles **before** removing the contents. Read the label three times:
    • Before you pick up the container.
    • When the container is in your hand.
    • When you put the bottle back.

12. Do not take reagent bottles to your work area unless instructed to do so. Use test tubes, paper, or beakers to obtain your chemicals. Take only small amounts. It is easier to get more than to dispose of excess.

13. Do not return unused chemicals to the stock bottle.

14. Do not insert droppers into reagent bottles. Pour a small amount of the chemical into a beaker.

15. **Never** taste any chemicals. **Never** draw any chemicals into a pipette with your mouth.

16. Keep combustible materials away from open flames.

17. Handle toxic and combustible gases only under the direction of your teacher. Use the fume hood when such materials are present.

18. When heating a substance in a test tube, be careful not to point the mouth of the test tube at another person or yourself. Never look down the mouth of a test tube.

19. Do not heat graduated cylinders, burettes, or pipettes with a laboratory burner.

20. Use caution and proper equipment when handling hot apparatus or glassware. Hot glass looks the same as cool glass.

21. Dispose of broken glass, unused chemicals, and products of reactions only as directed by your teacher.

22. Know the correct procedure for preparing acid solutions. **Always** add the acid slowly to the water.

23. Keep the balance area clean. Never place chemicals directly on the pan of a balance.

24. After completing an experiment, clean and put away your equipment. Clean your work area. Make sure the gas and water are turned off. Wash your hands with soap and water before you leave the lab.

---

## Portfolio

### Lab Safety

**Visual-Spatial** Have student groups create posters or a bulletin board that emphasizes safe lab procedures. Be sure the products reflect what the safe behavior is and why it should be used.
**L2 ELL P**

---

### Resource Manager

**Teaching Transparency 3 and Master**
**L2 ELL**
Lab Manual, pp. 1–4, 5–8 **L2**
ChemLab and MiniLab Worksheets,
p. 1 **L2**

## Benefits of Chemistry

It is easy to understand the purpose of applied research because it addresses a specific problem. It also is easier to see its immediate benefit. Yet, when a sudden, unexpected event occurs in the world, whether it's the ozone hole or the AIDS epidemic, the first line of defense is to look at the pure research that has already been conducted.

The products that we use to make our lives easier and more comfortable are the result of technological applications of pure and applied research. **Technology** is the practical use of scientific information. It is concerned with making improvements in human life and the world around us. As **Figure 1-15** shows, advances in technology can benefit us in many ways.

**Figure 1-15**

Nuclear power and artificial limbs and joints are just a few of the technological advances that have improved human life.

## Section 1.4 Assessment

**17.** Compare and contrast pure research and applied research.

**18.** What is technology? Is technology a product of pure research or applied research? Explain.

**19.** Explain why it is important to read each **CHEM-LAB** and **miniLAB** before you come to class.

**20. Thinking Critically** Explain the reason behind each of the following.

  **a.** Wear goggles and an apron in the lab even if you are only an observer.

  **b.** Report all accidents to your teacher.

  **c.** Do not return unused chemicals to the stock bottle.

**21. Interpreting Scientific Diagrams** What safety precautions should you take when you see the following safety symbols?

---

Ask students whether they think research on the Human Genome Project is pure or applied. If students are unfamiliar with the project, have them read the Chemistry and Society on page 20 of this text. Answers will vary but might include that it is pure research for knowledge of what's in the genome. Some students might say it is applied because of its use in gene therapy and cures for genetic diseases.

### Reteach

Emphasize that pure research is often a foundation for applied research. Pure research can create compounds or increase knowledge that scientists may not know how to use for years. However, when that knowledge or material is needed, it is readily available.

### Extension

Ask students to bring in newspaper or magazine articles about scientific research and explain to the class how that research applies to their lives. Examples may include a new drug or treatment for a disease that affects someone they know or new technology that affects the environment. L2

### Assessment

**Portfolio** Have students summarize articles brought in by some of the other students for the Extension above. Have students place the summaries into their portfolios. L2  P

---

## Section 1.4 Assessment

**17.** Pure research is done for the sake of knowledge. Applied research is done to solve a specific problem.

**18.** Technology is the practical use of scientific information and is the result of both pure and applied research.

**19.** You need to know what the objectives are, safety precautions, materials needed, and how to manage time.

**20. a.** Materials can spatter or spill.
   **b.** Specific means of disposal or cleanup might be needed.
   **c.** They might be contaminated.

**21.** Use proper protection when handling materials that are cold or hot. Make sure the area is well ventilated; never smell fumes directly; wear a mask. Wear dust mask and gloves; practice extra care when handling materials. Avoid open flames.

## Preparation

**Time Allotment**
One laboratory period

**Process Skills**
Analyzing and concluding, collecting and interpreting data, comparing and contrasting, designing an experiment, hypothesizing, measuring, observing and inferring, thinking critically

**Safety Precautions**
Remind students to use the rubber bands properly and responsibly. Ensure that students wear goggles throughout the activity. Rubber bands can accidentally injure eyes. Caution students that hair dryers become hot.

**Disposal**
Keep the rubber bands for reuse.

**Preparation**
• Give students some time before the lab period to plan how they will design their experiments.
• Ask students to bring in hair dryers from home.

### Pre-Lab

1. from the warmer object (your finger) to the cooler one (the object)
2. The sensitive skin on the forehead tells that an object is giving off heat if it feels warm on your forehead and absorbing heat if it feels cool.
3. What happens when you heat a stretched rubber band?
4. Check student procedures to assure they follow a correct scientific method.
5. See Expected Results.

### Procedure

• Check the students' experimental designs before they do the experiments.

**National Science Content Standards**
**Pages 18–19**
UCP.1, UCP.2; A.1, A.2; B.6

# The Rubber Band Stretch

Galileo Galilei (1564–1642) was an Italian philosopher, astronomer, and mathematician. Galileo pioneered the use of a systematic method of observation, experimentation, and analysis as a way to discover facts about nature. Modern science has its roots in Galileo's 17th-century work on the art of experimentation. This chapter introduced you to how scientists approach their work. In this **CHEMLAB**, you will have a chance to design a scientific method to study something you have observed many times before—the stretching of a rubber band.

**Problem**
What happens when you heat a stretched rubber band?

**Objectives**
• **Observe** the properties of a stretched and a relaxed rubber band.
• **Form a hypothesis** about the effect of heat on a stretched rubber band.
• **Design** an experiment to test your hypothesis.
• **Collect** and **analyze** data.
• **Draw conclusions** based on your analysis.

**Materials**
large rubber band
500-g mass
ring stand
clamp
hair dryer
meter stick or ruler

**Safety Precautions**

• Frequently observe the rubber band for any splits. Discard if rubber band is defective.
• The hair dryer can become hot, so handle it with care.

**Pre-Lab**

1. Heat is the transfer of energy from a warmer object to a cooler object. If an object feels warm to your finger, your finger is cooler than the object and energy is being transferred from the object to your finger. In what direction does the energy flow if an object feels cooler to you?

2. Your forehead is very sensitive to hot and cold. How can you use this fact to detect whether an object is giving off or absorbing heat?

3. Read the entire **CHEMLAB**. It is important to know exactly what you are going to do during all chemistry experiments so you can use your laboratory time efficiently and safely. What is the problem that this experiment is going to explore?

4. What typical steps in a scientific method will you use to explore the problem? Write down the procedure that you will use in each experiment that you design. Be sure to include all safety precautions.

5. You will need to record the data that you collect during each experiment. Prepare data tables that are similar to the one below.

| Rubber Band Data | |
|---|---|
| **Experiment #** | **Observations** |
| Trial 1 | |
| Trial 2 | |
| Trial 3 | |
| Trial 4 | |

## Expected Results

Observations should reflect that a rubber band gives off heat when it stretches, absorbs heat when it contracts, and contracts when heated.

## Analyze and Conclude

1. The rubber band feels warm. Energy was lost by the rubber band and gained by the forehead.

2. The rubber band feels cooler. Heat is gained by the rubber band and lost by the forehead.

3. When heated, a stretched rubber band contracts.

4. Most students would hypothesize that the rubber band would stretch when heated. The actual result refuted the hypothesis. The rubber band became shorter.

## Procedure

1. Obtain one large rubber band. Examine the rubber band for any splits or cracks. If you find any defects, discard it and obtain a new one.

2. Record detailed observations of the unstretched rubber band.

3. Design your first experiment to observe whether heat is given off or absorbed by a rubber band as it is stretched. Have your instructor approve your plan.

4. Do repeated trials of your experiment until you are sure of the results. **CAUTION:** *Do not bring the rubber band near your face unless you are wearing goggles.*

5. Design a second experiment to observe whether heat is given off or absorbed by a rubber band as it contracts after being stretched. Have your instructor approve your plan.

6. Do repeated trials of your experiment until you are sure of the results.

7. Use your observations in steps 2, 4, and 6 to form a hypothesis and make a prediction about what will happen to a stretched rubber band when it is heated.

8. Use the remaining items in the list of materials to design a third experiment to test what happens to a stretched rubber band as it is heated. Have your

instructor approve your plan. Be sure to record all observations before, during, and after heating.

## Cleanup and Disposal

1. Return the rubber band to your instructor to be reused by other classes.

2. Allow the hair dryer to cool before putting it away.

## Analyze and Conclude

1. **Observing and Inferring** What results did you observe in step 4 of the procedure? Was energy gained or lost by the rubber band? By your forehead? Explain.

2. **Observing and Inferring** What results did you observe in step 6 of the procedure? Was energy gained or lost by the rubber band? By your forehead? Explain.

3. **Applying** Many substances expand when they are heated. Did the rubber band behave in the same way? How do you know?

4. **Drawing a Conclusion** Did the result of heating the stretched rubber band in step 8 confirm or refute your hypothesis? Explain.

5. **Making Predictions** What would happen if you applied ice to the stretched rubber band?

6. Error Analysis Compare your results and conclusion with those of your classmates. What were your independent and dependent variables? Did you use a control? Did all of the lab teams measure the same variables? Were the data that you collected qualitative or quantitative? Does this make a difference when reporting your data to others? Do your results agree? Why or why not?

## Real-World Chemistry

1. When you put ice in a glass so that the ice rises higher than the rim, water does not overflow the glass when the ice melts. Explain.

2. Why do you think temperature extremes must be taken into account when bridges and highways are designed?

5. Predictions should include that it would stretch.

6. Student controls and variables will vary by student and by experiment. Sample answers might be: independent variable—degree of stretching; dependent variable—temperature; control—temperature of an unstretched rubber band. The data is qualitative because no actual measurements were made. A source of error might be time lags after stretching the rubber bands that allow temperature to change.

## Real-World Chemistry

1. Water expands when frozen. When ice melts, the water takes up less volume.

2. The materials that make up the bridge expand in warm weather and contract in cold weather. Bridge materials will crack if nothing is done to allow the bridge to expand and contract.

**Performance** Design an experiment like the one done in Procedure step 8, but cool the rubber band instead of heating it. Use the Performance Task Assessment List for Designing an Experiment in **PASC**, p. 23.

**Resource Manager**

ChemLab and MiniLab Worksheets, pp. 2–4 **L2**

## Internet Address Book

  Note Internet addresses that you find useful in the space below for quick reference.

_____

_____

_____

_____

## Purpose

Students will learn about the Human Genome Project, including how scientific methods are used to further project goals and societal issues raised by the research.

## Background

The goals of the Human Genome Project (HGP) included identifying all of the tens of thousands of genes in human DNA, determining the sequences of the 3 billion chemical bases that make up DNA, and storing this information in publicly accessible databases. It makes its findings available at no cost to other researchers around the world. The sequences identified by private companies are not available publicly. It is the first scientific effort of its size to address related legal, social, and ethical issues. HGP scientists are also decoding the genomes of the fruit fly, lab mouse, and *E. coli* bacterium. Studying nonhuman DNA may help researchers to address issues related to agriculture, energy, and environmental cleanup.

## Teaching Strategies

- Provide students with examples of genetic diversity in humans. Create a class list that shows some of the variety in traits expressed by human DNA.
- Have students research terminology associated with genetic research, including *genome, gene, chromosome,* and *protein.*
- Have students discuss their opinions about knowing what illnesses they are predisposed to develop, including conditions such as cancer, heart disease, and Alzheimer's. **L2**

## The Human Genome Project

From eye and skin color to the potential for developing disease, humans display remarkable and endless variety. Much of this variety is controlled by the human genome: the complete "instruction manual" found in the nucleus of all cells that is used to define a specific organism. Decoding and understanding these instructions is the goal of the Human Genome Project (HGP). The United States Department of Energy and the National Institutes of Health coordinated the project that began in 1990. Private industry also is involved. The HGP fosters cooperation as well as competition among researchers in a project that could hasten advances in treatment of human genetic conditions such as cancer and heart disease.

### A common goal, a common approach

The year 2003 marked the fiftieth anniversary of Watson and Crick's recognition of the structure of DNA. Chemicals called nitrogen bases connect the twisted strands that make up DNA. There are roughly three billion pairs of these bases in the human genome. Determining the sequence, or order, in which these base pairs occur was one common goal of researchers working on the HGP. Biologists, chemists, physicists, computer specialists, and engineers across the country approach the task from different angles. Use of scientific methods was the unifying theme in all of this work.

Prior to the HGP, researchers around the world used scientific methods to work independently on the mammoth task of decoding the human genome. Without coordination, however, the data they collected were analyzed and stored using different databases and were shared only through scientific journals and conferences. Those working on the HGP used common methods for gathering and analyzing data. Results were shared through databases that are rapidly available through the World Wide Web, enhancing communication, cooperation, and the flow of information. Because of this cooperation, a rough map of the human genome was completed in February 2001, several years ahead of schedule. Efforts are underway to determine the

exact location of every gene, however, and results will have to be shared by researchers working on the project.

### Looking toward the future

The HGP is spurring medical advances. But this powerful knowledge also raises important issues. For example, if a person's genome map shows a predisposition for a certain illness, should an employer or insurance company be informed? While the HGP is opening exciting doors, the associated ethical, legal, and societal issues must be acknowledged and addressed.

### Investigating the Issue

1. **Communicating Ideas** Research some of the ethical, legal, and societal issues being raised by genome research. Write a brief essay giving your opinion about how one or more of these issues could be addressed.

2. **Debating the Issue** The race to sequence the human genome took place in both the public and private sectors. Find information about several companies that worked independently on genome research. Is it ethical for them to sell this information, or should it be freely shared?

Visit the Chemistry Web site at **chemistrymc.com** to find links to more information about the Human Genome Project.

## Investigating the Issue

1. Students will have varying opinions on issues such as whether testing for genetic compatibility should be required prior to marriage; who should receive information about the results of genetic tests, including employers and insurance companies; and what is done if genetic testing shows a predisposition for developing certain illnesses.

2. Students will have a variety of reactions to a company's right to research, organize, and sell information it acquires using its own funds.

## Summary

### 1.1 The Stories of Two Chemicals

- The building blocks of the matter in the universe formed in the stars.
- A chemical is any substance that has a definite composition.
- Ozone is a chemical that forms a protective layer in Earth's atmosphere.
- Ozone is formed in the stratosphere when ultraviolet radiation from the Sun strikes oxygen gas.
- Thinning of the ozone layer over Antarctica is called the ozone hole.
- CFCs are synthetic chemicals made of chlorine, fluorine, and carbon.
- CFCs were used as refrigerants and as propellants in aerosol cans.
- CFCs can drift into the stratosphere.

### 1.2 Chemistry and Matter

- Chemistry is the study of matter and the changes that it undergoes.
- Matter is anything that has mass and takes up space.
- Mass is a measure of the amount of matter.
- Weight is a measure not only of an amount of matter but also the effect of Earth's gravitational pull on that matter.
- There are five traditional branches of chemistry: organic chemistry, inorganic chemistry, physical chemistry, analytical chemistry, and biochemistry.

- Macroscopic observations of matter reflect the actions of atoms on a submicroscopic scale.

### 1.3 Scientific Methods

- Typical steps of a scientific method include observation, hypothesis, experiments, data analysis, and conclusion.
- Qualitative data describe an observation; quantitative data use numbers.
- An independent variable is a variable that you change in an experiment.
- A dependant variable changes in response to a change in the independent variable.
- A theory is a hypothesis that has been supported by many experiments.
- A scientific law describes relationships in nature.

### 1.4 Scientific Research

- Scientific methods can be used in pure research for the sake of knowledge, or in applied research to solve a specific problem.
- Laboratory safety is the responsibility of anyone who conducts an experiment.
- Many of the conveniences we enjoy today are technological applications of chemistry.

## Vocabulary

- applied research (p. 14)
- chemistry (p. 7)
- conclusion (p. 12)
- control (p. 12)
- dependent variable (p. 12)
- experiment (p. 11)
- hypothesis (p. 11)
- independent variable (p. 12)
- mass (p. 8)
- matter (p. 8)
- model (p. 13)
- pure research (p. 14)
- qualitative data (p. 10)
- quantitative data (p. 11)
- scientific law (p. 13)
- scientific method (p. 10)
- technology (p. 17)
- theory (p. 13)
- weight (p. 8)

### Using the Vocabulary

To reinforce chapter vocabulary, have students write a sentence using each term. L2 ELL

### Review Strategies

- Have students define *chemistry, chemical, matter, mass,* and *weight.* L2
- Have students summarize the steps of a scientific method, giving examples of each step. L2
- Have students explain safe practices in the laboratory. L2

For additional help with vocabulary, have students access the Vocabulary PuzzleMaker online. chemistrymc.com/vocabulary_puzzlemaker

## EXAMVIEW® PRO

### Use ExamView® Pro Testmaker CD-ROM to:

- Create **multiple versions** of tests.
- Create **modified** tests with one mouse click for struggling students.
- **Edit** existing questions and add your own questions.
- **Build** tests based on national curriculum standards.

**National Science Content Standards**

**Pages 20–21**
UCP.1, UCP.2; A.1, A.2; B.2; E.2; F.1, F.6; G.1, G.2

**21**

## Concept Mapping

**22.** 1. ozone; 2. stratosphere;
3. ultraviolet radiation;
4. oxygen gas; 5. CFCs

## Mastering Concepts

**23.** any substance with a definite composition

**24.** 90% in the stratosphere

**25.** Chemical reactions in the atmosphere form ozone from oxygen and oxygen from ozone. Ozone protects Earth from UV rays.

**26.** refrigerants, foams, propellants for spray products

**27.** the study of matter and the changes it undergoes

**28.** An understanding of chemistry is central to all sciences and to our everyday lives.

**29.** Weight depends on gravitational force and changes as the gravitational force changes. Mass remains the same.

**30.** Analytical chemistry studies the composition of substances; environmental chemistry studies the environmental impact of chemicals.

**31.** Qualitative data, such as color or shape, are observed with the five senses. Quantitative data, such as mass or length, are measurements.

**32.** A control is a standard used for comparison.

**33.** A hypothesis is a tentative explanation about what has been observed. A theory is an explanation that has been supported by many experiments. A scientific law describes a relationship in nature.

**34.** Pure research might examine the properties of water. Applied research might ask what chemicals should be added to drinking water to promote health, such as fluoride to promote healthy tooth

formation. Technology might include creating filters to filter harmful contaminants out of water or machines to purify it.

## Chemistry Online

*Go to the Chemistry Web site at*
*chemistrymc.com for additional Chapter 1*
*Assessment.*

### Concept Mapping

**22.** Complete the concept map using the following terms: stratosphere, oxygen gas, CFCs, ozone, ultraviolet radiation.

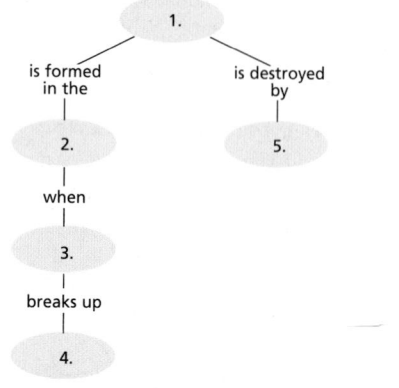

### Mastering Concepts

**23.** What is a chemical? (1.1)

**24.** Where is ozone located in Earth's atmosphere? (1.1)

**25.** Explain the balance between oxygen and ozone in the stratosphere. Why is it important? (1.1)

**26.** What were common uses of CFCs? (1.1)

**27.** What is chemistry? (1.2)

**28.** Why is chemistry called the central science? (1.2)

**29.** Which measurement depends on gravitational force—mass or weight? Explain. (1.2)

**30.** Which branch of chemistry studies the composition of substances? Environmental impact of chemicals? (1.2)

**31.** How does qualitative data differ from quantitative data? Give examples of each. (1.3)

**32.** What is the function of a control in an experiment? (1.3)

**33.** What is the difference between a hypothesis, a theory, and a law? (1.3)

**34.** In the study of water, what questions might be asked in pure research? Applied research? Technology? (1.4)

## Thinking Critically

**35. Compare and Contrast** Why is CFC depletion of the ozone layer a theory and not a scientific law?

**36. Classifying** CFCs break down to form chemicals that react with ozone. Is this a macroscopic or a microscopic observation?

**37. Communicating Ideas** Scientists often learn as much from an incorrect hypothesis as they do from one that is correct. Explain.

**38. Designing an Experiment** How would you design an experiment to evaluate the effectiveness of a "new and improved" chemical fertilizer on bean plants? Be sure to describe your hypothesis, procedure, variables, and control.

**39. Inferring** A newscaster reports, "The air quality today is poor. Visibility is only a quarter mile. Pollutants in the air are expected to rise above 0.085 parts per million (ppm) in the next eight hour average. Spend as little time outside today as possible if you suffer from asthma or other breathing problems." Which of these statements are qualitative and which are quantitative?

**40. Comparing and Contrasting** Match each of the following research topics with the branch of chemistry that would study it: water pollution, the digestion of food in the human body, the composition of a new textile fiber, metals to make new coins, a treatment for AIDS.

## Writing in Chemistry

**41.** Based on your beginning knowledge of chemistry, describe the research into depletion of the ozone layer by CFCs in a timeline.

**42.** Learn about the most recent measures taken by countries around the world to reduce CFCs in the atmosphere since the Montreal Protocol. Write a short report describing the Montreal Protocol and more recent environmental measures to reduce CFCs.

**43.** Name a technological application of chemistry that you use everyday. Prepare a booklet about its discovery and development.

## Cumulative Review

In chapters 2 through 26, this heading will be followed by questions that review your understanding of previous chapters.

chemistrymc.com/chapter_test

### Resource Manager

Chapter Assessment, pp. 1–6 **L2**
Supplemental Problems, Ch. 1
ExamView® Pro CD-ROM
MindJogger Videoquizzes VHS/DVD
Solutions Manual, Ch. 1
Chemistry Interactive CD-ROM,
 Ch. 1 quiz

*Use these questions and the test-taking tip to prepare for your standardized test.*

**1.** Matter is defined as anything that
   **a.** exists in nature.
   **b.** is solid to the touch.
   **c.** is found in the universe.
   **d.** has mass and takes up space.

**2.** Mass is preferred as a measurement over weight for all of the following reasons EXCEPT
   **a.** it has the same value everywhere on Earth.
   **b.** it is independent of gravitational forces.
   **c.** it becomes less in outer space, farther from Earth.
   **d.** it is a constant measure of the amount of matter.

**3.** Which of the following is an example of pure research?
   **a.** creating synthetic elements to study their properties
   **b.** producing heat-resistant plastics for use in household ovens
   **c.** finding ways to slow down the rusting of iron ships
   **d.** searching for fuels other than gasoline to power cars

**4.** When working with chemicals in the laboratory, which of the following is something you should NOT do?
   **a.** Read the label of chemical bottles before using their contents.
   **b.** Pour any unused chemicals back into their original bottles.
   **c.** Use lots of water to wash skin that has been splashed with chemicals.
   **d.** Take only as much as you need of shared chemicals.

**Interpreting Tables and Graphs** Use the table and graph to answer questions 5–7.

**5.** What must be a constant during the experiment?
   **a.** temperature
   **b.** mass of $CO_2$ dissolved in each sample
   **c.** amount of beverage in each sample
   **d.** independent variable

**6.** Assuming that all of the experimental data are correct, what is a reasonable conclusion for this experiment?
   **a.** Greater amounts of $CO_2$ dissolve in a liquid at lower temperatures.
   **b.** The different samples of beverage contained the same amount of $CO_2$ at each temperature.
   **c.** The relationship between temperature and solubility seen with solids is the same as the one seen with $CO_2$.
   **d.** $CO_2$ dissolves better in a liquid at higher temperatures.

### Page From a Student's Laboratory Notebook

| Step | Notes |
|---|---|
| Observation | Carbonated beverages taste fizzier (more gassy) when they are warm than when they are cold. (Carbonated beverages are fizzy because they contain dissolved carbon dioxide gas.) |
| Hypothesis | At higher temperatures, greater amounts of carbon dioxide gas will dissolve in a liquid. This is the same relationship between temperature and solubility seen with solids. |
| Experiment | Measure the mass of carbon dioxide ($CO_2$) in different samples of the same carbonated beverage at different temperatures. |
| Data Analysis | See graph below. |
| Conclusion | ? |

**Mass of $CO_2$ Dissolved in a Carbonated Beverage**

**7.** The scientific method used by this student showed that
   **a.** the hypothesis is supported by the experimental data.
   **b.** the observation accurately describes what occurs in nature.
   **c.** the experiment is poorly planned.
   **d.** the hypothesis should be thrown out.

### TEST-TAKING TIP

**More Than One Graphic** If a test question has more than one table, graph, diagram, or drawing with it, use them all. If you answer based on just one graphic, you've probably missed an important piece of information. For questions 5-7 above, make sure that you accurately analyzed both graphics before answering the questions.

Standardized Test Practice **23**

## Thinking Critically

**35.** It has been supported by many experiments but still relies on further experiments for support. It does not describe a law of nature that always occurs, such as gravity.

**36.** microscopic because it cannot be seen with human eyes

**37.** Data obtained testing an incorrect hypothesis provides useful information.

**38.** The hypothesis might say that the new fertilizer increases the number of beans produced by each bean plant. The procedure might be to have three groups of bean plants, one group with no fertilizer, one group with the unimproved fertilizer, and the other group with the new fertilizer. The independent variable would be the use of fertilizer. The dependent variable would be the number of beans produced by each plant. Constants are the amount of light and water received by each plant. The control would be the plants that received no fertilizer.

**39.** The qualitative statements are that air quality is poor and that people should spend little time outside. Quantitative statements include that visibility is only a quarter mile and that the pollutants will rise above 0.085 ppm in the next eight-hour average.

**40.** Answers will vary but might include environmental, biochemistry and organic, analytical, inorganic, and biochemistry, respectively.

### National Science Content Standards

**Pages 22–23**
UCP.1, UCP.2; A.2; B.2; E.2; F.4, F.6; G.2

## Standardized Test Practice

**1.** d          **6.** a
**2.** c          **7.** d
**3.** a
**4.** b
**5.** c

# Resource Manager

| Section | Objectives | Activities/Features |
|---|---|---|
| **Section 2.1**<br>**Units of Measurement**<br>$1/2$ session<br>📦 $1/2$ block | 1. **Define** SI base units for time, length, mass, and temperature.<br>2. **Explain** how adding a prefix changes a unit.<br>3. **Compare** the derived units for volume and density. | **Discovery Lab:** Layers of Liquids, p. 25<br>**Astronomy Connection,** p. 26<br>**MiniLab:** Density of an Irregular Solid, p. 28 |
| **Section 2.2**<br>**Scientific Notation and Dimensional Analysis**<br>2 sessions<br>📦 1 block | 4. **Express** numbers in scientific notation.<br>5. **Use** dimensional analysis to **convert** between units. | |
| **Section 2.3**<br>**How reliable are measurements?**<br>1 session<br>📦 $1/2$ block | 6. **Define** and **compare** accuracy and precision.<br>7. **Use** significant figures and rounding to reflect the certainty of data.<br>8. **Use** percent error to **describe** the accuracy of experimental data. | **Careers Using Chemistry:** Scientific Illustrator, p. 41 |
| **Section 2.4**<br>**Representing Data**<br>$2^1/2$ sessions<br>📦 1 block | 9. **Create** graphs to reveal patterns in data.<br>10. **Interpret** graphs. | **Problem-Solving Lab:** How does speed affect stopping distance? p. 44<br>**ChemLab:** Using Density to Find the Thickness of a Wire, pp. 46–47<br>**How It Works:** Ultrasound Devices, p. 48 |

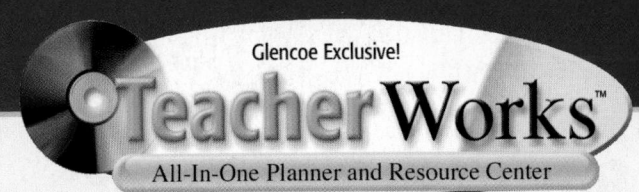

| National Science Content Standards | State/Local Standards | Reproducible Masters | Transparencies |
|---|---|---|---|
| UCP.1, UCP.3; A.1, A.2; B.2; G.1, G.2 | | **Study Guide for Content Mastery,** pp. 7–8 **L2**<br>**ChemLab and MiniLab Worksheets,** p. 5 **L2**<br>**Small-Scale Laboratory Manual,** pp. 1–4 **L2** | **Section Focus**<br>**Transparency 5** **L1** **ELL** |
| UCP.1, UCP.3; A.1, A.2; E.2 | | **Study Guide for Content Mastery,** p. 9 **L2** | **Section Focus**<br>**Transparency 6** **L1** **ELL**<br>**Teaching**<br>**Transparency 4** **L2** **ELL** |
| UCP.1, UCP.3; A.1, A.2; E.2; G2 | | **Study Guide for Content Mastery,** pp. 10–11 **L2** | **Section Focus**<br>**Transparency 7** **L1** **ELL**<br>**Teaching**<br>**Transparency 5** **L2** **ELL** |
| UCP.1, UCP.3; A.1, A.2; B.2; E.1, E.2; F.1; G.2 | | **Study Guide for Content Mastery,** p. 12 **L2**<br>**ChemLab and MiniLab Worksheets,** pp. 6–8 **L2**<br>**Laboratory Manual,** pp. 9–16 **L2**<br>**Challenge Problems,** p. 2 **L3** | **Section Focus**<br>**Transparency 8** **L1** **ELL**<br>**Math Skills**<br>**Transparency 1** **L2** **ELL**<br>**Teaching**<br>**Transparency 6** **L2** **ELL** |

**Key to National Science Content Standards:** UCP = Unifying Concepts and
Processes, A = Science as Inquiry, B = Physical Science, C = Life Science,
D = Earth and Space Sciences, E = Science and Technology,
F = Science in Personal and Social Perspectives, G = History and Nature of Science

Refer to pages 4T–5T of the Teacher Guide for an explanation of the
National Science Content Standards correlations.

# Resource Manager

## Materials List

**ChemLab** (pages 46–47)
small plastic cup, 100-mL graduated cylinder, balance, copper shot, 18-ga copper wire, 12-ga copper wire, ruler, pencil, graph paper, water, graphing calculator (optional)

**Discovery Lab** (page 25)
50-mL graduated cylinder, small plastic containers (4), alcohol, corn oil, water, glycerol, red food coloring, blue food coloring

**MiniLab** (page 28)
25-mL graduated cylinder, balance, washer or small object, water

**Demonstration** (pages 28–29)
1-L beakers (3), thermometers (3), ice, hot plate, paper towels, timer or stopwatch

## Preparation of Solutions

For a review of solution preparation, see page 46T of the Teacher Guide.

There are no solutions to be prepared for the activities in this chapter.

## Assessment Resources

**Chapter Assessment,** pp. 7–12
**MindJogger Videoquizzes DVD/VHS**
**Alternate Assessment in the Science Classroom**
**ExamView® Pro CD-ROM**
**Solutions Manual,** Chapter 2
**Supplemental Problems,** Chapter 2
**Performance Assessment in the Science Classroom**
**Chemistry Interactive CD-ROM,** Chapter 2 quiz
**Spanish Resources** **ELL**

## Additional Resources

**Guided Reading Audio Program,** Chapter 2 **ELL**
**Cooperative Learning in the Science Classroom**
**Lab and Safety Skills in the Science Classroom**
**Lesson Plans**
**Block Scheduling Lesson Plans**
**Chemistrymc.com**
   **/self_check_quiz**
   **/vocabulary_puzzlemaker**
   **/chapter_test**
   **/standardized_test**

## Glencoe Technology

The following multimedia for this chapter are available from Glencoe.

**VIDEOTAPE/DVD**
MindJogger Videoquizzes,
Chapter 2

**CD-ROM**
ExamView® Pro
    Testmaker

**CD-ROM**
Interactive Chalkboard

**CD-ROM**
TeacherWorks™

**CD-ROM**
**Chemistry: Matter and Change**
*Measurement of Density,* Experiment

## Multiple Learning Styles

Look for the following icons for strategies that emphasize different learning modalities.

**Kinesthetic**
Concept Development, p. 26; Meeting Individual Needs, pp. 27, 31, 44; Reteach, p. 30; Quick Demo, p. 36; Identifying Misconceptions, p. 38

**Interpersonal**
Chemistry Journal, p. 33; Reinforcement, p. 40; Extension, p. 37

**Intrapersonal**
Applying Chemistry, p. 33

**Linguistic**
Chemistry Journal, pp. 26, 36

**Logical-Mathematical**
Portfolio, p. 34; Reteach, p. 35; Chemistry Journal, p. 40; Differentiated Instruction, p. 41; Check for Understanding, p. 45

**Visual-Spatial**
Using the Photo, p. 24

## Key to Teaching Strategies

**L1** Level 1 activities should be appropriate for students with learning difficulties.

**L2** Level 2 activities should be within the ability range of all students.

**L3** Level 3 activities are designed for above-average students.

**ELL** ELL activities should be within the ability range of English Language Learners.

**COOP LEARN** Cooperative Learning activities are designed for small group work.

**P** These strategies represent student products that can be placed into a best-work portfolio.

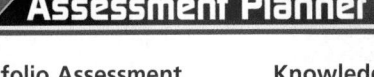 These strategies are useful in a block scheduling format.

## Assessment Planner

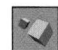

**Portfolio Assessment**
Portfolio, TWE, pp. 34, 49
Assessment, TWE, p. 45
ChemLab, TWE, p. 47

**Performance Assessment**
MiniLab, SE, p. 28
MiniLab, TWE, p. 28
ChemLab, SE, pp. 46–47
Discovery Lab, SE, p. 25

**Knowledge Assessment**
Assessment, TWE, pp. 26, 32, 42
Section Assessment, SE, pp. 30, 35, 42, 45
Chapter Assessment, SE, pp. 50–53

**Skill Assessment**
Assessment, TWE, pp. 30, 35, 44
Demonstration, TWE, p. 29
Problem-Solving Lab, TWE, p. 44

## Tying to Previous Knowledge

Have students review the following concepts before studying this chapter.
Chapter 1: qualitative and quantitative data, variables and analysis

## Using the Photo

 **Visual-Spatial** Ask students the importance of proper measurement of each piece of wood that is cut. Then, have each student in the class measure and cut out a narrow piece of paper exactly 15 cm long. Paste each strip of paper on poster board lengthwise so that the left sides of the strips line up. The right sides will show any differences in the lengths of the strips. Compare the different pieces of paper that should all be exactly 15 cm in length. How close are they? **L1** **ELL**

## Chapter Themes

The following themes from the National Science Education Standards are covered in this chapter.
Refer to page 4T of the Teacher Guide for an explanation of the correlations.
Systems, order, and organization (UCP.1)
Change, constancy, and measurement (UCP.2)

**PowerPoint® Presentations**
This CD-ROM is an editable Microsoft® PowerPoint® presentation that includes:
• Section presentations
• Section checks
• Image bank
• Links to Chemistry Online
• All transparencies
• Animations
• Audio

# Data Analysis

## What You'll Learn

▶ You will recognize SI units of measurement.
▶ You will convert data into scientific notation and from one unit to another.
▶ You will round off answers to the correct degree of certainty.
▶ You will use graphs to organize data.

## Why It's Important

What do planting a garden, painting a room, and planning a party have in common? For each task, you need to gather and analyze data.

Visit the Chemistry Web site at **chemistrymc.com** to find links about data analysis.

Carpenters learn from their mistakes to "measure twice and cut once."

## Purpose

Students will use various liquids to demonstrate the property of density.

## Safety and Disposal

Remind students to never taste anything in the laboratory. Have students add liquid soap to the contents of the cylinder, then flush them down the drain with plenty of water.

## Teaching Strategies

• Emphasize to students the importance of pouring the liquids slowly down the side of the cylinder. If they are poured quickly, the layers will mix at the boundaries.
• Be sure students add the liquids in the order specified. Adding a more dense liquid to one that is less dense might cause mixing of the layers.

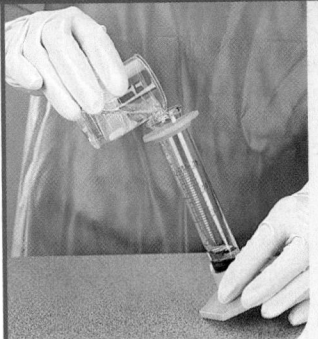

## Layers of Liquids

**H**ow many layers will four different liquids form when you add them to a graduated cylinder?

### Safety Precautions

Keep alcohol away from open flames.

### Procedure

1. Pour the blue-dyed glycerol from its small container into the graduated cylinder. Allow all of the glycerol to settle to the bottom.
2. Slowly add the water by pouring it down the inside of the cylinder as shown in the photograph.
3. Repeat step 2 with the corn oil.
4. Repeat step 2 with the red-dyed alcohol.

### Analysis

How are the liquids arranged in the cylinder? Hypothesize about what property of the liquids is responsible for this arrangement.

**Materials**

5 mL each in small, plastic containers:
alcohol
corn oil
glycerol
water
graduated cylinder

---

## Section 2.1 — Units of Measurement

### Objectives

- **Define** SI base units for time, length, mass, and temperature.
- **Explain** how adding a prefix changes a unit.
- **Compare** the derived units for volume and density.

### Vocabulary

base unit
second
meter
kilogram
derived unit
liter
density
kelvin

Suppose you get an e-mail from a friend who lives in Canada. Your friend complains that it has been too hot lately to play soccer or ride a bike. The high temperature each day has been about 35. You think that this figure must be wrong because a temperature of 35 is cold, not hot. Actually, 35 can be either hot or cold depending on which temperature units are used. For a measurement to be useful, it must include both a number and a unit.

### SI Units

Measurement is a part of daily activities. Hospitals record the weight and length of each baby. Meters on gasoline pumps measure the volume of gasoline sold. The highway sign in **Figure 2-1** gives the measured distance from the sign's location to two different destinations. In the United States, these distances are shown in both kilometers and miles.

For people born in the United States, the mile is a familiar unit. People in most other countries measure distances in kilometers. Kilometers and miles are units of length in different measurement systems. The system that includes kilometers is the system used by scientists worldwide.

**Figure 2-1**

How many miles apart are Baker and Barstow? Which is longer, a mile or a kilometer?

2.1 Units of Measurement **25**

---

## 1 Focus

### Focus Transparency

Before presenting the lesson, display **Section Focus Transparency 5** on the overhead projector. Have students answer the accompanying questions using **Section Focus Transparency Master 5.** L1 ELL

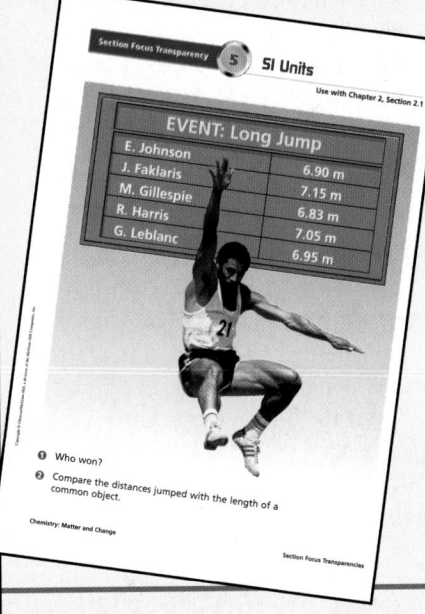

Section Focus Transparency **5** SI Units

Use with Chapter 2, Section 2.1

**EVENT: Long Jump**

| | |
|---|---|
| E. Johnson | 6.90 m |
| J. Faklaris | 7.15 m |
| M. Gillespie | 6.83 m |
| R. Harris | 7.05 m |
| G. Leblanc | 6.95 m |

❶ Who won?
❷ Compare the distances jumped with the length of a common object.

Chemistry: Matter and Change

Section Focus Transparencies

## 2 Teach

### Figure Caption Questions

**Figure 2-1** How many miles apart are Baker and Barstow? 62 mi Which is longer, a mile or a kilometer? A mile; have students look at the road sign in Figure 2-1. A given number of miles is equal to a greater number of kilometers. Therefore, a mile must be longer than a kilometer.

### Resource Manager

**Study Guide for Content Mastery,** pp. 7–8 L2
**Solving Problems: A Chemistry Handbook,** Section 2.1 L2
**Section Focus Transparency 5 and Master** L1 ELL

---

### Expected Results

The different liquids do not mix but form distinctive layers.

### Analysis

From bottom to top, the layers are glycerol, water, corn oil, and alcohol. Student hypotheses should reflect differences in densities of the liquids, although that term will probably not be used. Students might refer to differences in "heaviness."

**Page 26** Use Table 2-2 to figure out how many millimeters are in a meter and how many meters are in a kilometer. 1000; 1000

## Concept Development

 *Kinesthetic* Have students of varying heights count the number of paces they need to walk across the classroom. Elicit from students that a pace can vary in length from person to person, and that such differences are a problem when developing a system of measurement. Scientific measurements must be exact, and two scientists must be able to compare the same measurement. **L1** **ELL**

### ✔ Assessment

**Knowledge** Ask students to identify items that they would measure using the base units for time, length, and mass. Examples might include the amount of time it takes to bounce a ball (s), the distance across a room (m), and the mass of a student (kg).

### Quick Demo

Bring out weights of 1 g, 1 dg, 1 kg, and 1 Mg, if available. Have students feel the weights and compare them. Remind them that prefixes on the metric scale represent a 10-fold difference in the property measured (in this case, mass).

### Visual Learning

**Table 2-2** According to the table, which is greater, a nanosecond or a millisecond? a millisecond

---

**Table 2-1**

| SI Base Units | |
| --- | --- |
| **Quantity** | **Base unit** |
| Time | second (s) |
| Length | meter (m) |
| Mass | kilogram (kg) |
| Temperature | kelvin (K) |
| Amount of a substance | mole (mol) |
| Electric current | ampere (A) |
| Luminous intensity | candela (cd) |

**Try at Home LAB**

See page 952 in Appendix E for
**SI Measurement Around the Home**

### Astronomy
#### CONNECTION

A star's temperature and size determine its brightness, or luminous intensity. The SI base unit for luminous intensity is the candela. The more massive a star and the hotter its temperature, the brighter the star will be. How bright a star appears from Earth can be misleading because stars are at different distances from Earth. Light spreads out as it travels from its source. Thus, distant stars will appear less bright than stars of equal intensity that are closer to Earth.

**26** Chapter 2 Data Analysis

---

For centuries, units of measurement were fairly inexact. A person might mark off the boundaries of a property by walking and counting the number of steps. The passage of time could be estimated with a sundial or an hourglass filled with sand. Such estimates worked for ordinary tasks. Scientists, however, need to report data that can be reproduced by other scientists. They need standard units of measurement. In 1795, French scientists adopted a system of standard units called the metric system. In 1960, an international committee of scientists met to update the metric system. The revised system is called the Système Internationale d'Unités, which is abbreviated SI.

## Base Units

There are seven base units in SI. A **base unit** is a defined unit in a system of measurement that is based on an object or event in the physical world. A base unit is independent of other units. **Table 2-1** lists the seven SI base units, the quantities they measure, and their abbreviations. Some familiar quantities that are expressed in base units are time, length, mass, and temperature.

**Time** The SI base unit for time is the **second** (s). The frequency of microwave radiation given off by a cesium-133 atom is the physical standard used to establish the length of a second. Cesium clocks are more reliable than the clocks and stopwatches that you use to measure time. For ordinary tasks, a second is a short amount of time. Many chemical reactions take place in less than a second. To better describe the range of possible measurements, scientists add prefixes to the base units. This task is made easier because the metric system is a decimal system. The prefixes in **Table 2-2** are based on multiples, or factors, of ten. These prefixes can be used with all SI units. In Section 2.2, you will learn to express quantities such as 0.000 000 015 s in scientific notation, which also is based on multiples of ten.

**Length** The SI base unit for length is the **meter** (m). A meter is the distance that light travels through a vacuum in 1/299 792 458 of a second. A vacuum is a space containing no matter. A meter, which is close in length to a yard, is useful for measuring the length and width of a room. For distances between cities, you would use kilometers. The diameter of a drill bit might be reported in millimeters. Use **Table 2-2** to figure out how many millimeters are in a meter and how many meters are in a kilometer.

**Table 2-2**

| Prefixes Used with SI Units | | | | |
| --- | --- | --- | --- | --- |
| **Prefix** | **Symbol** | **Factor** | **Scientific notation** | **Example** |
| giga | G | 1 000 000 000 | $10^9$ | gigameter (Gm) |
| mega | M | 1 000 000 | $10^6$ | megagram (Mg) |
| kilo | k | 1000 | $10^3$ | kilometer (km) |
| deci | d | 1/10 | $10^{-1}$ | deciliter (dL) |
| centi | c | 1/100 | $10^{-2}$ | centimeter (cm) |
| milli | m | 1/1000 | $10^{-3}$ | milligram (mg) |
| micro | $\mu$ | 1/1 000 000 | $10^{-6}$ | microgram ($\mu$g) |
| nano | n | 1/1 000 000 000 | $10^{-9}$ | nanometer (nm) |
| pico | p | 1/1 000 000 000 000 | $10^{-12}$ | picometer (pm) |

---

### CHEMISTRY JOURNAL

#### Same Meaning, Different Language

*Linguistic* Have students write about times they disagreed with someone and later realized it was because they meant the same thing but used different language to say it. Ask them how SI units can solve that problem among scientists. **L2**

### CULTURAL DIVERSITY

#### Zero

The first known use of the zero was by a seventh-century Hindu, Brahmagupta. Ancient Egyptians and Greek mathematicians computed without a zero. Babylonians used a placeholder similar to the zero. Turkish and Greek mathematicians used an inverted *h* as a symbol for zero.

**Mass** Recall that mass is a measure of the amount of matter. The SI base unit for mass is the **kilogram** (kg). A kilogram is about 2.2 pounds. The kilogram is defined by the platinum-iridium metal cylinder shown in **Figure 2-2.** The cylinder is stored in a triple bell jar to keep air away from the metal. The masses measured in most laboratories are much smaller than a kilogram. For such masses, scientists use grams (g) or milligrams (mg). There are 1000 grams in a kilogram. How many milligrams are in a gram?

## Derived Units

Not all quantities can be measured with base units. For example, the SI unit for speed is meters per second (m/s). Notice that meters per second includes two SI base units—the meter and the second. A unit that is defined by a combination of base units is called a **derived unit.** Two other quantities that are measured in derived units are volume and density.

**Volume** Volume is the space occupied by an object. The derived unit for volume is the cubic meter, which is represented by a cube whose sides are all one meter in length. For measurements that you are likely to make, the more useful derived unit for volume is the cubic centimeter (cm³). The cubic centimeter works well for solid objects with regular dimensions, but not as well for liquids or for solids with irregular shapes. In the **miniLAB** on the next page, you will learn how to determine the volume of irregular solids.

**Figure 2-3** shows the relationship between different SI volume units, including the cubic decimeter (dm³). The metric unit for volume equal to one cubic decimeter is a **liter** (L). Liters are used to measure the amount of liquid in a container of bottled water or a carbonated beverage. One liter has about the same volume as one quart. For the smaller quantities of liquids that you will work with in the laboratory, volume is measured in milliliters (mL). A milliliter is equal in volume to one cubic centimeter. Recall that *milli* means one-thousandth. Therefore, one liter is equal to 1000 milliliters.

**Density** Why is it easier to lift a grocery bag full of paper goods than it is to lift a grocery bag full of soup cans? The volumes of the grocery bags are identical. Therefore, the difference in effort must be related to how much mass is packed into the same volume. **Density** is a ratio that compares the mass of an object to its volume. The units for density are often grams per cubic centimeter (g/cm³).

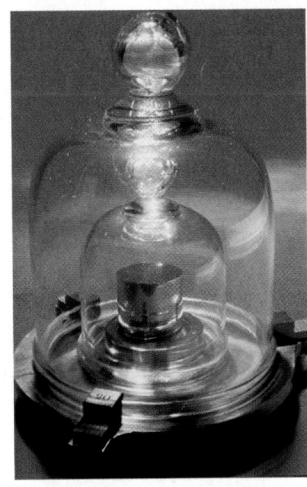

**Figure 2-2**

The kilogram is the only base unit whose standard is a physical object. The standard kilogram is kept in Sèvres, France. The kilogram in this photo is a copy kept at the National Institute of Standards and Technology in Gaithersburg, Maryland.

**Figure 2-3**

How many cubic centimeters (cm³) are in one liter?

2.1 Units of Measurement    **27**

## Figure Caption Question

**Figure 2-3** How many cubic centimeters (cm³) are in one liter?
1000

## In-Text Question

**Page 27** How many milligrams are in a gram? 1000

## Concept Development

Ask students why volume is considered to be a derived unit.
Volume is calculated as length × length × length. The SI unit of volume (m³) is derived from the SI base unit of length, the meter.

*GLENCOE*
*TECHNOLOGY*

**CD-ROM**
**Chemistry: Matter and Change**
Experiment:
*Measurement of Density*

**DIFFERENTIATED INSTRUCTION**

### Visually Impaired

*Kinesthetic* Have sighted students use paper to make cubes that are 1 cm and 1 dm on each side, with volumes of 1 cm³ and 1 dm³, respectively. Have visually impaired students determine tactilely the dimensions that must be measured to calculate volume. Explain how volume is a derived unit. **L1** **ELL**

**Resource Manager**

**ChemLab and MiniLab Worksheets,** p. 5 **L2**
**Small-Scale Lab Manual,** pp. 1–4 **L2**

**National Science Content Standards**
**Pages 26–27**
UCP.1, UCP.3; A.1, A.2; G.2

# miniLAB

## Purpose
Students will measure volume and mass and calculate density.

## Process Skills
Using numbers, measuring, acquiring and analyzing information

## Teaching Strategies
- Because of the small volume of the washer, students might obtain a more accurate measurement by determining the average volume of several washers.
- If students use washers or other objects of known composition, have them compare their calculated densities to the accepted density values for the substance.

## Expected Result
Density is determined in g/mL by dividing mass by volume.

## Analysis
1. $V_{final} - V_{initial} = V_{washer}$
2. mass/volume = density
3. Sugar dissolves in water.
4. Measure the diameter of the washer and calculate its area. Measure the diameter of the hole and calculate its area. Subtract the area of the hole from the area of the washer. Multiply the answer by the thickness of the washer.

## ✔ Assessment
**Performance** In cooking, water displacement can be used to measure volumes of ingredients that won't dissolve in water. Examples of such ingredients include solid shortening and peanut butter. Have student groups demonstrate how to measure one-fourth cup of one of these ingredients by using water displacement. Use the Performance Task Assessment List for Oral Presentation in **PASC**, p. 71.
**L1** **ELL**

National Science Content Standards
Pages 28–31
UCP.1, UCP.3; A.1, A.2; B.2; E.2; G.1, G.2

**28**

---

**Figure 2-4**

The piece of foam has the same mass as the quarter. Compare the densities of the quarter and the foam.

## Chemistry Online

**Topic: SI**
To learn more about SI, visit the Chemistry Web site at chemistrymc.com

**Activity:** Research three SI units not discussed in this section. Share with the class the units you selected and describe what the units measure.

Consider the quarter and the piece of foam in **Figure 2-4.** In this case, the objects have the same mass. Because the density of the quarter is much greater than the density of the foam, the quarter occupies a much smaller space. How does density explain what you observed in the **DISCOVERY LAB?**

You can calculate density using this equation:

$$\text{density} = \frac{\text{mass}}{\text{volume}}$$

If a sample of aluminum has a mass of 13.5 g and a volume of 5.0 cm³, what is its density? Insert the known quantities for mass and volume into the density equation.

$$\text{density} = \frac{13.5\ \text{g}}{5.0\ \text{cm}^3}$$

The density of aluminum is 2.7 g/cm³. Density is a property that can be used to identify an unknown sample of matter. Every sample of pure aluminum has the same density. **How It Works** at the end of the chapter explains how ultrasound testing relies on the variation in density among materials.

# miniLAB

## Density of an Irregular Solid

**Measuring** To calculate density, you need to know both the mass and volume of an object. You can find the volume of an irregular solid by displacing water.

**Materials** balance, graduated cylinder, water, washer or other small object

## Procedure
1. Find and record the mass of the washer.
2. Add about 15 mL of water to your graduated cylinder. Measure and record the volume. Because the surface of the water in the cylinder is curved, make volume readings at eye level and at the lowest point on the curve. The curved surface is called a *meniscus.*
3. Carefully add the washer to the cylinder. Then measure and record the new volume.

## Analysis
1. Use the initial and final volume readings to calculate the volume of the washer.
2. Use the calculated volume and the measured mass to find the density of the washer.
3. Explain why you cannot use displacement of water to find the volume of a sugar cube.
4. The washer is a short cylinder with a hole in the middle. Describe another way to find its volume.

---

## Demonstration

### Demonstration of Temperature

**Purpose**
Students will investigate the measurement of temperature by a thermometer and sensation of temperature by the skin.

**Materials**
1-L beakers (3); ice; hot plate; paper towels; timer; thermometers (3)

### Safety Precautions
Test warm water to make sure it will not burn the students. Be careful of slippery floors if water is spilled.

**Disposal** Items can be cleaned and reused.

### Procedure
Place three labeled beakers side by side. They should contain room-temperature water, ice water, and warm water, respectively. Measure

Your textbook includes example problems that explain how to solve word problems related to concepts such as density. Each example problem uses a three-part process for problem solving: analyze, solve, and evaluate. When you analyze a problem, you first separate what is known from what is unknown. Then you decide on a strategy that uses the known data to solve for the unknown. After you solve a problem, you need to evaluate your answer to decide if it makes sense.

## EXAMPLE PROBLEM 2-1

### Using Density and Volume to Find Mass

Suppose a sample of aluminum is placed in a 25-mL graduated cylinder containing 10.5 mL of water. The level of the water rises to 13.5 mL. What is the mass of the aluminum sample?

**1. Analyze the Problem**

The unknown is the mass of aluminum. You know that mass, volume, and density are related. The volume of aluminum equals the volume of water displaced in the graduated cylinder. You know that the density of aluminum is 2.7 g/cm³, or 2.7 g/mL, because 1 cm³ equals 1 mL.

| Known | Unknown |
|---|---|
| density = 2.7 g/mL | mass = ? g |
| volume = 13.5 mL − 10.5 mL = 3.0 mL | |

**2. Solve for the Unknown**

Rearrange the density equation to solve for mass.

$$density = \frac{mass}{volume}$$

$$mass = volume \times density$$

Substitute the known values for volume and density into the equation.

$$mass = 3.0 \text{ mL} \times 2.7 \text{ g/mL}$$

Multiply the values and the units. The mL units will cancel out.

$$mass = 3.0 \cancel{mL} \times \frac{2.7 \text{ g}}{\cancel{mL}} = 8.1 \text{ g}$$

**3. Evaluate the Answer**

You can check your answer by using it with the known data in the equation for density. The two sides of the equation should be equal.

density = mass/volume

2.7 g/mL = 8.1 g/3.0 mL

If you divide 8.1 g by 3.0 mL, you get 2.7 g/mL.

## PRACTICE PROBLEMS

**1.** A piece of metal with a mass of 147 g is placed in a 50-mL graduated cylinder. The water level rises from 20 mL to 41 mL. What is the density of the metal?

**2.** What is the volume of a sample that has a mass of 20 g and a density of 4 g/mL?

**3.** A metal cube has a mass of 20 g and a volume of 5 cm³. Is the cube made of pure aluminum? Explain your answer.

### Problem-Solving Process

**THE PROBLEM**
1. Read the problem carefully.
2. Be sure that you understand what it is asking you.

↓

**ANALYZE THE PROBLEM**
1. Read the problem again.
2. Identify what you are given and list the known data.
3. Identify and list the unknowns.
4. Gather information you need from graphs, tables, or figures.
5. Plan the steps you will follow to find the answer.

↓

**SOLVE FOR THE UNKNOWN**
1. Determine whether you need a sketch to solve the problem.
2. If the solution is mathematical, write the equation and isolate the unknown factor.
3. Substitute the known quantities into the equation.
4. Solve the equation.
5. Continue the solution process until you solve the problem.

↓

**EVALUATE THE ANSWER**
1. Re-read the problem. Is the answer reasonable?
2. Check your math. Are the units and the significant figures correct? (See Section 2.3.)

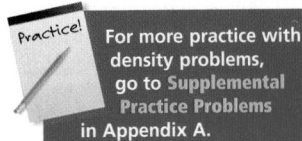

Practice! For more practice with density problems, go to **Supplemental Practice Problems** in Appendix A.

the temperature of the water in each beaker. Have a student place one hand in the ice water and the other hand in the warm water for two minutes. Ask the student to describe the temperature of each hand. Then, have the student simultaneously place both hands in the beaker containing room-temperature water. Have the student describe the temperature of this water as sensed by each hand.

### Results

The room-temperature water will feel warm to the hand coming from ice water but cool to the hand coming from warm water.

### Analysis

**1.** How do you classify something as hot or cold? By whether heat flows from it or to it; they are qualitative terms.

**2.** How does a thermometer classify something as hot or cold? It gives a numerical value to the temperature. It is quantitative.

### ✓ Assessment

**Skill** Have students do an Internet search to determine how a thermometer works. Visit science.glencoe.com. **L2**

## Check for Understanding

Ask students whether a liter is a base unit or a derived unit. A liter is a unit of volume; therefore, it is a derived unit. **L2**

## Reteach

**Kinesthetic** Have students hold a small piece of foam in one hand and a large piece in the other hand. Ask them if the two pieces of foam have the same mass. no Ask if they have the same volume. no Then, ask them if the densities of the two pieces of foam are the same. Have them justify their answers. Yes; they are the same material. **L2** **ELL**

## Extension

Ask students to explain the difference in how skin and a thermometer respond to temperature. Skin responds to temperature in a qualitative way by indicating the relative warmth or coldness of an object compared to your body's temperature. A thermometer measures temperature quantitatively, against a standard.

✔ **Assessment**

**Skill** Have students determine what 437 K is in Celsius. 164°C What is 23°C in kelvins? 296 K **L2**

---

**Figure 2-5**

One kelvin is equal in size to one degree on the Celsius scale. The degree sign ° is not used with temperatures on the Kelvin scale.

## Temperature

Suppose you run water into a bathtub. You control the temperature of the water by adjusting the flow from the hot and cold water pipes. When the streams mix, heat flows from the hot water to the cold water. You classify an object as hot or cold by whether heat flows from you to the object or from the object to you. The temperature of an object is a measure of how hot or cold the object is relative to other objects.

**Temperature scales** Hot and cold are qualitative terms. For quantitative descriptions of temperature, you need measuring devices such as thermometers. In a thermometer, a liquid expands when heated and contracts when cooled. The tube that contains the liquid is narrow so that small changes in temperature can be detected. Scientists use two temperature scales. The Celsius scale was devised by Anders Celsius, a Swedish astronomer. He used the temperatures at which water freezes and boils to establish his scale because these temperatures are easy to reproduce. He defined the freezing point as 0 and the boiling point as 100. Then he divided the distance between these points into 100 equal units, or degrees Celsius.

The Kelvin scale was devised by a Scottish physicist and mathematician, William Thomson, who was known as Lord Kelvin. A **kelvin** (K) is the SI base unit of temperature. On the Kelvin scale, water freezes at about 273 K and boils at about 373 K. **Figure 2-5** compares the two scales. You will use the Celsius scale for your experiments. In Chapter 14, you will learn why scientists use the Kelvin scale to describe the behavior of gases.

It is easy to convert from the Celsius scale to the Kelvin scale. For example, the element mercury melts at −39°C and boils at 357°C. To convert temperatures reported in degrees Celsius into kelvins, you just add 273.

$$-39°C + 273 = 234 \text{ K}$$
$$357°C + 273 = 630 \text{ K}$$

It is equally easy to convert from the Kelvin scale to the Celsius scale. For example, the element bromine melts at 266 K and boils at 332 K. To convert temperatures reported in kelvins into degrees Celsius, you subtract 273.

$$266 \text{ K} - 273 = -7°C$$
$$332 \text{ K} - 273 = 59°C$$

---

## Section 2.1 Assessment

**4.** List SI units of measurement for length, mass, time, and temperature.

**5.** Describe the relationship between the mass, volume, and density of a material.

**6.** Which of these samples have the same density?

| Density Data | | |
|---|---|---|
| Sample | Mass | Volume |
| A | 80 g | 20 mL |
| B | 12 g | 4 cm³ |
| C | 33 g | 11 mL |

**7.** What is the difference between a base unit and a derived unit?

**8.** How does adding the prefix *mega-* to a unit affect the quantity being described?

**9.** How many milliseconds are in a second? How many centigrams are in a gram?

**10. Thinking Critically** Why does oil float on water?

**11. Using Numbers** You measure a piece of wood with a meterstick and it is exactly one meter long. How many centimeters long is it?

chemistrymc.com/self_check_quiz

---

## Section 2.1 Assessment

**4.** length: meter, mass: kilogram; time: second; temperature: kelvin

**5.** Density is the mass-to-volume ratio of a material.

**6.** B and C

**7.** Base unit definitions are based on a physical object or process. Derived units use a combination of base units.

**8.** It multiplies it by $10^6$.

**9.** 1000 ms/s; 100 cg/g

**10.** Oil is less dense than water.

**11.** 100 cm

# Scientific Notation and Dimensional Analysis

A proton's mass is 0.000 000 000 000 000 000 000 000 001 672 62 kg. An electron's mass is 0.000 000 000 000 000 000 000 000 000 000 910 939 kg. If you try to compare the mass of a proton with the mass of an electron, the zeros get in the way. Numbers that are extremely small or large are hard to handle. You can convert such numbers into a form called scientific notation.

## Scientific Notation

**Scientific notation** expresses numbers as a multiple of two factors: a number between 1 and 10; and ten raised to a power, or exponent. The exponent tells you how many times the first factor must be multiplied by ten. The mass of a proton is $1.627\,62 \times 10^{-27}$ kg in scientific notation. The mass of an electron is $9.109\,39 \times 10^{-31}$ kg. When numbers larger than 1 are expressed in scientific notation, the power of ten is positive. When numbers smaller than 1 are expressed in scientific notation, the power of ten is negative.

### Objectives

- **Express** numbers in scientific notation.
- **Use** dimensional analysis to **convert** between units.

### Vocabulary

scientific notation
conversion factor
dimensional analysis

---

## EXAMPLE PROBLEM 2-2

### Convert Data into Scientific Notation

Change the following data into scientific notation.

**a.** The diameter of the Sun is 1 392 000 km.

**b.** The density of the Sun's lower atmosphere is 0.000 000 028 g/cm³.

**1. Analyze the Problem**

You are given two measurements. One measurement is much larger than 10. The other is much smaller than 10. In both cases, the answers will be factors between 1 and 10 that are multiplied by a power of ten.

**2. Solve for the Unknown**

Move the decimal point to produce a factor between 1 and 10. Count the number of places the decimal point moved and the direction.

| 1 392 000. | 0.000 000 028 |
|---|---|
| The decimal point moved 6 places to the left. | The decimal point moved 8 places to the right. |

Remove the extra zeros at the end or beginning of the factor. Multiply the result by $10^n$ where $n$ equals the number of places moved. When the decimal point moves to the *left, n* is a *positive* number. When the decimal point moves to the *right, n* is a *negative* number. Remember to add units to the answers.

**a.** $1\,392\,000 = 1.392 \times 10^6$ km

**b.** $0.000\,000\,028 = 2.8 \times 10^{-8}$ g/cm³

**3. Evaluate the Answer**

The answers have two factors. The first factor is a number between 1 and 10. Because the diameter of the Sun is a large number, 10 has a positive exponent. Because the density of the Sun's lower atmosphere is a small number, 10 has a negative exponent.

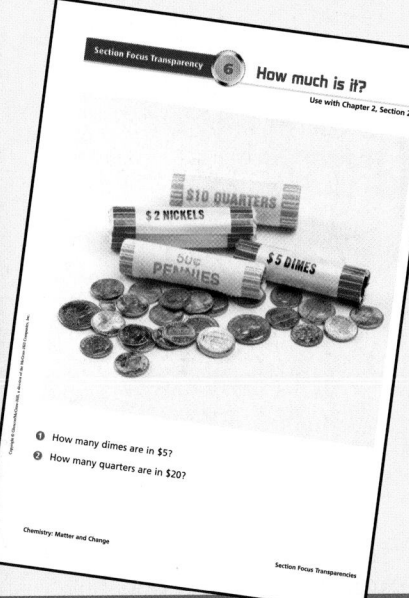

The density of the Sun's lower atmosphere is similar to the density of Earth's outermost atmosphere.

---

## DIFFERENTIATED INSTRUCTION

### Learning Disabled

 *Kinesthetic* Ask students to guess the number of beans in a pile of dried beans. Have them separate the pile into groups of ten beans and then use the number of piles to calculate the number of beans. Ask if it was easier to count the number of beans by grouping them into groups of ten. Relate the activity to scientific notation. **L1 ELL**

## Resource Manager

**Study Guide for Content Mastery,** p. 9 **L2**

**Solving Problems: A Chemistry Handbook,** Section 2.2 **L2**

**Section Focus Transparency 6 and Master L1 ELL**

---

## 1 Focus

### Focus Transparency

Before presenting the lesson, display **Section Focus Transparency 6** on the overhead projector. Have students answer the accompanying questions using **Section Focus Transparency Master 6. L1 ELL**

## 2 Teach

### Quick Demo

Show students a large jar of popcorn and have them guess the number of kernels. Then, show them the same number of kernels, but have the kernels divided equally into small paper cups. Tell the students approximately how many kernels are in each cup, and have them guess the number of kernels that would fill the large jar. Explain that scientific notation is similar to dividing the large number of kernels into smaller cups. It is easier to identify large or small quantities.

**31**

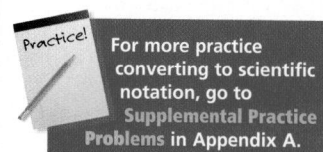

**For more practice** converting to scientific notation, go to **Supplemental Practice Problems** in Appendix A.

**Figure 2-6**

Population density is high in a city such as São Paulo, Brazil.

## PRACTICE PROBLEMS

**12.** Express the following quantities in scientific notation.

   **a.** 700 m

   **b.** 38 000 m

   **c.** 4 500 000 m

   **d.** 685 000 000 000 m

   **e.** 0.0054 kg

   **f.** 0.000 006 87 kg

   **g.** 0.000 000 076 kg

   **h.** 0.000 000 000 8 kg

**13.** Express the following quantities in scientific notation.

   **a.** 360 000 s

   **b.** 0.000 054 s

   **c.** 5060 s

   **d.** 89 000 000 000 s

**Adding and subtracting using scientific notation** When adding or subtracting numbers written in scientific notation, you must be sure that the exponents are the same before doing the arithmetic. Suppose you need to add $7.35 \times 10^2$ m $+ 2.43 \times 10^2$ m. You note that the quantities are expressed to the same power of ten. You can add 7.35 and 2.43 to get $9.78 \times 10^2$ m. What can you do if the quantities are not expressed to the same power of ten?

As shown in **Figure 2-6,** some of the world's cities are extremely crowded. In 1995, the population figures for three of the four largest cities in the world were: $2.70 \times 10^7$ for Tokyo, Japan; $15.6 \times 10^6$ for Mexico City, Mexico; and $0.165 \times 10^8$ for São Paulo, Brazil. To find the total population for these three cities in 1995, you first need to change the data so that all three quantities are expressed to the same power of ten. Because the first factor in the data for Tokyo is a number between 1 and 10, leave that quantity as is: $2.70 \times 10^7$. Change the other two quantities so that the exponent is 7. For the Mexico City data, you need to increase the power of ten from $10^6$ to $10^7$. You must move the decimal point one place to the left.

$$15.6 \times 10^6 = 1.56 \times 10^7$$

For the São Paulo data, you need to decrease the power of ten from $10^8$ to $10^7$. You must move the decimal point one place to the right.

$$0.165 \times 10^8 = 1.65 \times 10^7$$

Now you can add the quantities.

$$2.70 \times 10^7 + 1.56 \times 10^7 + 1.65 \times 10^7 = 5.91 \times 10^7$$

You can test this procedure by writing the original data in ordinary notation. When you add 27 000 000 + 15 600 000 + 16 500 000, you get 59 100 000. When you convert the answer back to scientific notation, you get $5.91 \times 10^7$.

## PRACTICE PROBLEMS

Solve the following addition and subtraction problems. Express your answers in scientific notation.

**14. a.** $5 \times 10^{-5}$ m $+ 2 \times 10^{-5}$ m

   **b.** $7 \times 10^8$ m $- 4 \times 10^8$ m

   **c.** $9 \times 10^2$ m $- 7 \times 10^2$ m

   **d.** $4 \times 10^{-12}$ m $+ 1 \times 10^{-12}$ m

   **e.** $1.26 \times 10^4$ kg $+ 2.5 \times 10^3$ kg

   **f.** $7.06 \times 10^{-3}$ kg $+ 1.2 \times 10^{-4}$ kg

   **g.** $4.39 \times 10^5$ kg $- 2.8 \times 10^4$ kg

   **h.** $5.36 \times 10^{-1}$ kg $- 7.40 \times 10^{-2}$ kg

## Internet Address Book

**Chemistry Online** Note Internet addresses that you find useful in the space below for quick reference.

_____

_____

_____

_____

**Multiplying and dividing using scientific notation** Multiplying and dividing also involve two steps, but in these cases the quantities being multiplied or divided do not have to have the same exponent. For multiplication, you multiply the first factors. Then, you add the exponents. For division, you divide the first factors. Then, you subtract the exponent of the divisor from the exponent of the dividend.

Take care when determining the sign of the exponent in an answer. Adding +3 to +4 yields +7, but adding +3 to −4 yields −1. Subtracting −6 from −4 yields +2, but subtracting −4 from −6 yields −2.

**EXAMPLE** PROBLEM 2-3

**Multiplying and Dividing Numbers in Scientific Notation**

Suppose you are asked to solve the following problems.
**a.** $(2 \times 10^3) \times (3 \times 10^2)$
**b.** $(9 \times 10^8) \div (3 \times 10^{-4})$

**1. Analyze the Problem**

You are given values to multiply and divide. For the multiplication problem, you multiply the first factors. Then you add the exponents. For the division problem, you divide the first factors. Then you subtract the exponent of the divisor from the exponent of the dividend.

$$\text{Quotient} = \frac{9 \times 10^8}{3 \times 10^{-4}} \quad \overset{\text{Dividend}}{\underset{\text{Divisor}}{}}$$

**2. Solve for the Unknown**

**a.** $(2 \times 10^3) \times (3 \times 10^2)$

Multiply the first factors.
$2 \times 3 = 6$

Add the exponents.
$3 + 2 = 5$

Combine the factors.
$6 \times 10^5$

**b.** $(9 \times 10^8) \div (3 \times 10^{-4})$

Divide the first factors.
$9 \div 3 = 3$

Subtract the exponents.
$8 - (-4) = 8 + 4 = 12$

Combine the factors.
$3 \times 10^{12}$

**3. Evaluate the Answer**

You can test these procedures by writing the original data in ordinary notation. For example, problem **a** becomes 2000 × 300. An answer of 600 000 seems reasonable.

**PRACTICE** PROBLEMS

Solve the following multiplication and division problems. Express your answers in scientific notation.

**15.** Calculate the following areas. Report the answers in square centimeters, cm².
  **a.** $(4 \times 10^2 \text{ cm}) \times (1 \times 10^8 \text{ cm})$
  **b.** $(2 \times 10^{-4} \text{ cm}) \times (3 \times 10^2 \text{ cm})$
  **c.** $(3 \times 10^1 \text{ cm}) \times (3 \times 10^{-2} \text{ cm})$
  **d.** $(1 \times 10^3 \text{ cm}) \times (5 \times 10^{-1} \text{ cm})$

**16.** Calculate the following densities. Report the answers in g/cm³.
  **a.** $(6 \times 10^2 \text{ g}) \div (2 \times 10^1 \text{ cm}^3)$
  **b.** $(8 \times 10^4 \text{ g}) \div (4 \times 10^1 \text{ cm}^3)$
  **c.** $(9 \times 10^5 \text{ g}) \div (3 \times 10^{-1} \text{ cm}^3)$
  **d.** $(4 \times 10^{-3} \text{ g}) \div (2 \times 10^{-2} \text{ cm}^3)$

**Math Handbook**

Review arithmetic operations with positive and negative numbers in the **Math Handbook** on pages 887 to 889 of this text.

Practice! For more practice doing arithmetic operations using scientific notation, go to **Supplemental Practice Problems in Appendix A.**

## Figure Caption Questions

**Figure 2-7** How many teaspoons are equivalent to two $\frac{1}{4}$ measuring cups? 12 teaspoons = 4 tablespoons = one $\frac{1}{4}$ measuring cup. So 2 × 12 teaspoons, or 24 teaspoons, equal two $\frac{1}{4}$ measuring cups.

**Figure 2-8** How can conversion factors be used to make a scale drawing? Actual measurements correspond to a certain number of smaller scale measurements. To find the number of smaller measurements on the scale drawing, multiply the actual measurement by the conversion factor represented by the scale. For example, if 8 km is represented by 1 cm on a map, 12 km is represented by 12 km × 1 cm/8 km, or 1.5 cm.

### Practice PROBLEMS

Have students refer to Appendix D for complete solutions to Practice Problems.

**17. a.** 360 000 ms
**b.** 4.8 kg
**c.** 560 m
**d.** 72 000 mg
**18. a.** 0.245 s
**b.** 500 cm
**c.** 68 m
**d.** 0.025 Mg

**Resource Manager**

Teaching Transparency 4 and Master **L2** **ELL**

**National Science Content Standards**
**Pages 34–35**
UCP.1, UCP.3; A.1, A.2; E.2

---

**Figure 2-7**

Twelve teaspoons equal four tablespoons; four tablespoons equal 1/4 of a cup. How many teaspoons are equivalent to two 1/4 measuring cups?

**Figure 2-8**

Blueprints are scale drawings. On a blueprint, objects and distances appear smaller than their actual sizes but the relative sizes of objects remain the same. How can conversion factors be used to make a scale drawing?

---

## Dimensional Analysis

Suppose you have a salad dressing recipe that calls for 2 teaspoons of vinegar. You plan to make 6 times as much salad dressing for a party. That means you need 12 teaspoons of vinegar. You could measure out 12 teaspoons or you could use a larger unit. According to **Figure 2-7,** 3 teaspoons are equivalent to 1 tablespoon and 4 tablespoons are equivalent to 1/4 of a cup. The relationship between teaspoons and tablespoons can be expressed as a pair of ratios. These ratios are conversion factors.

$$\frac{3 \text{ teaspoons}}{1 \text{ tablespoon}} = \frac{1 \text{ tablespoon}}{3 \text{ teaspoons}} = 1$$

A **conversion factor** is a ratio of equivalent values used to express the same quantity in different units. A conversion factor is always equal to 1. Because a quantity does not change when it is multiplied or divided by 1, conversion factors change the units of a quantity without changing its value. If you measure out 12 teaspoons of vinegar, 4 tablespoons of vinegar, or 1/4 of a cup of vinegar, you will get the same volume of vinegar.

**Dimensional analysis** is a method of problem-solving that focuses on the units used to describe matter. For example, if you want to convert a temperature in degrees Celsius to a temperature in kelvins, you focus on the relationship between the units in the two temperature scales. Scale drawings such as maps and the blueprint in **Figure 2-8** are based on the relationship between different units of length.

Dimensional analysis often uses conversion factors. Suppose you want to know how many meters are in 48 km. You need a conversion factor that relates kilometers to meters. You know that 1 km is equal to 1000 m. Because you are going to multiply 48 km by the conversion factor, you want to set up the conversion factor so the kilometer units will cancel out.

$$48 \text{ km} \times \frac{1000 \text{ m}}{1 \text{ km}} = 48\,000 \text{ m}$$

When you convert from a large unit to a small unit, the number of units must increase. A meter is a much smaller unit than a kilometer, one one-thousandth smaller to be exact. Thus, it is reasonable to find that there are 48 000 meters in 48 kilometers.

### PRACTICE PROBLEMS

Refer to **Table 2-2** to figure out the relationship between units.

**17. a.** Convert 360 s to ms.
**b.** Convert 4800 g to kg.
**c.** Convert 5600 dm to m.
**d.** Convert 72 g to mg.

**18. a.** Convert 245 ms to s.
**b.** Convert 5 m to cm.
**c.** Convert 6800 cm to m.
**d.** Convert 25 kg to Mg.

---

 **Portfolio**

### The Price of Gasoline

**Logical-Mathematical** Have students determine any needed conversion factors for the following problem, solve the problem, and place the solution in their portfolios. Assume that gasoline in Europe is currently sold at $0.989 per liter and the current price in the United States is $1.56/gallon. Where is gasoline more expensive?

1 L is equal to approximately 1 quart, and 4 quarts equals 1 gallon. The price of gas in Europe is $0.989/L × 1 L/1 quart × 4 quarts/1 gallon = $3.96/gallon. Gasoline is more expensive at the European price.

**L2** **P** 🎲

## EXAMPLE PROBLEM 2-4

### Using Multiple Conversion Factors

What is a speed of 550 meters per second in kilometers per minute?

**1. Analyze the Problem**

You are given a speed in meters per second. You want to know the equivalent speed in kilometers per minute. You need conversion factors that relate kilometers to meters and seconds to minutes.

**2. Solve for the Unknown**

First convert meters to kilometers. Set up the conversion factor so that the meter units will cancel out.

$$\frac{550 \cancel{m}}{s} \times \frac{1 \text{ km}}{1000 \cancel{m}} = \frac{0.55 \text{ km}}{s}$$

Next convert seconds to minutes. Set up the conversion factor so that the seconds cancel out.

$$\frac{0.55 \text{ km}}{\cancel{s}} \times \frac{60 \cancel{s}}{1 \text{ min}} = \frac{33 \text{ km}}{\text{min}}$$

**3. Evaluate the Answer**

To check your answer, you can do the steps in reverse order.

$$\frac{550 \text{ m}}{\cancel{s}} \times \frac{60 \cancel{s}}{1 \text{ min}} = \frac{33\,000 \cancel{m}}{\text{min}} \times \frac{1 \text{ km}}{1000 \cancel{m}} = \frac{33 \text{ km}}{\text{min}}$$

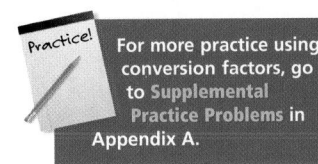

### Math Handbook

Review dimensional analysis and unit conversions in the **Math Handbook** on pages 900 and 901 of this text.

## PRACTICE PROBLEMS

**19.** How many seconds are there in 24 hours?

**20.** The density of gold is 19.3 g/mL. What is gold's density in decigrams per liter?

**21.** A car is traveling 90.0 kilometers per hour. What is its speed in miles per minute? One kilometer = 0.62 miles.

*Practice!* **For more practice using conversion factors, go to Supplemental Practice Problems in Appendix A.**

Using the wrong units to solve a problem can be a costly error. In 1999, the Mars Climate Orbiter crashed into the atmosphere of Mars instead of flying closely by as planned. The probe was destroyed before it could collect any data. Two teams of engineers working on the probe had used different sets of units—English and metric—and no one had caught the error in time.

## Section 2.2 Assessment

**22.** Is the number $5 \times 10^{-4}$ greater or less than 1.0? Explain your answer.

**23.** When multiplying numbers in scientific notation, what do you do with the exponents?

**24.** Write the quantities $3 \times 10^{-4}$ cm and $3 \times 10^4$ km in ordinary notation.

**25.** Write a conversion factor for cubic centimeters and milliliters.

**26.** What is dimensional analysis?

**27. Thinking Critically** When subtracting or adding two numbers in scientific notation, why do the exponents need to be the same?

**28. Applying Concepts** You are converting 68 km to meters. Your answer is 0.068 m. Explain why this answer is incorrect and the likely source of the error.

## Section 2.2 Assessment

**22.** less than one because the exponent is negative
**23.** Add them.
**24.** 0.0003 cm; 30 000 km
**25.** $1 \text{ cm}^3$/1 mL
**26.** a method of problem solving that focuses on the units used to describe matter

**27.** Equal place values should be added to each other.
**28.** Because meters are smaller than kilometers, there should be more meters than kilometers. The 68 km was divided by 1000, not multiplied by 1000.

**Practice** PROBLEMS

Have students refer to Appendix D for complete solutions to Practice Problems.

**19.** 86 400 s
**20.** 193 000 dg/L
**21.** 0.930 mi/min

# 3 Assess
## Check for Understanding

Ask students which metric prefix is equal to $1 \times 10^6$. mega, M

## Reteach

**Logical-Mathematical** Write additional problems involving calculations with scientific notation on pieces of poster board. Hang the pieces around the classroom. Have student groups complete the problems, then present their work to the rest of the class. **L2**

## Extension

Have students research the latest figure on the national debt and express it in scientific notation.

### ✓ Assessment

**Skill** Have students identify common conversion factors and prepare a table. Have each student write one question using a conversion factor and collect the questions for a class review. Conversion factors may be those used in the English system, in the metric system, or factors used to convert between the English and metric systems. **L2**

# 1 Focus

## Focus Transparency

Before presenting the lesson, display **Section Focus Transparency 7** on the overhead projector. Have students answer the accompanying questions using **Section Focus Transparency Master 7.** L1 ELL

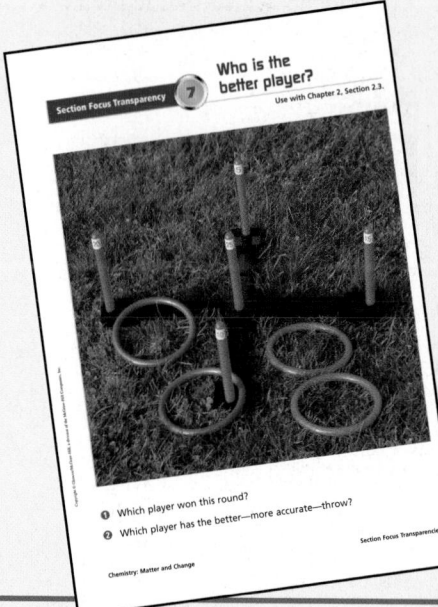

# 2 Teach

## Quick Demo

*Kinesthetic* Bring in a dartboard that uses Velcro darts and the darts. Have students break into teams of four and play a round of darts. Emphasize that even in science, accuracy and precision require skill and repeated effort. L1 ELL

### Objectives

- **Define** and **compare** accuracy and precision.
- **Use** significant figures and rounding to reflect the certainty of data.
- **Use** percent error to **describe** the accuracy of experimental data.

### Vocabulary

accuracy
precision
percent error
significant figure

Suppose someone is planning a bicycle trip from Baltimore, Maryland to Washington D.C. The actual mileage will be determined by where the rider starts and ends the trip, and the route taken. While planning the trip, the rider does not need to know the actual mileage. All the rider needs is an estimate, which in this case would be about 39 miles. People need to know when an estimate is acceptable and when it is not. For example, you could use an estimate when buying material to sew curtains for a window. You would need more exact measurements when ordering custom shades for the same window.

## Accuracy and Precision

When scientists make measurements, they evaluate both the accuracy and the precision of the measurements. **Accuracy** refers to how close a measured value is to an accepted value. **Precision** refers to how close a series of measurements are to one another. The archery target in **Figure 2-9** illustrates the difference between accuracy and precision. For this example, the center of the target is the accepted value.

In **Figure 2-9a,** the location of the arrow is accurate because the arrow is in the center. In **Figure 2-9b,** the arrows are close together but not near the center. They have a precise location but not an accurate one. In **Figure 2-9c,** the arrows are closely grouped in the center. Their locations are both accurate and precise. In **Figure 2-9d,** the arrows are scattered at a distance from the center. Their locations are neither accurate nor precise. Why does it make no sense to discuss the precision of the arrow location in **Figure 2-9a?**

Consider the data in **Table 2-3.** Students were asked to find the density of an unknown white powder. Each student measured the volume and mass of three separate samples. They reported calculated densities for each trial and an average of the three calculations. The powder was sucrose, also called table sugar, which has a density of 1.59 g/cm³. Who collected the most accurate data? Student A's measurements are the most accurate because they are closest to the accepted value of 1.59 g/cm³. Which student collected the most precise data? Student C's measurements are the most precise because they are the closest to one another.

### Figure 2-9

An archery target illustrates the difference between accuracy and precision.

Arrow in the center
= high accuracy

Arrows far from center
= low accuracy

Arrows close together
= high precision

Arrows in center
= high accuracy

Arrows close together
= high precision

Arrows far from center
= low accuracy

Arrows far apart
= low precision

**36**   Chapter 2 Data Analysis

## CHEMISTRY JOURNAL

### Applied Accuracy and Precision

*Linguistic* Have students write about areas of their lives where they need accuracy and precision. Some common examples may be sports, playing a musical instrument, a hobby, even academics. Ask students to identify the role of precision and accuracy in each example and strategies they use to accomplish their goal. L2

## Resource Manager

**Study Guide for Content Mastery,** pp. 10–11 L2
**Solving Problems: A Chemistry Handbook,** Section 2.3 L2
**Section Focus Transparency 7 and Master** L1 ELL
**Teaching Transparency 5 and Master** L2 ELL

**Table 2-3**

| | Student A | Student B | Student C |
|---|---|---|---|
| **Density Data Collected by Three Different Students** | | | |
| Trial 1 | 1.54 g/cm³ | 1.40 g/cm³ | 1.70 g/cm³ |
| Trial 2 | 1.60 g/cm³ | 1.68 g/cm³ | 1.69 g/cm³ |
| Trial 3 | 1.57 g/cm³ | 1.45 g/cm³ | 1.71 g/cm³ |
| Average | 1.57 g/cm³ | 1.51 g/cm³ | 1.70 g/cm³ |

**In-Text Question**

**Page 36** Why does it make no sense to discuss the precision of the arrow location in Figure 2-9a? To determine precision, a series of measurements is needed.

Recall that precise measurements may not be accurate. Looking at just the average of the densities can be misleading. Based solely on the average, Student B appears to have collected fairly reliable data. However, on closer inspection, Student B's data are neither accurate nor precise. The data are not close to the accepted value and they are not close to one another.

What factors could account for inaccurate or imprecise data? Perhaps Student A did not follow the procedure with consistency. He or she might not have read the graduated cylinder at eye level for each trial. Student C may have made the same slight error with each trial. Perhaps he or she included the mass of the filter paper used to protect the balance pan. Student B may have recorded the wrong data or made a mistake when dividing the mass by the volume. External conditions such as temperature and humidity also can affect the collection of data.

**Percent error** The density values reported in **Table 2-3** are experimental values, which are values measured during an experiment. The density of sucrose is an accepted value, which is a value that is considered true. To evaluate the accuracy of experimental data, you can calculate the difference between an experimental value and an accepted value. The difference is called an error. The errors for the data in **Table 2-3** are listed in **Table 2-4**.

Scientists want to know what percent of the accepted value an error represents. **Percent error** is the ratio of an error to an accepted value.

$$\text{Percent error} = \frac{\text{error}}{\text{accepted value}} \times 100$$

For this calculation, it does not matter whether the experimental value is larger or smaller than the accepted value. Only the size of the error matters. When you calculate percent error, you ignore plus and minus signs. Percent error is an important concept for the person assembling bicycle gears in **Figure 2-10**. The dimensions of a part may vary within narrow ranges of error called tolerances. Some of the manufactured parts are tested to see if they meet engineering standards. If one dimension of a part exceeds its tolerance, the item will be discarded or, if possible, retooled.

**Figure 2-10**

The dimensions for each part used to build a bicycle gear have accepted values.

**Extension**

**Interpersonal** After calculating the percent error for each student's data in Table 2-4, have student groups compare the percent error to the average density obtained by each student in Table 2-3. Ask them if it is easier to identify which student had the most accurate data by looking at the average in Table 2-3 or the percent error in Table 2-4. Help student groups to see the value in the percent error; it quickly and easily identifies the accuracy of a measurement. **L2** **COOP LEARN**

**Table 2-4**

| | Student A | Student B | Student C |
|---|---|---|---|
| **Errors for Data in Table 2-3** | | | |
| Trial 1 | –0.05 g/cm³ | –0.19 g/cm³ | +0.11 g/cm³ |
| Trial 2 | +0.01 g/cm³ | +0.09 g/cm³ | +0.10 g/cm³ |
| Trial 3 | –0.02 g/cm³ | –0.14 g/cm³ | +0.12 g/cm³ |

## Internet Address Book

**Chemistry Online** Note Internet addresses that you find useful in the space below for quick reference.

_____

_____

_____

_____

**National Science Content Standards**

**Pages 36–37**
UCP.1, UCP.3; A.1, A.2; E.2; G.2

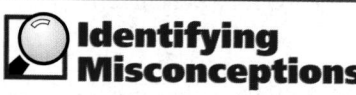
Have students refer to Appendix D for complete solutions to Practice Problems.

**29.** 11.9%; 5.66%; 8.80%

**30.** 6.92%; 6.29%; 7.55%

## Identifying Misconceptions

Many students confuse accuracy and precision.

### Uncover the Misconception

**Kinesthetic** Place a transparent container with a small target painted on the bottom on the overhead projector. Fill it three-fourths full with water. Have a student drop coins into the container, attempting to hit the target. After several coins are dropped, have students discuss the accuracy and precision of the results.

### Demonstrate the Concept

Divide students into groups. Give each group a balance. One balance has been properly zeroed and the others have not. Have each group take several mass readings of the same object.

### Assess New Knowledge

Have students discuss their results. They should note that, if readings were taken carefully, all are precise but only the readings from the zeroed balance are accurate. Emphasize the importance of using properly standardized laboratory equipment.

**Table 2-5**

| | Student A's Data | |
|---|---|---|
| Trial | Density (g/cm³) | Error (g/cm³) |
| 1 | 1.54 | −0.05 |
| 2 | 1.60 | +0.01 |
| 3 | 1.57 | −0.02 |

Practice! For more practice with percent error, go to **Supplemental Practice Problems** in Appendix A.

## EXAMPLE PROBLEM 2-5

### Calculating Percent Error

Calculate the percent errors. Report your answers to two places after the decimal point. **Table 2-5** summarizes Student A's data.

**1. Analyze the Problem**

You are given the errors for a set of density measurements. To calculate percent error, you need to know the accepted value for density, the errors, and the equation for percent error.

**Known**

accepted value for density = 1.59 g/cm³

errors: −0.05 g/cm³; 0.01 g/cm³; −0.02 g/cm³

**Unknown**

percent errors = ?

**2. Solve for the Unknown**

Substitute each error into the percent error equation. Ignore the plus and minus signs. Note that the units for density cancel out.

$$\text{percent error} = \frac{\text{error}}{\text{accepted value}} \times 100$$

$$\text{percent error} = \frac{0.05 \text{ g/cm}^3}{1.59 \text{ g/cm}^3} \times 100 = 3.14\%$$

$$\text{percent error} = \frac{0.01 \text{ g/cm}^3}{1.59 \text{ g/cm}^3} \times 100 = 0.63\%$$

$$\text{percent error} = \frac{0.02 \text{ g/cm}^3}{1.59 \text{ g/cm}^3} \times 100 = 1.26\%$$

**3. Evaluate the Answer**

The percent error is greatest for trial 1, which had the largest error, and smallest for trial 2, which was closest to the accepted value.

## PRACTICE PROBLEMS

Use data from **Table 2-4**. Remember to ignore plus and minus signs.

**29.** Calculate the percent errors for Students B's trials.

**30.** Calculate the percent errors for Student C's trials.

## Significant Figures

Often, precision is limited by the available tools. If you have a digital clock that displays the time as 12:47 or 12:48, you can record the time only to the nearest minute. If you have a clock with a sweep hand, you can record the time to the nearest second. With a stopwatch, you might record time elapsed to the nearest hundredth of a second. As scientists have developed better measuring devices, they have been able to make more precise measurements. Of course, the measuring devices must be in good working order. For example, a balance must read zero when no object is resting on it. The process for assuring the accuracy of a measuring device is called calibration. The person using the instrument must be trained and use accepted techniques.

Scientists indicate the precision of measurements by the number of digits they report. A value of 3.52 g is more precise than a value of 3.5 g. The digits that are reported are called significant figures. **Significant figures**

## DIFFERENTIATED INSTRUCTION

### Learning Disabled

Have student pairs explain to one another the concepts of accuracy and precision. Have the student pairs work on Example Problem 2-5 and Practice Problems 29 and 30. **L1** include all known digits plus one estimated digit. Consider the rod in **Figure 2-11.** The end of the rod falls somewhere between 5 and 6 cm. Counting over from the 5-cm mark, you can count 2 millimeter tick marks. Thus, the rod's length is between 5.2 cm and 5.3 cm. The 5 and 2 are known digits that correspond to marks on the ruler. You can add one estimated digit to reflect the rod's location relative to the 2 and 3 millimeter marks. The third digit is an estimate because the person reading the ruler must make a judgment call. One person may report the answer as 5.23 cm. Another may report it as 5.22 cm. Either way, the answer has three significant figures—two known and one estimated.

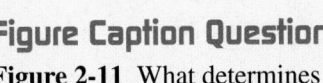

**Figure 2-11**

What determines whether a figure is known or estimated?

**Figure Caption Question**
**Figure 2-11** What determines whether a figure is known or estimated? The precision of the instrument used to take the measurement determines whether a figure is known or estimated.

### Rules for recognizing significant figures

1. *Non-zero numbers are always significant.* 72.3 g has three

2. *Zeros between non-zero numbers are always significant.* 60.5 g has three

3. *All final zeros to the right of the decimal place are significant.* 6.20 g has three

4. *Zeros that act as placeholders are not significant. Convert quantities to scientific notation to remove the placeholder zeros.* 0.0253 g and 4320 g each have three

5. *Counting numbers and defined constants have an infinite number of significant figures.* 6 molecules, 60 s = 1 min

## EXAMPLE PROBLEM 2-6

**Applying Significant Figure Rules**
Determine the number of significant figures in the following masses.
a. 0.000 402 30 g
b. 405 000 kg

**1. Analyze the Problem**

You are given two measurements of mass. Choose the rules that are appropriate to the problem.

**2. Solve for the Unknown**

Count all non-zero numbers (rule 1), zeros between non-zero numbers (rule 2), and final zeros to the right of the decimal place (rule 3). Ignore zeros that act as placeholders (rule 4).
a. 0.000 402 30 g has five significant figures.

b. 405 000 kg has three significant figures.

**3. Evaluate the Answer**

Write the data in scientific notation: $4.0230 \times 10^{-4}$ g and $4.05 \times 10^5$ kg. Without the placeholder zeros, it is clear that 0.000 402 30 g has five significant figures and 405 000 kg has three significant figures.

## PRACTICE PROBLEMS

Determine the number of significant figures in each measurement.

**31. a.** 508.0 L
 **b.** 820 400.0 L
 **c.** $1.0200 \times 10^5$ kg
 **d.** 807 000 kg

**32. a.** 0.049 450 s
 **b.** 0.000 482 mL
 **c.** $3.1587 \times 10^{-8}$ g
 **d.** 0.0084 mL

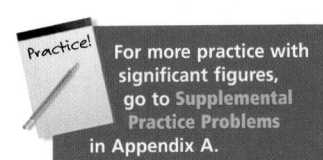

Practice! For more practice with significant figures, go to Supplemental Practice Problems in Appendix A.

**Math Handbook**

Review significant figures in the **Math Handbook** on page 893 of this text.

**Practice PROBLEMS**

Have students refer to Appendix D for complete solutions to Practice Problems.

**31. a.** 4
 **b.** 7
 **c.** 5
 **d.** 3
**32. a.** 5
 **b.** 3
 **c.** 5
 **d.** 2

**Discussion**

Discuss with students when approximate measurements that have fewer significant figures are adequate. Examples might include length measurements. When measuring wood for making a bookcase, the measurements should be as accurate as possible. To measure the distance traveled on a vacation, approximate values can be used. Usually, stating that you traveled 450 km is accurate enough. You probably don't need to know that you traveled 451.76 km.

## Internet Address Book

 Note Internet addresses that you find useful in the space below for quick reference.

**Figure 2-12**

The calculator often provides
more significant figures than
are appropriate for a given
calculation.

## Rounding Off Numbers

Suppose you are asked to find the density of an object whose mass is 22.44 g
and whose volume is 14.2 cm$^3$. When you use your calculator, you get a density of 1.580 281 7 g/cm$^3$, as shown in **Figure 2-12.** A calculated density with
eight significant figures is not appropriate if the mass has only four significant figures and the volume has only three. The answer should have no more
significant figures than the data with the fewest significant figures. The density must be rounded off to three significant figures, or 1.58 g/cm$^3$.

### Rules for rounding numbers

In the example for each rule, there are three significant figures.

**1.** *If the digit to the immediate right of the last significant figure is less
than five, do not change the last significant figure.*    2.532 → 2.53

**2.** *If the digit to the immediate right of the last significant figure is greater
than five, round up the last significant figure.*    2.536 → 2.54

**3.** *If the digit to the immediate right of the last significant figure is equal
to five and is followed by a nonzero digit, round up the last significant
figure.*    2.5351 → 2.54

**4.** *If the digit to the immediate right of the last significant figure is equal
to five and is not followed by a nonzero digit, look at the last significant
figure. If it is an odd digit, round it up. If it is an even digit, do not
round up.*    2.5350 → 2.54 but 2.5250 → 2.52

**EXAMPLE** PROBLEM 2-7

**Applying the Rounding Rules**

Round 3.515 014 to (a) five significant figures, then to (b) three significant figures, and finally to (c) one significant figure.

**1.** **Analyze the Problem**

You are given a number that has seven significant figures. You will
remove two figures with each step. You will need to choose the rule
that is appropriate for each step.

**2.** **Solve for the Unknown**

**a.** Round 3.515 014 to five significant figures.

Rule 1 applies. The last significant digit is 0. The number to its
immediate right is 1, which is less than 5. The zero does not change.
The answer is 3.5150.

**b.** Round 3.5150 to three significant figures.

Rule 4 applies. The last significant digit is 1. The number to its immediate right is a 5 that is not followed by a nonzero digit. Because the
1 is an odd number it is rounded up to 2.
The answer is 3.52.

**c.** Round 3.52 to one significant figure.

Rule 3 applies. The last significant digit is 3. The number to its
immediate right is a 5 that is followed by a nonzero digit. Thus, the
3 is rounded up to 4.
The answer is 4.

**3.** **Evaluate the Answer**

The final answer, 4, makes sense because 3.515 013 7 is greater than
the halfway point between 3 and 4, which is 3.5.

**CHEMISTRY JOURNAL**

## Everyday Estimation

**Logical-Mathematical** Have students
write examples of when they round
numbers in everyday life. Examples might
include estimating how much several
items cost to make sure they have enough
money or estimating the mass of something to determine whether it is too heavy
to lift. **L2**

**National Science Content Standards**

**Pages 40–41**
UCP.1, UCP.3; A.1, A.2; E.2

## PRACTICE PROBLEMS

**Round all numbers to four significant figures. Write the answers to problem 34 in scientific notation.**

**33. a.** 84 791 kg
   **b.** 38.5432 g
   **c.** 256.75 cm
   **d.** 4.9356 m

**34. a.** 0.000 548 18 g
   **b.** 136 758 kg
   **c.** 308 659 000 mm
   **d.** 2.0145 mL

**Addition and subtraction** When you add or subtract measurements, your answer must have the same number of digits to the right of the decimal point as the value with the fewest digits to the right of the decimal point. For example, the measurement 1.24 mL has two digits to the right of the decimal point. The measurement 12.4 mL has one digit to the right of the decimal point. The measurement 124 mL has zero digits to the right of the decimal point, which is understood to be to the right of the 4. The easiest way to solve addition and subtraction problems is to arrange the values so that the decimal points line up. Then do the sum or subtraction. Identify the value with the fewest places after the decimal point. Round the answer to the same number of places.

## EXAMPLE PROBLEM 2-8

### Applying Rounding Rules to Addition

Add the following measurements: 28.0 cm, 23.538 cm, and 25.68 cm.

**1. Analyze the Problem**

There are three measurements that need to be aligned on their decimal points and added. The measurement with the fewest digits after the decimal point is 28.0 cm, with one digit. Thus, the answer must be rounded to only one digit after the decimal point.

**2. Solve for the Unknown**

Line up the measurements.

```
    28.0   cm
    23.538 cm
+   25.68  cm
    77.218 cm
```

Because the digit immediately to the right of the last significant digit is less than 5, rule 1 applies. The answer is 77.2 cm.

**3. Evaluate the Answer**

The answer, 77.2 cm, has the same precision as the least precise measurement, 28.0 cm.

## PRACTICE PROBLEMS

**Complete the following addition and subtraction problems. Round off the answers when necessary.**

**35. a.** 43.2 cm + 51.0 cm + 48.7 cm
   **b.** 258.3 kg + 257.11 kg + 253 kg
   **c.** 0.0487 mg + 0.058 34 mg + 0.004 83 mg

**36. a.** 93.26 cm − 81.14 cm
   **b.** 5.236 cm − 3.14 cm
   **c.** $4.32 \times 10^3$ cm − $1.6 \times 10^3$ cm

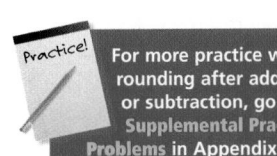

**For more practice with** rounding after addition or subtraction, go to **Supplemental Practice Problems** in Appendix A.

### Careers Using Chemistry

#### Scientific Illustrator

*Imagine the expertise that went into illustrating this book. You can combine a science background with your artistic ability in the technically demanding career of scientific illustrator.*

Scientific illustrations are a form of art required for textbooks, museum exhibits, Web sites, and publications of scientific research. These figures often show what photographs cannot—the reconstruction of an object from fragments, comparisons among objects, or the demonstration of a process or idea. Scientific illustrators use everything from paper and pencil to computer software to provide this vital link in the scientific process.

## Practice PROBLEMS

Have students refer to Appendix D for complete solutions to Practice Problems.

**33. a.** 84 790 kg
   **b.** 38.54 g
   **c.** 256.8 cm
   **d.** 4.936 m

**34. a.** $5.482 \times 10^{-4}$ g
   **b.** $1.368 \times 10^5$ kg
   **c.** $3.087 \times 10^8$ mm
   **d.** 2.014 mL

**35. a.** 142.9 cm
   **b.** 768 kg
   **c.** 0.1119 mg

**36. a.** 12.12 cm
   **b.** 2.10 cm
   **c.** $2.7 \times 10^3$ cm

### CAREERS USING CHEMISTRY

**Career Path** A career as a scientific illustrator requires science courses on the high school and college level. Art courses at a college or art school are also required.

**Career Issue** Have students investigate how computers are used in scientific illustration. Have them go through a chapter of this textbook and determine which illustrations were done using a computer and which were not.

**For More Information**
For more information about careers in scientific illustration, students can contact a local college, university, or art school.

2.3 How reliable are measurements?    **41**

### DIFFERENTIATED INSTRUCTION

#### Gifted

*Logical-Mathematical* Help capable students systematically explore the roles of accuracy, precision, and significant figures. Have students measure the volume and mass of a substance of known density. Have them obtain each measurement three times, calculate the density, and then calculate the percent error. **L3**

## Practice PROBLEMS

Have students refer to Appendix D for complete solutions to Practice Problems.

**37. a.** 78 m²
   **b.** 12 m²
   **c.** 2.5 m²
   **d.** 81.1 m²
**38. a.** 2.0 m/s
   **b.** 3.00 m/s
   **c.** 2.00 m/s
   **d.** 2.9 m/s

# 3 Assess

## Check for Understanding

Ask students to solve the following problem. A 5.00-m board is sold to a construction crew. They measure it four times and obtain the following values: 4.98 m, 4.95 m, 5.08 m, and 5.03 m. How precise are these values? Fairly precise; the error ranges from –0.05 m to +0.08 m. **L2**

## Reteach

Have students average the measurements for the board given above. Make sure they explain the number of significant figures in their answers. How accurate are the measurements? The average measurement is 5.01 m. The average measurement is very accurate. **L2**

## Extension

Ask students to calculate the percent error for the average length of the board. Make sure they explain the number of significant figures in their answer. The percent error is 0.2%. The error, 0.01 m, has only one significant figure, so the answer has only one. **L2**

 **Assessment**

**Knowledge** Continue the example of the construction crew by asking students whether the carpenters were sold a 5.00-m board. Have them explain their answers. Yes; the length of the board rounds off to 5 m. **L2**

**42**

---

**Multiplication and division** When you multiply or divide numbers, your answer must have the same number of significant figures as the measurement with the fewest significant figures.

To find the volume of a rectangular object, multiply the length of the base times the width times the height.

### EXAMPLE PROBLEM 2-9

**Applying Rounding Rules to Multiplication**

Calculate the volume of a rectangular object with the following dimensions: length = 3.65 cm; width = 3.20 cm; height = 2.05 cm.

**1. Analyze the Problem**

You are given measurements for the length, width, and height of a rectangular object. Because all three measurements have three significant figures, the answer will have three significant figures. Note that the units must be multiplied too.

**2. Solve for the Unknown**

To find the volume of a rectangular object, multiply the length times the width times the height.

3.20 cm × 3.65 cm × 2.05 cm = 23.944 cm³

Because the data have only three significant figures, the answer can have only three significant figures.

The answer is 23.9 cm³.

**3. Evaluate the Answer**

To test if your answer is reasonable, round the data to one significant figure. Multiply 3 cm × 4 cm × 2 cm to get 24 cm³. Your answer, 23.9 cm³, has the same number of significant figures as the data. All three measurements should have the same number of significant figures because the same ruler or tape measure was used to collect the data.

Practice! For more practice with rounding after multiplication, go to Supplemental Practice Problems in Appendix A.

### PRACTICE PROBLEMS

Complete the following calculations. Round off the answers to the correct number of significant figures.

**37. a.** 24 m × 3.26 m
   **b.** 120 m × 0.10 m
   **c.** 1.23 m × 2.0 m
   **d.** 53.0 m × 1.53 m

**38. a.** 4.84 m/2.4 s
   **b.** 60.2 m/20.1 s
   **c.** 102.4 m/51.2 s
   **d.** 168 m/58 s

## Section 2.3 Assessment

**39.** A piece of wood has a labeled length value of 76.49 cm. You measure its length three times and record the following data: 76.48 cm, 76.47 cm, and 76.59 cm. How many significant figures do these measurements have?

**40.** Are the measurements in problem 39 accurate? Are they precise? Explain your answers.

**41.** Calculate the percent error for each measurement in problem 39.

**42.** Round 76.51 cm to two significant figures. Then round your answer to one significant figure.

**43. Thinking Critically** Which of these measurements was made with the most precise measuring device: 8.1956 m, 8.20 m, or 8.196 m? Explain your answer.

**44. Using Numbers** Write an expression for the quantity 506 000 cm in which it is clear that all the zeros are significant.

chemistrymc.com/self_check_quiz

## Section 2.3 Assessment

**39.** four
**40.** Answers may vary but might include the following. They are not precise for values recorded to four significant figures. The first and second values are close enough to the accepted value to be called accurate.

**41.** 0.01307%; 0.02615%; 0.1307%
**42.** 77 cm, 80 cm
**43.** 8.1956 m because it has the greatest number of significant figures
**44.** 5.060 00 × 10⁵ cm

# 1 Focus

When you analyze data, you may set up an equation and solve for an unknown, but this is not the only method scientists have for analyzing data. A goal of many experiments is to discover whether a pattern exists in a certain situation. Does raising the temperature change the rate of a reaction? Does a change in diet affect a rat's ability to solve a maze? When data are listed in a table such as **Table 2-6,** a pattern may not be obvious.

## Graphing

Using data to create a graph can help to reveal a pattern if one exists. A **graph** is a visual display of data. Have you ever heard the saying, "A picture is worth a thousand words?"

**Circle graphs** If you read a paper or a news magazine, you will find many graphs. The circle graph in **Figure 2-13a** is sometimes called a pie chart because it is divided into wedges like a pie or pizza. A circle graph is useful for showing parts of a fixed whole. The parts are usually labeled as percents with the circle as a whole representing 100%. The graph in **Figure 2-13a** is based on the data in **Table 2-6.** What percent of the chlorine sources are natural? What percent are manufactured compounds? Which source supplies the most chlorine to the stratosphere?

**Bar graph** A bar graph often is used to show how a quantity varies with factors such as time, location, or temperature. In those cases, the quantity being measured appears on the vertical axis (*y*-axis). The independent variable appears on the horizontal axis (*x*-axis). The relative heights of the bars show how the quantity varies. A bar graph can be used to compare population figures for a country by decade. It can compare annual precipitation for different cities or average monthly precipitation for a single location, as in **Figure 2-13b.** The precipitation data was collected over a 30-year period (1961–1990). During which four months does Jacksonville receive about half of its annual precipitation?

### Objectives

• **Create** graphs to reveal patterns in data.

• **Interpret** graphs.

### Vocabulary

graph

**Table 2-6**

| Sources of Chlorine in the Stratosphere | |
|---|---|
| **Source** | **Percent** |
| Hydrogen chloride | 3 |
| Methyl chloride | 15 |
| Carbon tetrachloride | 12 |
| Methyl chloroform | 10 |
| CFC-11 | 23 |
| CFC-12 | 28 |
| CFC-113 | 6 |
| HCFC-22 | 3 |

**Figure 2-13**

What do circle graphs and bar graphs have in common?

**a**

CFC–12 28%
CFC–113 6%
HCFC–22 3%
Methyl chloroform 10%
Methyl chloride 15%
Hydrogen chloride 3%
Carbon tetrachloride 12%
CFC–11 23%

■ Manufactured compounds  □ Natural sources

**b**

**Precipitation in Jacksonville (1961–1990)**

Average precipitation (inches) vs. Months (Jan–Dec)

# 1 Focus

## Section 2.4

## Focus Transparency

Before presenting the lesson, display **Section Focus Transparency 8** on the overhead projector. Have students answer the accompanying questions using **Section Focus Transparency Master 8.** **L1** **ELL**

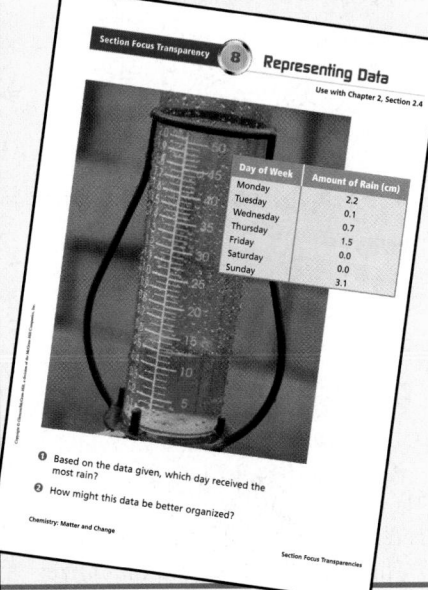

Section Focus Transparency 8 — Representing Data
Use with Chapter 2, Section 2.4

| Day of Week | Amount of Rain (cm) |
|---|---|
| Monday | 2.2 |
| Tuesday | 0.1 |
| Wednesday | 0.7 |
| Thursday | 1.5 |
| Friday | 0.0 |
| Saturday | 0.0 |
| Sunday | 3.1 |

❶ Based on the data given, which day received the most rain?
❷ How might this data be better organized?

Chemistry: Matter and Change
Section Focus Transparencies

# 2 Teach

## Figure Caption Question

**Figure 2-13** What do circle graphs and bar graphs have in common? Both compare relative amounts.

## In-Text Questions

**Page 43** What percent of chlorine sources are natural? 18%

**Page 43** What percent are manufactured compounds? 82%

**Page 43** Which source supplies the most chlorine to the stratosphere? CFC-12

**Page 43** During what four months does Jacksonville receive about half of its annual precipitation? June-September

### CHEMISTRY JOURNAL

**Visual Imagery**

Have students explain how circle graphs give both qualitative and quantitative information. A glance gives qualitative information, such as which wedge of the circle is largest. The precise percentage for each slice of the pie provides quantitative information. **L2**

### Resource Manager

**Study Guide for Content Mastery,** p. 12 **L2**
**Solving Problems: A Chemistry Handbook,** Section 2.4 **L2**
**Section Focus Transparency 8 and Master** **L1** **ELL**

**National Science Content Standards**

**Pages 42–45**
UCP.1, UCP.3; A.1, A.2; E.2; G.2

**Purpose** 🖐
Students will make a line graph.

**Process Skills**
Making and using graphs, using numbers, identifying variables

**Teaching Strategies**
- Emphasize the importance of the intervals on the axes being equal.
- Explain that functions such as $y = mx + b$ form a straight line on a graph, but measured data usually indicates only trends.

**Analysis**
Independent variable—speed; dependent variable—stopping distance; Graphs should show that as speed increases, so does stopping distance.

**Thinking Critically**
Reaction time should be fairly constant. Thus, braking distance must increase more rapidly.

### ✔ Assessment

**Skill** Have each student measure his or her height and arm length, collect class data, and create a line graph of height versus arm length from them. Emphasize that a general trend is observed, but not all the results are on the "best fit" line. **L2**

---

## In-Text Questions

**Page 44** What are the values for the independent variable and the dependent variable at Point B?
20.0 cm³; 54 g

**Page 45** Why might extrapolation be less reliable than interpolation?
Extrapolation deals with values beyond the range of those measured.

**Page 45** Based on the graph, was there an ozone hole in the 1957–1972 era? no

## Figure Caption Questions

**Figure 2-14** Compare the slopes of these graphs. graph a—positive; graph b—negative
**Figure 2-15** Why are there no measurements from May to July? They are difficult to obtain in winter.

**44**

---

ⓐ **Density of Aluminum**

B (20.0 cm³, 54 g)
A (10.0 cm³, 27 g)

Mass (g) — Volume (cm³)

ⓑ **Temperature Versus Elevation**

Temperature (°C) — Elevation (m)

**Figure 2-14**

Compare the slopes of these two graphs.

## Line Graphs

In chemistry, most graphs that you create and interpret will be line graphs. The points on a line graph represent the intersection of data for two variables. The independent variable is plotted on the *x*-axis. The dependent variable is plotted on the *y*-axis. Remember that the independent variable is the variable that a scientist deliberately changes during an experiment. In **Figure 2-14a**, the independent variable is volume and the dependent variable is mass. What are the values for the independent variable and the dependent variable at point B? **Figure 2-14b** is a graph of elevation versus temperature. Because the points are scattered, the line cannot pass through all the data points. The line must be drawn so that about as many points fall above the line as fall below it. This line is called a best fit line.

If the best fit line is straight, there is a linear relationship between the variables and the variables are *directly* related. This relationship can be further described by the steepness, or slope, of the line. If the line rises to the right, the slope is *positive*. A positive slope indicates that the dependent variable *increases* as the independent variable increases. If the line sinks to the right, the slope is *negative*. A negative slope indicates that the dependent variable *decreases* as the independent variable increases. Either way, the slope of the graph is constant. You can use the data points to calculate the slope of the line. The slope is the change in *y* divided by the change in *x*.

$$\text{slope} = \frac{y_2 - y_1}{x_2 - x_1} = \frac{\Delta y}{\Delta x}$$

Calculate the slope for the line in **Figure 2-14a** using data points A and B.

$$\text{slope} = \frac{54 \text{ g} - 27 \text{ g}}{20.0 \text{ cm}^3 - 10.0 \text{ cm}^3} = \frac{27 \text{ g}}{10.0 \text{ cm}^3} = 2.7 \text{ g/cm}^3$$

When the mass of a material is plotted against volume, the slope of the line is the density of the material. Do the **CHEMLAB** at the end of the chapter to learn more about using a graph to find density.

---

## problem-solving LAB

### How does speed affect stopping distance?

**Making and Using Graphs** Use the steps below and the data to make a line graph.

| Speed (m/s) | 11 | 16 | 20 | 25 | 29 |
|---|---|---|---|---|---|
| Stopping distance (m) | 18 | 32 | 49 | 68 | 92 |

1. Identify the independent and dependent variables.
2. Determine the range of data that needs to be plotted for each axis. Choose intervals for the axes that spread out the data. Make each square on the graph a multiple of 1, 2, or 5.
3. Number and label each axis.
4. Plot the data points.
5. Draw a best fit line for the data. The line may be straight or it may be curved. Not all points may fall on the line.
6. Give the graph a title.

**Analysis**
What does the graph tell you about the relationship between speed and stopping distance?

**Thinking Critically**
There are two components to stopping distance: reaction distance (distance traveled before the driver applies the brake) and braking distance (distance traveled after the brake is applied). Predict which component will increase more rapidly as the speed increases. Explain your choice.

**44** Chapter 2 Data Analysis

---

When the best fit line is curved, the relationship between the variables is nonlinear. In chemistry, you will study nonlinear relationships called inverse relationships. See pages 903–907 in the **Math Handbook** for more discussion of graphs. Do the **problem-solving LAB** to practice making line graphs.

## Interpreting Graphs

An organized approach can help you understand the information on a graph. First, identify the independent and dependent variables. Look at the ranges of the data and consider what measurements were taken. Decide if the relationship between the variables is linear or nonlinear. If the relationship is linear, is the slope positive or negative? If a graph has multiple lines or regions, study one area at a time.

When points on a line graph are connected, the data is considered continuous. You can read data from a graph that falls between measured points. This process is called interpolation. You can extend the line beyond the plotted points and estimate values for the variables. This process is called extrapolation. Why might extrapolation be less reliable than interpolation?

**Interpreting ozone data** Figure 2-15 is a graph of ozone measurements taken at a scientific settlement in Antarctica called Halley. The independent variable is months of the year. The dependent variable is total ozone measured in Dobson units (DU). The graph shows how ozone levels vary from August to April. There are two lines on the graph. Multiple lines allow scientists to introduce a third variable, in this case different periods of time. Having two lines on the same graph allows scientists to compare data gathered before the ozone hole developed with data from a recent season. They can identify a significant trend in ozone levels and verify the depletion in ozone levels over time.

The top line represents average ozone levels for the period 1957–1972. Follow the line from left to right. Ozone levels were about 300 DU in early October. By November, they rose to about 360 DU. Ozone levels slowly dropped back to around 290 DU by April. The bottom line shows the ozone levels from the 1999–2000 survey. The ozone levels were around 200 DU in August, dipped to about 150 DU during October, and slowly rose to a maximum of about 280 DU in January. At no point during this 9-month period were the ozone levels as high as they were at the corresponding points during 1957–1972. The "ozone hole" is represented by the dip in the bottom line. Based on the graph, was there an ozone hole in the 1957–1972 era?

**Ozone Measurements at Halley**

1957–1972

1999–2000

**Figure 2-15**

In Antarctica, spring begins in October and winter begins in April. Why are there no measurements from May to July?

## Section 2.4 Assessment

45. Explain why graphing can be an important tool for analyzing data.

46. What type of data can be displayed on a circle graph? On a bar graph?

47. If a linear graph has a negative slope, what can you say about the dependent variable?

48. When can the slope of a graph represent density?

49. **Thinking Critically** Why does it make sense for the line in **Figure 2-14a** to extend to 0, 0 even though this point was not measured?

50. **Interpreting Graphs** Using **Figure 2-15,** determine how many months the ozone hole lasts.

chemistrymc.com/self_check_quiz

2.4 Representing Data  **45**

## Section 2.4 Assessment

45. It provides visual information about relationships between variables, relative amounts, or parts of a whole.

46. parts of a whole; how a quantity varies with a factor

47. It decreases in value as the independent variable increases.

48. when mass is the *y* value and volume is the *x* value

49. Extrapolation of measured data extends the line to this point. The graph shows that an object with no mass will have no volume.

50. from September to November, or approximately three months

## Preparation

### Time Allotment
One laboratory period

### Process Skills
Collecting data, comparing and contrasting, making and using graphs, measuring, thinking critically, using numbers

### Disposal
Save the copper wire for reuse.

### Alternative Materials
Other gauges of copper wire can be used.

### Pre-Lab

**2.** $D = m/V$

**3.** by water displacement

**4.** It is the curved surface of a liquid. The bottom of the meniscus is considered to be the level of the liquid.

**5.** density

**6.** Choose two points on the line. Divide the difference in the $y$ values by the difference in the $x$ values.

**7.** $r = \sqrt{V/(\pi h)}$

**8.** $d = 2r$

**9.** See data tables.

### Sample Data

| | Density of Copper | | |
|---|---|---|---|
| Trial | Mass of copper added | Total mass of copper | Total volume of water displaced |
| 1 | 9.7 g | 9.7 g | 1.0 mL |
| 2 | 9.9 g | 19.6 g | 2.0 mL |
| 3 | 12.4 g | 32.0 g | 3.4 mL |
| 4 | 12.2 g | 44.2 g | 4.8 mL |

| Diameter of Copper Wire | | |
|---|---|---|
| | 12-gauge | 18-gauge |
| Length | 16.3 cm | 16.4 cm |
| Mass | 4.8 g | 1.2 g |
| Measured diameter | 0.20 cm | 0.10 cm |
| Calculated diameter | 0.21 cm | 0.10 cm |

---

# Using Density to Find the Thickness of a Wire

The thickness of wire often is measured using a system called the American Wire Gauge (AWG) standard. The smaller the gauge number, the larger the diameter of the wire. For example, 18-gauge copper wire has a diameter of about 0.102 cm; 12-gauge copper wire has a diameter of about 0.205 cm. Such small diameters are difficult to measure accurately with a metric ruler. In this experiment, you will plot measurements of mass and volume to find the density of copper. Then, you will use the density of copper to confirm the gauge of copper wire.

### Problem
How can density be used to verify the diameter of copper wire?

### Objectives
- **Collect** and **graph** mass and volume data to find the density of copper.
- **Measure** the length and volume of a copper wire, and **calculate** its diameter.
- **Calculate** percent errors for the results.

### Materials
tap water
100-mL graduated cylinder
small cup, plastic
balance
copper shot
copper wire (12-gauge, 18-gauge)
metric ruler
pencil
graph paper
graphing calculator (optional)

### Safety Precautions

- Always wear safety goggles and a lab apron.

### Pre-Lab

**1.** Read the entire **CHEMLAB.**

**2.** What is the equation used to calculate density?

**3.** How can you find the volume of a solid that has an irregular shape?

**4.** What is a meniscus and how does it affect volume readings?

**5.** If you plot mass versus volume, what property of matter will the slope of the graph represent?

**6.** How do you find the slope of a graph?

**7.** A piece of copper wire is a narrow cylinder. The equation for the volume of a cylinder is

$$V = \pi r^2 h$$

where $V$ is the volume, $r$ is the radius, $h$ is the height, and $\pi$ (pi) is a constant with a value of 3.14. Rearrange the equation to solve for $r$.

**8.** What is the relationship between the diameter and the radius of a cylinder?

**9.** Prepare two data tables.

| | Density of Copper | | |
|---|---|---|---|
| Trial | Mass of copper added | Total mass of copper | Total volume of water displaced |
| 1 | | | |
| 2 | | | |
| 3 | | | |
| 4 | | | |

| Diameter of Copper Wire | | |
|---|---|---|
| | 12-gauge | 18-gauge |
| Length | | |
| Mass | | |
| Measured diameter | | |
| Calculated diameter | | |

## Procedure
- Require that the students' notebooks contain objectives, outline or flow chart of the procedure, and data tables before they begin.
- Have paper towels available for cleanup of any spills.
- Have students practice reading a meniscus before beginning the activity.

## Expected Results
See the data tables.

## Procedure

*Record all measurements in your data tables.*

1. Pour about 20 mL of water into a 100-mL graduated cylinder. Read the actual volume.

2. Find the mass of the plastic cup.

3. Add about 10 g of copper shot to the cup and find the mass again.

4. Pour the copper shot into the graduated cylinder and read the new volume.

5. Repeat steps 3 and 4 three times. By the end of the four trials, you will have about 40 g of copper in the graduated cylinder.

6. Obtain a piece of 12-gauge copper wire and a piece of 18-gauge copper wire. Use a metric ruler to measure the length and diameter of each wire.

7. Wrap each wire around a pencil to form a coil. Remove the coils from the pencil. Find the mass of each coil.

## Cleanup and Disposal

1. Carefully drain off most of the water from the graduated cylinder. Make sure all of the copper shot remains in the cylinder.

2. Pour the copper shot onto a paper towel to dry. Both the copper shot and wire can be reused.

## Analyze and Conclude

1. **Using Numbers** Complete the table for the density of copper by calculating the total mass of copper and the total water displaced for each trial.

2. **Making and Using Graphs** Graph total mass versus total volume of copper. Draw a line that best fits the points. Then use two points on your line to find the slope of your graph. Because density equals mass divided by volume, the slope will give you the density of copper.

   If you are using a graphing calculator, select the 5:FIT CURVE option from the MAIN MENU of the ChemBio program. Choose 1:LINEAR L1,L2 from the REGRESSION/LIST to help you plot and calculate the slope of the graph.

3. **Using Numbers** Calculate the percent error for your value of density.

4. **Using Numbers** To complete the second data table, you must calculate the diameter for each wire. Use the accepted value for the density of copper and the mass of each wire to calculate volume. Then use the equation for the volume of a cylinder to solve for the radius. Double the radius to find the diameter.

5. **Comparing and Contrasting** How do your calculated values for the diameter compare to your measured values and to the AWG values listed in the introduction?

6. **Error Analysis** How could you change the procedure to reduce the percent error for density?

## Real-World Chemistry

1. There is a standard called the British Imperial Standard Wire Gauge (SWG) that is used in England and Canada. Research the SWG standard to find out how it differs from the AWG standard. Are they the only standards used for wire gauge?

2. Interview an electrician or a building inspector who reviews the wiring in new or remodeled buildings. Ask what the codes are for the wires used and how the diameter of a wire affects its ability to safely conduct electricity. Ask to see a wiring diagram.

## Analyze and Conclude

1. See Density of Copper table.

2. Density should equal approximately 8.96.

3. % error = $\frac{(D_{actual} - D_{calculated})}{D_{actual}} \times 100\%$

4. See Diameter of Copper Wire table.

5. Answers should be close to the values listed.

6. Answers might include using a smaller graduated cylinder so volume readings will be more accurate.

## Real-World Chemistry

1. Gauge 9 SWG is 0.144 in. and gauge 9 in AWG is 0.1144 in. AWG is also called Brown and Sharp. Other gauges include Birmingham or Stubbs, Washburn and Moen, metric wire gauge, and U.S. Government Standard.

2. Check students' results for consistency. Local electrical codes may vary. The National Electrical Code provides criteria for all electrical installations. Color codes for wires help electricians make correct connections. Wire is characterized by gauge number (diameter) and kind of insulation. Improper wire size may cause fire.

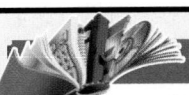 **Assessment**

**Portfolio** Have students write lab reports of the experiment and place them in their portfolios.
**L2** **P**

### Resource Manager

**ChemLab and MiniLab Worksheets,** pp. 6–8 **L2**

**National Science Content Standards**

**Pages 46–47**
UCP.1, UCP.3; A.1, A.2; B.2

# How It Works

## Purpose 🔲

Students will learn how different densities of human tissue are used to create ultrasound images.

## Background

Sound travels as waves. Waves are described by their frequency. The more waves passing a point in a given period of time, the higher the frequency. Ultrasound waves have a frequency higher than those perceived by the human ear.

Ultrasound devices are a noninvasive method of probing the body. Ultrasound waves are used rather than waves in the audible region because they have shorter wavelengths and can, therefore, produce more detailed images.

Ultrasound does not replace X rays in all situations, but it is helpful for certain kinds of diagnoses. For example, some tissues cannot be detected in X rays. Ultrasound waves, however, are reflected from their boundaries.

## Visual Learning

Have students use the illustration to explain orally their answers to Thinking Critically, question 1.

## Teaching Strategies

• Echolocation and sonar are applications of sound that are similar to ultrasound. Ask students to choose one process and relate it to making an ultrasound image.

**National Science Content Standards**

**Pages 48–49**
UCP.1, UCP.3; A.1, A.2; B.2; E.1, E.2; F.1

**48**

---

# How It Works
## Ultrasound Devices

An ultrasound device is a diagnostic tool that allows doctors to see inside the human body without having to perform surgery. With an ultrasound device, doctors can detect abnormal growths, follow the development of a fetus in the uterus, or study the action of heart valves.

An ultrasound device emits high-frequency sound waves that can pass through a material, be absorbed, or reflect off the surface of a material. Waves are reflected at the border between tissues with different densities, such as an organ and a tumor. The larger the difference in density, the greater the reflection.

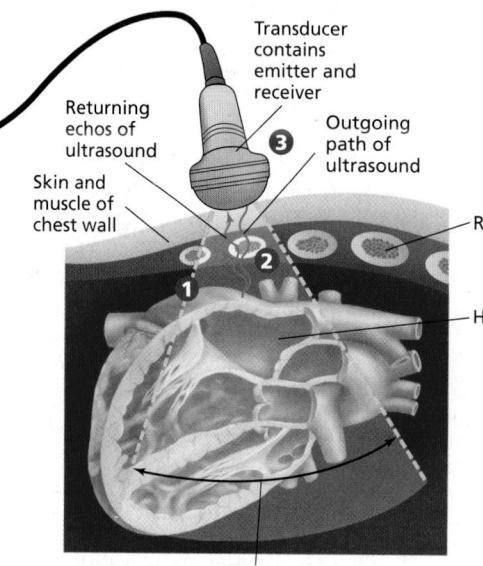

Transducer contains emitter and receiver

Returning echos of ultrasound

Outgoing path of ultrasound

Skin and muscle of chest wall

Rib

❸

❶ ❷

Heart

Path of beam's sweep

❶ In the transducer, electrical pulses are changed into sound waves, which are aimed at a specific part of the body.

❷ As the transducer is moved across the body, some sound is reflected back as echoes.

❸ A receiver detects the reflected waves and converts the sound back into electrical pulses.

❹ A computer analyzes the data and creates an image of an internal organ, such as the heart.

### Thinking Critically

**1. Predicting** If all parts of the heart had the same density, would doctors be able to use ultrasound to detect heart defects? Explain.

**2. Inferring** Why is it considered safe to use ultrasound but not X rays during pregnancy?

---

## Thinking Critically

**1.** No; the ultrasound device could not distinguish between the defect and the surrounding tissue. Ultrasound images are reflected at the boundary between tissues of different densities.

**2.** Ultrasound uses only high-energy sound waves, which are not as energetic as X rays. X rays can cause mutations in genetic material.

## Summary

### 2.1 Units of Measurement

- SI measurement units allow scientists to report data that can be reproduced by other scientists.

- Adding prefixes to SI units extends the range of possible measurements.

- SI base units include the meter for length, the second for time, the kilogram for mass, and the kelvin for temperature.

- Volume and density have derived units. Density is the ratio of mass to volume. Density can be used to identify a sample of matter.

### 2.2 Scientific Notation and Dimensional Analysis

- Scientific notation makes it easier to handle extremely large or small measurements.

- Numbers expressed in scientific notation are a product of two factors: (1) a number between 1 and 10 and (2) ten raised to a power.

- Numbers added or subtracted in scientific notation must be expressed to the same power of ten.

- When measurements are multiplied or divided in scientific notation, their exponents are added or subtracted, respectively.

- Dimensional analysis often uses conversion factors to solve problems that involve units. A conversion factor is a ratio of equivalent values.

### 2.3 How reliable are measurements?

- An accurate measurement is close to the accepted value. Precise measurements show little variation over a series of trials.

- The type of measurement instrument determines the degree of precision possible.

- Percent error compares the size of an error in experimental data to the size of the accepted value.

- The number of significant figures reflects the precision of reported data. Answers to calculations are rounded off to maintain the correct number of significant figures.

### 2.4 Representing Data

- Graphs are visual representations of data. Graphs can reveal patterns in data.

- Circle graphs show parts of a whole. Bar graphs can show how a factor varies with time, location, or temperature.

- The relationship between the independent and dependent variables on a line graph can be linear or nonlinear.

- Because the data on a line graph are considered continuous, you can interpolate or extrapolate data from a line graph.

## Key Equations and Relationships

- density: $density = \dfrac{mass}{volume}$ (p. 28)

- conversion between temperature scales: $°C + 273 = K$    $K - 273 = °C$ (p. 30)

- percent error: $percent\ error = \dfrac{error}{accepted\ value} \times 100$ (p. 37)

- slope of graph: $slope = \dfrac{y_2 - y_1}{x_2 - x_1} = \dfrac{\Delta y}{\Delta x}$ (p. 44)

## Vocabulary

- accuracy (p. 36)
- base unit (p. 26)
- conversion factor (p. 34)
- density (p. 27)
- derived unit (p. 27)
- dimensional analysis (p. 34)
- graph (p. 43)
- kelvin (p. 30)
- kilogram (p. 27)
- liter (p. 27)
- meter (p. 26)
- percent error (p. 37)
- precision (p. 36)
- scientific notation (p. 31)
- second (p. 26)
- significant figure (p. 38)

 chemistrymc.com/vocabulary_puzzlemaker

## Using the Vocabulary

To reinforce chapter vocabulary, have students write a sentence using each term. **L2** **ELL**

## Review Strategies

- Have students list and give examples of scientific notation with positive and negative exponents and explain the significance of each number. **L2**
- Have students list the rules for rounding significant figures and determining the correct number of significant figures following calculations. **L2**
- Problems from Appendix A or the **Supplemental Problems** booklet can be used for review. **L2**

## GLENCOE
### TECHNOLOGY

 **VIDEOTAPE/DVD**
**MindJogger Videoquizzes**
*Chapter 2: Data Analysis*
Have students work in groups as they play the videoquiz game to review key chapter concepts.

## VOCABULARY
### PuzzleMaker

For additional help with vocabulary, have students access the Vocabulary PuzzleMaker online.

chemistrymc.com/ vocabulary_puzzlemaker

 **Chemistry online**

## Concept Mapping

**51.** 1. base unit; 2. derived unit; 3. mass; 4. time; 5. length; 6. volume; 7. density

## Mastering Concepts

**52.** The number gives you the quantitative value, and the unit indicates what was measured.

**53.** Scientists from different countries have different languages and cultures but must be able to share and compare data.

**54.** It gives the magnitude of the measurement.

**55.** 1000; 0.1

**56.** The SI unit for volume is the cubic meter, m³, which is equal to three SI measurements of length multiplied together.

**57.** The sizes of the units are equal; °C + 273 = K.

**58.** Scientific notation uses a number between 1 and 10 times a power of ten to indicate the size of very large or small numbers.

**59.** positive

**60.** Subtract them.

**61.** It decreases.

**62.** You must know the accepted value to know if the measurements are accurate. They are fairly precise because there is only 0.14 g difference between the two measurements.

**63.** The starting unit (m) will be in the denominator so that the units will cancel. The final unit (cm) will be in the numerator. Coefficients in the conversion factor express an amount equal to one (100 cm/1 m).

**64.** You need to know only the difference between the measured value and the

magnitude of the accepted value.

**65.** the first one; placeholder

**66.** 3.448 and 3.450

**67.** the number that has the fewest digits to the right of the decimal point; it is less precise.

---

## Chemistry Online

Go to the Chemistry Web site at chemistrymc.com for additional Chapter 2 Assessment.

## Concept Mapping

**51.** Use the following terms to complete the concept map: volume, derived unit, mass, density, base unit, time, length.

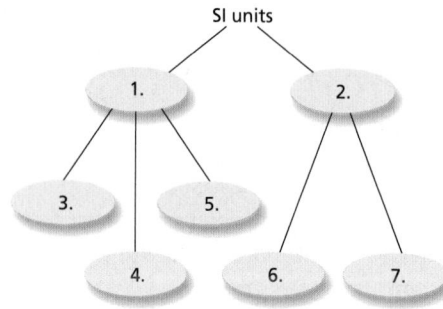

## Mastering Concepts

**52.** Why must a measurement include both a number and a unit? (2.1)

**53.** Explain why scientists, in particular, need standard units of measurement. (2.1)

**54.** What role do prefixes play in the metric system? (2.1)

**55.** How many meters are there in one kilometer? In one decimeter? (2.1)

**56.** What is the relationship between the SI unit for volume and the SI unit for length? (2.1)

**57.** Explain how temperatures on the Celsius and Kelvin scales are related. (2.1)

**58.** How does scientific notation differ from ordinary notation? (2.2)

**59.** If you move the decimal place to the left to convert a number into scientific notation, will the power of ten be positive or negative? (2.2)

**60.** When dividing numbers in scientific notation, what must you do with the exponents? (2.2)

**61.** When you convert from a small unit to a large unit, what happens to the number of units? (2.2)

---

**62.** If you report two measurements of mass, 7.42 g and 7.56 g, are the measurements accurate? Are they precise? Explain your answers. (2.3)

**63.** When converting from meters to centimeters, how do you decide which values to place in the numerator and denominator of the conversion factor? (2.2)

**64.** Why are plus and minus signs ignored in percent error calculations? (2.3)

**65.** In 50 540, which zero is significant? What is the other zero called? (2.3)

**66.** Which of the following three numbers will produce the same number when rounded to three significant figures: 3.456, 3.450, or 3.448? (2.3)

**67.** When subtracting 61.45 g from 242.6 g, which factor determines the number of significant figures in the answer? Explain. (2.3)

**68.** When multiplying 602.4 m by 3.72 m, which factor determines the number of significant figures in the answer? Explain. (2.3)

**69.** Which type of graph would you choose to depict data on how many households heat with gas, oil, or electricity? Explain. (2.4)

**70.** Which type of graph would you choose to depict changes in gasoline consumption over a period of ten years? Explain. (2.4)

**71.** How can you find the slope of a line graph? (2.4)

## Mastering Problems

### Density (2.1)

**72.** A 5-mL sample of water has a mass of 5 g. What is the density of water?

**73.** An object with a mass of 7.5 g raises the level of water in a graduated cylinder from 25.1 mL to 30.1 mL. What is the density of the object?

**74.** The density of aluminum is 2.7 g/mL. What is the volume of 8.1 g?

### Scientific Notation (2.2)

**75.** Write the following numbers in scientific notation.
- **a.** 0.004 583 4 mm
- **b.** 0.03054 g
- **c.** 438 904 s
- **d.** 7 004 300 000 g

**76.** Write the following numbers in ordinary notation.
- **a.** $8.348 \times 10^6$ km
- **b.** $3.402 \times 10^3$ g
- **c.** $7.6352 \times 10^{-3}$ kg
- **d.** $3.02 \times 10^{-5}$ s

chemistrymc.com/chapter_test

---

## Resource Manager

Chapter Assessment, pp. 7–12 **L2**
Supplemental Problems, Ch. 2
ExamView® Pro CD-ROM
MindJogger Videoquizzes
Solutions Manual, Ch. 2
Chemistry Interactive CD-ROM, Ch. 2 quiz

**77.** Complete the following addition and subtraction problems in scientific notation.

   **a.** $6.23 \times 10^6$ kL $+ 5.34 \times 10^6$ kL
   **b.** $3.1 \times 10^4$ mm $+ 4.87 \times 10^5$ mm
   **c.** $7.21 \times 10^3$ mg $+ 43.8 \times 10^2$ mg
   **d.** $9.15 \times 10^{-4}$ cm $+ 3.48 \times 10^{-4}$ cm
   **e.** $4.68 \times 10^{-5}$ cg $+ 3.5 \times 10^{-6}$ cg
   **f.** $3.57 \times 10^2$ mL $- 1.43 \times 10^2$ mL
   **g.** $9.87 \times 10^4$ g $- 6.2 \times 10^3$ g
   **h.** $7.52 \times 10^5$ kg $- 5.43 \times 10^5$ kg
   **i.** $6.48 \times 10^{-3}$ mm $- 2.81 \times 10^{-3}$ mm
   **j.** $5.72 \times 10^{-4}$ dg $- 2.3 \times 10^{-5}$ dg

**78.** Complete the following multiplication and division problems in scientific notation.

   **a.** $(4.8 \times 10^5$ km$) \times (2.0 \times 10^3$ km$)$
   **b.** $(3.33 \times 10^{-4}$ m$) \times (3.00 \times 10^{-5}$ m$)$
   **c.** $(1.2 \times 10^6$ m$) \times (1.5 \times 10^{-7}$ m$)$
   **d.** $(8.42 \times 10^8$ kL$) \div (4.21 \times 10^3$ kL$)$
   **e.** $(8.4 \times 10^6$ L$) \div (2.4 \times 10^{-3}$ L$)$
   **f.** $(3.3 \times 10^{-4}$ mL$) \div (1.1 \times 10^{-6}$ mL$)$

## Conversion Factors (2.2)

**79.** Write the conversion factor that converts

   **a.** grams to kilograms
   **b.** kilograms to grams
   **c.** millimeters to meters
   **d.** meters to millimeters
   **e.** milliliters to liters
   **f.** centimeters to meters

**80.** Convert the following measurements.

   **a.** 5.70 g to milligrams
   **b.** 4.37 cm to meters
   **c.** 783 kg to grams
   **d.** 45.3 mm to meters
   **e.** 10 m to centimeters
   **f.** 37.5 g/mL to kg/L

## Percent Error (2.3)

**81.** The accepted length of a steel pipe is 5.5 m. Calculate the percent error for each of these measurements.

   **a.** 5.2 m
   **b.** 5.5 m
   **c.** 5.7 m
   **d.** 5.1 m

**82.** The accepted density for copper is 8.96 g/mL. Calculate the percent error for each of these measurements.

   **a.** 8.86 g/mL
   **b.** 8.92 g/mL
   **c.** 9.00 g/mL
   **d.** 8.98 g/mL

## Significant Figures (2.3)

**83.** Round each number to four significant figures.

   **a.** 431 801 kg
   **b.** 10 235.0 mg
   **c.** 1.0348 m
   **d.** 0.004 384 010 cm
   **e.** 0.000 781 00 mL
   **f.** 0.009 864 1 cg

**84.** Round each figure to three significant figures.

   **a.** 0.003 210 g
   **b.** 3.8754 kg
   **c.** 219 034 m
   **d.** 25.38 L
   **e.** 0.087 63 cm
   **f.** 0.003 109 mg

**85.** Round the answers to each of the following problems to the correct number of significant figures.

   **a.** $7.31 \times 10^4 + 3.23 \times 10^3$
   **b.** $8.54 \times 10^{-3} - 3.41 \times 10^{-4}$
   **c.** 4.35 dm $\times$ 2.34 dm $\times$ 7.35 dm
   **d.** 4.78 cm $+$ 3.218 cm $+$ 5.82 cm
   **e.** 3.40 mg $+$ 7.34 mg $+$ 6.45 mg
   **f.** 45 m $\times$ 72 m $\times$ 132 m
   **g.** 38736 km/4784 km

## Representing Data (2.4)

**86.** Use the accompanying bar graph to answer the following questions.

   **a.** Which substance has the greatest density?
   **b.** Which substance has the least density?
   **c.** Which substance has a density of 7.87 g/cm³?
   **d.** Which substance has a density of 11.4 g/ cm³?

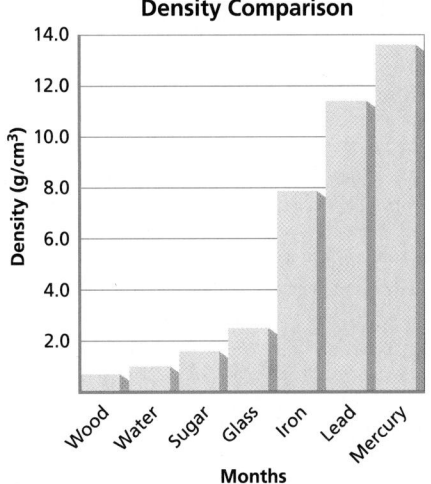

**Density Comparison**

**Months**

**68.** 3.72; it has the smaller number of significant figures.

**69.** A bar graph could be used with the method of heating on the x-axis and the number of households on the y-axis. If the data include all the households for a region, relative numbers could be converted to a percentage and expressed as a circle graph.

**70.** line or bar graph because they can show how consumption varies with time

**71.** Choose two points on the line. Divide the difference in the y values by the difference in the x values.

## Mastering Problems

Complete solutions to Chapter Assessment problems can be found in the **Solutions Manual.**

### Density (2.1)
**Level 1**
   **72.** 1 g/mL

**Level 2**
   **73.** 1.5 g/mL
   **74.** 3.0 mL

### Scientific Notation (2.2)
**Level 1**
   **75. a.** $4.5834 \times 10^{-3}$ mm
      **b.** $3.054 \times 10^{-2}$ g
      **c.** $4.389\ 04 \times 10^5$ s
      **d.** $7.0043 \times 10^9$ g
   **76. a.** 8 348 000 km
      **b.** 3402 g
      **c.** 0.007 635 2 kg
      **d.** 0.000 030 2 s

**Level 2**
   **77. a.** $1.157 \times 10^7$ kL
      **b.** $5.18 \times 10^5$ mm
      **c.** $1.159 \times 10^4$ mg
      **d.** $1.263 \times 10^{-3}$ cm
      **e.** $5.03 \times 10^{-5}$ cg
      **f.** $2.14 \times 10^2$ mL
      **g.** $9.25 \times 10^4$ g
      **h.** $2.09 \times 10^5$ kg
      **i.** $3.67 \times 10^{-3}$ mm
      **j.** $5.49 \times 10^{-4}$ dg
   **78. a.** $9.6 \times 10^8$ km²
      **b.** $9.99 \times 10^{-9}$ m²
      **c.** $1.8 \times 10^{-1}$ m²
      **d.** $2.00 \times 10^5$
      **e.** $3.5 \times 10^9$
      **f.** $3.0 \times 10^2$

## Conversion Factors (2.2)
### Level 1
**79. a.** 1 kg/1000 g
**b.** 1000 g/1 kg
**c.** 1 m/1000 mm
**d.** 1000 mm/1 m
**e.** 1 L/1000 mL
**f.** 1 m/100 cm

### Level 2
**80. a.** $5.70 \times 10^3$ mg
**b.** 0.0437 m
**c.** 783 000 g
**d.** 0.0453 m
**e.** 1000 cm
**f.** 37.5 kg/L

## Percent Error (2.3)
### Level 1
**81. a.** 5.5%
**b.** 0%
**c.** 3.6%
**d.** 7.3%

### Level 2
**82. a.** 1.12%
**b.** 0.446%
**c.** 0.446%
**d.** 0.223%

## Significant Figures
### Level 1
**83. a.** 431 800 kg
**b.** 10 240 mg
**c.** 1.035 m
**d.** 0.004 384 cm
**e.** 0.000 781 0 mL
**f.** 0.009 864 cg
**84. a.** 0.003 21 g
**b.** 3.88 kg
**c.** 219 000 m
**d.** 25.4 L
**e.** 0.0876 cm
**f.** 0.003 11 mg

### Level 2
**85. a.** $7.63 \times 10^4$
**b.** $8.20 \times 10^{-3}$
**c.** 74.8 dm$^3$
**d.** 13.82 cm
**e.** 17.19 mg
**f.** 430 000 m$^3$
**g.** 8.097

---

**87.** Graph the following data with the volume on the *x*-axis and the mass on the *y*-axis. Then calculate the slope of the line.

**Table 2-7**

| Density Data | |
|---|---|
| **Volume (mL)** | **Mass (g)** |
| 2.0 mL | 5.4 |
| 4.0 mL | 10.8 |
| 6.0 mL | 16.2 |
| 8.0 mL | 21. 6 |
| 10.0 mL | 27.0 |

## Mixed Review

*Sharpen your problem-solving skills by answering the following.*

**88.** You have a 23-g sample of ethanol with a density of 0.7893 g/mL. What volume of ethanol do you have?

**89.** Complete the following problems in scientific notation. Round off to the correct number of significant figures.
**a.** $(5.31 \times 10^{-2}$ cm$) \times (2.46 \times 10^5$ cm$)$
**b.** $(3.78 \times 10^3$ m$) \times (7.21 \times 10^2$ m$)$
**c.** $(8.12 \times 10^{-3}$ m$) \times (1.14 \times 10^{-5}$ m$)$
**d.** $(5.53 \times 10^{-6}$ km$) \times (7.64 \times 10^3$ km$)$
**e.** $(9.33 \times 10^4$ mm$) \div (3.0 \times 10^2$ mm$)$
**f.** $(4.42 \times 10^{-3}$ kg$) \div (2.0 \times 10^2$ kg$)$
**g.** $(6.42 \times 10^{-2}$ g$) \div (3.21 \times 10^{-3}$ g$)$

**90.** Evaluate the following conversion. Will the answer be correct? Explain.

$$\text{rate} = \frac{75 \text{ m}}{1 \text{ s}} \times \frac{60 \text{ s}}{1 \text{ min}} \times \frac{1 \text{ h}}{60 \text{ min}}$$

**91.** What mass of lead (density 11.4 g/cm$^3$) would have an identical volume to 15.0 g of mercury (density 13.6 g/cm$^3$)?

**92.** Three students use a meterstick to measure a length of wire. One student records a measurement of 3 cm. The second records 3.3 cm. The third records 2.87 cm. Explain which answer was recorded correctly.

**93.** Express each quantity in the unit listed to its right.
**a.** 3.01 g    cg    **d.** 0.2 L    dm$^3$
**b.** 6200 m    km    **e.** 0.13 cal/g    kcal/g
**c.** $6.24 \times 10^{-7}$ g    μg    **f.** 3.21 mL    L

**94.** The black hole in the galaxy M82 has a mass about 500 times the mass of our Sun. It has about the same volume as Earth's moon. What is the density of this black hole?

$$\text{mass}_{sun} = 1.9891 \times 10^{30} \text{ kg}$$
$$\text{volume}_{moon} = 2.1968 \times 10^{10} \text{ km}^3$$

**95.** The density of water is 1 g/cm$^3$. Use your answer to question 94 to compare the densities of water and a black hole.

## Thinking Critically

**96. Comparing and Contrasting** What advantages do SI units have over the units in common use in the United States? Is there any disadvantage to using SI units?

**97. Forming a Hypothesis** Why do you think the SI standard for time was based on the distance light travels through a vacuum?

**98. Inferring** Explain why the mass of an object cannot help you identify what material the object is made from.

**99. Drawing Conclusions** Why might property owners hire a surveyor to determine property boundaries rather than measure the boundaries themselves?

## Writing in Chemistry

**100.** Although the standard kilogram is stored at constant temperature and humidity, unwanted matter can build up on its surface. Scientists have been looking for a more reliable standard for mass. Research and describe alternate standards that have been proposed. Find out why no alternate standard has been chosen.

**101.** Research and report on some unusual units of measurement such as bushels, pecks, firkins, and frails.

**102.** Research the range of volumes used for packaging liquids sold in supermarkets.

**103.** Find out what the acceptable limits of error are for some manufactured products or for the doses of medicine given at a hospital.

## Cumulative Review

*Refresh your understanding of previous chapters by answering the following.*

**104.** You record the following in your lab book: A liquid is thick and has a density of 4.58 g/mL. Which data is qualitative? Which is quantitative? (Chapter 1)

---

## Representing Data (2.4)
### Level 1
**86. a.** mercury
**b.** wood
**c.** iron
**d.** lead

### Level 2
**87.** Graphs show a straight line with a slope of 2.7 g/mL. See the Solutions Manual.

*Use the questions and the test-taking tip to prepare for your standardized test.*

**1.** Which of the following is *not* an SI base unit?

a. second (s)
b. kilogram (kg)
c. degrees Celsius (°C)
d. meter (m)

**2.** Which of the following values is NOT equivalent to the others?

a. 500 meters
b. 0.5 kilometers
c. 5000 centimeters
d. $5 \times 10^{11}$ nanometers

**3.** What is the correct representation of 702.0 g using scientific notation?

a. $7.02 \times 10^3$ g
b. $70.20 \times 10^1$ g
c. $7.020 \times 10^2$ g
d. $70.20 \times 10^2$ g

**4.** Three students measured the length of a stamp whose accepted length is 2.71 cm. Based on the table, which statement is true?

a. Student 2 is both precise and accurate.
b. Student 1 is more accurate than Student 3.
c. Student 2 is less precise than Student 1.
d. Student 3 is both precise and accurate.

**Measured Values for a Stamp's Length**

|         | Student 1 | Student 2 | Student 3 |
|---------|-----------|-----------|-----------|
| Trial 1 | 2.60 cm   | 2.70 cm   | 2.75 cm   |
| Trial 2 | 2.72 cm   | 2.69 cm   | 2.74 cm   |
| Trial 3 | 2.65 cm   | 2.71 cm   | 2.64 cm   |
| Average | 2.66 cm   | 2.70 cm   | 2.71 cm   |

**5.** Chemists found that a complex reaction occurred in three steps. The first step takes $2.5731 \times 10^2$ s to complete, the second step takes $3.60 \times 10^{-1}$ s, and the third step takes $7.482 \times 10^1$ s. What is the total amount of time elapsed during the reaction?

a. $3.68 \times 10^1$ s      c. $1.37 \times 10^1$ s
b. $7.78 \times 10^1$ s      d. $3.3249 \times 10^2$ s

**6.** How many significant figures are there in a distance measurement of 20.070 km?

a. 2      c. 4
b. 3      d. 5

chemistrymc.com/standardized_test

**Interpreting Graphs** Use the graph to answer the following questions.

**Age of Ice Layers in Vostok Ice Sheet**

(y-axis: Age of ice layer (years), from 20 000 to 70 000; x-axis: Depth of ice layer below surface (m), from 500 to 1000)

**7.** Using the graph, a student reported the age of an ice layer at 705 m as $4.250 \times 10^4$ years. The accepted value for the age of this ice layer is $4.268 \times 10^4$ years. What is the percent error of the student's value?

a. 0.4217%      c. 0.4235%
b. 99.58%       d. 1.800%

**8.** The slope of the graph is about _____ .

a. 80 years/m      c. 0.015 years/m
b. 80 m/year       d. 1500 m/year

**9.** What age is an ice layer found at a depth of 1000 m?

a. $6.75 \times 10^4$ years
b. $7.00 \times 10^4$ years
c. $6.25 \times 10^4$ years
d. $6.5 \times 10^4$ years

---

### TEST-TAKING TIP

**Practice Under Test-Like Conditions**
Ask your teacher to set a time limit. Then do all of the questions in the time provided without referring to your book. Did you complete the test? Could you have made better use of your time? What topics do you need to review? Show your test to your teacher for an objective assessment of your performance.

---

Standardized Test Practice    **53**

---

**88.** 29 mL
**89.** a. $1.31 \times 10^4$ cm$^2$
     b. $2.73 \times 10^6$ m$^2$
     c. $9.26 \times 10^{-8}$ m$^2$
     d. $4.22 \times 10^{-2}$ km$^2$
     e. $3.1 \times 10^2$
     f. $2.2 \times 10^{-5}$
     g. $2.00 \times 10^1$
**90.** No; the last factor should be 60 min/1h.
**91.** 12.6 g
**92.** The third student (2.87 cm); a meterstick has markings to the millimeter. A third digit would be estimated.
**93.** a. 301 cg
     b. 6.2 km
     c. 0.624 µg
     d. 0.2 dm$^3$
     e. 0.000 13 kcal/g
     f. 0.003 21 L
**94.** $4.5273 \times 10^{10}$ g/cm$^3$
**95.** The black hole is $4.5273 \times 10^{10}$ times as dense.

**Thinking Critically**

**96.** Answers will vary but might include that units based on powers of ten are easy to convert from one to another. Most disadvantages involve the initial changing from another system to SI.
**97.** There is no chance for matter to interfere with the speed measurement in a vacuum.
**98.** Mass itself has no meaning without a measurement of its volume. If the object is a pure substance and its mass and volume are known, its density can help identify it.
**99.** Surveyors use equipment that is not affected by terrain or obstacles.

---

## Cumulative Review

**104.** Thick is qualitative; a density of 4.58 g/mL is quantitative.

## Standardized Test Practice

**1.** c     **6.** d
**2.** c     **7.** a
**3.** c     **8.** a
**4.** a     **9.** d
**5.** d

**National Science Content Standards**

**Pages 52–53**
UCP.1, UCP.3; A.1, A.2; B.2; E.2; G.2

# Resource Manager

| Section | Objectives | Activities/Features |
|---|---|---|
| **Section 3.1**<br>**Properties of Matter**<br>1 session<br>½ block | 1. **Identify** the characteristics of a substance.<br>2. **Distinguish** between physical and chemical properties.<br>3. **Differentiate** among the physical states of matter. | **Discovery Lab:** Observing Chemical Change, p. 55<br>**Careers Using Chemistry:** Science Writer, p. 56<br>**Problem-Solving Lab:** How is compressed gas released? p. 60 |
| **Section 3.2**<br>**Changes in Matter**<br>1 session<br>½ block | 4. **Define** physical change and list several common physical changes.<br>5. **Define** chemical change and list several indications that a chemical change has taken place.<br>6. **Apply** the law of conservation of mass to chemical reactions. | **ChemLab:** Matter and Chemical Reactions, pp. 78–79 |
| **Section 3.3**<br>**Mixtures of Matter**<br>2 sessions<br>1 block | 7. **Contrast** mixtures and substances.<br>8. **Classify** mixtures as homogeneous or heterogeneous.<br>9. **List** and **describe** several techniques used to separate mixtures. | **MiniLab:** Separating Ink Dyes, p. 68 |
| **Section 3.4**<br>**Elements and Compounds**<br>2 sessions<br>1 block | 10. **Distinguish** between elements and compounds.<br>11. **Describe** the organization of elements on the periodic table.<br>12. **Explain** how all compounds obey the laws of definite and multiple proportions. | **History Connection**, p. 75<br>**Chemistry and Society:** Green Buildings, p. 80 |

| National Science Content Standards | State/Local Standards | Reproducible Masters | Transparencies |
|---|---|---|---|
| UCP.1, UCP.2, UCP.3; A.1; B.2, B.3, B.4, B.5, B.6;G.1 | | **Study Guide for Content Mastery,** pp. 13–14 L2 <br> **Laboratory Manual,** pp. 17–20 L2 <br> **Small-Scale Laboratory Manual,** pp. 5–8 L2 | **Section Focus** <br> **Transparency 9** L1 ELL <br> **Teaching** <br> **Transparency 7** L2 ELL |
| UCP.1, UCP.2, UCP.3; B.2, B.3, B.5, B.6 | | **Study Guide for Content Mastery,** p. 15 L2 <br> **ChemLab and MiniLab Worksheets,** pp. 10–12 L2 <br> **Challenge Problems,** p. 3 L3 <br> **Laboratory Manual,** pp. 21–24 L2 | **Section Focus** <br> **Transparency 10** L1 ELL <br> **Teaching** <br> **Transparency 8** L2 ELL <br> **Math Skills** <br> **Transparency 2** L2 ELL |
| UCP.1, UCP.2, UCP.3; A.1; B.2; E.1 | | **Study Guide for Content Mastery,** p. 16 L2 <br> **ChemLab and MiniLab Worksheets,** p. 9 L2 <br> **Forensics Laboratory Manual,** pp. 1–12 L2 <br> **Small-Scale Laboratory Manual,** pp. 9–12 L2 | **Section Focus** <br> **Transparency 11** L1 ELL |
| UCP.1, UCP.2, UCP.3; A.1; B.1, B.2, B.3, B.6; E.2; F.4, F.6; G.1, G.2, G.3 | | **Study Guide for Content Mastery,** pp. 17–18 L2 <br> **ChemLab and MiniLab Worksheets,** pp. 10–12 L2 | **Section Focus** <br> **Transparency 12** L1 ELL <br> **Teaching** <br> **Transparencies 9, 10** L2 ELL <br> **Math Skills** <br> **Transparency 3** L2 ELL |

**Key to National Science Content Standards:** UCP = Unifying Concepts and Processes, A = Science as Inquiry, B = Physical Science, C = Life Science, D = Earth and Space Sciences, E = Science and Technology, F = Science in Personal and Social Perspectives, G = History and Nature of Science

Refer to pages 4T–5T of the Teacher Guide for an explanation of the National Science Content Standards correlations.

## Resource Manager

### Materials List

**ChemLab (pages 78–79)**

copper wire, $AgNO_3$ solution, sandpaper, stirring rod, 50-mL graduated cylinder, 50-mL beaker, funnel, filter paper, 250-mL Erlenmeyer flask, ring stand, small iron ring, petri dish, paper clip, Bunsen burner, tongs

**Discovery Lab (page 55)**

test tube, test-tube rack, 3$M$ hydrochloric acid (10 mL), zinc metal, wood splint, burner

**MiniLab (page 68)**

9-oz. plastic cup (2), filter paper (2), scissors, water-soluble black felt marker, large nail, water

**Demonstration (pages 62–63)**

piece of zinc (2 g), NaOH (5 g), porcelain evaporating dish, forceps, paper towel, hot plate, new pennies (3), water

### Preparation of Solutions

For a review of solution preparation, see page 46T of the Teacher Guide.

Quantities are for a class of 30 students.

**ChemLab (pages 78–79)**

**1$M$ silver nitrate ($AgNO_3$)** Dissolve 170 g $AgNO_3$ in 600 mL distilled water. Make up to 1 L final volume with distilled water. **CAUTION:** Silver nitrate is toxic and harmful to skin and clothing.

**Discovery Lab (page 55)**

**3$M$ hydrochloric acid** Add 100 mL concentrated (12$M$) hydrochloric acid to 300 mL distilled water while stirring. **CAUTION:** Do NOT add the water to the acid.

### Assessment Resources

**Chapter Assessment,** pp. 13–18
**MindJogger Videoquizzes DVD/VHSs**
**Alternate Assessment in the Science Classroom**
**ExamView® Pro CD-ROM**
**Solutions Manual,** Chapter 3
**Supplemental Problems,** Chapter 3
**Performance Assessment in the Science Classroom**
**Chemistry Interactive CD-ROM,** Chapter 3 quiz

### Additional Resources

**Spanish Resources** ELL
**Guided Reading Audio Program,** Chapter 3 ELL
**Cooperative Learning in the Science Classroom**
**Lab and Safety Skills in the Science Classroom**
**Lesson Plans**
**Block Scheduling Lesson Plans**
**Chemistrymc.com**

## Glencoe Technology

The following multimedia for this chapter are available from Glencoe.

**VIDEOTAPE/DVD**
MindJogger Videoquizzes,
Chapter 3

**CD-ROM**
**Chemistry: Matter and Change**
*Separating Substances,* Exploration
*Physical and Chemical Properties,* Video
*Separating Mixtures,* Exploration
*Metal Alloys,* Experiment

**CD-ROM**
**Interactive Chalkboard**

**CD-ROM**
**ExamView® Pro**
**Testmaker**

**CD-ROM**
**TeacherWorks™**

## Multiple Learning Styles

Look for the following icons for strategies that emphasize different learning modalities.

**Kinesthetic**
Meeting Individual Needs, pp. 58, 61, 66; Reteach, p. 59; Check for Understanding, p. 69; Extension, p. 77

**Visual-Spatial**
Check for Understanding, pp. 58, 65, 76; Chemistry Journal, pp. 67, 76; Differentiated Instruction, p. 70; Visual Learning, p. 73; Reteach, p. 77

**Interpersonal**
Reteach, p. 69; Reinforcement, p. 72

**Intrapersonal**
Extension, pp. 59, 72; Chemistry Journal, p. 71; Enrichment, p. 74

**Linguistic**
Chemistry Journal, pp. 56, 64; Portfolio, p. 57

## Key to Teaching Strategies

**L1** Level 1 activities should be appropriate for students with learning difficulties.

**L2** Level 2 activities should be within the ability range of all students.

**L3** Level 3 activities are designed for above-average students.

**ELL** ELL activities should be within the ability range of English Language Learners.

**COOP LEARN** Cooperative Learning activities are designed for small group work.

**P** These strategies represent student products that can be placed into a best-work portfolio.

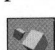 These strategies are useful in a block scheduling format.

## ✔ Assessment Planner

**Portfolio Assessment**
Problem-Solving Lab, TWE p. 60
Assessment, TWE, p. 66
ChemLab, TWE, p. 79
Portfolio, TWE, p. 81

**Performance Assessment**
Assessment, TWE, pp. 58, 62
Discovery Lab, SE, p. 55
MiniLab, SE, p. 68
ChemLab, SE, pp. 78–79

**Knowledge Assessment**
Assessment, TWE, pp. 59, 65
Demonstration, TWE, p. 63
Section Assessment, SE, pp. 60, 65, 69, 77
Chapter Assessment, SE, pp. 82–85

**Skill Assessment**
MiniLab, TWE, p. 68
Assessment, TWE, pp. 69, 73, 77

## Tying to Previous Knowledge

Have students review the following concepts before studying this chapter.

Chapter 1: matter, qualitative and quantitative aspects of chemistry

Chapter 2: significant figures

## Using the Photo

Ask students to identify the types of matter seen in this photograph. Encourage them to be specific in their descriptions. Solids are evident in the coral reef (mostly calcium carbonate); the divers' bodies (compounds of carbon, hydrogen, oxygen, nitrogen, phosphorus, calcium, sulfur, and trace amounts of other metals). Liquids are most evident in the solution of salt water. Gases are evident in the escaping oxygen bubbles.

**PowerPoint® Presentations**

This CD-ROM is an editable Microsoft® PowerPoint® presentation that includes:
- Section presentations
- Section checks
- Image bank
- Links to Chemistry Online
- All transparencies
- Animations
- Audio

# Matter–Properties and Changes

## What You'll Learn
▶ You will distinguish between physical and chemical properties.
▶ You will classify matter by composition: element, compound, or mixture.
▶ You will identify observable characteristics of chemical reactions.
▶ You will explain the fundamental law of conservation of mass.

## Why It's Important

You are completely surrounded by matter. To better understand this matter—how it affects you, how you affect it, and how it can be manipulated for the benefit of society—you need to build a basic understanding of the types and properties of matter.

**Chemistry Online**

Visit the Chemistry Web site at chemistrymc.com to find links about matter, properties, and changes.

Chemistry is the study of matter and its properties. Every aspect of these divers' environment, under water and on land, is some form of matter.

## DISCOVERY LAB

### Purpose
Students will examine several types of chemical changes.

### Safety and Disposal
Use gloves when handling HCl. The HCl can be washed down the sink with a lot of water. The unreacted zinc can be reused. $ZnCl_2$ solution can be flushed down the drain.

### Teaching Strategies
- If you are using smaller test tubes, about 3 to 5 mL of 6*M* HCl will work.
- See page 54C for preparation of solutions.

### Expected Results
The zinc reacts with hydrochloric acid to produce zinc chloride (which is soluble and, therefore, not easily seen) and hydrogen gas (seen as bubbles). When a

lighted splint is brought close to the mouth of the test tube, the hydrogen gas reacts with oxygen in the air to produce gaseous water. The reaction produces a pop or "bark."

### Analysis
Answers will vary. Students might have thought that no reaction would occur. The "bark" is the result of a reaction between the gas that was produced and oxygen.

## DISCOVERY LAB

### Observing Chemical Change

Consider the metal objects that are part of the everyday world. A mailbox, for example, stands outside day in and day out, without seeming to change. Under what conditions does metal exhibit chemical change?

### Safety Precautions

Always wear eye goggles, gloves, and an apron when experimenting with chemicals. Use caution when handling an open flame.

### Procedure

1. Place a piece of zinc metal in a large test tube.

2. Add approximately 10 mL of 3*M* hydrochloric acid (HCl) to the test tube. Record your observations.
   CAUTION: *HCl causes burns and hazardous fumes.*

3. When the zinc and HCl have reacted for approximately 1 min, bring a lighted, glowing wood splint to the mouth of the test tube. CAUTION: *Be sure the test tube is facing away from your face when the splint is brought near.* Again record your observations.

### Analysis

What may have caused the dynamic reaction you observed in step 3? Did you expect this reaction? Explain.

### Materials

large test tube
test-tube holder or rack
10 mL HCl
zinc metal
wood splint
match or burner

---

## Section 3.1 — Properties of Matter

### Objectives

- **Identify** the characteristics of a substance.
- **Distinguish** between physical and chemical properties.
- **Differentiate** among the physical states of matter.

### Vocabulary

substance
physical property
extensive property
intensive property
chemical property
states of matter
solid
liquid
gas
vapor

Imagine yourself scuba diving through a complex biological ecosystem such as a coral reef. What kinds of things fill your imagination? Regardless of what you envision, there is only one answer—you see matter. The diversity of matter in the world and in the universe is astounding. From pepperoni pizzas to supernovas, it's all matter. If we are to understand this diversity, we must start with a way of organizing and describing matter.

### Substances

Recall from Chapter 1 that chemistry is the study of matter, and matter is anything that has mass and takes up space. Everything around you is matter; including things such as air and microbes, which you cannot see. For example, table salt is a simple type of matter that you are probably familiar with. Table salt has a unique and unchanging chemical composition. It is always 100% sodium chloride and its composition does not change from one sample to another. Matter that has a uniform and unchanging composition is called a **substance**, also known as a pure substance. Table salt is a substance. Another example of a pure substance is water. Water is always composed of hydrogen and oxygen. Seawater, on the other hand, is not a substance because samples taken from different locations will probably have

3.1 Properties of Matter **55**

---

### Chapter Themes

The following themes from the National Science Education Standards are covered in this chapter. Refer to page 4T of the Teacher Guide for an explanation of the correlations.
Systems, order, and organization (UCP.1)
Evidence, models, and explanation (UCP.2)
Form and function (UCP.5)

### Resource Manager

**Study Guide for Content Mastery,** pp. 13–14 L2
**Solving Problems: A Chemistry Handbook,** Section 3.1 L2
**Section Focus Transparency 9 and Master** L1 ELL
**Lab Manual,** pp. 17–20 L2

---

## Section 3.1

## 1 Focus

### Focus Transparency

Before presenting the lesson, display **Section Focus Transparency 9** on the overhead projector. Have students answer the accompanying questions using **Section Focus Transparency Master 9.** L1 ELL

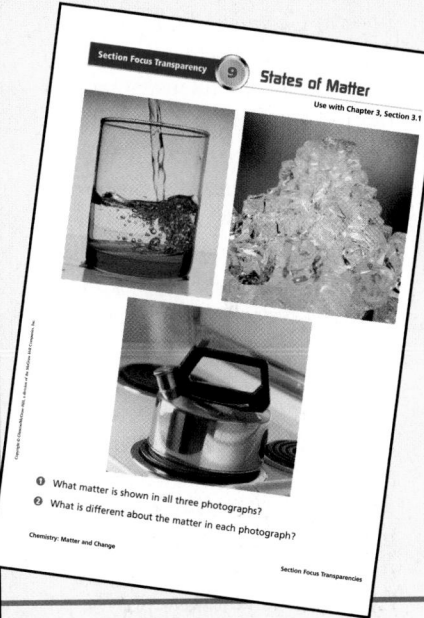

## 2 Teach

### Quick Demo

Show students a beaker of distilled water and a beaker of unsaturated salt solution. Ask them if the beakers contain pure substances and how they would confirm their hypothesis. A visual inspection would lead students to believe both were pure substances. However, some students may realize that further tests would be necessary to confirm this. Students may suggest evaporation or the use of a conductivity apparatus to show that the second beaker is actually a mixture of substances. It is a solution.

**55**

**National Science Content Standards**

Pages 54–57
UCP.1, UCP.2, UCP.3; A.1; B.2, B.3; G.1

**Figure 3-1**

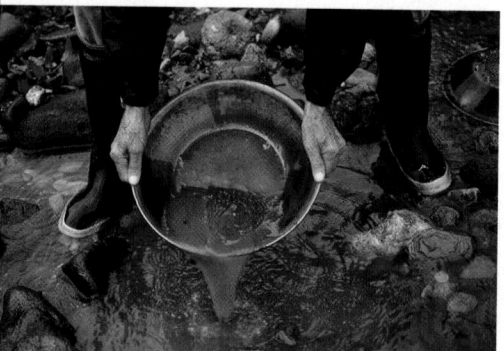

Miners relied on the physical property of density to distinguish gold (19 g/cm³) from the worthless minerals in their sluice pans. The density of pyrite, a worthless mineral often mistaken for gold, is 5 g/cm³.

differing compositions. That is, they will contain differing amounts of water, salts, and other dissolved substances. Given this definition, what other pure substances are you familiar with? Substances are important; much of your chemistry course will be focused on the processes by which substances are changed into different substances.

## Physical Properties of Matter

You are used to identifying objects by their properties—their characteristics and behavior. For example, you can easily identify a pencil in your backpack because you recognize its shape, color, weight, or some other property. These characteristics are all physical properties of the pencil. A **physical property** is a characteristic that can be observed or measured without changing the sample's composition. Physical properties describe pure substances, too. Because substances have uniform and unchanging compositions, they have consistent and unchanging physical properties as well. Density, color, odor, taste, hardness, melting point, and boiling point are common physical properties that scientists record as identifying characteristics of a substance. Sodium chloride forms solid, white crystals at room temperature, all having the same unique salty taste. **Table 3-1** lists several common substances and their physical properties.

**Table 3-1**

| Physical Properties of Common Substances | | | | | |
|---|---|---|---|---|---|
| Substance | Color | State at 25°C | Melting point (°C) | Boiling point (°C) | Density (g/cm³) |
| Oxygen | Colorless | Gas | −218 | −183 | 0.0014 |
| Mercury | Silver | Liquid | −39 | 357 | 13.5 |
| Water | Colorless | Liquid | 0 | 100 | 1.00 |
| Sucrose | White | Solid | 185 | Decomposes | 1.59 |
| Sodium chloride | White | Solid | 801 | 1413 | 2.17 |

**Extensive and intensive properties** Physical properties can be further described as being one of two types. **Extensive properties** are dependent upon the amount of substance present. For example, mass, which depends on the amount of substance there is, is an extensive property. Length and volume are also extensive properties. Density, on the other hand, is an example of an intensive property of matter. **Intensive properties** are independent of the amount of substance present. For example, density of a substance (at constant temperature and pressure) is the same no matter how much substance is present.

A substance can often be identified by its intensive properties. In some cases, a single intensive property is unique enough for identification. During the California gold rush, miners relied on gold's characteristic density (19 g/cm³) to separate valuable gold-containing flakes from riverbed sand. The process used by the miners is shown in **Figure 3-1**. Another intensive property of gold is its distinctive appearance. Unfortunately, miners often learned that identification of gold based on appearance alone was misleading. **Figure 3-2** shows a nugget of the relatively worthless

(a) Gold

(b) Pyrite

**Figure 3-2**

Gold (a) and pyrite, or "fool's gold" (b), have similar physical properties but are different samples of matter.

mineral pyrite, often called "fool's gold," which looks very similar to actual gold nuggets. Such errors in identification based on the intensive property of appearance fooled many miners into falsely thinking they had struck it rich!

## Chemical Properties of Matter

Some properties of a substance are not obvious unless the substance has changed composition as a result of its contact with other substances or the application of thermal or electrical energy. The ability of a substance to combine with or change into one or more other substances is called a **chemical property**. The ability of iron to form rust when combined with air is an example of a chemical property of iron. Similarly, the inability of a substance to change into another substance is also a chemical property. For example, when iron is placed in nitrogen gas at room temperature, no chemical change occurs. The fact that iron does not undergo a change in the presence of nitrogen is another chemical property of iron.

## Observing Properties of Matter

Every substance has its own unique set of physical and chemical properties. **Table 3-2** lists several of these properties of copper. **Figure 3-3** shows physical and chemical properties of copper. What physical and chemical properties are evident in these photos?

**Table 3-2**

| Properties of Copper | |
|---|---|
| **Physical properties** | **Chemical properties** |
| • Reddish brown, shiny | • Forms green copper carbonate compound when in contact with moist air |
| • Easily shaped into sheets (malleable) and drawn into wires (ductile) | |
| • Good conductor of heat and electricity | • Forms new substances when combined with nitric acid and sulfuric acid |
| • Density = 8.92 g/cm³ | |
| • Melting point = 1085°C | • Forms a deep blue solution when in contact with ammonia |
| • Boiling point = 2570°C | |

**Figure 3-3**

These photos illustrate some of the physical and chemical properties of copper as it exists in the form of hardware (a) and the Statue of Liberty (b).

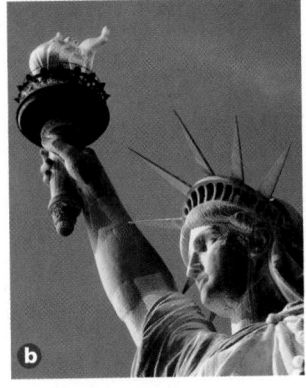

3.1 Properties of Matter    **57**

Observations of properties may vary depending on the conditions of the immediate environment. It is important to state the specific conditions in which observations are made because both chemical and physical properties depend on temperature and pressure. Consider the properties of water, for example. You may think of water as a liquid (physical property) that is not particularly chemically reactive (chemical property). You may also know that water has a density of 1.00 g/cm$^3$ (physical property). These properties, however, apply only to water at standard "room" temperature and pressure. At temperatures greater than 100°C, water is a gas (physical property) with a density of about 0.0006 g/cm$^3$ (physical property) that reacts rapidly with many different substances (chemical property). As you can see, the properties of water are dramatically different under different conditions.

## States of Matter

Imagine you are sitting on a bench, breathing heavily and drinking water after a tiring game of soccer. In this scenario, you are in contact with three different forms of matter; the bench is a solid, the water is a liquid, and the air you breathe is a gas. In fact, all matter that exists on Earth can be classified as one of these physical forms called **states of matter**. Scientists recognize a fourth state of matter called plasma, but it does not occur naturally on Earth except in the form of lightning bolts. The physical state of a substance is a physical property of that substance. Each of the three common states of matter can be distinguished by the way it fills a container.

**Solids** A **solid** is a form of matter that has its own definite shape and volume. Wood, iron, paper, and sugar are examples of solids. The particles of matter in a solid are very tightly packed; when heated, a solid expands, but only slightly. Because its shape is definite, a solid may not conform to the shape of the container in which it is placed. The tight packing of particles in a solid makes it incompressible; that is, it cannot be pressed into a smaller volume. It is important to understand that a solid is not defined by its rigidity or hardness; the marble statue in **Figure 3-4** is rigid whereas wax sculpture is soft, yet both are solids.

**Liquids** A **liquid** is a form of matter that flows, has constant volume, and takes the shape of its container. Common examples of liquids include water, blood, and mercury. The particles in a liquid are not rigidly held in place and are less closely packed than are the particles in a solid: liquid particles

**Figure 3-4**

The properties of the solid materials marble **a** and wax **b** make these sculptures possible. Particles in a solid are tightly packed **c**, giving definite shape and volume to the solid.

Solid

Liquid

**Figure 3-5**

**a** Despite having different shapes, each of these measuring cups holds the same volume of liquid.
**b** River water flows to fit within the boundaries of its banks, regardless of the curves along its path.
**c** Molecules in a liquid are closely packed but can still move relatively freely.

are able to move past each other. This allows a liquid to flow and take the shape of its container, although it may not completely fill the container. A liquid's volume is constant: regardless of the size and shape of the container in which the liquid is held, the volume of the liquid remains the same. This is why measuring cups used in cooking, such as those pictured in **Figure 3-5**, can be made in a variety of shapes yet still measure the same volume. Because of the way the particles of a liquid are packed, liquids are virtually incompressible. Like solids, liquids tend to expand when heated.

**Gases** A **gas** is a form of matter that flows to conform to the shape of its container and fills the entire volume of its container. Examples of gases include neon, which is used in the lighted artwork in **Figure 3-6**; methane, which is used in cooking; and air, which is a mixture of gases. Compared to solids and liquids, the particles of gases are very far apart. Because of the significant amount of space between particles, gases are easily compressed. The **problem-solving LAB** in this section poses several important questions about the practical use of compressed gas.

It is likely that you are familiar with the word vapor as it relates to the word gas. The words gas and vapor, while similar, do not mean the same thing and should not be used interchangeably. The word gas refers to a substance that is naturally in the gaseous state at room temperature. The word **vapor** refers to the gaseous state of a substance that is a solid or a liquid at room temperature. For example, steam is a vapor because at room temperature water exists as a liquid.

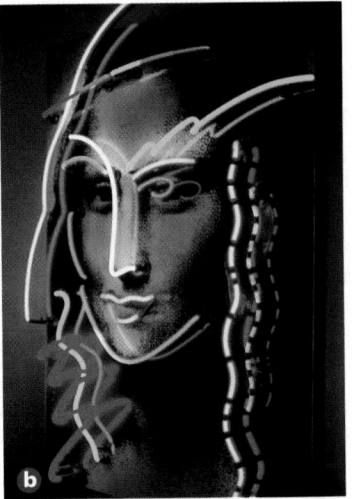

a        Gas

**Figure 3-6**

**a** Molecules in a gas are far apart and freely moving.
**b** Neon gas completely fills the tubes of the electric artwork.

## Reteach

**Kinesthetic** Have students act out the packing of the different states of matter by "becoming" atoms themselves. Isolate a particular area of the classroom as the stage so that students can visualize the relative packing of atoms in the different states. **L1** **ELL**

## Extension

**Intrapersonal** Have students search the Internet for examples of new materials being developed by various chemical manufacturers (DuPont, Dow, Kodak, for instance). Ask students to relate the properties of the new materials to the arrangement of the atoms or molecules as solids, liquids, or gases.

## ✔ Assessment

**Knowledge** Ask students to decide whether the following statements are true or false, and to support their choice with text references.
• A vapor and a gas are the same thing. F
• A liquid conforms to its container. T
• Particles of a gas are spaced closer together than particles of a liquid. F
• A solid has definite shape but changeable volume. F

---

**Internet Address Book**

**Chemistry Online**    Note Internet addresses that you find useful in the space below for quick reference.

_____

_____

_____

_____

_____

**National Science Content Standards**
**Pages 58–59**
UCP.1, UCP.2, UCP.3; B.2, B.4, B.5, B.6

## problem-solving LAB

### Purpose
Students will deduce the method by which the flow of gas out of a compressed tank is controlled.

### Process Skills
Inferring, predicting, thinking critically, recognizing cause and effect

### Teaching Strategies
- Identify several real-world situations (outside a laboratory) where compressed gases are used.
- Identify control and safety features in these situations.

### Thinking Critically
1. Some kind of valve must be attached that can limit the exit orifice, thereby limiting the amount of gas that is released.
2. Without the regulator device, the gas would rush out of the tank with a force powerful enough to transform it into a dangerous, uncontrolled projectile.

### ✓ Assessment
**Portfolio** Have students research the breathing apparatus that a scuba diver uses and compare that equipment with compressed gas equipment in a laboratory. Reports can be placed in students' portfolios. **L2** **P**

**National Science Content Standards**

**Pages 60–61**
UCP.1, UCP.2, UCP.3; B.2, B.5, B.6

## problem-solving LAB

### How is compressed gas released?

**Recognizing Cause and Effect** Tanks of compressed gases are a common sight in a chemistry laboratory. For example, nitrogen is often flowed over a reaction in progress to displace other gases that might interfere with the experiment. Given what you know about the properties of gases, explain how compressed nitrogen is released.

### Analysis
By definition, the particles of gases are far apart and gases tend to fill their container, even if the container is a laboratory room. Tanks of compressed gas come from the supplier capped to prevent the gas from escaping. In the lab a chemist or technician attaches a regulator to the tank and secures the tank to a stable fixture.

### Thinking Critically
1. Explain why the flow of compressed gas must be controlled for practical use.
2. Predict what would happen if the valve on a full tank of compressed gas were suddenly opened all the way or if the full tank were punctured.

The fact that substances can change form, as in the example of water changing to steam, is another important concept in chemistry. If you review what you just learned about physical properties of substances, you can see that because the particular form of a substance is a physical property, changing the form introduces or adds another physical property to its list of characteristics. In fact, resources that provide tables of physical and chemical properties of substances, such as the *CRC Handbook of Chemistry and Physics,* generally include the physical properties of substances in all of the states in which they can exist.

## Section  3.1 Assessment

1. Describe the characteristics that identify a sample of matter as being a substance.

2. Classify each of the following as a physical or chemical property.
   a. Iron and oxygen form rust.
   b. Iron is more dense than aluminum.
   c. Magnesium burns brightly when ignited.
   d. Oil and water do not mix.
   e. Mercury melts at −39°C.

3. Create a table that describes the three common states of matter in terms of their shape, volume, and compressibility.

4. **Thinking Critically** Using what you know about the compressibility of gases, explain why the oxygen in a SCUBA tank is compressed.

5. **Interpreting Data** Bromine is a reddish-brown liquid that boils at 59°C. Bromine is highly reactive with many metals. For example, it reacts with sodium to form a white solid. Classify each of these properties of bromine as either a physical or a chemical property.

chemistrymc.com/self_check_quiz

## Section 3.1 Assessment

1. The sample of matter must have a uniform and unchanging composition to be a substance.

2. a. chemical   d. physical
   b. physical    e. physical
   c. chemical

3. Table should list solid (definite volume, definite shape, incompressible); liquid (definite volume, fills container shape, virtually incompressible); gas (fills volume of container, takes shape of container, compressible).

4. Particles in a gas are spaced far apart and are easily compressed. Therefore, it is possible to put a significant volume of oxygen in a tank, which allows the diver to remain under water longer.

5. color, physical; boiling point, physical; reactive with metals, chemical

You learned in Section 3.1 that scientists can describe matter in terms of physical and chemical properties. For example, a physical property of copper allows it to be drawn into copper wire, and a chemical property of copper accounts for the fact that when a solution of copper ions is combined with ammonia, the copper solution changes to a deep blue color. The key concept in both of these examples is that the substance copper changed in some way. In this section, you'll explore how matter changes as a result of its physical and chemical properties.

## Physical Changes

A substance often undergoes changes that result in a dramatically different appearance yet leave the composition of the substance unchanged. An example is the crumpling of a sheet of aluminum foil. While the foil goes from a smooth, flat, mirrorlike sheet to a round, compact ball, the actual composition of the foil is unchanged—it is still aluminum. Changes such as this, which alter a substance without changing its composition, are known as **physical changes**. Cutting a sheet of paper and breaking a crystal are other examples of physical changes in matter. Can you name some other physical changes? Your list might include verbs such as bend, grind, crumple, split, and crush, all of which indicate physical change.

As with other physical properties, the state of matter depends on the temperature and pressure of the surroundings. As temperature and pressure change, most substances undergo a change from one state (or phase) to another. For example, at atmospheric pressure and at temperatures below 0°C, water is in its solid state, which is known as ice. As heat is added to the ice, it melts and becomes liquid water. This change of state is a physical change because even though ice and water have very different appearances, their composition is the same. If the temperature of the water increases to 100°C, the water begins to boil and liquid water is converted to steam. Melting and formation of a gas are both physical changes and phase changes. **Figure 3-7** shows condensation, another common phase change. When you encounter terms such as boil, freeze, condense, vaporize, or melt in your study of chemistry, the meaning generally refers to a phase change in matter.

### Objectives

- **Define** physical change and list several common physical changes.
- **Define** chemical change and list several indications that a chemical change has taken place.
- **Apply** the law of conservation of mass to chemical reactions.

### Vocabulary

physical change
chemical change
law of conservation of mass

### Try at Home LAB

See page 953 in Appendix E for **Comparing Frozen Liquids**

**Figure 3-7**

(a) Condensation on an icy beverage glass is the result of the phase change of water in a gaseous state to water in a liquid state.
(b) The characteristic "fog" of dry ice is actually fine water droplets formed by condensation of water vapor from the air surrounding the very cold dry ice. Refer to **Table C-1** in Appendix C for a key to atom color conventions.

3.2 Changes in Matter **61**

---

# 1 Focus

## Focus Transparency

Before presenting the lesson, display **Section Focus Transparency 10** on the overhead projector. Have students answer the accompanying questions using **Section Focus Transparency Master 10**. **L1** **ELL**

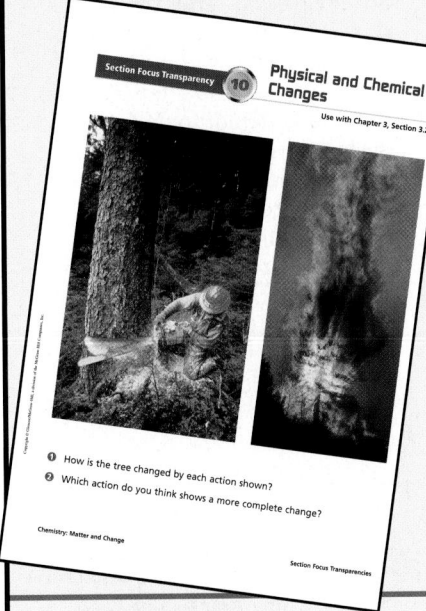

Section Focus Transparency **10** Physical and Chemical Changes

Use with Chapter 3, Section 3.2

❶ How is the tree changed by each action shown?
❷ Which action do you think shows a more complete change?

Chemistry: Matter and Change

Section Focus Transparencies

# 2 Teach

## Quick Demo

**CAUTION:** *Perform this demo under a hood.* Place several moth balls in a beaker. Place a flask half filled with cold water on top to serve as a condensing "lid." Heat the moth balls until they have melted and ask students to observe and diagram the changes. Remove the heat source and ask students to again observe the changes. With heat, students will see the change from solid to liquid, solid to vapor, and liquid to vapor. On cooling, students will see liquid to solid and vapor to solid, or

---

## DIFFERENTIATED INSTRUCTION

### Gifted

*Kinesthetic* Have gifted students identify an unknown from a list of possibilities based on the melting point and boiling point. Students should plot a heating/cooling graph of time on the x-axis versus temperature on the y-axis. **L3**

## Resource Manager

**Study Guide for Content Mastery,** p.15 **L2**
**Challenge Problems**, p. 3 **L3**
**Solving Problems: A Chemistry Handbook,** Section 3.2 **L2**
**Section Focus Transparency 10 and Master** **L1** **ELL**

Pour 20 to 25 mL of ethanol into an empty water cooler jug or plastic gallon milk bottle. Roll the ethanol around to coat the inside of the bottle and pour off the excess. Turn off the classroom lights and, with a lighted splint that is taped to a meter stick, ignite the top of the bottle. **CAUTION:** *Perform from behind an explosion shield and keep your hand clear of the bottle opening.* After the explosion, show the water that forms in the reaction by pouring it into a beaker. Students will frequently clamor for an encore performance, which is most often unsuccessful because of the presence of the other product of the reaction, carbon dioxide. Have the students identify the reactants (ethanol and oxygen) and the products (water and carbon dioxide). The carbon dioxide can be flushed out of the bottle by water displacement.

## Assessment

**Performance** The reaction of iron with oxygen costs American industry a great deal of money. Have the students choose a particular industry (such as agriculture, transportation, or construction) and give an oral report on how the industry deals with the problem of rust. Use the Performance Task Assessment List for Oral Presentation in **PASC**, p. 71.

---

The temperature and pressure at which a substance undergoes a phase change are important physical properties. These properties are listed as the melting and boiling points of the substance. **Table 3-1** on page 56 provides this information for several common substances. Like density, the melting point and boiling point are intensive physical properties that may be used to identify unknown substances. For example, if an unknown solid melts at 801°C and boils at 1413°C—very high temperatures—it is most probably sodium chloride, or common table salt. Tables of intensive properties, such as those given in the *CRC Handbook of Chemistry and Physics,* are indispensable tools in identifying unknown substances from experimental data.

## Chemical Changes

As you learned earlier, chemical properties relate to the ability of a substance to combine with or change into one or more substances. A process that involves one or more substances changing into new substances is called a **chemical change**, which is commonly referred to as a chemical reaction. The new substances formed in the reaction have different compositions and different properties from the substances present before the reaction occurred. For example, the crushing of grapes that is part of the wine-making process is a physical change, but the fermentation of the juice, sugars, and other ingredients to wine is a chemical change. The **Chemistry and Society** feature at the end of the chapter describes some interesting consequences of physical and chemical changes in the production of concrete.

Let's consider again the rusting of iron. When a freshly exposed iron surface is left in contact with air, it slowly changes into a new substance, namely, the rust shown in **Figure 3-8a**. The iron reacts with oxygen in the air to form a new substance, rust. Rust is a chemical combination of iron and oxygen. In chemical reactions, the starting substances are called reactants and the new substances that are formed are called products. Thus iron and oxygen are reactants and rust is a product. When you encounter terms such as explode, rust, oxidize, corrode, tarnish, ferment, burn, or rot, the meaning generally refers to a chemical reaction in which reactant substances produce different product substances.

**Figure 3-8**

**a** The formation of a gas or solid when reactants mix often indicates that a chemical reaction has taken place. Rust is the result of a chemical reaction. **b** Color changes generally indicate that a chemical reaction has taken place. One example is the color change of tree leaves in the fall.

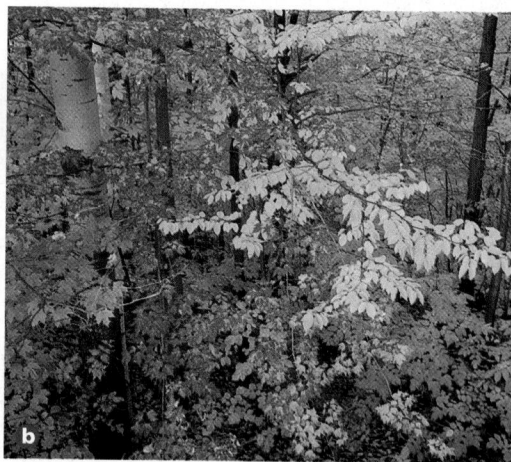

---

## Demonstration

### Atoms in Motion

#### Purpose
To observe atomic motion and the formation of an alloy, brass

#### Materials
New pennies (3); zinc (2 g); NaOH

(5 g); porcelain evaporating dish; forceps; paper towels; hot plate

#### Safety Precautions

**Disposal** Decant the cooled NaOH solution from the solid zinc. Neutralize the NaOH and rinse down the drain. Dry the zinc in an evaporating dish and reuse. Do not allow the zinc plating solution to come in contact with flammable materials.

#### Procedure
Dissolve 5 g NaOH in 25 mL of water in an evaporating dish. **CAUTION:** *NaOH causes severe burns; avoid skin contact. Rinse spills with plenty of water. Wear goggles and apron.* Add a 2 g piece of zinc to the NaOH solution. Place the solution on the hot plate and heat to just below the boiling point. Keep one penny as a control. Immerse two new pennies in the NaOH–zinc plating bath. After one minute,

**Evidence of a chemical reaction** As **Figure 3-8a** shows, rust is a brownish-orange powdery substance that looks very different from iron and oxygen. Rust is not attracted to a magnet, whereas iron is. The observation that the product (rust) has different properties than the reactants (iron and oxygen) is evidence that a chemical reaction has taken place. A chemical reaction always produces a change in properties. **Figures 3-8 and 3-9** illustrate several common indicators of chemical change. The **CHEMLAB** at the end of the chapter provides a practical laboratory experience with chemical reactions.

## Conservation of Mass

Although chemical reactions have been observed over the course of human history, it was only in the late eighteenth century that scientists began to use quantitative tools to monitor chemical changes. The revolutionary quantitative tool developed at this time was the analytical balance, which was capable of measuring very small changes in mass.

By carefully measuring mass before and after many chemical reactions, it was observed that, although chemical changes occurred, the total mass involved in the reaction remained constant. The constancy of mass in chemical reactions was observed so often that scientists assumed the phenomenon must be true for all reactions. They summarized this observation in a scientific law. The **law of conservation of mass** states that mass is neither created nor destroyed during a chemical reaction—it is conserved. This law was one of the great achievements of eighteenth-century science. The equation form of the law of conservation of mass is

$$\text{Mass}_{\text{reactants}} = \text{Mass}_{\text{products}}$$

The French scientist Antoine Lavoisier (1743–1794) was one of the first to use an analytical balance like the one shown in **Figure 3-10** to monitor chemical reactions. He studied the thermal decomposition of mercury(II) oxide, known then as calx of mercury. Mercury(II) oxide is a powdery red solid. When it is heated, the red solid reacts to form silvery liquid mercury and colorless oxygen gas as shown in **Figure 3-11** on the next page. The color change and production of a gas are indicators of a

**Figure 3-9**

ⓐ Energy changes indicate chemical reactions. For example, the burning of wood is a common example of a reaction that releases heat.
ⓑ The change in the smell of a substance or the production of an odor may be an indication of a chemical reaction.

**Figure 3-10**

The development of scientific tools such as this analytical balance gave a degree of precision to measurements that greatly improved general scientific understanding.

3.2 Changes in Matter   **63**

### Enrichment

The first true chemist is considered by many to be Robert Boyle (1627–1691), known for his work on the relationship between gas pressure and volume.

The German chemist Georg Stahl (1660–1734) was also interested in the chemistry and physics of gases, in particular, combustion. He believed that when a substance burned, "phlogiston" flowed out of the material.

The English scientist and clergyman Joseph Priestley (1773–1804) is credited with the discovery of the active role of oxygen in combustion. He called oxygen "dephlogisticated air."

Antoine Lavoisier, with carefully recorded measurements, showed that mass was conserved in combustion reactions involving oxygen. It was Lavoisier who named the gas that supports combustion "oxygene," meaning "generator of acid" (it was originally believed to be an important part of all acids).

Have students research and report on one of these early pioneers. **L2**

### CHEMLAB

ChemLab 3, located at the end of the chapter, can be used at this point in the lesson.

**Resource Manager**

Teaching Transparency 8 and Master **L2** **ELL**
Math Skills Transparency 2 and Master **L2** **ELL**

use forceps to turn the pennies over. Keep the pennies immersed until they are silver in color. Using forceps, remove the two coins from the hot bath, rinse with cold water, and pat dry with paper towels. Remove the evaporating dish from the hot plate. Place one of the plated pennies on the hot surface. In a few seconds, the plated coin will return to its original copper color. After a few more seconds, the color of the coin will appear golden. Remove the coin

from the hot plate and allow it to cool. **CAUTION:** *Do not touch the hot penny.* Display the three pennies to the class.

**Results**
The control penny remains copper colored. The zinc-plated penny is silver colored. The third penny is gold colored.

**Analysis**
Describe the alloy brass. Brass is a solid

solution of the metallic elements copper and zinc.

**✔ Assessment**

**Knowledge** Ask students why heat is needed to cause the zinc coating to diffuse into the copper. Heat increases the motion of the atoms and separates and expands the layers of atoms, thus allowing them to migrate more easily.

**Figure 3-11**

Lavoisier's experimental decomposition of mercury(II) oxide is one proof of the law of conservation of mass. Although a chemical reaction is obvious (powder to liquid mercury), matter was neither created nor destroyed.

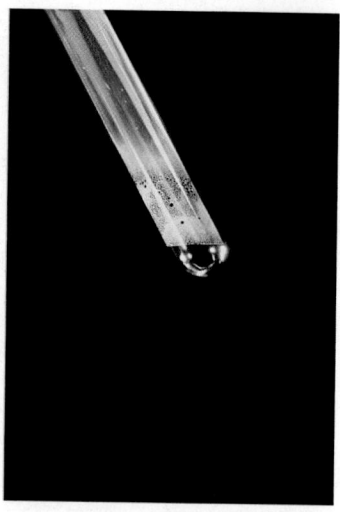

Mercury occurs naturally in air, water, soil, and living organisms. Seafood that is intended for human consumption is monitored to ensure that the products do not contain levels of mercury exceeding the established limits for public safety.

chemical reaction. When the reaction is performed in a closed container, the oxygen gas cannot escape and the mass before and after the reaction can be measured. The masses will be the same.

$$\text{Mercury(II) oxide yields mercury + oxygen}$$
$$2\ HgO \rightarrow 2\ Hg + O_2$$
$$\underset{\text{Mass of reactant}}{216\ g} = \underset{\text{mass of products}}{200\ g + 16\ g}$$

A more modern digital analytical balance can be used to prove the conservation of mass of this example. The law of conservation of mass is one of the most fundamental concepts of chemistry. Let's examine more closely some situations that illustrate the concept. Example Problem 3-1 leads you through a sample calculation. The practice problems also illustrate the law of conservation of mass.

### EXAMPLE PROBLEM 3-1

**Conservation of Mass**

In an experiment, 10.00 g of red mercury(II) oxide powder is placed in an open flask and heated until it is converted to liquid mercury and oxygen gas. The liquid mercury has a mass of 9.26 g. What is the mass of oxygen formed in the reaction?

**1. Analyze the Problem**

You are given the mass of a reactant and the mass of one of the products in a chemical reaction. Applying the law of conservation of mass, the total mass of the products must equal the total mass of the reactants. This means that the mass of the liquid mercury plus the mass of the oxygen gas must equal the mass of the mercury(II) oxide powder.

**Known**

Mass of mercury(II) oxide = 10.00 g

Mass of liquid mercury = 9.26 g

**Unknown**

Mass of oxygen formed = ? g

### CHEMISTRY JOURNAL

**The Conservation of Energy**

*Linguistic* The law of conservation of matter, formalized by Lavoisier, was a major achievement for the eighteenth century. However, it is really an incomplete statement without considering it with the law of conservation of energy. Have students research and write a short report on the experiments of the twentieth century that led to the formulation of the law of conservation of energy. L2

## 2. Solve for the Unknown

Write an equation showing conservation of mass of reactants and products.

$Mass_{reactants} = Mass_{products}$

$Mass_{mercury(II)\ oxide} = Mass_{mercury} + Mass_{oxygen}$

Solve the equation for $Mass_{oxygen}$.

$Mass_{oxygen} = Mass_{mercury(II)\ oxide} - Mass_{mercury}$

Substitute known values and solve.

$Mass_{oxygen} = 10.00\ g - 9.26\ g$

$Mass_{oxygen} = 0.74\ g$

## 3. Evaluate the Answer

The sum of the masses of the two products equals the mass of the reactant, verifying that mass has been conserved. The answer is correctly expressed to the hundredths place.

## PRACTICE PROBLEMS

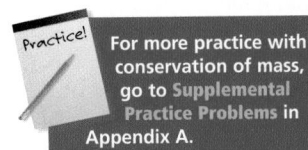

**Practice!** For more practice with conservation of mass, go to **Supplemental Practice Problems** in Appendix A.

6. From a laboratory process designed to separate water into hydrogen and oxygen gas, a student collected 10.0 g of hydrogen and 79.4 g of oxygen. How much water was originally involved in the process?

7. A student carefully placed 15.6 g of sodium in a reactor supplied with an excess quantity of chlorine gas. When the reaction was complete, the student obtained 39.7 g of sodium chloride. How many grams of chlorine gas reacted? How many grams of sodium reacted?

8. In a flask, 10.3 g of aluminum reacted with 100.0 g of liquid bromine to form aluminum bromide. After the reaction, no aluminum remained, and 8.5 grams of bromine remained unreacted. How many grams of bromine reacted? How many grams of compound were formed?

9. A 10.0-g sample of magnesium reacts with oxygen to form 16.6 g of magnesium oxide. How many grams of oxygen reacted?

## Section 3.2 Assessment

10. Describe the results of a physical change and list three examples of physical change.

11. Describe the results of a chemical change. List four indicators of chemical change.

12. Solve each of the following.

   a. In the complete reaction of 22.99 g of sodium with 35.45 g of chlorine, what mass of sodium chloride is formed?

   b. A 12.2-g sample of X reacts with a sample of Y to form 78.9 g of XY. What is the mass of Y that reacted?

13. **Thinking Critically** A friend tells you, "Because composition does not change during a physical change, the appearance of a substance does not change." Is your friend correct? Explain why.

14. **Classifying** Classify each of the following examples as a physical change or a chemical change.

   a. crushing an aluminum can

   b. recycling used aluminum cans to make new aluminum cans

   c. aluminum combining with oxygen to form aluminum oxide

3.2 Changes in Matter **65**

## Section 3.2 Assessment

10. During a physical change, a substance is altered but its composition does not change. Examples will vary but may include changes such as melting, freezing, boiling, bending, and tearing.

11. During a chemical change, the composition of a substance is altered. Possible indicators of chemical change include a change in color, odor, or temperature, and the formation of a gas or solid from a liquid.

12. **a.** 58.44 g of sodium chloride
    **b.** 66.7 g of Y

13. The statement is false. While the composition does not change, a change in appearance often accompanies a physical change.

14. **a.** physical; **b.** physical; **c.** chemical

---

## 3 Assess

### Check for Understanding

**Visual-Spatial** Set up simultaneous experiments. In one small beaker, place a scoop of baking soda (sodium hydrogen carbonate) and add 10 mL of vinegar (acetic acid). Invert another larger beaker over the top to capture the carbon dioxide–water that is produced. In the second experiment, pour several mL of carbonated beverage (club soda) into a small beaker and place on a hotplate. Again, invert a larger beaker over the top of the smaller beaker to capture the carbon dioxide–water that is produced. When both reactions are complete, slide a glass plate under each inverted beaker and test for the presence of carbon dioxide by extinguishing a splint or candle. Ask the students how the first experiment is different from the second. The first experiment generates carbon dioxide through a chemical change, the second through a physical change.

### Reteach

Set up a beaker of water and another beaker of ethanol. Place several ice cubes in each beaker. Ask students to relate their observations to the physical states of the matter involved. The ice will float on the water because the solid is less dense than the liquid; however, ice is more dense than liquid ethanol and will sink. To dispose of ethanol, evaporate under a hood.

### ✔ Assessment

**Knowledge** Set out a tray of objects (glassware, files, clamps, splints). Have the students team up and choose three objects from the tray and list the physical properties of each object and some physical changes that the object could undergo. Repeat for chemical properties and changes. **L2 ELL COOP LEARN**

**65**

# 1 Focus

Before presenting the lesson, display **Section Focus Transparency 11** on the overhead projector. Have students answer the accompanying questions using **Section Focus Transparency Master 11.** L1 ELL

# 2 Teach

### ✔ Assessment

**Portfolio** Have the students look around the room and generate a list of items that are mixtures and items that are substances. Have them identify the criteria they are using for classification and rough percentages of each item in each category. Lists can be placed in their portfolios. Answers will vary but there are usually higher percentages of materials that are classified as mixtures. L2 P

---

**National Science Content Standards**

**Pages 66–67**
UCP.1, UCP.2, UCP.3; B.2

---

### Objectives

- **Contrast** mixtures and substances.
- **Classify** mixtures as homogeneous or heterogeneous.
- **List** and **describe** several techniques used to separate mixtures.

### Vocabulary

mixture
heterogeneous mixture
homogeneous mixture
solution
filtration
distillation
crystallization
chromatography

**Figure 3-12**

**a** The components of the sand and water mixture (left) are obvious, whereas the components of the table salt and water mixture (right) are not.
**b** The salt component becomes obvious when the mixture is boiled.

When scientists speak of the composition of matter, they are referring to the kinds and amounts of components of which the matter is made. On the basis of composition alone, all matter can be classified into two broad categories: substances or mixtures. You have already learned that a pure substance is a form of matter with a uniform and unchanging composition. You also know that the intensive properties of pure substances do not change, regardless of the physical state or amount of the substance. But what is the result when two or more substances are combined?

## Mixtures

A **mixture** is a combination of two or more pure substances in which each pure substance retains its individual chemical properties. The composition of mixtures is variable, and the number of mixtures that can be created by combining substances is infinite. Although much of the focus of chemistry is the behavior of substances, it is important to remember that most everyday matter occurs as mixtures. Substances tend naturally to mix; it is difficult to keep things pure.

Two mixtures, sand and water, and table salt and water, are shown in **Figure 3-12a.** You know water to be a colorless liquid. Sand is a grainy solid that does not dissolve in water. When sand and water are mixed, the two substances are in contact, yet each substance retains its properties. The sand and water have not reacted. Just by looking at the sand–water mixture in beaker A, it is easy to see each separate substance. Some mixtures, however, may not look like mixtures at all. The mixture of table salt and water in the beaker labeled B is colorless and appears the same as pure water. How can you determine if it is a mixture? If you were to boil away the water, you would see a white residue. That residue, shown in **Figure 13-12b,** is the salt. Thus, the colorless mixture actually contained two separate substances. The salt and the water physically mixed but did not react and were separated by the physical method of boiling.

---

### DIFFERENTIATED INSTRUCTION

**Visually Impaired**

***Kinesthetic*** Set up stations with examples of heterogeneous and homogeneous mixtures that can be discerned by touch. Partner visually impaired students with sighted students and have them rotate through the stations to classify each type of mixture. L1 ELL

### Resource Manager

**Study Guide for Content Mastery,** p.16 L2
**Solving Problems: A Chemistry Handbook,** Section 3.3 L2
**Section Focus Transparency 11 and Master** L1 ELL

**Types of mixtures** The combinations of pure substances shown in **Figure 3-12** are indeed both mixtures, despite their obvious visual differences. Can you think of some way to further define mixtures? Mixtures themselves are classified as either heterogeneous or homogeneous. A **heterogeneous mixture** is one that does not blend smoothly throughout and in which the individual substances remain distinct. The sand and water mixture is an example of a heterogeneous mixture. Suppose you draw a drop from the top of the mixture using an eyedropper. The drop would be almost completely water. If you draw a second drop from the bottom of the mixture, that drop would contain mostly sand. Thus the composition of the sand–water mixture is not uniform—the substances have not blended smoothly and the two substances of the mixture (sand on the bottom and water on the top) remain distinct. In another example, fresh-squeezed orange juice is a mixture of juice and pulp. The pulp component floats on top of the juice component. Is your favorite pizza a mixture? The answer is yes when you consider that the pizza is a combination of distinct areas of dough, sauce, cheese, and toppings. We can therefore say that the existence of two or more distinct areas indicates a heterogeneous mixture.

A **homogeneous mixture** has constant composition throughout; it always has a single phase. Let's examine the salt–water mixture using the eyedropper. A drop of the mixture from the top of the beaker has the same composition as a drop from the bottom of the beaker. In fact, every drop of the mixture contains the same relative amounts of salt and water.

Homogeneous mixtures are also referred to as **solutions**. You are probably most familiar with solutions in a liquid form, such as cough suppressant medicine and lemonade, but solutions may contain solids, liquids, or gases. **Table 3-3** lists the various types of solution systems and gives an example of each. Solutions are very important in chemistry, and, in fact, this textbook devotes an entire chapter to the study of solutions.

The solid–solid solution known as steel is called an alloy. An alloy is a homogeneous mixture of metals, or a mixture of a metal and a nonmetal in which the metal substance is the major component. The U.S. Mint's golden dollar coin, shown in **Figure 3-13**, uses a metal alloy composed of 77% copper, 12% zinc, 7% manganese, and 4% nickel surrounding a copper core. Alloys are also used in spacecraft and automobiles. What might be the benefit of using alloys for these applications? Manufacturers combine the properties of various metals in an alloy to achieve greater strength and durability of their products.

**Figure 3-13**

Coins issued by the U.S. Mint are metal alloys. The combination of multiple metals gives the coins specific properties such as color, weight, and durability.

Table 3-3

| Types of Solution Systems | |
|---|---|
| **System** | **Example** |
| Gas–gas | Air is primarily a mixture of nitrogen, oxygen, and argon gases. |
| Gas–liquid | Carbonated beverages contain carbon dioxide gas in solution. |
| Liquid–gas | Moist air contains water droplets in air (which is a mixture of gases). |
| Liquid–liquid | Vinegar contains acetic acid in water. |
| Solid–liquid | Sweetened powder drink contains sugar and other solid ingredients in water. |
| Solid–solid | Steel is an alloy of iron containing carbon. |

## miniLAB

### Purpose

To separate a mixture by paper chromatography

### Process Skills

Applying concepts, collecting and interpreting data, comparing and contrasting, observing and inferring

### Safety Precautions

Be sure students wear safety goggles and aprons.

### Teaching Strategies

- Remind students to handle the filter paper as little as possible. The oil from their fingers will distort the results.
- Any size of round filter paper will work. Green and yellow dyes separate best if the paper is relatively large in diameter.
- Use several different types of black felt pens and black markers. Each brand and type has different ink combinations. This makes it more interesting when students compare their chromatograms. The inks must be water soluble.

### Expected Results

As the water spreads out on the paper, different dyes in the ink will spread out from the center and be deposited on the filter paper at different distances from the center.

### Analysis

1. Drawings should resemble the miniLab photo with correct labels.
2. Different components of the ink have varying attraction for the filter paper. Therefore, the colors that comprise the ink will be deposited at different distances from the center of the paper.
3. Answers will vary. Different makes and types of black ink have different dyes in them.

### Assessment

**Skill** Have students repeat the experiment using ethanol and permanent markers. Have them write a summary of both experiments in which they compare and contrast the results. L2

**Figure 3-14**

The physical properties of the iron filings on the plate allow them to be easily separated from the sand using a magnet.

## Separating Mixtures

Most matter exists naturally as mixtures. For students and scientists to gain a thorough understanding of matter, it is very important to be able to do the reverse of mixing, that is, to separate mixtures into their component substances. Because the substances in a mixture are physically combined, the processes used to separate a mixture are physical processes that are based on the difference in physical properties of the substances. Sometimes it is very easy to separate a mixture; separating a mixture of pennies and nickels is not a difficult task. More difficult would be separating a mixture of sand and iron filings. Or would it be? The demonstration illustrated in **Figure 3-14** shows how the sand–iron mixture is easily separated on the basis of the unique physical properties of the substances involved. Numerous techniques have been developed that take advantage of different physical properties in order to separate mixtures.

Heterogeneous mixtures composed of solids and liquids are easily separated by filtration. **Filtration** is a technique that uses a porous barrier to separate a solid from a liquid. As **Figure 3-15** shows, the mixture is poured through a piece of filter paper that has been folded into a cone shape. The liquid passes through, leaving the solids trapped in the filter paper.

## miniLAB

### Separating Ink Dyes

**Applying Concepts** Chromatography is an important diagnostic tool for chemists. Many types of substances can be separated and analyzed using this technique. In this experiment, you will use paper chromatography to separate the dyes in water-soluble black ink.

**Materials** 9-oz wide-mouth plastic cups (2); round filter paper; ¼ piece of 11-cm round filter paper; scissors; pointed object, approximately 3–4 mm diameter; water-soluble black felt pen or marker

### Procedure

1. Fill one of the wide-mouth plastic cups with water to about 2 cm from the top. Wipe off any water drops on the lip of the cup.
2. Place the round filter paper on a clean, dry surface. Make a concentrated ink spot in the center of the paper by firmly pressing the tip of the pen or marker onto the paper.
3. Use a sharp object to create a small hole, approximately 3–4 mm or about the diameter of a pen tip, in the center of the ink spot.
4. Roll the 1/4 piece of filter paper into a tight cone. This will act as a wick to draw the ink. Work the pointed end of the wick into the hole in the center of the round filter paper.
5. Place the paper/wick apparatus on top of the cup of water, with the wick in the water. The

water will move up the wick and outward through the round paper.

6. When the water has moved to within about 1 cm of the edge of the paper (about 20 minutes), carefully remove the paper from the water-filled cup and put it on the empty cup.

### Analysis

1. Make a drawing of the round filter paper and label the color bands. How many distinct dyes can you identify?
2. Why do you see different colors at different locations on the filter paper?
3. How does your chromatogram compare with those of your classmates who used other types of black felt pens or markers? Explain the differences.

## Resource Manager

ChemLab and MiniLab Worksheets, p. 9 L2
Small-Scale Laboratory Manual, pp. 9–12 L2
Forensics Lab Manual, pp. 1–12 L2

## GLENCOE TECHNOLOGY

**CD-ROM**
**Chemistry: Matter and Change**
Exploration: *Separating Mixtures*
Experiment: *Metal Alloys*

**Figure 3-15**

Filtration is a common technique used to remove impurities from drinking water. Clean water passes through the porous filter **ⓐ** leaving behind the impurities that can be easily discarded **ⓑ**.

Most homogeneous mixtures can be separated by distillation. **Distillation** is a separation technique that is based on differences in the boiling points of the substances involved. In distillation, a mixture is heated until the substance with the lowest boiling point boils to a vapor that can then be condensed into a liquid and collected. When precisely controlled, distillation can separate substances having boiling points that differ by only a few degrees.

Did you ever make rock candy as a child? Making rock candy from a sugar solution is an example of separation by crystallization. **Crystallization** is a separation technique that results in the formation of pure solid particles of a substance from a solution containing the dissolved substance. When the solution contains as much dissolved substance as it can possibly hold, the addition of a tiny amount more often causes the dissolved substance to come out of solution and collect as crystals on some available surface. In the rock candy example, as water evaporates from the sugar–water solution, the sugar is left behind as a solid crystal on the string. Crystallization produces highly pure solids.

**Chromatography** is a technique that separates the components of a mixture (called the mobile phase) on the basis of the tendency of each to travel or be drawn across the surface of another material (called the stationary phase). The **miniLAB** in this section describes how you can separate a solution such as ink into its components as it spreads across a stationary piece of paper. The separation occurs because the various components of the ink spread through the paper at different rates.

### Chemistry Online

**Topic: Mixtures**
To learn more about mixtures and separation techniques, visit the Chemistry Web site at chemistrymc.com

**Activity:** Use your research to make a poster showing several real-life mixtures, their uses, and techniques that might be used to separate each mixture.

## Section 3.3 Assessment

**15.** How do mixtures and substances differ?

**16.** Consider a mixture of water, sand, and oil. How many phases are present? How could you separate this mixture into individual substances?

**17.** Classify each of the following as either a heterogeneous or homogeneous mixture.
  **a.** orange juice
  **b.** tap water
  **c.** steel (a blend of iron and carbon)
  **d.** air
  **e.** raisin muffin

**18. Thinking Critically** When 50 mL of ethanol is mixed with 50 mL of water, a solution forms. The volume of the final solution is less than 100 mL. Propose an explanation for this phenomenon. (*Hint*: Consider what you know about the space between particles in liquids.)

**19. Applying Concepts** Describe the separation technique that could be used to separate each of the following mixtures.
  **a.** two colorless liquids
  **b.** a nondissolving solid mixed with a liquid
  **c.** red and blue marbles of same size and mass

---

# 1 Focus

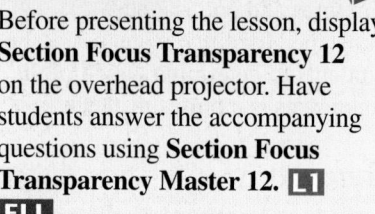

Before presenting the lesson, display **Section Focus Transparency 12** on the overhead projector. Have students answer the accompanying questions using **Section Focus Transparency Master 12. L1 ELL**

---

# Elements and Compounds

## Objectives

- **Distinguish** between elements and compounds.

- **Describe** the organization of elements on the periodic table.

- **Explain** how all compounds obey the laws of definite and multiple proportions.

## Vocabulary

element
periodic table
compound
law of definite proportions
percent by mass
law of multiple proportions

**Figure 3-16**

Although many early scientists have contributed to the modern organization of the elements, Mendeleev's system of rows and columns was a revolutionary advancement.

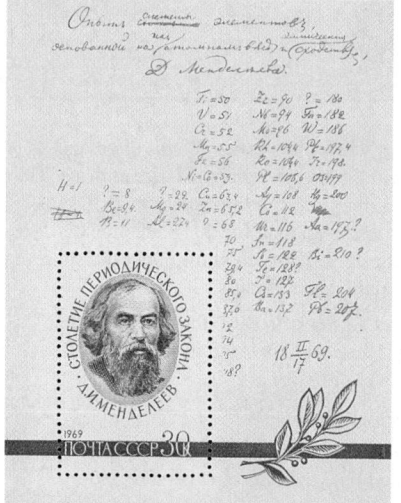

To this point you've examined many of the properties of matter. You've also learned how scientists have organized, classified, and described matter by arranging it into various subcategories of components. But there remains another fundamental level of classification of matter: the classification of pure substances as elements or compounds.

## Elements

Recall that earlier in this chapter you considered the diversity of your surroundings in terms of matter. Although the diversity is astounding, in reality all matter can be broken down into a relatively small number of basic building blocks called elements. An **element** is a pure substance that cannot be separated into simpler substances by physical or chemical means. On Earth, 91 elements occur naturally. Copper, oxygen, and gold are examples of naturally occurring elements. There are also several elements that do not exist naturally but have been developed by scientists.

Each element has a unique chemical name and symbol. The chemical symbol consists of one, two, or three letters; the first letter is always capitalized and the remaining letter(s) are always lowercase. Why has so much effort been given to naming the elements? The names and symbols of the elements are universally accepted by scientists in order to make the communication of chemical information possible.

The 91 naturally occurring elements are not equally abundant. For example, hydrogen is estimated to make up approximately 75% of the mass of the universe. Oxygen and silicon together comprise almost 75% of the mass of Earth's crust, while oxygen, carbon, and hydrogen account for more than 90% of the human body. Francium, on the other hand, is one of the least abundant naturally occurring elements. It is estimated that there is probably less than 20 grams of francium dispersed throughout Earth's crust. To put that into perspective, the total mass of francium is approximately equal to the mass of your pencil or pen.

**A first look at the periodic table** As many new elements were being discovered in the early nineteenth century, chemists began to see patterns of similarities in the chemical and physical properties of particular sets of elements. Several schemes for organizing the elements on the basis of these similarities were proposed, with varying degrees of success. In 1869, the Russian chemist Dmitri Mendeleev made a significant contribution to the effort. Mendeleev devised the chart shown in **Figure 3-16**, which organized all of the elements that were known at the time into rows and columns based on their similarities and their masses. Mendeleev's organizational table was the first version of what has been further developed into the **periodic table** of elements. The periodic table organizes the elements into a grid of horizontal rows called periods and vertical columns called groups or families. Elements in the same group have similar chemical and physical properties. The table is called "periodic" because the pattern of similar properties repeats as you move from period to period.

One of the brilliant aspects of Mendeleev's original table was that its structure could accommodate elements that were not known at

---

**DIFFERENTIATED INSTRUCTION**

## Learning Disabled

*Visual-Spatial* Decide which of the elements' symbols and name spellings you wish your students to know (generally 50 to 60 of the more commonly used elements). Have students make flashcards with the name of the element on one side and its corresponding symbol on the back. Provide some class time for students to quiz each other using the flashcards. **L1 ELL**

# of the Elements

| | | | | | | VIIIA 18 |
|---|---|---|---|---|---|---|
| | IIIA 13 | IVA 14 | VA 15 | VIA 16 | VIIA 17 | 4,0 2 He |

| | | | 10,8 5 B | 12,0 6 C | 14,0 7 N | 16,0 8 O | 19,0 9 F | 20,2 10 Ne |
|---|---|---|---|---|---|---|---|---|

| IB 11 | IIB 12 | | 27,0 13 Al | 28,1 14 Si | 31,0 15 P | 32,1 16 S | 35,5 17 Cl | 39,9 18 Ar |
|---|---|---|---|---|---|---|---|---|

| 10 | IB 11 | IIB 12 | | | | | | |
|---|---|---|---|---|---|---|---|---|
| 58,7 28 Ni | 63,5 29 Cu | 65,4 30 Zn | 69,7 31 Ga | 72,6 32 Ge | 74,9 33 As | 79,0 34 Se | 79,9 35 Br | 83,8 36 Kr |
| 106,4 46 Pd | 107,9 47 Ag | 112,4 48 Cd | 114,8 49 In | 118,7 50 Sn | 121,8 51 Sb | 127,6 52 Te | 126,9 53 I | 131,3 54 Xe |
| 195,1 78 Pt | 197,0 79 Au | 200,6 80 Hg | 204,4 81 Tl | 207,2 82 Pb | 209,0 83 Bi | 209 84 Po (102 a) | 210 85 At (8 h) | 222 86 Rn (3,8 d) |
| 273 110 (118 ms) | 272 111 (1,5 ms) | 277 112 (0,24 ms) | | | | | | |

| 150,4 62 Sm | 152,0 63 Eu | 157,3 64 Gd | 158,9 65 Tb | 162,5 66 Dy | 164,9 67 Ho | 167,3 68 Er | 168,9 69 Tm | 173,0 70 Yb | 175,0 71 Lu |
|---|---|---|---|---|---|---|---|---|---|
| 244 94 Pu (8,0·10⁷ a) | 243 95 Am (7400 a) | 247 96 Cm (1,6·10⁷ a) | 247 97 Bk (1400 a) | 251 98 Cf (900 a) | 252 99 Es (472 d) | 257 100 Fm (105 d) | 258 101 Md (53 d) | 259 102 No (58 min) | 262 103 Lr (3,6 h) |

3.4 Elements and Compounds 73

## Visual Learning

**Visual-Spatial** Have the students use the periodic table to determine the number of elements that are gaseous, liquid, solid, metallic, and radioactive at room temperature. L2

## ✓ Assessment

**Skill** Have students use the *CRC Handbook of Chemistry and Physics* (section on element information) to research the following sample questions about the elements.

- How many elements are named for people? Countries? Cities or states?
- How many elements are named for mythological figures or gods?
- What town has four elements named for it?
- What elements were known to ancient humans?
- What elements were discovered before 1800? Between 1801 and 1900? Between 1901 and the present?

Ask the students to choose one particular category and portray the information graphically. L2

Alchemists sought to find a mysterious substance that could be taken apart and recombined to form more precious elements, such as gold. Although the practice of alchemy was a dead end in itself, much useful chemical information and many processes were stumbled upon.

Early Chinese philosophers believed that all materials cycle through five fundamental stages: earth, wood, fire, metal, and water. Each step of the cycle led to a state of greater order. For instance, the earth allows a tree to grow, which in turn can be chopped down and burned to transform metals. In the heating process, condensation provides the water to renew the cycle.

**Figure 3-19**

This classic apparatus, called a Hoffman apparatus, and other similar designs are used to separate water into its components.

Unlike elements, compounds can be broken down into simpler substances by chemical means. In general, compounds that naturally occur are more stable than the individual component elements. To separate a compound into its elements often requires external energy such as heat or electricity. **Figure 3-19** shows the apparatus used to produce the chemical change of water into its component elements of hydrogen and oxygen through a process called electrolysis. Here, one end of a long platinum electrode is exposed to the water in the tube and the other end is attached to a power source. An electric current splits water into hydrogen gas in the compartment on the right and oxygen gas in the compartment on the left. Because water is composed of two parts hydrogen and one part oxygen, there is twice as much hydrogen gas than oxygen gas.

The properties of a compound are different from those of its component elements. The example of water in **Figure 3-19** illustrates this fact. Water is a stable compound that is liquid at room temperature. When water is broken down into its components, it is obvious that hydrogen and oxygen are dramatically different than the liquid they form when combined. Oxygen and hydrogen are tasteless, odorless gases that vigorously undergo chemical reactions with many elements. This difference in properties is a result of a chemical reaction between the elements. **Figure 3-20** shows the component elements (sodium and chlorine) of the compound commonly called table salt (sodium chloride). When sodium and chlorine react with each other, the compound sodium chloride is formed. Note how different the properties of sodium chloride are from its component elements. Sodium is a highly reactive element that fizzes and burns when added to water. Chlorine is a poisonous, pale green gas. Sodium chloride, however, is a white, unreactive solid that flavors many of the foods you eat.

**Figure 3-20**

Compounds such as sodium chloride (table salt) are often remarkably different from the components that comprise them.

Chlorine

Sodium

Sodium chloride

## Internet Address Book

**Chemistry Online** Note Internet addresses that you find useful in the space below for quick reference.

_____

_____

_____

_____

_____

**National Science Content Standards**

**Pages 74–75**
UCP.1, UCP.2, UCP.3; B.2, B.3

# Law of Definite Proportions

An important characteristic of compounds is that the elements comprising them combine in definite proportions by mass. This observation is so fundamental that it is summarized as the **law of definite proportions**. This law states that, regardless of the amount, a compound is always composed of the same elements in the same proportion by mass. For example, consider the compound table sugar (sucrose), which is composed of carbon, hydrogen, and oxygen. The analysis of 20.00 g of sucrose from a bag of sugar is given in **Table 3-4**. Note that in Column 1 the sum of the individual masses of the elements equals 20.00 g, the amount of sucrose that was analyzed. This demonstrates the law of conservation of mass as applied to compounds: The mass of the compound is equal to the sum of the masses of the elements that make up the compound. Column 2 shows the ratio of the mass of each element to the total mass of the compound as a percentage called the **percent by mass**.

$$\text{percent by mass (\%)} = \frac{\text{mass of element}}{\text{mass of compound}} \times 100$$

**Table 3-4**

| Sucrose Analysis from Bag Sugar | | |
|---|---|---|
| | **Column 1** | **Column 2** |
| **Element** | **Analysis by mass (g)** | **Percent by mass (%)** |
| Carbon | 8.44 g carbon | $\frac{8.44 \text{ g C}}{20.00 \text{ g sucrose}} \times 100 = 42.2\%$ carbon |
| Hydrogen | 1.30 g hydrogen | $\frac{1.30 \text{ g H}}{20.00 \text{ g sucrose}} \times 100 = 6.50\%$ hydrogen |
| Oxygen | 10.26 g oxygen | $\frac{10.26 \text{ g O}}{20.00 \text{ g sucrose}} \times 100 = 51.30\%$ oxygen |
| Total | 20.00 g sucrose | $= 100.0\%$ |

Now let's suppose you analyzed 500.0 g of sucrose isolated from a sample of sugar cane. The analysis is shown in **Table 3-5**. Note in Column 2 that the percent by mass values equal those in Column 2 in **Table 3-4**. According to the law of definite proportions, samples of a compound from any source must have the same mass proportions. Conversely, compounds with different mass proportions must be different compounds. Thus, you can conclude that samples of sucrose always will be composed of 42.2% carbon, 6.50% hydrogen, and 51.30% oxygen.

**Table 3-5**

| Sucrose Analysis from Sugar Cane | | |
|---|---|---|
| | **Column 1** | **Column 2** |
| **Element** | **Analysis by mass (g)** | **Percent by mass (%)** |
| Carbon | 211.0 g carbon | $\frac{211.0 \text{ g C}}{500.0 \text{ g sucrose}} \times 100 = 42.20\%$ carbon |
| Hydrogen | 32.5 g hydrogen | $\frac{32.5 \text{ g H}}{500.0 \text{ g sucrose}} \times 100 = 6.50\%$ hydrogen |
| Oxygen | 256.5 g oxygen | $\frac{256.5 \text{ g O}}{500.0 \text{ g sucrose}} \times 100 = 51.30\%$ oxygen |
| Total | 500.0 g sucrose | $= 100.00\%$ |

## Practice PROBLEMS

Have students refer to Appendix D for complete solutions to Practice Problems.

**20.** 15.9%

**21.** 5.0%

**22.** 25% X and 75% Y

**23.** When the composition by mass percentage is calculated for both compounds, it is found that the composition is not the same for the two compounds; therefore, they must be different.

**24.** No, you cannot be sure. Having the same mass percentage of a single element does not guarantee that the composition of each compound is the same.

# 3 Assess

## Check for Understanding

*Visual-Spatial* Have students draw diagrams featuring atoms and molecules that show packing arrangements in heterogeneous mixtures, solutions, and pure substances. **L2** **ELL**

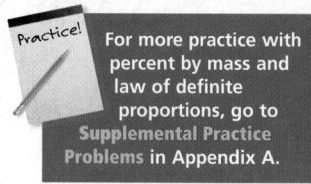

For more practice with percent by mass and law of definite proportions, go to **Supplemental Practice Problems** in Appendix A.

**ⓐ** Compound I

**ⓑ** Compound II

**ⓒ** Mass Ratio Comparison

**Figure 3-21**

Bar graph **ⓐ** compares the relative masses of copper and chlorine in Compound I and bar graph **ⓑ** compares the relative masses of copper and chlorine in Compound II. **ⓒ** A comparison between the relative masses of copper in both compounds shows a 2:1 ratio.

## PRACTICE PROBLEMS

**20.** A 78.0-g sample of an unknown compound contains 12.4 g of hydrogen. What is the percent by mass of hydrogen in the compound?

**21.** If 1.0 g of hydrogen reacts completely with 19.0 g of fluorine, what is the percent by mass of hydrogen in the compound that is formed?

**22.** If 3.5 g of X reacts with 10.5 g of Y to form the compound XY, what is the percent by mass of X in the compound? The percent by mass of Y?

**23.** Two unknown compounds are tested. Compound I contains 15.0 g of hydrogen and 120.0 g of oxygen. Compound II contains 2.0 g of hydrogen and 32.0 g of oxygen. Are the compounds the same?

**24.** All you know about two unknown compounds is that they have the same percent by mass of carbon. With only this information, can you be sure the two compounds are the same?

## Law of Multiple Proportions

Compounds composed of different elements are obviously different compounds. Can compounds that are composed of the same elements differ from each other? The answer is yes because those different compounds have different mass compositions. The **law of multiple proportions** states that when different compounds are formed by a combination of the same elements, different masses of one element combine with the same relative mass of the other element in a ratio of small whole numbers. Ratios compare the relative amounts of any items or substances. The comparison can be expressed using numbers separated by a colon or as a fraction. With regard to the law of multiple proportions, ratios express the relationship of elements in a compound.

The two distinct compounds water ($H_2O$) and hydrogen peroxide ($H_2O_2$) illustrate the law of multiple proportions. Each compound contains the same elements (hydrogen and oxygen). Water is composed of two parts hydrogen (the element that is present in the same amount in both compounds) to one part oxygen (the element that is present in different amounts in both compounds). Hydrogen peroxide is composed of two parts hydrogen and two parts oxygen. Hydrogen peroxide differs from water in that it has twice as much oxygen. When we compare the mass of oxygen in hydrogen peroxide to the mass of oxygen in water, we get the ratio 2:1.

In another example, copper (Cu) reacts with chlorine (Cl) under different sets of conditions to form two different compounds. **Table 3-6** provides an analysis of their composition. Note that the two copper compounds must be different because they have different percents by mass. Compound I contains 64.20% copper; compound II contains 47.27% copper. Compound I contains 35.80% chlorine; compound II contains 52.73% chlorine.

**Table 3-6**

| Analysis Data of Two Copper Compounds | | | | | |
|---|---|---|---|---|---|
| Compound | % Cu | % Cl | Mass copper (g) in 100.0 g of compound | Mass chlorine (g) in 100.0 g of compound | Mass ratio $\left(\dfrac{\text{mass Cu}}{\text{mass Cl}}\right)$ |
| I | 64.20 | 35.80 | 64.20 | 35.80 | 1.793 g Cu/1 g Cl |
| II | 47.27 | 52.73 | 47.27 | 52.73 | 0.8964 g Cu/1 g Cl |

---

## CHEMISTRY JOURNAL

### Same Elements, Major Differences

*Visual-Spatial* Have students use the *CRC Handbook of Chemistry and Physics* to look up the properties of compounds that exemplify the law of multiple proportions (for example, copper(I) chloride and copper(II) chloride; hydrogen peroxide and water). Have them organize the information in reference tables so they can clearly see distinctions between the two compounds. **L2**

**National Science Content Standards**

**Pages 76–77**
UCP.1, UCP.2, UCP.3; B.2; G.1, G.3

Figure 3-22

Analyses of the mass ratios of the two copper chloride compounds shown here indicate that they are indeed different compounds. The calculated mass ratio of compound I to compound II is 2.000 and fits the definition of the law of multiple proportions.

Compare the ratio of the mass of copper to the mass of chlorine for each compound (see the last column of **Table 3-6** and **Figure 3-21**). You'll notice that the mass ratio of copper to chlorine in compound I (1.793) is two times the mass ratio of copper to chlorine in compound II (0.8964).

$$\frac{\text{mass ratio compound I}}{\text{mass ratio compound II}} = \frac{1.793 \text{ g Cu/g Cl}}{0.8964 \text{ g Cu/g Cl}} = 2.000$$

As the law of multiple proportions states, the different masses of copper that combine with a fixed mass of chlorine in the two different copper compounds, shown in **Figure 3-22,** can be expressed as a small whole-number ratio, in this case 2:1.

Considering that there is a finite number of elements that exist today and an exponentially greater number of compounds that are composed of these elements under various conditions, it becomes clear how important the law of multiple proportions is in chemistry.

# Section 3.4 Assessment

**25.** How are elements and compounds similar? How are they different?

**26.** What is the basic organizing feature of the periodic table of elements?

**27.** Explain how the law of definite proportions applies to compounds.

**28.** What type of compounds are compared in the law of multiple proportions?

**29. Thinking Critically** Name two elements that have properties similar to those of element potassium (K). To those of krypton (Kr).

**30. Interpreting Data** Complete the following table and then analyze the data to determine if compounds I and II are the same compound. If the compounds are different, use the law of multiple proportions to show the relationship between them.

| Analysis Data of Two Iron Compounds | | | | | |
|---|---|---|---|---|---|
| Compound | Total mass (g) | Mass Fe (g) | Mass O (g) | Mass % Fe | Mass % O |
| I | 75.00 | 52.46 | 22.54 | | |
| II | 56.00 | 43.53 | 12.47 | | |

## Reteach

**Visual-Spatial** Students may find it easier to memorize a triangular arrangement of matter from most general at the bottom of the pyramid to most specific (element, compound, solution, heterogeneous mixture) at the top of the pyramid. Also, as you move from right to left on the base of the pyramid, classification becomes more ordered. **L1** **ELL**

## Extension

**Kinesthetic** Give each student a 10 cm × 10 cm "information square" on which they describe themselves by a category such as name, address, height, hair color, eye color, interests, pets, number of siblings. Have them put a small picture of themselves in the center. Then pass out reduced copies of the completed squares and ask the students to arrange the squares into as many meaningful patterns as possible. Once they have decided on a pattern, students should paste down their squares and describe their pattern in a presentation. This assignment may also be done as an entire class using the original squares and generating discussion about the best placement of each square. In order to obtain enough squares, consider combining classes. **L1** **ELL** **COOP LEARN**

## Assessment

**Skill** Clip photos of various mixtures from magazines or other sources and have students identify them as heterogeneous mixtures, solutions, or pure substances in various phases. **L2** **ELL**

---

# Section 3.4 Assessment

**25.** Compounds are composed of elements and can be broken down. Elements cannot be broken down into simpler substances.

**26.** The periodic table of elements is organized by similarities in physical and chemical properties.

**27.** The law of definite proportions describes the constant composition of a substance.

**28.** The law of multiple proportions relates the compositions of two compounds composed of the same elements.

**29.** Elements in group 1A have properties similar to K. Elements in group 8A have properties similar to Kr.

**30.** Compound I mass percent Fe = 69.95%; mass percent O = 30.05%. Compound II mass percent Fe = 77.73%; mass percent O = 22.27%. The compounds are not the same. The mass ratio of compound 1 to compound 2 is 2:3.

## Preparation 📦

**Time Allotment**
One laboratory period

**Process Skills**
Observing and inferring, classifying

**Safety Precautions**
Be sure students wear aprons and goggles. Remind students to tie back long hair and use caution around a flame. Paper clip will remain hot for several minutes. Do not allow solutions to contact skin or clothing.

**Disposal**
Rinse filtrate down the drain with lots of water. The solid wastes may be collected for recycling according to local regulations.

### Pre-Lab

**3.** A physical property is a characteristic that can be observed or measured without changing the substance's composition—for example, color, shape, or mass. A chemical property is the ability of a substance to combine with or change into one or more other substances—for example, reactivity with water.

**4. a.** You might observe a change in color or odor, the evolution of heat or light, the absorption of energy, or the formation of a gas, liquid, or different solid. A different product will form.

**b.** You might observe a change in shape or in physical state, such as boiling, condensing, freezing, melting, evaporating, dissolving, or crystallizing.

**5.** A homogeneous mixture is one in which one or more substances are evenly distributed throughout another substance. A heterogeneous mixture is one in which there is an observable separation of component substances.

# Matter and Chemical Reactions

**O**ne of the most interesting characteristics of matter, and one that drives the study and exploration of chemistry, is the fact that matter changes. By examining a dramatic chemical reaction, such as the reaction of the element copper and the compound silver nitrate in a water solution, you can readily observe chemical change. Drawing on one of the fundamental laboratory techniques introduced in this chapter, you can separate the products. Then, you will use a flame test to confirm the identity of the products.

**Problem**
Is there evidence of a chemical reaction between copper and silver nitrate? If so, which elements reacted and what is the name of the compound they formed?

**Objectives**
• **Observe** the reactants as they change into product.
• **Separate** a mixture by filtration.
• **Predict** the names of the products.

**Materials**
copper wire
$AgNO_3$ solution
sandpaper
stirring rod
50-mL graduated cylinder
50-mL beaker
funnel
filter paper
250-mL Erlenmeyer flask
ring stand
small iron ring
plastic petri dish
paper clip
Bunsen burner
tongs

**Safety Precautions**

• Always wear safety goggles, gloves, and lab apron.
• Silver nitrate is toxic and will harm skin and clothing.
• Use caution around a flame.

**Pre-Lab**

**1.** Read the entire **CHEMLAB**.

**2.** Prepare all written materials that you will take into the laboratory. Be sure to include safety precautions, procedure notes, and a data table in which to record your observations.

| Reaction Observations | |
|---|---|
| Time (min) | Observations |
| | |
| | |
| | |
| | |
| | |
| | |

**3.** Define the terms physical property and chemical property. Give an example of each.

**4.** Form a hypothesis regarding what you might observe if
  **a.** a chemical change occurs.
  **b.** a physical change occurs.

**5.** Distinguish between a homogeneous mixture and a heterogeneous mixture.

**Procedure**

**1.** Obtain 8 cm of copper wire. Rub the copper wire with the sandpaper until it is shiny.

**2.** Measure approximately 25 mL $AgNO_3$ (silver nitrate) solution into a 50-mL beaker. **CAUTION:** *Do not allow to contact skin or clothing.*

**3.** Make and record an observation of the physical properties of the copper wire and $AgNO_3$ solution.

**Procedure**
• The lengths of wire can be cut ahead.
• Copper coil can be allowed to sit in $AgNO_3$ solution overnight.
• Darken room to view flame color.

**4.** Coil the piece of copper wire to a length that will fit into the beaker. Make a hook on the end of the coil to allow the coil to be suspended from the stirring rod.

**5.** Hook the coil onto the middle of the stirring rod. Place the stirring rod across the top of the beaker immersing some of the coil in the $AgNO_3$ solution.

**6.** Make and record observations of the wire and the solution every five minutes for 20 minutes.

**7.** Use the ring stand, small iron ring, funnel, Erlenmeyer flask, and filter paper to set up a filtration apparatus. Attach the iron ring to the ring stand. Adjust the height of the ring so the end of the funnel is inside the neck of the Erlenmeyer flask.

**8.** To fold the filter paper, examine the diagram below. Begin by folding the circle in half, then fold in half again. Tear off the lower right corner of the flap that is facing you. This will help the filter paper stick better to the funnel. Open the folded paper into a cone. Place the filter paper cone in the funnel.

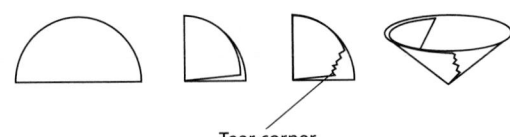

Tear corner

**9.** Remove the coil from the beaker and dispose of it as directed by your teacher. Some of the solid product may form a mixture with the liquid in the beaker. Decant the liquid by slowly pouring it down the stirring rod into the funnel. Solid product will be caught in the filter paper. Collect the filtrate—the liquid that runs through the filter paper—in the Erlenmeyer flask.

**10.** Transfer the clear filtrate to a petri dish.

**11.** Adjust a Bunsen burner flame until it is blue. Hold the paper clip with tongs in the flame until no additional color is observed. **CAUTION:** *The paper clip will be very hot.*

**12.** Using tongs, dip the hot paper clip in the filtrate. Then, hold the paper clip in the flame. Record the color you observe.

## Cleanup and Disposal

**1.** Dispose of materials as directed by your teacher.

**2.** Clean and return all lab equipment to its proper place.

**3.** Wash hands thoroughly.

## Analyze and Conclude

**1. Classifying** Which type of mixture is silver nitrate in water? Which type of mixture is formed in step 6? Explain.

**2. Observing and Inferring** Describe the changes you observed in step 6. Is there evidence a chemical change occurred? Why?

**3. Predicting** Predict the products formed in step 6. You may not know the exact chemical name, but you should be able to make an intuitive prediction.

**4. Using Resources** Use resources such as the *CRC Handbook of Chemistry and Physics*, the *Merck Index,* or the Internet to determine the colors of silver metal and copper nitrate in water. Compare this information with your observations of the reactants and products in step 6.

**5. Identifying** Metals emit characteristic colors in flame tests. Copper emits blue-green light. Do your observations in step 12 confirm the presence of copper in the filtrate collected in step 9?

**6. Communicating** Express in words the chemical equation that represents the reaction that occurred in step 6.

**7. Error Analysis** Compare your recorded observations with those of several other lab teams. Explain any differences.

## Real-World Chemistry

**1.** Analytical chemists determine the chemical composition of matter. Two major branches of analytical chemistry are qualitative analysis—determining what is in a substance—and quantitative analysis—measuring how much substance. Research and report on a career as an analytical chemist in the food industry.

## Expected Results

Step 3: Cu – reddish metal; $AgNO_3$– clear, colorless solution
Step 6: Solution will turn blue-green; grayish solid will "grow" on the wire.
Step 12: blue-green color

## Analyze and Conclude

**1.** homogeneous; heterogeneous and homogeneous

**2.** A grayish solid formed on the wire. The solution turned blue-green. Yes, a solid formed and a color change occurred.

**3.** silver and copper nitrate

**4.** Silver metal is white to gray. Copper nitrate is blue-green.

**5.** Experimental results should agree with blue-green light.

**6.** Copper and silver nitrate solution react to form silver and copper nitrate.

**7.** Copper wire may not have been clean. The better observations will be more detailed.

## Real-World Chemistry

**1.** Answers will vary but may include analysis of vitamin content, flavors, preservatives, or calorie content.

### ✔ Assessment

**Portfolio** Have each student place the laboratory report for this experiment in his or her portfolio. **L2** **P**

CHEMLAB **79**

### Resource Manager

**ChemLab and MiniLab Worksheets,** pp. 10–12 **L2**

**National Science Content Standards**

**Pages 78–79**
UCP.1, UCP.2, UCP.3; A.1; B.2, B.3

## Purpose

Students will learn about efforts to use chemistry to produce quality buildings while decreasing their negative impact on the environment.

## Background

While not always thought of among the top industries that pollute the atmosphere, cement production is one of the most energy-intensive industries in the world. This use of energy, along with chemical reactions involved in the production of cement, release huge amounts of carbon dioxide and other greenhouse gases into the atmosphere every year. Annually, cement production releases as much $CO_2$ as 350 million cars.

Researchers have found a way to use a waste product of coal-burning power plants to decrease the amount of cement used to make concrete. In addition to protecting the environment, the properties of this waste product, known as flyash, lead to a stronger, more durable concrete. Flyash starts out as impurities in coal. Since the impurities cannot be burned, they end up as ash. At high temperatures, they fuse and become glass. As the glass particles move at high speeds with the gases released during the burning of coal, the hot glass turns into tiny beads.

## Teaching Strategies

- Ask students to review the greenhouse effect and to prepare posters showing how it maintains the temperatures on Earth.
- Ask students to debate the possibility of decreasing the amount of concrete used throughout the world. Have them address the issue that the need for cement is expected to double in the next 25 years as developing countries expand their building.
- It takes between 1450 and 1600 kg (3200 to 3500 lb) of raw materials to produce about 907 kg

## Green Buildings

Until the Industrial Revolution, the amount of carbon dioxide ($CO_2$) in the atmosphere was fairly constant. Since the Industrial Revolution, however, the burning of fossil fuels has contributed to a significant increase in the amount of carbon dioxide in the atmosphere. As the level of carbon dioxide increases, Earth gradually warms up. Too much $CO_2$ in the atmosphere can change the conditions on Earth.

Another major source of carbon dioxide may be in the foundation of your building or on the sidewalks near your school. The production of cement, the key ingredient in concrete, releases tremendous amounts of carbon dioxide into the atmosphere. Chemistry may allow engineers to build "green buildings," that are still practical yet have less of an impact on the environment.

### Producing Cement

Cement generally begins with a mixture of limestone and sand placed in a kiln, which heats it to about 1480°C. As the mixture is heated, its chemical and physical properties change. After heating, the solid that remains is ground into a fine powder. This is cement. To make concrete, the cement is mixed with fine particles, such as sand, coarse particles, such as crushed stone, and water.

During the production of cement, carbon dioxide is released in two ways. First, when the limestone is heated it changes into lime and carbon dioxide. Second, the electrical energy used to heat the kiln is usually supplied by a power plant that burns fossil fuels, such as coal. Fossil fuels also release carbon dioxide and other substances.

### Using Flyash

One way to reduce the amount of carbon dioxide released into the atmosphere is to find a replacement for cement in concrete. One such replacement is a substance known as flyash. Flyash is a waste product that accumulates in the smokestacks of power plants when ground coal is burned. It is a fine gray powder that consists of tiny glass beads.

Using flyash offers several advantages. Flyash ordinarily is dumped in landfills. Replacing cement with flyash can reduce $CO_2$ emissions and prevent

tons of waste from piling up in landfills. Flyash also produces better concrete. Traditional concrete has weak zones where tiny cracks allow water to flow through. Flyash contains fine particles that fill spaces and keep moisture out. Flyash also protects the steel surrounding the concrete, makes the concrete easier to work with, and extends the life of the concrete structure. In fact, flyash is so reliable the Romans used natural materials similar to flyash to build the concrete dome of the Pantheon.

Solutions to environmental problems require a willing commitment from scientists, architects, builders, and owners to look for ways to build durable structures and protect the environment.

### Investigating the Issue

1. **Communicating Ideas** Write a pamphlet for people who are building new homes telling them about the importance of green buildings.

2. **Using Resources** Investigate issues that influence the decision to use flyash. Discuss the advantages and disadvantages of flyash.

## Chemistry Online

Visit the Chemistry Web site at **chemistrymc.com** to find links to more information about flyash and green buildings.

(1 ton) of finished cement. Ask students to research and present other statistics related to cement production.
- Some people are concerned about the use of flyash. For example, there is some concern about radioactivity. The EPA believes that flyash does not constitute a significant risk that is any greater than from the cement it replaces. Ask students to find out about any issues related to the use of flyash.

## Investigating the Issue

1. Answers will vary. Students should stress the importance of finding industrial methods that are safe for the environment yet still meet the objectives.
2. Students may consider cost, availability, processing ease, and safety in their discussions.

## Summary

### 3.1 Properties of Matter

- A substance is a form of matter with a uniform and unchanging composition.

- Physical properties can be observed without altering a substance's composition. Chemical properties describe a substance's ability to combine with or change into one or more new substances.

- Both physical and chemical properties are affected by external conditions such as temperature and pressure.

- The three common states of matter are solid, liquid, and gas.

### 3.2 Changes in Matter

- A physical change alters the physical properties of a substance without changing its composition.

- A chemical change, also known as a chemical reaction, involves a change in a substance's composition.

- In a chemical reaction, reactants form products.

- The law of conservation of mass states that mass is neither created nor destroyed during a chemical reaction; it is conserved.

### 3.3 Mixtures of Matter

- A mixture is a physical blend of two or more pure substances in any proportion.

- Solutions are homogeneous mixtures.

- Mixtures can be separated by physical means. Common separation techniques include filtration, distillation, crystallization, and chromatography.

### 3.4 Elements and Compounds

- Elements are substances that cannot be broken down into simpler substances by chemical or physical means.

- The elements are organized in the periodic table of elements.

- A compound is a chemical combination of two or more elements. Properties of compounds differ from the properties of their component elements.

- The law of definite proportions states that a compound is always composed of the same elements in the same proportions.

- The law of multiple proportions states that if elements form more than one compound, those compounds will have compositions that are small, whole-number multiples of each other.

## Key Equations and Relationships

- law of conservation of mass (p. 63)
  $$\text{Mass}_{reactants} = \text{Mass}_{products}$$

- percent by mass $= \dfrac{\text{Mass}_{element}}{\text{Mass}_{compound}} \times 100$

  (p. 75)

## Vocabulary

- chemical change (p. 62)
- chemical property (p. 57)
- chromatography (p. 69)
- compound (p. 71)
- crystallization (p. 69)
- distillation (p. 69)
- element (p. 70)
- extensive properties (p. 56)
- filtration (p. 68 )
- gas (p. 59)

- heterogeneous mixture (p. 67)
- homogeneous mixture (p. 67)
- intensive properties (p. 56)
- law of conservation of mass (p. 63)
- law of definite proportions (p. 75)
- law of multiple proportions (p. 76)
- liquid (p. 58)

- mixture (p. 66)
- percent by mass (p. 75)
- periodic table (p. 70)
- physical changes (p. 61)
- physical property (p. 56)
- solid (p. 58)
- solution (p. 67)
- states of matter (p. 58)
- substance (p. 55)
- vapor (p. 59)

## Using the Vocabulary

To reinforce chapter vocabulary, have students write a sentence using each term. **L2** **ELL**

## Review Strategies

- Have students summarize the differences between physical and chemical properties and physical and chemical change and give an example of each. **L2**
- Have students be able to use the symbols of the most frequently used elements. **L1**
- Have students be able to classify matter according to the scheme given in the chapter. **L1**
- Problems from Appendix A or the **Supplemental Problems** booklet can be used for review. **L2**

## VOCABULARY
## PuzzleMaker

For additional help with vocabulary, have students access the Vocabulary PuzzleMaker online.

**chemistrymc.com/ vocabulary_puzzlemaker**

## Chemistry online

**National Science Content Standards**

**Pages 80–81**
UCP.1, UCP.2, UCP.3; A.1; B.2, B.3, B.6; E.2; F.4, F.6

## Concept Mapping

**31. 1.** physical properties; **2.** state; **3.** solid; **4.** liquid; **5.** gas; **6.** tightly packed particles; **7.** loosely packed particles; **8.** particles far apart; **9.** incompressible; **10.** virtually incompressible; **11.** compressible

## Mastering Concepts

**32.** Answers will vary. Water, salt, and sugar are all substances. Each is a substance because it has a unique and unchanging composition.

**33.** Answers will vary. Tap water is colorless, a liquid, freezes at approximately 0°C, and boils at approximately 100°C.

**34. a.** intensive **c.** intensive
**b.** extensive **d.** extensive

**35.** The statement is false. Properties are affected by changes in temperature, pressure. Specific examples will vary.

**36. a.** liquid **d.** gas
**b.** gas **e.** solid
**c.** solid **f.** solid

**37. a.** physical **d.** physical
**b.** physical **e.** chemical
**c.** chemical **f.** physical

**38.** The volume of the milk remains unchanged. Milk, which is a liquid, conforms to the shape of its container, thus the shape of the milk changes as it is poured from the carton into the bowl.

**39. a.** physical **d.** chemical
**b.** physical **e.** chemical
**c.** chemical

**40.** A change in phase is a physical change because the composition of the substance is not altered.

**41.** Probable indicators of a chemical reaction include a change in color, odor, or temperature, and/or the production of a gas or a solid upon mixing.

**82**

### Chemistry Online

*Go to the Chemistry Web site at chemistrymc.com for additional Chapter 3 Assessment.*

## Concept Mapping

**31.** Organize the following terms into a logical concept map: state, physical properties, virtually incompressible, solid, gas, liquid, tightly packed particles, compressible, incompressible, particles far apart, loosely packed particles.

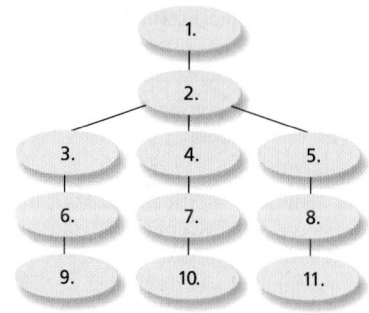

## Mastering Concepts

**32.** List three examples of substances. Explain why each is a substance. (3.1)

**33.** List at least three physical properties of tap water. (3.1)

**34.** Identify each of the following as an extensive or intensive physical property. (3.1)

   **a.** melting point
   **b.** mass
   **c.** density
   **d.** length

**35.** "Properties are not affected by changes in temperature and pressure." Is this statement true or false? Explain. (3.1)

**36.** Classify each of the following as either solid, liquid, or gas at room temperature. (3.1)

   **a.** milk
   **b.** air
   **c.** copper
   **d.** helium
   **e.** diamond
   **f.** candle wax

**37.** Classify each of the following as a physical property or a chemical property. (3.1)

   **a.** aluminum has a silvery color
   **b.** gold has a density of 19 $g/cm^3$
   **c.** sodium ignites when dropped in water
   **d.** water boils at 100°C
   **e.** silver tarnishes
   **f.** mercury is a liquid at room temperature

**38.** A carton of milk is poured into a bowl. Describe the changes that occur in the milk's shape and volume. (3.1)

**39.** Classify each of the following as a physical change or a chemical change. (3.2)

   **a.** breaking a pencil in two
   **b.** water freezing and forming ice
   **c.** frying an egg
   **d.** burning wood
   **e.** leaves turning color in the fall

**40.** Is a change in phase a physical change or a chemical change? Explain. (3.2)

**41.** List four indicators that a chemical change has probably taken place. (3.2)

**42.** Iron and oxygen combine to form iron oxide (rust). List the reactants and products of this reaction. (3.2)

**43.** Use **Table 3-1** to identify a substance that undergoes a phase change as its temperature increases from −250°C to −210°C. What phase change takes place? (3.2)

**44.** After burning for three hours, a candle has lost half of its mass. Explain why this example does not violate the law of conservation of mass. (3.2)

**45.** Describe the difference between a physical change and a chemical change. (3.2)

**46.** Describe the characteristics of a mixture. (3.3)

**47.** Describe a method that could be used to separate each of the following mixtures. (3.3)

   **a.** iron filings and sand
   **b.** sand and salt
   **c.** the components of ink
   **d.** helium and oxygen gases

**48.** "A mixture is the chemical bonding of two or more substances in any proportion." Is this statement true or false. Explain.

**42.** Iron and oxygen are the reactants, while iron oxide is the product formed. Iron + oxygen → iron oxide

## Resource Manager

**Chapter Assessment,** pp. 13–18 **L2**
**Supplemental Problems,** Ch. 3
**ExamView® Pro CD-ROM**
**MindJogger Videoquizzes**
**Solutions Manual,** Ch. 3
**Chemistry Interactive CD-ROM,**
 Ch. 3 quiz

**49.** Which of the following are the same and which are different? (3.3)

   **a.** a substance and a pure substance
   **b.** a heterogeneous mixture and a solution
   **c.** a substance and a mixture
   **d.** a homogeneous mixture and a solution

**50.** Describe how a homogeneous mixture differs from a heterogeneous mixture. (3.3)

**51.** A chemistry professor has developed a laboratory task to give her students practical experience using basic separation techniques. She prepares a liquid solution of water and another compound. Assuming you are a student in the class, name the technique you would use to separate and identify the components. Give specific details of the method.

**52.** State the definition of an element. (3.4)

**53.** Name the elements contained in the following compounds. (3.4)

   **a.** sodium chloride (NaCl)    **c.** ethanol ($C_2H_6O$)
   **b.** ammonia ($NH_3$)          **d.** bromine ($Br_2$)

**54.** How many naturally occurring elements are found on Earth? Approximately how many synthetic elements have been identified? (3.4)

**55.** What was Dmitri Mendeleev's major contribution to the field of chemistry? (3.4)

**56.** Is it possible to distinguish between an element and a compound? Explain. (3.4)

**57.** How are the properties of a compound related to those of the elements that comprise it? (3.4)

**58.** How are the elements contained within a group on the periodic table related? (3.4)

**59.** Which law states that a compound always contains the same elements in the same proportion by mass? (3.4)

## Mastering Problems

### Properties of Matter (3.1)

**60.** A scientist is given the task of identifying an unknown compound on the basis of its physical properties. The substance is a white solid at room temperature. Attempts to determine its boiling point were unsuccessful. Using **Table 3-1**, name the unknown compound.

### Conservation of Mass (3.2)

**61.** A 28.0-g sample of nitrogen gas combines completely with 6.0 g of hydrogen gas to form ammonia. What is the mass of ammonia formed?

**62.** A substance breaks down into its component elements when it is heated. If 68.0 grams of the substance is present before it is heated, what is the combined mass of the component elements after heating?

**63.** A 13.0-g sample of X combines with a 34.0-g sample of Y to form the compound $XY_2$. What is the mass of the reactants?

**64.** Sodium chloride can be formed by the reaction of sodium metal and chlorine gas. If 45.98 g of sodium combines with an excess of chlorine gas to form 116.89 g sodium chloride, what mass of chlorine gas is used in the reaction?

**65.** Copper sulfide is formed when copper and sulfur are heated together. In this reaction, 127 g of copper reacts with 41 g of sulfur. After the reaction is complete, 9 g of sulfur remains unreacted. What is the mass of copper sulfide formed?

### Law of Definite Proportions (3.4)

**66.** A 25.3-g sample of an unknown compound contains 0.8 g of oxygen. What is the percent by mass of oxygen in the compound?

**67.** Magnesium combines with oxygen to form magnesium oxide. If 10.57 g of magnesium reacts completely with 6.96 g of oxygen, what is the percent by mass of oxygen in magnesium oxide?

**68.** When mercury oxide is heated, it decomposes into mercury and oxygen. If 28.4 g of mercury oxide decomposes, producing 2.0 g oxygen, what is the percent by mass of mercury in mercury oxide?

### Law of Multiple Proportions (3.4)

**69.** Carbon reacts with oxygen to form two different compounds. Compound I contains 4.82 g carbon for every 6.44 g of oxygen. Compound II contains 20.13 g carbon for every 53.7 g of oxygen. What is the ratio of carbon to a fixed mass of oxygen for the two compounds?

## Mixed Review

*Sharpen your problem-solving skills by answering the following.*

**70.** Which state of matter is the most compressible? The least? Explain why.

Solid          Liquid          Gas

**43.** Oxygen undergoes a phase change as its temperature increases from −250°C to −210°C. Solid oxygen melts to form liquid oxygen at a temperature of −218°C.

**44.** The mass of the candle is conserved if you consider the gaseous products from the reaction.

**45.** A physical change alters a substance without changing its composition, while a chemical change involves a change in composition.

**46.** Mixtures are a physical blend of two or more substances in any proportion. Mixtures do not have a constant composition. The properties of the mixture are largely those of its component substances.

**47. a.** A magnet can be used to draw the iron filings from the sand.
   **b.** Add water to the mixture to dissolve the salt. Filter the mixture to remove the sand, and then boil off the water so only the salt remains.
   **c.** Paper chromatography should be used to separate the components of the ink. If enough ink is available, distillation may also be used, but is far more complicated than chromatography.
   **d.** Cool the gas mixture until it condenses, then distill the condensate.

**48.** The statement is false because mixtures are a physical blend of substances, not a chemical bonding of substances.

**49. a.** same    **c.** different
   **b.** different   **d.** same

**50.** Homogeneous mixtures contain a single phase. Heterogeneous mixtures may have many phases.

**51.** Using distillation, heat the solution until the boiling point of the aqueous component is reached, then note that temperature. Boil away the aqueous component and observe the remaining component. Use a table such as 3-1 or another resource to identify the components based on the information obtained from the distillation process.

**52.** An element is a substance that cannot be broken down into simpler substances by physical or chemical means.

**53. a.** sodium and chlorine
   **b.** nitrogen and hydrogen
   **c.** carbon, hydrogen, and oxygen
   **d.** bromine

National Science Content Standards

Pages 82–83
UCP.1, UCP.2, UCP.3; B.2, B.3; E.2; G.3

**54.** There are 91 naturally occurring elements. There are more than 20 synthetically produced elements.

**55.** Mendeleev developed the first widely accepted periodic table of elements.

**56.** Yes, elements can be distinguished from compounds. Compounds can be broken down into their component elements, whereas elements cannot be broken down into simpler substances.

**57.** The properties of a compound are unique to that compound and different from those of its component elements.

**58.** Elements within a group of the periodic table have similar chemical and physical properties.

**59.** the law of definite proportions

## Mastering Problems

Complete solutions to Chapter Assessment problems can be found in the **Solutions Manual.**

## Properties of Matter (3.1)
### Level 1
**60.** Table 3-1 shows two compounds that are white solids, but it is sucrose that decomposes before a boiling point is determined. Therefore the unknown substance is sucrose.

## Conservation of Mass (3.2)
### Level 1
**61.** $Mass_{ammonia} = 34.0$ g
**62.** 68.0 g
**63.** 47.0 g

### Level 2
**64.** $Mass_{chlorine} = 70.91$ g
**65.** $Mass_{copper\ sulfide} = 159$ g

## Law of Definite Proportions (3.4)
### Level 1
**66.** $Mass\ percentage_{oxygen} = 3\%$

**71.** Classify each of the following as a homogeneous mixture or a heterogeneous mixture. (3.3)

   **a.** brass (an alloy of zinc and copper)
   **b.** a salad
   **c.** blood
   **d.** powder drink mix dissolved in water

**72.** Phosphorus combines with hydrogen to form phosphine. In this reaction, 123.9 g of phosphorus combines with excess hydrogen to produce 129.9 g of phosphine. After the reaction, 310 g of hydrogen remains unreacted. What mass of hydrogen is used in the reaction? What was the initial mass of hydrogen before the reaction?

**73.** A sample of a certain lead compound contains 6.46 grams of lead for each gram of oxygen. A second sample has a mass of 68.54 g and contains 28.76 g of oxygen. Are the two samples the same?

## Thinking Critically

**74. Applying Concepts** Air is a mixture of many gases, primarily nitrogen, oxygen, and argon. Could distillation be used to separate air into its component gases? Explain.

**75. Interpreting Data** A compound contains elements X and Y. Four samples with different masses were analyzed, and the masses of X and Y in each sample were plotted on a graph. The samples are labeled I, II, III, and IV.

   **a.** Which samples are from the same compound? How do you know?
   **b.** What is the approximate ratio of mass X to mass Y in the samples that are from the same compound?
   **c.** What is the approximate ratio of mass X to mass Y in the sample(s) that are not from the same compound?

**67.** $Mass\ percentage_{oxygen} = 39.7\%$
**68.** $Mass\ percentage_{mercury} = 93.0\%$

## Law of Multiple Proportions (3.4)
### Level 2
**69.** The ratio of carbon to a fixed mass of oxygen in compound I is 0.748:1, while in compound II it is 0.375:1.

## Writing in Chemistry

**76.** Select a synthetic element and prepare a short written report on its development. Be sure to cover recent discoveries, list major research centers that conduct this type of research, and describe the properties of the synthesized element.

**77.** Research the life of a scientist, other than Mendeleev, who contributed to the development of the modern periodic table of elements. Write a brief biography of this person and detail his or her scientific accomplishments.

**78.** The results and interpretations of chemistry experiments and studies are recorded and published in literally hundreds of scientific journals around the world. Visit the local library and look at several of the articles in a chemistry journal such as *The Journal of the American Chemical Society*. Write a brief summary of your observations regarding the format and style of writing in chemistry.

## Cumulative Review

*Refresh your understanding of previous chapters by answering the following.*

**79.** What is chemistry? (Chapter 1)

**80.** What is mass? Weight? (Chapter 1)

**81.** Express the following in scientific notation. (Chapter 2)

   **a.** 34 500      **d.** 789
   **b.** 2665       **e.** 75 600
   **c.** 0.9640    **f.** 0.002 189

**82.** Perform the following operations. (Chapter 2)

   **a.** $10^7 \times 10^3$
   **b.** $(1.4 \times 10^{-3}) \times (5.1 \times 10^{-5})$
   **c.** $(2 \times 10^{-3}) \times (4 \times 10^5)$

**83.** Convert 65°C to Kelvins. (Chapter 2)

**84.** Graph the following data. What is the slope of the line? (Chapter 2)

| Energy Released by Carbon ||
|---|---|
| Mass (g) | Energy released (kJ) |
| 1.00 | 33 |
| 2.00 | 66 |
| 3.00 | 99 |
| 4.00 | 132 |

## Mixed Review

**70.** Gases are the most compressible state of matter, solids the least. Compressibility is determined by the amount of space between particles in each state. Gases have the greatest amount of space between particles, solids the least.

*Use these questions and the test-taking tip to prepare for your standardized test.*

**Interpreting Tables** Use the table to answer questions 1 and 2.

| Mass Analysis of Two Chlorine–Fluorine Compound Samples | | | | |
|---|---|---|---|---|
| Sample | Mass chlorine (g) | Mass fluorine (g) | %Cl | %F |
| I | 13.022 | 6.978 | 65.11 | 34.89 |
| II | 5.753 | 9.248 | ? | ? |

**1.** What are the values for %Cl and %F, respectively, for Sample II?

   **a.** 0.622 and 61.65
   **b.** 61.65 and 38.35
   **c.** 38.35 and 0.622
   **d.** 38.35 and 61.65

**2.** Which of the following statements best describes the relationship between the two samples?

   **a.** The compound in Sample I is the same as in Sample II. Therefore, the mass ratio of Cl to F in both samples will obey the law of definite proportions.
   **b.** The compound in Sample I is the same as in Sample II. Therefore, the mass ratio of Cl to F in both samples will obey the law of multiple proportions.
   **c.** The compound in Sample I is not the same as in Sample II. Therefore, the mass ratio of Cl to F in both samples will obey the law of proportions.
   **d.** The compound in Sample I is not the same as in Sample II. Therefore, the mass ratio of Cl to F in both samples will obey the law of multiple proportions.

**3.** After elements A and B react to completion in a closed container, the ratio of masses of A and B in the container will be the same as before the reaction. This is true because of the law of

   **a.** definite proportions.
   **b.** multiple proportions.
   **c.** conservation of mass.
   **d.** conservation of energy.

**4.** All of the following are physical properties of table sugar (sucrose) EXCEPT

   **a.** forms solid crystals at room temperature.
   **b.** appears as crystals white in color.
   **c.** breaks down into carbon and water vapor when heated.
   **d.** tastes sweet.

**5.** A substance is said to be in the solid state if

   **a.** it is hard and rigid.
   **b.** it can be compressed into a smaller volume.
   **c.** it takes the shape of its container.
   **d.** its matter particles are close together.

**6.** Na, K, Li, and Cs all share very similar chemical properties. In the periodic table of elements, they most likely belong to the same

   **a.** row.          **c.** group.
   **b.** period.       **d.** element.

**7.** A heterogeneous mixture

   **a.** cannot be separated by physical means.
   **b.** is composed of distinct areas of composition.
   **c.** is also called a solution.
   **d.** has the same composition throughout.

**8.** What is the percent by mass of sulfur in sulfuric acid, $H_2SO_4$?

   **a.** 32.69%        **c.** 16.31%
   **b.** 64.13%        **d.** 48.57%

**9.** Magnesium reacts explosively with oxygen to form magnesium oxide. All of the following are true of this reaction EXCEPT

   **a.** The mass of magnesium oxide produced equals the mass of magnesium consumed plus the mass of oxygen consumed.
   **b.** The reaction describes the formation of a new substance.
   **c.** The product of the reaction, magnesium oxide, is a chemical compound.
   **d.** Magnesium oxide has physical and chemical properties similar to both oxygen and magnesium.

**10.** Which of the following is NOT a chemical reaction?

   **a.** dissolution of sodium chloride in water
   **b.** combustion of gasoline
   **c.** fading of wallpaper by sunlight
   **d.** curdling of milk

---

**TEST-TAKING TIP**

**When Eliminating, Cross It Out** Consider each answer choice individually and cross out choices you've eliminated. If you can't write in the test booklet, use the scratch paper. List the answer choice letters on the scratch paper and cross them out there. You'll save time and stop yourself from choosing an answer you've mentally eliminated.

---

**71. a.** homogeneous
     **b.** heterogeneous
     **c.** heterogeneous
     **d.** homogeneous
**72.** $Mass_{hydrogen}$ = 6.0 g
     Initial $mass_{hydrogen}$ = 316 g
**73.** Sample I:
     $Mass_{lead}/Mass_{oxygen}$ = 6.46
     Sample II:
     $Mass_{lead}/Mass_{oxygen}$ = 1.381
     The two samples are not the same because the two $Mass_{lead}/Mass_{oxygen}$ ratios are not the same.

## Thinking Critically

**74.** If the mixture of gases is cooled sufficiently, it will condense into a mixture of liquids. This mixture could then be distilled.
**75. a.** Samples I, III, and IV are the same compound. A straight line can be drawn through these three plotted points. The slope of the line is equivalent to ratio $Mass_X/Mass_Y$. The fact that all three points are on the same line shows that they all have the same mass ratio of X to Y and must be the same compound.
     **b.** Mass ratio of X to Y for samples I, III, and IV is 3.75:1.
     **c.** Sample II mass ratio is 1.9:1

## Cumulative Review

**79.** Chemistry is the study of matter and the changes that it undergoes.
**80.** Mass is the measure of the amount of matter an object contains. It is measured on a balance.

---

The weight of an object is the amount of gravitational pull acting on the mass of an object. It is measured on a scale.
**81. a.** $3.45 \times 10^4$      **d.** $7.89 \times 10^2$
     **b.** $2.665 \times 10^3$    **e.** $7.56 \times 10^4$
     **c.** $9.640 \times 10^{-1}$  **f.** $2.189 \times 10^{-3}$
**82. a.** $10^{10}$

   **b.** $7.1 \times 10^{-8}$
   **c.** $8 \times 10^2$
**83.** 338 K
**84.** Slope = 33 kJ/g

## Standardized Test Practice

| | | | | |
|---|---|---|---|---|
| **1.** d | **3.** c | **5.** a | **7.** b | **9.** d |
| **2.** d | **4.** c | **6.** c | **8.** a | **10.** a |

---

**National Science Content Standards**

**Pages 84–85**
UCP.1, UCP.2, UCP.3; B.2, B.3; E.2; G.3

# Resource Manager

| Section | Objectives | Activities/Features |
|---|---|---|
| **Section 4.1**<br>**Early Theories of Matter**<br>1 session<br>1/2 block | **1. Compare** and **contrast** the atomic models of Democritus and Dalton.<br>**2. Define** an atom. | **Discovery Lab:** Observing Electrical Charge, p. 87<br>**History Connection,** p. 90 |
| **Section 4.2**<br>**Subatomic Particles and the Nuclear Atom**<br>1 session<br>1/2 block | **3. Distinguish** between the subatomic particles in terms of relative charge and mass.<br>**4. Describe** the structure of the nuclear atom, including the locations of the subatomic particles. | **Problem-Solving Lab:** Interpreting STM Images, p. 96 |
| **Section 4.3**<br>**How Atoms Differ**<br>2 sessions<br>1 block | **5. Explain** the role of atomic number in determining the identity of an atom.<br>**6. Define** an isotope and **explain** why atomic masses are not whole numbers.<br>**7. Calculate** the number of electrons, protons, and neutrons in an atom given its mass number and atomic number. | **MiniLab:** Modeling Isotopes, p. 102 |
| **Section 4.4**<br>**Unstable Nuclei and Radioactive Decay**<br>2 sessions<br>1 block | **8. Explain** the relationship between unstable nuclei and radioactive decay.<br>**9. Characterize** alpha, beta, and gamma radiation in terms of mass and charge. | **Careers Using Chemistry:** Radiation Protection Technician, p. 106<br>**ChemLab:** Very Small Particles, pp. 108–109<br>**Chemistry and Society:** Nanotechnology, p. 110 |

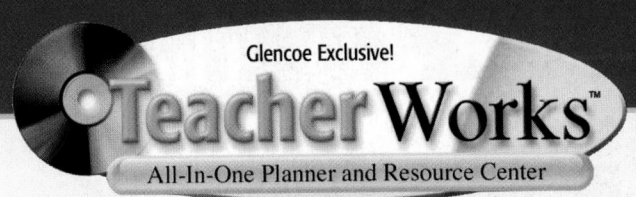

Glencoe Exclusive!
**TeacherWorks™**
All-In-One Planner and Resource Center

| National Science Content Standards | State/Local Standards | Reproducible Masters | Transparencies |
|---|---|---|---|
| UCP.1, UCP.2; A.1; B.1, B.2, B.4; G.2, G.3 | | **Study Guide for Content Mastery,** p. 19 L2 | **Section Focus** Transparency 13 L1 ELL |
| UCP.1, UCP.2; A.2; B.1, B.4; G.1, G.2, G.3 | | **Study Guide for Content Mastery,** p. 20 L2 <br> **Laboratory Manual,** pp. 25–28 L2 | **Section Focus** Transparency 14 L1 ELL <br> **Teaching** Transparencies 11, 12 L2 ELL |
| UCP.1, UCP.2; A.1; B.1, B.2; G.2 | | **Study Guide for Content Mastery,** pp. 21–23 L2 <br> **ChemLab and MiniLab Worksheets,** p. 13 L2 <br> **Challenge Problems,** p. 4 L3 | **Section Focus** Transparency 15 L1 ELL <br> **Teaching** Transparency 13 L2 ELL <br> **Math Skills** Transparency 4 L2 ELL |
| UCP.1, UCP.2; A.1; B.1, B.2, B.4, B.6; E.1, E.2; F.5, F.6; G.3 | | **Study Guide for Content Mastery,** p. 24 L2 <br> **ChemLab and MiniLab Worksheets,** pp. 14–16 L2 <br> **Laboratory Manual,** pp. 29–32 L2 | **Section Focus** Transparency 16 L1 ELL <br> **Teaching** Transparency 14 L2 ELL |

**Key to National Science Content Standards:** UCP = Unifying Concepts and Processes, A = Science as Inquiry, B = Physical Science, C = Life Science, D = Earth and Space Sciences, E = Science and Technology, F = Science in Personal and Social Perspectives, G = History and Nature of Science

Refer to pages 4T–5T of the Teacher Guide for an explanation of the National Science Content Standards correlations.

# The Structure of the Atom

## Resource Manager

### Materials List

**ChemLab** (pages 108–109)
vanilla extract (6 mL), 9-inch latex balloon (2), dropper

**Discovery Lab** (page 87)
plastic comb, hole punch, paper, ruler, clear plastic tape (four 10-cm long pieces)

**MiniLab** (page 102)
balance, bag of pre- and post-1982 pennies

**Demonstration** (pages 92–93)
Crooke's tube, high-voltage power supply, bar magnet

### Preparation of Solutions

For a review of solution preparation, see page 46T of the Teacher Guide.

There are no solutions to be prepared for the activities in this chapter.

### Assessment Resources

**Chapter Assessment,** pp. 19–24
**MindJogger Videoquizzes DVD/VHS**
**Alternate Assessment in the Science Classroom**
**ExamView® Pro CD-ROM**
**Solutions Manual,** Chapter 4
**Supplemental Problems,** Chapter 4
**Performance Assessment in the Science Classroom**
**Chemistry Interactive CD-ROM,** Chapter 4 quiz

### Additional Resources

**Spanish Resources** ELL
**Guided Reading Audio Program,** Chapter 4 ELL
**Cooperative Learning in the Science Classroom**
**Lab and Safety Skills in the Science Classroom**
**Lesson Plans**
**Block Scheduling Lesson Plans**
**Chemistrymc.com**

## Glencoe Technology

The following multimedia for this chapter are available from Glencoe.

**VIDEOTAPE/DVD**
MindJogger Videoquizzes,
Chapter 4

**CD-ROM**
**Chemistry: Matter and Change**
*History of the Atomic Theory,* Video
*Discovery of the Electron,* Experiment
*Thomson's Experiment,* Demonstration
*Rutherford's Gold,* Animation
*Evidence for Alpha Particles,*
   Demonstration

**CD-ROM**
**ExamView® Pro**
   **Testmaker**

**CD-ROM**
**Interactive Chalkboard**

**CD-ROM**
**TeacherWorks™**

## Multiple Learning Styles

Look for the following icons for strategies that emphasize different learning modalities.

***Kinesthetic***
Differentiated Instruction, pp. 95, 98, 106;
Reteach, p. 97

***Visual-Spatial***
Differentiated Instruction, p. 89; Chemistry
Journal, p. 94; Extension, p. 97; Enrichment, p. 103

***Interpersonal***
Check for Understanding, p. 107

***Intrapersonal***
Enrichment, p. 88; Extension, p. 89

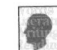
***Linguistic***
Chemistry Journal, pp. 88, 100; Reteach, p. 91;
Portfolio, p. 101; Enrichment, p. 93; Differentiated
Instruction, p. 94

***Logical-Mathematical***
Check for Understanding, p. 104

## Key to Teaching Strategies

**L1** Level 1 activities should be appropriate for students with
learning difficulties.

**L2** Level 2 activities should be within the ability range of
all students.

**L3** Level 3 activities are designed for above-average students.

**ELL** ELL activities should be within the ability range of
English Language Learners.

**COOP LEARN** Cooperative Learning activities are designed
for small group work.

**P** These strategies represent student products that can be
placed into a best-work portfolio.

These strategies are useful in a block scheduling format.

## Assessment Planner

**Portfolio Assessment**
Portfolio, TWE, pp. 101, 111
Assessment, p. 95

**Performance Assessment**
Assessment, TWE, pp. 91, 101
ChemLab, TWE, p. 109
Problem-Solving Lab, TWE,
   p. 96
MiniLab, TWE, p. 102
ChemLab, SE, pp. 108–109
Discovery Lab, SE, p. 87
MiniLab, SE, p. 102

**Knowledge Assessment**
Assessment, TWE, p. 107
Section Assessment, SE,
   pp. 91, 97, 104, 107
Chapter Assessment, SE,
   pp. 112–115

**Skill Assessment**
Assessment, TWE, pp. 89, 97,
   104
Demonstration, TWE, p. 93

## Tying to Previous Knowledge

Have students review the following concepts before studying this chapter.
Chapter 1: matter, scientific laws, theories
Chapter 3: elements, laws of definite and multiple proportions

## Using the Photo

Textbooks from 30 years ago claimed that no one could see atoms due to their extremely small size. Today, images of atoms are commonly seen in textbooks. Why? The development of the scanning tunneling microscope in 1981 has made these images possible.

### INTERACTIVE CHALKBOARD
#### with Image Bank

**PowerPoint® Presentations**
This CD-ROM is an editable Microsoft® PowerPoint® presentation that includes:
• Section presentations
• Section checks
• Image bank
• Links to Chemistry Online
• All transparencies
• Animations
• Audio

### Resource Manager

**Study Guide for Content Mastery**, p. 19 L2
**Solving Problems: A Chemistry Handbook**, Section 4.1 L2
**Section Focus Transparency 13 and Master** L1 ELL

# The Structure of the Atom

## What You'll Learn

▶ You will identify the experiments that led to the development of the nuclear model of atomic structure.
▶ You will describe the structure of the atom and differentiate among the subatomic particles that comprise it.
▶ You will explain the relationship between nuclear stability and radioactivity.

## Why It's Important

The world you know is made of matter, and all matter is composed of atoms. Understanding the structure of the atom is fundamental to understanding why matter behaves the way it does.

### Chemistry Online

Visit the Chemistry Web site at chemistrymc.com to find links about the structure of the atom.

Not only can individual atoms be seen, but scientists now have the ability to arrange them into patterns and simple devices. The atoms shown here have been arranged to form the Japanese kanji characters for atom.

**86** Chapter 4

## DISCOVERY LAB

### Purpose
Students will observe the behavior of charged objects.

### Teaching Strategies
• Any brand of plastic tape should give the same results.
• When rubbed, plastic and hard rubber gain a negative charge; glass, fur, and wool gain a positive charge.

• Remind students that charging the objects is a separation of existing electrical charge, not the creation of new electrical charge.
• Make a list of materials with the same charge as the tape stuck to the table and a list of those materials with the same charge as the pieces of tape that were stuck together.

## DISCOVERY LAB

### Observing Electrical Charge

Electrical charge plays an important role in atomic structure and throughout chemistry. How can you observe the behavior of electrical charge using common objects?

**Procedure**

1. Cut out small round pieces of paper using the hole punch and spread them out on a table. Run a plastic comb through your hair. Bring the comb close to the pieces of paper. Record your observations.

2. Fold a 1-cm long portion of each piece of tape back on itself to form a handle. Stick two pieces of tape firmly to your desktop. Quickly pull both pieces of tape off of the desktop and bring them close together so that their non-sticky sides face each other. Record your observations.

3. Firmly stick one of the remaining pieces of tape to your desktop. Firmly stick the last piece of tape on top of the first. Quickly pull the pieces of tape as one from the desktop and then pull them apart. Bring the two tape pieces close together so that their non-sticky sides face each other. Record your observations.

**Materials**

metric ruler
plastic comb
hole punch
paper

10-cm long
piece of
clear plastic
tape (4)

**Analysis**

Use your knowledge of electrical charge to explain your observations. Which charges are similar? Which are different? How do you know?

---

## Early Theories of Matter

### Section 4.1

**Objectives**

• **Compare** and **contrast** the atomic models of Democritus and Dalton.

• **Define** an atom.

**Vocabulary**

Dalton's atomic theory
atom

Perhaps you have never seen a photo of individual atoms as shown on the previous page, but chances are you've heard of atoms ever since you were in elementary school. From atom smashers and atomic power to the reality of the atomic bomb, you are already familiar with many modern atom-based processes. Surprisingly, the idea that matter is composed of tiny particles (which we now call atoms) did not even exist a few thousand years ago. In fact, for more than a thousand years, great thinkers of their day argued against the idea that atoms existed. As you will see, the development of the concept of the atom and our understanding of atomic structure are fascinating stories involving scores of great thinkers and scientists.

### The Philosophers

Science as we know it today did not exist several thousand years ago. No one knew what a controlled experiment was, and there were few tools for scientific exploration. In this setting, the power of mind and intellectual thought were considered the primary avenues to the truth. Curiosity sparked the interest of scholarly thinkers known as philosophers who considered the many mysteries of life. As they speculated about the nature of matter, many of the philosophers formulated explanations based on their own life experiences.

4.1 Early Theories of Matter **87**

---

### Focus Transparency

Before presenting the lesson, display **Section Focus Transparency 13** on the overhead projector. Have students answer the accompanying questions using **Section Focus Transparency Master 13.** L1 ELL

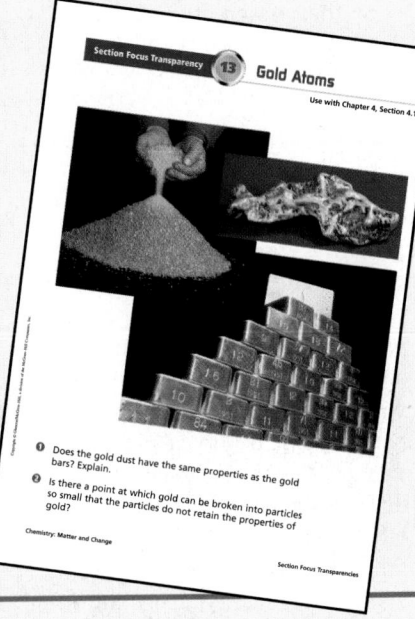

Section Focus Transparency 13 — Gold Atoms
Use with Chapter 4, Section 4.1

❶ Does the gold dust have the same properties as the gold bars? Explain.

❷ Is there a point at which gold can be broken into particles so small that the particles do not retain the properties of gold?

Chemistry: Matter and Change

Section Focus Transparencies

### Chapter Themes

The following themes from the National Science Education Standards are covered in this chapter. Refer to page 4T of the Teacher Guide for an explanation of the correlations.

Systems, order, and organization (UCP. 1); Evidence, models, and explanation (UCP.2); Change, constancy, and measurement (UCP. 3); Evolution and equilibrium (UCP. 4); Form and function (UCP. 5)

---

**Expected Results**

Step 1: The pieces of paper are attracted to the comb.
Step 2: The pieces of tape repel each other as they are brought together.
Step 3: The pieces of tape attract each other as they are brought together.

**Analysis**

Like electrical charges repel each other, whereas opposite electrical charges attract each other. The objects that repelled each other had similar charges. The objects that attracted each other had opposite charges.

### National Science Content Standards

**Pages 86–87**
UCP.1, UCP.2; A.1; B.1, B.2, B.4; G.2, G.3

Build a "mousetrap" sort of device using a marble that descends down a series of shoots, turns wheels, rings bells, and makes various noises. Many of these are available in children's board games. Shield the device with a cardboard box. You may wish to make part of the marble's descent visible through cutout windows. Ask the students to draw what they think is going on inside the box based on their observations and have them draw parallels to discovery of the parts of the atom.

## Enrichment

**Intrapersonal** Prior to the seventeenth century, scientists were known as natural philosophers who relied on the method of deductive reasoning to explain the world around them. In this method, philosophers observed events and extrapolated those observations through the use of reason back to other specific situations. The process was deductive because it went from general to specific, from universal to individual.

Sir Francis Bacon (1561–1626), an English lawyer and philosopher, argued passionately that although deductive reasoning might work in the realm of mathematics, the laws of science had to be induced, to be established as generalizations drawn from a vast amount of experimental observations. Have students compare inductive and deductive reasoning, citing examples of each. **L2**

**Figure 4-1**

Many Greek philosophers thought matter was formed of air, earth, fire, and water. They also associated properties with each of the four basic components of matter. The pairings of opposite properties, such as hot and cold, and wet and dry, mirrored the symmetry and balance the philosophers observed in nature. These early nonscientific and incorrect beliefs were not completely dispelled until the 1800s.

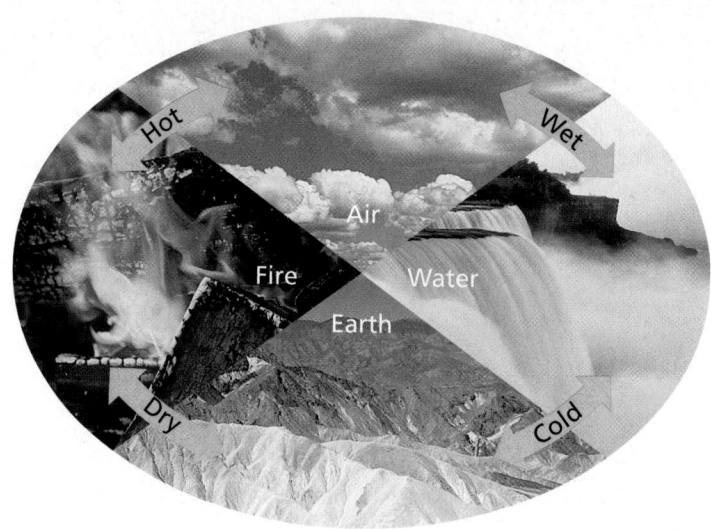

It wasn't surprising then, that many of them concluded that matter was composed of things such as earth, water, air, and fire. See **Figure 4-1.** It was also commonly accepted that matter could be endlessly divided into smaller and smaller pieces. While these early ideas were creative, there was no method for testing their validity.

The Greek philosopher Democritus (460–370 B.C.) was the first person to propose the idea that matter was not infinitely divisible. He believed matter was made up of tiny individual particles called *atomos,* from which the English word atom is derived. Democritus believed that atoms could not be created, destroyed, or further divided. Democritus and a summary of his ideas are shown in **Figure 4-2.**

While a fair amount of Democritus's ideas do not agree with modern atomic theory, his belief in the existence of atoms was amazingly ahead of his time. Despite this, his ideas did not turn out to be a major step toward our current understanding of matter. Over time, Democritus's ideas were met with criticism from other philosophers. "What holds the atoms together?" they asked. Democritus could not answer the question. Other criticisms came from Aristotle (384–322 B.C.), one of the most influential Greek philosophers. Aristotle is shown in **Figure 4-3.** He rejected the atomic "theory" entirely

**Figure 4-2**

The Greek philosopher Democritus (460–370 B.C.) proposed the concept of the atom more than two thousand years ago.

### Democritus's Ideas

- Matter is composed of empty space through which atoms move.
- Atoms are solid, homogeneous, indestructible, and indivisible.
- Different kinds of atoms have different sizes and shapes.
- The differing properties of matter are due to the size, shape, and movement of atoms.
- Apparent changes in matter result from changes in the groupings of atoms and not from changes in the atoms themselves.

**88      Chapter 4** The Structure of the Atom

### The Point of the Matter

**Linguistic** Show students a reproduction of any of Georges Seurat's artwork which use the pointillistic technique. *Sunday Afternoon on the Grande Jatte* is a good example. Show them the work at a distance and then gradually decrease the viewing distance. Ask them to write how the artwork parallels Democritus's ideas about the composition of matter. **L2**

### Aristotle

- One of the most influential philosophers.
- Wrote extensively on many subjects, including politics, ethics, nature, physics, and astronomy.
- Most of his writings have been lost through the ages.

**Figure 4-3**

The Greek philosopher Aristotle (384–322 B.C.) was influential in the rejection of the concept of the atom.

because it did not agree with his own ideas on nature. One of Aristotle's major criticisms concerned the idea that atoms moved through empty space. He did not believe that the "nothingness" of empty space could exist. Unable to answer the challenges to his ideas, Democritus's atomic theory was eventually rejected.

In fairness to Democritus, it was impossible for him or anyone else of his time to determine what held the atoms together. More than two thousand years would pass before the answer was known. However, it is important to realize that Democritus's ideas were just that—ideas and not science. Without the benefit of being able to conduct controlled experiments, Democritus could not test to see if his ideas were valid.

Unfortunately for the advancement of science, Aristotle was able to gain wide acceptance for his ideas on nature—ideas that denied the existence of atoms. Incredibly, the influence of Aristotle was so great and the development of science so primitive that his denial of the existence of atoms went largely unchallenged for two thousand years!

## John Dalton

Although the concept of the atom was revived in the 18th century, it took the passing of another hundred years before significant progress was made. The work done in the 19th century by John Dalton (1766–1844), a schoolteacher in England, marks the beginning of the development of modern atomic theory. Dalton revived and revised Democritus's ideas based upon the results of scientific research he conducted. The main points of **Dalton's atomic theory** are shown in **Figure 4-4**.

### Dalton's Atomic Theory

- All matter is composed of extremely small particles called atoms.
- All atoms of a given element are identical, having the same size, mass, and chemical properties. Atoms of a specific element are different from those of any other element.
- Atoms cannot be created, divided into smaller particles, or destroyed.
- Different atoms combine in simple whole-number ratios to form compounds.
- In a chemical reaction, atoms are separated, combined, or rearranged.

**Figure 4-4**

John Dalton's (1766–1844) atomic theory was a breakthrough in our understanding of matter.

4.1 Early Theories of Matter   **89**

## Extension

**Intrapersonal** John Dalton, a practicing Quaker, left school at age 11 and then returned to teach at the ripe old age of 12! Dalton's first love was meteorology, and he kept careful daily recordings of the weather for 57 years. His book *Meteorological Observations and Essays* (1793) qualified him as one of the pioneers in this area of study. Such meteorological studies led Dalton to think about the composition and properties of air. By studying the works of Democritus, Boyle, and Proust, Dalton went on to formalize his own atomic theory. This theory extended beyond simply gases—it encompassed all matter. Dalton advanced his theory in his book *New System of Chemical Philosophy* (1808). Have students research Dalton's original writings on his atomic theory, citing examples of where the theory has been found to be in error and where it is still held to be true. **L3**

## Enrichment

Obtain a video or videodisc of Ray and Charles Eames' "Powers of Ten," a short and excellent dramatization that takes students on a journey from the subatomic level to intergalactic space. The video also provides an excellent review of scientific notation.

### ✓ Assessment

**Skill** Given the number of atoms in a penny, have students calculate the approximate volume of a single atom of copper. Then have them determine the number of atoms it would take to fill up any volume of interest, such as a 2-liter soda bottle. **L2**

---

## *GLENCOE* TECHNOLOGY

**CD-ROM**
**Chemistry: Matter and Change**
Video: *History of the Atomic Theory*

### DIFFERENTIATED INSTRUCTION

## Hearing Impaired

**Visual-Spatial** John Dalton believed that chemical formulas should be encoded as pictographs, in which each element had a particular drawing associated with it. Have students research Dalton's pictographs and draw both the pictograph and its letter symbol counterpart. **L2**

National Science Content Standards
Pages 88–89
UCP.1, UCP.2; B.2; G.2, G.3

**Page 90** What similarities and differences can you find between the two theories? Similarities: matter composed of atoms; atoms are indestructible and indivisible; changes in matter are due to changes in groupings of atoms. Differences: Democritus states that matter is composed of empty space through which atoms move, whereas Dalton makes no such claims.

## Quick Demo

Place a 1-cm grid on an overhead projector. Place a clear lid or tray filled with water on top of the grid. Make an oleic acid solution (0.50% dissolved in methanol). Using a pipette and a small graduated cylinder, have students calculate the volume of a single drop of 0.50% oleic acid. Next, sprinkle the surface of the water with lycopodium or talcum powder. Place a single drop of the oleic acid in the middle of the water. The acid will spread out to the thickness of one molecule. Have students calculate the area by counting the cm squares. The density of oleic acid is 0.895 g/cm³ and the molecule has a length and width of 1/10 its thickness. Have students calculate the mass and thickness of the molecule. Dispose of the oleic acid, lycopodium powder, talcum powder, and methanol by rinsing them down the drain with a large volume of water. Tell students mass = (volume) (density) and thickness = (volume/area). **L2**

**National Science Content Standards**

**Pages 90–91**
UCP.1, UCP.2; B.2; G.2, G.3

---

**Figure 4-5**

Dalton's atomic theory explains the conservation of mass when a compound forms from its component elements. Atoms of elements A and B combine in a simple whole-number ratio, in this case two B atoms for each A atom, to form a compound. Because the atoms are only rearranged in the chemical reactions, their masses are conserved.

Atoms of element A
Total mass = mass A

Atoms of element B
Total mass = mass B

Compound composed
of elements A and B
Total mass = (mass A + mass B)

## History
### CONNECTION

Alchemy, a popular pursuit during the Middle Ages, was the search for a way to transform common metals into gold. "Scientists" who studied alchemy did not succeed in producing gold, but their experiments revealed the properties of various metals and helped advance our understanding of matter. During the seventeenth century some alchemists began focusing on identifying new compounds and reactions—these alchemists were probably the first true chemists. By the twentieth century, scientists could transform atoms of some elements into atoms of other elements by bombarding them with neutrons. Even this process, however, has not succeeded in producing gold.

The advancements in science since Democritus's day served Dalton well, as he was able to perform experiments that allowed him to refine and verify his theories. Dalton studied numerous chemical reactions, making careful observations and measurements along the way. He was able to accurately determine the mass ratios of the elements involved in the reactions. Based on this research, he proposed his atomic theory in 1803. In many ways Democritus's and Dalton's theories are similar. What similarities and differences can you find between the two theories?

Recall from Chapter 3 that the law of conservation of mass states that mass is conserved in any process, such as a chemical reaction. Dalton's atomic theory easily explains the conservation of mass in chemical reactions as being the result of the separation, combination, or rearrangement of atoms—atoms that are not created, destroyed, or divided in the process. The formation of a compound from the combining of elements and the conservation of mass during the process are shown in **Figure 4-5**. Dalton's convincing experimental evidence and clear explanation of the composition of compounds and conservation of mass led to the general acceptance of his atomic theory.

Was Dalton's atomic theory a huge step toward our current atomic model of matter? Yes. Was all of Dalton's theory accurate? No. As is often the case in science, Dalton's theory had to be revised as additional information was learned that could not be explained by the theory. As you will soon learn, Dalton was wrong about atoms being indivisible (they are divisible into several subatomic particles) and about all atoms of a given element having identical properties (atoms of an element may have slightly different masses).

## Defining the Atom

Many experiments since Dalton's time have proven that atoms do actually exist. So what exactly then is the definition of an atom? To answer this question, consider a gold ring. Suppose you decide to grind the ring down into a pile of gold dust. Each fragment of gold dust still retains all of the properties of gold. If it were possible—which it is not without special equipment—you could continue to divide the gold dust particles into still smaller particles. Eventually you would encounter a particle that could not be divided any further and still retain the properties of gold. This smallest particle of an element that retains the properties of the element is called an **atom**.

Just how small is a typical atom? To get some idea of its size, consider the population of the world. In the year 2000, the world population was approximately 6 000 000 000 (six billion) people. By comparison, a typical solid copper penny contains almost five billion times as many atoms of copper!

World population                                6 000 000 000
Atoms in a penny            29 000 000 000 000 000 000 000

**90**     **Chapter 4** The Structure of the Atom

---

## Section ④·① Assessment

1. Democritus could not explain what held atoms together or verify that atoms moved through empty space.
2. An atom is the fundamental building block of nature. It is the smallest component of an element that exhibits all of the characteristic properties of that element.

3. Dalton was wrong about atoms being indivisible (they are made up of subatomic protons, neutrons, and electrons) and about all atoms of a given element having identical properties (the masses of isotopes differ).
4. Democritus developed his ideas about atoms through intellectual thought, whereas Dalton developed his ideas by

The diameter of a single copper atom is $1.28 \times 10^{-10}$m. Placing six billion copper atoms (equal in number to the world's population) side by side would result in a line of copper atoms less than one meter long.

You might think that because atoms are so small there would be no way to actually see them. However, an instrument called the scanning tunneling microscope allows individual atoms to be seen. Do the **problem-solving LAB** on page 96 to analyze scanning tunneling microscope images and gain a better understanding of atomic size. As **Figures 4-6a** and **4-6b** illustrate, not only can individual atoms be seen, scientists are now able to move individual atoms around to form shapes, patterns, and even simple machines. This capability has led to the exciting new field of nanotechnology. The promise of nanotechnology is molecular manufacturing—the atom-by-atom building of machines the size of molecules. As you'll learn in later chapters, a molecule is a group of atoms that are bonded together and act as a unit. While this technology is not yet feasible for the production of consumer products, progress toward that goal has been made. To learn more about nanotechnology, read the **Chemistry and Society** at the end of this chapter.

The acceptance of atomic theory was only the beginning of our understanding of matter. Once scientists were fairly convinced of the existence of atoms, the next set of questions to be answered emerged. What is an atom like? How are atoms shaped? Is the composition of an atom uniform throughout, or is it composed of still smaller particles? While many scientists researched the atom in the 1800s, it was not until almost 1900 that answers to some of these questions were found. The next section explores the discovery of subatomic particles and the further evolution of atomic theory.

**Figure 4-6**

**a** This colorized scanning electron micrograph shows a microgear mechanism.
**b** A mound of gold atoms (yellow, red, and brown) is easily discerned from the graphite substrate (green) it rests on.

## Section 4.1 Assessment

1. Why were Democritus's ideas rejected by other philosophers of his time?

2. Define an atom using your own words.

3. Which statements in Dalton's original atomic theory are now considered to be incorrect? Describe how modern atomic theory differs from these statements.

4. **Thinking Critically** Democritus and Dalton both proposed the concept of atoms. Describe the method each of them used to reach the conclusion that atoms existed. How did Democritus's method hamper the acceptance of his ideas?

5. **Comparing and Contrasting** Compare and contrast the atomic theories proposed by Democritus and John Dalton.

chemistrymc.com/self_check_quiz

performing experiments and making careful measurements. Because Democritus used only thought and not controlled experiments, he had no observable facts to support his ideas and no means of testing his theories.

5. Both believed: matter composed of extremely small particles called atoms; all atoms of a given element are identical, but differ from the atoms of other elements; atoms could not be created, divided, or destroyed; apparent changes in matter result from changes in the groupings of atoms. Democritus further believed that matter is composed of empty space through which atoms move,

that different kinds of atoms come in different sizes and shapes, and that the differing properties of atoms are due to the size, shape, and movement of the atoms. Dalton further specified that different atoms combine in simple whole number ratios to form compounds.

**91**

# 1 Focus

Before presenting the lesson, display **Section Focus Transparency 14** on the overhead projector. Have students answer the accompanying questions using **Section Focus Transparency Master 14.** **L1** **ELL**

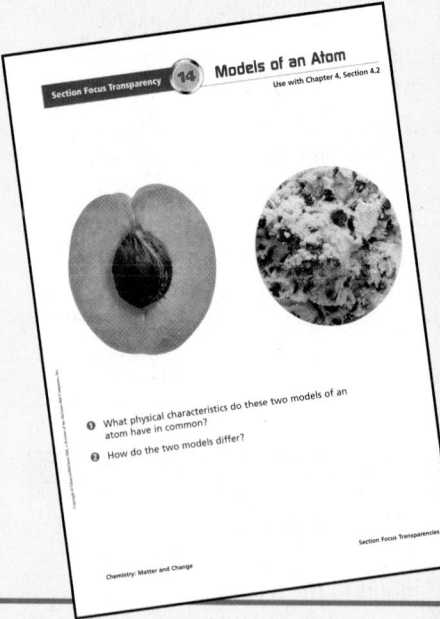

# 2 Teach

**Quick Demo**

Use an electroscope or pith balls to show the transfer of electrons and the consequences. Rub a Lucite wand with fur or silk (this pulls off the electrons from the material) and then touch the wand to the electroscope or pith balls. The foil leaves of the electroscope (or the pith balls themselves) will acquire a negative charge that will cause them to separate from each other. Reinforce that like charges repel.

**National Science Content Standards**

Pages 92–93
UCP.1, UCP.2; A.2; B.1, B.4; G.1, G.3

---

### Objectives

• **Distinguish** between the subatomic particles in terms of relative charge and mass.

• **Describe** the structure of the nuclear atom, including the locations of the subatomic particles.

### Vocabulary

cathode ray
electron
nucleus
proton
neutron

# Subatomic Particles and the Nuclear Atom

In 1839, American inventor Charles Goodyear accidentally heated a mixture of natural rubber and sulfur. The resulting reaction greatly strengthened the rubber. This new rubber compound revolutionized the rubber industry and was eventually used in the manufacturing of automobile tires. Accidental discoveries such as this have occurred throughout the history of science. Such is the case with the discovery of subatomic particles, the particles that make up atoms.

## Discovering the Electron

Has your hair ever clung to your comb? Have you ever received a shock from a metal doorknob after walking across a carpeted floor? Observations such as these led scientists in the 1800s to look for some sort of relationship between matter and electric charge. To explore the connection, some scientists wondered how electricity might behave in the absence of matter. With the help of the recently invented vacuum pump, they passed electricity through glass tubes from which most of the air (and most of the matter) had been removed.

A typical tube used by researchers studying the relationship between mass and charge is illustrated in **Figure 4-7.** Note that metal electrodes are located on opposite ends of the tube. The electrode connected to the negative terminal of the battery is called the cathode, and the electrode connected to the positive terminal is called the anode.

One day while working in a darkened laboratory, English physicist Sir William Crookes noticed a flash of light within one of the tubes. The flash was produced by some form of radiation striking a light-producing coating that had been applied to the end of the tube. Further work showed there were rays (radiation) traveling from the cathode to the anode within the tube. Because the ray of radiation originated from the cathode end of the tube, it became known as a **cathode ray.** The accidental discovery of the cathode ray led to the invention of one of the most important technological and social developments of the 20th century—the television. Television and computer monitor images are formed as radiation from the cathode strikes light-producing chemicals that coat the backside of the screen.

**Figure 4-7**

Examine the parts of a typical cathode ray tube. Note that the electrodes take on the charge of the battery terminal to which they are connected. The cathode ray travels from the cathode to the anode.

---

**Demonstration**

### Thomson's Experiment

**Purpose**
To observe the characteristics of a cathode-ray tube

**Materials**
Crookes's tube (cathode-ray tube); high-voltage DC power supply; bar magnet

**Safety Precautions**
**Disposal** Items can be saved and reused.

**Procedure**
Connect the two electrodes of the power supply to the ends of the tube using wires with alligator clips on each end. Turn on the power supply. **CAUTION:** *The high-voltage power supply can cause severe electric shocks.*

If the tube fails to light, increase the voltage from the power supply. If the tube still fails to light, turn off the power supply

Voltage source

Hole

Anode

Cathode

Gas at low pressure

**1** A tiny hole located in the center of the anode produces a thin beam of electrons. A phosphor coating allows the position of the beam to be determined as it strikes the end of the tube. Because altering the gas in the tube and the material used for the cathode have no effect on the cathode ray, the particles in the ray must be part of all matter.

**2** The fact that the cathode ray is deflected in a magnetic field indicates that it is composed of charged particles.

S

N

Magnet

Electrically charged plates

**3** Because the cathode ray is deflected toward the positively charged plate by an electric field, the particles in the ray must have a negative charge.

**Figure 4-8**

Multiple experiments helped determine the properties of cathode rays.

Scientists continued their research using cathode ray tubes, and by the end of the 1800s they were fairly convinced of the following:

• Cathode rays were actually a stream of charged particles.
• The particles carried a negative charge. (The exact value of the negative charge was not known, however.)

Because changing the type of electrode or varying the gas (at very low pressure) in the cathode ray tube did not affect the cathode ray produced, it was concluded that the ray's negative particles were found in all forms of matter. These negatively charged particles that are part of all forms of matter are now called **electrons**. The range of experiments used to determine the properties of the cathode ray are shown in **Figure 4-8**.

In spite of the progress made from all of the cathode ray tube experiments, no one had succeeded in determining the mass of a single cathode ray particle. Unable to measure the particle's mass directly, English physicist J.J. Thomson (1856–1940) began a series of cathode ray tube experiments in the late 1890s to determine the ratio of its charge to its mass. By carefully measuring the effect of both magnetic and electric fields on a cathode ray, Thomson was able to determine the charge-to-mass ratio of the charged particle. He then compared that ratio to other known ratios. Thomson concluded that the mass of the charged particle was much less than that of a hydrogen atom, the lightest known atom. The conclusion was shocking because it meant there were particles smaller than the atom. In other words, Dalton was wrong: Atoms were divisible into smaller subatomic particles. Because Dalton's atomic theory had become so widely accepted, and because Thomson's conclusion was so revolutionary, many fellow scientists found it hard to believe this new discovery. But Thomson was correct. He had identified the first subatomic particle—the electron.

The next significant development came in 1909, when an American physicist named Robert Millikan (1868–1953) determined the charge of an electron.

**Enrichment**

*Linguistic* The discovery of the inert gases in the 1890s led Dimitri Mendeleev to speculate about *ether*, which scientists of the time believed was the component of empty space through which light traveled. Because Mendeleev predicted the existence and properties of elements heavier than hydrogen, he felt that he could also predict the existence of an element lighter than hydrogen (element X).

In his writings, he noted that element X was "capable of moving freely everywhere throughout the universe, with an atomic weight nearly one millionth that of hydrogen and traveling with a velocity of about 2250 kilometers per second." He placed element X at the top of the family of inert gases.

Mendeleev resisted the concept of the electron because he felt that atoms had no further internal structure.

Have students investigate and write about other scientists who, while credited with one or more discoveries, were in error with some of their other theories. **L3**

**Resource Manager**

**Study Guide for Content Mastery,** p. 20 **L2**
**Solving Problems: A Chemistry Handbook,** Section 4.2 **L2**
**Section Focus Transparency 14 and Master L1 ELL**
**Teaching Transparency 11 and Master L2 ELL**

and reverse the wire connections on the tube. Have students observe the electron beam on the fluorescent screen. Deflect the beam with the magnet. Reverse the magnet's field by flipping it around and use it to show deflection of the beam in the opposite direction.

**Results**

Students will see evidence of an electron beam. The phosphors on the plate glow along the path of the beam. Point out that Thomson observed deflection by means of both magnets and charged plates.

**Analysis**

**1.** What properties account for the bending of the cathode ray in a magnetic field? The ray has an electrical charge.

**2.** What is the function of the electromagnets on a TV picture tube? They cause

the electron beam to move back and forth, forming an image on the inside face of the luminescent chemical-coated screen.

**Assessment**

**Skill** Have students research an article describing how a CRT or television works. **L2**

## Applying Chemistry

A more sophisticated version of the cathode ray tube can be found in most homes in the form of a television set or computer monitor. A television uses magnets to direct the electron beam back and forth across the backside of its screen. The screen is coated with luminescent chemicals that produce the colors we see when it is illuminated by the electron beam.

## GLENCOE TECHNOLOGY

**CD-ROM**
**Chemistry: Matter and Change**
Experiment: *Discovery of the Electron*
Demonstration:
*Thomson's Experiment*
Animation:
*Rutherford's Gold*

National Science Content Standards

Pages 94–95
UCP.1, UCP.2; A.2; B.1, B.4; G.2, G.3

**94**

---

**Figure 4-9**

J.J. Thomson's plum pudding atomic model proposed that negatively charged electrons were distributed throughout a uniform positive charge.

(Figure 4-9: diagram labeled "Matter containing evenly distributed positive charge" and "Electrons")

**Figure 4-10**

Ernest Rutherford expected most of the fast-moving and relatively massive alpha particles to pass straight through the gold atoms. He also expected a few of the alpha particles to be slightly deflected by the electrons in the gold atoms.

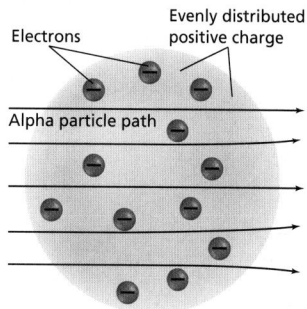

(Figure 4-10: diagram labeled "Electrons", "Evenly distributed positive charge", "Alpha particle path")

---

So good was Millikan's experimental setup and technique that the charge he measured almost one hundred years ago is within 1% of the currently accepted value. This charge has since been equated to a single unit of negative charge; in other words, a single electron carries a charge of 1–. Knowing the electron's charge and using the known charge-to-mass ratio, Millikan calculated the mass of a single electron.

$$\text{Mass of an electron} = 9.1 \times 10^{-28} \text{ g} = \frac{1}{1840} \text{ mass of a hydrogen atom}$$

As you can see, the mass of an electron is extremely small.

The existence of the electron and the knowledge of some of its properties raised some interesting new questions about the nature of atoms. It was known that matter is neutral. You know matter is neutral from everyday experience; you do not receive an electrical shock (except under certain conditions) when you touch an object. If electrons are part of all matter and they possess a negative charge, how is it that all matter is neutral? Also, if the mass of an electron is so extremely small, what accounts for the rest of the mass in a typical atom?

In an attempt to answer these questions, J.J. Thomson proposed a model of the atom that became known as the plum pudding model. As you can see in **Figure 4-9**, Thomson's model consisted of a spherically shaped atom composed of a uniformly distributed positive charge within which the individual negatively charged electrons resided. A more modern name for this model might be the chocolate-chip cookie dough model, where the chocolate chips are the electrons and the dough is the uniformly distributed positive charge. As you are about to learn, the plum pudding model of the atom did not last for very long.

## The Nuclear Atom

The story of the atom continues with the role played by Ernest Rutherford (1871–1937). As a youth, Rutherford, who was born in New Zealand, placed second in a scholarship competition to attend the prestigious Cambridge University in England. He received a fortunate break when the winner of the competition decided not to attend. By 1908, Rutherford won the Nobel Prize in chemistry and had many significant discoveries to his credit.

In 1911 Rutherford became interested in studying how positively charged alpha particles (radioactive particles you will learn more about later in this chapter) interacted with solid matter. A small group of scientists that included Rutherford designed and conducted an experiment to see if alpha particles would be deflected as they passed through a thin foil of gold. In the experiment, a narrow beam of alpha particles was aimed at a thin sheet of gold foil. A zinc sulfide coated screen surrounding the gold foil produced a flash of light whenever it was struck by an alpha particle. By noting where the flashes occurred, the scientists could determine if the atoms in the gold foil deflected the alpha particles.

Rutherford was aware of Thomson's plum pudding model of the atom and expected only minor deflections of the alpha particles. He thought the paths of the massive (relative to electrons) and fast-moving alpha particles would be only slightly altered by a nearby encounter or collision with an electron. And because the positive charge within the gold atoms was thought to be uniformly distributed, he thought it would not alter the paths of the alpha particles either. **Figure 4-10** shows the results Rutherford anticipated from the experiment. After a few days of testing, Rutherford and his fellow scientists were amazed to discover that a few of the alpha particles were deflected at

---

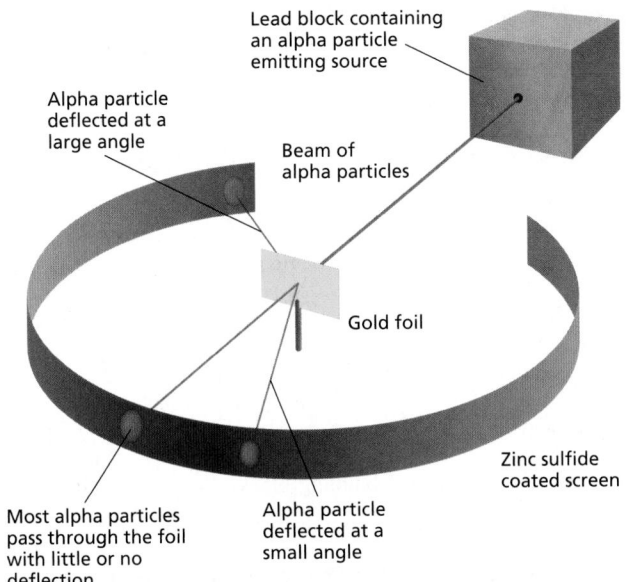

Lead block containing
an alpha particle
emitting source

Alpha particle
deflected at a
large angle

Beam of
alpha particles

Gold foil

Zinc sulfide
coated screen

Most alpha particles
pass through the foil
with little or no
deflection

Alpha particle
deflected at a
small angle

**Figure 4-11**

As Rutherford expected, most all of the alpha particles passed straight through the gold foil, without deflection. Surprisingly, however, some alpha particles were scattered at small angles, and on a few occasions they were deflected at very large angles.

very large angles. Several particles were even deflected straight back toward the source of the alpha particles. Rutherford likened the results to firing a large artillery shell at a sheet of paper and having the shell come back and hit you! These results, shown in **Figure 4-11**, were truly astounding.

Rutherford concluded that the plum pudding model was incorrect because it could not explain the results of the gold foil experiment. He set out to develop a new atomic model based upon his findings. Considering the properties of the alpha particles and the electrons, and the frequency of the deflections, he calculated that an atom consisted mostly of empty space through which the electrons move. He also concluded that there was a tiny, dense region, which he called the **nucleus**, centrally located within the atom that contained all of an atom's positive charge and virtually all of its mass. Because the nucleus occupies such a small space and contains most of an atom's mass, it is incredibly dense. Just how dense? If a nucleus were the size of the dot in the exclamation point at the end of this sentence, its mass would be approximately as much as that of 70 automobiles!

According to Rutherford's new nuclear atomic model, most of an atom consists of electrons moving rapidly through empty space. The electrons move through the available space surrounding the nucleus and are held within the atom by their attraction to the positively charged nucleus. The volume of space through which the electrons move is huge compared to the volume of the nucleus. A typical atom's diameter, which is defined by the volume of space through which the electrons move, is approximately 10 000 times the diameter of the nucleus. To put this in perspective, if an atom had a diameter of two football fields, the nucleus would be the size of a nickel!

The concentrated positive charge in the nucleus explains the deflection of the alpha particles—the repulsive force produced between the positive nucleus and the positive alpha particles causes the deflections. Alpha particles closely approaching the nucleus were deflected at small angles, while alpha particles directly approaching the nucleus were deflected at very large angles. You can see in **Figure 4-12** how Rutherford's nuclear atomic model explained the

**Figure 4-12**

Rutherford's nuclear model of the atom explains the results of the gold foil experiment. Most alpha particles pass straight through, being only slightly deflected by electrons, if at all. The strong force of repulsion between the positive nucleus and the positive alpha particles causes the large deflections.

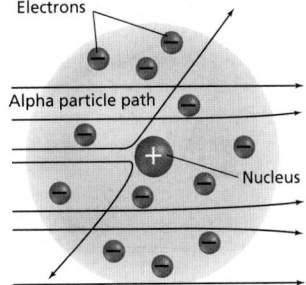

Electrons

Alpha particle path

Nucleus

4.2 Subatomic Particles and the Nuclear Atom    **95**

---

**DIFFERENTIATED INSTRUCTION**

**Learning Disabled**

*Kinesthetic* Consider creating a gold foil "shooting gallery" within a part of your classroom to conceptually recreate aspects of Rutherford's experiment. Using string, hang tennis balls from the ceiling at 2-foot intervals (horizontally and vertically) so that they form a small rectangular field. These tennis balls represent nuclei of the gold atoms in the foil. Have students take turns throwing a tennis ball "alpha particle" through the field of tennis ball "gold atoms." Record the number of throws that go through versus those that are deflected. Ask students to compare the in-classroom setup and results with the those of Rutherford's gold foil experiment. **L1** **ELL**

**Chemistry Online**

**Topic: Atomic Structure**
To learn more about the discovery of atomic structure, visit the Chemistry Web site at **chemistrymc.com**

**Activity:** Research Ernest Rutherford's work. Write a newspaper article announcing his model of the atom.

results of the gold foil experiment. The nuclear model also explains the neutral nature of matter: the positive charge of the nucleus balancing the negative charge of the electrons. However, the model still could not account for all of the atom's mass. Another 20 years would pass before this mystery was solved.

## Completing the Atom—The Discovery of Protons and Neutrons

By 1920, eight years after his revolutionary gold foil experiment, Rutherford had refined the concept of the nucleus. He concluded that the nucleus contained positively charged particles called protons. A **proton** is a subatomic particle carrying a charge equal to but opposite that of an electron; that is, a proton has a positive charge of 1+.

In 1932, Rutherford's coworker, English physicist James Chadwick (1891–1974), showed that the nucleus also contained another subatomic particle, a neutral particle called the neutron. A **neutron** has a mass nearly equal to that of a proton, but it carries no electrical charge. Thus, three subatomic particles are the fundamental building blocks from which all atoms are

## problem-solving LAB

### Interpreting STM Images

**Measuring** The invention of the scanning tunneling microscope (STM) in 1981 gave scientists the ability to visualize individual atoms, and also led to their being able to manipulate the positions of individual atoms. Use the information shown in the STM images to interpret sizes and make measurements.

### Analysis
**Figure A** is an STM image of silicon atoms that have been bonded together in a hexagonal pattern. The image is of an area 18.1nm wide by 19.0 nm high (1 nm = 1 x 10$^{-9}$ m).
**Figure B** is an STM image of 48 iron atoms that have been arranged into a circular "corral." The corral has a diameter of 1426 nm. There is a single electron trapped inside the "corral."

### Thinking Critically
1. Using a metric ruler and the dimensions of **Figure A** given above, develop a scale for making measurements off of the image. Use your scale to estimate the distance between adjacent silicon nuclei forming a hexagon.
2. What evidence is there that an electron is trapped inside the "corral" of iron atoms in **Figure B**? Estimate the distance between adjacent iron atoms. (Hint: Use the number of atoms and the formula circumference = $\pi \times$ diameter.)

**Figure A**

**Figure B**

---

## Internet Address Book

**Chemistry Online** Note Internet addresses that you find useful in the space below for quick reference.

_____

_____

_____

_____

_____

**Table 4-1**

| | | | | Properties of Subatomic Particles | |
| Particle | Symbol | Location | Relative electrical charge | Relative mass | Actual mass (g) |
|---|---|---|---|---|---|
| Electron | $e^-$ | In the space surrounding the nucleus | 1− | $\frac{1}{1840}$ | $9.11 \times 10^{-28}$ |
| Proton | $p^+$ | In the nucleus | 1+ | 1 | $1.673 \times 10^{-24}$ |
| Neutron | $n^0$ | In the nucleus | 0 | 1 | $1.675 \times 10^{-24}$ |

made—the electron, the proton, and the neutron. Together, electrons, protons, and neutrons account for all of the mass of an atom. The properties of electrons, protons, and neutrons are summarized in **Table 4-1**.

You know an atom is an electrically neutral particle composed of electrons, protons, and neutrons. Atoms are spherically shaped, with a tiny, dense nucleus of positive charge surrounded by one or more negatively charged electrons. Most of an atom consists of fast-moving electrons traveling through the empty space surrounding the nucleus. The electrons are held within the atom by their attraction to the positively charged nucleus. The nucleus, which is composed of neutral neutrons (hydrogen's single-proton nucleus is an exception) and positively charged protons, contains all of an atom's positive charge and more than 99.97% of its mass. Since an atom is electrically neutral, the number of protons in the nucleus equals the number of electrons surrounding the nucleus. The features of a typical atom are shown in **Figure 4-13**. To gain more perspective on the size of typical atoms, do the **CHEMLAB** at the end of this chapter.

Subatomic particle research is still a major interest of modern scientists. In fact, the three subatomic particles you have just learned about have since been found to have their own structures. That is, they contain sub-subatomic particles. These particles will not be covered in this textbook because it is not understood if or how they affect chemical behavior. As you will learn in coming chapters, behavior can be explained by considering only an atom's electrons, protons, and neutrons.

You should now have a solid understanding of the structure of a typical atom. But what makes an atom of one element different from an atom of another element? In the next section, you'll find out.

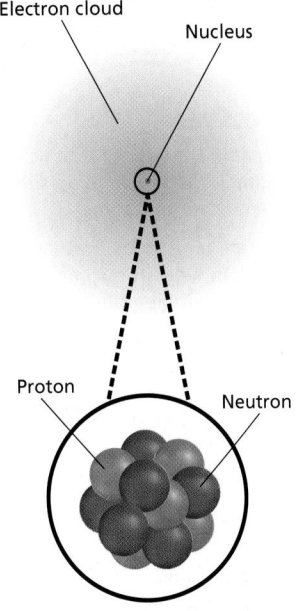

**Figure 4-13**

Atoms consist of a "cloud" of fast moving, negatively charged electrons surrounding a tiny, extremely dense nucleus containing positively charged protons and neutral neutrons. The nucleus contains virtually all of the atom's mass, but occupies only about one ten-thousandth the volume of the atom.

**Try at Home** **LAB**

See page 953 in Appendix E for **Comparing Atom Sizes**

Ask students to compare functions and dimensions of the basic unit of chemistry, the atom, with the basic unit of biology, the cell.

**Reteach**

*Kinesthetic* Have groups of students build the various atomic models using clay, construction paper, gum drops, or any other materials of their choice. **L1** **ELL**

**Extension**

*Visual-Spatial* Have students make a timeline of the events leading to our current understanding of the atom. The timeline should include anyone involved in the evolution of our understanding of the atom and also include a brief description of any related experiments. **L2**

✓ **Assessment**

**Skill** Using the mass of an electron as the basic unit of mass, have students set up a table that relates the masses of the other subatomic particles, other atoms, and other objects of their choosing. **L2**

---

**Section** **4.2** **Assessment**

6. Briefly evaluate the experiments that led to the conclusion that electrons were negatively charged particles found in all matter.

7. Describe the structure of a typical atom. Be sure to identify where each subatomic particle is located.

8. Make a table comparing the relative charge and mass of each of the subatomic particles.

9. **Thinking Critically** Compare and contrast Thomson's plum pudding atomic model with Rutherford's nuclear atomic model.

10. **Graphing** Make a timeline graph of the development of modern atomic theory. Be sure to include the discovery of each subatomic particle.

chemistrymc.com/self_check_quiz

4.2 Subatomic Particles and the Nuclear Atom **97**

---

**Section** **4.2** **Assessment**

6. The deflection toward positively charged plates demonstrated the negatively charged nature of electrons; the fact that changing the type of electrode or the type of gas used in the cathode ray tube did not affect the ray produced led to the conclusion that electrons are present in all matter.

7. A typical atom consists of a central, small, dense nucleus containing protons and neutrons. The nucleus is surrounded by a cloud of negatively charged electrons.

8.
| Particle | Relative charge | Relative mass |
|---|---|---|
| Electron | −1 | 1/1840 |
| Proton | +1 | 1 |
| Neutron | 0 | ~1 |

9. Thomson's plum pudding model describes atoms as spherical particles with uniformly distributed positive charge in which individual, negatively charged, electrons are located. In contrast, Rutherford's model states that an atom is mostly empty space, with a small, dense, central nucleus containing all of an atom's positive charge and most of its mass. The negatively charged electrons move through the empty space and are held in the atom by their attraction to the positively charged nucleus.

10. Timelines must include Democritus, Aristotle, Dalton, Crookes, Thomson, Millikan, and Rutherford.

# 1 Focus

Before presenting the lesson, display **Section Focus Transparency 15** on the overhead projector. Have students answer the accompanying questions using **Section Focus Transparency Master 15**. [L1] [ELL]

# 2 Teach

## In-Text Questions

**Page 98** How many protons does a gold atom contain? 79 A silver atom? 47 How many electrons does an atom of element 97 contain? 97

**Resource Manager**

**Study Guide for Content Mastery,** pp. 21–23 [L2]
**Solving Problems: A Chemistry Handbook,** Section 4.3 [L2]
**Section Focus Transparency 15 and Master** [L1] [ELL]

**National Science Content Standards**

**Pages 98–99**
UCP.1, UCP.2; B.1; B.2; G.2

**98**

---

## Objectives

- **Explain** the role of atomic number in determining the identity of an atom.
- **Define** an isotope and **explain** why atomic masses are not whole numbers.
- **Calculate** the number of electrons, protons, and neutrons in an atom given its mass number and atomic number.

## Vocabulary

atomic number
isotope
mass number
atomic mass unit (amu)
atomic mass

Look at the periodic table on the inside back cover of this textbook. As you can see, there are more than 110 different elements. This means that there are more than 110 different kinds of atoms. What makes an atom of one element different from an atom of another element? You know that all atoms are made up of electrons, protons, and neutrons. Thus, you might suspect that atoms somehow differ in the number of these particles. If so, you are correct.

### Atomic Number

Not long after Rutherford's gold foil experiment, the English scientist Henry Moseley (1887–1915) discovered that atoms of each element contain a unique positive charge in their nuclei. Thus, the number of protons in an atom identifies it as an atom of a particular element. The number of protons in an atom is referred to as the element's **atomic number**. Look again at the periodic table and you will see that the atomic number determines the element's position in the table. Consider hydrogen, located at the top left of the table. The information provided by the periodic table for hydrogen is shown in **Figure 4-14**. Note that above the symbol for hydrogen (H), you see the number 1. This number, which corresponds to the number of protons in a hydrogen atom, is the atomic number of hydrogen. Hydrogen atoms always contain a single proton. Moving across the periodic table to the right, you'll next come to helium (He). Helium has an atomic number of 2, and thus has two protons in its nucleus. The next row begins with lithium (Li), atomic number 3, followed by beryllium (Be), atomic number 4, and so on. As you can see, the periodic table is organized left-to-right and top-to-bottom by increasing atomic number. How many protons does a gold atom contain? A silver atom?

Remember that because all atoms are neutral, the number of protons and electrons in an atom must be equal. Thus, once you know the atomic number of an element, you know both the number of protons and the number of electrons an atom of that element contains.

Atomic number = number of protons = number of electrons

For instance, an atom of lithium, atomic number of 3, contains three protons and three electrons. How many electrons does an atom of element 97 contain?

**Figure 4-14**

The atomic number of an element equals the positive charge contained in its nucleus.

Hydrogen ——— Chemical name
1 ——— Atomic number
**H** ——— Chemical symbol
1.008 ——— Average atomic mass

Hydrogen, with an atomic number of 1, is the first element in the periodic table. A hydrogen atom has one proton and a charge of 1+ in its nucleus.

**98** Chapter 4 The Structure of the Atom

---

**DIFFERENTIATED INSTRUCTION**

## Learning Disabled

*Kinesthetic* Use three different colors of gum drops to allow students to build models of atoms that show the relationship of protons, neutrons, and electrons. Be sure to emphasize that the scaling of the model is in no way appropriate; electrons are 1/1840 the size of protons and neutrons, and the diameter of an atom is about 10 000 times the size of its nucleus. [L1] [ELL]

## EXAMPLE PROBLEM 4–1

### Using Atomic Number

Complete the following table.

| Composition of Several Elements | | | |
|---|---|---|---|
| | Element | Atomic number | Protons | Electrons |
| a. | Pb | 82 | ___ | ___ |
| b. | ___ | ___ | 8 | ___ |
| c. | ___ | ___ | ___ | 30 |

### 1. Analyze the Problem

You are given the information in the table. Apply the relationship among atomic number, number of protons, and number of electrons to complete most of the table. Once the atomic number is known, use the periodic table to identify the element.

### 2. Solve for the Unknown

Apply the atomic number relationship and then consult the periodic table to identify the element.

**a.** Atomic number = number of protons = number of electrons
82 = number of protons = number of electrons
Element 82 is lead (Pb).

**b.** Atomic number = number of protons = number of electrons
Atomic number = 8 = number of electrons
Element 8 is oxygen (O).

**c.** Atomic number = number of protons = number of electrons
Atomic number = number of protons = 30
Element 30 is zinc (Zn).

The completed table is shown below.

| Composition of Several Elements | | | |
|---|---|---|---|
| | Element | Atomic number | Protons | Electrons |
| a. | Pb | 82 | 82 | 82 |
| b. | O | 8 | 8 | 8 |
| c. | Zn | 30 | 30 | 30 |

### 3. Evaluate the Answer

The answers agree with atomic numbers and element symbols given in the periodic table.

## PRACTICE PROBLEMS

**11.** How many protons and electrons are in each of the following atoms?

    **a.** boron       **c.** platinum
    **b.** radon       **d.** magnesium

**12.** An atom of an element contains 66 electrons. What element is it?

**13.** An atom of an element contains 14 protons. What element is it?

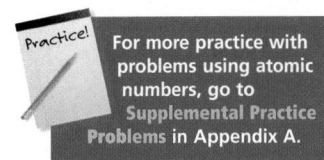

Practice! For more practice with problems using atomic numbers, go to **Supplemental Practice Problems in Appendix A.**

## Enrichment

Of the scientists working under Rutherford at Cambridge University, Henry Moseley was the youngest. He beamed X rays at samples of the different elements to find that the wavelength of the resultant X rays decreased with increasing atomic weight. Moseley attributed this to the increasing number of electrons in the atom and, consequently, the increasing number of protons in the nucleus. This led to the final arrangement of Mendeleev's periodic table—elements arranged by increasing number of protons (atomic number). This arrangement solved problems with the sequence of elements with nearly similar atomic masses and clearly identified "holes" in the table for yet-to-be discovered elements; as of 1914, there were seven undiscovered elements. Moseley's method was used to refute Urbain's claim of discovering a new element that he called "celtium" and to support Hevesey's discovery of hafnium. Have students compare Mendeleev's periodic table with Moseley's periodic table and identify discrepancies in the sequence of elements. **L3**

## Practice PROBLEMS

Have students refer to Appendix D for complete solutions to Practice Problems.

**11. a.** boron, 5
    **b.** radon, 86
    **c.** platinum, 78
    **d.** magnesium, 12

**12.** dysprosium

**13.** silicon

---

## CULTURAL DIVERSITY

### A Woman with Designs

In 1948, a high school career aptitude test indicated Patsy Sherman was best suited to be a housewife. Instead, she decided to attend college, where she earned degrees in chemistry and math. After graduation, she got a temporary job at the 3M Corporation in St. Paul, Minnesota.

One day, a lab assistant accidentally spilled some chemicals on Patsy's shoes. She noticed that the site of the spill was waterproof and stain-resistant. She decided to pursue the chemical mixture, which later was marketed as the fabric protectant Scotchgard. The protectant consists of a rubbery molecule, one side of which is sticky, allowing it to cling to fabric, while the other is slippery enough to repel stains.

3M liked the idea so well that it awarded Sherman with a full-time position. Scotchgard became one of 3M's most profitable products. Sherman has gone on to earn 16 U.S. patents and serves on the board of the National Inventors Hall of Fame.

**100**

**Figure 4-15**

Ag is the chemical symbol for the silver used in these coins. The silver in each coin is comprised of 51.84% silver-107 ($^{107}_{47}$Ag) isotopes and 48.16% silver-109 ($^{109}_{47}$Ag) isotopes.

## Isotopes and Mass Number

Earlier you learned that Dalton's atomic theory was wrong about atoms being indivisible. It was also incorrect in stating that all atoms of a particular element are identical. While it is true that all atoms of a particular element have the same number of protons and electrons, the number of neutrons on their nuclei may differ. For example, there are three different types of potassium atoms. All three types contain 19 protons (and thus 19 electrons). However, one type of potassium atom contains 20 neutrons, another contains 21 neutrons, and still another 22 neutrons. Atoms such as these, with the same number of protons but different numbers of neutrons, are called **isotopes**.

In nature most elements are found as a mixture of isotopes. Usually, no matter where a sample of an element is obtained, the relative abundance of each isotope is constant. For example, in a banana, which is a rich source of potassium, 93.25% of the potassium atoms have 20 neutrons, 6.7302% will have 22 neutrons, and a scant 0.0117% will have 21 neutrons. In another banana, or in a totally different source of potassium, the percentage composition of the potassium isotopes will still be the same.

As you might expect, the isotopes do differ in mass. Isotopes containing more neutrons have a greater mass. In spite of differences in mass and the number of neutrons, isotopes of an atom have essentially the same chemical behavior. Why? Because, as you'll learn in greater detail later in this textbook, chemical behavior is determined by the number of electrons an atom has, not by its number of neutrons and protons. To make it easy to identify each of the various isotopes of an element, chemists add a number after the element's name. The number that is added is called the **mass number**, and it represents the sum of the number of protons and neutrons in the nucleus. For example, the potassium isotope with 19 protons and 20 neutrons has a mass number of 39 (19 + 20 = 39), and the isotope is called potassium-39. The potassium isotope with 19 protons and 21 neutrons has a mass number of 40 (19 + 21 = 40), and is called potassium-40. What is the mass number and name of the potassium isotope with 19 protons and 22 neutrons?

Chemists often write out isotopes using a shortened type of notation involving the chemical symbol, atomic number, and mass number, as shown in **Figure 4-15**. Note that the mass number is written as a superscript to the left of the chemical symbol, and the atomic number is written as a subscript to the left of the chemical symbol. The three potassium isotopes you have just learned

**Figure 4-16**

The three naturally occurring potassium isotopes are potassium-39, potassium-40, and potassium-41. How do their masses compare? Their chemical properties?

| | Potassium-39 | Potassium-40 | Potassium-41 |
|---|---|---|---|
| Protons | 19 | 19 | 19 |
| Neutrons | 20 | 21 | 22 |
| Electrons | 19 | 19 | 19 |

19e⁻ 19e⁻ 19e⁻

19p⁺ 20n⁰      19p⁺ 21n⁰      19p⁺ 22n⁰

## CHEMISTRY JOURNAL

### Useful Isotopes

*Linguistic* Have students research the uses of isotopes in medicine and radiochemical dating. In their journals, have them describe how radiochemical dating makes use of radioactive isotopes. Also, have them list at least three isotopes used in medicine and describe how those isotopes are used. L2

about are summarized in **Figure 4-16**. The number of neutrons in an isotope can be calculated from the atomic number and mass number.

$$\text{Number of neutrons} = \text{mass number} - \text{atomic number}$$

## EXAMPLE PROBLEM 4–2

### Using Atomic Number and Mass Number

A chemistry laboratory has analyzed the composition of isotopes of several elements. The composition data is given in the table at the right. Data for one of neon's three isotopes is given in the table. Determine the number of protons, electrons, and neutrons in the isotope of neon. Name the isotope and give its symbol.

**Isotope Composition Data**

| Element | Atomic number | Mass number |
|---|---|---|
| **a.** Neon | 10 | 22 |
| **b.** Calcium | 20 | 46 |
| **c.** Oxygen | 8 | 17 |
| **d.** Iron | 26 | 57 |
| **e.** Zinc | 30 | 64 |
| **f.** Mercury | 80 | 204 |

### 1. Analyze the Problem

You are given some data for neon in the table. The symbol for neon can be found from the periodic table. From the atomic number, the number of protons and electrons in the isotope are known. The number of neutrons in the isotope can be found by subtracting the atomic number from the mass number.

**Known**

Element: neon
Atomic number = 10
Mass number = 22

**Unknown**

Number of protons, electrons, and neutrons = ?
Name of isotope = ?
Symbol for isotope = ?

### 2. Solve for the Unknown

The number of protons equals the number of electrons which equals the atomic number.

Number of protons = number of electrons = atomic number = 10

Use the atomic number and the mass number to calculate the number of neutrons.

Number of neutrons = mass number − atomic number

Number of neutrons = 22 − 10 = 12

Use the element name and mass number to write the isotope's name.

neon-22

Use the chemical symbol, mass number, and atomic number to write out the isotope in symbolic notation form.

$^{22}_{10}\text{Ne}$

### 3. Evaluate the Answer

The relationships among number of electrons, protons, and neutrons have been applied correctly. The isotope's name and symbol are in the correct format.

## PRACTICE PROBLEM

**14.** Determine the number of protons, electrons, and neutrons for isotopes b. through f. in the table above. Name each isotope, and write its symbol.

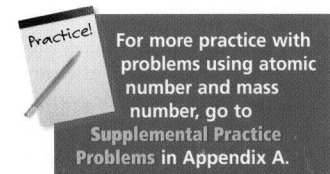 *Practice!* For more practice with problems using atomic number and mass number, go to **Supplemental Practice Problems** in Appendix A.

---

### Portfolio

#### Separating Isotopes

*Linguistic* Have students research how isotopes are separated for commercial, medical, and industrial purposes. For instance, in nuclear power plants, only the uranium-235 is suitable for use as a fissionable fuel and it must be separated from the more abundant uranium-238. Students may wish to diagram the sequence in addition to their writing. **L2** **P** 🗁

---

### Extension

Familiarize your students with the Table of Isotopes in the *CRC Handbook of Chemistry and Physics*. At this point, they should be able to identify how many isotopes are found per element and understand how the isotope notation is listed. Check student understanding by quizzing them on facts they look up in the table.

### ✓ Assessment

**Performance** Have students use the overhead projector and a set of colored dots (cut from colored acetate sheets) representing protons, neutrons, and electrons to build correct configurations for various isotopes. Use the Performance Task Assessment List for Model in **PASC**, p. 51. **L1** **ELL**

### Practice PROBLEMS

Have students refer to Appendix D for complete solutions to Practice Problems.

**14.**

| | Protons and electrons | Neutrons | Isotope | Symbol |
|---|---|---|---|---|
| **b.** | 20 | 26 | calcium-46 | $^{46}_{20}\text{Ca}$ |
| **c.** | 8 | 9 | oxygen-17 | $^{17}_{8}\text{O}$ |
| **d.** | 26 | 31 | iron-57 | $^{57}_{26}\text{Fe}$ |
| **e.** | 30 | 34 | zinc-64 | $^{64}_{30}\text{Zn}$ |
| **f.** | 80 | 124 | mercury-204 | $^{204}_{80}\text{Hg}$ |

### Resource Manager

ChemLab and MiniLab Worksheets, p. 13 **L2**
Challenge Problems, p. 4 **L3**
Math Skills Transparency 4 and Master **L2** **ELL**
Teaching Transparency 13 and Master **L2** **ELL**

# miniLAB

## Purpose

Students will determine the atomic mass of a penny given a mixture of its pre- and post-1982 "isotopes."

## Process Skills

Classifying, measuring, using numbers

## Teaching Strategies

- Review the reason for the change in composition of the penny in 1982 during the pre-lab discussion (cost savings).
- Students may have difficulty calculating the percent abundance and mass contribution of each isotope.

## Expected Results

Pre-1982 pennies have a greater mass than post-1982 pennies.
Mass of ten pre-1982 pennies
    = 31.10 g
Average mass of a pre-1982 penny
    = 3.11g
Mass of ten post-1982 pennies
    = 25.48 g
Average mass of a post-1982 penny
    = 2.55 g
The atomic mass depends on the mixture analyzed.

## Analysis

1. The relative number of pre- and post-1982 pennies in the bag determines the percentage abundance of each group. The two abundances must sum to 100%.
2. The atomic mass of a penny depends upon the mixture of pennies each student receives. Sample data is shown here.
    mass contribution (pre-1982)
        = (55.0%)(3.11 g) =1.71 g
    mass contribution (post-1982)
        = (45.0%)(2.55 g) = 1.15 g
    atomic mass =(1.71 g + 1.15 g)
        = 2.86 g
3. Atomic mass is dependent upon the relative abundance of each isotope. A different mixture of pennies would have a different atomic mass.
4. Masses of individual pennies will vary due to wear. Using an average mass of each penny minimizes the errors related to the variation.

**Table 4-2**

| Masses of Subatomic Particles | |
|---|---|
| Particle | Mass (amu) |
| Electron | 0.000 549 |
| Proton | 1.007 276 |
| Neutron | 1.008 665 |

## Mass of Individual Atoms

Recall from **Table 4-1** that the masses of both protons and neutrons are approximately $1.67 \times 10^{-24}$ g. While this is a very small mass, the mass of an electron is even smaller—only about $\frac{1}{1840}$ that of a proton or neutron. Because these extremely small masses expressed in scientific notation are difficult to work with, chemists have developed a method of measuring the mass of an atom relative to the mass of a specifically chosen atomic standard. That standard is the carbon-12 atom. Scientists assigned the carbon-12 atom a mass of exactly 12 atomic mass units. Thus, one **atomic mass unit (amu)** is defined as $\frac{1}{12}$ the mass of a carbon-12 atom. Although a mass of 1 amu is very nearly equal to the mass of a single proton or a single neutron, it is important to realize that the values are slightly different. As a result, the mass of silicon-30, for example, is 29.974 amu, and not 30 amu. **Table 4-2** gives the masses of the subatomic particles in terms of amu.

Because an atom's mass depends mainly on the number of protons and neutrons it contains, and because protons and neutrons have masses close to 1 amu, you might expect the atomic mass of an element to always be very near a whole number. This, however, is often not the case. The explanation involves how atomic mass is defined. The **atomic mass** of an element is the weighted

# miniLAB

## Modeling Isotopes

**Formulating Models** Because they have different compositions, pre- and post-1982 pennies can be used to model an element with two naturally occurring isotopes. From the penny "isotope" data, the mass of each penny isotope and the average mass of a penny can be determined.

**Materials** bag of pre- and post-1982 pennies, balance

### Procedure

1. Get a bag of pennies from your teacher, and sort the pennies by date into two groups: pre-1982 pennies and post-1982 pennies. Count and record the total number of pennies and the number of pennies in each group.
2. Use the balance to determine the mass of ten pennies from each group. Record each mass to the nearest 0.01 g. Divide the total mass of each group by ten to get the average mass of a pre- and post-1982 penny "isotope."

### Analysis

1. Using data from step 1, calculate the percentage abundance of each group. To do this, divide the number of pennies in each group by the total number of pennies.
2. Using the percentage abundance of each "isotope" and data from step 2, calculate the

atomic mass of a penny. To do this, use the following equation for each "isotope."

mass contribution = (% abundance)(mass)

Sum the mass contributions to determine the atomic mass.

3. Would the atomic mass be different if you received another bag of pennies containing a different mixture of pre- and post-1982 pennies? Explain.
4. In step 2, instead of measuring and using the mass of a single penny of each group, the average mass of each type of penny was determined. Explain why.

102    Chapter 4 The Structure of the Atom

## ✔ Assessment

**Performance** Have student groups design and carry out an experiment to determine the average mass of "isotopes" of an object such as beans or pasta. Use the Performance Task Assessment List of Designing an Experiment in **PASC**, p. 23.

## Calculating the Weighted Average Atomic Mass of Chlorine

$^{35}_{17}$Cl

17e⁻

17p⁺
18n⁰

Atomic mass: 34.969 amu
Percent abundance: 75.770%
Mass contribution:
(34.969 amu) (75.770%) = 26.496 amu

$^{37}_{17}$Cl

17e⁻

17p⁺
20n⁰

Atomic mass: 36.966 amu
Percent abundance: 24.230%
Mass contribution:
(36.966 amu) (24.230%) = 8.957 amu

Weighted average
atomic mass of chlorine = (26.496 amu + 8.957 amu) = 35.453 amu

**Figure 4-17**

To determine the weighted average atomic mass of chlorine, the mass contribution of each of the two isotopes is calculated, and then those two values are added together.

average mass of the isotopes of that element. For example, the atomic mass of chlorine is 35.453 amu. Chlorine exists naturally as a mixture of about 75% chlorine-35 and 25% chlorine-37. Because atomic mass is a weighted average, the chlorine-35 atoms, which exist in greater abundance than the chlorine-37 atoms, have a greater effect in determining the atomic mass. The atomic mass of chlorine is calculated by summing the products of each isotope's percent abundance times its atomic mass. See **Figure 4-17**. For hands-on practice in calculating atomic mass, do the **miniLAB** on the previous page.

You can calculate the atomic mass of any element if you know its number of naturally occurring isotopes, their masses, and their percent abundances. The following Example Problem and Practice Problems will provide practice in calculating atomic mass.

## EXAMPLE PROBLEM 4–3

### Calculating Atomic Mass

Given the data in the table at the right, calculate the atomic mass of unknown element *X*. Then, identify the unknown element, which is used medically to treat some mental disorders.

**1. Analyze the Problem**

You are given the data in the table. Calculate the atomic mass by multiplying the mass of each isotope by its percent abundance and summing the results. Use the periodic table to confirm the calculation and identify the element.

| | |
|---|---|
| **Known** | **Unknown** |
| For isotope $^6X$: | atomic mass of $X$ = ? amu |
|   mass = 6.015 amu | name of element $X$ = ? |
|   abundance = 7.50% = 0.0750 | |
| For isotope $^7X$: | |
|   mass = 7.016 amu | |
|   abundance = 92.5% = 0.925 | |

**2. Solve for the Unknown**

Calculate each isotope's contribution to the atomic mass.
For $^6X$: Mass contribution = (mass)(percent abundance)

mass contribution = (6.015 amu)(0.0750) = 0.451 amu

*Continued on next page*

| Isotope Abundance for Element *X* | | |
|---|---|---|
| **Isotope** | **Mass (amu)** | **Percent abundance** |
| $^6X$ | 6.015 | 7.5% |
| $^7X$ | 7.016 | 92.5% |

### Reinforcement
Point out to students that the answer to a weighted average atomic mass problem will probably be a mass that is closest to the element with the highest percent abundance.

### Enrichment
*Visual-Spatial* The mass spectrometer is an instrument that can be used to separate the isotopes of a particular element. A sample of the element is introduced into a vacuum and reduced to low pressure. Next, the vapor is passed through a beam of electrons, where ionization occurs. The ions produced are accelerated into a magnetic field. A charged particle traveling at high speeds follows a curved path whose radius depends on the speed of the particle and its mass-to-charge ratio (m/e). As a result of the differences of mass-to-charge, each isotope arrives at a different location on the collector plate, where a detector counts and displays a distribution of isotopes registered. This is called a mass spectrum. Have students research a mass spectrometer, sketching and labeling its main parts, and creating a flow chart of its function. **L3**

### Practice PROBLEMS
Have students refer to Appendix D for complete solutions to Practice Problems.
**15.** 10.81 amu
**16.** Helium-4 is more abundant in nature because the atomic mass of naturally occurring helium is closer to the mass of helium-4 (~4 amu) than to the mass of helium-3 (~3 amu).
**17.** 24.31 amu

## Internet Address Book

Note Internet addresses that you find useful in the space below for quick reference.

_____

_____

_____

_____

_____

National Science Content Standards
Pages 102–103
UCP.1, UCP.2; A.1; B.1

*Logical-Mathematical*
Obtain or create a copy of a mass spectrograph and have students analyze the abundance of each isotope and calculate an average atomic mass. The Internet or reference texts may be good sources for obtaining a mass spectrograph. **L2**

## Reteach

Compare the calculation of an average atomic mass with the calculation of a student's grade using weighted grades. For instance, suppose a student knew his or her grade in chemistry was weighted in the following way: 50% tests; 40% lab reports; 10% homework. If the student averaged 85 on tests, 95 on lab reports, and 70 on homework, what would be his final grade? 87.5

## Extension

Have students do a scavenger hunt through the Table of Isotopes in the *CRC Handbook of Chemistry and Physics*. Provide a list of clues (give an element with the highest number of isotopes; three isotopes; a weighted average of 24.305) and a prize for the student who arrives at the correct element the fastest. **L2**

### ✓ Assessment

**Skill** Pass around a sandwich bag that contains several varieties—or "isotopes"—of the same thing. Good choices are pastas, beans, and M&M candies. Have students calculate the weighted average mass of the "isotopes" present. **L2**

**National Science Content Standards**
**Pages 104–105**
UCP.1, UCP.2; B.1, B.6

**104**

---

For $^7X$: Mass contribution = (mass)(percent abundance)
mass contribution = (7.016 amu)(0.925) = 6.490 amu

Sum the mass contributions to find the atomic mass.
Atomic mass of $X$ = (0.451 amu + 6.490 amu) = 6.941 amu

Use the periodic table to identify the element.
The element with a mass of 6.941 amu is lithium (Li).

**3. Evaluate the Answer**

The result of the calculation agrees with the atomic mass given in the periodic table. The masses of the isotopes have four significant figures, so the atomic mass is also expressed with four significant figures.

## PRACTICE PROBLEMS

**15.** Boron has two naturally occurring isotopes: boron-10 (abundance = 19.8%, mass = 10.013 amu), boron-11 (abundance = 80.2%, mass = 11.009 amu). Calculate the atomic mass of boron.

**16.** Helium has two naturally occurring isotopes, helium-3 and helium-4. The atomic mass of helium is 4.003 amu. Which isotope is more abundant in nature? Explain.

**17.** Calculate the atomic mass of magnesium. The three magnesium isotopes have atomic masses and relative abundances of 23.985 amu (78.99%), 24.986 amu (10.00%), and 25.982 amu (11.01%).

Analyzing an element's mass can give you insight into what the most abundant isotope for the element may be. For example, note that fluorine (F) has an atomic mass that is extremely close to a value of 19 amu. If fluorine had several fairly abundant isotopes, it would be unlikely that its atomic mass would be so close to a whole number. Thus, you might conclude that virtually all naturally occurring fluorine is probably in the form of fluorine-19 ($^{19}_{9}F$). You would be correct, as 100% of naturally occurring fluorine is in the form of fluorine-19. While this type of reasoning generally works well, it is not foolproof. Consider bromine (Br), with an atomic mass of 79.904 amu. With a mass so close to 80 amu, it seems likely that the most common bromine isotope would be bromine-80 ($^{80}_{35}Br$). This is not the case, however. Bromine's two isotopes, bromine-79 (78.918 amu, 50.69%) and bromine-81 (80.917 amu, 49.31%), have a weighted average atomic mass of approximately 80 amu, but there is no bromine-80 isotope.

## Section 4.3 Assessment

**18.** Which subatomic particle identifies an atom as that of a particular element? How is this particle related to the atom's atomic number?

**19.** What is an isotope? Give an example of an element with isotopes.

**20.** Explain how the existence of isotopes is related to atomic masses not being whole numbers.

**21. Thinking Critically** Nitrogen has two naturally occurring isotopes, N-14 and N-15. The atomic mass of nitrogen is 14.007 amu. Which isotope is more abundant in nature? Explain.

**22. Communicating** List the steps in the process of calculating average atomic mass given data about the isotopes of an element.

chemistrymc.com/self_check_quiz

---

## Section 4.3 Assessment

**18.** The proton. The number of protons equals the atomic number.

**19.** Isotopes are atoms of the same element that have the same number of protons but different numbers of neutrons. Carbon has the three isotopes: C-12, C-13, and C-14.

**20.** Atomic masses aren't whole numbers because they represent weighted aver-

ages of the masses of the isotopes of an element.

**21.** N-14 must be more abundant because the atomic mass of nitrogen, which is a weighted average, is closer to the mass of N-14 than to the mass of N-15.

**22.** First, multiply the mass of each isotope by its percent abundance; then, sum the mass contributions of all the isotopes.

# Unstable Nuclei and Radioactive Decay

You now have a good understanding of the basic structure of matter and how matter interacts and changes through processes called chemical reactions. With the information you have just learned about the atom's nuclear nature, you are ready to learn about a very different type of reaction—the nuclear reaction. This section introduces you to some of the changes that can take place in a nucleus; you will revisit and further explore this topic in Chapter 25 when you study nuclear chemistry.

## Radioactivity

Recall from Chapter 3 that a chemical reaction involves the change of one or more substances into new substances. Although atoms may be rearranged, their identities do not change during the reaction. You may be wondering why atoms of one element do not change into atoms of another element during a chemical reaction. The reason has to do with the fact that chemical reactions involve only an atom's electrons—the nucleus remains unchanged.

As you learned in the previous section, the number of protons in the nucleus determines the identity of an atom. Thus, because there are no changes in the nuclei during a chemical reaction, the identities of the atoms do not change. There are, however, reactions that do involve an atom of one element changing into an atom of another element. These reactions, which involve a change in an atom's nucleus, are called **nuclear reactions**.

In the late 1890s, scientists noticed that some substances spontaneously emitted radiation in a process they called **radioactivity**. The rays and particles emitted by the radioactive material were called **radiation**. Scientists studying radioactivity soon made an important discovery—radioactive atoms undergo significant changes that can alter their identities. In other words, by emitting radiation, atoms of one element can change into atoms of another element. This discovery was a major breakthrough, as no chemical reaction had ever resulted in the formation of new kinds of atoms.

Radioactive atoms emit radiation because their nuclei are unstable. Unstable systems, whether they're atoms or the pencil standing on its sharpened tip shown in **Figure 4-18a**, gain stability by losing energy. As you can see in **Figure 4-18b** and **Figure 4-18c**, the pencil gains stability (and loses energy) by toppling over. When resting flat on the table top, the pencil has

### Objectives

- **Explain** the relationship between unstable nuclei and radioactive decay.

- **Characterize** alpha, beta, and gamma radiation in terms of mass and charge.

### Vocabulary

nuclear reaction
radioactivity
radiation
radioactive decay
alpha radiation
alpha particle
nuclear equation
beta radiation
beta particle
gamma ray

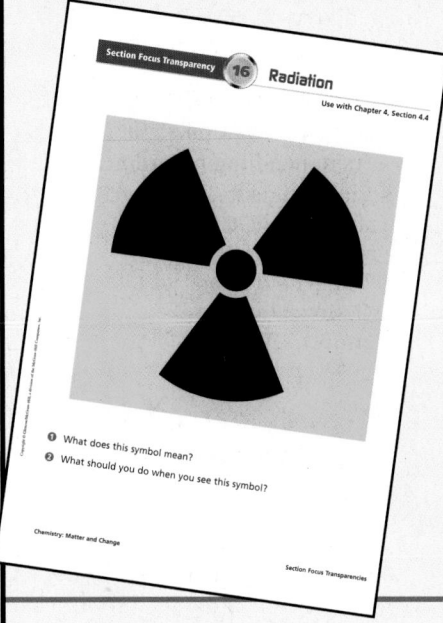

**Figure 4-18**

Unstable systems, such as this pencil momentarily standing on its tip, gain stability by losing energy. In this case, the pencil loses gravitational potential energy as it topples over. Unstable atoms also gain stability by losing energy—they lose energy by emitting radiation.

---

## GLENCOE TECHNOLOGY

**CD-ROM**
**Chemistry: Matter and Change**
Demonstration: *Evidence for Alpha Particles*

---

## CHEMISTRY JOURNAL

### Nuclear News

Have students scan through daily newspapers and magazines for articles dealing with nuclear phenomena. Have them keep a listing of the articles and classify them by categories, such as weaponry, power, food, medicine, and industrial. Based on their lists, have students estimate rough percentages for each category. **L2**

---

## 1 Focus

### Focus Transparency

Before presenting the lesson, display **Section Focus Transparency 16** on the overhead projector. Have students answer the accompanying questions using **Section Focus Transparency Master 16**. **L1 ELL**

**Section Focus Transparency** **16** **Radiation**

Use with Chapter 4, Section 4.4

❶ What does this symbol mean?
❷ What should you do when you see this symbol?

Chemistry: Matter and Change

Section Focus Transparencies

## 2 Teach

### Concept Development

Emphasize to students the three major kinds of changes: physical, chemical, and nuclear. Students should be able to describe the mechanism of each change and give clear examples of each.

### Resource Manager

**Study Guide for Content Mastery**, p. 24 **L2**
**Solving Problems: A Chemistry Handbook**, Section 4.4 **L2**
**Section Focus Transparency 16 and Master** **L1 ELL**
**Teaching Transparency 14 and Master** **L2 ELL**

**Career Path** A career in handling hazardous materials would include high school courses in chemistry and math. Technicians must complete high school and at least three months of training in handling nuclear waste, asbestos, and lead. They must also be licensed.

**Career Issue** Have students suggest reasons why radiation protection technicians are paid more than workers who remove lead or asbestos.

**For More Information**
For more information about careers in handling hazardous materials, students can contact:

Laborers—AGC Education
  and Training Fund
37 Deerfield Road
P.O. Box 37
Pomfret, CT 06259

## Quick Demo

To acquaint students with the concept of radiation, purchase an inexpensive radon kit from a local hardware store and test your classroom radon levels. These kits are sent through the mail for laboratory analysis. Radon, a byproduct of the decay of uranium-238 in soils and building materials, is considered hazardous due to the fact that it decays into radioactive isotopes of polonium, bismuth, and lead. These heavy metal ions are not easily eliminated from the body. It is estimated that 10 000 to 20 000 lung cancer deaths are caused by radon gas exposure in the United States each year.

National Science Content Standards

Pages 106–107
UCP.1, UCP.2; B.1, B.6; F.5

---

**Careers Using Chemistry**

### Radiation Protection Technician

*Do you like the idea of protecting the health of others? Would you enjoy the challenge of removing contaminated materials? If so, consider a career as a radiation protection technician.*

Radiation protection technicians use radiation measuring instruments to locate and assess the risk posed by contaminated materials. Then they decontaminate the area with high-pressure cleaning equipment and remove the radioactive materials. The work often requires the technicians to wear protective suits. The physically demanding work is carefully planned and carried out, with an emphasis on safety.

**Figure 4-19**

Because alpha, beta, and gamma radiation possess different amounts of electrical charge, they are affected differently by an electric field. Gamma rays, which carry no charge, are not deflected by the electric field.

---

less gravitational potential energy than it did in its upright position, and thus, it is more stable. Unstable nuclei lose energy by emitting radiation in a spontaneous process (a process that does not require energy) called **radioactive decay**. Unstable radioactive atoms undergo radioactive decay until they form stable nonradioactive atoms, often of a different element. Several types of radiation are commonly emitted during radioactive decay.

## Types of Radiation

Scientists began researching radioactivity in the late 1800s. By directing radiation from a radioactive source between two electrically charged plates, scientists were able to identify three different types of radiation. As you can see in **Figure 4-19**, some of the radiation was deflected toward the negatively charged plate, some was deflected toward the positively charged plate, and some was not deflected at all.

**Alpha radiation** Scientists named the radiation that was deflected toward the negatively charged plate **alpha radiation**. This radiation is made up of **alpha particles**. Each alpha particle contains two protons and two neutrons, and thus has a 2+ charge. As you know, opposite electrical charges attract. So the 2+ charge explains why alpha particles are attracted to the negatively charged plate shown in **Figure 4-19**. An alpha particle is equivalent to a helium-4 nucleus and is represented by $^4_2He$ or $\alpha$. The alpha decay of radioactive radium-226 into radon-222 is shown below.

$$^{226}_{88}Ra \rightarrow\ ^{222}_{86}Rn\ +\ ^4_2He$$
$$\text{radium-226} \qquad \text{radon-222} \qquad \text{alpha particle}$$

Note also that a new element, radon (Rn), is created as a result of the alpha decay of the unstable radium-226 nucleus. The type of equation shown above is known as a **nuclear equation** because it shows the atomic number and mass number of the particles involved. It is important to note that both mass number and atomic number are conserved in nuclear equations. The accounting of atomic numbers and mass numbers below shows that they are conserved.

$$^{226}_{88}Ra \rightarrow\ ^{222}_{86}Rn + ^4_2He$$
$$\text{Atomic number: } 88 \rightarrow 86 + 2$$
$$\text{Mass number: } 226 \rightarrow 222 + 4$$

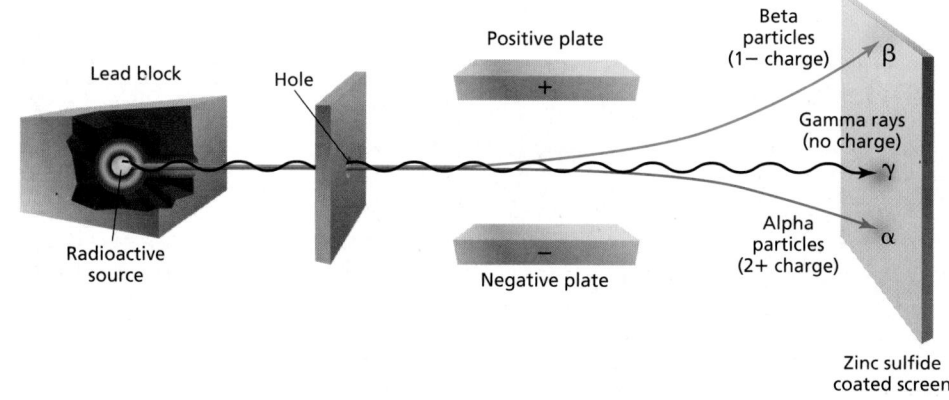

---

**DIFFERENTIATED INSTRUCTION**

### Visually Impaired

*Kinesthetic* Give students sets consisting of two differently shaped objects representing protons and neutrons. Use small containers, such as petri dishes, to represent the nucleus and contain the protons and neutrons. Ask students to model various isotopes and then follow up by asking them to demonstrate an alpha or beta decay by removing the appropriate numbers of protons or neutrons. **L1 ELL**

**Beta radiation** Scientists named the radiation that was deflected toward the positively charged plate **beta radiation**. This radiation consists of fast moving electrons called **beta particles**. Each beta particle is an electron with a 1– charge. The negative charge of the beta particle explains why it is attracted to the positively charged plate shown in **Figure 4-19**. Beta particles are represented by the symbol $_{-1}^{0}\beta$. The beta decay of radioactive carbon-14 into nitrogen-14 is shown below.

$$_{6}^{14}C \rightarrow {}_{7}^{14}N + {}_{-1}^{0}\beta$$

carbon-14     nitrogen-14     beta particle

The beta decay of unstable carbon-14 results in the creation of the new atom nitrogen (N).

**Gamma radiation** The third common type of radiation is called gamma radiation, or gamma rays. **Gamma rays** are high-energy radiation that possess no mass and are denoted by the symbol $_{0}^{0}\gamma$. Because they possess no electrical charge, gamma rays are not deflected by electric or magnetic fields. Gamma rays usually accompany alpha and beta radiation, and they account for most of the energy lost during the radioactive decay process. For example, gamma rays accompany the alpha decay of uranium-238.

$$_{92}^{238}U \rightarrow {}_{90}^{234}Th + {}_{2}^{4}He + 2{}_{0}^{0}\gamma$$

uranium-238     thorium-234     alpha particle     gamma rays

Because gamma rays are massless, the emission of gamma rays by themselves cannot result in the formation of a new atom. **Table 4-3** summarizes the basic characteristics of alpha, beta, and gamma radiation.

**Nuclear stability** You may be wondering why some atoms are stable while others are not. The primary factor in determining an atom's stability is its ratio of neutrons to protons. The details of how the neutron-to-proton ratio determines stability will be covered in Chapter 25. For now, it is enough that you know that atoms containing either too many or too few neutrons are unstable. Unstable nuclei lose energy through radioactive decay in order to form a nucleus with a stable composition of neutrons and protons. Alpha and beta particles are emitted during radioactive decay, and these emissions affect the neutron-to-proton ratio of the newly created nucleus. Eventually, radioactive atoms undergo enough radioactive decay to form stable, nonradioactive atoms. This explains why there are so few radioactive atoms found in nature—most of them have already decayed into stable atoms.

**Table 4-3**

| Characteristics of Alpha, Beta, and Gamma Radiation | | | |
|---|---|---|---|
| Radiation type | Symbol | Mass (amu) | Charge |
| Alpha | $_{2}^{4}He$ | 4 | 2+ |
| Beta | $_{-1}^{0}\beta$ | $\frac{1}{1840}$ | 1– |
| Gamma | $_{0}^{0}\gamma$ | 0 | 0 |

# 3 Assess

## Check for Understanding

**Interpersonal** Have student groups of three use the Table of Isotopes in the *CRC Handbook of Chemistry and Physics* to find any isotope that undergoes radioactive decay. The first student in the group writes down the listed isotope, then passes the paper to a second student in the group. The second student writes down the ejected particle listed, then passes it to the third student in the group. This student should complete the nuclear equation by writing the resulting nuclide. Have students continue with this process for five minutes. Each group should check with the teacher to see whether its equations are correct. The group with the most correct nuclear equations wins. **L2** **COOP LEARN**

## Reteach

Have students complete the following nuclear reactions.
$$_{27}^{60}Co \rightarrow {}_{28}^{60}Ni + ? {}_{-1}^{0}\beta$$
$$_{95}^{241}Am \rightarrow {}_{93}^{237}Np + ? {}_{2}^{4}He$$

## Extension

Have students research the use of radioactive isotopes in classical experiments in chemistry and physics. **L2**

## ✔ Assessment

**Knowledge** Have each student write two questions from each section of this chapter. Then use the questions for a game show similar to a quiz tournament. **L2**

## Section 4.4 Assessment

**23.** Explain how unstable atoms gain stability. What determines whether or not an atom is stable?

**24.** Create a table comparing the mass and charge of alpha, beta, and gamma radiation.

**25.** In writing a balanced nuclear equation, what must be conserved?

**26. Thinking Critically** Explain how a nuclear reaction differs from a chemical reaction.

**27. Classifying** Classify each of the following as a chemical reaction, a nuclear reaction, or neither.
   **a.** Thorium emits a beta particle.
   **b.** Two atoms share electrons to form a bond.
   **c.** A sample of pure sulfur emits heat energy as it slowly cools.
   **d.** A piece of iron rusts.

## Section 4.4 Assessment

**23.** Atoms can gain stability by losing energy (emitting radiation). Atomic stability is determined primarily by the ratio of the number of neutrons to the number of protons.

**24.**

| Particle | Symbol | Mass (amu) | Charge |
|---|---|---|---|
| $\alpha$ | $_{2}^{4}He$ | 4 | +2 |
| $\beta$ | $_{-1}^{0}\beta$ | 1/1840 | −1 |
| $\gamma$ | $_{0}^{0}\gamma$ | 0 | 0 |

**25.** In a balanced nuclear equation, both mass number and atomic number must be conserved.

**26.** Nuclear reactions involve changes in the nuclei of the atoms, usually resulting in changes of atoms of one element into atoms of another element. Chemical reactions involve changes of substances into new substances.

**27. a.** nuclear     **c.** neither
   **b.** chemical     **d.** chemical

**107**

## Preparation

**Time Allotment**
One laboratory period

**Process Skills**
Observing and inferring, formulating models, hypothesizing, comparing and contrasting

**Safety Precautions**
To avoid splashing your eyes or clothing with vanilla, do not deflate the balloon until the vanilla has dried inside.

**Disposal**
The deflated balloons can be placed in a solid waste container.

**Alternative Materials**
After-shave lotion or perfume can be used to replace the vanilla.

### Pre-Lab

2. A polymer is a large molecule made up of many repeating smaller molecules. Latex is an example.

3. The amount of vanilla placed into each balloon is constant. The chemical composition of the balloons is constant.

4. The purpose of the vanilla flavoring is to trace the movement of molecules using the sense of smell to detect their presence.

5. The high-energy molecules leave first, lowering the average kinetic energy of the remaining liquid. It is cooler.

6. You are smelling a gas or vapor.

### Data Table

| Observations | | Initial | Final |
|---|---|---|---|
| Balloon 1 with vanilla | Relative size | Same size | Same size |
| | Relative temp. | Cool | Room temp. |
| Balloon 2 without vanilla | Relative size | Same size | Same size |
| | Relative temp. | Room temp. | Room temp. |

---

# Very Small Particles

This laboratory investigation will help you conceptualize the size of an atom. You will experiment with a latex balloon containing a vanilla bean extract. Latex is a polymer, meaning that it is a large molecule (a group of atoms that act as a unit) that is made up of a repeating pattern of smaller molecules. The scent of the vanilla extract will allow you to trace the movement of its molecules through the walls of the solid latex balloon.

**Problem**
How small are the atoms that make up the molecules of the balloon and the vanilla extract? How can you conclude the vanilla molecules are in motion?

**Objectives**
• **Observe** the movement of vanilla molecules based on detecting their scent.
• **Infer** what the presence of the vanilla scent means in terms of the size and movement of its molecules.
• **Formulate models** that explain how small molecules in motion can pass through an apparent solid.
• **Hypothesize** about the size of atoms that make up matter.

**Materials**
vanilla extract or flavoring
9-inch latex balloon (2)
dropper

**Safety Precautions**

• Always wear safety goggles and a lab apron.
• Be careful not to cut yourself when using a sharp object to deflate the balloon.

**Pre-Lab**

1. Read the entire CHEMLAB.
2. Describe a polymer and give an example.
3. Identify constants in the experiment.
4. What is the purpose of the vanilla extract?
5. As a liquid evaporates, predict what you think will happen to the temperature of the remaining liquid.
6. When you smell an aroma, is your nose detecting a particle in the solid, liquid, or gas phase?
7. Prepare all written materials that you will take into the laboratory. Be sure to include safety precautions, procedure notes, and a data table in which to record your data and observations.

### Data Table

| Observations | | Initial | Final |
|---|---|---|---|
| Balloon 1 with vanilla | Relative size | | |
| | Relative temperature | | |
| Balloon 2 without vanilla | Relative size | | |
| | Relative temperature | | |

## Procedure

• Encourage students to blow up the balloon so the walls are stretched tight. In this way, the pores of the walls become larger.
• Use large balloons (9-inch). The necks are larger, making it easier to add the vanilla; they are also easier to inflate and tie shut.

## Expected Results

See data table.

## Analyze and Conclude

1. The volume of the balloons did not change.
2. Balloon 1 feels cool to the touch. The vanilla absorbs energy from the surroundings in changing to a vapor.
3. The vanilla's odor is outside the balloon and fills the small, enclosed space. The vanilla vaporizes and its molecules move through the pores in the wall of the balloon.

## Procedure

1. Using the medicine dropper, add 25 to 30 drops of vanilla extract to the first balloon.

2. Inflate the balloon so its walls are tightly stretched, but not stretched so tightly that the balloon is in danger of bursting. Try to keep the vanilla in one location as the balloon is inflated. Tie the balloon closed.

3. Feel the outside of the balloon where the vanilla is located and note the temperature of this area relative to the rest of the balloon. Record your observations in the data table.

4. Use only air to inflate a second balloon to approximately the same size as that of the first, and tie it closed. Feel the outside of the second balloon. Make a relative temperature comparison to that of the first balloon. Record your initial observations.

5. Place the inflated balloons in a small, enclosed area such as a closet or student locker.

6. The next day, repeat the observations in steps 3 and 4 after the vanilla has dried inside the balloon. Record these final observations.

7. To avoid splattering your clothes with dark brown vanilla, do not deflate the balloon until the vanilla has dried inside.

## Cleanup and Disposal

1. After the vanilla has dried, deflate the balloon by puncturing it with a sharp object.

2. Dispose of the pieces of the balloon as directed by your teacher.

## Analyze and Conclude

1. **Observing and Inferring** How did the relative volumes of balloons 1 and 2 change after 24 hours? Explain.

2. **Observing and Inferring** By comparing the relative temperatures of balloons 1 and 2, what can you conclude about the temperature change as the vanilla evaporated? Explain.

3. **Observing and Inferring** Did the vanilla's odor get outside the balloon and fill the enclosed space? Explain.

4. **Predicting** Do you think vanilla will leak more rapidly from a fully inflated balloon or from a half-inflated balloon? Explain.

5. **Hypothesizing** Write a hypothesis that explains your observations.

6. **Comparing and Contrasting** Compare your hypothesis to Dalton's atomic theory. In what ways is it similar? How is it different?

7. **Error Analysis** What factors might affect the results of different groups that performed the experiment? What types of errors might have occurred during the procedure?

## Real-World Chemistry

1. Explain why helium-filled, Mylar-foil balloons can float freely for several weeks, but latex balloons for less than 24 hours.

2. How are high-pressure gases stored for laboratory and industrial use to prevent loss?

CHEMLAB **109**

4. Vanilla will leak more rapidly from a fully inflated balloon. The thinner wall will allow more vanilla to pass through its pores because the polymer chains are stretched farther apart.

5. A possible hypothesis is that the latex polymer chains move apart as the balloon inflates. The stretching of the latex walls creates pores. The greater pressure inside the balloon causes the molecules to move from inside the balloon to the outside. The vanilla molecules are very small particles that fit through the pores and are detected by their aroma outside the balloon. The evaporation of the vanilla liquid requires energy. The wall of the balloon feels cool to the touch where the liquid is changing into a vapor. After 24 hours, the liquid evaporates and leaves a dried brown residue inside the balloon.

6. Dalton's atomic theory states that all matter is composed of extremely small particles. So does the hypothesis in question 5. The laboratory investigation does not address the many other aspects of Dalton's atomic theory.

7. Student answers will vary. Temperature and inflation of the balloon (tightness) will affect results. The balloon may not have been tightly closed.

### Real-World Chemistry

1. Metallic coated Mylar is a nonporous polymer film. Thus, helium does not escape Mylar.

2. High-pressure gases are stored in impermeable steel storage cylinders.

## Assessment

**Performance** Have a team of students repeat the laboratory investigation using small Mylar balloons. Ask the students to make a hypothesis, in writing, about what they think will happen before repeating the investigation. Use the Performance Task Assessment List for Formulating a Hypothesis in **PASC**, p. 21. **L2**

 **Resource Manager**

**ChemLab and MiniLab Worksheets,** pp. 14–16 **L2**

**National Science Content Standards**
**Pages 108–109**
UCP.1, UCP.2; A.1; B.2, B.4

## Purpose

Students will learn about nanotechnology and how it may affect the world in which they live.

## Background

Richard Feynmen, a scientist who won the 1965 Nobel prize in physics, first introduced the concept of nanotechnology in 1959. Since that time, many researchers have studied the possibilities. However, only recently, with the development of new and powerful scientific instruments and computer programs, is nanotechnology finally coming into reality. Scientists now have the ability not only to visualize individual atoms, but to move them around as well.

## Teaching Strategies

- Ask students to research the roles of enzymes, proteins, and ribosomes in the human body. Have them prepare posters, individually or in groups, in which they relate the roles of nanocomputers and nanorobots to naturally occurring processes in the human body.
- Ask students to choose an area that will be changed by nanotechnology, such as manufacturing, medicine, or environmental science. Have them consider what advances they would like to see in that area.
- Ask students to give an example of a revolutionary product that has been developed during their lifetimes. Have them explain how it has affected their lives.

## Investigating the Issue

1. The Industrial Revolution began in the eighteenth century in England and later spread to other parts of the world. Students should describe several advances in technology that occurred during the period. They should also mention how these advances

# CHEMISTRY and
## Society

# Nanotechnology

Imagine a technology able to produce roads that repave themselves, greenhouses productive enough to end starvation, and computers the size of cells. Sound like science fiction? It may not be.

### Starting at the bottom

This yet-to-be realized technology is generally known as nanotechnology. The prefix *nano-* means one billionth. A nanometer is roughly the size of several atoms put together. The goal of nanotechnology is to manipulate individual atoms in order to create a wide variety of products.

In order to manipulate the immense number of atoms required to make a product, scientists plan on constructing tiny robots called nanorobots. Nanorobots would have two objectives—to manipulate atoms and to copy themselves (self-replication). Through self-replication, countless nanorobots could be created. This work force of nanorobots would then work together to quickly and efficiently assemble new products.

### Possibilities and effects

The benefits of nanotechnology could potentially go beyond those of all other existing technologies. The quality and reliability of manufactured products could improve dramatically. For example, a brick could repair itself after cracks form, and a damaged road could repave itself. Furthermore, even as the quality and capability of products increase, their prices would decrease. With the use of nanorobot workforces and a readily available supply of atoms, the cost of atom-assembled products would be low.

Unlike many technological advances of the past, nanotechnology could also benefit the environment. The need for traditional raw materials, such as trees and coal, would be greatly reduced. Also, because the atoms are arranged individually, the amount of waste could be carefully controlled and limited. Thin materials called nanomembranes may even be able to filter existing pollutants out of air and water.

Advances in medicine could also be amazing. Nanodevices smaller than human cells could be used to detect health problems, repair cells, and carry medicines to specific sites in the body.

2 micron

### When will it happen?

The promise of nanotechnology is still years away. Some think nanodevices will be available in the next decade, whereas others expect the technology to take much longer to develop. So far, researchers have accomplished rearranging atoms into specific shapes such as letters and symbols, and have also succeeded in developing several very simple nanodevices. One such device, a nanoguitar, made of crystalline silicon, is about 1/20th the width of a single human hair. Another device under development will enable delivery of anti-cancer drugs to just the cancerous cells, while leaving normal cells unharmed.

### Investigating the Issue

1. **Communicating Ideas** Read about the Industrial Revolution and write a brief essay describing how technological advances affected society.

2. **Debating the Issue** Nanotechnology supporters argue that dangers posed by the technology will be addressed as nanotechnology is developed. Should researchers be prevented from developing nanotechnology?

**Chemistry Online**

Visit the Chemistry Web site at chemistrymc.com to find links to more information about nanotechnology and the issues that surround it.

lead to changes in socioeconomic structure and culture as society changed from agrarian to industrial. Finally, students should balance the positive results with a mention of the negative impact, such as increased pollution.

2. Answers will vary. Make sure that students back up their opinions with examples and facts. For example, one student might argue that nuclear technology offered many positive benefits but it has been used for horrible destruction and still poses military dangers. For this reason, they might oppose the development of the technology. Another might argue that the automobile poses dangers to both drivers and pedestrians. Yet laws and new technology, such as airbags, have been developed along the way to make driving as safe as possible. They might argue that similar developments would make nanotechnology safe.

## Summary

### 4.1 Early Theories of Matter
- The Greek philosopher Democritus was the first person to propose the existence of atoms.
- In 1808, Dalton proposed his atomic theory, which was based on numerous scientific experiments.
- All matter is composed of atoms. An atom is the smallest particle of an element that maintains the properties of that element. Atoms of one element are different from atoms of other elements.

### 4.2 Subatomic Particles and the Nuclear Atom
- Atoms are composed of negatively charged electrons, neutral neutrons, and positively charged protons. Electrons have a $1-$ charge, protons have a $1+$ charge, and neutrons have no charge. Both protons and neutrons have masses approximately 1840 times that of an electron.
- The nucleus of an atom contains all of its positive charge and nearly all of its mass.
- The nucleus occupies an extremely small volume of space at the center of an atom. Most of an atom consists of empty space surrounding the nucleus through which the electrons move.

### 4.3 How Atoms Differ
- The number of protons in an atom uniquely identifies an atom. This number of protons is the atomic number of the atom.

- Atoms have equal numbers of protons and electrons, and thus, no overall electrical charge.
- An atom's mass number is equal to its total number of protons and neutrons.
- Atoms of the same element with different numbers of neutrons and different masses are called isotopes.
- The atomic mass of an element is a weighted average of the masses of all the naturally occurring isotopes of that element.

### 4.4 Unstable Nuclei and Radioactive Decay
- Chemical reactions involve changes in the electrons surrounding an atom. Nuclear reactions involve changes in the nucleus of an atom.
- The neutron-to-proton ratio of an atom's nucleus determines its stability. Unstable nuclei undergo radioactive decay, emitting radiation in the process.
- Alpha particles are equivalent to the nuclei of helium atoms, and are represented by $_2^4\text{He}$ or $\alpha$. Alpha particles have a charge of $2+$.
- Beta particles are high-speed electrons and are represented by $_{-1}^{0}\beta$. Beta particles have a $1-$ charge.
- Gamma rays are high-energy radiation and are represented by the symbol $_0^0\gamma$. Gamma rays have no electrical charge and no mass.

## Key Equations and Relationships
- Determining the number of protons and electrons

  $$\text{Atomic number} = \text{number of protons} = \text{number of electrons} \quad \text{(p. 98)}$$

- Determining the number of neutrons

  $$\text{Number of neutrons} = \text{mass number} - \text{atomic number} \quad \text{(p. 101)}$$

## Vocabulary
- alpha particle (p. 106)
- alpha radiation (p. 106)
- atom (p. 90)
- atomic mass (p. 102)
- atomic mass unit (amu) (p. 102)
- atomic number (p. 98)
- beta particle (p. 107)
- beta radiation (p. 107)
- cathode ray (p. 92)
- Dalton's atomic theory (p. 89)
- electron (p. 93)
- gamma ray (p. 107)
- isotope (p. 100)
- mass number (p. 100)
- neutron (p. 96)
- nuclear equation (p. 106)
- nuclear reaction (p. 105)
- nucleus (p. 95)
- proton (p. 96)
- radiation (p. 105)
- radioactive decay (p. 106)
- radioactivity (p. 105)

chemistrymc.com/vocabulary_puzzlemaker

Study Guide **111**

## Using the Vocabulary
To reinforce chapter vocabulary, have students write a sentence using each term. **L2** **ELL**

## Review Strategies
- Have students summarize how the atomic model has changed from Dalton's concept to present understanding. **L2**
- Have students list the parts of the atom and give their charge, location, and relative size. **L2**
- Have students determine the average atomic mass for an element given isotope masses and corresponding percent abundance. **L2**
- Problems from Appendix A or the **Supplemental Problems** booklet can be used for review. **L2**

### VOCABULARY PuzzleMaker

For additional help with vocabulary, have students access the Vocabulary PuzzleMaker online.

chemistrymc.com/vocabulary_puzzlemaker

## EXAM*VIEW* ® PRO

### Use Exam*View*® Pro Testmaker CD-ROM to:
- Create **multiple versions** of tests.
- Create **modified** tests with one mouse click for struggling students.
- **Edit** existing questions and add your own questions.
- **Build** tests based on national curriculum standards.

**National Science Content Standards**

Pages 110–111
UCP.1, UCP.2; B.1, B.2, B.4; E.1, E.2; F.6; G.3

## Concept Mapping

**28.** 1. matter; 2. atoms;
3. electrons; 4. protons or
neutrons; 5. neutrons or
protons; 6. empty space
around nucleus; 7. nucleus

## Mastering Concepts

**29.** Democritus
**30.** John Dalton
**31.** The scientific instruments
necessary to research
matter at the atomic level
had not been invented yet.
**32.** See Figure 4-4. Dalton was
wrong about atoms being
indivisible and all atoms of
an element being identical.
**33.** Mass is conserved because
atoms cannot be created,
divided, or destroyed.
Chemical reactions involve
only the separation, combination, and rearrangement
of atoms.
**34.** the electron
**35.** changing the type of electrode or the type of gas did
not affect the ray produced
**36.** charge = −1;
mass = $9.11 \times 10^{-28}$ g
**37.** Strengths: Rutherford's
model explained the results
of the gold-foil experiment
and why an atom is electrically neutral.
Weaknesses: The model
could not account for the
total mass of an atom or
the arrangement of the
electrons.
**38.** protons and neutrons; net
positive charge equal to the
number of protons
**39.** attraction to the positively
charged nucleus
**40.** from cathode to anode
**41.** the plum pudding model
**42.** The $\alpha$ particles were
deflected by the positively
charged gold nuclei.

**National Science Content Standards**
Pages 112–113
UCP.1, UCP.2; B.1, B.2, B.4, B.6; G.3

**Chemistry** Online

*Go to the Chemistry Web site at*
chemistrymc.com *for additional*
*Chapter 4 Assessment.*

## Concept Mapping

**28.** Complete the concept map using the following terms:
electrons, matter, neutrons, nucleus, empty space
around nucleus, protons, and atoms.

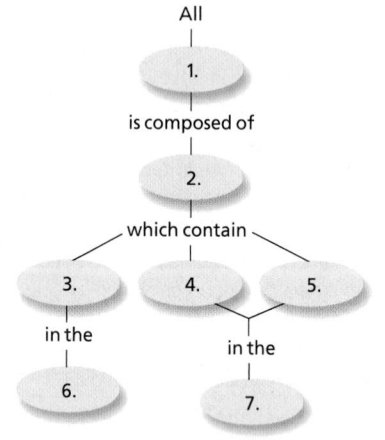

All
|
1.
|
is composed of
|
2.
|
which contain
|
3.   4.   5.
|        |
in the    in the
|        |
6.       7.

## Mastering Concepts

**29.** Who originally proposed the concept that matter was
composed of tiny indivisible particles? (4.1)

**30.** Whose work is credited with being the beginning of
modern atomic theory? (4.1)

**31.** Explain why Democritus was unable to experimentally
verify his ideas. (4.1)

**32.** State the main points of Dalton's atomic theory using
your own words. Which parts of Dalton's theory were
later found to be in error? Explain why. (4.1)

**33.** Explain how Dalton's atomic theory offered a convincing explanation of the observation that mass is
conserved in chemical reactions. (4.1)

**34.** Which subatomic particle was discovered by
researchers working with cathode ray tubes? (4.2)

**35.** What experimental results led to the conclusion that
electrons were part of all forms of matter? (4.2)

**36.** What is the charge and mass of a single electron? (4.2)

**37.** List the strengths and weaknesses of Rutherford's
nuclear model of the atom. (4.2)

**38.** What particles are found in the nucleus of an atom?
What is the net charge of the nucleus? (4.2)

**39.** Explain what keeps the electrons confined in the space
surrounding the nucleus. (4.2)

**40.** Describe the flow of a cathode ray inside a cathode
ray tube. (4.2)

**41.** Which outdated atomic model could be likened to
chocolate chip cookie dough? (4.2)

**42.** What caused the deflection of the alpha particles in
Rutherford's gold foil experiment? (4.2)

**43.** Which subatomic particles account for most all of an
atom's mass? (4.2)

**44.** How is an atom's atomic number related to its number
of protons? To its number of electrons? (4.2)

**45.** What is the charge of the nucleus of element 89? (4.2)

**46.** Explain why atoms are electrically neutral. (4.2)

**47.** Does the existence of isotopes contradict part of
Dalton's original atomic theory? Explain. (4.3)

**48.** How do isotopes of a given element differ? How are
they similar? (4.3)

**49.** How is the mass number related to the number of protons and neutrons an atom has? (4.3)

**50.** What do the superscript and subscript in the notation
$^{40}_{19}K$ represent? (4.3)

**51.** Explain how to determine the number of neutrons an
atom contains if you know its mass number and its
atomic number. (4.3)

**52.** Define the atomic mass unit. What were the benefits
of developing the atomic mass unit as a standard unit
of mass? (4.3)

**53.** What type of reaction involves changes in the nucleus
of an atom? (4.4)

**54.** Explain how energy loss and nuclear stability are
related to radioactive decay. (4.4)

**55.** Explain what must occur before a radioactive atom
ceases to undergo further radioactive decay. (4.4)

**56.** Write the symbols used to denote alpha, beta, and
gamma radiation and give their mass and charge. (4.4)

**57.** What change in mass number occurs when a radioactive atom emits an alpha particle? A beta particle? A
gamma particle? (4.4)

**58.** What is the primary factor determining whether or not
an atom is stable or unstable? (4.4)

chemistrymc.com/chapter_test

**43.** protons and neutrons
**44.** They are all equal.

**Resource Manager**

Chapter Assessment, pp. 19–24 **L2**
Supplemental Problems, Ch. 4
ExamView® Pro CD-ROM
MindJogger Videoquizzes DVD/VHS
Solutions Manual, Ch. 4
Chemistry Interactive CD-ROM,
Ch. 4 quiz

## Mastering Problems

### Atomic Number and Mass Number (4.3)

**59.** How many protons and electrons are contained in an atom of element 44?

**60.** For each of the following chemical symbols, determine the element name and the number of protons and electrons an atom contains.

a. V      c. Ir
b. Mn      d. S

**61.** A carbon atom has a mass number of 12 and an atomic number of 6. How many neutrons does it have?

**62.** An isotope of mercury has 80 protons and 120 neutrons. What is the mass number of this isotope?

**63.** An isotope of xenon has an atomic number of 54 and contains 77 neutrons. What is the xenon isotope's mass number?

**64.** How many electrons, protons, and neutrons are contained in each of the following atoms?

a. $^{132}_{55}$Cs      c. $^{163}_{69}$Tm
b. $^{59}_{27}$Co      d. $^{70}_{30}$Zn

**65.** How many electrons, protons, and neutrons are contained in each of the following atoms?

a. gallium-64      c. titanium-48
b. fluorine-23      d. helium-8

### Atomic Mass (4.3)

**66.** Chlorine, which has an atomic mass of 35.453 amu, has two naturally occurring isotopes, Cl-35 and Cl-37. Which isotope occurs in greater abundance? Explain.

**67.** Silver has two isotopes, $^{107}_{47}$Ag has a mass of 106.905 amu (52.00%), and $^{109}_{47}$Ag has a mass of 108.905 amu (48.00%). What is the atomic mass of silver?

**68.** Data for chromium's four naturally occurring isotopes is provided in the table below. Calculate chromium's atomic mass.

### Chromium Isotope Data

| Isotope | Percent abundance | Mass (amu) |
|---------|-------------------|------------|
| Cr-50 | 4.35% | 49.946 |
| Cr-52 | 83.79% | 51.941 |
| Cr-53 | 9.50% | 52.941 |
| Cr-54 | 2.36% | 53.939 |

## Mixed Review

*Sharpen your problem-solving skills by answering the following.*

**69.** Describe a cathode ray tube and how it operates.

**70.** Explain how J. J. Thomson's determination of the charge-to-mass ratio of the electron led to the conclusion that atoms were composed of subatomic particles.

**71.** How did the actual results of Rutherford's gold foil experiment differ from the results he expected?

**72.** Complete the table below.

### Composition of Various Isotopes

| Isotope | Atomic number | Mass number | Number of protons | Number of neutrons | Number of electrons |
|---------|---------------|-------------|-------------------|--------------------|--------------------|
|  |  | 32 | 16 |  |  |
|  |  |  |  | 24 | 20 |
| Zn-64 |  |  |  |  |  |
|  | 9 |  |  | 10 |  |
|  | 11 | 23 |  |  |  |

**73.** Approximately how many times greater is the diameter of an atom than the diameter of its nucleus? Knowing that most of an atom's mass is contained in the nucleus, what can you conclude about the density of the nucleus?

**74.** Is the charge of a nucleus positive, negative, or zero? The charge of an atom?

**75.** Why are electrons in a cathode ray tube deflected by magnetic and electric fields?

**76.** What was Henry Moseley's contribution to our understanding of the atom?

**77.** What is the mass number of potassium-39? What is the isotope's charge?

**78.** Boron-10 and boron-11 are the naturally occurring isotopes of elemental boron. If boron has an atomic mass of 10.81 amu, which isotope occurs in greater abundance?

**79.** Calculate the atomic mass of titanium. The five titanium isotopes have atomic masses and relative abundances of 45.953 amu (8.00%), 46.952 amu (7.30%), 47.948 amu (73.80%), 48.948 amu (5.50%), and 49.945 amu (5.40%).

**45.** 89+
**46.** The number of positively charged protons equals the number of negatively charged electrons.
**47.** Yes; not all atoms of an element are identical in mass.
**48.** differ: number of neutrons, masses; similar: chemical properties, number of protons and electrons
**49.** mass number = number of $p^+$ + number of $n^0$
**50.** The superscript represents the mass number (40) and the subscript represents the atomic number (19).
**51.** number of $n^0$ = mass number – atomic number
**52.** amu = 1/12 of the mass of a C-12 atom; Scientists defined the atomic mass unit as a relative standard that was closer in size to atomic and subatomic masses.
**53.** nuclear reaction
**54.** Radioactivity results when unstable nuclei emit energy in order to gain stability.
**55.** A stable, nonradioactive atom must be formed.
**56.**

| Particle | Symbol | Mass (amu) | Charge |
|----------|--------|------------|--------|
| α | $^4_2$He | 4 | +2 |
| β | $^0_{-1}$β | 1/1840 | −1 |
| γ | $^0_0$γ | 0 | 0 |

**57.** α, mass number decreases by 4; β, no change in mass number; γ, no change in mass number
**58.** the neutron-to-proton ratio

## Mastering Problems

Complete solutions to Chapter Assessment problems can be found in the **Solutions Manual.**

### Atomic Number and Mass Number (4.3)

**Level 1**

**59.** 44 protons, 44 electrons

**60.**

| | Element | Protons | Electrons |
|---|---------|---------|-----------|
| a. | vanadium | 23 | 23 |
| b. | manganese | 25 | 25 |
| c. | iridium | 77 | 77 |
| d. | sulfur | 16 | 16 |

**61.** 6 neutrons

**Level 2**

**62.** mass number is 200
**63.** mass number is 131

**64.**

| | Symbol | Electrons | Protons | Neutrons |
|---|--------|-----------|---------|----------|
| a. | $^{132}_{55}$Cs | 55 | 55 | 77 |
| b. | $^{59}_{27}$Co | 27 | 27 | 32 |
| c. | $^{163}_{69}$Tm | 69 | 69 | 94 |
| d. | $^{70}_{30}$Zn | 30 | 30 | 40 |

**65.**

| | Symbol | Electrons | Protons | Neutrons |
|---|--------|-----------|---------|----------|
| a. | Ga-64 | 31 | 31 | 33 |
| b. | F-23 | 9 | 9 | 14 |
| c. | Ti-48 | 22 | 22 | 26 |
| d. | He-8 | 2 | 2 | 6 |

## Atomic Mass (4.3)

### Level 1

**66.** Cl-35 must be more abundant because the atomic mass of chlorine is much closer to the mass Cl-35 than the mass of Cl-37.

### Level 2

**67.** 107.86 amu

**68.** 51.99 amu

## Mixed Review

**69.** A cathode ray tube has a metal electrode at each end and is filled with a gas at low pressure. One electrode is connected to the negative terminal of a battery (cathode), and the other is connected to the positive terminal (anode). When current flows, negatively charged particles called electrons are emitted from the cathode and travel through the tube to the anode.

**70.** Thomson determined that the electron's mass was much less than the mass of a hydrogen atom, the lightest atom. This showed that there were smaller, subatomic particles. Atoms are divisible.

**71.** Rutherford expected the $\alpha$ particles to be slightly deflected when they passed through a thin gold foil. Instead, he found that some were deflected at very large angles.

**72.**

| Isotope | Atomic number | Mass number | $p^+$ | $n^0$ | $e^-$ |
|---------|---------------|-------------|-------|-------|-------|
| S-32 | 16 | 32 | 16 | 16 | 16 |
| Ca-44 | 20 | 44 | 20 | 24 | 20 |
| Zn-64 | 30 | 64 | 30 | 34 | 30 |
| F-19 | 9 | 19 | 9 | 10 | 9 |
| Na-23 | 11 | 23 | 11 | 12 | 11 |

**73.** An atom's diameter is about 10 000 times the diameter of its nucleus. Consequently, the density of the nucleus must be enormous.

**80.** Identify the two types of radiation shown in the figure below. Explain your reasoning.

**81.** Describe how each type of radiation affects an atom's atomic number and mass number.

**82.** Silicon is very important to the semiconductor manufacturing industry. The three naturally occurring isotopes of silicon are silicon-28, silicon-29, and silicon-30. Write the symbol for each.

## Thinking Critically

**83.** **Applying Concepts** Which is greater, the number of compounds or the number of elements? The number of atoms or the number of isotopes? Explain.

**84.** **Analyzing Information** An element has three naturally occurring isotopes. What other information must you know in order to calculate the element's atomic mass?

**85.** **Applying Concepts** If atoms are primarily composed of empty space, why can't you pass your hand through a solid object?

**86.** **Formulating Models** Sketch a modern atomic model of a typical atom and identify where each type of subatomic particle would be located.

**87.** **Applying Concepts** Copper has two naturally occurring isotopes and an atomic mass of 63.546 amu. Cu-63 has a mass of 62.940 amu and an abundance of 69.17%. What is the identity and percent abundance of copper's other isotope?

## Writing in Chemistry

**88.** The Standard Model of particle physics describes all of the known building blocks of matter. Research the particles included in the Standard Model. Write a short report describing the known particles and those thought to exist but not detected experimentally.

**89.** Individual atoms can be seen using a sophisticated device known as a scanning tunneling microscope. Write a short report on how the scanning tunneling microscope works and create a gallery of scanning tunneling microscope images from sources such as books, magazines, and the Internet.

## Cumulative Review

*Refresh your understanding of previous chapters by answering the following.*

**90.** How is a qualitative observation different from a quantitative observation? Give an example of each. (Chapter 1)

**91.** A 1.0-cm³ block of gold can be flattened to a thin sheet that averages $3.0 \times 10^{-8}$ cm thick. What is the area (in cm²) of the flattened gold sheet? A letter size piece of paper has an area of 603 cm². How many sheets of paper would the gold cover? (Chapter 2)

**92.** Classify the following mixtures as heterogeneous or homogeneous. (Chapter 3)
  **a.** salt water
  **b.** vegetable soup
  **c.** 14-K gold
  **d.** concrete

**93.** Are the following changes physical or chemical? (Chapter 3)
  **a.** water boils
  **b.** a match burns
  **c.** sugar dissolves in water
  **d.** sodium reacts with water
  **e.** ice cream melts

**74.** The nucleus is positively charged, whereas the atom is neutral.

**75.** Because they are charged particles, and charged particles are affected by the electrostatic forces of attraction and repulsion from electric and magnetic fields.

**76.** Moseley discovered that each element contains a unique positive charge (or number of protons) in its nucleus.

Thus, the number of protons in an atom's nucleus uniquely identifies it as an atom of a particular element.

**77.** mass number = 39; charge = 0

**78.** B-11 must occur in greater abundance because the atomic weight of bromine is much closer to the mass of B-11 than to the mass of B-10.

**79.** 47.89 amu

*Use these questions and the test-taking tip to prepare for your standardized test.*

**1.** An atom of plutonium

  **a.** can be divided into smaller particles that retain all the properties of plutonium.

  **b.** cannot be divided into smaller particles that retain all the properties of plutonium.

  **c.** does not possess all the properties of a larger quantity of plutonium.

  **d.** cannot be seen using current technology.

**2.** Neptunium's only naturally occurring isotope, $^{237}_{93}Np$, decays by emitting one alpha particle, one beta particle, and one gamma ray. What is the new atom formed from this decay?

  **a.** $^{233}_{92}U$       **c.** $^{233}_{90}Th$

  **b.** $^{241}_{93}Np$      **d.** $^{241}_{92}U$

**3.** An atom has no net electrical charge because

  **a.** its subatomic particles carry no electrical charges.

  **b.** the positively charged protons cancel out the negatively charged neutrons.

  **c.** the positively charged neutrons cancel out the negatively charged electrons.

  **d.** the positively charged protons cancel out the negatively charged electrons.

**4.** $^{126}_{52}Te$ has

  **a.** 126 neutrons, 52 protons, and 52 electrons.

  **b.** 74 neutrons, 52 protons, and 52 electrons.

  **c.** 52 neutrons, 74 protons, and 74 electrons.

  **d.** 52 neutrons, 126 protons, and 126 electrons.

**5.** Assume the following three isotopes of element $Q$ exist: $^{248}Q$, $^{252}Q$, and $^{259}Q$. If the atomic mass of $Q$ is 258.63, which of its isotopes is the most abundant?

  **a.** $^{248}Q$       **c.** $^{259}Q$

  **b.** $^{252}Q$      **d.** they are all equally abundant

**Interpreting Tables** Use the table to answer questions 6–8.

| Characteristics of Naturally Occurring Neon Isotopes | | | |
|---|---|---|---|
| Isotope | Atomic number | Mass (amu) | Percent abundance |
| $^{20}Ne$ | 10 | 19.992 | 90.48 |
| $^{21}Ne$ | 10 | 20.994 | 0.27 |
| $^{22}Ne$ | 10 | 21.991 | 9.25 |

**6.** Based on the table, what is the mass of an atom of neon found in nature?

  **a.** 19.992 amu

  **b.** 20.179 amu

  **c.** 20.994 amu

  **d.** 21.991 amu

**7.** In which of the neon isotopes is the number of neutrons the same as the number of protons?

  **a.** $^{20}Ne$

  **b.** $^{21}Ne$

  **c.** $^{22}Ne$

  **d.** none of the above

**8.** The atomic mass of Ne is equal to _____ .

  **a.** $\dfrac{19.922 \text{ amu} + 20.994 \text{ amu} + 21.991 \text{ amu}}{3}$

  **b.** $\frac{1}{3}[(19.992 \text{ amu})(90.48\%) + (20.994 \text{ amu})(0.27\%) + (21.991 \text{ amu})(9.25\%)]$

  **c.** $(19.992 \text{ amu})(90.48\%) + (20.994 \text{ amu})(0.27\%) + (21.991 \text{ amu})(9.25\%)$

  **d.** $19.992 \text{ amu} + 20.994 \text{ amu} + 21.991 \text{ amu}$

**9.** Element X has an unstable nucleus due to an overabundance of neutrons. All of the following are likely to occur EXCEPT

  **a.** element X will undergo radioactive decay.

  **b.** element X will eventually become a stable, nonradioactive element.

  **c.** element X will gain more protons to balance the neutrons it possesses.

  **d.** element X will spontaneously lose energy.

**10.** The volume of an atom is made up mostly of

  **a.** protons.

  **b.** neutrons.

  **c.** electrons.

  **d.** empty space.

---

**TEST-TAKING TIP**

**Skip Around If You Can** The questions on some tests start easy and get progressively harder, while other tests mix easy and hard questions. You may want to skip over difficult questions and come back to them later, after you've answered all the easier questions. This will guarantee more points toward your final score. In fact, other questions may help you answer the ones you skipped. Just be sure you fill in the correct ovals on your answer sheet.

**80.** The deflected beam is α radiation because it is deflected toward the negatively charged plate. The undeflected beam must be neutral γ gamma radiation.

**81.** α, atomic number decreases by 2, mass number decreases by 4; β, atomic number increases by 1, mass number unchanged; γ, atomic number and mass number are unchanged

**82.** $^{28}_{14}Si$, $^{29}_{14}Si$, $^{30}_{14}Si$

## Thinking Critically

**83.** The number of compounds is greater than the number of elements because compounds are combinations of elements and the elements can be combined in many ways. The number of isotopes is greater than the number of atoms because each element has only one type of atom but may have more than one isotope.

**84.** You also need to know the mass and percent abundance of each isotope.

**85.** Atoms in a solid object are bonded together by electrical forces—bonds that are not easily broken. These tightly bonded atoms form solid objects.

**86.** Sketches should look similar to Figure 4-13.

**87.** The other isotope is Cu-65. Its percent abundance is 30.83%.

---

## Cumulative Review

**90.** A qualitative observation does not involve measurement (water is hot). A quantitative observation involves measurement (the water is 42°C).

**91.** area = $3.3 \times 10^7$ cm²; sheets = 55 000

**92. a.** homogeneous

  **b.** heterogeneous

  **c.** homogeneous

  **d.** heterogeneous

**93. a.** physical change

  **b.** chemical change

  **c.** physical change

  **d.** chemical change

  **e.** physical change

## Standardized Test Practice

| | | |
|---|---|---|
| **1.** b | **5.** c | **8.** c |
| **2.** a | **6.** a | **9.** c |
| **3.** d | **7.** a | **10.** d |
| **4.** b | | |

**National Science Content Standards**

Pages 114–115
UCP.1, UCP.2; B.1, B.6

# Resource Manager

| Section | Objectives | Activities/Features |
|---------|-----------|---------------------|
| **Section 5.1**<br>**Light and Quantized Energy**<br>1½ sessions<br>🖳 ½ block | **1. Compare** the wave and particle models of light.<br>**2. Define** a quantum of energy and **explain** how it is related to an energy change of matter.<br>**3. Contrast** continuous electromagnetic spectra and atomic emission spectra. | **Discovery Lab:** What's Inside?, p. 117<br>**MiniLab:** Flame Tests, p. 125<br>**ChemLab:** Line Spectra, pp. 142–143 |
| **Section 5.2**<br>**Quantum Theory and the Atom**<br>1½ sessions<br>🖳 1 block | **4. Compare** the Bohr and quantum mechanical models of the atom.<br>**5. Explain** the impact of de Broglie's wave-particle duality and the Heisenberg uncertainty principle on the modern view of electrons in atoms.<br>**6. Identify** the relationships among a hydrogen atom's energy levels, sublevels, and atomic orbitals. | **Problem-Solving Lab:** How was Bohr's atomic model able to explain the line spectrum of hydrogen? p. 130<br>**Physics Connection,** p. 131 |
| **Section 5.3**<br>**Electron Configurations**<br>3 sessions<br>🖳 1½ blocks | **7. Apply** the Pauli exclusion principle, the aufbau principle, and Hund's rule to write electron configurations using orbital diagrams and electron configuration notation.<br>**8. Define** valence electrons and draw electron-dot structures representing an atom's valence electrons. | **Careers Using Chemistry:** Spectroscopist, p. 136<br>**How It Works:** Lasers, p. 144 |

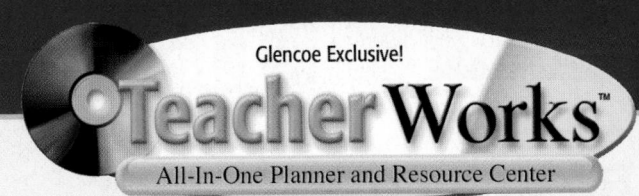

| National Science Content Standards | State/Local Standards | Reproducible Masters | Transparencies |
|---|---|---|---|
| UCP.1, UCP.2; A.1, A.2; B.1, B.6; G.1, G.2, G.3 | | **Study Guide for Content Mastery,** pp. 25–26 **L2**<br>**ChemLab and MiniLab Worksheets,** pp. 17–20 **L2** | **Section Focus**<br>**Transparency 17 L1 ELL**<br>**Teaching**<br>**Transparency 15 L2 ELL**<br>**Math Skills**<br>**Transparency 5 L2 ELL** |
| UCP.1, UCP.2; A.2; B.1, B.6; G.2, G.3 | | **Study Guide for Content Mastery,** pp. 27–28 **L2**<br>**Laboratory Manual,** pp. 33–36 **L2**<br>**Challenge Problems,** p. 5 **L3** | **Section Focus**<br>**Transparency 18 L1 ELL**<br>**Teaching**<br>**Transparency 16 L2 ELL** |
| UCP.1, UCP.2; A.1, A.2; B.1, B.6; E.2; F.6; G.2, G.3 | | **Study Guide for Content Mastery,** pp. 29–30 **L2**<br>**Laboratory Manual,** pp. 37–40 **L2** | **Section Focus**<br>**Transparency 19 L1 ELL**<br>**Teaching**<br>**Transparency 17 L2 ELL** |

**Key to National Science Content Standards:** UCP = Unifying Concepts and Processes, A = Science as Inquiry, B = Physical Science, C = Life Science, D = Earth and Space Sciences, E = Science and Technology, F = Science in Personal and Social Perspectives, G = History and Nature of Science

Refer to pages 4T–5T of the Teacher Guide for an explanation of the National Science Content Standards correlations.

# Resource Manager

## Materials List

### ChemLab (pages 142–143)
40-W tubular light bulb, light socket with power cord, spectrum tubes (hydrogen, neon, and mercury), spectrum tube power supplies (3), Flinn C-Spectra®, diffraction grating, colored pencils, food coloring (red, green, blue, and yellow), 275-mL polystyrene culture flasks (4), book, water

### Discovery Lab (page 117)
wrapped box containing small object

### MiniLab (page 125)
Bunsen burner, cotton swabs (6), distilled water, lithium chloride, sodium chloride, potassium chloride, calcium chloride, strontium chloride, unknown

### Demonstration (pages 136–137)
spectrum tubes (hydrogen and neon), spectrum tube power supply, Flinn C-Spectra®, diffraction grating, colored pencils or chalk

## Preparation of Solutions

For a review of solution preparation, see page 46T of the Teacher Guide.

There are no solutions to be prepared for the activities in this chapter.

## Assessment Resources

**Chapter Assessment,** pp. 25–30
**MindJogger Videoquizzes DVD/VHS**
**Alternate Assessment in the Science Classroom**
**ExamView® Pro CD-ROM**
**Solutions Manual,** Chapter 5
**Supplemental Problems,** Chapter 5
**Performance Assessment in the Science Classroom**
**Chemistry Interactive CD-ROM,** Chapter 5 quiz

## Additional Resources

**Spanish Resources** ELL
**Guided Reading Audio Program,** Chapter 5 ELL
**Cooperative Learning in the Science Classroom**
**Lab and Safety Skills in the Science Classroom**
**Lesson Plans**
**Block Scheduling Lesson Plans**
**Chemistrymc.com**

## Glencoe Technology

The following multimedia for this chapter are available from Glencoe.

**VIDEOTAPE/DVD**
MindJogger Videoquizzes,
Chapter 5

**CD-ROM**
**Chemistry: Matter and Change**
*Flame Test,* Video
*The Aurora,* Video
*Atomic Emissions,* Video
*Electrons and Energy Levels,* Animation
*Building Atoms,* Exploration

**CD-ROM**
**ExamView® Pro**
  **Testmaker**

**CD-ROM**
**Interactive Chalkboard**

**CD-ROM**
**TeacherWorks™**

## Multiple Learning Styles

Look for the following icons for strategies that emphasize different learning modalities.

*Kinesthetic*
Building a Model, p. 123; Differentiated
Instruction, pp. 127, 139; Quick Demo, p. 131

*Visual-Spatial*
Portfolio, p. 118; Chemistry Journal, p. 133;
Reteach, p. 141

*Intrapersonal*
English Language Learners, p. 121; Enrichment,
p. 122; Differentiated Instruction, p. 131; Chemistry
Journal, p. 129

*Linguistic*
Chemistry Journal, pp. 119, 122, 140; Portfolio,
p. 133

*Logical-Mathematical*
Differentiated Instruction, p. 128

## Key to Teaching Strategies

**L1** Level 1 activities should be appropriate for students with learning difficulties.

**L2** Level 2 activities should be within the ability range of all students.

**L3** Level 3 activities are designed for above-average students.

**ELL** ELL activities should be within the ability range of English Language Learners.

**COOP LEARN** Cooperative Learning activities are designed for small group work.

**P** These strategies represent student products that can be placed into a best-work portfolio.

 These strategies are useful in a block scheduling format.

## ✓ Assessment Planner

**Portfolio Assessment**
Portfolio, TWE, pp. 118, 120,
  133, 145
Assessment, p. 139

**Performance Assessment**
Assessment, TWE, pp. 122,
  128
MiniLab, SE, p. 125
ChemLab, SE, pp. 142-143
Discovery Lab, SE, p. 117

**Knowledge Assessment**
Assessment, TWE, pp. 126,
  134
Section Assessment, SE,
  pp. 126, 134, 141
Chapter Assessment, SE,
  pp. 146-149

**Skill Assessment**
Assessment, TWE, p. 141
Problem-Solving Lab, TWE,
  p. 130
ChemLab, TWE, p. 143
Demonstration, TWE, p. 137

## Tying to Previous Knowledge

Have students review the following concepts before studying this chapter.
Chapter 4: atomic structure

## Using the Photo

Point out that the vivid colors of light given off by fireworks are of different origin than colors produced by colored light bulbs or filters. Explain that energy transitions within atoms cause the distinctive colors—something that students will learn more about in the chapter.

## Chapter Themes

The following themes from the National Science Education Standards are covered in this chapter. Refer to page 4T of the Teacher Guide for an explanation of the correlations.
Systems, order, and organization (UCP.1)
Evidence, models, and explanation (UCP.2)
Form and function (UCP.5)

# Electrons in Atoms

## What You'll Learn

▶ You will compare the wave and particle models of light.
▶ You will describe how the frequency of light emitted by an atom is a unique characteristic of that atom.
▶ You will compare and contrast the Bohr and quantum mechanical models of the atom.
▶ You will express the arrangements of electrons in atoms through orbital notations, electron configurations, and electron dot structures.

## Why It's Important

Why are some fireworks red, some white, and others blue? The key to understanding the chemical behavior of fireworks, and all matter, lies in understanding how electrons are arranged in atoms of each element.

Visit the Chemistry Web site at chemistrymc.com to find links about electrons in atoms.

The colorful display from fireworks is due to changes in the electron configurations of atoms.

---

## DISCOVERY LAB

### Purpose
Students will make observations using all the senses except sight.

### Safety and Disposal
Keep boxes for use next year.

### Teaching Strategies
• Try to use objects in the box that are simple, but challenging.
• When students are through with the lab, you may want to identify the objects, or, to demonstrate that chemists can't always see what they are looking for, you may want to leave the object's identity a mystery!

### Expected Results
Results will vary. Students should try to use senses other than sight to determine the relative size, mass, shape, and number of objects.

### Analysis
Answers will vary. Students will determine that observations typically rely heavily upon sight, although touch and hearing are somewhat useful.

## DISCOVERY LAB

### What's Inside?

It's your birthday, and there are many wrapped presents for you to open. Much of the fun is trying to figure out what's inside the package before you open it. In trying to determine the structure of the atom, chemists had a similar experience. How good are your skills of observation and deduction?

**Procedure**

1. Obtain a wrapped box from your instructor.

2. Using as many observation methods as you can, and without unwrapping or opening the box, try to figure out what the object inside the box is.

3. Record the observations you make throughout this discovery process.

**Analysis**

How were you able to determine things such as size, shape, number, and composition of the object in the box? What senses did you use to make your observations? Why is it hard to figure out what type of object is in the box without actually seeing it?

**Materials**

a wrapped box from your instructor

## Section 5.1

# Light and Quantized Energy

### Objectives

- **Compare** the wave and particle models of light.

- **Define** a quantum of energy and explain how it is related to an energy change of matter.

- **Contrast** continuous electromagnetic spectra and atomic emission spectra.

### Vocabulary

electromagnetic radiation
wavelength
frequency
amplitude
electromagnetic spectrum
quantum
Planck's constant
photoelectric effect
photon
atomic emission spectrum

Although three subatomic particles had been discovered by the early-1900s, the quest to understand the atom and its structure had really just begun. That quest continues in this chapter, as scientists pursued an understanding of how electrons were arranged within atoms. Perform the **DISCOVERY LAB** on this page to better understand the difficulties scientists faced in researching the unseen atom.

## The Nuclear Atom and Unanswered Questions

As you learned in Chapter 4, Rutherford proposed that all of an atom's positive charge and virtually all of its mass are concentrated in a nucleus that is surrounded by fast-moving electrons. Although his nuclear model was a major scientific development, it lacked detail about how electrons occupy the space surrounding the nucleus. In this chapter, you will learn how electrons are arranged in an atom and how that arrangement plays a role in chemical behavior.

Many scientists in the early twentieth century found Rutherford's nuclear atomic model to be fundamentally incomplete. To physicists, the model did not explain how the atom's electrons are arranged in the space around the nucleus. Nor did it address the question of why the negatively charged electrons are not pulled into the atom's positively charged nucleus. Chemists found Rutherford's nuclear model lacking because it did not begin to account for the differences in chemical behavior among the various elements.

5.1 Light and Quantized Energy **117**

## Section 5.1

# 1 Focus

### Focus Transparency

Before presenting the lesson, display **Section Focus Transparency 17** on the overhead projector. Have students answer the accompanying questions using **Section Focus Transparency Master 17.** L1 ELL

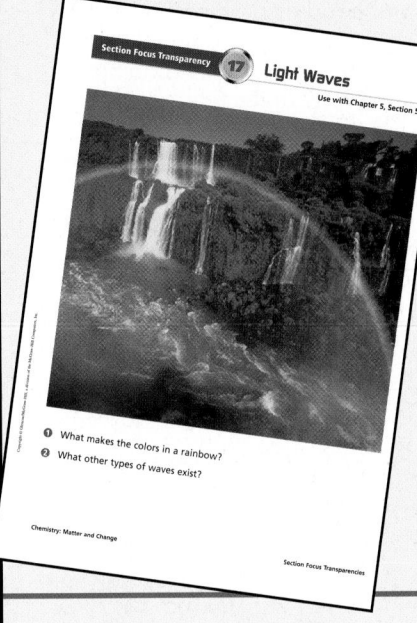

Section Focus Transparency 17 Light Waves
Use with Chapter 5, Section 5.1

❶ What makes the colors in a rainbow?
❷ What other types of waves exist?

Chemistry: Matter and Change

Section Focus Transparencies

# 2 Teach
## Concept Development

Explain that the concept that matter is made up of atoms is useful in many ways. For example, the fact that water contains two atoms of hydrogen for every atom of oxygen explains why the masses of the two elements are always in the same proportion in the compound. Point out, however, that something well beyond this concept must account for the vastly different chemical behaviors of hydrogen, oxygen, and the other chemical elements.

### Resource Manager

**Study Guide for Content Mastery,** pp. 25–26 L2
**Solving Problems: A Chemistry Handbook,** Section 5.1
**Section Focus Transparency 17 and Master** L1 ELL

**National Science Content Standards**

Pages 116–117
UCP.1, UCP.2; B.1, B.6; G.1, G.3

Demonstrate that unlike charges attract using the following materials, which can probably be obtained from your school's physics department: a hard rubber rod; either a piece of cat hide with the fur attached or a piece of wool; a glass rod; a piece of synthetic fabric, such as nylon. Use a Y-shaped piece of string to suspend the rubber rod horizontally from a support. Impart a negative charge to the rod by rubbing it with fur. Then, impart a positive charge to the glass rod by rubbing it with synthetic fabric. When you bring the glass rod close to the suspended rubber rod, the rubber rod will move toward the glass rod. Explain that the rods' unlike charges cause the attraction. Point out that an atom's positively charged nucleus exerts the same type of electrostatic attraction for its negatively charged electrons.

**Figure 5-1**

**a** Chlorine gas, shown here reacting vigorously with steel wool, reacts with many other atoms as well. **b** Argon gas fills the interior of this incandescent bulb. The nonreactive argon prevents the hot filament from oxidizing, thus extending the life of the bulb. **c** Solid potassium metal is submerged in oil to prevent it from reacting with air or water.

For example, consider the elements chlorine, argon, and potassium, which are found in consecutive order on the periodic table but have very different chemical behaviors. Atoms of chlorine, a yellow-green gas at room temperature, react readily with atoms of many other elements. **Figure 5-1a** shows chlorine atoms reacting with steel wool. The interaction of highly reactive chlorine atoms with the large surface area provided by the steel results in a vigorous reaction. Argon, which is used in the incandescent bulb shown in **Figure 5-1b**, also is a gas. Argon, however, is so unreactive that it is considered a noble gas. Potassium is a reactive metal at room temperature. In fact, as you can see in **Figure 5-1c,** because potassium is so reactive, it must be stored under kerosene or oil to prevent its atoms from reacting with the oxygen and water in the air. Rutherford's nuclear atomic model could not explain why atoms of these elements behave the way they do.

In the early 1900s, scientists began to unravel the puzzle of chemical behavior. They had observed that certain elements emitted visible light when heated in a flame. Analysis of the emitted light revealed that an element's chemical behavior is related to the arrangement of the electrons in its atoms. In order for you to better understand this relationship and the nature of atomic structure, it will be helpful for you to first understand the nature of light.

## Wave Nature of Light

**Electromagnetic radiation** is a form of energy that exhibits wavelike behavior as it travels through space. Visible light is a type of electromagnetic radiation. Other examples of electromagnetic radiation include visible light from the sun, microwaves that warm and cook your food, X rays that doctors and dentists use to examine bones and teeth, and waves that carry radio and television programs to your home.

All waves can be described by several characteristics, a few of which you may be familiar with from everyday experience. **Figure 5-2a** shows a standing wave created by rhythmically moving the free end of a spring toy. **Figure 5-2b** illustrates several primary characteristics of all waves, wavelength, frequency, amplitude, and speed. **Wavelength** (represented by $\lambda$, the Greek letter lambda) is the shortest distance between equivalent points on a continuous wave. For example, in **Figure 5-2b** the wavelength is measured from crest to crest or from trough to trough. Wavelength is usually expressed in meters, centimeters, or nanometers ($1 \text{ nm} = 1 \times 10^{-9}$ m). **Frequency** (represented by $\nu$, the Greek letter nu) is the number of waves that pass a given

---

### Portfolio

### Classical Physics and Electrons in Atoms

*Visual-Spatial* Have students research and explain how electrons in atoms should behave according to classical physics. Have them draw diagrams illustrating their findings. Students should include their explanations and diagrams in their portfolios. Negatively charged electrons orbiting the nucleus should spiral into the positively charged nucleus, giving off energy in the process. **L2** **ELL** **P**

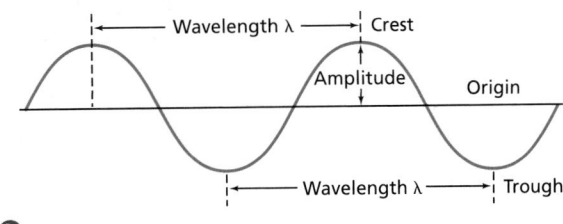

(a)

(b)

Project the beam from a high-intensity projector into the side of a large beaker of water. Darken the room and adjust the arrangement so students can see the visible portion of the electromagnetic spectrum on a wall or screen. Explain that reflection and refraction separate the component colors of white light from the projector as they pass through the beaker and water. Point out that rainbows are formed in much the same manner when the colors in sunlight separate as they are reflected and refracted by raindrops.

point per second. One hertz (Hz), the SI unit of frequency, equals one wave per second. In calculations, frequency is expressed with units of "waves per second," $\left(\frac{1}{s}\right)$ or $(s^{-1})$, where the term "waves" is understood. For example,

$$652 \text{ Hz} = 652 \text{ waves/second} = \frac{652}{s} = 652 \text{ s}^{-1}$$

The **amplitude** of a wave is the wave's height from the origin to a crest, or from the origin to a trough. To learn how lightwaves are able to form powerful laser beams, read the **How It Works** at the end of this chapter.

All electromagnetic waves, including visible light, travel at a speed of $3.00 \times 10^8$ m/s in a vacuum. Because the speed of light is such an important and universal value, it is given its own symbol, $c$. The speed of light is the product of its wavelength ($\lambda$) and its frequency ($\nu$).

$$c = \lambda \nu$$

Although the speed of all electromagnetic waves is the same, waves may have different wavelengths and frequencies. As you can see from the equation above, wavelength and frequency are inversely related; in other words, as one quantity increases, the other decreases. To better understand this relationship, examine the red and violet light waves illustrated in **Figure 5-3**. Although both waves travel at the speed of light, you can see that red light has a longer wavelength and lower frequency than violet light.

Sunlight, which is one example of what is called white light, contains a continuous range of wavelengths and frequencies. Sunlight passing through a prism

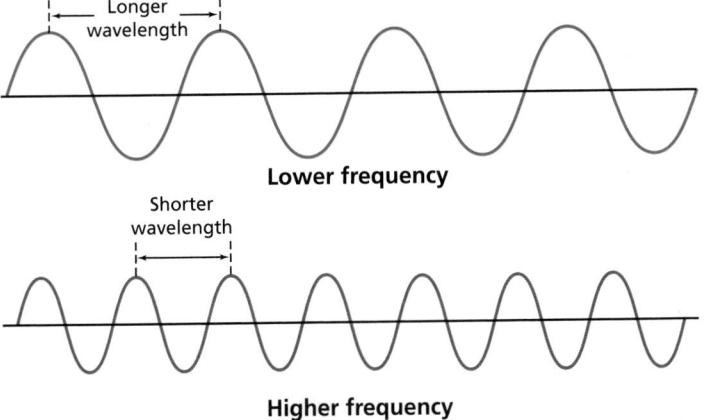

**Figure 5-2**

(a) The standing wave produced with this spring toy displays properties that are characteristic of all waves. (b) The primary characteristics of waves are wavelength, frequency, amplitude, and speed. What is the wavelength of the wave in centimeters?

**Figure 5-3**

The inverse relationship between wavelength and frequency of electromagnetic waves can be seen in these red and violet waves. As wavelength increases, frequency decreases. Wavelength and frequency do not affect the amplitude of a wave. Which wave has the larger amplitude?

5.1 Light and Quantized Energy **119**

**Figure Caption Questions**

**Figure 5-2** What is the wavelength of the wave in centimeters? ~4.5 cm

**Figure 5-3** Which wave has the larger amplitude? The red wave has a larger amplitude.

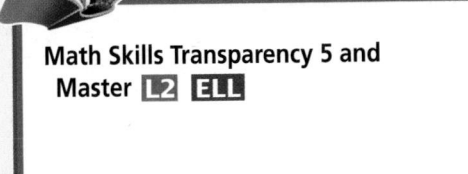

**CHEMISTRY JOURNAL**

**Frequencies and Daily Living**

*Linguistic* In order to reinforce the concept of frequency, have students think of and describe at least five phenomena they encounter that recur or occur at given frequencies in their daily lives. Have them describe these phenomena in their journals and, when possible, quantify the frequencies.

Borrow a Slinky from the physics department and attach it securely to an object on one side of the room. Demonstrate wave characteristics—wavelength, frequency, and energy—by generating standing waves. Start with a half wave, showing the longest wavelength, lowest frequency, and least energy. Work up to two or two and one-half standing waves. It will be obvious that you must use more energy as the number of standing waves increases. With each increase in the number of waves, ask students what is happening to frequency and wavelength, and how energy is changing. *Frequency is increasing, wavelength is decreasing, and energy is increasing.*

## Figure Caption Question

**Figure 5-5** Which types of waves or rays have the highest energy?
gamma rays and X rays

**Figure 5-4**

White light is separated into a continuous spectrum when it passes through a prism.

**Try at Home LAB**

See page 954 in Appendix E for
**Observing Light's Wave Nature**

**Figure 5-5**

The electromagnetic spectrum includes a wide range of wavelengths (and frequencies). Energy of the radiation increases with increasing frequency. Which types of waves or rays have the highest energy?

is separated into a continuous spectrum of colors. These are the colors of the visible spectrum. The spectrum is called continuous because there is no portion of it that does not correspond to a unique wavelength and frequency of light. You are already familiar with all of the colors of the visible spectrum from your everyday experiences. And if you have ever seen a rainbow, you have seen all of the visible colors at once. A rainbow is formed when tiny drops of water in the air disperse the white light from the sun into its component colors, producing a continuous spectrum that arches across the sky.

The visible spectrum of light shown in **Figure 5-4,** however, comprises only a small portion of the complete electromagnetic spectrum, which is illustrated in **Figure 5-5.** The **electromagnetic spectrum,** also called the EM spectrum, encompasses all forms of electromagnetic radiation, with the only differences in the types of radiation being their frequencies and wavelengths. Note in **Figure 5-4** that the short wavelengths bend more than long wavelengths as they pass through the prism, resulting in the sequence of colors red, orange, yellow, green, blue, indigo, and violet. This sequence can be remembered using the fictitious name Roy G. Biv as a memory aid. In examining the energy of the radiation shown in **Figure 5-5**, you should note that energy increases with increasing frequency. Thus, looking back at **Figure 5-3**, the violet light, with its greater frequency, has more energy than the red light. This relationship between frequency and energy will be explained in the next section.

Electromagnetic Spectrum

 **Portfolio**

## Electromagnetic Waves and Uses
Have students research and discuss the many ways humans use electromagnetic waves to transmit information and carry energy from place to place. Have them write up their findings in their portfolios.
L2 P

**Resource Manager**

**Teaching Transparency 15 and Master**
L2 ELL

Because all electromagnetic waves travel at the same speed, you can use the formula $c = \lambda\nu$ to calculate the wavelength or frequency of any wave. Example Problem 5-1 shows how this is done.

## EXAMPLE PROBLEM 5-1

### Calculating Wavelength of an EM Wave

Microwaves are used to transmit information. What is the wavelength of a microwave having a frequency of $3.44 \times 10^9$ Hz?

**1. Analyze the Problem**

You are given the frequency of a microwave. You also know that because microwaves are part of the electromagnetic spectrum, their speed, frequency, and wavelength are related by the formula $c = \lambda\nu$. The value of $c$ is a known constant. First, solve the equation for wavelength, then substitute the known values and solve.

| Known | Unknown |
|---|---|
| $\nu = 3.44 \times 10^9$ Hz | $\lambda = ?$ m |
| $c = 3.00 \times 10^8$ m/s | |

**2. Solve for the Unknown**

Solve the equation relating the speed, frequency, and wavelength of an electromagnetic wave for wavelength ($\lambda$).

$$c = \lambda\nu$$

$$\lambda = c/\nu$$

Substitute $c$ and the microwave's frequency, $\nu$, into the equation. Note that hertz is equivalent to 1/s or $s^{-1}$.

$$\lambda = \frac{3.00 \times 10^8 \text{ m/s}}{3.44 \times 10^9 \text{ s}^{-1}}$$

Divide the values to determine wavelength, $\lambda$, and cancel units as required.

$$\lambda = \frac{3.00 \times 10^8 \text{ m/s}}{3.44 \times 10^9 \text{ s}^{-1}} = 8.72 \times 10^{-2} \text{ m}$$

**3. Evaluate the Answer**

The answer is correctly expressed in a unit of wavelength (m). Both of the known values in the problem are expressed with three significant figures, so the answer should have three significant figures, which it does. The value for the wavelength is within the wavelength range for microwaves shown in **Figure 5-5**.

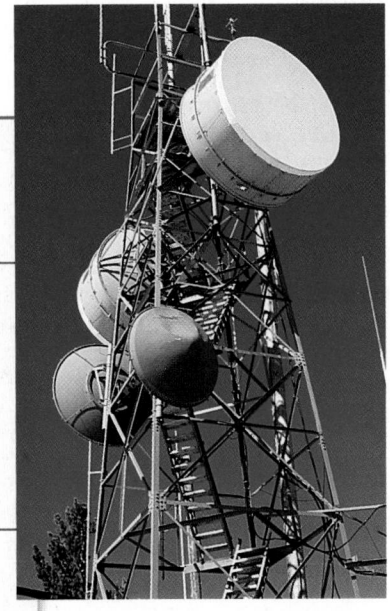

Microwave relay antennas are used to transmit voice and data from one area to another without the use of wires or cables.

## PRACTICE PROBLEMS

1. What is the frequency of green light, which has a wavelength of $4.90 \times 10^{-7}$ m?

2. An X ray has a wavelength of $1.15 \times 10^{-10}$ m. What is its frequency?

3. What is the speed of an electromagnetic wave that has a frequency of $7.8 \times 10^6$ Hz?

4. A popular radio station broadcasts with a frequency of 94.7 MHz. What is the wavelength of the broadcast? (1 MHz = $10^6$ Hz)

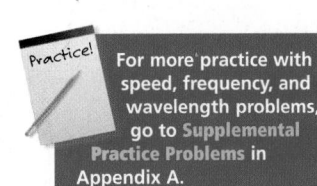

Practice! For more practice with speed, frequency, and wavelength problems, go to Supplemental Practice Problems in Appendix A.

### Practice PROBLEMS

Have students refer to Appendix D for complete solutions to Practice Problems.
1. $6.12 \times 10^{14}$ s$^{-1}$
2. $2.61 \times 10^{18}$ s$^{-1}$
3. $3.00 \times 10^8$ m/s
4. 3.17 m

### Reinforcement

When the people in a stadium make a "wave," the wave travels around the stadium as individual persons move their bodies and arms up and down. Point out, however, that each person transmitting the wave remains in the same place.

### Math in Chemistry

Explain that when two quantities are related mathematically in such a way that the increase in one quantity is proportional to the decrease in the other quantity, the two quantities are said to be inversely proportional. Point out that the relationship $c = \lambda\nu$ is valid only if the quantities $\lambda$ and $\nu$ are inversely related.

## DIFFERENTIATED INSTRUCTION

### English Language Learners

*Intrapersonal* Have English language learners look up and then explain the meanings of several key English words used in this section: *radiation, spectrum, constant, effect, emission, quantum.* Then ask them to use the words in a paragraph about waves. **L1** **ELL**

National Science Content Standards
**Pages 120–121**
UCP.1, UCP.2; B.1, B.6

**Chemistry Online**

**Topic: Forensics**
To learn more about chemical analytical techniques that use light, visit the Chemistry Web site at **chemistrymc.com**

**Activity:** Research the roles that infrared and ultraviolet light have played in forensic investigations. Share with the class a particular case that was solved with these tools.

**Figure 5-6**

These photos illustrate the phenomenon of heated objects emitting different frequencies of light. Matter, regardless of its form, can gain or lose energy only in small "quantized" amounts.

# Particle Nature of Light

While considering light as a wave does explain much of its everyday behavior, it fails to adequately describe important aspects of light's interactions with matter. The wave model of light cannot explain why heated objects emit only certain frequencies of light at a given temperature, or why some metals emit electrons when colored light of a specific frequency shines on them. Obviously, a totally new model or a revision of the current model of light was needed to address these phenomena.

**The quantum concept** The glowing light emitted by the hot objects shown in **Figure 5-6** are examples of a phenomenon you have certainly seen. Iron provides another example of the phenomenon. A piece of iron appears dark gray at room temperature, glows red when heated sufficiently, and appears bluish in color at even higher temperatures. As you will learn in greater detail later on in this course, the temperature of an object is a measure of the average kinetic energy of its particles. As the iron gets hotter it possesses a greater amount of energy, and emits different colors of light. These different colors correspond to different frequencies and wavelengths. The wave model could not explain the emission of these different wavelengths of light at different temperatures. In 1900, the German physicist Max Planck (1858–1947) began searching for an explanation as he studied the light emitted from heated objects. His study of the phenomenon led him to a startling conclusion: matter can gain or lose energy only in small, specific amounts called quanta. That is, a **quantum** is the minimum amount of energy that can be gained or lost by an atom.

Planck and other physicists of the time thought the concept of quantized energy was revolutionary—and some found it disturbing. Prior experience had led scientists to believe that energy could be absorbed and emitted in continually varying quantities, with no minimum limit to the amount. For example, think about heating a cup of water in a microwave oven. It seems that you can add any amount of thermal energy to the water by regulating the power and duration of the microwaves. Actually, the water's temperature increases in infinitesimal steps as its molecules absorb quanta of energy. Because these steps are so small, the temperature seems to rise in a continuous, rather than a stepwise, manner.

The glowing objects shown in **Figure 5-6** are emitting light, which is a form of energy. Planck proposed that this emitted light energy was quantized.

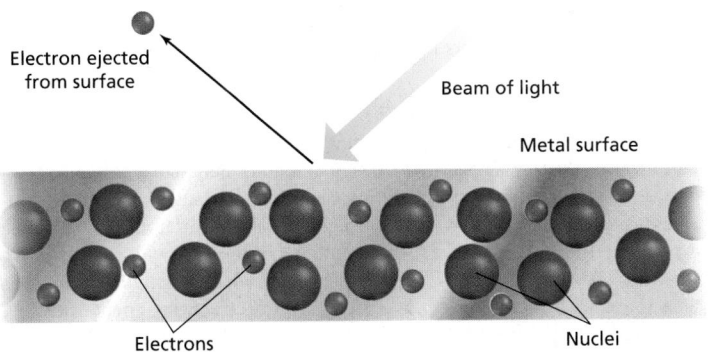

Electron ejected from surface

Beam of light

Metal surface

Electrons

Nuclei

Figure 5-7

In the photoelectric effect, light of a certain minimum frequency (energy) ejects electrons from the surface of a metal. Increasing the intensity of the incident light results in more electrons being ejected. Increasing the frequency (energy) of the incident light causes the ejected electrons to travel faster.

He then went further and demonstrated mathematically that the energy of a quantum is related to the frequency of the emitted radiation by the equation

$$E_{quantum} = h\nu$$

where $E$ is energy, $h$ is Planck's constant, and $\nu$ is frequency. **Planck's constant** has a value of $6.626 \times 10^{-34}$ J $\cdot$ s, where J is the symbol for the joule, the SI unit of energy. Looking at the equation, you can see that the energy of radiation increases as the radiation's frequency, $\nu$, increases. This equation explains why the violet light in **Figure 5-3** has greater energy than the red light.

According to Planck's theory, for a given frequency, $\nu$, matter can emit or absorb energy only in whole-number multiples of $h\nu$; that is, $1h\nu$, $2h\nu$, $3h\nu$, and so on. A useful analogy for this concept is that of a child building a wall of wooden blocks. The child can add to or take away height from the wall only in increments of a whole number of blocks. Partial blocks are not possible. Similarly, matter can have only certain amounts of energy—quantities of energy between these values do not exist.

**The photoelectric effect** Scientists knew that the wave model (still very popular in spite of Planck's proposal) could not explain a phenomenon called the photoelectric effect. In the **photoelectric effect**, electrons, called photoelectrons, are emitted from a metal's surface when light of a certain frequency shines on the surface, as shown in **Figure 5-7**. Perhaps you've taken advantage of the photoelectric effect by using a calculator, such as the one shown in **Figure 5-8**, that is powered by photoelectric cells. Photoelectric cells in these and many other devices convert the energy of incident light into electrical energy.

The mystery of the photoelectric effect concerns the frequency, and therefore color, of the incident light. The wave model predicts that given enough time, even low-energy, low-frequency light would accumulate and supply enough energy to eject photoelectrons from a metal. However, a metal will not eject photoelectrons below a specific frequency of incident light. For example, no matter how intense or how long it shines, light with a frequency less than $1.14 \times 10^{15}$ Hz does not eject photoelectrons from silver. But even dim light having a frequency equal to or greater than $1.14 \times 10^{15}$ Hz causes the ejection of photoelectrons from silver.

In explaining the photoelectric effect, Albert Einstein proposed in 1905 that electromagnetic radiation has both wavelike and particlelike natures. That is, while a beam of light has many wavelike characteristics, it also can be thought of as a stream of tiny particles, or bundles of energy, called photons. Thus, a **photon** is a particle of electromagnetic radiation with no mass that carries a quantum of energy.

Figure 5-8

The direct conversion of sunlight into electrical energy is a viable power source for low-power consumption devices such as this calculator. The cost of photoelectric cells makes them impractical for large-scale power production.

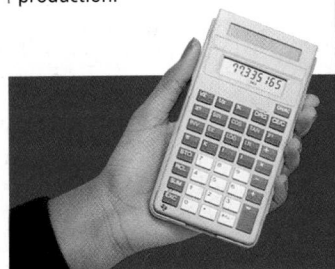

## Concept Development

Explain to students that they might think of the light emitted by an atom as a "window into the atom." Explain further that the chemical behaviors of the elements are related not to the number of subatomic particles in their atoms, but to the arrangement of electrons within their atoms.

## Building a Model

**Kinesthetic** Have student groups build a setup that models the photoelectric effect. For example, the setup might show that impacting small magnets attached to a heavy iron object with lightweight and low-energy objects such as marshmallows will not displace the magnets. Then, the setup could show that heavier objects with greater energy displace the magnets. Have students draw the analogy between the marshmallows and low-energy photons and between the heavier objects and high-energy photons.
**L2** **ELL** **COOP LEARN**

5.1 Light and Quantized Energy    **123**

---

## Internet Address Book

**Chemistry Online**

Note Internet addresses that you find useful in the space below for quick reference.

_____

_____

_____

_____

_____

**National Science Content Standards**

**Pages 122–123**
UCP.1, UCP.2; A.2; B.1, B.6; G.2, G.3

### Practice PROBLEMS

Have students refer to Appendix D for complete solutions to Practice Problems.

**5. a.** $4.19 \times 10^{-13}$ J
   **b.** $6.29 \times 10^{-20}$ J
   **c.** $6.96 \times 10^{-18}$ J
**6. a.** gamma ray or X ray
   **b.** infrared
   **c.** ultraviolet

# 3 Assess

## Check for Understanding

Ask students to explain why chemists found Rutherford's nuclear model of the atom lacking. It did not explain or account for the differences in the chemical behavior of the elements.

## GLENCOE
### TECHNOLOGY

**CD-ROM**
**Chemistry: Matter and Change**
Video: *Flame Test*
Video: *The Aurora*
Video: *Atomic Emissions*

### Resource Manager

**ChemLab and MiniLab Worksheets,** p. 17 **L2**

## Extension

Begin to extend students' understanding of wave-particle duality by explaining that not only do waves have a particle nature, but moving particles have a wave nature, a concept students will learn more about in the next section.

---

Extending Planck's idea of quantized energy, Einstein calculated that a photon's energy depends on its frequency.

$$E_{photon} = h\nu$$

Further, Einstein proposed that the energy of a photon of light must have a certain minimum, or threshold, value to cause the ejection of a photoelectron. That is, for the photoelectric effect to occur a photon must possess, at a minimum, the energy required to free an electron from an atom of the metal. According to this theory, even small numbers of photons with energy above the threshold value will cause the photoelectric effect. Although Einstein was able to explain the photoelectric effect by giving electromagnetic radiation particlelike properties, it's important to note that a dual wave-particle model of light was required.

Sunlight bathes Earth in white light—light composed of all of the visible colors of the electromagnetic spectrum.

## EXAMPLE PROBLEM 5-2

### Calculating the Energy of a Photon

Tiny water drops in the air disperse the white light of the sun into a rainbow. What is the energy of a photon from the violet portion of the rainbow if it has a frequency of $7.23 \times 10^{14}$ s$^{-1}$?

**1. Analyze the Problem**

You are given the frequency of a photon of violet light. You also know that the energy of a photon is related to its frequency by the equation $E_{photon} = h\nu$. The value of $h$, Planck's constant, is known. By substituting the known values, the equation can be solved for the energy of a photon of violet light.

**Known**

$\nu = 7.23 \times 10^{14}$ s$^{-1}$
$h = 6.626 \times 10^{-34}$ J · s

**Unknown**

$E_{photon} = ?$ J

**2. Solve for the Unknown**

Substitute the known values for frequency and Planck's constant into the equation relating energy of a photon and frequency.

$E_{photon} = h\nu$

$E_{photon} = (6.626 \times 10^{-34}$ J · s$)(7.23 \times 10^{14}$ s$^{-1})$

Multiply the known values and cancel units.

$E_{photon} = (6.626 \times 10^{-34}$ J · s$)(7.23 \times 10^{14}$ s$^{-1}) = 4.79 \times 10^{-19}$ J

The energy of one photon of violet light is $4.79 \times 10^{-19}$ J.

**3. Evaluate the Answer**

The answer is correctly expressed in a unit of energy (J). The known value for frequency has three significant figures, and the answer also is expressed with three significant figures, as it should be. As expected, the energy of a single photon of light is extremely small.

## PRACTICE PROBLEMS

Practice! For more practice with photon energy problems, go to Supplemental Practice Problems in Appendix A.

**5.** What is the energy of each of the following types of radiation?

   **a.** $6.32 \times 10^{20}$ s$^{-1}$     **b.** $9.50 \times 10^{13}$ Hz     **c.** $1.05 \times 10^{16}$ s$^{-1}$

**6.** Use **Figure 5-5** to determine the types of radiation described in problem 5.

---

## DIFFERENTIATED INSTRUCTION

### Gifted

Have capable students research and perhaps explain to the class how astrophysicists determine what elements make up Earth's Sun and other stars. In general, because a star is made up of hot, glowing gases, its emitted light can be gathered by a telescope and analyzed. From the atomic emission and absorption spectra of the light, the elements present in the star can be determined. **L3**

## Atomic Emission Spectra

Have you ever wondered how light is produced in the glowing tubes of neon signs? The process illustrates another phenomenon that cannot be explained by the wave model of light. The light of the neon sign is produced by passing electricity through a tube filled with neon gas. Neon atoms in the tube absorb energy and become excited. These excited and unstable atoms then release energy by emitting light. If the light emitted by the neon is passed through a glass prism, neon's atomic emission spectrum is produced. The **atomic emission spectrum** of an element is the set of frequencies of the electromagnetic waves emitted by atoms of the element. Neon's atomic emission spectrum consists of several individual lines of color, not a continuous range of colors as seen in the visible spectrum.

Each element's atomic emission spectrum is unique and can be used to determine if that element is part of an unknown compound. For example, when a platinum wire is dipped into a strontium nitrate solution and then inserted into a burner flame, the strontium atoms emit a characteristic red color. You can perform a series of flame tests yourself by doing the **miniLAB** below.

**Figure 5-9** on the following page shows an illustration of the characteristic purple-pink glow produced by excited hydrogen atoms and the visible portion of hydrogen's emission spectrum responsible for producing the glow. Note how the line nature of hydrogen's atomic emission spectrum differs from that of a continuous spectrum. To gain firsthand experience with types of line spectra, you can perform the **CHEMLAB** at the end of this chapter.

## miniLAB

### Flame Tests

**Classifying** When certain compounds are heated in a flame, they emit a distinctive color. The color of the emitted light can be used to identify the compound.

**Materials** Bunsen burner; cotton swabs (6); distilled water; crystals of lithium chloride, sodium chloride, potassium chloride, calcium chloride, strontium chloride, unknown

**Procedure**

1. Dip a cotton swab into the distilled water. Dip the moistened swab into the lithium chloride so that a few of the crystals stick to the cotton. Put the crystals on the swab into the flame of a Bunsen burner. Observe the color of the flame and record it in your data table.

2. Repeat step 1 for each of the metallic chlorides (sodium chloride, potassium chloride, calcium chloride, and strontium chloride). Be sure to record the color of each flame in your data table.

3. Obtain a sample of unknown crystals from your teacher. Repeat the procedure in step 1 using the unknown crystals. Record the color of the flame produced by the unknown crystals in your data table. Dispose of used cotton swabs as directed by your teacher.

### Analysis

1. Each of the known compounds tested contains chlorine, yet each compound produced a flame of a different color. Explain why this occurred.

2. How is the atomic emission spectrum of an element related to these flame tests?

3. What is the identity of the unknown crystals? Explain how you know.

| Flame Test Results | |
|---|---|
| Compound | Flame color |
| Lithium chloride | |
| Sodium chloride | |
| Potassium chloride | |
| Calcium chloride | |
| Strontium chloride | |
| Unknown | |

# Reteach

Reinforce the concept that red light has less energy than blue light. Explaining that you are making a solution of a fluorescent substance, prepare a solution of about 10 g fluorescein in 100 mL water in a 150 mL beaker. Turn out the room lights, and shine a flashlight's beam through a transparent red cellophane sheet into the fluorescein solution. When you turn out the flashlight, the solution will not fluoresce. Then, repeat the process, but use a blue cellophane sheet rather than a red one. The solution will fluoresce when you turn out the light. Ask students to explain the results. The blue light waves have a higher frequency, shorter wavelength, and greater energy than the red light waves. The solution may be flushed down the drain with water.

## CHEMLAB

ChemLab 5, located at the end of the chapter, can be used at this point in the lesson.

## Assessment

**Knowledge** Ask students to compare the wavelengths, frequencies, and energies of microwaves and X rays. Microwaves have longer wavelengths, lower frequencies, and lower energies than X rays. **L2**

## Figure Caption Question

**Figure 5-9** Which line has the highest energy? the violet line

Slit  Prism

410 nm  434 nm  486 nm  656 nm

$\lambda(nm)$ 400  450  500  550  600  650  700  750

Hydrogen gas discharge tube

Hydrogen's atomic emission spectrum

**Figure 5-9**

The atomic emission spectrum of hydrogen consists of four distinct colored lines of different frequencies. This type of spectrum is also known as a line spectrum. Which line has the highest energy?

An atomic emission spectrum is characteristic of the element being examined and can be used to identify that element. The fact that only certain colors appear in an element's atomic emission spectrum means that only certain specific frequencies of light are emitted. And because those emitted frequencies of light are related to energy by the formula $E_{photon} = h\nu$, it can be concluded that only photons having certain specific energies are emitted. This conclusion was not predicted by the laws of classical physics known at that time. Scientists found atomic emission spectra puzzling because they had expected to observe the emission of a continuous series of colors and energies as excited electrons lost energy and spiraled toward the nucleus. In the next section, you will learn about the continuing development of atomic models, and how one of those models was able to account for the frequencies of the light emitted by excited atoms.

## Section 5.1 Assessment

**7.** List the characteristic properties of all waves. At what speed do electromagnetic waves travel in a vacuum?

**8.** Compare the wave and particle models of light. What phenomena can only be explained by the particle model?

**9.** What is a quantum of energy? Explain how quanta of energy are involved in the amount of energy matter gains and loses.

**10.** Explain the difference between the continuous spectrum of white light and the atomic emission spectrum of an element.

**11. Thinking Critically** Explain how Einstein utilized Planck's quantum concept in explaining the photoelectric effect.

**12. Interpreting Scientific Illustrations** Use **Figure 5-5** and your knowledge of light to match the numbered items on the right with the lettered items on the left. The numbered items may be used more than once or not at all.

a. longest wavelength  1. gamma rays
b. highest frequency  2. infrared waves
c. greatest energy  3. radio waves

## Section 5.1 Assessment

**7.** speed, wavelength, frequency, and amplitude; EM waves travel at $c$.

**8.** The wave model treats light as an electromagnetic wave. The particle model treats light as being comprised of photons. The wave model could not explain the photoelectric effect, the color of hot objects, and emission spectra.

**9.** A quantum is the minimum amount of energy that can be lost or gained by an atom. Matter loses or gains energy in multiples of the quantum.

**10.** A continuous spectrum contains all the visible colors; an atomic emission spectrum contains only specific colors.

**11.** Einstein proposed that electromagnetic radiation has a wave-particle nature, that the energy of a photon depends on the frequency of the radiation, and that the photon's energy is given by the formula $E_{photon} = h\nu$.

**12.** a: 3, b: 1, c: 1

# Quantum Theory and the Atom

You now know that the behavior of light can be explained only by a dual wave-particle model. Although this model was successful in accounting for several previously unexplainable phenomena, an understanding of the relationships among atomic structure, electrons, and atomic emission spectra still remained to be established.

## Bohr Model of the Atom

Recall that hydrogen's atomic emission spectrum is discontinuous; that is, it is made up of only certain frequencies of light. Why are elements' atomic emission spectra discontinuous rather than continuous? Niels Bohr, a young Danish physicist working in Rutherford's laboratory in 1913, proposed a quantum model for the hydrogen atom that seemed to answer this question. Impressively, Bohr's model also correctly predicted the frequencies of the lines in hydrogen's atomic emission spectrum.

**Energy states of hydrogen** Building on Planck's and Einstein's concepts of quantized energy (quantized means that only certain values are allowed), Bohr proposed that the hydrogen atom has only certain allowable energy states. The lowest allowable energy state of an atom is called its **ground state**. When an atom gains energy, it is said to be in an excited state. And although a hydrogen atom contains only a single electron, it is capable of having many different excited states.

Bohr went even further with his atomic model by relating the hydrogen atom's energy states to the motion of the electron within the atom. Bohr suggested that the single electron in a hydrogen atom moves around the nucleus in only certain allowed circular orbits. The smaller the electron's orbit, the lower the atom's energy state, or energy level. Conversely, the larger the electron's orbit, the higher the atom's energy state, or energy level. Bohr assigned a quantum number, $n$, to each orbit and even calculated the orbit's radius. For the first orbit, the one closest to the nucleus, $n = 1$ and the orbit radius is 0.0529 nm; for the second orbit, $n = 2$ and the orbit radius is 0.212 nm; and so on. Additional information about Bohr's description of hydrogen's allowable orbits and energy levels is given in **Table 5-1**.

### Objectives

- **Compare** the Bohr and quantum mechanical models of the atom.
- **Explain** the impact of de Broglie's wave-particle duality and the Heisenberg uncertainty principle on the modern view of electrons in atoms.
- **Identify** the relationships among a hydrogen atom's energy levels, sublevels, and atomic orbitals.

### Vocabulary

ground state
de Broglie equation
Heisenberg uncertainty
   principle
quantum mechanical model
   of the atom
atomic orbital
principal quantum number
principal energy level
energy sublevel

**Table 5-1**

| | Bohr's Description of the Hydrogen Atom | | | |
|---|---|---|---|---|
| Bohr atomic orbit | Quantum number | Orbit radius (nm) | Corresponding atomic energy level | Relative energy |
| First | $n = 1$ | 0.0529 | 1 | $E_1$ |
| Second | $n = 2$ | 0.212 | 2 | $E_2 = 4E_1$ |
| Third | $n = 3$ | 0.476 | 3 | $E_3 = 9E_1$ |
| Fourth | $n = 4$ | 0.846 | 4 | $E_4 = 16E_1$ |
| Fifth | $n = 5$ | 1.32 | 5 | $E_5 = 25E_1$ |
| Sixth | $n = 6$ | 1.90 | 6 | $E_6 = 36E_1$ |
| Seventh | $n = 7$ | 2.59 | 7 | $E_7 = 49E_1$ |

## 1 Focus

### Focus Transparency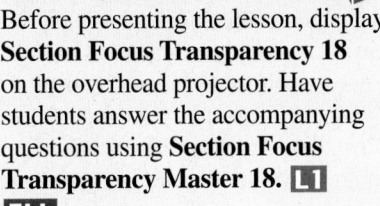

Before presenting the lesson, display **Section Focus Transparency 18** on the overhead projector. Have students answer the accompanying questions using **Section Focus Transparency Master 18.** L1 ELL

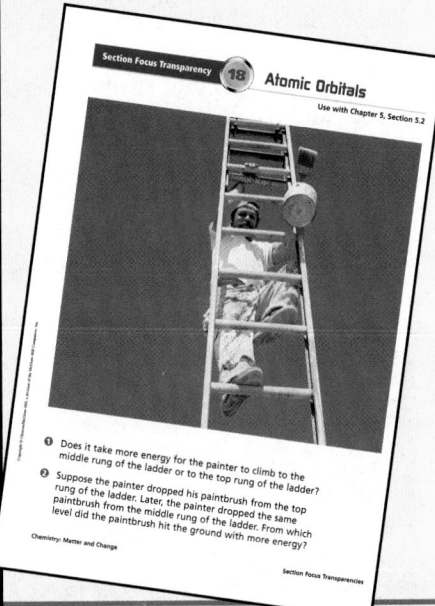

Section Focus Transparency 18 — Atomic Orbitals
Use with Chapter 5, Section 5.2

❶ Does it take more energy for the painter to climb to the middle rung of the ladder or to the top rung of the ladder?

❷ Suppose the painter dropped his paintbrush from the top rung of the ladder. Later, the painter dropped the same paintbrush from the middle rung of the ladder. From which level did the paintbrush hit the ground with more energy?

Chemistry: Matter and Change

Section Focus Transparencies

## 2 Teach

### Visual Learning

**Table 5-1** Ask students to examine the table's Relative energy column and determine Bohr's formula relating the hydrogen atom's relative energy to the electron's Bohr atomic orbit ($n$). $E_n = n^2E_1$ L2

---

## DIFFERENTIATED INSTRUCTION

### Learning Disabled

*Kinesthetic* Demonstrate the electron transitions associated with energy-level changes. Tell students that a book on the floor represents an electron in an atom's lowest-energy orbit. Raise the book to a higher energy level (their chair). Ask if energy is required. yes Ask what happens when the book returns to the floor. Energy is released. Explain the analogy between the book's energy levels and an electron's transitions between atomic orbits. Point out that the energy needed to raise an electron to a higher-energy orbit is exactly the same as the energy released when the electron returns to its original orbit. L1 ELL

National Science Content Standards

Pages 126–127
UCP.1, UCP.2; B.1, B.6; G.2, G.3

**An explanation of hydrogen's line spectrum** Bohr suggested that the hydrogen atom is in the ground state, also called the first energy level, when the electron is in the $n = 1$ orbit. In the ground state, the atom does not radiate energy. When energy is added from an outside source, the electron moves to a higher-energy orbit such as the $n = 2$ orbit shown in **Figure 5-10a**. Such an electron transition raises the atom to an excited state. When the atom is in an excited state, the electron can drop from the higher-energy orbit to a lower-energy orbit. As a result of this transition, the atom emits a photon corresponding to the difference between the energy levels associated with the two orbits.

$$\Delta E = E_{\text{higher-energy orbit}} - E_{\text{lower-energy orbit}} = E_{\text{photon}} = h\nu$$

### Figure 5-10

**a** When an electron drops from a higher-energy orbit to a lower-energy orbit, a photon with a specific energy is emitted. Although hydrogen has spectral lines associated with higher energy levels, only the visible, ultraviolet, and infrared series of spectral lines are shown in this diagram. **b** The relative energies of the electron transitions responsible for hydrogen's four visible spectral lines are shown. Note how the energy levels become more closely spaced as $n$ increases.

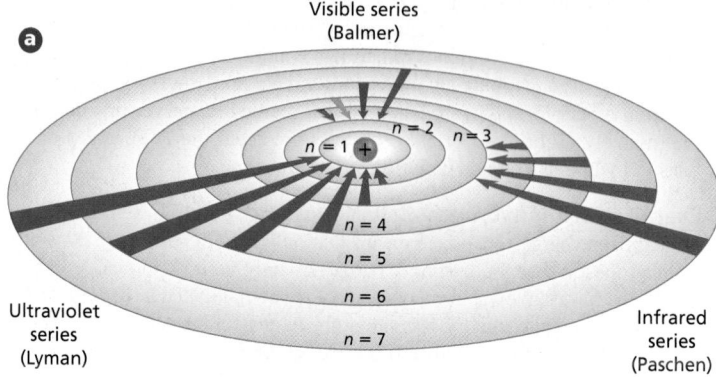

**a**

Visible series (Balmer)

$n = 1$  $n = 2$  $n = 3$  $n = 4$  $n = 5$  $n = 6$  $n = 7$

Ultraviolet series (Lyman)

Infrared series (Paschen)

**b**

Energy of hydrogen atom

$n$
∞
6
5
4
3
2
1

Note that because only certain atomic energies are possible, only certain frequencies of electromagnetic radiation can be emitted. You might compare hydrogen's seven atomic orbits to seven rungs on a ladder. A person can climb up or down the ladder only from rung to rung. Similarly, the hydrogen atom's electron can move only from one allowable orbit to another, and therefore, can emit or absorb only certain amounts of energy.

The four electron transitions that account for visible lines in hydrogen's atomic emission spectrum are shown in **Figure 5-10b**. For example, electrons dropping from the third orbit to the second orbit cause the red line. Note that electron transitions from higher-energy orbits to the second orbit account for all of hydrogen's visible lines. This series of visible lines is called the Balmer series. Other electron transitions have been measured that are not visible, such as the Lyman series (ultraviolet) in which electrons drop into the $n = 1$ orbit and the Paschen series (infrared) in which electrons drop into the $n = 3$ orbit. **Figure 5-10b** also shows that unlike rungs on a ladder, the hydrogen atom's energy levels are not evenly spaced. You will be able to see in greater detail how Bohr's atomic model was able to account for hydrogen's line spectrum by doing the **problem-solving LAB** later in this chapter.

Bohr's model explained hydrogen's observed spectral lines remarkably well. Unfortunately, however, the model failed to explain the spectrum of any other element. Moreover, Bohr's model did not fully account for the chemical behavior of atoms. In fact, although Bohr's idea of quantized energy levels laid the groundwork for atomic models to come, later experiments demonstrated that the Bohr model was fundamentally incorrect. The movements of electrons in atoms are not completely understood even now; however, substantial evidence indicates that electrons do not move around the nucleus in circular orbits.

## The Quantum Mechanical Model of the Atom

Scientists in the mid-1920s, by then convinced that the Bohr atomic model was incorrect, formulated new and innovative explanations of how electrons are arranged in atoms. In 1924, a young French graduate student in physics named Louis de Broglie (1892–1987) proposed an idea that eventually accounted for the fixed energy levels of Bohr's model.

**Electrons as waves** De Broglie had been thinking that Bohr's quantized electron orbits had characteristics similar to those of waves. For example, as **Figure 5-11b** shows, only multiples of half-wavelengths are possible on a plucked guitar string because the string is fixed at both ends. Similarly, de Broglie saw that only whole numbers of wavelengths are allowed in a circular orbit of fixed radius, as shown in **Figure 5-11c**. He also reflected on

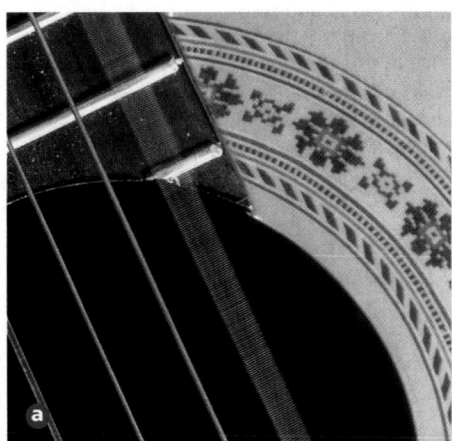

the fact that light—at one time thought to be strictly a wave phenomenon—has both wave and particle characteristics. These thoughts led de Broglie to pose a new question. If waves can have particlelike behavior, could the opposite also be true? That is, can particles of matter, including electrons, behave like waves?

### Figure 5-11

**a** A vibrating guitar string is constrained to vibrate between two fixed end points. **b** The possible vibrations of the guitar string are limited to multiples of half-wavelengths. Thus, the "quantum" of the guitar string is one-half wavelength. **c** The possible circular orbits of an electron are limited to whole numbers of complete wavelengths.

$n = 1$

1 half–wavelength

$n = 2$

2 half–wavelengths

$n = 3$

3 half–wavelengths

**b** Vibrating guitar string
Only multiples of half wavelengths allowed

$n = 3$ wavelengths

$n = 5$ wavelengths

$n \neq$ whole number (not allowed)

**c** Orbiting electron
Only whole numbers of wavelengths allowed

5.2 Quantum Theory and the Atom **129**

### Quick Demo

Have a fan rotating at high speed when students enter the classroom so that they will not have seen the fan's blades in a stopped position. As soon as the class period begins, ask them to describe the fan's blades. They will be able to tell the blades' approximate length and little else. Explain that scientists experience somewhat the same situation in trying to describe electrons in atoms. The electrons move about the nucleus and appear to fill the entire volume, yet occupy very little volume themselves. Explain that due to the motion of the electrons and certain limitations in our ability to view them (as described by Heisenberg's uncertainty principle), we are unable to simultaneously describe exactly where the electrons are and where they are going.

### Resource Manager

**Lab Manual,** pp. 33–36 **L2**

### DIFFERENTIATED INSTRUCTION

#### English Language Learners

Have English language learners look up and then explain the meanings of several key English words used in this section: *state* (as in ground state), *uncertainty, principal, level* (noun). Ask students to use each word in a sentence or a paragraph.
**L1 ELL**

### CHEMISTRY JOURNAL

#### Gases for IR and UV

*Intrapersonal* Have students research the types of gases used to emit infrared and ultraviolet electromagnetic radiation. Have them summarize their findings in their chemistry journals.
**L2**

**National Science Content Standards**
**Pages 128–129**
UCP.1, UCP.2; B.1, B.6; G.2, G.3

## problem-solving LAB

### Purpose

Students will explore the relationship between electron orbit radii and energy states of the hydrogen atom. This relationship will then be used to explain the characteristics of spectroscopic series that result from electron transitions between orbits.

### Process Skills

Constructing models, using numbers, acquiring and analyzing information, drawing conclusions, applying concepts, predicting

### Teaching Strategies

• Ask students to explain how the force between two magnets depends on the separation distance, and then relate this to the electric force of attraction between an electron and proton. The magnetic force decreases with the cube of the distance. Because of this, magnets are useful in modeling the behavior of electric force, which decreases with the square of the distance.

• Ask students to describe the full range of the electromagnetic spectrum and how frequency, $\nu$, wavelength, $\lambda$, and energy, $E$, are related. $c = \lambda\nu$ ($c$ is the speed of light) and $E = h\nu$

### Thinking Critically

1. The largest radius is $r_7$ (25.9 × $10^{-10}$ m). Thus, a scale of 1 cm = 1 × $10^{-10}$ m results in a graph about 26 cm in diameter, which will fit on the two sheets of paper. Energy increases with increasing radius.

2. See the Solutions Manual.

3. See the Solutions Manual.

4. greatest energy to least energy: Lyman, Balmer, Paschen, Brackett, and Pfund

5. See the Solutions Manual.

6. Lyman series, ultra-violet; Balmer series, visible; Paschen series, near infrared; Brackett series, middle infrared; Pfund series, far infrared

## problem-solving LAB

### How was Bohr's atomic model able to explain the line spectrum of hydrogen?

**Using Models** Niels Bohr proposed that electrons must occupy specific, quantized energy levels in an atom. He derived the following equations for hydrogen's electron orbit energies ($E_n$) and radii ($r_n$).

$$r_n = (0.529 \times 10^{-10} \text{ m})n^2$$
$$E_n = -(2.18 \times 10^{-18} \text{ J})/n^2$$

Where $n$ = quantum number (1, 2, 3...).

### Analysis

Using the orbit radii equation, calculate hydrogen's first seven electron orbit radii and then construct a scale model of those orbits. Use a compass and a metric ruler to draw your scale model on two sheets of paper that have been taped together. (Use caution when handling sharp objects.) Using the orbit energy equation, calculate the energy of each electron orbit and record the values on your model.

### Thinking Critically

1. What scale did you use to plot the orbits? How is the energy of each orbit related to its radius?

2. Draw a set of arrows for electron jumps that end at each energy level (quantum number). For example, draw a set of arrows for all transitions that end at $n = 1$, a set of arrows for all transitions that end at $n = 2$, and so on, up to $n = 7$.

3. Calculate the energy released for each of the jumps in step 2, and record the values on your model. The energy released is equal to the difference in the energies of each level.

4. Each set of arrows in step 2 represents a spectral emission series. Label five of the series, from greatest energy change to least energy change, as the Lyman, Balmer, Paschen, Brackett, and Pfund series.

5. Use the energy values in step 3 to calculate the frequency of each photon emitted in each series. Record the frequencies on your model.

6. Using the electromagnetic spectrum as a guide, identify in which range (visible, ultraviolet, infrared, etc.) each series falls.

In considering this question, de Broglie knew that if an electron has wave-like motion and is restricted to circular orbits of fixed radius, the electron is allowed only certain possible wavelengths, frequencies, and energies. Developing his idea, de Broglie derived an equation for the wavelength ($\lambda$) of a particle of mass ($m$) moving at velocity ($v$).

$$\lambda = \frac{h}{mv}$$

The **de Broglie equation** predicts that all moving particles have wave characteristics. Why, then, you may be wondering, haven't you noticed the wavelength of a fast-moving automobile? Using de Broglie's equation provides an answer. An automobile moving at 25 m/s and having a mass of 910 kg has a wavelength of $2.9 \times 10^{-38}$ m—a wavelength far too small to be seen or detected, even with the most sensitive scientific instrument. By comparison, an electron moving at the same speed has the easily measured wavelength of $2.9 \times 10^{-5}$ m. Subsequent experiments have proven that electrons and other moving particles do indeed have wave characteristics.

Step by step, scientists such as Rutherford, Bohr, and de Broglie had been unraveling the mysteries of the atom. However, a conclusion reached by the German theoretical physicist Werner Heisenberg (1901–1976), a contemporary of de Broglie, proved to have profound implications for atomic models.

**130** Chapter 5 Electrons in Atoms

### ✔ Assessment

**Skill** Have the students extend the ideas presented here to make a prediction concerning the spectrum that would be emitted from hydrogenlike atoms, such as He$^+$ or Li$^{2+}$. Or, have them predict what would happen to the continuous spectrum of light if it passed through a cell containing hydrogen gas. **L2**

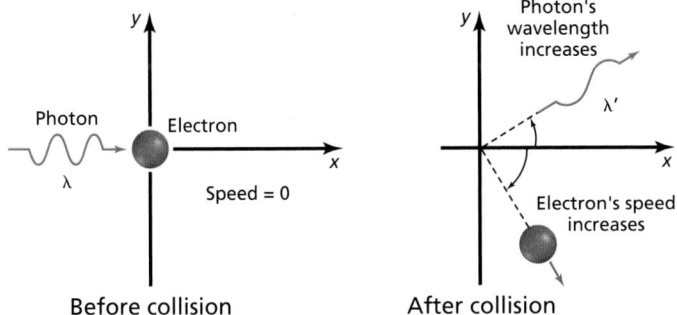

Photon
λ
Electron
Speed = 0

Before collision

Photon's wavelength increases
λ'
Electron's speed increases

After collision

**Figure 5-12**

A photon that strikes an electron at rest alters the position and velocity of the electron. This collision illustrates the Heisenberg uncertainty principle: It is impossible to simultaneously know both the position and velocity of a particle. Note that after the collision, the photon's wavelength is longer. How has the photon's energy changed?

## The Heisenberg Uncertainty Principle

Heisenberg concluded that it is impossible to make any measurement on an object without disturbing the object—at least a little. Imagine trying to locate a hovering, helium-filled balloon in a completely darkened room. When you wave your hand about, you'll locate the balloon's position when you touch it. However, when you touch the balloon, even gently, you transfer energy to it and change its position. Of course, you could also detect the balloon's position by turning on a flashlight. Using this method, photons of light that reflect from the balloon reach your eyes and reveal the balloon's location. Because the balloon is much more massive than the photons, the rebounding photons have virtually no effect on the balloon's position.

Can photons of light help determine the position of an electron in an atom? As a thought experiment, imagine trying to determine the electron's location by "bumping" it with a high-energy photon of electromagnetic radiation. Unfortunately, because such a photon has about the same energy as an electron, the interaction between the two particles changes both the wavelength of the photon and the position and velocity of the electron, as shown in **Figure 5-12**. In other words, the act of observing the electron produces a significant, unavoidable uncertainty in the position and motion of the electron. Heisenberg's analysis of interactions such as those between photons and electrons led him to his historic conclusion. The **Heisenberg uncertainty principle** states that it is fundamentally impossible to know precisely both the velocity and position of a particle at the same time.

Although scientists of the time found Heisenberg's principle difficult to accept, it has been proven to describe the fundamental limitations on what can be observed. How important is the Heisenberg uncertainty principle? The interaction of a photon with an object such as a helium-filled balloon has so little effect on the balloon that the uncertainty in its position is too small to measure. But that's not the case with an electron moving at $6 \times 10^6$ m/s near an atomic nucleus. The uncertainty in the electron's position is at least $10^{-9}$ m, about ten times greater than the diameter of the entire atom!

**The Schrödinger wave equation** In 1926, Austrian physicist Erwin Schrödinger (1887–1961) furthered the wave-particle theory proposed by de Broglie. Schrödinger derived an equation that treated the hydrogen atom's electron as a wave. Remarkably, Schrödinger's new model for the hydrogen atom seemed to apply equally well to atoms of other elements—an area in which Bohr's model failed. The atomic model in which electrons are treated as waves is called the wave mechanical model of the atom or, more commonly, the **quantum mechanical model of the atom**. Like Bohr's model,

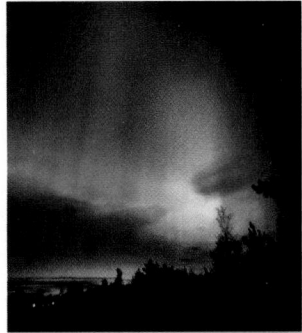

### Figure Caption Question
**Figure 5-12** How has the photon's energy changed? It has decreased.

### Enrichment
Make a sign that says "Heisenberg May Have Slept Here." Show it to students and ask how the uncertainty about whether or not Heisenberg slept in a given location is analogous to an electron's position in an atom. Heisenberg's principle states that it is fundamentally impossible to know both a particle's motion (actually momentum) and position at the same time.

### Quick Demo

*Kinesthetic* Give a heavy ball to a blindfolded student in the middle of an open space (about a 5-foot radius). Quietly, set a 50-mL, plastic graduated cylinder about 5 feet from the student. Surround the blindfolded student with a ring of other students about 10 feet distant, and instruct the student to gently roll the ball in various directions until the cylinder is located. When the ball finally hits the cylinder, it knocks the cylinder from its original position. Then, ask the students if the information gained from rolling the ball gives the cylinder's position *after* impact. The cylinder is no longer where it was before being hit with the ball. Then describe the analogy to the photon and electron. **L1** **ELL**

---

### DIFFERENTIATED INSTRUCTION

#### Gifted

*Intrapersonal* Have capable students investigate and report on whether quantum mechanics invalidates the laws and models of classical physics. In general, classical physics laws and models are valid approximations of the laws of quantum mechanics. As such, they accurately describe and predict behavior at the macroscopic level. However, quantum mechanics is needed to accurately describe and explain atomic and subatomic behavior. **L3**

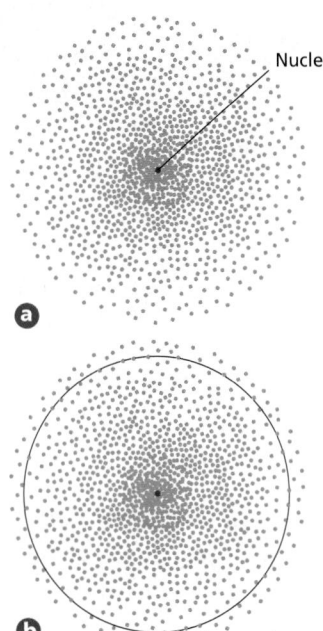

**a**

**b**

Nucleus

**Figure 5-13**

**a** This electron density diagram for a hydrogen atom represents the likelihood of finding an electron at a particular point in the atom. The greater the density of dots, the greater the likelihood of finding hydrogen's electron. **b** The boundary of an atom is defined as the volume that encloses a 90% probability of containing its electrons.

the quantum mechanical model limits an electron's energy to certain values. However, unlike Bohr's model, the quantum mechanical model makes no attempt to describe the electron's path around the nucleus.

The Schrödinger wave equation is too complex to be considered here. However, each solution to the equation is known as a wave function. And most importantly, the wave function is related to the probability of finding the electron within a particular volume of space around the nucleus. Recall from your study of math that an event having a high probability is more likely to occur than one having a low probability.

What does the wave function predict about the electron's location in an atom? A three-dimensional region around the nucleus called an **atomic orbital** describes the electron's probable location. You can picture an atomic orbital as a fuzzy cloud in which the density of the cloud at a given point is proportional to the probability of finding the electron at that point. **Figure 5-13a** illustrates the probability map, or orbital, that describes the hydrogen electron in its lowest energy state. It might be helpful to think of the probability map as a time-exposure photograph of the electron moving around the nucleus, in which each dot represents the electron's location at an instant in time. Because the dots are so numerous near the positive nucleus, they seem to form a dense cloud that is indicative of the electron's most probable location. However, because the cloud has no definite boundary, it also is possible that the electron might be found at a considerable distance from the nucleus.

## Hydrogen's Atomic Orbitals

Because the boundary of an atomic orbital is fuzzy, the orbital does not have an exactly defined size. To overcome the inherent uncertainty about the electron's location, chemists arbitrarily draw an orbital's surface to contain 90% of the electron's total probability distribution. In other words, the electron spends 90% of the time within the volume defined by the surface, and 10% of the time somewhere outside the surface. The spherical surface shown in **Figure 5-13b** encloses 90% of the lowest-energy orbital of hydrogen.

Recall that the Bohr atomic model assigns quantum numbers to electron orbits. In a similar manner, the quantum mechanical model assigns **principal quantum numbers** ($n$) that indicate the relative sizes and energies of atomic

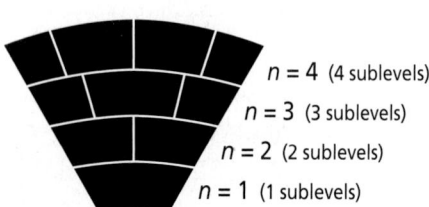

$n = 4$ (4 sublevels)
$n = 3$ (3 sublevels)
$n = 2$ (2 sublevels)
$n = 1$ (1 sublevels)

**Figure 5-14**

Energy sublevels can be thought of as a section of seats in a theater. The rows that are higher up and farther from the stage contain more seats, just as energy levels that are farther from the nucleus contain more sublevels.

## Internet Address Book

**Chemistry Online**

Note Internet addresses that you find useful in the space below for quick reference.

_____
_____
_____
_____
_____

orbitals. That is, as *n* increases, the orbital becomes larger, the electron spends more time farther from the nucleus, and the atom's energy level increases. Therefore, *n* specifies the atom's major energy levels, called **principal energy levels.** An atom's lowest principal energy level is assigned a principal quantum number of one. When the hydrogen atom's single electron occupies an orbital with $n = 1$, the atom is in its ground state. Up to seven energy levels have been detected for the hydrogen atom, giving *n* values ranging from 1 to 7.

Principal energy levels contain **energy sublevels.** Principal energy level 1 consists of a single sublevel, principal energy level 2 consists of two sublevels, principal energy level 3 consists of three sublevels, and so on. To better understand the relationship between the atom's energy levels and sublevels, picture the seats in a wedge-shaped section of a theater, as shown in **Figure 5-14.** As you move away from the stage, the rows become higher and contain more seats. Similarly, the number of energy sublevels in a principal energy level increases as *n* increases.

Sublevels are labeled s, p, d, or f according to the shapes of the atom's orbitals. All s orbitals are spherical and all p orbitals are dumbbell shaped; however, not all d or f orbitals have the same shape. Each orbital may contain at most two electrons. The single sublevel in principal energy level 1 consists of a spherical orbital called the 1s orbital. The two sublevels in principal energy level 2 are designated 2s and 2p. The 2s sublevel consists of the 2s orbital, which is spherical like the 1s orbital but larger in size. See **Figure 5-15a.** The 2p sublevel consists of three dumbbell-shaped p orbitals of equal energy designated $2p_x$, $2p_y$, and $2p_z$. The subscripts *x*, *y*, and *z* merely designate the orientations of p orbitals along the *x*, *y*, and *z* coordinate axes, as shown in **Figure 5-15b.**

Principal energy level 3 consists of three sublevels designated 3s, 3p, and 3d. Each d sublevel consists of five orbitals of equal energy. Four d orbitals have identical shapes but different orientations. However, the fifth, $d_{z^2}$ orbital is shaped and oriented differently from the other four. The shapes and orientations of the five d orbitals are illustrated in **Figure 5-16.** The fourth principal energy level ($n = 4$) contains a fourth sublevel, called the 4f sublevel, which consists of seven f orbitals of equal energy.

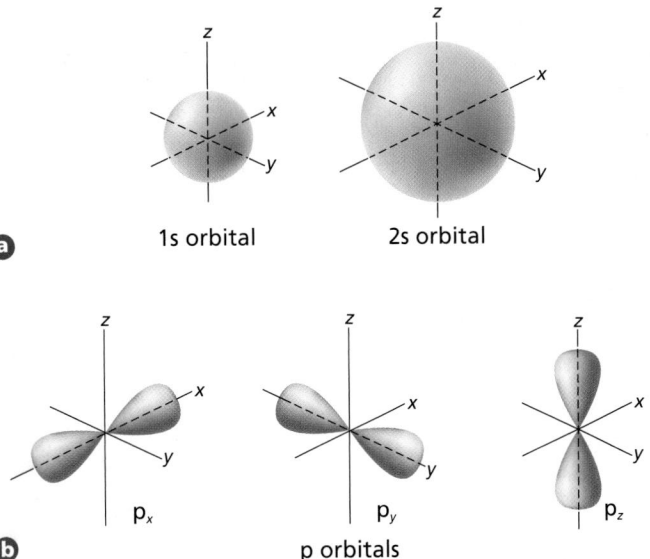

**(a)**

1s orbital          2s orbital

**(b)**

$p_x$          $p_y$          $p_z$

p orbitals

**Figure 5-15**

Atomic orbitals represent the electron probability clouds of an atom's electrons. **(a)** The spherical 1s and 2s orbitals are shown here. All s orbitals are spherical in shape and increase in size with increasing principal quantum number. **(b)** The three dumbbell-shaped p orbitals are oriented along the three perpendicular *x*, *y*, and *z* axes. Each of the p orbitals related to an energy sublevel has equal energy.

**Figure 5-16**

Four of five equal-energy d orbitals have the same shape. Notice how the $d_{xy}$ orbital lies in the plane formed by the *x* and *y* axes, the $d_{xz}$ orbital lies in the plane formed by the *x* and *z* axes, and so on. The $d_{z^2}$ orbital has it own unique shape.

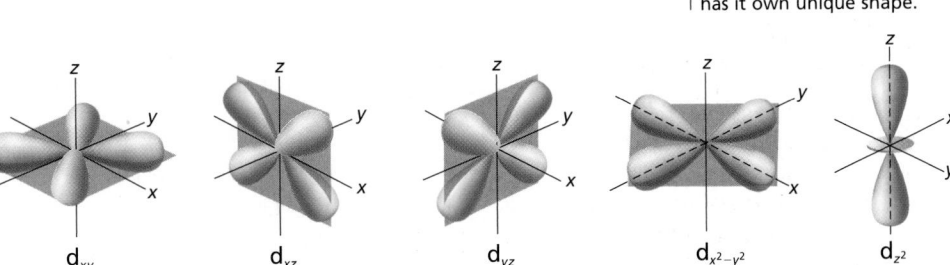

$d_{xy}$          $d_{xz}$          $d_{yz}$          $d_{x^2-y^2}$          $d_{z^2}$

Table 5-2

## Reteach

Explain that an electron's position and velocity within an atomic orbital are not known. Reiterate that at a given instant, there is a 10% probability that the electron is outside the orbital's 90% probability surface.

## Extension

According to quantum mechanics, each electron in an atom can be described by four quantum numbers. Three of these ($n$, $l$, and $m_l$) are related to the probability of finding the electron at various points in space. The fourth ($m_s$) is related to the direction of electron spin—either clockwise or counterclockwise. The principal quantum number, $n$, specifies the atom's energy level associated with the electron. $l$ specifies the energy sublevel and describes the shape of the region of space in which the electron moves. $m_l$ specifies the orientation in space of the orbital containing the electron. $m_s$ specifies the orientation of the electron's spin axis.

## ✔ Assessment

**Knowledge** Ask students which hydrogen energy-level transition accounts for the violet line in its emission spectrum.
$n = 6 \rightarrow n = 2$ **L2**

| Hydrogen's First Four Principal Energy Levels | | | |
|---|---|---|---|
| Principal quantum number (*n*) | Sublevels (types of orbitals) present | Number of orbitals related to sublevel | Total number of orbitals related to principal energy level ($n^2$) |
| 1 | s | 1 | 1 |
| 2 | s p | 1 3 | 4 |
| 3 | s p d | 1 3 5 | 9 |
| 4 | s p d f | 1 3 5 7 | 16 |

Hydrogen's first four principal energy levels, sublevels, and related atomic orbitals are summarized in **Table 5-2**. Note that the maximum number of orbitals related to each principal energy level equals $n^2$. Because each orbital may contain at most two electrons, the maximum number of electrons related to each principal energy level equals $2n^2$.

Given the fact that a hydrogen atom contains only one electron, you might wonder how the atom can have so many energy levels, sublevels, and related atomic orbitals. At any given time, the atom's electron can occupy just one orbital. So you can think of the other orbitals as unoccupied spaces—spaces available should the atom's energy increase or decrease. For example, when the hydrogen atom is in the ground state, the electron occupies the 1s orbital. However, the atom may gain a quantum of energy that excites the electron to the 2s orbital, to one of the three 2p orbitals, or to another vacant orbital.

You have learned a lot about electrons and quantized energy in this section: how Bohr's orbits explained the hydrogen atom's quantized energy states; how de Broglie's insight led scientists to think of electrons as both particles and waves; and how Schrödinger's wave equation predicted the existence of atomic orbitals containing electrons. In the next section, you'll learn how the electrons are arranged in atomic orbitals of atoms having more than one electron.

## Section 5.2 Assessment

**13.** According to the Bohr atomic model, why do atomic emission spectra contain only certain frequencies of light?

**14.** Why is the wavelength of a moving soccer ball not detectable to the naked eye?

**15.** What sublevels are contained in the hydrogen atom's first four energy levels? What orbitals are related to each s sublevel and each p sublevel?

**16. Thinking Critically** Use de Broglie's wave-particle duality and the Heisenberg uncertainty principle to explain why the location of an electron in an atom is uncertain.

**17. Comparing and Contrasting** Compare and contrast the Bohr model and quantum mechanical model of the atom.

## Section 5.2 Assessment

**13.** Because only certain atomic energies are possible, only certain frequencies of radiation can be emitted from an atom.
**14.** It is too small to see or detect.
**15.** First energy level, s; second energy level, s and p; third energy level, s, p, and d; fourth energy level, s, p, d, and f. Each s sublevel is related to a spherical s orbital. Each p sublevel is related to three dumb-bell-shaped orbitals ($p_x$, $p_y$, and $p_z$).
**16.** An electron has wave-particle characteristics and does not have a single, definite location in space.

The Heisenberg uncertainty principle states that it is fundamentally impossible to know precisely both the velocity and position of a particle at the same time.
**17.** Bohr model: the electron is a particle; the hydrogen atom has only certain allowable energy

**134**

# Electron Configurations

When you consider that atoms of the heaviest elements contain in excess of 100 electrons, that there are numerous principal energy levels and sublevels and their corresponding orbitals, and that each orbital may contain a maximum of two electrons, the idea of determining the arrangement of an atom's electrons seems daunting. Fortunately, the arrangement of electrons in atoms follows a few very specific rules. In this section, you'll learn these rules and their occasional exceptions.

## Ground-State Electron Configurations

The arrangement of electrons in an atom is called the atom's **electron configuration.** Because low-energy systems are more stable than high-energy systems, electrons in an atom tend to assume the arrangement that gives the atom the lowest possible energy. The most stable, lowest-energy arrangement of the electrons in atoms of each element is called the element's ground-state electron configuration. Three rules, or principles—the aufbau principle, the Pauli exclusion principle, and Hund's rule—define how electrons can be arranged in an atom's orbitals.

**The aufbau principle** The **aufbau principle** states that each electron occupies the lowest energy orbital available. Therefore, your first step in determining an element's ground-state electron configuration is learning the sequence of atomic orbitals from lowest energy to highest energy. This sequence, known as an aufbau diagram, is shown in **Figure 5-17**. In the diagram, each box represents an atomic orbital. Several features of the aufbau diagram stand out.

- *All orbitals related to an energy sublevel are of equal energy.* For example, all three 2p orbitals are of equal energy.
- *In a multi-electron atom, the energy sublevels within a principal energy level have different energies.* For example, the three 2p orbitals are of higher energy than the 2s orbital.

### Objectives

- **Apply** the Pauli exclusion principle, the aufbau principle, and Hund's rule to write electron configurations using orbital diagrams and electron configuration notation.

- **Define** valence electrons and draw electron-dot structures representing an atom's valence electrons.

### Vocabulary

electron configuration
aufbau principle
Pauli exclusion principle
Hund's rule
valence electron
electron-dot structure

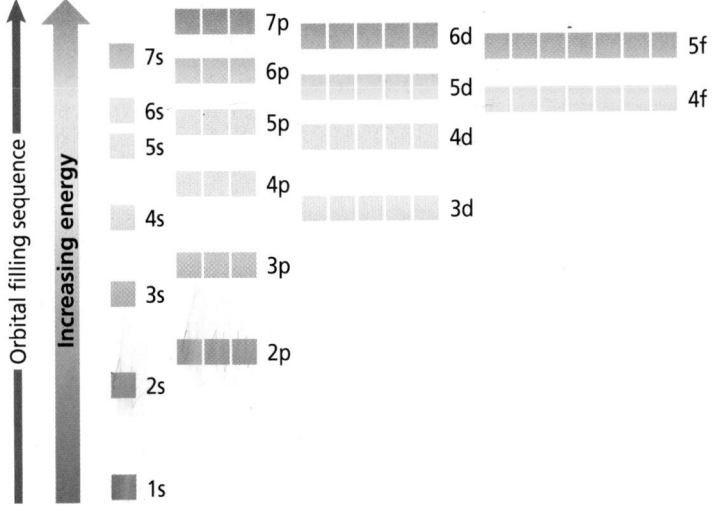

**Figure 5-17**

The aufbau diagram shows the energy of each sublevel. Each box on the diagram represents an atomic orbital. Does the 3d or 4s sublevel have greater energy?

## 1 Focus

Before presenting the lesson, display **Section Focus Transparency 19** on the overhead projector. Have students answer the accompanying questions using **Section Focus Transparency Master 19.** **L1** **ELL**

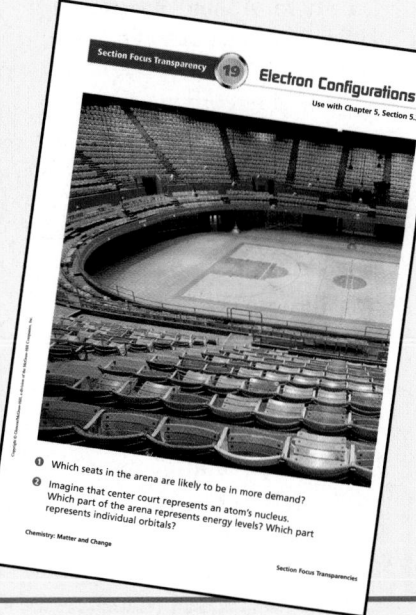

Section Focus Transparency **19**
**Electron Configurations**
Use with Chapter 5, Section 5.3

❶ Which seats in the arena are likely to be in more demand?

❷ Imagine that center court represents an atom's nucleus. Which part of the arena represents energy levels? Which part represents individual orbitals?

Chemistry: Matter and Change

Section Focus Transparencies

## 2 Teach

### Figure Caption Question

**Figure 5-17** Does the 3d or 4s sublevel have the greater energy? The 3d sublevel has the greater energy.

### Using Science Terms

Explain that the name aufbau is derived from the German *aufbauen,* which means "to build up."

states. Quantum mechanical model: the electron is a wave-particle phenomenon; an electron's energy is limited to certain values. Also, the quantum mechanical model makes no assertions regarding the electron's path around the nucleus.

## *GLENCOE* TECHNOLOGY

**CD-ROM**
**Chemistry: Matter and Change**
Animation: *Electrons and Energy Levels*
Exploration: *Building Atoms*

**National Science Content Standards**

Pages 134–135
UCP.1, UCP.2; B.1, B.6

• *In order of increasing energy, the sequence of energy sublevels within a principal energy level is s, p, d, and f.*

• *Orbitals related to energy sublevels within one principal energy level can overlap orbitals related to energy sublevels within another principal level.* For example, the orbital related to the atom's 4s sublevel has a lower energy than the five orbitals related to the 3d sublevel.

Although the aufbau principle describes the sequence in which orbitals are filled with electrons, it's important to know that atoms are not actually built up electron by electron.

**The Pauli exclusion principle** Each electron in an atom has an associated spin, similar to the way a top spins on its axis. Like the top, the electron is able to spin in only one of two directions. An arrow pointing up (↑) represents the electron spinning in one direction, an arrow pointing down (↓) represents the electron spinning in the opposite direction. The **Pauli exclusion principle** states that a maximum of two electrons may occupy a single atomic orbital, but only if the electrons have opposite spins. Austrian physicist Wolfgang Pauli proposed this principle after observing atoms in excited states. An atomic orbital containing paired electrons with opposite spins is written as ↑↓.

**Hund's rule** The fact that negatively charged electrons repel each other has an important impact on the distribution of electrons in equal-energy orbitals. **Hund's rule** states that single electrons with the same spin must occupy each equal-energy orbital before additional electrons with opposite spins can occupy the same orbitals. For example, let the boxes below represent the 2p orbitals. One electron enters each of the three 2p orbitals before a second electron enters any of the orbitals. The sequence in which six electrons occupy three p orbitals is shown below.

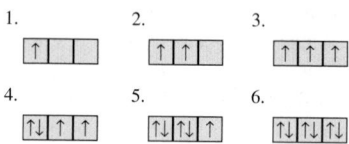

## Orbital Diagrams and Electron Configuration Notations

You can represent an atom's electron configuration using two convenient methods. One method is called an orbital diagram. An orbital diagram includes a box for each of the atom's orbitals. An empty box ▢ represents an unoccupied orbital; a box containing a single up arrow ↑ represents an orbital with one electron; and a box containing both up and down arrows ↑↓ represents a filled orbital. Each box is labeled with the principal quantum number and sublevel associated with the orbital. For example, the orbital diagram for a ground-state carbon atom, which contains two electrons in the 1s orbital, two electrons in the 2s orbital, and 1 electron in two of three separate 2p orbitals, is shown below.

---

## Demonstration

### Emission Spectra

#### Purpose
To illustrate the relationship between the electron configurations of nonmetals and their emission spectra

#### Materials
Spectrum tubes (H and Ne); spectrum tube

power supply; Flinn C-Spectra diffraction grating; colored pencils or chalk

#### Safety Precautions
Use care around the spectrum tube high voltage power supply. Spectrum tubes will get hot when used.

#### Procedure
An inexpensive alternative to a spectroscope is to tape a small piece of the Flinn C-Spectra diffraction grating to a 3 × 5

inch card. Have students view the spectrum emitted from the lights in the classroom. Then, darken the room and have them view the excited neon atoms in the powered neon spectrum tubes. Use colored pencils to record the emission spectrum of neon as seen through their diffraction gratings. Remind students that neon contains 10 electrons. Now repeat the process using a hydrogen spectrum tube. Since hydrogen has 1 electron, ask

**Table 5-3**

| | | Orbital diagram | Electron |
|---|---|---|---|
| Element | Atomic number | 1s  2s  $2p_x$ $2p_y$ $2p_z$ | configuration notation |
| Hydrogen | 1 | ↑ | $1s^1$ |
| Helium | 2 | ↑↓ | $1s^2$ |
| Lithium | 3 | ↑↓ ↑ | $1s^2 2s^1$ |
| Beryllium | 4 | ↑↓ ↑↓ | $1s^2 2s^2$ |
| Boron | 5 | ↑↓ ↑↓ ↑ | $1s^2 2s^2 2p^1$ |
| Carbon | 6 | ↑↓ ↑↓ ↑ ↑ | $1s^2 2s^2 2p^2$ |
| Nitrogen | 7 | ↑↓ ↑↓ ↑ ↑ ↑ | $1s^2 2s^2 2p^3$ |
| Oxygen | 8 | ↑↓ ↑↓ ↑↓ ↑ ↑ | $1s^2 2s^2 2p^4$ |
| Fluorine | 9 | ↑↓ ↑↓ ↑↓ ↑↓ ↑ | $1s^2 2s^2 2p^5$ |
| Neon | 10 | ↑↓ ↑↓ ↑↓ ↑↓ ↑↓ | $1s^2 2s^2 2p^6$ |

The table title spanning: **Electron Configurations and Orbital Diagrams for Elements in the First Two Periods**

Recall that the number of electrons in an atom equals the number of protons, which is designated by the element's atomic number. Carbon, which has an atomic number of six, has six electrons in its configuration.

Another shorthand method for describing the arrangement of electrons in an element's atoms is called electron configuration notation. This method designates the principal energy level and energy sublevel associated with each of the atom's orbitals and includes a superscript representing the number of electrons in the orbital. For example, the electron configuration notation of a ground-state carbon atom is written $1s^2 2s^2 2p^2$. Orbital diagrams and electron configuration notations for the elements in periods one and two of the periodic table are shown in **Table 5-3**. To help you visualize the relative sizes and orientations of atomic orbitals, the filled 1s, 2s, $2p_x$, $2p_y$, and $2p_z$ orbitals of the neon atom are illustrated in **Figure 5-18**.

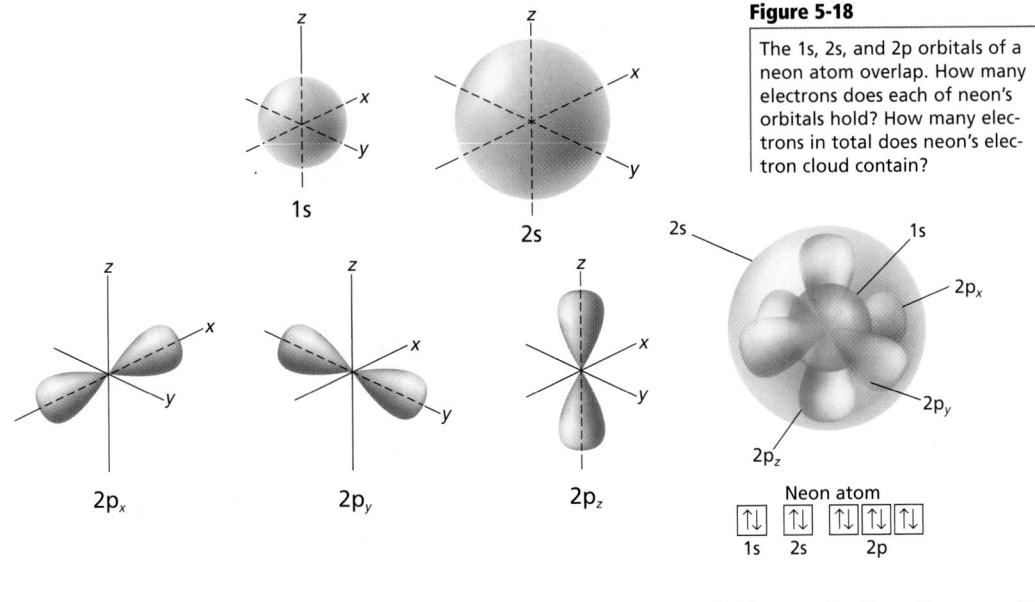

1s

2s

$2p_x$  $2p_y$  $2p_z$

**Figure 5-18**

The 1s, 2s, and 2p orbitals of a neon atom overlap. How many electrons does each of neon's orbitals hold? How many electrons in total does neon's electron cloud contain?

Neon atom

↑↓ ↑↓ ↑↓ ↑↓ ↑↓
1s  2s   2p

5.3 Electron Configurations   **137**

## Figure Caption Questions

**Figure 5-18** How many electrons does each of neon's orbitals hold? Each orbital contains two electrons. How many electrons in total does neon's electron cloud contain? ten electrons

## Visual Learning

**Table 5-3** Have students write an electron configuration notation that shows the orbital occupancy related to a phosphorus atom's 3p sublevel. $3p_x^1 3p_y^1 3p_z^1$ A chlorine atom's 3s and 3p sublevels. $3s^2 3p_x^2 3p_y^2 3p_z^1$

## Concept Development

Ask students to think about and explain the analogy between Hund's rule and the behavior of total strangers as they board an empty bus. By and large, passengers sit in separate rows until people occupy all rows. Only when no more empty rows are available do two passengers occupy a single row. For electrons, the situation is much the same as they occupy orbitals related to a sublevel. Chemistry's bus principle is known as Hund's rule.

students to predict if there will be more or fewer lines in hydrogen's spectrum.

**Results**
The red-orange spectrum of neon also contains some green lines. Usually only 3 of the 4 lines of hydrogen are visible.

**Analysis**
1. Write the electron configurations of neon and hydrogen. Ne: $1s^2 2s^2 2p^6$, H: $1s^1$
2. What is the appearance of neon in the

excited state? In the ground state, neon is a clear, colorless gas. In the excited state it gives off a red-orange light.
3. Of the two spectra viewed, did hydrogen or neon have more lines? Explain why. Neon has more lines than hydrogen because its ten electrons have a greater number of possible energy transitions.

### Assessment

**Skill** Have students view the excited spectral tube of another element such as mercury. Ask them to predict if Hg will have more lines than neon and hydrogen because it has 80 electrons. No, Hg actually has fewer lines in the visible spectrum. However, there are many additional lines in mercury's IR and UV spectra.

**137**

**Figure 5-19** Which is filled first, the 5s or 4p orbital? The 4p orbital is filled first.

## Reinforcement

Point out that some textbooks, reference books, and periodic tables show electron configurations written in energy-level sequence rather than in aufbau sequence. Reinforce that using the energy-level sequence for electron configurations does not render the aufbau sequence invalid.

**Figure 5-19**

This sublevel diagram shows the order in which the orbitals are usually filled. The proper sequence for the first seven orbitals is 1s, 2s, 2p, 3s, 3p, 4s, and 3d. Which is filled first, the 5s or the 4p orbital?

Note that electron configuration notation usually does not show the orbital distributions of electrons related to a sublevel. It's understood that a designation such as nitrogen's $2p^3$ represents the orbital occupancy $2p_x^1 2p_y^1 2p_z^1$.

For sodium, the first ten electrons occupy 1s, 2s, and 2p orbitals. Then, according to the aufbau sequence, the eleventh electron occupies the 3s orbital. The electron configuration notation and orbital diagram for sodium are written

$$\text{Na} \quad 1s^2 2s^2 2p^6 3s^1 \qquad \boxed{\uparrow\downarrow} \; \boxed{\uparrow\downarrow} \; \boxed{\uparrow\downarrow}\,\boxed{\uparrow\downarrow}\,\boxed{\uparrow\downarrow} \; \boxed{\uparrow}$$
$$\qquad\qquad\qquad\qquad\qquad\quad 1s \quad 2s \qquad 2p \qquad 3s$$

Noble-gas notation is a method of representing electron configurations of noble gases using bracketed symbols. For example, [He] represents the electron configuration for helium, $1s^2$, and [Ne] represents the electron configuration for neon, $1s^2 2s^2 2p^6$. Compare the electron configuration for neon with sodium's configuration above. Note that the inner-level configuration for sodium is identical to the electron configuration for neon. Using noble-gas notation, sodium's electron configuration can be shortened to the form $[\text{Ne}]3s^1$. The electron configuration for an element can be represented using the noble-gas notation for the noble gas in the previous period and the electron configuration for the energy level being filled. The complete and abbreviated (using noble-gas notation) electron configurations of the period 3 elements are shown in **Table 5-4**.

When writing electron configurations, you may refer to a convenient memory aid called a sublevel diagram, which is shown in **Figure 5-19**. Note that following the direction of the arrows in the sublevel diagram produces the sublevel sequence shown in the aufbau diagram of **Figure 5-17**.

**Exceptions to predicted configurations** You can use the aufbau diagram to write correct ground-state electron configurations for all elements up to and including vanadium, atomic number 23. However, if you were to proceed in this manner, your configurations for chromium, $[\text{Ar}]4s^2 3d^4$, and copper, $[\text{Ar}]4s^2 3d^9$, would prove to be incorrect. The correct configurations for these two elements are:

$$\text{Cr } [\text{Ar}]4s^1 3d^5 \qquad \text{Cu } [\text{Ar}]4s^1 3d^{10}$$

The electron configurations for these two elements, as well as those of several elements in other periods, illustrate the increased stability of half-filled and filled sets of s and d orbitals.

**Table 5-4**

| Electron Configurations for Elements in Period Three | | | |
|---|---|---|---|
| Element | Atomic number | Complete electron configuration | Electron configuration using noble-gas notation |
| Sodium | 11 | $1s^2 2s^2 2p^6 3s^1$ | $[\text{Ne}]3s^1$ |
| Magnesium | 12 | $1s^2 2s^2 2p^6 3s^2$ | $[\text{Ne}]3s^2$ |
| Aluminum | 13 | $1s^2 2s^2 2p^6 3s^2 3p^1$ | $[\text{Ne}]3s^2 3p^1$ |
| Silicon | 14 | $1s^2 2s^2 2p^6 3s^2 3p^2$ | $[\text{Ne}]3s^2 3p^2$ |
| Phosphorus | 15 | $1s^2 2s^2 2p^6 3s^2 3p^3$ | $[\text{Ne}]3s^2 3p^3$ |
| Sulfur | 16 | $1s^2 2s^2 2p^6 3s^2 3p^4$ | $[\text{Ne}]3s^2 3p^4$ |
| Chlorine | 17 | $1s^2 2s^2 2p^6 3s^2 3p^5$ | $[\text{Ne}]3s^2 3p^5$ |
| Argon | 18 | $1s^2 2s^2 2p^6 3s^2 3p^6$ | $[\text{Ne}]3s^2 3p^6$ or $[\text{Ar}]$ |

## CULTURAL DIVERSITY

### The Development of Fireworks

Explain that the Chinese likely first used fireworks about the second century B.C. After inventing explosive black powder, which they called "gung pow," the Chinese developed black-powder "crackers" that produced loud explosions. Most scholars believe that the Chinese used crackers to frighten off evil spirits and to celebrate weddings, births, battle victories, and eclipses of the Moon.

Fireworks became much more interesting and colorful in the 1830s, when Italian pyrotechnics experts added potassium chlorate to the mix. The potassium chlorate provided more oxygen for the chemical reaction, making it burn faster and hotter. This enabled the Italians to include various inorganic compounds that burn at high temperatures and create spectacular colors. Fireworks' colors are due to energy-level transitions of electrons in the metal atoms of these inorganic compounds.

## EXAMPLE PROBLEM 5-3

### Writing Electron Configurations

Germanium (Ge), a semiconducting element, is commonly used in the manufacture of computer chips. What is the ground-state electron configuration for an atom of germanium?

**1. Analyze the Problem**

You are given the semiconducting element, germanium (Ge). Consult the periodic table to determine germanium's atomic number, which also is equal to its number of electrons. Also note the atomic number of the noble gas element that precedes germanium in the table. Determine the number of additional electrons a germanium atom has compared to the nearest preceding noble gas, and then write out germanium's electron configuration.

**2. Solve for the Unknown**

From the periodic table, germanium's atomic number is determined to be 32. Thus, a germanium atom contains 32 electrons. The noble gas preceding germanium is argon (Ar), which has an atomic number of 18. Represent germanium's first 18 electrons using the chemical symbol for argon written inside brackets.

[Ar]

The remaining 14 electrons of germanium's configuration need to be written out. Because argon is a noble gas in the third period of the periodic table, it has completely filled 3s and 3p orbitals. Thus, the remaining 14 electrons fill the 4s, 3d, and 4p orbitals in order. [Ar]$4s^?3d^74p^?$

Using the maximum number of electrons that can fill each orbital, write out the electron configuration. [Ar]$4s^23d^{10}4p^2$

**3. Evaluate the Answer**

All 32 electrons in a germanium atom have been accounted for. The correct preceding noble gas (Ar) has been used in the notation, and the order of orbital filling for the fourth period is correct (4s, 3d, 4p).

Atoms of boron and arsenic are inserted into germanium's crystal structure in order to produce a semiconducting material that can be used to manufacture computer chips.

## PRACTICE PROBLEMS

**18.** Write ground-state electron configurations for the following elements.

   **a.** bromine (Br)      **d.** rhenium (Re)

   **b.** strontium (Sr)    **e.** terbium (Tb)

   **c.** antimony (Sb)    **f.** titanium (Ti)

**19.** How many electrons are in orbitals related to the third energy level of a sulfur atom?

**20.** How many electrons occupy p orbitals in a chlorine atom?

**21.** What element has the following ground-state electron configuration? [Kr]$5s^24d^{10}5p^1$

**22.** What element has the following ground-state electron configuration? [Xe]$6s^2$

*Practice!* **For more practice with electron configuration problems, go to Supplemental Practice Problems in Appendix A.**

## Practice PROBLEMS

Have students refer to Appendix D for complete solutions to Practice Problems.

**18. a.** [Ar]$4s^23d^{10}4p^5$

   **b.** [Kr]$5s^2$

   **c.** [Kr]$5s^24d^{10}5p^3$

   **d.** [Xe]$6s^24f^{14}5d^5$

   **e.** [Xe]$6s^24f^9$

   **f.** [Ar]$4s^23d^2$

**19.** 6

**20.** 11

**21.** indium

**22.** barium

### ✔ Assessment

**Portfolio** Ask students to write electron configurations and construct orbital notations and electron dot structures for atoms of all the elements in the third period on the periodic table. Have them include the configurations, notations, and structures in their portfolios. **L2** **P**

## DIFFERENTIATED INSTRUCTION

### Visually Impaired

*Kinesthetic* Make or purchase cellular polystyrene (Styrofoam) or papier-mâché models of s, p, and d orbitals. Allow visually impaired students to feel the models and trace their contours to gain a better appreciation of their shapes and orientations. **L1** **ELL**

**National Science Content Standards**

**Pages 136–139**
UCP.1, UCP.2; B.1, B.6

## Using Science Terms

Explain to students that some text-books and reference books use the word *valence* in place of oxidation state. For example, such books would say that oxygen has a valence of 2−.

## Content Background

**Valence Electrons** Explain to capable students that some inner-level d electrons are often considered valence electrons for transition elements. For example, although an atom of iron has just two electrons in its outermost (4s) orbitals, an additional electron associated with one of the atom's 3d orbitals is often involved in bonding. And in an atom of manganese, as many as five 3d-orbital electrons may be involved in bonding.

---

### Practice PROBLEMS

Have students refer to Appendix D for complete solutions to Practice Problems.

**23. a.** ·Mg·        **d.** Rb·

  **b.** :S̈:        **e.** ·T̈l:

  **c.** ·B̈r:        **f.** :Xë:

---

## 3 Assess

### Check for Understanding

Ask students to predict the maximum number of electrons that can exist in orbitals related to an atom's fourth and fifth energy levels—assuming an element existed that contained enough electrons. You may want to give students the formula $2n^2$, which can be used to calculate the number of electrons related to each value of $n$. 32 and 50 electrons, respectively

---

---

## Valence Electrons

Only certain electrons, called valence electrons, determine the chemical properties of an element. **Valence electrons** are defined as electrons in the atom's outermost orbitals—generally those orbitals associated with the atom's highest principal energy level. For example, a sulfur atom contains 16 electrons, only six of which occupy the outermost 3s and 3p orbitals, as shown by sulfur's electron configuration. Sulfur has six valence electrons.

$$S \ [Ne]3s^23p^4$$

Similarly, although a cesium atom contains 55 electrons, it has but one valence electron, the 6s electron shown in cesium's electron configuration.

$$Cs \ [Xe]6s^1$$

Francium, which belongs to the same group as cesium, also has a single valence electron.

$$Fr \ [Rn]7s^1$$

**Electron-dot structures** Because valence electrons are involved in forming chemical bonds, chemists often represent them visually using a simple shorthand method. An atom's **electron-dot structure** consists of the element's symbol, which represents the atomic nucleus and inner-level electrons, surrounded by dots representing the atom's valence electrons. The American chemist G. N. Lewis (1875–1946), devised the method while teaching a college chemistry class in 1902.

In writing an atom's electron-dot structure, dots representing valence electrons are placed one at a time on the four sides of the symbol (they may be placed in any sequence) and then paired up until all are used. The ground-state electron configurations and electron-dot structures for the elements in the second period are shown in **Table 5-5**.

Table 5-5

| Electron-Dot Structures for Elements in Period Two | | | |
|---|---|---|---|
| Element | Atomic number | Electron configuration | Electron-dot structure |
| Lithium | 3 | $1s^22s^1$ | Li· |
| Beryllium | 4 | $1s^22s^2$ | ·Be· |
| Boron | 5 | $1s^22s^22p^1$ | ·B̈· |
| Carbon | 6 | $1s^22s^22p^2$ | ·C̈· |
| Nitrogen | 7 | $1s^22s^22p^3$ | ·N̈· |
| Oxygen | 8 | $1s^22s^22p^4$ | :Ö· |
| Fluorine | 9 | $1s^22s^22p^5$ | :F̈· |
| Neon | 10 | $1s^22s^22p^6$ | :N̈e: |

---

## CHEMISTRY JOURNAL

### Another Solar System—What if?

**Linguistic** Ask students to write essays for their journals in which they speculate about flying a spacecraft to a planet in a different solar system. In the new solar system, they discover that each atomic orbital of the planet's solid, liquid, and gaseous matter may contain up to three electrons rather than just two. Their speculation should focus on the characteristics of the elements on this new planet. **L2**

## EXAMPLE PROBLEM 5-4

### Writing Electron-Dot Structures

Some sheet glass is manufactured using a process that makes use of molten tin. What is tin's electron-dot structure?

**1. Analyze the Problem**

You are given the element tin (Sn). Consult the periodic table to determine the total number of electrons an atom of tin has. Write out tin's electron configuration and determine the number of valence electrons it has. Then use the number of valence electrons and the rules for electron-dot structures to draw the electron-dot structure for tin.

**2. Solve for the Unknown**

From the periodic table, tin is found to have an atomic number of 50. Thus, a tin atom has 50 electrons. Write out the noble-gas form of tin's electron configuration.

$[Kr]5s^24d^{10}5p^2$

The two 5s and the two 5p electrons (the electrons in the orbitals related to the atom's highest principal energy level) represent tin's four valence electrons. Draw tin's electron-dot structure by representing its four valence electrons with dots, arranged one at a time, around the four sides of tin's chemical symbol (Sn).

$\cdot \overset{\cdot}{\underset{\cdot}{Sn}} \cdot$

**3. Evaluate the Answer**

The correct symbol for tin (Sn) has been used, and the rules for drawing electron-dot structures have been correctly applied.

Flat-surfaced window glass may be manufactured by floating molten glass on top of molten tin.

## PRACTICE PROBLEMS

**23.** Draw electron-dot structures for atoms of the following elements.

| | |
|---|---|
| **a.** magnesium | **d.** rubidium |
| **b.** sulfur | **e.** thallium |
| **c.** bromine | **f.** xenon |

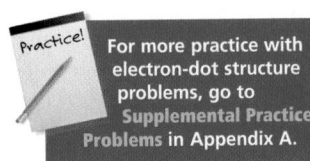

**Practice!** For more practice with electron-dot structure problems, go to **Supplemental Practice Problems** in Appendix A.

---

## Section 5.3 Assessment

**24.** State the aufbau principle in your own words.

**25.** Apply the Pauli exclusion principle, the aufbau principle, and Hund's rule to write out the electron configuration and draw the orbital diagram for each of the following elements.

| | |
|---|---|
| **a.** silicon | **c.** calcium |
| **b.** fluorine | **d.** krypton |

**26.** What is a valence electron? Draw the electron-dot structures for the elements in problem 25.

**27. Thinking Critically** Use Hund's rule and orbital diagrams to describe the sequence in which ten electrons occupy the five orbitals related to an atom's d sublevel.

**28. Interpreting Scientific Illustrations** Which of the following is the correct electron-dot structure for an atom of selenium? Explain.

**a.** $\cdot \overset{\cdot}{\underset{}{Se}} :$  **b.** $\cdot \cdot \overset{\cdot}{\underset{}{Se}} \cdot$  **c.** $\cdot \overset{\cdot}{\underset{\cdot\cdot}{Se}} \cdot$  **d.** $\overset{\cdot\cdot}{\underset{}{S}} \cdot$

---

## Section 5.3 Assessment

**24.** Electrons tend to occupy the lowest-energy orbital available.

**25. a.** Si $1s^22s^22p^63s^23p^2$

↑↓  ↑↓  ↑↓↑↓↑↓  ↑↓   ↑↑
1s    2s      2p        3s    3p

**b.** F $1s^22s^22p^5$

↑↓  ↑↓  ↑↓↑↓↑
1s    2s      2p

**c.** Ca $1s^22s^22p^63s^23p^64s^2$

↑↓  ↑↓  ↑↓↑↓↑↓  ↑↓  ↑↓↑↓↑↓  ↑↓
1s    2s      2p        3s       3p        4s

**d.** Kr $1s^22s^22p^63s^23p^64s^23d^{10}4p^6$

↑↓  ↑↓  ↑↓↑↓↑↓  ↑↓  ↑↓↑↓↑↓
1s    2s      2p        3s       3p        4s

↑↓↑↓↑↓↑↓↑↓      ↑↓↑↓↑↓
3d                          4p

---

### Reteach

**Visual-Spatial** Have students write the electron-dot structure of strontium. The structure includes the symbol Sr and two dots. Ask what the two dots represent. They represent the two electrons in a strontium atom's outermost, 5s, orbital. Then, ask what the electron-dot structure does not communicate about the strontium atom's electrons. It does not specify which orbital contains the two electrons, nor does it give any information about strontium's inner level electrons.

### ✔ Assessment

**Skill** Ask students to identify the elements that have the following ground-state electron configurations. $[Ar]4s^23d^5$ manganese $[Xe]6s^24f^{14}5d^{10}6p^3$ bismuth **L2**

**26.** A valence electron is an electron in an atom's outermost orbitals.

**a.** $\cdot \overset{\cdot}{\underset{}{Si}} \cdot$   **c.** $\cdot Ca \cdot$

**b.** $\overset{\cdot\cdot}{\underset{\cdot\cdot}{:F:}}$   **d.** $\overset{\cdot\cdot}{\underset{\cdot\cdot}{:Kr:}}$

**27.** 1 electron    ↑
2 electrons    ↑ ↑
3 electrons    ↑ ↑ ↑
4 electrons    ↑ ↑ ↑ ↑
5 electrons    ↑ ↑ ↑ ↑ ↑
6 electrons    ↑↓ ↑ ↑ ↑ ↑
7 electrons    ↑↓ ↑↓ ↑ ↑ ↑
8 electrons    ↑↓ ↑↓ ↑↓ ↑ ↑
9 electrons    ↑↓ ↑↓ ↑↓ ↑↓ ↑
10 electrons  ↑↓ ↑↓ ↑↓ ↑↓ ↑↓
Single electrons with the same spin occupy each equal-energy orbital before additional electrons with opposite spins occupy the same orbital.

**28.** c is correct; a shows three two-electron orbitals; b shows one three-electron orbital; d has the wrong symbol

**141**

## Preparation

### Time Allotment
One laboratory period

### Process Skills
Comparing and contrasting, predicting, thinking critically, classifying, observing and inferring, sequencing

### Safety Precautions
- Do not let students handle the spectrum power supplies or tubes. Warn students not to touch the gas spectrum tubes during use because they are very hot and can cause burns. Exercise caution around the spectrum power supplies, as they present a significant electrical shock hazard.

### Disposal
You may want to reuse the flasks of food coloring solutions.

### Preparation of Materials
- Set up light sockets with light bulbs prior to class and have them plugged in.
- Set up spectrum power supplies and tubes prior to class.

## Pre-Lab

2. When electrons drop from higher-energy orbitals to lower-energy orbitals, the atom emits energy in the form of light. Each orbital transition is associated with a characteristic spectral line.

3. A continuous spectrum contains a continuum of visible colors from red to violet. An absorption spectrum is a continuous spectrum containing black lines at wavelengths associated with the atoms' energy absorptions. An emission spectrum consists of colored lines associated with the atoms' energy-level transitions.

## Procedure

- Have several groups of students start their observations of the gas discharge tubes first so that the area doesn't become crowded by the end of the class period.

---

# Line Spectra

**Y**ou know that sunlight is made up of a continuous spectrum of colors that combine to form white light. You also have learned that atoms of gases can emit visible light of characteristic wavelengths when excited by electricity. The color you see is the sum of all of the emitted wavelengths. In this experiment, you will use a diffraction grating to separate these wavelengths into emission line spectra.

You also will investigate another type of line spectrum—the absorption spectrum. The color of each solution you observe is due to the reflection or transmission of unabsorbed wavelengths of light. When white light passes through a sample and then a diffraction grating, dark lines show up on the continuous spectrum of white light. These lines correspond to the wavelengths of the photons absorbed by the solution.

### Problem
What absorption and emission spectra do various substances produce?

### Objectives
- **Observe** emission spectra of several gases.
- **Observe** the absorption spectra of various solutions.
- **Analyze** patterns of absorption and emission spectra.

### Materials
(For each group)
ring stand with clamp
40-W tubular light bulb
light socket with power cord
275-mL polystyrene culture flask (4)
Flinn C-Spectra® or similar diffraction grating

food coloring (red, green, blue, and yellow)
set of colored pencils
book

(For entire class)
spectrum tubes (hydrogen, neon, and mercury)
spectrum tube power supplies (3)

### Safety Precautions

- Always wear safety goggles and a lab apron.
- Use care around the spectrum tube power supplies.
- Spectrum tubes will get hot when used.

### Pre-Lab
1. Read the entire **CHEMLAB**.
2. Explain how electrons in an element's atoms produce an emission spectrum.
3. Distinguish among a continuous spectrum, an emission spectrum, and an absorption spectrum.
4. Prepare your data tables.

| Drawings of Emission Spectra | |
|---|---|
| Hydrogen | |
| Neon | |
| Mercury | |

| Drawings of Absorption Spectra | |
|---|---|
| Red | |
| Green | |
| Blue | |
| Yellow | |

### Procedure
1. Use a Flinn C-Spectra® to view an incandescent light bulb. What do you observe? Draw the spectrum using colored pencils.

---

- The Flinn C-Spectra is much easier to use than a spectroscope for viewing spectra. It can be ordered from:
  Flinn Scientific, Inc.
  P.O. Box 219
  Batavia, IL 60510
  www.flinnsci.com.
- You may be able to borrow gas spectrum tubes and power supplies from a physics teacher.

## Expected Results
For each colored solution listed below, all colors are visible except as noted.
Red solution: blue and green
Green solution: red and orange
Blue solution: yellow, orange, and some red
Yellow solution: blue

2. Use the Flinn C-Spectra® to view the emission spectra from tubes of gaseous hydrogen, neon, and mercury. Use colored pencils to make drawings in the data table of the spectra observed.

3. Fill a 275-mL culture flask with about 100-mL water. Add 2 or 3 drops of red food coloring to the water. Shake the solution.

4. Repeat step 3 for the green, blue, and yellow food coloring. **CAUTION:** *Be sure to thoroughly dry your hands before handling electrical equipment.*

5. Set up the 40-W light bulb so that it is near eye level. Place the flask with red food coloring about 8 cm from the light bulb. Use a book or some other object to act as a stage to put the flask on. You should be able to see light from the bulb above the solution and light from the bulb projecting through the solution.

6. With the room lights darkened, view the light using the Flinn C-Spectra®. The top spectrum viewed will be a continuous spectrum of the white light bulb. The bottom spectrum will be the absorption spectrum of the red solution. The black areas of the absorption spectrum represent the colors absorbed by the red food coloring in the solution. Use colored pencils to make a drawing in the data table of the absorption spectra you observed.

7. Repeat steps 5 and 6 using the green, blue, and yellow colored solutions.

### Cleanup and Disposal

1. Turn off the light socket and spectrum tube power supplies.

2. Wait several minutes to allow the incandescent light bulb and the spectrum tubes to cool.

3. Follow your teacher's instructions on how to dispose of the liquids and how to store the light bulb and spectrum tubes.

### Analyze and Conclude

1. **Thinking Critically** How can the existence of spectra help to prove that energy levels in atoms exist?

2. **Thinking Critically** How can the single electron in a hydrogen atom produce all of the lines found in its emission spectrum?

3. **Predicting** How can you predict the absorption spectrum of a solution by looking at its color?

4. **Thinking Critically** How can spectra be used to identify the presence of specific elements in a substance?

### Real-World Chemistry

1. How can absorption and emission spectra be used by the Hubble space telescope to study the structures of stars or other objects found in deep space?

2. The absorption spectrum of chlorophyll *a* indicates strong absorption of red and blue wavelengths. Explain why leaves appear green.

CHEMLAB **143**

The approximate emission spectra of the gas spectrum tubes are shown below.

Hydrogen

Mercury

Neon

Blue Green    Yellow   Orange   Red

### Analyze and Conclude

1. The spectral lines indicate energy is absorbed or released as the atom transitions from one energy level to another.

2. At any given time, the electron occupies a single orbital. However, it can move into other, vacant orbitals as the atom absorbs or emits energy.

3. The color of a solution is due to the color of light it transmits. The colors not transmitted are absorbed, and these colors comprise the absorption spectrum.

4. The spectrum of each element is unique. Thus, the presence of a unique atomic spectrum indicates the presence of that element.

### Real-World Chemistry

1. The light emitted by stars can be analyzed for the presence of unique atomic spectra. Such spectra can identify the types of matter that comprise the star.

2. Leaves appear green because they reflect (do not absorb) green light. The reflected green light is what our eyes see.

**Resource Manager**

ChemLab and MiniLab Worksheets, pp. 18–20 **L2**

**Assessment**

**Skill** Have students look at the spectrum produced by a fluorescent light and compare this spectrum to the spectrum of an incandescent bulb. **L2**

National Science Content Standards

Pages 142–143
UCP.1, UCP.2; A.1, A.2; B.1, B.6

# How It Works

## How It Works

## Purpose

Students will learn how lasers are an application of quantum theory.

## Background

Most sources of light emit incoherent light. Incoherent light waves have different wavelengths, amplitudes, and frequencies, travel in all directions, and are not in phase with each other as they move through space. Laser light is coherent, traveling in the same direction while being in phase.

Two conditions must be met for a laser to work. First, the atoms must be excited to a higher state. Second, the atoms must remain in the higher state longer than usual so that they can be stimulated to emit light rather than to emit it spontaneously. How these conditions are achieved depends on the type of laser being used. In a ruby laser, for example, strong flashes of light excite the atoms. The atoms then drop to a lower state that is still excited, which leaves enough time for stimulated emission to occur.

## Visual Learning

Bring a laser pointer to class, and compare its light to that of an ordinary flashlight. **CAUTION:** *Be sure that students do not look directly into the laser light or shine it into anyone's eyes.*

## Teaching Strategies

• Ask students to list at least five different types of materials that can be used in a laser to produce light.
• Ask students to select an application of laser light to research. Have them create a poster summarizing how the laser is used in this way.

**L2** **ELL**

**National Science Content Standards**

**Pages 144–145**
UCP.1, UCP.2; B.1, B.6; E.2; F.6; G.3

---

# How It Works

## Lasers

A laser is a device that produces a beam of intense light of a specific wavelength (color). Unlike light from a flashlight, laser light is coherent; that is, it does not spread out as it travels through space. The precise nature of lasers led to their use in pointing and aiming devices, CD players, optical fiber data transmission, and surgery.

**1** The spiral-wound high-intensity lamp flashes, supplying energy to the helium-neon gas mixture inside the tube. The atoms of the gas absorb the light energy and are raised to an excited energy state.

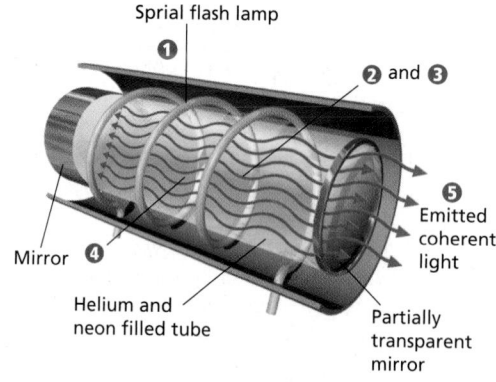

Sprial flash lamp
**1**
**2** and **3**
**5** Emitted coherent light
Mirror **4**
Helium and neon filled tube
Partially transparent mirror

**4** Photons traveling parallel to the tube are reflected back through the tube by the flat mirrors located at each end. The photons strike additional excited atoms and cause more photons to be released. The intensity of the light in the tube builds.

**5** Some of the laser's coherent light passes through the partially transparent mirror at one end of the tube and exits the laser. These photons make up the light emitted by the laser.

**2** The excited atoms begin returning to the ground state, emitting photons in the process. These initial photons travel in all directions.

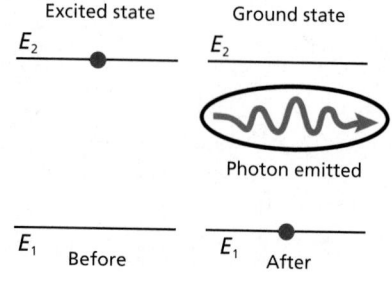

Excited state      Ground state
$E_2$                    $E_2$

Photon emitted

$E_1$    Before      $E_1$    After

**3** The emitted photons hit other excited atoms, causing them to release additional photons. These additional photons are the same wavelength as the photons that struck the excited atoms, and they are coherent (their waves are in sync because they are identical in wavelength and direction).

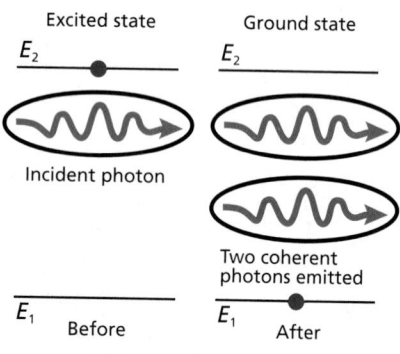

Excited state      Ground state
$E_2$                    $E_2$

Incident photon

Two coherent photons emitted

$E_1$    Before      $E_1$    After

### Thinking Critically

**1. Inferring** How does the material used in the laser affect the type of light emitted?

**2. Relating Cause and Effect** Why is one mirror partially transparent?

### Thinking Critically

**1.** The arrangement of electrons varies from one substance to another. As a result, the characteristics of light emitted by the laser also vary. The material in the laser determines the characteristics of the light produced.

**2.** If one of the mirrors were not partially transparent, the photons would have no way to escape the laser. If the mirror were totally transparent, the photons would exit the laser after just one pass through the tube. Thus, the photons could not stimulate the emission of additional photons; the laser would soon weaken.

## Summary

### 5.1 Light and Quantized Energy

- All waves can be described by their wavelength, frequency, amplitude, and speed.

- Light is an electromagnetic wave. In a vacuum, all electromagnetic waves travel at a speed of $3.00 \times 10^8$ m/s.

- All electromagnetic waves may be described as both waves and particles. Particles of light are called photons.

- Energy is emitted and absorbed by matter in quanta.

- In contrast to the continuous spectrum produced by white light, an element's atomic emission spectrum consists of a series of fine lines of individual colors.

### 5.2 Quantum Theory and the Atom

- According to the Bohr model of the atom, hydrogen's atomic emission spectrum results from electrons dropping from higher-energy atomic orbits to lower-energy atomic orbits.

- The de Broglie equation predicts that all moving particles have wave characteristics and relates each particle's wavelength to its mass, its velocity, and Planck's constant.

- The quantum mechanical model of the atom is based on the assumption that electrons are waves.

- The Heisenberg uncertainty principle states that it is not possible to know precisely the velocity and the position of a particle at the same time.

- Electrons occupy three-dimensional regions of space called atomic orbitals. There are four types of orbitals, denoted by the letters s, p, d, and f.

### 5.3 Electron Configurations

- The arrangement of electrons in an atom is called the atom's electron configuration. Electron configurations are prescribed by three rules: the aufbau principle, the Pauli exclusion principle, and Hund's rule.

- Electrons related to the atom's highest principal energy level are referred to as valence electrons. Valence electrons determine the chemical properties of an element.

- Electron configurations may be represented using orbital diagrams, electron configuration notation, and electron-dot structures.

## Key Equations and Relationships

- EM Wave relationship: $c = \lambda\nu$
  (p. 119)

- Energy of a quantum: $E_{quantum} = h\nu$
  (p. 123)

- Energy of a photon: $E_{photon} = h\nu$
  (p. 124)

- Energy change of an electron:
  $$\Delta E = E_{\text{higher-energy orbit}} - E_{\text{lower-energy orbit}}$$
  $$\Delta E = E_{photon} = h\nu$$
  (p. 128)

- de Broglie's equation: $\lambda = \dfrac{h}{mv}$
  (p. 130)

## Vocabulary

- amplitude (p. 119)
- atomic emission spectrum (p. 125)
- atomic orbital (p. 132)
- aufbau principle (p. 135)
- de Broglie equation (p. 130)
- electromagnetic radiation (p. 118)
- electromagnetic spectrum (p. 120)
- electron configuration (p. 135)
- electron-dot structure (p. 140)
- energy sublevel (p. 133)
- frequency (p. 118)
- ground state (p. 127)
- Heisenberg uncertainty principle (p. 131)
- Hund's rule (p. 136)
- Pauli exclusion principle (p. 136)
- photoelectric effect (p. 123)
- photon (p. 123)
- Planck's constant (p. 123)
- principal energy level (p. 133)
- principal quantum number (p. 132)
- quantum (p. 122)
- quantum mechanical model of the atom (p. 131)
- valence electron (p. 140)
- wavelength (p. 118)

chemistrymc.com/vocabulary_puzzlemaker

Study Guide **145**

## Using the Vocabulary

To reinforce chapter vocabulary, have students write a sentence using each term. **L2** **ELL**

## Review Strategies

- Have students describe the electromagnetic spectrum and differentiate between visible light and infrared radiation. **L2**

- Ask students to write the equation that relates an electromagnetic wave's frequency and wavelength. **L2**

- Have students write the equation that relates the energy of a quantum of electromagnetic radiation to the frequency of an associated wave. **L2**

- Ask students to explain the significance of Heisenberg's uncertainty principle as it relates to electrons in atoms. **L2**

- Have students explain the relationship between an atom's orbitals and its energy levels. **L2**

- Problems from Appendix A or the **Supplemental Problems** booklet can be used for review. **L2**

### VOCABULARY PuzzleMaker

For additional help with vocabulary, have students access the Vocabulary PuzzleMaker online.

chemistrymc.com/ vocabulary_puzzlemaker

### Chemistry Online

## Concept Mapping

**29.** 1. electromagnetic waves;
2. characteristic properties;
3. frequency; 4. wavelength; 5. speed; 6. hertz;
7. $c = \lambda\nu$; 8. $c$

## Mastering Concepts

**30. a.** Frequency is the number of waves that pass a given point per second.
**b.** Wavelength is the shortest distance between equivalent points on a continuous wave.
**c.** A quantum is the minimum amount of energy that can be lost or gained by an atom.
**d.** An atom's ground state is its lowest allowable energy state.

**31.** Typical answers will say that the model did not explain the following: how the atom's negatively charged electrons occupy the space around the nucleus; why the electrons are not drawn into the atom's positively charged nucleus; a rationale for the chemical properties of the elements.

**32.** light, microwaves, X rays, radio waves

**33.** Electricity passing through the tube excites neon atoms to higher energy levels. As the excited atoms drop back to lower energy levels, they emit light.

**34.** a particle of electromagnetic radiation having a rest mass of zero and carrying a quantum of energy

**35.** a phenomenon in which a metal emits electrons when light of a sufficient frequency shines on it

**36.** According to Planck, for a given frequency, $\nu$, matter can emit or absorb energy only in discrete quanta that are whole-number multiples of $h\nu$.

## Chemistry Online

*Go to the Chemistry Web site at* chemistrymc.com *for additional Chapter 5 Assessment.*

## Concept Mapping

**29.** Complete the concept map using the following terms: speed, $c = \lambda\nu$, electromagnetic waves, wavelength, characteristic properties, frequency, $c$, and hertz.

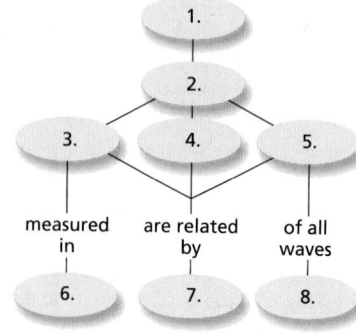

## Mastering Concepts

**30.** Define the following terms.
  **a.** frequency (5.1)    **c.** quantum (5.1)
  **b.** wavelength (5.1)    **d.** ground state (5.2)

**31.** Why did scientists consider Rutherford's nuclear model of the atom incomplete? (5.1)

**32.** Name one type of electromagnetic radiation. (5.1)

**33.** Explain how the gaseous neon atoms in a neon sign emit light. (5.1)

**34.** What is a photon? (5.1)

**35.** What is the photoelectric effect? (5.1)

**36.** Explain Planck's quantum concept as it relates to energy lost or gained by matter. (5.1)

**37.** How did Einstein explain the previously unexplainable photoelectric effect? (5.1)

**38.** Arrange the following types of electromagnetic radiation in order of increasing wavelength. (5.1)
  **a.** ultraviolet light   **c.** radio waves
  **b.** microwaves     **d.** X rays

**39.** What is the difference between an atom's ground state and an excited state? (5.2)

**40.** According to the Bohr model, how do electrons move in atoms? (5.2)

**41.** What does $n$ designate in Bohr's atomic model? (5.2)

**42.** Why are you unaware of the wavelengths of moving objects such as automobiles and tennis balls? (5.2)

**43.** What is the name of the atomic model in which electrons are treated as waves? Who first wrote the electron wave equations that led to this model? (5.2)

**44.** What is an atomic orbital? (5.2)

**45.** What is the probability that an electron will be found within an atomic orbital? (5.2)

**46.** What does $n$ represent in the quantum mechanical model of the atom? (5.2)

**47.** How many energy sublevels are contained in each of the hydrogen atom's first three energy levels? (5.2)

**48.** What atomic orbitals are related to a p sublevel? To a d sublevel? (5.2)

**49.** Which of the following atomic orbital designations are incorrect? (5.2)
  **a.** 7f   **b.** 3f   **c.** 2d   **d.** 6p

**50.** What do the sublevel designations s, p, d, and f specify with respect to the atom's orbitals? (5.2)

**51.** What do subscripts such as $y$ and $xz$ tell you about atomic orbitals? (5.2)

**52.** What is the maximum number of electrons an orbital may contain? (5.2)

**53.** Why is it impossible to know precisely the velocity and position of an electron at the same time? (5.2)

**54.** What shortcomings caused scientists to finally reject Bohr's model of the atom? (5.2)

**55.** Describe de Broglie's revolutionary concept involving the characteristics of moving particles. (5.2)

**56.** How is an orbital's principal quantum number related to the atom's major energy levels? (5.2)

**57.** Explain the meaning of the aufbau principle as it applies to atoms with many electrons. (5.3)

**58.** In what sequence do electrons fill the atomic orbitals related to a sublevel? (5.3)

**59.** Why must the two arrows within a single block of an orbital diagram be written in opposite (up and down) directions? (5.3)

**60.** How does noble-gas notation shorten the process of writing an element's electron configuration? (5.3)

**61.** What are valence electrons? How many of a magnesium atom's 12 electrons are valence electrons? (5.3)

chemistrymc.com/chapter_test

**37.** He proposed that photons must have a certain minimum, or threshold, value to cause the ejection of a photoelectron.

**38.** d. X rays, a. ultraviolet light, b. microwaves, c. radio waves

**62.** Light is said to have a dual wave-particle nature. What does this statement mean? (5.3)

**63.** Describe the difference between a quantum and a photon. (5.3)

**64.** How many electrons are shown in the electron-dot structures of the following elements? (5.3)

   **a.** carbon      **c.** calcium
   **b.** iodine      **d.** gallium

## Mastering Problems

### Wavelength, Frequency, Speed, and Energy (5.1)

**65.** What is the wavelength of electromagnetic radiation having a frequency of $5.00 \times 10^{12}$ Hz? What kind of electromagnetic radiation is this?

**66.** What is the frequency of electromagnetic radiation having a wavelength of $3.33 \times 10^{-8}$ m? What type of electromagnetic radiation is this?

**67.** The laser in a compact disc (CD) player uses light with a wavelength of 780 nm. What is the frequency of this light?

**68.** What is the speed of an electromagnetic wave having a frequency of $1.33 \times 10^{17}$ Hz and a wavelength of 2.25 nm?

**69.** Use **Figure 5-5** to determine each of the following types of radiation.

   **a.** radiation with a frequency of $8.6 \times 10^{11}$ s$^{-1}$
   **b.** radiation with a wavelength 4.2 nm
   **c.** radiation with a frequency of 5.6 MHz
   **d.** radiation that travels at a speed of $3.00 \times 10^8$ m/s

**70.** What is the energy of a photon of red light having a frequency of $4.48 \times 10^{14}$ Hz?

**71.** Mercury's atomic emission spectrum is shown below. Estimate the wavelength of the orange line. What is its frequency? What is the energy of an orange photon emitted by the mercury atom?

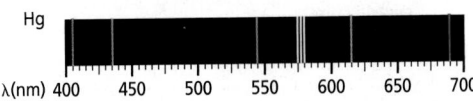

Hg
λ(nm) 400    450    500    550    600    650    700

**72.** What is the energy of an ultraviolet photon having a wavelength of $1.18 \times 10^{-8}$ m?

**73.** A photon has an energy of $2.93 \times 10^{-25}$ J. What is its frequency? What type of electromagnetic radiation is the photon?

**74.** A photon has an energy of $1.10 \times 10^{-13}$ J. What is the photon's wavelength? What type of electromagnetic radiation is it?

**75.** How long does it take a radio signal from the Voyager spacecraft to reach Earth if the distance between Voyager and Earth is $2.72 \times 10^9$ km?

**76.** If your favorite FM radio station broadcasts at a frequency of 104.5 MHz, what is the wavelength of the station's signal in meters? What is the energy of a photon of the station's electromagnetic signal?

### Electron Configurations (5.3)

**77.** List the aufbau sequence of orbitals from 1s to 7p.

**78.** Write orbital notations and complete electron configurations for atoms of the following elements.

   **a.** beryllium
   **b.** aluminum
   **c.** nitrogen
   **d.** sodium

**79.** Use noble-gas notation to describe the electron configurations of the elements represented by the following symbols.

   **a.** Mn      **f.** W
   **b.** Kr      **g.** Pb
   **c.** P       **h.** Ra
   **d.** Zn      **i.** Sm
   **e.** Zr      **j.** Bk

**80.** What elements are represented by each of the following electron configurations?

   **a.** $1s^2 2s^2 2p^5$
   **b.** $[Ar]4s^2$
   **c.** $[Xe]6s^2 4f^4$
   **d.** $[Kr]5s^2 4d^{10} 5p^4$
   **e.** $[Rn]7s^2 5f^{13}$
   **f.** $1s^2 2s^2 2p^6 3s^2 3p^6 4s^2 3d^{10} 4p^5$

**81.** Draw electron-dot structures for atoms of each of the following elements.

   **a.** carbon
   **b.** arsenic
   **c.** polonium
   **d.** potassium
   **e.** barium

**82.** An atom of arsenic has how many electron-containing orbitals? How many of the orbitals are completely filled? How many of the orbitals are associated with the atom's $n = 4$ principal energy level?

**39.** An atom's ground state is its lowest energy state, while any energy state higher than the ground state is an excited state.

**40.** Electrons move in circular orbits around the nucleus.

**41.** The quantum number $n$ specifies the electron's orbit.

**42.** Their wavelengths are too small to be seen.

**43.** the quantum mechanical model of the atom; Erwin Schrödinger

**44.** a three-dimensional region around the nucleus describing an electron's probable location

**45.** The probability is 90%.

**46.** $n$ represents an orbital's principal quantum number, which indicates the relative size and energy of the orbital.

**47.** energy level 1 has one sublevel, energy level 2 has two sublevels, energy level 3 has three sublevels

**48.** p sublevel: $x$, $y$, and $z$ orbitals; d sublevel: $xy$, $xz$, $yz$, $x^2 - y^2$, and $z^2$ orbitals

**49.** b, c are incorrect

**50.** their shapes

**51.** their orientations

**52.** two electrons

**53.** The photon required to measure an electron's velocity or position changes both the position and velocity of the electron.

**54.** Bohr's model did not explain the spectra of atoms having more than one electron and did not fully explain the chemical behavior of atoms.

**55.** de Broglie proposed that all moving particles have wave characteristics.

**56.** Because the orbital's principal quantum number indicates the orbital's relative size and energy, it also specifies the atom's major energy level.

**57.** The aufbau principle describes the sequence in which an atom's orbitals are filled with electrons.

**58.** Each orbital must contain a single electron before any orbital contains two electrons.

**59.** Two electrons occupying a single atomic orbital must have opposite spins.

**60.** The noble-gas notation uses the bracketed symbol of the preceding noble gas in the periodic table to represent an atom's inner electrons.

**61.** Valence electrons are the electrons in an atom's outermost orbitals; 2

**62.** Light exhibits wavelike behavior in some situations and particlelike behavior in others.

National Science Content Standards

Pages 146–147
UCP.1, UCP.2; B.1, B.6; G.2, G.3

**63.** A quantum is the minimum amount of energy that can be lost or gained by an atom, while a photon is a particle of light that carries a quantum of energy.

**64. a.** 4   **c.** 2
**b.** 7   **d.** 3

## Mastering Problems

Complete solutions to Chapter Assessment problems can be found in the **Solutions Manual.**

### Wavelength, Frequency, Speed, and Energy (5.1)
#### Level 1

**65.** $\lambda = 6.00 \times 10^{-5}$ m; infrared radiation
**66.** $\nu = 9.01 \times 10^{15}$ s$^{-1}$; ultraviolet radiation
**67.** $\nu = 3.8 \times 10^{14}$ s$^{-1}$
**68.** $v = 3.00 \times 10^8$ m/s
**69. a.** infrared
**b.** X ray
**c.** AM radio
**d.** any EM wave

#### Level 2

**70.** $E_{photon} = 2.97 \times 10^{-19}$ J
**71.** $\lambda = 615$ nm, $4.88 \times 10^{14}$ s$^{-1}$, $E_{photon} = 3.23 \times 10^{-19}$ J
**72.** $E_{photon} = 1.68 \times 10^{-17}$ J
**73.** $\nu = 4.42 \times 10^8$ s$^{-1}$; TV or FM wave
**74.** $\lambda = 1.81 \times 10^{-12}$ m, an X ray or gamma ray
**75.** $t = 9070$ s, or 151 min
**76.** $\lambda = 2.87$ m, $E_{photon} = 6.92 \times 10^{-26}$ J

### Electron Configurations (5.3)
#### Level 1

**77.** 1s, 2s, 2p, 3s, 3p, 4s, 3d, 4p, 5s, 4d, 5p, 6s, 4f, 5d, 6p, 7s, 5f, 6d, 7p

**78. a.** Be 1s$^2$2s$^2$

⇅ ⇅
1s   2s

**b.** Al 1s$^2$2s$^2$2p$^6$3s$^2$3p$^1$

⇅ ⇅ ⇅⇅⇅ ⇅ ↑
1s   2s      2p      3s 3p

**c.** N 1s$^2$2s$^2$2p$^3$

⇅ ⇅ ↑ ↑ ↑
1s   2s      2p

**d.** Na 1s$^2$2s$^2$2p$^6$3s$^1$

⇅ ⇅ ⇅⇅⇅ ↑
1s   2s      2p      3s

**79. a.** Mn [Ar]4s$^2$3d$^5$
**b.** Kr [Ar]4s$^2$3d$^{10}$4p$^6$
**c.** P [Ne]3s$^2$3p$^3$
**d.** Zn [Ar]4s$^2$3d$^{10}$
**e.** Zr [Kr]5s$^2$4d$^2$
**f.** W [Xe]6s$^2$4f$^{14}$5d$^4$
**g.** Pb [Xe]6s$^2$4f$^{14}$5d$^{10}$6p$^2$
**h.** Ra [Rn]7s$^2$
**i.** Sm [Xe]6s$^2$4f$^6$
**j.** Bk [Rn]7s$^2$5f$^9$

#### Level 2

**80. a.** F   **c.** Nd   **e.** Md
**b.** Ca   **d.** Te   **f.** Br

**81. a.** ·Ċ·   **d.** ·K
**b.** ·Äs·   **e.** Ba·
**c.** :Ṗo·

**82.** 18; 15; 4

---

## Mixed Review

*Sharpen your problem-solving skills by answering the following.*

**83.** What is the frequency of electromagnetic radiation having a wavelength of 1.00 m?

**84.** What is the maximum number of electrons that can be contained in an atom's orbitals having the following principal quantum numbers?

**a.** 3   **b.** 4   **c.** 6   **d.** 7

**85.** What is the wavelength of light with a frequency of $5.77 \times 10^{14}$ Hz?

**86.** Using the waves shown below, identify the wave or waves with the following characteristics.

**1.**   **3.**
**2.**   **4.**

**a.** longest wavelength   **c.** largest amplitude
**b.** greatest frequency   **d.** shortest wavelength

**87.** How many orientations are possible for the orbitals related to each of the following sublevels?

**a.** s   **b.** p   **c.** d   **d.** f

**88.** Describe the electrons in an atom of nickel in the ground state using the electron configuration notation and the noble-gas notation.

**89.** Which of the following elements have two electrons in their electron-dot structures: hydrogen, helium, lithium, aluminum, calcium, cobalt, bromine, krypton, and barium?

**90.** In Bohr's atomic model, what electron orbit transition produces the blue-green line in hydrogen's atomic emission spectrum?

**91.** A zinc atom contains a total of 18 electrons in its 3s, 3p, and 3d orbitals. Why does its electron-dot structure show only two dots?

**92.** An X-ray photon has an energy of $3.01 \times 10^{-18}$ J. What is its frequency and wavelength?

**93.** Which element has the following orbital diagram?

⇅ ⇅ ↑ □ □
1s   2s      2p

**94.** Which element has the ground-state electron configuration represented by the noble-gas notation [Rn]7s$^1$?

**95.** How many photons of infrared radiation having a frequency of $4.88 \times 10^{13}$ Hz are required to provide an energy of 1.00 J?

---

## Thinking Critically

**96. Comparing and Contrasting** Briefly discuss the difference between an orbit in Bohr's model of the atom and an orbital in the quantum mechanical view of the atom.

**97. Applying Concepts** Scientists use atomic emission spectra to determine the elements in materials of unknown composition. Explain what makes this method possible.

**98. Using Numbers** It takes $8.17 \times 10^{-19}$ J of energy to remove one electron from a gold surface. What is the maximum wavelength of light capable of causing this effect?

**99. Drawing a Conclusion** The elements aluminum, silicon, gallium, germanium, arsenic, selenium are all used in making various types of semiconductor devices. Write electron configurations and electron-dot structures for atoms of each of these elements. What similarities among the elements' electron configurations do you notice?

## Writing in Chemistry

**100.** In order to make "neon" signs emit a variety of colors, manufacturers often fill the signs with gases other than neon. Research the use of gases in neon signs and specify the colors produced by the gases.

## Cumulative Review

*Refresh your understanding of previous chapters by answering the following.*

**101.** Round 20.561 20 g to three significant figures. (Chapter 2)

**102.** Identify each of the following as either chemical or physical properties of the substance. (Chapter 3)

**a.** mercury is a liquid at room temperature
**b.** sucrose is a white, crystalline solid
**c.** iron rusts when exposed to moist air
**d.** paper burns when ignited

**103.** Identify each of the following as a pure substance or a mixture. (Chapter 3)

**a.** distilled water   **d.** diamond
**b.** orange juice with pulp   **e.** milk
**c.** smog   **f.** copper metal

**104.** An atom of gadolinium has an atomic number of 64 and a mass number of 153. How many electrons, protons, and neutrons does it contain? (Chapter 4)

*Use these questions and the test-taking tip to prepare for your standardized test.*

**1.** Cosmic rays are high-energy radiation from outer space. What is the frequency of a cosmic ray that has a wavelength of $2.67 \times 10^{-13}$ m when it reaches Earth? (The speed of light is $3.00 \times 10^8$ m/s.)

  **a.** $8.90 \times 10^{-22}$ s$^{-1}$
  **b.** $3.75 \times 10^{12}$ s$^{-1}$
  **c.** $8.01 \times 10^{-5}$ s$^{-1}$
  **d.** $1.12 \times 10^{21}$ s$^{-1}$

**2.** Wavelengths of light shorter than about $4.00 \times 10^{-7}$ m are not visible to the human eye. What is the energy of a photon of ultraviolet light having a frequency of $5.45 \times 10^{16}$ s$^{-1}$? (Planck's constant is $6.626 \times 10^{-34}$ J·s.)

  **a.** $3.61 \times 10^{-17}$ J
  **b.** $1.22 \times 10^{-50}$ J
  **c.** $8.23 \times 10^{49}$ J
  **d.** $3.81 \times 10^{-24}$ J

**Interpreting Charts** Use the periodic table and the chart below to answer questions 3–6.

### Electron Configurations for Selected Transition Metals

| Element | Symbol | Atomic number | Electron configuration |
|---------|--------|---------------|------------------------|
| Vanadium | V | 23 | [Ar]4s$^2$3d$^3$ |
| Yttrium | Y | 39 | [Kr]5s$^2$4d$^1$ |
| _____ | — | — | [Xe]6s$^2$4f$^{14}$5d$^6$ |
| Scandium | Sc | 21 | [Ar]4s$^2$3d$^1$ |
| Cadmium | Cd | 48 | _____ |

**3.** Using noble-gas notation, what is the ground-state electron configuration of Cd?

  **a.** [Kr]4d$^{10}$4f$^2$
  **c.** [Kr]5s$^2$4d$^{10}$
  **b.** [Ar]4s$^2$3d$^{10}$
  **d.** [Xe]5s$^2$4d$^{10}$

**4.** What is the element that has the ground-state electron configuration [Xe]6s$^2$4f$^{14}$5d$^6$?

  **a.** La
  **c.** W
  **b.** Ti
  **d.** Os

**5.** What is the complete electron configuration of a scandium atom?

  **a.** 1s$^2$2s$^2$2p$^6$3s$^2$3p$^6$4s$^2$3d$^1$
  **b.** 1s$^2$2s$^2$2p$^7$3s$^2$3p$^7$4s$^2$3d$^1$
  **c.** 1s$^2$2s$^2$2p$^5$3s$^2$3p$^5$4s$^2$3d$^1$
  **d.** 1s$^2$2s$^1$2p$^7$3s$^1$3p$^7$4s$^2$3d$^1$

**6.** Which of the following is the correct orbital diagram for the third and fourth principal energy levels of vanadium?

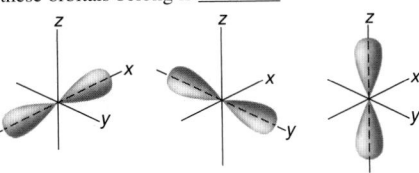

**a.** 3s 3p 4s 3d
**b.** 3s 3p 4s 3d
**c.** 3s 3p 4s 3d
**d.** 3s 3p 4s 3d

**7.** Which of the following orbitals has the highest energy?

  **a.** 4f
  **b.** 5p
  **c.** 6s
  **d.** 3d

**8.** What is the electron-dot structure for indium?

  **a.** ·In
  **c.** ·In·
  **b.** ·In·
  **d.** ·In·

**9.** The picture below shows all of the orbitals related to one type of sublevel. The type of sublevel to which these orbitals belong is _____ .

  **a.** s
  **c.** d
  **b.** p
  **d.** f

**10.** What is the maximum number of electrons related to the fifth principal energy level of an atom?

  **a.** 10
  **c.** 25
  **b.** 20
  **d.** 50

---

### TEST-TAKING TIP

**Do Some Reconnaissance** Find out what the conditions will be for taking the test. Is it timed or untimed? Can you eat a snack at the break? Can you use a calculator or other tools? Will those tools be provided? Will mathematical constants be given? Know these things in advance so that you can practice taking tests under the same conditions.

## Mixed Review

**83.** $\nu = 3.00 \times 10^8$ s$^{-1}$
**84. a.** 18   **c.** 72
  **b.** 32   **d.** 98
**85.** $\lambda = 5.20 \times 10^{-7}$ m
**86. a.** longest wavelength: 4
  **b.** greatest frequency: 3
  **c.** largest amplitude: 1 and 3
  **d.** shortest wavelength: 3
**87. a.** 1   **c.** 5
  **b.** 3   **d.** 7
**88.** 1s$^2$2s$^2$2p$^6$3s$^2$3p$^6$4s$^2$3d$^8$ [Ar]4s$^2$3d$^8$
**89.** helium, calcium, cobalt, barium
**90.** $n = 4 \rightarrow n = 2$
**91.** The two dots are the atom's two 4s valence electrons.
**92.** $\nu = 4.54 \times 10^{15}$ s$^{-1}$; $\lambda = 6.60 \times 10^{-8}$ m
**93.** boron
**94.** francium
**95.** $3.10 \times 10^{19}$ photons

## Thinking Critically

**96.** In the Bohr model, an orbit is a circular path taken by an electron as it moves around the atomic nucleus. In the quantum mechanical model, an orbital is a three-dimensional region around the nucleus that describes the electron's probable location.
**97.** Each element emits a characteristic, unique atomic emission spectrum.
**98.** $\lambda = 2.43 \times 10^{-7}$ m
**99.** Al [Ne]3s$^2$3p$^1$
Si [Ne]3s$^2$3p$^2$
Ga [Ar]4s$^2$3d$^{10}$4p$^1$
Ge [Ar]4s$^2$3d$^{10}$4p$^2$
As [Ar]4s$^2$3d$^{10}$4p$^3$
Se [Ar]4s$^2$3d$^{10}$4p$^4$
The atoms have filled s orbitals and p orbitals containing 1 to 4 electrons. See the Solutions Manual for electron dot structures.

---

## Cumulative Review

**101.** 20.6 g
**102. a.** physical property
  **b.** physical property
  **c.** chemical property
  **d.** chemical property
**103. a.** pure substance
  **b.** mixture
  **c.** mixture
  **d.** pure substance
  **e.** mixture
  **f.** pure substance
**104.** 64 electrons, 64 protons, 89 neutrons

## Standardized Test Practice

| | | | |
|---|---|---|---|
| **1.** d | **4.** d | **7.** a | **9.** b |
| **2.** a | **5.** a | **8.** c | **10.** d |
| **3.** c | **6.** b | | |

### National Science Content Standards

**Pages 148–149**
UCP.1, UCP.2; B.1, B.6; E.2

# Resource Manager

| Section | Objectives | Activities/Features |
|---------|-----------|---------------------|
| **Section 6.1**<br>**Development of the Modern Periodic Table**<br>1 session<br>½ block | **1. Trace** the development and **identify** key features of the periodic table. | **Discovery Lab:** Versatile Metals, p. 151<br>**Astronomy Connection,** p. 152<br>**Problem-Solving Lab:** Francium—solid, liquid, or gas? p. 155 |
| **Section 6.2**<br>**Classification of the Elements**<br>2 sessions<br>1 block | **2. Explain** why elements in the same group have similar properties.<br>**3. Identify** the four blocks of the periodic table based on electron configuration. | **Careers Using Chemistry:** Medical Lab Technician, p. 160<br>**ChemLab:** Descriptive Chemistry of the Elements, pp. 170–171 |
| **Section 6.3**<br>**Periodic Trends**<br>3 sessions<br>1½ blocks | **4. Compare** period and group trends of several properties.<br>**5. Relate** period and group trends in atomic radii to electron configuration. | **MiniLab:** Periodicity of Molar Heats of Fusion and Vaporization, p. 164<br>**ChemLab:** Descriptive Chemistry of the Elements, pp. 170–171<br>**How It Works:** Television Screen, p. 172 |

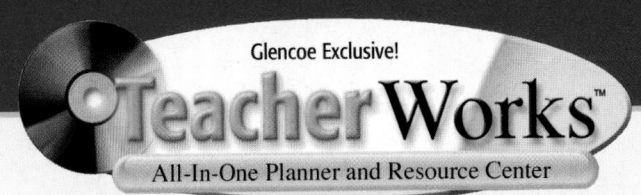

| National Science Content Standards | State/Local Standards | Reproducible Masters | Transparencies |
|---|---|---|---|
| UCP.1, UCP.2, UCP.5; A.1, A.2; B.1, B.2; E.2; G.1, G.2, G.3 | | **Study Guide for Content Mastery,** pp. 31–32 **L2** | **Section Focus Transparency 20** **L1** **ELL** <br> **Teaching Transparency 18** **L2** **ELL** |
| UCP.1, UCP.2, UCP.5; A.1; B.1, B.2 | | **Study Guide for Content Mastery,** pp. 33–34 **L2** <br> **ChemLab and MiniLab Worksheets,** pp. 22–24 **L2** <br> **Challenge Problems,** p. 6 **L3** | **Section Focus Transparency 21** **L1** **ELL** <br> **Teaching Transparency 19** **L2** **ELL** <br> **Math Skills Transparency 6** **L2** **ELL** |
| UCP.1, UCP.2, UCP.5; A.1, A.2; B.1, B.2, B.6; E.1, E.2; G.2, G.3 | | **Study Guide for Content Mastery,** pp. 35–36 **L2** <br> **ChemLab and MiniLab Worksheets,** pp. 21–24 **L2** <br> **Laboratory Manual,** pp. 41–48 **L2** | **Section Focus Transparency 22** **L1** **ELL** <br> **Teaching Transparencies 20, 21** **L2** **ELL** |

**Key to National Science Content Standards:** UCP = Unifying Concepts and Processes, A = Science as Inquiry, B = Physical Science, C = Life Science, D = Earth and Space Sciences, E = Science and Technology, F = Science in Personal and Social Perspectives, G = History and Nature of Science

Refer to pages 4T–5T of the Teacher Guide for an explanation of the National Science Content Standards correlations.

# Resource Manager

## Materials List

### ChemLab (pages 170–171)
stoppered test tubes containing small samples of elements, plastic dishes containing samples of elements, conductivity tester, 1.0$M$ HCl, test tubes (6), test-tube rack, 10-mL graduated cylinder, spatula, small hammer, glass marking pencil

### Discovery Lab (page 151)
samples of copper (coins, wire, shot, strips, etc.), masking tape, low-voltage light bulb with socket, connecting wires, battery

### MiniLab (page 164)
graphing calculator or computer graphing program or graph paper and pencil, data table of molar heats of fusion and vaporization

### Demonstration (pages 166–167)
overhead projector, explosion shield, 600-mL beakers (3), phenolphthalein indicator, clear plastic wrap, wire screen (10 cm × 10 cm), small cubes (approximately 2 mm) of lithium, sodium, and potassium, water

## Preparation of Solutions

For a review of solution preparation, see page 46T of the Teacher Guide.

Quantities are for a class of 30 students.

**ChemLab (pages 170–171)**
  **1.0$M$ hydrochloric acid**  Add 25 mL concentrated (12$M$) hydrochloric acid to 275 mL distilled water while stirring. **CAUTION:** Do NOT add the water to the acid.

**Demonstration (pages 166–167)**
  **phenolphthalein indicator solution**  Dissolve 0.1 g phenolphthalein powder in 70 mL 95% ethanol. Make up to 100 mL final volume with distilled water.

## Assessment Resources

**Chapter Assessment,** pp. 31–36
**MindJogger Videoquizzes** DVD/VHS
**Alternate Assessment in the Science Classroom**
**ExamView® Pro CD-ROM**
**Solutions Manual,** Chapter 6
**Supplemental Problems,** Chapter 6
**Performance Assessment in the Science Classroom**
**Chemistry Interactive CD-ROM,** Chapter 6 quiz

## Additional Resources

**Spanish Resources** ELL
**Guided Reading Audio Program,** Chapter 6 ELL
**Cooperative Learning in the Science Classroom**
**Lab and Safety Skills in the Science Classroom**
**Lesson Plans**
**Block Scheduling Lesson Plans**
**Chemistrymc.com**

## Glencoe Technology

The following multimedia for this chapter are available from Glencoe.

**VIDEOTAPE/DVD**
MindJogger Videoquizzes,
Chapter 6

**CD-ROM**
**Chemistry: Matter and Change**
*The Periodic Table,* Exploration
*Transuranium Elements,* Video
*Activity of Alkali Metals,* Demonstration

**CD-ROM**
**ExamView® Pro**
**Testmaker**

**CD-ROM**
**Interactive Chalkboard**

**CD-ROM**
**TeacherWorks™**

## Multiple Learning Styles

Look for the following icons for strategies that emphasize different learning modalities.

*Kinesthetic*
Differentiated Instruction, pp. 156, 160; Quick Demo, p. 161

*Visual-Spatial*
Visual Learning, pp. 153, 154; Portfolio, p. 159; Check for Understanding, p. 161; Reteach, pp. 162, 169; Differentiated Instruction, p. 165; Math in Chemistry, p. 165

*Interpersonal*
Chemistry Journal, p. 157; Reteach, p. 158

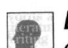
*Intrapersonal*
Differentiated Instruction, p. 153; Chemistry Journal, p. 168

*Linguistic*
Check for Understanding, p. 158; Chemistry Journal, p. 161

*Logical-Mathematical*
Math in Chemistry, p. 167

## Key to Teaching Strategies

**L1** Level 1 activities should be appropriate for students with learning difficulties.

**L2** Level 2 activities should be within the ability range of all students.

**L3** Level 3 activities are designed for above-average students.

**ELL** ELL activities should be within the ability range of English Language Learners.

**COOP LEARN** Cooperative Learning activities are designed for small group work.

**P** These strategies represent student products that can be placed into a best-work portfolio.

These strategies are useful in a block scheduling format.

## Assessment Planner

**Portfolio Assessment**
Portfolio, TWE, pp. 159, 173
Assessment, TWE, p. 161

**Performance Assessment**
Assessment, TWE, p. 166
ChemLab, SE, pp. 170–171
Discovery Lab, SE, p. 151
MiniLab, SE, p. 164
Problem-Solving Lab, TWE, p. 155
MiniLab, TWE, p. 164

**Knowledge Assessment**
Assessment, TWE, p. 156
Section Assessment, SE, pp. 158, 162, 169
Chapter Assessment, SE, pp. 174–177
Demonstration, TWE, p. 167

**Skill Assessment**
Assessment, TWE, pp. 158, 162, 169
ChemLab, TWE, p. 171

**CHAPTER**  6

## Tying to Previous Knowledge

Have students review the following concepts before studying this chapter.
Chapter 4: atomic structure
Chapter 5: electron configurations, valence electrons, electron-dot structures

## Using the Photo

Ask students to estimate the period of each of the two periodic events shown in the photo—the tides and the phases of the Moon. The Moon cycles through its phases in approximately 29.5 days. Two high tides and two low tides occur every 24 hours in most locations.

## Chapter Themes

The following themes from the National Science Education Standards are covered in this chapter. Refer to page 4T of the Teacher Guide for an explanation of the correlations.
Systems, order, and organization (UCP.1)
Evidence, models, and explanation (UCP.2)
Form and function (UCP.5)

**PowerPoint® Presentations**
This CD-ROM is an editable Microsoft® PowerPoint® presentation that includes:
• Section presentations
• Section checks
• Image bank
• Links to Chemistry Online
• All transparencies
• Animations
• Audio

**150**

# The Periodic Table and Periodic Law

### What You'll Learn
▶ You will explain why elements in a group have similar properties.
▶ You will relate the group and period trends seen in the periodic table to the electron configuration of atoms.
▶ You will identify the s-, p-, d-, and f-blocks of the periodic table.

### Why It's Important
The periodic table is the single most powerful chemistry reference tool available to you. Understanding its organization and interpreting its data will greatly aid you in your study of chemistry.

**Chemistry Online**
Visit the Chemistry Web site at chemistrymc.com to find links about the periodic table and periodic law.

The phases of the moon and the cycle of ocean tides are both periodic events, that is, they repeat in a regular manner.

## DISCOVERY LAB

**Purpose** P
Students will observe several characteristics of metals that make them versatile.

**Safety and Disposal**
Warn students to exercise caution when bending the copper samples, as they may have sharp edges that could cause cuts.

**Teaching Strategies**
• Form sets of the following types of copper samples: wires of different gauges, round shot, flat strips, granules, and shiny and dull pennies. If all of these are not available, use whatever kinds of copper samples you can find.
• Have as many samples of copper available as possible. Remind students to bend samples gently so that they do not break. Review the terms *ductile* (drawn into wire) and *malleable* (bendable).

## Versatile Metals

A variety of processes can be used to shape metals into different forms. Because of their physical properties, metals are used in a wide range of applications.

### Safety Precautions

 Be careful when bending the copper samples, as they may have sharp edges.

### Procedure

1. Observe the different types of copper metal that your teacher gives you. Write down as many observations as you can about each of the copper samples.

2. Try gently bending each copper sample (do not break the samples). Record your observations.

3. Connect each copper sample to the circuit as shown in the photo. Record your observations.

### Analysis

What properties of copper are similar in all of the samples? How do the samples of copper differ? List several common applications of copper. What properties make metals such as copper so versatile?

**Materials**

tape
samples of copper
light socket with bulb, wires, and battery

# 1 Focus

Before presenting the lesson, display **Section Focus Transparency 20** on the overhead projector. Have students answer the accompanying questions using **Section Focus Transparency Master 20.** L1 ELL

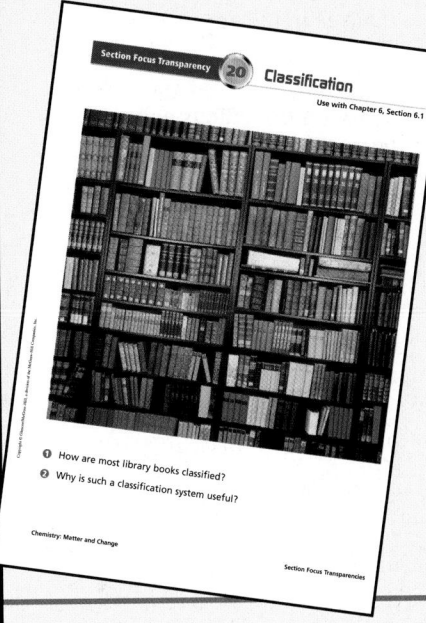

Section Focus Transparency 20 **Classification**
Use with Chapter 6, Section 6.1

❶ How are most library books classified?
❷ Why is such a classification system useful?

Chemistry: Matter and Change

Section Focus Transparencies

# Development of the Modern Periodic Table

## Objectives

• **Trace** the development and **identify** key features of the periodic table.

## Vocabulary

periodic law
group
period
representative element
transition element
metal
alkali metal
alkaline earth metal
transition metal
inner transition metal
nonmetal
halogen
noble gas
metalloid

You have already learned much in your study of chemistry. Wouldn't it be nice if you could easily organize the chemistry knowledge you are acquiring? You can, with the help of the *periodic* table. It is called a periodic table because, much like the phases of the moon, one of which is shown in the chapter opening photo, the properties of the elements in the table repeat in a periodic way. The periodic table will be an invaluable tool as you continue this course in chemistry. However, before you learn about the modern periodic table, a recounting of the history behind the table's development will help you understand its significance.

## History of the Periodic Table's Development

In the late 1790s, French scientist Antoine Lavoisier compiled a list of elements known at the time. The list contained 23 elements. Many of these elements, such as silver, gold, carbon, and oxygen, were known since prehistoric times. The 1800s brought many changes to the world, including an explosion in the number of known elements. The advent of electricity, which was used to break compounds down into their component elements, and the development of the spectrometer, which was used to identify the newly isolated elements, played major roles in the advancement of chemistry. So did the industrial revolution

## Expected Results

Observations should include color (orange-red); descriptions of shapes; that all shapes are bendable except penny and shot; and that all samples conduct electricity.

## Analysis

All samples are hard, shiny, conduct electricity, and similar in color (though some may be duller than others). Except for the shot and the penny, all the samples can be bent fairly easily. The samples differ primarily in shape and surface texture. Copper wires are often used to transmit electricity and copper coatings are often used in cookware. Metals are very versatile because of their malleability, ductility, strength, and good thermal and electrical conductivity.

### Resource Manager

**Study Guide for Content Mastery,** pp. 31–32 L2
**Section Focus Transparency 20 and Master** L1 ELL
**Solving Problems: A Chemistry Handbook,** Section 6.1 L2

**National Science Content Standards**

**Pages 150-151**
UCP.1, UCP.2, UCP.5; A.1; B.1, B.2; G.3

**Figure 6-1**

A resident of London, England invented the word smog to describe the city's filthy air, a combination of smoke and natural fog. The quality of London's air became so poor that in 1952 about 4000 Londoners died during a four-day period. This incident led to the passage of England's Clean Air Act in 1956.

Go to the **Chemistry Interactive CD-ROM** to find additional resources for this chapter.

## Astronomy
### CONNECTION

The element technetium does not occur naturally on Earth. It has been found in stars. Astronomers analyze the chemical composition of stellar matter by using an instrument called a spectroscope, which separates the light from a star into individual colors, much as a prism does. Although each star has a unique composition of elements, all stars are composed mainly of the gases hydrogen and helium. The Sun, for example, is estimated to be about 70 percent hydrogen and 28 percent helium. A tiny fraction of a star's mass may come from heavier elements such as oxygen, carbon, nitrogen, calcium, or sodium. Two percent of our Sun's mass comes from these heavier elements.

of the mid-1800s, which led to the development of many new chemistry-based industries, such as the manufacture of petrochemicals, soaps, dyes, and fertilizers. By 1870, there were approximately 70 known elements—almost triple the number known in Lavoisier's time. As you can see in **Figure 6-1,** the industrial revolution also created problems, such as increased chemical pollution.

Along with the discovery of new elements came volumes of new scientific data related to the elements and their compounds. Chemists of the time were overwhelmed with learning the properties of so many new elements and compounds. What chemists needed was a tool for organizing the many facts associated with the elements. A significant step toward this goal came in 1860, when chemists agreed upon a method for accurately determining the atomic masses of the elements. Until this time, different chemists used different mass values in their work, making the results of one chemist's work hard to reproduce by another. With newly agreed upon atomic masses for the elements, the search for relationships between atomic mass and elemental properties began in earnest.

**John Newlands** In 1864, English chemist John Newlands (1837–1898), who is shown in **Figure 6-2,** proposed an organization scheme for the elements. Newlands noticed that when the elements were arranged by increasing atomic mass, their properties repeated every eighth element. In other words, the first and eighth elements had similar properties, the second and ninth elements had similar properties, and so on. A pattern such as this is called periodic because it repeats in a specific manner. Newlands named the periodic relationship that he observed in chemical properties the law of octaves, because an octave is a group of musical notes that repeats every eighth tone. **Figure 6-2** also shows how Newlands organized the first 14 "known" elements (as of the mid-1860s). If you compare Newlands's arrangement of the elements with the modern periodic table on the inside back cover of your textbook, you'll see that some of his rows correspond to columns on the modern periodic table. Acceptance of the law of octaves was hampered because the law did not work for all of the known elements. Also, unfortunately for Newlands, the use of the word octave was harshly criticized by fellow scientists who thought that the musical analogy was unscientific. While Newlands's law was not generally accepted, the passage of a few years would show that he was basically correct; the properties of elements do repeat in a periodic way.

**Meyer, Mendeleev, and Moseley** In 1869, German chemist Lothar Meyer (1830–1895) and Russian chemist Dmitri Mendeleev (1834–1907) each demonstrated a connection between atomic mass and elemental properties. Mendeleev, however, is generally given more credit than Meyer because he published his organization scheme first and went on to better demonstrate its usefulness. Like Newlands several years earlier, Mendeleev noticed that when the elements were ordered by increasing atomic mass, there was a repetition, or periodic pattern, in their properties. By arranging the elements in order of increasing atomic mass into columns with similar properties, Mendeleev organized the elements into the first periodic table. Mendeleev and part of his periodic table are shown in **Figure 6-3.** Part of the reason Mendeleev's table was widely accepted was that he predicted the existence and properties of undiscovered elements. Mendeleev left blank spaces in the table where he thought the undiscovered elements should go. By noting trends in the properties of known elements, he was able to predict the properties of the yet-to-be discovered elements scandium, gallium, and germanium.

---

## Internet Address Book

**Chemistry Online**    Note Internet addresses that you find useful in the space below for quick reference.

_____

_____

_____

_____

_____

**Elements with similar properties are in the same row**

| | | | | | |
|---|---|---|---|---|---|
| A | **H** | 1 | A | **F** | 8 — and so on → |
| B | **Li** | 2 | B | **Na** | 9 → |
| C | **G** | 3 | C | **Mg** | 10 → |
| D | **Bo** | 4 | D | **Al** | 11 → |
| E | **C** | 5 | E | **Si** | 12 → |
| F | **N** | 6 | F | **P** | 13 → |
| G | **O** | 7 | G | **S** | 14 → |

1 octave

**Figure 6-2**

John Newlands noticed that the properties of elements repeated in a manner similar to an octave on a musical scale (A, B, C, D, E, F, G, A, and so on). While there are some similarities between the law of octaves and the modern periodic table, there also are significant differences. You'll notice that some of the chemical symbols do not match. For example, beryllium (Be) was also known as glucinum (G). What similarities and differences can you identify?

## Quick Demo

Randomly display about 30 stock bottles of elements and compounds. Ask students whether such an arrangement facilitates being able to locate a particular substance. Have students suggest better ways to arrange the substances.

## Figure Caption Question

**Figure 6-2** What similarities and differences can you identify?
similarities: elements arranged in groups with repeating properties; properties repeat every eight elements (elements with atomic numbers ≤ 20)
differences: columns and rows are interchanged; element names differ

## Visual Learning

*Visual-Spatial* Have your class create a classroom periodic table that describes the characteristics of each of the students. Each student will be a cell in the classroom periodic table. Provide each student with a one-foot square poster board. In the center of the square, each student should write his or her two-letter student symbol (capped initial of last name followed by lower-case initial of first name). Pick student-based characteristics such as shoe size, hair color, sports interest, favorite school subject, etc. Define a location on the card for each characteristic. Have each student complete his or her card; then, have the class determine an appropriate method for organizing the squares, so that, if possible, a periodic pattern is developed. **L2** **ELL**

Mendeleev's table, however, was not completely correct. After several new elements were discovered and atomic masses of the known elements were more accurately determined, it became apparent that several elements in his table were not in the correct order. Arranging the elements by mass resulted in several elements being placed in groups of elements with differing properties. The reason for this problem was determined in 1913 by English chemist Henry Moseley. As you may recall from Chapter 4, Moseley discovered that atoms of each element contain a unique number of protons in their nuclei—the number of protons being equal to the atom's atomic number. By arranging the elements in order of increasing atomic number instead of increasing atomic mass, as Mendeleev had done, the problems with the order of the elements in the periodic table were solved. Moseley's arrangement of elements by atomic number resulted in a clear periodic pattern of properties. The statement that there is a periodic repetition of chemical and physical properties of the elements when they are arranged by increasing atomic number is called the **periodic law.**

**Figure 6-3**

Dmitri Mendeleev produced the first useful and widely accepted periodic table. The monument shown on the right is located in St. Petersburg, Russia, and shows an early version of Mendeleev's periodic table. The blank areas on the table show the positions of elements that had not yet been discovered.

6.1 Development of the Modern Periodic Table **153**

**DIFFERENTIATED INSTRUCTION**

## Gifted

*Intrapersonal* Mendeleev predicted properties of several elements that had not been discovered at the time he published his periodic table. Provide students with several of the properties he predicted and have them research the properties of the actual element that was discovered. One example is *ekasilicon,* which was named gallium once it was discovered.

Mendeleev predicted that ekasilicon would have an atomic mass of 68 amu, a low melting point, a density of 5.9 g/cm³, and an oxide formula of $Ea_2O_3$. Have students research the actual properties of gallium and evaluate how close Mendeleev's predictions were to the actual properties. Ask students what they think the prefix *eka-* means. **L3**

## National Science Content Standards

Pages 152-153
UCP.1, UCP.2, UCP.5; A.2; B.2; G.1, G.2, G.3

## Visual Learning

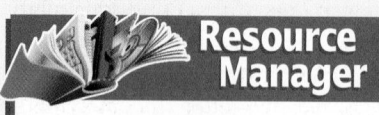 **Visual-Spatial** Provide students with a list of element names and their dates of discovery, or have students research these dates. Give each student a set of colored pencils and a basic periodic table that contains only element names or symbols. Have students color each of the following sets of elements a different color.

- elements known by the year 100
- elements discovered from 101 to 1600
- elements discovered from 1601 to 1799
- elements discovered from 1800 through the time Mendeleev published his first periodic table (~1870)
- elements discovered from 1871 to 1980
- elements discovered since 1981

**L2** **ELL**

## In-Text Questions

**Page 154** What group is oxygen in? 6A What period contains potassium and calcium? 4

**Resource Manager**

Teaching Transparency 18 and Master **L2** **ELL**

**National Science Content Standards**

**Pages 154-155**
UCP.1, UCP.2, UCP.5; B.1, B.2; G.2

**154**

PERIODIC TABLE OF THE ELEMENTS

**Figure 6-4**

The modern periodic table arranges the elements by increasing atomic number. The columns are known as groups or families, and the rows are known as periods.

**Figure 6-5**

A typical box from the periodic table contains important information about an element.

The periodic table became a significant tool for chemists working in the new industries created during the industrial revolution. The table brought order to seemingly unrelated facts. You, too, will find the periodic table a valuable tool. Among other things, it is a useful reference for understanding and predicting the properties of elements and for organizing your knowledge of atomic structure. Do the **problem-solving LAB** on the next page to see how the periodic law can be used to predict unknown elemental properties.

## The Modern Periodic Table

The modern periodic table is shown in **Figure 6-4** and on the inside back cover of your textbook. A larger, two-page version of the table appears in **Figure 6-7** on pages 156-157. The table consists of boxes, each containing an element name, symbol, atomic number, and atomic mass. A typical box from the table is shown in **Figure 6-5.** The boxes are arranged in order of increasing atomic number into a series of columns, called **groups** or families, and rows, called **periods.** Beginning with hydrogen in period 1, there are a total of seven periods. Each group is numbered 1 through 8, followed by the letter A or B. For example, scandium (Sc) is in the third column from the left, group 3B. What group is oxygen in? What period contains potassium and calcium? The groups designated with an A (1A through 8A) are often referred to as the main group, or **representative elements** because they possess a wide range of chemical and physical properties. The groups designated with a B (1B through 8B) are referred to as the **transition elements.** A more recent numbering system, which uses the numbers 1 through 18, also appears above each group. The number-and-letter system is used throughout this textbook.

## CULTURAL DIVERSITY

### International Tables

Collect periodic tables from a variety of countries, such as Japan, Russia, Germany, Spain, and Mexico. Display these periodic tables and have students examine them for similarities and differences. For example, a Japanese periodic table uses the same symbol (Na) for sodium as an English table, but the element name is written in Kanji or Japanese calligraphy. If time permits, have students further investigate how the English translation for the element name compares to the English name for the element. While there are alternative forms of the periodic table, students will find that the shape of the periodic table is relatively universal.

**Classifying the elements** There are three main classifications for the elements—metals, nonmetals, and metalloids. **Metals** are elements that are generally shiny when smooth and clean, solid at room temperature, and good conductors of heat and electricity. Most metals also are malleable and ductile, meaning that they can be pounded into thin sheets and drawn into wires, respectively. **Figure 6-6** shows several applications that make use of the physical properties of metals.

Most group A elements and all group B elements are metals. If you look at boron (B) in column 3A, you see a heavy stair-step line that zigzags down to astatine (At) at the bottom of group 7A. This stair-step line serves as a visual divider between the metals and the nonmetals on the table. Metals are represented by the light blue boxes in **Figure 6-7**. Except for hydrogen, all of the elements on the left side of the table are metals. The group 1A elements (except for hydrogen) are known as the **alkali metals;** the group 2A elements are known as the **alkaline earth metals.** Both the alkali metals and the alkaline earth metals are chemically reactive, with the alkali metals being the more reactive of the two groups.

**Try at Home LAB**

See page 954 in Appendix E for **Turning up the Heat**

**Figure 6-6**

Metals are used in a wide variety of applications. The excellent electrical conductivity of metals such as copper, makes them a good choice for transmitting electrical power. Ductility and malleability allow metals to be formed into coins, tools, fasteners, and wires.

## problem-solving LAB

### Francium—solid, liquid or gas?

**Predicting** Of the first 101 elements, francium is the least stable. Its most stable isotope has a half-life of just 22 minutes! Use your knowledge about the properties of other alkali metals to predict some of francium's properties.

**Analysis**

In the spirit of Dimitri Mendeleev's prediction of the properties of several, as of then, undiscovered elements, use the given information about the known properties of the alkali metals to devise a method for determining the corresponding property of francium.

**Thinking Critically**

1. Using the periodic law as a guide, devise an approach that clearly displays the trends for each of the properties given in the table and allows you to extrapolate a value for francium.

2. Predict whether francium is a solid, liquid, or gas. How can you support your prediction?

| **Alkali Metals Data** | | | |
|---|---|---|---|
| Element | Melting point (°C) | Boiling point (°C) | Radius (pm) |
| lithium | 180.5 | 1347 | 152 |
| sodium | 97.8 | 897 | 186 |
| potassium | 63.3 | 766 | 227 |
| rubidium | 39.31 | 688 | 248 |
| cesium | 28.4 | 674.8 | 265 |
| francium | ? | ? | ? |

3. Which of the given columns of data presents the greatest possible error in making a prediction? Explain.

4. Currently, scientists can produce about one million francium atoms per second. Explain why this is still not enough to make basic measurements such as density or melting point.

## problem-solving LAB

**Purpose**

Students will use the periodic law to determine the melting point, boiling point, and heat of vaporization of francium.

**Process Skills**

Predicting, identifying variables, making and using graphs, interpreting data, observing and inferring, applying concepts

**Teaching Strategies**

• Review the periodic law and ask students how the law can be used to predict the melting point, boiling point, and heat of vaporization of francium. By plotting a graph of these properties versus atomic number for the known alkali metals, francium's values can be extrapolated from the graph.

• Explain why there is so little francium in Earth's crust. Francium-223 is the only naturally occurring isotope of the element. It is produced from the alpha decay of actinium-227, which itself is produced from the decay of uranium-238. For one ton of U-238, only 0.2 mg of Ac-227 is formed. Ac-227, with a half-life of 22 years, produces only $3.8 \times 10^{-10}$ g of Fr-223. The unstable Fr-223 decays very quickly, having a half-life of only 22 minutes.

**Thinking Critically**

1. A graph of each property versus atomic number is the best approach. See the Solutions Manual. By extending the data curve through to francium's atomic number of 87, its radius, melting point, and boiling point can be determined. R ≈ 280–290 pm, MP ≈ 25°C, and BP ≈ 675°C.

2. Francium is probably a liquid at room temperature. Its melting point is probably below 20°C, according to the trend shown in the table.

3. The radius prediction is most inaccurate. The affect of the principal energy level on the radius is harder to extrapolate accurately because it varies from period to period.

4. Even one million atoms collected together as a solid are microscopic. A grain of salt contains about $10^{15}$ sodium atoms.

### ✓ Assessment

**Performance** Give students another characteristic property, such as heat of vaporization, and have them predict francium's value. Use the Performance Task Assessment List for Making Observations and Inferences in **PASC**, p. 17. **L2**

**Knowledge** Point out that the placement of several pairs of elements on Mendeleev's table were incorrect. Argon and potassium are one pair whose correct positions were reversed. Ask students to suggest reasons why Mendeleev used atomic mass instead atomic number to organize the elements. The property of atomic number was not discovered until the early 1900s, thus making it impossible for Mendeleev to base his periodic table on it. **L2**

**Figure 6-7**

# PERIODIC TABLE OF THE ELEMENTS

| Element | → Hydrogen |
| Atomic number | → 1 | → State of matter |
| Symbol | → H |
| Atomic mass | → 1.008 |

Gas
Liquid
Solid
Synthetic

**1A** 1

**2A** 2

**3B** 3
**4B** 4
**5B** 5
**6B** 6
**7B** 7
**8B** 8   9

| Period | 1A | 2A | 3B | 4B | 5B | 6B | 7B | 8B | |
|---|---|---|---|---|---|---|---|---|---|
| 1 | Hydrogen 1 H 1.008 | | | | | | | | |
| 2 | Lithium 3 Li 6.941 | Beryllium 4 Be 9.012 | | | | | | | |
| 3 | Sodium 11 Na 22.990 | Magnesium 12 Mg 24.305 | | | | | | | |
| 4 | Potassium 19 K 39.098 | Calcium 20 Ca 40.078 | Scandium 21 Sc 44.956 | Titanium 22 Ti 47.867 | Vanadium 23 V 50.942 | Chromium 24 Cr 51.996 | Manganese 25 Mn 54.938 | Iron 26 Fe 55.845 | Cobalt 27 Co 58.933 |
| 5 | Rubidium 37 Rb 85.468 | Strontium 38 Sr 87.62 | Yttrium 39 Y 88.906 | Zirconium 40 Zr 91.224 | Niobium 41 Nb 92.906 | Molybdenum 42 Mo 95.94 | Technetium 43 Tc (98) | Ruthenium 44 Ru 101.07 | Rhodium 45 Rh 102.906 |
| 6 | Cesium 55 Cs 132.905 | Barium 56 Ba 137.327 | Lanthanum 57 La 138.906 | Hafnium 72 Hf 178.49 | Tantalum 73 Ta 180.948 | Tungsten 74 W 183.84 | Rhenium 75 Re 186.207 | Osmium 76 Os 190.23 | Iridium 77 Ir 192.217 |
| 7 | Francium 87 Fr (223) | Radium 88 Ra (226) | Actinium 89 Ac (227) | Rutherfordium 104 Rf (261) | Dubnium 105 Db (262) | Seaborgium 106 Sg (266) | Bohrium 107 Bh (264) | Hassium 108 Hs (277) | Meitnerium 109 Mt (268) |

The number in parentheses is the mass number of the longest lived isotope for that element.

**Lanthanide series**

| Cerium 58 Ce 140.116 | Praseodymium 59 Pr 140.908 | Neodymium 60 Nd 144.24 | Promethium 61 Pm (145) | Samarium 62 Sm 150.36 | Europium 63 Eu 151.964 |
|---|---|---|---|---|---|

**Actinide series**

| Thorium 90 Th 232.038 | Protactinium 91 Pa 231.036 | Uranium 92 U 238.029 | Neptunium 93 Np (237) | Plutonium 94 Pu (244) | Americium 95 Am (243) |
|---|---|---|---|---|---|

## DIFFERENTIATED INSTRUCTION

### English Language Learners

**Kinesthetic** Have students create a dot-to-dot puzzle using chemical symbols as clues. Draw the outline of a piece of lab equipment, a lab setup, or some other chemistry-related picture using a dark felt tip marker. Place another sheet of paper over the first and mark dots along the image, especially at critical direction changes. Label the dots with chemical symbols instead of by number. The atomic number of each chemical symbol represents the number of each dot (H is 1, He is 2, Li is 3, etc.). Students should exchange and complete each other's puzzles. **L2** **ELL**

## Chemistry Online

Visit the Chemistry Web site at
chemistrymc.com to find
updates on the periodic table.

**Legend (cube key):**
- Metal
- Metalloid
- Nonmetal
- Recently discovered

| | | 3A 13 | 4A 14 | 5A 15 | 6A 16 | 7A 17 | 8A 18 |
|---|---|---|---|---|---|---|---|
| | | | | | | | Helium 2 **He** 4.003 |
| | | Boron 5 **B** 10.811 | Carbon 6 **C** 12.011 | Nitrogen 7 **N** 14.007 | Oxygen 8 **O** 15.999 | Fluorine 9 **F** 18.998 | Neon 10 **Ne** 20.180 |

| 10 | 1B 11 | 2B 12 | Aluminum 13 **Al** 26.982 | Silicon 14 **Si** 28.086 | Phosphorus 15 **P** 30.974 | Sulfur 16 **S** 32.065 | Chlorine 17 **Cl** 35.453 | Argon 18 **Ar** 39.948 |
|---|---|---|---|---|---|---|---|---|
| Nickel 28 **Ni** 58.693 | Copper 29 **Cu** 63.546 | Zinc 30 **Zn** 65.39 | Gallium 31 **Ga** 69.723 | Germanium 32 **Ge** 72.64 | Arsenic 33 **As** 74.922 | Selenium 34 **Se** 78.96 | Bromine 35 **Br** 79.904 | Krypton 36 **Kr** 83.80 |
| Palladium 46 **Pd** 106.42 | Silver 47 **Ag** 107.868 | Cadmium 48 **Cd** 112.411 | Indium 49 **In** 114.818 | Tin 50 **Sn** 118.710 | Antimony 51 **Sb** 121.760 | Tellurium 52 **Te** 127.60 | Iodine 53 **I** 126.904 | Xenon 54 **Xe** 131.293 |
| Platinum 78 **Pt** 195.078 | Gold 79 **Au** 196.967 | Mercury 80 **Hg** 200.59 | Thallium 81 **Tl** 204.383 | Lead 82 **Pb** 207.2 | Bismuth 83 **Bi** 208.980 | Polonium 84 **Po** (209) | Astatine 85 **At** (210) | Radon 86 **Rn** (222) |
| Darmstadtium 110 **Ds** (281) | * Unununium 111 **Uuu** (272) | * Ununbium 112 **Uub** (285) | | * Ununquadium 114 **Uuq** (289) | | | | |

* Names not officially assigned. Discovery of element 114 recently reported. Further information not yet available.

| Gadolinium 64 **Gd** 157.25 | Terbium 65 **Tb** 158.925 | Dysprosium 66 **Dy** 162.50 | Holmium 67 **Ho** 164.930 | Erbium 68 **Er** 167.259 | Thulium 69 **Tm** 168.934 | Ytterbium 70 **Yb** 173.04 | Lutetium 71 **Lu** 174.967 |
|---|---|---|---|---|---|---|---|
| Curium 96 **Cm** (247) | Berkelium 97 **Bk** (247) | Californium 98 **Cf** (251) | Einsteinium 99 **Es** (252) | Fermium 100 **Fm** (257) | Mendelevium 101 **Md** (258) | Nobelium 102 **No** (259) | Lawrencium 103 **Lr** (262) |

## Applying Chemistry

**TECH PREP**

Gemstones often owe their color to atoms of transition elements that are substituted into a crystal structure. For example, consider the mineral corundum ($Al_2O_3$). If chromium atoms replace a few aluminum atoms in the crystal structure, the resulting crystal has a brilliant red color. This crystal is the gemstone known as a ruby. The substitution of iron atoms results in the gemstone known as topaz. The substitution of titanium atoms results in a sapphire. Another example occurs in the mineral known as beryl ($Be_3Al_2Si_6O_{18}$). If a few of the aluminum atoms in the crystal are replaced with chromium atoms, the result is a brilliant green emerald. The substitution of one atom for another occurs because the atoms have similar atomic radii and valence electrons.

## CHEMISTRY JOURNAL

### Student News Correspondents

**Interpersonal** Have students pretend they are newspaper reporters and their assignment is to interview Mendeleev and Moseley. They should conduct some background research in order to be effective reporters. In addition to asking about their subjects' respective chemical discoveries, suggest that some of the interview questions relate to the subjects' experiences during the time period in which they lived, their educational backgrounds, and the countries in which they lived. **L2**

**National Science Content Standards**

**Pages 156-157**
UCP.1, UCP.2, UCP.5; B.1, B.2; E.2

## Check for Understanding

 *Linguistic* Have students write a paragraph using each of the vocabulary words listed for the section. **L2**

## Reteach

*Interpersonal* Pair students. Have one student select an element that the other student must classify using the terms introduced in this section. Have students reverse roles so that both students have the opportunity to respond. **L2** **COOP LEARN**

## Extension

Have students predict the properties for element 117. They should offer supporting reasons for their predictions. **L2**

**CHEMLAB**

ChemLab 6, located at the end of the chapter, can be used at this point in the lesson.

**✓ Assessment**

**Skill** Display samples of elements that represent metals, nonmetals, and metalloids. Have students record their observations of each sample and classify it as a metal, nonmetal, or metalloid. If possible, students should identify each element and state its group. **L2**

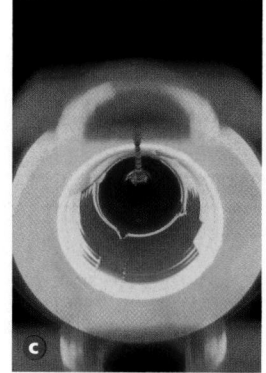

**Figure 6-8**

**a** A mountain climber breathes from a container of compressed oxygen gas, a nonmetal. **b** This Persian brass bowl contains inlays of the transition metals silver and gold. **c** Silicon crystals, a metalloid, are grown in an inert atmosphere of argon, a nonmetal. The crystals are used in the manufacture of computer chips.

The group B elements, or transition elements, are divided into **transition metals** and **inner transition metals.** The two sets of inner transition metals, known as the lanthanide and actinide series, are located along the bottom of the periodic table. The rest of the group B elements make up the transition metals. Elements from the lanthanide series are used extensively as phosphors, substances that emit light when struck by electrons. The **How It Works** at the end of the chapter explains more about phosphors and how images are formed on a television screen.

Nonmetals occupy the upper right side of the periodic table. They are represented by the yellow boxes in **Figure 6-7. Nonmetals** are elements that are generally gases or brittle, dull-looking solids. They are poor conductors of heat and electricity. The only nonmetal that is a liquid at room temperature is bromine (Br). The highly reactive group 7A elements are known as **halogens,** and the extremely unreactive group 8A elements are commonly called the **noble gases.**

Examine the elements in green boxes bordering the stair-step line in **Figure 6-7.** These elements are called metalloids, or semimetals. **Metalloids** are elements with physical and chemical properties of both metals and nonmetals. Silicon and germanium are two of the most important metalloids, as they are used extensively in computer chips and solar cells. Applications that make use of the properties of nonmetals, transition metals, and metalloids are shown in **Figure 6-8.** Do the **CHEMLAB** at the end of this chapter to observe trends among various elements.

This introduction to the periodic table only touches the surface of its usefulness. In the next section, you will discover how an element's electron configuration, which you learned about in Chapter 5, is related to its position on the periodic table.

## Section 6.1 Assessment

1. Describe the development of the modern periodic table. Include contributions made by Lavoisier, Newlands, Mendeleev, and Moseley.

2. Sketch a simplified version of the periodic table and indicate the location of groups, periods, metals, nonmetals, and metalloids.

3. Describe the general characteristics of metals, nonmetals, and metalloids.

4. Identify each of the following as a representative element or a transition element.
   **a.** lithium (Li)       **c.** promethium (Pm)
   **b.** platinum (Pt)      **d.** carbon (C)

5. **Thinking Critically** For each of the given elements, list two other elements with similar chemical properties.
   **a.** iodine (I)
   **b.** barium (Ba)
   **c.** iron (Fe)

6. **Interpreting Data** An unknown element has chemical behavior similar to that of silicon (Si) and lead (Pb). The unknown element has a mass greater than that of sulfur (S), but less than that of cadmium (Cd). Use the periodic table to determine the identity of the unknown element.

## Section 6.1 Assessment

1. Newlands was the first to organize the elements and show that properties repeated in a periodic way. Mendeleev and Meyer proposed periodic tables showing a relationship between atomic mass and elemental properties. Moseley orga-

nized the elements by atomic number instead of atomic mass.

2. Simplified tables should resemble Figure 6-7 with the groups and periods labeled. See the Solutions Manual.

3. metals: shiny, ductile, malleable, good conductors of heat and electricity; nonmetals: dull, brittle, poor

conductors of heat and electricity; metalloids: properties midway between metals and nonmetals

4. **a.** representative; **b.** transition; **c.** transition; **d.** representative

5. **a.** any other group 7A element; **b.** any other group 2A element; **c.** any other group 8B element

6. germanium (Ge)

In Chapter 5, you learned how to write the electron configuration for an atom. This is an important skill because the electron configuration determines the chemical properties of the element. However, the process of writing out electron configurations using the aufbau diagram can be tedious. Fortunately, by noting an atom's position on the periodic table, you can determine its electron configuration and its number of valence electrons.

## Organizing the Elements by Electron Configuration

Take a look at the electron configurations for the group 1A elements listed below. These elements comprise the first four periods of group 1A.

| Period 1 | hydrogen | $1s^1$ | $1s^1$ |
| Period 2 | lithium | $1s^22s^1$ | $[He]2s^1$ |
| Period 3 | sodium | $1s^22s^22p^63s^1$ | $[Ne]3s^1$ |
| Period 4 | potassium | $1s^22s^22p^63s^23p^64s^1$ | $[Ar]4s^1$ |

What do the four configurations have in common? The answer is that they all have a single electron in their outermost energy level.

**Valence electrons** Recall from Chapter 5 that electrons in the highest principal energy level of an atom are called valence electrons. Each of the group 1A elements has one electron in its highest energy level; thus, each element has one valence electron. This is no coincidence. The group 1A elements have similar chemical properties because they all have the same number of valence electrons. This is one of the most important relationships in chemistry; *atoms in the same group have similar chemical properties because they have the same number of valence electrons.* Each group 1A element has a valence electron configuration of $s^1$. Likewise, each group 2A element has a valence electron configuration of $s^2$. Each column of group A elements on the periodic table has its own unique valence electron configuration.

**Valence electrons and period** The energy level of an element's valence electrons indicates the period on the periodic table in which it is found. For example, lithium's valence electron is in the second energy level and lithium is found in period 2. Now look at gallium, with its electron configuration of $[Ar]4s^23d^{10}4p^1$. Gallium's valence electrons are in the fourth energy level, and gallium is found in the fourth period. What is the electron configuration for the group 1A element in the sixth period?

**Valence electrons and group number** A representative element's group number and the number of valence electrons it contains also are related. Group 1A elements have one valence electron, group 2A elements have two valence electrons, and so on. There are several exceptions to this rule, however. The noble gases in group 8A each have eight valence electrons, with the exception of helium, which has only two valence electrons. Also, the group number rule applies only to the representative elements (the group A elements). See **Figure 6-9** on the next page. The electron-dot structures you learned in Chapter 5 illustrate the connection between group number and number of valence electrons.

## Objectives

- **Explain** why elements in the same group have similar properties.

- **Identify** the four blocks of the periodic table based on electron configuration.

**Chemistry Online**

**Topic: Alternate Periodic Tables**

To learn more about alternate periodic tables, visit the Chemistry Web site at chemistrymc.com

**Activity:** Research periodic tables that differ from the standard periodic table on pages 156–157. List three alternate versions of the standard periodic table and describe their differences.

## 1 Focus

**Focus Transparency**

Before presenting the lesson, display **Section Focus Transparency 21** on the overhead projector. Have students answer the accompanying questions using **Section Focus Transparency Master 21.** L1 ELL

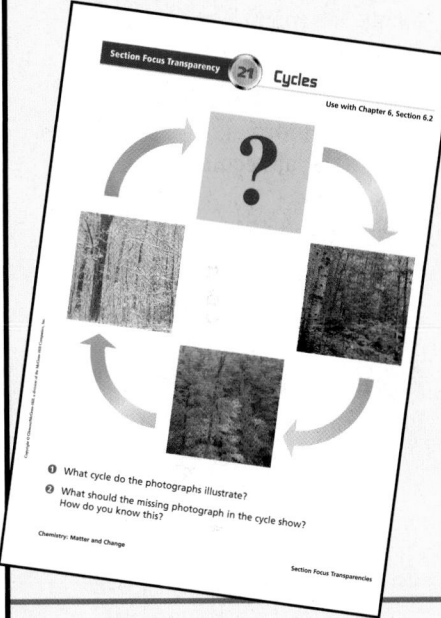

## 2 Teach
### Concept Development

Emphasize that electron configuration is a periodic trend and that it determines an element's chemical properties.

### In-Text Question

**Page 159** What is the electron configuration for the group 1A element in the sixth period? $[Xe]6s^1$

---

**Portfolio**

### Time Line Comparisons

*Visual-Spatial* Have students create a time line that includes all of the people discussed in Chapters 5 and 6 and their contributions to chemistry. Students should then pick another topic, such as famous inventions, to plot on the time line. Have them compare the events on the time line and look for ways in which they may be related. They should place the time lines in their portfolios. L2 ELL P

**GLENCOE**
**TECHNOLOGY**

CD-ROM
**Chemistry: Matter and Change**
Experiment: *Classify the Elements*

# The s-, p-, d-, and f-Block Elements

The periodic table has columns and rows of varying sizes. The reason behind the table's odd shape becomes clear if it is divided into sections, or blocks, representing the atom's energy sublevel being filled with valence electrons. Because there are four different energy sublevels (s, p, d, and f), the periodic table is divided into four distinct blocks, as shown in **Figure 6-10.**

**s-block elements** The s-block consists of groups 1A and 2A, and the elements hydrogen and helium. In this block, the valence electrons, represented in **Figure 6-9,** occupy only s orbitals. Group 1A elements have partially filled s orbitals containing one valence electron and electron configurations ending in $s^1$. Group 2A elements have completely filled s orbitals containing two valence electrons and electron configurations ending in $s^2$. Because s orbitals hold a maximum of two electrons, the s-block portion of the periodic table spans two groups.

**p-block elements** After the s sublevel is filled, the valence electrons, represented in **Figure 6-9,** next occupy the p sublevel and its three p orbitals. The p-block of the periodic table, comprised of groups 3A through 8A, contains elements with filled or partially filled p orbitals. Why are there no p-block elements in period 1? The answer is that the p sublevel does not exist for the first principal energy level ($n = 1$). Thus, the first p-block element is boron (B), in the second period. The p-block spans six groups on the periodic table because the three p orbitals can hold a maximum of six electrons. Together, the s- and p-blocks comprise the representative, or group A, elements.

The group 8A, or noble gas, elements are unique members of the p-block because of their incredible stability. Noble gas atoms are so stable that they undergo virtually no chemical reactions. The reason for their stability lies in their electron configurations. Look at the electron configurations of the first four noble gas elements shown in **Table 6-1.** Notice that *both* the s and p orbitals corresponding to the period's principal energy level are *completely filled.* This arrangement of electrons results in an unusually stable atomic structure. You soon will learn that this stable configuration plays an important role in the formation of ions and chemical bonds.

**d-block elements** The d-block contains the transition metals and is the largest of the blocks. Although there are a number of exceptions, d-block elements are characterized by a filled outermost s orbital of energy level *n*, and filled or partially filled d orbitals of energy level *n* − 1. As you move across the period, electrons fill the d orbitals. For example, scandium (Sc), the first d-block element, has an electron configuration of $[Ar]4s^23d^1$. Titanium, the next element on the table, has an electron configuration of $[Ar]4s^23d^2$. Note that titanium's filled outermost s orbital has an energy level of $n = 4$, while the partially filled d orbital has an energy level of $n − 1$, or 3. The five d orbitals can hold a total of ten electrons; thus, the d-block spans ten groups on the periodic table.

### Figure 6-9

The electron-dot structures of most of the representative elements are shown here. The number of valence electrons is the same for all members of a group. For the group A elements, an atom's number of valence electrons is equal to its group number (in the 1A, 2A, . . . numbering system).

| 1A 1 | 2A 1 | | 3A 13 | 4A 14 | 5A 15 | 6A 16 | 7A 17 | 8A 18 |
|---|---|---|---|---|---|---|---|---|
| 1 | H. | | | | | | | He: |
| 2 | Li. | Be. | | .B. | .C. | .N. | .O. | :F. | :Ne: |
| 3 | Na. | Mg. | | .Al. | .Si. | .P. | .S. | :Cl. | :Ar: |
| 4 | K. | Ca. | | .Ga. | .Ge. | .As. | .Se. | :Br. | :Kr: |
| 5 | Rb. | Sr. | | .In. | .Sn. | .Sb. | .Te. | :I. | :Xe: |
| 6 | Cs. | Ba. | | .Tl. | .Pb. | .Bi. | .Po. | | :Rn: |

**Table 6-1**

| Period | Principal energy level | Element | Electron configuration | Electron dot structure |
|--------|----------------------|---------|----------------------|----------------------|
| 1 | $n = 1$ | helium | $1s^2$ | He: |
| 2 | $n = 2$ | neon | $[He]2s^22p^6$ | :N̈e: |
| 3 | $n = 3$ | argon | $[Ne]3s^23p^6$ | :Är: |
| 4 | $n = 4$ | krypton | $[Ar]4s^23d^{10}4p^6$ | :K̈r: |

**Electron Configurations of Helium, Neon, Argon, and Krypton**

**f-block elements** The f-block contains the inner transition metals. The f-block elements are characterized by a filled, or partially filled outermost s orbital, and filled or partially filled 4f and 5f orbitals. The electrons of the f sublevel do not fill their orbitals in a predictable manner. Because there are seven f orbitals holding up to a maximum of 14 electrons, the f-block spans 14 columns of the periodic table.

Thus, the s-, p-, d-, and f-blocks determine the shape of the periodic table. As you proceed down through the periods, the principal energy level increases, as does the number of energy sublevels containing electrons. Period 1 contains only s-block elements, periods 2 and 3 contain both s- and p-block elements, periods 4 and 5 contain s-, p-, and d-block elements, and periods 6 and 7 contain s-, p-, d-, and f-block elements.

**Figure 6-10**

Although electrons fill the orbitals of s- and p-block elements in a predictable manner, there are a number of exceptions in the d- and f-block elements. What is the relationship between the maximum number of electrons an energy sublevel can hold and the size of that block on the diagram?

[Periodic table diagram showing s block, p block, d block, and f block]

6.2 Classification of the Elements **161**

**7.** Electron
configuration Group Period Block
**a.** [Ne]3s$^2$    2A    3    s-block
**b.** [He]2s$^2$    2A    2    s-block
**c.** [Kr]5s$^2$4d$^{10}$5p$^5$    7A    5    p-block

**8.** See the Solutions Manual.

**9. a.** Sc, Y, La, Ac
    **b.** N, P, As, Sb, Bi
    **c.** Ne, Ar, Kr, Xe, Rn

## Reteach

*Visual-Spatial* Have student groups make four flashcards. Each card should identify an element by its period number, group number, valence electrons, and family name, respectively. Student groups should challenge one another to identify the elements. **L2** **COOP LEARN**

## ✔ Assessment

**Skill** A student is given clues about three elements. One of the elements is an alkali metal, one is from the carbon family, and one is from the nitrogen family.
- Element A is metallic, shiny, a good conductor, and reacts slowly with HCl to form H$_2$ gas.
- Element B is a yellow solid and is not a good conductor.
- Element C exhibits a metallic luster, conducts electricity, and forms a white powder when exposed to air.

Have students propose identities for each element, support their choices, and write electron configurations for each. **L2**

A: Most likely lithium because it is an alkali metal that, in its group, reacts the slowest with HCl. [He]2s$^1$

B: Must be sulfur because of its yellow color, nonconductive properties, and the fact that it is in the same group as oxygen. [Ne]3s$^2$3p$^4$

C: Must be lead because it's gray, malleable, and in the same group as carbon. [Xe]6s$^2$4f$^{14}$5d$^{10}$6p$^2$

---

**Electron Configuration and the Periodic Table**
Strontium has an electron configuration of [Kr]5s$^2$. Without using the periodic table, determine the group, period, and block in which strontium is located on the periodic table.

**1. Analyze the Problem**
You are given the electron configuration of strontium. The energy level of the valence electrons can be used to determine the period in which strontium is located. The electron configuration of the valence electrons can be used to determine the group and the block in which strontium is located.

**2. Solve for the Unknown**
**Group** The valence electron configuration of s$^2$ indicates that strontium is in group 2A. All group 2A elements have the s$^2$ configuration.
**Period** The 5 in 5s$^2$ indicates that strontium is in period 5.
**Block** The s$^2$ indicates that strontium's valence electrons fill the s sublevel. Thus, strontium is in the s-block.

**3. Evaluate the Answer**
The relationships among electron configuration and position on the periodic table have been correctly applied. The given information identifies a unique position on the table, as it must.

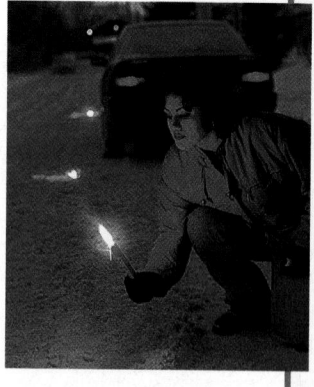

Strontium-containing compounds are used to produce the bright red seen in these road flares.

*Practice!* For more practice with electron configuration problems, go to **Supplemental Practice Problems in Appendix A.**

### PRACTICE PROBLEMS

**7.** Without using the periodic table, determine the group, period, and block of an atom with the following electron configurations.
   **a.** [Ne]3s$^2$    **b.** [He]2s$^2$    **c.** [Kr]5s$^2$4d$^{10}$5p$^5$

**8.** Write the electron configuration of the element fitting each of the following descriptions.
   **a.** The group 2A element in the fourth period
   **b.** The noble gas in the fifth period
   **c.** The group 2B element in the fourth period
   **d.** The group 6A element in the second period

**9.** What are the symbols for the elements with the following valence electron configurations?
   **a.** s$^2$d$^1$    **b.** s$^2$p$^3$    **c.** s$^2$p$^6$

## Section 6.2 Assessment

**10.** Explain why elements in the same group on the periodic table have similar chemical properties.

**11.** Given each of the following valence electron configurations, determine which block of the periodic table the element is in.
   **a.** s$^2$p$^4$    **b.** s$^1$    **c.** s$^2$d$^1$    **d.** s$^2$p$^1$

**12.** Describe how each of the following are related.
   **a.** Group number and number of valence electrons for representative elements
   **b.** Principal energy level of valence electrons and period number

**13.** Without using the periodic table, determine the group, period, and block of an atom with an electron configuration of [Ne]3s$^2$3p$^4$.

**14. Thinking Critically** A gaseous element is a poor conductor of heat and electricity, and is extremely nonreactive. Is the element likely to be a metal, nonmetal, or metalloid? Where would the element be located on the periodic table? Explain.

**15. Formulating Models** Make a simplified sketch of the periodic table and label the s-, p-, d-, and f-blocks.

---

## Section 6.2 Assessment

**10.** Chemical behavior is determined by the number of valence electrons. Elements in the same group have the same valence electron configurations.

**11. a.** p-block; **b.** s-block; **c.** d-block; **d.** p-block

**12. a.** They are the same number.
   **b.** They are the same number.

**13.** group 6A, period 3; p-block

**14.** It is most likely a nonmetal noble gas located on the extreme right side of the periodic table. Other gases are reactive.

**15.** Sketches should look similar to Figure 6-10. See the Solutions Manual for a sample sketch.

Many properties of the elements tend to change in a predictable way, known as a trend, as you move across a period or down a group. You will explore several periodic trends in this section. Do the **miniLAB** on the next page to explore several properties that behave periodically.

## Atomic Radius

The electron cloud surrounding a nucleus is based on probability and does not have a clearly defined edge. It is true that the outer limit of an electron cloud is defined as the spherical surface within which there is a 90% probability of finding an electron. However, this surface does not exist in a physical way, as the outer surface of a golf ball does. Atomic size is defined by how closely an atom lies to a neighboring atom. Because the nature of the neighboring atom can vary from one substance to another, the size of the atom itself also tends to vary somewhat from substance to substance.

For metals such as sodium, the atomic radius is defined as half the distance between adjacent nuclei in a crystal of the element. See **Figure 6-11a.** For elements that commonly occur as molecules, such as many nonmetals, the

### Objectives

- **Compare** period and group trends of several properties.
- **Relate** period and group trends in atomic radii to electron configuration.

### Vocabulary

ion
ionization energy
octet rule
electronegativity

**Figure 6-11**

The table gives atomic radii of the representative elements.

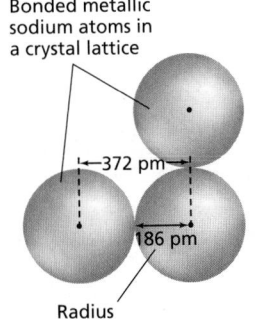

Bonded metallic sodium atoms in a crystal lattice

372 pm

186 pm

Radius

**a** The radius of a metal atom in a metallic crystal is one-half the distance between two adjacent atoms in the crystal.

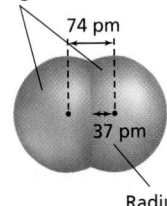

Bonded nonmetal hydrogen atoms

74 pm

37 pm

Radius

**b** The radius of a nonmetal atom is often determined from a diatomic molecule of an element.

| 1A | | | | | | | 8A |
|---|---|---|---|---|---|---|---|
| H 37 | | Chemical symbol — K 227 — Atomic radius — Relative size | | | | | He 31 |
| | 2A | 3A | 4A | 5A | 6A | 7A | |
| Li 152 | Be 112 | B 85 | C 77 | N 75 | O 73 | F 72 | Ne 71 |
| Na 186 | Mg 160 | Al 143 | Si 118 | P 110 | S 103 | Cl 100 | Ar 98 |
| K 227 | Ca 197 | Ga 135 | Ge 122 | As 120 | Se 119 | Br 114 | Kr 112 |
| Rb 248 | Sr 215 | In 167 | Sn 140 | Sb 140 | Te 142 | I 133 | Xe 131 |
| Cs 265 | Ba 222 | Tl 170 | Pb 146 | Bi 150 | Po 168 | At 140 | Rn 140 |

**c** The atomic radii of the representative elements are given in picometers ($1 \times 10^{-12}$ meters) and their relative sizes are shown. The radii for the transition metals have been omitted because they exhibit many exceptions to the general trends shown here. What causes the increase in radii as you move down a group?

6.3 Periodic Trends    **163**

## 1 Focus

**Focus Transparency**

Before presenting the lesson, display **Section Focus Transparency 22** on the overhead projector. Have students answer the accompanying questions using **Section Focus Transparency Master 22.** **L1** **ELL**

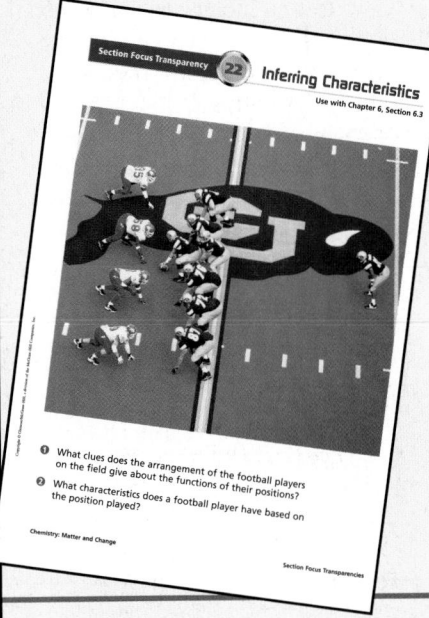

Section Focus Transparency 22    Inferring Characteristics
Use with Chapter 6, Section 6.3

❶ What clues does the arrangement of the football players on the field give about the functions of their positions?
❷ What characteristics does a football player have based on the position played?

Chemistry: Matter and Change

Section Focus Transparencies

## 2 Teach

### Concept Development

Help students develop the concept of periodic trends by providing them with opportunities to plot specific data and analyze the resulting graphs.

### Figure Caption Question

**Figure 6-11c** What causes the increase in radii as you move down a group? Electrons occupy larger, higher-energy orbitals; inner core electrons shield valence electrons from the increased charge in the nucleus.

**National Science Content Standards**

Pages 162-163
UCP.1, UCP.2, UCP.5; A.1; B.1, B.2

## miniLAB

### Purpose

Students will use graphs to determine if molar heats of fusion and vaporization behave in a periodic way.

### Process Skills

Comparing and contrasting, making and using graphs, sequencing, thinking critically, using numbers

### Teaching Strategies

- Students can use sources other than Appendix Tables C-6 and C-13 to find molar heats of fusion and vaporization. The Internet is also a good source for periodic table information.
- If students use TI graphing calculators, remind them to reset the $x$ and $y$ values in the WINDOW of the calculator so that all of the data can be seen.

### Expected Results

**Molar Heat Data**

| Element | Atomic number | $H_f$ (kJ/mol) | $H_v$ (kJ/mol) |
|---------|---------------|----------------|----------------|
| Li | 3 | 3 | 148 |
| Be | 4 | 7.9 | 298 |
| B | 5 | 50.2 | 504 |
| C | 6 | 104.6 | 711 |
| N | 7 | 0.072 | 5.58 |
| O | 8 | 0.44 | 6.82 |
| F | 9 | 0.51 | 6.54 |
| Ne | 10 | 0.34 | 1.77 |
| Na | 11 | 2.06 | 97.4 |
| Mg | 12 | 8.5 | 127 |
| Al | 13 | 10.7 | 291 |
| Si | 14 | 50.2 | 359 |
| P | 15 | 0.659 | 362 |
| S | 16 | 1.73 | 9.62 |
| Cl | 17 | 6.41 | 20.4 |
| Ar | 18 | 1.18 | 6.52 |

**National Science Content Standards**

Pages 164-165
UCP.1, UCP.2, UCP.5; B.1, B.2

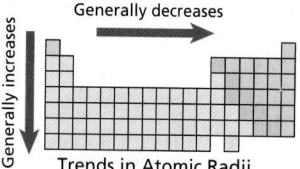

Generally decreases →

Generally increases ↓

Trends in Atomic Radii

### Figure 6-12

This small table provides a summary of the general trends in atomic radii.

atomic radius is defined as half the distance between nuclei of identical atoms that are chemically bonded together. The atomic radius of a nonmetal diatomic hydrogen molecule ($H_2$) is shown in **Figure 6-11b**.

**Trends within periods** A pattern in atomic size emerges as you look across a period in **Figure 6-11c**. In general, there is a decrease in atomic radii as you move left-to-right across a period. This trend is caused by the increasing positive charge in the nucleus and the fact that the principal energy level within a period remains the same. Each successive element has one additional proton and electron, and each additional electron is added to the same principal energy level. Moving across a period, no additional electrons come between the valence electrons and the nucleus. Thus, the valence electrons are not shielded from the increased nuclear charge. The result is that the increased nuclear charge pulls the outermost electrons closer to the nucleus.

**Trends within groups** Atomic radii generally increase as you move down a group. The nuclear charge increases and electrons are added to successively higher principal energy levels. Although you might think the increased nuclear charge would pull the outer electrons toward the nucleus and make the atom smaller, this effect is overpowered by several other factors. Moving down a group, the outermost orbital increases in size along with the increasing principal energy level; thus, making the atom larger. The larger orbital means that the outer electrons are farther from the nucleus. This increased distance offsets the greater pull of the increased nuclear charge. Also, as additional orbitals between the nucleus and the outer electrons are occupied, these electrons shield the outer electrons from the pull of the nucleus. **Figure 6-12** summarizes the group and period trends in atomic radii.

## miniLAB

### Periodicity of Molar Heats of Fusion and Vaporization

**Making and Using Graphs** The heats required to melt or to vaporize a mole (a specific amount of matter) of matter are known as the molar heat of fusion ($H_f$) and the molar heat of vaporization ($H_v$), respectively. These heats are unique properties of each element. You will investigate if the molar heats of fusion and vaporization for the period 2 and 3 elements behave in a periodic fashion.

**Materials** either a graphing calculator, a computer graphing program, or graph paper; Appendix **Table C-6** or access to comparable element data references

### Procedure

Use **Table C-6** in Appendix C to look up and record the molar heat of fusion and the molar heat of vaporization for the period 3 elements listed in the table. Then, record the same data for the period 2 elements.

**Molar Heat Data**

| Element | Atomic number | $H_f$ (kJ/mol) | $H_v$ (kJ/mol) |
|---------|---------------|----------------|----------------|
| Na | 11 | | |
| Mg | 12 | | |
| Al | 13 | | |
| Si | 14 | | |
| P | 15 | | |
| S | 16 | | |
| Cl | 17 | | |
| Ar | 18 | | |

### Analysis

1. Graph molar heats of fusion versus atomic number. Connect the points with straight lines and label the curve. Do the same for molar heats of vaporization.

2. Do the graphs repeat in a periodic fashion? Describe the graphs to support your answer.

### Analysis

1. See sample graph in the Solutions Manual. Graphs should reflect data shown in data table.

2. Yes, both molar heat of fusion and vaporization repeat in a periodic fashion, and, therefore, are periodic properties of elements.

### ✔ Assessment

**Performance** Have students graph other properties, such as density or specific heat, to see if they behave in a periodic way. Use the Performance Task Assessment List for Graph from Data in **PASC**, p. 39. **L2**

## EXAMPLE PROBLEM 6-2

### Interpreting Trends in Atomic Radii

Which has the largest atomic radius: carbon (C), fluorine (F), beryllium (Be), or lithium (Li)? Do not use **Figure 6-11** to answer the question. Explain your answer in terms of trends in atomic radii.

**1. Analyze the Problem**

You are given four elements. First, determine the groups and periods the elements occupy. Then apply the general trends in atomic radii to determine which has the largest atomic radius.

**2. Solve for the Unknown**

From the periodic table, all the elements are found to be in period 2. Ordering the elements from left-to-right across the period yields:
Li, Be, C, F

Applying the trend of decreasing radii across a period means that lithium, the first element in period 2, has the largest radius.

**3. Evaluating the Answer**

The group trend in atomic radii has been correctly applied. Checking radii values from **Figure 6-11** verifies the answer.

## PRACTICE PROBLEMS

Answer the following questions using your knowledge of group and period trends in atomic radii. Do not use the atomic radii values in **Figure 6-11** to answer the questions.

**16.** Which has the largest radius: magnesium (Mg), silicon (Si), sulfur (S), or sodium (Na)? The smallest?

**17.** Which has the largest radius: helium (He), xenon (Xe), or argon (Ar)? The smallest?

**18.** Can you determine which of two unknown elements has the larger radius if the only known information is that the atomic number of one of the elements is 20 greater than the other?

*Practice!* **For more practice with periodic trend problems, go to Supplemental Practice Problems in Appendix A.**

## Ionic Radius

Atoms can gain or lose one or more electrons to form ions. Because electrons are negatively charged, atoms that gain or lose electrons acquire a net charge. Thus, an **ion** is an atom or a bonded group of atoms that has a positive or negative charge. You'll learn about ions in detail in Chapter 8, but for now, let's look at how the formation of an ion affects the size of an atom.

When atoms lose electrons and form positively charged ions, they always become smaller. For example, as shown in **Figure 6-13a** on the next page a sodium atom with a radius of 186 pm shrinks to a radius of 95 pm when it forms a positive sodium ion. The reason for the decrease in size is twofold. The electron lost from the atom will always be a valence electron. The loss of a valence electron may leave a completely empty outer orbital, which results in a smaller radius. Furthermore, the electrostatic repulsion between the now fewer number of remaining electrons decreases, allowing them to be pulled closer to the nucleus.

When atoms gain electrons and form negatively charged ions, they always become larger, as shown in **Figure 6-13b**. The addition of an electron to an

6.3 Periodic Trends **165**

Have students refer to Appendix D for complete solutions to Practice Problems.

**16.** largest: Na
smallest: S

**17.** largest: Xe
smallest: He

**18.** No. If all you know is that the atomic number of one element is 20 greater than that of the other, then you will be unable to determine the specific groups and periods that the elements are in. Without this information, you cannot apply the periodic trends in atomic size to determine which element has the larger radius.

## Math in Chemistry

*Visual-Spatial* Students often have difficulty interpreting graphs and generalizing the information.

- Provide students with several graphs and ask them to write several sentences describing any trends they see in the data. The graphs they analyze do not have to be of periodic trends; select a wide variety of graphs, such as business trends, seasonal temperature, population over time, crop yields, and rainfall.

- Select a new scientific graph and ask students specific questions that require them to read and analyze data points on the graph. Ask them to summarize any trends shown in the graph. Then, ask a question that requires them to apply the trends in order to answer.

## Resource Manager

ChemLab and MiniLab Worksheets, p. 21 **L2**

---

## DIFFERENTIATED INSTRUCTION

### Learning Disabled

*Visual-Spatial* Draw an atomic model of sodium on the board. The atom should have eleven protons in the nucleus, two electrons in the first shell, eight electrons in the second shell, and one electron in the third shell. Ask students what happens to the size of the atom if the outermost valence electron is removed. Have students draw atomic models of other elements within the same group or period. Make sure they understand that as they move across a period, the increase in the nuclear charge has a greater impact on the atomic radii than the increasing number of electrons around the nucleus. This results in the trend of decreasing atomic radii. **L2** **ELL**

Sodium atom (Na)
[Ne]3s¹

Sodium ion (Na⁺)
[Ne]

**a**

Chlorine atom (Cl)
[Ne]3s²3p⁵

Chlorine ion (Cl⁻)
[Ne]3s²3p⁶ or [Ar]

**b**

## Figure Caption Questions

**Figure 6-13** How is each ion's electron configuration related to those of the noble gas elements? Ions have the same electron configuration as the nearest noble gas in the periodic table.

**Figure 6-16** What trend in first ionization energies do you observe as you move down a group? Ionization energies generally decrease down a group.

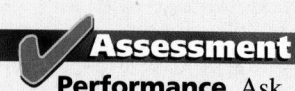

**Performance** Ask students to draw a metal atom and its ion, showing relative sizes. The ion will be smaller. Ask students to repeat the procedure with a halogen atom and its ion. The ion will be larger. Use the Performance Task Assessment List for Scientific Drawing in **PASC**, p. 55. **L2** **ELL**

**Teaching Transparencies 20, 21 and Masters** **L2** **ELL**
**Lab Manual,** pp. 45–48 **L2**

**National Science Content Standards**
Pages 166–167
UCP.1, UCP.2, UCP.5; B.1, B.2

**Figure 6-13**

Atoms undergo significant changes in size when forming ions. **a** The sodium atom loses an electron and becomes smaller. **b** The chlorine ion gains an electron and becomes larger. How is each ion's electron configuration related to those of the noble gas elements?

atom increases the electrostatic repulsion between the atom's outer electrons, forcing them to move farther apart. The increased distance between the outer electrons results in a larger radius.

**Trends within periods** The ionic radii of most of the representative elements are shown in **Figure 6-14.** Note that elements on the left side of the table form smaller positive ions, and elements on the right side of the table form larger negative ions. In general, as you move left-to-right across a period, the size of the positive ions gradually decreases. Then, beginning in group 5A or 6A, the size of the much larger negative ions also gradually decreases.

**Trends within groups** As you move down a group, an ion's outer electrons are in higher principal energy levels, resulting in a gradual increase in ionic size. Thus, the ionic radii of both positive and negative ions increase as you move down a group. **Figure 6-15** on the next page summarizes the group and period trends in ionic radii.

**Figure 6-14**

The table shows the ionic radii of most of the representative elements. The ion sizes are shown relative to one another, while the actual radii are given in picometers (1 × 10⁻¹² meters). Note that the elements on the left side of the table form positive ions, and those on the right form negative ions.

Chemical symbol — K 138 — Ionic radius
Charge — 1+ — Relative size

## Demonstration

### Activity of Alkali Metals

**Purpose**
To demonstrate that chemical reactivity follows a predictable pattern

**Materials**
Overhead projector; explosion shield; 600-mL beakers (3); phenolphthalein indi-cator (10 drops); clear plastic wrap; cubes of Li, Na, and K, (~ 2 mm on a side); wire screen (10 cm × 10 cm)
See page 150C for preparation of solutions.

**Safety Precautions**

Wear safety goggles and an apron. Use an explosion shield. Make sure there are no open flames or possible ignition sources.

**Disposal** Neutralize the solutions formed using acetic acid or dilute HCl. Flush the neutralized solutions down the drain with copious amounts of water.

**Procedure**
Cover the stage and lower lens of an overhead projector with clear plastic wrap. Place a 600-mL beaker containing 100 mL of water on the projector. **CAUTION:** *Place*

## Ionization Energy

To form a positive ion, an electron must be removed from a neutral atom. This requires energy. The energy is needed to overcome the attraction between the positive charge in the nucleus and the negative charge of the electron. **Ionization energy** is defined as the energy required to remove an electron from a gaseous atom. For example, $8.64 \times 10^{-19}$ J is required to remove an electron from a gaseous lithium atom. The energy required to remove the first electron from an atom is called the first ionization energy. Therefore, the first ionization energy of lithium equals $8.64 \times 10^{-19}$ J. The loss of the electron results in the formation of a Li$^+$ ion. The first ionization energies of the elements in periods 1 through 5 are plotted on the graph in **Figure 6-16.**

Think of ionization energy as an indication of how strongly an atom's nucleus holds onto its valence electrons. A high ionization energy value indicates the atom has a strong hold on its electrons. Atoms with large ionization energy values are less likely to form positive ions. Likewise, a low ionization energy value indicates an atom loses its outer electron easily. Such atoms are likely to form positive ions.

Take a close look at the graph in **Figure 6-16.** Each set of connected points represents the elements in a period. From the graph, it is clear that the group 1A metals have low ionization energies. Thus, group 1A metals (Li, Na K, Rb) are likely to form positive ions. It also is clear that the group 8A elements (He, Ne, Ar, Kr, Xe) have high ionization energies and are unlikely to form ions. Gases of group 8A are extremely unreactive—their stable electron configuration greatly limits their reactivity.

After removing the first electron from an atom, it is possible to remove additional electrons. The amount of energy required to remove a second electron from a 1+ ion is called the second ionization energy, the amount of energy required to remove a third electron from a 2+ ion is called the third ionization energy, and so on. **Table 6-2** on the next page lists the first through ninth ionization energies for elements in period 2.

Reading across **Table 6-2** from left-to-right, you see that the energy required for each successive ionization always increases. However, the increase in energy does not occur smoothly. Note that for each element there is an ionization for which the required energy jumps dramatically. For example, the second ionization energy of lithium (7300 kJ/mol) is much greater than its first ionization energy (520 kJ/mol). This means a lithium atom is relatively likely to lose its first valence electron, but extremely unlikely to lose its second.

If you examine the table, you'll see that the ionization at which the large jump in energy occurs is related to the atom's number of valence electrons. Lithium has one valence electron and the jump occurs after the first ionization energy. Lithium easily forms the common lithium 1+ ion, but is unlikely to form a lithium 2+ ion. The jump in ionization energy shows that atoms hold

**Figure 6-15**

This small table provides a summary of the general trends in ionic radii.

**Figure 6-16**

The graph shows the first ionization energies for elements in periods 1 through 5. Note the high energies required to remove an electron from a noble gas element. What trend in first ionization energies do you observe as you move down a group?

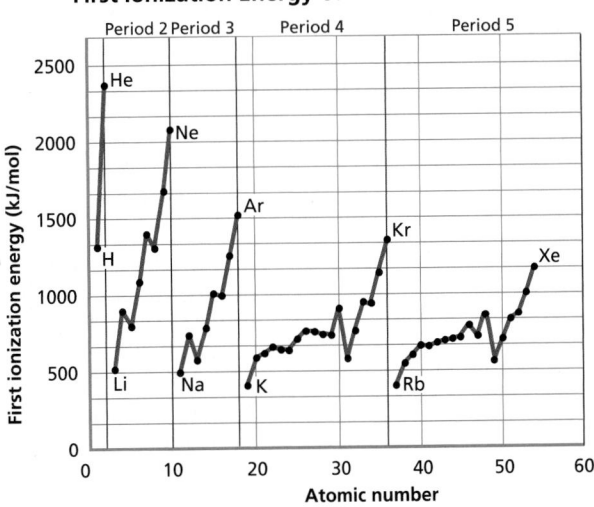

First Ionization Energy of Elements in Periods 1–5

## Math in Chemistry

*Logical-Mathematical* Assign a trend to each group of students and have them create a table of data for that trend for the first 40 elements of the periodic table. Assigned trends should include ionization energy, electron affinity, electronegativity, atomic radii, ionic radii, density, and melting point. Students may need a variety of resources, such as the text, a *CRC Handbook of Chemistry and Physics,* a periodic table, Internet sites, or other reference materials, to complete their data table.

Have students enter the data as a set of lists into a graphing calculator. The first list should be the atomic numbers 1 through 40. These data should be graphed on the *x*-axis. The specific data related to the trend should be graphed on the *y*-axis. Have students display and print the graph. On the printed graph, have them draw a vertical line through each alkali metal (explain that the interval between each vertical line represents a period). They should then select a color and color-code each data point that represents an alkali metal. A different color should be used to color-code each noble gas. Repeat this process with a third color for the halogens. Finally, have students write a paragraph describing the trend that results when comparing elements within a period and elements in the same group. **L2** **COOP LEARN**

---

*an explosion shield around the projector.* Turn on the projector and darken the room. Drop a *small* piece of lithium into the water. **CAUTION:** *Quickly cover the beaker with a wire screen. The gas produced is flammable.* In separate beakers, repeat the procedure using Na and K.

**Results**

Metals skim across the water with speeds related to their activity. Li: slow, least

active; Na: fast, active; K: flammable, very active.

**Analysis**

1. Which metal reacts the fastest? K
2. How does the element's position in the column on the periodic table relate to its reactivity? Li is first and least reactive; K is third and most reactive.
3. Which metal has its outer-level electron farthest from the nucleus? K

---

### Assessment

**Knowledge** Have students apply the trend in reactivities they observed to predict how the activity of Rb and Cs will compare with that of Li, Na, and K. Rb and Cs will be more reactive, with Cs being the most reactive. **L2**

**Table 6-2** Have students study the table for the period 2 elements. Ask them to predict how they could use the chart of ionization energies to predict the number of electrons an atom would lose when forming an ion. **L2**

Ask students to predict which element, magnesium or calcium, will be more reactive. Drop a small piece of magnesium into several milliliters of water in a test tube. Have students record their observations. Repeat this procedure with a small piece of calcium metal in a second test tube. Make sure to use a fresh piece of calcium that has not started to oxidize. After students record their observations, add several drops of phenolphthalein to both test tubes and discuss what the color change indicates.

Students should notice that calcium is noticeably more reactive than the magnesium. A slow reaction between the magnesium and the water does occur, as evidenced by the small bubbles and slight color change. Repeat the reaction with hot water, and students should note that the reaction occurs more vigorously for both metals. Neutralize the solutions created and flush them down the drain with water.

**In-Text Question**

**Page 168** Where does the jump in ionization energy occur for oxygen, an atom with six valence electrons?
after the sixth electron is removed

Table 6-2

| Element | Valence electrons | Ionization energy (kJ/mol)* | | | | | | | | |
|---------|-------------------|------|------|------|------|------|------|------|------|------|
| | | 1st | 2nd | 3rd | 4th | 5th | 6th | 7th | 8th | 9th |
| Li | 1 | 520 | 7300 | | | | | | | |
| Be | 2 | 900 | 1760 | 14 850 | | | | | | |
| B | 3 | 800 | 2430 | 3660 | 25 020 | | | | | |
| C | 4 | 1090 | 2350 | 4620 | 6220 | 37 830 | | | | |
| N | 5 | 1400 | 2860 | 4580 | 7480 | 9440 | 53 270 | | | |
| O | 6 | 1310 | 3390 | 5300 | 7470 | 10 980 | 13 330 | 71 330 | | |
| F | 7 | 1680 | 3370 | 6050 | 8410 | 11 020 | 15 160 | 17 870 | 92 040 | |
| Ne | 8 | 2080 | 3950 | 6120 | 9370 | 12 180 | 15 240 | 20 000 | 23 070 | 115 380 |

* mol is an abbreviation for mole, a quantity of matter.

**Figure 6-17**

This small table provides a summary of the general trends in first ionization energies.

onto their inner core electrons much more strongly than they hold onto their valence electrons. Where does the jump in ionization energy occur for oxygen, an atom with six valence electrons?

**Trends within periods** As shown in **Figure 6-16** and by the values in **Table 6-2**, first ionization energies generally increase as you move left-to-right across a period. The increased nuclear charge of each successive element produces an increased hold on the valence electrons.

**Trends within groups** First ionization energies generally decrease as you move down a group. This decrease in energy occurs because atomic size increases as you move down the group. With the valence electrons farther from the nucleus, less energy is required to remove them. **Figure 6-17** summarizes the group and period trends in first ionization energies.

**Octet rule** When a sodium atom loses its single valence electron to form a 1+ sodium ion, its electron configuration changes as shown below.

Sodium atom $1s^22s^22p^63s^1$ Sodium ion $1s^22s^22p^6$

Note that the sodium ion has the same electron configuration as neon $(1s^22s^22p^6)$, a noble gas. This observation leads to one of the most important principles in chemistry, the octet rule. The **octet rule** states that atoms tend to gain, lose, or share electrons in order to acquire a full set of eight valence electrons. This reinforces what you learned earlier that the electron configuration of filled s and p orbitals of the same energy level (consisting of eight valence electrons) is unusually stable. Note that the first period elements are an exception to the rule, as they are complete with only two valence electrons.

The octet rule is useful for determining the type of ions likely to form. Elements on the right side of the periodic table tend to gain electrons in order to acquire the noble gas configuration; therefore, these elements tend to form negative ions. In a similar manner, elements on the left side of the table tend to lose electrons and form positive ions.

## Electronegativity

The **electronegativity** of an element indicates the relative ability of its atoms to attract electrons in a chemical bond. **Figure 6-18** lists the electronegativity values for most of the elements. These values are calculated based upon a number of factors, and are expressed in terms of a numerical

**Group Numbering Systems**

*Intrapersonal* Have students investigate and report on different numbering systems used on periodic tables. Have students summarize their findings and place them in their journals. **L2**

**CD-ROM**
**Chemistry: Matter and Change**
Animation: *Electronegativity*

value of 3.98 or less. The units of electronegativity are arbitrary units called Paulings, named after American scientist Linus Pauling (1901–1994).

Note that because the noble gases form very few compounds, they have been left out of **Figure 6-18.** Fluorine is the most electronegative element, with a value of 3.98, and cesium and francium are the least electronegative elements, with values of 0.79 and 0.7, respectively. In a chemical bond, the atom with the greater electronegativity more strongly attracts the bond's electrons. You will use electronegativity values in upcoming chapters to help determine the types of bonds that exist between elements in a compound.

**Trends within periods and groups** Electronegativity generally decreases as you move down a group, and increases as you move left-to-right across a period; therefore, the lowest electronegativities are found at the lower left side of the periodic table, while the highest electronegativities are found at the upper right.

**Figure 6-18**

The table shows the electronegativity values for most of the elements. In which areas of the periodic table do the highest electronegativities tend to occur? The lowest?

**Electronegativity Values in Paulings**

## Section 6.3 Assessment

19. Sketch a simplified periodic table and use arrows and labels to compare period and group trends in atomic and ionic radii, ionization energies, and electronegativities.

20. Explain how the period and group trends in atomic radii are related to electron configuration.

21. Which has the largest atomic radius: nitrogen (N), antimony (Sb), or arsenic (As)? The smallest?

22. For each of the following properties, indicate whether fluorine or bromine has a larger value.
    a. electronegativity
    c. atomic radius
    b. ionic radius
    d. ionization energy

23. **Thinking Critically** Explain why it takes more energy to remove the second electron from a lithium atom than it does to remove the fourth electron from a carbon atom.

24. **Making and Using Graphs** Graph the atomic radii of the group A elements in periods 2, 3, and 4 versus their atomic numbers. Connect the points of elements in each period, so that there are three separate curves on the graph. Summarize the trends in atomic radii shown on your graph. Explain.

## Figure Caption Questions

**Figure 6-18** In which areas of the periodic table do the highest electronegativities tend to occur? top right The lowest? bottom left

# 3 Assess
## Check for Understanding

Informally quiz students on periodic trends by giving them pairs of elements and asking them to identify which is larger, smaller, more reactive, or more electronegative. **L2**

## Reteach

**Visual-Spatial** Have students label the trends on an outline of a periodic table by using arrows pointing in the direction that the trend increases. Repeat this labeling process with the other trends studied. **L2**

### Assessment

**Skill** Given the following letters representing elements in groups (CNJ, ADG, EOSU, BZ, DT, FH, KV, IM), have students place them in the correct place on a blank periodic table.

A: a gas, no assigned electronegativity; B: a halogen; E: 1 proton; O, S, and U: alkali metals; U: largest atomic size in its group; S: smallest atomic size in its group; B: greater atomic mass than Z; A: 2 protons; D: 8 more electrons than G; J: smaller atomic radii than N; D and T: 3 valence electrons; D: lower ionization energy than T; K: has 6 electrons; C: alkaline earth metal with the highest ionization energy is its group; F: lower electronegativity than B but higher than I

Periods 1–4: E A / S C T K M H Z G / O J D V I F B D / U N **L3**

## Section 6.3 Assessment

19. See the Solutions Manual for a sample sketch.
20. Atomic radii increase down a group as electrons are added to higher energy levels and inner core electrons shield the valence electrons from the increased nuclear charge. Atomic radii decrease across a period as increased nuclear charge coupled with unchanging shielding by inner core electrons pulls the valence electrons (being added to the same energy level) closer to the nucleus.
21. antimony (Sb); nitrogen (N)
22. a. fluorine    c. bromine
    b. bromine    d. fluorine
23. Lithium's second removed electron is an inner core electron, not a valence electron. Carbon's fourth removed electron is still a valence electron.
24. See Solutions Manual. In general, atomic radii decrease across a period due to increased nuclear charge and increase down a group due to shielding from increased nuclear charge.

**169**

# CHEMLAB  6

## Preparation

### Time Allotment
One and a half laboratory periods

### Process Skills
Observing and inferring, interpreting data, classifying, comparing and contrasting

### Safety Precautions
Students must wear aprons and goggles because the elements could shatter when struck with the hammer. Also caution students about the risk of hydrochloric acid to eyes and clothes. Remind students that they should never taste a chemical substance.

### Disposal
The HCl solution may be flushed down the drain with a large amount of water.

### Preparation of Materials
- The following element samples should be obtained for use in this lab. Test tubes samples: carbon, nitrogen, oxygen, magnesium, aluminum, silicon, red phosphorus, sulfur, chlorine, calcium, selenium, tin, iodine, and lead.
- Dish samples: carbon, magnesium, aluminum, silicon, sulfur, and tin
- The lab can be performed even if some of the listed elements are not available.
- If other elements are substituted, make sure they do not produce hazardous reactions.
- See page 150C for preparation of all solutions.

## Pre-Lab

**3.** All naturally occurring metals are solids, except for mercury, which is a liquid at room temperature. All metalloids are solids. Nonmetals are primarily gases and solids, with bromine being the only liquid.

**4.** Luster: shininess; malleability: capable of being flattened into sheets or formed into shapes; electrical conductivity: capable of transmitting an electric current; They are properties commonly associated with metals.

**170**

---

# CHEMLAB 6

# Descriptive Chemistry of the Elements

What do elements look like? How do they behave? Can periodic trends in the properties of elements be observed? You cannot examine all of the elements on the periodic table because of limited availability, cost, and safety concerns. However, you can observe several of the representative elements, classify them, and compare their properties. The observation of the properties of elements is called descriptive chemistry.

### Problem
What is the pattern of properties of the representative elements?

### Objectives
- **Observe** properties of various elements.
- **Classify** elements as metals, nonmetals, and metalloids.
- **Examine** general trends within the periodic table.

### Materials
stoppered test tubes containing small samples of elements
plastic dishes containing samples of elements
conductivity apparatus

1.0*M* HCl
test tubes (6)
test tube rack
10-mL graduated cylinder
spatula
small hammer
glass marking pencil

### Safety Precautions

- Wear safety goggles and a lab apron at all times.
- Do not handle elements with bare hands.
- 1.0*M* HCl is harmful to eyes and clothing.
- Never test chemicals by tasting.
- Follow any additional safety precautions provided by your teacher.

### Pre-Lab

**1.** Read the entire **CHEMLAB.**

**2.** Prepare a data table similar to the one below to record the observations you make during the lab.

**3.** Examine the periodic table. What is the physical state of most metals? Nonmetals? Metalloids?

**4.** Look up the definitions of the terms luster, malleability, and electrical conductivity. To what elements do they apply?

| Observation of Elements | | | | | |
|---|---|---|---|---|---|
| Element | Appearance and physical state | Malleable or brittle? | Reactivity with HCl | Electrical conductivity | Classification |
| | | | | | |
| | | | | | |
| | | | | | |
| | | | | | |
| | | | | | |
| | | | | | |

**170**   Chapter 6 The Periodic Table and Periodic Law

| Observation of Elements | | | | | |
|---|---|---|---|---|---|
| Element | Appearance and physical state | Malleable or brittle? | Reactivity with HCl | Electrical conductivity | Classification |
| carbon | gray/black, dull solid | brittle | no | yes | metalloid |
| oxygen | colorless gas | ---- | ---- | ---- | nonmetal |
| magnesium | shiny, silver solid | malleable | yes | yes | metal |
| silicon | shiny, gray solid | brittle | no | yes | metalloid |
| sulfur | dull, yellow solid | brittle | no | yes | nonmetal |
| chlorine | yellow-green gas | not tested | not tested | not tested | nonmetal |

## Procedure

1. Observe and record the appearance of the element sample in each test tube. Observations should include physical state, color, and other characteristics such as luster and texture. **CAUTION:** *Do not remove the stoppers from the test tubes.*

2. Remove a small sample of each of the elements contained in a dish and place it on a hard surface designated by your teacher. Gently tap each element sample with a small hammer. **CAUTION:** *Safety goggles must be worn.* If the element is malleable it will flatten. If it is brittle, it will shatter. Record your observations.

3. Use the conductivity tester to determine which elements conduct electricity. An illuminated light bulb is evidence of electrical conductivity. Record your results in your data table. Clean the electrodes with water and make sure they are dry before testing each element.

4. Label each test tube with the symbol for one of the elements in the plastic dishes. Using a graduated cylinder, add 5 mL of water to each test tube.

5. Use a spatula to put a small amount of each of the six elements (approximately 0.2 g or a 1-cm long ribbon) into the test tube labeled with its chemical symbol. Using a graduated cylinder, add 5 mL of 1.0*M* HCl to each test tube. Observe each test tube for at least one minute. The formation of bubbles is evidence of a reaction between the acid and the element. Record your observations.

## Cleanup and Disposal

Dispose of all materials as instructed by your teacher.

## Analyze and Conclude

1. **Interpreting Data** Metals are usually malleable and good conductors of electricity. They are generally lustrous and silver or white in color. Many react with acids. Write the word "metal" beneath the Classification heading in the data table for those element samples that display the general characteristics of metals.

2. **Interpreting Data** Nonmetals can be solids, liquids, or gases. They do not conduct electricity and do not react with acids. If a nonmetal is a solid, it is likely to be brittle and have color (other than white or silver). Write the word "nonmetal" beneath the Classification heading in the data table for those element samples that display the general characteristics of nonmetals.

3. **Interpreting Data** Metalloids combine some of the properties of both metals and nonmetals. Write the word "metalloid" beneath the Classification heading in the data table for those element samples that display the general characteristics of metalloids.

4. **Making a Model** Construct a periodic table and label the representative elements by group (1A through 7A). Using the information in your data table and the periodic table, record the identities of elements observed during the lab in your periodic table.

5. **Interpreting** Describe any trends among the elements you observed in the lab.

## Real-World Chemistry

1. Why did it take so long to discover the first noble gas element?

2. Research one of the most recently discovered elements. New elements are created in particle accelerators and tend to be very unstable. Because of this, many of the properties of a new element can not be determined. Using periodic group trends in melting and boiling point, predict whether the new element you selected is likely to be a solid, liquid, or gas.

## Procedure

- Set up stations at various locations in the lab.

## Expected Results

See data tables.

## Analyze and Conclude

**1.–3.** See completed Observation of Elements table.

**4.** See periodic table below.

**5.** Students may note that the metallic characteristic increases from right-to-left, and from top-to-bottom.

## Real-World Chemistry

1. Many elements were discovered by using electricity to break down compounds into their component elements. Because noble gases form virtually no compounds, the electrical decomposition technique could not be used.

2. Answers will vary. For example, 114 may be a solid with high melting point.

### ✓ Assessment

**Skill** Give each student a blank periodic table. Ask them to draw an arrow on their tables showing the direction of increasing metallic properties across the table and another showing increasing metallic properties within a group.
**L2** **ELL**

**ChemLab and MiniLab Worksheets, pp. 22–24** **L2**

**National Science Content Standards**

**Pages 170-171**
UCP.1, UCP.2, UCP.5; A.1, A.2; B.2

| | 1A | 2A | 3A | 4A | 5A | 6A | 7A |
|---|---|---|---|---|---|---|---|
| 2 | | | | 6, C, metalloid | 7, N, nonmetal | 8, O, nonmetal | |
| 3 | | 12, Mg, metal | 13, Al, metal | 14, Si, metalloid | 15, P, nonmetal | 16, S, nonmetal | 17, Cl, nonmetal |
| 4 | | 20, Ca, metal | | | 33, As, uncertain | 34, Se, uncertain | |
| 5 | | | | 50, Sn, metal | | | 53, I, uncertain |
| 6 | | | | 82, Pb, metal | | | |

# How It Works

## Purpose 📦

Students will learn how electron beams and phosphors are used to create images on television screens.

## Background

In electroluminescence, solid materials called phosphors emit light when exposed to radiation. Phosphors generally consist of lanthanide series elements. For example, a small amount of europium oxide added to yttrium oxide results in a bright red phosphor. Hundreds of thousands of types of phosphors have now been synthesized. Phosphors are commonly used in computer and radar screens and fluorescent lamps.

## Visual Learning

Phosphors are arranged in clusters of dots called pixels. Turn on a television. Allow students to hold a hand lens up to the screen to look for the individual pixels. They should stand about an arm's length away from the screen.

## Teaching Strategies

Ask students to think about how the speed at which the electron beams scan the screen affects the clarity of the pictures. Have students research and summarize the technology of high definition television.

## Thinking Critically

1. The phosphors used in a television screen are stimulated to glow when they are hit with a beam of electrons. These beams are created only when the television is turned on and is receiving an electronic signal.
2. The phosphors must glow long enough for an entire picture to form. If the first phosphors scanned by the beam no longer glow by the time the

# How It Works
## Television Screen

Most television screens are part of a cathode ray tube. As you know, a cathode ray tube is an evacuated chamber which produces a beam of electrons, known as a cathode ray. Electronic circuitry inside the television processes an electronic signal received from the television station. The processed signal is used to vary the strength of several electron beams, while magnetic fields are used to direct the beams to different parts of the screen.

1 The television receives an electronic signal from a television station by way of an antenna or cable.

2 Electronic circuits process and amplify the signal.

3 Electron beams are directed at the screen end of the cathode ray tube.

Electron beams

Glass screen

Mask

Cathodes

Anodes

Horizontal and vertical deflecting electromagnets

Coating of phosphor strips

4 Phosphors in the screen glow in red, green, and blue. Combinations of the phosphor colors form the screen image.

### Thinking Critically

1. **Relating Cause and Effect** Why don't the phosphors in a television screen glow when the television is turned off?

2. **Inferring** Why is the length of time over which a phosphor emits light an important factor to consider when designing a television screen?

172    **Chapter 6** The Periodic Table and Periodic Law

last phosphors are scanned, a complete image could not be formed. However, it is also important that the phosphors do not glow for too long, as this would not allow for new images to form quickly.

## Summary

### 6.1 Development of the Modern Periodic Table

- Periodic law states that when the elements are arranged by increasing atomic number, there is a periodic repetition of their chemical and physical properties.

- Newlands's law of octaves, which was never accepted by fellow scientists, organized the elements by increasing atomic mass. Mendeleev's periodic table, which also organized elements by increasing atomic mass, became the first widely accepted organization scheme for the elements. Moseley fixed the errors inherent in Mendeleev's table by organizing the elements by increasing atomic number.

- The periodic table organizes the elements into periods (rows) and groups (columns) by increasing atomic number. Elements with similar properties are in the same group.

- Elements are classified as either metals, nonmetals, or metalloids. The stair-step line on the table separates metals from nonmetals. Metalloids border the stair-step line.

### 6.2 Classification of the Elements

- Elements in the same group on the periodic table have similar chemical properties because they have the same valence electron configuration.

- The four blocks of the periodic table can be characterized as follows:

  s-block: filled or partially filled s orbitals.
  p-block: filled or partially filled p orbitals.
  d-block: filled outermost s orbital of energy level $n$, and filled or partially filled d orbitals of energy level $n - 1$.
  f-block: filled outermost s orbital, and filled or partially filled 4f and 5f orbitals.

- For the group A elements, an atom's group number equals its number of valence electrons.

- The energy level of an atom's valence electrons equals its period number.

- The $s^2p^6$ electron configuration of the group 8A elements (noble gases) is exceptionally stable.

### 6.3 Periodic Trends

- Atomic radii generally decrease as you move left-to-right across a period, and increase as you move down a group.

- Positive ions are smaller than the neutral atoms from which they form. Negative ions are larger than the neutral atoms from which they form.

- Ionic radii of both positive and negative ions decrease as you move left-to-right across a period. Ionic radii of both positive and negative ions increase as you move down a group.

- Ionization energy indicates how strongly an atom holds onto its electrons. After the valence electrons have been removed from an atom, there is a tremendous jump in the ionization energy required to remove the next electron.

- Ionization energies generally increase as you move left-to-right across a period, and decrease as you move down a group.

- The octet rule states that atoms gain, lose, or share electrons in order to acquire the stable electron configuration of a noble gas.

- Electronegativity, which indicates the ability of atoms of an element to attract electrons in a chemical bond, plays a role in determining the type of bond formed between elements in a compound.

- Electronegativity values range from 0.7 to 3.96, and generally increase as you move left-to-right across a period, and decrease as you move down a group.

## Vocabulary

- alkali metal (p. 155)
- alkaline earth metal (p. 155)
- electronegativity (p. 168)
- group (p. 154)
- halogen (p. 158)
- inner transition metal (p. 158)
- ion (p. 165)
- ionization energy (p. 167)
- metal (p. 155)
- metalloid (p. 158)
- noble gas (p. 158)
- nonmetal (p. 158)
- octet rule (p. 168)
- period (p. 154)
- periodic law (p. 153)
- representative element (p. 154)
- transition element (p. 154)
- transition metal (p. 158)

chemistrymc.com/vocabulary_puzzlemaker

## Using the Vocabulary

To reinforce chapter vocabulary, have students write a sentence using each term. **L2** **ELL**

## Review Strategies

- Have students work in cooperative groups to create a puzzle of scrambled words using the vocabulary from Chapter 6. When complete, the puzzle should be handed to another group to solve. The group completing the puzzle will unscramble the words and provide a definition. **L2**
- Have students label a blank periodic table with as many of the trends as they have studied. **L2**
- Problems from Appendix A or the **Supplemental Problems** booklet can be used for review. **L2**

**VOCABULARY PuzzleMaker**

For additional help with vocabulary, have students access the Vocabulary PuzzleMaker online.

**chemistrymc.com/ vocabulary_puzzlemaker**

**Chemistry Online**

## EXAM*VIEW*® PRO

### Use Exam*View*® Pro Testmaker CD-ROM to:

- Create **multiple versions** of tests.
- Create **modified** tests with one mouse click for struggling students.
- **Edit** existing questions and add your own questions.
- **Build** tests based on national curriculum standards.

**National Science Content Standards**

**Pages 172-173**
UCP.1, UCP.2, UCP.5; B.6; E.1, E.2; G.2, G.3

## Concept Mapping

**25.** 1. periodic table;
2. electron configuration;
3. periodic trends;
4.–7. electronegativity, ionic radius, atomic radius, ionization energy

## Mastering Concepts

**26.** Mendeleev used atomic mass instead of atomic number to order the elements. This resulted in some elements being out of order. Moseley used atomic number.

**27.** Newlands introduced the idea of periodically repeating properties.

**28.** Mendeleev's work was published first, he did more to show periodic trends, and he predicted properties of several yet-to-be-discovered elements.

**29.** The elements were arranged by increasing atomic mass into columns with similar properties.

**30.** When the elements are arranged by increasing atomic number, there is a periodic repetition of their chemical and physical properties.

**31. a.** nonmetal **d.** metal
**b.** metal **e.** nonmetal
**c.** metalloid **f.** metal

**32.** Metals are generally dense, solid, shiny, ductile, malleable, and good conductors of heat and electricity.

**33. a.** 2; **b.** 4; **c.** 3; **d.** 1

**34. a.** rep.; **b.** rep.; **c.** rep.; **d.** trans.; **e.** rep.; **f.** trans.

**35.** See the Solutions Manual for a sample table.

**36.** properties describe a metal; left of the stair step line

**37.** Metalloids have properties intermediate between metals and nonmetals.

# Chemistry Online

Go to the Chemistry Web site at chemistrymc.com for additional Chapter 6 Assessment.

## Concept Mapping

**25.** Complete the concept map using the following terms: electronegativity, electron configuration, periodic trends, ionic radius, atomic radius, ionization energy, and periodic table.

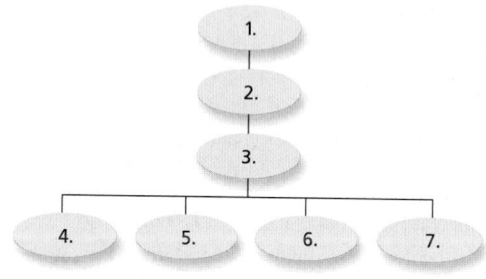

## Mastering Concepts

**26.** Explain how Mendeleev's periodic table was in error. How was this error fixed? (6.1)

**27.** Explain the contribution of Newlands's law of octaves to the development of the modern periodic table. (6.1)

**28.** German chemist Lothar Meyer and Russian chemist Dmitri Mendeleev both proposed similar periodic tables in 1869. Why is Mendeleev generally given credit for the periodic table? (6.1)

**29.** How was Mendeleev's periodic table organized? (6.1)

**30.** What is the periodic law? (6.1)

**31.** Identify each of the following as a metal, nonmetal, or metalloid. (6.1)

**a.** oxygen **d.** iron
**b.** barium **e.** neon
**c.** germanium **f.** praseodymium

**32.** Describe the general characteristics of metals. (6.1)

**33.** Match each numbered item on the right with the lettered item that it is related to on the left. (6.1)

**a.** alkali metals **1.** group 8A
**b.** halogens **2.** group 1A
**c.** alkaline earth metals **3.** group 2A
**d.** noble gases **4.** group 7A

**34.** Identify each of the elements in problem 31 as a representative element or a transition element. (6.1)

**35.** Sketch a simplified periodic table and use labels to identify the alkali metals, alkaline earth metals, transition metals, inner transition metals, noble gases, and halogens. (6.1)

**36.** A shiny solid element also is ductile. What side of the periodic table is it likely to be found? (6.1)

**37.** What are the general properties of a metalloid? List three metalloid elements. (6.1)

**38.** What is the purpose of the heavy stair-step line on the periodic table? (6.1)

**39.** Describe the two types of numbering used to identify groups on the periodic table. (6.1)

**40.** Give the chemical symbol of each of the following elements. (6.1)

**a.** the two elements that are liquids at room temperature
**b.** the noble gas with the greatest atomic mass
**c.** any metal from group 4A
**d.** any inner transition metal

**41.** Why do the elements chlorine and iodine have similar chemical properties? (6.2)

**42.** How are the numbers of valence electrons of the group A elements related to the group number? (6.2)

**43.** How is the energy level of an atom's valence electrons related to the period it is in on the periodic table? (6.2)

**44.** How many valence electrons do each of the noble gases have? (6.2)

**45.** What are the four blocks of the periodic table? (6.2)

**46.** In general, what electron configuration has the greatest stability? (6.2)

**47.** Determine the group, period, and block in which each of the following elements is located on the periodic table. (6.2)

**a.** $[Kr]5s^24d^1$ **c.** $[He]2s^22p^6$
**b.** $[Ar]4s^23d^{10}4p^3$ **d.** $[Ne]3s^23p^1$

**48.** Categorize each of the elements in problem 47 as a representative element or a transition metal. (6.2)

**49.** Explain how an atom's valence electron configuration determines its place on the periodic table. (6.2)

**50.** Write the electron configuration for the element fitting each of the following descriptions. (6.2)

**a.** the metal in group 5A
**b.** the halogen in period 3
**c.** the alkali metal in period 2
**d.** the transition metal that is a liquid at room temperature

chemistrymc.com/chapter_test

**38.** The line separates metals from nonmetals. Most elements bordering the line are metalloids.

**37.** Metalloids have properties intermediate between metals and nonmetals. (B, Si, Ge, As, Sb, Te, Po, At) are metalloids.

### Resource Manager

Chapter Assessment, pp. 31–36 **L2**
Supplemental Problems, Ch. 6
ExamView® Pro CD-ROM
MindJogger Videoquizzes DVD/VHS
Solutions Manual, Ch. 6
Chemistry Interactive CD-ROM,
Ch. 6 quiz

51. Explain why the radius of an atom cannot be measured directly. (6.3)

52. Given any two elements within a group, is the element with the larger atomic number likely to have a larger or smaller atomic radius than the other element? (6.2)

53. Which elements are characterized as having their d orbitals fill with electrons as you move left-to-right across a period? (6.2)

54. Explain why is it harder to remove an inner shell electron than a valence electron from an atom. (6.3)

55. An element forms a negative ion when ionized. On what side of the periodic table is the element located? Explain. (6.3)

56. Of the elements magnesium, calcium, and barium, which forms the ion with the largest radius? The smallest? What periodic trend explains this? (6.3)

57. What is ionization energy? (6.3)

58. Explain why each successive ionization of an electron requires a greater amount of energy. (6.3)

59. Which group has the highest ionization energies? Explain why. (6.3)

60. Define an ion. (6.3)

61. How does the ionic radius of a nonmetal compare with its atomic radius? Explain why the change in radius occurs. (6.3)

62. Explain why atomic radii decrease as you move left-to-right across a period. (6.3)

63. Which element in each pair has the larger ionization energy? (6.3)
   **a.** Li, N
   **b.** Kr, Ne
   **c.** Cs, Li

64. Explain the octet rule. (6.3)

65. Use the illustration of spheres A and B to answer each of the following questions. Explain your reasoning for each answer. (6.3)
   **a.** If A is an ion and B is an atom of the same element, is the ion a positive or negative ion?

   **b.** If A and B represent the atomic radii of two elements in the same period, what is their correct order (left-to-right)?
   **c.** If A and B represent the ionic radii of two elements in the same group, what is their correct order (top-to-bottom)?

66. How many valence electrons do elements in each of the following groups have? (6.3)
   **a.** group 8A
   **b.** group 3A
   **c.** group 1A

67. $Na^+$ and $Mg^{2+}$ ions each have ten electrons surrounding their nuclei. Which ion would you expect to have the larger radius? Why? (6.3)

## Mixed Review

*Sharpen your problem-solving skills by answering the following.*

68. Match each numbered item on the right with the lettered item that it is related to on the left.
   **a.** group A elements    **1.** periods
   **b.** columns    **2.** representative elements
   **c.** group B elements    **3.** groups
   **d.** rows    **4.** transition elements

69. Which element in each pair is more electronegative?
   **a.** K, As
   **b.** N, Sb
   **c.** Sr, Be

70. Explain why the s-block of the periodic table is two groups wide, the p-block is six groups wide, and the d-block is ten groups wide.

71. Arrange the elements oxygen, sulfur, tellurium, and selenium in order of increasing atomic radii. Is your order an example of a group trend or a period trend?

72. Identify the elements with the following valence electron configurations.
   **a.** $5s^1$    **c.** $3s^2$
   **b.** $4s^2 3d^2$    **d.** $4s^2 4p^3$

73. Which of the following is not a reason why atomic radii increase as you move down a group?
   **a.** shielding of inner electrons
   **b.** valence electrons in larger orbitals
   **c.** increased charge in the nucleus

74. Explain why there are no p-block elements in the first period of the periodic table.

75. Identify each of the following as an alkali metal, alkaline earth metal, transition metal, or inner transition metal.
   **a.** cesium    **d.** ytterbium
   **b.** zirconium    **e.** uranium
   **c.** gold    **f.** francium

76. An element is a brittle solid that does not conduct electricity well. Is the element a metal, nonmetal, or metalloid?

39. One system uses 1A–8A for representative elements, and 1B–8B for transition elements. The other system numbers the columns 1–18 left to right.

40. **a.** Br, Hg; **b.** Rn; **c.** Sn or Pb; **d.** elements 58–71 or 90–103

41. They have the same valence electron configuration ($s^2 p^5$).

42. The number of valence electrons equals the group number for group A elements.

43. The energy level of an atom's valence electrons equals its period number.

44. All noble gases have eight valence electrons, except for helium, which has two.

45. s-, p-, d-, and f-block

46. $ns^2 np^6$, where $n$ is the energy level

47. **a.** 3B, period 5, d-block
   **b.** 5A, period 4, p-block
   **c.** 8A, period 2, p-block
   **d.** 3A, period 3, p-block

48. **a.** trans. metal  **c.** rep.
   **b.** rep.    **d.** rep.

49. Elements in a given column have the same number of valence electrons. The energy level of an atom's valence electrons determines its period.

50. **a.** Bi: $[Xe]6s^2 4f^{14} 5d^{10} 6p^3$
   **b.** Cl: $[Ne]3s^2 3p^5$
   **c.** Li : $[He]2s^1$
   **d.** Hg: $[Xe]6s^2 4f^{14} 5d^{10}$

51. because the boundaries of an atom are indistinct

52. larger

53. transition metals

54. There are fewer shielding electrons between inner electrons and the nucleus. Thus, the inner electrons are more tightly bound to

the nucleus by attractive electrostatic forces.

55. Elements on the right side of the periodic table gain electrons to gain a stable octet.

56. $Ba^{2+}$ is the largest; $Mg^{2+}$ is the smallest; ionic size increases down a group.

57. Ionization energy is the energy needed to remove an electron from a neutral atom in its gaseous state.

58. With each removed electron, there

are fewer electrons to shield the remaining electrons from the electrostatic force of attraction of the nucleus. The increased nuclear attraction makes it more difficult to remove subsequent electrons.

59. The group 8A elements have the highest ionization energies because their electron configurations are the most stable.

60. An ion is an atom or a bonded group

**National Science Content Standards**

**Pages 174-175**
UCP.1, UCP.2, UCP.5; B.1, B.2; E.2; G.2, G.3

## CHAPTER 6 ASSESSMENT (left column)

of atoms with a positive or negative charge.

**61.** The ionic radius of a nonmetal is larger than its neutral atom. Nonmetals tend to gain electrons in the atom's current energy level; these additional electrons repel each other and increase the size of the ion.

**62.** Atomic radii decrease left-to-right because the nuclear charge increases as the shielding of inner core electrons remains constant. The increased attraction of the nucleus for its electrons pulls the electrons inward, resulting in a decreased atomic size.

**63. a.** N; **b.** Ne; **c.** Li

**64.** The $ns^2np^6$ electron configuration, known as the octet configuration, contains eight electrons and generally has the lowest energy and is the most stable. Atoms gain, lose, or share electrons in order to obtain the stable octet configuration.

**65. a.** The ion is negative. A negative ion is always larger than its atom.
**b.** A is to the left of B. Atomic radius in a period decreases left-to-right.
**c.** A is below B. Ionic radius increases down a group.

**66. a.** 8; **b.** 3; **c.** 1

**67.** $Na^+$ has the larger radius. The greater nuclear charge of $Mg^{2+}$ produces an increased inward pull on its ten electrons and results in a smaller radius.

## Thinking Critically

**77. Interpreting Data** Given the following data about an atom's ionization energies, predict its valence electron configuration. Explain your reasoning.

| Ionization Data | |
|---|---|
| **Ionization** | **Ionization Energy (kJ/mol)** |
| First | 734 |
| Second | 1850 |
| Third | 16 432 |

**78. Applying Concepts** Sodium forms a 1+ ion, while fluorine forms a 1− ion. Write the electron configuration for each ion. Why don't these two elements form 2+ and 2− ions, respectively?

**79. Interpreting Data** The melting points of the period 6 elements are plotted versus atomic number in the graph shown below. Determine the trends in melting point by analyzing the graph and the orbital configurations of the elements. Form a hypothesis that explains the trends. (Hint: In Chapter 5, you learned that half-filled sets of orbitals are more stable than other configurations of partially filled orbitals.)

**Melting Points of the Period 6 Elements**

| Group 5A Density Data | | |
|---|---|---|
| **Element** | **Atomic Number** | **Density (g/cm³)** |
| nitrogen | 7 | $1.25 \times 10^{-3}$ |
| phosphorus | 15 | 1.82 |
| arsenic | 33 | 5.73 |
| antimony | 51 | 6.70 |
| bismuth | 83 | 9.78 |

**80. Making and Using Graphs** The densities of the group 5A elements are given in the table above. Plot density versus atomic number and state any trends you observe.

## Writing in Chemistry

**81.** In the early 1800s, German chemist J. W. Dobereiner proposed that some elements could be classified into sets of three, called triads. Research and write a report on Dobereiner's triads. What elements comprised the triads? How were the properties of elements within a triad similar?

**82.** Electron affinity is another periodic property of the elements. Research and write a report on what electron affinity is and describe its group and period trends.

## Cumulative Review

*Refresh your understanding of previous chapters by answering the following.*

**83.** Define matter. Identify whether or not each of the following is a form of matter. (Chapter 1)
  **a.** microwaves
  **b.** helium inside a balloon
  **c.** heat from the Sun
  **d.** velocity
  **e.** a speck of dust
  **f.** the color blue

**84.** Convert the following mass measurements as indicated. (Chapter 2)
  **a.** 1.1 cm to meters
  **b.** 76.2 pm to millimeters
  **c.** 11 Mg to kilograms
  **d.** 7.23 micrograms to kilograms

**85.** How is the energy of a quantum of emitted radiation related to the frequency of the radiation? (Chapter 5)

**86.** What element has the ground-state electron configuration of $[Ar]4s^23d^6$? (Chapter 5).

## Mixed Review

**68. a.** 2; **b.** 3; **c.** 4; **d.** 1
**69. a.** As ; **b.** N; **c.** Be
**70.** The s block represents the filling of the s orbital, which holds a maximum of two electrons. The p-block represents the filling of the three p orbitals, which hold a maximum of six electrons. The d-block represents the filling of the five d orbitals, which hold a maximum of ten electrons.

**71.** The order is O, S, Se, and Te. This is an example of a group trend.
**72. a.** Rb; **b.** Ti; **c.** Mg; **d.** As
**73.** c

**74.** The p orbital does not exist for energy level 1. The first energy level consists only of a single s orbital that holds a maximum of two electrons.
**75. a.** alkali metal; **b.** transition metal; **c.** transition metal; **d.** transition metal; **e.** inner transition metal; **f.** alkali metal
**76.** The element is most likely a nonmetal.

*Use these questions and the test-taking tip to prepare for your standardized test.*

**1.** Periodic law states that elements show a

  **a.** repetition of their physical properties when arranged by increasing atomic radius.

  **b.** repetition of their chemical properties when arranged by increasing atomic mass.

  **c.** periodic repetition of their properties when arranged by increasing atomic number.

  **d.** periodic repetition of their properties when arranged by increasing atomic mass.

**2.** Elements in the same group of the periodic table have the same

  **a.** number of valence electrons.

  **b.** physical properties.

  **c.** number of electrons.

  **d.** electron configuration.

**3.** All of the following are true EXCEPT

  **a.** atomic radius of Na < atomic radius of Mg.

  **b.** electronegativity of C > electronegativity of B.

  **c.** ionic radius of Br$^-$ > atomic radius of Br.

  **d.** first ionization energy of K > first ionization energy of Rb.

**4.** Which of the following is NOT true of an atom obeying the octet rule?

  **a.** obtains a full set of eight valence electrons

  **b.** acquires the valence configuration of a noble gas

  **c.** possesses eight electrons in total

  **d.** has a $s^2p^6$ valence configuration

**5.** What is the group, period, and block of an atom with the electron configuration $[Ar]4s^23d^{10}4p^4$?

  **a.** group 4A, period 4, d-block

  **b.** group 6A, period 3, p-block

  **c.** group 4A, period 4, p-block

  **d.** group 6A, period 4, p-block

**6.** Moving down a group on the periodic table, which two atomic properties follow the same trend?

  **a.** atomic radius and ionization energy

  **b.** ionic radius and atomic radius

  **c.** ionization energy and ionic radius

  **d.** ionic radius and electronegativity

**Interpreting Tables** Use the periodic table and the table at the bottom of the page to answer questions 7 and 8.

**7.** It can be predicted that silicon will experience a large jump in ionization energy after its

  **a.** second ionization.

  **b.** third ionization.

  **c.** fourth ionization.

  **d.** fifth ionization.

**8.** Which of the following requires the most energy?

  **a.** second ionization of Li

  **b.** fourth ionization of N

  **c.** first ionization of Ne

  **d.** third ionization of Be

**9.** Niobium (Nb) is a(n)

  **a.** nonmetal.          **c.** alkali metal.

  **b.** transition metal.   **d.** halogen.

**10.** It can be predicted that element 118 would have properties similar to a(n)

  **a.** alkali earth metal. **c.** metalloid.

  **b.** halogen.            **d.** noble gas.

---

### TEST-TAKING TIP

**Practice, Practice, Practice** Practice to improve your performance on standardized tests. Don't compare yourself to anyone else.

---

## Thinking Critically

**77.** It's a 2A element with a $ns^2$ configuration. The two s electrons are easily removed, but the third electron must be removed from the ($n$-1) p orbital, which is much more tightly held.

**78.** Both ions have the configuration $1s^22s^22p^6$, a stable, noble gas configuration.

**79.** For the d-block elements, the highest values occur for half-filled and near half-filled d orbitals. (Re with a configuration of $5d^5$ has the highest melting point.) Relating to Hund's rule, it seems that metallic bonding strengthens as the number of unpaired electrons increases, reaching a maximum when the orbital is half-filled. Note that Hg and Rn have no unpaired electrons and substantially lower melting points. For the p-block elements (81–86), again the elements with unpaired p electrons tend to have higher melting points.

**80.** The graph should show density increasing with increasing atomic number. Note that the density of nitrogen is so low because it is the only element that exists as a gas (the others are solids). See the Solutions Manual for graph.

---

| | | Ionization energy (kJ/mol)* | | | | | | | | |
|---|---|---|---|---|---|---|---|---|---|---|
| Element | Valence electrons | 1st | 2nd | 3rd | 4th | 5th | 6th | 7th | 8th | 9th |
| Li | 1 | 520 | 7300 | | | | | | | |
| Be | 2 | 900 | 1760 | 14 850 | | | | | | |
| B | 3 | 800 | 2430 | 3660 | 25 020 | | | | | |
| C | 4 | 1090 | 2350 | 4620 | 6220 | 37 830 | | | | |
| N | 5 | 1400 | 2860 | 4580 | 7480 | 9440 | 53 270 | | | |
| O | 6 | 1310 | 3390 | 5300 | 7470 | 10 980 | 13 330 | 71 330 | | |
| F | 7 | 1680 | 3370 | 6050 | 8410 | 11 020 | 15 160 | 17 870 | 92 040 | |
| Ne | 8 | 2080 | 3950 | 6120 | 9370 | 12 180 | 15 240 | 20 000 | 23 070 | 115 380 |

**Successive Ionization Energies for the Period 2 Elements**

\* mol is an abbreviation for mole, a quantity of matter.

 chemistrymc.com/standardized_test

---

## Cumulative Review

**83.** Matter is anything that has mass and takes up space.

  **a.** no      **d.** no

  **b.** yes     **e.** yes

  **c.** no      **f.** no

**84. a.** $1.1 \times 10^{-2}$ m

  **b.** $7.62 \times 10^{-8}$ mm

  **c.** $1.1 \times 10^4$ kg

  **d.** $7.23 \times 10^{-9}$ kg

**85.** The energy of a quantum equals the frequency times Planck's constant.

**86.** iron

## Standardized Test Practice

**1.** c      **6.** b

**2.** a      **7.** c

**3.** a      **8.** d

**4.** c      **9.** b

**5.** d      **10.** d

---

**National Science Content Standards**

Pages 176-177
UCP.1, UCP.2, UCP.5; B.1, B.2; G.3

# Resource Manager

| Section | Objectives | Activities/Features |
|---|---|---|
| **Section 7.1**<br>**Properties of s-Block Elements**<br>1 session<br>🔲 ½ block | 1. **Explain** how elements in a given group are both similar and different.<br>2. **Discuss** the properties of hydrogen.<br>3. **Describe** and **compare** the properties of alkali metals and alkaline earth metals. | **Discovery Lab:** Magnetic Materials, p. 179<br>**Careers Using Chemistry:** Dietician, p. 182<br>**MiniLab:** Properties of Magnesium, p. 184 |
| **Section 7.2**<br>**Properties of p-Block Elements**<br>1½ sessions<br>🔲 ½ block | 4. **Describe** and **compare** properties of p-block elements.<br>5. **Define** allotropes and provide examples.<br>6. **Explain** the importance to organisms of selected p-block elements. | **History Connection**, p. 190<br>**Problem-Solving Lab:** Cost of Fertilizer, p. 191 |
| **Section 7.3**<br>**Properties of d-Block and f-Block Elements**<br>2½ sessions<br>🔲 1 block | 7. **Compare** the electron configurations of transition and inner transition metals.<br>8. **Describe** the properties of transition elements.<br>9. **Explain** why some transition metals form compounds with color and some have magnetic properties. | **ChemLab:** Hard Water, pp. 202–203<br>**How It Works:** Semiconductor Chips, p. 204 |

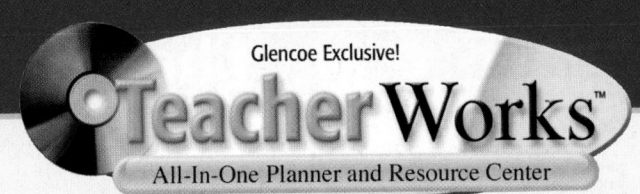

| National Science Content Standards | State/Local Standards | Reproducible Masters | Transparencies |
|---|---|---|---|
| UCP.1, UCP.2, UCP.5; A.1; B.1, B.2, B.3, B.6; E.2; F.5; G.3 | | **Study Guide for Content Mastery,** pp. 37–38 **L2** <br> **ChemLab and MiniLab Worksheets,** pp. 25–28 **L2** <br> **Challenge Problems,** p. 7 **L3** <br> **Small-Scale Laboratory Manual,** pp. 13–15 **L2** | **Section Focus** <br> **Transparency 23** **L1** **ELL** <br> **Teaching** <br> **Transparency 22** **L2** **ELL** |
| UCP.1, UCP.2, UCP.5; B.1, B.2, B.3; E.1, E.2; F.1, F.4, F.5, F.6; G.3 | | **Study Guide for Content Mastery,** pp. 39–40 **L2** | **Section Focus** <br> **Transparency 24** **L1** **ELL** <br> **Teaching** <br> **Transparency 23** **L2** **ELL** |
| UCP.1, UCP.2, UCP.5; A.1, A.2; B.1, B.2, B.3, B.6; E.1, E.2; F.1, F.4, F.6; G.1 | | **Study Guide for Content Mastery,** pp. 41–42 **L2** <br> **Small-Scale Laboratory Manual,** pp. 17–20 **L2** | **Section Focus** <br> **Transparency 25** **L1** **ELL** <br> **Teaching** <br> **Transparency 24** **L2** **ELL** |

**Key to National Science Content Standards:** UCP = Unifying Concepts and Processes, A = Science as Inquiry, B = Physical Science, C = Life Science, D = Earth and Space Sciences, E = Science and Technology, F = Science in Personal and Social Perspectives, G = History and Nature of Science

Refer to pages 4T–5T of the Teacher Guide for an explanation of the National Science Content Standards correlations.

# Resource Manager

## Materials List

### ChemLab (pages 202–203)

large test tubes (3), stoppers (3), test-tube rack, grease pencil, 25-mL graduated cylinder, distilled water, hard water, 250-mL beaker, balance, filter paper, dish detergent, dropper, washing soda ($Na_2CO_3 \cdot 10H_2O$), metric ruler

### Discovery Lab (page 179)

bar magnet, aluminum foil, paper clips, coins, hair pin, soda can, empty soup cans, assorted metal items

### MiniLab (page 184)

test tube, test-tube rack, 10-mL graduated cylinder, hydrochloric acid, magnesium ribbon, sandpaper, cardboard, wood splint, matches

### Demonstration (pages 192–193)

roll sulfur (20 g), distilled water, hammer, cloth towel, laboratory burner, 250-mL beaker, test tube, test-tube holder, conductivity tester, spatula

## Preparation of Solutions

For a review of solution preparation, see page 46T of the Teacher Guide.

Quantities are for a class of 30 students.

### ChemLab (pages 202–203)

**hard water**  Dissolve 1.0 g anhydrous magnesium sulfate ($MgSO_4$) in 1 L distilled water. As an alternative, you may use 2.1 g Epsom salts (magnesium sulfate heptahydrate, $MgSO_4 \cdot 7H_2O$).

### MiniLab (page 184)

**hydrochloric acid (1$M$)**  Add 10 mL concentrated (12$M$) hydrochloric acid to 110 mL distilled water. **CAUTION:** Do not add the water to the acid.

## Assessment Resources

**Chapter Assessment,** pp. 37–42
**MindJogger Videoquizzes DVD/VHS**
**Alternate Assessment in the Science Classroom**
**ExamView® Pro CD-ROM**
**Solutions Manual,** Chapter 7
**Supplemental Problems,** Chapter 7
**Performance Assessment in the Science Classroom**
**Chemistry Interactive CD-ROM,** Chapter 7 quiz

## Additional Resources

**Spanish Resources** ELL
**Guided Reading Audio Program,** Chapter 7 ELL
**Cooperative Learning in the Science Classroom**
**Lab and Safety Skills in the Science Classroom**
**Lesson Plans**
**Block Scheduling Lesson Plans**
**Chemistrymc.com**

## Glencoe Technology

The following multimedia for this chapter are available from Glencoe.

**VIDEOTAPE/DVD**
MindJogger Videoquizzes,
Chapter 7

**CD-ROM**
**Chemistry: Matter and Change**
*Organizing Elements in a Periodic Table,* Exploration
*Synthetic Gems,* Video
*Nonmetallic Elements,* Experiment
*Semiconductors,* Video
*Shape of Memory Metals,* Video

**CD-ROM**
**ExamView® Pro Testmaker**

**CD-ROM**
**Interactive Chalkboard**

**CD-ROM**
**TeacherWorks**™

## Multiple Learning Styles

Look for the following icons for strategies that emphasize different learning modalities.

***Kinesthetic***
Portfolio, p. 180; Enrichment, p. 183; Differentiated Instruction, p. 200

***Visual-Spatial***
Reinforcement, p. 179; Differentiated Instruction, p. 181; Concept Development, p. 186; Portfolio, p. 195; Portfolio, p. 199; Enrichment, p. 200; Reteach, p. 201

***Interpersonal***
Differentiated Instruction, p. 191; Concept Development, p. 195; Check for Understanding, p. 196

***Intrapersonal***
Concept Development, p. 189; Differentiated Instruction, p. 189

***Linguistic***
Chemistry Journal, pp. 181, 187, 198

***Logical-Mathematical***
Math in Chemistry, p. 192

***Auditory-Musical***
Portfolio, p. 194

## Key to Teaching Strategies

**L1** Level 1 activities should be appropriate for students with learning difficulties.

**L2** Level 2 activities should be within the ability range of all students.

**L3** Level 3 activities are designed for above-average students.

**ELL** ELL activities should be within the ability range of English Language Learners.

**COOP LEARN** Cooperative Learning activities are designed for small group work.

**P** These strategies represent student products that can be placed into a best-work portfolio.

 These strategies are useful in a block scheduling format.

## Assessment Planner

**Portfolio Assessment**
Portfolio, TWE, pp. 180, 194, 195, 199, 205
MiniLab, TWE, p. 184
Demonstration, TWE, p. 193
ChemLab, TWE, p. 203

**Performance Assessment**
Discovery Lab, SE, p. 179
MiniLab, SE, p. 184
ChemLab, SE, pp. 202–203

**Knowledge Assessment**
Assessment, TWE, pp. 183, 185, 196, 199, 201
Section Assessment, SE, pp. 185, 196, 201
Problem-Solving Lab, TWE, p. 191
Chapter Assessment, SE, pp. 206–209

**Skill Assessment**
Assessment, TWE, p. 195

**CHAPTER**

## Tying to Previous Knowledge

Have students review the following concepts before studying this chapter.
Chapter 5: electron configuration
Chapter 6: periodic trends; properties of metals, nonmetals, and metalloids

## Using the Photo

Have students look at the opening photo of the amphora. Explain that an amphora was used to store food and wine, and the inside was usually coated with a lead glaze to make it waterproof. Ask why that is significant. Lead is toxic. Why do we line steel cans with tin? To prevent corrosion of the steel, and because tin is nontoxic.

## Chapter Themes

The following themes from the National Science Education Standards are covered in this chapter. Refer to page 4T of the Teacher Guide for an explanation of the correlations.
Systems, order, and organization (UCP.1)
Evidence, models, and explanation (UCP.2)

**PowerPoint® Presentations**
This CD-ROM is an editable Microsoft® PowerPoint® presentation that includes:
• Section presentations
• Section checks
• Image bank
• Links to Chemistry Online
• All transparencies
• Animations
• Audio

# The Elements

## What You'll Learn
▶ You will classify elements based on their electron configurations.
▶ You will relate electron configurations to the properties of elements.
▶ You will identify the sources and uses of selected elements.

## Why It's Important
What you know about an element can affect the choices you make. Before all of its properties were known, toxic lead glazes were used to seal clay storage containers. Modern steel cans are lined with tin, which is a non-toxic element similar to lead.

Visit the Chemistry Web site at **chemistrymc.com** to find links about the elements.

Some historians think that drinking wine from lead-glazed vases contributed to the fall of the Roman Empire.

## DISCOVERY LAB

### Purpose
Students will observe the interaction of a magnet with various substances.

### Process Skills
Acquiring and analyzing information, classifying, comparing and contrasting, observing and inferring

### Safety and Disposal
Magnets can damage or erase data on floppy disks and cassette tapes. All materials can be reused.

### Teaching Strategies
• Encourage students to test as many substances as possible.
• Some soda pop cans are made of steel and are magnetic; others are made from

## DISCOVERY LAB

### Magnetic Materials

**Y**ou know that magnets can attract some materials. In this lab, you will classify materials based on their interaction with a magnet and look for a pattern in your data.

#### Safety Precautions

 Always wear your safety goggles during lab.

#### Procedure

1. Working with a partner, review the properties of magnets. Arrange the bar magnets so that they are attracted to one another. Then arrange them so that they repel one another.

2. Test each item with your magnet. Record your observations.

3. Test as many other items in the classroom as time allows. Predict the results before testing each item.

#### Analysis

Look at the group of items that were attracted to the magnet. What do these items have in common? In Section 7.3, you will learn more about what determines whether a material is magnetic.

**Materials**

bar magnet
aluminum foil
paper clips
coins
hair pin

soda cans
empty soup cans
variety of other items

Before presenting the lesson, display **Section Focus Transparency 23** on the overhead projector. Have students answer the accompanying questions using **Section Focus Transparency Master 23.** L1 ELL

---

## Section 7.1 — Properties of s-Block Elements

### Objectives

- **Explain** how elements in a given group are both similar and different.

- **Discuss** the properties of hydrogen.

- **Describe** and **compare** the properties of alkali metals and alkaline earth metals.

### Vocabulary

diagonal relationship

If you could travel through the universe to collect samples of matter, you would find 92 naturally occurring elements. The amount of each element would vary from location to location. Helium, which is the second most common element in the universe, is much less abundant here on Earth. Oxygen is the most abundant element on Earth. Per kilogram of Earth's crust, there are $4.64 \times 10^5$ mg of oxygen, but only $8 \times 10^{-3}$ mg of helium. Elements with atomic numbers greater than 92 do not exist in nature. These synthetic elements must be created in laboratories or nuclear reactors.

### Representative Elements

Recall from Chapter 6 that no one element can represent the properties of all elements. However, the elements in groups 1A through 8A are called representative elements because, as a group, they display a wide range of physical and chemical properties. For example, groups 1A through 8A include metals and nonmetals; highly reactive elements and some that hardly react at all; and elements that are solids, liquids, and gases at room temperature.

Elements in any given group on the periodic table have the same number of valence electrons. The number and location of valence electrons determine the chemistry of an element. Thus, elements within a group have similar physical and chemical properties. Representative elements display the range of possible valence electrons from one in group 1A to eight in group 8A. The valence electrons of representative elements are in s or p orbitals.

7.1 Properties of s-Block Elements **179**

### Resource Manager

**Study Guide for Content Mastery,** p. 38 L2
**Challenge Problems,** p. 7 L3
**Solving Problems: A Chemistry Handbook,** Section 7.1 L2
**Section Focus Transparency 23 and Master** L1 ELL
**Teaching Transparency 22 and Master** L2 ELL

---

aluminum and are not. Have both types available for students to test.
- Students may wonder why a nickel— which has magnetic character—is not attracted to the magnet. A nickel contains only about 25% nickel, so it will not react strongly to a magnet.

**Expected Results**
See analysis answers.

**Analysis**
Substances that are attracted to the magnet are metal and plastic-coated paper clips, bobby pins, some types of chalkboards, and any substance containing iron or steel. (Substances that are not attracted are nonmetals, wood, plastics, pennies, nickels, dimes, quarters, and aluminum foil and cans.)

**National Science Content Standards**

Pages 178–179
UCP.1, UCP.2, UCP.5; A.1; B.2; F.5

As students study the periodic properties of the elements, point out that chemical bonding, as well as group characteristics and properties of the elements, depends on the position of the elements in the periodic table.

Fill two balloons, one with helium and the other with hydrogen, and attach each to a long string. Separate the balloons and attach them to lab tables. Ask students to compare the balloons. Answers will vary. Both contain gas that is lighter than air. Ask students if both balloons have the same gas. Answers will vary. Attach a wood splint (or a small candle) to the end of a meter stick and light it. Bring the lit wood splint near the helium balloon first. It will pop. Then bring it near the hydrogen filled balloon. It will burst into flames. Ask students again if both balloons contained the same gas. Discuss the properties of hydrogen. Have students look at Figure 7-2, and discuss why hydrogen is no longer used in airships.

## In-Text Questions

**Page 180** Of the representative elements, which is the most reactive metal? Francium is the most reactive metal. Which is the most reactive nonmetal? Fluorine is the most reactive nonmetal.

## GLENCOE
### TECHNOLOGY

CD-ROM
**Chemistry: Matter and Change**
Exploration: *Organizing Elements in a Periodic Table*

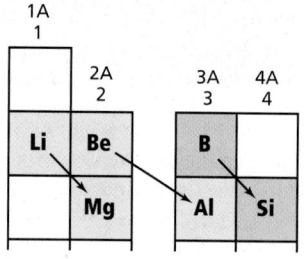

**Figure 7-1**

The diagonal arrows connect pairs of elements that have similar properties.

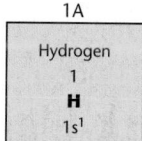

**Figure 7-2**

When the *Hindenburg* crashed in New Jersey, the hydrogen that kept the airship aloft came in contact with oxygen and exploded.

Why are the properties of elements within a group similar but not identical? Although elements within a group have the same number of valence electrons, they have different numbers of nonvalence electrons. Remember what happens as the atomic number increases within a group. As new levels of electrons are added, the atomic radius increases and the shielding effect increases. As a result, the ionization energy decreases. A lower ionization energy makes it easier for an element to lose electrons.

Recall that metals tend to lose electrons. Thus, the lower the ionization energy, the more reactive the metal. For a group of metals, reactivity *increases* as the atomic number increases. The opposite is true for nonmetals because nonmetals tend to gain electrons. The higher the ionization energy of a nonmetal, the more reactive the nonmetal. For a group of nonmetals, reactivity *decreases* as the atomic number increases. Of the representative elements, which is the most reactive metal? Which is the most reactive nonmetal? (Hint: What is the trend for ionization energy across a period?)

**Diagonal relationships** Some period 2 elements do not behave as predicted by their locations on the table. Often, the lightest element in a group is the least representative. These light elements have more in common with the period-3 element in the next group than with the period-3 element in their own group. These close relationships between elements in neighboring groups are called **diagonal relationships.** Three diagonal relationships that you will study later in this chapter are shown in **Figure 7-1.**

## Hydrogen

Hydrogen is placed in group 1A because it has one valence electron. This placement does not mean that hydrogen has the same properties as the metals in group 1A. In fact, hydrogen shares many properties with the nonmetals in group 7A. Because hydrogen has both metallic and nonmetallic properties, it is not considered part of any group.

When Henry Cavendish discovered hydrogen in 1766, he called it "flammable air" because it burned when ignited in air. In 1783, Antoine Lavoisier named hydrogen for the water that forms when hydrogen and oxygen combine. Lavoisier used the Greek roots for water (*hydro*) and to form (*genes*). **Figure 7-2** shows the explosive reaction of hydrogen and oxygen that occurred when a passenger airship crashed in 1937. The airship was kept aloft by hydrogen, which is a colorless, odorless, lighter-than-air gas under normal conditions of temperature and pressure. As a part of water and most other compounds found in organisms, hydrogen is essential to life.

The universe contains more than 90% hydrogen by mass. There are three naturally occurring hydrogen isotopes: protium, deuterium, and tritium. The vast majority of hydrogen, 99.985%, is protium (hydrogen-1), which has no neutrons. Deuterium (hydrogen-2), which makes up 0.015% of hydrogen, has one neutron. Tritium (hydrogen-3), which has two neutrons, is a radioactive isotope. It is produced when cosmic rays bombard water in the atmosphere.

The physical properties of isotopes differ slightly because of differences in atomic mass. For example, water that contains deuterium is called heavy water because the neutrons in deuterium add mass to the water molecule. Some nuclear reactors use heavy water to help keep the chain reaction going. The heavy water slows down (or moderates) the neutrons produced during nuclear fission so that they can be absorbed by the uranium fuel. You will learn more about nuclear reactions in Chapter 25.

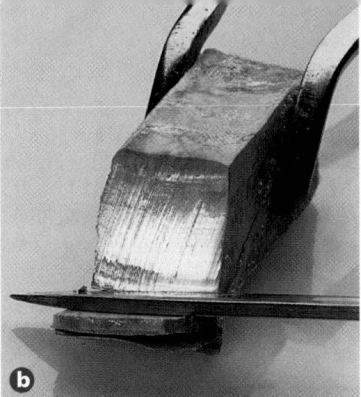

**Figure 7-3**

**a** The reaction of potassium and water produces hydrogen gas and an alkaline solution of potassium hydroxide. The heat produced by the reaction ignites the hydrogen.
**b** Sodium is as soft as cold butter. The shiny surface dulls as it reacts with oxygen.

Hydrogen's single valence electron explains its unusual set of metallic and nonmetallic properties. When a hydrogen atom acts like a nonmetal, it gains an electron and achieves the stable electron configuration of helium. When hydrogen reacts with a nonmetal such as oxygen, it acts like a metal. Hydrogen loses its single electron and forms a hydrogen ion ($H^+$). A hydrogen ion is a nucleus with a single proton. Does a hydrogen ion contain any neutrons? In Chapter 19, you will learn the role hydrogen ions play in the chemistry of acids and bases.

Hydrogen can be produced in the laboratory when a metal reacts with an acid or when electricity is used to separate water into hydrogen and oxygen. Large quantities of industrial hydrogen are produced when water reacts with methane, which is the main ingredient in natural gas. The major industrial use of hydrogen is in the production of ammonia from nitrogen and hydrogen gases. Hydrogen also is used to convert liquid vegetable oils into solid fats such as shortening. You will learn more about hydrogenation in Chapter 23, and fats and oils in Chapter 24.

## Group 1A: Alkali Metals

People used to pour water over the ashes from a wood-burning fire to produce a compound of sodium called lye. They boiled the lye with animal fat to make soap. Lye, which is the active ingredient in drain cleansers, is an example of an alkaline solution. The term *alkali* comes from the Arabic *al-qili* meaning "ashes of the saltwort plant." Saltworts grow on beaches or near salt marshes. Because group 1A metals react with water to form alkaline solutions, as shown in **Figure 7-3a,** they are called alkali metals.

Alkali metals easily lose a valence electron and form an ion with a 1+ charge. They are soft enough to cut with a knife. Sodium, shown in **Figure 7-3b,** has the consistency of cold butter. Because alkali metals are highly reactive, they are found combined with other elements in nature. Lab samples are stored in oil to prevent a reaction with oxygen in the air. Alkali metals are good conductors of heat and electricity.

**Lithium** Trace amounts of lithium, the lightest alkali metal, are found in water, soil, and rocks. Lithium is the least reactive of the alkali metals. Its compounds are less likely to dissolve in water. In these and other properties, lithium is more closely related to magnesium than to the other alkali metals. Lithium has an atomic radius of 152 pm and an ionic radius of 76 pm. Magnesium has an atomic radius of 160 pm and an ionic radius of 72 pm. These similar physical properties lead to similar chemical properties, which is why lithium and magnesium have a diagonal relationship.

| 1A |
|---|
| Lithium |
| 3 |
| **Li** |
| [He]2s¹ |
| Sodium |
| 11 |
| **Na** |
| [Ne]3s¹ |
| Potassium |
| 19 |
| **K** |
| [Ar]4s¹ |
| Rubidium |
| 37 |
| **Rb** |
| [Kr]5s¹ |
| Cesium |
| 55 |
| **Cs** |
| [Xe]6s¹ |
| Francium |
| 87 |
| **Fr** |
| [Rn]7s¹ |

7.1 Properties of s-Block Elements **181**

Long-lasting lithium batteries may extend the range of electric automobiles. Compounds of lithium are used in dehumidifiers to absorb water. Lithium carbonate is used to strengthen glass and as a drug to treat bipolar disorders. Such disorders involve mood swings from mania to depression. Alloys of lithium, magnesium, and aluminum are used for items such as airplane parts because these parts must be strong, yet lightweight. Remember that an alloy is a solid solution. A chemist can fine-tune the properties of an alloy by varying the amount of each element.

**Sodium and potassium** The most abundant alkali metals are sodium and potassium. Sodium is used in sodium vapor lamps and as a heat exchanger in nuclear reactors. Because potassium is more reactive than sodium and more expensive to produce, elemental potassium has fewer industrial uses.

Humans and other vertebrates must have sodium and potassium in their diets because many biological functions are controlled by sodium and potassium ions. Potassium ions are the most common positive ions within cells. Sodium ions are the most common positive ions in the fluid that surrounds cells. When a nerve cell is stimulated, sodium ions flow into the cell and potassium ions flow out. This flow of ions across the cell membrane carries the nerve impulse along the cell. After the impulse passes, a compound attached to the cell membrane uses energy to move the ions back across the membrane so that they are in position for the next impulse.

**Figure 7-4a** shows a deposit of sodium chloride, or table salt—the most common sodium compound. Table salt occurs naturally in many foods. It is used to keep food from spoiling and to preserve foods for long-term storage, as shown in **Figure 7-4b.** These roles were especially important before the widespread use of refrigeration. Potassium chloride serves as a salt substitute for people whose intake of sodium must be limited. Potassium compounds are included in fertilizers because potassium is an important factor for plant growth and development. Potassium nitrate is used as an explosive for large-scale fireworks displays.

**Other alkali metals** The most reactive alkali metals—rubidium, cesium, and francium—have little commercial use. Rubidium, with a melting point of only 40°C, melts on a hot day. It will burst into flames if exposed to air. Francium, the most reactive alkali metal, is a rare radioactive element. For which SI base unit is cesium the atomic standard?

**Figure 7-4**

(a) The Bonneville Salt Flats in Utah formed when a vast land-locked salt lake evaporated.
(b) People started to use salt as a preservative in the days when the only food to which people had access in winter was the food they had dried, cured, or canned.

## Group 2A: Alkaline Earth Metals

Medieval alchemists classified solids that did not melt in their fires as "earths." Group 2A elements form compounds with oxygen, called oxides, that qualify as "earths" by this definition. Except for beryllium oxide, these oxides produce alkaline solutions when they react with water. The label alkaline earth reflects these two properties.

Alkaline earth metals are shiny solids that are harder than alkali metals. Although alkaline earth metals are less reactive than alkali metals, they are usually found combined with oxygen and other nonmetals in Earth's crust. Alkaline earth metals lose their two valence electrons to form ions with a 2+ charge. Reactions with water reveal the relative reactivity of the alkaline earth metals. Calcium, strontium, and barium react vigorously with room temperature water. Magnesium will react in hot water. Beryllium does not appear to react with water. When exposed to oxygen, alkaline earth metals form a thin oxide coating. Most compounds of alkaline earth metals do not dissolve easily in water. Do the **miniLAB** on the next page to observe some properties of an alkaline earth metal.

**Beryllium**  The lightest member of group 2A, beryllium, is found combined with aluminum, silicon, and oxygen in a material called beryl. **Figure 7-5** shows two highly prized forms of beryl. Finding aluminum and beryllium together is not surprising because these elements have a diagonal relationship and, thus, similar chemical properties. Beryllium is used to moderate neutrons in nuclear reactors. Tools made from an alloy of beryllium and copper are used in situations where a spark from steel tools touching steel equipment could cause a fire or explosion. For example, beryllium–copper tools are used in petroleum refineries.

**Calcium**  Calcium is an essential element for humans, especially in maintaining healthy bones and teeth. Calcium is found widely in nature, mainly combined with carbon and oxygen in calcium carbonate. This compound is the main ingredient in rocks such as limestone, chalk, and marble. Coral reefs build up from calcium carbonate exoskeletons that are created by marine animals called corals. Calcium carbonate is used in antacid tablets and as an abrasive in toothpaste. An abrasive is a hard material used to polish, smooth, or grind a softer material. Emery boards and sandpaper are examples of abrasive materials.

| 2A |
| --- |
| Beryllium<br>4<br>**Be**<br>[He]2s² |
| Magnesium<br>12<br>**Mg**<br>[Ne]3s² |
| Calcium<br>20<br>**Ca**<br>[Ar]4s² |
| Strontium<br>38<br>**Sr**<br>[Kr]5s² |
| Barium<br>56<br>**Ba**<br>[Xe]6s² |
| Radium<br>88<br>**Ra**<br>[Rn]7s² |

**Figure 7-5**

Beryllium-containing **a** emerald and **b** aquamarine get their brilliant colors from impurities—traces of chromium in emerald and traces of scandium in aquamarine.

7.1  Properties of s-Block Elements   **183**

---

## miniLAB

**Purpose**
Students will mix magnesium with HCl and observe the results.

**Process Skills**
Observing and inferring, comparing and contrasting, drawing a conclusion

**Safety Precautions**
Remind students to wear a lab apron and safety goggles.

**Disposal**
Collect the used hydrochloric acid in a large beaker. Neutralize the acid with $NaHCO_3$ before washing it down the drain with large quantities of water.

**Teaching Strategies**
- See page 178C for preparation of solutions.
- Have students investigate practical uses of magnesium, such as in the manufacture of tools, auto parts, and sports equipment and the construction of aircraft and missiles. Ask them to relate these applications to magnesium's properties. Magnesium is light, but strong; objects made of magnesium have a protective layer of magnesium oxide that forms by the reaction of magnesium with oxygen in the air. The magnesium oxide protects the remaining material from corrosion.
- Explain to students that they are using the reaction $Mg + 2HCl \rightarrow MgCl_2 + H_2$ to produce $H_2$ gas.
- Have students research the production and uses of hydrogen gas as a fuel and in fuel cells. After they complete their research, ask them if hydrogen could be the fuel of the future.
- Have students research the production of hydrogen by Cavendish (1766) and Lavoisier (1783). **L2**

**Expected Results**
The sandpaper removes the oxide coating from the gray Mg ribbon, exposing a shiny silver-colored surface. When the Mg ribbon is dropped into the HCl solution in the test tube, the magnesium reacts with HCl and hydrogen gas bubbles

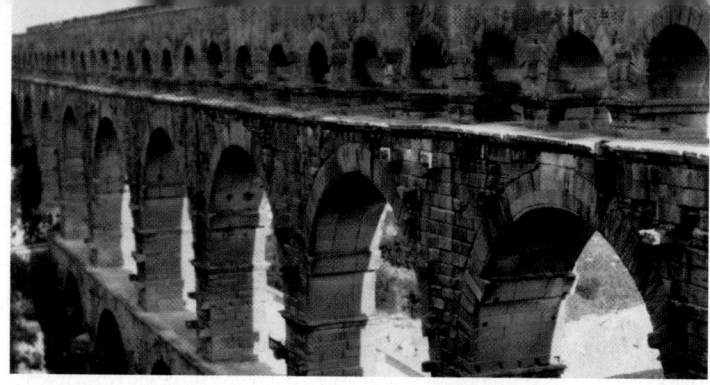

**Figure 7-6**

Limestone is a relatively light building material that is easy to work with and durable.

Calcium carbonate as limestone was used to build the Roman aqueduct in **Figure 7-6**. When calcium carbonate decomposes, it forms an oxide of calcium called lime. Lime is one of the most important industrial compounds. For example, lime plays a role in the manufacture of steel, paper, and glass. Gardeners use lime to make soil less acidic. Wastewater treatment plants use lime, as do devices that remove pollutants from smokestacks. Lime is mixed with sand and water to form a paste called mortar.

**Magnesium** Magnesium is an abundant element that can be formed into almost any shape. Alloys of magnesium with aluminum and zinc are much lighter than steel but equally strong. The backpack frame in **Figure 7-7a** is made from a magnesium alloy, as are many bicycle frames and the "mag" wheels on the sports car in **Figure 7-7b**. The oxide of magnesium has such a high melting point that it is used to line furnaces. Plants cannot function

## miniLAB

### Properties of Magnesium

**Observing and Inferring** In this activity, you will mix magnesium with hydrochloric acid and observe the result.

**Materials** test tube, test tube rack, 10-mL graduated cylinder, hydrochloric acid, magnesium ribbon, sandpaper, cardboard, wood splint, safety matches

**Procedure**

**Record all of your observations.**
1. Place your test tube in a test tube rack. For safety, the test tube should remain in the rack throughout the lab.
2. Use a 10-mL graduated cylinder to measure out about 6 mL of hydrochloric acid. Pour the acid slowly into the test tube.
   **CAUTION:** *If acid gets on your skin, flush with cold running water. Use the eyewash station if acid gets in your eye.*
3. Use sandpaper to clean the surface of a 3-cm length of magnesium ribbon.
4. Drop the ribbon into the acid and immediately cover the test tube with a cardboard lid.
5. As the reaction appears to slow down, light a wood splint in preparation for step 6.
6. As soon as the reaction stops, uncover the test tube and drop the burning splint into it.
7. Pour the contents of the test tube into a container specified by your teacher. Then rinse the test tube with water. Do not place your fingers inside the unwashed tube.

### Analysis
1. Compare the appearance of the magnesium ribbon before and after you used the sandpaper. What did the sandpaper remove?
2. What happened when you placed the ribbon in the acid? How did you decide when the reaction was over?
3. What did you observe when you placed the burning splint in the test tube?
4. What gas can ignite explosively when exposed to oxygen in the air? (Hint: The gas is lighter than air.)

**184** Chapter 7 The Elements

are produced. The burning splint causes the gas to ignite. A sound is produced by the explosive reaction of $H_2$ and $O_2$.

### Analysis
1. The gray coating from the Mg ribbon was removed to expose a shiny silver-colored surface.
2. Magnesium ribbon reacted with HCl to produce a gas. The bubbling stopped.
3. The burning splint ignited the gas.
4. hydrogen

**✓ Assessment**
**Portfolio** Have students write a lab report and place it in their portfolios. **L2** **P**

**Figure 7-7**

**a** The lighter the backpack frame, the more supplies a person can carry.
**b** Reducing a car's weight improves its engine performance, which is why sports cars were the first to use wheels made from a lightweight magnesium alloy.

without a supply of magnesium because each chlorophyll molecule contains a magnesium ion. Your body depends on magnesium ions, too; they play key roles in muscle function and metabolism.

When large quantities of calcium and magnesium ions are found in the water supply, the water is referred to as hard water. Hard water makes it difficult to wash oil from your hair or grease from your dishes because the ions interfere with the action of soaps and detergents. If there are large amounts of hydrogen carbonate ions in the water, they can combine with the calcium and magnesium ions to form deposits that can clog pipes, water heaters, and appliances such as steam irons. Devices called water softeners exchange sodium or hydrogen ions for the calcium and magnesium ions. Do the **CHEMLAB** at the end of the chapter to compare the cleaning ability of hard water and softened water.

**Uses of other alkaline earth metals** Strontium gives some fireworks their crimson color. Colorful barium compounds are used in paints and some types of glass. Barium also is used as a diagnostic tool for internal medicine. Radium is a highly radioactive element. Radium atoms emit alpha, beta, and gamma rays. Before people understood the danger, they used radium compounds to paint the hands on watches because paint containing radium glows in the dark.

## Section 7.1 Assessment

1. Why are elements in groups 1A through 8A called representative elements?
2. What determines the chemical behavior of an element?
3. Why are alkali metals stored in oil?
4. What do group 1A and group 2A elements have in common? Give at least three examples.
5. What types of ions make water hard? What is the main problem with using hard water?
6. Name three factors that make magnesium a good choice for alloys.
7. **Thinking Critically** Lithium behaves more like magnesium than sodium. Use what you learned in Chapter 6 about trends in atomic sizes to explain this behavior.
8. **Applying Concepts** Hydrogen can gain one electron to reach a stable electron configuration. Why isn't hydrogen placed in group 7A with the other elements that share this behavior?

# 1 Focus

## Focus Transparency

Before presenting the lesson, display **Section Focus Transparency 24** on the overhead projector. Have students answer the accompanying questions using **Section Focus Transparency Master 24.** L1 ELL

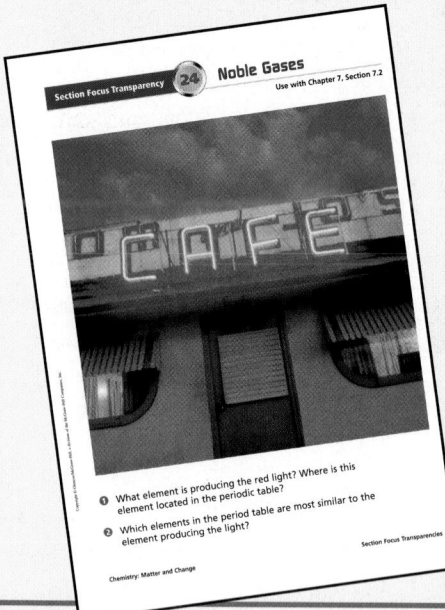

### Objectives

• **Describe** and **compare** properties of p-block elements.

• **Define** allotropes and provide examples.

• **Explain** the importance to organisms of selected p-block elements.

### Vocabulary

mineral
ore
allotrope

| 3A |
|---|
| Boron 5 **B** [He]$2s^2 2p^1$ |
| Aluminum 13 **Al** [Ne]$3s^2 3p^1$ |
| Gallium 31 **Ga** [Ar]$4s^2 3d^{10} 4p^1$ |
| Indium 49 **In** [Kr]$5s^2 4d^{10} 5p^1$ |
| Thallium 81 **Tl** [Xe]$6s^2 4f^{14} 5d^{10} 6p^1$ |

**Figure 7-8**

ⓐ How might using borosilicate glassware contribute to lab safety?
ⓑ Cookware made from borosilicate glass is designed to go directly from the refrigerator to the oven.

Differences among the s-block metals are slight in comparison to the range of properties found among the p-block elements. Remember that some p-block elements are metals, some are metalloids, and some are nonmetals. Some are solids and some are gases at room temperature. Even individual p-block elements display a greater range of properties; for example, many form more than one type of ion. As you might expect, the explanation for this property lies with the electron configurations, especially those configurations that are not close to a stable, noble-gas electron configuration.

## Group 3A: The Boron Group

Group 3A elements are always found combined with other elements in nature. They are most often found as oxides in Earth's crust. This group contains one metalloid (boron), one familiar and abundant metal (aluminum), and three rare metals (gallium, indium, and thallium). Based on the group number, you would expect group 3A elements to lose three valence electrons to form ions with a 3+ charge. Boron, aluminum, gallium, and indium form such ions. Thallium does not. Thallium is the most metallic member of the group with properties similar to those of alkali metals. Thallium loses only the p valence electron to form ions with a 1+ charge. Gallium and indium also can form ions with a 1+ charge.

**Boron** Although group 3A is named for the metalloid boron, as with other groups, the lightest member is the least representative. Boron has more in common with silicon in group 4A than with the metallic members of group 3A. Boron and silicon oxides combine to form borosilicate glass, which can withstand extreme differences in temperature without shattering. This property makes borosilicate glass ideal for the laboratory equipment and cookware shown in **Figure 7-8.**

The main source of boron is a complex compound of boron called borax. About half of the world supply of borax comes from a large deposit in California's Mojave Desert. Borax is used as a cleaning agent and as fireproof insulation. Another compound of boron, boric acid, is used as a disinfectant and as an eye wash. A form of boron nitride is the second hardest known material; only diamond is harder. These materials are classified as superabrasives. They are used in grinding wheels, which shape manufactured parts and tools.

# 2 Teach

## Concept Development

🔲 *Visual-Spatial* Have students locate the p block of elements on the periodic table. Show students samples of p-block elements, including sulfur, bromine, silicon, carbon, lead, tin, and aluminum. Ask students to locate metals, nonmetals, and metalloids. L2

## Figure Caption Question

**Figure 7-8a** How might using borosilicate glassware contribute to lab safety? It can withstand extremes of temperature without shattering.

## Resource Manager

**Study Guide for Content Mastery,** pp. 39–40 L2
**Solving Problems: A Chemistry Handbook,** Section 7.2 L2
**Section Focus Transparency 24 and Master** L1 ELL
**Teaching Transparency 23 and Master** L2 ELL

## GLENCOE TECHNOLOGY

**CD-ROM**
**Chemistry: Matter and Change**
Video: *Synthetic Gems*

**Aluminum** Aluminum is the most abundant metal and the third most abundant element in Earth's crust. It usually occurs combined with oxygen or silicon. Because removing aluminum from its ore, bauxite, requires a great deal of energy, it is cost effective to recycle the aluminum in products such as the cans shown in **Figure 7-9.** Aluminum oxide is the major compound in bauxite. It is used as an abrasive, to strengthen ceramics, and in heat-resistant fabrics. Many gems, including ruby and sapphires, are crystals of aluminum oxide with traces of other metals. Chromium gives ruby its red color; iron and titanium give sapphire its bright blue color. The compound aluminum sulfate, known as alum, is used in antiperspirants and to remove suspended particles during water purification.

**Gallium** Gallium can literally melt in your hand. It is used in some thermometers because it remains a liquid over a wide temperature range—from 30°C to 2403°C. A compound of gallium and arsenic called gallium arsenide produces an electric current when it absorbs light. This property makes gallium arsenide ideal for the semiconductor chips used in light-powered calculators and solar panels. These chips are ten times more efficient than silicon-based chips. Read **How It Works** at the end of the chapter to learn more about semiconductors.

Scientists are using a compound of gallium and nitrogen, gallium nitride, to develop lasers that emit blue rather than red light. Using the shorter wavelengths of blue light would triple the storage capacity of a DVD, making room for three two-hour movies. Blue lasers could increase the speed and resolution of laser printers. Medical devices for detecting cancer cells could be less expensive if they used low-cost, blue-light lasers.

## Group 4A: The Carbon Group

Based on the trends discussed in Chapter 6, the metallic properties of the elements in group 4A should increase as the atomic number increases. Carbon is a nonmetal; silicon and germanium are metalloids; tin and lead are metals. With such a wide range of properties, there are few rules that apply to all members of the group. One general trend does apply. The period-2 element, carbon, is not representative of the other elements within the group.

**Carbon** Group 4A contains one of the most important elements on Earth: carbon. Except for water and ions such as sodium, most substances that control what happens in cells contain carbon. The branch of chemistry that studies these carbon compounds is called organic chemistry. Until 1828 when the first organic compound was synthesized in the laboratory, scientists thought that organic compounds could be created only in organisms. Chapter 9 will help you understand how carbon can form so many different compounds. Chapters 22 through 24 will provide more details about organic chemistry.

The branch of chemistry that deals with all other compounds is called inorganic chemistry, meaning "not organic." Carbonates, cyanides, carbides, sulfides, and oxides of carbon are classified as inorganic compounds. Geologists call these compounds minerals. A **mineral** is an element or inorganic compound that is found in nature as solid crystals. Minerals usually are found mixed with other materials in ores. An **ore** is a material from which a mineral can be removed at a reasonable cost. In other words, the cost of extraction cannot approach or exceed the economic value of the mineral.

Although both diamond and graphite contain only carbon atoms, they display different properties. Graphite is one of the softest known materials; diamond is one of the hardest. These different forms of the same element are

**Figure 7-9**

The energy used to recycle aluminum is about 5% of the energy needed to extract aluminum from its ore.

**Try at Home** **LAB**

See page 955 in Appendix E for
**Amazing Aluminum**

| 4A |
|---|
| Carbon<br>6<br>**C**<br>$[He]2s^22p^2$ |
| Silicon<br>14<br>**Si**<br>$[Ne]3s^23p^2$ |
| Germanium<br>32<br>**Ge**<br>$[Ar]4s^23d^{10}4p^2$ |
| Tin<br>50<br>**Sn**<br>$[Kr]5s^24d^{10}5p^2$ |
| Lead<br>82<br>**Pb**<br>$[Xe]6s^24f^{14}5d^{10}6p^2$ |

## Content Background

### Allotropes of Carbon

Diamond and graphite are the 2 most common allotropes of carbon, but others are found in nature. The allotrope fullerene is formed when carbon atoms bond to form sphere-like structures. The most famous fullerene is $C_{60}$, known as buckminsterfullerene (after the architect Buckminster Fuller) or buckyball. The 60 carbon atoms of the molecule bond together forming pentagons and hexagons similar to the panels of a soccer ball. Buckminsterfullerene has unique chemical, magnetic, and electric properties. Fullerenes are being studied for their usefulness. Derivatives of buckminsterfullerene have been used to treat cancer and block the active sites of enzymes; certain compounds of fullerenes are superconductors. Two rare forms of carbon that are believed to form only in meteorites are lonsdaleite, found in the Barringer Crater in Arizona, and chaoite, found in Mottigen Rise Crater, Germany.

**Figure 7-10**

Comparing the diagrams to the photos should help explain why graphite and diamond have such different properties.

**Figure 7-11**

(a) Quartz crystals, (b) white sand, and (c) glass all contain silicon dioxide.

examples of allotropes. **Allotropes** are forms of an element in the same physical state—solid, liquid, or gas—that have different structures and properties. Because diamond and graphite are both solids made of carbon, they are allotropes. So is the amorphous form of carbon found in coal.

As shown in **Figure 7-10,** each carbon atom in graphite shares electrons with three other carbon atoms to form flat layers that can slide over one another. When you use a pencil, layers of carbon atoms slide onto your paper. This "slippery" property makes graphite a good lubricant. In diamond, each carbon atom shares electrons with four other carbon atoms to form a three-dimensional solid. Because of this arrangement, diamonds on grinding wheels are hard enough to sharpen tools and cut through granite or concrete.

**Silicon** Silicon, which is used in computer chips and solar cells, is the second most abundant element in Earth's crust after oxygen. Silicon occurs most often combined with oxygen in the compound silicon dioxide, which also is known as silica. Silica can be found in the quartz crystals, sand, and glass shown in **Figure 7-11.** When rocks containing quartz crystals weather, they produce white sand, which is the type of sand found on most beaches. If white sand is melted and allowed to cool rapidly, glass forms. A glass blower can shape glass into many different forms.

A compound of silicon and carbon, silicon carbide, is a major industrial abrasive. Its common name is carborundum. People who have a home workshop use silicon carbide sticks to sharpen their tools.

## CULTURAL DIVERSITY

### Glassmaking

Glassmaking dates back to 2500 B.C. in Mesopotamia, where glass was used to make beads, architectural decorations, and seals. Glass is formed from sand, which is composed of sodium carbonate, limestone, and silicon dioxide. To make glass, sand is melted and then held in the molten state for more than 24 hours to

allow the air bubbles to escape. The molten mixture is poured into molds or shaped and allowed to cool. As it cools, the glass solidifies into the desired shapes. The glass formed is hard and resists scratches, but it breaks when it is exposed to extreme ranges in temperature.

In 1912, borosilicate glass was devel-

oped to withstand extreme changes in temperature. This heat-resistant glass, known as Pyrex, was formed by replacing the sodium carbonate with boric acid. Today, glass made of pure silicon dioxide is used to make windows in space shuttles because it can withstand temperatures up to 2200 degrees Fahrenheit.

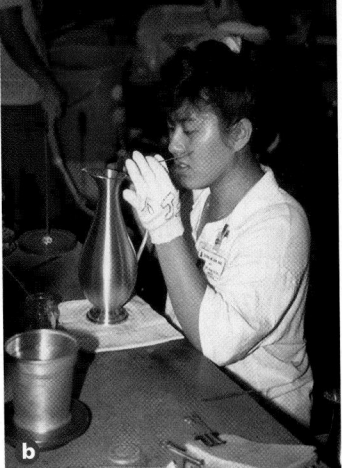

**Figure 7-12**

**ⓐ** The bronze used in this statue of a bull located in New York City's financial district is an alloy of tin and copper. **ⓑ** This pewter vase is lead free. About 8% antimony is mixed with tin to make the pewter harder.

**Lead and tin** Recall from the chapter opener that the metals tin and lead are similar with one key difference. Lead is toxic. The uses of pure tin are limited because tin is softer than most metals. For years, tin was used as a coating to keep steel cans from rusting, but aluminum cans are now more common. The decorative items in **Figure 7-12** are made from bronze and pewter. Bronze is an alloy of tin and copper with copper predominating. Some zinc is included to make the alloy harder. Pewter was made from about 40% lead and 60% tin until the toxic effects of lead became known.

Lead may have been the first pure metal obtained from its ores because of its low melting point. Analysis of ancient skeletons shows significant levels of lead. Until people realized the dangers of lead poisoning, lead was used for eating utensils, pipes for plumbing, as an additive in gasoline, and in paint. Paint at the hardware store no longer contains lead, but in older houses with layers of paint, lead may still be present. Lead is especially harmful for preschool children who may inhale it in dust or chew on scraps of peeling paint. In many states, a landlord cannot rent to a family with young children until the lead paint is removed. Currently, the major use of lead is in storage batteries for automobiles, which you will learn about in Chapter 21.

## Group 5A: The Nitrogen Group

Although the nonmetals (N and P), metalloids (As and Sb), and metal (Bi) in group 5A each have five valence electrons, they display a wide variety of physical and chemical properties. Nitrogen, which you inhale with every breath, forms some of the most explosive compounds known. Phosphorus has three solid allotropes. Antimony and bismuth expand when they change from a liquid to a solid. Nitrogen can gain three electrons and form ions with a 3− charge; bismuth can lose three electrons and form ions with a 3+ charge.

**Nitrogen** Nitrogen gas is colorless, odorless, and relatively unreactive. About 78% of Earth's atmosphere is nitrogen. Proteins and other essential organic compounds contain nitrogen. However, most organisms cannot use the nitrogen in air to create these compounds. Bacteria in the soil and roots of plants such as clover convert, or "fix," molecular nitrogen into nitrogen compounds. These compounds are then used by plants and the animals that consume plants. Some essential organic compounds contain both nitrogen and phosphorus. In Chapter 24, you will learn how these compounds control the movement of energy and transfer of genetic information within cells.

| 5A |
|---|
| Nitrogen<br>7<br>**N**<br>$[He]2s^22p^3$ |
| Phosphorus<br>15<br>**P**<br>$[Ne]3s^23p^3$ |
| Arsenic<br>33<br>**As**<br>$[Ar]4s^23d^{10}4p^3$ |
| Antimony<br>51<br>**Sb**<br>$[Kr]5s^24d^{10}5p^3$ |
| Bismuth<br>83<br>**Bi**<br>$[Xe]6s^24f^{14}5d^{10}6p^3$ |

## Concept Development

**Intrapersonal** A semiconductor is a solid or liquid that can conduct an electrical current at room temperature better than an insulator, but not as readily as a metal. The elements selenium, germanium, and silicon, as well as the compounds gallium arsenate, lead telluride, and zinc selenide, are common semiconductors. Doping is a method of adding impurities to a semiconductor to increase its ability to carry an electric charge. Have students investigate the use of semiconductors in solar cells. In their research, they should trace the history of solar cells, the materials used in their construction, and their potential as an energy source. Students can summarize their findings in a "news report" format, poster, or oral report for presentation to the class. **L2**

## Content Background

**Allotropes of Tin** Tin has two allotropes, white tin and gray tin. White tin has metallic properties and is used in bakeware and as a thin interior coating on steel cans. Gray tin has no metallic properties and is a dull gray, powdery material with no known uses. When white tin is at temperatures below 13°C, it slowly changes into gray tin. This change from white to gray tin is known as tin plague or tin pest. In the nineteenth century, the organ pipes in the cathedrals of northern Europe were made of white tin. During the long cold winters, many of the white-tin organ pipes became covered with gray-tin patches that gradually spread, causing the pipes to lose their structural integrity and crumble.

---

**DIFFERENTIATED INSTRUCTION**

### Gifted

**Intrapersonal** Have students research the band theory and present models of this theory to the class. The band theory, based on the molecular orbital theory, explains the conductivity of metals and semiconductors. It states that empty orbitals form a conduction band, filled orbitals form a valence band, and a "forbidden zone" separates the two bands. By heating semiconductors or adding impurities to them, electrons are better able to cross the forbidden zone, increasing conductivity. **L3**

**National Science Content Standards**

Pages 188–189
UCP.1, UCP.2, UCP.5; B.1, B.2; E.2, F.1, F.5

## Applying Chemistry

**TECH PREP**

Nitroglycerin ($C_3H_5N_3O_9$), a very unstable oil, can be used as both a fuel and oral medication. It was discovered accidentally when an Italian chemist, Ascano Sobrero, mixed nitric acid with the organic compound glycerol. Nitroglycerin is the main ingredient in dynamite and is extremely explosive. Despite its dangerous nature, nitroglycerin can be compounded with mannitol to form a lifesaving drug for people with coronary artery disease. Nitroglycerin dilates the blood vessels of the heart, increasing blood flow to the heart muscle.

### Figure Caption Question

**Figure 7-13** Why must white phosphorus be stored in water?

because it bursts into flames in air

## History

### CONNECTION

The Swedish chemist Alfred Nobel (1833–1896) invented a safe way to use nitroglycerine. He mixed liquid nitroglycerine with sand to form a paste that could be shaped into rods. Nobel patented the mixture, which he called dynamite, and the blasting caps used to detonate the rods. The invention of dynamite greatly reduced the cost of drilling road and railway tunnels through rock. Nobel left most of his money to endow annual prizes in peace, chemistry, physics, medicine, and literature. These prizes are called Nobel Prizes.

**Figure 7-13**

White phosphorus is toxic and flammable. Why must white phosphorus be stored in water? Red phosphorus is an amorphous solid, which means that there is no definite pattern to the arrangement of its atoms.

As you learned in Section 7.1, the major industrial use of hydrogen is in the production of the nitrogen compound ammonia, which is a colorless gas with an irritating odor. Many cleaning products contain ammonia. Liquid ammonia can be used as a source of nitrogen for plants. It is stored under pressure and pumped directly into the soil. About 25% of ammonia is converted into nitric acid, which is used to produce explosives, dyes, and solid fertilizers. Artists use nitric acid to etch designs into metal plates. When ink is applied to the etched plate and then transferred to paper, a mirror image of the design appears. Some nitrogen compounds are extremely unstable. These include TNT (trinitrotoluene) and nitroglycerine.

**Phosphorus** Two of the three solid allotropes of phosphorus are shown in **Figure 7-13**. White phosphorus bursts into flames in air and must be stored in water. Red phosphorus is less reactive. It forms when white phosphorus is heated in the absence of air. Red phosphorus is used on the striking surface of matchboxes. The third allotrope, black phosphorus, is produced when either red or white phosphorus is heated under high pressure.

Most phosphorus is used to make phosphoric acid, which in turn is converted into phosphate compounds. These compounds have many uses. Some are found in processed cheese, laxatives, and baking powders. Others are used as a flame-retardant coating for fabrics and as a grease remover in cleaning products. Because phosphorus is essential for plant growth, fertilizers often contain phosphates. Do the **problem-solving LAB** on the next page to explore the role of fertilizers in the economics of farming.

The use of fertilizers containing phosphates can be harmful to the environment. In a lake, bacteria break down waste products and dead organisms into nutrients. Algae feed on these nutrients, which include phosphate ions. Small animals called zooplankton eat the algae; fish eat the zooplankton. If phosphate ions from fertilized fields reach the lake, they cause an increase in algae. Layers of algae form on the surface of the lake and keep light from reaching the algae below, which cannot survive if they do not have light for photosynthesis. Bacterial decay of dead algae uses large amounts of the dissolved oxygen in the water. There is not enough oxygen left to sustain other organisms. Over a long period of time, if algal growth is left unchecked, layers of waste can slowly build up on the lake bottom and the lake can evolve into a marsh or pond. Detergents that are sold in the United States no longer contain phosphate compounds because phosphate ions can be released into water by sewage treatment plants.

---

## Internet Address Book

**Chemistry Online**

Note Internet addresses that you find useful in the space below for quick reference.

**Figure 7-14**

**ⓐ** Britannia metal is harder than pewter. This tin-antimony alloy's properties can be varied by the addition of zinc, copper, lead, or bismuth. **ⓑ** When heat from a fire melts the Wood's metal plug in a sprinkler head, water that was held back by the plug is freed.

**Arsenic, antimony, and bismuth** These group 5A elements are less abundant than nitrogen and phosphorus. However, they are among the oldest known elements. Although arsenic is toxic, for centuries physicians used small amounts of an arsenic and sulfur compound, arsenic sulfide, to treat some illnesses. A black compound of antimony and sulfur, antimony sulfide, was used as a cosmetic to darken eyebrows and make the eyes appear larger. Britannia metal, an alloy of tin and antimony, can be shaped by stamping or spinning, and cast in molds, as shown by the tableware in **Figure 7-14a.** Today, lead storage batteries contain 5% antimony. A compound of bismuth is the active ingredient in a popular, pink remedy for diarrhea and nausea. A low-melting alloy of bismuth, lead, tin, and cadmium called Wood's metal is used as a plug in automatic sprinkler systems, as shown in **Figure 7-14b.**

## problem-solving **LAB**

### Cost of Fertilizer

**Interpreting Data** Farmers deduct expenses from income to determine profit. The United States Department of Agriculture (USDA) collects annual data on production expenses from United States farmers, including data on fertilizer.

#### Analysis

1. What percent of the total expenses was spent on fertilizer and lime for each of the years shown? Round your answers to three significant figures.

2. What trend is revealed by your answers to question 1?

#### Thinking Critically

3. The table shows that farmers spent more money each year on fertilizer from 1993 to 1996. From this data, can you conclude that farmers increased their use of fertilizer at the same rate? Give a reason for your answer.

| Production expenses (in millions) | | |
|---|---|---|
| **Year** | **Total expenses ($)** | **Fertilizer* ($)** |
| 1993 | 160 548 | 8398 |
| 1994 | 167 547 | 9180 |
| 1995 | 174 161 | 10 033 |
| 1996 | 181 303 | 10 934 |

\* This category includes money spent on lime, which is a soil conditioner.

4. Suppose the USDA data were altered to exclude farmers who raise livestock. Predict how this change would affect expenditures for fertilizer and lime as a percent of total expenses.

5. Use the Internet to find out if data since 1996 has confirmed the trend you identified in question 2.

---

## problem-solving **LAB**

### Purpose
Students will analyze data on the cost of fertilizer over time and draw conclusions.

### Process Skills
Interpreting data, drawing conclusions, hypothesizing

### Teaching Strategies
• To help students analyze the data in the chart and observe trends in the data, have them calculate the percent of total expenses for each year and plot the percents against the years on a graph.

### Analysis
1. 1993: 5.23%; 1994: 5.48%; 1995: 5.76%; 1996: 6.03%
2. Expenditures for fertilizer as a percent of total expenses increased from 1993 to 1996.

### Thinking Critically
3. A portion of the increased costs could be attributed to increased prices.
4. Given that farmers who grow crops (as opposed to livestock farmers) are the most likely users of fertilizer, the percent of total expenses should increase noticeably if farmers who raise livestock are excluded.
5. Answers will vary, but if prices for feed drop, then the percent spent on fertilizer might increase.

### ✔ **Assessment**
**Knowledge** Ask students what factors might affect the percent of total expenses spent on fertilizer. the quantity of fertilizer used or the price per unit quantity **L2**

---

### ▶ DIFFERENTIATED INSTRUCTION

#### Gifted

**Interpersonal** Have students in a group research the work of Henry Cavendish, Karl Scheele, Jons Jakob Berzelius, Joseph Priestley, Humphry Davy, and William Ramsay. Then, ask each group to use its findings to write a dialogue for a dinner conversation among these scientists; to write a poem or song about each scientist; or to write an ad for a product based on each scientist's work. **L3** **COOP LEARN**

**National Science Content Standards**

**Pages 190–191**
UCP.1, UCP.2, UCP.5; B.2; E.2; F.4

*Logical-Mathematical*
The following density data were gathered for the elements in group 4A.

| Element | Atomic number | Density (g/cm³ at 300 K) |
|---------|---------------|--------------------------|
| C | 6 | 2.26 |
| Si | 14 | 2.33 |
| Sn | 50 | 7.31 |
| Pb | 82 | 11.35 |

Using a graphing calculator, show students how to plot the data in two lists and display the data as a scatter plot. Have them calculate the linear regression of the line and display the function on a graph with the data. Then, ask students to predict the density of germanium (Ge, atomic number 32), by tracing the line. 5.10 g/cm³ They could also use the Value Operation or Table Functions of their calculators to predict the density. 5.06 g/cm³ The actual density of germanium is 5.32 g/cm³. Have students determine the percent error in their density predictions. 4.13%; 4.89%
**L3**

## In-Text Questions

**Page 192** Based on their names, what other nonmetals are found in these compounds? carbon and the metalloid, silicon

**Page 192** Which oxide is essential to life and which is life-threatening? Carbon dioxide is essential to life; carbon monoxide is life-threatening.

**6A**

| Oxygen |
|---|
| 8 |
| **O** |
| [He]$2s^2 2p^4$ |

| Sulfur |
|---|
| 16 |
| **S** |
| [Ne]$3s^2 3p^4$ |

| Selenium |
|---|
| 34 |
| **Se** |
| [Ar]$4s^2 3d^{10} 4p^4$ |

| Tellurium |
|---|
| 52 |
| **Te** |
| [Kr]$5s^2 4d^{10} 5p^4$ |

| Polonium |
|---|
| 84 |
| **Po** |
| [Xe]$6s^2 4f^{14} 5d^{10} 6p^4$ |

## Group 6A: The Oxygen Group

Polonium is the most metallic member of group 6A. But it is not a typical metal. It is rare, radioactive, and extremely toxic. Polonium is important historically because it was discovered by Marie and Pierre Curie in 1898 and named for Marie's native land, Poland. Selenium and tellurium are metalloids; oxygen and sulfur are nonmetals. There are some trends to note in group 6A. With six valence electrons, the elements act mainly as nonmetals. They tend to gain two electrons to form ions with a 2− charge; they also can share two electrons to achieve a stable electron configuration.

**Oxygen** Oxygen has two allotropes. You studied ozone ($O_3$) in Chapter 1. Remember that ozone is an unstable gas with a pungent odor and that it decomposes when exposed to heat or ultraviolet light. The odor of ozone is noticeable during electrical storms and near high-voltage motors such as those used in subway stations. Ozone produced in automobile emissions can irritate eyes, harm lung cells, and affect plant growth.

The allotrope that makes up about 21% of Earth's atmosphere is a colorless, odorless gas ($O_2$). Joseph Priestley (1733–1804) usually is credited with the discovery of oxygen. When he heated an oxide of mercury, the gas produced caused a candle to burn more brightly than it would in air. This experiment showed that air was a mixture and that one gas in air, not air as a whole, was responsible for combustion. When fuels burn, they release energy to heat homes, run automobiles, and operate machinery. The oxygen produced by plants during photosynthesis is used by both plants and animals during cellular respiration—the process that releases energy from carbohydrates. Like all organisms, the fish in **Figure 7-15a** needs a constant supply of oxygen.

Oxygen is separated from the other gases in air through a distillation process that is based on differences in boiling point among the gases. Oxygen is stored as a liquid under pressure in cylinders. These cylinders are too massive for all situations where oxygen may be needed, for example, on an airplane. Instead, a small canister is stored above each seat on the plane. The canister contains chemicals that can react to produce oxygen in an emergency.

Oxygen is the most abundant element in Earth's crust. It is found combined with metals in silicates and carbonates. Based on their names, what other elements are found in these compounds? Oxygen forms at least one oxide with every element except helium, neon, and argon. Oxygen combines with hydrogen to form two oxides—water and hydrogen peroxide, which is used as a bleach. **Figure 7-15b** shows another use of hydrogen peroxide. Oxygen also forms two oxides with carbon—carbon monoxide and carbon dioxide. Which oxide is essential to life and which is life-threatening?

**Figure 7-15**

ⓐ Fish use their gills to remove oxygen from water.
ⓑ A 3% solution of hydrogen peroxide in water can help disinfect an open wound.

---

## Demonstration

### Allotropes of Sulfur

#### Purpose
Students will observe orthorhombic sulfur and its conversion to the amorphous form, called plastic sulfur.

#### Materials
Roll sulfur (20 g); distilled water; hammer; cloth towel; laboratory burner; 250-mL beaker; test tube; test-tube holder; conductivity tester; spatula

#### Safety Precautions
**Disposal** Product can be thrown in the trash.

#### Procedure
Use a piece of roll sulfur (the orthorhombic form) to visually reinforce the properties of nonmetals. First, show the class the dull surface. Cover it with a cloth, and use a hammer to break off a piece. Students will see that orthorhombic sulfur is brittle, powdery, and unmalleable. Use a conductivity tester to demonstrate that sulfur does not conduct an electric current. Half-fill a 250-mL beaker with distilled water. Half-fill a test tube with sulfur. Heat the sulfur until it begins to boil and turns dark in color. Pour the hot sulfur into the beaker of water.

**Sulfur** Sulfur can be found combined with mercury in cinnabar or with lead in galena. It also is found uncombined in underground deposits. When water heated to 160°C and compressed air are pumped into a deposit, the yellow solid melts and is forced to the surface. Sulfur has ten allotropes, more than carbon and oxygen combined. **Figure 7-16** shows how a brittle allotrope that can be ground into a powder can be changed into one that is elastic.

When sulfur is burned in air, it reacts with oxygen to form sulfur dioxide, which is used to preserve fruit and as an antibacterial agent. Sulfur dioxide released into the atmosphere reacts with water vapor to form one of the acids in acid rain. More than 90% of the sulfur dioxide produced is used to make sulfuric acid. This inexpensive acid is used by so many industries that the amount of it produced can indicate the strength of an economy. About half the sulfuric acid produced is used to make fertilizers. Products ranging from steel to paper to paints also depend on this acid.

Scientists have discovered places in the deep ocean where heat from Earth's interior is released through vents, or openings, in Earth's crust. Because light does not reach the depth shown in **Figure 7-17,** the food chain cannot begin with photosynthesis. Instead, it begins with hydrogen sulfide, which also is released through the vents. (Hydrogen sulfide gives a rotten egg its vile odor.) Some unusual bacteria that live near these vents use hydrogen sulfide as an energy source. Other organisms feed on these bacteria. Volcanoes also release hydrogen sulfide from Earth's interior into the atmosphere. When silver dulls, this is a sign that it has reacted with atmospheric hydrogen sulfide to form silver sulfide, which is called tarnish.

**Figure 7-16**

**ⓐ** When brittle, yellow sulfur is heated, **ⓑ** it melts at 112°C. **ⓒ** Further heating produces a thick, red-brown syrup. When the syrup is poured into cold water, an amorphous solid forms. This allotrope is called plastic sulfur because it stretches like a rubber band.

## Applying Chemistry

**TECH PREP** Ruby red glass has a rich red color and was first produced by the Egyptians by adding copper to glass. In A.D. 4, the Romans added both gold and silver to glass to produce ruby red glass. The Lycurgus Cup, a Roman goblet of ruby red glass, appears red in transmitted light and green in reflected light. Today, most red and pink glass is made from selenium. Incorporating cadmium selenide and zinc sulfide in the mixture makes the glass red. When cadmium sulfide is present, the glass is yellow, but when selenium is added, the glass changes from yellow to orange to a bright ruby red.

**Figure 7-17**

Heat and hydrogen sulfide released at deep ocean vents support many organisms.

**National Science Content Standards**

Pages 192–193
UCP.1, UCP.2, UCP.5; B.2; E.2; G.3

7.2 Properties of p-Block Elements **193**

---

**CAUTION:** *The sulfur vapor can ignite.* After the amorphous sulfur cools, remove it from the water with a spatula.

### Results

Physical properties of orthorhombic sulfur include yellow color, hardness, brittleness, low melting point, and nonconductivity. Amorphous sulfur is black or dark red in color and elastic, but slowly changes back to the orthorhombic form.

### Analysis

1. **What are allotropes?** They are two or more forms of an element in the same physical state that differ in molecular structure.

2. Oxygen, like sulfur, is in group 6A of the periodic table. What are the allotropes of oxygen? $O_2$ and ozone ($O_3$)

### ✓ Assessment

**Portfolio** Have students research whether two other members of group 6A, selenium and tellurium, form allotropes. They should summarize their findings and include their written summaries in their portfolios. **L2** **P**

Mix 1.0 mL chlorine water ($Cl_2$ aq) with 1.0 mL hexane. Ask students to describe the hexane layer. colorless layer Repeat, adding 1.0 mL bromine water ($Br_2$ aq) to a fresh sample of hexane, yellow/orange layer and again using 1.0 mL iodine water ($I_2$ aq). pink/purple layer Observe the hexane layer after combining 1.0 mL of hexane with the following combinations:

| 1 | 1.0 mL $Cl_2$ (aq) | 1.0 mL of 1.0$M$ NaBr |
|---|---|---|
| 2 | 1.0 mL $Cl_2$ (aq) | 1.0 mL of 1.0$M$ NaI |
| 3 | 1.0 mL $Br_2$ (aq) | 1.0 mL of 1.0$M$ NaCl |
| 4 | 1.0 mL $Br_2$ (aq) | 1.0 mL of 1.0$M$ NaI |
| 5 | 1.0 mL $I_2$ (aq) | 1.0 mL of 1.0$M$ NaCl |
| 6 | 1.0 mL $I_2$ (aq) | 1.0 mL of 1.0$M$ NaBr |

Based on their observations, have students draw conclusions about the trend of reactivity among the halogens. Reactivity of Cl > Br > I
Disposal: Check with a waste-water treatment plant to determine if the materials can be disposed of down the drain. If they cannot, evaporate or burn off the hexane mixtures under the hood in small quantities.

## Figure Caption Question

**Figure 7-18** What connection might there be between the name of the locoweed plant and the plant's effect on an animal's behavior? When eaten by livestock, it causes locoism—severe poisoning characterized by weakness, lack of coordination, trembling, and paralysis.

### Figure 7-18

What connection might there be between the name of the locoweed plant and the plant's effect on an animal's behavior?

| 7A |
|---|
| Fluorine 9 **F** [He]$2s^2 2p^5$ |
| Chlorine 17 **Cl** [Ne]$3s^2 3p^5$ |
| Bromine 35 **Br** [Ar]$4s^2 3d^{10} 4p^5$ |
| Iodine 53 **I** [Kr]$5s^2 4d^{10} 5p^5$ |
| Astatine 85 **At** [Xe]$6s^2 4f^{14} 5d^{10} 6p^5$ |

### Figure 7-19

Three states of matter are represented by solid iodine (left), chlorine gas (middle), and liquid bromine (right) at room temperature.

**Selenium** Some people supplement their diet with tablets that contain essential vitamins and minerals. These supplements may include a small amount of sodium selenate. Selenium also can be found in such foods as fish, eggs, and grains. Selenium works with vitamin E to prevent cell damage. It may help to inhibit the growth of cancer cells. However, in the case of nutrients, more is not always better. The locoweed plant shown in **Figure 7-18** provides an example of this principle related to selenium. When a locoweed plant absorbs selenium from the soil, the concentration of selenium increases to a toxic level. Grazing animals that feed on locoweed can become quite ill.

Because selenium can convert light into electricity, it is used in solar panels. Selenium's ability to conduct electricity increases as its exposure to light increases. Meters that photographers use to measure the level of available light contain selenium. Photocopiers work because charged particles of selenium create an "image" of the item being copied. Selenium also is used in semiconductors, as is tellurium, which is a relatively rare element.

## Group 7A: The Halogens

The elements in group 7A are named for their ability to form compounds with almost all metals. Because these compounds are called salts, the group 7A elements are called "salt formers," or halogens. You are familiar with one salt, sodium chloride, which is known as table salt. The halogens differ in their physical properties, as shown in **Figure 7-19.** Chlorine is a gas at room temperature. Bromine is a liquid, but it evaporates easily. Iodine is a solid that can change directly into a vapor.

The chemical behavior of the halogens is quite similar with one exception. Astatine is a radioactive element with no known uses. The other halogens share the following general properties. They are reactive nonmetals that are always found combined with other elements in nature. Because they have seven valence electrons, halogens tend to share one electron or gain one electron to attain a stable, noble-gas electron configuration. They tend to form ions with a 1− charge.

### Portfolio

## Elements and Families

*Auditory-Musical* Play the song *The Elements* by Tom Lehrer, available on Rhino Record CD, *Songs and More Songs* by Tom Lehrer. Have students choose a melody and write their own song lyrics about the groups of elements and present the song to the class. Students should add their songs to their portfolios. **L1** **P**

**Fluorine** Because fluorine is the halogen with the lowest atomic number, it has a small atom that provides little shielding of its valence electrons from the nucleus. Fluorine is the most electronegative element on the periodic table; that is, it has the greatest tendency to attract electrons. Thus, it is logical that fluorine also is the most active of all elements. In fact, it reacts with every element except helium, neon, and argon.

Fluorine comes from the Latin word *fluere,* which means "to flow." The mineral fluorite, which contains fluorine and calcium, is used to lower the melting points of other minerals to make it easier to separate them from their ores. Fluorine compounds are added to toothpaste and drinking water to protect tooth enamel from decay. A compound of fluorine and carbon provides a non-stick coating for the cookware shown in **Figure 7-20a.** When fluorine reacts with isotopes of uranium, the gases that form are separated by differences in mass. This process is called uranium enrichment; it provides the uranium-235 fuel for nuclear reactors.

**Chlorine** Chlorine reacts with nearly all of the elements. Although chlorine is a deadly gas, compounds of chlorine have many uses, including some that can save lives. In 1848, a cholera epidemic began in London. About 25 000 people died during the epidemic, which was blamed on raw sewage flowing into the river Thames. In 1855, London became the first city to use chlorine compounds to disinfect sewage.

Chlorine compounds are used as bleaching agents by the textile and paper industries. Homeowners use chlorine bleach to remove stains from clothing. The substances dentists use to block the nerves that carry pain signals to the brain often are chlorine compounds. Hydrochloric acid in your stomach helps you digest food; this acid also is used to remove rust from steel in a process called pickling. Much of the chlorine gas produced is combined with products from oil refineries to make plastics such as polyvinyl chloride (PVC). Floor tiles, pipes for indoor plumbing, and the garden hose in **Figure 7-20b** are a few of the products made from PVC.

**Bromine and iodine** Compared to chlorine, much less bromine and iodine are produced annually because there are fewer commercial uses for their compounds. Silver bromide and silver iodide are used to coat photographic film. Your body needs iodine to maintain a healthy thyroid gland. This gland produces hormones that control growth and your metabolic rate—the speed at which biochemical reactions occur. A lack of iodine causes the thyroid gland to enlarge, a condition called goiter. Seafood is an excellent source of iodine. So is iodized salt, which contains potassium iodide or sodium iodide in addition to sodium chloride. Because iodine kills bacteria, campers use iodine tablets or crystals to disinfect water.

**Figure 7-20**

**ⓐ** Cookware with a non-stick surface is easy to clean and can reduce the use of cooking oils and fats. **ⓑ** A garden hose made from polyvinyl chloride is sturdy and flexible.

7.2 Properties of p-Block Elements **195**

**Concept Development**

*Interpersonal* Divide the class into teams, each team representing one of the six noble gases. Using their class notes and textbooks, have each team complete a chart that summarizes the properties, characteristics, and uses of each gas. Then, have students share their charts with the class. As an extension, each team could perform independent research on the gas to find out more distinguishing features and possible uses. **L2** **COOP LEARN**

### ✔ Assessment

**Skill** Cover all periodic tables in the classroom and give students a blank periodic table. List properties or uses of a p-block element. Once students identify the element, have them place the symbol of the element in the correct location on the periodic table. **L2**

### ✔ Portfolio

#### Neon Lights

 *Visual-Spatial* Have interested students research neon lights and the different gases used to produce different colors. Have them design neon signs and identify the gases used to produce the colors. Students may display their signs for the class and place them in their portfolios. **L2** **ELL** **P**

**National Science Content Standards**

**Pages 194–195**
UCP.1, UCP.2, UCP.5; B.1, B.2, B.3; E.2; F.4, F.6

## In-Text Question

**Page 196** Why did Neil Bartlett choose fluorine for his experiment? *because it is so reactive*

# 3 Assess

## Check for Understanding

 **Interpersonal** Put index cards with symbols of p-block elements or group names into a container. Have students, or teams of students, draw cards from the container, one at a time. Ask students to list the properties or uses of the element, or the characteristics of the group. If students work in teams, have them share their work with the class. **L2**
**COOP LEARN**

## Reteach

To review the properties of the p-block elements, make a blank chart of the elements. To fill in the chart, elicit from students the group characteristics and properties, uses, and occurrence of each element. **L2**

## Extension

Have students research the pros and cons of fluoridating drinking water. Based on their research, have them form panels either for or against fluoridation, and debate whether or not fluoride should be added to drinking water. **L2**

### ✔ Assessment

**Knowledge** List the physical and chemical properties of the p-block elements and have students identify the elements. **L2**

---

8A

| Helium |
| 2 |
| **He** |
| $1s^2$ |

| Neon |
| 10 |
| **Ne** |
| $[He]2s^22p^6$ |

| Argon |
| 18 |
| **Ar** |
| $[Ne]3s^23p^6$ |

| Krypton |
| 36 |
| **Kr** |
| $[Ar]4s^23d^{10}4p^6$ |

| Xenon |
| 54 |
| **Xe** |
| $[Kr]5s^24d^{10}5p^6$ |

| Radon |
| 86 |
| **Rn** |
| $[Xe]6s^24f^{14}5d^{10}6p^6$ |

---

## Group 8A: Noble Gases

The noble gases were among the last naturally occurring elements to be discovered because they are colorless and unreactive. Scientists assumed that noble gases could not form compounds. In 1962, the inorganic chemist Neil Bartlett created compounds from xenon and fluorine. Why do you think he chose fluorine for his experiments?

Despite this breakthrough, group 8A elements are still known primarily for their stability. Remember that noble gases have the maximum number of electrons in their outermost energy levels—eight—except for helium, which has two. Noble gases rarely react because of their stable electron configurations. In fact, there are no known compounds of helium, neon, or argon.

**Helium** The lightest noble gas, helium, was discovered first in the emission spectrum of the Sun. Although helium is light enough to escape Earth's gravity, it can be found on Earth in natural-gas wells. Helium is the lighter-than-air gas used in blimps, airships, and balloons. A mixture of helium and oxygen is used by deep-sea divers. By replacing the nitrogen in air with helium, divers can return to the surface quickly without experiencing a painful condition called the "bends." Liquid helium is used as a coolant for superconducting magnets.

**Neon** Neon is used in light displays that are commonly referred to as neon lights. When high-voltage electricity passes through the neon gas stored in a gas discharge tube, electrons in the atoms become excited. When the electrons return to a lower energy state, the atoms emit a bright orange light. The color of neon lights is not a constant because gases other than neon can be used in the displays. For example, argon emits blue light and helium emits a pale yellow light.

**Argon and krypton** Argon is the most abundant of the noble gases on Earth; it makes up about 1% of Earth's atmosphere. Argon provides an inert atmosphere for procedures such as high-temperature welding. This substitution avoids the dangerous mixture of electrical sparks, heat, and oxygen. Argon and krypton are used to prolong the life of filaments in incandescent light bulbs and as a layer of insulation between panes of glass. In Chapter 25, you will learn about another noble gas, the radioactive gas radon, which can be dangerous when inhaled.

---

## Section 7.2 Assessment

**9.** In general, how do p-block elements differ from s-block elements?

**10.** How do animals obtain the nitrogen they need to build compounds such as proteins?

**11.** Explain why noble gases were among the last naturally occurring elements to be discovered.

**12.** What is an allotrope? Describe two allotropes of carbon.

**13.** Compare the physical and chemical properties of fluorine, chlorine, bromine, and iodine.

**14.** How do a mineral and an ore differ?

**15. Thinking Critically** Although carbon and lead are in the same group, one is a nonmetal and the other a metal. Explain how two elements with the same number of valence electrons can have such different properties.

**16. Predicting** A place has been left for element 113 on the periodic table. To what group does it belong? How many valence electrons will it have? What element will it most closely resemble?

chemistrymc.com/self_check_quiz

---

## Section 7.2 Assessment

**9.** There is a wider range of properties among p-block elements.

**10.** Bacteria in soil and plant roots convert $N_2$ to N compounds, which are used by plants and by animals that consume them.

**11.** They are colorless and unreactive.

**12.** form of an element that has different structures and properties in the same physical state; graphite is a layered, soft solid; diamond is a hard 3-dimensional solid.

**13.** At room temperature, F and Cl are gases, Br is a volatile liquid, and I is a solid that sublimes. From F to I, reactivity decreases.

**14.** A mineral is an inorganic element or compound; an ore is a mixture from which a mineral can be mined.

**15.** Carbon has a small atomic radius and a high ionization energy. Lead has a large atomic radius and a low ionization energy. In a group, as atomic number increases, elements tend to be more metallic and form

**196**

# Properties of d-Block and f-Block Elements

Beginning with period 4, the periodic table is expanded to make room for the elements whose d or f orbitals are being filled. These elements are called transition elements. They are subdivided into d-block and f-block elements—the transition metals and inner transition metals, respectively. Note that the groups of transition elements are labeled "B" to distinguish them from the groups containing representative elements. Recall that a transition metal is any element whose final electron enters a d sublevel. An inner transition metal is any element whose final electron enters an f sublevel.

**Figure 7-21** reviews the locations of the d-block and f-block elements on the periodic table. Recall that the f-block elements are placed below the main body of the periodic table with an arrow to indicate their proper locations on the table. The f-block elements are further divided into two series of elements that reflect those locations. The f-block elements from period 6 are named the **lanthanide series** because they follow the element lanthanum. The f-block elements from period 7 are named the **actinide series** because they follow the element actinium.

## Transition Metals

Transition metals share properties such as electrical conductivity, luster, and malleability with other metals. There is little variation in atomic size, electronegativity, and ionization energy across a period. However, there are differences in properties among these elements, especially physical properties. For example, silver is the best conductor of electricity. Iron and titanium are used as structural materials because of their relative strength.

The physical properties of transition metals are determined by their electron configurations. Most transition metals are hard solids with relatively high melting and boiling points. Differences in properties among transition metals are based on the ability of unpaired d electrons to move into the valence level. The more unpaired electrons in the d sublevel, the greater the hardness and the higher the melting and boiling points.

### Objectives
- **Compare** the electron configurations of transition and inner transition metals.
- **Describe** the properties of transition elements.
- **Explain** why some transition metals form compounds with color and some have magnetic properties.

### Vocabulary
lanthanide series
actinide series
ferromagnetism
metallurgy

**Figure 7-21**

In which periods are the d-block and f-block elements located?

d-block transition metals

f-block inner transition metals

## 1 Focus

### Focus Transparency

Before presenting the lesson, display **Section Focus Transparency 25** on the overhead projector. Have students answer the accompanying questions using **Section Focus Transparency Master 25.** **L1** **ELL**

## 2 Teach
### Figure Caption Question

**Figure 7-21** In which periods are the d-block and f-block elements located? They are located in periods 4 through 7.

| National Science Content Standards |
| --- |
| Pages 196–199 |
| UCP.1, UCP.2, UCP.5; B.1, B.2; B.6; E.2 |

positive ions because larger atoms have more inner electrons and a lower ionization energy. Inner electrons shield valence electrons from the nuclear charge.

**16.** Group 3A; 3; element 81, thallium

## CULTURAL DIVERSITY

### Metallurgy

Metallurgy, extracting metals from their ores, can be traced back to 6000 B.C. Early civilizations were based on seven metals—gold, copper, silver, lead, tin, iron, and mercury. The Egyptians, Mesopotamians, Greeks, and Romans all used these metals. The first tools and weapons, dating to 5000 B.C., were produced from copper. Gold and silver were used for jewelry. Pliny, the Roman scientist and chronicler, described how to purify mercury in 1600 B.C. Around 1200 B.C., wrought iron implements were made. Because of its low melting point, lead was used to make containers and conduits. The predominant metal alloy was bronze, a mixture of tin and copper.

## Identifying Misconceptions

Students often mistakenly think that metals have the same degree of strength, luster, reactivity, hardness, conductivity, and malleability. Students also may believe that individual atoms of metals have these properties as well.

### Uncover the Misconception

Have students describe the characteristics of metals. Clarify that a metal's properties depend on its location on the periodic table. Generally, elements at the bottom of a column are more metallic. To illustrate this, choose a group of transition metals or assign the group to students and have them research the elements' metallic properties.

### Demonstrate the Concept

Show students samples of metals, including mercury, gold, silver, copper, iron, sodium, potassium, calcium, and magnesium. Ask them if all the metals have the same reactivity. Tell students that gold is the most unreactive metal, but it does react to form gold chloride and gold cyanide. Ask students to describe the metals' hardness and to identify which chemical property determines hardness. Explain that the number of unpaired d electrons determines hardness. Iron is the hardest metal of the samples listed. Have students investigate the number of unpaired d electrons in each metal. Discuss students' findings as they relate to the hardness of the metals. Ask what other properties are determined by the number of unpaired d electrons.
melting and boiling points

### Assess New Knowledge

Have students compare and contrast the hardness and melting and boiling points of several transition metals in the same period. Ask students to relate these properties to the number of unpaired d electrons.

**Figure 7-22**

From left to right, the compounds contain the following transition metals: scandium (white), titanium (white), vanadium (light blue), chromium (yellow), manganese (light pink), iron (red-orange), cobalt (violet), nickel (green), copper (blue), and zinc (white).

Consider, for example, the period 4 transition metals. Moving from left to right across the period, scandium has one unpaired d electron, titanium has two, vanadium has three, and manganese has five unpaired d electrons. Chromium, with six unpaired electrons—five unpaired d electrons and one unpaired s electron—is the hardest, and has a high melting point. Iron, cobalt, nickel, and copper form pairs of d electrons. Thus, their melting points, and hardness decrease from left to right. Zinc has the lowest melting and boiling points and is a relatively soft metal because its 3d and 4s orbitals are completely filled.

**Formation of ions** Transition metals can lose two s electrons and form ions with a $2+$ charge. Because unpaired d electrons can move to the outer energy level, these elements also can form ions with a charge of $3+$ or higher. When a transition metal reacts with a highly electronegative element such as fluorine or oxygen, the positive ions formed can have a charge as high as $6+$.

**Figure 7-22** shows a compound of each transition metal in period 4 in order from left to right. Note that most of the compounds have color. The metal ions in these compounds have partially filled d sublevels. Electrons in these sublevels can absorb visible light of specific wavelengths. The exceptions are the white compounds that contain scandium, titanium, or zinc. The scandium and titanium ions have an empty d sublevel. The zinc ion has a completely filled and stable d sublevel. Electrons in zinc, scandium, and titanium can be excited to higher levels, but not by wavelengths of visible light. The energy required corresponds to wavelengths in the ultraviolet range of the electromagnetic spectrum.

For those transition metals that can form more than one type of ion, a change from one to another often can be detected by a color change, as shown in **Figure 7-23**. There are vanadium ions in all four solutions. The ions in the yellow solution have a $5+$ charge. When zinc is added to the solution, a reaction occurs that changes the charge on vanadium from $5+$ to $4+$. This change is indicated by a color change in the solution from yellow to blue. If the reaction is allowed to continue, the charge changes from $4+$ to $3+$ and the color of the solution changes from blue to green. The final change in charge is from $3+$ to $2+$ with a corresponding color change from green to violet.

**Figure 7-23**

Each solution contains different vanadium ions.

## CHEMISTRY JOURNAL

### History of Metals

**Linguistic** Before 1800, there were only 12 metals in common use: antimony, arsenic, bismuth, copper, gold, iron, lead, mercury, platinum, silver, tin, and zinc. Have students research one of these metals and write a report for their chemistry journals. **L2**

### Resource Manager

**Study Guide for Content Mastery,** pp. 41–42 **L2**
**Solving Problems: A Chemistry Handbook,** Section 7.3 **L2**
**Section Focus Transparency 25 and Master** **L1** **ELL**
**Teaching Transparency 24 and Master** **L2** **ELL**

**Magnetism and metals** The ability of a substance to be affected by a magnetic field is called *magnetism*. A moving electron creates a magnetic field. Because paired electrons spin in opposite directions, their magnetic fields tend to cancel out. When all of the electrons in atoms or ions are paired, the substance is either unaffected or slightly repelled by a magnetic field. This property is called *diamagnetism*. When there is an unpaired electron in the valence orbital of an atom or ion, the electron is attracted to a magnetic field. This property is called *paramagnetism*. Most substances act as temporary magnets; that is, their magnetic properties disappear after the magnetic field is removed.

Now recall the materials you tested in the **DISCOVERY LAB.** Did any of them contain iron? The transition metals iron, cobalt, and nickel have a property called ferromagnetism. **Ferromagnetism** is the strong attraction of a substance to a magnetic field. **Figure 7-24** shows how the ions in a ferromagnetic metal respond to a magnetic field. The ions align themselves in the direction of the field. When the field is removed, the ions stay aligned and the metal continues to act as a magnet. Thus, iron, cobalt, and nickel can form permanent magnets.

**Sources of transition metals** Copper, silver, gold, platinum, and palladium are the only transition metals that are unreactive enough to be found in nature uncombined with other elements. All other transition metals are found in nature combined with nonmetals in minerals such as oxides and sulfides. Recall that minerals are mixed with other materials in ores. **Metallurgy** is the branch of applied science that studies and designs methods for extracting metals and their compounds from ores. The methods are divided into those that rely on high temperatures to extract the metal, those that use solutions, and those that rely on electricity. Electricity also is used to purify a metal extracted by high temperatures or solutions.

**Figure 7-25** shows a blast furnace in which iron is extracted from its ore. Ore enters the furnace at the top, where the temperature is about 200°C. As the ore travels down through the furnace, carbon monoxide reacts with compounds in iron ore to remove the iron. The temperature increases along the way until molten iron at about 2000°C flows from the bottom. The product, which is called pig iron, contains about 3%–4% carbon. Most pig iron is purified and mixed with other elements in alloys called steel.

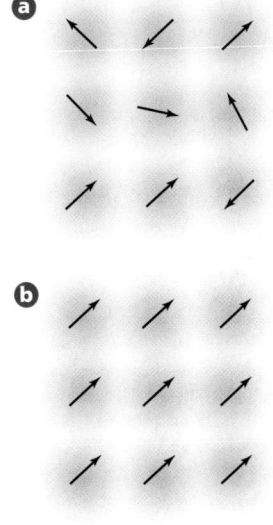

**Figure 7-24**

ⓐ Each ion in a ferromagnetic metal acts as a magnet. ⓑ If all of the ions are aligned in the same direction, they can form a permanent magnet.

**Figure 7-25**

This blast furnace is named for the blast of hot air that moves rapidly up the furnace. The hot air carries carbon monoxide, which reacts with compounds in iron ore to remove the iron.

7.3 Properties of d-Block and f-Block Elements **199**

### Quick Demo

Iron, cobalt, and nickel form permanent magnets. Magnetite, a naturally occurring magnet, is also called lodestone. Obtain a piece of lodestone and show students its magnetic properties. Nickel also exhibits magnetic properties. Add 2 to 3 grams solid $Ni(NO_3)_2$ and a 4 cm × 4 cm piece of aluminum foil, shined with sandpaper or steel wool, to a beaker. Test for magnetism with a magnet. There is no magnetism. Add 10 mL of water to dissolve the nickel nitrate and allow the substances to react for 24 hours. Solid nickel will be on the bottom of the beaker. Test for magnetism by moving a magnet under the beaker. Nickel is attracted to the magnetic field. Point out Figure 7-24, and discuss ferromagnetism. Disposal: Filter out the nickel and recycle it or place it wrapped in a solid-waste container.

### ✓ Assessment

**Knowledge** Hand each student an index card labeled on one side with the symbol for a transition element or an inner transition element. Have students write the electron configuration for the element and list its properties on the other side. If they are unsure of the properties, have them predict properties based on group characteristics. Students could also work in groups. **L2** **COOP LEARN**

### In-Text Question

**Page 199** Did any of the materials that you tested in the Discovery Lab contain iron? Answers will vary; examples are paper clips and soup cans.

---

## GLENCOE TECHNOLOGY

**CD-ROM**
Chemistry: Matter and Change
Video: *Shape of Memory Metals*

### ✓ Portfolio

**Uses of Metals**

*Visual-Spatial* Have students cut pictures from newspapers and magazines of products that are made of metals or metal alloys. Students can make a collage or poster of their pictures to place in their portfolios or use as a bulletin-board display. **L1** **ELL** **P**

### Resource Manager

Lab Manual, pp. 49–52, 53–56
**L2**

**TECH PREP**

Ask students if they know how paints are made. Explain that painting dates back to prehistoric times. Early paints were composed of materials such as crushed berries, vegetable pigments, blood, milkweed sap, and colored soils mixed with water or animal fat. As knowledge of minerals grew, the composition of paint changed. In the 1400s, paint was made by grinding up minerals and mixing them with egg yolks and water. Leonardo da Vinci was the first Italian painter to make oil paints by mixing ground minerals with linseed oil and water.

Many paint colors are due to transition metals in ground minerals. Paints with iron oxide are yellow or orange; those containing cobalt compounds are violet or blue. White paint has zinc oxide or titanium oxide; reds may contain compounds of mercury or gold.

## Figure Caption Question

**Figure 7-26** Are any strategic materials found in only one location? strontium—Mexico, tungsten—Zaire, vanadium—South Africa

## In-Text Question

**Page 200** Which elements would qualify as trace elements? chromium, copper, iodine, manganese, molybdenum, selenium, zinc

## Enrichment

*Visual-Spatial* Have students research the 12 birthstones, their basic composition, the impurities each gem contains, and the color. Ask students to summarize their research in a table, chart, or poster. Students could add their summaries to their portfolios, or share their posters in a class presentation. **L2** **P**

**Resource Manager**

Small-Scale Laboratory Manual, pp. 17–20 **L2**

**200**

---

## Locations of Some Strategic Metals

**Figure 7-26**

Are any strategic materials found in only one location?

**Table 7-1**

| Supplement Contents Per Tablet | | |
|---|---|---|
| **Element** | **Amount** | **% DV** |
| Calcium | 161 mg | 16% |
| Chromium | 25 µg | 20% |
| Copper | 2 mg | 100% |
| Iodine | 150 µg | 100% |
| Manganese | 2.5 mg | 125% |
| Magnesium | 100 mg | 25% |
| Molybdenum | 25 µg | 33% |
| Phosphorus | 109 mg | 11% |
| Potassium | 40 mg | 1% |
| Selenium | 20 µg | 28% |
| Zinc | 15 mg | 100% |

Transition metals play a vital role in the economy of many countries because they have a wide variety of uses. As the uses of transition metals increase, so does the demand for these valuable materials. Ores that contain transition metals are located throughout the world, as shown in **Figure 7-26.** The United States now imports more than 60 materials that are classified as "strategic and critical" because the economy and the military are dependent on these materials. The list includes platinum, chromium, cobalt, manganese, and tungsten.

**Uses of transition metals** Copper is used in electrical wiring, zinc as a protective coating for other metals, and iron in making steel. Many transition metals are found in alloys used to make items such as jet engines, drill bits, surgical instruments, and armor. The plastics, petroleum, and food industries use transition metals such as platinum, palladium, and nickel to control the conditions at which a reaction will occur. In Chapter 17, you will learn how some elements and compounds affect the rate of reactions and increase the amount of products produced in a reaction.

Your body needs large amounts of a few elements to function: carbon, oxygen, hydrogen, nitrogen, sulfur, phosphorus, sodium, potassium, calcium, magnesium, and chlorine. Other elements are essential, but are required only in trace amounts. Many trace elements are transition metals. Except for scandium and titanium, all period 4 transition metals play vital roles in organisms. An iron ion is in the center of each hemoglobin molecule. Hemoglobin picks up oxygen from blood vessels in the lungs and carries it to cells throughout the body. Molecules that help your body digest proteins and eliminate carbon dioxide contain zinc. Manganese and copper are involved in cell respiration. Cobalt is needed for the development of red blood cells.

**Table 7-1** shows some of the elements included in vitamin and mineral supplements. The contents and quantities vary among supplements. Daily value (DV) means the amount of each element recommended daily. Which elements would qualify as trace elements?

---

## DIFFERENTIATED INSTRUCTION

### Learning Disabled

*Kinesthetic* Many transition metals are essential to both plants and animals. Place a single serving of an iron-fortified cereal in a beaker. Add water to the cereal and stir the mixture until the cereal becomes soggy. Place a magnetic stirring bar in the mixture and stir for 20 to 30 minutes. Carefully remove the magnetic stirring bar and observe the iron filings that are covering the magnet. Ask students what phenomenon they have observed. Ferromagnetism, the strong attraction of a substance to a magnetic field. Discuss why iron is needed by the body. It is essential to the formation of hemoglobin, which carries oxygen in red blood cells. **L1** **ELL**

**Figure 7-27**

**a** What protection do the lanthanide compounds in tinted sunglass lenses provide?
**b** This smoke detector needs to be replaced after about 10 years because the amount of americium steadily decreases.

## Inner Transition Metals

The inner transition metals are divided into two groups: the period 6 lanthanide series and the period 7 actinide series.

**Lanthanide series** Lanthanides are silvery metals with relatively high melting points. Because there is so little variation in properties among inner transition metals, they are found mixed together in nature and are extremely hard to separate. The name of one lanthanide, dysprosium, comes from a Greek word meaning "hard to get at." Lanthanide ores were first mined in Ytterby, Sweden. Which four elements are named for this town?

The glass in welder's goggles contains neodymium and praseodymium, which absorb high-energy radiation that can damage the eyes. Oxides of yttrium and europium are found in television screens and color computer monitors. The yttrium and europium ions in the oxides emit bright red light when excited by a beam of electrons. An alloy called misch metal, which is 50% cerium, is used by the steel industry to remove carbon from iron and steel. Compounds of lanthanides are used in movie projectors, high-intensity searchlights, lasers, and tinted sunglasses such as those in **Figure 7-27a.**

**Actinide series** Actinides are radioactive elements. Only three actinides exist in nature. The rest are synthetic elements called transuranium elements. A transuranium element is an element whose atomic number is greater than 92, the atomic number of uranium. Transuranium elements are created in particle accelerators or nuclear reactors. Most transuranium elements decay quickly. One notable exception is plutonium-239. A sample of this isotope can remain radioactive for thousands of years. Plutonium is used as a fuel in nuclear power plants. The home smoke detector in **Figure 7-27b** uses americium.

**Chemistry Online**

**Topic: Forensics**
To learn more about elements, visit the Chemistry Web site at **chemistrymc.com**

**Activity:** Choose one brand of forensic investigation, such as arson, anthopology, firearms, or toxicology, and report on the elements that provide the most important clues to investigators.

**Figure Caption Question**

**Figure 7-27a** What protection do the lanthanide compounds in tinted sunglasses provide? They may be used in antireflective coatings—layers of metal oxides that reduce the reflection of light entering from behind and bouncing off the lens' surface into the eyes. The result is a reduction in glare.

**In-Text Question**

**Page 201** Which 4 transition elements are named for Ytterby, Sweden? the lanthanides Ytterbium, Terbium, and Erbium; the non-lanthanide Yttrium

## 3 Assess
### Check for Understanding

List the properties of transition metals and inner transition metals on the overhead. Ask students to identify examples of elements that exhibit the properties listed. **L2**

### Reteach

**Visual-Spatial** Make a chart on an overhead transparency. In each of 8 blocks, write identifying properties or uses of a transition metal. On another 8-block sheet, identify the transition metal. Have students play the game *Concentration*, matching the element with its properties or uses. **L2**

### Assessment

**Knowledge** Divide the class into 3 groups. Have the first group write a true/false quiz of the properties of d- and f-block elements, the second group a crossword puzzle, and the third group a fill-in or multiple-choice quiz. Have the groups exchange their work.

---

## Section 7.3 Assessment

**17.** How do the electron configurations of transition and inner transition metals differ?

**18.** Why do transition metals share properties with other transition metals in their period?

**19.** How do transuranium elements differ from other inner transition metals?

**20.** Explain how some transition metals can form ions with more than one charge.

**21.** What factor determines the magnetic properties of an element and the color of its compounds?

**22.** What is metallurgy?

**23.** Compare and contrast the lanthanide series and the actinide series.

**24. Thinking Critically** Why is silver not used for electrical wires if it is such a good conductor of electricity?

**25. Using a Database** Vanadium, manganese, and titanium are used to make different types of steel. Find one use for each type of steel alloy.

**chemistrymc.com/self_check_quiz**

7.3 Properties of d-Block and f-Block Elements **201**

---

## Section 7.3 Assessment

**17.** The final electron of a transition metal enters the d sublevel; the final electron of an inner transition metal enters the f sublevel.

**18.** They all have two s valence electrons.

**19.** They are synthetic elements with atomic numbers above 92.

**20.** They can lose 2s electrons and form ions with a 2+ charge. When d electrons are lost, ions with a charge of 3+ or higher can form.

**21.** the presence or absence of unpaired valence electrons

**22.** the science of extracting metals from ores

**23.** Lanthanides are silvery metals with high melting points. Actinides are radioactive; all but three are synthetic.

**24.** Silver is too soft. Wires made from silver are likely to bend.

**25.** Vanadium steel is used for truck springs and axles; manganese steel for armor and bulldozer blades; titanium steel for jet engines.

**201**

## Preparation 🔖

### Time Allotment
One laboratory period

### Purpose
Students will compare hard and soft water and their effect on detergent sudsing, calculate the hardness of water, and soften hard water.

### Process Skills
Acquiring and analyzing information, classifying, comparing and contrasting, drawing a conclusion, hypothesizing, measuring, observing and inferring, thinking critically, using numbers

### Safety Precautions
Remind students to wear a lab apron and safety goggles. Hard water containing magnesium sulfate can irritate the eyes and respiratory tract. Washing soda is a skin and eye irritant.

### Disposal
All solutions can be washed down the sink drain with lots of water.

### Preparation of Solutions
• See page 178C for preparation of solutions.

### Alternative Materials
• You may want to use several different types of packaged water softeners. White Rain, Blue Raindrops, and Spring Rain are nonprecipitating types. Arm and Hammer Washing Soda (used for sample data for this lab), Raindrops, Blue Dew, Borax, Climalene, Mel, White King Water Softener, and Borateem are precipitating types. Calgon is a mixture of nonprecipitating and precipitating chemicals.
• Any type of liquid detergent will work. Lemon-Fresh Joy was used for gathering data for this experiment.

## Pre-Lab

2. Students may hypothesize that hard water and detergent produce less suds. Relative sudsiness: distilled water > soft water > hard water

---

# Hard Water

The contents of tap water vary among communities. In some areas the water is hard. Hard water is water that contains large amounts of calcium or magnesium ions. Hardness can be measured in milligrams per liter (mg/L) of calcium or magnesium ions. Hard water makes it difficult to get hair, clothes, and dishes clean. In this lab, you will learn how hard water is softened and how softening water affects its ability to clean. You will also collect, test, and classify local sources of water.

### Problem
How can hard water be softened? How do hard and soft water differ in their ability to clean?

### Objectives
• **Compare** the effect of distilled water, hard water, and soft water on the production of suds.
• **Calculate** the hardness of a water sample.

### Materials
3 large test tubes with stoppers
test tube rack
grease pencil
25-mL graduated cylinder
distilled water
dropper

hard water
250-mL beaker
balance
filter paper
washing soda
dish detergent
metric ruler

### Safety Precautions

• **Always wear safety goggles and a lab apron.**
• **Washing soda is a skin and eye irritant.**

### Pre-Lab

1. Read the entire **CHEMLAB**.
2. Hypothesize about the effect hard and soft water will have on the ability of a detergent to produce suds. Then, predict the relative sudsiness of the three soap solutions.
3. Prepare a data table similar to the one shown below. Leave space to record your qualitative observations.

| Production of Suds | |
|---|---|
| **Sample** | **Level of suds (cm)** |
| Distilled water | |
| Hard water | |
| Soft water | |

4. Are there any other safety precautions you need to consider?

5. Suppose you accidentally add more than one drop of detergent to one of the test tubes. Is there a way to adjust for this error or must you discard the sample and start over?

6. The American Society of Agricultural Engineers, the U.S. Department of the Interior, and the Water Quality Association agree on the following classification of water hardness. GPG stands for grains per gallon. One GPG equals 17.1 mg/L. If a sample of water has 150 mg/L of magnesium ions, what is its hardness in grains per gallon?

| Classification of Water Hardness | | |
|---|---|---|
| **Classification** | **mg/L** | **GPG** |
| Soft | 0–60 | 0–3.5 |
| Moderate | 61–120 | 3.5–7 |
| Hard | 121–180 | 7–10.5 |
| Very hard | > 180 | > 10.5 |

---

4. Safety glasses and lab apron; washing soda can irritate the skin and eyes.
5. You could adjust by adding the same number of additional drops of detergent to the other tubes.
6. 8.8 GPG

### Sample Data Table

| Distilled water | Suds level: 5.5 cm |
|---|---|
| Hard water | Suds level: 4.0 cm |
| Soft water | Suds level: 9.0 cm |

## Procedure

• This lab can also be set up outdoors near sources of water, and it can be used to test streams, ponds, etc.

## Procedure

1. Use a grease pencil to label three large test tubes D (for distilled water), H (for hard water), and S (for soft water).

2. Use a 25-mL graduated cylinder to measure out 20-mL of distilled water. Pour the water into test tube D. Stopper the tube.

3. Place test tube H next to test tube D and make a mark on test tube H that corresponds to the height of the water in test tube D. Repeat the procedure with test tube S.

4. Obtain about 50-mL of hard water in a beaker from your teacher. Slowly pour hard water into test tube H until you reach the marked height.

5. Place a piece of filter paper on a balance and set the balance to zero. Then measure about 0.2 g of washing soda. Remove the filter paper and washing soda. Reset the balance to zero.

6. Use the filter paper to transfer the washing soda to the beaker containing the remainder of the hard water. Swirl the mixture to soften the water. Record any observations.

7. Slowly pour soft water into test tube S until you reach the marked height.

8. Add one drop of dish detergent to each test tube. Stopper the tubes tightly. Then shake each sample to produce suds. Use a metric ruler to measure the height of the suds.

9. Collect water samples from reservoirs, wells, or rain barrels. Use the sudsiness test to determine the hardness of your samples. If access to a source is restricted, ask a local official to collect the sample.

## Cleanup and Disposal

1. Use some of the soapy solutions to remove the grease marks from the test tubes.

2. Rinse all of the liquids down the drain with lots of tap water.

## Analyze and Conclude

1. **Comparing and Contrasting** Which sample produced the most suds? Which sample produced the least suds? Set up your own water hardness scale based on your data. What is the relative hardness of the local water samples?

2. **Using Numbers** The hard water you used was prepared by adding 1 gram of magnesium sulfate per liter of distilled water. Magnesium sulfate contains 20.2% magnesium ions by mass. What is its hardness in grains per gallon?

3. **Drawing a Conclusion** The compound in washing soda is sodium carbonate. How did the sodium carbonate soften the hard water?

4. **Thinking Critically** Remember that most compounds of alkaline earth metals do not dissolve easily in water. What is the white solid that formed when washing soda was added to the solution of magnesium sulfate?

5. **Error Analysis** Could the procedure be changed to make the results more quantitative? Explain.

## Real-World Chemistry

1. Water softeners for washing machines are sold in the detergent section of a store. Look at some of the packages and compare ingredients. Do packages that have different ingredients also have different instructions for how the water softener should be used?

2. Suppose a family notices that the water pressure in their house is not good enough to flush a toilet on the second floor. Other than a leak, what could be interfering with the flow of water?

3. Explain why drinking hard water might be better for your health than drinking soft water. How could a family have the benefit of hard water for drinking and soft water for washing?

## Analyze and Conclude

1. The test tube that contained the soft water had the largest volume of suds. The one with the hard water had the smallest volume. Answers will vary with local water.

2. Hardness would be $2.0 \times 10^2$ mg/L or 12 GPG.

3. Sodium carbonate combines with the magnesium sulfate in hard water to form an insoluble precipitate, which removes magnesium ions from the water.

4. The white solid is magnesium carbonate.

5. The volumes of the liquids and the detergent could be measured with more precision.

## Real-World Chemistry

1. yes

2. Hard-water deposits can form in pipes, causing corrosion and blocking the flow of water.

3. Calcium and magnesium ions are important minerals for health, so having some of these ions in water is beneficial; by adding water softeners to water used for washing

 **Assessment**

**Portfolio** Have students research how mechanical water softeners/conditioners work. In their research, students should find out the importance of using resin pellets and brine solution in maintaining soft water. Have students summarize their findings in a brief essay of three to four paragraphs.
**L2**  **P**

---

- The same size test tubes must be used.
- Make sure students rinse out the test tubes when finished.
- Make sure that the lab supplies of magnesium sulfate and washing soda are covered, because both are hygroscopic and will absorb water from the air.

## Expected Results

See the data table.

## Resource Manager

**ChemLab and MiniLab Worksheets,** pp. 26–28 **L2**

**National Science Content Standards**

**Pages 200–203**
UCP.1, UCP.2, UCP.5; A.1, A.2; B.2; E.1, E.2; F.1, F.6

# How It Works

## Purpose

Students will learn how electrons move through a semiconductor chip.

## Background

In order to improve electronic devices, the process of doping is used to increase the conductivity of semiconductors. Doping involves adding certain other elements, known as dopants. For example, the addition of just one dopant atom per million silicon atoms will significantly change the conducting properties of silicon.

## Visual Learning

Tell students that a copper wire conducts electricity because copper's valence electrons are not tightly held to individual atoms and are free to move through the wire. Have students compare the pathway of an electron through a p-type and n-type semiconductor. Ask why electrons are free to move through a doped semiconductor chip. In an n-type semiconductor, each phosphorus provides an extra electron to the crystal structure. These electrons are free to move throughout the crystal. In a p-type semiconductor, boron has one less electron than silicon, so there are holes in the crystal through which electrons can move.

## Teaching Strategies

• Have students compare the electron configurations of silicon, phosphorus, and boron. Ask them how many valence electrons each element contains. Si:4; P:5; B:3.

### National Science Content Standards

Pages 204–205
UCP.1, UCP.2, UCP.5; B.1, B.2, B.3; E.1, E.2; F.6

**204**

# How It Works
## Semiconductor Chips

All of the miniature electrical circuits in your television, computer, calculator, and cell phone depend on elements that are semiconductors. Some metalloids, such as silicon and germanium, are semiconductors.

An electric current is a flow of electrons. This movement of electrons can be used to carry information. Metals are good conductors of electricity; nonmetals are poor conductors. Semiconductors fall somewhere in between. Silicon's conductivity can be improved by the addition of phosphorus or boron—a process called doping.

**1** Hundreds of tiny electronic circuits form an integrated circuit on a thin slice of silicon called a chip.

**2** Valence electrons hold silicon atoms together. No electrons are available to carry electric current.

**3** Extra valence electrons from phosphorus are not needed to hold the crystal together. They are free to move throughout the crystal and form an electric current.

**4** Boron has fewer valence electrons than silicon. When boron is added to silicon, there are spaces lacking electrons. "Holes" are created in the crystal structure. Movement of electrons into and out of these holes produces an electric current.

Phosphorus-doped silicon
*n*-type semiconductor

• = 1 electron
● = Silicon atom

Silicon crystal

Before doping

Boron-doped silicon
*p*-type semiconductor

After doping

### Thinking Critically

**1.** Explain why you would expect germanium to have the same type of structure and semiconducting properties as silicon.

**2.** What type of semiconductor would you expect arsenic-doped germanium to be?

**Chapter 7** The Elements

• Some students think that n-type semiconductors have a net negative charge and that p-type semiconductors have a net positive charge. Explain that the silicon and dopant atoms are neutral, so the doped semiconductor must also be neutral.

## Thinking Critically

1. Silicon and germanium have the same number of valence electrons and similar atomic radii.

2. Arsenic has five valence electrons and germanium has four. Therefore, arsenic-doped germanium would be an n-type semiconductor.

## Summary

### 7.1 Properties of s-Block Elements

- The number and location of valence electrons determine an element's position on the periodic table and its chemistry.

- Properties within a group are not identical because members have different numbers of inner electrons.

- Similarities between period-2 elements and period-3 elements in neighboring groups are called diagonal relationships.

- The representative elements in groups 1A through 8A have only s and p electrons.

- Because hydrogen has a single electron, it can behave as a metal and lose an electron or behave as a nonmetal and gain an electron.

- The alkali and alkaline earth metals in groups 1A and 2A are the most reactive metals.

- Metals form mixtures called alloys, whose composition can be adjusted to produce different properties.

- Sodium and potassium are the most abundant alkali metals. Many biological functions are controlled by sodium and potassium ions.

- Calcium is essential for healthy teeth and bones. It is most often found as calcium carbonate, which can decompose to form lime—one of the most important industrial compounds.

- Magnesium is used in lightweight, yet strong alloys. Magnesium ions are essential for metabolism, muscle function, and photosynthesis.

### 7.2 Properties of p-Block Elements

- p-block elements include metals, metalloids, nonmetals, and inert gases.

- Aluminum is the most abundant metal in Earth's crust. Much more energy is needed to extract aluminum from its ore than to recycle aluminum.

- Because a carbon atom can join with up to four other carbon atoms, carbon forms millions of organic compounds.

- Graphite and diamond are allotropes of carbon.

- The most abundant elements in Earth's crust, silicon and oxygen, are usually found in silica, which can be melted and rapidly cooled to form glass.

- Lead, which is still used in storage batteries, was used in pipes, paint, and gasoline until people realized the danger of lead poisoning.

- Nitrogen combines with hydrogen in ammonia, which is used in cleaning products. Nitric acid, which is produced from ammonia, is used to make solid fertilizers, explosives, and dyes.

- Phosphates in fertilizers and cleaning products can harm the environment.

- Sulfur dioxide reacts with water to form one of the acids in acid rain. Most sulfur dioxide is used to make sulfuric acid.

- Halogens are extremely reactive nonmetals. Their compounds are used in toothpaste, disinfectants, and bleaches. Many plastics contain chlorine. Silver bromide or iodide is used to coat photographic film.

- The stable noble gases are used in lighter-than-air blimps, in neon lights, as a substitute for nitrogen in diving tanks, and as an inert atmosphere for welding.

### 7.3 Properties of d-Block and f-Block Elements

- The d-block transition metals and f-block inner transition metals are more similar across a period than are the s-block and p-block elements.

- The more unpaired electrons in the d sublevel, the harder the transition metal and the higher its melting and boiling points. Ions with partially filled d sublevels often form compounds with color.

- In ferromagnetic metals, ions are permanently aligned in the direction of a magnetic field.

- Many transition metals are strategic materials.

- Lanthanides are silvery metals with high melting points that are found mixed in nature and are hard to separate. Actinides are radioactive elements.

## Vocabulary

- actinide series (p. 197)
- allotrope (p. 188)
- diagonal relationship (p. 180)
- ferromagnetism (p. 199)
- lanthanide series (p. 197)
- metallurgy (p. 199)
- mineral (p. 187)
- ore (p. 187)

chemistrymc.com/vocabulary_puzzlemaker

## Using the Vocabulary

To reinforce chapter vocabulary, have students write a sentence using each term. **L2** **ELL**

## Review Strategies

- Have students locate on the periodic table the s-block elements: groups of elements (1A and 2A) that have only s valence electrons. Have them list the characteristics of each group and examples of elements. **L2**

- Have students locate the p-block elements: the groups of elements (3A through 8A) that have s and p valence electrons. Have them list the characteristics of each group and examples of elements. **L2**

- Have students locate the d-block (transition) and f-block (inner transition) elements. Have them list the characteristics of each group and examples of elements. Discuss the similarities and differences of each block of elements. **L2**

VOCABULARY PuzzleMaker

For additional help with vocabulary, have students access the Vocabulary PuzzleMaker online.

chemistrymc.com/ vocabulary_puzzlemaker

Chemistry Online

## EXAMVIEW® PRO

### Use ExamView® Pro Testmaker CD-ROM to:

- Create **multiple versions** of tests.
- Create **modified** tests with one mouse click for struggling students.
- **Edit** existing questions and add your own questions.
- **Build** tests based on national curriculum standards.

## Concept Mapping

**26.** 1. alkaline earth metals;
2. calcium, strontium, barium; 3. magnesium;
4. beryllium

## Mastering Concepts

**27.** Elements within a group have the same number of valence electrons.

**28.** groups 1A through 8A

**29.** the close relationships between elements in neighboring groups, such as similarities in properties between a period 2 element and a period 3 element in the next group

**30.** Hydrogen loses an electron and forms an ion with a 1+ charge.

**31.** Heavy water contains deuterium, an isotope of hydrogen with one neutron.

**32.** 1+ and 2+, respectively

**33. a.** sodium
**b.** calcium
**c.** francium

**34.** Group 2A elements have an additional valence electron, are less reactive, harder, and form compounds that are less soluble in water.

**35.** Sodium, atomic number 11, has a smaller atomic radius and a larger ionization energy than cesium. Cesium, atomic number 55, has a larger atomic radius and more inner electrons to shield the valence electrons from the nucleus. With a larger shielding effect and a lower ionization energy, cesium loses electrons more easily than sodium.

**36.** Calcium has two valence electrons, and it takes more energy to remove two valence electrons than one. Potassium has only one valence electron and is larger than calcium; there-

## Chemistry Online

*Go to the Chemistry Web site at* chemistrymc.com *for additional Chapter 7 Assessment.*

## Concept Mapping

**26.** Complete the following concept map using the following terms: beryllium; magnesium; calcium, strontium, and barium; alkaline earth metals.

```
        Representative
        elements that have
        two valence electrons
                |
              ( 1. )
             /        \
      Reacts          Does not
    vigorously        react with
    with water          water
        |                 |
      ( 2. )           ( 4. )
          \   Will react  /
           \    with     /
            \  hot water/
              ( 3. )
```

## Mastering Concepts

**27.** Why are elements within a group similar in chemical and physical properties? (7.1)

**28.** Which groups have representative elements? (7.1)

**29.** What is a diagonal relationship? (7.1)

**30.** What happens when hydrogen reacts with a nonmetal element? (7.1)

**31.** What is heavy water? (7.1)

**32.** What is the charge on alkali metal ions? On alkaline earth metal ions? (7.1)

**33.** Identify the element that fits each description. (7.1)
**a.** element in baking soda that turns a flame yellow
**b.** metallic element found in limestone
**c.** radioactive alkali metal

**34.** List some ways group 2A elements differ from group 1A elements. (7.1)

**35.** Explain why cesium is a more reactive alkali metal than sodium. (7.1)

**36.** Use their electron configurations to explain why calcium is less reactive than potassium. (7.1)

**37.** List at least one use for each of the following compounds. (7.1)
**a.** sodium chloride (table salt)
**b.** calcium oxide (lime)
**c.** potassium chloride

**38.** List three types of information that you can obtain from the periodic table. (7.1)

**39.** Explain why the halogens are extremely reactive non-metals. (7.2)

**40.** Explain why most carbon compounds are classified as organic compounds. (7.2)

**41.** What is the charge on halogen ions? (7.2)

**42.** Argon has only one more proton than chlorine. Explain why these two gases have such different chemical properties. (7.2)

**43.** Why is red phosphorus classified as an amorphous solid? (7.2)

**44.** Why is lead no longer used in paints or for plumbing pipes? (7.2)

**45.** Compare the allotropes of oxygen. (7.2)

**46.** Identify the element that fits each description. (7.2)
**a.** greenish-yellow gas used to disinfect water
**b.** main element in emeralds and aquamarines
**c.** lightweight metal extracted from bauxite ore
**d.** the most abundant element in Earth's crust

**47.** What could account for the change in color within the mineral in the photograph below? (7.2)

chemistrymc.com/chapter_test

fore, it takes less energy to remove its valence electron.

**37. a.** food additive, preservative, source of dietary sodium ions
**b.** makes soil less acidic; removes pollutants from smokestacks; is an ingredient in mortar; used in manu-

## Resource Manager

**Chapter Assessment,** pp. 37–42 **L2**
**Supplemental Problems,** Ch. 7
**ExamView® Pro CD-ROM**
**MindJogger Videoquizzes DVD/VHS**
**Solutions Manual,** Ch. 7
**Chemistry Interactive CD-ROM,**
  Ch. 7 quiz

**48.** Explain why iodine can be substituted for bromine in some compounds. (7.2)

**49.** Explain why fluorine reacts with all elements except helium, neon, and argon. (7.2)

**50.** Name the element that combines with oxygen to form a compound that fits each description. (7.2)
   **a.** the compound that can be melted to form glass
   **b.** the main compound in ruby and sapphire
   **c.** a compound used to preserve fruit and produce an inexpensive acid

**51.** List at least one use for each compound. (7.2)
   **a.** silicon carbide (carborundum)
   **b.** aluminum sulfate (alum)
   **c.** boric acid
   **d.** nitric acid

**52.** When the metal gallium melts, is the liquid that forms an allotrope? Explain your answer. (7.2)

**53.** How do transition metals differ from inner transition metals in their electron configurations? (7.3)

**54.** Explain why compounds of zinc are white but compounds containing copper have a color. (7.3)

**55.** Name three general methods for extracting a metal from its ore. (7.3)

**56.** What does it mean for a metal to be listed as strategic or critical? (7.3)

**57.** Predict which of the transition metals in period 4 is diamagnetic. Explain your answer. (7.3)

**58.** Explain how the electron configurations of chromium and copper determine that one is used to strengthen alloys and the other to make jewelry. (7.3)

## Mixed Review

*Sharpen your problem-solving skills by answering the following.*

**59.** What distinguishes a metal from a nonmetal?

**60.** Where are the most reactive nonmetals located on the periodic table? The most reactive metals?

**61.** Which families contain metalloids?

**62.** What chemical property does zinc share with calcium?

**63.** Name at least three elements that are commonly found in fertilizers.

**64.** What physical property is shown by the element in the photograph? Identify the element.

**65.** Of the period-5 elements, palladium, tin, and silver, which will display noticeably different properties from the other two? Explain your choice.

**66.** What do rubidium and white phosphorus have in common?

**67.** Identify the block on the periodic table where you are likely to find:
   **a.** a synthetic radioactive element.
   **b.** a highly reactive element that forms salts with halogens.
   **c.** an element that forms millions of compounds.

**68.** For each period-3 element, Na through Cl, identify the following:
   **a.** the metals, nonmetals, and metalloids.
   **b.** the appearance of the element and its state at room temperature.

**69.** What is the most common ion or ions for each of these elements: sodium, bromine, neon, cadmium, boron, and hydrogen?

## Thinking Critically

**70. Applying Concepts** Which element would be easiest to extract from its ore, gold or iron? Explain your choice.

**71. Hypothesizing** Why might countries have different lists of strategic and critical materials?

**72. Applying Concepts** In 1906, Ferdinand Moissan won a Nobel Prize for producing fluorine in its pure elemental form. Why do you think his achievement was considered worthy of such a prize?

**73. Analyze and Conclude** Why were metals such as copper and gold discovered long before gases such as oxygen and nitrogen?

facture of steel, paper, and glass
   **c.** dietary substitute for table salt

**38.** whether an element is a metal, nonmetal, or metalloid; what type of ion an element is likely to form; what group an element is found in (which indicates its reactivity)

**39.** With seven valence electrons, halogens need only one electron to achieve a stable noble gas electron configuration.

**40.** Many carbon compounds play key roles in the chemistry of living organisms.

**41.** Halogens form ions with a $1^-$ charge.

**42.** Argon, an element with a stable noble gas configuration of eight valence electrons, is unreactive. Chlorine, with seven valence electrons, must gain one electron to achieve a noble gas electron configuration.

**43.** There is no definite pattern to the arrangement of its atoms.

**44.** Lead is toxic.

**45.** Both are gases formed from oxygen atoms. Oxygen gas ($O_2$) is colorless, odorless, essential for most living organisms, and abundant in the lower atmosphere. Ozone ($O_3$) is an unstable gas with an irritating odor that is found mainly in the upper atmosphere.

**46. a.** chlorine   **c.** aluminum
     **b.** beryllium  **d.** oxygen

**47.** The change in color may be due to the presence of different trace element impurities.

**48.** Iodine and bromine are group 7A nonmetals that have similar chemical properties.

**49.** Fluorine is the most electronegative element on the periodic table and therefore the most reactive.

**50. a.** silicon
     **b.** aluminum
     **c.** sulfur

**51. a.** an industrial abrasive
     **b.** used in antiperspirants and to remove suspended particles during water purification
     **c.** a disinfectant and eye wash
     **d.** used to etch metal plates; to produce solid fertilizers, explosives, and dyes

**52.** No; the liquid is in a different state and is not a different structure in the same state.

**National Science Content Standards**

Pages 206–207
UCP.1, UCP.2, UCP.5; B.1, B.2, B.3; E.2

53. In transition metals, the final electron enters a d sublevel; in inner transition metals, the final electron enters an f sublevel.

54. Copper has d electrons in its partially filled d sublevel that can absorb wavelengths of visible light. Zinc has a filled d sublevel, and transitions in zinc require the higher energy of UV radiation.

55. heat, solutions, and electrolysis

56. Either the metal or its compounds have critical applications that affect industries or the military.

57. zinc, because it has no unpaired electrons

58. Chromium has six unpaired electrons and is a hard metal with a high melting point; copper has only one unpaired electron, making it softer and more malleable.

## Mixed Review

59. Metals, located on the left of the periodic table, tend to lose electrons, are conductors, have luster, and are malleable/ductile; nonmetals, located on the right of the periodic table, tend to gain electrons, are dull, brittle, and nonconductors.

60. group 7A; group 1A

61. groups 3A, 4A, 5A, and 6A

62. Both metals can lose two electrons, forming ions with a 2+ charge.

63. potassium, nitrogen, phosphorus, and sulfur

64. It is a silvery liquid. It is mercury.

65. Tin is a representative element in group 4A; palladium and silver are transition metals that have similar sizes and ionization energies and similar properties.

74. **Drawing a Conclusion** The most important function of blood is to carry oxygen to all cells in the body. What could happen if blood flow to a cell were blocked?

75. **Using a Database** Find out the following:
    **a.** the trend for the melting point of alkali metals
    **b.** the color of copper compounds
    **c.** the colors of the ions of chromium

76. **Observing and Predicting** If you were given two solutions, one colorless and the other a light blue, which solution would probably contain an ion from a transition metal? Explain your answer.

## Writing in Chemistry

77. Research the local city or state regulations for removal of lead paint and write a report on your findings.

78. Use the example of ozone to argue that a single chemical can be both beneficial and harmful.

79. Describe the uses of fluorine, chlorine, and iodine compounds related to drinking water and wastewater.

80. Research and write a report on the use of silver iodide for seeding clouds.

81. Research the history of the term *bromide*, which is used to describe a remedy designed to ease tension.

82. Find out how the daily values for vitamins and minerals are determined. Compare supplements to see whether they all contain the same minerals in the same quantities per tablet. In your report, suggest reasons for any variations you discover.

83. Research the processes of recycling aluminum, plastic, and glass. Design a poster or a multimedia presentation for members of your community about one of the processes. Include the following considerations: Why is it cost effective to recycle? What resources are conserved? What recycling is available in your area? How can the members of your community use this information to make responsible choices about the products they purchase?

84. Find out how the elements are assigned their names. What elements are named after people? Choose one and research why this person was given such an honor.

## Cumulative Review

*Refresh your understanding of previous chapters by answering the following.*

85. Determine the correct number of significant figures in each of the following. (Chapter 2)
    **a.** 708.4 mL
    **b.** 1.0050 g
    **c.** 1.000 mg
    **d.** $6.626 \times 10^{-34}$ s
    **e.** 2000 people

86. A quarter has a mass of 5.627 g. What is its mass in milligrams? (Chapter 2)

87. A solution of sugar has a density of 1.05 g/cm³. If you have 300.0 mL of sugar solution, what is the mass of the solution? (Chapter 2)

88. A substance is said to be volatile if it readily changes from a liquid to a gas at room temperature. Is this a physical change or a chemical change? (Chapter 3)

89. How many electrons, protons, and neutrons are there is the following: (Chapter 4)
    **a.** carbon-13
    **b.** chromium-50
    **c.** tin-119

90. An AM radio signal broadcasts at $6.00 \times 10^5$ Hz. What is the wavelength of this signal in meters? What is the energy of one photon of this signal? (Chapter 5)

91. Determine the energy of a photon with a wavelength of $4.80 \times 10^2$ nm. (Chapter 5)

92. Identify which of the following orbitals cannot exist according to quantum theory: 4s, 1p, 2p, 3f, 2d. Briefly explain your answer. (Chapter 5)

93. Mendeleev left a space on his periodic table for the undiscovered element germanium and in 1886 Winkler discovered it. Write the electron configuration for germanium. (Chapter 6)

94. Select the atom or ion in each pair that has the larger radius. (Chapter 6)
    **a.** Cs or Fr
    **b.** Br or As
    **c.** $O^{2-}$ or O

95. Arrange the following in order of increasing ionization energy: Li, C, Si, Ne. (Chapter 6)

96. Arrange the following in order of increasing ionization energy: K, Ca, Fr, Mg. (Chapter 6)

66. They burst into flame if exposed to air.

67. **a.** f block
    **b.** s block
    **c.** p block

68. **a.** Metals: Na, Mg, Al; metalloids: Si; Nonmetals: P, S, Cl
    **b.** Na, Mg, Al, and Si are silvery gray solids; P is a white, black, or red solid; the common allotrope of S is a yellow solid; Cl is a greenish-yellow gas.

69. $Na^+$, $Br^-$, none, $Cd^{2+}$, $B^{3+}$, $H^+$ or $H^-$

## Thinking Critically

70. Gold would be easier to extract because it exists uncombined in nature.

71. Countries may have their own deposits of critical minerals. They may have different needs based on their industries.

*Use these questions and the test-taking tip to prepare for your standardized test.*

**1.** Which of the following descriptions does NOT apply to gold?

   **a.** transition metal
   **b.** ferromagnetic
   **c.** element
   **d.** nonconductor

**2.** On the periodic table, metalloids are found only in

   **a.** the d-block.
   **b.** groups 3A through 6A.
   **c.** the f-block.
   **d.** groups 1A and 2A.

**3.** The majority of _____ are radioactive.

   **a.** actinides
   **b.** lanthanides
   **c.** halogens
   **d.** alkali metals

**4.** Which of the following groups is composed entirely of nonmetals?

   **a.** 1A
   **b.** 3A
   **c.** 5A
   **d.** 7A

**5.** Which is a major component of organic compounds?

   **a.** sodium
   **b.** calcium
   **c.** carbon
   **d.** potassium

**6.** Although metals in the same group on the periodic table have the same number of valence electrons, they do not have identical properties. Which of the following is NOT an explanation for differences in properties within a group?

   **a.** The metals have different numbers of nonvalence electrons.
   **b.** The reactivity of metals increase as their ionization energies decrease.
   **c.** The ionization energies of metals decrease as their atomic masses increase.
   **d.** The reactivity of metals increase as their atomic masses decrease.

**7.** Throughout history, dangerous products were used before people understood their harmful effects. Which of the following historic practices was NOT discontinued because of the health hazard it posed?

   **a.** using radium paint to make watch hands glow in the dark
   **b.** lining steel cans with tin to prevent corrosion
   **c.** using arsenic sulfide to treat illnesses
   **d.** adding lead to gasoline to increase engine efficiency

**Interpreting Tables** Use the table to answer questions 8 through 10.

| Characteristics of Elements | | |
|---|---|---|
| **Element** | **Block** | **Characteristic** |
| X | s | soft solid; reacts readily with oxygen |
| Y | p | gas at room temperature; forms salts |
| Z | — | inert gas |

**8** In which group does Element X most likely belong?

   **a.** 1A
   **b.** 7A
   **c.** 8A
   **d.** 4B

**9.** Element Y is probably

   **a.** an alkaline metal.
   **b.** an alkaline earth metal.
   **c.** a halogen.
   **d.** a transition metal.

**10.** Element Z is most likely found in the

   **a.** s-block.
   **b.** p-block.
   **c.** d-block.
   **d.** f-block.

---

### TEST-TAKING TIP

**Plan Your Work and Work Your Plan**
Plan your workload so that you do a little work each day rather than a lot of work all at once. The key to retaining information is repeated review and practice. You will retain more if you study one hour a night for five days in a row instead of cramming for five hours on a Sunday night.

 chemistrymc.com/standardized_test

Standardized Test Practice   **209**

**72.** Because fluorine reacts with almost every element, it took decades to find a way to isolate elemental fluorine.
**73.** They are visible solids often found uncombined in nature. Oxygen and nitrogen are colorless, odorless gases.
**74.** The cell would not receive the oxygen it needs to release energy.
**75. a.** Melting point decreases with an increase in atomic number.
   **b.** Copper compounds are green and blue.
   **c.** $Cr^{2+}$ is red, $Cr^{3+}$ is green, $Cr^{4+}$ is brown-black, and $Cr^{6+}$ is orange.
**76.** The blue solution is most likely to contain transition metal ions because transition metal ions with partially filled d sublevels display color. However, some transition metal ions are colorless, e.g., zinc ions.

## Cumulative Review

**85. a.** 4
   **b.** 5
   **c.** 4
   **d.** 4
   **e.** 1, unless it is an exact count; then infinite
**86.** $5.627 \times 10^3$ mg
**87.** 315 g
**88.** physical change
**89. a.** 6 e, 6 p, 7 n
   **b.** 24 e, 24 p, 26 n
   **c.** 50 e, 50 p, 69 n
**90.** $5.00 \times 10^2$ m; $3.98 \times 10^{-28}$ J
**91.** $4.14 \times 10^{-19}$ J
**92.** 1p, 3f, and 2d cannot exist; the n = 1 energy level can have only one sublevel; when n = 3, there are

3 sublevels, s, p, and d; when n = 2, there are only 2 sublevels, s and p.
**93.** $[Ar]4s^2 3d^{10} 4p^2$
**94. a.** Fr
   **b.** As
   **c.** $O^{2-}$
**95.** Li, Si, C, Ne
**96.** Fr, K, Ca, Mg

## Standardized Test Practice

  **1.** b      **6.** d
  **2.** b      **7.** b
  **3.** a      **8.** a
  **4.** d      **9.** c
  **5.** c    **10.** b

**National Science Content Standards**

**Pages 208–209**
UCP.1, UCP.2, UCP.5; B.1, B.2; E.2; F.4, F.6; G.1

# Resource Manager

| Section | Objectives | Activities/Features |
|---|---|---|
| **Section 8.1**<br>**Forming Chemical Bonds**<br>1 session<br>½ block | 1. **Define** chemical bond.<br>2. **Relate** chemical bond formation to electron configuration.<br>3. **Describe** the formation of positive and negative ions. | **Discovery Lab:** An Unusual Alloy, p. 211 |
| **Section 8.2**<br>**The Formation and Nature of Ionic Bonds**<br>1½ sessions<br>1 block | 4. **Describe** the formation of ionic bonds.<br>5. **Account** for many of the physical properties of an ionic compound.<br>6. **Discuss** the energy involved in the formation of an ionic bond. | **Problem-Solving Lab:** How is color related to a transferred electron? p. 219<br>**ChemLab:** Making Ionic Compounds, pp. 232–233 |
| **Section 8.3**<br>**Names and Formulas for Ionic Compounds**<br>1½ sessions<br>1 block | 7. **Write** formulas for ionic compounds and oxyanions.<br>8. **Name** ionic compounds and oxyanions. | **Careers Using Chemistry:** Wastewater Treatment Operator, p. 222<br>**Earth Science Connection**, p. 226 |
| **Section 8.4**<br>**Metallic Bonds and Properties of Metals**<br>2 sessions<br>1 block | 9. **Describe** a metallic bond.<br>10. **Explain** the physical properties of metals in terms of metallic bonds.<br>11. **Define** and **describe** alloys. | **MiniLab:** Heat Treatment of Steel, p. 230<br>**Everyday Chemistry:** Colors of Gems, p. 234 |

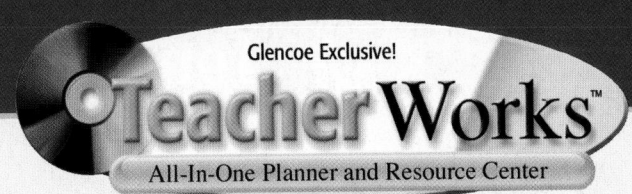

| National Science Content Standards | State/Local Standards | Reproducible Masters | Transparencies |
|---|---|---|---|
| UCP.1, UCP.2; A.1; B.1, B.2 | | **Study Guide for Content Mastery,** p. 43 L2 <br> **Challenge Problems,** p. 8 L3 | **Section Focus** <br> **Transparency 26** L1 ELL <br> **Teaching** <br> **Transparency 25** L2 ELL <br> **Math Skills** <br> **Transparency 7** L2 ELL |
| UCP.1, UCP.2; B.1, B.2, B.3, B.4, B.6 | | **Study Guide for Content Mastery,** pp. 44–45 L2 <br> **ChemLab and MiniLab Worksheets,** pp. 30–32 L2 <br> **Laboratory Manual,** pp. 57–64 L2 <br> **CBL Laboratory Manual,** pp. 5–8 L2 | **Section Focus** <br> **Transparency 27** L1 ELL <br> **Teaching** <br> **Transparency 26** L2 ELL |
| UCP.1, UCP.2; B.2; E.2; G.2 | | **Study Guide for Content Mastery,** pp. 46–47 L2 | **Section Focus** <br> **Transparency 28** L1 ELL <br> **Teaching** <br> **Transparency 27** L2 ELL <br> **Math Skills** <br> **Transparency 8** L2 ELL |
| UCP.1, UCP.2; A.1; B.1, B.2, B.3, B.4, B.6; E.1 | | **Study Guide for Content Mastery,** p. 48 L2 <br> **ChemLab and MiniLab Worksheets,** p. 29 L2 | **Section Focus** <br> **Transparency 29** L1 ELL <br> **Teaching** <br> **Transparency 28** L2 ELL |

**Key to National Science Content Standards:** UCP = Unifying Concepts and Processes, A = Science as Inquiry, B = Physical Science, C = Life Science, D = Earth and Space Sciences, E = Science and Technology, F = Science in Personal and Social Perspectives, G = History and Nature of Science

Refer to pages 4T–5T of the Teacher Guide for an explanation of the National Science Content Standards correlations.

# Resource Manager

## Materials List

### ChemLab (pages 232–233)
magnesium ribbon, crucible, ring stand, ring stand ring, clay triangle, crucible tongs, balance, 100-mL beaker, distilled water, conductivity tester, laboratory burner, stirring rod

### Discovery Lab (page 211)
Onion's Fusible Alloy, 250-mL beaker, laboratory burner or hot plate, thermometer, water

### MiniLab (page 230)
laboratory burner, forceps (2), hairpins (3), 250-mL beaker, water

### Demonstration (pages 222–223)
granular zinc-mercury(II) chloride(aq) amalgam, ammonium metavanadate solution, 250-mL graduated cylinder, powder funnel, 500-mL Erlenmeyer flask, stopper

## Preparation of Solutions

For a review of solution preparation, see page 46T of the Teacher Guide.

Quantities are for a class of 30 students.

**Demonstration (pages 222–223)**

**Ammonium metavanadate solution** Dissolve 0.7 g ammonium metavanadate ($NH_4VO_3$) in 150 mL distilled water. **CAUTION:** Solution is moderately toxic.

## Assessment Resources

**Chapter Assessment,** pp. 43–48
**MindJogger Videoquizzes DVD/VHS**
**Alternate Assessment in the Science Classroom**
**ExamView® Pro CD-ROM**
**Solutions Manual,** Chapter 8
**Supplemental Problems,** Chapter 8
**Performance Assessment in the Science Classroom**
**Chemistry Interactive CD-ROM,** Chapter 8 quiz

## Additional Resources

**Spanish Resources** ELL
**Guided Reading Audio Program,** Chapter 8 ELL
**Cooperative Learning in the Science Classroom**
**Lab and Safety Skills in the Science Classroom**
**Lesson Plans**
**Block Scheduling Lesson Plans**
**Chemistrymc.com**

## Glencoe Technology

The following multimedia for this chapter are available from Glencoe.

**VIDEOTAPE/DVD**
MindJogger Videoquizzes,
Chapter 8

**CD-ROM**
**Chemistry: Matter and Change**
*Forming an Ionic Compound,* Experiment
*Variable Oxidation States,* Demonstration
*Determining a Formula,* Exploration
*Oxidation States of Vanadium,*
   Demonstration

**CD-ROM**
**ExamView® Pro**
   **Testmaker**

**CD-ROM**
**Interactive Chalkboard**

**CD-ROM**
**TeacherWorks™**

## Multiple Learning Styles

Look for the following icons for strategies that emphasize different learning modalities.

***Kinesthetic***
Differentiated Instruction, pp. 221, 228;
Reinforcement, p. 225; Portfolio, p. 225

***Visual-Spatial***
Reinforcement, p. 212, Concept Development,
p. 212; Differentiated Instruction, p. 212; Chemistry
Journal, pp. 213, 217, 229; Extension, p. 214; Portfolio,
p. 226

***Interpersonal***
Extension, p. 215

***Intrapersonal***
Differentiated Instruction, p. 219, Chemistry
Journal, p. 225; Check for Understanding, p. 227;
Portfolio, p. 230; Extension, p. 231

***Linguistic***
Portfolio, pp. 213, 215

***Logical-Mathematical***
Math in Chemistry, p. 218

## Key to Teaching Strategies

**L1** Level 1 activities should be appropriate for students with learning difficulties.

**L2** Level 2 activities should be within the ability range of all students.

**L3** Level 3 activities are designed for above-average students.

**ELL** ELL activities should be within the ability range of English Language Learners.

**COOP LEARN** Cooperative Learning activities are designed for small group work.

**P** These strategies represent student products that can be placed into a best-work portfolio.

These strategies are useful in a block scheduling format.

## Assessment Planner

**Portfolio Assessment**
Portfolio, TWE, pp. 213, 215,
   225, 226, 230, 235
Assessment, TWE, p. 227
Problem-Solving Lab,
   TWE, p. 219
MiniLab, TWE, p. 230

**Performance Assessment**
Assessment, TWE, p. 218
MiniLab, SE, p. 230
ChemLab, SE, pp. 232–233
Discovery Lab, SE, p. 211

**Knowledge Assessment**
Assessment, TWE, pp. 214,
   220, 225, 229
Demonstration, TWE,
   p. 223
ChemLab, TWE, p. 233
Section Assessment, SE,
   pp. 214, 220, 227, 231
Chapter Assessment, SE,
   pp. 236–239

**Skill Assessment**
Assessment, TWE, pp. 212,
   225, 231

## Tying to Previous Knowledge

Have students review the following concepts before studying this chapter:
Chapter 4: atomic structure
Chapter 5: electron configuration
Chapter 6: periodic trends
Chapter 7: periodic properties

## Using the Photo

Have students observe the opening photo of the rock climbers. Ask students what items are composed of only one kind of atom. Answers will vary but might include certain gases in the air or any free elements they might see. Are most of the materials composed of more than one element? yes

### PowerPoint® Presentations

This CD-ROM is an editable Microsoft® PowerPoint® presentation that includes:
• Section presentations
• Section checks
• Image bank
• Links to Chemistry Online
• All transparencies
• Animations
• Audio

---

# Ionic Compounds

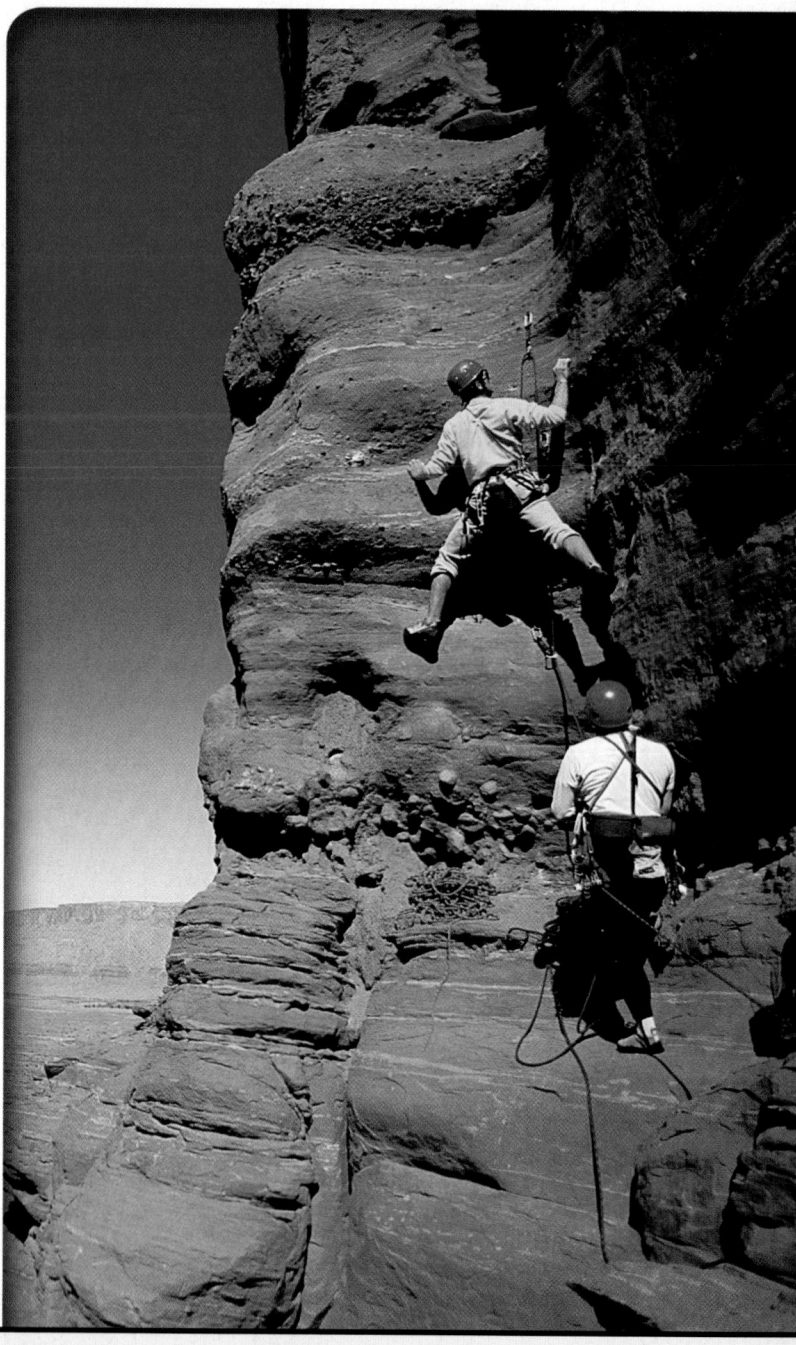

## What You'll Learn

▶ You will define a chemical bond.
▶ You will describe how ions form.
▶ You will identify ionic bonding and the characteristics of ionic compounds.
▶ You will name and write formulas for ionic compounds.
▶ You will relate metallic bonds to the characteristics of metals.

## Why It's Important

The world around you is composed mainly of compounds. The properties of each compound are based on how the compound is bonded. The salts dissolved in Earth's oceans and the compounds that make up most of Earth's crust are held together by ionic bonds.

Visit the Chemistry Web site at chemistrymc.com to find links about ionic compounds.

The rock surface, the climbers' equipment, the atmosphere, and even the climbers are composed almost entirely of compounds and mixtures of compounds.

210     Chapter 8

---

## DISCOVERY LAB

### Purpose
Students will observe a metal alloy that has a low melting point.

### Safety and Disposal
Remind students to be careful around hot materials. Keep the alloy for reuse.

### Teaching Strategies
• After the alloy melts, tell students to make sure it solidifies in one piece.
• Tell interested students that Onion's Fusible Alloy contains approximately 50% bismuth, 30% lead, and 20% tin.

### Expected Results
Onion's Fusible Alloy melts at approximately 92°C.

### Analysis
Onion's Fusible Alloy melts at a much lower temperature than other metals. The melting point of bismuth is 271°C; lead, 327°C; and tin, 232°C. Students should conclude that a mixture of metals does not necessarily have the properties of the metals that comprise it.

## DISCOVERY LAB

### An Unusual Alloy

**M**ost metals that you encounter are solids. Can a metal melt at a temperature below the boiling point of water? You will use a metal alloy called Onion's Fusible Alloy to answer this question.

#### Safety Precautions

 Use caution around the heat source and the heated beaker and its contents.

#### Procedure

1. Carefully place a small piece of Onion's Fusible Alloy into a 250-mL beaker. Add about 100 mL of water to the beaker.

2. Heat the beaker and its contents with a laboratory burner or a hot plate. Monitor the temperature with a thermometer. When the temperature rises above 85°C, carefully observe the Onion's Fusible Alloy. Record your observations. Remove the beaker from the heat when the water begins to boil. Allow the contents to cool before handling the Onion's Fusible Alloy.

#### Analysis

What is unusual about Onion's Fusible Alloy compared to other metals? Onion's Fusible Alloy contains bismuth, lead, and tin. Compare the melting points of these metals to the melting point of Onion's Fusible Alloy.

**Materials**

Onion's Fusible Alloy
250-mL beaker
laboratory burner or
  hot plate
Celsius thermometer

---

## Section 8.1

## Forming Chemical Bonds

### Objectives

- **Define** chemical bond.
- **Relate** chemical bond formation to electron configuration.
- **Describe** the formation of positive and negative ions.

### Vocabulary

chemical bond
cation
anion

Ascending to the summit of a mountain peak, a rock climber can survey the surrounding world. This world is composed of many different kinds of compounds, ranging from simple ones such as the sodium chloride found in the perspiration on the climber's skin to more complex ones such as the calcite or pyrite found in certain rocks. How do these and thousands of other compounds form from the relatively few elements known to exist?

### Chemical Bonds

The answer to this question lies in the electron structure of the atoms of the elements involved and the nature of the attractive forces between these atoms. The force that holds two atoms together is called a **chemical bond**. Chemical bonds may form by the attraction between a positive nucleus and negative electrons or the attraction between a positive ion and a negative ion.

In previous chapters, you learned about atomic structure, electron arrangement, and periodic properties of the elements. The elements within a group on the periodic table have similar properties. Many of these properties are due to the number of valence electrons. These same electrons are involved in the formation of chemical bonds between two atoms.

8.1 Forming Chemical Bonds **211**

---

## 1 Focus

### Focus Transparency

Before presenting the lesson, display **Section Focus Transparency 26** on the overhead projector. Have students answer the accompanying questions using **Section Focus Transparency Master 26. L1 ELL**

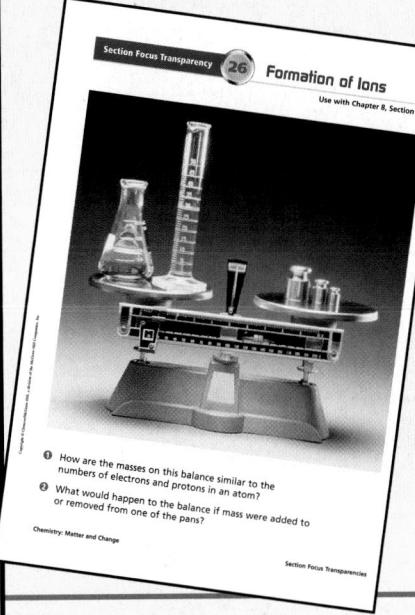

Section Focus Transparency **26** Formation of Ions

Use with Chapter 8, Section 8.1

❶ How are the masses on this balance similar to the numbers of electrons and protons in an atom?
❷ What would happen to the balance if mass were added to or removed from one of the pans?

Chemistry: Matter and Change

Section Focus Transparencies

### Chapter Themes

The following themes from the National Science Education Standards are covered in this chapter. Refer to page 4T of the Teacher Guide for an explanation of the correlations.
Systems, order, and organization (UCP.1)
Evidence, models, and explanation (UCP.2)

---

### Resource Manager

**Study Guide for Content Mastery,**
   p. 43 L2
**Solving Problems: A Chemistry**
   **Handbook,** Section 8.1 L2
**Section Focus Transparency 26 and**
   **Master** L1 ELL

---

**National Science Content Standards**

**Pages 210–211**
UCP.1, UCP.2; A.1; B.1, B.2

**Table 8-1** Tell students that G. N. Lewis suggested a simple way to show and keep track of valence electrons. Have students look at Table 8-1. Up to two dots can be placed on each of the four sides of a symbol. Tell students that all four sides of the symbol are equivalent. Have students write and compare electron dot diagrams for several different elements. **L2**

**Reinforcement**

**Visual-Spatial** Hand students a blank periodic table and have them locate several elements and draw several electron dot diagrams for atoms of those elements. Remind students that valence electrons can be only s and p electrons. **L2** **ELL**

**Concept Development**

**Visual-Spatial** On the chalkboard or overhead projector, write the complete electron configurations of potassium and argon. Ask students to compare and contrast them. They are the same except that potassium also has a $4s^1$ electron. Ask students why argon is particularly stable. It is a noble gas and has eight valence electrons. Ask students how potassium could achieve a noble gas configuration. lose the $4s^1$ electron Remind students that potassium becomes 1+ due to the extra proton in the nucleus. Continue the discussion with calcium, then gallium. **L2**

**Assessment**

**Skill** Have students write the electron configuration for each of the following ions and determine which ions possess noble gas configurations and which possess pseudo-noble gas configurations: $Ti^{4+}$, $Se^{2-}$, $Ge^{3+}$, $Sc^{3+}$. All but $Ge^{3+}$ form noble gas configurations. **L2**

---

**Table 8-1**

| | | | | | | | | |
|---|---|---|---|---|---|---|---|---|
| **Electron-Dot Structures** | | | | | | | | |
| **Group** | **1A** | **2A** | **3A** | **4A** | **5A** | **6A** | **7A** | **8A** |
| **Diagram** | Li· | ·Be· | ·B̈· | ·C̈· | ·N̈· | ·Ö· | :F̈· | :N̈e: |

Recall that an electron-dot structure is a type of diagram used to keep track of valence electrons and is especially useful when illustrating the formation of chemical bonds. **Table 8-1** shows several examples of electron-dot structures. For example, carbon has an electron configuration of $1s^22s^22p^2$. Its valence electrons are those in the second energy level, as can be seen in the electron-dot structure for carbon in the table.

Recall from Chapter 6 that ionization energy refers to how easily an atom loses an electron. The term electron affinity indicates how much attraction an atom has for electrons. Noble gases, having high ionization energies and low electron affinities, show a general lack of chemical reactivity. Other elements on the periodic table react with each other, forming numerous compounds. The difference in reactivity is directly related to the valence electrons.

All atoms have valence electrons. Why does this difference in reactivity of elements exist? Noble gases have electron configurations that have a full outermost energy level. This level is full with two electrons for helium ($1s^2$). The other noble gases have electron configurations consisting of eight electrons in the outermost energy level, $ns^2np^6$. As you will recall, the presence of eight valence electrons in the outer energy level is chemically stable and is called a stable octet. Elements tend to react to acquire the stable electron structure of a noble gas.

**Formation of positive ions** Recall that a positive ion forms when an atom loses one or more valence electrons in order to attain a noble gas configuration. To understand the formation of a positive ion, compare the electron configurations of the noble gas neon, atomic number 10, and the alkali metal sodium, atomic number 11.

Neon     $1s^22s^22p^6$
Sodium   $1s^22s^22p^63s^1$

Note that the sodium atom has one 3s valence electron; it differs from the noble gas neon by that single valence electron. If sodium loses this outer valence electron, the resulting electron configuration will be identical to that of neon. **Figure 8-1** shows how a sodium atom loses its valence electron to become a positive sodium ion. A positively charged ion is called a **cation**.

**Figure 8-1**

In the formation of a positive ion, a neutral atom loses one or more valence electrons. Note that the number of protons is equal to the number of electrons in the uncharged atom, but the ion contains more protons than electrons, making the overall charge on this ion positive.

11 electrons (11−)      10 electrons (10−)

$+ \; 498 \frac{kJ}{mol} \rightarrow \qquad\qquad + \; e^-$

11 protons (11+)      11 protons (11+)

Sodium atom + ionization → Sodium ion (Na+) + electron
                 energy

**212**     **Chapter 8** Ionic Compounds

---

**DIFFERENTIATED INSTRUCTION**

**Learning Disabled**

**Visual-Spatial** Show that when an atom becomes stable, it does not actually become a noble gas. Place a circle of transparency film on an overhead projector. In the center, place 11 small beads to represent the positive sodium nucleus. Ask students to determine the charge on the nucleus. 11+ Place beads in three concentric circles to represent energy levels in the elec-

tron cloud. Determine the charge in the electron cloud. 11− Remove the outermost bead, which represents the valence electron, and have students determine the charge of the ion. 1+ Remind students that the number of protons, not the number of electrons, determines what element is present. **L1** **ELL**

By losing an electron, the sodium atom acquired the stable outer electron configuration of neon. It is important to understand that although sodium now has the electron configuration of neon, it is not neon. It is a sodium ion with a single positive charge. The 11 protons that establish the character of sodium still remain within its nucleus.

Reactivity of metals is based on the ease with which they lose valence electrons to achieve a stable octet, or noble gas configuration. Group 1A elements, [noble gas]ns$^1$, lose their one valence electron, forming an ion with a 1+ charge. Group 2A elements, [noble gas]ns$^2$, lose their two valence electrons and form ions with a 2+ charge. For example, potassium, a group 1A element, forms a K$^+$ ion; magnesium, a group 2A element, forms a Mg$^{2+}$ ion. These two groups contain the most active metals on the periodic table. Some elements in group 3A, [noble gas]ns$^2$np$^1$, also lose electrons and form positive ions. What is the charge on these ions? What is the formula for the aluminum ion?

Recall that, in general, transition metals have an outer energy level of ns$^2$. Going from left to right across a period, atoms of each element are filling an inner d sublevel. When forming positive ions, transition metals commonly lose their two valence electrons, forming 2+ ions. However, it is also possible for d electrons to be lost. Thus transition elements also commonly form ions of 3+ or greater, depending on the number of d electrons in the electron structure. It is difficult to predict the number of electrons lost by transition elements. A useful rule of thumb for these metals is that they form ions with a 2+ or 3+ charge.

Although the formation of an octet is the most stable electron configuration, other electron configurations provide some stability. For example, elements in groups 1B through 4A in periods 4 through 6 lose electrons to form an outer energy level containing full s, p, and d sublevels. These relatively stable electron arrangements are referred to as *pseudo-noble gas configurations*. Let's examine the formation of the zinc ion, which is shown in **Figure 8-2**. The zinc atom has the electron configuration of 1s$^2$2s$^2$2p$^6$3s$^2$3p$^6$4s$^2$3d$^{10}$. When forming an ion, the zinc atom loses the two 4s electrons in the outer energy level, and the stable configuration of 1s$^2$2s$^2$2p$^6$3s$^2$3p$^6$3d$^{10}$ results in a pseudo-noble gas configuration.

### Figure 8-2

Orbital notation provides a convenient way to visualize the loss or gain of valence electrons. When zinc metal reacts with sulfuric acid, the zinc forms a Zn$^{2+}$ ion with a pseudo-noble gas configuration.

8.1 Forming Chemical Bonds **213**

## Concept Development

The electron configurations of some transition metals show a limitation of the octet rule. Transition metals generally do not form ions with noble-gas configurations. In forming ions, transition metals lose the valence s electrons first, but they can also lose d electrons. Write the electron configuration for the element iron. [Ar] 3d$^6$4s$^2$ Iron forms two ions, Fe$^{2+}$ and Fe$^{3+}$. When forming Fe$^{2+}$, the two 4s electrons are lost, resulting in [Ar]3d$^6$. This configuration is only somewhat stable, and the ion will readily lose a 3d electron, forming Fe$^{3+}$. The electron configuration for Fe$^{3+}$ is [Ar]3d$^5$. This half-full d sublevel is not as stable as an octet, but it is more stable than the original configuration for iron or that for Fe$^{2+}$.

## In-Text Questions

**Page 213** What is the charge on these ions? 3+ What is the formula for the aluminum ion? Al$^{3+}$

### Resource Manager

Challenge Problems, p. 8 **L3**
Math Skills Transparency 7 and Master **L2** **ELL**
Teaching Transparency 25 and Master **L2** **ELL**

**National Science Content Standards**

**Pages 212–213**
UCP.1, UCP.2; B.1, B.2

## CHEMISTRY JOURNAL

### Summary of Ion Formation

*Visual-Spatial* In their chemistry journals, have students make charts with the following column heads: Symbol of element, Electron configuration, Electron dot diagram, Ion with charge, Number of electrons lost or gained, and Name of ion. Using the elements cesium, barium, arsenic, iodine, zinc, and phosphorus, have students complete the charts. **L2**

## ✔ Portfolio

### Ions in Biology

*Linguistic* Many ions are important in biological life forms. These ions include the ions of sodium, potassium, magnesium, and calcium, and chloride, iodide, and fluoride. Have interested students research the importance of these ions and write a report to be placed in their portfolios. **L2** **P**

**Page 214** What is the name of the anion formed from nitrogen? nitride

# 3 Assess

## Check for Understanding

Ask students to determine the ions formed from strontium, aluminum, and sulfur. $Sr^{2+}$, $Al^{3+}$, $S^{2-}$

## Reteach

Write the symbol for calcium on the chalkboard. Have students write the electron configuration. $1s^22s^22p^63s^23p^64s^2$ Determine the number of valence electrons. 2 Ask students what ion is formed when calcium reacts. $Ca^{2+}$ Write the symbol for fluorine on the chalk-board and have students determine its electron configuration. $1s^22s^22p^5$ Ask students the number of valence electrons. 7 Ask students what ion will form when fluorine reacts. $F^-$ What is this ion named? fluoride
**L2**

## Extension

 **Visual-Spatial** On a blank periodic table, have students write formulas for and name the ions formed from various elements.
**L2**

✔ **Assessment**

**Knowledge** Have each student write five representative elements that have an atomic number of 54 or lower on a piece of paper. Another student should write the electron configuration for each element, draw the electron dot diagram, and determine what type of ion is most likely formed. **L2**

---

**Figure 8-3**

In the formation of a negative ion, a neutral atom gains one or more electrons. Again, note that in the neutral atom the number of protons equals the number of electrons. However, the ion contains more electrons than protons, making this over-all charge on this ion negative.

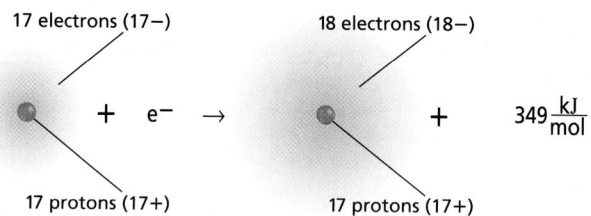

17 electrons (17−)     18 electrons (18−)

$+ \quad e^- \quad \rightarrow$     $+ \quad 349\frac{kJ}{mol}$

17 protons (17+)     17 protons (17+)

Chlorine atom + electron → Chloride ion (Cl−) + electron affinity

**Formation of negative ions** Recall that nonmetals, located on the right side of the periodic table, have a great attraction for electrons and form a stable outer electron configuration by gaining electrons. The chlorine atom, a halogen from group 7A, provides a good example.

Chlorine   $1s^22s^22p^63s^23p^5$

Examine **Figure 8-3**. To attain a noble gas configuration, chlorine gains one electron, forming a negative ion with a 1− charge. By gaining the single electron, the chlorine atom now has the electron configuration of argon.

Ar   $1s^22s^22p^63s^23p^6$

Cl−   $1s^22s^22p^63s^23p^6$

With the addition of one electron, chlorine becomes an **anion**, which is another name for a negative ion. To designate an anion, the ending -*ide* is added to the root name of the element. Thus the anion of chlorine is called the chloride ion. What is the name of the anion formed from nitrogen?

Nonmetals gain the number of electrons that, when added to their valence electrons, equals eight. Phosphorus, a group 5A element with the electron configuration of [Ne]$3s^23p^3$, has five valence electrons. To form a stable octet, the phosphorus atom may gain three electrons and form the phosphide ion with a 3− charge. If an oxygen atom, a group 6A element, gains two electrons, the oxide ion with a charge of 2− results.

Some nonmetals can lose or gain other numbers of electrons to form an octet. For example, in addition to gaining three electrons, phosphorus can lose five. However, in general, group 5A elements gain three electrons, group 6A gain two, and group 7A gain one to achieve an octet.

## Section 8.1 Assessment

1. What is a chemical bond?
2. Why do ions form?
3. What family of elements is relatively unreactive and why?
4. Describe the formation of both positive and negative ions.
5. **Thinking Critically** Predict the change that must occur in the electron configuration if each of the following atoms is to achieve a noble gas configuration.

   **a.** nitrogen     **c.** barium
   **b.** sulfur     **d.** lithium

6. **Formulating Models** Draw models to represent the formation of the positive calcium ion and the negative bromide ion.

chemistrymc.com/self_check_quiz

---

## Section 8.1 Assessment

1. a force that holds two atoms together
2. Atoms gain more stable electron configurations by losing or gaining electrons.
3. Noble gases are relatively unreactive because they have eight electrons in the outermost energy level, which is a stable configuration.
4. Positive ions form when atoms lose valence electrons. Negative ions form when valence electrons are added to an atom.
5. **a.** gain 3 electrons (3− ion) or lose 5 electrons (5+ ion)
   **b.** gain 2 electrons (2− ion)
   **c.** lose 2 electrons (2+ ion)
   **d.** lose 1 electron (1+ ion)
6. Models should show that the calcium atom loses two electrons, forming $Ca^{2+}$, and that bromine gains one electron, forming Br−.

Look at the photos in **Figure 8-4a** and **b**. What do these reactions have in common? As you can see, in both cases, elements react with each other to form a compound. What happens in the formation of a compound?

## Formation of an Ionic Bond

**Figure 8-4a** shows the reaction between the elements sodium and chlorine. During this reaction, a sodium (Na) atom transfers its valence electron to a chlorine (Cl) atom and becomes a positive ion. The chlorine atom accepts the electron into its outer energy level and becomes a negative ion. The compound sodium chloride forms because of the attraction between oppositely charged sodium and chloride ions. The electrostatic force that holds oppositely charged particles together in an ionic compound is referred to as an **ionic bond**. Compounds that contain ionic bonds are ionic compounds. If ionic bonds occur between metals and the nonmetal oxygen, oxides form. Most other ionic compounds are called salts.

Hundreds of compounds contain ionic bonds. Many ionic compounds are binary, which means that they contain only two different elements. Binary ionic compounds contain a metallic cation and a nonmetallic anion. Magnesium oxide, MgO, is a binary compound because it contains the two different elements magnesium and oxygen. However, $CaSO_4$ is not a binary compound. Can you explain why?

Consider the formation of the ionic compound calcium fluoride from calcium (Ca) and fluorine (F). Calcium, a group 2A metal with the electron configuration $[Ar]4s^2$, has two valence electrons. Fluorine, a group 7A nonmetal with the electron configuration $[He]2s^2 2p^5$, must gain one electron to attain the noble gas configuration of neon.

Because the number of electrons lost must equal the number of electrons gained, it will take two fluorine atoms to gain the two electrons lost from one

## Objectives

• **Describe** the formation of ionic bonds.

• **Account** for many of the physical properties of an ionic compound.

• **Discuss** the energy involved in the formation of an ionic bond.

## Vocabulary

ionic bond
electrolyte
lattice energy

### Figure 8-4

These chemical reactions that produce ionic compounds also release a large amount of energy.
ⓐ The reaction that occurs between elemental sodium and chlorine gas produces a white crystalline solid.
ⓑ This sparkler contains iron, which burns in air to produce an ionic compound that contains iron and oxygen.

### Resource Manager

**Study Guide for Content Mastery,** pp. 44–45 **L2**
**Solving Problems: A Chemistry Handbook,** Section 8.2 **L2**
**Section Focus Transparency 27 and Master** **L1** **ELL**
**Lab Manual,** pp. 57–60, 61–64 **L2**

 **Portfolio**

### Forming an Ionic Bond

*Linguistic* Have students write a story or create a model about the formation of an ionic bond. Then, have them present their models to the class.
**L2** **ELL** **P**

# 1 Focus

### Focus Transparency

Before presenting the lesson, display **Section Focus Transparency 27** on the overhead projector. Have students answer the accompanying questions using **Section Focus Transparency Master 27.** **L1** **ELL**

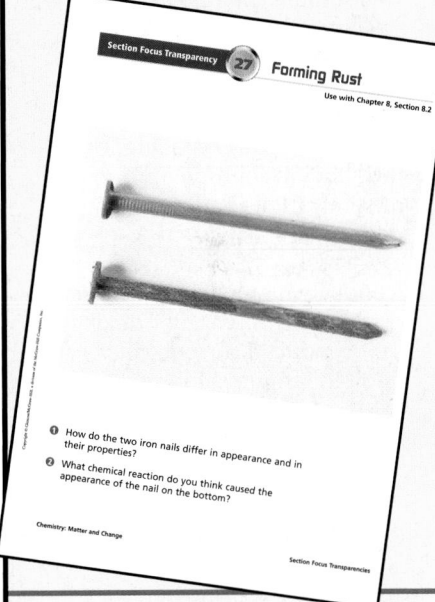

Section Focus Transparency **27** Forming Rust
Use with Chapter 8, Section 8.2

❶ How do the two iron nails differ in appearance and in their properties?
❷ What chemical reaction do you think caused the appearance of the nail on the bottom?

Chemistry: Matter and Change
Section Focus Transparencies

# 2 Teach

### Extension

*Interpersonal* Have students check the label of ingredients on paint cans, either from their home or a neighborhood paint supplier. With students working in groups, determine which of the compounds listed are ionic. Answers will vary; ionic compounds present are usually titanium dioxide, calcium carbonate, calcium silicate, and aluminum silicate. **L2**
**COOP LEARN**

### In-Text Question

**Page 215** Can you explain why $CaSO_4$ is not a binary compound? It contains more than two elements.

Demonstrate that ionic compounds do not conduct an electric current in the solid state, but they conduct in both the molten state and as a solution. Place some sodium chloride crystals in a watch glass. Insert a conductivity apparatus and have the students observe. The bulb will not light, indicating no flow of electricity. Remove the tester and dissolve the sodium chloride in water. Insert the conductivity apparatus and observe. The bulb will light. Ask students why the sodium chloride did not conduct in the crystalline form but does in solution. Ions in a solid have no movement from one place to another. In a solution, they do. Use the conductivity tester to confirm that solid lithium chloride does not conduct a current but molten lithium chloride does. If your laboratory heat source will not melt the compound, discuss with students what would happen.

## Applying Chemistry

**TECH PREP**

The following table lists a few common household items and the ionic compounds that are used to produce them.

| Item | Ionic compound needed |
|------|----------------------|
| Carpet | Calcium carbonate |
| Ceramics/ Glass | Calcium carbonate Lithium borate Magnesium silicate Sodium carbonate |
| Glossy Paper | Aluminum silicate Calcium carbonate Sodium sulfate Calcium oxide Sodium carbonate Titanium(IV) oxide |
| Toothpaste | Calcium carbonate Sodium carbonate Sodium hydrogen carbonate Sodium fluoride |

calcium atom. The compound formed will contain one calcium ion with a charge of 2+ for every two fluoride ions, each with a charge of 1−. Note that the overall charge on one unit of this compound is zero.

$$1 \text{ Ca ion} \left( \frac{2+}{\text{Ca ion}} \right) + 2 \text{ F ions} \left( \frac{1-}{\text{F ion}} \right) = (2+) + 2(1-) = 0$$

**Figure 8-5** summarizes the formation of an ionic compound from the elements sodium and chlorine using four different methods: electron configuration, orbital notation, electron-dot structures, and atomic models.

**Figure 8-5**

Several methods are used to show how an ionic compound forms.

Electron configuration

$e^-$

$[Ne]3s^1 + [Ne]3s^23p^5 \rightarrow [Ne] + [Ar] + energy$

Na          Cl          Na⁺    Cl⁻

Orbital notation

$e^-$

1s 2s  2p  3s    1s 2s  2p  3s  3p  →

Na                      Cl

1s 2s  2p    1s 2s  2p  3s  3p  + energy

Na⁺                  Cl⁻

Electron-dot structures

$Na\cdot + \cdot\ddot{Cl}: \rightarrow [Na]^+ + [:\ddot{Cl}:]^- + energy$

Atomic models

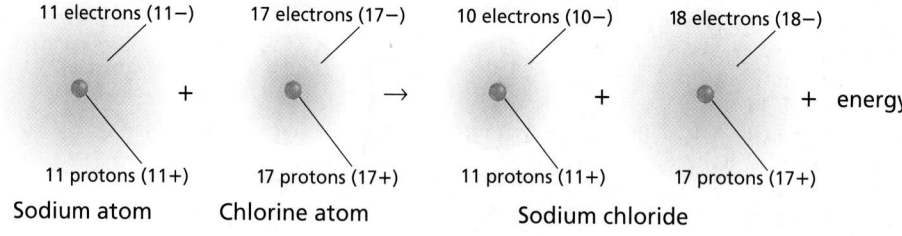

| 11 electrons (11−) | 17 electrons (17−) | 10 electrons (10−) | 18 electrons (18−) |
| 11 protons (11+) | 17 protons (17+) | 11 protons (11+) | 17 protons (17+) |
| Sodium atom | Chlorine atom | Sodium chloride | |

## Internet Address Book

**Chemistry Online**

Note Internet addresses that you find useful in the space below for quick reference.

## EXAMPLE PROBLEM 8-1

### Formation of an Ionic Compound

Unprotected aluminum metal reacts with oxygen in air, forming the white coating you can observe on aluminum objects such as lawn furniture. Explain the formation of an ionic compound from the elements aluminum and oxygen.

**1. Analyze the Problem**

You are given that aluminum and oxygen react to form an ionic compound. Aluminum is a group 3A element with three valence electrons, and oxygen is a group 6A element with six valence electrons. To acquire a noble gas configuration, each aluminum atom must lose three electrons and each oxygen atom must gain two electrons.

**2. Solve for the Unknown**

Remember that the number of electrons lost must equal the number of electrons gained. The smallest number evenly divisible by the three electrons lost by aluminum and the two gained by oxygen is six. Three oxygen atoms are needed to gain the six electrons lost by two aluminum atoms.

**3. Evaluate the Answer**

The overall charge on one unit of this compound is zero.

$$2 \text{ Al ions} \left(\frac{3+}{\text{Al ion}}\right) + 3 \text{ O ions} \left(\frac{2-}{\text{O ion}}\right) = 2(3+) + 3(2-) = 0$$

## PRACTICE PROBLEMS

Explain the formation of the ionic compound composed of each pair of elements.

7. sodium and nitrogen
8. lithium and oxygen
9. strontium and fluorine
10. aluminum and sulfur
11. cesium and phosphorus

## Properties of Ionic Compounds

The chemical bonds that occur between the atoms in a compound determine many of the physical properties of the compound. During the formation of an ionic compound, the positive and negative ions are packed into a regular repeating pattern that balances the forces of attraction and repulsion between the ions. This particle packing forms an ionic crystal, as shown in **Figure 8-6**. No single unit consisting of only one ion attracting one other ion is formed. Large numbers of positive ions and negative ions exist together in a ratio determined by the number of electrons transferred from the metal to the nonmetal.

Examine the pattern of the ions in the sodium chloride crystal shown in the figure. What shape would you expect a large crystal of this compound to be? This one-to-one ratio of ions produces a cubic crystal. Examine some table salt (NaCl) under a magnifying glass. What shape are these small salt crystals?

**Chemistry Online**

**Topic: Ionic Compounds**
To learn more about ionic compounds, visit the Chemistry Web site at **chemistrymc.com**

**Activity:** Research the colors of minerals and their chemical formulas. Which elements seem to be in the most colored compounds? What are their uses? Make a chart to report your findings.

**Practice!** For more practice with forming ionic compounds, go to **Supplemental Practice Problems** in Appendix A.

### Figure 8-6

In this ionic compound, each sodium ion is surrounded by six chloride ions, and each chloride ion is surrounded by six sodium ions. Refer to **Table C-1** in Appendix C for a key to atom color conventions.

---

### In-Text Question

**Page 217** What shape are these small salt crystals? cubic

### Practice PROBLEMS

Have students refer to Appendix D for complete solutions to Practice Problems.

7. Three Na atoms each lose 1 e⁻, forming 1+ ions. One N atom gains 3 e⁻, forming a 3− ion. The ions attract, forming $Na_3N$.

8. Two Li atoms each lose 1 e⁻, forming 1+ ions. One O atom gains 2 e⁻, forming a 2− ion. The ions attract, forming $Li_2O$.

9. One Sr atom loses 2 e⁻, forming a 2+ ion. Two F atoms each gain 1 e⁻, forming 1− ions. The ions attract, forming $SrF_2$.

10. Two Al atoms each lose 3 e⁻, forming 3+ ions. Three S atoms gain 2 e⁻ each, forming 2− ions. The ions attract, forming $Al_2S_3$.

11. Three Cs atoms each lose 1 e⁻, forming 1+ ions. One P atom gains 3 e⁻, forming a 3− ion. The ions attract, forming $Cs_3P$.

### CHEMLAB

ChemLab 8, located at the end of the chapter, can be used at this point in the lesson.

---

## CHEMISTRY JOURNAL

### Forming an Ionic Compound

*Visual-Spatial* Using the methods shown in Figure 8-5, have students show how an ionic compound between calcium and phosphorus forms. Have them place the diagrams in their journals. **L2** **ELL**

**National Science Content Standards**

**Pages 214–217**
UCP.1, UCP.2; B.1, B.2, B.3, B.4

***Logical-Mathematical***
Lattice energy is a result of the electrostatic attractions between oppositely charged ions. There is a relationship between lattice energy and the interionic distance, which is the sum of the ionic radii of a positive and a negative ion. Have students determine the interionic distance for LiF, LiCl, and LiI using the following ionic radii. $Li^+ = 76$ pm, $F^- = 133$ pm, $Cl^- = 181$ pm, and $I^- = 220$ pm. The lattice energy for each of these compounds is: LiF = $-1032$ kJ/mol, LiCl = $-852$ kJ/mol, LiI = $-761$ kJ/mol. Have them graph the interionic radii on the $X$ axis and lattice energy as a positive value on the $Y$ axis. What does the graph indicate? An inverse relationship; as interionic distance increases, lattice energy decreases. Use the graph to estimate the lattice energy for LiBr. The ionic radius of $Br^- = 196$ pm. $-817$ kJ/mol **L3**

## Assessment

**Performance** Using the following data, have students design a graph or table to show trends in lattice energy.

| Compound | Lattice energy (kJ/mol) |
|----------|-------------------------|
| LiF | −1032 |
| LiCl | −852 |
| LiBr | −815 |
| LiI | −761 |
| NaF | −926 |
| NaCl | −786 |
| NaBr | −752 |
| NaI | −702 |
| KF | −813 |
| KCl | −717 |
| KBr | −689 |
| KI | −649 |

Have students predict the shape of the graph of the lattice energies of RbF, RbCl, RbBr, and RbI. Have them make graphs that test their predictions. Use the Performance Task Assessment List for Graph from Data in **PASC**, p. 39. **L2** **ELL**

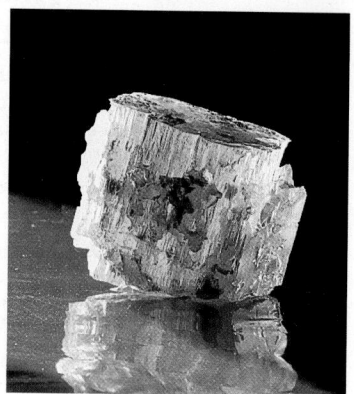

**Figure 8-7**

Aragonite ($CaCO_3$), barite ($BaSO_4$), and beryl ($Be_3Al_2Si_6O_{18}$) are examples of minerals that are ionic compounds. The ions that form them are bonded together in a crystal lattice.

**Try at Home** **LAB**

See page 955 in Appendix E for
**Comparing Sport Drink Electrolytes**

The strong attraction of positive ions and negative ions in an ionic compound results in a crystal lattice. A crystal lattice is a three-dimensional geometric arrangement of particles. In a crystal lattice, each positive ion is surrounded by negative ions and each negative ion is surrounded by positive ions. Ionic crystals vary in shape due to the sizes and relative numbers of the ions bonded, as shown in **Figure 8-7**.

Melting point, boiling point, and hardness are physical properties that depend on how strongly the particles are attracted to each other. Because ionic bonds are relatively strong, the crystals that result require a large amount of energy to be broken apart. Therefore, ionic crystals have high melting points and boiling points, as shown in **Table 8-2**. Their color may be related to their structure. See the **problem-solving LAB** on the next page and **Everyday Chemistry** at the end of this chapter. These crystals are also hard, rigid, and brittle solids due to the strong attractive forces that hold the ions in place. When an external force large enough to overcome the attraction of ions in the crystal is applied, the crystal cracks. The force repositions the like-charged ions next to each other, and the repulsive force cracks the crystal.

**Table 8-2**

| Melting and Boiling Points of Some Ionic Compounds | | |
|----------|-------------------|-------------------|
| Compound | Melting point (°C) | Boiling point (°C) |
| NaI | 660 | 1304 |
| KBr | 734 | 1435 |
| NaBr | 747 | 1390 |
| $CaCl_2$ | 782 | >1600 |
| $CaI_2$ | 784 | 1100 |
| NaCl | 801 | 1413 |
| MgO | 2852 | 3600 |

Charged particles must be free to move for a material to conduct an electric current. In the solid state, ionic compounds are nonconductors of electricity because of the fixed positions of the ions. However, in a liquid state or when dissolved in water, ionic compounds are electrical conductors because the ions are free to move. An ionic compound whose aqueous solution conducts an electric current is called an **electrolyte**. You will learn more about solutions of electrolytes in Chapter 15.

## Resource Manager

CBL Lab Manual, pp. 5–8 **L2**
Teaching Transparency 26 and Master
**L2** **ELL**

**Energy and the ionic bond** During any chemical reaction, energy is either absorbed or released. When energy is absorbed during a chemical reaction, the reaction is endothermic. If energy is released, it is exothermic. As you will see in the **CHEMLAB** at the end of this chapter, energy is released when magnesium reacts with oxygen.

Energy changes also occur during the formation of ionic bonds from the ions formed during a chemical reaction. The formation of ionic compounds from positive and negative ions is always exothermic. The attraction of the positive ion for the negative ions close to it forms a more stable system that is lower in energy than the individual ions. If the amount of energy released during bond formation is added to an ionic compound, the bonds that hold the positive and negative ions together break.

You just learned that the ions in an ionic compound are arranged in a pattern in a crystal lattice. The energy required to separate one mole of the ions of an ionic compound is referred to as the **lattice energy.** The strength of the forces holding ions in place is reflected by the lattice energy. The more negative the lattice energy, the stronger the force of attraction.

# problem-solving LAB

## How is color related to a transferred electron?

**Factors that Affect Color of an Ionic Compound**

| Compound | Color | Anion radius (Å) | Visible absorption band |
|---|---|---|---|
| AgF | Yellow | 1.36 | Blue-violet |
| AgCl | White | 1.81 | None |
| AgBr | Cream | 1.95 | Violet |
| AgI | Yellow | 2.16 | Blue-violet |
| $Ag_2S$ | Black | 1.84 | All |
| $Al_2O_3$ | White | 1.40 | None |
| $Sb_2O_3$ | White | 1.40 | None |
| $Bi_2O_3$ | ? | 1.40 | Violet |

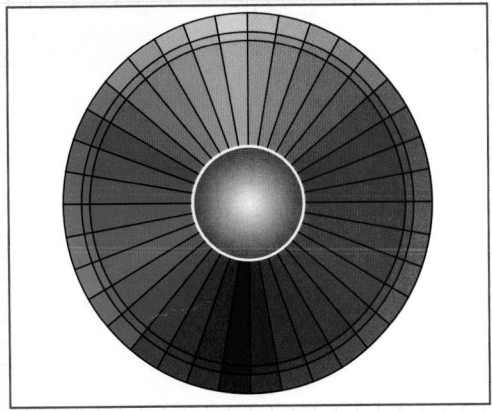

**Predicting** Once an ionic bond is formed, the cation has a tendency to pull the transferred electron toward the nucleus. The appearance of color is directly related to the strength of the pull, which depends upon the size of the ions involved and their oxidation numbers. If visible light of a certain color can send the electron back to the cation momentarily, then the light reflected from a crystal of the compound will be missing this color from its spectrum. The resulting color of the crystal will be the complement of this color of light and can be predicted using the color wheel that is shown here. Complementary colors are across from each other on the color wheel.

**Analysis**
The information in the table can be used to make some general conclusions about a compound's color and the strength of the cation's pull on the transferred electron. Using this information, the color of a compound can be predicted.

**Thinking Critically**

1. A larger anion radius results in a more pronounced color. What reason can you give for this fact?

2. Which do you think produces a more pronounced color, a high oxidation state for the anions or a low one? Explain.

3. Use the color wheel to predict the color of $Bi_2O_3$, the last compound on the list.

---

# GLENCOE TECHNOLOGY

**CD-ROM**
**Chemistry: Matter and Change**
*Experiment: Forming an Ionic Compound*

---

# DIFFERENTIATED INSTRUCTION

## Gifted

*Intrapersonal* Have capable students research the Born-Haber cycle for the energy changes in sodium chloride formation and design a Born-Haber cycle for the formation of potassium fluoride.

L3

---

# problem-solving LAB

**Purpose**
Students will correlate properties of the ions forming binary compounds and the color of the resulting crystal.

**Process Skills**
Recognizing cause and effect, drawing conclusions, applying concepts, classifying, predicting

**Teaching Strategies**
• Ask students to recall how light is emitted and absorbed by atoms and how it relates to energy. Light is emitted or absorbed when an electron moves from one energy level to another. The larger the jump, the greater the energy of the photon released or absorbed.

• Ask students to identify and explain the trends in size of ions. Ions get larger as the atomic number increases in a group. Metallic ions become smaller as atomic number increases in a period. The opposite tendency occurs with the nonmetallic ions because the charge is being added to a neutral atom. The larger oxidation state will have the larger size in a period.

**Thinking Critically**
1. The larger electron cloud is more easily polarized by the cation.
2. A larger oxidation number would increase the polarizing effect, causing a more pronounced color.
3. $Bi_2O_3$ is yellow.

## ✓ Assessment

**Portfolio** Ask students to extend the ideas presented in this exercise to the effect of ligands on the colors produced by transition metals and to the brilliant colors found in gemstones, such as rubies.

L2  P

**National Science Content Standards**
**Pages 218–221**
UCP.1, UCP.2; B.1, B.2, B.4, B.6; G.2

**Page 220** Which would have a more negative lattice energy, LiCl or LiBr? LiCl

**Page 220** How do they confirm that lattice energy is related to ion size? K⁺ has a smaller ionic radius than Rb⁺. KF has greater lattice energy than RbF.

**Page 220** How do SrCl₂ and AgCl show the relationship between lattice energy and the charge of the ions involved? $Sr^{2+}$ has the greater charge. The lattice energy of $SrCl_2$ is greater than AgCl.

# 3 Assess

## Check for Understanding

Ask students to determine the ionic compound formed from Mg and Cl and explain how it was formed. $MgCl_2$; magnesium loses two valence electrons, while chlorine gains only one valence electron. The ratio of $Mg^{2+}$ to $Cl^-$ is 1:2. **L2**

## Reteach

Using the elements aluminum and oxygen, have students determine the formula for the ionic compound formed. $Al_2O_3$ **L2**

## ✔ Assessment

**Knowledge** Have each student list a metal and a nonmetal. Have another student determine the ionic compound formed between them. **L2** **COOP LEARN**

---

Lattice energy is directly related to the size of the ions bonded. Smaller ions generally have a more negative value for lattice energy because the nucleus is closer to and thus has more attraction for the valence electrons. Thus, the lattice energy of a lithium compound is more negative than that of a potassium compound containing the same anion because the lithium ion is smaller than the potassium ion. Which would have a more negative lattice energy, lithium chloride or lithium bromide?

The value of lattice energy is also affected by the charge of the ion. The ionic bond formed from the attraction of ions with larger positive or negative charges generally has a more negative lattice energy. The lattice energy of MgO is almost four times greater than the lattice energy of NaF because the charge of the ions is greater. The lattice energy of $SrCl_2$ is between the lattice energies of MgO and NaF because $SrCl_2$ contains ions with both higher and lower charges.

**Table 8-3** shows the lattice energies of some ionic compounds. Examine the lattice energies of RbF and KF. How do they confirm that lattice energy is related to ion size? Look at the lattice energies of $SrCl_2$ and AgCl. How do they show the relationship between lattice energy and the charge of the ions involved?

**Table 8-3**

| Lattice Energies of Some Ionic Compounds | | | |
|---|---|---|---|
| Compound | Lattice energy (kJ/mol) | Compound | Lattice energy (kJ/mol) |
| KI | −632 | KF | −808 |
| KBr | −671 | AgCl | −910 |
| RbF | −774 | NaF | −910 |
| NaI | −682 | LiF | −1030 |
| NaBr | −732 | SrCl₂ | −2142 |
| NaCl | −769 | MgO | −3795 |

## Section 8.2 Assessment

**12.** What is an ionic bond?

**13.** How does an ionic bond form?

**14.** List three physical properties associated with an ionic bond.

**15.** Describe the arrangement of ions in a crystal lattice.

**16.** What is lattice energy and how is it involved in an ionic bond?

**17. Thinking Critically** Using the concepts of ionic radii and lattice energy, account for the trend in melting points shown in the following table.

| Trend in Melting Points | |
|---|---|
| Ionic compound | Melting point in °C |
| KF | 858 |
| KCl | 770 |
| KBr | 734 |
| KI | 681 |

**18. Formulating Models** Use electron configurations, orbital notation, and electron-dot structures to represent the formation of an ionic compound from the metal strontium and the nonmetal chlorine.

chemistrymc.com/self_check_quiz

---

## Section 8.2 Assessment

**12.** the electrostatic attraction between oppositely charged ions

**13.** Ions form from electron transfer. Oppositely charged ions attract.

**14.** exist as crystals; have high melting and boiling points; are hard, rigid, and brittle; conductive when dissolved or molten but not solid

**15.** Each ion is surrounded by oppositely charged ions.

**16.** It is the energy required to separate the ions of an ionic compound and is the energy given off when positive and negative ions attract.

**17.** As the ionic radius of the nonmetallic ion increases, the melting point and lattice energy decrease.

**18.** Drawing should include an Sr atom losing 2 e⁻, becoming $Sr^{2+}$, and two Cl atoms, each gaining 1 e⁻, forming two Cl⁻. These ions attract, forming $SrCl_2$. See the Solutions Manual.

# Names and Formulas for Ionic Compounds

One of the most important requirements of chemistry is communicating information to others. Chemists discuss compounds by using both chemical formulas and names. The chemical formula and the name for the compound must be understood universally. Therefore, a set of rules is used in the naming of compounds. This system of naming allows everyone to write a chemical formula when given a compound name and to name the compound from a given chemical formula.

## Formulas for Ionic Compounds

Recall from Section 8.2 that a sample of an ionic compound contains crystals formed from many ions arranged in a pattern. Because no single particle of an ionic compound exists, ionic compounds are represented by a formula that provides the simplest ratio of the ions involved. The simplest ratio of the ions represented in an ionic compound is called a **formula unit**. For example, the formula KBr represents a formula unit for potassium bromide because potassium and bromide ions are in a one-to-one ratio in the compound. A formula unit of magnesium chloride is $MgCl_2$ because two chloride ions exist for each magnesium ion in the compound. In the compound sodium phosphide, three sodium ions exist for every phosphide ion. What is the formula unit for sodium phosphide?

Because the total number of electrons gained by the nonmetallic atoms must equal the total number of electrons lost by the metallic atoms, the overall charge of a formula unit is zero. The formula unit for $MgCl_2$ contains one $Mg^{2+}$ ion and two $Cl^-$ ions, for a total charge of zero.

**Determining charge** Binary ionic compounds are composed of positively charged monatomic ions of a metal and negatively charged monatomic ions of a nonmetal. A **monatomic ion** is a one-atom ion, such as $Mg^{2+}$ or $Br^-$. **Table 8-4** indicates the charges of common monatomic ions according to the location of their atoms on the periodic table. What is the formula for the beryllium ion? The iodide ion? The nitride ion? Transition metals, which are in groups 3B through 2B, and metals in groups 3A and 4A are not included in this table because of the variance in ionic charges of atoms in the groups. Most transition metals and those in groups 3A and 4A can form several different positive ions.

### Objectives

- **Write** formulas for ionic compounds and oxyanions.
- **Name** ionic compounds and oxyanions.

### Vocabulary

formula unit
monatomic ion
oxidation number
polyatomic ion
oxyanion

**Table 8-4**

| Common Ions Based on Groups | | |
|---|---|---|
| Group | Atoms that commonly form ions | Charge on ions |
| 1A | H, Li, Na, K, Rb, Cs | 1+ |
| 2A | Be, Mg, Ca, Sr, Ba | 2+ |
| 5A | N, P, As | 3− |
| 6A | O, S, Se, Te | 2− |
| 7A | F, Cl, Br, I | 1− |

## 1 Focus

### Focus Transparency

Before presenting the lesson, display **Section Focus Transparency 28** on the overhead projector. Have students answer the accompanying questions using **Section Focus Transparency Master 28.** **L1** **ELL**

## 2 Teach

### In-Text Questions

**Page 221** What is the formula unit for sodium phosphide? $Na_3P$ What is the formula for the beryllium ion? $Be^{2+}$ The iodide ion? $I^-$ The nitride ion? $N^{3-}$

### Resource Manager

**Study Guide for Content Mastery**, pp. 46–47 **L2**
**Solving Problems: A Chemistry Handbook**, Section 8.3 **L2**
**Section Focus Transparency 28 and Master** **L1** **ELL**
**Math Skills Transparency 8 and Master** **L2** **ELL**
**Teaching Transparency 27 and Master** **L2** **ELL**

## Demonstration

The following demonstration is available as a kit from Flinn Scientific, Inc., catalog no. AP8472, by calling (800) 452-1261.

A detailed set of instructions developed by Jim and Julie Ealy is available from Flinn Scientific as Chem Fax publication no. 8472, P.O. Box 219, Batavia, IL 60510. The demonstration is used by permission of Flinn Scientific, Inc.

# GLENCOE TECHNOLOGY

**CD-ROM**
**Chemistry: Matter and Change**
Demonstration: *Variable Oxidation States*
Exploration: *Determining a Formula*
Demonstration: *Oxidation States of Vanadium*

**Table 8-5**

| Group | Common ions |
|---|---|
| \multicolumn{2}{c}{Common Ions of Transition Metals and Groups 3A and 4A} | |
| 3B | $Sc^{3+}$, $Y^{3+}$, $La^{3+}$ |
| 4B | $Ti^{2+}$, $Ti^{3+}$ |
| 5B | $V^{2+}$, $V^{3+}$ |
| 6B | $Cr^{2+}$, $Cr^{3+}$ |
| 7B | $Mn^{2+}$, $Mn^{3+}$, $Tc^{2+}$ |
| 8B | $Fe^{2+}$, $Fe^{3+}$ |
| 8B | $Co^{2+}$, $Co^{3+}$ |
| 8B | $Ni^{2+}$, $Pd^{2+}$, $Pt^{2+}$, $Pt^{4+}$ |
| 1B | $Cu^{+}$, $Cu^{2+}$, $Ag^{+}$, $Au^{+}$, $Au^{3+}$ |
| 2B | $Zn^{2+}$, $Cd^{2+}$, $Hg_2^{2+}$, $Hg^{2+}$ |
| 3A | $Al^{3+}$, $Ga^{2+}$, $Ga^{3+}$, $In^{+}$, $In^{2+}$, $In^{3+}$, $Tl^{+}$, $Tl^{3+}$ |
| 4A | $Sn^{2+}$, $Sn^{4+}$, $Pb^{2+}$, $Pb^{4+}$ |

The charge of a monatomic ion is its **oxidation number**. Most transition metals and group 3A and 4A metals have more than one oxidation number, as shown in **Table 8-5**. The oxidation numbers given in the table are the most common ones for many of the elements listed but might not be the only ones possible.

The term *oxidation state* is sometimes used and means the same thing as oxidation number. The oxidation number, or oxidation state, of an element in an ionic compound equals the number of electrons transferred from an atom of the element to form the ion. For example, when sodium and chlorine atoms react, the sodium atom transfers one electron to the chlorine atom, forming $Na^{+}$ and $Cl^{-}$. Thus, in the compound formed, the oxidation state of sodium is $1+$ because one electron is transferred from the sodium atom. The oxidation state of chlorine is $1-$. One electron is transferred, and the negative sign shows that the electron transferred to, not from, the chlorine atom.

The oxidation numbers of ions are used to determine the formulas for the ionic compounds they form. Recall that in ionic compounds, oppositely charged ions combine chemically in definite ratios to form a compound that has no charge. If you add the oxidation number of each ion multiplied by the number of these ions in a formula unit, the total must be zero.

In the chemical formula for any ionic compound, the symbol of the cation is always written first, followed by the symbol of the anion. Subscripts, which are small numbers to the lower right of a symbol, are used to represent the number of ions of each element in an ionic compound. If no subscript is written, it is assumed to be one.

Suppose you need to determine the formula for one formula unit of the compound that contains sodium and chloride ions. Write the symbol and charge for each ion.

$$Na^{+} \qquad Cl^{-}$$

The ratio of ions must be such that the number of electrons lost by the metal is equal to the number of electrons gained by the nonmetal. Because the sum of the oxidation numbers of these ions is zero, these ions must be present in a one-to-one ratio. One sodium ion transfers one electron to one chloride ion, and the formula unit is NaCl.

---

## Demonstration

### Oxidation States of Vanadium

#### Purpose
To demonstrate the colorful ions formed as the oxidation number of vanadium changes from $5+$ to $4+$, $3+$, and $2+$.

#### Materials
Granular zinc-mercury(II) chloride(aq)

amalgam, ammonium metavanadate ($NH_4VO_3$) solution, 500-mL Erlenmeyer flask with stopper, powder funnel, 250-mL graduated cylinder. See page 210C for preparation of solutions.

#### Safety Precautions 🥽 🧤 🚫 ☣ ⚗ ✋

**Disposal** Hazardous waste as described by EPA regulators will be produced and should be disposed of accordingly.

#### Procedure
The zinc-mercury amalgam is stored under water. After pouring off the water, pour 63 g of the zinc-mercury amalgam into a 500-mL Erlenmeyer flask through a powder funnel. Add 140 mL of ammonium metavanadate solution to the zinc-mercury amalgam in the flask.
**CAUTION:** *The solutions are toxic and corrosive.* Note the color change as vanadium with oxidation number $5+$ ($VO_2^{+}$,

## EXAMPLE PROBLEM 8-2

### Determining the Formula for an Ionic Compound

The ionic compound formed from potassium and oxygen is used as a dehydrating agent because it reacts readily with water. Determine the correct formula for the ionic compound formed from potassium and oxygen.

**1. Analyze the Problem**

It is given that potassium and oxygen ions form an ionic compound. The first thing to do is determine the symbol and oxidation number for each ion involved in the ionic compound and write them as shown.

$$K^+ \quad O^{2-}$$

If the charges are not the same, subscripts must be determined to indicate the ratio of positive ions to negative ions.

**2. Solve for the Unknown**

A potassium atom loses one electron while an oxygen atom gains two electrons. If combined in a one-to-one ratio, the number of electrons lost by potassium will not balance the number of electrons gained by oxygen. To have the same number of electrons lost and gained, you must have two potassium ions for every oxide ion. The correct formula is $K_2O$.

**3. Evaluate the Answer**

The overall charge on one formula unit of this compound is zero.

$$2 \text{ K ions} \left(\frac{1+}{\text{K ion}}\right) + 1 \text{ O ions} \left(\frac{2-}{\text{O ion}}\right) = 2(1+) + 1(2-) = 0$$

## EXAMPLE PROBLEM 8-3

### Determining the Formula for an Ionic Compound

Determine the correct formula for the yellowish-gray compound formed from aluminum ions and sulfide ions. This compound decomposes in moist air.

**1. Analyze the Problem**

You are given that aluminum and sulfur ions form an ionic compound. First, determine the charge of each ion involved.

$$Al^{3+} \quad S^{2-}$$

Each aluminum atom loses three electrons while each sulfur atom gains two. The number of electrons lost must equal the number of electrons gained.

**2. Solve for the Unknown**

The smallest number that both two and three divide into evenly is six. Therefore, a total of six electrons was transferred. Three sulfur atoms accept the six electrons lost by two aluminum atoms. The correct formula will show two aluminum ions bonded to three sulfur ions, or $Al_2S_3$.

**3. Evaluate the Answer**

The overall charge on one formula unit of this compound is zero.

$$2 \text{ Al ions} \left(\frac{3+}{\text{Al ion}}\right) + 3 \text{ S ions} \left(\frac{2-}{\text{S ion}}\right) = 2(3+) + 3(2-) = 0$$

Review least common multiple in the **Math Handbook** on page 909 of this text.

## Concept Development

Using the oxidation numbers for monatomic ions in Tables 8-4 and 8-5, work through several examples following Example Problem 8-2. Avoid using the technique that crosses oxidation numbers to get subscripts. This technique is quick and it is accurate if subscripts are reduced to the simplest ratio, but it does not lead to an understanding of balanced charges.

### Identifying Misconceptions

Students often think that formula units represent actual numbers of atoms.

**Uncover the Misconception**
Display crystals of different ionic compounds. Each ion in the crystal is surrounded by ions oppositely charged. Students should define formula units as the ratios of these ions.

**Demonstrate the Concept**
Set up a microscope and allow students to view the cubic crystals of NaCl. Using toothpicks and small and large marshmallows representing $Na^+$ and $Cl^-$, respectively, form the NaCl crystal lattice. Point out that one $Na^+$ is surrounded by six $Cl^-$ and one $Cl^-$ is surrounded by six $Na^+$. The ratio of $Na^+$ to $Cl^-$ is one-to-one, and the formula unit is NaCl.

**Assess New Knowledge**
Have students determine the cation to anion ratio for the formula units that represent $Ag_2S$, $MgCl_2$, $Al_2O_3$, $SnF_4$, FeO. 2:1, 1:2, 2:3, 1:4, 1:1

yellow) is converted to vanadium with oxidation number 4+ ($VO^{2+}$, blue). The yellow and blue of the two ions mix to give a green color. Stopper the flask and shake gently until the color of the solution changes from green to blue to blue-green as vanadium with oxidation number 4+ ($VO^{2+}$, blue) is converted to $V^{3+}$ (blue-green). Finally, shake the stoppered flask vigorously to change $V^{3+}$ to $V^{2+}$ (violet).

### Results
Equilibrium reactions account for the mixtures of colors.
$$Zn + 2VO_2^+ + 4H^+ \leftrightarrows 2VO^{2+} + Zn^{2+} + 2H_2O$$
$$Zn + 2VO^{2+} + 4H^+ \leftrightarrows 2V^{3+} + Zn^{2+} + 2H_2O$$
$$2V^{3+} + Zn \leftrightarrows 2V^{2+} + Zn^{2+}$$

### Analysis
**1.** Where is vanadium found on the periodic table? group 5B, period 4, among the transition elements

### ✔ Assessment
**Knowledge** Have students explain which electrons are lost as vanadium's oxidation number changes from 0 to 5+. the 4s and 3d electrons **L2**

Practice! For more practice with writing formulas for ionic compounds, go to **Supplemental Practice Problems** in Appendix A.

## PRACTICE PROBLEMS

Write the correct formula for the ionic compound composed of the following pairs of ions.

19. potassium and iodide
20. magnesium and chloride
21. aluminum and bromide
22. cesium and nitride
23. barium and sulfide

**Compounds that contain polyatomic ions** Many ionic compounds contain **polyatomic ions**, which are ions made up of more than one atom. **Table 8-6** lists the formulas and the charges for several polyatomic ions.

The charge given to a polyatomic ion applies to the entire group of atoms. Although an ionic compound containing one or more polyatomic ions contains more than two atoms, the polyatomic ion acts as an individual ion. Therefore, the chemical formula for the compound can be written following the same rules used for a binary compound.

Because a polyatomic ion exists as a unit, never change subscripts of the atoms within the ion. If more than one polyatomic ion is needed, place parentheses around the ion and write the appropriate subscript outside the parentheses. For example, the formula for magnesium chlorate is $Mg(ClO_3)_2$. Note that the ammonium ion is the only common polyatomic cation.

How can you determine the formula unit for an ionic compound containing a polyatomic ion? Chemists use a naming system called the Stock System, after the German chemist Alfred Stock. Let's consider the compound formed from the ammonium ion and the chloride ion.

$$NH_4^+ \qquad Cl^-$$

Because the sum of the charges on the ions is zero, the ions are in a one-to-one ratio. The correct formula unit for this compound is $NH_4Cl$.

**Table 8-6**

| Common Polyatomic Ions | | | |
|---|---|---|---|
| Ion | Name | Ion | Name |
| $NH_4^+$ | ammonium | $IO_4^-$ | periodate |
| $NO_2^-$ | nitrite | $C_2H_3O_2^-$ | acetate |
| $NO_3^-$ | nitrate | $H_2PO_4^-$ | dihydrogen phosphate |
| $HSO_4^-$ | hydrogen sulfate | $CO_3^{2-}$ | carbonate |
| $OH^-$ | hydroxide | $SO_3^{2-}$ | sulfite |
| $CN^-$ | cyanide | $SO_4^{2-}$ | sulfate |
| $MnO_4^-$ | permanganate | $S_2O_3^{2-}$ | thiosulfate |
| $HCO_3^-$ | hydrogen carbonate | $O_2^{2-}$ | peroxide |
| $ClO^-$ | hypochlorite | $CrO_4^{2-}$ | chromate |
| $ClO_2^-$ | chlorite | $Cr_2O_7^{2-}$ | dichromate |
| $ClO_3^-$ | chlorate | $HPO_4^{2-}$ | hydrogen phosphate |
| $ClO_4^-$ | perchlorate | $PO_4^{3-}$ | phosphate |
| $BrO_3^-$ | bromate | $AsO_4^{3-}$ | arsenate |
| $IO_3^-$ | iodate | | |

## CULTURAL DIVERSITY

### Pottery

One of the most ancient arts is the making of pottery. The oldest known pottery dates back to 400 B.C. in Japan. Chinese, Middle Eastern, and Native American potters also produced a variety of pottery. Basically, the chemical composition of pottery is that of clay or clay blends, $Al_2O_3 \cdot 2SiO_2 \cdot 2H_2O$. When formed to the desired shape, the clay piece is baked hard and the intensity of the heat determines the degree of hardness. Pottery is often coated with glaze to render it waterproof and add decoration. Pottery glaze has a composition similar to that of pottery clay, as well as a mixture of ionically bonded metal oxides. The addition of metal oxides to the glaze results in many properties, including hardness, color, surface character, crystal development, and chemical stability. Adding $Fe_2O_3$ produces a rich red color, while CuO produces a clear green color. The addition of $Al_2O_3$ adds hardness and durability to the pottery.

## Determining the Formula for an Ionic Compound Containing a Polyatomic Ion

The ionic compound formed from the calcium ion and the phosphate ion is a common ingredient in fertilizers. Write the formula for this compound.

**1. Analyze the Problem**

It is given that calcium and phosphate ions form an ionic compound. You should first write each ion along with its charge.

$$Ca^{2+} \qquad PO_4^{3-}$$

Because the numerical values of the charges differ, a one-to-one ratio is not possible.

**2. Solve for the Unknown**

Six is the smallest number evenly divisible by both ionic charges. Therefore, a total of six electrons were transferred. The amount of negative charge of two phosphate ions equals the amount of positive charge of three calcium ions. To use a subscript to indicate more than one unit of a polyatomic ion, you must place the polyatomic ion in parentheses and add the subscript to the outside. The correct formula is $Ca_3(PO_4)_2$.

**3. Evaluate the Answer**

The overall charge on one formula unit of calcium phosphate is zero.

$$3 \text{ calcium ions} \left( \frac{2+}{\text{calcium ion}} \right) + 2 \text{ phosphate ions} \left( \frac{3-}{\text{phosphate ion}} \right) =$$

$$3(2+) + 2(-3) = 0$$

### PRACTICE PROBLEMS

Determine the correct formula for the ionic compound composed of the following pairs of ions.

24. sodium and nitrate

27. potassium and chromate

25. calcium and chlorate

28. magnesium and carbonate

26. aluminum and carbonate

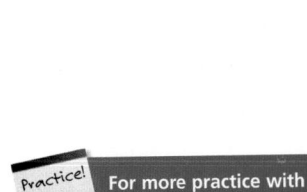

**Math Handbook**

Review positive and negative numbers in the **Math Handbook** on page 887 of this text.

**Practice!** For more practice with writing formulas for ionic compounds that contain polyatomic ions, go to Supplemental Practice Problems in Appendix A.

## Naming Ions and Ionic Compounds

You already know how to name monatomic ions. How do you name polyatomic ions? Most polyatomic ions are oxyanions. An **oxyanion** is a polyatomic ion composed of an element, usually a nonmetal, bonded to one or more oxygen atoms. Many oxyanions contain the same nonmetal and have the same charges but differ in the number of oxygen atoms. More than one oxyanion exists for some nonmetals, such as nitrogen and sulfur. These ions are easily named using the following conventions.

- *The ion with more oxygen atoms is named using the root of the nonmetal plus the suffix -ate.*
- *The ion with fewer oxygen atoms is named using the root of the nonmetal plus the suffix -ite.*

For example:

| $NO_3^-$ | $NO_2^-$ | $SO_4^{2-}$ | $SO_3^{2-}$ |
|----------|----------|-------------|-------------|
| nitrate  | nitrite  | sulfate     | sulfite     |

8.3 Names and Formulas for Ionic Compounds    **225**

**Practice PROBLEMS**

Have students refer to Appendix D for complete solutions to Practice Problems.

**24.** $NaNO_3$    **27.** $K_2CrO_4$
**25.** $Ca(ClO_3)_2$   **28.** $MgCO_3$
**26.** $Al_2(CO_3)_3$

### ✓ Assessment

**Skill** Play a game of Concentration using names and formulas for ionic compounds. On an overhead transparency, draw a 4 × 4 chart. Place the names for eight compounds in eight of the squares and the formulas for the same compounds in the other eight squares. Cover each square, and have students turn the covers over two at a time to match each formula with its name. **L2**

### ✓ Assessment

**Knowledge** Have students draw a 5 × 5 chart on a piece of paper. Have them write five metal ions in the left margin, including the ammonium ion, and five nonmetal ions at the top, including at least two polyatomic anions. Have them trade charts with another student. Have each student write the correct formulas for the ionic compounds formed in the square. Hand the completed chart to another student to evaluate the responses. **L2**

### Reinforcement

**Kinesthetic** Have students make flash cards to help them remember the names, formulas, and charges of polyatomic ions. **L1** **ELL**

### CHEMISTRY JOURNAL

#### Composition of Ocean Water

**Intrapersonal** Ocean water contains potassium, sodium, magnesium, hydrogen carbonate, sulfate, chloride, and bromide ions. Have students write and name all the formula units that can be composed from a combination of these ions. **L2**

### ✓ Portfolio

#### Pottery Glazes

**Kinesthetic** Have interested students ask the art instructor to explain the difference in pottery glazes. Have students coat small pottery pieces with a basic glaze recipe plus one of the metal oxides and fire in a kiln. Have them observe the properties given to the pottery by the glaze. **L1** **ELL** **P**

**National Science Content Standards**

Pages 222–225
UCP.1, UCP.2; B.2

## Using Science Terms

Discuss the rules used in naming ionic compounds. Remind students that systematic naming requires the use of Roman numerals to indicate the oxidation state of the ions of transition metals as well as several group 3A and 4A metals.

Tell students that an older system of naming uses the Latin name of the metal with the suffixes *-ic* and *-ous* to designate the higher and lower oxidation numbers of the metals, respectively.

| Compound | Latin name |
|---|---|
| $FeO$ | Ferrous oxide |
| $Fe_2O_3$ | Ferric oxide |
| $CuCl$ | Cuprous chloride |
| $CuCl_2$ | Cupric chloride |
| $Hg_2Br_2$ | Mercurous bromide |
| $HgBr_2$ | Mercuric bromide |
| $PbO$ | Plumbous oxide |
| $PbO_2$ | Plumbic oxide |
| $SnF_2$ | Stannous fluoride |
| $SnF_4$ | Stannic fluoride |

### Practice PROBLEMS

Have students refer to Appendix D for complete solutions to Practice Problems.

**29.** sodium bromide
**30.** calcium chloride
**31.** potassium hydroxide
**32.** copper(II) nitrate
**33.** silver chromate

## Earth Science
### CONNECTION

Mineralogists, the scientists who study minerals, use various classification schemes to organize the thousands of known minerals. Color; crystal structure; hardness; chemical, magnetic, and electrical properties; and numerous other characteristics are used to classify minerals.

The types of anions minerals contain also can identify them. For example, more than one-third of all known minerals are silicates, which are minerals that contain an anion that is a combination of silicon and oxygen. Halides contain fluoride, chloride, bromide, or iodide ions. Minerals in which the anions contain boron are called borates.

Practice! For more practice with naming ionic compounds, go to Supplemental Practice Problems in Appendix A.

Chlorine in group 7A, the halogens, forms four oxyanions. These oxyanions are named according to the number of oxygen atoms present. The following conventions are used to name these oxyanions.

- *The oxyanion with the greatest number of oxygen atoms is named using the prefix* per-, *the root of the nonmetal, and the suffix* -ate.
- *The oxyanion with one less oxygen atom is named with the root of the nonmetal and the suffix* -ate.
- *The oxyanion with two fewer oxygen atoms is named using the root of the nonmetal plus the suffix* -ite.
- *The oxyanion with three fewer oxygen atoms is named using the prefix* hypo-, *the root of the nonmetal, and the suffix* -ite.

| $ClO_4^-$ | $ClO_3^-$ | $ClO_2^-$ | $ClO^-$ |
|---|---|---|---|
| perchlorate | chlorate | chlorite | hypochlorite |

Other halogens form oxyanions that are named similarly to the oxyanions chlorine forms. Bromine forms $BrO_3^-$, the bromate ion. Iodine forms the periodate ion ($IO_4^-$) and the iodate ion ($IO_3^-$).

**Naming ionic compounds** Chemical nomenclature is a systematic way of naming compounds. Now that you are familiar with writing chemical formulas, you will use the following general rules in naming ionic compounds when their formulas are known.

**1.** *Name the cation first and the anion second.* Remember that the cation is always written first in the formula. For example, CsBr is a compound used in X-ray fluorescent screens. In the formula CsBr, $Cs^+$ is the cation and is named first. The anion is $Br^-$ and is named second.

**2.** *Monatomic cations use the element name.* The name of the cation $Cs^+$ is cesium, the name of the element.

**3.** *Monatomic anions take their name from the root of the element name plus the suffix* -ide. The compound CsBr contains the bromide anion.

**4.** *Group 1A and group 2A metals have only one oxidation number. Transition metals and metals on the right side of the periodic table often have more than one oxidation number.* To distinguish between multiple oxidation numbers of the same element, the name of the chemical formula must indicate the oxidation number of the cation. The oxidation number is written as a Roman numeral in parentheses after the name of the cation. For example, the compound formed from $Fe^{2+}$ and $O^{2-}$ has the formula FeO and is named iron(II) oxide. The compound formed from $Fe^{3+}$ and $O^{2-}$ has the formula $Fe_2O_3$ and is named iron(III) oxide.

**5.** *If the compound contains a polyatomic ion, simply name the ion.* The name of the compound that contains the sodium cation and the polyatomic hydroxide anion, NaOH, is sodium hydroxide. The compound $(NH_4)_2S$ is ammonium sulfide.

### PRACTICE PROBLEMS

Name the following compounds.

**29.** NaBr

**30.** $CaCl_2$

**31.** KOH

**32.** $Cu(NO_3)_2$

**33.** $Ag_2CrO_4$

## ✔ Portfolio

### Naming Ionic Compounds

*Visual-Spatial* Have students design flow charts to be used to name ionic compounds or to determine the formula unit of ionic compounds. Have them explain their flow charts to the class. **L2**

P 📦

National Science Content Standards
Pages 226–227
UCP.1, UCP.2; B.1, B.2; E.2

Determine the cation and anion of the given formula.

Does the cation have only one oxidation number?

Yes

Write the name of the cation and then write the name of the anion. $Na_3PO_4$ = sodium phosphate

No

Write the name of the cation followed by a Roman numeral to represent the charge. Next write the name of the anion. $Fe_2O_3$ = iron(III) oxide

**Figure 8-8**

This diagram summarizes how to name ionic compounds from their formulas.

## 3 Assess
### Check for Understanding

**Intrapersonal** Use the ingredients list from a bottle of vitamins to write the names or formulas of the ionic compounds that make up the tablets on the chalkboard. Have students determine the correct formula unit or name for each compound. Compounds often present are calcium phosphate, magnesium phosphate, copper(II) oxide, zinc oxide, calcium carbonate, magnesium oxide, titanium(IV) oxide, potassium chloride, potassium iodide, tin(II) chloride, and chromium(III) chloride. **L2**

### Reteach

Review naming ionic compounds and writing their formula units. Tell students that artificial ocean water, as is used in saltwater aquariums, is made by mixing the following: 24.72 g NaCl, 0.67 g KCl, 1.36 g $CaCl_2$, 4.66 g $MgCl_2$, 6.29 g $MgSO_4$, and 0.18 g $NaHCO_3$. Have students name each ionic compound present.

### Extension

Have students design Jeopardy questions and answers for categories such as oxidation numbers, formula units for ionic compounds, and names for ionic compounds. **L2**

### ✔ Assessment

**Portfolio** Write formulas for several ions, both positive and negative, on a transparency. Point out one positive and one negative ion, and have students determine the correct formula and name of the ionic compound formed. Have students place their work in their portfolios. **L2 P**

**Figure 8-8** reviews the steps used in naming ionic compounds if the formula is known. Naming ionic compounds is important in communicating the cation and anion present in a crystalline solid or aqueous solution. How might you change the diagram to help you write the formulas for ionic compounds if you know their names?

All the ion-containing substances you have investigated so far have been ionic compounds. Do any other substances contain ions? Can certain elements contain ions and still be electrically neutral? Do the properties of other ion-containing substances differ from the properties of ionic compounds? In the next section, you will learn the answers to these questions by examining how ions relate to the structure and properties of metals.

## Section 8.3 Assessment

**34.** What is the difference between a monatomic ion and a polyatomic ion? Give an example of each.

**35.** How do you determine the correct subscripts in a chemical formula?

**36.** How are metals named in an ionic compound? Nonmetals? Polyatomic ions?

**37.** What is an oxyanion and how is it named?

**38. Thinking Critically** What subscripts would most likely be used if the following substances formed an ionic compound?

a. an alkali metal and a halogen
b. an alkali metal and a nonmetal from group 6A
c. an alkaline earth metal and a halogen
d. an alkaline earth metal and a nonmetal from group 6A
e. a metal from group 3A and a halogen

**39. Making and Using Tables** Complete the table below by providing the correct formula for each compound formed from the listed ions.

| Formulas for Some Ionic Compounds | | | | |
|---|---|---|---|---|
| | Oxide | Chloride | Sulfate | Phosphate |
| Potassium | | | | |
| Barium | | | | |
| Aluminum | | | | |
| Ammonium | | | | |

## Section 8.3 Assessment

**34.** monatomic: one-atom ion, $Cl^-$; polyatomic: contains two or more atoms grouped together with a net charge, $ClO_3^-$

**35.** Subscripts are the number of atoms that must be used so that charges in the formula total zero.

**36.** Metals: use the name with a Roman numeral if needed. Nonmetals: use a form of the root of the nonmetal plus the suffix -ide. Polyatomic ions: use the ion name.

**37.** It is a polyatomic ion containing oxygen. For any particular element, the ion with the most oxygen atoms is named by using the root of the nonmetal plus -ate; the ion with one less oxygen atom is named by the root of the nonmetal plus -ite.

**38. a.** 1, 1    **c.** 1, 2    **e.** 1, 3
**b.** 2, 1    **d.** 1, 1

**39.** Left to right, top to bottom: $K_2O$, KCl, $K_2SO_4$, $K_3PO_4$, BaO, $BaCl_2$, $BaSO_4$, $Ba_3(PO_4)_2$, $Al_2O_3$, $AlCl_3$, $Al_2(SO_4)_3$, $AlPO_4$, $(NH_4)_2O$, $NH_4Cl$, $(NH_4)_2SO_4$, and $(NH_4)_3PO_4$.

# 1 Focus

## Section 8.4

# Metallic Bonds and Properties of Metals

## Focus Transparency

Before presenting the lesson, display **Section Focus Transparency 29** on the overhead projector. Have students answer the accompanying questions using **Section Focus Transparency Master 29. L1 ELL**

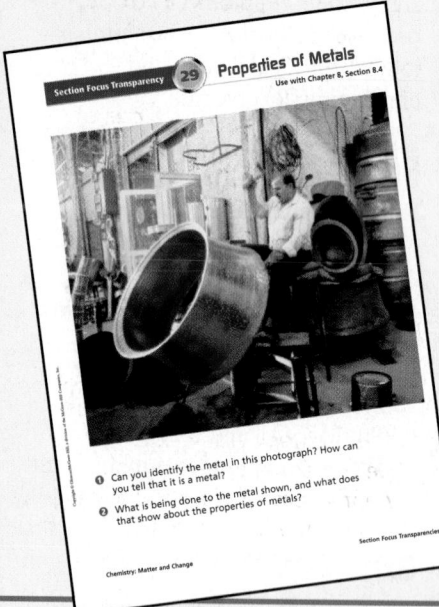

## Objectives

- **Describe** a metallic bond.
- **Explain** the physical properties of metals in terms of metallic bonds.
- **Define** and **describe** alloys.

## Vocabulary

electron sea model
delocalized electrons
metallic bond
alloy

Although metals are not ionic, they share several properties with ionic compounds. Properties of materials are based on bonding, and the bonding in both metals and ionic compounds is based on the attraction of particles with unlike charges.

## Metallic Bonds

Although metals do not bond ionically, they often form lattices in the solid state. These lattices are similar to the ionic crystal lattices that were discussed in Section 8.2. In such a lattice, eight to 12 other metal atoms surround each metal atom. Although metal atoms have at least one valence electron, they do not share these electrons with neighboring atoms nor do they lose electrons to form ions.

Instead, in this crowded condition, the outer energy levels of the metal atoms overlap. The **electron sea model** proposes that all the metal atoms in a metallic solid contribute their valence electrons to form a "sea" of electrons. The electrons present in the outer energy levels of the bonding metallic atoms are not held by any specific atom and can move easily from one atom to the next. Because they are free to move, they are often referred to as **delocalized electrons**. When the atom's outer electrons move freely throughout the solid, a metallic cation is formed. Each such ion is bonded to all neighboring metal cations by the "sea" of valence electrons shown in **Figure 8-9**. A **metallic bond** is the attraction of a metallic cation for delocalized electrons.

**Properties of metals** The typical physical properties of metals can be explained by metallic bonding. These properties provide evidence of the strength of metallic bonds.

The melting points of metals vary greatly. Mercury is a liquid at room temperature, which makes it useful in scientific instruments such as thermometers and barometers. On the other hand, tungsten has a melting point of 3422°C, which makes it useful by itself or in combination with other metals

# 2 Teach

## Visual Learning

**Figure 8-9** Have students observe the figure and discuss how metallic bonds have metal cations surrounded by a "sea" of mobile electrons. Using a conductivity device, touch the surface of a piece of zinc or copper. The bulb will light up. Ask students why the bulb lights up. mobile electrons Point out that unlike ionic compounds, where bonding electrons are attached to the ions, bonding electrons in metals are free to move throughout the crystal.

**Figure 8-9**

The valence electrons in metals (shown in blue) are evenly distributed among the metallic cations (shown in red). Attractions between the positive cations and negative "sea" hold the metal atoms together in a lattice.

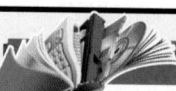

Group 1A

Group 2A

## DIFFERENTIATED INSTRUCTION

### Gifted

*Kinesthetic* Have students research the thermal conductivity of metals. Obtain different metal wires, such as Al, Zn, Cu, and Fe, of equal gauge and length. On one end of each wire, place a small bead of wax. Using tongs, have students heat the opposite end of the wire and determine and compare the times needed to melt the wax. **L3 ELL**

## Resource Manager

**Study Guide for Content Mastery,** p. 48 **L2**
**Solving Problems: A Chemistry Handbook,** Section 8.4 **L2**
**Section Focus Transparency 29 and Master L1 ELL**
**Teaching Transparency 28 and Master L2 ELL**

Metal is deformed →

External force

Figure 8-10

An applied force causes metal ions to move through delocalized electrons, making metals malleable and ductile.

for purposes that involve high temperatures or strength. Lightbulb filaments are usually made from tungsten, as are certain spacecraft parts. In general, metals have moderately high melting points and high boiling points, as shown in **Table 8-7.** The melting points are not as extreme as the boiling points because the cations and electrons are mobile in a metal. It does not take an extreme amount of energy for them to be able to move past each other. However, during boiling, atoms must be separated from the group of cations and electrons, which requires much more energy.

Metals are malleable, which means they can be hammered into sheets, and they are ductile, which means they can be drawn into wire. **Figure 8-10** shows how the mobile particles involved in metallic bonding can be pushed or pulled past each other, making metals malleable and ductile.

Metals are generally durable. Although metallic cations are mobile in a metal, they are strongly attracted to the electrons surrounding them and aren't easily removed from the metal.

Delocalized electrons in a metal are free to move, keeping metallic bonds intact. The movement of mobile electrons around positive metallic cations explains why metals are good conductors. The delocalized electrons move heat from one place to another much more quickly than the electrons in a material that does not contain mobile electrons. Mobile electrons easily move as a part of an electric current when electrical potential is applied to a metal. These same delocalized electrons interact with light, absorbing and releasing photons, thereby creating the property of luster in metals.

The mobile electrons in transition metals consist not only of the two outer s electrons but also the inner d electrons. As the number of delocalized electrons increases, so do the properties of hardness and strength. For example, strong metallic bonds are found in transition metals such as chromium, iron, and nickel, whereas alkali metals are considered soft because they have only one delocalized electron, $ns^1$.

Table 8-7

| Melting Points and Boiling Points of Some Metals | | |
|---|---|---|
| Element | Melting point (°C) | Boiling point (°C) |
| Lithium | 180 | 1347 |
| Tin | 232 | 2623 |
| Aluminum | 660 | 2467 |
| Barium | 727 | 1850 |
| Silver | 961 | 2155 |
| Copper | 1083 | 2570 |

## Quick Demo

In an evaporating dish, dissolve 5.0 g of sodium hydroxide in 25 mL of water. Add 2.0 g of zinc to the solution, and place on a hot plate. Heat the mixture to just below the boiling point. Place some new pennies into the evaporating dish, and turn pennies several times with forceps. When the pennies are silver in color, take the evaporating dish off the hot plate and remove the pennies. Rinse and dry the pennies. Ask students what has happened. The pennies are coated with zinc. Place one of the pennies on the hot plate. The penny will turn golden. Ask students what happened. The zinc and the copper on the surface of the penny mixed. Discuss alloys, and tell students that the heat increased the motion of the atoms and allowed them to mix faster. Allow the students to examine a new penny, a zinc-coated penny, and a brass-coated penny. Ask what type of alloy was formed. a substitutional alloy because copper and zinc atoms are almost identical in size Disposal: wash remaining zinc with cold water, drain, and place in the trash. Dilute the NaOH solution and flush down the drain.

## Assessment

**Knowledge** Show students an iron nail and a piece of copper wire. Ask what they have in common and how they are different. Both have metallic bonds and are malleable, ductile, and conductors. Iron is stronger because it has more delocalized electrons. They are different elements.

## CHEMISTRY JOURNAL

### Types of Alloys

**Visual-Spatial** Have students diagram microscopic views of both a substitutional alloy and an interstitial alloy in their journals. **L2** **ELL**

**National Science Content Standards**

Pages 228–229
UCP.1, UCP.2; B.2, B.4

## Metal Alloys

Due to the nature of a metallic bond, it is relatively easy to introduce other elements into a metallic crystal, forming an alloy. An **alloy** is a mixture of elements that has metallic properties. **Table 8-8** lists some commercially important alloys and their uses. A company that manufactures trophies probably would use which alloy listed in the table?

The properties of alloys differ somewhat from the properties of the elements they contain. For example, steel is iron mixed with at least one other element. Some properties of iron are present, but steel has additional properties, such as increased strength. Some alloys, such as that used in the **miniLAB,** vary in properties depending on how they are manufactured.

# miniLAB

## Heat Treatment of Steel

**Recognizing Cause and Effect** People have treated metals with heat for many centuries. Different properties result when the metal is slowly or rapidly cooled. Can you determine how and why the properties change?

**Materials** laboratory burner, forceps (2), hairpins (3), 250-mL beaker

### Procedure 🥽 👐 👟 🔥

1. Examine a property of spring steel by trying to bend open one of the hairpins. Record your observations.

2. Hold each end of a hairpin with forceps. Place the curved central loop in the top of the burner's flame. When it turns red, pull it open into a straight piece of metal. Allow it to cool as you record your observations. Repeat this procedure for the remaining two hairpins. CAUTION: *Do not touch the hot metal.*

3. To make softened steel, use forceps to hold all three hairpins vertically in the flame until they glow red all over. Slowly raise the three hairpins straight up and out of the flame so they cool slowly. Slow cooling results in the formation of large crystals.

4. After cooling, bend each of the three hairpins into the shape of the letter J. Record how the metal feels as you bend it.

5. To harden the steel, use tongs to hold two of the bent hairpins in the flame until they are glowing red all over. Quickly plunge the hot metals into a 250-mL beaker containing approximately 200 mL of cold water. Quick-cooling causes the crystal size to be small.

6. Attempt to straighten one of the bends. Record your observations.

7. To temper the steel, use tongs to briefly hold the remaining hardened metal bend above the flame. Slowly move the metal back and forth just above the flame until the gray metal turns to an iridescent blue-gray color. Do not allow the metal to glow red. Slowly cool the metal and then try to unbend it using the end of your finger. Record your observations.

### Analysis

1. State a use for spring steel that takes advantage of its unique properties.
2. What are the advantages and disadvantages of using softened steel for body panels on automobiles?
3. What is the major disadvantage of hardened steel? Do you think this form of iron would be wear resistant and retain a sharpened edge?
4. Which two types of steel appear to have their properties combined in tempered steel?
5. State a hypothesis that explains how the different properties you have observed relate to crystal size.

230    Chapter 8 Ionic Compounds

## ✓ Portfolio

### Chemistry at Work

👤 *Intrapersonal* Have students research the alloys used in the manufacture of the lightweight bicycles used in racing and write a report for their portfolios. L2 P 📦

Table 8-8

| Some Commercially Important Alloys | | |
|---|---|---|
| Common name | Composition | Uses |
| Alnico | Fe 50%, Al 20%, Ni 20%, Co 10% | Magnets |
| Brass | Cu 67-90%, Zn 10-33% | Plumbing, hardware, lighting |
| Bronze | Cu 70-95%, Zn 1-25%, Sn 1-18% | Bearings, bells, medals |
| Cast iron | Fe 96-97%, C 3-4% | Casting |
| Dental amalgam | Hg 50%, Ag 35%, Sn 15% | Dental fillings |
| Gold, 10 carat | Au 42%, Ag 12-20%, Cu 38-46% | Jewelry |
| Lead shot | Pb 99.8%, As 0.2% | Shotgun shells |
| Pewter | Sn 70-95%, Sb 5-15%, Pb 0-15% | Tableware |
| Stainless steel | Fe 73-79%, Cr 14-18%, Ni 7-9% | Instruments, sinks |
| Sterling silver | Ag 92.5%, Cu 7.5% | Tableware, jewelry |

Alloys most commonly form when the elements involved are either similar in size or the atoms of one element are considerably smaller than the atoms of the other. Thus, two basic types of alloys exist, substitutional and interstitial, and many industries depend on their production. A substitutional alloy has atoms of the original metallic solid replaced by other metal atoms of similar size. Sterling silver is an example of a substitutional alloy. When copper atoms replace silver atoms in the original metallic crystal, a solid with properties of both silver and copper is formed. Brass, pewter, and 10-carat gold are all examples of substitutional alloys.

An interstitial alloy is formed when the small holes (interstices) in a metallic crystal are filled with smaller atoms. Forming this type of alloy is similar to pouring sand into a bucket of gravel. Even if the gravel is tightly packed, holes exist between the pieces. The sand does not replace any of the gravel but fills in the spaces. The best-known interstitial alloy is carbon steel. Holes in the iron crystal are filled with carbon atoms, and the physical properties of iron are changed. Iron is relatively soft and malleable. However, the presence of carbon makes the solid harder, stronger, and less ductile than pure iron, increasing its uses.

## Section 8.4 Assessment

**40.** What is a metallic bond?

**41.** Explain how conductivity of electricity and high melting point of metals are explained by metallic bonding.

**42.** What is an alloy?

**43.** How does a substitutional alloy differ from an interstitial alloy?

**44. Thinking Critically** In the laboratory, how could you determine if a solid has an ionic bond or a metallic bond?

**45. Formulating Models** Draw a model to represent the ductility of a metal using the electron sea model shown in **Figure 8-10**.

### Check for Understanding

Ask students to compare and contrast ionic compounds and metallic solids. Accept any reasonable answer.

### Reteach

Show students several metallic and ionic solids. Demonstrate the differences in physical properties.

### Extension

*Intrapersonal* Have interested students research industrial alloys and report to the class. Ask students to find out if industries in their area use the alloys they researched. **L2**

### Assessment

**Skill** Have students complete a chart that compares metallic bonding to ionic bonding. Charts might include types of particles, bond formation, structure, physical properties, and possible laboratory identification. **L2**

### Resource Manager

ChemLab and MiniLab Worksheets, p. 29 **L2**

**National Science Content Standards**

Pages 230–231
UCP.1, UCP.2; A.1; B.2; E.1

## Section 8.4 Assessment

**40.** the attraction of a positive metallic ion for delocalized electrons

**41.** Delocalized electrons can move through the solid to conduct an electric current. The number of delocalized electrons and the strength of a metallic bond determine the melting point.

**42.** a mixture of a metal and at least one other element

**43.** A substitutional alloy has metal atoms that are of similar size, while an interstitial alloy has the spaces in a metallic crystal filled with smaller atoms.

**44.** A metallic solid will conduct and is malleable and ductile, but an ionic solid will not conduct and is brittle.

**45.** Diagrams should show metal ions being moved into a longer, thinner form through a sea of electrons. See the Solutions Manual.

## Preparation

### Time Allotment
One laboratory period

### Process Skills
Classifying, observing and inferring, using numbers, comparing and contrasting, predicting

### Safety Precautions
Have students wear an apron and goggles. The exothermic reaction produces a very bright light. Do not allow them to look directly at the light. Advise them that the crucible will remain hot enough to burn the skin for about five minutes.

### Disposal
Have students either place the magnesium product in a receptacle for solid waste or rinse it from the beaker and wash it down the drain.

## Pre-Lab

**1.** Variable: mass of Mg; Constant: there must be an excess of oxygen

**2.** Mg $1s^2\ 2s^2\ 2p^6\ 3s^2$
   **a.** lose electrons
   **b.** $Mg^{2+}\ 1s^2\ 2s^2\ 2p^6$
   **c.** neon

**3.** O $1s^2\ 2s^2\ 2p^4$, N $1s^2\ 2s^2\ 2p^3$
   **a.** Both will gain electrons.
   **b.** $O^{2-}\ 1s^2\ 2s^2\ 2p^6$, $N^{3-}\ 1s^2\ 2s^2\ 2p^6$
   **c.** Both have the configuration of neon.

**5.** The mass of the magnesium and the mass of the magnesium products are calculated. Other mass values are measured directly.

**6.** The mass of magnesium ribbon is calculated by subtracting the mass of the crucible from the mass of the crucible and magnesium. The mass of the magnesium products is calculated by subtracting the mass

### National Science Content Standards
**Pages 232–233**
UCP.1, UCP.2; A.1; B.3

# Making Ionic Compounds

**E**lements combine to form compounds. If energy is released as the compound is formed, the resulting product is more stable than the reacting elements. In this investigation you will react elements to form two compounds. You will test the compounds to determine several of their properties. Ionic compounds have properties that are different from those of other compounds. You will decide if the products you formed are ionic compounds.

### Problem
What are the formulas and names of the products that are formed? Do the properties of these compounds classify them as having ionic bonds?

### Objectives
- **Observe** evidence of a chemical reaction.
- **Acquire** and **analyze** information that will enable you to decide if a compound has an ionic bond.
- **Classify** the products as ionic or not ionic.

### Materials
magnesium ribbon
crucible
ring stand and ring
clay triangle
laboratory burner
stirring rod

crucible tongs
centigram balance
100-mL beaker
distilled water
conductivity tester

### Safety Precautions

- Always wear safety glasses and a lab apron.
- Do not look directly at the burning magnesium. The intensity of the light can damage your eyes.
- Avoid handling heated materials until they have cooled.

### Pre-Lab

**1.** Read the entire procedure. Identify the variables. List any conditions that must be kept constant.

**2.** Write the electron configuration of the magnesium atom.
   **a.** Based on this configuration, will magnesium lose or gain electrons to become a magnesium ion?
   **b.** Write the electron configuration of the magnesium ion.
   **c.** The magnesium ion has an electron configuration like that of which noble gas?

**3.** Repeat question 2 for oxygen and nitrogen.

**4.** Prepare your data table.

**5.** In your data table, which mass values will be measured directly? Which mass values will be calculated?

**6.** Explain what must be done to calculate each mass value that is not measured directly.

| Mass Data | |
|---|---|
| **Material(s)** | **Mass (g)** |
| Empty crucible | |
| Crucible and Mg ribbon before heating | |
| Magnesium ribbon | |
| Crucible and magnesium products after heating | |
| Magnesium products | |

of the crucible from the mass of the crucible and its contents after heating.

## Procedure

- The lengths of magnesium can be cut in advance.
- The laboratory burners should be adjusted so as to produce the hottest possible flame.

- Point out to students that, at high temperatures, oxygen and nitrogen from the air will react with magnesium.
- **Troubleshooting** To prevent direct observation of the burning magnesium, place a piece of shiny metal behind the crucible and a piece of cardboard in front of it. Then, the flame can be observed indirectly.

## Procedure

1. Arrange the ring on the ring stand so that it is about 7 cm above the top of the Bunsen burner. Place the clay triangle on the ring.

2. Measure the mass of the clean, dry crucible, and record the mass in the data table.

3. Roll 25 cm of magnesium ribbon into a loose ball. Place it in the crucible. Measure the mass of the magnesium and crucible and record this mass in the data table.

4. Place the crucible on the clay ring. Heat the crucible with a hot flame, being careful to position the crucible near the top of the flame.

5. When the magnesium metal ignites and begins to burn with a bright white light, immediately turn off the laboratory burner. **CAUTION:** *Do not look directly at the burning magnesium.* After the magnesium product and crucible have cooled, measure their mass and record it in the data table.

6. Place the dry solid product in a small beaker for further testing.

7. Add 10 mL of distilled water to the dry magnesium product in the beaker and stir. Check the mixture with a conductivity checker, and record your results.

## Cleanup and Disposal

1. Wash out the crucible with water.

2. Dispose of the product as directed by your teacher.

3. Return all lab equipment to its proper place.

## Analyze and Conclude

1. **Analyzing Data** Use the masses in the table to calculate the mass of the magnesium ribbon and the mass of the magnesium product. Record these masses in the table.

2. **Classifying** What kind of energy was released by the reaction? What can you conclude about the product of this reaction?

3. **Using Numbers** How do you know that the magnesium metal reacts with certain components of the air?

4. **Predicting** Magnesium reacts with both oxygen and nitrogen from the air at the high temperature of the crucible. Predict the binary formulas for both products. Write the names of these two compounds.

5. **Analyzing and Concluding** The product formed from magnesium and oxygen is white, and the product formed from magnesium and nitrogen is yellow. From your observations, which compound makes up most of the product?

6. **Analyzing and Concluding** Did the magnesium compounds and water conduct an electric current? Do the results indicate whether or not the compounds are ionic?

7. **Error Analysis** If the magnesium lost mass instead of gaining mass, what do you think was a possible source of the error?

## Real-World Chemistry

1. The magnesium ion plays an important role in a person's biochemistry. Research the role of this electrolyte in your physical and mental health. Is magnesium listed as a component in a multi-vitamin and mineral tablet?

2. Research the use of $Mg(OH)_2$ in everyday products. What is $Mg(OH)_2$ commonly called in over-the-counter drugs?

**Resource Manager**

ChemLab and MiniLab Worksheets, pp. 30–32 **L2**

## Expected Results

### Sample Data and Observations
Mass of empty crucible
7.65 g
Mass of crucible and Mg ribbon before heating
7.85 g
Mass of magnesium ribbon
0.20 g
Mass of crucible and magnesium products after heating
7.93 g
Mass of magnesium products
0.28 g

## Analyze and Conclude

1. See Expected Results.
2. Heat and light; It is more stable than the reacting elements.
3. There is an increase in mass from 0.20 g to 0.28 g.
4. MgO, magnesium oxide; $Mg_3N_2$, magnesium nitride
5. MgO; the product appears white.
6. Yes; ionic compounds conduct a current in solution.
7. Possible answers include that some of the product blew away or that the reaction was incomplete.

## Real-World Chemistry

1. Answers may include that it is important in nerve impulse transmission. Mg is present in vitamin-mineral tablets.
2. Answers might include that it is used in over-the-counter antacids and laxatives, where it is known as milk of magnesia.

### ✓ Assessment

**Knowledge** Have students list the properties of the product that they observed in this investigation that are characteristic of an ionic compound. produced by an exothermic reaction, hard, rigid, brittle, aqueous solution conducts a current, and high melting point

# Everyday Chemistry

## Purpose

Students will learn how transition metals give gems and glass their colors.

## Teaching Strategies

- Remind students that color is related to the wavelength or frequency of light.
- Use a flashlight and colored filters to show students that white light is an additive mixture of red, blue, and green light. Demonstrate how combinations of the filters make other colors.
- Explain how transition metals produce color. When white light shines on transition metals, d electrons of the metals absorb certain frequencies of the light and are excited to a higher energy state. The light that is not absorbed is no longer white, but a combination of the unabsorbed frequencies. This light is transmitted or reflected by the object and perceived by the eye.

## Testing Your Knowledge

1. Iron(III) sulfate and iron(II) thiocyanate have different colors because iron has different oxidation numbers in the two compounds. Iron is in the 3+ oxidation state in both iron(III) thiocyanate and iron(III) sulfate. Therefore, the difference in color is due to the different anions.
2. amethyst: iron and manganese; rose quartz: manganese and titanium oxide; citrine: iron(II) oxide
3. The chemical and physical properties are generally identical. Synthetics have superior quality because natural gems may contain impurities.

**National Science Content Standards**

**Pages 234–235**
UCP.1, UCP.2; B.1, B.2, B.3, B.4

## Colors of Gems

Have you ever wondered what produces the gorgeous colors in a stained-glass window or in the rubies, emeralds, and sapphires mounted on a ring? Compounds of transition elements are responsible for creating the entire spectrum of colors.

### Transition elements color gems and glass

Transition elements have many important uses, but one that is often overlooked is their role in giving colors to gemstones and glass. Although not all compounds of transition elements are colored, most inorganic colored compounds contain a transition element such as chromium, iron, cobalt, copper, manganese, nickel, cadmium, titanium, gold, or vanadium. The color of a compound is determined by the identity of the metal, its oxidation number, and the negative ion combined with it.

### Impurities give gemstones their color

Crystals have fascinating properties. A clear, colorless quartz crystal is pure silicon dioxide ($SiO_2$). But a crystal that is colorless in its pure form may exist as a variety of colored gemstones when tiny amounts of transition element compounds, usually oxides, are present. Amethyst (purple), citrine (yellow-brown), and rose quartz (pink) are quartz crystals with transition element impurities scattered throughout. Blue sapphires are composed of aluminum oxide ($Al_2O_3$) with the impurities iron(II) oxide (FeO) and titanium(IV) oxide ($TiO_2$). If trace amounts of chromium(III) oxide ($Cr_2O_3$) are

present in the $Al_2O_3$, the resulting gem is a red ruby. A second kind of gemstone is one composed entirely of a colored compound. Most are transition element compounds, such as rose-red rhodochrosite ($MnCO_3$), black-grey hematite ($Fe_2O_3$), or green malachite ($CuCO_3 \cdot Cu(OH)_2$).

### How metal ions interact with light to produce color

Why does the presence of $Cr_2O_3$ in $Al_2O_3$ make a ruby red? The $Cr^{3+}$ ion absorbs yellow-green colors from white light striking the ruby, and the remaining red-blue light is transmitted, resulting in a deep red color. This same process occurs in all gems. Trace impurities absorb certain colors of light from white light striking or passing through the stone. The remaining colors of light that are reflected or transmitted produce the color of the gem.

### Adding transition elements to molten glass for color

Glass is colored by adding transition element compounds to the glass while it is molten. This process is used for stained glass, glass used in glass blowing, and even glass in the form of ceramic glazes. Most of the coloring agents are oxides. When oxides of copper or cobalt are added to molten glass, the glass is blue; oxides of manganese produce purple glass; iron oxides, green; gold oxides, deep ruby red; copper or selenium oxides, red; and antimony oxides, yellow. Some coloring compounds are not oxides. Chromates, for example, produce green glass, and iron sulfide gives a brown color.

### Testing Your Knowledge

1. **Applying** Explain why iron(III) sulfate is yellow, iron(II) thiocyanate is green, and iron(III) thiocyanate is red.

2. **Acquiring Information** Find out what impurities give amethyst, rose quartz, and citrine their colors.

3. **Comparing and Contrasting** Conduct research to find the similarities and differences between synthetic and natural gemstones.

**234**   **Chapter 8** Ionic Compounds

## Summary

### 8.1 Forming Chemical Bonds

- A chemical bond is the force that holds two atoms together.

- Atoms that form ions gain or lose valence electrons to achieve the same electron arrangement as that of a noble gas, which is a stable configuration. This noble gas configuration involves a complete outer electron energy level, which usually consists of eight valence electrons.

- A positive ion, or cation, forms when valence electrons are removed and a stable electron configuration is obtained.

- A negative ion, or anion, forms when valence electrons are added to the outer energy level, giving the ion a stable electron configuration.

### 8.2 The Formation and Nature of Ionic Bonds

- An ionic bond forms when anions and cations close to each other attract, forming a tightly packed geometric crystal lattice.

- Lattice energy is needed to break the force of attraction between oppositely charged ions arranged in a crystal lattice.

- The physical properties of ionic solids, such as melting point, boiling point, hardness, and the ability to conduct electricity in the molten state and as an aqueous solution, are related to the strength of the ionic bonds and the presence of ions.

- An ionic compound is an electrolyte because it conducts an electric current when it is liquid or in aqueous solution.

### 8.3 Names and Formulas for Ionic Compounds

- Subscripts in an ionic compound indicate the ratio of cations and anions needed to form electrically neutral compounds. The formula unit represents the ratio of these ions in the crystal lattice.

- If the element that forms the cation has more than one possible oxidation number, Roman numerals are used to indicate the oxidation number present for that element in the compound.

- Ions formed from only one atom are monatomic ions. The charge on a monatomic ion is its oxidation number, or oxidation state.

- Polyatomic ions are two or more atoms bonded together that act as a single unit with a net charge. Many polyatomic ions are oxyanions, containing an atom, usually a nonmetal, and oxygen atoms.

- In a chemical formula, polyatomic ions are placed inside parentheses when using a subscript.

- Ionic compounds are named by the name of the cation followed by the name of the anion.

### 8.4 Metallic Bonds and Properties of Metals

- Metallic bonds are formed when metal cations attract free valence electrons. A "sea" of electrons moves throughout the entire metallic crystal, producing this attraction.

- The electrons involved in metallic bonding are called delocalized electrons because they are free to move throughout the metal and are not attached to a particular atom.

- The electron sea model can explain the melting point, boiling point, malleability, conductivity, and ductility of metallic solids.

- Metal alloys are formed when a metal is mixed with one or more other elements. The two common types of alloys are substitutional and interstitial.

## Vocabulary

- alloy (p. 230)
- anion (p. 214)
- cation (p. 212)
- chemical bond (p. 211)
- delocalized electrons (p. 228)
- electrolyte (p. 218)
- electron sea model (p. 228)
- formula unit (p. 221)
- ionic bond (p. 215)
- lattice energy (p. 219)
- metallic bond (p. 228)
- monatomic ion (p. 221)
- oxidation number (p. 222)
- oxyanion (p. 225)
- polyatomic ion (p. 224)

## Using the Vocabulary

To reinforce chapter vocabulary, have students write a sentence using each term. L2 ELL

## Review Strategies

- Have students describe the formation of cations and anions and give an example of each. L2

- Have students summarize the formation of ionic compounds, discuss the nature of ionic bonds, and identify physical properties associated with ionic bonds. L2

- Have students name and write formulas for ionic compounds. L2

- Have students summarize a metallic bond, identify physical properties associated with metallic bonding, and discuss the formation of alloys. L2

- Problems from Appendix A can be used for review. L2

### VOCABULARY PuzzleMaker

For additional help with vocabulary, have students access the Vocabulary PuzzleMaker online.
chemistrymc.com/vocabulary_puzzlemaker

### EXAM*VIEW* PRO

## Use Exam*View*® Pro Testmaker CD-ROM to:

- Create **multiple versions** of tests.
- Create **modified** tests with one mouse click for struggling students.
- **Edit** existing questions and add your own questions.
- **Build** tests based on national curriculum standards.

**National Science Content Standards**
Pages 236–239
UCP.1, UCP.2; B.1, B.2, B.3, B.4, B.6

## Concept Mapping

**46.** 1. cation; 2. anion;
3. positive; 4. negative

## Mastering Concepts

**47.** when a positive nucleus attracts electrons of another atom, or oppositely charged ions attract

**48.** An atom gains or loses electrons to achieve a stable electron configuration.

**49.** Halogens need to gain one electron to have a noble gas configuration. Alkali metals need to lose one.

**50.** High electron affinity: atom easily gains an electron; low ionization energy: atom easily loses an electron

**51.** A positive ion is attracted to a negative ion and lattice energy is released.

**52.** exist as crystals; have high melting and boiling points

**53.** The number of electrons lost is equal to the number of electrons gained.

**54.** the metallic ion and the nonmetallic ion, including their charges

**55.** when more than one unit of an ion is in the simplest ratio of the ions

**56.** See page 226.

**57.** Each positive metal ion is attracted to delocalized valence electrons.

**58.** When a force is applied to a metallic solid, the metal ions move as well as the delocalized electrons.

**59.** A substitutional alloy has metal atoms that are similar in size. An interstitial alloy has two differently sized atoms.

*Go to the Chemistry Web site at chemistrymc.com for additional Chapter 8 Assessment.*

## Concept Mapping

**46.** Complete the concept map, showing what type of ion is formed in each case and what type of charge the ion has.

## Mastering Concepts

**47.** When do chemical bonds form? (8.1)

**48.** Why do positive ions and negative ions form? (8.1)

**49.** Why are halogens and alkali metals likely to form ions? Explain your answer. (8.1)

**50.** Discuss the importance of electron affinity and ionization energy in the formation of ions. (8.1)

**51.** Discuss the formation of ionic bonds. (8.2)

**52.** Briefly discuss three physical properties of ionic solids that are linked to ionic bonds. (8.2)

**53.** What does the term *electrically neutral* mean when discussing ionic compounds? (8.2)

**54.** What information is needed to write a correct chemical formula to represent an ionic compound? (8.3)

**55.** When are subscripts used in formulas for ionic compounds? (8.3)

**56.** Discuss how an ionic compound is named. (8.3)

**57.** Describe a metallic bond. (8.4)

**58.** Briefly explain how malleability and ductility of metals are explained by metallic bonding. (8.4)

**59.** Compare and contrast the two types of metal alloys. (8.4)

## Mastering Problems

### Ion Formation (8.1)

**60.** Explain why noble gases are not likely to form chemical bonds.

**61.** Give the number of valence electrons in an atom of each of the following:

a. cesium      d. zinc
b. rubidium     e. strontium
c. gallium

**62.** Discuss the formation of the barium ion.

**63.** Explain how an anion of nitrogen forms.

**64.** The more reactive an atom, the higher its potential energy. Which atom has higher potential energy, neon or fluorine? Explain.

**65.** Predict the reactivity of the following atoms based on their electron configurations.

a. potassium
b. fluorine
c. neon

**66.** Discuss the formation of the iron ion that has a 3+ oxidation number.

### Ionic Bonds and Ionic Compounds (8.2)

**67.** Determine the ratio of cations to anions for the following ionic compounds.

a. potassium chloride, a salt substitute
b. calcium fluoride, used in the steel industry
c. aluminum oxide, known as corundum in the crystalline form
d. calcium oxide, used to remove sulfur dioxide from power plant exhaust
e. strontium chloride, used in fireworks

**68.** Using orbital notation, diagram the formation of an ionic bond between aluminum and fluorine.

**69.** Using electron configurations, diagram the formation of an ionic bond between barium and nitrogen.

**70.** Discuss the formation of an ionic bond between zinc and oxygen.

**71.** Under certain conditions, ionic compounds conduct an electric current. Describe these conditions and explain why ionic compounds are not always used as conductors.

**72.** Which of the following compounds are not likely to occur: $CaKr$, $Na_2S$, $BaCl_3$, $MgF$? Explain your choices.

**73.** Using **Table 8-2**, determine which of the following ionic compounds will have the highest melting point: $MgO$, $KI$, or $AgCl$. Explain your answer.

chemistrymc.com/chapter_test

## Mastering Problems

Complete solutions to Chapter Assessment Problems can be found in the **Solutions Manual.**

### Ion Formation (8.1)
**Level 1**

**60.** They already have a full, stable outer energy level.

### Resource Manager

Chapter Assessment, pp. 43–48 **L2**
Supplemental Problems, Ch. 8
ExamView® Pro CD-ROM
MindJogger Videoquizzes DVD/VHS
Solutions Manual, Ch. 8
Chemistry Interactive CD-ROM,
   Ch. 8 quiz

## Formulas and Names for Ionic Compounds (8.3)

**74.** Give the formula for each of the following ionic compounds.

    **a.** calcium iodide    **d.** potassium periodate
    **b.** silver(I) bromide    **e.** silver(I) acetate
    **c.** copper(II) chloride

**75.** Name each of the following ionic compounds.

    **a.** $K_2O$    **d.** $NaClO$
    **b.** $CaCl_2$    **e.** $KNO_3$
    **c.** $Mg_3N_2$

**76.** Complete **Table 8-9** by placing the symbols, formulas, and names in the blanks.

**Table 8-9**

| Identifying Ionic Compounds | | | |
|---|---|---|---|
| Cation | Anion | Name | Formula |
| | | ammonium sulfate | |
| | | | $PbF_2$ |
| | | lithium bromide | |
| | | | $Na_2CO_3$ |
| $Mg^{2+}$ | $PO_4^{3-}$ | | |

**77.** Chromium, a transition metal, forms both the $Cr^{2+}$ and $Cr^{3+}$ ions. Write the formulas for the ionic compounds formed when each of these ions react with

    **a.** fluorine    **b.** oxygen

**78.** Which of the following are correct formulas for ionic compounds? For those that are not correct, give the correct formula and justify your answer.

    **a.** $AlCl$    **d.** $BaOH_2$
    **b.** $Na_3SO_4$    **e.** $Fe_2O$
    **c.** $MgCO_3$

**79.** Write the formulas for all of the ionic compounds that can be formed by combining each of the cations with each of the anions listed below. Name each compound formed.

**Table 8-10**

| Cations | Anions |
|---|---|
| $K^+$ | $SO_3^{2-}$ |
| $NH_4^+$ | $I^-$ |
| $Fe^{3+}$ | $NO_3^-$ |

## Metals and Metallic Bonds (8.4)

**80.** How is a metallic bond different from an ionic bond?

**81.** Briefly explain why silver is a good conductor of electricity.

**82.** Briefly explain why iron is used in making the structures of many buildings.

**83.** The melting point of beryllium is 1287°C, while that of lithium is 180°C. Account for the large difference in values.

**84.** Describe the difference between the metal alloy sterling silver and carbon steel in terms of the types of alloys involved.

# Mixed Review

*Sharpen your problem-solving skills by answering the following.*

**85.** Give the number of valence electrons for atoms of oxygen, sulfur, arsenic, phosphorus, and bromine.

**86.** Explain why calcium can form a $Ca^{2+}$ ion but not a $Ca^{3+}$ ion.

**87.** Which of the following ionic compounds would have the most negative lattice energy: NaCl, KCl, or $MgCl_2$? Explain your answer.

**88.** Give the formula for each of the following ionic compounds.

    **a.** sodium sulfide    **d.** calcium phosphate
    **b.** iron(III) chloride    **e.** zinc nitrate
    **c.** sodium sulfate

**89.** Cobalt, a transition metal, forms both the $Co^{2+}$ and $Co^{3+}$ ions. Write the correct formulas and give the name for the oxides formed by the two different ions.

**90.** Briefly explain why gold can be used as both a conductor in electronic devices and in jewelry.

**91.** Discuss the formation of the nickel ion with a 2+ oxidation number.

**92.** Using electron-dot structure, diagram the formation of an ionic bond between potassium and iodine.

**93.** Magnesium forms both an oxide and a nitride when burned in air. Discuss the formation of magnesium oxide and magnesium nitride when magnesium atoms react with oxygen and nitrogen atoms.

**94.** An external force easily deforms sodium metal, while sodium chloride shatters when the same amount of force is applied. Why do these two solids behave so differently?

**61. a.** 1   **c.** 3   **e.** 2
    **b.** 1   **d.** 2

**62.** Ba will lose two electrons and form $Ba^{2+}$, which has the stable electron configuration of Xe.

**63.** N gains three electrons, forming $N^{3-}$, which has the stable electron configuration of Ne.

**64.** F, because it will gain one more electron to fill its outer energy level

### Level 2

**65. a.** Potassium ([Ar] $4s^1$) will lose one outer electron and form a 1+ ion.
    **b.** Fluorine ([He] $2s^22p^5$) will gain one more electron and form a 1− ion.
    **c.** Neon ($1s^22s^22p^6$) will not react because it already has eight electrons in its outer energy level.

**66.** Iron will lose two outer 4s electrons and one 3d electron.

## Ionic Bonds and Ionic Compounds (8.2)
### Level 1

**67. a.** 1:1   **c.** 2:3   **e.** 1:2
    **b.** 1:2   **d.** 1:1

**68.** The diagram in the Solutions Manual should show the transfer of three electrons from one Al atom to three F atoms.

**69.** Use the configuration of Ba as [Xe]$6s^2$ and that of N as [He] $2s^22p^3$ to show how three Ba atoms transfer a total of six electrons to two N atoms, forming $Ba^{2+}$ as [Xe] and $N^{3-}$ as [Ne].

**70.** Zn will lose its outer 4s electrons, forming $Zn^{2+}$. Oxygen will gain the two electrons forming $O^{2-}$. $Zn^{2+}$ attracts $O^{2-}$, forming ZnO.

### Level 2

**71.** Ionic compounds will conduct in the molten state or dissolved in water but are nonconducting solids at room temperature.

**72.** CaKr, because Kr is a noble gas; $BaCl_3$ and MgF, because charges are not balanced.

**73.** MgO; it has the highest lattice energy.

## Formulas and Names for Ionic Compounds (8.3)

### Level 1

**74. a.** $CaI_2$   **d.** $KIO_4$
    **b.** AgBr   **e.** $AgC_2H_3O_2$
    **c.** $CuCl_2$

**75. a.** potassium oxide
    **b.** calcium chloride
    **c.** magnesium nitride
    **d.** sodium hypochlorite
    **e.** potassium nitrate

**76.** left to right, top to bottom: $NH_4^+$, $SO_4^{2-}$, $(NH_4)_2SO_4$; $Pb^{2+}$, $F^-$, lead(II) fluoride; $Li^+$, $Br^-$, LiBr; $Na^+$, $CO_3^{2-}$, sodium carbonate; magnesium phosphate, $Mg_3(PO_4)_2$

**77. a.** $CrF_2$, $CrF_3$
**b.** $CrO$, $Cr_2O_3$

**Level 2**

**78. a.** $AlCl_3$; one $Al^{3+}$ ion bonds to three $Cl^-$ ions.
**b.** $Na_2SO_4$; two $Na^+$ ions bond to $SO_4^{2-}$.
**c.** correct
**d.** $Ba(OH)_2$; if a polyatomic ion needs a subscript, parentheses must be used.
**e.** $Fe_2O_3$; or $FeO$; iron forms either $Fe^{2+}$ or $Fe^{3+}$.

**79.** $K_2SO_3$, potassium sulfite; $KI$, potassium iodide; $KNO_3$, potassium nitrate; $(NH_4)_2SO_3$, ammonium sulfite; $NH_4I$, ammonium iodide; $NH_4NO_3$, ammonium nitrate; $Fe_2(SO_3)_3$, iron(III) sulfite; $FeI_3$, iron(III) iodide; $Fe(NO_3)_3$, iron(III) nitrate

## Metals and Metallic Bonds (8.4)

**Level 1**

**80.** Metallic bond: electrostatic attraction between a positive metal ion and free valence electrons; ionic bond: between a positive metallic ion and a negative nonmetallic ion

**81.** It has delocalized electrons that are free to move.

**82.** Iron forms a strong metallic bond, giving solid iron hardness and strength.

**Level 2**

**83.** Beryllium has two delocalized electrons per atom. Lithium has one.

**84.** Sterling silver is substitutional, formed from silver and copper. Carbon steel is interstitial, formed from iron and carbon.

## Mixed Review

**85.** 6, 6, 5, 5, and 7, respectively
**86.** Ca ($[Ar]\,4s^2$) will lose 2 electrons. If it loses an inner 3p electron, it is unstable.

**95.** Name each of the following ionic compounds.
**a.** $CaO$
**b.** $BaS$
**c.** $AlPO_4$
**d.** $Ba(OH)_2$
**e.** $Sr(NO_3)_2$

**96.** Write the formulas for all of the ionic compounds that can be formed by combining each of the cations with each of the anions listed below. Name each compound formed.

**Table 8-11**

| Cations | Anions |
|---------|--------|
| $Ba^{2+}$ | $S_2O_3^{2-}$ |
| $Cu^+$ | $Br^-$ |
| $Al^{3+}$ | $NO_2^-$ |

## Thinking Critically

**97. Concept Mapping** Design a concept map to explain the physical properties of both ionic compounds and metallic solids.

**98. Predicting** Predict which solid in each of the following will have the higher melting point. Explain your answer.
**a.** NaCl or CsCl
**b.** Ag or Cu
**c.** $Na_2O$ or MgO

**99. Comparing and Contrasting** Compare and contrast cations and anions.

**100. Observing and Inferring** From the following incorrect formulas and formula names, identify the mistakes and design a flow chart to prevent the mistakes.
**a.** copper acetate
**b.** $Mg_2O_2$
**c.** $Pb_2O_5$
**d.** disodium oxide
**e.** $Al_2SO_{43}$

**101. Hypothesizing** Look at the locations of potassium and calcium on the periodic table. Form a hypothesis as to why the melting point of calcium is considerably higher than the melting point of potassium.

**102. Drawing a Conclusion** Explain why the term *delocalized* is an appropriate term for the electrons involved in metallic bonding.

**103. Applying Concepts** All uncharged atoms have valence electrons. Explain why elements such as iodine and sulfur don't have metallic bonds.

**104. Drawing a Conclusion** Explain why lattice energy is a negative quantity.

## Writing in Chemistry

**105.** Many researchers believe that free radicals are responsible for the effects of aging and cancer. Research free radicals and write about the cause and what can be done to prevent free radicals.

**106.** Crystals of ionic compounds can be easily grown in the laboratory setting. Research the growth of crystals and try to grow one crystal in the laboratory.

## Cumulative Review

*Refresh your understanding of previous chapters by answering the following.*

**107.** You are given a liquid of unknown density. The mass of a graduated cylinder containing 2.00 mL of the liquid is 34.68 g. The mass of the empty graduated cylinder is 30.00 g. What is the density of the liquid? (Chapter 2)

**108.** A mercury atom drops from $1.413 \times 10^{-18}$ J to $1.069 \times 10^{-18}$ J. (Chapter 5)
**a.** What is the energy of the photon emitted by the mercury atom?
**b.** What is the frequency of the photon emitted by the mercury atom?
**c.** What is the wavelength of the photon emitted by the mercury atom?

**109.** Which element has the greater ionization energy, chlorine or carbon? (Chapter 6)

**110.** Compare and contrast the way metals and nonmetals form ions and explain why they are different. (Chapter 6)

**111.** What are transition elements? (Chapter 6)

**112.** Write the symbol and name of the element that fits each description. (Chapter 6)
**a.** the second-lightest of the halogens
**b.** the metalloid with the lowest period number
**c.** the only group 6A element that is a gas at room temperature
**d.** the heaviest of the noble gases
**e.** the group 5A nonmetal that is a solid at room temperature

**113.** Which group 4A element is (Chapter 7)
**a.** a metalloid that occurs in sand?
**b.** a nonmetal?
**c.** used in electrodes in car batteries?
**d.** a component in many alloys?

**87.** $MgCl_2$; lattice energy increases with increased charge.
**88. a.** $Na_2S$  **c.** $Na_2SO_4$  **e.** $Zn(NO_3)_2$
**b.** $FeCl_3$  **d.** $Ca_3(PO_4)_2$
**89.** $CoO$, cobalt(II) oxide; $Co_2O_3$, cobalt(III) oxide
**90.** Delocalized electrons allow it to conduct. It is malleable and ductile.
**91.** Nickel, $[Ar]3d^84s^2$, will lose the two outer 4s electrons.

**92.** The electron dot structure for potassium shows one valence electron, and that for iodine shows seven. One potassium atom transfers its valence electron to one iodine atom.

**93.** A Mg atom loses two valence electrons, forming $Mg^{2+}$. An O atom gains two electrons, forming $O^{2-}$. One magnesium ion attracts one oxygen ion, forming MgO. Three Mg atoms each lose two

*Use these questions and the test-taking tip to prepare for your standardized test.*

**1.** Which of the following is NOT true of the $Sc^{3+}$ ion?

  **a.** It has the same electron configuration as Ar.
  **b.** It is a scandium ion with three positive charges.
  **c.** It is considered to be a different element than a neutral Sc atom.
  **d.** It was formed by the removal of the valence electrons of Sc.

**2.** Of the salts below, it would require the most energy to break the ionic bonds in

  **a.** $BaCl_2$.          **c.** NaBr.
  **b.** LiF.           **d.** KI.

**3.** What is the correct chemical formula for the ionic compound formed by the calcium ion ($Ca^{2+}$) and the acetate ion ($C_2H_3O_2^-$)?

  **a.** $CaC_2H_3O_2$
  **b.** $CaC_4H_6O_8$
  **c.** $(Ca)_2C_2H_3O_2$
  **d.** $Ca(C_2H_3O_2)_2$

**4.**

The model above has been proposed to explain why

  **a.** metals are shiny, reflective substances.
  **b.** metals are excellent conductors of heat and electricity.
  **c.** ionic compounds are malleable compounds.
  **d.** ionic compounds are good conductors of electricity.

**5.** Yttrium, a metallic element with atomic number 39, will form

  **a.** positive ions.
  **b.** negative ions.
  **c.** both positive and negative ions.
  **d.** no ions at all.

**6.** The high strength of its ionic bonds results in all of the following properties of NaCl EXCEPT

  **a.** hard crystals.
  **b.** high boiling point.
  **c.** high melting point.
  **d.** low solubility.

chemistrymc.com/standardized_test

**Interpreting Tables** Use the table below to answer questions 7–10.

| Properties of Some Ionic Compounds | | | |
|---|---|---|---|
| Compound | Lattice Energy (kJ/mol) | Melting Point (°C) | Color |
| $Ag_2Se$ | −2686 | ? | gray |
| $AlPO_4$ | ? | 1460 | white |
| $FeI_2$ | −2439 | ? | reddish–purple |
| $RbClO_4$ | ? | 281 | white |

**7.** What is the correct name of the compound with the formula $RbClO_4$?

  **a.** rubidium chlorine oxide
  **b.** rubidium chloride tetroxide
  **c.** rubidium perchlorate
  **d.** rubidium chlorate

**8.** Rank the compounds in order of increasing melting point.

  **a.** $Ag_2Se$, $AlPO_4$, $FeI_2$, $RbClO_4$
  **b.** $RbClO_4$, $FeI_2$, $Ag_2Se$, $AlPO_4$
  **c.** $AlPO_4$, $Ag_2Se$, $FeI_2$, $RbClO_4$
  **d.** $RbClO_4$, $AlPO_4$, $Ag_2Se$, $FeI_2$

**9.** Which compound is expected to have the strongest attraction between its ions?

  **a.** $Ag_2Se$
  **b.** $AlPO_4$
  **c.** $FeI_2$
  **d.** $RbClO_4$

**10.** What is the charge on the anion in $AlPO_4$?

  **a.** 2+
  **b.** 3+
  **c.** 2−
  **d.** 3−

---

### TEST-TAKING TIP

**Work Weak Muscles; Maintain Strong Ones** If you're preparing for a standardized test that covers many topics, it's sometimes difficult to focus on all the topics that require your attention. Ask yourself "What's my strongest area?" and "What's my weakest area?" Focus most of your energy on your weaker area and review your stronger topics less frequently.

electrons, forming $Mg^{2+}$, while two N atoms each gain three electrons, forming two $N^{3-}$. The ions attract each other, forming $Mg_3N_2$.

**94.** Sodium metal contains metallic bonds. Sodium chloride is an ionic solid.

**95. a.** calcium oxide
  **b.** barium sulfide
  **c.** aluminum phosphate
  **d.** barium hydroxide
  **e.** strontium nitrate

**96.** $BaS_2O_3$, barium thiosulfate; $BaBr_2$, barium bromide; $Ba(NO_2)_2$, barium nitrite; $Cu_2S_2O_3$, copper(I) thiosulfate; CuBr, copper(I) bromide; $CuNO_2$, copper(I) nitrite; $Al_2(S_2O_3)_3$, aluminum thiosulfate; $AlBr_3$, aluminum bromide; $Al(NO_2)_3$, aluminum nitrite

## Thinking Critically

**97.** Concept maps will vary.
**98. a.** NaCl; smaller ion size
  **b.** Cu; it is smaller.
  **c.** MgO; Mg has a greater charge.
**99.** Cations are formed from the loss of electrons. Anions are formed from gaining electrons.
**100.** Flow charts will vary.
  **a.** Identify the metal as copper(II) or copper(I).
  **b.** The formula unit is not in the simplest ratio.
  **c.** Lead can have only the oxidation state of 2+ or 4+, not 5+.
  **d.** Prefixes are not used in ionic compounds.
  **e.** If a polyatomic ion requires a subscript, use parentheses.
**101.** Calcium has two delocalized electrons for every one for potassium.
**102.** They are free to move.
**103.** They gain electrons. Thus, their electrons are not delocalized.
**104.** Energy given off when bonds form is considered negative.

---

## Cumulative Review

**107.** 2.34 g/mL
**108. a.** $3.44 \times 10^{-19}$ J
  **b.** $5.19 \times 10^{14} \, s^{-1}$
  **c.** $5.78 \times 10^{-7}$ m or 578 nm
**109.** chlorine
**110.** Metals lose electrons to form cations; nonmetals gain electrons to form anions. Both form ions to gain stability.
**111.** the d block elements

**112. a.** Cl, chlorine      **d.** Rn, radon
  **b.** B, boron        **e.** P, phosphorus
  **c.** O, oxygen
**113. a.** Si          **c.** Pb
  **b.** C          **d.** Sn

### Standardized Test Practice

| 1. c | 3. d | 5. a | 7. c | 9. b |
|---|---|---|---|---|
| 2. a | 4. b | 6. d | 8. b | 10. d |

# Resource Manager

| Section | Objectives | Activities/Features |
|---|---|---|
| **Section 9.1**<br>**The Covalent Bond**<br>1 session<br>⬛ 1/2 block | **1. Apply** the octet rule to atoms that bond covalently.<br>**2. Describe** the formation of single, double, and triple covalent bonds.<br>**3. Compare** and **contrast** sigma and pi bonds.<br>**4. Relate** the strength of covalent bonds to bond length and bond dissociation energy. | **Discovery Lab:** Oil and Vinegar Dressing, p. 241 |
| **Section 9.2**<br>**Naming Molecules**<br>1 session<br>⬛ 1/2 block | **5. Identify** the names of binary molecular compounds from their formulas.<br>**6. Name** acidic solutions. | **Careers Using Chemistry:** Organic Chemist, p. 250 |
| **Section 9.3**<br>**Molecular Structures**<br>2 sessions<br>⬛ 1 block | **7. List** five basic steps used in drawing Lewis structures.<br>**8. Explain** why resonance occurs, and **identify** resonance structures.<br>**9. Explain** three exceptions to the octet rule, and **identify** molecules in which these exceptions occur. | |
| **Section 9.4**<br>**Molecular Shape**<br>2 sessions<br>⬛ 1 block | **10. Discuss** the VSEPR bonding theory.<br>**11. Predict** the shape of and the bond angles in a molecule.<br>**12. Define** hybridization. | **MiniLab:** Building VSEPR Models, p. 261 |
| **Section 9.5**<br>**Electronegativity and Polarity**<br>2 sessions<br>⬛ 1 block | **13. Describe** how electronegativity is used to determine bond type.<br>**14. Compare** and **contrast** polar and nonpolar covalent bonds and polar and nonpolar molecules.<br>**15. Describe** the characteristics of compounds that are covalently bonded. | **History Connection,** p. 264<br>**Problem-Solving Lab:** How do dispersion forces determine the boiling point of a substance? p. 267<br>**ChemLab:** Chromatography, pp. 268–269<br>**How It Works:** Microwave Oven, p. 270 |

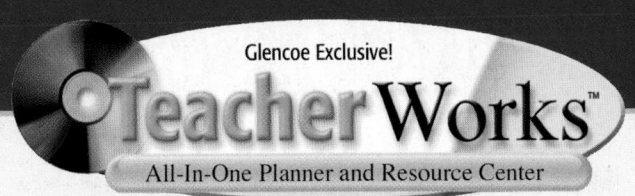

Glencoe Exclusive!
## TeacherWorks™
All-In-One Planner and Resource Center

| National Science Content Standards | State/Local Standards | Reproducible Masters | Transparencies |
|---|---|---|---|
| UCP.2, UCP.3, UCP.5; A.1; B.1, B.2, B.3, B.4, B.6 | | **Study Guide for Content Mastery,** p. 49 L2 | **Section Focus** Transparency 30 L1 ELL |
| UCP.2, UCP.3, UCP.5; B.2; G.2 | | **Study Guide for Content Mastery,** p. 50 L2 | **Section Focus** Transparency 31 L1 ELL **Math Skills** Transparency 9 L2 ELL |
| UCP.2, UCP.3, UCP.5; B.2 | | **Study Guide for Content Mastery,** p. 51 L2 **Challenge Problems,** p. 9 L3 | **Section Focus** Transparency 32 L1 ELL **Teaching** Transparency 29 L2 ELL |
| UCP.2, UCP.3, UCP.5; A.1; B.2, B.4 | | **Study Guide for Content Mastery,** p. 52 L2 **ChemLab and MiniLab Worksheets,** p. 33 L2 **Laboratory Manual,** pp. 65–68 L2 | **Section Focus** Transparency 33 L1 ELL **Teaching** Transparency 30 L2 ELL |
| UCP.2, UCP.3, UCP.5; A.1, A.2; B.1, B.2, B.4, B.6; E.2; G.3 | | **Study Guide for Content Mastery,** pp. 53–54 L2 **ChemLab and MiniLab Worksheets,** pp. 34–36 L2 **Laboratory Manual,** pp. 69–72 L2 | **Section Focus** Transparency 34 L1 ELL **Teaching** Transparency 31 L2 ELL **Math Skills** Transparency 10 L2 ELL |

**Key to National Science Content Standards:** UCP = Unifying Concepts and Processes, A = Science as Inquiry, B = Physical Science, C = Life Science, D = Earth and Space Sciences, E = Science and Technology, F = Science in Personal and Social Perspectives, G = History and Nature of Science

Refer to pages 4T–5T of the Teacher Guide for an explanation of the National Science Content Standards correlations.

# Resource Manager

## Materials List

### ChemLab (pages 268–269)
chromatography paper (3 pieces), 2-L plastic soft-drink bottle, pencils (2), ruler, tape, scissors, aluminum foil, acetone, fresh leaf samples from three different species of deciduous trees or outdoor plants

### Discovery Lab (page 241)
Beral-type pipette, vinegar, cooking oil

### MiniLab (page 261)
regular-sized marshmallows (3), mini-sized marshmallows (9), small gumdrops (3), toothpicks

### Demonstration (pages 248–249)
magnesium ribbon (5 cm), roll sulfur (2 g), tongs, large metal can, deflagrating spoon, laboratory burner

## Preparation of Solutions

For a review of solution preparation, see page 46T of the Teacher Guide.

There are no solutions to be prepared for the activities in this chapter.

## Assessment Resources

**Chapter Assessment,** pp. 49–54
**MindJogger Videoquizzes DVD/VHS**
**Alternate Assessment in the Science Classroom**
**ExamView® Pro CD-ROM**
**Solutions Manual,** Chapter 9
**Supplemental Problems,** Chapter 9
**Performance Assessment in the Science Classroom**
**Chemistry Interactive CD-ROM,** Chapter 9 quiz

## Additional Resources

**Spanish Resources** ELL
**Guided Reading Audio Program,** Chapter 9 ELL
**Cooperative Learning in the Science Classroom**
**Lab and Safety Skills in the Science Classroom**
**Lesson Plans**
**Block Scheduling Lesson Plans**
**Chemistrymc.com**

## Glencoe Technology

The following multimedia for this chapter are available from Glencoe.

 **VIDEOTAPE/DVD**
MindJogger Videoquizzes,
Chapter 9

 **CD-ROM**
**Chemistry: Matter and Change**
*Covalent Bonding,* Animation
*Forming Ionic and Covalent Bonds,*
  Demonstration
*Ionic and Covalent Compounds,* Video
*Lewis Structures,* Video
*Molecular Geometry,* Experiment

 **CD-ROM**
**ExamView® Pro**
  **Testmaker**

 **CD-ROM**
**Interactive Chalkboard**

 **CD-ROM**
**TeacherWorks**™

## Multiple Learning Styles

Look for the following icons for strategies that emphasize different learning modalities.

 **Kinesthetic**
Differentiated Instruction, pp. 246, 264;
Reinforcement, p. 249; Quick Demo, p. 252

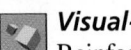 **Visual-Spatial**
Reinforcement, p. 243; Differentiated Instruction,
pp. 244, 255, 260; Check for Understanding, pp. 247, 251,
257, 262; Portfolio, p. 253; Math in Chemistry, p. 260;
Extension, pp. 260, 266

 **Intrapersonal**
Chemistry Journal, pp. 250, 254, 261; Reteach,
p. 251; Portfolio, p. 261

 **Linguistic**
Portfolio, p. 242; Chemistry Journal, p. 243

 **Logical-Mathematical**
Enrichment, p. 246; Extension, p. 247;
Differentiated Instruction, p. 250

## Key to Teaching Strategies

**L1** Level 1 activities should be appropriate for students with
learning difficulties.

**L2** Level 2 activities should be within the ability range of
all students.

**L3** Level 3 activities are designed for above-average students.

**ELL** ELL activities should be within the ability range of
English Language Learners.

**COOP LEARN** Cooperative Learning activities are designed
for small group work.

**P** These strategies represent student products that can be
placed into a best-work portfolio.

These strategies are useful in a block scheduling format.

## ✓ Assessment Planner

**Portfolio Assessment**
Portfolio, TWE, pp. 242, 253,
  261
Assessment, TWE, pp. 265

**Performance Assessment**
Assessment, TWE, pp. 261,
  262
MiniLab, SE, p. 261
ChemLab, SE, pp. 268–269
ChemLab, TWE, p. 269
MiniLab, TWE, p. 261
Discovery Lab, SE, p. 241

**Knowledge Assessment**
Demonstration, TWE, p. 249
Assessment, TWE, pp. 250,
  251, 257, 266, 267
Section Assessment, SE,
  pp. 247, 251, 258, 262, 267
Problem-Solving Lab,
  TWE, p. 267
Chapter Assessment, SE,
  pp. 272–275

**Skill Assessment**
Assessment, TWE, pp. 245,
  247, 258

## Tying to Previous Knowledge

Have students review the following concepts before studying this chapter:
Chapter 4: atomic structure
Chapter 5: electron configuration
Chapter 6: periodic trends
Chapter 7: periodic properties of elements
Chapter 8: ionic bonding

## Using the Photo

Have students look at the photo of a plane crop dusting. Ask them what types of materials the plane might be using. Possible answers include pesticides and fertilizers. Tell them that these materials contain covalent bonds.

### PowerPoint® Presentations
This CD-ROM is an editable Microsoft® PowerPoint® presentation that includes:
• Section presentations
• Section checks
• Image bank
• Links to Chemistry Online
• All transparencies
• Animations
• Audio

**National Science Content Standards**

**Pages 240–241**
UCP.2, UCP.3, UCP.5; A.1; B.1, B.2, B.3

---

# CHAPTER 9

# Covalent Bonding

### What You'll Learn

▶ You will analyze the nature of a covalent bond.
▶ You will name covalently bonded groups of atoms.
▶ You will determine the shapes of molecules.
▶ You will describe characteristics of covalent molecules.
▶ You will compare and contrast polar and nonpolar molecules.

### Why It's Important

Most compounds, including those in living organisms, are covalently bonded.

Visit the Chemistry Web site at chemistrymc.com to find links about covalent bonding.

Herbicides and fertilizers used on crops are covalent compounds.

## DISCOVERY LAB

### Purpose
Students will observe the interaction of polar and nonpolar substances.

### Safety and Disposal
Because oil makes cleanup of the pipette difficult, throw the pipette and its contents in the trash.

### Teaching Strategies
Show students a bottle of oil and vinegar salad dressing to show how the substances separate after shaking.

### Expected Results
After shaking, the mixture appears relatively uniform. After a little time, the two components separate. The oil floats on top of the vinegar.

### Oil and Vinegar Dressing

**W**hen preparing a meal, you combine different types of food. But when you mix different substances, do they always "mix"? How about making oil and vinegar dressing for tonight's salad?

#### Safety Precautions

#### Procedure

1. Fill the bulb of a Beral-type pipet about 1/3 full of vinegar and 1/3 full of vegetable oil. Shake the pipet and its contents. Record your observations.
2. Allow the contents to sit for about five minutes. Record your observations.

#### Analysis

Do oil and vinegar mix? What explanation can you give for your observations in this experiment? Why do the instructions on many types of salad dressings read "shake well before using"?

**Materials**
Beral-type pipette
vinegar
vegetable oil

---

## Section 9.1 — The Covalent Bond

### Objectives

- **Apply** the octet rule to atoms that bond covalently.
- **Describe** the formation of single, double, and triple covalent bonds.
- **Compare** and **contrast** sigma and pi bonds.
- **Relate** the strength of covalent bonds to bond length and bond dissociation energy.

### Vocabulary

covalent bond
molecule
Lewis structure
sigma bond
pi bond
endothermic
exothermic

Worldwide, scientists are studying ways to increase food supplies, reduce pollution, and prevent disease. Understanding the chemistry of compounds that make up fertilizers, pollutants, and materials that carry genetic information is essential in developing new technologies in these areas. An understanding of the chemistry of compounds requires an understanding of their bonding.

### Why do atoms bond?

You learned in Chapter 6 that all noble gases have particularly stable electron arrangements. This stable arrangement consists of a full outer energy level. A full outer energy level consists of two valence electrons for helium and eight valence electrons for all other noble gases. Because of this stability, noble gases, in general, don't react with other elements to form compounds.

You also learned in Chapter 8 that when metals and nonmetals react to form binary ionic compounds, electrons are transferred, and the resulting ions have noble-gas electron configurations. But sometimes two atoms that both need to gain valence electrons to become stable have a similar attraction for electrons. Sharing of electrons is another way that these atoms can acquire the electron configuration of noble gases. Recall from Chapter 6 that the octet rule states that atoms lose, gain, or share electrons to achieve a stable configuration of eight valence electrons, or an octet. Although exceptions to the octet rule exist, the rule provides a useful framework for understanding chemical bonds.

9.1 The Covalent Bond    **241**

---

## Section 9.1

## 1 Focus

### Focus Transparency

Before presenting the lesson, display **Section Focus Transparency 30** on the overhead projector. Have students answer the accompanying questions using **Section Focus Transparency Master 30. L1 ELL**

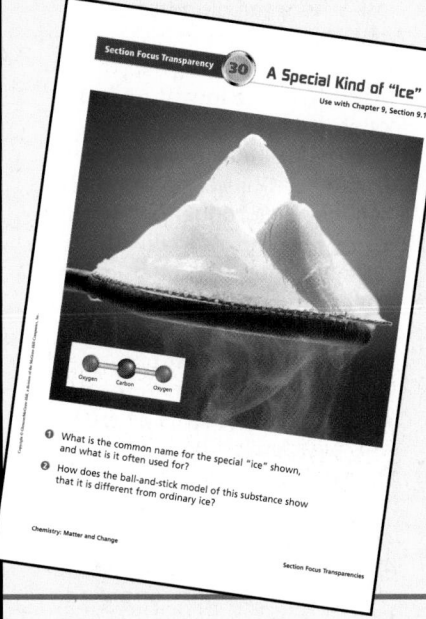

### Chapter Themes

The following themes from the National Science Education Standards are covered in this chapter. Refer to page 4T of the Teacher Guide for an explanation of the correlations.
Systems, order, and organization (UCP.1)
Evidence, models, and explanation (UCP.2)

---

### Analysis

The oil and vinegar separate immediately. Explanations might include that oil and vinegar are different types of liquids. The oil and vinegar separate in the salad dressing bottle, so they need to be shaken to mix just before pouring onto a salad.

### Resource Manager

**Study Guide for Content Mastery,** p. 49 L2
**Solving Problems: A Chemistry Handbook,** Section 9.1 L2
**Section Focus Transparency 30 and Master L1 ELL**

The atoms that make up molecules achieve their lowest potential energy state when they form covalent bonds. Remind students of the definition of potential energy.

Use the following demonstration to relate potential energy to stability. Hang a foam rubber ball from a string or spring to form a pendulum and ask where the highest potential energy position is. where the pendulum is pulled up Ask where the lowest potential energy would be found. where the pendulum hangs without any force being applied Use a second foam rubber ball to form a second pendulum next to the first one. Show students that the two pendulums can be pulled apart or pushed together. The lowest potential energy occurs when no force is applied. Ask students where this position is. where the pendulums hang without any outside force Remind students that the potential energy increases when the pendulums are pushed together or pulled apart.

## Visual Learning

**Figure 9-1** Have students look at the figure and discuss the potential energy change as the fluorine atoms approach each other in terms of attractive forces and repulsive forces. When the attractive force equals the repulsive force, a bond forms. If the repulsive force is greater, no bond forms and the atoms stay separated. **L2**

**GLENCOE
TECHNOLOGY**

CD-ROM
**Chemistry: Matter and Change**
Animation: *Covalent Bonding*

242

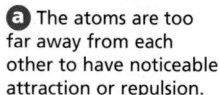

**a** The atoms are too far away from each other to have noticeable attraction or repulsion.

**b** Each nucleus attracts the other atom's electron cloud, but the electron clouds repel each other.

**c** The distance is right for the attraction of one atom's protons for the other atom's electrons to make the bond stable.

**d** If the atoms are forced closer together, the nuclei and electrons repel.

**Figure 9-1**

The overall force between two atoms is the result of electron-electron repulsion, nucleus-nucleus repulsion, and nucleus-electron attraction. The arrows in this diagram show the net force acting on two fluorine atoms as they move toward each other.

## What is a covalent bond?

You know that certain atoms, such as magnesium and chlorine, transfer electrons from one atom to another, forming an ionic bond. However, the number of ionic compounds is quite small compared with the total number of known compounds. What type of bonding is found in all these other compounds that are not ionically bonded?

The atoms in these other compounds share electrons. The chemical bond that results from the sharing of valence electrons is a **covalent bond.** In a covalent bond, the shared electrons are considered to be part of the complete outer energy level of both atoms involved. Covalent bonding generally occurs when elements are relatively close to each other on the periodic table. The majority of covalent bonds form between nonmetallic elements.

A **molecule** is formed when two or more atoms bond covalently. The carbohydrates and simple sugars you eat; the proteins, fats, and DNA found in your body; and the wool, cotton, and synthetic fibers in the clothes you wear all consist of molecules formed from covalently bonded atoms.

**Formation of a covalent bond** Hydrogen ($H_2$), nitrogen ($N_2$), oxygen ($O_2$), fluorine ($F_2$), chlorine ($Cl_2$), bromine ($Br_2$), and iodine ($I_2$) occur in nature as diatomic molecules, not as single atoms because the molecules formed are more stable than the indiviual atoms. How do two atoms that do not give up electrons bond with each other?

Consider fluorine ($F_2$), which has an electron configuration of $1s^2 2s^2 2p^5$. Each fluorine atom has seven valence electrons and must have one additional electron to form an octet. As two fluorine atoms approach each other, as shown in **Figure 9-1**, two forces become important. A repulsive force occurs between the like-charged electrons and between the like-charged protons of the two atoms. An attractive force also occurs between the protons of one fluorine atom and the electrons of the other atom. As the fluorine atoms move closer, the attraction of both nuclei for the other atom's electrons increases until the maximum attraction is achieved. At the point of maximum attraction, the attractive forces balance the repulsive forces.

If the two nuclei move even closer, the repulsion between the like-charged nuclei and electron clouds will increase, resulting in repulsive forces that exceed attractive forces. Thus the most stable arrangement of atoms exists at the point of maximum attraction. At that point, the two atoms bond covalently and a molecule forms. Fluorine exists as a diatomic molecule because the sharing of one pair of electrons will give both fluorine atoms stable noble gas configurations. Each fluorine atom in the fluorine molecule has one bonding pair of electrons and three *lone pairs*, which are unshared pairs of electrons.

**Portfolio**

### Bonding Limerick

*Linguistic* Read students a limerick that appeared in *Chem 13 News,* May 1988, p. 7.
Bond formation can me unwell
(Electrons join up in a shell)
For it doesn't seem fine
To say they combine
When we know very well they repel!

Have students develop limericks, poems, or rhymes that depict some aspect of covalent bonds and place them in their portfolios.
**L2** **P**

## Single Covalent Bonds

Consider the formation of a hydrogen molecule, which is shown in **Figure 9-2**. Each covalently bonded atom equally attracts one pair of shared electrons. Thus, two electrons shared by two hydrogen nuclei belong to each atom simultaneously. Both hydrogen atoms have the noble gas configuration of helium ($1s^2$). The hydrogen molecule is more stable than individual hydrogen atoms.

When a single pair of electrons is shared, such as in a hydrogen molecule, a single covalent bond forms. The shared electron pair, often referred to as the bonding pair, is represented by either a pair of dots or a line in the Lewis structure for the molecule. **Lewis structures** use electron-dot diagrams to show how electrons are arranged in molecules. For example, a hydrogen molecule is represented as H : H or H—H. Hydrogen gas also is represented by the molecular formula $H_2$, which reflects the number of atoms in each molecule.

As you have seen, the halogens—group 7A elements—such as fluorine, have seven valence electrons. To attain an octet, one more electron is necessary. Therefore, group 7A elements will form a single covalent bond. You have seen how an atom from group 7A will form a covalent bond with another identical atom. Fluorine exists as $F_2$. Similarly, chlorine exists as $Cl_2$, bromine as $Br_2$, and iodine as $I_2$ because the molecule formed is more stable than the individual atoms. In addition, such bonds are often formed between the halogen and another element, such as carbon.

Group 6A elements share two electrons to form two covalent bonds. Oxygen is a group 6A element with an electron configuration of $1s^2 2s^2 2p^4$. Water is composed of two hydrogen atoms and one oxygen atom. Each hydrogen atom attains the noble gas configuration of helium as it shares one electron with oxygen. Oxygen, in turn, attains the noble gas configuration of neon by sharing one electron with each hydrogen atom. **Figure 9-3a** shows the Lewis structure for a molecule of water. Notice that two single covalent bonds are formed and two lone pairs remain on the oxygen atom.

Likewise, group 5A elements form three covalent bonds with atoms of non-metals. Nitrogen is a group 5A element with the electron configuration of $1s^2 2s^2 2p^3$. Ammonia ($NH_3$) contains three single covalent bonds and one lone pair of electrons on the nitrogen atom. **Figure 9-3b** shows the Lewis structure

**Figure 9-2**

By sharing a pair of electrons, these hydrogen atoms have a full outer electron energy level and are stable. Refer to **Table C-1** in Appendix C for a key to atom color conventions.

**Figure 9-3**

These chemical equations show how atoms share electrons to become stable. As can be seen by the Lewis structures (left side) for the molecules, after a reaction, all atoms in the molecules are stable according to the octet rule.

9.1 The Covalent Bond **243**

## Concept Development

It is important for students to understand that electrons are identical regardless of which atom or energy level is their source. Students must also understand that electrons in the electron cloud are not static. They move at nearly the speed of light, yet are attracted to the positively charged nucleus. When a covalent bond forms, nuclei of both atoms contribute to the force that attracts the electrons. A single atom does not have sole ownership of the shared electrons.

## Reinforcement

*Visual-Spatial* Review the electron dot diagrams used in Chapter 8. Point out that covalent bonds can be represented in a variety of ways.

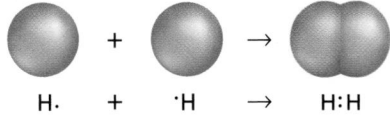

## CHEMISTRY JOURNAL

### Why Covalent Bonds Form

*Linguistic* Have students write a paragraph explaining why a covalent bond can form between a chlorine atom and a fluorine atom. **L2**

National Science Content Standards
Pages 242–243
UCP.2, UCP.3, UCP.5; B.1, B.2, B.3

Have students refer to Appendix D for complete solutions to Practice Problems.

**1.**

:Ö:
:Ö—Cl—

**2.** H—S̈:
        |
        H

**3.** H—C̈l:

**4.** :C̈l:
   :C̈l—C—C̈l:
        :C̈l:

**5.**     H
           |
      H—Si—H
           |
           H

## Concept Development

Students must understand that each orbital can contain only two electrons at any one time. If an orbital has only one electron, it can share electrons only with another orbital that has one electron. A double covalent bond involves two orbitals sharing four electrons between two atoms. When drawing an electron dot diagram, remind students that the bonding electrons are always rotated into the space between the elements. A triple covalent bond involves three orbitals sharing six electrons between two atoms.

**National Science Content Standards**

**Pages 244–245**
UCP.2, UCP.3, UCP.5; B.1, B.2, B.4

**244**

for an ammonia molecule. Nitrogen also forms similar compounds with group 7A elements, such as nitrogen trifluoride ($NF_3$), nitrogen trichloride ($NCl_3$), and nitrogen tribromide ($NBr_3$). Each of these group 7A atoms shares a pair of electrons with the nitrogen atom.

Group 4A elements will form four covalent bonds. A methane molecule ($CH_4$) is formed when one carbon atom bonds with four hydrogen atoms. Carbon, a group 4A element, has an electron configuration of $1s^22s^22p^2$. With four valence electrons, it must obtain four more electrons for a noble gas configuration. Therefore, when carbon bonds with other atoms, it forms four bonds. Because hydrogen, a group 1A element, has one valence electron, four hydrogen atoms are necessary to provide the four electrons needed by the carbon atom. The Lewis structure for methane is shown in **Figure 9-3c**. Carbon also forms single covalent bonds with other nonmetals, including group 7A elements.

### EXAMPLE PROBLEM 9-1

**Lewis Structure for a Molecule**

Hydrogen bromide (HBr) is used to manufacture several other bromides and has been medically used as a sedative. Draw the Lewis structure for this molecule.

**1. Analyze the Problem**

You are given that hydrogen and bromine form the molecule hydrogen bromide. Hydrogen, a group 1A element, has only one valence electron. Therefore, when hydrogen bonds with any nonmetal, it must share one pair of electrons. Bromine, a group 7A element, also needs one electron to complete its octet. Hydrogen and bromine bond with each other by one single covalent bond.

**2. Solve for the Unknown**

To draw the Lewis structure, first draw the electron-dot structure for each of the two atoms. Then show the sharing of the pairs of electrons by a single line.

H· + ·B̈r: → H—B̈r:
Hydrogen   Bromine   Hydrogen bromide
atom       atom      molecule

**3. Evaluate the Answer**

Each atom in the molecule has achieved a noble gas configuration and thus is stable.

When hydrogen bromide is dissolved in water, hydrobromic acid forms. This acid must be kept in a dark bottle because it decomposes when exposed to light.

### PRACTICE PROBLEMS

Draw the Lewis structure for each of these molecules.
**1.** $PH_3$
**2.** $H_2S$
**3.** HCl
**4.** $CCl_4$
**5.** $SiH_4$

Practice! For more practice with drawing Lewis structures, go to **Supplemental Practice Problems** in Appendix A.

### DIFFERENTIATED INSTRUCTION

#### Learning Disabled

**Visual-Spatial** Using a piece of acetate, draw circles to represent atoms. In each circle, represent a single atom by using its electron dot diagram. Show students two F atoms, and ask what each one needs to become stable. one electron Overlap the circles so each F atom has eight electrons and ask students how many electrons each atom has. eight Tell students that the shared electrons form a covalent bond. Overlap two H atoms and one O atom. Ask students how many electrons O has. eight How many electrons does each H atom have? two Ask students if H is stable with two electrons. Yes, because it has the noble gas configuration of He. Ask students how many bonds are formed. two single covalent bonds **L1**

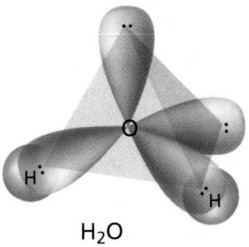

CH₄                          NH₃                          H₂O

**Figure 9-4**

The sigma bonds form in these molecules as the atomic orbitals of hydrogen atoms overlap end to end with the orbitals of the central atoms.

**The sigma bond** Single covalent bonds also are called **sigma bonds,** symbolized by the Greek letter sigma ($\sigma$). A sigma bond occurs when the electron pair is shared in an area centered between the two atoms. When two atoms share electrons, the valence atomic orbital of one atom overlaps or merges with the valence atomic orbital of the other atom. A sigma bond results if the atomic orbitals overlap end to end, concentrating the electrons in a bonding orbital between the two atoms. A bonding orbital is a localized region where bonding electrons will most likely be found. **Figure 9-4** indicates the sigma bonds found in methane ($CH_4$), ammonia ($NH_3$), and water ($H_2O$). Sigma bonds can form from the overlap of an s orbital with another s orbital, an s orbital with a p orbital, or a p orbital with another p orbital. Does hydrogen use s or p orbitals to form bonds in **Figure 9-4**?

## Multiple Covalent Bonds

In many molecules, atoms attain a noble-gas configuration by sharing more than one pair of electrons between two atoms, forming a multiple covalent bond. Atoms of the elements carbon, nitrogen, oxygen, and sulfur most often form multiple bonds. How do you know when two atoms will form a multiple bond? The number of valence electrons of an element is associated with the number of shared electron pairs needed to complete the octet and gives a clue as to how many covalent bonds can form.

Double and triple covalent bonds are examples of multiple bonds. A double covalent bond occurs when two pairs of electrons are shared. The atoms in an oxygen molecule ($O_2$) share two electron pairs, forming a double bond. Each oxygen atom has six valence electrons and must obtain two additional electrons for a noble-gas configuration. If each oxygen atom shares two electrons, a total of two pairs of electrons is shared between the two atoms. A double covalent bond results. See **Figure 9-5a**.

A triple covalent bond is formed when three pairs of electrons are shared between two atoms. Nitrogen ($N_2$) shares three electron pairs, producing a triple bond. One nitrogen atom needs three additional electrons to attain a noble-gas configuration. **Figure 9-5b** shows the triple bond formed between two nitrogen atoms.

**ⓐ** $:\ddot{O}\cdot \; + \; \cdot\ddot{O}: \; \rightarrow \; :\ddot{O}=\ddot{O}:$

**ⓑ** $:\dot{N}\cdot \; + \; \cdot\dot{N}: \; \rightarrow \; :N\equiv N:$

**Figure 9-5**

Multiple bonds form when more than one pair of electrons are shared. **ⓐ** The two pairs of electrons shared by oxygen atoms form a double bond. **ⓑ** Nitrogen shares three pairs of electrons, forming a triple bond.

9.1 The Covalent Bond    **245**

## Concept Development

An important factor in determining the chemical reactivity of a molecule is the strength of the covalent bonds holding the molecule together. When comparing two molecules with similar composition, the one with weaker bonds is usually more reactive. Have students compare the bond energies of the molecules $CH_3Cl$ and $CH_2Cl_2$. 1567 kJ/mol, 1482 kJ/mol Ask students which molecule is more likely to react. $CH_2Cl_2$ **L2**

## ✔ Assessment

**Skill** Divide students into groups. Hand each group a set of cards that contain electron dot diagrams of atoms. The set should include two carbon atoms, two nitrogen atoms, two oxygen atoms, six hydrogen atoms, and four chlorine atoms. Place a hydrogen card next to a chlorine card. Show students that by sharing a pair of electrons each atom obtains a stable outer electron configuration. Have students determine the Lewis structure for as many molecules as possible by combining the cards. Remind students that multiple bonds are possible with carbon, nitrogen, and oxygen atoms. **L2** **ELL**

## In-Text Question

**Page 245** Does hydrogen use s or p orbitals to form bonds in Figure 9-4? s orbital

## Content Background

**Exceptional Oxygen** Spins of unpaired electrons in atoms or ions cause a substance to be paramagnetic, that is, attracted to an external magnetic field. A substance is diamagnetic, unaffected by the magnetic field, if all of the electrons are paired. Although the Lewis structure and bond strength for diatomic oxygen indicates there is a double bond between the two atoms, oxygen exhibits exceptional behavior in the laboratory. It is paramagnetic. The electrons associated with the $\pi$ bond have unpaired, or parallel, spins.

## Enrichment

*Logical-Mathematical* To calculate the change in enthalpy of a chemical reaction, the equation $\triangle H = \sum$(bond energies of broken bonds) $- \sum$(bond energies of formed bonds) is used. Have students determine the total enthalpy change when $Cl_2$ reacts with $CH_4$ to form $CH_3Cl$ and $HCl$. Have them draw the Lewis structures of the molecules and predict which bonds are broken and which are formed. Bonds broken are one Cl—Cl and four C—H. Bonds formed are one H—Cl, three C—H, and one C—Cl. The enthalpy change is −104 kJ. A negative enthalpy change indicates that the reaction is exothermic, and the bonds in the product molecules are stronger than the bonds in the reactant molecules. **L3**

## In-Text Questions

**Page 247** Based on bond length, which of these three molecules would you predict to have the greatest bond energy? $N_2$ The least? $F_2$ Do the bond dissociation energies supplied in the previous paragraph confirm your predictions? Yes

---

**Figure 9-6**

Notice how the multiple bond between carbon atoms in ethene ($C_2H_4$) consists of one sigma bond and one pi bond. The carbon atoms are close enough that the side-by-side p orbitals overlap. The p-overlap that forms the pi bond results in a donut-shaped cloud around the sigma bond.

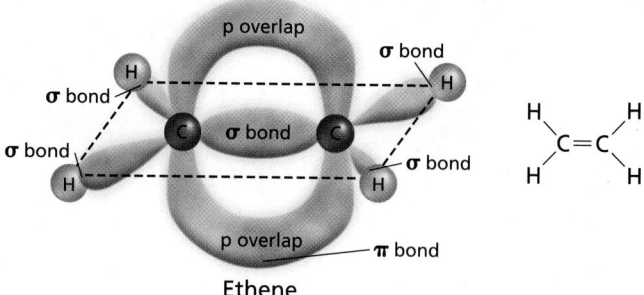

Ethene

**The pi bond** A **pi bond**, denoted by the Greek symbol pi ($\pi$), is formed when parallel orbitals overlap to share electrons, as shown in **Figure 9-6**. The shared electron pair of a pi bond occupies the space above and below the line that represents where the two atoms are joined together. A multiple bond consists of one sigma bond and at least one pi bond. A double covalent bond has one sigma bond and one pi bond. A triple covalent bond consists of one sigma bond and two pi bonds. See **Figure 9-6**. A pi bond always accompanies a sigma bond when forming double and triple bonds.

## Strength of Covalent Bonds

Remember that a covalent bond involves attractive and repulsive forces. In a molecule, nuclei and electrons attract each other, but nuclei repel other nuclei, and electrons repel other electrons. When this balance of forces is upset, the covalent bond can be broken. Some covalent bonds are broken more easily than others because they differ in strength. Several factors control the strength of covalent bonds.

The strength of a covalent bond depends on how much distance separates bonded nuclei. The distance between the two bonding nuclei at the position of maximum attraction is called *bond length*, which is determined by the size of the atoms and how many electron pairs are shared. See **Figure 9-7**. The bond length of the single bond in an $F_2$ molecule is $1.43 \times 10^{-10}$ m. The bond length of the double bond in $O_2$ is $1.21 \times 10^{-10}$ m. The bond length of the triple bond in $N_2$ is $1.10 \times 10^{-10}$ m. Although the sizes of the atoms are not the same, not much difference exists in the size of these molecules. How does the number of pairs of electrons shared in $F_2$, $O_2$, and $N_2$ relate to the bond lengths in each of these molecules? As the number of shared electron pairs increases, bond length decreases. A triple bond, sharing three electron pairs, has a shorter bond length than a single bond where only two electrons are shared. The shorter the bond length, the stronger the bond. Thus, single bonds, such as those in $F_2$, are weaker than double bonds, such as those in $O_2$. Double bonds are weaker than triple bonds, such as those in $N_2$.

An energy change accompanies the forming or breaking of a bond between atoms in a molecule. Energy is released when a bond forms. Energy must be added to break the bonds in a molecule. The amount of energy required to break a specific covalent bond is called *bond dissociation energy*. Breaking bonds always requires the addition of energy. Thus, bond dissociation energy is always a positive value. The bond dissociation energy of $F_2$ is 159 kJ/mol, of $O_2$ is 498 kJ/mol, and of $N_2$ is 945 kJ/mol. The sum of the bond dissociation energy values for all bonds in a compound is used to determine the

**Figure 9-7**

Bond length is the distance from the center of one nucleus to the center of the other nucleus of two bonded atoms.

---

**DIFFERENTIATED INSTRUCTION**

### Learning Disabled

*Kinesthetic* Have students place a single toothpick between two gumdrops to form a single bond. Then have them break 1 cm off each of two toothpicks, and place them between two gumdrops to form a double bond. Then have them break 2 cm off each of three toothpicks, and place them between two gumdrops to represent a triple bond. Have students identify the shortest and longest bonds. Ask students to carefully break the bonds to determine which bond is easiest and which is the most difficult to break. A triple bond is the shortest, is the most difficult to break, and has the highest bond energy. The single bond is the longest, is the easiest to break, and has the lowest bond energy. **L1** **ELL** amount of chemical potential energy available in a molecule of that compound.

Bond dissociation energy indicates the strength of a chemical bond because a direct relationship exists between bond energy and bond length. As two atoms are bonded closer together, greater amounts of bond energy are needed to separate them. Think back to the relative bond lengths of $F_2$, $O_2$, and $N_2$. Based on bond length, which of these three molecules would you predict to have the greatest bond energy? The least? Do the bond dissociation energies supplied in the previous paragraph confirm your predictions?

In chemical reactions, bonds in reactant molecules are broken and new bonds are formed as product molecules form. See **Figure 9-8.** The total energy change of the chemical reaction is determined from the energy of the bonds broken and formed. **Endothermic** reactions occur when a greater amount of energy is required to break the existing bonds in the reactants than is released when the new bonds form in the product molecules. **Exothermic** reactions occur when more energy is released forming new bonds than is required to break bonds in the initial reactants. You will learn more about energy and chemical processes in Chapter 16.

**Figure 9-8**

Energy is used to break C–C bonds in coal and O–O bonds of oxygen in air. Energy is released as heat and light due to the formation of $CO_2$. Coal burning is an exothermic reaction.

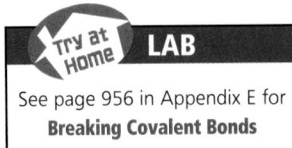

Try at Home **LAB**

See page 956 in Appendix E for
**Breaking Covalent Bonds**

## Section 9.1 Assessment

6. What is a covalent bond? How does it differ from an ionic bond?

7. What is a single covalent bond? Why does it form?

8. Why do multiple bonds form?

9. What is the difference between a sigma bond and a pi bond?

10. How is bond length related to bond dissociation energy?

11. **Thinking Critically** From the following structures, predict the relative bond energies needed to break all of the bonds present.

 **a.** H—C ≡ C—H       **b.**

$$\begin{array}{ccc} H & & H \\ & C = C & \\ H & & H \end{array}$$

12. **Making Predictions** Draw the electron-dot diagrams for the elements sulfur, carbon, bromine, oxygen, and hydrogen. Using Lewis structures, predict the number of covalent bonds formed when
 **a.** one atom of sulfur bonds with two atoms of hydrogen.
 **b.** one atom of carbon bonds with two atoms of sulfur.
 **c.** two atoms of bromine bond with one atom of sulfur.
 **d.** one atom of carbon bonds with four atoms of bromine
 **e.** one atom of sulfur bonds with two atoms of oxygen.

# 3 Assess
## Check for Understanding

 **Visual-Spatial** Ask students to draw the Lewis structure for the molecule $H_2S$.

$$H—\overset{\cdot\cdot}{\underset{|}{S}}:$$
$$H$$

## Reteach

Draw the structural formulas for $C_2H_6$, $C_2H_4$, and $C_2H_2$. Ask students to identify all sigma and pi bonds. Using a table of bond energies and bond length, compare the bond lengths and bond energies of C—C, C=C, and C≡C. Remind students that as the number of bonds between two atoms increases, the bond length becomes shorter and the bond itself becomes stronger.

## Extension

**Logical-Mathematical** Have interested students research trinitrotoluene (TNT) and determine the available bond energy if all bonds in a molecule of this compound were broken. **L3**

## ✓ Assessment

**Skill** Give groups of students note cards with the formulas for the molecules $NCl_3$, $CF_2Cl_2$, and $SiO_2$ on one side. Have the students draw the covalent bonds formed and identify all sigma and pi bonds. **L2**
**COOP LEARN**

**National Science Content Standards**

**Pages 246–247**
UCP.2, UCP.3, UCP.5; B.2, B.4, B.6

## Section 9.1 Assessment

6. Two atoms share electrons. An ionic bond forms when electrons are transferred between atoms.

7. One pair of electrons is shared between two atoms so each atom can achieve an octet through sharing.

8. More than one pair of electrons are shared between two atoms because each atom needs more than one electron to form an octet.

9. A sigma bond is a single covalent bond formed from the direct overlap of orbitals. A pi bond is the parallel overlap of p orbitals.

10. As bond length decreases, bond dissociation energy increases.

11. **a.** C—H: less energy than C≡C
 **b.** C—H: less energy  than C=C

12. See Solutions Manual.
 **a.** two H—S bonds
 **b.** four; two C=S double bonds
 **c.** two S—Br bonds
 **d.** four C—Br bonds
 **e.** one S—O single bond; one S—O double bond

**247**

Choose three students to represent atoms in the polyatomic ion $NO_2^-$. Arrange the three students in a sequence with the nitrogen atom as the central atom. One bond is a double bond and the other bond is a single bond. Ask students to determine the resonance structures. Place blue dye and red dye in separate containers to represent the two structures. Mix the dyes and have students notice that the resulting color is not red or blue but an intermediate of the two colors. A resonance hybrid is the intermediate of the two individual structures. **L1**
**ELL**

## Practice PROBLEMS

Have students refer to Appendix D for complete solutions to Practice Problems.

**35.**
$$\left[ :\ddot{O}=S-\ddot{O}: \atop \quad\quad | \atop \quad\quad :\ddot{O}: \right]^{2-}$$

$$\left[ :\ddot{O}-S=\ddot{O}: \atop \quad\quad | \atop \quad\quad :\ddot{O}: \right]^{2-}$$

$$\left[ :\ddot{O}-S-\ddot{O}: \atop \quad\quad \| \atop \quad\quad :\ddot{O}: \right]^{2-}$$

**36.** $:\ddot{O}=S:$
$\quad\quad |$
$\quad\quad :\ddot{O}:$

$:\ddot{O}-S:$
$\quad\quad \|$
$\quad\quad :\ddot{O}:$

**37.** $:\ddot{O}-O=\ddot{O}:$

$:\ddot{O}=O-\ddot{O}:$

**38.**
$$\left[ :\ddot{O}=\ddot{N} \atop \quad\quad | \atop \quad\quad :\ddot{O}: \right]^{-}$$

$$\left[ :\ddot{O}-\ddot{N} \atop \quad\quad \| \atop \quad\quad :\ddot{O}: \right]^{-}$$

### Figure 9-11

The nitrate ion ($NO_3^-$) exhibits resonance. **ⓐ** These resonance structures differ only in the location of the double bond. The locations of the nitrogen and oxygen atoms stay the same. **ⓑ** The actual nitrate ion is like an average of the three resonance structures in **ⓐ**. The dotted line indicates possible locations of the double bond.

## Resonance Structures

Using the same sequence of atoms, it is possible to have more than one correct Lewis structure when a molecule or polyatomic ion has both a double bond and a single bond. Consider the polyatomic ion nitrate ($NO_3^-$) shown in **Figure 9-11a**. Three equivalent structures can be used to represent the nitrate ion. **Resonance** is a condition that occurs when more than one valid Lewis structure can be written for a molecule or ion. The two or more correct Lewis structures that represent a single molecule or ion are often referred to as *resonance structures*. Resonance structures differ only in the position of the electron pairs, never the atom positions. The location of the lone pairs and bonding pairs differs in resonance structures. The molecule $O_3$ and the polyatomic ions $NO_3^-$, $NO_2^-$, $SO_3^{2-}$ and $CO_3^{2-}$ commonly form resonance structures.

It is important to note that each actual molecule or ion that undergoes resonance behaves as if it has only one structure. See **Figure 9-11b**. Experimentally measured bond lengths show that the bonds are identical to each other. They are shorter than single bonds but longer than double bonds. The actual bond length is an average of the bonds in the resonance structures.

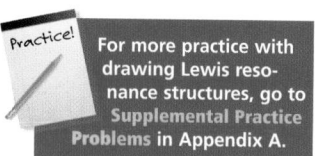

Practice! For more practice with drawing Lewis resonance structures, go to **Supplemental Practice Problems in Appendix A.**

## PRACTICE PROBLEMS

Draw the Lewis resonance structures for the following.

**35.** $SO_3$          **37.** $O_3$

**36.** $SO_2$          **38.** $NO_2^-$

## Exceptions to the Octet Rule

The Lewis structure is focused on the attainment of an octet by all atoms when they bond with other elements. Some molecules and ions, however, do not obey the octet rule. Three reasons exist for these exceptions.

First, a small group of molecules has an odd number of valence electrons and cannot form an octet around each atom. For example, $NO_2$ has five valence electrons from nitrogen and 12 from oxygen, totaling 17, which cannot form an exact number of electron pairs. $ClO_2$ and $NO$ are other examples of molecules with odd numbers of valence electrons.

$$:\ddot{O}-\overset{\textstyle\cdot}{N}=\ddot{O}:$$

## Internet Address Book

 Chemistry Online    Note Internet addresses that you find useful in the space below for quick reference.

amount of chemical potential energy available in a molecule of that compound.

Bond dissociation energy indicates the strength of a chemical bond because a direct relationship exists between bond energy and bond length. As two atoms are bonded closer together, greater amounts of bond energy are needed to separate them. Think back to the relative bond lengths of $F_2$, $O_2$, and $N_2$. Based on bond length, which of these three molecules would you predict to have the greatest bond energy? The least? Do the bond dissociation energies supplied in the previous paragraph confirm your predictions?

In chemical reactions, bonds in reactant molecules are broken and new bonds are formed as product molecules form. See **Figure 9-8.** The total energy change of the chemical reaction is determined from the energy of the bonds broken and formed. **Endothermic** reactions occur when a greater amount of energy is required to break the existing bonds in the reactants than is released when the new bonds form in the product molecules. **Exothermic** reactions occur when more energy is released forming new bonds than is required to break bonds in the initial reactants. You will learn more about energy and chemical processes in Chapter 16.

**Figure 9-8**
Energy is used to break C–C bonds in coal and O–O bonds of oxygen in air. Energy is released as heat and light due to the formation of $CO_2$. Coal burning is an exothermic reaction.

Try at Home **LAB**
See page 956 in Appendix E for
**Breaking Covalent Bonds**

 **Section 9.1 Assessment**

6. What is a covalent bond? How does it differ from an ionic bond?

7. What is a single covalent bond? Why does it form?

8. Why do multiple bonds form?

9. What is the difference between a sigma bond and a pi bond?

10. How is bond length related to bond dissociation energy?

11. **Thinking Critically** From the following structures, predict the relative bond energies needed to break all of the bonds present.

a. $H—C \equiv C—H$     b.
$$
\begin{array}{cc}
H & H \\
\backslash & / \\
C & = C \\
/ & \backslash \\
H & H
\end{array}
$$

12. **Making Predictions** Draw the electron-dot diagrams for the elements sulfur, carbon, bromine, oxygen, and hydrogen. Using Lewis structures, predict the number of covalent bonds formed when

a. one atom of sulfur bonds with two atoms of hydrogen.

b. one atom of carbon bonds with two atoms of sulfur.

c. two atoms of bromine bond with one atom of sulfur.

d. one atom of carbon bonds with four atoms of bromine

e. one atom of sulfur bonds with two atoms of oxygen.

chemistrymc.com/self_check_quiz

9.1 The Covalent Bond     **247**

**Check for Understanding**

 **Visual-Spatial** Ask students to draw the Lewis structure for the molecule $H_2S$.

$$H—\overset{\displaystyle ..}{\underset{\displaystyle |}{S}}:$$
$$H$$

**Reteach**

Draw the structural formulas for $C_2H_6$, $C_2H_4$, and $C_2H_2$. Ask students to identify all sigma and pi bonds. Using a table of bond energies and bond length, compare the bond lengths and bond energies of C—C, C=C, and C≡C. Remind students that as the number of bonds between two atoms increases, the bond length becomes shorter and the bond itself becomes stronger.

**Extension**

**Logical-Mathematical** Have interested students research trinitrotoluene (TNT) and determine the available bond energy if all bonds in a molecule of this compound were broken. **L3**

✔ **Assessment**
**Skill** Give groups of students note cards with the formulas for the molecules $NCl_3$, $CF_2Cl_2$, and $SiO_2$ on one side. Have the students draw the covalent bonds formed and identify all sigma and pi bonds. **L2**
**COOP LEARN**

**National Science Content Standards**
**Pages 246–247**
UCP.2, UCP.3, UCP.5; B.2, B.4, B.6

---

**Section 9.1 Assessment**

6. Two atoms share electrons. An ionic bond forms when electrons are transferred between atoms.

7. One pair of electrons is shared between two atoms so each atom can achieve an octet through sharing.

8. More than one pair of electrons are shared between two atoms because each atom needs more than one electron to form an octet.

9. A sigma bond is a single covalent bond formed from the direct overlap of orbitals. A pi bond is the parallel overlap of p orbitals.

10. As bond length decreases, bond dissociation energy increases.

11. a. C—H: less energy than C≡C
    b. C—H: less energy   than C=C

12. See Solutions Manual.
    a. two H—S bonds
    b. four; two C=S double bonds
    c. two S—Br bonds
    d. four C—Br bonds
    e. one S—O single bond; one S—O double bond

**247**

# 1 Focus

Section **9.2**

## Naming Molecules

### Focus Transparency

Before presenting the lesson, display **Section Focus Transparency 31** on the overhead projector. Have students answer the accompanying questions using **Section Focus Transparency Master 31.** **L1** **ELL**

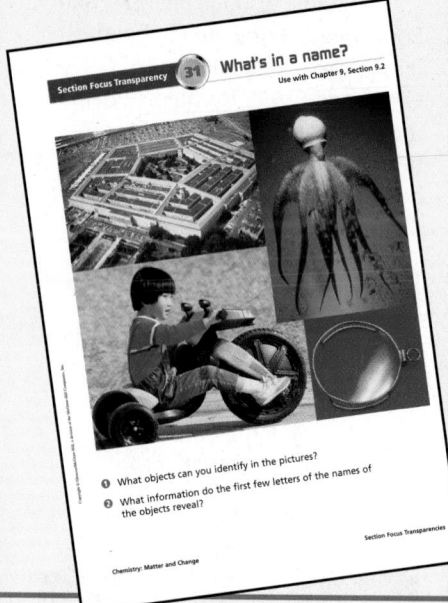

## Objectives

- **Identify** the names of binary molecular compounds from their formulas.
- **Name** acidic solutions.

## Vocabulary

oxyacid

You know that many atoms covalently bond to form molecules that behave as a single unit. These units can be represented by chemical formulas and names that are used to identify them. When naming molecules, the system of rules is similar to the one you used to name ionic compounds.

## Naming Binary Molecular Compounds

The anesthetic dinitrogen oxide ($N_2O$), commonly known as nitrous oxide, is a covalently bonded compound. Because it contains only two different elements, it is a binary molecular compound. Binary molecular compounds are composed of two different nonmetals and do not contain metals or ions. Although many of these compounds have common names, they also have scientific names that reveal their composition. Use the following simple rules to name binary molecular compounds.

1. *The first element in the formula is always named first, using the entire element name.*
2. *The second element in the formula is named using the root of the element and adding the suffix -ide.*
3. *Prefixes are used to indicate the number of atoms of each type that are present in the compound.* The most common prefixes are shown in **Table 9-1**.

Table 9-1

| Prefixes in Covalent Compounds | | | |
|---|---|---|---|
| **Number of atoms** | **Prefix** | **Number of atoms** | **Prefix** |
| 1 | mono- | 6 | hexa- |
| 2 | di- | 7 | hepta- |
| 3 | tri- | 8 | octa- |
| 4 | tetra- | 9 | nona- |
| 5 | penta- | 10 | deca- |

One exception to using these prefixes is that the first element in the formula never uses the prefix *mono-*. Also, to avoid awkward pronunciation, drop the final letter in the prefix when the element name begins with a vowel. For example, CO is carbon monoxide, not monocarbon monooxide.

# 2 Teach

## Visual Learning

**Table 9-1** Review oxidation numbers, naming ionic compounds and writing formula units. Unlike ionic compounds, the number of each atom that makes up a molecule is identified by a prefix. Write several molecular formulas on the chalkboard and have students use Table 9-1 to practice naming molecules.

### EXAMPLE PROBLEM 9-2

**Naming Binary Molecular Compounds**

Name the compound $P_2O_5$, which is used as a drying and dehydrating agent.

**1. Analyze the Problem**

You are given the formula for a compound. This formula reveals what elements are present and how many atoms of each element exist in a molecule. Because only two different elements are present and both

## Demonstration

### Forming Ionic and Covalent Bonds

#### Purpose
To demonstrate the formation of ionic and covalent bonds

#### Materials
Magnesium ribbon (5 cm); roll sulfur (2 g);

tongs; large metal can; deflagrating spoon; laboratory burner

#### Safety Precautions

**Disposal** Dispose of the solid in a landfill approved to receive chemical waste.

#### Procedure
Place a large can in the sink. Hold the magnesium ribbon with tongs and carefully

ignite it. Hold the burning magnesium ribbon in the can. If the room lights are turned off, students can safely observe the reflected light. **CAUTION:** Wear goggles when burning magnesium. Do not look directly at the burning metal. In a darkened room, place a small piece of roll sulfur in a deflagrating spoon and briefly heat it in a burner flame. The sulfur will ignite and burn with a low blue flame. **CAUTION:** Use a fume hood; $SO_2$ vapor is toxic.

are nonmetals, the compound can be named using the rules for naming binary molecular compounds.

## 2. Solve for the Unknown

Name the first element present in the compound.

phosphorus

The second element is oxygen. The root of this name is *ox-*, so the second part of the name is *oxide*.

phosphorus oxide

From the formula $P_2O_5$, two phosphorus atoms and five oxygen atoms make up a molecule of the compound. From **Table 9-1**, *di-* is the prefix for two, and *penta-* is the prefix for five.

diphosphorus pentoxide.

The *a-* of *penta-* is not used because *oxide* begins with a vowel.

## 3. Evaluate the Answer

The name diphosphorus pentoxide shows that a molecule of the compound contains two phosphorus atoms and five oxygen atoms, which agrees with the chemical formula for the compound, $P_2O_5$.

Diphosphorus pentoxide releases energy and produces fumes when it dissolves in water to form phosphoric acid.

## PRACTICE PROBLEMS

Name the following binary covalent compounds.

**13.** $CCl_4$

**14.** $As_2O_3$

**15.** CO

**16.** $SO_2$

**17.** $NF_3$

Practice!
For more practice with naming binary covalent compounds, go to **Supplemental Practice Problems** in Appendix A.

**Common names of some molecular compounds** How frequently have you drunk an icy, cold glass of dihydrogen monoxide? Quite frequently, but you probably didn't call it that. You called it by its more common name, which is water. Remember from Chapter 8 that many ionic compounds have common names in addition to their scientific ones. Baking soda is sodium hydrogen carbonate and common table salt is sodium chloride. Many covalent compounds also have both common and scientific names.

Many binary molecular compounds were discovered and given common names long before the modern naming system was developed. **Table 9-2** lists some of these molecules, their common names, and the binary molecular compound names.

Table 9-2

| Formulas and Names of Some Covalent Compounds | | |
|---|---|---|
| Formula | Common name | Molecular compound name |
| $H_2O$ | water | dihydrogen monoxide |
| $NH_3$ | ammonia | nitrogen trihydride |
| $N_2H_4$ | hydrazine | dinitrogen tetrahydride |
| $N_2O$ | nitrous oxide (laughing gas) | dinitrogen monoxide |
| NO | nitric oxide | nitrogen monoxide |

**Practice** PROBLEMS

Have students refer to Appendix D for complete solutions to Practice Problems.

**13.** carbon tetrachloride

**14.** diarsenic trioxide

**15.** carbon monoxide

**16.** sulfur dioxide

**17.** nitrogen trifluoride

## Reinforcement

**Kinesthetic** Have students make a mobile that can be used to name molecules. Display the mobile in the classroom. **L1** **ELL**

## GLENCOE TECHNOLOGY

**CD-ROM**
**Chemistry: Matter and Change**
Video: *Ionic and Covalent Compounds*
Demonstration: *Forming Ionic and Covalent Bonds*

## Resource Manager

**Study Guide for Content Mastery,** p. 50 **L2**
**Solving Problems: A Chemistry Handbook,** Section 9.2 **L2**
**Section Focus Transparency 31 and Master** **L1** **ELL**
**Math Skills Transparency 9 and Master** **L2** **ELL**

## Results

Magnesium burns with a bright, white-hot flame. Sulfur burns with a low blue flame. The stability of MgO is evidenced by the large amount of heat and light produced when it is formed compared to the heat and light produced in the formation of $SO_2$. Point out to students that the greater energy released in the formation of MgO indicates that the ionic bond in MgO is stronger (more stable) than the covalent bonds in $SO_2$.

## Analysis

Ask these questions.

**1.** With what element do magnesium and sulfur react? oxygen

**2.** Write balanced chemical equations for the chemical reactions. $2Mg(s) + O_2(g) \rightarrow 2MgO(s)$; $S(s) + O_2(g) \rightarrow SO_2(g)$

## Assessment

**Knowledge** If Mg forms an ionic bond, and S forms a covalent bond, which bond type is the stronger bond? Why? The ionic bond is stronger because more energy is released during its formation.

## Naming Acids

Water solutions of some molecules are acidic and are named as acids. Acids are important compounds with specific properties that will be discussed at length in Chapter 19. If the compound produces hydrogen ions ($H^+$) in solution, it is an acid. For example, HCl produces $H^+$ in solution and is an acid. Two common types of acids exist—binary acids and oxyacids.

**Naming binary acids** A binary acid contains hydrogen and one other element. When naming a binary acid, use the prefix *hydro-* to name the hydrogen part of the compound. The rest of the name consists of a form of the root of the second element plus the suffix *-ic*, followed by the word *acid*. For example, HBr in a water solution is called hydrobromic acid.

Although the term *binary* indicates exactly two elements, a few acids that contain more than two elements are named according to the rules for naming binary acids. If no oxygen is present in the formula for the acidic compound, the acid is named in the same way as a binary acid, except that the root of the second part of the name is the root of the polyatomic ion that the acid contains. For example, HCN, which is composed of hydrogen and the cyanide ion, is called hydrocyanic acid.

**Naming oxyacids** Another set of rules is used to name an acid that contains an oxyanion. An oxyanion is a polyatomic ion that contains oxygen. Any acid that contains hydrogen and an oxyanion is referred to as an **oxyacid.**

Because the name of an oxyacid depends on the oxyanion present in the acid, you must first identify the anion present. The name of an oxyacid consists of a form of the root of the anion, a suffix, and the word *acid*. If the anion suffix is *-ate*, it is replaced with the suffix *-ic*. When the anion ends in *-ite*, the suffix is replaced with *-ous*. Consider the oxyacid $HNO_3$. Its oxyanion is nitrate ($NO_3^-$). Following this rule, $HNO_3$ is named nitric acid. The anion of $HNO_2$ is the nitrite ion ($NO_2^-$). $HNO_2$ is nitrous acid. Notice that the hydrogen in an oxyacid is not part of the name.

It's important to remember that these hydrogen-containing compounds are named as acids only when they are in water solution. For example, at room temperature and pressure HCl is hydrogen chloride, a gas. When HCl is dissolved in water, it is hydrochloric acid.

### PRACTICE PROBLEMS

Name the following acids. Assume each compound is dissolved in water.

**18.** HI      **21.** $H_2SO_4$
**19.** $HClO_3$   **22.** $H_2S$
**20.** $HClO_2$

## Writing Formulas from Names

The name of a molecular compound reveals its composition and is important in communicating the nature of the compound. **Figure 9-9** can help you determine the name of a molecular covalent compound.

The name of any binary molecule allows you to write the correct formula with ease. Subscripts are determined from the prefixes used in the name because the name indicates the exact number of each atom present in the molecule. The formula for an acid can be derived from the name as well.

Figure 9-9

This flow chart summarizes how to name molecular compounds when their formulas are known.

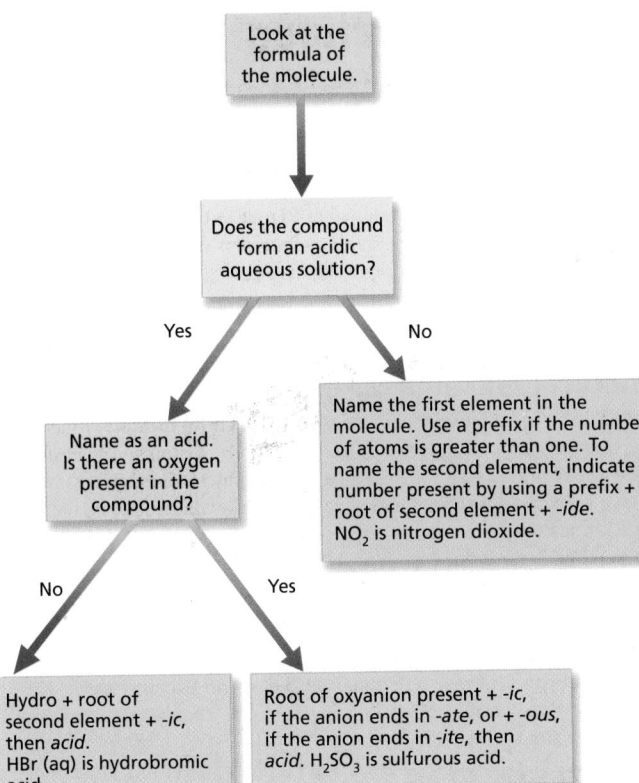

Look at the formula of the molecule.

↓

Does the compound form an acidic aqueous solution?

Yes → Name as an acid. Is there an oxygen present in the compound?

No → Name the first element in the molecule. Use a prefix if the number of atoms is greater than one. To name the second element, indicate the number present by using a prefix + root of second element + -ide. NO₂ is nitrogen dioxide.

Name as an acid. Is there an oxygen present in the compound?

No → Hydro + root of second element + -ic, then acid. HBr (aq) is hydrobromic acid.

Yes → Root of oxyanion present + -ic, if the anion ends in -ate, or + -ous, if the anion ends in -ite, then acid. H₂SO₃ is sulfurous acid.

## Section 9.2 Assessment

**23.** What is a binary molecular compound?

**24.** Using the system of rules for naming binary molecular compounds, describe how you would name the molecule $N_2O_4$.

**25.** Compare and contrast naming binary acids and naming other binary covalent molecules.

**26.** What is the difference between a binary acid and an oxyacid?

**27.** Write the molecular formula for each of the following compounds.
a. disulfur trioxide
b. iodic acid
c. dinitrogen monoxide
d. hydrofluoric acid
e. phosphorus pentachloride

**28. Thinking Critically** Write the molecular formula for each listed compound.
a. dinitrogen trioxide and nitrogen monoxide
b. hydrochloric acid and chloric acid
c. sulfuric acid and sulfurous acid

**29. Making and Using Tables** Complete the following table.

| Formulas and Names of Covalent Compounds | |
|---|---|
| **Formula** | **Name** |
| $PCl_5$ | |
| | hydrobromic acid |
| $H_3PO_4$ | |
| | oxygen difluoride |
| $SO_2$ | |

## Section 9.2 Assessment

**23.** a molecule composed of only two elements

**24.** There are two atoms of nitrogen; use the prefix *di–* with the name nitrogen. There are four atoms of oxygen, so use the prefix *tetra–* + the root of oxygen + the ending –ide. The name is dinitrogen tetroxide.

**25.** Acids are named using *hydro–* + the root of the nonmetal + –ic, but a binary covalent molecule is named using the name of the first element + the root of the second element + –ide.

**26.** A binary acid contains hydrogen and one other element. An oxyacid contains hydrogen, another element, and oxygen.

**27. a.** $S_2O_3$  **c.** $N_2O$  **e.** $PCl_5$
**b.** $HIO_3$  **d.** HF

**28. a.** $N_2O_3$ and NO
**b.** HCl and $HClO_3$
**c.** $H_2SO_4$ and $H_2SO_3$

**29.** phosphorus pentachloride, HBr, phosphoric acid, $OF_2$, sulfur dioxide

251

## 3 Assess
### Check for Understanding

**Visual-Spatial** Place a 4 × 4 grid containing eight molecules and their names at random on the overhead projector. Cover each square and play a game of Concentration by matching the formula of the molecule with its correct name. **L1 ELL**

### Reteach

**Intrapersonal** Many common air pollutants form acids in water solution. Have students create tables that have the following column heads: Formula of pollutant, Name of molecule, Formula of acid, and Name of acid. For each of the following pollutants, provide information for one column and have students complete the table: $SO_2$ (sulfur dioxide, $H_2SO_3$, sulfurous acid), $CO_2$ (carbon dioxide, $H_2CO_3$, carbonic acid), $SO_3$ (sulfur trioxide, $H_2SO_4$, sulfuric acid), $NO_2$ (nitrogen dioxide, $HNO_3$, nitric acid). **L2**

### Extension

Have students write answers and questions for a game of Jeopardy using the categories Molecular Formulas, Names of Molecules, Names of Acids, and Formulas for Acids. **L2**

### Assessment

**Knowledge** Have students write molecular formulas, names of molecules, names of acids, or formulas of acids on the front of note cards. Have another student write the correct formula or name on the back of each note card. Use these note cards for review. **L2**

# 1 Focus

## Focus Transparency

Before presenting the lesson, display **Section Focus Transparency 32** on the overhead projector. Have students answer the accompanying questions using **Section Focus Transparency Master 32.** **L1** **ELL**

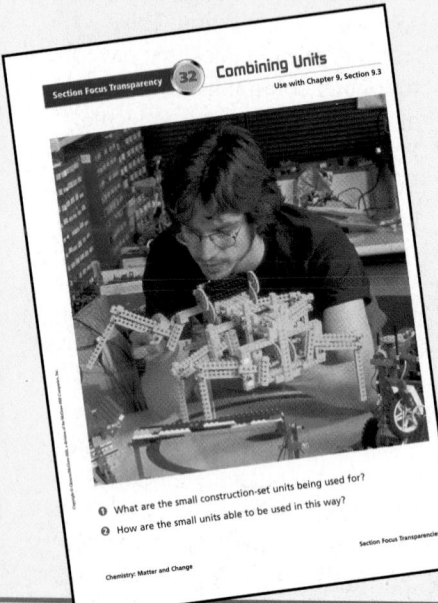

## Objectives

- **List** five basic steps used in drawing Lewis structures.

- **Explain** why resonance occurs, and **identify** resonance structures.

- **Explain** three exceptions to the octet rule, and **identify** molecules in which these exceptions occur.

## Vocabulary

structural formula
resonance
coordinate covalent bond

You can now identify atoms that bond covalently and name the molecular compounds formed through covalent bonding. In order to predict the arrangement of atoms in each molecule, a model, or representation is used. Several different models can be used, as shown in **Figure 9-10**. Note that in the ball-and-stick and space-filling molecular models, atoms of each specific element are represented by spheres of a representative color, as shown in **Table C-1** in Appendix C. These colors are used for identification of the atoms if the chemical symbol of the element is not present.

## Structural Formulas

One of the most useful molecular models is the **structural formula,** which uses letter symbols and bonds to show relative positions of atoms. The structural formula can be predicted for many molecules by drawing the Lewis structure. You have already seen some simple examples of Lewis structures, but more involved structures are needed to help you determine the shapes of molecules.

Although it is fairly easy to draw Lewis structures for most compounds formed by nonmetals, it is a good idea to follow a regular procedure. The following steps should be used to determine Lewis structures.

1. Predict the location of certain atoms.
   a. Hydrogen is always a terminal, or end, atom. Because it can share only one pair of electrons, hydrogen can be connected to only one other atom.
   b. The atom with the least attraction for shared electrons in the molecule is the central atom. This element usually is the one closer to the left on the periodic table. The central atom is located in the center of the molecule, and all other atoms become terminal atoms.

2. Find the total number of electrons available for bonding. This total is the number of valence electrons in the atoms in the molecule.

3. Determine the number of bonding pairs by dividing the number of electrons available for bonding by two.

4. Place one bonding pair (single bond) between the central atom and each of the terminal atoms.

# 2 Teach

## Quick Demo

**Kinesthetic** Place a circle with the electron dot diagram of a sulfur atom and two circles with the electron dot diagram of oxygen on a felt board. Ask students how these atoms could be arranged to satisfy the octet rule. Students will use trial and error methods. Tell students that a systematic approach can be used to determine the Lewis structure of molecules, including those that show exceptions to the octet rule. **L2** **ELL**

$PH_3$
Molecular formula

Space-filling
molecular model

H — P̈ — H
     |
     H
Lewis structure

Ball-and-stick
molecular model

**Figure 9-10**

All of these models can be used to show the relative locations of atoms and electrons in the phosphorus trihydride (phosphine) molecule.

H — P — H
     |
     H
Structural formula

**252    Chapter 9  Covalent Bonding**

## Internet Address Book

  Note Internet addresses that you find useful in the space below for quick reference.

_____

_____

_____

_____

**5.** Subtract the number of pairs you used in step 4 from the number of bonding pairs you determined in step 3. The remaining electron pairs include lone pairs as well as pairs used in double and triple bonds. Place lone pairs around each terminal atom bonded to the central atom to satisfy the octet rule. Any remaining pairs are assigned to the central atom.

**6.** If the central atom is not surrounded by four electron pairs, it does not have an octet. You must convert one or two of the lone pairs on the terminal atoms to a double bond or a triple bond between the terminal atom and the central atom. These pairs are still associated with the terminal atom as well as with the central atom. Remember that, in general, carbon, nitrogen, oxygen, and sulfur can form double or triple bonds with the same element or with another element.

---

**EXAMPLE** PROBLEM 9-3

**Lewis Structure: Covalent Compound with Single Bonds**

Ammonia is a raw material for the manufacture of many materials, including fertilizers, cleaning products, and explosives. Draw the Lewis structure for ammonia ($NH_3$).

**1. Analyze the Problem**

You are given that the ammonia molecule consists of one nitrogen atom and three hydrogen atoms. Because hydrogen must be a terminal atom, nitrogen is the central atom.

**2. Solve for the Unknown**

Find the total number of valence electrons.

$$1 \text{ N atom} \times \frac{5 \text{ valence electrons}}{\text{N atom}} + 3 \text{ H atoms} \times \frac{1 \text{ valence electron}}{\text{H atom}}$$

= 8 valence electrons

Determine the total number of bonding pairs.

$$\frac{8 \text{ electrons}}{2 \text{ electrons/pair}} = 4 \text{ pairs}$$

Draw single bonds from each H to the N.

$$
\begin{array}{c}
\text{H} - \text{N} - \text{H} \\
| \\
\text{H}
\end{array}
$$

Subtract the number of pairs used in these bonds from the total number of pairs of electrons available.

4 pairs total − 3 pairs used = 1 pair available

One lone pair remains to be added to either the terminal atoms or the central atom. Because hydrogen atoms can have only one bond, they have no lone pairs. Place the remaining lone pair on the central atom, N.

$$
\begin{array}{c}
\text{H} - \ddot{\text{N}} - \text{H} \\
| \\
\text{H}
\end{array}
$$

**3. Evaluate the Answer**

Each hydrogen atom shares one pair of electrons, as required, and the central nitrogen atom shares three pairs of electrons and has one lone pair, providing a stable octet.

Ammonia is a common ingredient in many cleaning products.

---

## Applying Chemistry

**TECH PREP**

Organic dyes are organic molecules that absorb select wavelengths of visible light and reflect all other light wavelengths to produce colors. These dyes are used to produce colorful fabrics. They are also used in recordable compact discs. Recordable CDs have a layer of colored organic dye sandwiched between a clear rigid backing and a reflective surface. A laser is used to "burn" data onto the CD. The bonds in the organic dye molecule absorb the laser light and change the structure of the molecule, producing an opaque substance. This change in structure is irreversible; therefore, data can be written only once on any part of the compact disc.

## Reinforcement

Point out that Lewis structures and structural formulas are both used to show the arrangement and ratio of atoms in a compound. Lewis structures can be used to represent both ionic and covalent compounds. Structural formulas are used only to represent molecules. Structural formulas use a line to represent a shared pair of electrons. However, unshared lone pairs of electrons are still represented by electron dots.

---

## GLENCOE TECHNOLOGY

**CD-ROM**
**Chemistry: Matter and Change**
Video: *Lewis Structures*

---

## Resource Manager

**Study Guide for Content Mastery,** p. 51 **L2**
**Solving Problems: A Chemistry Handbook,** Section 9.3 **L2**
**Section Focus Transparency 32 and Master L1 ELL**

## Portfolio

**Gilbert Lewis**

*Visual-Spatial* Have interested students research Gilbert Newton Lewis and make posters depicting his original Lewis structures. Students should share the posters with the class and then place them in their portfolios. **L2 ELL P**

**National Science Content Standards**

Pages 252–253
UCP.2, UCP.3, UCP.5; B.2

## Concept Development

Using the systematic approach, have students draw Lewis structures for several molecules. Remind students that carbon atoms can form chains with other carbon atoms. The carbon atoms will bond together with a single, double, or triple bond, depending on the available electron pairs. Have students draw the Lewis structure for ethane ($C_2H_6$), ethene ($C_2H_4$), and ethyne ($C_2H_2$), using the systematic technique. **L2**

## Content Background

**Space Molecules** Astronomers, using radio telescopes, have searched the dust clouds throughout the universe for space molecules. In these clouds, the dust particles provide a surface for chemical reactions to take place. Atoms join together, one atom at a time, and create larger molecules. As these molecules tumble through space, they change energy and give off radiation in the form of radio waves. In May 2000, scientists discovered the simple sugar molecule ribose floating in the dust cloud called Sagittarius B2. This sugar molecule is made up of two carbon atoms, four hydrogen atoms, and two oxygen atoms. Ribose is a building block for more complex molecules, such as glucose and RNA. Throughout the year 2000, astronomers identified more than 120 space molecules. Among these molecules are many simple molecules, such as water, and more complex molecules, such as acetic acid and methanol.

As a waste product, carbon dioxide is one of the gases exhaled.

---

**EXAMPLE** PROBLEM 9-4

### Lewis Structure: Covalent Compound with Multiple Bonds

Carbon dioxide is a product of all cellular respiration. Draw the Lewis structure for carbon dioxide ($CO_2$).

**1. Analyze the Problem**

You are given that the carbon dioxide molecule consists of one carbon atom and two oxygen atoms. Because carbon has less attraction for shared electrons, carbon is the central atom, and the two oxygen atoms are terminal.

**2. Solve for the Unknown**

Find the total number of valence electrons.

$$1 \text{ C atom} \times \frac{4 \text{ valence electrons}}{\text{C atom}} + 2 \text{ O atoms} \times \frac{6 \text{ valence electrons}}{\text{O atom}}$$

$$= 16 \text{ valence electrons}$$

Determine the total number of bonding pairs.

$$\frac{16 \text{ electrons}}{2 \text{ electrons/pair}} = 8 \text{ pairs}$$

Draw single bonds from each O to the central C atom.

O—C—O

Subtract the number of pairs used in these bonds from the total number of pairs of electrons available.

8 pairs total − 2 pairs used = 6 pairs available

Add three lone pairs to each terminal oxygen. Subtract the lone pairs used from the pairs available.

6 pairs available − 6 lone pairs used = 0

No electron pairs remain available for the carbon atom.

$$\ddot{\text{O}} - \text{C} - \ddot{\text{O}}$$

Carbon does not have an octet, so use a lone pair from each oxygen atom to form a double bond with the carbon atom.

$$\ddot{\text{O}} = \text{C} = \ddot{\text{O}}$$

**3. Evaluate the Answer**

Both carbon and oxygen now have an octet, which satisfies the octet rule.

---

The polyatomic ions you learned about in Chapter 8 are related to covalent compounds. Although the unit acts as an ion, the atoms within the ion itself are covalently bonded. The structures of these ions can also be represented by Lewis structures.

The procedure for drawing Lewis structures for polyatomic ions is similar to drawing them for covalent compounds. The main difference is in finding the total number of electrons available for bonding. Compared to the number of valence electrons present in the atoms that make up the ion, more electrons are present if the ion is negatively charged and fewer are present if the ion is positive. To find the total number of electrons available for bonding, first find the number available in the atoms present in the ion. Then, subtract the ion charge if the ion is positive, and add the ion charge if the ion is negative.

**254** Chapter 9 Covalent Bonding

---

**CHEMISTRY JOURNAL**

### Lewis Structures

*Intrapersonal* In their chemistry journals, have students predict the Lewis structures for the following common molecules: carbon monoxide (CO), carbon dioxide ($CO_2$), sulfur dioxide ($SO_2$), sulfur trioxide ($SO_3$), hydrogen cyanide (HCN), dinitrogen monoxide ($N_2O$), nitrogen dioxide ($NO_2$), and nitrogen monoxide (NO). **L2**

---

**Resource Manager**

**Teaching Transparency 29 and Master**
**L2** **ELL**
**Challenge Problems,** p. 9 **L3**

## Lewis Structure: Polyatomic Ion

Draw the correct Lewis structure for the polyatomic ion phosphate ($PO_4^{3-}$).

### 1. Analyze the Problem

You are given that the phosphate ion consists of one phosphorus atom and four oxygen atoms and has a charge of −3. Phosphorus has less attraction for shared electrons, so it is the central atom, and the four oxygen atoms are terminal.

### 2. Solve for the Unknown

Find the total number of valence electrons.

$$1 \; \text{P atom} \times \frac{5 \text{ valence electrons}}{\text{P atom}} + 4 \; \text{O atoms} \times \frac{6 \text{ valence electrons}}{\text{O atom}}$$

+ 3 electrons from the negative charge = 32 valence electrons

Determine the total number of bonding pairs.

$$\frac{32 \text{ electrons}}{2 \text{ electrons/pair}} = 16 \text{ pairs}$$

Draw single bonds from each O to the central P.

```
        O
        |
   O — P — O
        |
        O
```

Subtract the number of pairs used in these bonds from the total number of pairs of electrons available.

16 pairs total − 4 pairs used = 12 pairs available

Add three lone pairs to each terminal oxygen. Subtract the lone pairs used from the pairs available.

12 pairs available − 12 lone pairs used = 0

No electron pairs remain available for the phosphorus atom, resulting in the following Lewis structure for the phosphate ion.

```
        ..            3−
       :O:
        |
  ..    |    ..
 :O — P — O:
  ..    |    ..
       :O:
        ..
```

### 3. Evaluate the Answer

Phosphorus and all four oxygen atoms have an octet, and the group of atoms has a net charge of −3.

One phosphate compound, $MgH_4(PO_4)_2$, is used to fireproof wood. This compound contains the polyatomic ion phosphate.

## PRACTICE PROBLEMS

**Draw a Lewis structure for each of the following:**

**30.** $NF_3$

**31.** $CS_2$

**32.** $BH_3$

**33.** $ClO_4^-$

**34.** $NH_4^+$

**Practice!** For more practice with drawing Lewis structures, go to **Supplemental Practice Problems in Appendix A.**

---

## Applying Chemistry

**TECH PREP**

Fruits and vegetables naturally produce ethylene gas ($C_2H_4$) as they ripen. Also, the ripening process is accelerated when fruits and vegetables are exposed to ethylene. It will turn green bananas yellow and green tomatoes red. Unfortunately, this process gives only the appearance of ripeness because the taste of ripe fruit is due to the production of sugars or other substances that require the correct amount of growing time. The effect of ethylene on fruits and vegetables is dependent on the sensitivity of the item. Corn, radishes, and cherries are not sensitive to ethylene. Apples, avocados, and peaches, which are high producers of ethylene, are sensitive to the gas. Broccoli and brussels sprouts, although low producers of ethylene, are also sensitive to the gas. Tell students that they can accelerate the ripening of fruit at home by placing unripe fruit in a closed paper bag. Trapped ethylene gas produced by ripening fruit will accelerate the ripening process.

## Practice PROBLEMS

Have students refer to Appendix D for complete solutions to Practice Problems.

**30.**
```
        ..
       :F:
        |
  ..    |    ..
 :F — N — F:
  ..         ..
```

**31.**
```
  ..        ..
  S = C = S
  ..        ..
```

**32.**
```
        H
        |
        B
       / \
      H   H
```

**33.**
```
            ..           −
           :O:
            |
  ..    ..  |  ..    ..
 :O — Cl — O:
  ..    ..  |  ..    ..
           :O:
            ..
```

**34.**
```
        H        +
        |
   H — N — H
        |
        H
```

---

## Concept Development

Choose three students to represent atoms in the polyatomic ion $NO_2^-$. Arrange the three students in a sequence with the nitrogen atom as the central atom. One bond is a double bond and the other bond is a single bond. Ask students to determine the resonance structures. Place blue dye and red dye in separate containers to represent the two structures. Mix the dyes and have students notice that the resulting color is not red or blue but an intermediate of the two colors. A resonance hybrid is the intermediate of the two individual structures. **L1**
**ELL**

### Practice PROBLEMS

Have students refer to Appendix D for complete solutions to Practice Problems.

**35.** $\left[\begin{array}{c} :\overset{..}{O}=S—\overset{..}{\underset{..}{O}}: \\ | \\ :\overset{..}{\underset{..}{O}}: \end{array}\right]^{2-}$

$\left[\begin{array}{c} :\overset{..}{\underset{..}{O}}—S=\overset{..}{O}: \\ | \\ :\overset{..}{\underset{..}{O}}: \end{array}\right]^{2-}$

$\left[\begin{array}{c} :\overset{..}{\underset{..}{O}}—S—\overset{..}{\underset{..}{O}}: \\ || \\ :\overset{..}{O}: \end{array}\right]^{2-}$

**36.** $:\overset{..}{O}=S:$
   $|$
   $:\overset{..}{\underset{..}{O}}:$

$:\overset{..}{\underset{..}{O}}—S:$
   $||$
   $:\overset{..}{O}:$

**37.** $:\overset{..}{\underset{..}{O}}—O=\overset{..}{O}:$

$:\overset{..}{O}=O—\overset{..}{\underset{..}{O}}:$

**38.** $\left[\begin{array}{c} :\overset{..}{O}=N \\ | \\ :\overset{..}{\underset{..}{O}}: \end{array}\right]^-$

$\left[\begin{array}{c} :\overset{..}{\underset{..}{O}}—N \\ || \\ :\overset{..}{O}: \end{array}\right]^-$

---

### Figure 9-11

The nitrate ion ($NO_3^-$) exhibits resonance. **a** These resonance structures differ only in the location of the double bond. The locations of the nitrogen and oxygen atoms stay the same. **b** The actual nitrate ion is like an average of the three resonance structures in **a**. The dotted line indicates possible locations of the double bond.

## Resonance Structures

Using the same sequence of atoms, it is possible to have more than one correct Lewis structure when a molecule or polyatomic ion has both a double bond and a single bond. Consider the polyatomic ion nitrate ($NO_3^-$) shown in **Figure 9-11a.** Three equivalent structures can be used to represent the nitrate ion. **Resonance** is a condition that occurs when more than one valid Lewis structure can be written for a molecule or ion. The two or more correct Lewis structures that represent a single molecule or ion are often referred to as *resonance structures*. Resonance structures differ only in the position of the electron pairs, never the atom positions. The location of the lone pairs and bonding pairs differs in resonance structures. The molecule $O_3$ and the polyatomic ions $NO_3^-$, $NO_2^-$, $SO_3^{2-}$ and $CO_3^{2-}$ commonly form resonance structures.

It is important to note that each actual molecule or ion that undergoes resonance behaves as if it has only one structure. See **Figure 9-11b.** Experimentally measured bond lengths show that the bonds are identical to each other. They are shorter than single bonds but longer than double bonds. The actual bond length is an average of the bonds in the resonance structures.

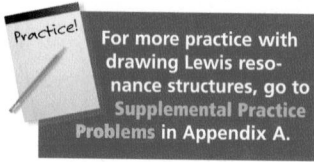

For more practice with drawing Lewis resonance structures, go to **Supplemental Practice Problems** in Appendix A.

### PRACTICE PROBLEMS

Draw the Lewis resonance structures for the following.

**35.** $SO_3$       **37.** $O_3$

**36.** $SO_2$       **38.** $NO_2^-$

## Exceptions to the Octet Rule

The Lewis structure is focused on the attainment of an octet by all atoms when they bond with other elements. Some molecules and ions, however, do not obey the octet rule. Three reasons exist for these exceptions.

First, a small group of molecules has an odd number of valence electrons and cannot form an octet around each atom. For example, $NO_2$ has five valence electrons from nitrogen and 12 from oxygen, totaling 17, which cannot form an exact number of electron pairs. $ClO_2$ and NO are other examples of molecules with odd numbers of valence electrons.

$:\overset{..}{\underset{..}{O}}\overset{\displaystyle N}{\diagdown}\underset{\displaystyle O}{\|}:$

---

## Internet Address Book

  Note Internet addresses that you find useful in the space below for quick reference.

_____

_____

_____

_____

_____

$$H-B + :N-H \rightarrow H-B-N-H$$

(with H atoms above and below B and N as shown in the structures)

Second, some compounds form with fewer than eight electrons present around an atom. This group is relatively rare, and $BH_3$ is an example. Boron, a group 3A nonmetal, forms three covalent bonds with other nonmetallic atoms.

$$H-B-H$$
$$\quad\quad |$$
$$\quad\quad H$$

A total of six electrons is shared by the boron atom, which is two less than the number needed for an octet. Such compounds tend to be reactive and can share an entire pair of electrons donated by another atom. When one atom donates a pair of electrons to be shared with an atom or ion that needs two electrons to become stable, a **coordinate covalent bond** forms, as in **Figure 9-12**. Atoms or ions with lone pairs often form coordinate covalent bonds with atoms or ions that need two more electrons.

The third group of compounds that does not follow the octet rule has central atoms that contain more than eight valence electrons. This electron arrangement is referred to as an *expanded octet*. An expanded octet can be explained by considering the d orbital that occurs in the energy levels of elements in period three or higher. An example of an expanded octet is the bond formation in the molecule $PCl_5$. Five bonds are formed with ten electrons shared in one s orbital, three p orbitals, and one d orbital. Another example is the molecule $SF_6$, which has six bonds sharing 12 electrons in an s orbital, three p orbitals, and two d orbitals. When you draw the Lewis structure for these compounds, extra lone pairs are added to the central atom or more than four bonding atoms are present in the molecule.

## EXAMPLE PROBLEM 9-6

### Lewis Structure: Exception to the Octet Rule

Xenon is a noble gas that will form a few compounds with nonmetals that strongly attract electrons. Draw the correct Lewis structure for xenon tetrafluoride ($XeF_4$).

**1. Analyze the Problem**

You are given that a molecule of xenon tetrafluoride consists of one xenon atom and four fluorine atoms. Xenon has less attraction for electrons, so it is the central atom.

**2. Solve for the Unknown**

Find the total number of valence electrons.

$$1 \text{ Xe atom} \times \frac{8 \text{ valence electrons}}{\text{Xe atom}} + 4 \text{ F atoms} \times \frac{7 \text{ valence electrons}}{\text{F atom}}$$

$$= 36 \text{ valence electrons}$$

Determine the number of bonding pairs.

$$\frac{36 \text{ electrons}}{2 \text{ electrons/pair}} = 18 \text{ pairs}$$

*Continued on next page*

**Figure 9-12**

In this reaction between boron trihydride ($BH_3$) and ammonia ($NH_3$), the nitrogen atom donates both electrons that are shared by boron and ammonia, forming a coordinate covalent bond.

## Content Background
### Exceptions to the Octet Rule

When drawing Lewis structures for simple molecules, the octet rule is a useful guide. However, many compounds form that do not have eight electrons around each atom. Compounds that contain beryllium and boron as the central atom are often deficient in electrons. An important example of these odd-electron molecules is the free radical $NO_2$. When two $NO_2$ molecules collide, they form $N_2O_4$, and each nitrogen atom obtains an octet. Expanded octets, those having more than eight electrons, occur only around a central nonmetallic atom from period 3 or higher because they have d orbitals available.

### ✓ Assessment

**Knowledge** Phosgene is a colorless, highly toxic gas used in warfare. The formula for this molecule is $CCl_2O$. Have students draw two resonance structures for this molecule. **L2**

## 3 Assess
### Check for Understanding

**Visual-Spatial** Write a molecular formula on the overhead projector and have students draw the correct Lewis structure for the molecule. **L2**

### Reteach

Review the steps used in drawing Lewis structures using the molecules $N_2O$ and $BeF_2$. Have students determine whether these molecules are exceptions to the octet rule or if they exhibit resonance. **L2**

## DIFFERENTIATED INSTRUCTION

### Learning Disabled

Use the following analogy to clarify coordinate covalent bonds to students. You borrow a CD from a friend. While using the CD, you treat the CD as belonging to you, yet at the same time your friend counts that CD as part of his or her CD collection. **L1**

**National Science Content Standards**

Pages 256–257
UCP.2, UCP.3, UCP.5; B.2

Have students refer to Appendix D for complete solutions to Practice Problems.

**39.**

**40.**

**41.**

:F:
|
:Cl:
/    \
:F      F:

## Extension

Have students research the compounds formed from the noble gas xenon. Have them draw the Lewis structure that represents each molecule formed. **L2**

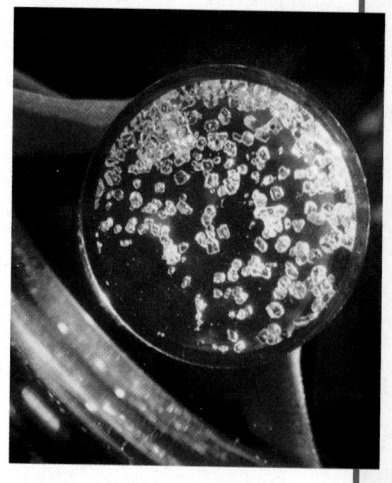

Xenon compounds, such as the XeF₄ shown here, are highly toxic because they are so reactive.

Use four bonding pairs to bond the four F atoms to the central Xe atom.

Determine the number of remaining pairs.

18 pairs available − 4 pairs used = 14 pairs available

Add three pairs to each F atom to obtain an octet. Determine how many pairs remain.

$$14 \text{ pairs} - 4 \text{ F atoms} \times \frac{3 \text{ pairs}}{\text{F atom}} = 2 \text{ pairs unused}$$

Place the two remaining pairs on the central Xe atom.

**3. Evaluate the Answer**

This structure gives xenon 12 total electrons, an expanded octet, for a total of six bond positions.

**For more practice with drawing Lewis structures, go to Supplemental Practice Problems in Appendix A.**

Draw the correct Lewis structures for the following molecules, which contain expanded octets.

**39.** SF₆

**40.** PCl₅

**41.** ClF₃

You now know how to draw Lewis structures for molecules and polyatomic ions. You can use them to determine the number of bonding pairs between atoms and the number of lone pairs present. Next, you will learn to describe molecular structure and predict the angles in a molecule, both of which determine the three-dimensional molecular shape.

## Section 9.3 Assessment

**42.** What is the role of the central atom when drawing the Lewis structure for a molecule?

**43.** What is resonance?

**44.** List three exceptions to the octet rule.

**45.** What is a coordinate covalent bond?

**46.** What is an expanded octet?

**47. Thinking Critically** Draw the resonance structures for the N₂O molecule.

**48. Formulating Models** Draw the Lewis structures for the following molecules and ions.
  **a.** CN⁻
  **b.** SiF₄
  **c.** HCO₃⁻
  **d.** AsF₆⁻

chemistrymc.com/self_check_quiz

---

**42.** All terminal atoms are bonded to it.

**43.** when two or more correct Lewis structures can be written for a molecule

**44.** The molecule has an odd number of valence electrons. The atoms have fewer than eight electrons around an atom. The central atom

has more than eight valence electrons and has an expanded octet.

**45.** One atom donates a pair of electrons to be shared with an atom or ion that needs two electrons.

**46.** More than eight electrons surround one atom. This involves the s orbital, three p orbitals, and one or two d orbitals.

**47.** :N̈=N=Ö: or :N≡N—Ö:

**48. a.** [:C≡N:]⁻    **b.**

:F:
|
:F—Si—F:
|
:F:

The shape of a molecule determines many of its physical and chemical properties. Molecular shape, in turn, is determined by the overlap of orbitals that share electrons. Theories have been developed to explain the overlap of bonding orbitals and are used to predict the shape of the molecule.

## VSEPR Model

Many chemical reactions, especially those in living things, depend on the ability of two compounds to contact each other. The shape of the molecule determines whether or not molecules can get close enough to react.

Once a Lewis structure is drawn, you can determine the molecular geometry, or shape, of the molecule. The model used to determine the molecular shape is referred to as the **Valence Shell Electron Pair Repulsion model**, or **VSEPR model.** This model is based on an arrangement that minimizes the repulsion of shared and unshared pairs of electrons around the central atom.

The repulsions among electron pairs in a molecule result in atoms existing at fixed angles to each other. The angle formed by any two terminal atoms and the central atom is a *bond angle*. Bond angles predicted by VSEPR are supported by experimental evidence. Shared electron pairs repel one another. Lone pairs of electrons also are important in determining the shape of the molecule. Because lone pairs are not shared between two nuclei, they occupy a slightly larger orbital than shared electrons. Shared bonding orbitals are pushed together slightly by lone pairs.

To make sense of the VSEPR model, consider balloons of similar size tied together, as shown in **Figure 9-13**. Each balloon represents an orbital and, therefore, the repulsive force that keeps other electrons from entering this space. When each set of balloons is connected at a central point that represents the central atom, the balloons naturally form a shape that minimizes interactions between the balloons. You will build additional examples of VSEPR models in the **miniLAB** on page 261.

Examine **Table 9-3**, which indicates some common shapes of molecules. First, consider molecules that contain no lone pairs of electrons. When only two pairs of electrons are shared off the central atom ($BeCl_2$), these bonding electrons will seek the maximum separation, which is a bond angle of $180°$, and the molecular shape is linear. Three bonding electron pairs also will separate as much as possible ($AlCl_3$), forming a trigonal planar shape with $120°$ bond angles. When the central atom has four pairs of bonding electrons ($CH_4$), the shape is tetrahedral with bond angles of $109.5°$.

It is important to remember that a lone pair also occupies a position in space. Recall phosphine ($PH_3$) shown in **Figure 9-10,** which has three single covalent bonds and one lone pair. You might expect the structure to be tetrahedral because of the four bonding positions around the central atom. However, the lone pair takes up a greater amount of space than the shared pairs. The geometry of $PH_3$ is trigonal pyramidal, and the bond angles are $107.3°$.

Now consider a water molecule ($H_2O$), which has two single covalent bonds and two lone pairs according to its Lewis structure. Although a water molecule has four electron pairs off the central atom, it is not tetrahedral because the two lone pairs occupy more space than do the paired electrons. The water molecule has a bent shape with a bond angle of $104.5°$.

### Objectives

- **Discuss** the VSEPR bonding theory.
- **Predict** the shape of and the bond angles in a molecule.
- **Define** hybridization.

### Vocabulary

VSEPR model
hybridization

**Figure 9-13**

Electrons in a molecule are located as far apart as they can be, just as these balloons are arranged.

## Resource Manager

**Study Guide for Content Mastery,** p. 52 **L2**

**Solving Problems: A Chemistry Handbook,** Section 9.4 **L2**

**Section Focus Transparency 33 and Master **L1** **ELL**

**Teaching Transparency 30 and Master **L2** **ELL**

**Lab Manual,** pp. 65–68 **L2**

---

# 1 Focus

## Focus Transparency

Before presenting the lesson, display **Section Focus Transparency 33** on the overhead projector. Have students answer the accompanying questions using **Section Focus Transparency Master 33. L1** **ELL**

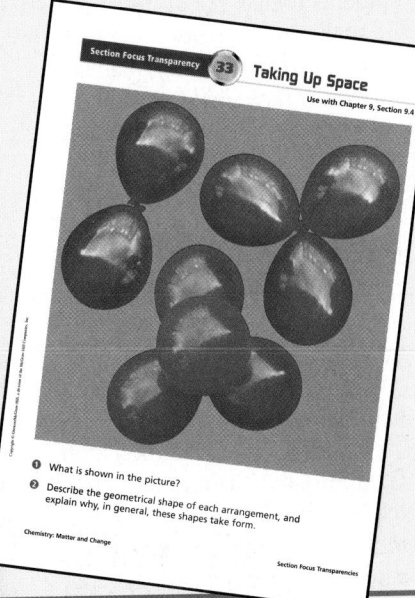

# 2 Teach

## Quick Demo

Using small balloons to represent shared pairs of electrons and larger balloons to represent unshared pairs of electrons, make models to represent HCl, $H_2O$, $NH_3$, and $CH_4$. HCl, one small and three large; $H_2O$, two small and two large; $NH_3$, three small and one large; $CH_4$, four small Tie the balloons together and ask students to notice the shape of the resultant molecules.

## National Science Content Standards

Pages 258–259
UCP.2, UCP.3, UCP.5; B.2, B.4

# Math in Chemistry

**Visual-Spatial** In their study of geometry, students have had experience drawing and constructing geometric shapes. Using a molecular model set, construct molecules, beginning with $H_2$. Ask students why a hydrogen molecule is considered linear. A single line can be drawn through all atoms in the molecule. Next, construct $BeH_2$, and ask students to determine its shape. linear Construct $BH_3$, and have students notice that all four atoms lie in the same plane. Cut a triangle from transparency film, place it on top of the molecule, then have students determine the bond angle. 120° The molecular shape is referred to as trigonal planar. Construct a $CH_4$ molecule, and have students cut four equilateral triangles and assemble them over the molecular model, forming a geometric model. Students will notice the shape is that of a tetrahedron, a hydrogen atom occupies each vertex, and the carbon atom occupies an interior point in the tetrahedron. Construct the $NH_3$ molecule and have students assemble a geometric shape that will encompass the molecule. trigonal pyramid Students should notice that there are no interior points in this molecular shape, and each atom aligns with a vertex. Construct an $H_2O$ molecule and ask students to determine the shape. bent Point out that this molecular shape is planar and the atoms form an obtuse angle. **L2** **ELL**

## Extension

**Visual-Spatial** Repeat the Math in Chemistry activity above with a $PCl_5$ molecule and the $SF_6$ molecule. Have students determine the geometric shapes of the molecules. trigonal bipyramidal, octahedral **L3** **ELL**

**Table 9-3**

| | | | | | | |
|---|---|---|---|---|---|---|
| **Molecular Shapes** | | | | | | |
| **Example** | **Total pairs** | **Shared pairs** | **Lone pairs** | ***Molecular shape** | **Bond Angle** | **Hybrid Orbitals** |
| $BeCl_2$ | 2 | 2 | 0 | Linear | 180° | sp |
| $AlCl_3$ | 3 | 3 | 0 | Trigonal planar | 120° | sp² |
| $CH_4$ | 4 | 4 | 0 | Tetrahedral | 109.5° | sp³ |
| $PH_3$ | 4 | 3 | 1 | Trigonal pyramidal | 107.3° | sp³ |
| $H_2O$ | 4 | 2 | 2 | Bent | 104.5° | sp³ |
| $NbBr_5$ | 5 | 5 | 0 | Trigonal bipyramidal | (vertical to horizontal) 90° /120° (horizontal to horizontal) | sp³d |
| $SF_6$ | 6 | 6 | 0 | Octahedral | 90° | sp³d² |

*Balls represent atoms; sticks represent bonds; and lobes represent lone pairs of electrons.

## DIFFERENTIATED INSTRUCTION

### Gifted

**Visual-Spatial** Have capable students research the molecular orbital theory. This theory describes electrons in molecules by using molecular orbitals instead of atomic orbitals. Students should use diagrams and report their finding to the class. **L3**

## GLENCOE TECHNOLOGY

**CD-ROM**
**Chemistry: Matter and Change**
Experiment: *Molecular Geometry*

## Hybridization

A hybrid results from combining two of the same type of object, and it has characteristics of both. Atomic orbitals undergo hybridization during bonding. Let's consider the bonding involved in the methane molecule ($CH_4$). The carbon atom has four valence electrons with the electron configuration of $[He]2s^22p^2$. You might expect the two unpaired p electrons to bond with other atoms and the 2s electrons to remain a lone pair. However, carbon atoms undergo **hybridization,** a process in which atomic orbitals are mixed to form new, identical *hybrid orbitals*. Each hybrid orbital contains one electron that it can share with another atom, as shown in **Figure 9-14.** Carbon is the most common element that undergoes hybridization. Because the four hybrid orbitals form from one s and three p orbitals, this hydrid orbital is called an $sp^3$ orbital.

Look again at **Table 9-3** on the previous page. Notice that the number of atomic orbitals mixed to form the hybrid orbital equals the total number of pairs of electrons. In addition, the number of hybrid orbitals formed equals the number of atomic orbitals mixed. For example, $AlCl_3$ has a total of three pairs of electrons and VSEPR predicts a trigonal planar molecular shape. To have this shape, one s and two p orbitals on the central atom Al must mix to form three identical $sp^2$ hybrid orbitals.

Lone pairs also occupy hybrid orbitals. Compare the hybrid orbitals of $BeCl_2$ and $H_2O$ in **Table 9-3.** Both compounds contain three atoms. Why is $H_2O$ $sp^3$? There are two lone pairs on the central atom (oxygen) in $H_2O$. Therefore, there must be four hybrid orbitals—two for bonding and two for the lone pairs.

Recall from Section 9.1 that multiple covalent bonds consist of one sigma bond and one or more pi bonds. Only the two electrons in the sigma bond occupy hybrid orbitals such as sp and $sp^2$. The remaining unhybridized p orbitals overlap to form pi bonds.

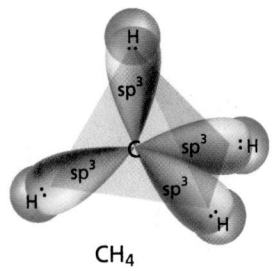

**$CH_4$**

**Figure 9-14**

One s and three p orbitals hybridize to form four $sp^3$ orbitals. According to VSEPR, a tetrahedral shape minimizes repulsion between the orbitals.

## miniLAB

### Building VSEPR Models

**Formulating Models** The VSEPR model states that pairs of valence electrons on a central atom repel each other and are arranged so that the repulsions are as small as possible. In this **miniLAB**, you will use marshmallows and gumdrops to build models of substances, showing examples of the VSEPR model.

**Materials** regular-sized marshmallows (3); mini-sized marshmallows (9); small gumdrops (3); toothpicks, cut in half

### Procedure

1. Draw Lewis structures for methane ($CH_4$), ammonia ($NH_3$), and water ($H_2O$). Notice the location of each shared and unshared pair of electrons.
2. Using your Lewis structures, build a VSEPR model for each molecule. Use a mini-marshmallow to represent both the hydrogen atom and the region of space containing the pair of electrons shared by hydrogen and the central atom. Use a regular-sized marshmallow to represent the space occupied by an unshared pair of electrons and a small gumdrop to represent a central atom. Use small pieces of toothpicks to attach the marshmallows and gumdrops to each other. Sketch each of your models.

### Analysis

1. How did drawing a Lewis structure help you to determine the geometry of each of your substances?
2. Why was a mini-marshmallow used to show a shared pair of electrons and a regular marshmallow an unshared pair?
3. How can the VSEPR model help to predict the bond angles for these substances?

### ✓ Portfolio

**Sulforaphane**

*Intrapersonal* The compound sulforaphane is an ingredient in broccoli and has been discovered to be a potent anticancer agent. Have students research sulforaphane ($C_5H_{11}OS$) and draw models to represent this molecule. Have students place the reports and models in their portfolios. **L3** **P**

### CHEMISTRY JOURNAL

**Molecular Shape**

*Intrapersonal* Have students predict the molecular shape and bond angle of the common molecules $CO_2$, $NO_2$, $CH_2O$, $CCl_4$, $H_2S$, and HF. **L2**

### Resource Manager

ChemLab and MiniLab Worksheets, p. 33 **L2**

## Practice PROBLEMS

Have students refer to Appendix
D for complete solutions.
**49.** trigonal planar, 120°, sp²
**50.** tetrahedral, 109°, sp³
**51.** bent, 104.5°, sp³
**52.** linear, 180°, sp
**53.** tetrahedral, 109°, sp³

# 3 Assess
## Check for Understanding

**Visual-Spatial** Have the
students use the Lewis structure for $AsH_3$ to predict the shape
of the molecule, the bond angle,
and the hybrid orbitals of arsenic.
**L2**

## Reteach

Have students use balls of modeling
clay to represent nuclei and nonvalence electrons, colored toothpicks
to represent bonded electrons, and
noncolored toothpicks to represent
lone pairs. Construct $CH_4$, and
have students determine the hybrid
orbitals of carbon and the shape
of the molecule. sp³, tetrahedral
Repeat for $NH_3$. sp³, trigonal pyramidal Continue with $H_2O$. sp³,
bent **L2**

### ✓ Assessment

**Performance** Have
students write the formula of a
simple molecule on a sheet of
paper. Have another student draw a
model of the molecule, predict the
geometry, the hybrid, and the bond
angle. Use the Performance Task
Assessment List for Scientific
Drawing in **PASC**, p. 55. **L2**

---

## EXAMPLE PROBLEM 9-7

### Finding the Shape of a Molecule

Phosphorus trihydride is produced when organic materials rot, and it
smells like rotten fish. What is the shape of a molecule of phosphorus
trihydride? Determine the bond angle, and identify the type of hybrid.

**1. Analyze the Problem**

You are given a molecule of phosphorus trihydride that contains one
phosphorus atom bonded to three hydrogen atoms. The hydrogen
atoms are terminal atoms, and phosphorus is the central atom.

**2. Solve for the Unknown**

Find the total number of valence electrons and the number of electron pairs.

$$1 \text{ P atom} \times \frac{5 \text{ valence electrons}}{\text{P atom}} + 3 \text{ H atoms} \times \frac{1 \text{ valence electron}}{\text{H atom}}$$

= 8 valence electrons

$$\frac{8 \text{ available electrons}}{2 \text{ electrons/pair}} = 4 \text{ available pairs}$$

Draw the Lewis structure, using one pair of electrons to bond each H
to the central P and assigning the lone pair to the phosphorus atom.

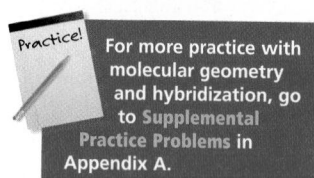

Lewis structure        Molecular shape

The molecular geometry is trigonal pyramidal with a bond angle of
107°. With four bonding positions, the molecule is an sp³ hybrid.

**4. Evaluate the Answer**

Each atom has a stable electron configuration, and all electron pairs
are accounted for.

---

**Practice!** For more practice with
molecular geometry
and hybridization, go
to *Supplemental
Practice Problems* in
Appendix A.

Phosphine, or phosphorus trihydride, is formed when phospho-
rus-containing organic material,
such as this potato, rots.

## PRACTICE PROBLEMS

Determine the molecular geometry, bond angle, and type of hybridization
for the following.

**49.** $BF_3$          **51.** $OCl_2$          **53.** $CF_4$
**50.** $NH_4^+$        **52.** $BeF_2$

---

## Section 9.4 Assessment

**54.** What is the VSEPR model?
**55.** What are the bond angles in a molecule with a
tetrahedral shape?
**56.** What is hybridization?
**57.** What are the hybrid orbitals in a molecule with
a tetrahedral shape?
**58. Thinking Critically** Compare the molecules $PF_3$
and $PF_5$. What is the molecular shape of each of

the two molecules? What type of hybrid orbital is
in each molecule? Why is the shape different?
**59. Making and Using Tables** Make a table that
contains the Lewis structure, molecular shape,
bond angle, and type of hybrid for the following
molecules: $CS_2$, $CH_2O$, $H_2Se$, $CCl_2F_2$, and $NCl_3$.

chemistrymc.com/self_check_quiz

---

## Section 9.4 Assessment

**54.** a theory based on the repulsive
nature of electron pairs around a
central atom that is used to determine molecular geometry
**55.** 109°
**56.** a theory used to explain why all
bonding orbitals around certain
atoms are the same

**57.** sp³
**58.** $PF_3$ is trigonal pyramidal with sp³
hybrid orbitals. $PF_5$ is trigonal
bipyramidal with sp³d hybrid
orbitals. Shape is determined by
the type of hybrid orbital.

**59.** :S̈=C=S̈: linear, 180°, sp

H\
  C=Ö:  trigonal planar,
H/        120°, sp²

H—S̈e:  bent, 104.5°, sp³
     \H

# Electronegativity and Polarity

You now know that the type of bond that forms when two elements react depends on which elements are involved. What makes one type of bond form when carbon burns and another type form when iron corrodes? The answer lies in how much attraction each type of atom has for electrons.

## Electronegativity Difference and Bond Character

Electron affinity is a measure of the tendency of an atom to accept an electron. Excluding noble gases, electron affinity increases as the atomic number increases within a given period and decreases with an increase in atomic number within a group. The scale of electronegativities allows a chemist to evaluate the electron affinity of specific atoms when they are incorporated into a compound. Recall from Chapter 6 that electronegativity indicates the relative ability of an atom to attract electrons in a chemical bond.

Look at the electronegativity values shown in **Figure 9-15.** Can you observe any trends? Note that fluorine has the highest electronegativity value (3.98), while francium has the lowest (0.7). The same trends appear with electronegativities that can be observed with electron affinities. Because noble gases do not generally form compounds, individual electronegativity values for helium, neon, and argon are not given. However, larger noble gases like xenon do occasionally bond with highly electronegative atoms such as fluorine.

### Objectives
- **Describe** how electronegativity is used to determine bond type.
- **Compare** and **contrast** polar and nonpolar covalent bonds and polar and nonpolar molecules.
- **Describe** the characteristics of compounds that are covalently bonded.

### Vocabulary
polar covalent

**Figure 9-15**

Electronegativity values are not measured quantities. They are values assigned by Linus Pauling comparing the abilities of atoms to attract shared electrons with the ability of fluorine to do so.

## Electronegativities

| 1 H 2.20 | | | | | | | | | | | | | | | | | |
|---|---|---|---|---|---|---|---|---|---|---|---|---|---|---|---|---|---|
| 3 Li 0.98 | 4 Be 1.57 | | | | | | | | | | | 5 B 2.04 | 6 C 2.55 | 7 N 3.04 | 8 O 3.44 | 9 F 3.98 |
| 11 Na 0.93 | 12 Mg 1.31 | | | | | | | | | | | 13 Al 1.61 | 14 Si 1.90 | 15 P 2.19 | 16 S 2.58 | 17 Cl 3.16 |
| 19 K 0.82 | 20 Ca 1.00 | 21 Sc 1.36 | 22 Ti 1.54 | 23 V 1.63 | 24 Cr 1.66 | 25 Mn 1.55 | 26 Fe 1.83 | 27 Co 1.88 | 28 Ni 1.91 | 29 Cu 1.90 | 30 Zn 1.65 | 31 Ga 1.81 | 32 Ge 2.01 | 33 As 2.18 | 34 Se 2.55 | 35 Br 2.96 |
| 37 Rb 0.82 | 38 Sr 0.95 | 39 Y 1.22 | 40 Zr 1.33 | 41 Nb 1.6 | 42 Mo 2.16 | 43 Tc 2.10 | 44 Ru 2.2 | 45 Rh 2.28 | 46 Pd 2.20 | 47 Ag 1.93 | 48 Cd 1.69 | 49 In 1.78 | 50 Sn 1.96 | 51 Sb 2.05 | 52 Te 2.1 | 53 I 2.66 |
| 55 Cs 0.79 | 56 Ba 0.89 | 57 La 1.10 | 72 Hf 1.3 | 73 Ta 1.5 | 74 W 1.7 | 75 Re 1.9 | 76 Os 2.2 | 77 Ir 2.2 | 78 Pt 2.2 | 79 Au 2.4 | 80 Hg 1.9 | 81 Tl 1.8 | 82 Pb 1.8 | 83 Bi 1.9 | 84 Po 2.0 | 85 At 2.2 |
| 87 Fr 0.7 | 88 Ra 0.9 | 89 Ac 1.1 | | | | | | | | | | | | | | |

Metal
Metalloid
Nonmetal

Elements not included on this table have no measured electronegativity or form relatively few bonds.

| | 58 Ce 1.12 | 59 Pr 1.13 | 60 Nd 1.14 | 61 Pm — | 62 Sm 1.17 | 63 Eu — | 64 Gd 1.20 | 65 Tb — | 66 Dy 1.22 | 67 Ho 1.23 | 68 Er 1.24 | 69 Tm 1.25 | 70 Yb — | 71 Lu 1.0 |
|---|---|---|---|---|---|---|---|---|---|---|---|---|---|---|
| **Lanthanide series** | | | | | | | | | | | | | | |
| **Actinide series** | 90 Th 1.3 | 91 Pa 1.5 | 92 U 1.7 | 93 Np 1.3 | 94 Pu 1.3 | | | | | | | | | |

---

Section 9.5

## 1 Focus

### Focus Transparency

Before presenting the lesson, display **Section Focus Transparency 34** on the overhead projector. Have students answer the accompanying questions using **Section Focus Transparency Master 34.** L1 ELL

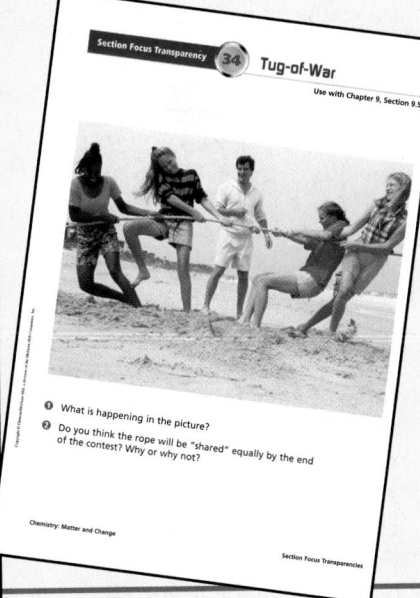

Section Focus Transparency 34 Tug-of-War
Use with Chapter 9, Section 9.5

① What is happening in the picture?
② Do you think the rope will be "shared" equally by the end of the contest? Why or why not?

Chemistry: Matter and Change

Section Focus Transparencies

## 2 Teach

### Quick Demo

Pour water into one buret and paint thinner into another. Rub a rubber rod with fur or silk to induce a charge. Open the water buret, and bring the charged rod near the stream of water. Have students observe that the water moves toward the charged rod. Repeat the procedure with the paint thinner. Nothing happens. Have students try to explain the results. When polarity is discussed in this section, refer to this Quick Demo and point out that water is a polar molecule, and paint thinner is nonpolar. Partial charges on water molecules are attracted to opposite charges.

---

tetrahedral, 109°, sp³

trigonal pyramidal, 107°, sp³

## CHEMISTRY JOURNAL

### Bond Type
Using the electronegativity difference, have students determine if the bonds in the following molecules are polar covalent, nonpolar covalent, or ionic: $H_2S$, $CH_4$, $NH_3$, KCl, $N_2$, CaO, $CO_2$, HCl. KCl and CaO are ionic, $N_2$ is nonpolar covalent, and the rest are polar covalent. L2

## Identifying Misconceptions

A common misconception is that the bond between two atoms is purely covalent or purely ionic.

**Uncover the Misconception**
Have students write analogies to represent nonpolar covalent bonds, polar covalent bonds, and ionic bonds. They should place the analogies in their portfolios.

**Demonstrate the Concept**
Have students imagine that they are eating at a restaurant with another person and each orders a different type of sandwich to be shared. If they share equally, what would they do? They would cut the sandwich in half and each would get a half. Ask students what unequal sharing would be. The shared portions are not equal. Finally, if one person eats his or her entire sandwich and then takes some of the other person's sandwich, what bond type does this represent? ionic

**Assess New Knowledge**
Using the table of electronegativities and the percent ionic character, have students determine the bond type that is likely to occur in the following pairs of atoms and identify which atom is more likely to have the electron: H and Br polar covalent, Br; C and O polar covalent, O; Li and F ionic, F; O and O nonpolar covalent, the electrons are shared equally.

---

## In-Text Questions

**Page 264** What percent ionic character is a bond between two atoms that have an electronegativity difference of 2.00? 64% Where would LiBr be plotted on the graph? just to the left of NaBr on the curve, at an electronegativity difference of 1.98

## Figure Caption Question

**Figure 9-16** What is the percent ionic character of a pure covalent bond? zero

**264**

---

### History
#### CONNECTION

In the 1940s, while experimenting with a device called a magnetron that generates microwaves, a scientist noticed that a candy bar in his pocket was melting. This accidental discovery led to the creation of the microwave oven, which cooks foods based on the polarity of the molecules involved. Early microwave ovens did not sell well because they were about the size and weight of a refrigerator and cost several thousand dollars. Eventually, smaller, lower-cost versions appeared for the home kitchen.

**Figure 9-16**

This graph shows how the percent ionic character of a bond depends on the difference in electronegativity of the atoms that form it. Above 50% ionic character, bonds are mostly ionic. What is the percent ionic character of a pure covalent bond?

---

The character and type of a chemical bond can be predicted using the electronegativity difference of the elements that are bonded. For identical atoms, which have an electronegativity difference of zero, the electrons in the bond are equally shared between the two atoms and the bond is considered nonpolar covalent, which is a pure covalent bond. Chemical bonds between atoms of different elements are never completely ionic or covalent, and the character of the bond depends on how strongly the bonded atoms attract electrons. A covalent bond formed between atoms of different elements does not have equal sharing of the electron pair because there is a difference in electronegativity. Unequal sharing results in a **polar covalent** bond. Large differences in electronegativity indicate that an electron was transferred from one atom to another, resulting in bonding that is primarily ionic.

Bonding often is not clearly ionic or covalent. As the difference in electronegativity increases, the bond becomes more ionic in character. An electronegativity difference of 1.70 is considered 50 percent covalent and 50 percent ionic. Generally, ionic bonds form when the electronegativity difference is greater than 1.70. However, this cutoff is sometimes inconsistent with experimental observations of two nonmetals bonding together. **Figure 9-16** summarizes the range of chemical bonding between two atoms. What percent ionic character is a bond between two atoms that have an electronegativity difference of 2.00? Where would LiBr be plotted on the graph?

## Polar Covalent Bonds

Why are some bonds polar covalent? Sharing is not always equal. Consider a tug-of-war when the two sides are not of equal strength. Although both sides share the rope, one side pulls more of the rope toward its side. Polar covalent bonds form because not all atoms that share electrons attract them equally. When a polar bond forms, the shared pair of electrons is pulled toward one of the atoms. The electrons spend more time around that atom than they do around the other atom. Partial charges occur at the ends of the bond. Using the symbols $\delta^-$, partially negative, and $\delta^+$, partially positive, next to a model of the molecule indicates the polarity of a polar covalent bond. See **Figure 9-17**. The more electronegative atom is located at the partially negative end, while the less electronegative atom is found at the partially positive end. The resulting polar bond often is referred to as a a dipole (two poles).

**Electronegativity and Bond Character**

---

Electronegativity Cl = 3.16
Electronegativity H = 2.20
Difference      = 0.96

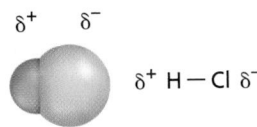

$$\delta^+ \;\; \delta^-$$
$$\delta^+ \text{ H} - \text{Cl } \delta^-$$

**Figure 9-17**

In a molecule containing hydro-gen and chlorine, chlorine has the higher electronegativity. Therefore, the shared pair of electrons is with the chlorine atom more often than it is with the hydrogen atom. The symbols indicating partial charge of each end of the molecule reflect this unequal sharing of electrons.

**Molecular polarity** Molecules are either nonpolar or polar, depending on the location and nature of the covalent bonds they contain. One way to distinguish polar from nonpolar molecules is that nonpolar molecules are not attracted by an electric field. Polar molecules tend to align with an electric field because polar molecules have a greater electron density on one side of the molecule. A polar molecule has a partial negative charge on one side, while the other side of the molecule has a partial positive charge. The molecule is a dipole because of the two partial charges.

**Polar molecule or not?** Let's compare water ($H_2O$) and carbon tetrachloride ($CCl_4$) molecules to see why some molecules are polar and some are not. Both molecules contain polar covalent bonds. Using **Figure 9-15** on page 263, you can see that the electronegativity difference between one hydrogen atom and one oxygen atom is 1.24. The electronegativity difference between one chlorine atom and one carbon atom is 0.61. Although these electronegativity differences vary quite a bit, both the H—O and the C—Cl bonds are considered to be polar covalent.

$$\delta^+ \; \delta^- \qquad\qquad \delta^+ \; \delta^-$$
$$\text{H}-\text{O} \qquad\qquad \text{C}-\text{Cl}$$

Both molecules contain more than one polar covalent bond. But water molecules are polar and carbon tetrachloride molecules are not. Examine the geometry of the molecules to see the reason for this difference.

The shape of $H_2O$ determined by VSEPR is bent because there are two lone pairs of electrons on the central oxygen atom. Because the polar H—O bonds are not symmetric in a water molecule, the molecule has a definite positive end and a definite negative end. Thus, it is polar.

**Figure 9-18**

Ammonia, represented by the Lewis structure, is used in the manufacture of certain synthetic fibers.

$$\begin{matrix} \delta^+ & & \delta^- \\ \text{H} & -\text{O} & \\ & \searrow & \\ & \text{H} \; \delta^+ & \end{matrix}$$

$$H_2O \qquad\qquad\qquad CCl_4$$

The shape of $CCl_4$ is tetrahedral. This molecule is symmetric. The electrical charge measured at any distance from its center is identical to the charge measured at the same distance on the opposite side. The average center of the negative charge is located on the carbon atom. The positive center also is located on the carbon atom. Because the partial charges are balanced, $CCl_4$ is a nonpolar molecule. Note that symmetric molecules are usually nonpolar, and molecules that are asymmetric are polar as long as the bond type is polar.

Is the molecule of ammonia ($NH_3$) shown in **Figure 9-18** polar or not? It contains a central nitrogen atom and three terminal hydrogen atoms. It has a trigonal pyramidal shape because of the lone pair of electrons present on the nitrogen atom. Using **Figure 9-15**, you can find that the electronegativity difference of hydrogen and nitrogen is 0.84. So, each N—H bond is polar covalent.

9.5 Electronegativity and Polarity   **265**

**Resource Manager**

**Math Skills Transparency 10 and Master** [L2] [ELL]
**Teaching Transparency 31 and Master** [L2] [ELL]
**Lab Manual**, pp. 69–72 [L2]

## Quick Demo

Place two or three Teflon-coated stirring bars on the overhead projector. The stirring bars should be spaced away from each other and have random orientation. Bring a magnet near the stirring bars. The stirring bars will align themselves with the magnet's magnetic field. Tell students that polar molecules behave much the same way in an electric field because the molecule has both a positive and a negative pole.

## Assessment

**Portfolio** Show students molecular models of common molecules. Have them determine the bond type present and then determine the type of molecule based on its symmetry. The molecules $SO_2$, $CS_2$, $CH_3Cl$, $CH_2O$, HCl, and $H_2S$ can be used. Student work can be placed in their portfolios. [L2] [P]

## Quick Demo

Show students two test tubes, one containing sugar and the other salt. Ask students how they could tell them apart without tasting the solids. Have students examine samples of sugar and salt with magnifying glasses or microscopes. Salt has cubic crystals. Place some salt and sugar into test tubes of water and check for conductivity. Ask students which solution conducts an electric current. salt solution Place some salt crystals and sugar crystals on watch glasses and heat them. Ask students which solid melted. sugar

**National Science Content Standards**

Pages 262–265
UCP.2, UCP.3, UCP.5; B.2, B.4; G.3

## Practice PROBLEMS

Have students refer to Appendix D for complete solutions to Practice Problems.

**60.** polar

**61.** polar

**62.** nonpolar

**63.** nonpolar

# 3 Assess
## Check for Understanding

Ask students to compare the characteristics of ionic solids to those of covalent and network solids. **L2**

## Reteach

Have students make a chart and discuss the properties of ionic, metallic, covalent, and network solids. Point out that a high melting point is a result of a three-dimensional attraction of an atom or ion for electrons. This occurs in network solids, metallic solids, and ionic solids. Covalent solids are held together by intermolecular attractions and have lower melting points. **L2**

## Extension

**Visual-Spatial** Have students investigate intermolecular bonds. Students should use drawings to represent each type of van der Waals force and give an example. Display the students' work. **L2**

## ✓ Assessment

**Knowledge** Write chemical formulas on the chalkboard and have students predict some of the physical properties of the compound based on bond type. **L2**

National Science Content Standards

Pages 266–267
UCP.2, UCP.3, UCP.5; B.2, B.4

**Figure 9-19**

Oil, most petroleum products, and other symmetric covalent molecules are nonpolar, whereas water and other asymmetric molecules are usually polar. When polar and nonpolar substances are mixed, they separate into two layers, as seen when oil floats on water.

**Chemistry Online**

**Topic: Molecular Shapes**
To learn more about molecular shapes and behavior, visit the Chemistry Web site at **chemistrymc.com**

**Activity:** Research the structure of an amino acid, lipid, or other biological molecule. Make a model or poster to explain how the polarity of each bond and the overall molecule affect the shape, function, and reactivity of the molecule.

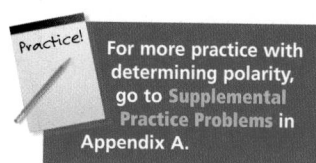

**Practice!** For more practice with determining polarity, go to Supplemental Practice Problems in Appendix A.

The charge distribution is unequal because the molecule is not symmetric. Thus, the molecule is polar. The **CHEMLAB** and the **How it Works** feature at the end of this chapter are based on the polarity of molecules.

**Solubility of polar molecules** The ability of a substance to dissolve in another substance is known as the physical property solubility. The bond type and the shape of the molecules present determine solubility. Polar molecules and ionic compounds usually are soluble in polar substances, but nonpolar molecules dissolve only in nonpolar substances. See **Figure 9-19.** Solubility will be covered in detail in Chapter 15.

## Properties of Covalent Compounds

You've probably noticed how similar table salt, an ionic solid, and table sugar, a covalent solid, are in appearance. But if you heat salt on the stove, it won't melt, even if the temperature is high. Sugar, on the other hand, melts at a relatively low temperature. Does type of bonding affect properties?

Differences in properties are a result of differences in attractive forces. In a covalent compound, the covalent bond between atoms in molecules is quite strong, but the attraction between individual molecules is relatively weak. The weak forces of attraction between individual molecules are known as *intermolecular forces*, or *van der Waals forces*. Intermolecular forces, which are discussed at length in Chapter 13, vary in strength but are weaker than the bonds that join atoms in a molecule or ions in an ionic compound.

There are different types of intermolecular forces. For nonpolar substances, the attraction between the molecules is weak and is called a dispersion force, or induced dipole. The effect of dispersion forces is investigated in the **problem-solving LAB** on the next page. The force between polar molecules is stronger and is called a dipole-dipole force. This force is the attraction of one end of the dipole to the oppositely charged end of another dipole. The more polar the molecule, the stronger the dipole-dipole force. The third force, a hydrogen bond, is an especially strong intermolecular force that is formed between the hydrogen end of one dipole and a fluorine, oxygen, or nitrogen atom on another dipole.

Many physical properties of covalent molecular solids are due to intermolecular forces. The melting and boiling points of molecular substances are relatively low compared with those of ionic substances. That's why salt doesn't melt when you heat it but sugar does. Many molecular substances exist as gases or vaporize readily at room temperature. Oxygen ($O_2$), carbon dioxide ($CO_2$), and hydrogen sulfide ($H_2S$) are examples of covalent gases. Hardness is also due to the intermolecular forces between individual molecules, so covalent molecules form relatively soft solids. Paraffin is a common example of a covalent solid.

In the solid state, molecules line up in a pattern forming a crystal lattice similar to that of an ionic solid, but with less attraction between particles. The structure of the crystal lattice depends on the shape of the molecule and the type of intermolecular force. Most information about molecules, including properties, molecular shape, bond length, and bond angle, has been determined by studying molecular solids.

## PRACTICE PROBLEMS

Decide whether each of the following molecules is polar or nonpolar.

**60.** $SCl_2$      **61.** $H_2S$      **62.** $CF_4$      **63.** $CS_2$

## CULTURAL DIVERSITY

### Medical Research

Do you have an allergy? Make a tea of beetle legs, lichens, toadstools, and some mysterious colored powders. The use of herbal remedies has been well documented in China over at least the past 2500 years. Western scientists and pharmaceutical companies are looking at covalent compounds contained in these remedies as sources of possible drugs for the treatment of cancer and AIDS. The National

Cancer Institute recently compiled data that catalogs the medicinal effects of Chinese herbs. In 1992, the National Institute of Health created an Office of Alternative Medicine to evaluate a variety of medical therapies, including five related to Chinese herbal medicine. Several U.S. pharmaceutical companies have formed over the past few years to develop drugs from Chinese plants.

# problem-solving LAB

## How do dispersion forces determine the boiling point of a substance?

**Making and Using Graphs** The strength of the dispersion force between nonpolar molecules determines the temperature at which these substances boil. Measuring the boiling point allows one to get a fairly good estimate of the relative strength of this force among different molecules.

**Analysis**

The table lists the molecular masses and boiling points for eight compounds composed of carbon and hydrogen atoms. Construct a graph showing the relationship between these quantities. Infer from the graph how dispersion forces change with increasing molecular mass. Then, draw the molecular structure for each molecule.

**Thinking Critically**

1. How do the relationship demonstrated by the graph and the geometry of the different hydrocarbons help to explain the effect the dispersion force has on molecules of different size?

2. How would you use your graph to predict the properties of similar but larger compounds, such as decane ($C_{10}H_{22}$)?

| Name | Formula | M (amu) | $T_{bp}$ (°C) |
|------|---------|---------|---------------|
| Methane | $CH_4$ | 16 | −161.48 |
| Ethane | $C_2H_6$ | 30 | −88.6 |
| Propane | $C_3H_8$ | 44 | −42.1 |
| Butane | $C_4H_{10}$ | 58 | −0.5 |
| Pentane | $C_5H_{12}$ | 72 | 36.06 |
| Hexane | $C_6H_{14}$ | 86 | 68.73 |
| Heptane | $C_7H_{16}$ | 100 | 98.5 |
| Octane | $C_8H_{18}$ | 114 | 125.7 |

## Covalent Network Solids

A number of solids are composed only of atoms interconnected by a network of covalent bonds. These solids are often called covalent network solids. Quartz is a network solid, as is diamond. See **Figure 9-20.** In contrast to molecular solids, network solids are typically brittle, nonconductors of heat or electricity, and extremely hard. In a diamond, four other carbon atoms surround each carbon atom. This tetrahedral arrangement forms a strongly bonded crystal system that is extremely hard and has a very high melting point.

**Figure 9-20**

In diamond, each carbon atom is bonded to four other carbon atoms. Network solids, such as diamond, are often used in cutting tools because of their hardness.

# problem-solving LAB

**Purpose** 📦
Students will use graphs to explore the effects forces have on carbon chains of different lengths.

**Process Skills**
Making and using graphs, drawing conclusions, applying concepts, predicting, hypothesizing

**Teaching Strategy**
Explain to students that the force between nonpolar molecules is the result of mutual polarization that is induced when the atoms pass near each other. Because electrons have little mass, they are easily displaced, creating momentary dipoles that can attract other nearby dipoles with the opposite polarization. For straight-chain hydrocarbons, an increase in the length of the molecule produces more dipole interactions, thus affecting properties such as boiling point.

**Analysis**
See Solutions Manual for graph. Dispersion forces increase with increasing molecular mass due to an increase in the number of electrons.

**Thinking Critically**
1. As the molecule gets longer, the force of attraction increases. The longer shape allows more contact between electron clouds.
2. by extrapolating the graph to the mass of decane (142 amu)

✔ **Assessment**
**Knowledge** Have students explain why the graph of boiling point shows a slight leveling off as the molecular mass increases. **L2**

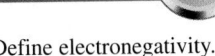

## Section 9.5 Assessment

64. Define electronegativity.

65. How is electronegativity difference used in determining the type of bond that occurs between two atoms?

66. Describe a polar covalent bond.

67. What is a polar molecule?

68. List three properties of a covalent compound.

69. **Thinking Critically** Predict the type of bond that will form between the following atoms.
    **a.** H and S     **b.** C and H     **c.** Na and S

70. **Drawing Conclusions** Draw the Lewis structure for the $SF_4$ and $SF_6$ molecules and determine if each molecule is polar or nonpolar.

## Section 9.5 Assessment

64. the tendency of an atom to attract electrons to itself

65. If the difference is zero, the bond is considered nonpolar covalent; if between 0 and 1.7, polar covalent; if greater than 1.7, ionic.

66. A polar covalent bond has unequal sharing of electrons. The electrons are pulled toward one of the atoms, generating partial charges on the ends.

67. It has a greater electron density on one side of the molecule.

68. The solid state of a molecule is crystalline. A molecular solid is a nonconductor, is soft, and has a low melting point.

69. **a.** polar covalent **b.** polar covalent **c.** ionic

70.

polar                nonpolar

**267**

## Preparation

**Time Allotment**
One laboratory period

**Process Skills**
Applying concepts, collecting data, interpreting data, comparing and contrasting, measuring, observing and inferring, using numbers, predicting

**Safety Precaution**
Caution students to use care when cutting the bottle.

**Disposal**
Paper can be discarded in the trashcan. Bottles should either be kept for reuse or recycled.

**Preparation of Materials**
Ask students to bring in 2-liter bottles ahead of time.

## Pre-Lab

**3.** Polarity relates to an uneven distribution of charge. Because of differences in polarity, different materials will travel through a chromatographic medium at different rates because they are attracted to the medium differently.

**4.** Predictions might include that different components of the pigment mixture will separate and move at different rates.

**5.** Hypotheses might include that the more soluble pigment is probably more polar and its $R_f$ will be greater because it will travel more at the speed of the solvent.

## Procedure

- Require that students' notebooks contain the following items before they begin: Objectives, Safety Precaution, Outline or Flow Chart of the Procedure, Data Table.
- If possible, allow chromatograms to develop for a longer period of time.

# Chromatography

Paper chromatography is a common way to separate various components of a mixture. The components of the mixture separate because different substances are selectively absorbed by paper due to differences in polarity. In this field or laboratory investigation, you will separate the various pigments found in leaves. You also will calculate the ratio called $R_f$ for each of them. The ratio $R_f$ compares the distance traveled by a substance, $D_s$, to the distance traveled by the solvent, $D_f$. The ratio is written as $R_f = D_s / D_f$.

**Problem**
How can a mixture be separated based on the polarity of substances in the mixture?

**Objectives**
- **Separate** pigments found in leaves.
- **Determine** the $R_f$ value for each of the pigments in the leaves.

**Materials**
chromatography paper (3 pieces)
2-L plastic soft drink bottle
pencils (2)
metric ruler
tape
scissors or metal snips
aluminum foil
acetone
fresh leaf samples from three different species of deciduous trees or outdoor plants.

**Safety Precautions**

- Acetone is a flammable liquid. Do not use near flames or sparks.
- Do not allow acetone to contact skin.
- Perform procedure in an area with proper ventilation.

**Pre-Lab**

1. Read the entire **CHEMLAB**.
2. Prepare all written materials that you will take into the laboratory. Be sure to include safety precautions, procedure notes, and a data table in which to record your observations.
3. What is polarity? How is polarity related to how chromatography works?
4. Predict what will happen when a mixture of leaf pigments is placed on a piece of paper and a solvent is allowed to move through the paper, moving the pigment with it.
5. Suppose that the pigments in two samples contain red pigment and that the red pigment in sample A is more soluble in acetone than the red pigment in sample B. Form a hypothesis regarding which red pigment has the higher $R_f$ value. Explain your answer.

| Paper Chromatography | | | | |
|---|---|---|---|---|
| Leaf sample | $D_f$ (cm) | Colors | $D_s$ (cm) | $R_f$ |
| 1 | | | | |
| | | | | |
| | | | | |
| 2 | | | | |
| | | | | |
| | | | | |
| 3 | | | | |
| | | | | |
| | | | | |

## Sample Data and Observations

| Paper Chromatography | | | | |
|---|---|---|---|---|
| Leaf sample | $D_f$ (cm) | Colors | $D_s$ (cm) | $R_f$ |
| 1 | 4.9 | green | 3.1 | 0.63 |
| | | yellow | 3.9 | 0.80 |
| | | orange | 4.8 | 0.98 |
| 2 | 4.8 | yellow | 2.5 | 0.52 |
| | | green | 3.0 | 0.63 |
| | | orange | 4.4 | 0.92 |
| 3 | 5.6 | yellow-orange | 0.5 | 0.089 |
| | | green | 3.5 | 0.63 |
| | | orange | 3.9 | 0.70 |

## Expected Results

Different components of the mixture would be expected to travel at different speeds. See the Data Table for sample results.

## Analyze and Conclude

1. See Data Table.
2. See Data Table.
3. See Data Table.

## Procedure

1. For each leaf sample, crush the leaves and soak them in a small amount of acetone to make a concentrated solution of the pigments in the leaves.

2. Cut the top off a 2-liter bottle. Cut small notches, as shown in the figure, so that a pencil can rest across the top of the bottle.

3. Cut three pieces of 3-cm wide chromatography paper to a length of about 18 cm. Label the top of each paper with a number. Assign a number to each pigment sample used. Draw pencil lines about 5 cm from the bottom of the end of each paper.

4. On the pencil line of paper 1, put a dot from the first sample. Make sure the dot is concentrated but not wide. Do the same for the other samples on their respective papers. Tape the papers to the pencil, as shown in the figure.

5. Put enough acetone in the 2-liter bottle so that when the papers are put in the bottle, the solvent touches only the bottom 1 cm of each paper, as shown in the figure. **CAUTION:** *Do not allow acetone to come in contact with skin. Use in area with proper ventilation.*

6. Carefully lower the chromatography papers into the acetone and put the pencil into the notches at the top of the bottle. Cover the top with aluminum foil. Allow the chromatograms to develop for about 35-40 minutes.

7. When the chromatograms are finished, remove them from the bottle. Mark the highest point reached by the solvent. Then, allow the papers to air dry.

## Cleanup and Disposal

1. Dispose of the acetone as directed by your teacher.

2. Throw the chromatography paper in the trash can.

## Analyze and Conclude

1. **Observing and Inferring** Record in the data table the colors that are found in each of the chromatograms. Space is allowed for three colors, but some samples may contain fewer or more than three colors.

2. **Measuring** For each strip, measure the distance the solvent traveled from the pencil line ($D_f$). For each color, measure from the top of the original marker dot to the farthest point the color traveled ($D_s$). Record these values in your data table.

3. **Interpreting Data** Calculate the $R_f$ values for each of the pigments in each chromatogram and record them in the data table.

4. **Comparing and Contrasting** Describe the differences between the pigments in each of the samples.

5. **Applying Concepts** Will a polar solvent, such as water, cause a difference in how the pigments are separated? Explain your answer.

6. **Error Analysis** What could be done to improve the measurements you used to calculate $R_f$?

## Real-World Chemistry

1. Use your results to explain what happens to leaves in autumn.

2. How might chromatography be used to analyze the composition of the dye in a marker?

4. Different colored pigments travel different distances. The pigments that have the greatest attraction to the paper don't travel as far.

5. Polar components in the pigment mixture will be more attracted to water and will travel farther with it than nonpolar components will.

6. Answers might include having more than one person measuring $D_s$ so all could be measured at the same time.

## Real-World Chemistry

1. Answers might include that the pigments change in cold weather and those remaining are carried to different parts of the leaves based on polarity.

2. Choose an appropriate solvent (water for a water-soluble marker and a nonpolar solvent for a permanent marker) and use a dot from the marker instead of a drop from the pigment mixture.

### ✔ Assessment

**Performance** Have students test a permanent marker using a solvent such as ethanol. Compare the dyes that separate out. Use the Performance Task Assessment List for Carrying Out a Strategy and Collecting Data in **PASC**, p. 25.

## Resource Manager

**ChemLab and MiniLab Worksheets,** pp. 34–36 L2

**National Science Content Standards**

**Pages 268–269**
UCP.2, UCP.3, UCP.5; A.1, A.2; B.2, B.4

# How It Works

## Purpose

Students will learn how the polarity of water is the basis of the operation of a microwave oven.

## Background

Water molecules are constantly jostled about as they align themselves with the changing polarity of the microwave energy field. In a microwave oven, these alignment changes take place about five billion times every second. The increased kinetic energy of the molecules raises their temperature. Because the microwave energy penetrates the food and generates heat within it, a microwave oven cooks food more quickly than a conventional oven.

## Visual Learning

Have students study the steps involved in using microwaves to heat food. Then have them work in pairs to explain the procedure to another student.

## Teaching Strategies

- If a microwave oven is available, heat equal masses of different food substances for equal lengths of time. Have students use what they know about how a microwave oven operates to explain the differences in the final temperatures.
- Point out that all foods contain water, even if it is a small amount.
- Explain to students that the reason popcorn pops in the microwave is that water contained in the kernels changes to water vapor, causing pressure that pops the kernel open.

**National Science Content Standards**

**Pages 270–271**
UCP.2, UCP.3, UCP.5; B.1, B.2, B.4, B.6; E.2

**270**

# How It Works
## Microwave Oven

Today, about 90 percent of home kitchens in the United States have a microwave oven. The polar nature and small size of water molecules allow a microwave oven to cook food without a conventional source of heat. Many large molecules, such as those in sugars and fats, are nonpolar and are not easily heated by microwaves because the molecules cannot easily and rapidly realign themselves. Also, substances that are in the form of crystals usually do not heat well because the bonds that form the crystal structure prevent the molecules from easily realigning themselves.

❸ Stirrer distributes microwaves throughout the cooking chamber.

❷ Microwaves travel through a hollow tube called a waveguide.

❶ Electrons moving in both a magnetic and electric field generate microwaves.

❼ Increased molecular motion generates heat — raising the temperature of the food.

❹ Microwaves penetrate the food.

❻ Water molecules flip back and forth as the microwave field oscillates.

❺ Polar water molecules align themselves with the microwave field.

## Thinking Critically

1. **Predicting** How well would you expect a microwave oven to heat liquid carbon dioxide ($CO_2$)? $CO_2$ is a small molecule and its structure is O=C=O. Explain your reasoning.

2. **Predicting** Would microwaves have the same heating effect on ice as they have on liquid water? What about table salt (NaCl)? Justify your predictions.

**Chapter 9** Covalent Bonding

## Thinking Critically

1. Students should predict that a microwave oven would not heat the $CO_2$ to any substantial extent. Although it is a small molecule that could easily move in response to the microwave field, it is nonpolar. The molecule would not become aligned. No increase in molecular motion is equivalent to no change in temperature.

2. The heating effect will not be as great on ice and almost none for table salt. In ice, the water molecules are not free to move about. Table salt is not a molecular compound and the individual ions in table salt crystals are not free to move.

## Summary

### 9.1 The Covalent Bond

- A covalent bond is formed when atoms share one or more pairs of electrons.

- Molecules, formed when atoms share electrons, are more stable than their constituent atoms.

- Sharing a single pair of electrons results in a single covalent bond. Two atoms sharing more than one pair of electrons results in a multiple bond.

- A double covalent bond results when two pairs of electrons are shared between atoms. Sharing three pairs of electrons results in a triple covalent bond.

- When an electron pair is shared by the direct overlap of bonding orbitals, a sigma bond results. The overlap of parallel orbitals forms a pi bond. Single bonds are sigma bonds. Multiple bonds involve both sigma and pi bonds.

- Bond length depends on the sizes of the bonded atoms and the number of electron pairs they share. Bond dissociation energy is the energy needed to break a covalent bond. Bond length and bond dissociation energy are directly related.

### 9.2 Naming Molecules

- Names of covalent molecular compounds include prefixes that tell the number of each atom present.

- Molecules that produce hydrogen ions in solution are acids and are named accordingly.

### 9.3 Molecular Structures

- The Lewis structure is used to show the distribution of shared and lone pairs of electrons in a molecule.

- Resonance occurs when more than one valid Lewis structure exists for the same molecule.

- Exceptions to the octet rule occur when an odd number of valence electrons exists between the bonding atoms, not enough electrons are available for an octet, or more than eight electrons are shared.

- Coordinate covalent bonding occurs when one atom of the bonding pair supplies both shared electrons.

### 9.4 Molecular Shape

- The valence shell electron pair repulsion, or VSEPR, model can be used to predict the three-dimensional shape of a molecule. Electron pairs repel each other and determine both the shape of and bond angles in a molecule.

- Hybridization explains the observed shapes of molecules by the presence of equivalent hybrid orbitals.

- Two orbitals form two sp hybrid orbitals, and the molecule is linear. Three orbitals, forming three $sp^2$ hybrid orbitals, form a molecule that is trigonal planar. Four orbitals, forming four $sp^3$ hybrid orbitals, form a molecule that is tetrahedral.

### 9.5 Electronegativity and Polarity

- Electronegativity is the tendency of an atom to attract electrons and is related to electron affinity. The electronegativity difference between two bonded atoms is used to determine the type of bond that most likely occurs.

- Polar bonds occur when electrons are not shared equally, resulting in an unequal distribution of charge and the formation of a dipole.

- The spatial arrangement of polar bonds in a molecule determines the overall polarity of a molecule.

- Weak intermolecular forces, also called van der Waals forces, hold molecules together in the liquid and solid phases. These weak attractive forces determine properties. Molecular solids tend to be soft and have low melting and boiling points.

- Covalent network solids result when each atom is covalently bonded to many other atoms in the solid. These solids are hard and have high melting points.

## Vocabulary

- coordinate covalent bond (p. 257)
- covalent bond (p. 242)
- endothermic (p. 247)
- exothermic (p. 247)
- hybridization (p. 261)
- Lewis structure (p. 243)
- molecule (p. 242)
- oxyacid (p. 250)
- pi bond (p. 246)
- polar covalent (p. 264)
- resonance (p. 256)
- sigma bond (p. 245)
- structural formula (p. 252)
- VSEPR model (p. 259)

chemistrymc.com/vocabulary_puzzlemaker

## Using the Vocabulary

To reinforce chapter vocabulary, have students write a sentence using each term. **L2** **ELL**

## Review Strategies

- Have students locate the nonmetals on the periodic table and summarize the formation of covalent bonds. **L2**

- Have students name and write formulas for molecular compounds and acids. **L2**

- Have students review the steps used in writing correct Lewis structures. Discuss resonance hybrids and exceptions to the octet rule. **L2**

- Have students determine the shape of a molecule, the bond angles present, and the hybrid orbitals. **L2**

- Have students use electronegativity difference to determine predominant bond type and determine polarity. List the properties of molecules. **L2**

- Problems from Appendix A can be used for review. **L2**

For additional help with vocabulary, have students access the Vocabulary PuzzleMaker online.

chemistrymc.com/
vocabulary_puzzlemaker

## EXAMVIEW® PRO

### Use ExamView® Pro Testmaker CD-ROM to:

- Create **multiple versions** of tests.
- Create **modified** tests with one mouse click for struggling students.
- **Edit** existing questions and add your own questions.
- **Build** tests based on national curriculum standards.

## Concept Mapping

**71.** 1. single bonds, 2. double bonds, 3. triple bonds, 4. one, 5. two, 6. three, 7. sigma, 8. sigma, 9. pi, 10. sigma, 11. pi

## Mastering Concepts

**72.** Atoms lose, gain, or share electrons to end with a full outer energy level. Certain atoms share electrons to achieve an octet.

**73.** The nucleus of one atom attracts the electrons of the other atom, and they share one or more pairs of electrons.

**74.** Molecules bond covalently.

**75.** See Figure 9-1 on page 242.

**76.** single bond: sigma bond; double bond: a sigma bond and a pi bond; triple bond: one sigma and two pi bonds

**77.** Answers should agree with Figure 9-9 on page 251.

**78.** when it releases $H^+$ in water solution

**79.** the number of valence electrons for each atom

**80.** the repulsive nature of electron pairs around a central atom

**81.** **a.** linear, 180°
**b.** linear, 180°
**c.** trigonal planar, 120°
**d.** tetrahedral, 109°

**82.** four

**83.** five identical $sp^3d$ orbitals formed

**84.** It increases left to right in a period and decreases top to bottom in a group.

**85.** A nonpolar molecule has a symmetric distribution of charge, while a polar molecule has a concentration of electrons on one side of the molecule.

**86.** Electrons in a polar bond are closer to the more electronegative atom because of unequal sharing. Those in a nonpolar bond are shared equally.

---

Go to the Chemistry Web site at chemistrymc.com for additional Chapter 9 Assessment.

## Concept Mapping

**71.** Complete the concept map using the following terms: double bonds, one, pi, sigma, single bonds, three, triple bonds, two. Each term can be used more than once.

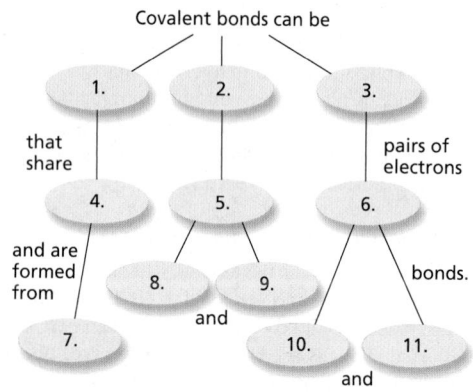

## Mastering Concepts

**72.** What is the octet rule, and how is it used in covalent bonding? (9.1)

**73.** Describe the formation of a covalent bond. (9.1)

**74.** Describe the bonding in molecules. (9.1)

**75.** Describe the forces, both attractive and repulsive, that occur as two atoms come closer together. (9.1)

**76.** How could you predict the presence of a sigma or pi bond in a molecule? (9.1)

**77.** Explain how molecular compounds are named. (9.2)

**78.** When is a molecular compound named as an acid? (9.2)

**79.** What must be known in order to draw the Lewis structure for a molecule? (9.3)

**80.** On what is the VSEPR model based? (9.4)

**81.** What is the molecular shape of each of the following molecules? Estimate the bond angle for each assuming no lone pair. (9.4)

  **a.** A—B
  **b.** A—B—A

---

**c.**
$$A-B-A$$
$$|$$
$$A$$

**d.**
$$A$$
$$|$$
$$A-B-A$$
$$|$$
$$A$$

**82.** What is the maximum number of hybrid orbitals a carbon atom can form? (9.4)

**83.** Explain the theory of hybridization and determine the number of hybrid orbitals present in the molecule $PCl_5$. (9.4)

**84.** Describe the trends in electronegativity in the periodic table. (9.5)

**85.** Explain the difference between nonpolar molecules and polar molecules. (9.5)

**86.** Compare the location of bonding electrons in a polar covalent bond with those in a nonpolar covalent bond. Explain your answer. (9.5)

**87.** What is the difference between a covalent molecular solid and a covalent network solid? Do their physical properties differ? Explain your answer. (9.5)

## Mastering Problems

### Covalent Bonds (9.1)

**88.** Give the number of valence electrons in N, As, Br, and Se. Predict the number of covalent bonds needed for each of these elements to satisfy the octet rule.

**89.** Locate the sigma and pi bonds in the following molecule.

$$\overset{\displaystyle O}{\underset{\displaystyle}{\overset{\|}{H-C-H}}}$$

**90.** Locate the sigma and pi bonds in the following molecule.

$$H-C \equiv C-H$$

### Bond Length (9.1)

**91.** Consider the molecules CO, $CO_2$, and $CH_2O$. Which C—O bond is shorter? In which molecule is the C—O bond stronger?

**92.** Consider the carbon-nitrogen bonds in the following:

$$C \equiv N^- \quad \text{and} \quad \overset{\displaystyle H \;\; H}{\underset{\displaystyle H \;\; H}{H-C-N}}$$

Which bond is shorter? Which is stronger?

chemistrymc.com/chapter_test

---

**87.** A covalent molecular solid is soft and has a low melting point because of weak intermolecular forces. A covalent network solid has a high melting point and is very hard because of the strength of the network of covalent bonds.

### Resource Manager

Chapter Assessment, pp. 49–54 **L2**
Supplemental Problems, Ch. 9
ExamView® Pro CD-ROM
MindJogger Videoquizzes DVD/VHS
Solutions Manual, Ch. 9
Chemistry Interactive CD-ROM,
  Ch. 9 quiz

**93.** Rank each of the molecules below in order of the shortest to the longest sulfur-oxygen bond length.

**a.** $SO_2$    **b.** $SO_3^{2-}$    **c.** $SO_4^{2-}$

## Naming Covalent Compounds (9.2)

**94.** Name each of the following solutions as an acid.

**a.** $HClO_2$    **c.** $H_2Se$
**b.** $H_3PO_4$    **d.** $HClO_3$

**95.** Name each of the following molecules.

**a.** $NF_3$    **c.** $SO_3$
**b.** $NO$    **d.** $SiF_4$

**96.** Name each of the following molecules.

**a.** $SeO_2$    **c.** $N_2F_4$
**b.** $SeO_3$    **d.** $S_4N_4$

## Writing Formulas (9.2)

**97.** Write the formula for each of the following.

**a.** sulfur difluoride
**b.** silicon tetrachloride
**c.** carbon tetrafluoride
**d.** sulfurous acid

**98.** Write the formula for each of the following.

**a.** silicon dioxide
**b.** bromous acid
**c.** chlorine trifluoride
**d.** hydrobromic acid

## Lewis Structures (9.3)

**99.** Draw the Lewis structure for each of these molecules or ions.

**a.** $H_2S$    **c.** $SO_2$
**b.** $BF_4^-$    **d.** $SeCl_2$

**100.** Draw the Lewis structure for each of these molecules or ions.

**a.** $SeF_2$    **d.** $POCl_3$
**b.** $ClO_2^-$    **e.** $GeF_4$
**c.** $PO_3^{3-}$

**101.** Which of the following elements are capable of forming molecules in which an atom has an expanded octet? Explain your answer.

**a.** B    **d.** O
**b.** C    **e.** Se
**c.** P

**102.** Draw three resonance structures for the polyatomic ion $CO_3^{2-}$.

**103.** Draw two resonance structures for the polyatomic ion $CHO_2^-$.

**104.** Draw the Lewis structure for each of the following molecules that have central atoms that do not obey the octet rule.

**a.** $PCl_5$    **c.** $ClF_5$
**b.** $BF_3$    **d.** $BeH_2$

## Molecular Shape (9.4)

**105.** Predict the molecular shape and bond angle, and identify the hybrid orbitals for each of the following. Drawing the Lewis structure may help you.

**a.** $SCl_2$
**b.** $NH_2Cl$
**c.** HOF
**d.** $BF_3$

**106.** For each of the following, predict the molecular shape.

**a.** COS    **b.** $CF_2Cl_2$

**107.** Identify the expected hybrid on the central atom for each of the following. Drawing the Lewis structure may help you.

**a.** $XeF_4$    **c.** $KrF_2$
**b.** $TeF_4$    **d.** $OF_2$

## Electronegativity and Polarity (9.5)

**108.** For each pair, indicate the more polar bond by circling the negative end of its dipole.

**a.** C−S, C−O
**b.** C−F, C−N
**c.** P−H, P−Cl

**109.** For each of the bonds listed, tell which atom is more negatively charged.

**a.** C−H    **c.** C−S
**b.** C−N    **d.** C−O

**110.** Predict which of the following bonds is the most polar.

**a.** C−O    **c.** C−Cl
**b.** Si−O    **d.** C−Br

**111.** Rank the following bonds according to increasing polarity.

**a.** C−H    **d.** O−H
**b.** N−H    **e.** Cl−H
**c.** Si−H

**112.** Consider the following and determine if they are polar. Explain your answers.

**a.** $H_3O^+$    **c.** $H_2S$
**b.** $PCl_5$    **d.** $CF_4$

**113.** Why is the $CF_4$ molecule nonpolar even though it contains polar bonds?

## Mastering Problems

Complete solutions to Chapter Assessment problems can be found in the **Solutions Manual.**

### Covalent Bonds (9.1)
**Level 1**
**88.** N: 5, 3; As: 5, 3; Br: 7, 1; Se: 6, 2

**Level 2**
**89.** single bonds: sigma bonds; double bond: one sigma bond and one pi bond
**90.** single bonds: sigma bonds; triple bond: one sigma and two pi bonds

### Bond Length (9.1)
**Level 1**
**91.** It is shortest and strongest in the triple bond in CO.
**92.** The triple bond in C≡N⁻ is shorter and stronger.

**Level 2**
**93.** a, b, c

### Naming Covalent Compounds (9.2)
**Level 1**
**94. a.** chlorous acid
    **b.** phosphoric acid
    **c.** hydroselenic acid
    **d.** chloric acid
**95. a.** nitrogen trifluoride
    **b.** nitrogen monoxide
    **c.** sulfur trioxide
    **d.** silicon tetrafluoride

**Level 2**
**96. a.** selenium dioxide
    **b.** selenium trioxide
    **c.** dinitrogen tetrafluoride
    **d.** tetrasulfur tetranitride

### Writing Formulas (9.2)
**Level 1**
**97. a.** $SF_2$ **b.** $SiCl_4$ **c.** $CF_4$
    **d.** $H_2SO_3$

**Level 2**
**98. a.** $SiO_2$    **c.** $ClF_3$
    **b.** $HBrO_2$    **d.** HBr

## Lewis Structures (9.3)
**Level 1**
**99. a.**

**b.**

**c.** :Ö=S̈
    :Ö:

**d.** :C̈l—S̈e:
    :C̈l:

**100. a.** :F̈—S̈e:
    :F̈:

**b.** [:Ö—C̈l: ]⁻
    :Ö:

**c.** [:Ö—P—Ö: ]³⁻
    :Ö:

273

**d.**

**e.**

## Level 2

**101.** P and Se because they are in period 3 and higher and have a d sublevel available

**102.**

**103.**

**104. a.**

**b.**

**c.**

**d.** H—Be—H

---

**114.** Use Lewis structures to predict the molecular polarities for sulfur difluoride, sulfur tetrafluoride, and sulfur hexafluoride.

## Mixed Review

*Sharpen your problem solving skills by answering the following.*

**115.** Consider the following molecules and determine which of the molecules are polar. Explain your answer.
- **a.** $CH_3Cl$
- **b.** ClF
- **c.** $NCl_3$
- **d.** $BF_3$
- **e.** $CS_2$

**116.** Arrange the following bonds in order of least to greatest polar character.
- **a.** C—O
- **b.** Si—O
- **c.** Ge—O
- **d.** C—Cl
- **e.** C—Br

**117.** Draw the Lewis structure for $ClF_3$ and identify the hybrid orbitals.

**118.** Use the Lewis structure for $SF_4$, to predict the molecular shape and identify the hybrid orbitals.

**119.** Write the formula for each of these molecules.
- **a.** chlorine monoxide
- **b.** arsenic acid
- **c.** phosphorus pentachloride
- **d.** hydrosulfuric acid

**120.** Name each of the following molecules.
- **a.** $PCl_3$
- **b.** $Cl_2O_7$
- **c.** $P_4O_6$
- **d.** NO

## Thinking Critically

**121. Concept Mapping** Design a concept map that will link both the VSEPR model and the hybridization theory to molecular shape.

**122. Making and Using Tables** Complete the table using Chapters 8 and 9.

**Table 9-4**

| Properties and Bonding | | | |
|---|---|---|---|
| **Solid** | **Bond description** | **Characteristic of solid** | **Example** |
| Ionic | | | |
| Covalent molecular | | | |
| Metallic | | | |
| Covalent network | | | |

**123. Drawing Conclusions** Consider each of the following characteristics and determine whether the molecule is more likely to be polar or nonpolar.
- **a.** a solid at room temperature
- **b.** a gas at room temperature
- **c.** attracted to an electric current

## Writing in Chemistry

**124.** Research chromatography and write a paper discussing how it is used to separate mixtures.

**125.** Research laundry detergents. Write a paper to explain why they are used to clean oil and grease out of fabrics.

## Cumulative Review

*Refresh your understanding of previous chapters by answering the following.*

**126.** The mass of the same liquid is given in the table below for the following volumes. Graph the volume on the *x*-axis and the mass on the *y*-axis. Calculate the slope of the graph. What information will the slope give you? (Chapter 2)

**Table 9-5**

| Mass vs. Volume | |
|---|---|
| **Volume** | **Mass** |
| 4.1 mL | 9.36 g |
| 6.0 mL | 14.04 g |
| 8.0 mL | 18.72 g |
| 10.0 mL | 23.40 g |

**127.** Which group 3A element is expected to exhibit properties that are significantly different from the remaining family members? (Chapter 7)

**128.** Write the correct chemical formula or name the following compounds. (Chapter 8)
- **a.** NaI
- **b.** calcium carbonate
- **c.** $Fe(NO_3)_3$
- **d.** $Sr(OH)_2$
- **e.** potassium chlorate
- **f.** copper(II) sulfate
- **g.** $CoCl_2$
- **h.** ammonium phosphate
- **i.** silver acetate
- **j.** $Mg(BrO_3)_2$

---

## Molecular Shape (9.4)
### Level 1
**105. a.** bent, 104.5°, sp³
   **b.** trigonal pyramidal, 107°, sp³
   **c.** bent, 104.5°, sp³
   **d.** trigonal planar, 120°, sp²

### Level 2
**106. a.** linear    **b.** tetrahedral
**107. a.** sp³d²    **c.** sp³d
   **b.** sp³d    **d.** sp³

## Electronegativity and Polarity (9.5)
### Level 1
**108.** The following are circled:
   **a.** O  **b.** F  **c.** Cl
**109. a.** C  **b.** N  **c.** S  **d.** O
**110.** Si—O
**111.** c, a, b, e, d

### Level 2
**112. a.** polar, asymmetrical
   **b.** nonpolar, symmetrical

*Use the questions and the test-taking tip to prepare for your standardized test.*

**1.** The common name of SiI₄ is tetraiodosilane. What is its molecular compound name?

  **a.** silane tetraiodide
  **b.** silane tetraiodine
  **c.** silicon iodide
  **d.** silicon tetraiodide

**2.** Which of the following compounds contains at least one pi bond?

  **a.** $CO_2$     **c.** $AsI_3$
  **b.** $CHCl_3$    **d.** $BeF_2$

**3.** What is the Lewis structure for silicon disulfide?

  **a.** $Si::\ddot{S}:$

  **b.** $\ddot{S}::Si::\ddot{S}$

  **c.** $\ddot{S}:Si:\ddot{S}$

  **d.** $:S::Si::S:$

**4.** The central selenium atom in selenium hexafluoride forms an expanded octet. How many electron pairs surround the central Se atom?

  **a.** 4     **c.** 6
  **b.** 5     **d.** 7

**5.** Chloroform ($CHCl_3$) was one of the first anesthetics used in medicine. The chloroform molecule contains 26 valence electrons in total. How many of these valence electrons take part in covalent bonds?

  **a.** 26     **c.** 8
  **b.** 13     **d.** 4

**6.** Which is the strongest type of intermolecular bond?

  **a.** ionic bond
  **b.** dipole-dipole force
  **c.** dispersion force
  **d.** hydrogen bond

**7.** All of the following compounds have bent molecular shapes EXCEPT _____.

  **a.** $BeH_2$    **c.** $H_2O$
  **b.** $H_2S$    **d.** $SeH_2$

**8.** Which of the following compounds is NOT polar?

  **a.** $H_2S$    **c.** $SiH_3Cl$
  **b.** $CCl_4$    **d.** $AsH_3$

**Interpreting Tables** Use the table to answer the following questions.

| Bond Dissociation Energies at 298 K | | | |
|---|---|---|---|
| **Bond** | **kJ/mol** | **Bond** | **kJ/mol** |
| Cl—Cl | 242 | N≡N | 945 |
| C—C | 345 | O—H | 467 |
| C—H | 416 | C—O | 358 |
| C—N | 305 | C=O | 745 |
| H—I | 299 | O=O | 498 |
| H—N | 391 | | |

**9.** Which of the following diatomic gases has the shortest bond between its two atoms?

  **a.** HI     **c.** $Cl_2$
  **b.** $O_2$     **d.** $N_2$

**10.** Approximately how much energy will it take to break all of the bonds present in the molecule below?

  **a.** 5011 kJ/mol    **c.** 4318 kJ/mol
  **b.** 3024 kJ/mol    **d.** 4621 kJ/mol

---

### TEST-TAKING TIP

**Wear A Watch** If you are taking a timed test, you should make sure that you pace yourself and do not spend too much time on any one question, but you shouldn't spend time staring at the clock. When each section of the test begins, set your watch for noon. This will make it very easy for you to figure out how many minutes have passed. After all, it is much easier to know that you started at 12:00 (according to your watch) and you'll be done at 12:30 than it is to figure out that you started at 10:42 and that time will run out at 11:12.

  **c.** polar, asymmetrical
  **d.** nonpolar, symmetrical
**113.** equal distribution of charge
**114.** $SF_2$ and $SF_4$ are polar. $SF_6$ is nonpolar.

## Mixed Review

**115.** The polar molecules are $CH_3Cl$, ClF, and $NCl_3$ because each molecule is asymmetric and the charge is not distributed evenly.
**116.** e, d, a, c, b
**117.**   $sp^3d$

**118.** $sp^3d$; see the Solutions Manual
**119.** **a.** ClO     **c.** $PCl_5$
    **b.** $H_3AsO_4$  **d.** $H_2S$
**120.** **a.** phosphorus trichloride
    **b.** dichlorine heptoxide
    **c.** tetraphosphorus hexoxide
    **d.** nitrogen monoxide

## Thinking Critically

**121.** Concept maps will vary.
**122.** **Column 2:** the electrostatic attraction of a positive ion for a negative ion; the sharing of electrons between two atoms; the attraction of a positive ion for delocalized electrons; atoms covalently bonded to many other atoms in a crystal lattice **Column 3:** hard, rigid, brittle, crystalline, high melting point, nonconductor in the solid state; soft, low melting point, nonconductor in the solid state; a crystal that conducts heat and electricity, malleable, ductile, high melting point; crystal is hard, rigid, brittle, nonconductor **Sample answers for Column 4:** NaCl, $CO_2$, Ag, diamond

National Science Content Standards

Pages 272–275
UCP.2, UCP.3, UCP.5; B.1, B.2, B.4

---

**123. a.** polar    **b.** nonpolar   **c.** polar

## Cumulative Review

**126.** 2.34 g/mL; density
**127.** boron
**128. a.** sodium iodide
    **b.** $CaCO_3$
    **c.** iron(III) nitrate
    **d.** strontium hydroxide

  **e.** $KClO_3$
  **f.** $CuSO_4$
  **g.** cobalt(II) chloride
  **h.** $(NH_4)_3PO_4$
  **i.** $AgC_2H_3O_2$
  **j.** magnesium bromate

## Standardized Test Practice

**1.** d   **3.** b   **5.** c   **7.** a   **9.** d
**2.** a   **4.** c   **6.** d   **8.** b  **10.** a

# Resource Manager

| Section | Objectives | Activities/Features |
|---|---|---|
| **Section 10.1**<br>**Reactions and Equations**<br>2 sessions<br>1 block | 1. **Recognize** evidence of chemical change.<br>2. **Represent** chemical reactions with equations. | **Discovery Lab:** Observing a Change, p. 277<br>**Earth Science Connection,** p. 281 |
| **Section 10.2**<br>**Classifying Chemical Reactions**<br>1 session<br>½ block | 3. **Classify** chemical reactions.<br>4. **Identify** the characteristics of different classes of chemical reactions. | **Problem-Solving Lab:** Can you predict the reactivities of halogens? p. 288<br>**ChemLab Small Scale:** Activities of Metals, pp. 300–301 |
| **Section 10.3**<br>**Reactions in Aqueous Solutions**<br>3 sessions<br>1½ blocks | 5. **Describe** aqueous solutions.<br>6. **Write** complete ionic and net ionic equations for chemical reactions in aqueous solutions.<br>7. **Predict** whether reactions in aqueous solutions will produce a precipitate, water, or a gas. | **MiniLab:** Observing a Precipitate-Forming Reaction, p. 295<br>**Careers Using Chemistry:** Pastry Chef, p. 297<br>**How It Works:** Hot and Cold Packs, p. 302 |

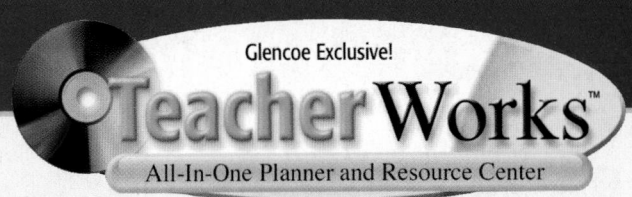

| National Science Content Standards | State/Local Standards | Reproducible Masters | Transparencies |
|---|---|---|---|
| UCP.3, UCP.5; A.1; B.2, B.3, B.6 | | **Study Guide for Content Mastery,** pp. 55–56 **L2** <br> **Challenge Problems,** p. 10 **L3** | **Section Focus** <br> **Transparency 35** **L1** **ELL** <br> **Teaching** <br> **Transparencies 32, 33** **L2** **ELL** <br> **Math Skills** <br> **Transparency 11** **L2** **ELL** |
| UCP.3, UCP.5; A.1; B.2, B.3 | | **Study Guide for Content Mastery,** pp. 57–58 **L2** <br> **ChemLab and MiniLab Worksheets,** pp. 38–40 **L2** <br> **Laboratory Manual,** pp. 73–80 **L2** | **Section Focus** <br> **Transparency 36** **L1** **ELL** <br> **Teaching** <br> **Transparencies 34, 35** **L2** **ELL** |
| UCP.3, UCP.5; A.1, A.2; B.2, B.3, B.6 | | **Study Guide for Content Mastery,** pp. 59–60 **L2** <br> **ChemLab and MiniLab Worksheets,** p. 37 **L2** <br> **Small-Scale Laboratory Manual,** pp. 25–28 **L2** | **Section Focus** <br> **Transparency 37** **L1** **ELL** <br> **Teaching** <br> **Transparency 36** **L2** **ELL** <br> **Math Skills** <br> **Transparency 12** **L2** **ELL** |

**Key to National Science Content Standards:** UCP = Unifying Concepts and
Processes, A = Science as Inquiry, B = Physical Science, C = Life Science,
D = Earth and Space Sciences, E = Science and Technology,
F = Science in Personal and Social Perspectives, G = History and Nature of Science

Refer to pages 4T–5T of the Teacher Guide for an explanation of the
National Science Content Standards correlations.

# Resource Manager

## Materials List

### ChemLab (pages 300–301)
1.0*M* zinc nitrate, 1.0*M* aluminum nitrate, 1.0*M* copper(II) nitrate, 1.0*M* magnesium nitrate, pipettes (4), wire cutters, copper wire, aluminum wire, magnesium ribbon, zinc strips (4), fine sandpaper, 24-well microscale reaction plate

### Discovery Lab (page 277)
25-mL graduated cylinder, 100-mL beaker, pipettes (2), stirring rod, thermometer, effervescent antacid tablet (Alka-Seltzer®), 0.1*M* ammonia solution, universal indicator, distilled water

### MiniLab (page 295)
150-mL beakers (2), 100-mL graduated cylinder, stirring rods (2), spatulas (2), weighing paper, NaOH, Epsom salts ($MgSO_4 \cdot 7H_2O$), distilled water, balance

### Demonstration (pages 280–281)
zinc dust (1 g), iodine crystals (3 g), test tube with stopper, evaporating dish, widemouth glass bottle with stopper, dropper, water

## Preparation of Solutions

For a review of solution preparation, see page 46T of the Teacher Guide.

Quantities are for a class of 30 students.

### ChemLab (pages 300–301)
**1*M* copper(II) nitrate ($Cu(NO_3)_2$)** Dissolve 242 g $Cu(NO_3)_2 \cdot 3H_2O$ in 600 mL distilled water. Make up to 1 L final volume with distilled water.

**1*M* aluminum nitrate ($Al(NO_3)_3$)** Dissolve 375 g $Al(NO_3)_3 \cdot 9H_2O$ in 600 mL distilled water. Make up to 1 L final volume with distilled water.

**1*M* magnesium nitrate ($Mg(NO_3)_2$)** Dissolve 256 g $Mg(NO_3)_2 \cdot 6H_2O$ in 600 mL distilled water. Make up to 1 L final volume with distilled water.

**1*M* zinc nitrate ($Zn(NO_3)_2$)** Dissolve 298 g $Zn(NO_3)_2 \cdot 6H_2O$ in 600 mL distilled water. Make up to 1 L final volume with distilled water.

### Discovery Lab (page 277)
**0.1*M* ammonia solution** Add 1 mL concentrated (15*M*) $NH_3$ (aq) to 150 mL distilled water.

## Assessment Resources

**Chapter Assessment**, pp. 55–60
**MindJogger Videoquizzes** DVD/VHS
**Alternate Assessment in the Science Classroom**
**ExamView® Pro CD-ROM**
**Solutions Manual**, Chapter 10
**Supplemental Problems**, Chapter 10
**Performance Assessment in the Science Classroom**
**Chemistry Interactive CD-ROM**, Chapter 10 quiz

## Additional Resources

**Spanish Resources** ELL
**Guided Reading Audio Program**, Chapter 10 ELL
**Cooperative Learning in the Science Classroom**
**Lab and Safety Skills in the Science Classroom**
**Lesson Plans**
**Block Scheduling Lesson Plans**
**Chemistrymc.com**

## Glencoe Technology

The following multimedia for this chapter are available from Glencoe.

**VIDEOTAPE/DVD**
MindJogger Videoquizzes,
Chapter 10

**CD-ROM**
**Chemistry: Matter and Change**
*Balancing an Equation,* Exploration
*A Metal and Nonmetal React,*
  Demonstration
*Properties of Oxygen Gas,* Demonstration
*Combustion of Ethanol,* Demonstration
*Exothermic Reactions,* Video
*Five Types of Chemical Reactions,*
  Animation
*Types of Chemical Reactions,* Video
*Precipitation Reactions,* Experiment

**CD-ROM**
**ExamView® Pro**
  **Testmaker**

**CD-ROM**
**Interactive Chalkboard**

**CD-ROM**
**TeacherWorks™**

## Multiple Learning Styles

Look for the following icons for strategies that emphasize different learning modalities.

**Kinesthetic**
Differentiated Instruction, p. 294

**Visual-Spatial**
Identifying Misconceptions, p. 281; Portfolio,
p. 290

**Intrapersonal**
Chemistry Journal, pp. 278, 289

**Linguistic**
Portfolio, p. 279; Using Science Terms, p. 284;
Chemistry Journal, pp. 292, 297

**Logical-Mathematical**
Differentiated Instruction, p. 288

## Key to Teaching Strategies

 **L1** Level 1 activities should be appropriate for students with learning difficulties.

**L2** Level 2 activities should be within the ability range of all students.

**L3** Level 3 activities are designed for above-average students.

**ELL** ELL activities should be within the ability range of English Language Learners.

**COOP LEARN** Cooperative Learning activities are designed for small group work.

 **P** These strategies represent student products that can be placed into a best-work portfolio.

 These strategies are useful in a block scheduling format.

## Assessment Planner

**Portfolio Assessment**
Assessment, TWE, pp. 279,
  284, 290, 291, 303
MiniLab, TWE, p. 295

**Performance Assessment**
Problem-Solving Lab, TWE,
  p. 288
Discovery Lab, SE, p. 277
MiniLab, SE, p. 295
ChemLab, SE, pp. 300–301

**Knowledge Assessment**
Assessment, TWE, pp. 282,
  283, 299
ChemLab, TWE, p. 301
Section Assessment, SE,
  pp. 283, 291, 299
Chapter Assessment, SE,
  pp. 304–307

**Skill Assessment**
Assessment, TWE, p. 298
Demonstration, TWE, p. 281

## Tying to Previous Knowledge

Have students review the following concepts before studying this chapter.
Chapter 8: writing formulas for ionic compounds
Chapter 9: writing formulas for molecular compounds

## Using the Photo

Students may not consider that a strong thunderstorm involves myriad chemical reactions. Discuss with the students the chemical reactions that accompany a lightning bolt, rain formation and acid rain, and cloud seeding.

### INTERACTIVE CHALKBOARD with Image Bank

**PowerPoint® Presentations**
This CD-ROM is an editable Microsoft® PowerPoint® presentation that includes:
• Section presentations
• Section checks
• Image bank
• Links to Chemistry Online
• All transparencies
• Animations
• Audio

# Chemical Reactions

## What You'll Learn

▶ You will write chemical equations to describe chemical reactions.
▶ You will classify and identify chemical reactions.
▶ You will write ionic equations for reactions that occur in aqueous solutions.

## Why It's Important

Chemical reactions affect you every second of every day. For example, life-sustaining chemical reactions occur continuously in your body. Other chemical reactions occur in less likely situations, such as in a thunderstorm.

### Chemistry Online

Visit the Chemistry Web site at **chemistrymc.com** to find links about chemical reactions.

The electricity of a lightning bolt provides the energy that sparks chemical reactions among substances in the atmosphere.

## DISCOVERY LAB

**Purpose**
Students will classify an observed change as either chemical or physical and identify the evidence of a chemical change.

**Safety and Disposal**
Cover the desktop with an absorbent cloth that can catch any overflow from the reaction. Contents of the test tube may be flushed down the drain.

**Teaching Strategies**
• Make sure the effervescent tablet contains a carbonate or hydrogen carbonate and a weak acid such as citric acid.
• See page 276C for preparation of solutions.

**Expected Results**
Citric acid in the tablet dissolves in water, turning the indicator from blue to red. The acid reacts with sodium hydrogen

carbonate, producing carbon dioxide gas. As the gas escapes, the solution is buffered and the acidity decreases. The red color quickly changes to orange, then yellow, and after standing, to green. The contents of the test tube foam and overflow. The temperature of the solution decreases 2°C.

**Analysis**
Each of the characteristics of the reaction is evidence of a chemical change; therefore, a chemical change is observed.

## DISCOVERY LAB

### Observing a Change

An indicator is a chemical that shows when change occurs during a chemical reaction.

#### Safety Precautions

Always wear goggles and an apron in the laboratory.

#### Procedure

1. Measure 10.0 mL distilled water in a graduated cylinder and pour it into the beaker. Add one drop of 0.1*M* ammonia to the water.

2. Stir 15 drops of indicator into the solution with the stirring rod. Observe the solution's color. Measure its temperature with the thermometer.

3. Drop the effervescent tablet into the solution. Observe what happens. Record your observations, including any temperature change.

#### Analysis

Did a color change and a temperature change occur? Was a gas produced? Did a physical change or a chemical change occur? Explain.

### Materials

distilled water
25-mL graduated cylinder
100-mL beaker
pipettes (2)
0.1*M* ammonia
universal indicator
stirring rod
thermometer
effervescent tablet

---

## Section 10.1

# Reactions and Equations

### Objectives

- **Recognize** evidence of chemical change.

- **Represent** chemical reactions with equations.

### Vocabulary

chemical reaction
reactant
product
chemical equation
coefficient

Do you know that the foods you eat, the fibers in your clothes, and the plastic in your CDs have something in common? Foods, fibers, and plastic are produced when the atoms in substances are rearranged to form different substances. Atoms are rearranged during the flash of lightning shown in the photo on the opposite page. They were also rearranged when you dropped the effervescent tablet into the beaker of water and indicator in the **DISCOVERY LAB.**

## Evidence of Chemical Reactions

The process by which the atoms of one or more substances are rearranged to form different substances is called a **chemical reaction**. A chemical reaction is another name for a chemical change, which you read about in Chapter 3. Chemical reactions affect every part of your life. They break down your food, producing the energy you need to live. They produce natural fibers such as cotton and wool in the bodies of plants and animals. In factories, they produce synthetic fibers such as nylon and polyesters. Chemical reactions in the engines of cars and buses provide the energy to power the vehicles.

How can you tell when a chemical reaction has taken place? Although some chemical reactions are hard to detect, many reactions provide evidence that they have occurred. A temperature change can indicate a chemical reaction. Many reactions, such as those that occur during a forest fire, release energy in the form of heat and light. Other reactions absorb heat.

In addition to a temperature change, other types of evidence may indicate that a chemical reaction has occurred. One indication of a chemical reaction is

---

## 1 Focus

### Focus Transparency

Before presenting the lesson, display **Section Focus Transparency 35** on the overhead projector. Have students answer the accompanying questions using **Section Focus Transparency Master 35.** L1 ELL

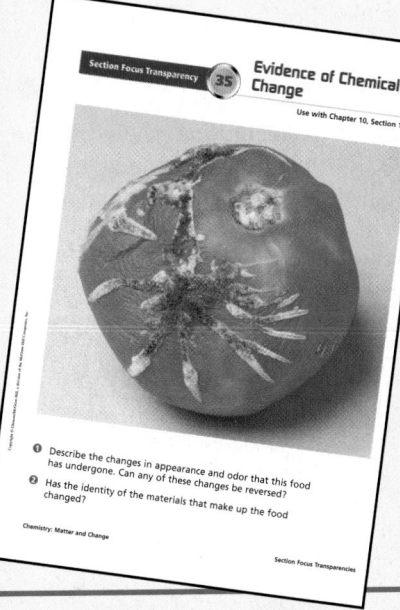

Section Focus Transparency 35
Evidence of Chemical Change

Use with Chapter 10, Section 10.1

① Describe the changes in appearance and odor that this food has undergone. Can any of these changes be reversed?
② Has the identity of the materials that make up the food changed?

Chemistry: Matter and Change

Section Focus Transparencies

### Chapter Themes

The following themes from the National Science Education Standards are covered in this chapter. Refer to page 4T of the Teacher Guide for an explanation of the correlations.

Systems, order, and organization (UCP.1)

Evidence, models, and explanation (UCP.2)

Change, constancy, and measurement (UCP.3)

Form and function (UCP.5)

---

## Resource Manager

**Study Guide for Content Mastery,** pp. 55–56 L2

**Solving Problems: A Chemistry Handbook,** Section 10.1 L2

**Section Focus Transparency 35 and Master** L1 ELL

National Science Content Standards

Pages 276–277
UCP.3, UCP.5; A.1; B.2, B.3

## Concept Development

Ask students to write a word equation for putting together a made-from-scratch cake, a process that requires energy. Student answers may be something like this: energy + salt + sugar + baking powder + eggs + water + shortening + flour → cake. Emphasize that the amounts of reactants and products in a chemical reaction (and equation) are critical. For example, 5 lb salt, 1 tsp sugar, 1 gal water, 4 doz eggs, etc. will likely produce a mess, not a cake. **L2**

## Math in Chemistry

Remind students that when writing the formula for a compound, the oxidation numbers of the component elements or ions must add to zero. For example: $H_2O$ $(2\times(1+)) + (2-) = 0$; $(NH_4)_2S$ $(2\times(1+)) + (2-) = 0$; $Ti(NO_2)_4$ $(1\times(4+)) + (4\times(1-)) = 0$.

### Figure 10-1

Each of these photos illustrates evidence of a chemical reaction.
**a** Reactions that happened when the marshmallow was burned are obvious by the color change.
**b** Chemical reactions occur in the oven when a cake mix is baked, namely, the formation of gas bubbles that cause the cake to rise.
**c** The tarnish that appears on silver and other metals is actually a solid that forms as a result of chemical reactions that take place when the metal is exposed to traces of sulfur compounds in the air.
**d** Numerous chemical reactions happen in an explosion. The appearance of smoke, the release of energy in the form of heat, and the permanent color change of materials involved are all evidence of chemical reactions.

 a
 b
 c
 d

a color change. For example, you may have noticed that the color of some nails that are left outside changes from silver to orange-brown in a short time. The color change is evidence that a chemical reaction occurred between the iron in the nail and the oxygen in air. Odor, gas bubbles, and/or the appearance of a solid are other indications of chemical change. Each of the photographs in **Figure 10-1** shows evidence of a chemical reaction. Do you recognize the evidence in each?

## Representing Chemical Reactions

Chemists use statements called equations to represent chemical reactions. Their equations show a reaction's **reactants**, which are the starting substances, and **products**, which are the substances formed during the reaction. Chemical equations do not express numerical equalities as do mathematical equations because during chemical reactions the reactants are used up as the products form. Instead, the equations used by chemists show the direction in which the reaction progresses. Therefore, an arrow rather than an equal sign is used to separate the reactants from the products. You read the arrow as "react to produce" or "yield". The reactants are written to the arrow's left, and the products are written to its right. When there are two or more reactants, or two or more products, a plus sign separates each reactant or each product. These elements of equation notation are shown below.

reactant 1 + reactant 2 → product 1 + product 2

### Table 10-1

| Symbols Used in Equations | |
|---|---|
| **Symbol** | **Meaning** |
| + | Separates two or more reactants or products |
| → | Separates reactants from products |
| (s) | Identifies solid state |
| (l) | Identifies liquid state |
| (g) | Identifies gaseous state |
| (aq) | Identifies water solution |

## CHEMISTRY JOURNAL

### Observing Chemical Change

 *Intrapersonal* Have students keep a running list in their chemistry journals of chemical reactions they use or observe. Have students also describe and include the evidence for each listed reaction. **L2**

## Resource Manager

**Teaching Transparency 32 and Master**
**L2** **ELL**

In equations, symbols are used to show the physical states of the reactants and products. Reactants and products can exist as solids, liquids, and gases. When they are dissolved in water, they are said to be aqueous. It is important to show the physical states of a reaction's reactants and products in an equation because the physical states provide clues about how the reaction occurs. Some basic symbols used in equations are shown in **Table 10-1**.

**Word equations** You can use statements called word equations to indicate the reactants and products of chemical reactions. The word equation below describes the reaction between iron and chlorine, which is shown in **Figure 10-2**. Iron is a solid and chlorine is a gas. The brown cloud in the photograph is composed of the reaction's product, which is solid particles of iron(III) chloride.

$$\text{reactant 1} + \text{reactant 2} \rightarrow \text{product 1}$$

$$\text{iron(s)} + \text{chlorine(g)} \rightarrow \text{iron(III) chloride(s)}$$

This word equation is read, "Iron and chlorine react to produce iron(III) chloride."

**Skeleton equations** Although word equations help to describe chemical reactions, they are cumbersome and lack important information. A skeleton equation uses chemical formulas rather than words to identify the reactants and the products. For example, the skeleton equation for the reaction between iron and chlorine uses the formulas for iron, chlorine, and iron(III) chloride in place of the words.

$$\text{iron(s)} + \text{chlorine(g)} \rightarrow \text{iron(III) chloride(s)}$$

$$\text{Fe(s)} + \text{Cl}_2\text{(g)} \rightarrow \text{FeCl}_3\text{(s)}$$

How would you write the skeleton equation that describes the reaction between carbon and sulfur to form carbon disulfide? Carbon and sulfur are solids. First, write the chemical formulas for the reactants to the left of an arrow. Then, separate the reactants with a plus sign and indicate their physical states.

$$\text{C(s)} + \text{S(s)} \rightarrow$$

Finally, write the chemical formula for the product, liquid carbon disulfide, to the right of the arrow and indicate its physical state. The result is the skeleton equation for the reaction.

$$\text{C(s)} + \text{S(s)} \rightarrow \text{CS}_2\text{(l)}$$

This skeleton equation tells us that carbon in the solid state reacts with sulfur in the solid state to produce carbon disulfide, which is in the liquid state.

## PRACTICE PROBLEMS

Write skeleton equations for the following word equations.

**1.** hydrogen(g) + bromine(g) → hydrogen bromide(g)

**2.** carbon monoxide(g) + oxygen(g) → carbon dioxide(g)

**3.** potassium chlorate(s) → potassium chloride(s) + oxygen(g)

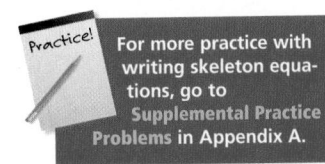
Practice! For more practice with writing skeleton equations, go to **Supplemental Practice Problems in Appendix A.**

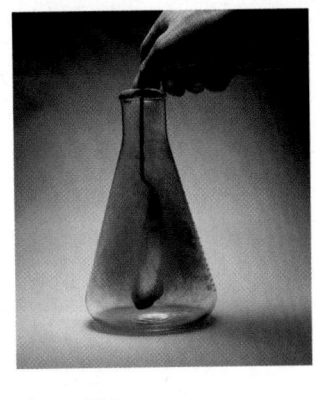

**Figure 10-2**

Science, like all other disciplines, has a specialized language that allows specific information to be communicated in a uniform manner. This reaction between iron and chlorine can be described by a word equation, skeleton equation, or balanced chemical equation.

## Reinforcement

Emphasize the importance of writing correct formulas for all reactants and products in the skeleton equation and not changing them during the balancing process. Point out that once correct formulas are written, only coefficients may be added and changed to balance the equation.

## Practice PROBLEMS

Have students refer to Appendix D for complete solutions to Practice Problems.

**1.** $\text{H}_2\text{(g)} + \text{Br}_2\text{(g)} \rightarrow \text{HBr(g)}$

**2.** $\text{CO(g)} + \text{O}_2\text{(g)} \rightarrow \text{CO}_2\text{(g)}$

**3.** $\text{KClO}_3\text{(s)} \rightarrow \text{KCl(s)} + \text{O}_2\text{(g)}$

## Quick Demo

**Caution:** Silver nitrate is toxic and will stain skin and clothing.

Pour approximately 5 mL of 0.1$M$ silver nitrate solution into one small test tube and 5 mL of 0.1$M$ potassium iodide solution into another. Carefully lower both test tubes into a small flask so that the tubes remain upright, stopper the flask, and weigh the flask and contents. Tip the flask so that the test tubes spill their contents into the flask, causing the formation of yellow, insoluble, silver iodide. Ask students to predict any change in mass. Because a dense solid formed, students may predict that the mass increased. Then weigh the flask and contents to demonstrate the law of conservation of mass.

## Portfolio

**Writing Chemical Equations**

*Linguistic* Ask students to consider some of the chemical reactions they have described in their journals. Have them write word, skeleton, and balanced chemical equations for any reactions they can. **L2** **P**

National Science Content Standards

Pages 278–279
UCP.3, UCP.5; A.1; B.3, B.6

**Figure 10-3**

The information conveyed by skeleton equations is limited. In this case, the skeleton equation (top) is correct, but it does not show the exact number of atoms that actually interact. Refer to **Table C-1** in Appendix C for a key to atom color conventions.

$$Fe(s) \quad + \quad Cl_2(g) \quad \rightarrow \quad FeCl_3(s)$$

One iron atom
Two chlorine atoms

One iron atom
Three chlorine atoms

**Chemical equations** Writing a skeleton equation is an important step toward using an equation to completely describe a chemical reaction. But, like word equations, skeleton equations also lack important information about reactions. Recall from Chapter 3 that the law of conservation of mass states that in a chemical change, matter is neither created nor destroyed. Chemical equations must show that matter is conserved during a reaction, and skeleton equations lack that information.

Look at **Figure 10-3**. The skeleton equation for the reaction between iron and chlorine shows that one iron atom and two chlorine atoms react to produce a substance containing one iron atom and three chlorine atoms. Was a chlorine atom created in the reaction? Atoms are not created in chemical reactions, and to accurately show what happened, more information is needed.

To accurately represent a chemical reaction by an equation, the equation must show how the law of conservation of mass is obeyed. In other words, the equation must show that the number of atoms of each reactant and each product is equal on both sides of the arrow. Such an equation is called a balanced **chemical equation.** A chemical equation is a statement that uses chemical formulas to show the identities and relative amounts of the substances involved in a chemical reaction. It is chemical equations that chemists use most often to represent chemical reactions.

## Balancing Chemical Equations

The balanced equation for the reaction between iron and chlorine, shown below, reflects the law of conservation of mass.

$$2Fe(s) + 3Cl_2(g) \rightarrow 2FeCl_3(s)$$

Two iron atoms
Six chlorine atoms

Two iron atoms
Six chlorine atoms

To balance an equation, you must find the correct coefficients for the chemical formulas in the skeleton equation. A **coefficient** in a chemical equation is the number written in front of a reactant or product. Coefficients are usually whole numbers, and are usually not written if the value is 1. A coefficient

---

## Demonstration

### A Metal and a Nonmetal React

#### Purpose
To combine a metal and nonmetal into a stable compound by releasing energy

#### Materials
zinc dust (1 g); iodine crystals (3 g); dry test tube with stopper; evaporating dish; widemouth glass bottle with stopper; dropper

#### Safety Precautions
Always perform this demonstration in a fume hood. Use caution when working with chemicals and extreme temperatures.

**Disposal** This demonstration produces hazardous waste as described by EPA regulators and should be disposed of accordingly.

#### Procedure
Put 1 g of zinc dust and 3 g of iodine crystals into a dry test tube. Stopper the test tube and mix by shaking. Transfer the mixture to an evaporating dish. In the fume hood, carefully add a few drops of water to the mixture using a dropper. **CAUTION:** *This demonstration should be*

tells you the smallest number of particles of the substance involved in the reaction. That is, the coefficients in a balanced equation describe the lowest whole-number ratio of the amounts of all of the reactants and products.

**Steps for balancing equations**   Most chemical equations can be balanced by following the steps given below. For example, you can use these steps to write the chemical equation for the reaction between hydrogen and chlorine that produces hydrogen chloride.

**Step 1** *Write the skeleton equation for the reaction.* Make sure that the chemical formulas correctly represent the substances. An arrow separates the reactants from the products, and a plus sign separates multiple reactants and products. Show the physical states of all reactants and products.

$$H_2(g) + Cl_2(g) \rightarrow HCl(g)$$

Two hydrogen       Two chlorine        One hydrogen atom
atoms              atoms               One chlorine atom

**Step 2** *Count the atoms of the elements in the reactants.* If a reaction involves identical polyatomic ions in the reactants and products, count the ions as if they are elements. This reaction does not involve any polyatomic ions. Two atoms of hydrogen and two atoms of chlorine are reacting.

$$H_2 \quad + \quad Cl_2 \quad \rightarrow$$
2 atoms H     2 atoms Cl

**Step 3** *Count the atoms of the elements in the products.* One atom of hydrogen and one atom of chlorine are produced.

HCl
1 atom H + 1 atom Cl

**Step 4** *Change the coefficients to make the number of atoms of each element equal on both sides of the equation.* Never change a subscript in a chemical formula to balance an equation because doing so changes the identity of the substance.

$$H_2 \quad + \quad Cl_2 \quad \rightarrow \quad 2HCl$$
2 atoms H       2 atoms Cl       2 atoms H + 2 atoms Cl

Two hydrogen       Two chlorine        Two hydrogen atoms
atoms              atoms               Two chlorine atoms

**Step 5** *Write the coefficients in their lowest possible ratio.* The coefficients should be the smallest possible whole numbers. The ratio 1 hydrogen to 1 chlorine to 2 hydrogen chloride (1:1:2) is the lowest possible ratio because the coefficients cannot be reduced and still remain whole numbers.

**Step 6** *Check your work.* Make sure that the chemical formulas are written correctly. Then, check that the number of atoms of each element is equal on both sides of the equation.

## Earth Science
### CONNECTION

Weathering is the general term used to describe the ways in which rock is broken down at or near Earth's surface. Soils are the result of weathering and the activities of plants and animals.

Physical weathering, also called mechanical weathering, involves expansion and contraction with changes in temperature, pressure, and the growth of plants and organisms in the rock. Water in rock fissures and crevices cause rock to fracture when water expands during freezing. Freeze-thaw physical weathering is more likely to occur in sub-Arctic climates.

Chemical weathering involves the break down of rock by chemical reactions. The mineral composition of the rock is changed, reorganized, or redistributed. For example, minerals that contain iron may react with oxygen in the air. Water in which carbon dioxide is dissolved will dissolve limestone. Chemical weathering is more likely to take place in humid tropical climates.

## Identifying Misconceptions

Students may think that the coefficients in a chemical equation must balance.

**Uncover the Misconception**
Have students write the balanced equation for the reaction between carbon (graphite) and gaseous oxygen yielding gaseous carbon dioxide. $C(s) + O_2(g) \rightarrow CO_2(g)$ Now ask them to compare the sum of the coefficients on the two sides of the balanced equation. The sum on the reactant side is two, and the sum on the product side is one, showing that the sums do not have to be equal.

**Demonstrate the Concept**
*Visual-Spatial* Use ball-and-stick molecular models to model the reaction between gaseous acetylene ($C_2H_2$) and gaseous oxygen yielding gaseous carbon dioxide and liquid water: $2C_2H_2(g) + 5O_2(g) \rightarrow 4CO_2(g) + 2H_2O(l)$. Show that the number of atoms of each element in the products equals the number in the reactants, but the sum of reactant coefficients (7) does not equal the sum of product coefficients (6).

**Assess New Knowledge**
Have students write the balanced equation for the reaction between solid phosphorus ($P_4$) and liquid bromine yielding solid phosphorus pentabromide. $P_4(s) + 10Br_2(l) \rightarrow 4PBr_5(s)$ Emphasize the point by having them compare the sum of reactant coefficients (11) with the sum of product coefficients (4).

---

done only in a fume hood. $I_2$ vapors are toxic. The dish will become hot. Collect the toxic, violet-colored iodine vapors in a widemouth glass bottle that is inverted and clamped over the evaporating dish. Immediately stopper the bottle.

**Results**
Violet fumes are given off from the reacting mixture as an exothermic reaction proceeds.

**Analysis**
1. Examine these electron dot diagrams of zinc and iodine.

·Zn·   :Ï·

Do these dot diagrams show the correct number of valence electrons for zinc and iodine? Yes
2. In forming zinc iodide, one zinc atom reacts with two iodine atoms. Use this information and the dot diagrams to

explain how the reaction occurred. Zinc shares one electron with each iodine atom.

## Assessment
**Skill**  Ask students to mark on a blank periodic table the position of the dividing line between metals and nonmetals. **L2**

## Practice PROBLEMS

Have students refer to Appendix D for complete solutions to Practice Problems.

**4.** $FeCl_3(aq) + 3NaOH(aq) \rightarrow Fe(OH)_3(s) + 3NaCl(aq)$

**5.** $CS_2(l) + 3O_2(g) \rightarrow CO_2(g) + 2SO_2(g)$

**6.** $Zn(s) + H_2SO_4(aq) \rightarrow H_2(g) + ZnSO_4(aq)$

**National Science Content Standards**

Pages 282–283
UCP.3, UCP.5; B.3

---

## EXAMPLE PROBLEM 10-1

### Writing a Balanced Chemical Equation

Write the balanced chemical equation for the reaction in which sodium hydroxide and calcium bromide react to produce solid calcium hydroxide and sodium bromide. The reaction occurs in water.

**1. Analyze the Problem**

You are given the reactants and products in a chemical reaction. Start with a skeleton equation and use the steps given in the text for balancing chemical equations.

**2. Solve for the Unknown**

*Step 1* Write the skeleton equation. Be sure to put the reactants on the left side of an arrow and the products on the right. Separate the substances with plus signs and indicate physical states.

$$NaOH(aq) + CaBr_2(aq) \rightarrow Ca(OH)_2(s) + NaBr(aq)$$

*Step 2* Count the atoms of each element in the reactants.

1 Na, 1 O, 1 H, 1 Ca, 2 Br

*Step 3* Count the atoms of each element in the products.

1 Na, 2 O, 2 H, 1 Ca, 1 Br

*Step 4* Adjust the coefficients.
Insert the coefficient 2 in front of NaOH to balance the hydroxide ions.

$$2NaOH + CaBr_2 \rightarrow Ca(OH)_2 + NaBr$$

Insert the coefficient 2 in front of NaBr to balance the Na and Br atoms.

$$2NaOH + CaBr_2 \rightarrow Ca(OH)_2 + 2NaBr$$

*Step 5* Write the coefficients in their lowest possible ratio. The ratio of the coefficients is 2:1:1:2.

*Step 6* Check to make sure that the number of atoms of each element is equal on both sides of the equation.
Reactants:   2 Na, 2 OH, 1 Ca, 2 Br
Products:    2 Na, 2 OH, 1 Ca, 2 Br

**3. Evaluate the Answer**

The chemical formulas for all substances are written correctly. The number of atoms of each element is equal on both sides of the equation. The coefficients are written in the lowest possible ratio. The balanced chemical equation for the reaction is

$$2NaOH(aq) + CaBr_2(aq) \rightarrow Ca(OH)_2(s) + 2NaBr(aq)$$

The brick and mortar used in many construction applications involves chemical reactions with calcium and other substances. Although these materials have been used for centuries, chemistry continues to improve their durability and performance.

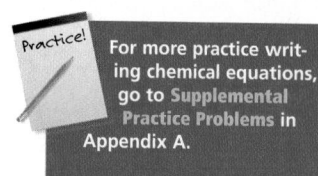

**Practice!** For more practice writing chemical equations, go to Supplemental Practice Problems in Appendix A.

## PRACTICE PROBLEMS

Write chemical equations for each of the following reactions.

**4.** In water, iron(III) chloride reacts with sodium hydroxide, producing solid iron(III) hydroxide and sodium chloride.

**5.** Liquid carbon disulfide reacts with oxygen gas, producing carbon dioxide gas and sulfur dioxide gas.

**6.** Solid zinc and aqueous hydrogen sulfate react to produce hydrogen gas and aqueous zinc sulfate.

---

## Internet Address Book

**Chemistry Online** Note Internet addresses that you find useful in the space below for quick reference.

**Balancing Chemical Equations**

```
Reactants on          Reactants            Number of atoms
left side                                  of each element
                                           on the left
```

```
Write a          Count           Add/adjust      must      Reduce              Check your
skeleton    →    atoms      →     coefficients    equal     coefficients to  →  work
equation                                          ↕         lowest possible
                                                            ratio
```

```
Products on          Products             Number of atoms
right side                                of each element
                                          on the right
```

**Figure 10-4**

It is imperative to your study of chemistry to be able to balance chemical equations. Use this flowchart to help you master the skill.

Probably the most fundamental concept of chemistry is the law of conservation of mass that you first encountered in Chapter 3. All chemical reactions obey the law that matter is neither created nor destroyed. Therefore, it is also fundamental that the equations that represent chemical reactions include sufficient information to show that the reaction obeys the law of conservation of mass. You have learned how to show this relationship with balanced chemical equations. The flowchart shown in **Figure 10-4** summarizes the steps for balancing equations. You will undoubtedly find that some chemical equations can be balanced easily, whereas others are more difficult to balance. All chemical equations, however, can be balanced by the process you learned in this section.

## Section 10.1 Assessment

**7.** List three types of evidence that indicate a chemical reaction has occurred.

**8.** Compare and contrast a skeleton equation and a chemical equation.

**9.** Why is it important that a chemical equation be balanced?

**10.** When balancing a chemical equation, can you adjust the number that is subscripted to a substance formula? Explain your answer.

**11.** Why is it important to reduce coefficients in a balanced equation to the lowest possible whole-number ratio?

**12. Thinking Critically** Explain how an equation can be balanced even if the number of reactant particles differs from the number of product particles.

**13. Using Numbers** Is the following equation balanced? If not, correct the coefficients.

$$2K_2CrO_4(aq) + Pb(NO_3)_2(aq) \rightarrow 2KNO_3(aq) + PbCrO_4(s)$$

chemistrymc.com/self_check_quiz

10.1 Reactions and Equations **283**

## Section 10.1 Assessment

**7.** Answers may include release or absorption of energy, change in color, change in odor, formation of a gas, formation of a solid.

**8.** The skeleton equation includes the formulas of reactants and products. The chemical equation gives the relative amounts of reactants and products.

**9.** Because mass is neither created nor destroyed in chemical reactions, the numbers of atoms of all elements must be equal on both sides of the reaction arrow.

**10.** No. Doing so changes the identity of the substance.

**11.** Coefficients in the lowest ratio most

# 3 Assess

## Check for Understanding

On the chalkboard, write $N_2(g) + O_2(g) \rightarrow N_2O_5(s)$. Ask students why it's incorrect to balance the equation by changing the formula for the reacting oxygen to $O_5$. Although the equation would be balanced, it would be incorrect because oxygen is diatomic ($O_2$), not pentatomic ($O_5$).

## Reteach

Have each student pick one interesting reaction that they have recorded in their chemistry journal and write a balanced equation for that reaction. **L2**

## Extension

For reactions in which polyatomic ions obviously remain intact, students may consider them as units to simplify the balancing process. For example, in the reaction $2Li_3PO_4(aq) + 3CaCl_2(aq) \rightarrow 6LiCl(aq) + Ca_3(PO_4)_2(s)$, two phosphate ions on each side of the equation balance phosphorus and oxygen. Have students balance several equations containing intact polyatomic ions. **L2**

## ✓ Assessment

**Knowledge** Ask students to write the balanced chemical equation for the reaction in the Quick Demo on page 279.
$$Pb(NO_3)_2(aq) + 2KI(aq) \rightarrow PbI_2(s) + 2KNO_3(aq)$$

clearly indicate the relative amounts of substances in a reaction.

**12.** The number of atoms of each element can be balanced while numbers of reactant and product molecules or other particles are different. For example, $2C_6H_6 + 15O_2 \rightarrow 12CO_2 + 6H_2O$ is balanced, but 17 molecules react and 18 molecules are produced.

**13.** No. The correct equation is $K_2CrO_4(aq) + Pb(NO_3)_2(aq) \rightarrow 2KNO_3(aq) + PbCrO_4(s)$

**283**

# 1 Focus

## Focus Transparency

Before presenting the lesson, display **Section Focus Transparency 36** on the overhead projector. Have students answer the accompanying questions using **Section Focus Transparency Master 36.** **L1** **ELL**

## Objectives

- **Classify** chemical reactions.
- **Identify** the characteristics of different classes of chemical reactions.

## Vocabulary

synthesis reaction
combustion reaction
decomposition reaction
single-replacement reaction
double-replacement
  reaction
precipitate

**Figure 10-5**

Without some level of organization, it would be difficult to shelve and maintain the huge number of books that have been published. Chemistry, too, hinges on strict rules of organization. Chemical reactions are classified as synthesis, combustion, decomposition, single-replacement, and double-replacement reactions.

How long do you think it would take you to find your favorite author's new novel in an unorganized book store? Because there are so many books in book stores, it could take you a very long time. Book stores, such as the store shown in **Figure 10-5,** supermarkets, and music stores are among the many places where things are classified and organized. Chemists classify chemical reactions in order to organize the many reactions that occur daily in living things, laboratories, and industry. Knowing the categories of chemical reactions can help you remember and understand them. It also can help you recognize patterns and predict the products of many chemical reactions.

Chemists classify reactions in different ways. One way is to distinguish among five types of chemical reactions: synthesis, combustion, decomposition, single-replacement, and double-replacement reactions. Some reactions fit equally well into more than one of these classes.

## Synthesis Reactions

In the previous section, you read about the reaction that occurs between iron and chlorine gas to produce iron(III) chloride. In this reaction, two elements (A and B) combine to produce one new compound (AB).

$$A + B \rightarrow AB$$

$$2Fe(s) + 3Cl_2(g) \rightarrow 2FeCl_3(s)$$

The reaction between iron and chlorine gas is an example of a **synthesis reaction**—a chemical reaction in which two or more substances react to produce a single product. When two elements react, the reaction is always a synthesis reaction. Another example of a synthesis reaction is shown below. In this reaction, sodium and chlorine react to produce sodium chloride.

$$2Na(s) + Cl_2(g) \rightarrow 2NaCl(s)$$

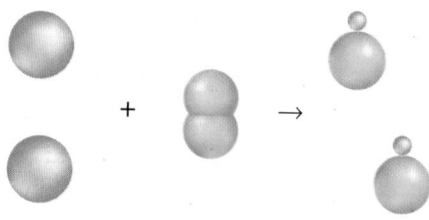

Just as two elements can combine, two compounds can also combine to form one compound. For example, the reaction between calcium oxide and water to form calcium hydroxide is a synthesis reaction.

$$CaO(s) + H_2O(l) \rightarrow Ca(OH)_2(s)$$

Another type of synthesis reaction may involve a reaction between a compound and an element, as happens when sulfur dioxide gas reacts with oxygen gas to form sulfur trioxide.

$$2SO_2(g) + O_2(g) \rightarrow 2SO_3(g)$$

# 2 Teach

## Using Science Terms

**Linguistic** Have students write statements explaining the meaning of the terms *synthesize* and *decompose*. Ask them to write four illustrative sentences—two that include each word. **L2** **ELL**

## National Science Content Standards

Pages 284–285
UCP.3, UCP.5; B.2, B.3

**284**

## Portfolio

### Identifying Reaction Types

**Intrapersonal** Ask students to cite chemical reactions that do not fit into the categories discussed in this chapter. Have them write the equations for these reactions in their portfolios and, if they are able, specify the reaction type. Examples include combinations of these categories plus reactions such as redox, saponification, and polymerization. **L2** **P**

## Resource Manager

**Study Guide For Content Mastery,** pp. 57–58 **L2**
**Solving Problems: A Chemistry Handbook,** Section 10.2 **L2**
**Section Focus Transparency 36 and Master** **L1** **ELL**
**Teaching Transparency 35 and Master** **L2** **ELL**

## Combustion Reactions

The synthesis reaction between sulfur dioxide and oxygen can be classified also as a combustion reaction. In a **combustion reaction**, oxygen combines with a substance and releases energy in the form of heat and light. Oxygen can combine in this way with many different substances, making combustion reactions common.

A combustion reaction, such as the one shown in **Figure 10-6**, occurs between hydrogen and oxygen when hydrogen is heated. Water is formed during the reaction and a large amount of energy is released.

$$2H_2(g) \ + \ O_2(g) \ \rightarrow \ 2H_2O(g)$$

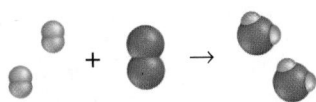

Another important combustion reaction occurs when coal is burned to produce energy. Coal is called a fossil fuel because it contains the remains of plants that lived long ago. It is composed primarily of the element carbon. Coal-burning power plants generate electric power in many parts of the United States. The primary reaction that occurs in these plants is between carbon and oxygen.

$$C(s) + O_2(g) \rightarrow CO_2(g)$$

Note that the combustion reactions just mentioned are also synthesis reactions. However, not all combustion reactions are synthesis reactions. For example, the reaction involving methane gas, $CH_4$, and oxygen illustrates a combustion reaction in which one substance replaces another in the formation of products.

$$CH_4(g) + 2O_2(g) \rightarrow CO_2(g) + 2H_2O(g)$$

Methane, which belongs to a group of substances called hydrocarbons, is the major component of natural gas. All hydrocarbons contain carbon and hydrogen and burn in oxygen to yield the same products as methane does—carbon dioxide and water. For example, most cars and trucks are powered by gasoline, which contains hydrocarbons. In engines, gasoline is combined with oxygen, producing carbon dioxide, water, and energy that powers the vehicles. You will learn more about hydrocarbons in Chapter 22.

### PRACTICE PROBLEMS

**Write chemical equations for the following reactions. Classify each reaction into as many categories as possible.**

**14.** The solids aluminum and sulfur react to produce aluminum sulfide.

**15.** Water and dinitrogen pentoxide gas react to produce aqueous hydrogen nitrate.

**16.** The gases nitrogen dioxide and oxygen react to produce dinitrogen pentoxide gas.

**17.** Ethane gas ($C_2H_6$) burns in air, producing carbon dioxide gas and water vapor.

**Figure 10-6**

The tragedy of the *Challenger* space mission was the result of a combustion reaction between oxygen and hydrogen.

Have
D for co
Practice P

**14.** 2Al(s) +
synthesis

**15.** H₂O(l) + N₂O₅(g
2HNO₃(aq) synthe

**16.** 4NO₂(g) + O₂(g) →
2N₂O₅(g) synthesis and
combustion

**17.** 2C₂H₆(g) + 7O₂(g) →
4CO₂(g) + 6H₂O(g)
combustion

## GLENCOE
### TECHNOLOGY

**CD-ROM**
**Chemistry: Matter and Change**
Demonstration: *Properties of Oxygen Gas*
Demonstration: *Combustion of Ethanol*
Video: *Exothermic Reactions*

Practice!

For more practice with writing synthesis and combustion equations, go to Supplemental Practice Problems in Appendix A.

---

## CULTURAL DIVERSITY

### The Language of Chemistry

Ask students if they can tell what subject is being discussed in the following passage from a Spanish chemistry textbook: "El gas cloro se representa por la fórmula Cl₂. Otros seis elementos comunes que existen normalmente como moléculas diatómicas son el hidrógeno (H₂), el nitrógeno (N₂), el oxígeno (O₂) y el flúor (F₂). El bromo (Br₂) existe en su estado gaseoso a una temperatura sobre 58.8°C. El yodo (I₂) se transforma en gas a la temperatura de 184°C."

On the basis of the chemical formulas, students will probably notice that the subject is chemistry. Explain that although scientists in different countries communicate with each other using various written and spoken languages, scientists the world over represent chemical reactions using the same chemical symbols and equations.

Content Ba~~~
**Products**~~~ons
Reacti~~~

reac~~~ oxide
~~~
~~~tal chloride

metal hydroxide → metal oxide + H₂O
metal oxide → metal + oxygen
oxyacid → nonmetal oxide + H₂O

---

**Practice** PROBLEMS

Have students refer to Appendix D for complete solutions to the Practice Problems.

**18.** $2Al_2O_3(s) \rightarrow 4Al(s) + 3O_2(g)$

**19.** $Ni(OH)_2(s) \rightarrow NiO(s) + H_2O(l)$

**20.** $2NaHCO_3(s) \rightarrow Na_2CO_3(aq) + CO_2(g) + H_2O(l)$

---

## GLENCOE
### TECHNOLOGY

**CD-ROM**
**Chemistry: Matter and Change**
Animation: *Five Types of Chemical Reactions*
Video: *Types of Chemical Reactions*

---

**Figure 10-7**

The decomposition of sodium azide, which produces a gas, is the key to inflatable air bags.

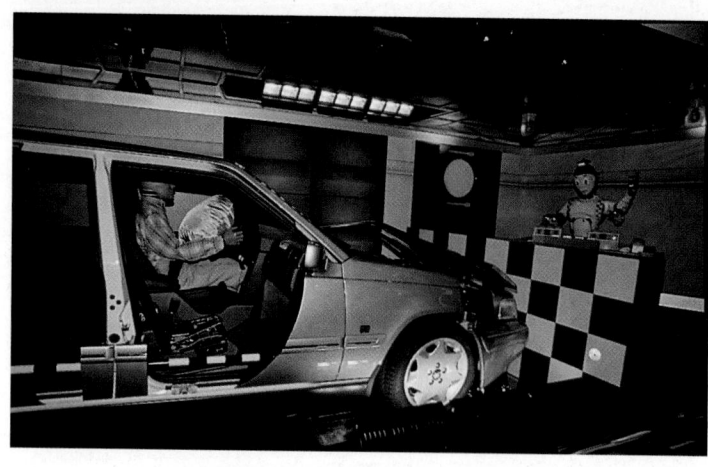

## Decomposition Reactions

Some chemical reactions are essentially the opposite of synthesis reactions. These reactions are classified as decomposition reactions. A **decomposition reaction** is one in which a single compound breaks down into two or more elements or new compounds. In generic terms, decomposition reactions look like the following.

$$AB \rightarrow A + B$$

Decomposition reactions often require an energy source, such as heat, light, or electricity, to occur. For example, ammonium nitrate breaks down into dinitrogen monoxide and water when the reactant is heated to high temperature.

$$NH_4NO_3(s) \rightarrow N_2O(g) + 2H_2O(g)$$

You can see that this decomposition reaction involves one reactant breaking down into more than one product.

The outcome of another decomposition reaction is shown in **Figure 10-7**. Automobile safety air bags inflate rapidly as sodium azide pellets decompose. A device that can provide an electric signal to start the reaction is packaged inside air bags along with the sodium azide pellets. When the device is activated, sodium azide decomposes, producing nitrogen gas that quickly inflates the safety bag.

$$2NaN_3(s) \rightarrow 2Na(s) + 3N_2(g)$$

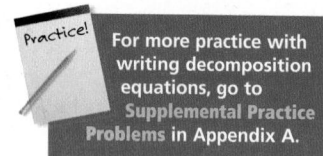

Practice!

For more practice with writing decomposition equations, go to **Supplemental Practice Problems** in Appendix A.

**PRACTICE** PROBLEMS

Write chemical equations for the following decomposition reactions.

**18.** Aluminum oxide(s) decomposes when electricity is passed through it.

**19.** Nickel(II) hydroxide(s) decomposes to produce nickel(II) oxide(s) and water.

**20.** Heating sodium hydrogen carbonate(s) produces sodium carbonate(aq), carbon dioxide(g), and water.

---

## Internet Address Book

**Chemistry** online

Note Internet addresses that you find useful in the space below for quick reference.

_____

_____

_____

_____

H$_2$    Li$^+$

H$_2$O    OH$^-$

Figure 10-8

The reaction of lithium and water is a single-replacement reaction. Lithium replaces a hydrogen in water, and the products of the reaction are aqueous lithium hydroxide and hydrogen gas. Lithium hydroxide exists as lithium and hydroxide ions in solution.

## Replacement Reactions

In contrast to synthesis, combustion, and decomposition reactions, many chemical reactions involve the replacement of an element in a compound. There are two types of replacement reactions: single-replacement reactions and double-replacement reactions.

**Single-replacement reactions** Now that you've seen how atoms and molecules rearrange in synthesis and combustion reactions, look closely at the reaction between lithium and water that is shown in **Figure 10-8**. The expanded view of the reaction at the molecular level shows that a lithium atom replaces one of the hydrogen atoms in a water molecule. The following chemical equation describes this activity.

$$2Li(s) + 2H_2O(l) \rightarrow 2LiOH(aq) + H_2(g)$$

A reaction in which the atoms of one element replace the atoms of another element in a compound is called a **single-replacement reaction**.

$$A + BX \rightarrow AX + B$$

The reaction between lithium and water is one type of single-replacement reaction in which a metal replaces a hydrogen in a water molecule. Another type of single-replacement reaction occurs when one metal replaces another metal in a compound dissolved in water. For example, **Figure 10-9** shows a single-replacement reaction occurring when a spiral of pure copper wire is placed in aqueous silver nitrate. The shiny crystals that are accumulating on the copper wire are the silver atoms that the copper atoms replaced.

$$Cu(s) + 2AgNO_3(aq) \rightarrow 2Ag(s) + Cu(NO_3)_2(aq)$$

A metal will not always replace another metal in a compound dissolved in water. This is because metals differ in their reactivities. A metal's reactivity is its ability to react with another substance. In **Figure 10-10** you see an activity series of some metals. This series orders metals by their reactivity with other metals. Single-replacement reactions like the one between copper and aqueous silver nitrate determine a metal's position on the list. The most active

Figure 10-9

The chemical equation for the single-replacement reaction involving copper and silver nitrate clearly describes the replacement of silver by copper, but the visual evidence of this chemical reaction is a solid precipitate.

lving

correlate
with the

Skills

·izing caus
·ying concep
·dicting

fu
des
occu
compo
with larg
Bubbles
time. Then,
slows consi
that a single-re
tion has occurred
hydrochloric acid and
galvanized iron's zinc co
Ask students to write the u
ical equation for the reaction
and identify the gas produced.
Zn(s) + 2HCl(aq) → ZnCl$_2$(aq)
+ H$_2$(g) The gas is hydrogen.
Ask students why the iron
metal under the zinc coating
reacts more slowly than did
zinc. The activity series of
metals shows that zinc is
more reactive than iron.

## CHEMISTRY JOURNAL

### Single-Replacement Reactions

Have students write chemical equations for the single-replacement reactions that occur when aluminum metal is placed in aqueous solutions of nickel(II) nitrate, sodium nitrate, lead(IV) nitrate, and gold(III) nitrate. If no reaction occurs, have them write NR in place of the products. Have students include the equations in their chemistry journals. 2Al(s) + 3Ni(NO$_3$)$_2$(aq) → 2Al(NO$_3$)$_3$(aq) + 3Ni(s), Al(s) + NaNO$_3$(aq) → NR, 4Al(s) + 3Pb(NO$_3$)$_4$(aq) → 4Al(NO$_3$)$_3$(aq) + 3Pb(s), Al(s) + Au(NO$_3$)$_3$(aq) → Al(NO$_3$)$_3$(aq) + Au(s)

the proper-
ur chemical

e and effect,
ts, classifying,

rategies
ts what properties
considered in deter-
he relative reactivity of
als. Electronegativity,
tion states, atomic radius,
zation energy, and effective
lear charge are properties
at exhibit periodic trends.
Ask students to explore how each
of their suggestions would help
predict the reactivity of a particular element. Generally, metals
with a low ionization energy
and large radius react more
easily. Further consideration
must be given to the stability
of the shell structure.

## Thinking Critically

1. With increasing atomic
   number, atomic radius
   increases, ionization energy
   decreases, and electronegativity decreases.
2. These trends correlate with
   the decrease in reactivity
   down the period.
3. Astatine is a group 7A element
   and follows the trends
   described for the halogens.
   Therefore, At would be at the
   bottom of the activity series
   on the basis of its periodic
   trends.

### ✓ Assessment

**Performance** Students
should write an account of their
findings and explain how the interpretations of their findings were
used to place the other given
elements in the reactive series. Use
the Performance Task Assessment
List for Writing in Science in
**PASC,** p. 87.

---

Most active → Least active

**METALS**
Lithium
Rubidium
Potassium
Calcium
Sodium
Magnesium
Aluminum
Manganese
Zinc
Iron
Nickel
Tin
Lead
Copper
Silver
Platinum
Gold

Most active → Least active

**HALOGENS**
Fluorine
Chlorine
Bromine
Iodine

**Figure 10-10**

An activity series, similar to the
series shown here for various
metals and halogens, is a useful
tool for determining whether a
chemical reaction will take place
and for determining the result
of a replacement reaction.

---

metals, which are those that do replace the metal in a compound, are at the
top of the list. The least active metals are at the bottom.

You can use **Figure 10-10** to predict whether or not certain reactions will
occur. A specific metal can replace any metal listed below it that is in a compound. It cannot replace any metal listed above it. For example, you saw in
**Figure 10-9** that copper atoms replace silver atoms in a solution of silver
nitrate. However, if you place a silver wire in aqueous copper(II) nitrate, the
silver atoms will not replace the copper. Silver is listed below copper in the
activity series and no reaction occurs. The letters NR (no reaction) are commonly used to indicate that a reaction will not occur.

$$Ag(s) + Cu(NO_3)_2(aq) \rightarrow NR$$

The **CHEMLAB** at the end of this chapter gives you an opportunity to
explore the activities of metals in the laboratory.

A third type of single-replacement reaction involves the replacement of a
nonmetal in a compound by another nonmetal. Halogens are frequently
involved in these types of reactions. Like metals, halogens exhibit different
activity levels in single-replacement reactions. The reactivities of halogens,
determined by single-replacement reactions, are also shown in **Figure 10-10.**
The most active halogen is fluorine, and the least active is iodine. A more reactive halogen replaces a less reactive halogen that is part of a compound dissolved in water. For example, fluorine replaces bromine in water containing
dissolved sodium bromide. However, bromine does not replace fluorine in
water containing dissolved sodium fluoride.

$$F_2(g) + 2NaBr(aq) \rightarrow 2NaF(aq) + Br_2(l)$$

$$Br_2(g) + 2NaF(aq) \rightarrow NR$$

The **problem-solving LAB** below will help you to relate periodic trends of
the halogens to their reactivities.

## problem-solving LAB

### Can you predict the reactivities of halogens?

**Analyzing and Concluding** The location of all
the halogens in group 7A in the periodic table
tells you that halogens have common characteristics. Indeed, halogens are all nonmetals and have
seven electrons in their outermost orbitals.
However, each halogen has its own characteristics, too, such as its ability to react with other
substances.

**Analysis**

Examine the accompanying table. It includes data
about the atomic radii, ionization energies, and
electronegativities of the halogens.

**Thinking Critically**

1. Describe any periodic trends that you identify
   in the table data.

| | Properties of Halogens | | |
|---|---|---|---|
| Halogen | Atomic radius (pm) | Ionization energy (kJ/mol) | Electro-negativity |
| Fluorine | 72 | 1681 | 3.98 |
| Chlorine | 100 | 1251 | 3.16 |
| Bromine | 114 | 1140 | 2.96 |
| Iodine | 133 | 1008 | 2.66 |
| Astatine | 140 | — | 2.2 |

2. Relate any periodic trends that you identify
   among the halogens to the activity series of
   halogens shown in **Figure 10-10.**
3. Predict the location of the element astatine in
   the activity series of halogens. Explain your
   answer.

---

### DIFFERENTIATED INSTRUCTION

**Gifted**

*Logical-Mathematical* Ask gifted students to devise and explain an experimental procedure they would use to place
an unknown metal in the activity series of
metals. Typical student procedures will
involve putting samples of the metal in
aqueous solutions of the salts of other,
known metals. Such experiments provide
data that allow students to place the
unknown metal above metals it replaces
and below metals it does not replace. **L3**

**Single-Replacement Reactions**

Predict the products that will result when these reactants combine and write a balanced chemical equation for each reaction.

$Fe(s) + CuSO_4(aq) \rightarrow$

$Br_2(l) + MgCl_2(aq) \rightarrow$

$Mg(s) + AlCl_3(aq) \rightarrow$

**1.** **Analyze the Problem**

You are given three sets of reactants. Using **Figure 10-10,** you must first determine if each reaction takes place. Then, if a reaction is predicted, you can determine the product(s) of the reaction. With this information you can write a skeleton equation for the reaction. Finally, you can use the steps for balancing chemical equations to write the complete balanced chemical equation.

**2.** **Solve for the Unknown**

Iron is listed above copper in the metals activity series. Therefore, the first reaction will take place because iron is more reactive than copper. In this case, iron will replace copper. The skeleton equation for this reaction is

$Fe(s) + CuSO_4(aq) \rightarrow FeSO_4(aq) + Cu(s)$

This equation is balanced.

In the second reaction, chlorine is more reactive than bromine because bromine is listed below chlorine in the halogen activity series. Therefore, the reaction will not take place. The skeleton equation for this situation is $Br(l) + MgCl_2(aq) \rightarrow$ NR. No balancing is required. Magnesium is listed above aluminum in the metals activity series. Therefore, the third reaction will take place because magnesium is more reactive than aluminum. In this case, magnesium will replace aluminum. The skeleton equation for this reaction is

$Mg(s) + AlCl_3(aq) \rightarrow Al(s) + MgCl_2(aq)$

This equation is not balanced. The balanced equation is

$3Mg(s) + 2AlCl_3(aq) \rightarrow 2Al(s) + 3MgCl_2(aq)$

**3.** **Evaluate the Answer**

The activity series shown in **Figure 10-10** supports the reaction predictions. The chemical equations are balanced because the number of atoms of each substance is equal on both sides of the equation.

Magnesium is an essential element for the human body. You can ensure an adequate magnesium intake by eating magnesium-rich foods.

**PRACTICE** PROBLEMS

Predict if the following single-replacement reactions will occur. If a reaction occurs, write a balanced equation for the reaction.

**21.** $K(s) + ZnCl_2(aq) \rightarrow$

**22.** $Cl_2(g) + HF(aq) \rightarrow$

**23.** $Fe(s) + Na_3PO_4(aq) \rightarrow$

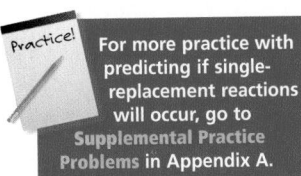

**Practice!** For more practice with predicting if single-replacement reactions will occur, go to **Supplemental Practice Problems** in Appendix A.

---

**CHEMLAB**

ChemLab 10, located at the end of the chapter, can be used at this point in the lesson.

**Content Background**

**Activity Series of Metals**

Explain to students that the reactivities of metals in the activity series may be described in greater detail than shown in Figure 10-10. Metals from magnesium down to iron react with steam (but not cold water). Metals from nickel to lead react with neither water nor steam. All metals above silver react with oxygen, forming oxides, while silver, platinum, and gold form oxides only indirectly.

**Practice** PROBLEMS

Have students refer to Appendix D for complete solutions to Practice Problems.

**21.** yes; $2K(s) + ZnCl_2(aq) \rightarrow 2KCl(aq) + Zn(s)$

**22.** no

**23.** no

**Resource Manager**

**Teaching Transparency 34 and Master** L2 ELL
**Lab Manual,** pp. 73–76, 77–80 L2

---

**CHEMISTRY JOURNAL**

**An Analogy for Reactions**

*Intrapersonal* Have students compare reaction types with dance activities and record their comparisons in their chemistry journals. Synthesis—two people come together to dance. Decomposition—two people part when dance is over. Single-replacement—another person cuts in and replaces one of the two partners. Double-replacement—two couples switch partners. L2

**National Science Content Standards**

**Pages 288–289**
UCP.3, UCP.5; A.1; B.2, B.3

Have students refer to Appendix D for complete solutions to Practice Problems.

24. $LiI(aq) + AgNO_3(aq) \rightarrow AgI(s) + LiNO_3(aq)$

25. $BaCl_2(aq) + K_2CO_3(aq) \rightarrow BaCO_3(s) + 2KCl(aq)$

26. $Na_2C_2O_4(aq) + Pb(NO_3)_2(aq) \rightarrow PbC_2O_4(s) + 2NaNO_3(aq)$

# 3 Assess

## Check for Understanding

Ask students to explain why reaction 1 occurs but reaction 2 does not.

1. $2KBr(aq) + Cl_2(g) \rightarrow 2KCl(aq) + Br_2(l)$
2. $2KBr(aq) + I_2(s) \rightarrow 2KI(aq) + Br_2(l)$

Chlorine is above bromine in the activity series of halogens; however, iodine is below bromine in the series.

**National Science Content Standards**

**Pages 290–291**
UCP.3, UCP.5; B.2, B.3

**290**

**Double-replacement reactions** The final type of replacement reaction which involves an exchange of ions between two compounds is called a **double-replacement reaction.**

$$AX + BY \rightarrow AY + BX$$

In this generic equation, A and B represent positively charged ions (cations), and X and Y represent negatively charged ions (anions). You can see that the anions have switched places and are now bonded to the other cations in the reaction. In other words, X replaces Y and Y replaces X—a double replacement. More simply, you might say that the positive and negative ions of two compounds switch places. The reaction between calcium hydroxide and hydrochloric acid is a double-replacement reaction.

$$Ca(OH)_2(aq) + 2HCl(aq) \rightarrow CaCl_2(aq) + 2H_2O(l)$$

The ionic components of the reaction are $Ca^{2+}$, $OH^-$, $H^+$, and $Cl^-$. Knowing this, you can now see the two replacements of the reaction. The anions ($OH^-$ and $Cl^-$) have changed places and are now bonded to the other cations ($Ca^{2+}$ and $H^+$) in the reaction.

The reaction between sodium hydroxide and copper(II) chloride in solution is also a double-replacement reaction.

$$2NaOH(aq) + CuCl_2(aq) \rightarrow 2NaCl(aq) + Cu(OH)_2(s)$$

In this case, the anions ($OH^-$ and $Cl^-$) changed places and are now associated with the other cations ($Na^+$ and $Cu^{2+}$). The result of this reaction is a solid product, copper(II) hydroxide. A solid produced during a chemical reaction in a solution is called a **precipitate.**

One of the key characteristics of double-replacement reactions is the type of product that is formed when the reaction takes place. All double-replacement reactions produce either a precipitate, a gas, or water. An example of a double-replacement reaction that forms a gas is that of potassium cyanide and hydrobromic acid.

$$KCN(aq) + HBr(aq) \rightarrow KBr(aq) + HCN(g)$$

It is important to be able to evaluate the chemistry of double-replacement reactions and predict the products of these reactions. The basic steps to do this are given in **Table 10-2.**

**Table 10-2**

| Guidelines for Double-Replacement Reactions | |
|---|---|
| **Step** | **Example** |
| 1. Write the components of the reactants in a skeleton equation. | $Al(NO_3)_3 + H_2SO_4$ |
| 2. Identify the cations and anions in each compound. | $Al(NO_3)_3$ has $Al^{3+}$ and $NO_3^-$ $H_2SO_4$ has $H^+$ and $SO_4^{2-}$ |
| 3. Pair up each cation with the anion from the other compound. | $Al^{3+}$ pairs with $SO_4^{2-}$ $H^+$ pairs with $NO_3^-$ |
| 4. Write the formulas for the products using the pairs from step 3. | $Al_2(SO_4)_3$ $HNO_3$ |
| 5. Write the complete equation for the double-replacement reaction. | $Al(NO_3)_3 + H_2SO_4 \rightarrow Al_2(SO_4)_3 + HNO_3$ |
| 6. Balance the equation. | $2Al(NO_3)_3 + 3H_2SO_4 \rightarrow Al_2(SO_4)_3 + 6HNO_3$ |

✔ **Portfolio**

## Chemistry in Industry

*Visual-Spatial* Ask students to research how scrubbers remove sulfur and nitrogen oxides from power plant emissions. Ask them to make posters illustrating their findings, write equations for any chemical reactions involved, and classify each reaction. Have them include the posters in their portfolios. **L2** **ELL**

Now use this information to work the following practice problems.

## PRACTICE PROBLEMS

**Write the balanced chemical equations for the following double-replacement reactions.**

**24.** Aqueous lithium iodide and aqueous silver nitrate react to produce solid silver iodide and aqueous lithium nitrate.

**25.** Aqueous barium chloride and aqueous potassium carbonate react to produce solid barium carbonate and aqueous potassium chloride.

**26.** Aqueous sodium oxalate and aqueous lead(II) nitrate react to produce solid lead(II) oxalate and aqueous sodium nitrate.

**For more practice with writing double-replacement equations, go to Supplemental Practice Problems in Appendix A.**

Now that you have learned about the various types of chemical reactions, you can use **Table 10-3** to help you organize them in a way such that you can identify each and predict its products.

As the table indicates, the components of double-replacement reactions are dissolved in water. As you continue with Section 10.3, you will learn more about double-replacement reactions in aqueous solutions.

### Chemistry Online

**Topic: Chemical Reactions in Forensics**

To learn more about chemical reactions in forensics, visit the Chemistry Web site at chemistrymc.com

**Activity:** Research the types of chemical tests that investigators use to gather forensic evidence after a crime. Prepare a media article explaining the forensics investigation to the public.

**Table 10-3**

| Predicting Products of Chemical Reactions | | |
|---|---|---|
| **Class of reaction** | **Reactants** | **Probable products** |
| Synthesis | Two or more substances | One compound |
| Combustion | A metal and oxygen<br>A nonmetal and oxygen<br>A compound and oxygen | The oxide of the metal<br>The oxide of the nonmetal<br>Two or more oxides |
| Decomposition | One compound | Two or more elements and/or compounds |
| Single-replacement | A metal and a compound<br>A nonmetal and a compound | A new compound and the replaced metal<br>A new compound and the replaced nonmetal |
| Double-replacement | Two compounds | Two different compounds, one of which is often a solid, water, or a gas |

## Section 10.2 Assessment

**27.** What are the five classes of chemical reactions?

**28.** Identify two characteristics of combustion reactions.

**29.** Compare and contrast single-replacement reactions and double-replacement reactions.

**30.** Describe the result of a double-replacement reaction.

**31. Thinking Critically** Does the following reaction occur? Explain your answer.

$$3Ni + 2AuBr_3 \rightarrow 3NiBr_2 + 2Au$$

**32. Classifying** What type of reaction is most likely to occur when barium reacts with fluorine? Write the chemical equation for the reaction.

chemistrymc.com/self_check_quiz

10.2 Classifying Chemical Reactions    **291**

## Section 10.2 Assessment

**27.** synthesis, combustion, decomposition, single replacement, double replacement

**28.** In combustion reactions, oxygen combines with a substance and releases energy in the form of heat and light.

**29.** In a single-replacement reaction, atoms of one element replace atoms of another element in a compound. In a double-replacement reaction, two compounds dissolved in water exchange positive ions.

**30.** Double-replacement reactions produce two different compounds, one being a solid precipitate, water, or gas.

**31.** The reaction does occur because nickel is more reactive than gold.

**32.** A synthesis reaction will likely occur. $Ba + F_2 \rightarrow BaF_2$

**291**

## 1 Focus

### Focus Transparency

Before presenting the lesson, display **Section Focus Transparency 37** on the overhead projector. Have students answer the accompanying questions using **Section Focus Transparency Master 37.** L1, ELL

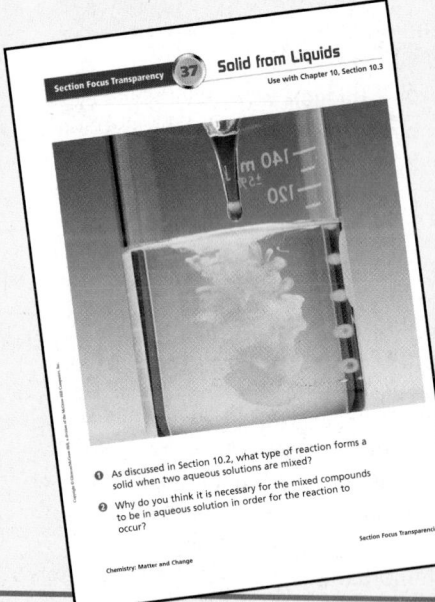

## 2 Teach
### Visual Learning

**Figures 10-11** and **10-12** Briefly explain and use models to show students how compounds form ions when they dissolve in water. Show how molecular compounds such as HCl form ions as they dissolve, a process known as ionization. Also, demonstrate how the positive and negative ions that make up ionic compounds such as NaOH merely separate as the compound dissolves in water, a process known as dissociation. L2 ELL

**292**

### Objectives

- **Describe** aqueous solutions.
- **Write** complete ionic and net ionic equations for chemical reactions in aqueous solutions.
- **Predict** whether reactions in aqueous solutions will produce a precipitate, water, or a gas.

### Vocabulary

solute
solvent
aqueous solution
complete ionic equation
spectator ion
net ionic equation

**Figure 10-11**

In an aqueous solution, hydrogen chloride (HCl) breaks apart into hydrogen ions (H⁺) and chloride ions (Cl⁻).

Many of the reactions discussed in the previous section involve substances dissolved in water. When a substance dissolves in water, a solution forms. You learned in Chapter 3 that a solution is a homogeneous mixture. A solution contains one or more substances called **solutes** dissolved in the water. In this case, water is the **solvent,** the most plentiful substance in the solution. An **aqueous solution** is a solution in which the solvent is water. Read the **How It Works** feature at the end of this chapter to see how aqueous solutions are used in hot and cold packs.

## Aqueous Solutions

Although water is always the solvent in aqueous solutions, there are many possible solutes. Some solutes, such as sucrose (table sugar) and ethanol (grain alcohol), are molecular compounds that exist as molecules in aqueous solutions. Other solutes are molecular compounds that form ions when they dissolve in water. For example, the molecular compound hydrogen chloride forms hydrogen ions and chloride ions when it dissolves in water, as shown in **Figure 10-11.** An equation can be used to show this process.

$$HCl(g) \rightarrow H^+(aq) + Cl^-(aq)$$

Compounds such as hydrogen chloride that produce hydrogen ions in aqueous solution are acids. In fact, an aqueous solution of hydrogen chloride is often referred to as hydrochloric acid. You'll learn more about acids in Chapter 19.

In addition to molecular compounds, ionic compounds may be solutes in aqueous solutions. Recall from Chapter 8 that ionic compounds consist of positive ions and negative ions held together by ionic bonds. When ionic compounds dissolve in water, their ions can separate. The equation below shows an aqueous solution of the ionic compound sodium hydroxide.

$$NaOH(aq) \rightarrow Na^+(aq) + OH^-(aq)$$

When two aqueous solutions that contain ions as solutes are combined, the ions may react with one another. These reactions are always double-replacement reactions. The solvent molecules, which are all water molecules, do not usually react. Three types of products can form from the double-replacement reaction: precipitate, water, or gas. You can observe a precipitate forming when you do the **miniLAB** for this chapter.

## Reactions That Form Precipitates

Some reactions that occur in aqueous solutions produce precipitates. For example, when aqueous solutions of sodium hydroxide and copper(II) chloride are mixed, a double-replacement reaction occurs in which the precipitate copper(II) hydroxide forms.

$$2NaOH(aq) + CuCl_2(aq) \rightarrow 2NaCl(aq) + Cu(OH)_2(s)$$

This is shown in **Figure 10-12.**

**292** Chapter 10 Chemical Reactions

### Resource Manager

**Study Guide for Content Mastery,** pp. 59–60 L2

**Solving Problems: A Chemistry Handbook,** Section 10.3 L2

**Section Focus Transparency 37 and Master** L1 ELL

### CHEMISTRY JOURNAL

#### Ions in Groundwater

**Linguistic** Have students research the types of ions found in groundwater in various parts of your county or state. Find out which ions, if any, are beneficial and which ions are usually removed (or partially removed) in water-treatment plants. Ask students to summarize their findings in their chemistry journals. L2

Note that the chemical equation does not show some details of this reaction. Sodium hydroxide and copper(II) chloride are ionic compounds. Therefore, in aqueous solutions they exist as $Na^+$, $OH^-$, $Cu^{2+}$, and $Cl^-$ ions. When their solutions are combined, $Cu^{2+}$ ions in one solution and $OH^-$ ions in the other solution react to form the precipitate copper(II) hydroxide, $Cu(OH)_2(s)$. The $Na^+$ and $Cl^-$ ions remain dissolved in the new solution.

To show the details of reactions that involve ions in aqueous solutions, chemists use ionic equations. Ionic equations differ from chemical equations in that substances that are ions in solution are written as ions in the equation. Look again at the reaction between aqueous solutions of sodium hydroxide and copper(II) chloride. To write the ionic equation for this reaction, you must show the reactants NaOH(aq) and $CuCl_2(aq)$ and the product NaCl(aq) as ions.

$$2Na^+(aq) + 2OH^-(aq) + Cu^{2+}(aq) + 2Cl^-(aq) \rightarrow$$
$$2Na^+(aq) + 2Cl^-(aq) + Cu(OH)_2(s)$$

An ionic equation that shows all of the particles in a solution as they realistically exist is called a **complete ionic equation**. Note that the sodium ions and the chloride ions are both reactants and products. Because they are both reactants and products, they do not participate in the reaction. Ions that do not participate in a reaction are called **spectator ions** and usually are not shown in ionic equations. Ionic equations that include only the particles that participate in the reaction are called **net ionic equations**. Net ionic equations are written from complete ionic equations by crossing out all spectator ions. For example, a net ionic equation is what remains after the sodium and chloride ions are crossed out of this complete ionic equation.

$$\cancel{2Na^+(aq)} + 2OH^-(aq) + Cu^{2+}(aq) + \cancel{2Cl^-(aq)} \rightarrow$$
$$\cancel{2Na^+(aq)} + \cancel{2Cl^-(aq)} + Cu(OH)_2(s)$$

Only the hydroxide and copper ions are left in the net ionic equation shown below.

$$2OH^-(aq) + Cu^{2+}(aq) \rightarrow Cu(OH)_2(s)$$

**Figure 10-12**

Like the aqueous solution of HCl you saw in **Figure 10-11**, sodium hydroxide (NaOH) in an aqueous solution dissociates into its ions sodium ($Na^+$) and hydroxide ($OH^-$). Copper chloride ($CuCl_2$) also dissociates into its ions, $Cu^{2+}$ and $Cl^-$.

10.3 Reactions in Aqueous Solutions    **293**

Have students refer to Appendix D for complete solutions to Practice Problems.

**33.** Chemical equation:
$KI(aq) + AgNO_3(aq) \rightarrow$
$KNO_3(aq) + AgI(s)$
Complete ionic equation:
$K^+(aq) + I^-(aq) + Ag^+$
$(aq) + NO_3^-(aq) \rightarrow K^+$
$(aq) + NO_3^-(aq) + AgI(s)$
Net ionic equation:
$I^-(aq) + Ag^+(aq) \rightarrow AgI(s)$

**34.** Chemical equation:
$2(NH_4)_3PO_4(aq) +$
$3Na_2SO_4(aq) \rightarrow NR$

**35.** Chemical equation:
$AlCl_3(aq) + 3NaOH(aq) \rightarrow$
$Al(OH)_3(s) + 3NaCl(aq)$
Complete ionic equation:
$Al^{3+}(aq) + 3Cl^-(aq) +$
$3Na^+(aq) + 3OH^-(aq) \rightarrow$
$Al(OH)_3(s) + 3Na^+(aq) +$
$3Cl^-(aq)$
Net ionic equation:
$Al^{3+}(aq) + 3OH^-(aq) \rightarrow$
$Al(OH)_3(s)$

**36.** Chemical equation:
$Li_2SO_4(aq) + Ca(NO_3)_2(aq)$
$\rightarrow 2LiNO_3(aq) + CaSO_4(s)$
Complete ionic equation:
$2Li^+(aq) + SO_4^{2-}(aq) +$
$Ca^{2+}(aq) + 2NO_3^-(aq) \rightarrow$
$2Li^+(aq) + 2NO_3^-(aq) +$
$CaSO_4(s)$
Net ionic equation:
$SO_4^{2-}(aq) + Ca^{2+}(aq) \rightarrow$
$CaSO_4(s)$

**37.** Chemical equation:
$5Na_2CO_3(aq) + 2MnCl_5$
$(aq) \rightarrow 10NaCl(aq) +$
$Mn_2(CO_3)_5(s)$
Complete ionic equation:
$10Na^+(aq) + 5CO_3^{2-}(aq) +$
$2Mn^{5+}(aq) + 10Cl^-(aq) \rightarrow$
$10Na^+(aq) + 10Cl^-(aq) +$
$Mn_2(CO_3)_5(s)$
Net ionic equation:
$5CO_3^{2-}(aq) + 2Mn^{5+}(aq) \rightarrow$
$Mn_2(CO_3)_5(s)$

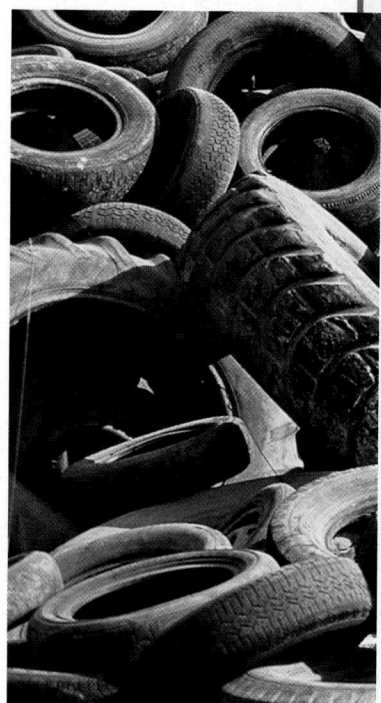

Barium carbonate ($BaCO_3$) is used in the rubber that is eventually processed into tires.

### Reactions That Form a Precipitate

Write the chemical, complete ionic, and net ionic equations for the reaction between aqueous solutions of barium nitrate and sodium carbonate that forms the precipitate barium carbonate.

**1. Analyze the Problem**

You are given the word equation for the reaction between barium nitrate and sodium carbonate. You must determine the chemical formulas and relative amounts of all reactants and products to write the chemical equation. To write the complete ionic equation, you need to show the ionic states of the reactants and products. By crossing out the spectator ions from the complete ionic equation you can write the net ionic equation. The net ionic equation will include fewer substances than the other equations.

**2. Solve for the Unknown**

Write the correct chemical formulas and physical states for all substances involved in the reaction.
$Ba(NO_3)_2(aq) + Na_2CO_3(aq) \rightarrow BaCO_3(s) + NaNO_3(aq)$

Balance the skeleton equation.
$Ba(NO_3)_2(aq) + Na_2CO_3(aq) \rightarrow BaCO_3(s) + 2NaNO_3(aq)$

Show the ionic states of the reactants and products.
$Ba^{2+}(aq) + 2NO_3^-(aq) + 2Na^+(aq) + CO_3^{2-}(aq) \rightarrow$
$\qquad\qquad BaCO_3(s) + 2Na^+(aq) + 2NO_3^-(aq)$

Cross out the spectator ions from the complete ionic equation.
$Ba^{2+}(aq) + \cancel{2NO_3^-(aq)} + \cancel{2Na^+(aq)} + CO_3^{2-}(aq) \rightarrow$
$\qquad\qquad BaCO_3(s) + \cancel{2Na^+(aq)} + \cancel{2NO_3^-(aq)}$

Write the net ionic equation.
$Ba^{2+}(aq) + CO_3^{2-}(aq) \rightarrow BaCO_3(s)$

**3. Evaluate the Answer**

The net ionic equation includes fewer substances than the other equations because it shows only the reacting particles. The particles that compose the solid precipitate that is the result of the reaction are no longer ions.

Practice! For more practice with writing ionic equations, go to **Supplemental Practice Problems** in Appendix A.

Write chemical, complete ionic, and net ionic equations for the following reactions that may produce precipitates. Use NR to indicate that no reaction occurs.

**33.** Aqueous solutions of potassium iodide and silver nitrate are mixed, forming the precipitate silver iodide.

**34.** Aqueous solutions of ammonium phosphate and sodium sulfate are mixed. No precipitate forms and no gas is produced.

**35.** Aqueous solutions of aluminum chloride and sodium hydroxide are mixed, forming the precipitate aluminum hydroxide.

**36.** Aqueous solutions of lithium sulfate and calcium nitrate are mixed, forming the precipitate calcium sulfate.

**37.** Aqueous solutions of sodium carbonate and manganese(V) chloride are mixed, forming the precipitate manganese(V) carbonate.

## DIFFERENTIATED INSTRUCTION

### Gifted

**Kinesthetic** Assemble an apparatus that includes a 20 mm × 150 mm test tube, a one-hole stopper that fits the test tube and has a short glass tube in the hole, a 30-cm length of rubber tubing attached to the short glass tube, and a 10-cm length of glass tubing attached to the other end of the rubber tubing. Have students pour approximately 5 mL of vinegar into the test tube and pour approximately 100 mL of limewater (saturated calcium hydroxide solution) into a 150-mL beaker. Then, have students add about one teaspoon of baking soda to the vinegar and quickly insert the one-hole stopper into the test tube so that the evolved gas passes through the tubing

## Observing a Precipitate-Forming Reaction

**Applying Concepts** When two clear, colorless solutions are mixed, a chemical reaction may occur, resulting in the formation of a precipitate.

**Materials** 150-mL beakers (2); 100-mL graduated cylinder; stirring rod (2); spatula (2); weighing paper (2); NaOH; Epsom salts ($MgSO_4 \cdot 7H_2O$); distilled water, balance

**Procedure**

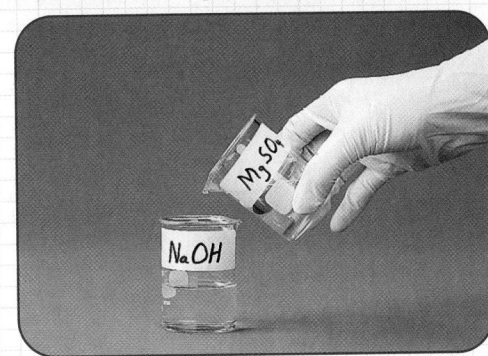

1. CAUTION: *Use gloves when working with NaOH.* Measure about 4 g NaOH and place it in a 150-mL beaker. Add 50 mL distilled water to the NaOH. Mix with a stirring rod until the NaOH dissolves.

2. Measure about 6 g Epsom salts and place it in another 150-mL beaker. Add 50 mL distilled water to the Epsom salts. Mix with another stirring rod until the Epsom salts dissolve.

3. Slowly pour the Epsom salts solution into the NaOH solution. Record your observations.

4. Stir the new solution. Record your observations.

5. Allow the precipitate to settle, then decant the liquid from the solid. Dispose of the solid as your teacher instructs.

**Analysis**

1. Write a chemical equation for the reaction between the NaOH and $MgSO_4$. Most sulfate compounds exist as ions in aqueous solutions.

2. Write the complete ionic equation for this reaction.

3. Write the net ionic equation for this reaction.

## Reactions That Form Water

Another type of double-replacement reaction that occurs in an aqueous solution produces water molecules. The water molecules produced in the reaction increase the number of solvent particles. Unlike reactions in which a precipitate forms, no evidence of a chemical reaction is observable because water is colorless and odorless and already makes up most of the solution. For example, when you mix hydrobromic acid with a sodium hydroxide solution, a double-replacement reaction occurs and water is formed.

$$HBr(aq) + NaOH(aq) \rightarrow H_2O(l) + NaBr(aq)$$

In this case, the reactants and the product sodium bromide exist as ions in an aqueous solution. The complete ionic equation for this reaction shows these ions.

$$H^+(aq) + Br^-(aq) + Na^+(aq) + OH^-(aq) \rightarrow H_2O(l) + Na^+(aq) + Br^-(aq)$$

Look carefully at the complete ionic equation. The reacting solute ions are the hydrogen and hydroxide ions because the sodium and bromine ions are both spectator ions. If you cross out the spectator ions, you are left with the ions that take part in the reaction.

$$H^+(aq) + OH^-(aq) \rightarrow H_2O(l)$$

This equation is the net ionic equation for the reaction.

**LAB**

See page 956 in Appendix E for **Preventing a Chemical Reaction**

---

**Purpose**
Students will write a balanced chemical equation, a complete ionic equation, and a net ionic equation for a chemical reaction that produces a precipitate.

**Process Skills**
Classifying, observing, inferring

**Safety Precautions**
Be sure students wear apron and goggles. NaOH is corrosive to skin. Epsom salts are a skin irritant.

**Disposal**
The magnesium hydroxide precipitate can be placed in the trash. Don't put it down the drain.

**Teaching Strategies**
• Show students how to decant a liquid that contains a solid.

**Expected Results**
The reaction will form a white precipitate. When the precipitate is mixed, the solution resembles milk. The precipitate is magnesium hydroxide. Sodium sulfate is also formed, but it is soluble in water and is not seen in the solution.

**Analysis**

1. $MgSO_4(aq) + 2NaOH(aq) \rightarrow Mg(OH)_2(s) + Na_2SO_4(aq)$

2. $Mg^{2+} + SO_4^{2-} + 2Na^+ + 2OH^- \rightarrow Mg(OH)_2(s) + 2Na^+ + SO_4^{2-}$

3. $Mg^{2+} + 2OH^- \rightarrow Mg(OH)_2(s)$

**✓ Assessment**

**Portfolio** Have students write a lab report for their portfolios. **L2** **P**

---

and bubbles through the limewater. Have them observe what happens. As the carbon dioxide gas produced by the reaction bubbles through the limewater, a cloud of insoluble calcium carbonate forms—a test for carbon dioxide. Ask students to write chemical equations for the reaction between the acetic acid in vinegar and sodium hydrogen carbonate and the reaction between carbon dioxide and aqueous calcium hydroxide to form insoluble calcium carbonate. **L2** **ELL**

$HC_2H_3O_2(aq) + NaHCO_3(s) \rightarrow H_2O(l) + CO_2(g) + NaC_2H_3O_2(aq)$; $CO_2(g) + Ca(OH)_2(aq) \rightarrow CaCO_3(s) + H_2O(l)$

National Science Content Standards

Pages 294–295
UCP.3, UCP.5; A.1; B.3

Have students refer to Appendix D for complete solutions to Practice Problems.

**38.** Chemical equation:
$$H_2SO_4(aq) + 2KOH(aq) \rightarrow 2H_2O(l) + K_2SO_4(aq)$$
Complete ionic equation:
$$2H^+(aq) + SO_4{}^{2-}(aq) + 2K^+(aq) + 2OH^-(aq) \rightarrow 2H_2O(l) + 2K^+(aq) + SO_4{}^{2-}(aq)$$
Net ionic equation:
$$H^+(aq) + OH^-(aq) \rightarrow H_2O(l)$$

**39.** Chemical equation:
$$2HCl(aq) + Ca(OH)_2(aq) \rightarrow 2H_2O(l) + CaCl_2(aq)$$
Complete ionic equation:
$$2H^+(aq) + 2Cl^-(aq) + Ca^{2+}(aq) + 2OH^-(aq) \rightarrow 2H_2O(l) + Ca^{2+}(aq) + 2Cl^-(aq)$$
Net ionic equation:
$$H^+(aq) + OH^-(aq) \rightarrow H_2O(l)$$

**40.** Chemical equation:
$$HNO_3(aq) + NH_4OH(aq) \rightarrow H_2O(l) + NH_4NO_3(aq)$$
Complete ionic equation:
$$H^+(aq) + NO_3{}^-(aq) + NH_4{}^+(aq) + OH^-(aq) \rightarrow H_2O(l) + NH_4{}^+(aq) + NO_3{}^-(aq)$$
Net ionic equation:
$$H^+(aq) + OH^-(aq) \rightarrow H_2O(l)$$

**41.** Chemical equation:
$$H_2S(aq) + Ca(OH)_2(aq) \rightarrow 2H_2O(l) + CaS(aq)$$
Complete ionic equation:
$$2H^+(aq) + S^{2-}(aq) + Ca^{2+}(aq) + 2OH^-(aq) \rightarrow 2H_2O(l) + Ca^{2+}(aq) + S^{2-}(aq)$$
Net ionic equation:
$$H^+(aq) + OH^-(aq) \rightarrow H_2O(l)$$

**42.** Chemical equation:
$$2H_3PO_4(aq) + 3Mg(OH)_2(aq) \rightarrow 6H_2O(l) + Mg_3(PO_4)_2(aq)$$
Complete ionic equation:
$$6H^+(aq) + 2PO_4{}^{3-}(aq) + 3Mg^{2+}(aq) + 6OH^-(aq) \rightarrow 6H_2O(l) + 3Mg^{2+}(aq) + 2PO_4{}^{3-}(aq)$$
Net ionic equation:
$$H^+(aq) + OH^-(aq) \rightarrow H_2O(l)$$

---

### EXAMPLE PROBLEM 10-4

**Reactions That Form Water**

Write the chemical, complete ionic, and net ionic equations for the reaction between hydrochloric acid and aqueous lithium hydroxide, which produces water.

**1. Analyze the Problem**

You are given the word equation for the reaction that occurs between hydrochloric acid and lithium hydroxide. You must determine the chemical formulas for and relative amounts of all reactants and products to write the chemical equation. To write the complete ionic equation, you need to show the ionic states of the reactants and products. By crossing out the spectator ions from the complete ionic equation you can write the net ionic equation.

**2. Solve for the Unknown**

Write the skeleton equation for the reaction and balance it.
$$HCl(aq) + LiOH(aq) \rightarrow H_2O(l) + LiCl(aq)$$

Show the ionic states of the reactants and products.
$$H^+(aq) + Cl^-(aq) + Li^+(aq) + OH^-(aq) \rightarrow H_2O(l) + Li^+(aq) + Cl^-(aq)$$

Cross out the spectator ions from the complete ionic equation.
$$H^+(aq) + \cancel{Cl^-(aq)} + \cancel{Li^+(aq)} + OH^-(aq) \rightarrow H_2O(l) + \cancel{Li^+(aq)} + \cancel{Cl^-(aq)}$$

Write the net ionic equation.
$$H^+(aq) + OH^-(aq) \rightarrow H_2O(l)$$

**3. Evaluate the Answer**

The net ionic equation includes fewer substances than the other equations because it shows only those particles involved in the reaction that produces water. The particles that compose the product water are no longer ions.

Hearing aids often use lithium batteries because batteries made with lithium are lightweight and have a long lifetime.

Practice! For more practice with writing ionic equations, go to Supplemental Practice Problems in Appendix A.

### PRACTICE PROBLEMS

Write chemical, complete ionic, and net ionic equations for the reactions between the following substances, which produce water.

**38.** Sulfuric acid ($H_2SO_4$) and aqueous potassium hydroxide

**39.** Hydrochloric acid (HCl) and aqueous calcium hydroxide

**40.** Nitric acid ($HNO_3$) and aqueous ammonium hydroxide

**41.** Hydrosulfuric acid ($H_2S$) and aqueous calcium hydroxide

**42.** Phosphoric acid ($H_3PO_4$) and aqueous magnesium hydroxide

## Reactions That Form Gases

A third type of double-replacement reaction that occurs in aqueous solutions results in the formation of a gas. Some gases commonly produced in these reactions are carbon dioxide, hydrogen cyanide, and hydrogen sulfide.

A gas-producing reaction occurs when you mix hydroiodic acid (HI) with an aqueous solution of lithium sulfide. Bubbles of hydrogen sulfide gas form in the container during the reaction. Lithium iodide is also produced in this reaction and remains dissolved in the solution.

$$2HI(aq) + Li_2S(aq) \rightarrow H_2S(g) + 2LiI(aq)$$

**296** Chapter 10 Chemical Reactions

### Resource Manager

**ChemLab and MiniLab Worksheets,** p. 37 **L2**

The reactants hydroiodic acid and lithium sulfide exist as ions in aqueous solution. Therefore, you can write an ionic equation for this reaction. The complete ionic equation includes all of the substances in the solution.

$$2H^+(aq) + 2I^-(aq) + 2Li^+(aq) + S^{2-}(aq) \rightarrow H_2S(g) + 2Li^+(aq) + 2I^-(aq)$$

Note that there are many spectator ions in the equation. When the spectator ions are crossed out, only the substances involved in the reaction remain in the equation.

$$2H^+(aq) + 2\cancel{I^-(aq)} + 2\cancel{Li^+(aq)} + S^{2-}(aq) \rightarrow H_2S(g) + 2\cancel{Li^+(aq)} + 2\cancel{I^-(aq)}$$

This is the net ionic equation.

$$2H^+(aq) + S^{2-}(aq) \rightarrow H_2S(g)$$

You observed another gas-producing reaction in the **DISCOVERY LAB** at the beginning of this chapter. In that reaction carbon dioxide gas was produced and bubbled out of the solution. Another reaction that produces carbon dioxide gas occurs in your kitchen when you mix vinegar and baking soda. Vinegar is an aqueous solution of acetic acid and water. Baking soda essentially consists of sodium hydrogen carbonate. Rapid bubbling occurs when vinegar and baking soda are combined. The bubbles are carbon dioxide gas escaping from the solution. You can see this reaction occurring in **Figure 10-13**.

A reaction similar to the one between vinegar and baking soda occurs when you combine any acidic solution and sodium hydrogen carbonate. In all cases, two reactions must occur almost simultaneously in the solution to produce the carbon dioxide gas. One reaction is double-replacement and the other is decomposition.

For example, when you dissolve sodium hydrogen carbonate in hydrochloric acid, a gas-producing double-replacement reaction occurs. The hydrogen in the hydrochloric acid and the sodium in the sodium hydrogen carbonate replace each other.

$$HCl(aq) + NaHCO_3(aq) \rightarrow H_2CO_3(aq) + NaCl(aq)$$

Sodium chloride is an ionic compound and its ions remain separate in the aqueous solution. However, as the carbonic acid ($H_2CO_3$) forms, it decomposes immediately into water and carbon dioxide.

$$H_2CO_3(aq) \rightarrow H_2O(l) + CO_2(g)$$

**Figure 10-13**

When vinegar and baking soda (sodium hydrogen carbonate, $NaHCO_3$) combine, the result is a vigorous bubbling that releases carbon dioxide ($CO_2$).

**Applying Chemistry**

**TECH PREP** Explain to students that some biscuits and other baked goods rise during baking because of trapped carbon dioxide gas produced by the reaction between baking powder and water. Baking powder is a mixture of baking soda (sodium hydrogen carbonate, $NaHCO_3$), a dry acid such as tartaric acid ($H_2C_4H_4O_6$), and usually starch to keep the mixture dry. Water added to baking powder dissolves the baking soda and tartaric acid, which facilitates the following chemical reaction: $H_2C_4H_4O_6(aq) + 2NaHCO_3(aq) \rightarrow 2H_2O(l) + 2CO_2(g) + Na_2C_4H_4O_6(aq)$. You may want to demonstrate the reaction by adding some water to a small sample of baking powder in a watch glass on an overhead projector.

**CAREERS USING CHEMISTRY**

**TECH PREP** **Career Path** A career as a pastry chef would include these high school courses: chemistry, math, and food science.

**Career Issue** Have students investigate how to cut down on fats and cholesterol and maintain taste and texture in desserts. Have them include some of the chemistry of the foods to explain.

**For More Information**
For more information about careers in the culinary arts, students can contact

The Culinary Institute of America
1946 Campus Drive
Hyde Park, NY 12538-1499

---

**CHEMISTRY JOURNAL**

**What's a hydrogen to do?**

**Linguistic** Have students write journal entries that describe the "activities" and "travels" of a hydrogen atom during the following reactions and processes: a gaseous hydrogen molecule reacts with a gaseous iodine molecule to form gaseous hydrogen iodide; gaseous hydrogen iodide dissolves in water to form hydroiodic acid; hydroiodic acid reacts with aqueous lithium sulfide to form hydrogen sulfide gas. Encourage students to look up the physical and chemical properties of iodine and hydrogen sulfide and possibly include these properties in their stories. **L2**

Refer to Appendix D for complete solutions.

**43.** Chemical equation:
$2HClO_4(aq) + K_2CO_3(aq) \rightarrow$
$H_2O(l) + CO_2(g) +$
$2KClO_4(aq)$
Complete ionic equation:
$2H^+(aq) + 2ClO_4^-(aq) +$
$2K^+(aq) + CO_3^{2-}(aq) \rightarrow$
$H_2O(l) + CO_2(g) + 2K^+$
$(aq) + 2ClO_4^-(aq)$
Net ionic equation:
$2H^+(aq) + CO_3^{2-}(aq) \rightarrow$
$H_2O(l) + CO_2(g)$

**44.** Chemical equation:
$H_2SO_4(aq) + 2NaCN(aq) \rightarrow$
$2HCN(g) + Na_2SO_4(aq)$
Complete ionic equation:
$2H^+(aq) + SO_4^{2-}(aq) +$
$2Na^+(aq) + 2CN^-(aq) \rightarrow$
$2HCN(g) + 2Na^+(aq) +$
$SO_4^{2-}(aq)$
Net ionic equation:
$H^+(aq) + CN^-(aq) \rightarrow$
$HCN(g)$

**45.** Chemical equation:
$2HBr(aq) + (NH_4)_2CO_3$
$(aq) \rightarrow H_2O(l) + CO_2(g) +$
$2NH_4Br(aq)$
Complete ionic equation:
$2H^+(aq) + 2Br^-(aq) +$
$2NH_4^+(aq) + CO_3^{2-}(aq) \rightarrow$
$H_2O(l) + CO_2(g) +$
$2NH_4^+(aq) + 2Br^-(aq)$
Net ionic equation:
$2H^+(aq) + CO_3^{2-}(aq) \rightarrow$
$H_2O(l) + CO_2(g)$

**46.** Chemical equation:
$2HNO_3(aq) + KRbS(aq) \rightarrow$
$H_2S(g) + KRb(NO_3)_2(aq)$
Complete ionic equation:
$2H^+(aq) + 2NO_3^-(aq) +$
$K^+(aq) + Rb^+(aq) +$
$S^{2-}(aq) \rightarrow H_2S(g) + K^+(aq)$
$+ Rb^+(aq) + 2NO_3^-(aq)$
Net ionic equation:
$2H^+(aq) + S^{2-}(aq) \rightarrow H_2S(g)$

The two reactions can be combined and represented by one chemical equation in a process similar to adding mathematical equations. An equation that combines two reactions is called an overall equation. To write an overall equation, the reactants in the two reactions are written on the reactant side of the combined equation, and the products of the two reactions are written on the product side. Then any substances that are on both sides of the equation are crossed out.

**Reaction 1**    $HCl(aq) + NaHCO_3(aq) \rightarrow H_2CO_3(aq) + NaCl(aq)$

**Reaction 2**    $\underline{H_2CO_3(aq) \rightarrow H_2O(l) + CO_2(g)}$

**Combined equation**  $HCl(aq) + NaHCO_3(aq) + \cancel{H_2CO_3(aq)} \rightarrow$
$\cancel{H_2CO_3(aq)} + NaCl(aq) + H_2O(l) + CO_2(g)$

**Overall equation**  $HCl(aq) + NaHCO_3(aq) \rightarrow$
$H_2O(l) + CO_2(g) + NaCl(aq)$

In this case, the reactants in the overall equation exist as ions in aqueous solutions. Therefore, a complete ionic equation can be written for the reaction.

$$H^+(aq) + Cl^-(aq) + Na^+(aq) + HCO_3^-(aq) \rightarrow$$
$$H_2O(l) + CO_2(g) + Na^+(aq) + Cl^-(aq)$$

Note that the sodium and chloride ions are the spectator ions. When you cross them out only the substances that take part in the reaction remain.

$$H^+(aq) + \cancel{Cl^-(aq)} + \cancel{Na^+(aq)} + HCO_3^-(aq) \rightarrow$$
$$H_2O(l) + CO_2(g) + \cancel{Na^+(aq)} + \cancel{Cl^-(aq)}$$

The net ionic equation shows that both water and carbon dioxide gas are produced in this reaction.

$$H^+(aq) + HCO_3^-(aq) \rightarrow H_2O(l) + CO_2(g)$$

This is an important reaction in your life. This reaction is occurring in the blood vessels of your lungs as you read these words. The carbon dioxide gas produced in your cells is transported in your blood in the form of the bicarbonate ion ($HCO_3^-$). In the blood vessels of your lungs, the $HCO_3^-$ ions combine with $H^+$ ions to produce $CO_2$, which you exhale. This reaction also occurs in sodium bicarbonate products, such as those shown in **Figure 10-14,** that are made with baking soda.

**Figure 10-14**

The reactions of sodium bicarbonate in aqueous solution have many household applications. This sampling of products shows a variety of products that involve a chemical reaction of sodium bicarbonate.

## Internet Address Book

**Chemistry Online**    Note Internet addresses that you find useful in the space below for quick reference.

_____

_____

_____

_____

_____

**Reactions That Form Gases**

Write the chemical, complete ionic, and net ionic equations for the reaction between hydrochloric acid and aqueous sodium sulfide, which produces hydrogen sulfide gas.

**1. Analyze the Problem**

You are given the word equation for the reaction between hydrochloric acid and sodium sulfide. You must write the skeleton equation and balance it. To write the complete ionic equation, you need to show the ionic states of the reactants and products. By crossing out the spectator ions in the complete ionic equation, you can write the net ionic equation.

**2. Solve for the Unknown**

Write the correct skeleton equation for the reaction and balance it.

$$2HCl(aq) + Na_2S(aq) \rightarrow H_2S(g) + 2NaCl(aq)$$

Show the ionic states of the reactants and products.

$$2H^+(aq) + 2Cl^-(aq) + 2Na^+(aq) + S^{2-}(aq) \rightarrow$$
$$H_2S(g) + 2Na^+(aq) + 2Cl^-(aq)$$

Cross out the spectator ions from the complete ionic equation.

$$2H^+(aq) + 2\cancel{Cl^-(aq)} + 2\cancel{Na^+(aq)} + S^{2-}(aq) \rightarrow$$
$$H_2S(g) + 2\cancel{Na^+(aq)} + 2\cancel{Cl^-(aq)}$$

Write the net ionic equation in its smallest whole number ratio.

$$2H^+(aq) + S^{2-}(aq) \rightarrow H_2S(g)$$

**3. Evaluate the Answer**

The net ionic equation includes fewer substances than the other equations because it shows only those particles involved in the reaction that produces hydrogen sulfide. The particles that compose the product are no longer ions.

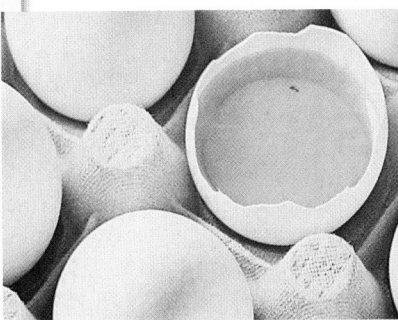

Many chemical reactions are obvious by the results that can be detected by the senses. The chemical reaction that occurs when eggs rot gives off hydrogen sulfide ($H_2S$) gas, which has a pungent, distinctive odor.

**PRACTICE** PROBLEMS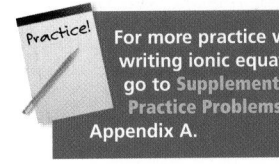

Write chemical, complete ionic, and net ionic equations for these reactions.

**43.** Perchloric acid ($HClO_4$) reacts with aqueous potassium carbonate.

**44.** Sulfuric acid ($H_2SO_4$) reacts with aqueous sodium cyanide.

**45.** Hydrobromic acid (HBr) reacts with aqueous ammonium carbonate.

**46.** Nitric acid ($HNO_3$) reacts with aqueous potassium rubidium sulfide.

*Practice!* **For more practice with writing ionic equations, go to Supplemental Practice Problems in Appendix A.**

## Section 10.3 Assessment

**47.** Describe an aqueous solution.

**48.** Distinguish between a complete ionic equation and a net ionic equation.

**49.** What are three common types of products produced by reactions that occur in aqueous solutions?

**50. Thinking Critically** Explain why net ionic equations communicate more than chemical equations about reactions in aqueous solutions.

**51. Communicating** Describe the reaction of aqueous solutions of sodium sulfide and copper(II) sulfate, producing the precipitate copper(II) sulfide.

## Section 10.3 Assessment

**47.** one in which water is the solvent

**48.** In a complete ionic equation, all dissolved ionic compounds and highly ionized molecular compounds are shown as free ions. A net ionic equation includes only the particles that take part in the reaction.

**49.** precipitates, water, and gases

**50.** The net ionic equation shows only the particles that react.

**51.** Sodium sulfide and copper(II) sulfate dissociate in water to form sodium ions, sulfide ions, copper(II) ions, and sulfate ions. The copper(II) ions and sulfide ions form the precipitate copper sulfide. Sodium ions and sulfate ions are spectator ions that remain dissolved in the solution.

---

# 3 Assess
## Check for Understanding

Ask students to predict which of the following double-replacement reactions occur. Have them explain their reasoning.

**1.** $CuCl_2(aq) + 2NaNO_3(aq) \rightarrow Cu(NO_3)_2(aq) + 2NaCl(aq)$

**2.** $CuCl_2(aq) + Na_2CO_3(aq) \rightarrow CuCO_3(s) + 2NaCl(aq)$

**3.** $2HCl(aq) + Na_2CO_3(aq) \rightarrow H_2O(l) + CO_2(g) + 2NaCl(aq)$

Reactions 2 and 3 occur. Reaction 2 forms a solid, and reaction 3 forms water and a gas.

## Reteach

Ask students to identify any spectator ions in the following complete ionic equation. Then, have them write the net ionic equation. $H^+(aq) + BrO_3^-(aq) + K^+(aq) + OH^-(aq) \rightarrow H_2O(l) + BrO_3^-(aq) + K^+(aq)$ Spectator ions are $BrO_3^-$ and $K^+$. The net ionic equation is $H^+(aq) + OH^-(aq) \rightarrow H_2O(l)$.

## Extension

Invite a chemistry professor or graduate student to your class to discuss the importance of balanced equations in graduate-level research. Prepare some equations representing chemical reactions and ask the guest speaker to demonstrate how he or she balances chemical equations.

 **Assessment**

**Knowledge** Ask students to predict the formula of the missing product (X) in each of the following reactions and tell why the reaction occurs:

**1.** $BaCl_2(aq) + K_2SO_4(aq) \rightarrow 2KCl(aq) + X$   X is $BaSO_4$, an insoluble product.

**2.** $HI(aq) + LiOH(aq) \rightarrow LiI(aq) + X$   X is $H_2O$.

**3.** $2HCl(aq) + (NH_4)_2S(aq) \rightarrow 2NH_4Cl(aq) + X$   X is $H_2S$, a gas.

**National Science Content Standards**

**Pages 298–299**
UCP.3, UCP.5; B.3

## Preparation 📖

**Time Allotment**
One laboratory period

**Process Skills**
Observing and inferring, sequencing, comparing and contrasting, applying concepts, predicting

**Safety Precautions**
Be sure students wear an apron and goggles and wash hands with soap after the lab.

**Disposal**
Unreacted metal can be reclaimed and reused. The contents of the well plate can be emptied into a waste container and evaporated to dryness in the fume hood. Dispose of the solid waste at an approved chemical disposal site.

**Preparation of Solutions**
Use the following masses of nitrate salts to prepare 1.0 L of a 1.0$M$ solution:
298 g $Zn(NO_3)_2 \cdot 6H_2O$
375 g $Al(NO_3)_3 \cdot 9H_2O$
242 g $Cu(NO_3)_2 \cdot 3H_2O$
256 g $Mg(NO_3)_2 \cdot 6H_2O$
See page 276C for preparation of all solutions.

**Alternative Materials**
Other metals and their nitrate salts can be substituted for the ones listed.

### Pre-Lab

3. Table should resemble the table shown on the next page.
4. Answers may vary. Students should predict (a) that no reaction will occur when a metal is placed in an aqueous solution of a more reactive metal and (b) that a metal that is placed in an aqueous solution of a less reactive metal replaces the less reactive metal.
5. independent: solution concentration, amount of each type of metal, reaction time; dependent: reaction (no reaction), evidence of reaction, specific products of reaction

---

# Activities of Metals

Some metals are more reactive than others. By comparing how different metals react with the same ions in aqueous solutions, an activity series for the tested metals can be developed. The activity series will reflect the relative reactivity of the tested metals. It can be used to predict whether reactions will occur.

### Problem
Which is the most reactive metal tested? Which is the least reactive metal tested? Can this information be used to predict whether reactions will occur?

### Objectives
- **Observe** chemical reactions.
- **Sequence** the activities of some metals.
- **Predict** if reactions will occur between certain substances.

### Materials
1.0$M$ $Zn(NO_3)_2$
1.0$M$ $Al(NO_3)_3$
1.0$M$ $Cu(NO_3)_2$
1.0$M$ $Mg(NO_3)_2$
pipettes (4)
wire cutters
Cu wire
Al wire
Mg ribbon
Zn metal strips (4)
emery cloth or fine sandpaper
24-well microscale reaction plate

### Safety Precautions

- Always wear safety goggles and a lab apron.
- Use caution when using sharp and coarse equipment.

### Pre-Lab

1. Read the entire **CHEMLAB**.
2. Make notes about procedures and safety precautions to use in the laboratory.
3. Prepare your data table.

| Reactions Between Solutions and Metals | | | | |
|---|---|---|---|---|
| | $Al(NO_3)_3$ | $Mg(NO_3)_2$ | $Zn(NO_3)_2$ | $Cu(NO_3)_2$ |
| Al | | | | |
| Mg | | | | |
| Zn | | | | |
| Cu | | | | |

4. Form a hypothesis about what reactions will occur.
5. What are the independent and dependent variables?
6. What gas is produced when magnesium and hydrochloric acid react? Write the chemical equation for the reaction.
7. Why is it important to clean the magnesium ribbon? How might not polishing a piece of metal affect the reaction involving that metal?

### Procedure

1. Use a pipette to fill each of the four wells in column 1 of the reaction plate with 2 mL of 1.0$M$ $Al(NO_3)_3$ solution.
2. Repeat the procedure in step 1 to fill the four wells in column 2 with 2 mL of 1.0$M$ $Mg(NO_3)_2$ solution.
3. Repeat the procedure in step 1 to fill the four wells in column 3 with 2 mL of 1.0$M$ $Zn(NO_3)_2$ solution.
4. Repeat the procedure in step 1 to fill the four wells in column 4 with 2 mL of 1.0$M$ $Cu(NO_3)_2$ solution.
5. With the emery paper or sandpaper, polish 10 cm of aluminum wire until it is shiny. Use wire cutters to cut the aluminum wire into four 2.5-cm pieces. Place a piece of the aluminum wire in each row A well that contains solution.
6. Repeat the procedure in step 5 using 10 cm of magnesium ribbon. Place a piece of the Mg ribbon in each row B well that contains solution.
7. Use the emery paper or sandpaper to polish small strips of zinc metal. Place a piece of Zn metal in each row C well that contains solution.

---

6. hydrogen; $Mg + 2HCl \rightarrow MgCl_2 + H_2$
7. Oxidation or a coating on the metal may prevent it from making chemical contact with the solution.

## Procedure

- 2 mL of solution will half-fill a well in the reaction plate.
- The metal must be cleaned with emery cloth or sandpaper and have a luster.
- **Troubleshooting** Remind students that if a shiny piece of metal darkens, that is evidence of a chemical change.

8. Repeat the procedure in step 5 using 10 cm of copper wire. Place a piece of Cu wire in each row D well that contains solution.

9. Observe what happens in each cell. After five minutes, record your observations on the data table you made.

## Cleanup and Disposal

1. Dispose of all chemicals and solutions as directed by your teacher.

2. Clean your equipment and return it to its proper place.

3. Wash your hands thoroughly before you leave the lab.

## Analyze and Conclude

1. **Observing and Inferring** In which wells of the reaction plate did chemical reactions occur? Which metal reacted with the most solutions? Which metal reacted with the fewest solutions? Which metal is the most reactive?

2. **Sequencing** The most active metal reacted with the most solutions. The least active metal reacted with the fewest solutions. Order the four metals from the most active to the least active.

3. **Comparing and Contrasting** Compare your activity series with the activity series shown here. How does the order you determined for the four metals you tested compare with the order of these metals?

4. **Applying Concepts** Write a chemical equation for each single-replacement reaction that occurred on your reaction plate.

5. **Predicting** Use the diagram below to predict if a single-replacement reaction will occur between the following reactants. Write a chemical equation for each reaction that will occur.
   a. Ca and $Sn(NO_3)_2$
   b. Ag and $Ni(NO_3)_2$
   c. Cu and $Pb(NO_3)_3$

6. **Error Analysis** If the activity series you sequenced does not agree with the order in the diagram below, propose a reason for the disagreement.

| | **METALS** |
|---|---|
| Most active | Lithium |
| | Rubidium |
| | Potassium |
| | Calcium |
| | Sodium |
| | Magnesium |
| | Aluminum |
| | Manganese |
| | Zinc |
| | Iron |
| | Nickel |
| | Tin |
| | Lead |
| | Copper |
| | Silver |
| Least active | Platinum |
| | Gold |
| | **HALOGENS** |
| Most active | Fluorine |
| | Chlorine |
| Least active | Bromine |
| | Iodine |

## Real-World Chemistry

1. Under what circumstances might it be important to know the activity tendencies of a series of elements?

2. Describe some of the environmental impacts of nitrates.

## Analyze and Conclude

1. A3, A4, B1, B3, B4, C4
   Mg– 3 reactions
   Cu – 0 reactions
   Magnesium is the most reactive.

2. Mg, Al, Zn, Cu

3. The order is the same.

4. A3: $2Al + 3Zn(NO_3)_2 \rightarrow$
   $2Al(NO_3)_3 + 3Zn$
   A4: $2Al + 3Cu(NO_3)_2 \rightarrow$
   $2Al(NO_3)_3 + 3Cu$
   B1: $3Mg + 2Al(NO_3)_3 \rightarrow$
   $3Mg(NO_3)_2 + 2Al$
   B3: $Mg + Zn(NO_3)_2 \rightarrow$
   $Mg(NO_3)_2 + Zn$
   B4: $Mg + Cu(NO_3)_2 \rightarrow$
   $Mg(NO_3)_2 + Cu$
   C4: $Zn + Cu(NO_3)_2 \rightarrow$
   $Zn(NO_3)_2 + Cu$

5. a. yes, $Ca + Sn(NO_3)_2 \rightarrow$
   $Ca(NO_3)_2 + Sn$
   b. no, c. no

6. Answers may vary. If the procedure was not followed or if the contents of two wells mixed due to over-filling, then the activity series would not agree.

## Real-World Chemistry

1. Answers may vary. For example, industrial chemists could use the information to fine-tune a product or process.

2. Answers may vary. For example, students may discuss nitrates as fertilizers or the dangers of nitrates in water supplies. They may also describe nitrate removal procedures.

### ✔ Assessment

**Knowledge** Have students use Figure 10-10 to predict if a reaction will occur between potassium (K) and a mercury(II) iodide solution. Yes, K will replace Hg.
$2K + HgI_2 \rightarrow 2KI + Hg$

**National Science Content Standards**
**Pages 300–301**
UCP.3, UCP.5; A.1, A.2; B.2, B.3

## Expected Results

| | $Al(NO_3)_3$ | $Mg(NO_3)_2$ | $Zn(NO_3)_2$ | $Cu(NO_3)_2$ |
|---|---|---|---|---|
| **Al** | No | No | Yes | Yes |
| **Mg** | Yes | No | Yes | Yes |
| **Zn** | No | No | No | Yes |
| **Cu** | No | No | No | No |

## Resource Manager

**ChemLab and MiniLab Worksheets,**
pp. 38–40 **L2**

# How It Works

## How It Works

## Purpose

Students will understand that a salt dissolving to form an aqueous solution absorbs or releases heat that can be used to alter the temperature of an object.

## Background

Heat is absorbed or released when most ionic compounds form aqueous solutions. In many cases the amount of heat transferred is small, but for some there is a substantial transfer. Most hot and cold packs utilize substances that generate or absorb substantial amounts of heat when they dissolve in water. A few hot packs utilize the oxidation of magnesium or iron to generate heat.

## Visual Learning

Refer students to the diagram of the cold pack to emphasize how it works. You can demonstrate the generation of heat by dissolving calcium chloride in water. Add 20 grams of calcium chloride to 100 mL of water in a small beaker along with a thermometer. Have students observe the temperature rise as the calcium chloride dissolves.

## Teaching Strategies

- Ask students why the type of pack shown is not reusable. The process is not easily reversed. The solution in the used pack would have to be evaporated to restore the salt to crystals.

- Ask students to do research on packs that use the oxidation of a metal to generate heat. Tell them to also look for the *field ration heaters* developed to heat food for military personnel.

**National Science Content Standards**

**Pages 302–303**
UCP.3, UCP.5; B.2, B.3, B.6

# How It Works
## Hot and Cold Packs

Athletes know that the application of heat or cold to a strain or sprain usually relieves the pain and may lessen the severity of the injury. Instant hot and cold packs allow you to quickly and easily apply the appropriate remedy to the injury.

Hot and cold packs create aqueous solutions of a soluble salt. A salt such as ammonium nitrate is used in the cold pack and heat is absorbed as the salt dissolves in the water. Hot packs release heat when a salt such as calcium chloride dissolves in the water.

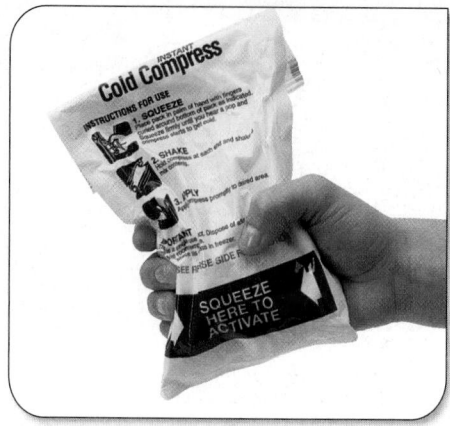

**1** The outside of the pouch is flexible and strong enough to resist breaking.

**2** The water is stored in an inner chamber made from thin, easily broken plastic membrane.

**3** Salt is stored between the outer covering and the water container.

**4** The water is released from the inner chamber when you squeeze or strike the pack.

**5** Heat is absorbed as the salt mixes with and dissolves in the water.

Plastic pouch

Soluble salt

Membrane of water pack

Water

### Thinking Critically

**1. Predicting** An aqueous solution of sodium thiosulfate releases heat when it crystallizes. What would happen when sodium thiosulfate crystals dissolve in water?

**2. Hypothesizing** One type of heat pack contains fine iron particles. These packs are kept in a sealed container and release heat when they are exposed to air. How does this type of pack work?

### Thinking Critically

**1.** Answers may vary. Students should correctly predict that when the sodium thiosulfate dissolves in water, it absorbs heat and the solution becomes cold.

**2.** When the seal is broken, the iron is exposed to the oxygen in the air and it oxidizes (rusts). Oxidation is a slow combustion reaction and combustion reactions usually generate heat.

## Summary

### 10.1 Reactions and Equations

- Some chemical reactions release energy in the form of heat and light, and some absorb energy.

- Changes in temperature, color, odor, and physical state are all types of evidence that indicate a chemical reaction has occurred.

- Word and skeleton equations provide important information about a chemical reaction, such as the reactants and products involved in the reaction and their physical states.

- A chemical equation gives the identities and relative amounts of the reactants and products that are involved in a chemical reaction. Chemical equations are balanced.

- Balancing an equation involves adjusting the coefficients of the chemical formulas in the skeleton equation until the number of atoms of each element is equal on both sides of the equation.

### 10.2 Classifying Chemical Reactions

- Classifying chemical reactions makes them easier to understand, remember, and recognize.

- Synthesis, combustion, decomposition, single-replacement, and double-replacement reactions are five classes of chemical reactions.

- A synthesis reaction occurs when two substances react to yield a single product. The substances that react can be two elements, a compound and an element, or two compounds.

- A combustion reaction occurs when a substance reacts with oxygen, producing heat and light.

- A decomposition reaction occurs when a single compound breaks down into two or more elements or new compounds.

- A single-replacement reaction occurs when the atoms of one element replace the atoms of another element in a compound.

- In single-replacement reactions, a metal may replace hydrogen in water, a metal may replace another metal in a compound dissolved in water, and a non-metal may replace another nonmetal in a compound.

- Metals and halogens can be ordered according to their reactivities. These listings, which are called activity series, can be used to predict if single-replacement reactions will occur.

- A double-replacement reaction involves the exchange of positive ions between two compounds.

### 10.3 Reactions in Aqueous Solutions

- In aqueous solutions, the solvent is always water. There are many possible solutes.

- Many molecular compounds form ions when they dissolve in water. When most ionic compounds dissolve in water, their ions separate.

- When two aqueous solutions that contain ions as solutes are combined, the ions may react with one another. The solvent molecules do not usually react.

- Reactions that occur in aqueous solutions are double-replacement reactions.

- Three types of products produced during reactions in aqueous solutions are precipitates, water, and gases.

- An ionic equation shows the details of reactions in aqueous solutions. A complete ionic equation shows all the particles in a solution as they exist. A net ionic equation includes only the particles that participate in a reaction in a solution.

## Using the Vocabulary

To reinforce chapter vocabulary, have students write a sentence using each term. **L2** **ELL**

## Review Strategies

- Have students list the various factors that may indicate a chemical reaction has occurred. **L2**

- Have students describe the steps involved in writing word equations, skeleton equations, and chemical equations. **L2**

- Ask students to describe each of the five classes of chemical reactions studied in this chapter. **L2**

- Have students write word equations, skeleton equations, chemical equations, complete ionic equations, and net ionic equations for several reactions that occur in aqueous solution. **L2**

- Problems from Appendix A or the **Supplemental Problems** booklet can be used for review. **L2**

VOCABULARY PuzzleMaker CHEMISTRY ONLINE

For additional help with vocabulary, have students access the Vocabulary PuzzleMaker online.

chemistrymc.com/ vocabulary_puzzlemaker

## Vocabulary

- aqueous solution (p. 292)
- chemical equation (p. 280)
- chemical reaction (p. 277)
- coefficient (p. 280)
- combustion reaction (p. 285)
- complete ionic equation (p.293)
- decomposition reaction (p. 286)
- double-replacement reaction (p. 290)
- net ionic equation (p. 293)
- precipitate (p. 290)
- product (p. 278)
- reactant (p. 278)
- single-replacement reaction (p. 287)
- solute (p. 292)
- solvent (p. 292)
- spectator ion (p. 293)
- synthesis reaction (p. 284)

Chemistry Online

chemistrymc.com/vocabulary_puzzlemaker

## Concept Mapping

**52. 1.** change in energy, **2.** change in physical state, **3.** change in odor, **4.** change in color, **5.** word equation, **6.** chemical equation, **7.** net ionic equation, **8.** complete ionic equation **9.** synthesis, **10.** decomposition, **11.** single-replacement, **12.** double-replacement, **13.** combustion

## Mastering Concepts

**53.** Reactants are the initial components and products are the resultant components.

**54.** Arrows separate reactants from products and specify direction of reaction. Coefficients specify the relative amount of the components.

**55. a.** $NO_2(g)$; **b.** $Ga(l)$; **c.** $BaCl_2(aq)$; **d.** $(NH_4)_2CO_3(s)$

**56.** K and $Zn(NO_3)_2(aq)$

**57.** energy release and formation of gases

**58.** magnesium(s) + iron(III) chloride(aq)→iron(s) + magnesium(II) chloride(aq)

**59.** $3Mg(s) + 2FeCl_3(aq) \rightarrow 2Fe(s) + 3MgCl_2(aq)$

**60.** synthesis, combustion, decomposition, single replacement, double replacement

**61.** It is a synthesis reaction.

**62.** In a single-replacement reaction, the atoms of an element react with a compound, whereas in a double-replacement reaction, two compounds react.

**63.** when the reaction occurs in aqueous solution and the product of the reaction is insoluble

**64.** single-replacement

**65. a.** Na replaces Sn; **b.** F replaces I; **c.** Pb replaces Ag; **d.** Ni replaces Cu.

**66.** solids, water, and gases

**67.** A chemical equation gives formulas and relative amounts of all substances. A complete ionic equation shows the particles as they exist in solution.

## Chemistry Online

*Go to the Chemistry Web site at* **chemistrymc.com** *for additional Chapter 10 Assessment.*

## Concept Mapping

**52.** Use the following terms and phrases to complete the concept map: synthesis, net ionic equation, change in energy, change in physical state, single-replacement, word equation, decomposition, complete ionic equation, double-replacement, combustion, change in odor, chemical equation, change in color.

Chemical Reactions

evidence of — classes of — described by

1. 9. 5.
2. 10. 6.
3. 11. 7.
4. 12. 8.
13.

## Mastering Concepts

**53.** Explain the difference between reactants and products. (10.1)

**54.** What do the arrows and coefficients used by chemists in equations communicate? (10.1)

**55.** Write formulas for the following substances and designate their physical states. (10.1)

**a.** nitrogen dioxide gas
**b.** liquid gallium
**c.** barium chloride dissolved in water
**d.** solid ammonium carbonate

**56.** Identify the reactants in the following reaction: When potassium is dropped into aqueous zinc nitrate, zinc and aqueous potassium nitrate form. (10.1)

**57.** When gasoline is burned in an automobile engine, what evidence indicates that a chemical change has occurred? (10.1)

**58.** Write the word equation for this skeleton equation. (10.1)

$$Mg(s) + FeCl_3(aq) \rightarrow Fe(s) + MgCl_2(aq)$$

**59.** Balance the equation in question 58. (10.1)

**60.** What are five classes of chemical reactions? (10.2)

**61.** How would you classify a chemical reaction between two reactants that produces one product? (10.2)

**62.** Explain the difference between a single-replacement reaction and a double-replacement reaction. (10.2)

**63.** Under what conditions does a precipitate form in a chemical reaction? (10.2)

**64.** Classify the chemical reaction in question 58. (10.2)

**65.** In each of the following pairs, which element will replace the other in a reaction? (10.2)

**a.** tin and sodium
**b.** fluorine and iodine
**c.** lead and silver
**d.** copper and nickel

**66.** When reactions occur in aqueous solutions what common types of products are produced? (10.3)

**67.** Compare and contrast chemical equations and ionic equations. (10.3)

**68.** What is a net ionic equation? How does it differ from a complete ionic equation? (10.3)

**69.** Define spectator ion. (10.3)

**70.** Write the net ionic equation for a chemical reaction that occurs in an aqueous solution and produces water. (10.3)

## Mastering Problems
### Balancing Chemical Equations (10.1)

**71.** Write skeleton equations for these reactions.

**a.** hydrogen iodide(g) $\rightarrow$ hydrogen(g) + iodine(g)
**b.** aluminum(s) + iodine(s) $\rightarrow$ aluminum iodide(s)
**c.** iron(II) oxide(s) + oxygen(g) $\rightarrow$ iron(III) oxide(s)

**72.** Write skeleton equations for these reactions.

**a.** butane $(C_4H_{10})(l)$ + oxygen(g) $\rightarrow$ carbon dioxide(g) + water(l)
**b.** aluminum carbonate(s) $\rightarrow$ aluminum oxide(s) + carbon dioxide(g)
**c.** silver nitrate(aq) + sodium sulfide(aq) $\rightarrow$ silver sulfide(s) + sodium nitrate(aq)

chemistrymc.com/chapter_test

**68.** A net ionic equation shows only the reactive particles. A complete ionic equation also shows ions that do not react (free ions from dissolved ionic compounds and highly ionized molecular compounds).

**69.** A spectator ion is an ion that is present in solution but does not participate in the reaction.

### Resource Manager

**Chapter Assessment**, pp. 55–60 L2
**Supplemental Problems**, Ch. 10
**ExamView® Pro CD-ROM**
**MindJogger Videoquizzes DVD/VHS**
**Solutions Manual**, Ch. 10
**Chemistry Interactive CD-ROM**, Ch. 10 quiz

**73.** Write skeleton equations for these reactions.

  **a.** iron(s) + fluorine(g) → iron(III) fluoride(s)
  **b.** sulfur trioxide(g) + water(l) → sulfuric acid(aq)
  **c.** sodium(s) + magnesium iodide(aq) → sodium iodide(aq) + magnesium(s)
  **d.** vanadium(s) + oxygen(g) → vanadium(V) oxide(s)

**74.** Write skeleton equations for these reactions.

  **a.** lithium(s) + gold(III) chloride(aq) → lithium chloride(aq) + gold(s)
  **b.** iron(s) + tin(IV) nitrate(aq) → iron(III) nitrate(aq) + tin(s)
  **c.** nickel(II) chloride(s) + oxygen(g) → nickel(II) oxide(s) + dichlorine pentoxide(g)
  **d.** lithium chromate(aq) + barium chloride(aq) → lithium chloride(aq) + barium chromate(s)

**75.** Balance the skeleton equations for the reactions described in question 71.

**76.** Balance the skeleton equations for the reactions described in question 72.

**77.** Balance the skeleton equations for the reactions described in question 73.

**78.** Balance the skeleton equations for the reactions described in question 74.

**79.** Write chemical equations for these reactions.

  **a.** When solid naphthalene ($C_{10}H_8$) burns in air, the products are gaseous carbon dioxide and liquid water.
  **b.** Bubbling hydrogen sulfide gas through manganese(II) chloride dissolved in water results in the formation of the precipitate manganese(II) sulfide and hydrochloric acid.
  **c.** Solid magnesium reacts with nitrogen gas to produce solid magnesium nitride.
  **d.** Heating oxygen difluoride gas yields oxygen gas and fluorine gas.

## Classifying Chemical Reactions (10.2)

**80.** Classify each of the reactions represented by the chemical equations in question 75.

**81.** Classify each of the reactions represented by the chemical equations in question 76.

**82.** Classify each of the reactions represented by the chemical equations in question 77.

**83.** Classify each of the reactions represented by the chemical equations in question 78.

**84.** Classify each of the reactions represented by the chemical equations in question 79.

**85.** Write chemical equations for each of the following synthesis reactions.

  **a.** boron + fluorine →
  **b.** germanium + sulfur →
  **c.** zirconium + nitrogen →
  **d.** tetraphosphorus decoxide + water → phosphoric acid

**86.** Write a chemical equation for the combustion of each of the following substances. If a compound contains the elements carbon and hydrogen, assume that carbon dioxide gas and liquid water are produced.

  **a.** solid barium
  **b.** solid boron
  **c.** liquid acetone ($C_3H_6O$)
  **d.** liquid octane ($C_8H_{18}$)

**87.** Write chemical equations for each of the following decomposition reactions. One or more products may be identified.

  **a.** magnesium bromide →
  **b.** cobalt(II) oxide →
  **c.** titanium(IV) hydroxide → titanium(IV) oxide + water
  **d.** barium carbonate → barium oxide + carbon dioxide

**88.** Write chemical equations for the following single-replacement reactions that may occur in water. If no reaction occurs, write NR in place of the products.

  **a.** nickel + magnesium chloride →
  **b.** calcium + copper(II) bromide →
  **c.** potassium + aluminum nitrate →
  **d.** magnesium + silver nitrate →

**89.** Write chemical equations for each of the following double-replacement reactions that occur in water.

  **a.** rubidium iodide + silver nitrate →
  **b.** sodium phosphate + manganese(II) chloride →
  **c.** lithium carbonate + molybdenum(VI) bromide →
  **d.** calcium nitrate + aluminum hydroxide →

## Reactions in Aqueous Solutions (10.3)

**90.** Write complete ionic and net ionic equations for each of the following reactions.

  **a.** $K_2S(aq) + CoCl_2(aq) → 2KCl(aq) + CoS(s)$
  **b.** $H_2SO_4(aq) + CaCO_3(s) → H_2O(l) + CO_2(g) + CaSO_4(s)$
  **c.** $2HClO(aq) + Ca(OH)_2(aq) → 2H_2O(l) + Ca(ClO)_2(aq)$

**91.** A reaction occurs when hydrosulfuric acid ($H_2S$) is mixed with an aqueous solution of iron(III) bromide. Solid iron(III) sulfide is produced. Write the chemical and net ionic equations for the reaction.

**70.** $H^+(aq) + OH^-(aq) → H_2O(l)$

## Mastering Problems

Complete solutions to Chapter Assessment Problems can be found in the **Solutions Manual.**

### Balancing Chemical Equations(10.1)

#### Level 1

**71. a.** $HI(g) → H_2(g) + I_2(g)$
  **b.** $Al(s) + I_2(s) → AlI_3(s)$
  **c.** $FeO(s) + O_2(g) → Fe_2O_3(s)$

**72. a.** $C_4H_{10}(l) + O_2(g) → CO_2(g) + H_2O(l)$
  **b.** $Al_2(CO_3)_3(s) → Al_2O_3(s) + CO_2(g)$
  **c.** $AgNO_3(aq) + Na_2S(aq) → Ag_2S(s) + NaNO_3(aq)$

**73. a.** $Fe(s) + F_2(g) → FeF_3(s)$
  **b.** $SO_3(g) + H_2O(l) → H_2SO_4(aq)$
  **c.** $Na(s) + MgI_2(aq) → NaI(aq) + Mg(s)$
  **d.** $V(s) + O_2(g) → V_2O_5(s)$

**74. a.** $Li(s) + AuCl_3(aq) → LiCl(aq) + Au(s)$
  **b.** $Fe(s) + Sn(NO_3)_4(aq) → Fe(NO_3)_3(aq) + Sn(s)$
  **c.** $NiCl_2(s) + O_2(g) → NiO(s) + Cl_2O_5(g)$
  **d.** $Li_2CrO_4(aq) + BaCl_2(aq) → LiCl(aq) + BaCrO_4(s)$

#### Level 2

**75. a.** $2HI(g) → H_2(g) + I_2(g)$
  **b.** $2Al(s) + 3I_2(s) → 2AlI_3(s)$
  **c.** $4FeO(s) + O_2(g) → 2Fe_2O_3(s)$

**76. a.** $2C_4H_{10}(l) + 13O_2(g) → 8CO_2(g) + 10H_2O(l)$
  **b.** $Al_2(CO_3)_3(s) → Al_2O_3(s) + 3CO_2(g)$
  **c.** $2AgNO_3(aq) + Na_2S(aq) → Ag_2S(s) + 2NaNO_3(aq)$

**77. a.** $2Fe(s) + 3F_2(g) → 2FeF_3(s)$
  **b.** $SO_3(g) + H_2O(l) → H_2SO_4(aq)$
  **c.** $2Na(s) + MgI_2(aq) → 2NaI(aq) + Mg(s)$
  **d.** $4V(s) + 5O_2(g) → 2V_2O_5(s)$

**National Science Content Standards**

Pages 304–307
UCP.3, UCP.5; B.2, B.3

**78. a.** $3Li(s) + AuCl_3(aq) → 3LiCl(aq) + Au(s)$
  **b.** $4Fe(s) + 3Sn(NO_3)_4(aq) → 4Fe(NO_3)_3(aq) + 3Sn(s)$
  **c.** $NiCl_2(s) + 3O_2(g) → NiO(s) + Cl_2O_5(g)$
  **d.** $Li_2CrO_4(aq) + BaCl_2(aq) → 2LiCl(aq) + BaCrO_4(s)$

**79. a.** $C_{10}H_8(s) + 12O_2(g) → 10CO_2(g) + 4H_2O(l)$
  **b.** $H_2S(g) + MnCl_2(aq) → MnS(s) + 2HCl(aq)$
  **c.** $3Mg(s) + N_2(g) → Mg_3N_2(s)$

  **d.** $2OF_2(g) → O_2(g) + 2F_2(g)$

## Classifying Chemical Reactions (10.2)
### Level 1

**80. a.** decomp.; **b.** synthesis; **c.** synthesis

**81. a.** combustion; **b.** decomp.; **c.** double rep.

**82. a.** synthesis; **b.** synthesis; **c.** single rep.; **d.** combustion

**83. a.** single rep.; **b.** single rep.; **c.** combustion; **d.** double rep.

**84. a.** combustion; **b.** double rep.; **c.** synthesis; **d.** decomp.

## Level 2

**85. a.** $2B(s) + 3F_2(g) \rightarrow 2BF_3(g)$
**b.** $Ge(s) + 2S(s) \rightarrow GeS_2(s)$
**c.** $3Zr(s) + 2N_2(g) \rightarrow Zr_3N_4(s)$
**d.** $P_4O_{10}(s) + 6H_2O(l) \rightarrow 4H_3PO_4(aq)$

**86. a.** $2Ba(s) + O_2(g) \rightarrow 2BaO(s)$
**b.** $4B(s) + 3O_2(g) \rightarrow 2B_2O_3(s)$
**c.** $C_3H_6O(l) + 4O_2(g) \rightarrow 3CO_2(g) + 3H_2O(l)$
**d.** $2C_8H_{18}(l) + 25O_2(g) \rightarrow 16CO_2(g) + 18H_2O(l)$

**87. a.** $MgBr_2(s) \rightarrow Mg(s) + Br_2(l)$
**b.** $2CoO(s) \rightarrow 2Co(s) + O_2(g)$
**c.** $Ti(OH)_4(s) \rightarrow TiO_2(s) + 2H_2O(l)$
**d.** $BaCO_3(s) \rightarrow BaO(s) + CO_2(g)$

**88. a.** $Ni(s) + MgCl_2(aq) \rightarrow$ NR
**b.** $Ca(s) + CuBr_2(aq) \rightarrow Cu(s) + CaBr_2(aq)$
**c.** $3K(s) + Al(NO_3)_3(aq) \rightarrow Al(s) + 3KNO_3(aq)$
**d.** $Mg(s) + 2AgNO_3(aq) \rightarrow 2Ag(s) + Mg(NO_3)_2(aq)$

**89. a.** $RbI(aq) + AgNO_3(aq) \rightarrow RbNO_3(aq) + AgI(s)$
**b.** $2Na_3PO_4(aq) + 3MnCl_2(aq) \rightarrow 6NaCl(aq) + Mn_3(PO_4)_2(s)$
**c.** $3Li_2CO_3(aq) + MoBr_6(aq) \rightarrow 6LiBr(aq) + Mo(CO_3)_3(s)$
**d.** $Ca(NO_3)_2(aq) + 2Al(OH)_3(aq) \rightarrow 3Ca(OH)_2(s) + 2Al(NO_3)_3(aq)$

## Reactions in Aqueous Solutions (10.3)
### Level 1

**90. a.** Complete: $2K^+(aq) + S^{2-}(aq) + Co^{2+}(aq) + 2Cl^-(aq) \rightarrow 2K^+(aq) + 2Cl^-(aq) + CoS(s)$
Net: $S^{2-}(aq) + Co^{2+}(aq) \rightarrow CoS(s)$
**b.** Complete: $2H^+(aq) + SO_4^{2-}(aq) + CaCO_3(s) \rightarrow H_2O(l) + CO_2(g) + CaSO_4(s)$ Net: $2H^+(aq) + SO_4^{2-}(aq) + CaCO_3(s) \rightarrow H_2O(l) + CO_2(g) + CaSO_4(s)$ **c.** Complete: $2H^+(aq) + 2ClO^-(aq) + Ca^{2+}(aq) + 2OH^-(aq) \rightarrow 2H_2O(l) + Ca^{2+}(aq) + 2ClO^-(aq)$
Net: $H^+(aq) + OH^-(aq) \rightarrow H_2O(l)$
**92. a.** Complete: $3H^+(aq) + PO_4^{3-}(aq) + 3Rb^+(aq) + 3OH^-(aq) \rightarrow 3H_2O(l) + 3Rb^+(aq) + PO_4^{3-}(aq)$

**306**

**92.** Write complete ionic and net ionic equations for each of the following reactions.
**a.** $H_3PO_4(aq) + 3RbOH(aq) \rightarrow 3H_2O(l) + Rb_3PO_4(aq)$
**b.** $HCl(aq) + NH_4OH(aq) \rightarrow H_2O(l) + NH_4Cl(aq)$
**c.** $2HI + (NH_4)_2S(aq) \rightarrow H_2S(g) + 2NH_4I(aq)$
**d.** $HNO_3(aq) + KCN(aq) \rightarrow HCN(g) + KNO_3(aq)$

**93.** A reaction occurs when sulfurous acid ($H_2SO_3$) is mixed with an aqueous solution of sodium hydroxide. Aqueous sodium sulfite is produced. Write the chemical and net ionic equations for the reaction.

**94.** A reaction occurs when nitric acid ($HNO_3$) is mixed with an aqueous solution of potassium hydrogen carbonate. Aqueous potassium nitrate is produced. Write the chemical and net ionic equations for the reaction.

## Mixed Review

*Sharpen your problem-solving skills by answering the following.*

**95.** Identify the products in the following reaction that occurs in plants: Carbon dioxide and water react to produce glucose and oxygen.

**96.** How will aqueous solutions of sucrose and hydrogen chloride differ?

**97.** Write the word equation for each of these skeleton equations. $C_6H_6$ is the formula for benzene.
**a.** $C_6H_6(l) + O_2(g) \rightarrow CO_2(g) + H_2O(l)$
**b.** $CO(g) + O_2(g) \rightarrow CO_2(g)$

**98.** Write skeleton equations for the following reactions.
**a.** ammonium phosphate(aq) + chromium(III) bromide(aq) → ammonium bromide(aq) + chromium(III) phosphate(s)
**b.** chromium(VI) hydroxide(s) → chromium(VI) oxide(s) + water(l)
**c.** aluminum(s) + copper(I) chloride(aq) → aluminum chloride(aq) + copper(s)
**d.** potassium iodide(aq) + mercury(I) nitrate(aq) → potassium nitrate(aq) + mercury(I) iodide(s)

**99.** Balance the skeleton equations for the reactions described in question 98.

**100.** Classify each of the reactions represented by the chemical equations in question 99.

**101.** Predict whether each of the following reactions will occur in aqueous solutions. If you predict that a reaction will not occur, explain your reasoning. Note: Barium sulfate and silver bromide precipitate in aqueous solutions.

**306**     Chapter 10  Chemical Reactions

**a.** sodium hydroxide + ammonium sulfate →
**b.** niobium(V) sulfate + barium nitrate →
**c.** strontium bromide + silver nitrate →

## Thinking Critically

**102. Predicting** A piece of aluminum metal is placed in aqueous KCl. Another piece of aluminum is placed in an aqueous $AgNO_3$ solution. Explain why a chemical reaction does or does not occur in each instance.

**103. Designing an Experiment** You suspect that the water in a lake close to your school may contain lead in the form of $Pb^{2+}(aq)$ ions. Formulate your suspicion as a hypothesis and design an experiment to test your theory. Write the net ionic equations for the reactions of your experiment. (Hint: In aqueous solution, $Pb^{2+}$ forms compounds that are solids with $Cl^-$, $Br^-$, $I^-$, and $SO_4^{2-}$ ions.)

**104. Applying Concepts** Write the chemical equations and net ionic equations for each of the following reactions that may occur in aqueous solutions. If a reaction does not occur, write NR in place of the products. Magnesium phosphate precipitates in an aqueous solution.
**a.** $KNO_3 + CsCl \rightarrow$
**b.** $Ca(OH)_2 + KCN \rightarrow$
**c.** $Li_3PO_4 + MgSO_4 \rightarrow$
**d.** $HBrO + NaOH \rightarrow$

## Writing in Chemistry

**105.** Prepare a poster describing types of chemical reactions that occur in the kitchen.

**106.** Write a report in which you compare and contrast chemical and mathematical equations.

## Cumulative Review

*Refresh your understanding of previous chapters by answering the following.*

**107.** Distinguish among a mixture, a solution, and a compound. (Chapter 3)

**108.** Write the formula for the compounds made from each of the following pairs of ions. (Chapter 9)
**a.** copper(I) and sulfite
**b.** tin(IV) and fluoride
**c.** gold(III) and cyanide
**d.** lead(II) and sulfide

Net: $H^+(aq) + OH^-(aq) \rightarrow H_2O(l)$
**b.** Complete: $H^+(aq) + Cl^-(aq) + NH_4^+(aq) + OH^-(aq) \rightarrow H_2O(l) + NH_4^+(aq) + Cl^-(aq)$ Net: $H^+(aq) + OH^-(aq) \rightarrow H_2O(l)$ **c.** Complete: $2H^+(aq) + 2I^-(aq) + 2NH_4^+(aq) + S^{2-}(aq) \rightarrow H_2S(g) + 2NH_4^+(aq) + 2I^-(aq)$ Net: $2H^+(aq) + S^{2-}(aq) \rightarrow H_2S(g)$ **d.** Complete: $H^+(aq) + NO_3^-(aq) + K^+(aq) + CN^-(aq) \rightarrow HCN(g) + K^+(aq) + NO_3^-(aq)$ Net: $H^+(aq) + CN^-(aq) \rightarrow HCN(g)$

## Level 2
**91.** Chemical: $3H_2S(aq) + 2FeBr_3(aq) \rightarrow 6HBr(aq) + Fe_2S_3(s)$ Net: $3S^{2-}(aq) + 2Fe^{3+}(aq) \rightarrow Fe_2S_3(s)$
**93.** Chemical: $H_2SO_3(aq) + 2NaOH(aq) \rightarrow 2H_2O(l) + Na_2SO_3(aq)$ Net: $H^+(aq) + OH^-(aq) \rightarrow H_2O(l)$
**94.** Chemical: $HNO_3(aq) + KHCO_3(aq) \rightarrow H_2O(l) + CO_2(g) + KNO_3(aq)$ Net: $H^+(aq) + HCO_3^-(aq) \rightarrow H_2O(l) + CO_2(g)$

*Use these questions and the test-taking tip to prepare for your standardized test.*

**1.** Potassium chromate and lead(II) acetate are both dissolved in a beaker of water, where they react to form solid lead(II) chromate. What is the balanced net ionic equation describing this reaction?

a. $Pb^{2+}(aq) + C_2H_3O_2^-(aq) \rightarrow Pb(C_2H_3O_2)_2(s)$
b. $Pb^{2+}(aq) + 2CrO_4^-(aq) \rightarrow Pb(CrO_4)_2(s)$
c. $Pb^{2+}(aq) + CrO_4^{2-}(aq) \rightarrow PbCrO_4(s)$
d. $Pb^+(aq) + C_2H_3O_2^-(aq) \rightarrow PbC_2H_3O_2(s)$

**2.** What type of reaction is described by the following equation?

$$Cs(s) + H_2O(l) \rightarrow CsOH(aq) + H_2(g)$$

a. synthesis
b. combustion
c. decomposition
d. replacement

**3.** Which of the following reactions between halogens and halide salts will occur?

a. $F_2(g) + FeI_2(aq) \rightarrow FeF_2(aq) + I_2(l)$
b. $I_2(s) + MnBr_2(aq) \rightarrow MnI_2(aq) + Br_2(g)$
c. $Cl_2(s) + SrF_2(aq) \rightarrow SrCl_2(aq) + F_2(g)$
d. $Br_2(l) + CoCl_2(aq) \rightarrow CoBr_2(aq) + Cl_2(g)$

**Interpreting Tables** Use the table to answer questions 4–6.

### Physical Properties of Select Ionic Compounds

| Compound | Name | Physical state at room temp. | Soluble in water? | Melting point (°C) |
|---|---|---|---|---|
| $NaClO_3$ | sodium chlorate | solid | yes | 248 |
| $Na_2SO_4$ | sodium sulfate | solid | yes | 884 |
| $NiCl_2$ | nickel(II) chloride | solid | yes | 1009 |
| $Ni(OH)_2$ | nickel(II) hydroxide | solid | no | 230 |
| $AgNO_3$ | silver nitrate | solid | yes | 212 |

**4.** An aqueous solution of nickel(II) sulfate is mixed with aqueous sodium hydroxide. Will a visible reaction occur?

a. No, solid nickel(II) hydroxide is soluble in water.
b. No, solid sodium sulfate is soluble in water.
c. Yes, solid sodium sulfate will precipitate out of solution.
d. Yes, solid nickel(II) hydroxide will precipitate out of solution.

**5.** When $AgClO_3(aq)$ and $NaNO_3(aq)$ are mixed,

a. no visible reaction occurs.
b. solid $NaClO_3$ precipitates out of solution.
c. $NO_2$ gas is released from the reaction.
d. solid Ag metal is produced.

**6.** Finely ground nickel(II) hydroxide is placed in a beaker of water. It sinks to the bottom of the beaker and remains unchanged. An aqueous solution of hydrochloric acid (HCl) is then added the beaker, and the $Ni(OH)_2$ disappears. Which of the following equations best describes what occurred in the beaker?

a. $Ni(OH)_2(s) + HCl(aq) \rightarrow NiO(aq) + H_2(g) + HCl(aq)$
b. $Ni(OH)_2(s) + 2HCl(aq) \rightarrow NiCl_2(aq) + 2H_2O(l)$
c. $Ni(OH)_2(s) + 2H_2O(l) \rightarrow NiCl_2(aq) + 2H_2O(l)$
d. $Ni(OH)_2(s) + 2H_2O(l) \rightarrow NiCl_2(aq) + 3H_2O(l) + O_2(g)$

**7.** The combustion of ethanol, $C_2H_6O$, produces carbon dioxide and water vapor. What equation best describes this process?

a. $C_2H_6O(l) + O_2(g) \rightarrow CO_2(g) + H_2O(l)$
b. $C_2H_6O(l) \rightarrow 2CO_2(g) + 3H_2O(l)$
c. $C_2H_6O(l) + 3O_2(g) \rightarrow 2CO_2(g) + 3H_2O(g)$
d. $C_2H_6O(l) \rightarrow 3O_2(l) + 2CO_2(g) + 3H_2O(l)$

**8.** What is the product of this synthesis reaction?

$$Cl_2(g) + 2NO(g) \rightarrow ?$$

a. $NCl_2$
b. $2NOCl$
c. $N_2O_2$
d. $2ClO$

---

### TEST-TAKING TIP

**Tables** If a test question involves a table, skim the table before reading the question. Read the title, column heads, and row heads. Then read the question and interpret the information in the table.

Standardized Test Practice **307**

---

## Mixed Review

**95.** glucose and oxygen

**96.** An aqueous sucrose solution contains water molecules and sucrose molecules. An aqueous hydrogen chloride solution contains water molecules, hydrogen ions, and chloride ions.

**97. a.** benzene(l)+oxygen(g)→ carbon dioxide(g)+water (l)
**b.** carbon monoxide(g)+ oxygen(g) → carbon dioxide(g)

**98. a.** $(NH_4)_3PO_4(aq) + CrBr_3(aq) \rightarrow NH_4Br(aq) + CrPO_4(s)$
**b.** $Cr(OH)_6(s) \rightarrow CrO_3(s) + H_2O(l)$
**c.** $Al(s) + CuCl(aq) \rightarrow AlCl_3(aq) + Cu(s)$
**d.** $KI(aq) + HgNO_3(aq) \rightarrow KNO_3(aq) + HgI(s)$

**99. a.** $(NH_4)_3PO_4(aq) + CrBr_3(aq) \rightarrow 3NH_4Br(aq) + CrPO_4(s)$
**b.** $Cr(OH)_6(s) \rightarrow CrO_3(s) + 3H_2O(l)$
**c.** $Al(s) + 3CuCl(aq) \rightarrow AlCl_3(aq) + 3Cu(s)$
**d.** $KI(aq) + HgNO_3(aq) \rightarrow KNO_3(aq) + HgI(s)$

**100. a.** double rep.; **b.** decomp.; **c.** single rep.; **d.** double rep.

**101. a.** No reaction; products are soluble and no water or gas is formed. **b.** and **c.** reaction occurs.

## Thinking Critically

**102.** No reaction occurs when Al is placed in KCl(aq) because Al does not replace K. However, Al reacts with an aqueous $AgNO_3$ solution because Al is above Ag in the activity series.

**103.** If lead is present, a reaction can be performed to precipitate a solid so it can be analyzed and confirmed as lead. Experiment: Allow a water sample to react with an excess amount of solution containing aqueous chloride, bromide, iodide, or sulfate ions. If the lead concentration is high, a lead-containing precipitate will form.

---

**104. a.** NR **b.** NR **c.** Chemical: $2Li_3PO_4(aq) + 3MgSO_4(aq) \rightarrow 3Li_2SO_4(aq) + Mg_3(PO_4)_2(s)$ Net ionic: $2PO_4^{3-}(aq) + 3Mg^{2+}(aq) \rightarrow Mg_3(PO_4)_2(s)$
**d.** Chemical: $HBrO(aq) + NaOH(aq) \rightarrow H_2O(l) + NaBrO(aq)$ Net ionic: $H^+(aq) + OH^-(aq) \rightarrow H_2O(l)$

## Cumulative Review

**107.** Refer to the glossary for definitions.
**108. a.** $Cu_2SO_3$; **b.** $SnF_4$; **c.** $AuCN$; **d.** PbS

## Standardized Test Practice

**1.** c  **3.** a  **5.** a  **7.** c
**2.** d  **4.** d  **6.** b  **8.** b

# Resource Manager

| Section | Objectives | Activities/Features |
|---------|-----------|---------------------|
| **Section 11.1**<br>**Measuring Matter**<br>1½ sessions<br>1 block | 1. **Describe** how a mole is used in chemistry.<br>2. **Relate** a mole to common counting units.<br>3. **Convert** moles to number of representative particles and number of representative particles to moles. | **Discovery Lab:** How much is a mole? p. 309<br>**History Connection,** p. 311 |
| **Section 11.2**<br>**Mass and the Mole**<br>1½ sessions<br>1 block | 4. **Relate** the mass of an atom to the mass of a mole of atoms.<br>5. **Calculate** the number of moles in a given mass of an element and the mass of a given number of moles of an element.<br>6. **Calculate** the number of moles of an element when given the number of atoms of the element.<br>7. **Calculate** the number of atoms of an element when given the number of moles of the element. | **Problem-Solving Lab:** Molar Mass, Avogadro's Number and the Atomic Nucleus, p. 314 |
| **Section 11.3**<br>**Moles of Compounds**<br>1½ sessions<br>1 block | 8. **Recognize** the mole relationships shown by a chemical formula.<br>9. **Calculate** the molar mass of a compound.<br>10. **Calculate** the number of moles of a compound from a given mass of the compound, and the mass of a compound from a given number of moles of the compound.<br>11. **Determine** the number of atoms or ions in a mass of a compound. | |
| **Section 11.4**<br>**Empirical and Molecular Formulas**<br>2 sessions<br>1 block | 12. **Explain** what is meant by the percent composition of a compound.<br>13. **Determine** the empirical and molecular formulas for a compound from mass percent and actual mass data. | **Careers Using Chemistry:** Analytical Chemist, p. 329<br>**MiniLab:** Percent Composition and Gum, p. 329 |
| **Section 11.5**<br>**The Formula for a Hydrate**<br>2½ sessions<br>1½ blocks | 14. **Explain** what a hydrate is and how its name reflects its composition.<br>15. **Determine** the formula for a hydrate from laboratory data. | **ChemLab:** Hydrated Crystals, pp. 342–343<br>**Chemistry and Technology:** Making Medicines, p. 344 |

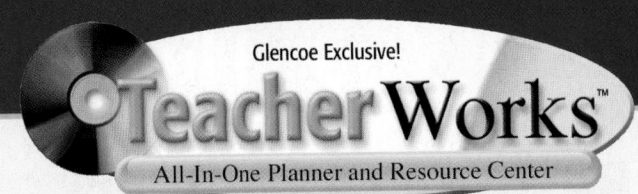

| National Science Content Standards | State/Local Standards | Reproducible Masters | Transparencies |
|---|---|---|---|
| UCP.1; A.1; B.2; E.2; G.2, G.3 | | **Study Guide for Content Mastery,** p. 61 **L2**<br>**Small-Scale Laboratory Manual,** pp. 29–32 **L2** | **Section Focus**<br>**Transparency 38** **L1** **ELL** |
| UCP.1; B.1, B.2; E.2 | | **Study Guide for Content Mastery,** p. 62 **L2** | **Section Focus**<br>**Transparency 39** **L1** **ELL**<br>**Math Skills**<br>**Transparency 13** **L2** **ELL** |
| UCP.1; B.2; E.2 | | **Study Guide for Content Mastery,** p. 63 **L2**<br>**Laboratory Manual,** pp. 81–84 **L2**<br>**Challenge Problems,** p. 11 **L3** | **Section Focus**<br>**Transparency 40** **L1** **ELL**<br>**Teaching**<br>**Transparency 37** **L2** **ELL**<br>**Math Skills**<br>**Transparency 14** **L2** **ELL** |
| UCP.1; A.1, A.2; B.2; E.2; G.1 | | **Study Guide for Content Mastery,** pp. 64–65 **L2**<br>**ChemLab and MiniLab Worksheets,** p. 41 **L2**<br>**Laboratory Manual,** pp. 85–88 **L2** | **Section Focus**<br>**Transparency 41** **L1** **ELL** |
| UCP.1; A.1, A.2; B.2, B.3, B.6; E.1, E.2; F.5, F.6 | | **Study Guide for Content Mastery,** p. 66 **L2**<br>**ChemLab and MiniLab Worksheets,** pp. 42–44 **L2** | **Section Focus**<br>**Transparency 42** **L1** **ELL** |

# Resource Manager

## Materials List

### ChemLab (pages 342–343)
Bunsen burner, ring stand, ring stand ring, crucible with cover, clay triangle, crucible tongs, balance, Epsom salts, spatula, spark lighter or matches

### Discovery Lab (page 309)
metric ruler, paper clip

### MiniLab (page 329)
balance, weighing paper, 250-mL beakers (2), water, paper towels, chewing gum pieces (2), stirring rod, scissors, window screen (10 cm × 10 cm), clock or timer

### Demonstration (pages 332–333)
large test tube, 2-hole stopper, glass tubing, rubber tubing, Bunsen burner, ring stand, test tube holder, copper(II) oxide, scupula

## Preparation of Solutions

For a review of solution preparation, see page 46T of the Teacher Guide.

There are no solutions to be prepared for the activities in this chapter.

## Assessment Resources

Chapter Assessment, pp. 61–66
MindJogger Videoquizzes DVD/VHS
Alternate Assessment in the Science Classroom
ExamView® Pro CD-ROM
Solutions Manual, Chapter 11
Supplemental Problems, Chapter 11
Performance Assessment in the Science Classroom
Chemistry Interactive CD-ROM, Chapter 11 quiz

## Additional Resources

Spanish Resources **ELL**
Guided Reading Audio Program, Chapter 11 **ELL**
Cooperative Learning in the Science Classroom
Lab and Safety Skills in the Science Classroom
Lesson Plans
Block Scheduling Lesson Plans
Chemistrymc.com

## Glencoe Technology

The following multimedia for this chapter are available from Glencoe.

**VIDEOTAPE/DVD**
MindJogger Videoquizzes,
Chapter 11

**CD-ROM**
**Chemistry: Matter and Change**
*Avogadro's Number,* Video
*Molar Mass,* Video
*Combustion Analysis,* Experiment
*Percent Sugar in Bubblegum,*
Demonstration

**CD-ROM**
**ExamView® Pro**
**Testmaker**

**CD-ROM**
**Interactive Chalkboard**

**CD-ROM**
**TeacherWorks™**

## Multiple Learning Styles

Look for the following icons for strategies that emphasize different learning modalities.

**Kinesthetic**
Check for Understanding, p 318; Extension,
p. 319; Differentiated Instruction, pp. 321, 338;
Chemistry Journal, p. 330; Concept Development,
pp. 331, 332

**Visual-Spatial**
Concept Development, p. 311; Extension, p. 312;
Math in Chemistry, p. 315

**Interpersonal**
Reteach, p. 319

**Intrapersonal**
Portfolio, pp. 325, 336; Chemistry Journal, p. 326;
Extension, p. 334

**Linguistic**
Portfolio, pp. 313, 335; Chemistry Journal,
pp. 310, 316, 323

**Logical-Mathematical**
Differentiated Instruction, pp. 311, 317; Quick
Demo, p. 313; Chemistry Journal, pp. 315, 322

## Key to Teaching Strategies

**L1** Level 1 activities should be appropriate for students with
learning difficulties.

**L2** Level 2 activities should be within the ability range of
all students.

**L3** Level 3 activities are designed for above-average students.

**ELL** ELL activities should be within the ability range of
English Language Learners.

**COOP LEARN** Cooperative Learning activities are designed
for small group work.

**P** These strategies represent student products that can be
placed into a best-work portfolio.

These strategies are useful in a block scheduling format.

## Assessment Planner

**Portfolio Assessment**
Portfolio, TWE, pp. 313, 323,
325, 331, 335, 336, 345
Assessment, TWE, pp. 317,
323

**Performance Assessment**
Assessment, TWE p. 341
Problem-Solving Lab,
TWE, p. 314
ChemLab, TWE, p. 343
MiniLab, TWE, p. 329
Demonstration, TWE, p. 333
Discovery Lab, SE, p. 309

ChemLab, SE, pp. 342–343
MiniLab SE, p. 329

**Knowledge Assessment**
Assessment, TWE pp. 312,
322, 324, 327, 330, 335, 337
Section Assessment, SE,
pp. 312, 319, 327, 337, 341
Chapter Assessment, SE,
pp. 346–351

**Skill Assessment**
Assessment, TWE, pp. 310,
319, 325

## Tying to Previous Knowledge

Have students review the following concepts before studying this chapter.

Chapter 2: scientific notation, significant figures

Chapter 2: dimensional analysis

Chapter 4: average atomic mass

## Using the Photo

Ask students what they expect to receive when they purchase a dozen roses. 12 roses because a dozen is 12 items Ask if they can think of any other words that mean a specific number of flowers. half-dozen Ask if they can think of other words that are used to represent a counted amount. pair, trio, quartet, six-pack, gross, ream

## Chapter Themes

The following themes from the National Science Education Standards are covered in this chapter. Refer to page 4T of the Teacher Guide for an explanation of the correlations.

Systems, order, and organization (UCP.1)

Evidence, models, and explanation (UCP.2)

Change, constancy, and measurement (UCP.3)

## PowerPoint® Presentations

This CD-ROM is an editable Microsoft® PowerPoint® presentation that includes:
- Section presentations
- Section checks
- Image bank
- Links to Chemistry Online
- All transparencies
- Animations
- Audio

# The Mole

## What You'll Learn

▶ You will use the mole and molar mass to make conversions among moles, mass, and number of representative particles.

▶ You will determine the percent composition of the components of compounds.

▶ You will calculate the empirical and molecular formulas for compounds and determine the formulas for hydrates.

## Why It's Important

New materials, new products, new consumer goods of all kinds come on the market regularly. But before manufacturing begins on most new products, calculations involving the mole must be done.

Visit the Chemistry Web site at chemistrymc.com to find links to the mole.

Florists often sell flowers, such as roses, carnations, and tulips, by the dozen. A dozen is a counting unit for 12 items.

## DISCOVERY LAB

### Purpose
Students will develop a mental picture of the size of a mole.

### Teaching Strategies
- Have students review conversions of metric units and scientific notation.
- Discuss the meaning of a light year—the distance traveled by light in one year in a vacuum. The speed of light is $3.00 \times 10^8$ m/sec.

- Have students calculate the actual distance traveled by light in one year. $3.00 \times 10^8$ m/sec $\times$ 60 sec/min $\times$ 60 min/hr $\times$ 24 hr/day $\times$ 365 days/year = $9.46 \times 10^{15}$ m

- Students can convert the distance of one light year in meters to the distance in miles. The conversion factor is $9.61 \times 10^3$ m/mile. $9.46 \times 10^{15}$ m $\times$ 1 mile/$9.61 \times 10^3$ m = $9.84 \times 10^{11}$ miles

## DISCOVERY LAB

### How much is a mole?

Counting large numbers of items is easier when you use counting units like the dozen. Chemists use a counting unit called the mole.

**Procedure**

1. Measure the length of a paper clip to the nearest 0.1 cm.
2. If a mole is $6.02 \times 10^{23}$ items, how far will a mole of paper clips, placed end to end lengthwise, reach into space?

**Analysis**

How many light-years (ly) would the paper clips extend into space? (1 light-year = $9.46 \times 10^{15}$ m). How does the distance you calculated compare with the following astronomical distances: nearest star (other than the sun) = 4.3 ly, center of our galaxy = 30 000 ly, nearest galaxy = $2 \times 10^6$ ly?

**Materials**
centimeter ruler
paper clip

---

# Measuring Matter

### Objectives

- **Describe** how a mole is used in chemistry.
- **Relate** a mole to common counting units.
- **Convert** moles to number of representative particles and number of representative particles to moles.

### Vocabulary

mole
Avogadro's number

If you were buying a bouquet of roses for a special occasion, you probably wouldn't ask for 12 or 24; you'd ask for one or two dozen. Similarly, you might buy a pair of gloves, a ream of paper for your printer, or a gross of pencils. Each of the units shown in **Figure 11-1**—a pair, a dozen, a gross, and a ream—represents a specific number of items. These units make counting objects easier. It's easier to buy and sell paper by the ream—500 sheets—than by the individual sheet.

## Counting Particles

Each of the counting units shown in **Figure 11-1** is appropriate for certain kinds of objects depending primarily on their size and the use they serve. But regardless of the object—boots, eggs, pencils, paper—the number that the unit represents is always constant.

**Figure 11-1**

A pair is always two objects, a dozen is 12, a gross is 144, and a ream is 500. Can you think of any other counting units?

11.1 Measuring Matter    **309**

---

## 1 Focus

### Focus Transparency

Before presenting the lesson, display **Section Focus Transparency 38** on the overhead projector. Have students answer the accompanying questions using **Section Focus Transparency Master 38.** L1 ELL

### Resource Manager

**Study Guide for Content Mastery,** p. 61 L2
**Solving Problems: A Chemistry Handbook,** Section 11.1 L2
**Section Focus Transparency 38 and Master** L1 ELL
**Small-Scale Laboratory Manual,** pp. 29–32 L2

**National Science Content Standards**

Pages 308–309
UCP.1, UCP.3; A.1; B.2

**309**

---

- Ask students to compare the miles traveled by light in one year to the distance across the United States (3000 miles) or the circumference of Earth (25 000 miles). $9.84 \times 10^{11}$ miles/25 000 miles = 39 000 000 Earth circumferences
- Paper clips of any uniform length may be used.

**Expected Results**
The length of a #1 paper clip is 3.2 cm. One mole of paperclips reaches $1.9 \times 10^{25}$ cm.

**Analysis**
$6.02 \times 10^{23}$ paper clips $\times \frac{3.2 \text{ cm}}{1 \text{ paper clip}} \times \frac{1 \text{ m}}{100 \text{ cm}} \times \frac{1 \text{ ly}}{9.46 \times 10^{15} \text{ m}} = 2.0$ million ly

This compares to the distance to the nearest galaxy.

Chemists also need a convenient method for counting accurately the number of atoms, molecules, or formula units in a sample of a substance. As you know, atoms and molecules are extremely small. There are so many of them in even the smallest sample that it's impossible to actually count them. That's why chemists created their own counting unit called the mole. In the **DISCOVERY LAB**, you found that a mole of paper clips is an enormous number of items.

**What is a mole?** The **mole**, commonly abbreviated mol, is the SI base unit used to measure the amount of a substance. It is the number of representative particles, carbon atoms, in exactly 12 g of pure carbon-12. Through years of experimentation, it has been established that a mole of anything contains $6.022\ 136\ 7 \times 10^{23}$ representative particles. A representative particle is any kind of particle such as atoms, molecules, formula units, electrons, or ions. The number $6.022\ 136\ 7 \times 10^{23}$ is called **Avogadro's number** in honor of the Italian physicist and lawyer Amedeo Avogadro who, in 1811, determined the volume of one mole of a gas. In this book, Avogadro's number will be rounded to three significant figures—$6.02 \times 10^{23}$.

If you write out Avogadro's number, it looks like this.

$$602\ 000\ 000\ 000\ 000\ 000\ 000\ 000\ 000$$

Avogadro's number is an enormous number, as it must be in order to count extremely small particles. As you can imagine, Avogadro's number would not be convenient for measuring a quantity of marbles. Avogadro's number of marbles would cover the surface of Earth to a depth of more than six kilometers! But you can see in **Figure 11-2** that it is convenient to use the mole to measure substances. One-mole quantities of three substances are shown, each with a different representative particle. The representative particle in a mole of water is the water molecule, the representative particle in a mole of copper is the copper atom, and the representative particle in a mole of sodium chloride is the formula unit.

**Figure 11-2**

The amount of each substance shown is $6.02 \times 10^{23}$ or one mole of representative particles. The representative particle for each substance is shown in a box. Refer to **Table C-1** in Appendix C for a key to atom color conventions.

Molecule     Atom     Formula unit

$H_2O$     Cu     NaCl

## Converting Moles to Particles and Particles to Moles

Suppose you buy three and a half dozen roses and want to know how many roses you have. Recall what you have learned about conversion factors. You can multiply the known quantity (3.5 dozen roses) by a conversion factor to express the quantity in the units you want (number of roses). You must set up your calculation as shown here so that all units cancel except those required for the answer.

$$\text{Conversion factor: } \frac{12 \text{ roses}}{1 \text{ dozen}}$$

$$3.5 \cancel{\text{ dozen}} \times \frac{12 \text{ roses}}{1 \cancel{\text{ dozen}}} = 42 \text{ roses}$$

Note that the units cancel and the answer tells you that 42 roses are in 3.5 dozen.

Now, suppose you want to determine how many particles of sucrose are in 3.50 moles of sucrose. You know that one mole contains $6.02 \times 10^{23}$ representative particles. Therefore, you can write a conversion factor, Avogadro's number, that relates representative particles to moles of a substance.

$$\text{Conversion factor: } \frac{6.02 \times 10^{23} \text{ representative particles}}{1 \text{ mole}}$$

You can find the number of representative particles in a number of moles just as you found the number of roses in 3.5 dozen.

$$\text{number of moles} \times \frac{6.02 \times 10^{23} \text{ representative particles}}{1 \text{ mole}}$$

$$= \text{number of representative particles}$$

For sucrose, the representative particle is a molecule, so the number of molecules of sucrose is obtained by multiplying 3.50 moles of sucrose by the conversion factor, Avogadro's number.

$$3.50 \cancel{\text{ mol sucrose}} \times \frac{6.02 \times 10^{23} \text{ molecules sucrose}}{1 \cancel{\text{ mol sucrose}}}$$

$$= 2.11 \times 10^{24} \text{ molecules sucrose}$$

There are $2.11 \times 10^{24}$ molecules of sucrose in 3.50 moles.

### PRACTICE PROBLEMS

**1.** Determine the number of atoms in 2.50 mol Zn.

**2.** Given 3.25 mol $AgNO_3$, determine the number of formula units.

**3.** Calculate the number of molecules in 11.5 mol $H_2O$.

Now, suppose you want to find out how many moles are represented by a certain number of representative particles. You can use the inverse of Avogadro's number as a conversion factor.

$$\text{number of representative particles} \times \frac{1 \text{ mole}}{6.02 \times 10^{23} \text{ representative particles}}$$

$$= \text{number of moles}$$

## History
### CONNECTION

Lorenzo Romano Amedeo Carlo Avogadro, Conte di Quaregna e Ceretto was born in Turin, Italy in 1776 and was educated as a church lawyer. During the early 1800s, he studied mathematics and physics and was appointed to a professorship at the Royal College of Vercelli where he produced his hypothesis on gases. From 1820 until his death, Avogadro was professor of physics at the University of Turin where he conducted research on electricity and the physical properties of liquids.

Avogadro's hypothesis did not receive recognition for more than fifty years. Although Avogadro did nothing to measure the number of particles in equal volumes of gases, his hypothesis did lead to the eventual calculation of the number, $6.02 \times 10^{23}$.

National Mole Day is celebrated on October 23 (10/23) from 6:02 A.M. to 6:02 P.M. to commemorate Avogadro's contribution to modern chemistry.

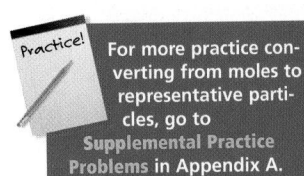

Practice! For more practice converting from moles to representative particles, go to **Supplemental Practice Problems** in Appendix A.

## Concept Development

*Visual-Spatial* Measure 27.0 g of aluminum foil (one mole) and place it on the overhead. Tell students it is one mole and ask how many representative particles are present. $6.02 \times 10^{23}$ representative particles because it is one mole Crumple the foil and ask what changed and what stayed the same. Students should understand that although the size and shape have changed, the crumpled foil is still one mole because nothing has been added or taken away. Tear the foil into two pieces and ask what changed. Each piece contains less than one mole of aluminum. **L2** **ELL**

### Practice PROBLEMS

Have students refer to Appendix D for complete solutions to Practice Problems.

**1.** $1.51 \times 10^{24}$ atoms Zn

**2.** $1.96 \times 10^{24}$ formula units $AgNO_3$

**3.** $6.92 \times 10^{24}$ molecules $H_2O$

---

## DIFFERENTIATED INSTRUCTION

### Learning Disabled

*Logical-Mathematical* Using conversion factors may confuse some students. Have them make an index card with Avogadro's number/1mol on one side and 1mol/Avogadro's number on the opposite side. As students analyze a problem, they can flip the card from side to side to determine which side leads to cancellation of units and the desired unit for the answer. **L1** **ELL**

National Science Content Standards

**Pages 310–311**
UCP.1, UCP.3; B.2; E.2; G.2, G.3

# 3 Assess

## Check for Understanding

Mass one mole of a substance such as copper shot (**63.5 g**). Ask students how many atoms of copper are on the balance. $6.02 \times 10^{23}$ atoms of copper Reduce the mass by one-half and ask students to explain how much substance is present in terms of moles and representative particles. 0.50 mol or $3.01 \times 10^{23}$ representative particles

## Reteach

Ask students why it's important to have a counting unit as large as the mole. A large counting unit like the mole allows you to count many very small particles.

## Extension

*Visual-Spatial* Ask students to invent a new counting unit that might be useful for counting marbles, CDs, baseballs, or books in the library. **L2**

## ✔ Assessment

**Knowledge** Have students write on a card a problem requiring a conversion from moles of a substance to representative particles. Each student will pass the card to a neighboring student to solve. The neighbor will solve the conversion and write a problem requiring a conversion from representative particles to moles and pass it back for solution. Both students must agree on the two answers. **L2 COOP LEARN**

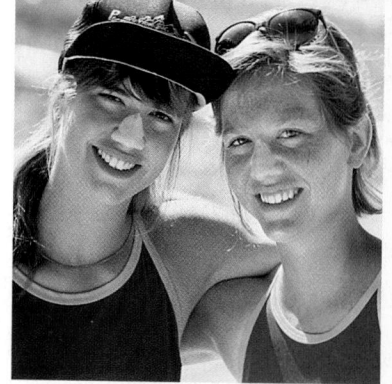

Ointments containing zinc oxide provide protection from sunburn and are used to treat some skin diseases.

The number of moles of substance is obtained by multiplying the number of particles by this factor, as you will see in Example Problem 11-1.

## EXAMPLE PROBLEM 11-1

**Converting Number of Representative Particles to Moles**

Zinc is used as a corrosion-resistant coating on iron and steel. It is also an essential trace element in your diet. Calculate the number of moles that contain $4.50 \times 10^{24}$ atoms of zinc (Zn).

### 1. Analyze the Problem

You are given the number of atoms of zinc and must find the equivalent number of moles. If you compare $4.50 \times 10^{24}$ atoms Zn with $6.02 \times 10^{23}$, the number of atoms in one mole, you can predict that the answer should be less than 10 moles.

| Known | Unknown |
|---|---|
| number of atoms = $4.50 \times 10^{24}$ atoms Zn | mol Zn = ? mol |
| 1 mol Zn = $6.02 \times 10^{23}$ atoms Zn | |

### 2. Solve for the Unknown

Multiply the number of zinc atoms by the conversion factor that is the inverse of Avogadro's number.

$$\text{number of atoms} \times \frac{1 \text{ mole}}{6.02 \times 10^{23} \text{ atoms}} = \text{number of moles}$$

$$4.50 \times 10^{24} \text{ atoms Zn} \times \frac{1 \text{ mol Zn}}{6.02 \times 10^{23} \text{ atoms Zn}} = 7.48 \text{ mol Zn}$$

### 3. Evaluate the Answer

The number of atoms of zinc and Avogadro's number have three significant figures. Therefore, the answer is expressed correctly with three digits. The answer is less than 10 moles, as predicted, and has the correct unit.

## PRACTICE PROBLEMS

**4.** How many moles contain each of the following?
   **a.** $5.75 \times 10^{24}$ atoms Al
   **b.** $3.75 \times 10^{24}$ molecules $CO_2$
   **c.** $3.58 \times 10^{23}$ formula units $ZnCl_2$
   **d.** $2.50 \times 10^{20}$ atoms Fe

*Practice!* For more practice converting from representative particles to moles, go to **Supplemental Practice Problems in Appendix A.**

## Section 11.1 Assessment

**5.** How is a mole similar to a dozen?

**6.** What is the relationship between Avogadro's number and one mole?

**7.** Explain how you can convert from the number of representative particles of a substance to moles of that substance.

**8.** Explain why chemists use the mole.

**9. Thinking Critically** Arrange the following from the smallest number of representative particles to the largest number of representative particles: $1.25 \times 10^{25}$ atoms Zn; 3.56 mol Fe; $6.78 \times 10^{22}$ molecules glucose ($C_6H_{12}O_6$).

**10. Using Numbers** Determine the number of representative particles in each of the following and identify the representative particle: 11.5 mol Ag; 18.0 mol $H_2O$; 0.150 mol NaCl.

chemistrymc.com/self_check_quiz

## Section 11.1 Assessment

**5.** The mole is a unit for counting $6.02 \times 10^{23}$ representative particles. The dozen is used to count 12 items.

**6.** One mole contains Avogadro's number ($6.02 \times 10^{23}$) of representative particles.

**7.** Multiply the number of representative particles by 1 mol/$6.02 \times 10^{23}$ representative particles.

**8.** Chemists use the mole because it is a convenient way of knowing how many representative particle are in a sample.

**9.** From smallest to largest: $6.78 \times 10^{22}$ molecules glucose, $2.14 \times 10^{24}$ atoms Fe, $1.25 \times 10^{25}$ atoms Zn.

**10.** $6.92 \times 10^{24}$ atoms Ag, $1.08 \times 10^{25}$ molecules $H_2O$, $9.03 \times 10^{22}$ formula units NaCl

You wouldn't expect a dozen limes to have the same mass as a dozen eggs. Eggs and limes differ in size and composition, so it's not surprising that they have different masses, as **Figure 11-3** shows. Moles of substances also have different masses for the same reason—the substances have different compositions. If you put a mole of carbon on a balance beside a mole of metallic copper, you would see a difference in mass just as you do for a dozen eggs and a dozen limes. Carbon atoms differ from copper atoms. Thus, the mass of $6.02 \times 10^{23}$ atoms of carbon does not equal the mass of $6.02 \times 10^{23}$ atoms of copper. How do you determine the mass of a mole?

## The Mass of a Mole

In Chapter 4, you learned that the relative scale of atomic masses uses the isotope carbon-12 as the standard. Each atom of carbon-12 has a mass of 12 atomic mass units (amu). The atomic masses of all other elements are established relative to carbon-12. For example, an atom of hydrogen-1 has a mass of 1 amu. The mass of an atom of helium-4 is 4 amu. Therefore, the mass of one atom of hydrogen-1 is one-twelfth the mass of one atom of carbon-12. The mass of one atom of helium-4 is one-third the mass of one atom of carbon-12.

You can find atomic masses on the periodic table, but notice that the values shown are not exact integers. For example, you'll find 12.011 amu for carbon, 1.008 amu for hydrogen, and 4.003 amu for helium. These differences occur because the recorded values are weighted averages of the masses of all the naturally occurring isotopes of each element.

How does the mass of one atom relate to the mass of a mole of that atom? You know that the mole is defined as the number of representative particles, or carbon-12 atoms, in exactly 12 g of pure carbon-12. Thus, the mass of one mole of carbon-12 atoms is 12 g. What about other elements? Whether you are considering a single atom or Avogadro's number of atoms (a mole), the masses of all atoms are established relative to the mass of carbon-12. The mass of a mole of hydrogen-1 is one-twelfth the mass of a mole of carbon-12 atoms, or 1.0 g. The mass of a mole of helium-4 atoms is one-third the mass of a mole of carbon-12 atoms, or 4.0 g. The mass in grams of one mole of any pure substance is called its **molar mass**. The molar mass of any element is numerically equal to its atomic mass and has the units g/mol. An atom of manganese has an atomic mass of 54.94 amu. Therefore, the molar mass of manganese is 54.94 g/mol. When you measure 54.94 g of manganese on a balance,

### Objectives

- **Relate** the mass of an atom to the mass of a mole of atoms.

- **Calculate** the number of moles in a given mass of an element and the mass of a given number of moles of an element.

- **Calculate** the number of moles of an element when given the number of atoms of the element.

- **Calculate** the number of atoms of an element when given the number of moles of the element.

### Vocabulary

molar mass

**Figure 11-3**

A dozen limes has approximately twice the mass of a dozen eggs. The difference in mass is reasonable because limes are different from eggs in composition and size.

---

## 1 Focus

### Focus Transparency

Before presenting the lesson, display **Section Focus Transparency 39** on the overhead projector. Have students answer the accompanying questions using **Section Focus Transparency Master 39.** [L1] [ELL]

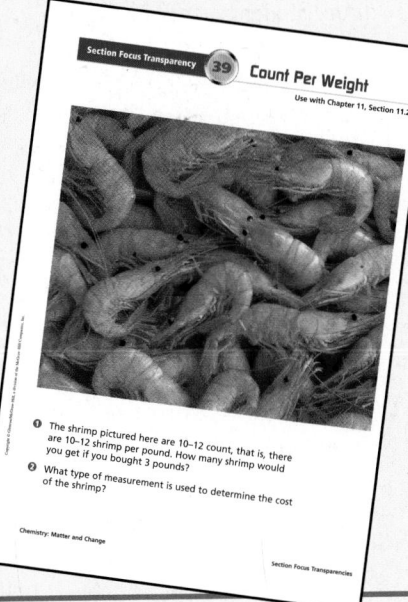

Section Focus Transparency **39** **Count Per Weight**
Use with Chapter 11, Section 11.2

❶ The shrimp pictured here are 10–12 count, that is, there are 10–12 shrimp per pound. How many shrimp would you get if you bought 3 pounds?
❷ What type of measurement is used to determine the cost of the shrimp?

*Chemistry: Matter and Change*                       Section Focus Transparencies

## 2 Teach

### Quick Demo

*Logical-Mathematical* Place a sack of pre-1982 pennies on a balance and determine the mass. The average mass of a pre-1982 penny is 3.10 g. Ask students how they can determine the number of pennies in the bag. Divide the total mass by 3.10 g. After students have calculated the number of pennies, have them verify their results by counting. [L2]

---

### Portfolio

#### How many moles?

*Linguistic* Give groups of students two bags of different numbers of iron nails, a bag containing one mole of iron filings, and an empty bag. Ask how they could determine the molar mass of iron and the number of moles of iron in each bag of nails. Have students carry out the procedure and write a report. [L2]

[P] **COOP LEARN**

### Resource Manager

Study Guide for Content Mastery, p. 62 [L2]
Solving Problems: A Chemistry Handbook, Section 11.2 [L2]
Section Focus Transparency 39 and Master [L1] [ELL]
Math Skills Transparency 13 and Master [L2] [ELL]

---

**National Science Content Standards**

Pages 312–313
UCP.1, UCP.3; B.2; E.2

## Purpose 🧊

Students will develop the relationship among atomic mass, molar mass, and Avogadro's number.

## Process Skills

Formulating models, drawing conclusions, using numbers

## Teaching Strategies

• Although the masses of protons and neutrons are known to eight or ten significant digits, the figures used in this lab are rounded to three. Students should expect to calculate approximate values.

• Students may ask how 12 nuclear particles, each with a mass of 1.007 amu, can be in the nucleus of a carbon atom with a mass of exactly 12 amu. The answer involves the mass equivalent of the binding energy of the electrons, which is being neglected in these calculations.

## Analysis

1. $$\frac{1.67 \times 10^{-24} \text{ g}}{} \times$$

$$\frac{4 \text{ nuclear particles}}{1 \text{ atom helium}} =$$

$$6.68 \times 10^{-24} \text{ g/He atom}$$

2. A model of C should have six protons and six neutrons.

$$\frac{1.67 \times 10^{-24} \text{ g}}{} \times$$

$$\frac{12 \text{ nuclear particles}}{1 \text{ atom C}} =$$

$$2.00 \times 10^{-23} \text{ g/C atom}$$

The carbon atom = 12 amu.

## Thinking Critically

1. $$1.007 \text{ g} \times \frac{1 \text{ H atom}}{1.67 \times 10^{-24} \text{ g}} =$$

$$6.0 \times 10^{23} \text{ H atoms}$$

2. $$\frac{6.68 \times 10^{-24} \text{ g}}{\text{He atom}} \times 6.0 \times$$

$$10^{23} \text{ He atom} = 4.0 \text{ g}$$

$$\frac{2.00 \times 10^{-23} \text{ g}}{\text{C atom}} \times 6.0 \times$$

$$10^{23} \text{ C atom} = 12 \text{ g}$$

3. The mass of one mole of any atom is the same value in grams as the mass of one atom in amu units.

---

**Figure 11-4**

One mole of manganese, represented by a bag of particles, contains Avogadro's number of atoms and has a mass equal to its atomic mass in grams. The same is true for all the elements.

1 mole manganese = $6.02 \times 10^{23}$ atoms of manganese

you indirectly count $6.02 \times 10^{23}$ atoms of manganese. **Figure 11-4** shows the relationship between molar mass and one mole of an element. The **problem-solving LAB** will further clarify these relationships.

## Using Molar Mass

Imagine that your class bought jellybeans in bulk to sell by the dozen at a candy sale. You soon realize that it's too much work counting out each dozen, so instead you decide to measure the jellybeans by mass. You find that 1 dozen jellybeans has a mass of 35 g. What mass of jellybeans should you measure if a customer wants 5 dozen? The conversion factor that relates mass and dozens of jellybeans is

$$\frac{35 \text{ g jellybeans}}{1 \text{ dozen}}$$

---

## problem-solving LAB

### Molar Mass, Avogadro's Number and the Atomic Nucleus

**Formulating models** A nuclear model of mass can provide a simple picture of the connections between the mole, molar mass, and the number of representative particles in a mole.

Hydrogen - 1          Helium - 4

#### Analysis

The diagram shows models of the nuclei of hydrogen-1 and helium-4. The hydrogen-1 nucleus contains one proton with a mass of 1.007 amu. The mass of the proton in grams has been found experimentally to be $1.672 \times 10^{-24}$ g. Helium-4 contains two protons and two neutrons and has a mass of approximately 4 amu.

1. What is the mass in grams of one helium atom? (The mass of a neutron is approximately the same as the mass of a proton.)

2. Carbon-12 contains six protons and six neutrons. Draw a model of the nucleus of

carbon-12 and calculate the mass of one atom in amu and in grams.

#### Thinking Critically

1. How many atoms of hydrogen-1 are in a 1.007-g sample? Recall that 1.007 amu is the mass of one atom of hydrogen-1. Round your answer to two significant digits.

2. If you had samples of helium and carbon that contained the same number of atoms as you calculated in question 1, what would be the mass in grams of each sample?

3. What can you conclude about the relationship between the number of atoms and the mass of each sample?

---

## ✓ Assessment

**Performance** Have students, working in groups of three, make a presentation of their understanding of the use of the nuclear model to explain the mass of a mole of an element. To make each presentation unique and to illustrate the fact that the molar mass of an element is the weighted average of all the

isotopes of the element, have each group explain the atomic mass of a different element having a number of different isotopes, chlorine, for example. Use the Performance Task Assessment List for Oral Presentation in **PASC**, p. 71. **L2** **COOP LEARN**

You would multiply the number of dozens to be sold by this conversion factor.

$$5 \text{ dozen} \times \frac{35 \text{ g jellybeans}}{1 \text{ dozen}} = 175 \text{ g jellybeans}$$

Note how the units cancel to give you the mass of 5 dozen jellybeans.

Now, suppose that while working in chemistry lab, you need 3.00 moles of manganese (Mn) for a chemical reaction. How can you measure that amount? Like the 5 dozen jellybeans, the number of moles of manganese can be converted to an equivalent mass and measured on a balance. To calculate mass from the number of moles, you need to multiply the number of moles of manganese required in the reaction (3.00 moles of Mn) by a conversion factor that relates mass and moles of manganese. That conversion factor is the molar mass of manganese (54.9 g/mol).

$$\text{number of moles} \times \frac{\text{number of grams}}{1 \text{ mole}} = \text{mass}$$

$$3.00 \text{ mol Mn} \times \frac{54.9 \text{ g Mn}}{1 \text{ mol Mn}} = 165 \text{ g Mn}$$

If you measure 165 g of manganese on a balance, you will have the 3.00 moles of manganese you need for the reaction. The reverse conversion—from mass to moles—also involves the molar mass as a conversion factor, but it is the inverse of the molar mass that is used. Can you explain why?

## EXAMPLE PROBLEM 11-2

### Mole to Mass Conversion

Chromium (Cr) is a transition element used as a coating on metals and in steel alloys to control corrosion. Calculate the mass in grams of 0.0450 moles of chromium.

**1. Analyze the Problem**

You are given the number of moles of chromium and must convert it to an equivalent mass using the molar mass of chromium from the periodic table. Because the sample is less than one-tenth mole, the answer should be less than one-tenth the molar mass.

| Known | Unknown |
|---|---|
| number of moles = 0.0450 mol Cr | mass = ? g Cr |
| molar mass Cr = 52.00 g/mol Cr | |

**2. Solve for the Unknown**

Multiply the known number of moles of chromium by the conversion factor that relates grams of chromium to moles of chromium, the molar mass.

$$\text{moles Cr} \times \frac{\text{grams Cr}}{1 \text{ mol Cr}} = \text{grams Cr}$$

$$0.0450 \text{ mol Cr} \times \frac{52.00 \text{ g Cr}}{1 \text{ mol Cr}} = 2.34 \text{ g Cr}$$

**3. Evaluate the Answer**

The known number of moles of chromium has the smallest number of significant figures (3), so the answer is correctly stated with three digits. The answer is less than one-tenth the mass of one mole as predicted and has the correct unit.

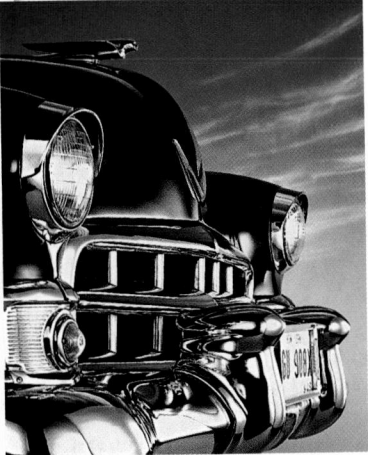

Chromium resists corrosion, which means it doesn't react readily with oxygen in the air. It was used in this 1948 Cadillac to protect the steel and add glitter.

## Practice PROBLEMS

Have students refer to Appendix D for complete solutions to Practice Problems.

**11. a.** 96.3 g Al
   **b.** $1.20 \times 10^3$ g Si
   **c.** 203 g Co
   **d.** $1.60 \times 10^2$ g Zn

**12. a.** 0.236 mol Ag
   **b.** 9.355 mol S
   **c.** 1.91 mol Zn
   **d.** 17.9 mol Fe

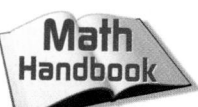

Review the meaning of inverse in the **Math Handbook** on page 905 of this text.

Practice!

For more practice with mass and mole conversions, go to **Supplemental Practice Problems** in Appendix A.

## PRACTICE PROBLEMS

**11.** Determine the mass in grams of each of the following.

   **a.** 3.57 mol Al        **c.** 3.45 mol Co
   **b.** 42.6 mol Si        **d.** 2.45 mol Zn

## EXAMPLE PROBLEM 11-3

### Mass to Mole Conversion

Calcium, the fifth most abundant element on Earth, is always found combined with other elements because of its high reactivity. How many moles of calcium are in 525 g calcium (Ca)?

#### 1. Analyze the Problem

You are given the mass of calcium and must convert the mass to moles of calcium. The mass of calcium is more than ten times larger than the molar mass. Therefore, the answer should be greater than ten moles.

**Known**

mass = 525 g Ca
molar mass Ca = 40.08 g/mol Ca

**Unknown**

number of moles = ? mol Ca

#### 2. Solve for the Unknown

Multiply the known amount of calcium by the conversion factor that relates moles of calcium to grams of calcium, the inverse of molar mass.

$$\text{mass} \times \frac{1 \text{ mole}}{\text{number of grams}} = \text{number of moles}$$

$$525 \text{ g Ca} \times \frac{1 \text{ mol Ca}}{40.08 \text{ g Ca}} = 13.1 \text{ mol Ca}$$

#### 3. Evaluate the Answer

The mass of calcium has the smaller number of significant figures (3), so the answer is expressed correctly with three digits. As predicted, the answer is greater than 10 moles and has the expected unit.

## PRACTICE PROBLEMS

**12.** Determine the number of moles in each of the following.

   **a.** 25.5 g Ag        **c.** 125 g Zn
   **b.** 300.0 g S        **d.** 1.00 kg Fe

**Conversions from mass to atoms and atoms to mass** So far, you have learned how to convert mass to the number of moles and the number of moles to mass. You can go one step further and convert mass to the number of atoms. Recall the jellybeans you were selling at the candy sale. At the end of the day, you find that 550 g of jellybeans are left unsold. Without counting, can you determine how many jellybeans this is? You know that one dozen jellybeans has a mass of 35 g and that 1 dozen contains 12 jellybeans. Thus, you can first convert the 550 g to dozens of jellybeans by using the conversion factor that relates dozens and mass.

$$550 \text{ g jellybeans} \times \frac{1 \text{ dozen jellybeans}}{35 \text{ g jellybeans}} = 16 \text{ dozen jellybeans}$$

## CHEMISTRY JOURNAL

### Mass, Moles, and Particles

*Linguistic* Ask students to write statements that relate mass to moles, moles to mass, moles to particles, and particles to moles. L2

Next, you can determine how many jellybeans are in 16 dozen by multiplying by the conversion factor that relates number of particles (jellybeans) and dozens.

$$16 \text{ dozen} \times \frac{12 \text{ jellybeans}}{1 \text{ dozen}} = 192 \text{ jellybeans}$$

The 550 g of leftover jellybeans is equal to 192 jellybeans.

Just as you cannot make a direct conversion from the mass of jellybeans to the number of jellybeans, you cannot make a direct conversion from the mass of a substance to the number of representative particles in that substance. You must first convert the mass to moles by multiplying by a conversion factor that relates moles and mass. Can you identify the conversion factor? The number of moles must then be multiplied by a conversion factor that relates the number of representative particles to moles. That conversion factor is Avogadro's number.

## EXAMPLE PROBLEM 11-4

### Mass to Atoms Conversion

Gold is one of a group of metals called the coinage metals (copper, silver, and gold). How many atoms of gold (Au) are in a pure gold nugget having a mass of 25.0 g.

**1. Analyze the Problem**

You are given a mass of gold and must determine how many atoms it contains. Because you cannot go directly from mass to the number of atoms, you must first convert mass to moles using molar mass. Then, you can convert moles to the number of atoms using Avogadro's number. The given mass of the gold nugget is about one-eighth the molar mass of gold (196.97 g/mol), so the number of gold atoms should be approximately one-eighth Avogadro's number.

**Known**

mass = 25.0 g Au
molar mass Au = 196.97 g/mol Au

**Unknown**

number of atoms = ? atoms Au

**2. Solve for the Unknown**

Multiply the known amount of gold by the inverse of the molar mass as the conversion factor.

$$\text{mass Au} \times \frac{1 \text{ mole Au}}{\text{number of grams Au}} = \text{moles Au}$$

$$25.0 \text{ g Au} \times \frac{1 \text{ mol Au}}{196.97 \text{ g Au}} = 0.127 \text{ mol Au}$$

Multiply the calculated number of moles of gold by Avogadro's number as a conversion factor.

$$\text{moles Au} \times \frac{6.02 \times 10^{23} \text{ atoms Au}}{1 \text{ mole Au}} = \text{atoms Au}$$

$$0.127 \text{ mol Au} \times \frac{6.02 \times 10^{23} \text{ atoms Au}}{1 \text{ mol Au}} = 7.65 \times 10^{22} \text{ atoms Au}$$

**3. Evaluate the Answer**

The mass of gold has the smallest number of significant figures (3), so the answer is expressed correctly with three digits. The answer is approximately one-eighth Avogadro's number as predicted, and the unit is correct.

Gold is called a noble metal because it doesn't react readily with other elements. Early civilizations used nearly pure gold for coins and ornaments such as this gold mask from Quimbaya, Columbia, A.D. 1000-1500.

11.2 Mass and the Mole **317**

Have students refer to Appendix D for complete solutions to Practice Problems.

**13. a.** $4.79 \times 10^{24}$ atoms Li
   **b.** $6.68 \times 10^{20}$ atoms Pb
   **c.** $3.45 \times 10^{22}$ atoms Hg
   **d.** $9.77 \times 10^{23}$ atoms Si
   **e.** $1.51 \times 10^{24}$ atoms Ti
**14. a.** $2.09 \times 10^{3}$ g Bi
   **b.** 91.3 g Mn
   **c.** 0.226 g He
   **d.** $3.49 \times 10^{-8}$ g N
   **e.** $5.93 \times 10^{-7}$ g U

# 3 Assess
## Check for Understanding

*Kinesthetic* Give each group of students a test tube containing a different mass of lead shot. Have each group determine the mass, moles, and number of atoms of lead in their test tube. Ask students what would change if the test tubes contained the same mass of iron filings instead of lead. Because the molar mass of iron is 55.85 g/mol and the molar mass of lead is 207.2 g/mol, the test tube containing iron will have 3.71 times as many moles and atoms as the test tube containing the same mass of lead.

**PRACTICE** PROBLEMS

**13.** How many atoms are in each of the following samples?
   **a.** 55.2 g Li
   **b.** 0.230 g Pb
   **c.** 11.5 g Hg
   **d.** 45.6 g Si
   **e.** 0.120 kg Ti

## EXAMPLE PROBLEM 11-5

**Atoms to Mass Conversion**

Helium is an unreactive noble gas often found in underground deposits mixed with methane. The mixture is separated by cooling the gaseous mixture until all but the helium has liquified.

A party balloon contains $5.50 \times 10^{22}$ atoms of helium (He) gas. What is the mass in grams of the helium?

**1. Analyze the Problem**

You are given the number of atoms of helium and must find the mass of the gas.

| Known | Unknown |
|---|---|
| number of atoms = $5.50 \times 10^{22}$ atoms He | mass = ? g He |
| molar mass He = 4.00 g/mol He | |

**2. Solve for the Unknown**

Multiply the number of atoms of helium by the inverse of Avogadro's number as a conversion factor.

$$\text{atoms He} \times \frac{1 \text{ mol He}}{6.02 \times 10^{23} \text{ atoms He}} = \text{moles He}$$

$$5.50 \times 10^{22} \text{ atoms He} \times \frac{1 \text{ mol He}}{6.02 \times 10^{23} \text{ atoms He}} = 0.0914 \text{ mol He}$$

Multiply the calculated number of moles of helium by the conversion factor that relates mass of helium to moles of helium, molar mass.

$$\text{moles He} \times \frac{\text{number of grams He}}{1 \text{ mole He}} = \text{mass He}$$

$$0.0914 \text{ mol He} \times \frac{4.00 \text{ g He}}{1 \text{ mol He}} = 0.366 \text{ g He}$$

**3. Evaluate the Answer**

The answer is expressed correctly with three significant figures and has the expected unit.

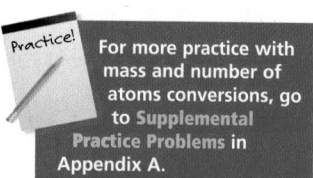

Helium gas, used in party balloons, is heavier than hydrogen gas but safer because it is unreactive and will not burn as hydrogen does.

*Practice!* For more practice with mass and number of atoms conversions, go to **Supplemental Practice Problems** in Appendix A.

**PRACTICE** PROBLEMS

**14.** What is the mass in grams of each of the following?
   **a.** $6.02 \times 10^{24}$ atoms Bi
   **b.** $1.00 \times 10^{24}$ atoms Mn
   **c.** $3.40 \times 10^{22}$ atoms He
   **d.** $1.50 \times 10^{15}$ atoms N
   **e.** $1.50 \times 10^{15}$ atoms U

318   **Chapter 11** The Mole

---

## Internet Address Book

**Chemistry Online** Note Internet addresses that you find useful in the space below for quick reference.

_____

_____

_____

_____

_____

Now that you have learned about and practiced conversions between mass, moles, and representative particles, you can see that the mole is at the center of these calculations. Mass must always be converted to moles before being converted to atoms, and atoms must similarly be converted to moles before calculating their mass. **Figure 11-5** shows the steps to follow as you work with these conversions.

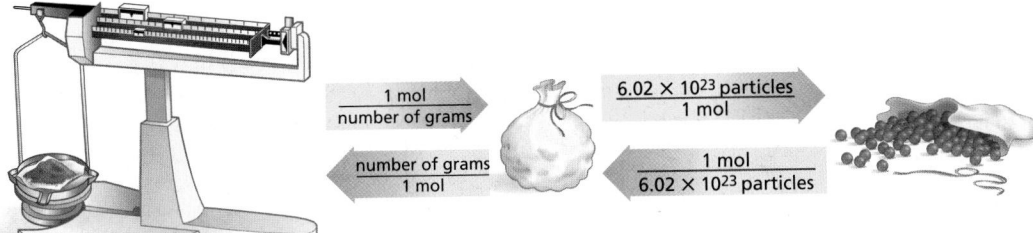

In **Figure 11-5**, mass is represented by a laboratory balance, moles are represented by a bag or bundle of particles, and representative particles are represented by the contents that are spilling out of the bag. You can see that two steps are needed to convert from mass on the left to representative particles on the right or to convert from representative particles on the right to mass on the left. The conversion factors for these conversions are given on the arrows pointing left and right. In the Example Problems, you have been making each of these conversions in separate steps, but you could make the same conversions in one calculation. For example, suppose you want to find out how many molecules of water are in 1.00 g of water. This calculation involves the conversion factors on the arrows pointing to the right. You could set up your calculation like this.

$$1.00 \text{ g H}_2\text{O} \times \frac{1 \text{ mol H}_2\text{O}}{18.02 \text{ g H}_2\text{O}} \times \frac{6.02 \times 10^{23} \text{ molecules H}_2\text{O}}{1 \text{ mol H}_2\text{O}}$$

$$= 3.34 \times 10^{22} \text{ molecules H}_2\text{O}$$

Note that the units cancel to give the answer in molecules of water. Do the reverse calculation yourself using the conversion factors on the arrows pointing from right to left. What is the mass of $3.34 \times 10^{22}$ molecules of water? What answer should you expect? What unit?

**Figure 11-5**

The mole is at the center of conversions between mass and particles. Two steps are needed to go from mass to representative particles or the reverse.

---

## Section 11.2 Assessment

15. Explain what is meant by molar mass.

16. What conversion factor should be used to convert from mass to moles? Moles to mass?

17. Explain the steps needed to convert the mass of an element to the number of atoms of the element.

18. **Thinking Critically** The mass of a single atom is usually given in the unit amu. Would it be possible to express the mass of a single atom in grams? Explain.

19. **Sequencing** Arrange the following in order of mass from the smallest mass to the largest: 1.0 mol Ar, $3.0 \times 10^{24}$ atoms Ne, 20 g Kr.

chemistrymc.com/self_check_quiz

11.2 Mass and the Mole    **319**

---

## Section 11.2 Assessment

15. Molar mass is the mass in grams of one mole of any pure substance.

16. Mass-to-mole conversions use the conversion factor 1 mol/number of grams. Moles-to-mass conversions use the conversion factor number of grams/1 mol.

17. Multiply the mass by the inverse of molar mass, and then multiply by Avogadro's number.

18. Because one mole is equal to $6.02 \times 10^{23}$ atoms and the molar mass of an element is equal to one mole, the mass of a single atom can be calculated by dividing the mass of one mole by Avogadro's number.

19. 20 g Kr, 1.0 mol Ar, $3.0 \times 10^{24}$ atoms Ne

**319**

# 1 Focus

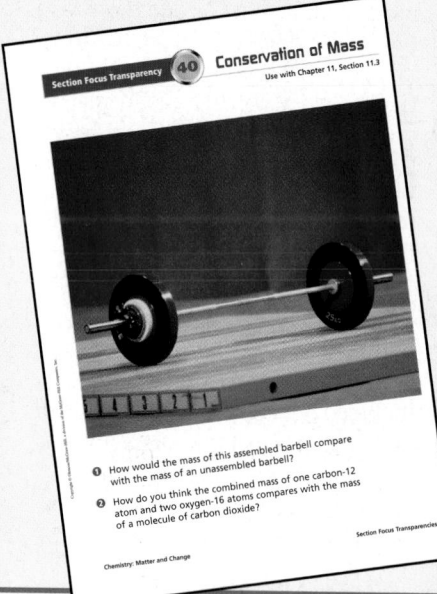

# 2 Teach

**Figure Caption Question**

**Figure 11-6** How many of each kind of atom are contained in one mole of Freon? $6.02 \times 10^{23}$ atoms C, $1.20 \times 10^{24}$ atoms Cl, and $1.20 \times 10^{24}$ atoms F

---

## Objectives

- **Recognize** the mole relationships shown by a chemical formula.

- **Calculate** the molar mass of a compound.

- **Calculate** the number of moles of a compound from a given mass of the compound, and the mass of a compound from a given number of moles of the compound.

- **Determine** the number of atoms or ions in a mass of a compound.

---

**Figure 11-6**

A dozen freon molecules contains one dozen carbon atoms, two dozen chlorine atoms, and two dozen fluorine atoms. How many of each kind of atom are contained in one mole of freon?

---

You have learned that different kinds of representative particles are counted using the mole, but so far you have applied this counting unit only to atoms of elements. Can you make similar conversions for compounds and ions? If so, you will need to know the molar mass of the compounds and ions.

## Chemical Formulas and the Mole

Recall that the chemical formula for a compound indicates the types of atoms and the number of each contained in one unit of the compound. For example, freon has the formula $CCl_2F_2$. The subscripts in the formula tell you that one molecule of $CCl_2F_2$ consists of one atom of carbon, two atoms of chlorine, and two atoms of fluorine that have chemically combined. The ratio of carbon to chlorine to fluorine is $1 : 2 : 2$.

But suppose you had a mole of freon. The representative particles would be molecules of freon. A mole of freon would contain Avogadro's number of freon molecules, which means that instead of one carbon atom, you would have a mole of carbon atoms. And instead of two chlorine atoms and two fluorine atoms, you would have two moles of chlorine atoms and two moles of fluorine atoms. The ratio of carbon to chlorine to fluorine in one mole of freon would still be $1 : 2 : 2$, as it is in one molecule of freon.

**Figure 11-6** illustrates this principle for a dozen freon molecules. Check for yourself that a dozen freon molecules contains one dozen carbon atoms, two dozen chlorine atoms, and two dozen fluorine atoms. The chemical formula $CCl_2F_2$ not only represents an individual molecule of freon, it also represents a mole of the compound.

In some chemical calculations, you may need to convert from moles of a compound to moles of individual atoms in the compound or from moles of individual atoms in a compound to moles of the compound. The following conversion factors can be written for use in these calculations for the molecule freon.

$$\frac{1 \text{ mol C atoms}}{1 \text{ mol } CCl_2F_2} \qquad \frac{2 \text{ mol Cl atoms}}{1 \text{ mol } CCl_2F_2} \qquad \frac{2 \text{ mol F atoms}}{1 \text{ mol } CCl_2F_2}$$

To find out how many moles of fluorine atoms are in 5.50 moles of freon, you would multiply the moles of freon by the conversion factor that relates moles of fluorine atoms to moles of $CCl_2F_2$.

$$\text{moles } CCl_2F_2 \times \frac{\text{moles F atoms}}{1 \text{ mole } CCl_2F_2} = \text{moles F atoms}$$

$$5.50 \text{ mol } CCl_2F_2 \times \frac{2 \text{ mol F atoms}}{1 \text{ mol } CCl_2F_2} = 11.0 \text{ mol F atoms}$$

Therefore, 11.0 mol F atoms are in 5.50 mol $CCl_2F_2$.

---

 **Resource Manager**

**Study Guide for Content Mastery,** p. 63 **L2**

**Solving Problems: A Chemistry Handbook,** Section 11.3 **L2**

**Section Focus Transparency 40 and Master** **L1** **ELL**

**Challenge Problems,** p. 11 **L3**

Conversion factors such as the one just used for fluorine can be written for any element in a compound. The number of moles of the element that goes in the numerator of the conversion factor is the subscript for that element in the chemical formula.

## EXAMPLE PROBLEM 11-6

### Mole Relationships from a Chemical Formula

Aluminum oxide ($Al_2O_3$), often called alumina, is the principal raw material for the production of aluminum. Alumina occurs in the minerals corundum and bauxite. Determine the moles of aluminum ions ($Al^{3+}$) in 1.25 moles of aluminum oxide.

**1. Analyze the Problem**

You are given the number of moles of $Al_2O_3$ and must determine the number of moles of $Al^{3+}$ ions. Use a conversion factor based on the chemical formula that relates moles of $Al^{3+}$ ions to moles of $Al_2O_3$. Every mole of $Al_2O_3$ contains two moles of $Al^{3+}$ ions. Thus, the answer should be two times the number of moles of $Al_2O_3$.

**Known**

number of moles = 1.25 mol $Al_2O_3$

**Unknown**

number of moles = ? mol $Al^{3+}$ ions

**2. Solve for the Unknown**

1 mol $Al_2O_3$ contains 2 mol $Al^{3+}$ ions. Determine the conversion factor relating moles of $Al^{3+}$ ions to moles of $Al_2O_3$.

$$\frac{2\ \text{mol}\ Al^{3+}\ \text{ions}}{1\ \text{mol}\ Al_2O_3}$$

Multiply the known number of moles of $Al_2O_3$ by the conversion factor.

$$\text{moles}\ Al_2O_3 \times \frac{\text{moles}\ Al^{3+}\ \text{ions}}{\text{mole}\ Al_2O_3} = \text{moles}\ Al^{3+}\ \text{ions}$$

$$1.25\ \text{mol}\ Al_2O_3 \times \frac{2\ \text{mol}\ Al^{3+}\ \text{ions}}{1\ \text{mol}\ Al_2O_3} = 2.50\ \text{mol}\ Al^{3+}\ \text{ions}$$

**3. Evaluate the Answer**

Because the conversion factor is a ratio of whole numbers, the number of significant digits is based on the moles of $Al_2O_3$. Therefore, the answer is expressed correctly with three significant figures. As predicted, the answer is twice the number of moles of $Al_2O_3$.

The capstone placed at the top of the Washington Monument in 1884 is a 22.86-cm pyramid of pure aluminum. Until an inexpensive purification process was developed, aluminum was considered a rare and precious metal.

## PRACTICE PROBLEMS

20. Determine the number of moles of chloride ions in 2.50 mol $ZnCl_2$.

21. Calculate the number of moles of each element in 1.25 mol glucose ($C_6H_{12}O_6$).

22. Determine the number of moles of sulfate ions present in 3.00 mol iron(III) sulfate ($Fe_2(SO_4)_3$).

23. How many moles of oxygen atoms are present in 5.00 mol diphosphorus pentoxide ($P_2O_5$)?

24. Calculate the number of moles of hydrogen atoms in 11.5 mol water.

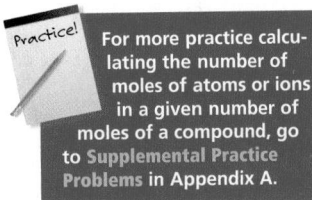

Practice! For more practice calculating the number of moles of atoms or ions in a given number of moles of a compound, go to Supplemental Practice Problems in Appendix A.

11.3 Moles of Compounds    **321**

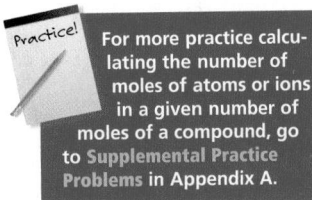
### Identifying Misconceptions

Students may recognize that a mole of a compound is $6.02 \times 10^{23}$ representative particles, but they may not realize that there are other molar relationships that can be defined in that mole, for example, the number of moles of fluorine atoms in one mole of freon molecules.

**Uncover the Misconception**
Analogies are helpful. Ask students how many legs a cat has. four How many legs do a dozen cats have? 48 How many cats have 200 legs? 50 How many legs would a mole of cats have? $2.41 \times 10^{24}$ Then, ask how many atoms of fluorine are in one freon molecule. two Finally, how many atoms of fluorine are in one mole of freon? $1.20 \times 10^{24}$

**Demonstrate the Concept**
Make a model of $CH_4$. Take the model apart and ask students the number of hydrogen atoms per methane molecule. four Ask how many hydrogen atoms would be in one mole of methane. $4 \times 6.02 \times 10^{23} = 2.41 \times 10^{24}$.

**Assess New Knowledge**
Have students write mole ratios for the methane molecule.

### Practice PROBLEMS

Have students refer to Appendix D for complete solutions to Practice Problems.

**20.** 5.00 mol $Cl^-$
**21.** 7.50 mol C, 15.0 mol H, 7.50 mol O
**22.** 9.00 mol $SO_4^{2-}$
**23.** 25.0 mol O
**24.** 23.0 mol H

## DIFFERENTIATED INSTRUCTION

### Learning Disabled

*Kinesthetic* Have groups of students make 12 molecular models of $CO_2$ using molecular model kits or gumdrops and toothpicks. Have them put their $CO_2$ models in an empty egg carton. Ask students to write down the number of $CO_2$ molecules. Then, have students take apart the molecules and place the carbon atoms in the egg carton. Have them record how many carbon atoms are present. Students can then put the oxygen atoms in two cartons and record the number of oxygen atoms present. Ask how many dozen carbon atoms and oxygen atoms are present in one dozen $CO_2$ molecules. Finally, ask how many moles of carbon atoms and oxygen atoms are present in one mole of $CO_2$. L1 ELL COOP LEARN

**National Science Content Standards**

Pages 320–321
UCP.1, UCP.3; B.2

## Assessment

**Knowledge** Give each student a different chemical formula and have them identify the number of each atom per single formula unit or molecule. Then, have them identify the number of moles of each atom per mole of the same substance. **L2**

## Reinforcement

To help students arrive at the same answers provided in the text, have them use the molar masses of the elements expressed to the second decimal place. Have students determine the molar mass of sodium thiosulfate ($Na_2S_2O_3$) using molar masses from the periodic table. 158.12 g/mol. Remind students that when adding measured values, the measurement with the digit having the lowest decimal value determines the number of significant figures in the answer.

## Practice PROBLEMS

Have students refer to Appendix D for complete solutions to Practice Problems.

**25.** 40.00 g/mol NaOH
110.98 g/mol $CaCl_2$
98.14 g/mol $KC_2H_3O_2$
211.64 g/mol $Sr(NO_3)_2$
149.10 g/mol $(NH_4)_3PO_4$

**26.** 46.07 g/mol $C_2H_5OH$
342.30 g/mol $C_{12}H_{22}O_{11}$
27.03 g/mol HCN
153.81 g/mol $CCl_4$
18.02 g/ mol $H_2O$

### Resource Manager

**Math Skills Transparency 14 and Master** **L2** **ELL**

## The Molar Mass of Compounds

The mass of your backpack is the sum of the mass of the pack plus the masses of the books, notebooks, pencils, lunch, and miscellaneous items you put into it. You could find its mass by determining the mass of each item separately and adding them together. Similarly, the mass of a mole of a compound equals the sum of the masses of every particle that makes up the compound. You know how to use the molar mass of an element as a conversion factor in calculations. You also know that a chemical formula indicates the number of moles of each element in a compound. With this information, you can now determine the molar mass of a compound.

Suppose you want to determine the molar mass of potassium chromate ($K_2CrO_4$). Using the periodic table, the mass of one mole of each element present in potassium chromate can be determined. That mass is then multiplied by the number of moles of that element in the chemical formula. Adding the masses of all elements present will yield the molar mass of $K_2CrO_4$.

$$\text{number of moles} \times \text{molar mass} = \text{number of grams}$$

$$2.000 \text{ mol K} \times \frac{39.10 \text{ g K}}{1 \text{ mol K}} = 78.20 \text{ g}$$

$$1.000 \text{ mol Cr} \times \frac{52.00 \text{ g Cr}}{1 \text{ mol Cr}} = 52.00 \text{ g}$$

$$4.000 \text{ mol O} \times \frac{16.00 \text{ g O}}{1 \text{ mol O}} = \underline{64.00 \text{ g}}$$

$$\text{molar mass } K_2CrO_4 = 194.20 \text{ g}$$

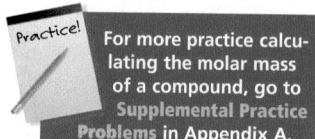

Practice! For more practice calculating the molar mass of a compound, go to **Supplemental Practice Problems** in Appendix A.

## PRACTICE PROBLEMS

**25.** Determine the molar mass of each of the following ionic compounds: NaOH, $CaCl_2$, $KC_2H_3O_2$, $Sr(NO_3)_2$, and $(NH_4)_3PO_4$.

**26.** Calculate the molar mass of each of the following molecular compounds: $C_2H_5OH$, $C_{12}H_{22}O_{11}$, HCN, $CCl_4$, and $H_2O$.

The molar mass of a compound demonstrates the law of conservation of mass. The sum of the masses of the elements that reacted to form the compound equals the mass of the compound. **Figure 11-7** shows 194 g, or one mole, of $K_2CrO_4$ and masses equal to one mole of two other substances.

**Figure 11-7**

Each substance contains different numbers and kinds of atoms so their molar masses are different. The molar mass of each compound is the sum of the masses of all the elements contained in the compound.

Potassium chromate ($K_2CrO_4$)    Sodium chloride (NaCl)    Sucrose ($C_{12}H_{22}O_{11}$)

### CHEMISTRY JOURNAL

## Molar Masses

**Logical-Mathematical** Have students determine the molar masses of $CaCO_3$, $C_{12}H_{22}O_{11}$ (sucrose), NaCl, $KNO_3$, and $C_8H_{18}$ (octane) and record their calculations and answers in their journals. The molar masses of these compounds will be used in future journal entries. **L2**

# Converting Moles of a Compound to Mass

Suppose you need to measure a certain number of moles of a compound for an experiment. First, you must calculate the mass in grams that corresponds to the necessary number of moles. Then, that mass can be measured on a balance. In Example Problem 11-2, you learned how to convert the number of moles of elements to mass using molar mass as the conversion factor. The procedure is the same for compounds except that you must first calculate the molar mass of the compound.

## EXAMPLE PROBLEM 11-7

**Mole-to-Mass Conversion for Compounds**

The characteristic odor of garlic is due to the compound allyl sulfide $((C_3H_5)_2S)$. What is the mass of 2.50 moles of allyl sulfide?

**1. Analyze the Problem**

You are given 2.50 mol $(C_3H_5)_2S$ and must convert the moles to mass using the molar mass as a conversion factor. The molar mass is the sum of the molar masses of all the elements in $(C_3H_5)_2S$.

**Known**

number of moles = 2.50 mol $(C_3H_5)_2S$

**Unknown**

molar mass $(C_3H_5)_2S$ = ? g/mol $(C_3H_5)_2S$
mass = ? g $(C_3H_5)_2S$

**2. Solve for the Unknown**

Calculate the molar mass of $(C_3H_5)_2S$.

$$1 \text{ mol S} \times \frac{32.07 \text{ g S}}{1 \text{ mol S}} = 32.07 \text{ g S}$$

$$6 \text{ mol C} \times \frac{12.01 \text{ g C}}{1 \text{ mol C}} = 72.06 \text{ g C}$$

$$10 \text{ mol H} \times \frac{1.008 \text{ g H}}{1 \text{ mol H}} = \underline{10.08 \text{ g H}}$$

molar mass $(C_3H_5)_2S$ = 114.21 g/mol $(C_3H_5)_2S$

Convert mol $(C_3H_5)_2S$ to g $(C_3H_5)_2S$ by using the molar mass as a conversion factor.

$$\text{moles } (C_3H_5)_2S \times \frac{\text{number of grams } (C_3H_5)_2S}{1 \text{ mole } (C_3H_5)_2S} = \text{mass } (C_3H_5)_2S$$

$$2.50 \text{ mol } (C_3H_5)_2S \times \frac{114.21 \text{ g } (C_3H_5)_2S}{1 \text{ mol } (C_3H_5)_2S} = 286 \text{ g } (C_3H_5)_2S$$

**3. Evaluate the Answer**

Mol $(C_3H_5)_2S$ has the smaller number of significant figures (3), so the answer is expressed correctly with three digits. The unit, g, is correct.

The pungent odor of garlic is characteristic of sulfides. Sulfides, including hydrogen sulfide, are noted for their strong, often unpleasant odors. The sulfur atom in allyl sulfide forms a chemical bond to each of the two $C_3H_5$ groups in the molecule.

## PRACTICE PROBLEMS

**27.** What is the mass of 3.25 moles of sulfuric acid $(H_2SO_4)$?

**28.** What is the mass of $4.35 \times 10^{-2}$ moles of zinc chloride $(ZnCl_2)$?

**29.** How many grams of potassium permanganate are in 2.55 moles?

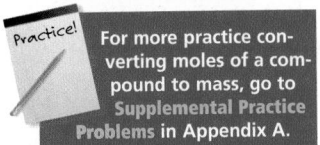

**Practice!** For more practice converting moles of a compound to mass, go to **Supplemental Practice Problems in Appendix A.**

11.3 Moles of Compounds **323**

---

---

## CHEMISTRY JOURNAL

### Knowing Your Antacid

*Linguistic* Have students examine the label on a bottle of antacid tablets, a brand that contains calcium carbonate. Ask them to record in their journals all information needed to determine the mass of calcium carbonate per tablet. Then, have them determine the moles of calcium carbonate per tablet, the moles of calcium ions per tablet, and the moles of carbonate ions per tablet. **L2**

## Converting the Mass of a Compound to Moles

Imagine that the experiment you are doing in the laboratory produces 5.55 g of a compound. How many moles is this? To find out, you calculate the molar mass of the compound and determine it to be 185.0 g/mol. The molar mass relates grams and moles, but this time you need the inverse of the molar mass as the conversion factor.

$$5.50 \ \text{g compound} \times \frac{1 \ \text{mol compound}}{185.0 \ \text{g compound}} = 0.0297 \ \text{mol compound}$$

### EXAMPLE PROBLEM 11-8

**Mass-to-Mole Conversion for Compounds**

Calcium hydroxide (Ca(OH)₂) is used to remove sulfur dioxide from the exhaust gases emitted by power plants and for softening water by the elimination of Ca²⁺ and Mg²⁺ ions. Calculate the number of moles of calcium hydroxide in 325 g.

**1. Analyze the Problem**

You are given 325 g Ca(OH)₂ and are solving for the number of moles of Ca(OH)₂. You must first calculate the molar mass of Ca(OH)₂.

**Known**

mass = 325 g Ca(OH)₂

**Unknown**

molar mass = ? g/mol Ca(OH)₂

number of moles = ? mol Ca(OH)₂

**2. Solve for the Unknown**

Determine the molar mass of Ca(OH)₂.

$$1 \ \text{mol Ca} \times \frac{40.08 \ \text{g Ca}}{1 \ \text{mol Ca}} = 40.08 \ \text{g}$$

$$2 \ \text{mol O} \times \frac{16.00 \ \text{g O}}{1 \ \text{mol O}} = 32.00 \ \text{g}$$

$$2 \ \text{mol H} \times \frac{1.008 \ \text{g H}}{1 \ \text{mol H}} = 2.016 \ \text{g}$$

molar mass of Ca(OH)₂ = 74.096 g/mol = 74.10 g/mol

Use the inverse of molar mass as the conversion factor to calculate moles.

$$325 \ \text{g Ca(OH)}_2 \times \frac{1 \ \text{mol Ca(OH)}_2}{74.10 \ \text{g Ca(OH)}_2} = 4.39 \ \text{mol Ca(OH)}_2$$

**3. Evaluate the Answer**

The given mass of Ca(OH)₂ has fewer digits than any other value in the calculations so it determines the number of significant figures in the answer (3). To check the reasonableness of the answer, round off the molar mass of Ca(OH)₂ to 75 g/mol and the given mass of Ca(OH)₂ to 300 g. Seventy- five is contained in 300 four times. Thus, the answer is reasonable.

This compound, commonly called lime, is calcium oxide (CaO). Calcium oxide reacts with water to produce calcium hydroxide. Lime is a component of cement and is used to counteract excess acidity in soil.

### PRACTICE PROBLEMS

For more practice converting the mass of a compound to moles, go to **Supplemental Practice Problems** in Appendix A.

**30.** Determine the number of moles present in each of the following.

**a.** 22.6 g AgNO₃      **d.** 25.0 g Fe₂O₃

**b.** 6.50 g ZnSO₄      **e.** 254 g PbCl₄

**c.** 35.0 g HCl

## Internet Address Book

**Chemistry Online**  Note Internet addresses that you find useful in the space below for quick reference.

_____

_____

_____

_____

_____

# Converting the Mass of a Compound to Number of Particles

Example Problem 11-8 illustrated how to find the number of moles of a compound contained in a given mass. Now, you will learn how to calculate the number of representative particles—molecules or formula units—contained in a given mass and, in addition, the number of atoms or ions. Recall that no direct conversion is possible between mass and number of particles. You must first convert the given mass to moles by multiplying by the inverse of the molar mass. Then, you can convert moles to the number of representative particles by multiplying by Avogadro's number. To determine numbers of atoms or ions in a compound, you will need conversion factors that are ratios of the number of atoms or ions in the compound to one mole of compound. These are based on the chemical formula. Example Problem 11-9 provides practice in solving this type of problem.

## EXAMPLE PROBLEM 11-9

**Conversion from Mass to Moles to Particles**

Aluminum chloride is used in refining petroleum and manufacturing rubber and lubricants. A sample of aluminum chloride ($AlCl_3$) has a mass of 35.6 g.

**a.** How many aluminum ions are present?

**b.** How many chloride ions are present?

**c.** What is the mass in grams of one formula unit of aluminum chloride?

### 1. Analyze the Problem

You are given 35.6 g $AlCl_3$ and must calculate the number of $Al^{3+}$ ions, the number of $Cl^-$ ions, and the mass in grams of one formula unit of $AlCl_3$. Molar mass, Avogadro's number, and ratios from the chemical formula are the necessary conversion factors. The ratio of $Al^{3+}$ ions to $Cl^-$ ions in the chemical formula is 1:3. Therefore, the calculated numbers of ions should be in that ratio. The mass of one formula unit in grams should be an extremely small number.

| Known | Unknown |
|---|---|
| mass = 35.6 g $AlCl_3$ | number of ions = ? $Al^{3+}$ ions |
| | number of ions = ? $Cl^-$ ions |
| | mass = ? g/formula unit $AlCl_3$ |

### 2. Solve for the Unknown

Determine the molar mass of $AlCl_3$.

$$1 \text{ mol Al} \times \frac{26.98 \text{ g Al}}{1 \text{ mol Al}} = 26.98 \text{ g Al}$$

$$3 \text{ mol Cl} \times \frac{35.45 \text{ g Cl}}{1 \text{ mol Cl}} = \underline{106.35 \text{ g Cl}}$$

Molar mass of $AlCl_3$ = 133.33 g/mol $AlCl_3$

Multiply by the inverse of the molar mass as a conversion factor to convert the mass of $AlCl_3$ to moles.

$$\text{grams } AlCl_3 \times \frac{1 \text{ mol } AlCl_3}{\text{grams } AlCl_3} = \text{moles } AlCl_3$$

$$35.6 \text{ g } AlCl_3 \times \frac{1 \text{ mol } AlCl_3}{133.33 \text{ g } AlCl_3} = 0.267 \text{ mol } AlCl_3$$

*Continued on next page*

At ordinary temperatures, aluminum chloride is a solid with the formula $AlCl_3$. In the vapor phase, however, aluminum chloride exists as a doubled molecule, or dimer, with the formula $Al_2Cl_6$.

## Portfolio

### Avogadro's Number

*Intrapersonal* Have interested students research the history of Avogadro's number and make class reports. When Avogadro proposed his hypothesis, there were no data to confirm it. Several other scientists were involved in determining the number of particles in one mole: Robert Brown, Jean-Baptiste Perrin, Albert Einstein, R. A. Millikan, and Stanislao Cannizzaro. **L2** **P**

**31. a.** $9.36 \times 10^{22}$ ions $Ag^+$
   **b.** $4.68 \times 10^{22}$ ions $CrO_4^{2-}$
   **c.** $5.51 \times 10^{-22}$ g/formula unit $Ag_2CrO_4$

**32.** 445 g NaCl

**33. a.** $1.19 \times 10^{24}$ atoms C
   **b.** $3.58 \times 10^{24}$ atoms H
   **c.** $5.96 \times 10^{23}$ atoms O

**34. a.** $2.16 \times 10^{22}$ ions $Na^+$
   **b.** $1.08 \times 10^{22}$ ions $SO_3^{2-}$
   **c.** $2.09 \times 10^{-22}$ g/formula unit

**35. a.** $7.11 \times 10^{23}$ atoms C
   **b.** $1.42 \times 10^{24}$ atoms O
   **c.** $7.31 \times 10^{-23}$ g/molecule $CO_2$

# 3 Assess

## Check for Understanding

Ask students to determine the molar mass of table sugar (sucrose, $C_{12}H_{22}O_{11}$). 342.3 g/mol Have them determine the mass of one cup of sugar and calculate the number of moles of sugar in one cup. Answers will depend on the mass of one cup; mass of 1 cup $\times$ 1 mol/342.3 g = number of moles of sugar. Ask how many atoms of carbon, hydrogen, and oxygen are in one cup of sugar. Answers will vary; moles of sucrose $\times$ 12 C atoms/1 mol $C_{12}H_{22}O_{11}$ = number of atoms C, moles of sucrose $\times$ 22 atoms H/1 mol $C_{12}H_{22}O_{11}$ = number of atoms H, and moles of sucrose $\times$ 11 O atoms/1 mol $C_{12}H_{22}O_{11}$ = number of atoms O.

National Science Content Standards

Pages 326–327
UCP.1, UCP.3; B.2; E.2

Multiply by Avogadro's number to calculate the number of formula units of $AlCl_3$.

$$0.267 \; \text{mol AlCl}_3 \times \frac{6.02 \times 10^{23} \; \text{formula units}}{1 \; \text{mol AlCl}_3} =$$

$$1.61 \times 10^{23} \; \text{formula units AlCl}_3$$

To calculate the number of $Al^{3+}$ and $Cl^-$ ions, use the ratios from the chemical formula as conversion factors.

$$1.61 \times 10^{23} \; \text{AlCl}_3 \; \text{formula unit} \times \frac{1 \; Al^{3+} \; \text{ion}}{1 \; \text{AlCl}_3 \; \text{formula unit}} =$$

$$1.61 \times 10^{23} \; Al^{3+} \; \text{ions}$$

$$1.61 \times 10^{23} \; \text{AlCl}_3 \; \text{formula unit} \times \frac{3 \; Cl^- \; \text{ions}}{1 \; \text{AlCl}_3 \; \text{formula unit}} =$$

$$4.83 \times 10^{23} \; Cl^- \; \text{ions}$$

Calculate the mass in grams of one formula unit of $AlCl_3$. Start with molar mass and use the inverse of Avogadro's number as a conversion factor.

$$\frac{133.33 \; \text{g AlCl}_3}{1 \; \text{mol}} \times \frac{1 \; \text{mol}}{6.02 \times 10^{23} \; \text{formula unit}} =$$

$$2.21 \times 10^{-22} \; \text{g AlCl}_3/\text{formula unit}$$

**3. Evaluate the Answer**

A minimum of three significant figures is used in each value in the calculations. Therefore, the answers have the correct number of digits. The number of $Cl^-$ ions is three times the number of $Al^{3+}$ ions, as predicted. The mass of a formula unit of $AlCl_3$ can be checked by calculating it in a different way: Divide the mass of $AlCl_3$ (35.6 g) by the number of formula units contained in the mass ($1.61 \times 10^{23}$ formula units) to obtain the mass of one formula unit. The two answers are the same.

## PRACTICE PROBLEMS

**31.** A sample of silver chromate ($Ag_2CrO_4$) has a mass of 25.8 g.
   **a.** How many $Ag^+$ ions are present?
   **b.** How many $CrO_4^{2-}$ ions are present?
   **c.** What is the mass in grams of one formula unit of silver chromate?

**32.** What mass of sodium chloride contains $4.59 \times 10^{24}$ formula units?

**33.** A sample of ethanol ($C_2H_5OH$) has a mass of 45.6 g.
   **a.** How many carbon atoms does the sample contain?
   **b.** How many hydrogen atoms are present?
   **c.** How many oxygen atoms are present?

**34.** A sample of sodium sulfite ($Na_2SO_3$) has a mass of 2.25 g.
   **a.** How many $Na^+$ ions are present?
   **b.** How many $SO_3^{2-}$ ions are present?
   **c.** What is the mass in grams of one formula unit of $Na_2SO_3$?

**35.** A sample of carbon dioxide has a mass of 52.0 g.
   **a.** How many carbon atoms are present?
   **b.** How many oxygen atoms are present?
   **c.** What is the mass in grams of one molecule of $CO_2$?

**Practice!** For more practice calculating the number of ions or atoms in a mass of a compound and the mass in grams of one formula unit, go to **Supplemental Practice Problems** in Appendix A.

## CHEMISTRY JOURNAL

### Moles of Gasoline

*Intrapersonal* Have students find out and record the price of one gallon of gasoline. As they study Section 11.3, have them answer the following questions.

**1.** A gallon of gasoline is 3.78 L and has a density of 0.70 g/mL. What is the mass of one gallon of gas?

**2.** The formula for gasoline can be taken to be $C_8H_{18}$. Determine the moles of gasoline in one gallon.

**3.** How many atoms of carbon are in one gallon of gasoline?

**4.** What is the price per mole of gasoline?

**5.** If you purchased $10.00 worth of gas, how many moles did you put into the tank? **L2**

Moles of atoms or ions

Mass of compound

Moles of compound

Representative particles

Conversions among mass, moles, and the number of particles are summarized in **Figure 11-8**. Refer to this diagram often until you become familiar with the calculations. Note that the molar mass (number of grams/1 mol) and the inverse of molar mass (1 mol/number of grams) are the conversion factors between the mass of a substance and the number of moles of the substance. Avogadro's number and its inverse are the conversion factors between the moles of a substance and the number of representative particles. To convert between the number of moles of a compound and the number of moles of atoms or ions contained in the compound, you need the ratio of moles of atoms or ions to 1 mole of compound or its inverse, which are shown on the upward and downward arrows in **Figure 11-8**. These ratios are derived from the subscripts in the chemical formula. What ratio would you use to find the moles of hydrogen atoms in four moles of water?

**Figure 11-8**

Note the central position of the mole. To go from the left, right, or top of the diagram to any other place, you must go through the mole. The conversion factors on the arrows provide the means for making the conversions.

## Section 11.3 Assessment

**36.** Describe how you can determine the molar mass of a compound.

**37.** What three conversion factors are often used in mole conversions?

**38.** Explain how you can determine the number of atoms or ions in a given mass of a compound.

**39.** If you know the mass in grams of a molecule of a substance, could you obtain the mass of a mole of that substance? Explain.

**40. Thinking Critically** Design a bar graph that will show the number of moles of each element present in 500 g dioxin ($C_{12}H_4Cl_4O_2$), a powerful poison.

**41. Applying Concepts** The recommended daily allowance of calcium is 1000 mg of $Ca^{2+}$ ions. Calcium carbonate is used to supply the calcium in vitamin tablets. How many moles of calcium ions does 1000 mg represent? How many moles of calcium carbonate are needed to supply the required amount of calcium ions? What mass of calcium carbonate must each tablet contain?

chemistrymc.com/self_check_quiz

11.3 Moles of Compounds    **327**

## Section 11.3 Assessment

**36.** Multiply the mass of one mole of each element by the ratio of that element to one mole of the compound. Add the resulting masses.

**37.** $\dfrac{\text{number of grams}}{1 \text{ mol}}$,

$\dfrac{6.02 \times 10^{23} \text{ representative particles}}{1 \text{ mol}}$,

$\dfrac{\text{number of atoms of element}}{1 \text{ mol compound}}$

**38.** Convert the mass to moles, multiply the number of moles by the ratio of the number of atoms or ions to one mole, multiply by Avogadro's number.

**39.** Yes, multiply the mass in grams of the molecule by Avogadro's number.

**40.** The graph should show 24 mol C, 8 mol H, 8 mol Cl, 4 mol O. See Solutions Manual.

**41.** 0.02 mol $Ca^{2+}$, 0.02 mol $CaCO_3$, 2 g $CaCO_3$

**327**

---

## Section 11.4

# Empirical and Molecular Formulas

### Objectives

- **Explain** what is meant by the percent composition of a compound.
- **Determine** the empirical and molecular formulas for a compound from mass percent and actual mass data.

### Vocabulary

percent composition
empirical formula
molecular formula

Chemists, such as those shown in **Figure 11-9**, are often involved in developing new compounds for industrial, pharmaceutical, and home uses. After a synthetic chemist (one who makes new compounds) has produced a new compound, an analytical chemist analyzes the compound to provide experimental proof of its composition and its chemical formula. You can learn more about the work of chemists by reading **Chemistry and Technology** at the end of this chapter.

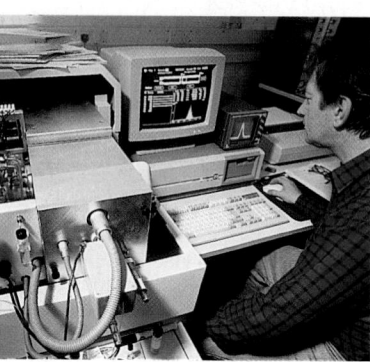

#### Figure 11-9

New compounds are first made on a small scale by a synthetic chemist like the one on the left. Then, an analytical chemist, like the one on the right, analyzes the compound to verify its structure and percent composition.

## Percent Composition

It's the analytical chemist's job to identify the elements a compound contains and determine their percent by mass. Gravimetric and volumetric analyses are experimental procedures based on the measurement of mass for solids and liquids, respectively. For example, a 100-g sample of a new compound contains 55 g of element X and 45 g of element Y. The percent by mass of any element in a compound can be found by dividing the mass of the element by the mass of the compound and multiplying by 100.

$$\frac{\text{mass of element}}{\text{mass of compound}} \times 100 = \text{percent by mass}$$

$$\frac{55 \text{ g element X}}{100 \text{ g compound}} \times 100 = 55\% \text{ element X}$$

$$\frac{45 \text{ g element Y}}{100 \text{ g compound}} \times 100 = 45\% \text{ element Y}$$

Because percent means parts per 100, the percents by mass of all the elements of a compound must always add up to 100. The percent composition of the compound is 55% X and 45% Y. The percent by mass of each element in a compound is called the **percent composition** of a compound.

**Percent composition from the chemical formula** If you already know the chemical formula for a compound such as water ($H_2O$), can you calculate its percent composition? The answer is yes. You can use the chemical formula to calculate the molar mass of water (18.02 g/mol) and assume you have an 18.02-g sample. Because the percent composition of a compound is always the same, no matter the size of the sample, you can assume that the sample size is one mole. To find the mass of each element in a mole of water, multiply the molar mass of the element by its subscript in the chemical formula. Because one mole of water contains two moles of hydrogen atoms, the mass of hydrogen in a mole of water is (2 mol)(1.01 g/mol) = 2.02 g. To find the percent by mass of hydrogen in water, divide the mass of hydrogen by the molar mass of water (18.02 g/mol) and multiply by 100.

$$\frac{2.02 \text{ g H}}{18.02 \text{ g H}_2\text{O}} \times 100 = 11.2\% \text{ H}$$

One mole of water contains one mole of oxygen. Thus, the mass of oxygen in one mole of water is 16.00 g. The percent by mass of oxygen is

$$\frac{16.00 \text{ g O}}{18.02 \text{ g H}_2\text{O}} \times 100 = 88.80\% \text{ O}$$

The percent composition of water is 11.2% hydrogen and 88.80% oxygen.
The general equation for calculating the percent by mass of any element in a compound is

$$\frac{\text{mass of element in 1 mol compound}}{\text{molar mass of compound}} \times 100 = \% \text{ by mass element}$$

The **miniLAB** provides an opportunity to practice calculating percents.

## miniLAB

### Percent Composition and Gum

**Interpreting Data** Water soluble sweeteners and flavorings are added to chewing gum. Are these chemicals added as an outside coating or are they mixed throughout the gum?

**Materials** balance, weighing paper, 250-mL beakers (2), pieces of chewing gum (2), stirring rod, paper towels, window screen (10 cm × 10 cm), scissors, clock or timer

### Procedure

CAUTION: *Do not taste or eat any items used in the lab.*

1. Unwrap two pieces of chewing gum. Measure the mass of each separately on a piece of weighing paper. Label the weighing papers with the masses to avoid mixing up your data. Record the masses.
2. Add 150 mL of cold tap water to a 250-mL beaker. Place one piece of chewing gum in the water and stir for two minutes.
3. Remove the gum from the water and pat dry using paper towels. Measure and record the mass of the dried gum.
4. Use scissors to cut the second piece of gum into small pieces, each about the width of a pea. Repeat step 2 using fresh water. Use the stirring rod to keep the pieces of gum from clumping together.
5. Use the window screen to strain the water from the gum. Pat the gum dry using paper towels. Measure and record the mass of the dried gum.
6. Discard the gum in a waste container.

### Analysis

1. For the uncut piece of gum, calculate the mass of sweeteners and flavorings that dissolved in the water. The mass of sweeteners and flavorings is the difference between the original mass of the gum and the mass of the dried gum.
2. For the gum that was in small pieces, calculate the mass of dissolved sweeteners and flavorings.
3. For both pieces of gum, calculate the percent of the original mass that was soluble sweeteners and flavorings. For help, refer to *Percents* in the **Math Handbook** on page 909 of this text.
4. What can you infer from the two percentages? Is the gum sugar-coated or are the sweeteners and flavorings mixed throughout?

## miniLAB

### Purpose
Students will calculate the percent composition of solid sweeteners in gum to infer whether the sugar is a coating or is mixed throughout the gum

### Process Skills
Observing and inferring, measuring

### Safety Precautions
Students should not place the gum in their mouths. Avoid using sharp pointed scissors.

### Disposal
Discard the gum in a waste container.

### Teaching Strategies
- Avoid using hard, candy-coated gums.
- Ask students if the percentage will change for a chunky piece of gum when compared to a long flat piece of gum.
- Have students compare the masses of all the pieces of gum. Ask them if they think the gum is machine made, and why. The masses are precise, i.e., 3.11g, 3.09g, 3.12g.

### Expected Results
The gum will lose mass after being placed in water because the sweeteners are water-soluble. The cut piece with the larger surface area will expose more of the soluble chemicals to the water, and will have a greater loss of mass.

### Analysis
1. 3.11 g (initial mass) − 2.84 g (final mass) = 0.27 g dissolved sweeteners and flavorings
2. 3.11 g (initial mass) − 2.75 g (final mass) = 0.36 g dissolved sweeteners and flavorings
3. whole piece of gum: $\frac{0.27 \text{ g}}{3.11 \text{ g}} \times 100 = 8.7\%$ small pieces of gum: $\frac{0.36 \text{ g}}{3.11 \text{ g}} \times 100 = 12\%$
4. Because more sweetener dissolves when the surface area is larger, the inference is that the sweeteners are mixed throughout the gum.

### Assessment

**Performance** Have students measure the mass of a bag of microwave popcorn before it is heated and again after popping. Caution students not to open the microwaved popcorn until the steam has had time to dissipate. Have them calculate the percent of water lost during popping. Use the Performance Task Assessment List for Carrying Out a Strategy and Collecting Data in PASC, p. 25.

Scratch the edge of a post-1982 penny to expose the zinc core. Measure and record the mass of the penny. Place the penny into 6.0M HCl and have students observe the reaction of zinc with HCl. **CAUTION:** *6.0M HCl will burn skin and irritate nasal linings. Do not take a deep breath over it. If spilled on skin, wash the area with soap and water, then neutralize it with a baking soda paste.* When the reaction stops, remove the penny with plastic forceps, rinse several times with water, and then with alcohol. Allow the penny to dry. Remass the penny. Have students calculate what mass of the penny was zinc (the part that dissolved) and what mass was copper (the remaining penny). Determine the mass percent of zinc and the mass percent of copper in the penny. Disposal: Dilute the acid solution with more water and flush it down the drain. Post-1982 pennies are 2.4% Cu and 97.6% Zn. Pre-1982 pennies are 95% Cu and 5% zinc. **L2**

## Assessment

**Knowledge** Give each student a card with a chemical formula on it. Have them determine the percent by mass of each element in the compound. Have students exchange cards with a partner and determine the percent by mass of another formula. Partners should compare answers and settle any discrepancies in results. Answers will vary depending on the chemical formulas used. Possible formulas and answers are the following. NaCl: 39.3% Na, 60.7% Cl $H_2O$: 11.2% H, 88.8% O $CO_2$: 27.3% C, 72.7% O NaOH: 57.5% Na, 40.0% O, 2.5% H

---

**Try at Home LAB**

See page 957 in Appendix E for **Calculating Carbon Percentages**

Antacids often contain carbonates, for example, sodium hydrogen carbonate, calcium carbonate, and magnesium carbonate. A carbonate-containing antacid neutralizes excess stomach acid by reacting with acid to produce carbon dioxide.

---

**EXAMPLE** PROBLEM 11-10

### Calculating Percent Composition

Sodium hydrogen carbonate, also called baking soda, is an active ingredient in some antacids used for the relief of indigestion. Determine the percent composition of sodium hydrogen carbonate ($NaHCO_3$).

**1. Analyze the Problem**

You are given only the chemical formula. Assume you have one mole of $NaHCO_3$. Calculate the molar mass and the mass of each element in one mole to determine the percent by mass of each element in the compound. The sum of all percents should be 100%.

**Known**

formula = $NaHCO_3$

**Unknown**

percent Na = ? % Na
percent H = ? % H
percent C = ? % C
percent O = ? % O

**2. Solve for the Unknown**

Determine the mass of each element present and the molar mass of $NaHCO_3$.

$$1 \text{ mol Na} \times \frac{22.99 \text{ g Na}}{1 \text{ mol Na}} = 22.99 \text{ g Na}$$

$$1 \text{ mol H} \times \frac{1.008 \text{ g H}}{1 \text{ mol H}} = 1.008 \text{ g H}$$

$$1 \text{ mol C} \times \frac{12.01 \text{ g C}}{1 \text{ mol C}} = 12.01 \text{ g C}$$

$$3 \text{ mol O} \times \frac{16.00 \text{ g O}}{1 \text{ mol O}} = 48.00 \text{ g O}$$

molar mass $NaHCO_3$ = 84.008 g/mol $NaHCO_3$ = 84.01g/mol $NaHCO_3$

Determine the percent by mass of each element by dividing the mass of the element by the molar mass of the compound and multiplying by 100.

$$\% \text{ mass element} = \frac{\text{mass of element in 1 mol compound}}{\text{molar mass of compound}} \times 100$$

$$\text{percent Na} = \frac{22.99 \text{ g Na}}{84.01 \text{ g } NaHCO_3} \times 100 = 27.37\% \text{ Na}$$

$$\text{percent H} = \frac{1.008 \text{ g H}}{84.01 \text{ g } NaHCO_3} \times 100 = 1.200\% \text{ H}$$

$$\text{percent C} = \frac{12.01 \text{ g C}}{84.01 \text{ g } NaHCO_3} \times 100 = 14.30\% \text{ C}$$

$$\text{percent O} = \frac{48.00 \text{ g O}}{84.01 \text{ g } NaHCO_3} \times 100 = 57.14\% \text{ O}$$

The percent composition of $NaHCO_3$ is 27.37% Na, 1.200% H, 14.30% C, and 57.14% O.

**3. Evaluate the Answer**

All masses and molar masses contain four significant figures. Therefore, the percents are correctly stated to four signigicant figures. The sum of the mass percents is 100.00% as required.

---

## CHEMISTRY JOURNAL

### Percent Composition of Coins

**Kinesthetic** Ask students to take the coins they have in their pockets and use the data below to determine the percent by mass of Ag, Cu, Zn, and Ni in each coin. Quarters and dimes minted before 1965 are 100% silver. Quarters and dimes minted after 1965 contain 75% Cu and 25% Ni by mass. Nickels are 75% Cu and 25% Ni by mass. Pre-1982 pennies are 95% Cu and 5% Zn, and post-1982 pennies are 2.4% Cu and 97.6% Zn. Have students mass their coins and write the calculations in their journals. **L2**

42. Determine the percent by mass of each element in calcium chloride.

43. Calculate the percent composition of sodium sulfate.

44. Which has the larger percent by mass of sulfur, $H_2SO_3$ or $H_2S_2O_8$?

45. What is the percent composition of phosphoric acid ($H_3PO_4$)?

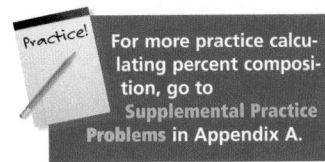

Practice! For more practice calculating percent composition, go to **Supplemental Practice Problems** in Appendix A.

## Empirical Formula

Suppose that the identities of the elements in a sample of a new compound have been determined and the compound's percent composition is known. These data can be used to find the formula for the compound. First, you must determine the smallest whole number ratio of the moles of the elements in the compound. This ratio provides the subscripts in the empirical formula. The **empirical formula** for a compound is the formula with the smallest whole-number mole ratio of the elements. The empirical formula may or may not be the same as the actual molecular formula. If the two formulas are different, the molecular formula will always be a simple multiple of the empirical formula. The empirical formula for hydrogen peroxide is HO; the molecular formula is $H_2O_2$. In both formulas, the ratio of oxygen to hydrogen is 1:1.

The data used to determine the chemical formula for a compound may be in the form of percent composition or it may be the actual masses of the elements in a given mass of the compound. If percent composition is given, you can assume that the total mass of the compound is 100.00 g and that the percent by mass of each element is equal to the mass of that element in grams. For example, the percent composition of an oxide of sulfur is 40.05% S and 59.95% O. Thus, as you can see in **Figure 11-10**, 100.00 g of the oxide contains 40.05 g S and 59.95 g O. The mass of each element can be converted to a number of moles by multiplying by the inverse of the molar mass. Recall that the number of moles of S and O are calculated in this way.

$$40.05 \text{ g S} \times \frac{1 \text{ mol S}}{32.07 \text{ g S}} = 1.249 \text{ mol S}$$

$$59.95 \text{ g O} \times \frac{1 \text{ mol O}}{16.00 \text{ g O}} = 3.747 \text{ mol O}$$

The mole ratio of S atoms to O atoms in the oxide is 1.249 : 3.747. As you can see, these values are not whole numbers and cannot be used as subscripts in a chemical formula.

How, then, can the mole ratio be converted to whole numbers? As a starting point, recognize that the element with the smaller number of moles, in this case sulfur, might have the smallest subscript possible, 1. You can make the mole value of sulfur equal to 1 if you divide both mole values by the value of sulfur (1.249). In doing so, you do not change the ratio between the two elements because both are divided by the same number.

$$\frac{1.249 \text{ mol S}}{1.25} = 1 \text{ mol S}$$

$$\frac{3.747 \text{ mol O}}{1.25} = 3 \text{ mol O}$$

The simplest whole number mole ratio of S atoms to O atoms is 1:3. Thus, the empirical formula for the oxide of sulfur is $SO_3$.

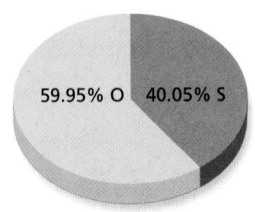

59.95% O 40.05% S

100.00% $SO_3$

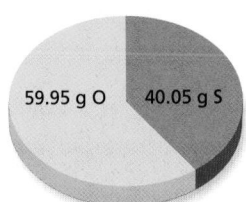

59.95 g O 40.05 g S

100.00 g $SO_3$

**Figure 11-10**

Keep this figure in mind when doing problems using percent composition. You can always assume that you have a 100-g sample of the compound and use the percents of the elements as masses of the elements.

11.4 Empirical and Molecular Formulas **331**

# Concept Development

**Kinesthetic** Continue the activity described in the Concept Development on the previous page by giving students another box to represent another compound. This box should have the same ratio of items, but different substances, for example, two wooden beads and one glass marble. Have students calculate the percent by mass of each item and the simplest whole-number ratio of items. Ask students if the boxes represent the same compound. Students should notice that although the empirical formula is the same, the mass percent is different, so the boxes contain models of different compounds.
L2

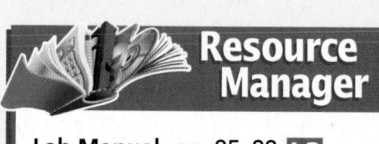

Lab Manual, pp. 85–88 L2

**National Science Content Standards**
Pages 332–333
UCP.1, UCP.3; B.2

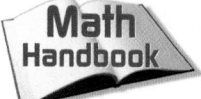

Review ratios in the **Math Handbook** on page 908 of this text.

---

Often in determining empirical formulas, the calculated mole values are still not whole numbers, as they are in the preceding example. In such cases, all the mole values must be multiplied by the smallest factor that will make them whole numbers. This is shown in Example Problem 11-11.

## EXAMPLE PROBLEM 11-11

### Calculating an Empirical Formula from Percent Composition

Methyl acetate is a solvent commonly used in some paints, inks, and adhesives. Determine the empirical formula for methyl acetate, which has the following chemical analysis: 48.64% carbon, 8.16% hydrogen, and 43.20% oxygen.

**1. Analyze the Problem**

You are given the percent composition of methyl acetate and must find the empirical formula. Because you can assume that each percent by mass represents the mass of the element in a 100.00-g sample, the percent sign can be replaced with the unit grams. Then, you can convert from grams to moles using the molar mass and find the smallest whole-number ratio of moles of the elements.

**Known**

percent by mass = 48.64% C
percent by mass = 8.16% H
percent by mass = 43.20% O

**Unknown**

empirical formula = ?

**2. Solve for the Unknown**

The mass of C is 48.64 g, the mass of H is 8.16 g, and the mass of O is 43.20 g. Multiply the mass of each element by the conversion factor that relates moles to grams based on molar mass.

$$48.64 \text{ g C} \times \frac{1 \text{ mol C}}{12.01 \text{ g C}} = 4.050 \text{ mol C}$$

$$8.16 \text{ g H} \times \frac{1 \text{ mol H}}{1.008 \text{ g H}} = 8.10 \text{ mol H}$$

$$43.20 \text{ g O} \times \frac{1 \text{ mol O}}{16.00 \text{ g O}} = 2.700 \text{ mol O}$$

Methyl acetate has a mole ratio of 4.050 mol C : 8.10 mol H : 2.700 mol O.

Calculate the simplest ratio of moles of the elements by dividing each number of moles by the smallest value in the mole ratio.

$$\frac{4.050 \text{ mol C}}{2.700} = 1.500 \text{ mol C} = 1.5 \text{ mol C}$$

$$\frac{8.10 \text{ mol H}}{2.700} = 3.00 \text{ mol H} = 3 \text{ mol H}$$

$$\frac{2.700 \text{ mol O}}{2.700} = 1.000 \text{ mol O} = 1 \text{ mol O}$$

The simplest ratio is 1.5 mol C : 3 mol H : 1 mol O.

Multiply the numbers of moles in the ratio by the smallest number that will produce a ratio of whole numbers.

$2 \times 1.5$ mol C = 3 mol C

$2 \times 3$ mol H = 6 mol H

$2 \times 1$ mol O = 2 mol O

The simplest whole-number ratio of C atoms to H atoms to O atoms is 3 : 6 : 2. The empirical formula is $C_3H_6O_2$.

---

## Demonstration

### Empirical Formulas

**Purpose**
To emphasize the information needed to determine an empirical formula.

**Materials**
Large test tube with two-hole stopper; glass and rubber tubing; Bunsen burner; ring stand with test tube holder; copper(II) oxide; scupula

**Safety Precautions** 🥽 🧤 🚫 ✋
**Disposal** Copper product can be reused.

**Procedure**
Set up the equipment as shown in the diagram. Close off the air supply to the burner. Turn on the gas and light the burner. When the flame turns yellow, all air has been removed and the reaction can begin. Adjust the air control to get a hot, blue flame. Heat the sample gently at first and then strongly. Note any changes. Heat for about 10 minutes. After the reaction is complete, remove the burner from the test tube and let the tube cool. Do not turn off the burner so that gas will be in contact with the product as it cools. Turn off the burner when the test tube is cool.

**3.** **Evaluate the Answer**

The calculations are correct and significant figures have been observed. To check that the formula is correct, the percent composition represented by the formula can be calculated. The percent composition checks exactly with the data given in the problem.

## PRACTICE PROBLEMS

**46.** A blue solid is found to contain 36.84% nitrogen and 63.16% oxygen. What is the empirical formula for this solid?

**47.** Determine the empirical formula for a compound that contains 35.98% aluminum and 64.02% sulfur.

**48.** Propane is a hydrocarbon, a compound composed only of carbon and hydrogen. It is 81.82% carbon and 18.18% hydrogen. What is the empirical formula?

**49.** The chemical analysis of aspirin indicates that the molecule is 60.00% carbon, 4.44% hydrogen, and 35.56% oxygen. Determine the empirical formula for aspirin.

**50.** What is the empirical formula for a compound that contains 10.89% magnesium, 31.77% chlorine, and 57.34% oxygen?

Practice! For more practice calculating an empirical formula from percent composition, go to **Supplemental Practice Problems** in Appendix A.

## Molecular Formula

Would it surprise you to learn that two or more substances with distinctly different properties can have the same percent composition and the same empirical formula? How is this possible? Remember that the subscripts in an empirical formula indicate the simplest whole-number ratio of moles of the elements in the compound. But the simplest ratio does not always indicate the actual number of moles in the compound. To identify a new compound, a chemist must go one step further and determine the **molecular formula**, which specifies the actual number of atoms of each element in one molecule or formula unit of the substance. **Figure 11-11** shows an important use of the gas, acetylene. It has the same percent composition and empirical formula, CH, as benzene which is a liquid. Yet chemically and structurally acetylene and benzene are very different.

To determine the molecular formula for a compound, the molar mass of the compound must be determined through experimentation and compared with the mass represented by the empirical formula. For example, the molar mass of acetylene is 26.04 g/mol and the mass of the empirical formula, CH, is 13.02 g/mol. Dividing the actual molar mass by the mass of the empirical formula indicates that the molar mass of acetylene is two times the mass of the empirical formula.

$$\frac{\text{experimentally determined molar mass of acetylene}}{\text{mass of empirical formula CH}} =$$

$$\frac{26.04 \text{ g/mol}}{13.02 \text{ g/mol}} = 2.000$$

The result shows that the molar mass of acetylene is two times the mass represented by the empirical formula. Thus, the molecular formula of acetylene must contain twice the number of carbon atoms and twice the number of hydrogen atoms represented by the empirical formula.

**Figure 11-11**

Acetylene is a gas used for welding because of the high-temperature flame produced when it is burned with oxygen.

---

**Results**

The black copper(II) oxide will turn to reddish-brown copper metal.

**Analysis**

**1.** What is the product of this reaction? copper metal

**2.** From the results of the experiment, can you identify the formula for the copper oxide? Why or why not? No, you do not know the amount of oxygen that was produced.

✓ **Assessment**

**Performance** Have students design an experiment to determine the empirical formula for the copper oxide. Determine the mass of the copper oxide before heating and determine the mass of the product. Calculate the empirical formula from this data. Use the Performance Task Assessment List for Designing an Experiment in **PASC,** p. 23.

To gas jet    Rubber tubing

## Concept Development

Have students refer to the data they obtained from the boxes of beads in the Concept Developments on pages 331 and 332. Tell them that each box represents a different molecule. Ask them what is the same for each molecule? The ratio of small to large beads (atoms) is two to one. What is different for each box? the total mass Using the mass of two small beads and one large bead, ask students to calculate the number of 2:1 units in their boxes. Answers will vary depending upon the number of beads in each box. Have students multiply the numbers in the ratio (2:1) by the number of units in their boxes and ask if the sum of the numbers in the new ratio is the same as the number of beads in their boxes. They should be the same. **L2**

## Extension

*Intrapersonal* Have interested and capable students investigate the operation of a gas chromatograph. Have them write a report or make a class presentation that explains how the instrument can be used to determine the concentrations of the capsaicinoids discussed in Cultural Diversity below. **L3**

**Chemistry Online**

**Topic: Empirical Formulas**
To learn more about empirical formulas, visit the Chemistry Web site at **chemistrymc.com**

**Activity:** Research how empirical formulas are used in mineral identification. Prepare a chart comparing the formulas of the minerals with their properties.

Succinic acid occurs naturally in fossils and fungi, and in lichens such as those shown. Succinic acid produced commercially is used to make compounds used in perfumes (esters) and in lacquers and dyes.

Similarly, when the experimentally determined molar mass of benzene, 78.12 g/mol, is compared with the mass of the empirical formula, the molar mass of benzene is found to be six times the mass of the empirical formula.

$$\frac{\text{experimentally determined molar mass of benzene}}{\text{mass of empirical formula CH}} =$$

$$\frac{78.12 \text{ g/mol}}{13.02 \text{ g/mol}} = 6.000$$

The molar mass of benzene is six times the mass represented by the empirical formula, so the molecular formula for benzene must represent six times the number of carbon and hydrogen atoms shown in the empirical formula. You can conclude that the molecular formula for acetylene is (CH)2 or $C_2H_2$ and the molecular formula for benzene is (CH)6 or $C_6H_6$.

A molecular formula can be represented as the empirical formula multiplied by an integer *n*.

$$\text{molecular formula} = (\text{empirical formula})n$$

The integer is the factor (6 in the example above) by which the subscripts in the empirical formula must be multiplied to obtain the molecular formula.

### **EXAMPLE** PROBLEM 11-12

**Determining a Molecular Formula**

Succinic acid is a substance produced by lichens. Chemical analysis indicates it is composed of 40.68% carbon, 5.08% hydrogen, and 54.24% oxygen and has a molar mass of 118.1 g/mol. Determine the empirical and molecular formulas for succinic acid.

**1. Analyze the Problem**

You are given the percent composition that allows you to calculate the empirical formula. Assume that each percent by mass represents the mass of the element in a 100.00-g sample. You can compare the given molar mass with the mass represented by the empirical formula to find *n*.

**Known**

percent by mass = 40.68% C
percent by mass = 5.08% H
percent by mass = 54.24 % O
molar mass = 118.1 g/mol succinic acid

**Unknown**

empirical formula = ?
molecular formula = ?

**2. Solve for the Unknown**

Use the percents by mass as grams of elements and convert to the number of moles by multiplying by the conversion factor that relates moles to mass based on molar mass.

$$40.68 \text{ g C} \times \frac{1 \text{ mol C}}{12.01 \text{ g C}} = 3.387 \text{ mol C}$$

$$5.08 \text{ g H} \times \frac{1 \text{ mol H}}{1.008 \text{ g H}} = 5.04 \text{ mol H}$$

$$54.24 \text{ g O} \times \frac{1 \text{ mol O}}{16.00 \text{ g O}} = 3.390 \text{ mol O}$$

Succinic acid has a mole ratio of C : H : O of 3.387 : 5.04 : 3.390.

---

## **CULTURAL DIVERSITY**

### Is it spicy?

If the restaurant you choose serves Mexican, Spanish, Thai, South American, Indian, or Chinese (Hunan or Szechuan) cuisine, the food is likely to be hot and spicy. The use of hot peppers in food is common among people of these countries, all of which have a hot climate. Not

only do these spicy foods taste good, they also provide an added advantage. They make you sweat. The evaporation of sweat absorbs heat and cools you off.

Capsaicinoids are the class of compounds responsible for the "heat" in spicy foods. The two most common capsaicinoids are capsaicin and dihydrocap-

saicin. These compounds are found in the white tissue inside a pepper. To determine the concentration of capsaicinoids in peppers, analytical chemists use an extract from the pepper and an instrument called a gas chromatograph.

Until recently, the "heat" in peppers was determined by a panel of tasters

Calculate the simplest ratio among the elements by dividing each mole value by the smallest value in the mole ratio.

$$\frac{3.387 \text{ mol C}}{3.387} = 1 \text{ mol C}$$

$$\frac{5.040 \text{ mol H}}{3.387} = 1.49 \text{ mol H} = 1.5 \text{ mol H}$$

$$\frac{3.390 \text{ mol O}}{3.387} = 1.001 \text{ mol O} = 1 \text{ mol O}$$

The simplest ratio is 1 mol C : 1.5 mol H : 1 mol O.

The simplest mol ratio includes a fractional value that cannot be used as a subscript in a formula. Multiply all mole values by 2.

$2 \times 1 \text{ mol C} = 2 \text{ mol C}$

$2 \times 1.5 \text{ mol H} = 3 \text{ mol H}$

$2 \times 1 \text{ mol O} = 2 \text{ mol O}$

The simplest whole-number ratio of C atoms to H atoms to O atoms is 2 : 3 : 2. The empirical formula is $C_2H_3O_2$

Calculate the empirical formula mass using the molar mass of each element.

$$2 \text{ mol C} \times \frac{12.01 \text{ g C}}{1 \text{ mol C}} = 24.02 \text{ g C}$$

$$3 \text{ mol H} \times \frac{1.008 \text{ g H}}{1 \text{ mol H}} = 3.024 \text{ g H}$$

$$2 \text{ mol O} \times \frac{16.00 \text{ g O}}{1 \text{ mol O}} = 32.00 \text{ g O}$$

molar mass $C_2H_3O_2 = 59.04$ g/mol $C_2H_3O_2$

Divide the experimentally determined molar mass of succinic acid by the mass of the empirical formula to determine $n$.

$$n = \frac{\text{molar mass of succinic acid}}{\text{molar mass of } C_2H_3O_2}$$

$$n = \frac{118.1 \text{ g/mol}}{59.04 \text{ g/mol}} = 2.000$$

Multiply the subscripts in the empirical formula by 2 to determine the actual subscripts in the molecular formula.

$(C_2H_3O_2)(2) = C_4H_6O_4$

The molecular formula for succinic acid is $C_4H_6O_4$.

**3. Evaluate the Answer**

Calculation of the molar mass from the molecular formula gives the same result as the experimental molar mass.

## PRACTICE PROBLEMS

**51.** Analysis of a chemical used in photographic developing fluid indicates a chemical composition of 65.45% C, 5.45% H, and 29.09% O. The molar mass is found to be 110.0 g/mol. Determine the molecular formula.

**52.** A compound was found to contain 49.98 g carbon and 10.47 g hydrogen. The molar mass of the compound is 58.12 g/mol. Determine the molecular formula.

**53.** A colorless liquid composed of 46.68% nitrogen and 53.32% oxygen has a molar mass of 60.01 g/mol. What is the molecular formula?

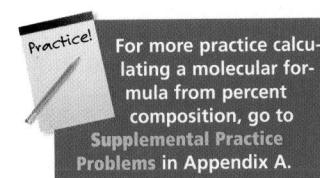

For more practice calculating a molecular formula from percent composition, go to **Supplemental Practice Problems** in Appendix A.

11.4 Empirical and Molecular Formulas **335**

## Practice PROBLEMS

Have students refer to Appendix D for complete solutions to Practice Problems.

**51.** $C_6H_6O_2$

**52.** $C_4H_{10}$

**53.** $N_2O_2$

 **Assessment**

**Knowledge** Have students determine the empirical formula and molecular formula for a compound with the following percent composition, 26.7% P, 12.1% N, and 61.2% Cl. The molar mass is 695 g/mol $PNCl_2$. $P_6N_6Cl_{12}$

who used their sense of "heat" to rank individual peppers in Scoville units. Scoville units range from zero for bell peppers to 300 000 for habanero peppers. Today, an analytical chemist in the laboratory reports chromatographic results in Scoville units.

 **Portfolio**

## Medicines from Plants

*Linguistic* Many medications, such as digoxin, quinine, digitalis, and ephedrine, have been obtained by extracting them from plants. Ask interested students to research one of these substances and write an article to share with the class and place in their porfolios.

L2  P

**National Science Content Standards**

**Pages 334–335**
UCP.1, UCP.3; B.2

## Concept Development

Have students refer to the data they obtained from the boxes of beads in Concept Development activities on pages 331 and 332. Using the masses of the two different sets of beads and the total masses, determine the percent composition of the two modeled compounds. **L2**

# 3 Assess

## Check for Understanding

Have each student determine the percent composition and molar mass of an assigned compound. Pairs of students should then exchange data and determine the empirical and molecular formulas of the compounds. The pairs of students should be expected to work out any discrepancies in the calculations. **L2** **COOP LEARN**

Because titanium is stable under severe conditions of heat and cold, it is used in aircraft engines, missiles, and space vehicles.

---

### EXAMPLE PROBLEM 11-13

#### Calculating an Empirical Formula from Mass Data

Although the mineral ilmenite contains more iron than titanium, the ore is usually mined and processed for titanium, a strong, light, and flexible metal. A sample of ilmenite is found to contain 5.41 g iron, 4.64 g titanium, and 4.65 g oxygen. Determine the empirical formula for ilmenite.

#### 1. Analyze the Problem

You are given the masses of the elements found in a known mass of ilmenite and must determine the empirical formula of the mineral. Convert the known masses of each element to moles using the conversion factor that relates moles to grams, the inverse of molar mass. Then, find the smallest whole-number ratio of the moles of the elements.

| Known | Unknown |
|---|---|
| mass of iron = 5.41 g Fe | empirical formula = ? |
| mass of titanium = 4.64 g Ti | |
| mass of oxygen = 4.65 g O | |

#### 2. Solve for the Unknown

Multiply the known mass of each element by the conversion factor that relates moles to grams based on the molar mass.

$$5.41 \text{ g Fe} \times \frac{1 \text{ mol Fe}}{55.85 \text{ g Fe}} = 0.0969 \text{ mol Fe}$$

$$4.64 \text{ g Ti} \times \frac{1 \text{ mol Ti}}{47.88 \text{ g Ti}} = 0.0969 \text{ mol Ti}$$

$$4.65 \text{ g O} \times \frac{1 \text{ mol O}}{16.00 \text{ g O}} = 0.291 \text{ mol O}$$

Ilmenite has a mole ratio of Fe : Ti : O of 0.0969 : 0.0969 : 0.291. Calculate the simplest ratio by dividing each mol value by the smallest value in the ratio. Fe and Ti have the same lower value (0.0969).

$$\frac{0.0969 \text{ mol Fe}}{0.0969} = 1 \text{ mol Fe}$$

$$\frac{0.0969 \text{ mol Ti}}{0.0969} = 1 \text{ mol Ti}$$

$$\frac{0.291 \text{ mol O}}{0.0969} = 3 \text{ mol O}$$

All the mol values are whole numbers. Thus, the simplest whole-number ratio of Fe : Ti : O is 1 : 1 : 3. The empirical formula for ilmenite is $FeTiO_3$.

#### 3. Evaluate the Answer

The mass of iron is slightly greater than the mass of titanium, but the molar mass of iron is also slightly greater than that of titanium. Thus, it is reasonable that the number of moles of iron and titanium are equal. The mass of titanium is approximately the same as the mass of oxygen, but the molar mass of oxygen is about 1/3 that of titanium. Thus, a 3:1 ratio of oxygen to titanium is reasonable.

336    **Chapter 11** The Mole

---

### ✓ Portfolio

#### What is a mass spectrometer?

*Intrapersonal* Have interested students research mass spectrometers and write a report on this analytical instrument and what information it can provide. Students can share their findings with the class and place their reports in their portfolios. **L2** **P**

**54.** When an oxide of potassium is decomposed, 19.55 g K and 4.00 g O are obtained. What is the empirical formula for the compound?

**55.** Analysis of a compound composed of iron and oxygen yields 174.86 g Fe and 75.14 g O. What is the empirical formula for this compound?

**56.** The pain reliever morphine contains 17.900 g C, 1.680 g H, 4.225 g O, and 1.228 g N. Determine the empirical formula.

**57.** An oxide of aluminum contains 0.545 g Al and 0.485 g O. Find the empirical formula for the oxide.

> **Practice!** For more practice calculating an empirical formula from mass data, go to **Supplemental Practice Problems** in Appendix A.

The steps in determining empirical and molecular formulas from percent composition or mass data are outlined below. As in other calculations, the route leads from mass through moles because formulas are based on the relative numbers of moles of elements in each mole of compound.

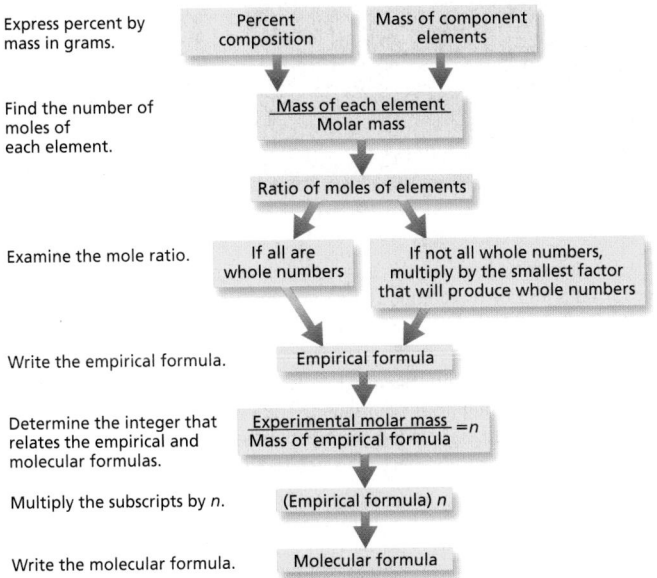

**Express percent by mass in grams.** → Percent composition / Mass of component elements

**Find the number of moles of each element.** → $\dfrac{\text{Mass of each element}}{\text{Molar mass}}$

→ Ratio of moles of elements

**Examine the mole ratio.** → If all are whole numbers / If not all whole numbers, multiply by the smallest factor that will produce whole numbers

**Write the empirical formula.** → Empirical formula

**Determine the integer that relates the empirical and molecular formulas.** → $\dfrac{\text{Experimental molar mass}}{\text{Mass of empirical formula}} = n$

**Multiply the subscripts by n.** → (Empirical formula) n

**Write the molecular formula.** → Molecular formula

## Section 11.4 Assessment

**58.** Explain how percent composition data for a compound are related to the masses of the elements in the compound.

**59.** What is the difference between an empirical formula and a molecular formula?

**60.** Explain how you can find the mole ratio in a chemical compound.

**61. Thinking Critically** An analysis for copper was performed on two pure solids. One solid was found to contain 43.0% copper; the other contained 32.0% copper. Could these solids be samples of the same copper-containing compound? Explain your answer.

**62. Inferring** Hematite ($Fe_2O_3$) and magnetite ($Fe_3O_4$) are two ores used as sources of iron. Which ore provides the greater percent of iron per kilogram?

---

### Reteach

Ask students to outline the procedure for determining an empirical formula.

### Extension

Challenge students to find the molecular formulas for sets of compounds that have the same empirical formula. A good place to look is in the Molecular Formulas Index of Organic Compounds in the *Handbook of Chemistry and Physics.* **L3**

### ✓ Assessment

**Knowledge** When heated in an atmosphere of pure nitrogen, magnesium reacts to form a nitride. Give students the following data and have them determine the formula of the compound.

Mass of empty crucible = 15.05 g

Mass of crucible + Mg ribbon = 17.45 g

Mass of crucible + product = 18.37 g

$Mg_3N_2$

### Practice PROBLEMS

Have students refer to Appendix D for complete solutions to Practice Problems.

**54.** $K_2O$
**55.** $Fe_2O_3$
**56.** $C_{17}H_{19}NO_3$
**57.** $Al_2O_3$

---

## Section 11.4 Assessment

**58.** Percent composition is numerically equal to the mass in grams of each element in a 100.0-g sample.

**59.** The empirical formula is the simplest whole-number ratio of the atoms in a compound. The molecular formula is the actual ratio of atoms in the compound.

**60.** The mole ratio is determined by calculating the moles of each element in the compound and dividing each number of moles by the smallest number of moles. It is sometimes necessary to multiply the ratio by an integer to obtain whole numbers.

**61.** No, a compound will always have the same chemical analysis.

Therefore, if two solids have different percents of copper, they are different compounds.

**62.** Hematite is 69.9% Fe, magnetite is 72.4% Fe. Magnetite contains a greater percentage of iron per kilogram than hematite

## 1 Focus

Section 11.5

# The Formula for a Hydrate

### Focus Transparency

Before presenting the lesson, display **Section Focus Transparency 42** on the overhead projector. Have students answer the accompanying questions using **Section Focus Transparency Master 42.** **L1** **ELL**

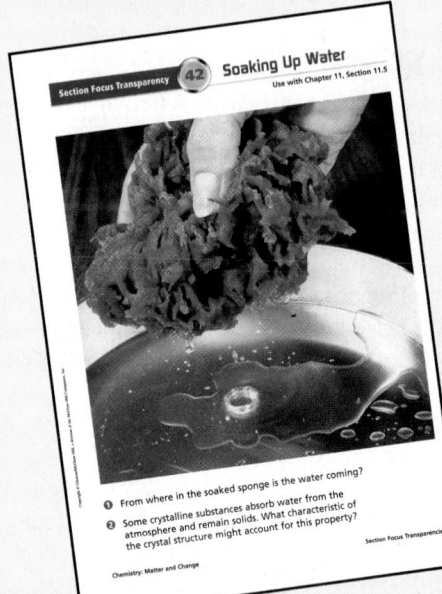

### Objectives

• **Explain** what a hydrate is and how its name reflects its composition.

• **Determine** the formula for a hydrate from laboratory data.

### Vocabulary

hydrate

#### Figure 11-12

The presence of water and various mineral impurities account for the variety of different colored opals. Further changes in color occur when opals are allowed to dry out.

Have you ever watched crystals slowly form from a water solution? Sometimes water molecules adhere to the ions as the solid forms. These water molecules become part of the crystal and are called water of hydration. Solids in which water molecules are trapped are called hydrates. A **hydrate** is a compound that has a specific number of water molecules bound to its atoms. **Figure 11-12** shows examples of a common gemstone called opal, which is composed of silicon dioxide ($SiO_2$). The unusual coloring is the result of the presence of water in the mineral.

## Naming Hydrates

In the formula for a hydrate, the number of water molecules associated with each formula unit of the compound is written following a dot: for example, $Na_2CO_3 \cdot 10H_2O$. This compound is called sodium carbonate decahydrate. In the word *decahydrate*, the prefix *deca-* means ten and the root word *hydrate* refers to water. Decahydrate means that ten molecules of water are associated with one formula unit of compound. The mass of water associated with a formula unit must be included in molar mass calculations. Hydrates are found with a variety of numbers of water molecules. **Table 11-1** lists some common hydrates.

#### Table 11-1

| Formulas for Hydrates | | | |
|---|---|---|---|
| Prefix | Molecules $H_2O$ | Formula | Name |
| Mono- | 1 | $(NH_4)_2C_2O_4 \cdot H_2O$ | Ammonium oxalate monohydrate |
| Di- | 2 | $CaCl_2 \cdot 2H_2O$ | Calcium chloride dihydrate |
| Tri- | 3 | $NaC_2H_3O_2 \cdot 3H_2O$ | Sodium acetate trihydrate |
| Tetra- | 4 | $FePO_4 \cdot 4H_2O$ | Iron(III) phosphate tetrahydrate |
| Penta- | 5 | $CuSO_4 \cdot 5H_2O$ | Copper(II) sulfate pentahydrate |
| Hexa- | 6 | $CoCl_2 \cdot 6H_2O$ | Cobalt(II) chloride hexahydrate |
| Hepta- | 7 | $MgSO_4 \cdot 7H_2O$ | Magnesium sulfate heptahydrate |
| Octa- | 8 | $Ba(OH)_2 \cdot 8H_2O$ | Barium hydroxide octahydrate |
| Deca- | 10 | $Na_2CO_3 \cdot 10H_2O$ | Sodium carbonate decahydrate |

## 2 Teach

### Visual Learning

**Figure 11-12** Some opals with orange-red coloring are referred to as "fire." The greater the water concentration in the opal, the greater the fire. Some fire opals have up to 10% water by mass. Ask students to infer why opals are often stored on damp cotton. To maintain the high water concentration. Opals often crack if heated. Ask students to infer an explanation. Heating an opal drives off the water.

**338**     **Chapter 11** The Mole

---

### DIFFERENTIATED INSTRUCTION

#### Gifted

*Kinesthetic* Ask capable students to measure and record the mass of a quantity of plaster of paris. Add water and have students mold the paste into a shape. Allow the product to dry and remass. Ask students to determine how much water was absorbed by the calcium sulfate. Have them determine the formula for the compound formed and compare their results with the formula for gypsum. Plaster of paris has one water molecule per two formula units of $CaSO_4$. Gypsum is calcium sulfate dihydrate. **L3**

## Analyzing a Hydrate

To analyze hydrates, you must drive off the water of hydration. Often this is done by heating the compound. The substance remaining after heating is anhydrous, or "without water." For example, hydrated cobalt(II) chloride is a pink solid that turns a deep blue when the water of hydration is driven off and anhydrous cobalt(II) chloride is produced. See **Figure 11-13.**

**Figure 11-13**

Hydrated $CoCl_2$, shown on the left, is pink. Its anhydrous form, on the right, is blue. The transition from pink to blue was accomplished by heating the hydrate until all water of hydration was removed.

**Formula for a hydrate** How can you determine the formula for a hydrate? You must find the number of moles of water associated with one mole of the hydrate. Suppose you have a 5.00-g sample of a hydrate of barium chloride. You know that the formula is $BaCl_2 \cdot xH_2O$. You must determine $x$, the coefficient of $H_2O$ in the hydrate formula that indicates the number of moles of water associated with one mole of $BaCl_2$. To find $x$, you would heat the sample of the hydrate to drive off the water of hydration. After heating, the dried substance, which is anhydrous $BaCl_2$, has a mass of 4.26 g. The mass of the water of hydration is the difference between the mass of the hydrate (5.00 g) and the mass of the anhydrous compound (4.26 g).

$$5.00 \text{ g } BaCl_2 \text{ hydrate} - 4.26 \text{ g anhydrous } BaCl_2 = 0.74 \text{ g } H_2O$$

You now know the masses of $BaCl_2$ and $H_2O$ in the sample. You can convert these masses to moles using the molar masses. The molar mass of $BaCl_2$ is 208.23 g/mol and the molar mass of $H_2O$ is 18.02 g/mol.

$$4.26 \text{ g } BaCl_2 \times \frac{1 \text{ mol } BaCl_2}{208.23 \text{ g } BaCl_2} = 0.0205 \text{ mol } BaCl_2$$

$$0.74 \text{ g } H_2O \times \frac{1 \text{ mol } H_2O}{18.02 \text{ g } H_2O} = 0.041 \text{ mol } H_2O$$

Now that the moles of $BaCl_2$ and $H_2O$ have been determined, you can calculate the ratio of moles of $H_2O$ to moles of $BaCl_2$ which is $x$, the coefficient that precedes $H_2O$ in the formula for the hydrate.

$$x = \frac{\text{moles } H_2O}{\text{moles } BaCl_2} = \frac{0.041 \text{ mol } H_2O}{0.0205 \text{ mol } BaCl_2} = \frac{2.0 \text{ mol } H_2O}{1.00 \text{ mol } BaCl_2} = \frac{2}{1}$$

The ratio of moles of $H_2O$ to moles of $BaCl_2$ is 2:1, so two moles of water are associated with one mole of barium chloride. The value of the coefficient $x$ is 2 and the formula for the hydrate is $BaCl_2 \cdot 2H_2O$. What is the name of the hydrate? The **CHEMLAB** at the end of this chapter will give you experience determining the formula of a hydrate.

11.5  The Formula for a Hydrate    **339**

## Quick Demo

 Clean a flask and add 5 mL of cooking oil. Make an aluminum foil lid with holes for the flask. Mass 20 kernels of popcorn and add them to the flask. Place the aluminum lid on the flask and measure and record the mass of the entire assembly. Heat the flask over a burner or on a hot plate until the popcorn is popped. The flask will be hot. Measure and record the final mass when the flask is cool. Ask students to determine the percent water in the popcorn. Results will vary. Point out that this type of experiment can be used to determine the amount of water in hydrates.

### Concept Development

Discuss how to calculate the molar mass of a hydrate. Remind students that the dot in the formula of a hydrate means *plus* water and should not be confused with the dot used in mathematics to mean multiplication. The formula $CaSO_4 \cdot 2H_2O$ indicates one mole of $CaSO_4$ plus 2 moles of water. The molar mass is 172.18 g/mol.

### In-Text Question

**Page 339** What is the name of the hydrate? barium chloride dihydrate

### CHEMLAB

ChemLab 11, located at the end of the chapter, can be used at this point in the lesson.

### Resource Manager

**Study Guide for Content Mastery,**
  p. 66 L2
**Solving Problems: A Chemistry**
  **Handbook,** Section 11.5 L2
**Section Focus Transparency 42 and**
  **Master** L1 ELL

### CHEMISTRY JOURNAL

**Hydrates**

Have students pick one of the hydrates in Table 11-1 for investigation. Have them determine the molar mass and the percent composition in terms of the percent anhydrous compound and the percent water. Students can record their calculations in their journals. L2

**National Science Content Standards**

**Pages 338–339**
UCP.1, UCP.3; B.2

## Applying Chemistry

Gypsum, calcium sulfate dihydrate ($CaSO_4 \cdot 2H_2O$), is an abundant compound that has been used by humans since early Egyptian times. Plaster of paris is gypsum that has been heated and ground into a fine powder. When water is added, the plaster can be molded into a desired shape and then allowed to harden. Gypsum is the only natural substance that, when heated, can be restored to its original rocklike state by the addition of water alone. Ask students why gypsum is heated. to drive out the water What happens when water is added to the plaster of paris? It hydrates and turns back into gypsum. Gypsum is also used in cement production and as a component of wallboard. Anhydrous calcium sulfate is commonly called anhydrite, meaning "without water." Although large deposits of anhydrite exist, they are of little economic value. However, experiments are ongoing to convert these deposits to valuable gypsum. Ask students what task the scientists are trying to do. add water to the compound

### Practice PROBLEMS

Have students refer to Appendix D for complete solutions to Practice Problems.

**63.** $MgSO_4 \cdot 7H_2O$ (magnesium sulfate heptahydrate)

**64.** $CoCl_2 \cdot 2H_2O$ (cobalt(II) chloride dihydrate)

### Figure Caption Question

**Example Problem 11-14** How could you convert anhydrous copper sulfate to its blue hydrated form?
Add water.

### National Science Content Standards
**Pages 340–341**
UCP.1, UCP.3; B.2; E.2

Heating blue anhydrous copper sulfate drives off the water of hydration and converts it to white anhydrous copper sulfate. How could you convert anhydrous copper sulfate to its blue hydrated form?

**Practice!** For more practice calculating the formula for a hydrate, go to **Supplemental Practice Problems in Appendix A.**

## EXAMPLE PROBLEM 11-14

### Determining the Formula for a Hydrate

A mass of 2.50 g of blue, hydrated copper sulfate ($CuSO_4 \cdot xH_2O$) is placed in a crucible and heated. After heating, 1.59 g white anhydrous copper sulfate ($CuSO_4$) remains. What is the formula for the hydrate? Name the hydrate.

### 1. Analyze the Problem

You are given a mass of hydrated copper sulfate. The mass after heating is the mass of the anhydrous compound. You know the formula for the compound except for $x$, the number of moles of water of hydration.

**Known**

mass of hydrated compound = 2.50 g $CuSO_4 \cdot xH_2O$
mass of anhydrous compound = 1.59 g $CuSO_4$
molar mass = 18.02 g/mol $H_2O$
molar mass = 159.6 g/mol $CuSO_4$

**Unknown**

formula for hydrate = ?
name of hydrate = ?

### 2. Solve for the Unknown

Subtract the mass of the anhydrous copper sulfate from the mass of the hydrated copper sulfate to determine the mass of water lost.

| | |
|---|---|
| mass of hydrated copper sulfate | 2.50 g |
| mass of anhydrous copper sulfate | −1.59 g |
| mass of water lost | 0.91 g |

Calculate the number of moles of $H_2O$ and anhydrous $CuSO_4$ using the conversion factor that relates moles and mass based on the molar mass.

$$1.59 \text{ g } CuSO_4 \times \frac{1 \text{ mol } CuSO_4}{159.6 \text{ g } CuSO_4} = 0.00996 \text{ mol } CuSO_4$$

$$0.91 \text{ g } H_2O \times \frac{1 \text{ mol } H_2O}{18.02 \text{ g } H_2O} = 0.050 \text{ mol } H_2O$$

Determine the value of $x$.

$$x = \frac{\text{moles } H_2O}{\text{moles } CuSO_4}$$

$$x = \frac{0.050 \text{ mol } H_2O}{0.00996 \text{ mol } CuSO_4} = \frac{5.0 \text{ mol } H_2O}{1.00 \text{ mol } CuSO_4} = 5$$

The ratio of $H_2O$ to $CuSO_4$ is 5 : 1, so the formula for the hydrate is $CuSO_4 \cdot 5H_2O$, copper(II) sulfate pentahydrate.

### 3. Evaluate the Answer

Copper(II) sulfate pentahydrate is listed as a hydrate in **Table 11-1**.

## PRACTICE PROBLEMS

**63.** A hydrate is found to have the following percent composition: 48.8% $MgSO_4$ and 51.2% $H_2O$. What is the formula and name for this hydrate?

**64.** **Figure 11-13** shows a common hydrate of cobalt(II) chloride. If 11.75 g of this hydrate is heated, 9.25 g of anhydrous cobalt chloride remains. What is the formula and name for this hydrate?

**Uses of hydrates** The ability of the anhydrous form of a hydrate to absorb water into its crystal structure has some important applications. Anhydrous calcium chloride and calcium sulfate are used as desiccants or drying agents in the laboratory because they can absorb water from the air or from their liquid surroundings. For example, calcium sulfate is often added to solvents such as ethanol and ethyl ether to keep them free of water. Anhydrous calcium chloride is placed in the bottom of tightly sealed containers called desiccators. The calcium chloride absorbs moisture from the air inside the desiccator, thus creating a dry atmosphere in which other substances can be placed to be kept dry. Calcium chloride forms a monohydrate, a dihydrate, and a hexahydrate. Electronic and optical equipment, particularly that transported overseas by ship, is packaged with packets of desiccants that absorb water from the air and prevent moisture from interfering with sensitive circuitry. Some of these uses are illustrated in **Figure 11-14**.

Some hydrates, sodium sulfate decahydrate ($Na_2SO_4 \cdot 10H_2O$) for example, are used to store solar energy. When the Sun's energy heats the hydrate to a temperature greater than 32°C, the single formula unit of $Na_2SO_4$ in the hydrate dissolves in the 10 moles of water of hydration. In the process, energy is absorbed by the hydrate. This solar energy, stored in the solution of the hydrate, is released when the temperature decreases and the hydrate crystallizes again.

**Figure 11-14**

Calcium sulfate is not soluble in ethanol so it remains on the bottom of the ethanol bottle and absorbs any water dissolved in the ethanol. Calcium chloride, in the bottom of the desiccator, keeps the air inside the desiccator dry. Porous packets of desiccants can be packaged with materials that need to be kept moisture free.

## Section 11.5 Assessment

**65.** What is a hydrate? What does its name indicate about its composition?

**66.** Describe the experimental procedure for determining the formula for a hydrate. Explain the reason for each step.

**67.** Name the compound having the formula $SrCl_2 \cdot 6H_2O$.

**68. Thinking Critically** Explain how the hydrate illustrated in **Figure 11-13** might be used as a means of roughly determining the probability of rain.

**69. Sequencing** Arrange these hydrates in order of increasing percent water content: $MgSO_4 \cdot 7H_2O$, $Ba(OH)_2 \cdot 8H_2O$, $CoCl_2 \cdot 6H_2O$.

chemistrymc.com/self_check_quiz

11.5 The Formula for a Hydrate    **341**

### Reteach
Soak two pieces of filter paper in a strong solution of cobalt chloride and allow the paper to dry. **CAUTION:** *Wear gloves. $CoCl_2$ is moderately toxic if ingested.* Place one piece of the dried paper in a humid environment. It will turn pink. Place another piece in a beaker and heat it for a few minutes. It will turn blue. Ask students to explain their observations. The cobalt chloride forms a pink hydrate when it absorbs water. When heated, the hydrate loses water and turns blue.

### Extension
Have students solve this problem. Equal molar amounts of barium hydroxide and a hydrate of barium hydroxide have these masses: 21.4 g barium hydroxide and 39.4 g barium hydroxide hydrate. What is the formula for the hydrate? $Ba(OH)_2 \cdot 8H_2O$

### ✔ Assessment
**Performance** Give each student a formula for a hydrate from Table 11-1 and have them determine the percent ionic compound and the percent water in the compound. Have each student write a problem providing the calculated data and asking for the formula for the hydrate. Students can exchange problems. Use the Performance Task Assessment List for Using Math in Science in **PASC,** p. 29.

## Section 11.5 Assessment

**65.** A hydrate is a compound that has a specific number of water molecules associated with it. The name indicates the name of the compound and the number of water molecules associated with each formula unit of compound.

**66.** Mass an empty crucible. Add some hydrate and remass. Heat the crucible to drive out the water. Cool and remass. Determine the moles of the anhydrous compound. Subtract the mass of the crucible after heating from the mass of the crucible with the hydrate. The difference is the mass of the water lost. Determine the moles of water. Determine the simplest whole-number ratio of moles of water to moles of anhydrous compound, which will yield the formula for the hydrate.

**67.** strontium chloride hexahydrate
**68.** The hydrate is pink in moist air.
**69.** $CoCl_2 \cdot 6H_2O$; $Ba(OH)_2 \cdot 8H_2O$; $MgSO_4 \cdot 7H_2O$

**341**

## Preparation 📦

### Time Allotment
One laboratory period

### Process Skills
Acquiring and analyzing information, interpreting data, hypothesizing, using numbers

### Safety Precautions
- Advise students to use Bunsen burners with care.
- Remind them that a crucible can be hot even though it does not look hot.
- Epsom salts is a mild skin irritant.

### Disposal
Anhydrous Epsom salts can be put into the trash. The Epsom salts can also be reclaimed and used again for this experiment by allowing the crystals to hydrate with water vapor from the air.

### Alternative Materials
- A hot plate with an evaporating dish can be used in place of the Bunsen burner and crucible, but this method does not heat the Epsom salts hot enough to remove all the water. The experimental result using this method is likely to be $MgSO_4 \cdot 3H_2O$.
- Other hydrates, such as $BaCl_2 \cdot 2H_2O$, $Na_2CO_3 \cdot H_2O$, and $CuSO_4 \cdot 5H_2O$, can be used. Epsom salts does not decompose with heating and produce fumes.

## Pre-Lab

**2.** See data table on the opposite page.

**3.** To obtain the mass of water, subtract the mass of the crucible, cover, and anhydrous $MgSO_4$ from the mass of the crucible, cover, and hydrated $MgSO_4$. To obtain the mass of anhydrous $MgSO_4$, subtract the mass of the crucible and cover from the mass of the crucible, cover, and anhydrous $MgSO_4$.

**4.** Divide by the molar mass.

**5.** Calculate the ratio of moles of water to moles of anhydrous $MgSO_4$.

---

# Hydrated Crystals

**H**ydrates are compounds that incorporate water molecules in their crystalline structures. The ratio of moles of water to one mole of the compound is a small whole number. For example, in the hydrated compound copper(II) sulfate pentahydrate ($CuSO_4 \cdot 5H_2O$), the ratio is 5:1. The ratio of moles of water to one mole of a hydrate can be determined experimentally by heating the hydrate to remove water.

### Problem
How can you determine the moles of water in a mole of a hydrated compound?

### Objectives
- **Heat** a known mass of hydrated compound until the water is removed.
- **Calculate** the formula for a hydrate using the mass of the hydrated compound and the mass of the anhydrous compound.

### Materials
Bunsen burner
ring stand and ring
crucible and lid
clay triangle
crucible tongs
balance
Epsom salts (hydrated $MgSO_4$)
spatula
spark lighter or matches

### Safety Precautions
- Always wear safety goggles and a lab apron.
- Hot objects will not appear to be hot.
- Use the Bunsen burner carefully.
- Turn off the Bunsen burner when not in use.

### Pre-Lab

1. Read the entire **CHEMLAB**.
2. Prepare all written materials that you will take into the laboratory. Be sure to include safety precautions, procedure notes, and a data table.
3. Explain how you will obtain the mass of water and the mass of anhydrous $MgSO_4$ contained in the hydrate.
4. How will you convert the masses of anhydrous $MgSO_4$ and water to moles?
5. How can you obtain the formula for the hydrate from the moles of anhydrous $MgSO_4$ and the moles of water?

## Procedure
- Show students the proper way to heat the crucible beginning with a low flame and gradually increasing the intensity.
- Although Epsom salts does not require the bottom of the crucible to get red hot, heating should be long enough and strong enough to completely remove the water of hydration.
- Students will be able to see water boiling out of the Epsom salts. They will know the water is removed when the boiling stops.

### Resource Manager

**ChemLab and MiniLab Worksheets,**
pp. 42–44 **L2**

### Mass Data and Observations of Epsom Salts

| | |
|---|---|
| Observations of hydrated $MgSO_4$ | |
| Mass of crucible and lid | |
| Mass of crucible, lid, and hydrated $MgSO_4$ | |
| Mass of hydrated $MgSO_4$ | |
| Mass of crucible, lid, and anhydrous $MgSO_4$ | |
| Mass of anhydrous $MgSO_4$ | |
| Mass of water in hydrated $MgSO_4$ | |
| Moles of anhydrous $MgSO_4$ | |
| Moles of water in hydrated $MgSO_4$ | |
| Observation of anhydrous $MgSO_4$ | |

## Procedure

1. Measure to the nearest 0.01 g the mass of a clean, dry crucible with a lid. Record the mass.

2. Add about 3 g hydrated $MgSO_4$ to the crucible. Measure the mass of the crucible, lid, and hydrate to the nearest 0.01 g and record the mass.

3. Record your observations of the hydrate.

4. Place the triangle on the ring of the ring stand. Carefully place the crucible in the triangle as shown in the photo.

5. Place the crucible lid on the crucible slightly cocked to help prevent spattering and allow vapor to escape. Begin heating with a low flame, then gradually progress to a stronger flame. Heat for about 10 minutes.

6. When heating is complete, remove the crucible using tongs. Place the lid on the crucible and allow the crucible and contents to cool.

7. Measure the mass of the crucible, lid, and $MgSO_4$ and record the mass in the data table.

8. Observe the anhydrous $MgSO_4$ and record your observations.

## Cleanup and Disposal

1. Discard the anhydrous $MgSO_4$ in a trash container or as directed by your teacher.

2. Return all lab equipment to its proper place and clean your lab station.

3. Wash your hands thoroughly when all lab work and cleanup are complete.

## Analyze and Conclude

1. **Using Numbers** Use your experimental data to calculate the formula for hydrated $MgSO_4$.

2. **Observing and Inferring** How did your observations of the hydrated $MgSO_4$ crystals compare with those of the anhydrous $MgSO_4$ crystals?

3. **Drawing Conclusions** Why might the method used in this experiment not be suitable for determining the water of hydration for all hydrates?

4. **Error Analysis** What is the percent error of your calculation of the water of hydration for $MgSO_4$ if the formula for the hydrate is $MgSO_4 \cdot 7H_2O$? What changes would you make in the procedure to reduce error?

5. **Predicting** What might you observe if the anhydrous crystals were left uncovered overnight?

## Real-World Chemistry

1. Packets of the anhydrous form of a hydrate are sometimes used to keep cellars from being damp. Is there a limit to how long a packet could be used?

2. Gypsum ($CaSO_4 \cdot 2H_2O$) is a mineral used for making wallboard for construction. The mineral is stripped of three-quarters of its water of hydration in a process called calcinning. Then, after mixing with water, it hardens to a white substance called plaster of paris. Infer what happens as calcinned gypsum becomes plaster of paris.

## Expected Results
See the data table below.

## Analyze and Conclude

1. Calculation of mole ratio:
Moles of $MgSO_4 = 1.47$ g $\times$ $\frac{1 \text{ mol}}{120.4 \text{ g}} = 0.0122$ mol $MgSO_4$
Moles of water $= 1.53$ g $\times$ $\frac{1 \text{ mol}}{18.02 \text{ g}} = 0.0849$ mol water
Mole ratio $= \frac{0.0849 \text{ mol } H_2O}{0.0122 \text{ mol } MgSO_4}$
$= 6.96$ or approximately 7
The formula is $MgSO_4 \cdot 7H_2O$.

2. The hydrated $MgSO_4$ is shiny and translucent. The anhydrous $MgSO_4$ is opaque and bright white.

3. Some hydrates may decompose when heated.

4. Answers will vary. $\frac{7.00 - 6.96}{7.00} \times 100 = 0.57\%$ error Students may suggest longer heating and guarding against loss of salt by spattering.

5. The anhydrous $MgSO_4$ may absorb water.

## Real-World Chemistry

1. Yes, eventually, the anhydrous compound will absorb as much water as is possible and can no longer act as a desiccant.

2. The addition of water causes the anhydrous compound to become hydrated.

### ✔ Assessment

**Performance** Students can allow anhydrous Epsom salts to remain exposed to air overnight. They then can repeat the experiment to determine how much water was reabsorbed by the Epsom salts. Use the Performance Task Assessment List for Carrying Out a Strategy and Collecting Data in **PASC,** p. 25.

### National Science Content Standards
**Pages 342–343**
UCP.1, UCP.3; A.1; B.2, B.6; E.2

| | |
|---|---|
| Observation of hydrated $MgSO_4$ | Shiny, translucent crystals |
| Mass of crucible and lid | 11.36 g |
| Mass of crucible, lid, and hydrated $MgSO_4$ | 14.36 g |
| Mass of hydrated $MgSO_4$ | 3.00 g |
| Mass of crucible, lid, and anhydrous $MgSO_4$ | 12.83 g |
| Mass of anhydrous $MgSO_4$ | 1.47 g |
| Mass of water in hydrated $MgSO_4$ | 1.53 g |
| Moles of anhydrous $MgSO_4$ | 0.0122 mol |
| Moles of water in hydrated $MgSO_4$ | 0.0849 mol |
| Observation of anhydrous $MgSO_4$ | Bright white, opaque, powdery |

# CHEMISTRY and
## Technology

## Purpose

Students will learn why and how chemists synthesize compounds in the laboratory.

## Background

The process of combinatorial chemistry can be traced to 1963 when Bruce Merrifield won a Nobel prize in chemistry for synthesizing specific compounds. The approach did not become widespread until the mid-1990s because advanced screening techniques were required to make the process useful. In the near future, the process may take place on a silicon chip and the screening will be achieved with a computer.

## Teaching Strategies

- Give students identical sets of 10 colored, interlocking blocks and have them arrange the blocks in as many ways as possible.
- As a class, have students use the blocks to create 10 structures that each differ by only one block. Discuss how tedious it is to build the same basic structure over and over again. Ask how robots could help this process.
- As chemical companies synthesize molecule after molecule, they need to have records of what they have synthesized. Have students discuss the challenges involved in the management of such huge amounts of information and how computers might play a role in this task.

## Investigating the Technology

1. In combinatorial chemistry, many chemical reactions occur at the same time. Because the goal is to produce variations of the same basic structure, chemists must keep the variables almost constant for every reaction.
2. Students may learn some of

## Making Medicines

In 1859, a chemist named Herman Kolbe identified the chemical structure of the compound that made willow bark an effective herbal medicine. Unfortunately, many people who took the medicine suffered upset stomachs from it. One such person was the father of a chemist named Felix Hoffman. To help his father, Hoffman changed the compound in such a way that it eased his father's arthritis without irritating his stomach. The new compound was acetylsalicylic acid, now known as aspirin.

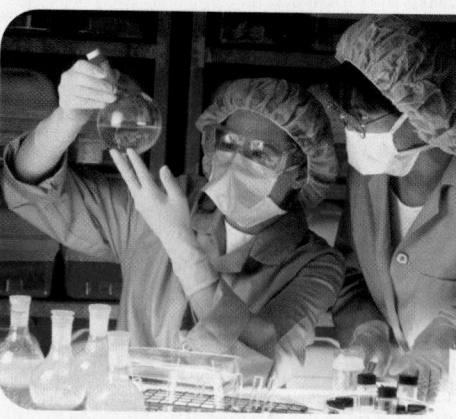

## Chemical Synthesis

Like aspirin, many medicines are compounds synthesized in the laboratory. During chemical synthesis, chemists combine simple compounds to form more complex compounds. Often, several chemical reactions must occur in a particular sequence to produce the desired product. The process is like putting building blocks together one at a time as the chemist carries out several chemical reactions in a particular sequence. The final product is then tested, or screened, to see if it has the desired effect. In the case of a medicine, the compound must be designed to interact with a molecule in the body known as the target molecule. The compound must have a particular shape and characteristics to be effective against the target molecule. If chemists know the shape and chemical properties of the target molecule, they try to design a compound to fit it exactly. More often, chemists must try as many compounds as possible until they find one that works.

## Combinatorial Chemistry

In the past, finding a potentially successful medicine would take many years. Now, chemists may be able to speed up the process by turning to the techniques of combinatorial chemistry. In combinatorial chemistry, chemists use robots to put chemical building blocks together in every possible combination at the same time. Instead of chemists making one compound per week, combinatorial chemistry enables chemists to produce as many as 100 compounds a day and up to tens of thousands of compounds a year!

## Looking to the Future

The goal of combinatorial chemistry is not to produce as many compounds as possible but to try to identify a basic structure that is effective and then develop variations of that structure. It's too soon to tell if combinatorial chemistry will revolutionize the way medicines are developed because the process has been used only within the last decade. However, some promising leads have been generated in months rather than years, and compounds produced from combinatorial chemistry are currently being tested.

### Investigating the Technology

1. **Controlling Variables** Why would it be important for chemists to control the variables of the reactions involved in combinatorial chemistry?

2. **Using Resources** Research the two main approaches to combinatorial chemistry. Find out how they are alike and how they are different.

Visit the Chemistry Web site at **chemistrymc.com** to find links to more information about combinatorial chemistry.

the following. There are two basic approaches to combinatorial chemistry. In the split synthesis method, chemists create compounds on tiny plastic beads that are divided among different containers. Chemists add a different chemical building block to the beads in each container. The beads are then mixed, split again, and reacted with different substances. The process is repeated a certain number of times. This method can result in small amounts of up to one million compounds. In the parallel synthesis method, a series of individual reactions are completed in separate vessels. Laboratory robots are programmed to add specific substances to each vessel. This method generally takes longer than the split synthesis method and results in larger amounts of fewer compounds.

## Summary

### 11.1 Measuring Matter

- The mole is a unit used to count particles indirectly. One mole is the amount of a pure substance that contains $6.02 \times 10^{23}$ representative particles.

- One mole of carbon-12 atoms contains 12 grams of the isotope carbon-12.

### 11.2 Mass and the Mole

- The molar mass of an element is the numerical equivalent of the atomic mass (amu) in grams.

- The molar mass of any substance is the mass in grams of Avogadro's number of representative particles of the substance.

- Molar mass is used to convert from moles of an element to mass, and the inverse of molar mass is used to convert from mass of an element to moles.

### 11.3 Moles of Compounds

- Subscripts in a chemical formula indicate how many moles of each element are in one mole of the compound.

- The molar mass of a compound is the sum of the masses of all the moles of elements present in the compound.

### 11.4 Empirical and Molecular Formulas

- The percent composition of a known compound can be calculated by dividing the mass of each element in one mole by the mass of a mole of the compound and multiplying by 100.

- The subscripts in an empirical formula are in a ratio of the smallest whole numbers of moles of the elements in the compound.

- The molecular formula for a compound can be determined by finding the integer by which the mass of the empirical formula differs from the molar mass of the compound.

### 11.5 The Formula for a Hydrate

- The formula for a hydrate consists of the formula for the ionic compound and the number of water molecules associated with one formula unit.

- The name of a hydrate consists of the compound name followed by the word *hydrate* with a prefix indicating the number of water molecules associated with one mole of compound.

- Anhydrous compounds are formed when hydrates are heated and the water of hydration is driven off.

## Using Vocabulary

To reinforce chapter vocabulary, have students write a sentence using each term. **L2** **ELL**

## Review Strategies

- Have students define and give an example of each type of mole conversion. **L2**

- Have students summarize how to calculate the percent composition of a compound, how to determine the empirical and molecular formulas of a compound, and how to determine the formula of a hydrate. **L2**

- Problems from Appendix A or the **Supplemental Problems** booklet can be used for review. **L2**

For additional help with vocabulary, have students access the Vocabulary PuzzleMaker online.

chemistrymc.com/
vocabulary_puzzlemaker

## Key Equations and Relationships

- number of representative particles = number of moles $\times \dfrac{6.02 \times 10^{23} \text{ representative particles}}{1 \text{ mole}}$ (p. 311)

- number of moles = number of representative particles $\times \dfrac{1 \text{ mole}}{6.02 \times 10^{23} \text{ representative particles}}$ (p. 311)

- mass = number of moles $\times \dfrac{\text{number of grams}}{1 \text{ mole}}$ (p. 315)

- number of moles = mass $\times \dfrac{1 \text{ mole}}{\text{number of grams}}$ (p. 316 Example Problem)

- percent by mass = $\dfrac{\text{mass of element}}{\text{mass of compound}} \times 100$ (p. 328)

- molecular formula = (empirical formula)$n$ (p. 334)

## Vocabulary

- Avogadro's number (p. 310)
- empirical formula (p. 331)
- hydrate (p. 338)
- molar mass (p. 313)
- mole (p. 310)
- molecular formula (p. 333)
- percent composition (p. 328)

chemistrymc.com/vocabulary_puzzlemaker

Study Guide **345**

## EXAMVIEW® PRO

### Use ExamView® Pro Testmaker CD-ROM to:

- Create **multiple versions** of tests.
- Create **modified** tests with one mouse click for struggling students.
- **Edit** existing questions and add your own questions.
- **Build** tests based on national curriculum standards.

**National Science Content Standards**

Pages 344–345
UCP.1, UCP.3; B.2, B.3, B.6; E.1; F.5, F.6

## Concept Mapping

**70.**

1. $\dfrac{1\ mol}{number\ of\ grams}$

2. $\dfrac{6.02 \times 10^{23}\ representative\ particles}{1\ mol}$

3. $\dfrac{1\ mol}{6.02 \times 10^{23}\ representative\ particles}$

4. $\dfrac{number\ of\ grams}{1\ mol}$

## Mastering Concepts

**71.** The mole allows a chemist to accurately measure the number of atoms, molecules, or formula units in a substance.

**72.** A mole, like a dozen, contains a specific number of items.

**73.** $6.02 \times 10^{23}$

**74.** Molar mass is the mass in grams of one mole of any element or compound.

**75.** They both contain the same number of atoms because a mole of anything contains $6.02 \times 10^{23}$ representative particles.

**76.** Molar mass is the mass in grams of one mole of any pure substance. Avogadro's number is the number of representative particles in one mole. The mass of $6.02 \times 10^{23}$ representative particles of a substance is the molar mass of the substance.

**77.** The molar mass of Au is 197.0 g/mol; the molar mass of Ag is 107.9 g/mol. Thus, a mole of Au has a greater mass.

**78.** Atomic mass (amu) is the mass of an individual particle (atom, molecule). Molar mass (grams) is the mass of a mole of particles.

**79.** the mass of one atom of the element

---

## Chemistry Online

Go to the Chemistry Web site at chemistrymc.com *for additional Chapter 11 Assessment.*

## Concept Mapping

**70.** Complete this concept map by placing in each box the conversion factor needed to convert from each measure of matter to the next.

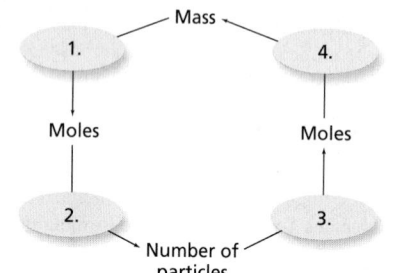

## Mastering Concepts

**71.** Why is the mole an important unit to chemists? (11.1)

**72.** How is a mole similar to a dozen? (11.1)

**73.** What is the numerical value of Avogadro's number? (11.1)

**74.** What is molar mass? (11.2)

**75.** Which contains more atoms, a mole of silver atoms or a mole of gold atoms? Explain your answer. (11.2)

**76.** Discuss the relationships that exist between the mole, molar mass, and Avogadro's number. (11.2)

**77.** Which has a greater mass, a mole of silver atoms or a mole of gold atoms? Explain your answer. (11.2)

**78.** Explain the difference between atomic mass (amu) and molar mass (gram). (11.2)

**79.** If you divide the molar mass of an element by Avogadro's number, what is the meaning of the quotient? (11.2)

**80.** List three conversion factors used in molar conversions. (11.3)

**81.** What information is provided by the formula for potassium chromate ($K_2CrO_4$)? (11.3)

---

**82.** Which of the following molecules contains the most moles of carbon atoms per mole of the compound: ascorbic acid ($C_6H_8O_6$), glycerin ($C_3H_8O_3$), or vanillin ($C_8H_8O_3$)? Explain. (11.3)

**83.** Explain what is meant by percent composition. (11.4)

**84.** What is the difference between an empirical formula and a molecular formula? Use an example to illustrate your answer. (11.4)

**85.** Do all pure samples of a given compound have the same percent composition? Explain. (11.4)

**86.** What information must a chemist obtain in order to determine the empirical formula of an unknown compound? (11.4)

**87.** What is a hydrated compound? Use an example to illustrate your answer. (11.5)

**88.** Explain how hydrates are named. (11.5)

## Mastering Problems
### Mole-Particle Conversions (11.1)

**89.** Determine the number of representative particles in each of the following.
- **a.** 0.250 mol silver
- **b.** $8.56 \times 10^{-3}$ mol sodium chloride
- **c.** 35.3 mol carbon dioxide
- **d.** 0.425 mol nitrogen ($N_2$)

**90.** Determine the number of moles in each of the following.
- **a.** $3.25 \times 10^{20}$ atoms lead
- **b.** $4.96 \times 10^{24}$ molecules glucose
- **c.** $1.56 \times 10^{23}$ formula units sodium hydroxide
- **d.** $1.25 \times 10^{25}$ copper(II) ions

**91.** Make the following conversions.
- **a.** $1.51 \times 10^{15}$ atoms Si to mol Si
- **b.** $4.25 \times 10^{-2}$ mol $H_2SO_4$ to molecules $H_2SO_4$
- **c.** $8.95 \times 10^{25}$ molecules $CCl_4$ to mol $CCl_4$
- **d.** 5.90 mol Ca to atoms Ca

**92.** How many molecules are contained in each of the following?
- **a.** 1.35 mol carbon disulfide ($CS_2$)
- **b.** 0.254 mol diarsenic trioxide ($As_2O_3$)
- **c.** 1.25 mol water
- **d.** 150.0 mol HCl

**93.** How many moles contain each of the following?
- **a.** $1.25 \times 10^{15}$ molecules carbon dioxide
- **b.** $3.59 \times 10^{21}$ formula units sodium nitrate
- **c.** $2.89 \times 10^{27}$ formula units calcium carbonate

chemistrymc.com/chapter_test

**80.**

$\dfrac{1\ mol}{number\ of\ grams}$ ,

$\dfrac{6.02 \times 10^{23}\ representative\ particles}{1\ mol}$ ,

$\dfrac{1\ mol}{6.02 \times 10^{23}\ representative\ particles}$ ,

$\dfrac{number\ of\ grams}{1\ mol}$

## Resource Manager

**Chapter Assessment,** pp. 61–66
**Supplemental Problems,** Ch. 11
**ExamView® Pro CD-ROM**
**MindJogger Videoquizzes**
**Solutions Manual,** Ch. 11
**Chemistry Interactive CD-ROM,**
 Ch. 11 quiz

**94.** A bracelet containing 0.200 mol of metal atoms is 75% gold. How many particles of gold atoms are in the bracelet?

**95.** A solution containing 0.250 mol $Cu^{2+}$ ions is added to another solution containing 0.130 mol $Ca^{2+}$ ions. What is the total number of metal ions in the combined solution?

**96.** If a snowflake contains $1.9 \times 10^{18}$ molecules of water, how many moles of water does it contain?

**97.** If you could count two atoms every second, how long would it take you to count a mole of atoms? Assume that you counted continually 24 hours every day. How does the time you calculated compare with the age of Earth, which is estimated to be $4.5 \times 10^9$ years old?

## Mole-Mass Conversions (11.2)

**98.** Calculate the mass of the following.

   **a.** 5.22 mol He    **c.** 2.22 mol Ti
   **b.** 0.0455 mol Ni   **d.** 0.00566 mol Ge

**99.** Make the following conversions.

   **a.** 3.50 mol Li to g Li
   **b.** 7.65 g Co to mol Co
   **c.** 5.62 g Kr to mol Kr
   **d.** 0.0550 mol As to g As

**100.** Determine the mass in grams of the following.

   **a.** $1.33 \times 10^{22}$ mol Sb
   **b.** $4.75 \times 10^{14}$ mol Pt
   **c.** $1.22 \times 10^{23}$ mol Ag
   **d.** $9.85 \times 10^{24}$ mol Cr

## Particle-Mass Conversions (11.2)

**101.** Convert the following to mass in grams.

   **a.** $4.22 \times 10^{15}$ atoms U
   **b.** $8.65 \times 10^{25}$ atoms H
   **c.** $1.25 \times 10^{22}$ atoms O
   **d.** $4.44 \times 10^{23}$ atoms Pb

**102.** A sensitive balance can detect masses of $1 \times 10^{-8}$ g. How many atoms of silver would be in a sample having this mass?

**103.** Calculate the number of atoms in each of the following.

   **a.** 25.8 g Hg    **c.** 150 g Ar
   **b.** 0.0340 g Zn   **d.** 0.124 g Mg

**104.** Which has more atoms, 10.0 g of carbon or 10.0 g of calcium? How many atoms does each have?

**105.** Which has more atoms, 10.0 moles of carbon or 10.0 moles of calcium? How many does each have?

**106.** A mixture contains 0.250 mol Fe and 1.20 g C. What is the total number of atoms in the mixture?

## Chemical Formulas (11.3)

**107.** In the formula for sodium phosphate ($Na_3PO_4$) how many moles of sodium are represented? How many moles of phosphorus? How many moles of oxygen?

**108.** How many moles of oxygen atoms are contained in the following?

   **a.** 2.50 mol $KMnO_4$
   **b.** 45.9 mol $CO_2$
   **c.** $1.25 \times 10^{-2}$ mol $CuSO_4 \cdot 5H_2O$

**109.** The graph shows the numbers of atoms of each element in a compound. What is its formula? What is its molar mass?

**The Composition of a Compound**

**110.** How many carbon tetrachloride molecules are in 3.00 mol carbon tetrachloride ($CCl_4$)? How many carbon atoms? How many chlorine atoms? How many total atoms?

## Molar Mass (11.3)

**111.** Determine the molar mass of each of the following.

   **a.** nitric acid ($HNO_3$)
   **b.** ammonium nitrate ($NH_4NO_3$)
   **c.** zinc oxide (ZnO)
   **d.** cobalt chloride ($CoCl_2$)

**112.** Calculate the molar mass of each of the following.

   **a.** ascorbic acid ($C_6H_8O_6$)
   **b.** sulfuric acid ($H_2SO_4$)
   **c.** silver nitrate ($AgNO_3$)
   **d.** saccharin ($C_7H_5NO_3S$)

**113.** Determine the molar mass of allyl sulfide, the compound responsible for the smell of garlic. The chemical formula of allyl sulfide is ($C_3H_5$)$_2$S.

**81.** One mole of $K_2CrO_4$ contains two moles of $K^+$ ions and one mole of $CrO_4^{2-}$ ions.

**82.** The formula for vanillin ($C_8H_8O_3$) shows there are eight carbon atoms per molecule, more than ascorbic acid or glycerin.

**83.** Percent composition is the percent by mass of each element in a compound.

**84.** An empirical formula is the smallest whole-number ratio of elements that make up a compound (CH). A molecular formula specifies the actual number of atoms of each element in one molecule of the substance ($C_6H_6$).

**85.** Yes, for every pure substance, the percent by mass of each element is the same regardless of the size of the sample.

**86.** the percent composition of the compound

**87.** A hydrated compound is a compound that has a specific number of water molecules associated with its atoms, for example, $Na_2CO_3 \cdot 10H_2O$ and $CuSO_4 \cdot 5H_2O$.

**88.** First, name the compound. Then, add a prefix (mono- di- tri-) that indicates how many water molecules are associated with one mole of compound.

## Mastering Problems

Complete solutions to Chapter Assessment problems can be found in the **Solutions Manual**.

## Mole-Particle Conversions (11.1)

### Level 1

**89. a.** $1.51 \times 10^{23}$ atoms Ag
   **b.** $5.15 \times 10^{21}$ formula units NaCl
   **c.** $2.13 \times 10^{25}$ molecules $CO_2$
   **d.** $2.56 \times 10^{23}$ molecules $N_2$

**90. a.** $5.39 \times 10^{-4}$ mol Pb
   **b.** 8.24 mol of glucose
   **c.** $2.59 \times 10^{-1}$ mol NaOH
   **d.** $2.08 \times 10^1$ mol $Cu^{2+}$ ions

**91. a.** $2.51 \times 10^{-9}$ mol Si
   **b.** $2.56 \times 10^{22}$ molecules $H_2SO_4$
   **c.** $1.49 \times 10^2$ mol $CCl_4$
   **d.** $3.55 \times 10^{24}$ atoms Ca

**92. a.** $8.13 \times 10^{23}$ molecules $CS_2$
   **b.** $1.53 \times 10^{23}$ molecules $As_2O_3$
   **c.** $7.53 \times 10^{23}$ molecules $H_2O$
   **d.** $9.030 \times 10^{25}$ molecules HCl

**93. a.** $2.08 \times 10^{-9}$ mol $CO_2$
   **b.** $5.96 \times 10^{-3}$ mol $NaNO_3$
   **c.** $4.80 \times 10^3$ mol $CaCO_3$

## Level 2
**94.** $9.03 \times 10^{22}$ atoms Au
**95.** $2.29 \times 10^{23}$ $Cu^{2+}$ and $Ca^{2+}$ ions
**96.** $3.2 \times 10^{-6}$ mol $H_2O$
**97.** $9.5 \times 10^{15}$ yr; about 2 million times longer

## Mole-Mass Conversions (11.2)
### Level 1
**98. a.** 20.9 g He
   **b.** 2.67 g Ni
   **c.** 106 g Ti
   **d.** 0.411 g Ge
**99. a.** 24.3 g Li
   **b.** 0.130 mol Co
   **c.** 0.0671 mol Kr
   **d.** 4.12 g As

### Level 2
**100. a.** $1.62 \times 10^{24}$ g Sb
    **b.** $9.27 \times 10^{16}$ g Pt
    **c.** $1.32 \times 10^{25}$ g Ag
    **d.** $5.12 \times 10^{26}$ g Cr

## Particle-Mass Conversions (11.2)
### Level 1
**101. a.** $1.67 \times 10^{-6}$ g U
    **b.** 145 g H
    **c.** 0.332 g O
    **d.** 153 g Pb
**102.** $5 \times 10^{13}$ atoms Ag
**103. a.** $7.74 \times 10^{22}$ atoms Hg
    **b.** $3.13 \times 10^{20}$ atoms Zn
    **c.** $2.3 \times 10^{24}$ atoms Ar
    **d.** $3.07 \times 10^{21}$ atoms Mg
**104.** C; atom C = $5.01 \times 10^{23}$; atom Ca = $1.50 \times 10^{23}$
**105.** atom C = atom Ca; $6.02 \times 10^{24}$ atoms

### Level 2
**106.** $2.11 \times 10^{23}$ atoms Fe and C

## Chemical Formulas (11.3)
### Level 1
**107.** 3 mol Na, 1 mol P, 4 mol O
**108. a.** 10.0 mol O
    **b.** 91.8 mol O
    **c.** 0.113 mol O

### Level 2
**109.** $CaC_4H_6O_4$ (calcium acetate), 158.18 g/mol
**110.** $1.81 \times 10^{24}$ molecules $CCl_4$
$1.81 \times 10^{24}$ atoms C

## Mass-Mole Conversions (11.3)
**114.** How many moles are in 100.0 g of each of the following compounds?
    **a.** dinitrogen oxide ($N_2O$)
    **b.** methanol ($CH_3OH$)
**115.** What is the mass of each of the following?
    **a.** $4.50 \times 10^{-2}$ mol $CuCl_2$
    **b.** $1.25 \times 10^2$ mol $Ca(OH)_2$
**116.** Determine the number of moles in each of the following.
    **a.** $1.25 \times 10^2$ g $Na_2S$    **b.** 0.145 g $H_2S$
**117.** Benzoyl peroxide is a substance used as an acne medicine. What is the mass in grams of $3.50 \times 10^{-2}$ moles of benzoyl peroxide ($C_{14}H_{10}O_4$)?
**118.** Hydrofluoric acid is a substance used to etch glass. Determine the mass of $4.95 \times 10^{25}$ HF molecules.
**119.** How many moles of aluminum ions are in 45.0 g of aluminum oxide?
**120.** How many moles of ions are in the following?
    **a.** 0.0200 g $AgNO_3$    **c.** 0.500 g $Ba(OH)_2$
    **b.** 0.100 mol $K_2CrO_4$    **d.** $1.00 \times 10^{-9}$ mol $Na_2CO_3$

## Mass-Particle Conversions (11.3)
**121.** Calculate the values that will complete the table.

**Table 11-2**

| Moles, Mass, and Representative Particles | | | |
|---|---|---|---|
| Compound | Number of moles | Mass (g) | Representative particles |
| Silver acetate $Ag(C_2H_3O_2)$ | 2.50 | | |
| Glucose $C_6H_{12}O_6$ | | 324.0 | |
| Benzene $C_6H_6$ | | | $5.65 \times 10^{21}$ |
| Lead(II) sulfide PbS | | 100.0 | |

**122.** How many formula units are present in 500.0 g lead(II) chloride?
**123.** Determine the number of atoms in 3.50 g gold.
**124.** Calculate the mass of $3.62 \times 10^{24}$ molecules of glucose ($C_6H_{12}O_6$).
**125.** Determine the number of molecules of ethanol ($C_2H_5OH$) in 47.0 g.

**126.** What mass of iron(III) chloride contains $2.35 \times 10^{23}$ chloride ions?
**127.** How many moles of iron can be recovered from 100.0 kg $Fe_3O_4$?
**128.** The mass of an electron is $9.11 \times 10^{-28}$ g. What is the mass of a mole of electrons?
**129.** Vinegar is 5.0% acetic acid ($CH_3COOH$). How many molecules of acetic acid are present in 25.0 g vinegar?
**130.** The density of lead is 11.3 $g/cm^3$. Calculate the volume of one mole lead.
**131.** Calculate the moles of aluminum ions present in 250.0 g aluminum oxide ($Al_2O_3$).
**132.** Determine the number of chloride ions in 10.75 g of magnesium chloride.
**133.** Acetaminophen, a common aspirin substitute, has the formula $C_8H_9NO_2$. Determine the number of molecules of acetaminophen in a 500 mg tablet.
**134.** Calculate the number of sodium ions present in 25.0 g sodium chloride.
**135.** Determine the number of oxygen atoms present in 25.0 g carbon dioxide.

## Percent Composition (11.4)
**136.** Express the composition of each of the following as the mass percent of its elements (percent composition).
    **a.** sucrose ($C_{12}H_{22}O_{11}$)
    **b.** magnetite ($Fe_3O_4$)
    **c.** aluminum sulfate ($Al_2(SO_4)_3$)
**137.** Which of the following iron compounds contain the greatest percentage of iron: pyrite ($FeS_2$), hematite ($Fe_2O_3$), or siderite ($FeCO_3$)?
**138.** Determine the empirical formula for each of the following compounds.
    **a.** ethylene ($C_2H_4$)
    **b.** ascorbic acid ($C_6H_8O_6$)
    **c.** naphthalene ($C_{10}H_8$)
**139.** Caffeine, a stimulant found in coffee, has the chemical formula $C_8H_{10}N_4O_2$.
    **a.** Calculate the molar mass of caffeine.
    **b.** Determine the percent composition of caffeine.
**140.** Which of the titanium-containing minerals rutile ($TiO_2$) or ilmenite ($FeTiO_3$) has the larger percent of titanium?
**141.** Vitamin E, found in many plants, is thought to retard the aging process in humans. The formula for vitamin E is $C_{29}H_{50}O_2$. What is the percent composition of vitamin E?

$7.24 \times 10^{24}$ atoms Cl
$9.05 \times 10^{24}$ total atoms

## Molar Mass (11.3)
### Level 1
**111. a.** 63.02 g/mol $HNO_3$
    **b.** 80.05 g/mol $NH_4NO_3$
    **c.** 81.39 g/mol ZnO
    **d.** 129.83 g/mol $CoCl_2$

**112. a.** 176.12 g/mol $C_6H_8O_6$
    **b.** 98.09 g/mol $H_2SO_4$
    **c.** 169.88 g/mol $AgNO_3$
    **d.** 183.19 g/mol $C_7H_5NO_3S$
**113.** 114.21 g/mol $(C_3H_5)_2S$

**142.** Aspartame, an artificial sweetener, has the formula $C_{14}H_{18}N_2O_5$. Determine the percent composition of aspartame.

## Empirical and Molecular Formulas (11.4)

**143.** The hydrocarbon used in the manufacture of foam plastics is called styrene. Analysis of styrene indicates the compound is 92.25% C and 7.75% H and has a molar mass of 104 g/mol. Determine the molecular formula for styrene.

**144.** Monosodium glutamate (MSG) is sometimes added to food to enhance flavor. Analysis determined this compound to be 35.5% C, 4.77% H, 8.29% N, 13.6% Na, and 37.9% O. What is the empirical formula for MSG?

**145.** Determine the molecular formula for ibuprofen, a common headache remedy. Analysis of ibuprofen yields a molar mass of 206 g/mol and a percent composition of 75.7% C, 8.80% H and 15.5% O.

**146.** Vanadium oxide is used as an industrial catalyst. The percent composition of this oxide is 56.0% vanadium and 44.0% oxygen. Determine the empirical formula for vanadium oxide.

**147.** What is the empirical formula of a compound that contains 10.52 g Ni, 4.38 g C, and 5.10 g N?

**148.** The Statue of Liberty turns green in air because of the formation of two copper compounds, $Cu_3(OH)_4SO_4$ and $Cu_4(OH)_6SO_4$. Determine the mass percent of copper in these compounds.

**149.** Analysis of a compound containing chlorine and lead reveals that the compound is 59.37% lead. The molar mass of the compound is 349.0 g/mol. What is the empirical formula for the chloride? What is the molecular formula?

**150.** Glycerol is a thick, sweet liquid obtained as a byproduct of the manufacture of soap. Its percent composition is 39.12% carbon, 8.75% hydrogen, and 52.12% oxygen. The molar mass is 92.11 g/mol. What is the molecular formula for glycerol?

## The Formula for a Hydrate (11.5)

**151.** Determine the mass percent of anhydrous sodium carbonate ($Na_2CO_3$) and water in sodium carbonate decahydrate ($Na_2CO_3 \cdot 10H_2O$).

**152.** What is the formula and name of a hydrate that is 85.3% barium chloride and 14.7% water?

**153.** Gypsum is hydrated calcium sulfate. A 4.89-g sample of this hydrate was heated, and after the water was driven off, 3.87 g anhydrous calcium sulfate remained. Determine the formula of this hydrate and name the compound.

**154.** The table shows data from an experiment to determine the formulas of hydrated barium chloride. Determine the formula for the hydrate and its name.

**Table 11-3**

| Data for $BaCl_2 \cdot xH_2O$ | |
|---|---|
| Mass of empty crucible | 21.30 g |
| Mass of hydrate + crucible | 31.35 g |
| Initial mass of hydrate | |
| Mass after heating 5 min | 29.87 g |
| Mass of anhydrous solid | |

**155.** A 1.628-g sample of a hydrate of magnesium iodide is heated until its mass is reduced to 1.072 g and all water has been removed. What is the formula of the hydrate?

**156.** Hydrated sodium tetraborate ($Na_2B_4O_7 \cdot xH_2O$) is commonly called borax. Chemical analysis indicates that this hydrate is 52.8% sodium tetraborate and 47.2% water. Determine the formula and name the hydrate.

## Mixed Review

*Sharpen your problem-solving skills by answering the following.*

**157.** Determine the following:
   **a.** the number of representative particles in 3.75 g Zn
   **b.** the mass of $4.32 \times 10^{22}$ atoms Ag
   **c.** the number of sodium ions in 25.0 g of $Na_2O$

**158.** Which of the following has the greatest number of oxygen atoms?
   **a.** 17.63 g $CO_2$
   **b.** $3.21 \times 10^{22}$ molecules $CH_3OH$
   **c.** 0.250 mol $C_6H_{12}O_6$

**159.** Which of the following compounds has the greatest percent of oxygen by mass: $TiO_2$, $Fe_2O_3$, $Al_2O_3$?

**160.** Naphthalene, commonly known as moth balls, is composed of 93.7% carbon and 6.3% hydrogen. The molar mass of napthalene is 128 g/mol. Determine the empirical and molecular formulas for naphthalene.

**161.** Which of the following molecular formulas are also empirical formulas: ethyl ether ($C_4H_{10}O$), aspirin ($C_9H_8O_4$), butyl dichloride ($C_4H_8Cl_2$), glucose ($C_6H_{12}O_6$).

## Mass-Mole Conversions (11.3)

### Level 1
**114. a.** 2.27 mol $N_2O$
      **b.** 3.12 mol $CH_3OH$
**115. a.** 6.05 g $CuCl_2$
      **b.** $9.26 \times 10^2$ g $Ca(OH)_2$
**116. a.** 1.60 mol $Na_2S$
      **b.** $4.25 \times 10^{-3}$ mol $H_2S$

### Level 2
**117.** 8.48 g $C_{14}H_{10}O_4$
**118.** $1.65 \times 10^3$ g HF
**119.** 0.883 mol $Al^{3+}$ ion
**120. a.** $2.35 \times 10^{-4}$ mol ions
      **b.** 0.300 mol ions
      **c.** $8.75 \times 10^{-3}$ mol ions
      **d.** $3.00 \times 10^{-9}$ mol ions

## Mass-Particle Conversions (11.3)

### Level 1
**121.** Silver acetate: 417 g, $1.51 \times 10^{24}$ representative particles
      Glucose: 1.798 mol, $1.082 \times 10^{24}$ representative particles
      Benzene: 0.00939 mol, 0.733 g
      PbS: 0.4178 mol, $2.516 \times 10^{23}$ representative particles
**122.** $1.082 \times 10^{24}$ formula units $PbCl_2$
**123.** $1.07 \times 10^{22}$ atoms Au
**124.** 1080 g $C_6H_{12}O_6$
**125.** $6.14 \times 10^{23}$ molecules $C_2H_5OH$
**126.** 21.1 g $FeCl_3$
**127.** 1296 mol Fe
**128.** $5.48 \times 10^{-4}$ g
**129.** $1.25 \times 10^{22}$ molecules $CH_3COOH$
**130.** 18.3 $cm^3$
**131.** 4.90 mol ions $Al^{3+}$

### Level 2
**132.** $1.37 \times 10^{23}$ $Cl^-$ ions
**133.** $2 \times 10^{21}$ $C_8H_9NO_2$ molecules
**134.** $2.58 \times 10^{23}$ Na ions
**135.** $6.84 \times 10^{23}$ oxygen atoms

National Science Content Standards

Pages 348–349
UCP.1, UCP.3; A.1; B.2; E.2

## Percent Composition (11.4)

### Level 1
**136. a.** 42.10% C, 6.480% H, 51.42% O
      **b.** 72.360% Fe, 27.64% O
      **c.** 15.77% Al, 28.12% S, 56.11% O
**137.** Hematite, with 69.944% Fe has the greastest percentage of iron.
**138. a.** $CH_2$
      **b.** $C_3H_4O_3$
      **c.** $C_5H_4$
**139. a.** 194.20 g/mol
      **b.** 49.47% C, 5.191% H, 28.86% N, 16.48% O
**140.** $TiO_2$
**141.** 80.87% C, 11.70% H, 7.430% O
**142.** 57.13% C, 6.165% H, 9.521% N, 27.18% O

# CHAPTER 11 ASSESSMENT

## Empirical and Molecular Formulas (11.4)

### Level 1
**143.** $C_8H_8$
**144.** $C_5H_8NO_4Na$
**145.** $C_{13}H_{18}O_2$

### Level 2
**146.** $V_2O_5$
**147.** $Ni(CN)_2$
**148.** $Cu_3(OH)_4SO_4$, 53.74% Cu
$Cu_4(OH)_6SO_4$, 56.20% Cu
**149.** $PbCl_4$, $PbCl_4$
**150.** $C_3H_8O_3$

## The Formula for a Hydrate (11.5)

### Level 1
**151.** 37.03% $Na_2CO_3$, 62.97% $H_2O$
**152.** $BaCl_2\cdot2H_2O$, barium chloride dihydrate
**153.** $CaSO_4\cdot2H_2O$, calcium sulfate dihydrate

### Level 2
**154.** Initial mass of the hydrate = 10.05 g Mass of anhydrous solid = 8.57 g $BaCl_2 \cdot 2H_2O$, barium chloride dihydrate
**155.** $MgI_2\cdot8H_2O$
**156.** $Na_2B_4O_7\cdot10H_2O$, sodium tetraborate decahydrate

## Mixed Review

**157. a.** $3.45 \times 10^{22}$ atom Zn
**b.** 7.74 g Ag
**c.** $4.86 \times 10^{23}$ $Na^+$ ions
**158.** 0.250 mol $C_6H_{12}O_6$
**159.** $Al_2O_3$
**160.** $C_5H_4$, $C_{10}H_8$
**161.** $C_4H_{10}O$, $C_9H_8O_4$
**162. a.** 0.109 mol $Na_2SO_4$
**b.** $1.54 \times 10^{23}$ formula units NaCl
**c.** 113 g $SF_6$
**d.** $1.83 \times 10^{23}$ ions $Cl^-$
**163.** 52.42 g O, 22.95 g N, 19.68 g C, 4.96 g H
**164.** $5.39 \times 10^{22}$ atoms He
**165.** empirical formula, $CF_2$; molecular formula, $C_2F_4$
**166.** $3.44 \times 10^{-22}$ g/atom Pb
**167.** $2.5 \times 10^{21}$ atoms C
**168.** $3.58 \times 10^{24}$ molecules $C_8H_{18}$
**169.** $1.34 \times 10^{32}$ molecules $H_2O$

**350**

**162.** Calculate each of the following:

**a.** the number of moles in 15.5 g $Na_2SO_4$
**b.** the number of formula units in 0.255 mol NaCl
**c.** the mass in grams of 0.775 mol $SF_6$
**d.** the number of $Cl^-$ ions in 14.5 g $MgCl_2$.

**163.** The graph shows the percent composition of a compound containing carbon, hydrogen, oxygen, and nitrogen. How many grams of each element are present in 100 g of the compound?

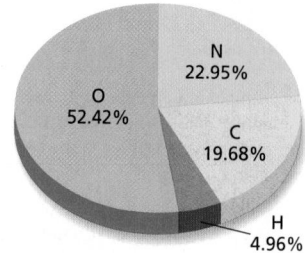

**164.** A party balloon was filled with $9.80 \times 10^{22}$ atoms of helium. After 24 hours, 45% of the helium had escaped. How many atoms of helium remained?

**165.** Tetrafluoroethylene, which is used in the production of Teflon, is composed of 24.0% carbon and 76.0% fluorine and has a molar mass of 100.0 g/mol. Determine the empirical and molecular formulas of this compound.

**166.** Calculate the mass in grams of one atom of lead.

**167.** Diamond is a naturally occurring form of carbon. If you have a 0.25-carat diamond, how many carbon atoms are present? (1 carat = 0.200 g)

**168.** How many molecules of isooctane ($C_8H_{18}$) are present in 1.00 L? (density of isooctane = 0.680 g/mL)

**169.** Calculate the number of molecules of water in a swimming pool which is 40.0 m in length, 20.0 m in width, and 5.00 m in depth. Assume that the density of water is 1.00 g/cm³.

## Thinking Critically

**170. Analyze and Conclude** A mining company has two possible sources of copper: chalcopyrite ($CuFeS_2$) and chalcocite ($Cu_2S$). If the mining conditions and the extraction of copper from the ore were identical for each of the ores, which ore would yield the greater quantity of copper? Explain your answer.

**350** Chapter 11 The Mole

**171. Designing an Experiment** Design an experiment that can be used to determine the amount of water in alum ($KAl(SO_4)_2\cdot xH_2O$).

**172. Concept Mapping** Design a concept map that illustrates the mole concept. Include moles, Avogadro's number, molar mass, number of particles, percent composition, empirical formula, and molecular formula.

**173. Communicating** If you use the expression "a mole of nitrogen," is it perfectly clear what you mean, or is there more than one way to interpret the expression? Explain. How could you change the expression to make it more precise?

## Writing in Chemistry

**174.** Octane ratings are used to identify certain grades of gasoline. Research *octane rating* and prepare a pamphlet for consumers identifying the different types of gasoline, the advantages of each, and when each grade is used.

**175.** Research the life of the Italian chemist Amedeo Avogadro (1776–1856) and how his work led scientists to the number of particles in a mole.

## Cumulative Review

*Refresh your understanding of previous chapters by answering the following.*

**176.** Express the following answers with the correct number of significant figures. (Chapter 2)

**a.** $18.23 - 456.7$
**b.** $4.233 \div 0.0131$
**c.** $(82.44 \times 4.92) + 0.125$

**177.** Distinguish between atomic number and mass number. How do these two numbers compare for isotopes of an element? (Chapter 4)

**178.** Write balanced equations for the following reactions. (Chapter 10)

**a.** Magnesium metal and water combine to form solid magnesium hydroxide and hydrogen gas.
**b.** Dinitrogen tetroxide gas decomposes into nitrogen dioxide gas.
**c.** Aqueous solutions of sulfuric acid and potassium hydroxide undergo a double replacement reaction.

**179.** How can you tell if a chemical equation is balanced? (Chapter 10)

## Thinking Critically

**170.** Chalcopyrite ($CuFeS_2$) is 34.6% copper by mass (determined from percent composition) and chalcocite ($Cu_2S$) is 79.9% copper by mass. Chalcocite would yield the greater quantity of copper because the ore has the greater percentage copper by mass.

**171.** Determine and record the mass of an empty evaporating dish. Add about 2 g

of the hydrate. Measure and record the mass. Heat the evaporating dish gently for five minutes, and strongly for another five minutes to evaporate all the water. Allow the dish to cool, and measure and record the mass. Determine the masses of the anhydrous solid and the water lost. Calculate the number of moles of anhydrous compound and water. Determine the

*Use these questions and the test-taking tip to prepare for your standardized test.*

**Interpreting Graphs** Use the graph to answer questions 1–4.

**Percent Composition of Some Organic Compounds**

1. Acetaldehyde and butanoic acid must have the same
   a. molecular formula.
   b. empirical formula.
   c. molar mass.
   d. chemical properties.

2. If the molar mass of butanoic acid is 88.1 g/mol, then what is its molecular formula?
   a. $CH_2O$
   b. $C_2H_4O$
   c. $C_6HO_2$
   d. $C_4H_8O_2$

3. What is the empirical formula of ethanol?
   a. $C_4HO_3$
   b. $C_{52}H_{13}O_{35}$
   c. $C_2H_6O$
   d. $C_4H_{13}O_2$

4. The empirical formula of formaldehyde is the same as its molecular formula. How many grams are in 2.000 moles of formaldehyde?
   a. 30.00 g
   b. 60.06 g
   c. 182.0 g
   d. 200.0 g

5. A mole is all of the following EXCEPT
   a. the atomic or molar mass of an element or compound.
   b. Avogadro's number of molecules of a compound.
   c. the number of atoms in exactly 12 g of pure $^{12}C$.
   d. the SI measurement unit for the amount of a substance.

6. How many atoms are in 0.625 moles of Ge (atomic mass = 72.59 amu)?
   a. $2.73 \times 10^{25}$
   b. $6.99 \times 10^{25}$
   c. $3.76 \times 10^{23}$
   d. $9.63 \times 10^{23}$

7. What is the molar mass of fluorapatite $(Ca_5(PO_4)_3F)$?
   a. 314 g/mol
   b. 344 g/mol
   c. 442 g/mol
   d. 504 g/mol

8. How many moles of cobalt(III) titanate $(Co_2TiO_4)$ are in 7.13 g of the compound?
   a. $2.39 \times 10^1$ mol
   b. $3.14 \times 10^{-2}$ mol
   c. $3.22 \times 10^1$ mol
   d. $4.17 \times 10^{-2}$ mol

9. Magnesium sulfate $(MgSO_4)$ is often added to water-insoluble liquid products of chemical reactions to remove any unwanted water. $MgSO_4$ readily absorbs water to form two different hydrates. One of these hydrates is found to contain 13.0% $H_2O$ and 87.0% $MgSO_4$. What is the name of this hydrate?
   a. magnesium sulfate monohydrate
   b. magnesium sulfate dihydrate
   c. magnesium sulfate hexahydrate
   d. magnesium sulfate heptahydrate

10. What is the mass of one molecule of barium hexafluorosilicate $(BaSiF_6)$?
    a. $1.68 \times 10^{26}$ g
    b. $2.16 \times 10^{21}$ g
    c. $4.64 \times 10^{-22}$ g
    d. $6.02 \times 10^{-23}$ g

### TEST-TAKING TIP

**Your Answers Are Better Than The Test's** When you know how to answer a question, answer it in your own words before looking at the answer choices. Often more than one answer choice will look good, so do the calculations first, and arm yourself with your answer before looking. If you need to, cover the choices with one hand until you're ready.

ratio of moles of water to moles of anhydrous compound. Use the whole-number ratio of the moles as the coefficient of $H_2O$ in the formula.

172. Concept maps will vary.

173. The phrase could be interpreted to mean a mole of nitrogen atoms or a mole of nitrogen molecules. Specify atoms or molecules.

## Cumulative Review

176. a. −438.5
     b. 323
     c. 406

177. Atomic number equals the number of protons. Mass number equals the number of protons plus the number of neutrons. Two isotopes of an element will have the same atomic number but different mass numbers.

178. a. $Mg(s) + 2H_2O(l) \rightarrow Mg(OH)_2(s) + H_2(g)$
     b. $N_2O_4(g) \rightarrow 2NO_2(g)$
     c. $H_2SO_4(aq) + 2KOH(aq) \rightarrow K_2SO_4(aq) + 2H_2O(l)$

179. There are equal numbers of each kind of atom on both sides of the equation.

## Standardized Test Practice

| | |
|---|---|
| **1.** b | **6.** c |
| **2.** d | **7.** d |
| **3.** c | **8.** b |
| **4.** b | **9.** a |
| **5.** a | **10.** c |

**National Science Content Standards**

**Pages 350–351**
UCP.1, UCP.3; B.2, B.3; E.2

# Resource Manager

| Section | Objectives | Activities/Features |
|---|---|---|
| **Section 12.1**<br>**What is stoichiometry?**<br>1 session<br>½ block | **1. Identify** the quantitative relationships in a balanced chemical equation.<br>**2. Determine** the mole ratios from a balanced chemical equation. | **Discovery Lab:** Observing a Chemical Reaction, p. 353<br>**Careers Using Chemistry:** Pharmacist, p. 354 |
| **Section 12.2**<br>**Stoichiometric Calculations**<br>3 sessions<br>3 blocks | **3. Explain** the sequence of steps used in solving stoichiometric problems.<br>**4. Use** the steps to solve stoichiometric problems. | **MiniLab:** Baking Soda Stoichiometry, p. 362<br>**ChemLab:** A Mole Ratio, pp. 374–375 |
| **Section 12.3**<br>**Limiting Reactants**<br>2 sessions<br>1 block | **5. Identify** the limiting reactant in a chemical equation.<br>**6. Identify** the excess reactant and **calculate** the amount remaining after the reaction is complete.<br>**7. Calculate** the mass of a product when the amounts of more than one reactant are given. | **Biology Connection,** p. 366 |
| **Section 12.4**<br>**Percent Yield**<br>3 sessions<br>1½ blocks | **8. Calculate** the theoretical yield of a chemical reaction from data.<br>**9. Determine** the percent yield for a chemical reaction. | **Problem-Solving Lab:** How does the surface area of a solid reactant affect percent yield? p. 372<br>**How It Works:** Air Bags, p. 376 |

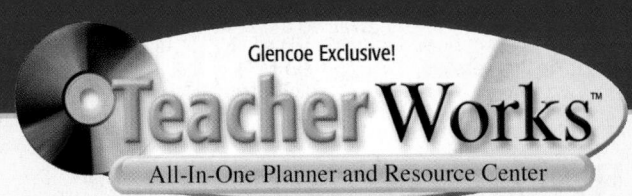

Glencoe Exclusive!
**TeacherWorks™**
All-In-One Planner and Resource Center

| National Science Content Standards | State/Local Standards | Reproducible Masters | Transparencies |
|---|---|---|---|
| UCP.1, UCP.3; A.1; B.3; E.1 | | **Study Guide for Content Mastery,** pp. 67–68 L2 | **Section Focus** Transparency 43 L1 ELL **Math Skills** Transparency 15 L2 ELL |
| UCP.1, UCP.3; A.1; B.3; E.1 | | **Study Guide for Content Mastery,** pp. 69–70 L2 **ChemLab and MiniLab Worksheets,** pp. 45–48 L2 **Challenge Problems,** p. 12 L3 | **Section Focus** Transparency 44 L1 ELL **Teaching** Transparency 38 L2 ELL **Math Skills** Transparencies 16, 17 L2 ELL |
| UCP.1, UCP.3; B.3; E.1, E.2; F.1 | | **Study Guide for Content Mastery,** p. 71 L2 **Laboratory Manual,** pp. 89–96 L2 | **Section Focus** Transparency 45 L1 ELL **Teaching** Transparency 39 L2 ELL |
| UCP.1, UCP.3; A.1, A.2; B.3, B.6; E.1, E.2; F.4, F.5, F.6; G.1 | | **Study Guide for Content Mastery,** p. 72 L2 | **Section Focus** Transparency 46 L1 ELL |

**Key to National Science Content Standards:** UCP = Unifying Concepts and Processes, A = Science as Inquiry, B = Physical Science, C = Life Science, D = Earth and Space Sciences, E = Science and Technology, F = Science in Personal and Social Perspectives, G = History and Nature of Science

Refer to pages 4T–5T of the Teacher Guide for an explanation of the National Science Content Standards correlations.

# Resource Manager

## Materials List

**ChemLab** (pages 374–375)

iron filings (20 mesh), copper(II) sulfate pentahydrate ($CuSO_4 \cdot 5H_2O$), distilled water, stirring rod, 150-mL beaker, 400-mL beaker, 100-mL graduated cylinder, weighing paper, balance, hot plate, beaker tongs

**Discovery Lab** (page 353)

10-mL graduated cylinder, 100-mL beaker, stirring rod, $0.01M$ potassium permanganate solution, $0.01M$ sodium hydrogen sulfite solution

**MiniLab** (page 362)

ring stand, ring, clay triangle, crucible, crucible tongs, Bunsen burner, balance, 3.0 g baking soda ($NaHCO_3$)

**Demonstration** (pages 366–367)

burets (2), stirring rods (8), test tubes (8), test-tube rack, centrifuge, $0.10M$ copper sulfate ($CuSO_4 \cdot 5H_2O$), $0.20M$ potassium hydroxide (KOH), distilled water, metric ruler, 25-mL graduated cylinder

## Preparation of Solutions

For a review of solution preparation, see page 46T of the Teacher Guide.

Quantities are for a class of 30 students.

**Discovery Lab** (page 353)

**$0.01M$ potassium permanganate** Dissolve 0.3 g potassium permanganate ($KMnO_4$) in 200 mL distilled water.

**$0.01M$ sodium hydrogen sulfite** Dissolve 0.2 g sodium hydrogen sulfite ($NaHSO_3$) in 200 mL distilled water.

**Demonstration** (pages 366–367)

**$0.10M$ copper sulfate** Dissolve 2.50 g copper sulfate ($CuSO_4 \cdot 5H_2O$) in 50 mL distilled water. Make up to 100 mL final volume with distilled water. **CAUTION:** $CuSO_4$ is toxic and corrosive.

**$0.20M$ potassium hydroxide** Dissolve 1.12 g potassium hydroxide (KOH) in 50 mL distilled water. Make up to 100 mL final volume with distilled water. **CAUTION:** KOH is toxic and corrosive.

## Assessment Resources

**Chapter Assessment,** pp. 67–72
**MindJogger Videoquizzes** DVD/VHS
**Alternate Assessment in the Science Classroom**
**ExamView® Pro CD-ROM**
**Solutions Manual,** Chapter 12
**Supplemental Problems,** Chapter 12
**Performance Assessment in the Science Classroom**
**Chemistry Interactive CD-ROM,** Chapter 12 quiz

## Additional Resources

**Spanish Resources** ELL
**Guided Reading Audio Program,** Chapter 12 ELL
**Cooperative Learning in the Science Classroom**
**Lab and Safety Skills in the Science Classroom**
**Lesson Plans**
**Block Scheduling Lesson Plans**
**Chemistrymc.com**

## Glencoe Technology

The following multimedia for this chapter are available from Glencoe.

**VIDEOTAPE/DVD**
MindJogger Videoquizzes,
Chapter 12

**CD-ROM**
**Chemistry: Matter and Change**
*How Much Oxygen Is Available?*
 Experiment
*Predicting Mass of Product,* Exploration

**CD-ROM**
**ExamView® Pro**
 **Testmaker**

**CD-ROM**
**Interactive Chalkboard**

**CD-ROM**
**TeacherWorks**™

## Multiple Learning Styles

Look for the following icons for strategies that emphasize different learning modalities.

**Visual-Spatial**
Quick Demo, p. 354; Differentiated Instruction;
pp. 354, 359

**Interpersonal**
Portfolio, p. 364; Differentiated Instruction,
p. 365

**Intrapersonal**
Check for Understanding, p. 355; Differentiated
Instruction, p. 358; Extension, p. 373

**Linguistic**
Chemistry Journal, pp. 355, 368; Reteach, p. 363

**Logical-Mathematical**
Quick Demo, p. 360; Chemistry Journal, p. 362;
Check for Understanding, pp. 363, 368; Differentiated
Instruction, p. 371

## Key to Teaching Strategies

 **L1** Level 1 activities should be appropriate for students with learning difficulties.

 **L2** Level 2 activities should be within the ability range of all students.

**L3** Level 3 activities are designed for above-average students.

**ELL** ELL activities should be within the ability range of English Language Learners.

**COOP LEARN** Cooperative Learning activities are designed for small group work.

 **P** These strategies represent student products that can be placed into a best-work portfolio.

 These strategies are useful in a block scheduling format.

## Assessment Planner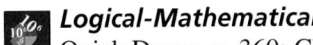

**Portfolio Assessment**
Portfolio, TWE, pp. 364, 370,
 377
Assessment, TWE, p. 367

**Performance Assessment**
MiniLab, SE, p. 362
Assessment, TWE, p. 373
ChemLab, SE. pp. 374–375

**Knowledge Assessment**
Section Assessment, SE,
 pp. 357, 363, 369, 373

Assessment, TWE, pp. 360,
 363, 365
Demonstration, TWE, p. 367
ChemLab, TWE, p. 375
Chapter Assessment, TWE,
 pp. 378–383

**Skill Assessment**
Assessment, TWE, pp. 355,
 369
MiniLab, TWE, p. 362
Problem-Solving Lab,
 TWE, p. 372

## Tying to Previous Knowledge

Have students review the following concepts before studying this chapter.
Chapter 2: scientific notation, significant figures, dimensional analysis
Chapter 4: average atomic mass
Chapter 11: mole conversions

## Using the Photo

Ask what substances are reacting. candle wax and oxygen Ask what would happen if a bell jar were put over the candle. The candle would go out as soon as the oxygen inside was used up. Point out that if the amount of oxygen available to react were known, they could calculate how much candle wax would be consumed.

## PowerPoint® Presentations

This CD-ROM is an editable Microsoft® PowerPoint® presentation that includes:
• Section presentations
• Section checks
• Image bank
• Links to Chemistry Online
• All transparencies
• Animations
• Audio

# Stoichiometry

## What You'll Learn

▶ You will write mole ratios from balanced chemical equations.
▶ You will calculate the number of moles and the mass of a reactant or product when given the number of moles or the mass of another reactant or product.
▶ You will identify the limiting reactant in a chemical reaction.
▶ You will determine the percent yield of a chemical reaction.

## Why It's Important

The cost of the things you buy is lower because chemists use stoichiometric calculations to increase efficiency in laboratories, decrease waste in manufacturing, and produce products more quickly.

Visit the Chemistry Web site at chemistrymc.com to find links to stoichiometry.

The candle will continue to burn as long as oxygen and candle wax are present.

352    Chapter 12

## DISCOVERY LAB

### Purpose
Students will observe a chemical reaction in which one of the reactants is completely used up and the other is in excess.

### Safety and Disposal
Be sure students wear aprons and goggles. Contents of the beaker can be flushed down the drain with water.

### Teaching Strategies
• Place five test tubes and ten rubber stoppers on the desk. Show students that one stopper fits into a test tube. Ask them which item is in excess.
• See page 352C for preparation of all solutions.

### Expected Results
Initially, the $KMnO_4$ solution is dark purple. The solution gradually becomes colorless as $NaHSO_3$ solution is added.

Expect that 5 mL $KMnO_4$ solution will require 27 mL $NaHSO_3$ solution to change it to a clear, colorless solution.

### Analysis
As colorless sodium hydrogen sulfite was added to the purple potassium permanganate solution, a color change from purple to colorless was observed. Nothing more will happen because the solution is colorless, meaning that there is no more potassium permanganate to react.

## DISCOVERY LAB

### Observing a Chemical Reaction

Reactants are consumed in a chemical reaction as products are produced. What evidence can you observe that a reaction takes place?

### Safety Precautions

### Procedure

1. Measure 5.0 mL of 0.01$M$ potassium permanganate solution ($KMnO_4$) and pour it into a 100-mL beaker.

2. Add 5.0 mL of 0.01$M$ sodium hydrogen sulfite solution ($NaHSO_3$) to the potassium permanganate solution while stirring. Record your observations.

3. Slowly add additional 5.0-mL portions of the $NaHSO_3$ solution until the $KMnO_4$ solution turns colorless. Record your observations.

4. Record the total volume of the $NaHSO_3$ solution you used to cause the beaker's contents to become colorless.

### Analysis

What evidence do you have that a reaction occurred? Would anything more have happened if you continued to add $NaHSO_3$ solution to the beaker? Explain.

### Materials

10-mL graduated cylinder
100-mL beaker
stirring rod
0.01$M$ potassium permanganate ($KMnO_4$)
0.01$M$ sodium hydrogen sulfite ($NaHSO_3$)

---

# 1 Focus

## Focus Transparency

Before presenting the lesson, display **Section Focus Transparency 43** on the overhead projector. Have students answer the accompanying questions using **Section Focus Transparency Master 43.** L1 ELL

---

## Section 12.1

# What is stoichiometry?

### Objectives

- **Identify** the quantitative relationships in a balanced chemical equation.

- **Determine** the mole ratios from a balanced chemical equation.

### Vocabulary

stoichiometry
mole ratio

Were you surprised when, in doing the **DISCOVERY LAB,** you saw the purple color of potassium permanganate disappear as you added sodium hydrogen sulfite? If you concluded that the potassium permanganate had been used up and the reaction had stopped, you are right. The photo on the opposite page shows the combustion of a candle using the oxygen in the surrounding air. What would happen if a bell jar was lowered over the burning candle blocking off the supply of oxygen? You know that oxygen is needed for the combustion of candle wax, so when the oxygen inside the bell jar is used up, the candle will go out.

Chemical reactions, such as the reaction of potassium permanganate with sodium hydrogen sulfite and the combustion of a candle, stop when one of the reactants is used up. Thus, in planning the reaction of potassium permanganate and sodium hydrogen sulfite, a chemist needs to know how many grams of potassium permanganate are needed to react completely with a known mass of sodium hydrogen sulfite. You might ask, "How much oxygen is required to completely burn a candle of known mass, or how much product will be produced if a given amount of a reactant is used?" Stoichiometry is the tool for answering these questions.

12.1  What is stoichiometry?    **353**

---

# 2 Teach

## Using Science Terms

Stoichiometry describes the quantitative relationships among masses and volumes. The word stoichiometry is a combination of two Greek words which, when used together, mean "to measure the elements."

## Resource Manager

**Study Guide for Content Mastery,** pp. 67–68 L2
**Solving Problems: A Chemistry Handbook,** Section 12.1 L2
**Section Focus Transparency 43 and Master** L1 ELL
**Math Skills Transparency 15 and Master** L2 ELL

---

## Chapter Themes

The following themes from the National Science Education Standards are covered in this chapter. Refer to page 4T of the Teacher Guide for an explanation of the correlations.
Systems, order, and organization (UCP.1)
Evidence, models, and explanation (UCP.2)
Change, constancy, and measurement (UCP.3)

National Science Content Standards

**Pages 352–353**
UCP.1, UCP.3; A.1; B.3

**Visual-Spatial** Attach a small glass funnel to one end of a rubber hose. Attach the other end of the hose to a gas jet. In a petri dish, place either a prepared bubble mixture or a soap solution containing 10% dish-washing soap and a few drops of glycerol. Dip the funnel into the bubble mixture. Attach a small wooden splint to the end of a meter stick and ignite the splint with a match. Turn on the gas jet just enough to slowly produce bubbles in the funnel. Shake the bubbles loose from the funnel and have a student touch each bubble with the burning splint. The bubbles will ignite. Remind students that you are igniting bubbles of natural gas or methane ($CH_4$). Ask students to write the combustion equation. $CH_4 + 2O_2 \rightarrow CO_2 + 2H_2O$

## Visual Learning

**Table 12-1** Ask students to use the table as a guide for interpreting the equation for the combustion of methane. Make a drawing of the reaction to help students.

**CAREERS USING CHEMISTRY**

**Career Path** A career as a pharmacist would include high school courses in biology, anatomy and physiology, chemistry, math, and physics.
**Career Issue** Have students investigate the role of the Food and Drug Administration in the approval of new prescription drugs.

## For More Information

For more information about a career as a pharmacist, students can contact
American Council on Pharmaceutical Education
311 West Superior Street
Suite 512
Chicago, IL 60610

**354**

**Figure 12-1**

If you know the equation for this reaction between iron and oxygen, you can calculate the number of moles and the mass of each reactant and product.

**354**     Chapter 12 Stoichiometry

## Mole-Mass Relationships in Chemical Reactions

The study of quantitative relationships between amounts of reactants used and products formed by a chemical reaction is called **stoichiometry**. Stoichiometry is based on the law of conservation of mass, which was introduced by Antoine Lavoisier in the eighteenth century. The law states that matter is neither created nor destroyed in a chemical reaction. Chemical bonds in reactants break and new chemical bonds form to produce products, but the amount of matter present at the end of the reaction is the same as was present at the beginning. Therefore, the mass of the reactants equals the mass of the products.

**Stoichiometry and the balanced chemical equation** Look at the reaction of powdered iron with oxygen shown in **Figure 12-1**. As tiny particles of iron react with oxygen in the air, iron(III) oxide ($Fe_2O_3$) is produced.

$$4Fe(s) + 3O_2(g) \rightarrow 2Fe_2O_3(s)$$

You can interpret this equation in terms of representative particles by saying that four atoms of iron react with three molecules of oxygen to produce two formula units of iron(III) oxide. But, remember that coefficients in an equation represent not only numbers of individual particles but also numbers of moles of particles. Therefore, you can also say that four moles of iron react with three moles of oxygen to produce two moles of iron(III) oxide.

Does the chemical equation tell you anything about the masses of the reactants and products? Not directly. But as you learned in Chapter 11, the mass of any substance can be determined by multiplying the number of moles of the substance by the conversion factor that relates mass and number of moles, which is the molar mass. Thus, the mass of the reactants can be calculated in this way.

$$4 \text{ mol Fe} \times \frac{55.85 \text{ g Fe}}{1 \text{ mol Fe}} = 223.4 \text{ g Fe}$$

$$3 \text{ mol O}_2 \times \frac{32.00 \text{ g O}_2}{1 \text{ mol O}_2} = 96.00 \text{ g O}_2$$

The total mass of the reactants = 319.4 g

Similarly, the mass of the product is

$$2 \text{ mol Fe}_2O_3 \times \frac{159.7 \text{ g Fe}_2O_3}{1 \text{ mol Fe}_2O_3} = 319.4 \text{ g}$$

The total mass of the reactants equals the mass of the product, as predicted by the law of conservation of mass. **Table 12-1** summarizes the relationships that can be determined from a balanced chemical equation.

**Table 12-1**

| Relationships Derived from a Balanced Chemical Equation | | | | |
|---|---|---|---|---|
| Iron | + | Oxygen | → | Iron(III) oxide |
| 4Fe(s) | + | $3O_2(g)$ | → | $2Fe_2O_3(s)$ |
| 4 atoms Fe | + | 3 molecules $O_2$ | → | 2 formula units $Fe_2O_3$ |
| 4 moles Fe | + | 3 moles $O_2$ | → | 2 moles $Fe_2O_3$ |
| 223.4 g Fe | + | 96.0 g $O_2$ | → | 319.4 g $Fe_2O_3$ |
| | | 319.4 g reactants | → | 319.4 g product |

**DIFFERENTIATED INSTRUCTION**

## Learning Disabled

**Visual-Spatial** Using a molecular model kit, make a model of $CH_4$ and two $O_2$ molecules. Ask students to identify the models. Make models of $CO_2$ and two $H_2O$ molecules and ask students to identify these models. Tell students that the two sets of models represent the reactants and the products of the combustion of methane. Arrange the reactants and products on opposite sides of a cardboard arrow. Ask students to count the number of each atom before and after the reaction. one carbon, four hydrogen, and four oxygen atoms Remind them that coefficients indicate the number of moles as well as the number of molecules. Have them interpret the equation in moles. 1 mol $CH_4$ + 2 mol $O_2 \rightarrow$ 1 mol $CO_2$ + 2 mol $H_2O$ **L2** **ELL**

## EXAMPLE PROBLEM 12-1

**Interpreting Chemical Equations**

The combustion of propane ($C_3H_8$) provides energy for heating homes, cooking food, and soldering metal parts. Interpret the equation for the combustion of propane in terms of representative particles, moles, and mass. Show that the law of conservation of mass is observed.

**1. Analyze the Problem**

The formulas in the equation represent both representative particles (molecules) and moles. Therefore, the equation can be interpreted in terms of molecules and moles. The law of conservation of mass will be verified if the masses of the reactants and products are equal.

**Known**

$C_3H_8(g) + 5O_2(g) \rightarrow 3CO_2(g) + 4H_2O(g)$

**Unknown**

The equation in terms of molecules = ?
The equation in terms of moles = ?
The equation in terms of mass = ?

**2. Solve for the Unknown**

The coefficients indicate the number of molecules.

1 molecule $C_3H_8$ + 5 molecules $O_2 \rightarrow$ 3 molecules $CO_2$ + 4 molecules $H_2O$

The coefficients indicate the number of moles.

1 mole $C_3H_8$ + 5 moles $O_2 \rightarrow$ 3 moles $CO_2$ + 4 moles $H_2O$

Calculate the mass of each reactant and product by multiplying the number of moles by the conversion factor molar mass.

$$\text{moles reactant or product} \times \frac{\text{grams reactant or product}}{\text{1 mole reactant or product}} =$$

$$\text{grams reactant or product}$$

$$1 \text{ mol } C_3H_8 \times \frac{44.09 \text{ g } C_3H_8}{1 \text{ mol } C_3H_8} = 44.09 \text{ g } C_3H_8$$

$$5 \text{ mol } O_2 \times \frac{32.00 \text{ g } O_2}{1 \text{ mol } O_2} = 160.0 \text{ g } O_2$$

$$3 \text{ mol } CO_2 \times \frac{44.01 \text{ g } CO_2}{1 \text{ mol } CO_2} = 132.0 \text{ g } CO_2$$

$$4 \text{ mol } H_2O \times \frac{18.02 \text{ g } H_2O}{1 \text{ mol } H_2O} = 72.08 \text{ g } H_2O$$

Add the masses of the reactants.
44.09 g $C_3H_8$ + 160.0 g $O_2$ = 204.1 g reactants

Add the masses of the products.
132.0 g $CO_2$ + 72.08 g $H_2O$ = 204.1 g products

204.1 g reactants = 204.1 g products

The law of conservation of mass is observed.

**3. Evaluate the Answer**

The sums of the reactants and the products are correctly stated to the first decimal place because each mass is accurate to the first decimal place. The mass of reactants equals the mass of products as predicted by the law of conservation of mass.

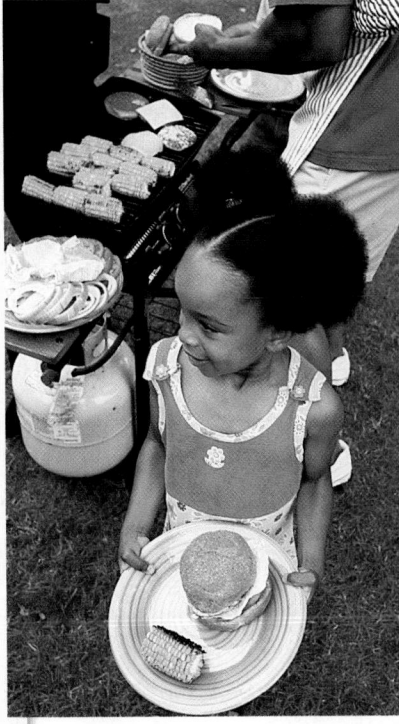

Because propane gas is readily liquified, it can be stored in tanks and transported to wherever it is needed.

12.1 What is stoichiometry? **355**

---

# 3 Assess
## Check for Understanding

*Intrapersonal* Place a small piece of calcium into a test tube containing 3.0$M$ HCl. In a second test tube, collect the hydrogen gas. Demonstrate the presence of hydrogen in the test tube using a burning splint. Note the characteristic pop. On the chalkboard, write the word equation for the reaction: calcium plus hydrochloric acid produces calcium chloride and hydrogen. Ask students to write the balanced equation. Ca + 2HCl → CaCl$_2$ + H$_2$ Have students write at least two mole ratios for the equation. **L2**

## Reteach

Pour 10 mL of 0.10$M$ Ba(OH)$_2$ into a test tube. Add 10 mL of 0.10$M$ sulfuric acid. Ask students to write the equation for the reaction that occurs and all the possible mole ratios. Ba(OH)$_2$ + H$_2$SO$_4$ → BaSO$_4$ + 2H$_2$O **L2**

### ✔ Assessment

**Skill** Have each student write a balanced equation on a sheet of paper and give it to another student who will write the mole ratios found in the equation. **L2**

---

## GLENCOE TECHNOLOGY

**CD-ROM**
**Chemistry: Matter and Change**
Experiment: *How Much Oxygen Is Available?*
Exploration: *Predicting Mass of Products*

---

## CHEMISTRY JOURNAL

**Interpreting Chemical Equations**

*Linguistic* Have students interpret the following equations in terms of particles, moles, and mass.

$2KClO_3 \rightarrow 2KCl + 3O_2$
$Fe_2O_3 + 3H_2 \rightarrow 2Fe + 3H_2O$

Have them demonstrate in their journals that the law of conservation of mass is observed. **L2**

National Science Content Standards
**Pages 354–355**
UCP.1, UCP.3; B.3, E.1

**1. a.** 1 molecule $N_2$ + 3 molecules $H_2$ → 2 molecules $NH_3$

1 mol $N_2$ + 3 mol $H_2$ → 2 mol $NH_3$

28.02 g $N_2$ + 6.06 g $H_2$ → 34.08 g $NH_3$

**b.** 1 molecule HCl + 1 formula unit KOH → 1 formula unit KCl + 1 molecule $H_2O$

1 mol HCl + 1 mol KOH → 1 mol KCl + 1 mol $H_2O$

36.46 g HCl + 56.11 g KOH → 74.55 g KCl + 18.02 g $H_2O$

**c.** 4 atoms Zn + 10 molecules $HNO_3$ → 4 formula units $Zn(NO_3)_2$ + 1 molecule $N_2O$ + 5 molecules $H_2O$

4 mol Zn + 10 mol $HNO_3$ → 4 mol $Zn(NO_3)_2$ + 1 mol $N_2O$ + 5 mol $H_2O$

261.56 g Zn + 630.20 g $HNO_3$ → 757.56 g $Zn(NO_3)_2$ + 44.02 g $N_2O$ + 90.10 g $H_2O$

**d.** 2 atoms Mg + 1 molecule $O_2$ → 2 formula units MgO

2 mol Mg + 1 mol $O_2$ → 2 mol MgO

48.62 g Mg + 32.00 g $O_2$ → 80.62 g MgO

**e.** 2 atoms Na + 2 molecules $H_2O$ → 2 formula units NaOH + 1 molecule $H_2$

2 mol Na + 2 mol $H_2O$ → 2 mol NaOH + 1 mol $H_2$

45.98 g Na + 36.04 g $H_2O$ → 80.00 g NaOH + 2.02 g $H_2$

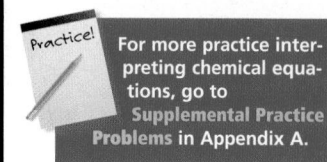

Practice! **For more practice interpreting chemical equations, go to Supplemental Practice Problems in Appendix A.**

**Figure 12-2**

Bromine is one of the two elements that are liquids at room temperature. Mercury is the other. Aluminum is a lightweight metal that resists corrosion. Aluminum and bromine react vigorously to form the ionic compound aluminum bromide.

## PRACTICE PROBLEMS

**1.** Interpret the following balanced chemical equations in terms of particles, moles, and mass. Show that the law of conservation of mass is observed.

**a.** $N_2(g) + 3H_2(g) \rightarrow 2NH_3(g)$

**b.** $HCl(aq) + KOH(aq) \rightarrow KCl(aq) + H_2O(l)$

**c.** $4Zn(s) + 10HNO_3(aq) \rightarrow 4Zn(NO_3)_2(aq) + N_2O(g) + 5H_2O(l)$

**d.** $2Mg(s) + O_2(g) \rightarrow 2MgO(s)$

**e.** $2Na(s) + 2H_2O(l) \rightarrow 2NaOH(aq) + H_2(g)$

**Mole ratios** You have seen that the coefficients in a chemical equation indicate the relationships among moles of reactants and products. For example, return to the reaction between iron and oxygen described in **Table 12-1**. The equation indicates that four moles of iron react with three moles of oxygen. It also indicates that four moles of iron react to produce two moles of iron(III) oxide. How many moles of oxygen react to produce two moles of iron(III) oxide? You can use the relationships between coefficients to write conversion factors called mole ratios. A **mole ratio** is a ratio between the numbers of moles of any two substances in a balanced chemical equation. As another example, consider the reaction shown in **Figure 12-2**. Aluminum reacts with bromine to form aluminum bromide. Aluminum bromide is used as a catalyst to speed up a variety of chemical reactions.

$$2Al(s) + 3Br_2(l) \rightarrow 2AlBr_3(s)$$

What mole ratios can be written for this reaction? Starting with the reactant aluminum, you can write a mole ratio that relates the moles of aluminum to the moles of bromine. Another mole ratio shows how the moles of aluminum relate to the moles of aluminum bromide.

$$\frac{2 \text{ mol Al}}{3 \text{ mol Br}_2} \quad \text{and} \quad \frac{2 \text{ mol Al}}{2 \text{ mol AlBr}_3}$$

Two other mole ratios show how the moles of bromine relate to the moles of the other two substances in the equation, aluminum and aluminum bromide.

$$\frac{3 \text{ mol Br}_2}{2 \text{ mol Al}} \quad \text{and} \quad \frac{3 \text{ mol Br}_2}{2 \text{ mol AlBr}_3}$$

Similarly, two ratios relate the moles of aluminum bromide to the moles of aluminum and bromine.

$$\frac{2 \text{ mol AlBr}_3}{2 \text{ mol Al}} \quad \text{and} \quad \frac{2 \text{ mol AlBr}_3}{3 \text{ mol Br}_2}$$

Six ratios define all the mole relationships in this equation. Each of the three substances in the equation forms a ratio with the two other substances.

What mole ratios can be written for the decomposition of potassium chlorate ($KClO_3$)? This reaction is sometimes used to obtain small amounts of oxygen in the laboratory.

$$2KClO_3(s) \rightarrow 2KCl(s) + 3O_2(g)$$

Each substance forms a mole ratio with the two other substances in the reaction. Thus, each substance should be the numerator of two mole ratios.

---

## Section **12.1** Assessment

**4.** the study of quantitative relationships among amounts of reactants and products

**5.** particles (atoms, molecules, formula units), moles, and mass

**6.** a ratio between the moles of any two substances in a balanced chemical equation

**7. a.** $N_2(g) + 3H_2(g) \rightarrow 2NH_3(g)$
1 mol $N_2$/3 mol $H_2$, 1 mol $N_2$/2 mol $NH_3$, 3 mol $H_2$/1 mol $N_2$, 3 mol $H_2$/2 mol $NH_3$, 2 mol $NH_3$/1 mol $N_2$, 2 mol $NH_3$/3 mol $H_2$

**b.** $2H_2O_2 \rightarrow 2H_2O + O_2$
2 mol $H_2O_2$/2 mol $H_2O$, 2 mol $H_2O_2$/1 mol $O_2$, 2 mol $H_2O$/2 mol $H_2O_2$,

$$\frac{2 \text{ mol } KClO_3}{2 \text{ mol } KCl} \quad \text{and} \quad \frac{2 \text{ mol } KClO_3}{3 \text{ mol } O_2}$$

$$\frac{2 \text{ mol } KCl}{2 \text{ mol } KClO_3} \quad \text{and} \quad \frac{2 \text{ mol } KCl}{3 \text{ mol } O_2}$$

$$\frac{3 \text{ mol } O_2}{2 \text{ mol } KClO_3} \quad \text{and} \quad \frac{3 \text{ mol } O_2}{2 \text{ mol } KCl}$$

Can you explain why each reactant and product is in the numerator two times?

Six mole ratios define all the relationships in this reaction, which has three participating species. How many could you write for a reaction involving a total of four reactants and products? A simple way to find out is to multiply the number of species in the equation by the next lower number. Thus, you could write 12 mole ratios for a reaction involving four species.

### PRACTICE PROBLEMS

**2.** Determine all possible mole ratios for the following balanced chemical equations.

   **a.** $4Al(s) + 3O_2(g) \rightarrow 2Al_2O_3(s)$
   **b.** $3Fe(s) + 4H_2O(l) \rightarrow Fe_3O_4(s) + 4H_2(g)$
   **c.** $2HgO(s) \rightarrow 2Hg(l) + O_2(g)$

**3.** Balance the following equations and determine the possible mole ratios.

   **a.** $ZnO(s) + HCl(aq) \rightarrow ZnCl_2(aq) + H_2O(l)$
   **b.** butane $(C_4H_{10})$ + oxygen $\rightarrow$ carbon dioxide + water

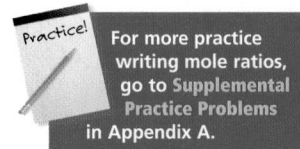

For more practice writing mole ratios, go to **Supplemental Practice Problems** in Appendix A.

You may be wondering why you need to learn to write mole ratios. As you will see in the next section, mole ratios are the key to calculations based upon a chemical equation. Suppose you know the amount of one reactant you will use in a chemical reaction. With the chemical equation and the mole ratios, you can calculate the amount of any other reactant in the equation and the maximum amount of product you can obtain.

## Section 12.1 Assessment

**4.** What is stoichiometry?

**5.** List three ways in which a balanced chemical equation can be interpreted.

**6.** What is a mole ratio?

**7. Thinking Critically** Write a balanced chemical equation for each reaction and determine the possible mole ratios.

   **a.** Nitrogen reacts with hydrogen to produce ammonia.
   **b.** Hydrogen peroxide $(H_2O_2)$ decomposes to produce water and oxygen.

   **c.** Pieces of zinc react with a phosphoric acid solution to produce solid zinc phosphate and hydrogen gas.

**8. Formulating Models** Use the balanced chemical equation to determine the mole ratios for the reaction of hydrogen and oxygen, $2H_2(g) + O_2(g) \rightarrow 2H_2O$. Make a drawing showing six molecules of hydrogen reacting with the correct number of oxygen molecules. Show the number of molecules of water produced.

---

2 mol $H_2O$/1 mol $O_2$, 1 mol $O_2$/2 mol $H_2O_2$, 1 mol $O_2$/2 mol $H_2O$

**c.** $3Zn(s) + 2H_3PO_4(aq) \rightarrow Zn_3(PO_4)_2(aq) + 3H_2(g)$
3 mol Zn/2 mol $H_3PO_4$, 3 mol Zn/1 mol $Zn_3(PO_4)_2$, 3 mol Zn/3 mol $H_2$, 2 mol $H_3PO_4$/3 mol Zn, 2 mol $H_3PO_4$/1 mol $Zn_3PO_4$, 2 mol $H_3PO_4$/3 mol $H_2$, 1 mol

$Zn_3(PO_4)_2$/3 mol Zn, 1 mol $Zn_3(PO_4)_2$/2 mol $H_3PO_4$, 1 mol $Zn_3(PO_4)_2$/3 mol $H_2$, 3 mol $H_2$/3 mol Zn, 3 mol $H_2$/2 mol $H_3PO_4$, 3 mol $H_2$/1 mol $Zn_3(PO_4)_2$

**8.** Drawing should show six molecules of $H_2$, three molecules of $O_2$, and six molecules of $H_2O$. See Solutions Manual.

---

# 1 Focus

Before presenting the lesson, display **Section Focus Transparency 44** on the overhead projector. Have students answer the accompanying questions using **Section Focus Transparency Master 44. L1 ELL**

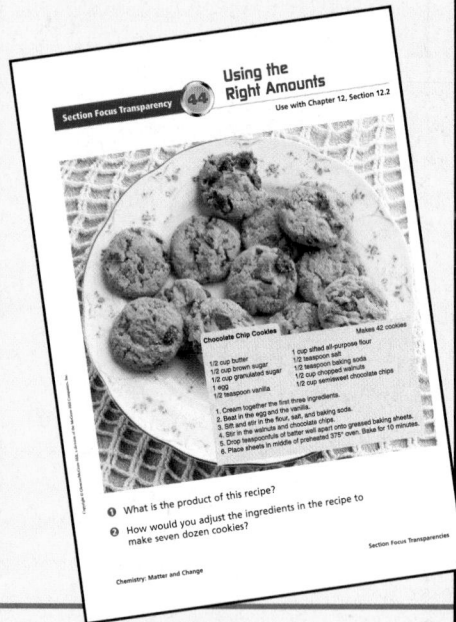

# 2 Teach
## Concept Development

Point out to students that moles are always involved when solving stiochiometry problems. Remind them that the mole ratio is needed to convert from one substance in the balanced equation to another substance. If they are in doubt about how to proceed in solving a problem, remind them to "go to moles first."

**National Science Content Standards**

Pages 356–359
UCP.1, UCP.3; B.3; E.1

### Objectives

- **Explain** the sequence of steps used in solving stoichiometric problems.
- **Use** the steps to solve stoichiometric problems.

Suppose a chemist needs to obtain a certain amount of product from a reaction. How much reactant must be used? Or, suppose the chemist wants to know how much product will form if a certain amount of reactant is used. Chemists use stoichiometric calculations to answer these questions.

## Using Stoichiometry

Recall that stoichiometry is the study of quantitative relationships between the amounts of reactants used and the amounts of products formed by a chemical reaction. What are the tools needed for stoichiometric calculations? All stoichiometric calculations begin with a balanced chemical equation, which indicates relative amounts of the substances that react and the products that form. Mole ratios based on the balanced chemical equation are also needed. You learned to write mole ratios in Section 12.1. Finally, mass-to-mole conversions similar to those you learned about in Chapter 11 are required.

**Stoichiometric mole-to-mole conversion** The vigorous reaction between potassium and water is shown in **Figure 12-3**. How can you determine the number of moles of hydrogen produced when 0.0400 mole of potassium is used? Start by writing the balanced chemical equation.

$$2K(s) + 2H_2O(l) \rightarrow 2KOH(aq) + H_2(g)$$

Then, identify the substance that you know and the substance that you need to determine. The given substance is 0.0400 mole of potassium. The unknown is the number of moles of hydrogen. Because the quantity of the given substance is in moles and the unknown substance is to be determined in moles, this problem is a mole-to-mole conversion.

To solve the problem, you need to know how the unknown moles of hydrogen are related to the known moles of potassium. In Section 12.1 you learned to use the balanced chemical equation to write mole ratios that describe mole relationships. Mole ratios are used as conversion factors to convert a known number of moles of one substance to moles of another substance in the same chemical reaction. What mole ratio could be used to convert moles of potassium to moles of hydrogen? In the correct mole ratio, the moles of unknown ($H_2$) should be the numerator and the moles of known (K) should be the denominator. The correct mole ratio is

$$\frac{1 \text{ mol } H_2}{2 \text{ mol } K}$$

This mole ratio can be used to convert the known number of moles of potassium to a number of moles of hydrogen. Remember that when you use a conversion factor, the units must cancel.

$$\text{moles of known} \times \frac{\text{moles of unknown}}{\text{moles of known}} = \text{moles of unknown}$$

$$0.0400 \text{ mol K} \times \frac{1 \text{ mol } H_2}{2 \text{ mol K}} = 0.0200 \text{ mol } H_2$$

If you put 0.0400 mol K into water, 0.0200 mol $H_2$ will be produced. The **How It Works** feature at the end of this chapter shows the importance of mole ratios.

**Figure 12–3**

Potassium metal reacts vigorously with water, releasing so much heat that the hydrogen gas formed in the reaction catches fire.

---

**DIFFERENTIATED INSTRUCTION**

### Learning Disabled

*Intrapersonal* Stress the importance of solving stoichiometric problems step by step and understanding the reason for each step. Ask students why the balanced chemical equation is important. It determines the mole ratios. Give them an equation and ask them to explain how they would convert from moles of one substance to moles of another substance in the same equation.

Use the mole ratio: moles of unknown substance divided by moles of known substance. This may be a point of confusion. Have students write a mole ratio on one side of an index card and the inverse of the same ratio on the other side. As they solve a problem, they can look at the index card to determine which ratio gives the correct unit for the answer. **L2**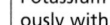

**Stoichiometric Mole-to-Mole Conversion**

One disadvantage of burning propane ($C_3H_8$) is that carbon dioxide ($CO_2$) is one of the products. The released carbon dioxide increases the growing concentration of $CO_2$ in the atmosphere. How many moles of carbon dioxide are produced when 10.0 moles of propane are burned in excess oxygen in a gas grill?

**1. Analyze the Problem**

You are given moles of the reactant propane, and moles of the product carbon dioxide must be found. The balanced chemical equation must be written. Conversion from moles of $C_3H_8$ to moles of $CO_2$ is required. The correct mole ratio has moles of unknown substance in the numerator and moles of known substance in the denominator.

**Known**

moles of propane = 10.0 mol $C_3H_8$

**Unknown**

moles of carbon dioxide = ? mol $CO_2$

**2. Solve for the Unknown**

Write the balanced chemical equation. Label the known substance and the unknown substance.

$$\overset{10.0\ mol}{C_3H_8(g)} + 5O_2(g) \rightarrow \overset{?\ mol}{3CO_2(g)} + 4H_2O(g)$$

Determine the mole ratio that relates mol $CO_2$ to mol $C_3H_8$.

$$\frac{3\ mol\ CO_2}{1\ mol\ C_3H_8}$$

Multiply the known number of moles of $C_3H_8$ by the mole ratio.

$$10.0\ mol\ C_3H_8 \times \frac{3\ mol\ CO_2}{1\ mol\ C_3H_8} = 30.0\ mol\ CO_2$$

Burning 10.0 mol $C_3H_8$ produces 30.0 mol $CO_2$.

**3. Evaluate the Answer**

The given number of moles has three significant figures. Therefore, the answer must have three digits. The balanced chemical equation indicates that 1 mol $C_3H_8$ produces 3 mol $CO_2$. Thus, 10.0 mol $C_3H_8$ would produce three times as many moles of $CO_2$, or 30.0 mol.

**PRACTICE** PROBLEMS

9. Sulfuric acid is formed when sulfur dioxide reacts with oxygen and water. Write the balanced chemical equation for the reaction. If 12.5 mol $SO_2$ reacts, how many mol $H_2SO_4$ can be produced? How many mol $O_2$ is needed?

10. A reaction between methane and sulfur produces carbon disulfide ($CS_2$), a liquid often used in the production of cellophane.

_____ $CH_4(g)$ + _____ $S_8(s)$ → _____ $CS_2(l)$ + _____ $H_2S(g)$

a. Balance the equation.

b. Calculate the mol $CS_2$ produced when 1.50 mol $S_8$ is used.

c. How many mol $H_2S$ is produced?

**Math Handbook**

Review dimensional analysis in the **Math Handbook** on page 900 of this text.

**Practice!** For more practice converting from moles of one substance to moles of another substance in a chemical equation, go to **Supplemental Practice Problems** in Appendix A.

12.2 Stoichiometric Calculations **359**

**Quick Demo**

**Quick Demo**

Punch a small hole in the center of the bottom of a potato chip or tennis ball can. Punch another hole in the side of the can an inch from the top. Tape a wood splint to a meter stick. Place the lid on the can and purge the can with hydrogen from a tank of hydrogen using the hole near the lid. Then, fill the can with hydrogen. Place tape over each hole. Place the closed can with its lid on the floor. Quickly remove the tape from both openings and light the top opening with the burning splint. Hydrogen will burn quietly with a blue flame. After several minutes, the hydrogen and oxygen mixture will ignite and the can will launch into the air. Ask students why, at first, the hydrogen burned only at the opening of the can. There was no oxygen in the can so hydrogen could combine with oxygen only at the opening. Ask why the hydrogen burned quietly, not explosively. There was only a limited amount of hydrogen in a large amount of air. Ask why the can exploded after a time. Oxygen was pulled into the can.

**Practice** PROBLEMS

Have students refer to Appendix D for complete solutions to Practice Problems.

9. $2SO_2 + 2H_2O + O_2 \rightarrow 2H_2SO_4$
12.5 mol $H_2SO_4$, 6.25 mol $O_2$

10. a. $2CH_4(g) + S_8(s) \rightarrow 2CS_2(l) + 4H_2S(g)$

b. 3.00 mol $CS_2$

c. 6.00 mol $H_2S$

**DIFFERENTIATED INSTRUCTION**

**Hearing Impaired**

**Visual-Spatial** Have students view a video clip of a shuttle launch. Show on the chalkboard that the fuel for the launch is a mixture of hydrogen and oxygen. Have students write a paragraph describing what factors engineers had to consider when using these fuels. how much hydrogen is present, how much oxygen is needed **L2**

**Resource Manager**

**Study Guide for Content Mastery,** pp. 69–70 **L2**
**Solving Problems: A Chemistry Handbook,** Section 12.2 **L2**
**Section Focus Transparency 44 and Master L1 ELL**
**Math Skills Transparency 16 and Master L2 ELL**

Using a straw, exhale into a test tube of limewater. Explain that the limewater becomes cloudy because insoluble calcium carbonate is formed. Write the equation for the reaction on the chalkboard or overhead: $CO_2(g) + CaO(aq) \rightarrow CaCO_3(s)$. Ask students to determine the mass of calcium carbonate that would be produced if you exhaled 0.0900 mol $CO_2$ into the test tube. 9.00 g $CaCO_3$ **L2**

## Assessment

**Knowledge** Have students consider the reaction of 2.50 mol calcium hydride with excess water according to this equation. $CaH_2 + 2H_2O \rightarrow Ca(OH)_2 + 2H_2$ Ask the following questions. What mass of calcium hydroxide will be produced? 185 g What mass of water is needed? 90.1 g What mass of hydrogen is produced? 10.1 g What is the mass of 2.50 mol calcium hydride? 105 g Have students verify the law of conservation of mass. 105 g $CaH_2$ + 90.1 g $H_2O$ = 185 g $Ca(OH)_2$ + 10.1 g $H_2$ **L2**

## Practice PROBLEMS

Have students refer to Appendix D for complete solutions to Practice Problems.
**11.** 177 g $Cl_2$
**12.** 88.6 g $Cl_2$

**Stoichiometric mole-to-mass conversion** Now, suppose you know the number of moles of a reactant or product in a reaction and you want to calculate the mass of another product or reactant. This situation is an example of a mole-to-mass conversion.

## EXAMPLE PROBLEM 12-3

The reaction of sodium and chlorine to form sodium chloride releases a large amount of energy in the form of light and heat. It should not surprise you, then, that a large amount of energy is required to decompose sodium chloride.

### Stoichiometric Mole-to-Mass Conversion
Determine the mass of sodium chloride or table salt (NaCl) produced when 1.25 moles of chlorine gas reacts vigorously with sodium.

**1. Analyze the Problem**

You are given the moles of the reactant $Cl_2$ and must determine the mass of the product NaCl. You must convert from moles of $Cl_2$ to moles of NaCl using the mole ratio from the equation. Then, you need to convert moles of NaCl to grams of NaCl using the molar mass as the conversion factor.

**Known**

moles of chlorine = 1.25 mol $Cl_2$

**Unknown**

mass of sodium chloride = ? g NaCl

**2. Solve for the Unknown**

Write the balanced chemical equation and identify the known and unknown substances.

$$\underset{2Na(s) \;+\;}{\overset{1.25 \text{ mol}}{}} \underset{Cl_2(g)}{} \rightarrow \underset{2NaCl(s)}{\overset{? \text{ g}}{}}$$

Write the mole ratio that relates mol NaCl to mol $Cl_2$.

$$\frac{2 \text{ mol NaCl}}{1 \text{ mol } Cl_2}$$

Multiply the number of moles of $Cl_2$ by the mole ratio.

$$1.25 \text{ mol } Cl_2 \times \frac{2 \text{ mol NaCl}}{1 \text{ mol } Cl_2} = 2.50 \text{ mol NaCl}$$

Multiply mol NaCl by the molar mass of NaCl.

$$2.50 \text{ mol NaCl} \times \frac{58.44 \text{ g NaCl}}{1 \text{ mol NaCl}} = 146 \text{ g NaCl}$$

**3. Evaluate the Answer**

The given number of moles has three significant figures, so the mass of NaCl is correctly stated with three digits. The computations are correct and the unit is as expected.

## PRACTICE PROBLEMS

Practice! For more practice converting from moles of one substance to mass of another substance in a chemical equation, go to **Supplemental Practice Problems** in Appendix A.

**11.** Titanium is a transition metal used in many alloys because it is extremely strong and lightweight. Titanium tetrachloride ($TiCl_4$) is extracted from titanium oxide using chlorine and coke (carbon).

$$TiO_2(s) + C(s) + 2Cl_2(g) \rightarrow TiCl_4(s) + CO_2(g)$$

If you begin with 1.25 mol $TiO_2$, what mass of $Cl_2$ gas is needed?

**12.** Sodium chloride is decomposed into the elements sodium and chlorine by means of electrical energy. How many grams of chlorine gas can be obtained from 2.50 mol NaCl?

## CULTURAL DIVERSITY

### Stoichiometry in Soap Making

Soap making dates to 2800 B.C. in Babylonia, where soap was used to clean wool. A fully functioning soap factory was discovered in the ruins of the Roman city of Pompeii.

Although soap-making guilds were documented during the seventh century, soap was a luxury item for the wealthy.

However, as materials became more readily available, more households made this valued substance. During the nineteenth century, soap was made in almost every household.

Crude stoichiometric techniques were used by all early soap-making peoples. Soap making requires three steps. The

first step is making lye. A soap maker in northern Europe would mix two parts potash ($K_2CO_3$) and one part of quicklime (CaO) with water until an egg would float on the mixture. The equation for the reaction is $K_2CO_3 + CaO + H_2O \rightarrow 2KOH + CaCO_3$. The second step required fat to be rendered or cleaned. In the third step, the

**Stoichiometric mass-to-mass conversion** If you were preparing to carry out a chemical reaction in the laboratory, you would need to know how much of each reactant to use in order to produce the mass of product you required. Example Problem 12-4 will demonstrate how you can use a measured mass of the known substance, the balanced chemical equation, and mole ratios from the equation to find the mass of the unknown substance. The **CHEMLAB** at the end of this chapter will provide you with laboratory experience determining a mole ratio.

**LAB**

See page 957 in Appendix E for
**Baking Soda Stoichiometry**

---

## EXAMPLE PROBLEM 12-4

### Stoichiometric Mass-to-Mass Conversion

Ammonium nitrate ($NH_4NO_3$), an important fertilizer, produces $N_2O$ gas and $H_2O$ when it decomposes. Determine the mass of water produced from the decomposition of 25.0 g of solid ammonium nitrate.

**1. Analyze the Problem**

You are given the mass of the reactant and will need to write the balanced chemical equation. You then must convert from the mass of the reactant to moles of the reactant. You will next use a mole ratio to relate moles of the reactant to moles of the product. Finally, you will use the molar mass to convert from moles of the product to the mass of the product.

**Known**

mass of ammonium nitrate = 25.0 g $NH_4NO_3$

**Unknown**

mass of water = ? g $H_2O$

**2. Solve for the Unknown**

Write the balanced chemical equation for the reaction and identify the known and unknown substances.

$$\underset{25.0\ g}{NH_4NO_3(s)} \rightarrow N_2O(g) + \underset{?g}{2H_2O(g)}$$

Convert grams of $NH_4NO_3$ to moles of $NH_4NO_3$ using the inverse of molar mass as the conversion factor.

$$25.0\ g\ NH_4NO_3 \times \frac{1\ mol\ NH_4NO_3}{80.04\ g\ NH_4NO_3} = 0.312\ mol\ NH_4NO_3$$

Determine from the equation the mole ratio of mol $H_2O$ to mol $NH_4NO_3$. The unknown quantity is the numerator.

$$\frac{2\ mol\ H_2O}{1\ mol\ NH_4NO_3}$$

Multiply mol $NH_4NO_3$ by the mole ratio.

$$0.312\ mol\ NH_4NO_3 \times \frac{2\ mol\ H_2O}{1\ mol\ NH_4NO_3} = 0.624\ mol\ H_2O$$

Calculate the mass of $H_2O$ using molar mass as the conversion factor.

$$0.624\ mol\ H_2O \times \frac{18.02\ g\ H_2O}{1\ mol\ H_2O} = 11.2\ g\ H_2O$$

**3. Evaluate the Answer**

The number of significant figures in the answer, three, is determined by the given moles of ammonium nitrate. The calculations are correct and the unit is appropriate.

The vigorous decomposition of ammonium nitrate attests to its use in explosives. However, ammonium nitrate is also widely used as a fertilizer because it is 100 percent available for plant use.

---

## Applying Chemistry

**TECH PREP**

Prior to 1940, the primary pigment in lead-based paints was $PbCO_3 \cdot Pb(OH)_2$. Today, we know that lead in household products poses a health hazard, but old paint is still found in many homes. The level of lead in homes can be determined using a lead detection kit. One lead test kit uses a swab containing potassium rhodizonate ($C_6K_2O_6$). The swab is rubbed over the surface to be tested. If lead is present, a pink color appears on the swab due to the presence of lead(II) rhodizonate. The reaction is a single replacement described by the equation $Pb^{2+} + C_6K_2O_6 \rightarrow C_6PbO_6 + 2K^+$. The larger the amount of lead, the redder the swab becomes. This kit can detect amounts of lead as low as 0.006 g.

## CHEMLAB

ChemLab 12, located at the end of the chapter, can be used at this point in the chapter.

### Resource Manager

Math Skills Transparency 17 and Master **L2** **ELL**
ChemLab and MiniLab Worksheets, p. 45 **L2**
Teaching Transparency 38 and Master **L2** **ELL**
Challenge Problems, p. 12 **L3**

**National Science Content Standards**

Pages 360–361
UCP.1, UCP.3; B.3

---

fat and lye were mixed in a ratio of eight pots of lye for every pot of rendered fat. This mixture was heated in a large-bottomed vessel. NaOH or KOH (lye) + fat → soap + glycerol. If a chicken feather dissolved in the soap mixture, the lye wasn't used up and the mixture was left in the

sun for a week. This recipe produced a soft soap; sodium chloride was added to make the soap hard. Scents were also added and the soap was rolled into balls or cut into bars to be stored.

Deer fat, whale blubber, tallow, and olive oil have been used as sources of fat

in soap depending upon which was available in the area. Countries bordering the Mediterranean Sea used the ashes of Mediterranean shrubs instead of potash ($K_2CO_3$). Ashes from these plants are rich in sodium carbonate, and were a valuable trade item called barilla.

Have students refer to Appendix D for complete solutions to Practice Problems.

**13.** 64.64 g $N_2$

**14.** $2SO_2(g) + O_2(g) + 2H_2O(l) \rightarrow 2H_2SO_4(aq)$, 3.83 g $H_2SO_4$

## miniLAB

### Purpose
Students will use stoichiometry to predict the mass of a product and compare it with the experimental mass.

### Process Skills
Collecting and interpreting data, predicting, using numbers

### Safety Precautions
Warn students about the hot crucible. Goggles and an apron should be worn.

### Disposal
The sodium carbonate product can be put into the trash.

### Teaching Strategies
• Have students calculate the final mass of the product before performing the experiment.
• Moderate heat will drive off the carbon dioxide and water.

### Expected Results
A mass of 3.12 g baking soda may yield approximately 1.90 g $Na_2CO_3$.

### Analysis
1. During heating, the product started looking "wet" and bubbles appeared. In time, the product "dried out."
2. Percent yield = 1.90 g/1.97 g × 100 = 96.4%; calculated and actual masses should be similar. Experimental error could explain a difference.

### ✓ Assessment
**Skill** Calculate the mass of $CO_2$ produced in the experiment. (3.12 g $NaHCO_3$) × (1 mol $NaHCO_3$/90.01 g $NaHCO_3$) × (1 mol $CO_2$/2 mol $NaHCO_3$) × (44.01 g $CO_2$/1mol $CO_2$) = 0.763 g $CO_2$ **L2**

**Practice!** For more practice converting from mass of one substance to mass of another substance in a chemical equation, go to Supplemental Practice Problems in Appendix A.

**13.** One in a series of reactions that inflate air bags in automobiles is the decomposition of sodium azide ($NaN_3$).

$$2NaN_3(s) \rightarrow 2Na(s) + 3N_2(g)$$

Determine the mass of $N_2$ produced if 100.0 g $NaN_3$ is decomposed.

**14.** In the formation of acid rain, sulfur dioxide reacts with oxygen and water in the air to form sulfuric acid. Write the balanced chemical equation for the reaction. If 2.50 g $SO_2$ react with excess oxygen and water, how many grams of $H_2SO_4$ are produced?

The steps you followed in Example Problem 12-4 are illustrated in **Figure 12-4** and described below it. Use the steps as a guide when you do stoichiometric calculations until you become thoroughly familiar with the procedure. Study **Figure 12-4** as you read.

The specified unit of the given substance determines at what point you will start your calculations. If the amount of the given substance is in moles, step 2 is omitted and step 3, mole-to-mole conversion, becomes the starting point for the calculations. However, if mass is the starting unit, calculations begin with step 2. The end point of the calculation depends upon the specified unit of the unknown substance. If the answer is to be obtained in moles, the calculation is finished with step 3. If the mass of the unknown is to be determined, you must go on to step 4.

Like any other type of problem, stoichiometric calculations require practice. You can begin to practice your skills in the **miniLAB** that follows.

## miniLAB

### Baking Soda Stoichiometry

**Predicting** When baking soda is an ingredient in your recipe, its purpose is to make the batter rise and produce a product with a light and fluffy texture. That's because baking soda, or sodium hydrogen carbonate ($NaHCO_3$), decomposes upon heating to form carbon dioxide gas.

$$2NaHCO_3 \rightarrow Na_2CO_3 + CO_2 + H_2O$$

Predict how much sodium carbonate ($Na_2CO_3$) is produced when baking soda decomposes.

**Materials** ring stand, ring, clay triangle, crucible, crucible tongs, Bunsen burner, balance, 3.0 g baking soda ($NaHCO_3$)

**Procedure**

1. Measure the mass of a clean, dry crucible. Add about 3.0 g of $NaHCO_3$ and measure the combined mass of the crucible and $NaHCO_3$. Record both masses in your data table and calculate the mass of the $NaHCO_3$.

2. Use this starting mass of baking soda and the balanced chemical equation to calculate the mass of $Na_2CO_3$ that will be produced.

3. Set up a ring stand with a ring and clay triangle for heating the crucible.

4. Heat the crucible slowly at first and then with a stronger flame for 7–8 min. Use tongs to remove the hot crucible. Record your observations during the heating.

5. Allow the crucible to cool and then obtain the mass of the crucible and sodium carbonate.

### Analysis

1. What were your observations during the heating of the baking soda?

2. How did your calculated mass of sodium carbonate compare with the actual mass you obtained from the experiment? If the two masses are different, suggest reasons for the difference.

## CHEMISTRY JOURNAL

### How much acid is neutralized?

**Logical-Mathematical** Have students find the active ingredients on the label of a container of antacid tablets and identify the compound that neutralizes stomach acid. Have them note the recommended dosage and the amount of the neutralizing ingredient per tablet. Ask students to determine the mass of the active ingredient per dose. If the active ingredient is a metal hydroxide, the hydroxide reacts with HCl to produce a metal chloride and water. If the active ingredient is a metal carbonate, the products are a metal chloride, carbon dioxide, and water. Have students write the equation of the reaction of the antacid. Using the mass of the active ingredient per dose, have them determine the mass of hydrochloric acid neutralized per dose. **L2**

Mass of given substance

no direct conversion

Mass of unknown substance

Step 1
Start with a
balanced equation

Step 2
Convert
from grams
to moles

$\frac{1\ mol}{number\ of\ grams}$

Step 4
Convert
from moles
to grams

$\frac{number\ of\ grams}{1\ mol}$

Mole of given substance

$\frac{moles\ of\ unknown}{moles\ of\ given}$

Step 3
Convert from moles
of given to moles of
unknown

Moles of unknown substance

**Figure 12-4**

Follow the steps from the balanced equation to the mass of the unknown. Note that there is no shortcut from the mass of the given substance to the mass of the unknown substance. The route goes through the mole. However, you can follow the arrow from step 1 to step 3 if the amount of the given substance is in moles.

### Steps in Stoichiometric Calculations

1. *Write a balanced chemical equation.* Interpret the equation in terms of moles.

2. *Determine the moles of the given substance using a mass-to-mole conversion.* Use the inverse of the molar mass as the conversion factor.

3. *Determine the moles of the unknown substance from the moles of the given substance.* Use the appropriate mole ratio from the balanced chemical equation as the conversion factor.

4. *From the moles of the unknown substance, determine the mass of the unknown substance using a mole-to-mass conversion.* Use the molar mass as the conversion factor.

## Section 12.2 Assessment

**15.** Why is a balanced chemical equation needed in solving stoichiometric calculations?

**16.** When solving stoichiometric problems, how is the correct mole ratio expressed?

**17.** List the four steps used in solving stoichiometric problems.

**18.** **Thinking Critically** In a certain industrial process, magnesium reacts with liquid bromine. How would a chemical engineer determine the mass of bromine needed to react completely with a given mass of magnesium?

**19.** **Concept Mapping** Many cities use calcium chloride to prevent ice from forming on roadways. To produce calcium chloride, calcium carbonate (limestone) is reacted with hydrochloric acid according to this equation.

$$CaCO_3(s) + 2HCl(aq) \rightarrow$$
$$CaCl_2(aq) + H_2O(l) + CO_2(g)$$

Create a concept map that describes how you can determine the mass of calcium chloride produced if the mass of hydrochloric acid is given.

## 3 Assess
### Check for Understanding

 *Logical-Mathematical* Write the balanced equation for the reaction between iron and sulfur on the chalkboard. $16Fe + 3S_8 \rightarrow 8Fe_2S_3$ Have students determine the mass of iron(III) sulfide produced if 7.00 g of iron is used. 13.0 g $Fe_2S_3$ **L2**

### Reteach

 *Linguistic* Write the equation for the production of glucose on the chalkboard or overhead. $6CO_2 + 6H_2O \rightarrow C_6H_{12}O_6 + 6O_2$ Tell students that 88.0 g of carbon dioxide reacts and they must calculate how many grams of glucose are produced. Before they pick up their pencils and calculators, have them verbalize each step in the solution and explain why each step is needed. Once they can explain each step, they will be able to solve the problem. 60.0 g $C_6H_{12}O_6$

### ✔ Assessment

**Knowledge** Have each student write a balanced chemical equation on a piece of paper and give the mass of one of the products or reactants. The student can then exchange papers with a classmate and each calculate the mass of another substance in the equation. The paper can then be passed to other students until the masses of all products and reactants have been calculated. Using the results of the calculations, have each student verify the law of conservation of mass for the equation that he or she wrote. **L2** **COOP LEARN**

## Section 12.2 Assessment

**15.** The coefficients in the balanced equation indicate the molar relationship between each pair of reactants and products.

**16.** moles of unknown/moles of known

**17.** 1. Balance the equation.
2. Convert the mass of the known substance to moles of known substance.
3. Use the mole ratio to convert from moles of the known to moles of the unknown.
4. Convert moles of unknown to mass of the unknown.

**18.** Write a balanced equation. Convert the given mass of magnesium to moles. Use the mole ratio from the balanced equation to convert moles of magnesium to moles of bromine. Convert from moles of bromine to mass of bromine.

**19.** Concept maps will vary, but all should show the use of these conversion factors: the inverse of molar mass, the mole ratio, the molar mass.

**363**

# 1 Focus

Before presenting the lesson, display **Section Focus Transparency 45** on the overhead projector. Have students answer the accompanying questions using **Section Focus Transparency Master 45.** L1 ELL

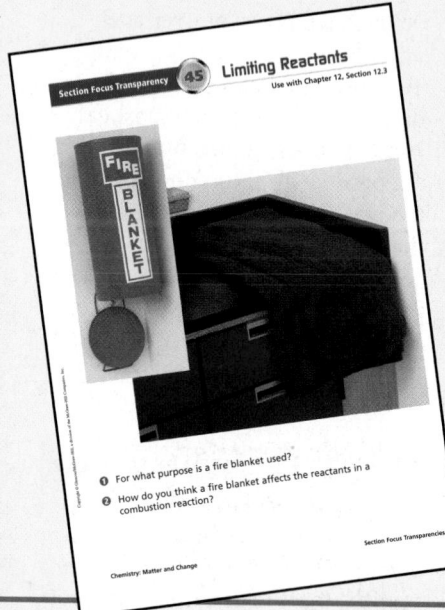

# 2 Teach

### Figure Caption Questions

**Figure 12-5** Which tool is limiting? Which tools are in excess? *hammer; two screw drivers and one pliers*

**Figure 12-6** Which reactant is in excess? *nitrogen*

### In-Text Question

**Page 364** What was the excess reactant in the reaction of potassium permanganate and sodium hydrogen sulfite? *sodium hydrogen sulfite*

### National Science Content Standards

**Pages 362–365**
UCP.1, UCP.3; A.1; B.3; E.1, E.2; F.1

**364**

---

## Section 12.3  Limiting Reactants

### Objectives

- **Identify** the limiting reactant in a chemical equation.
- **Identify** the excess reactant and **calculate** the amount remaining after the reaction is complete.
- **Calculate** the mass of a product when the amounts of more than one reactant are given.

### Vocabulary

limiting reactant
excess reactant

**Figure 12-5**

Each tool set must have one hammer so only four sets can be assembled. Which tool is limiting? Which tools are in excess?

At a school dance, the music begins and boys and girls pair up to dance. If there are more boys than girls, some boys will be left without partners. The same is true of reactants in a chemical reaction. Rarely in nature are reactants in a chemical reaction present in the exact ratios specified by the balanced equation. Generally, one or more reactants are in excess and the reaction proceeds until all of one reactant is used up.

### Why do reactions stop?

When a chemical reaction is carried out in the laboratory, the same principle applies. Usually, one or more reactants are in excess, while one is limited. The amount of product depends upon the reactant that is limited.

Remember the reaction between potassium permanganate and sodium hydrogen sulfite in the **DISCOVERY LAB.** As you added colorless sodium hydrogen sulfite to purple potassium permanganate, the color faded as a reaction took place. Finally, the solution was colorless. You could have continued adding sodium hydrogen sulfite, but would any further reaction have taken place? You are correct if you said that no further reaction could take place because no potassium permanganate was available to react. Potassium permanganate was a limiting reactant. As the name implies, the **limiting reactant** limits the extent of the reaction and, thereby, determines the amount of product. A portion of all of the other reactants remains after the reaction stops. These left-over reactants are called **excess reactants**. What was the excess reactant in the reaction of potassium permanganate and sodium hydrogen sulfite?

To help you understand limiting reactants, consider the analogy in **Figure 12-5**. How many tool sets can be assembled from the items shown if each complete tool set consists of one pair of pliers, one hammer, and two screwdrivers? You can see that four complete tool sets can be assembled. The number of tool sets is limited by the number of available hammers. Pliers and screwdrivers remain in excess. Chemical reactions work in a similar way.

**Tools available**

**Sets of tools**

**Set 1**

**Set 2**

**Set 3**

**Set 4**

**Extra tools**

---

## Maximum Yield of Carbon Dioxide

*Interpersonal* Have interested student groups design an experiment to determine the maximum yield of carbon dioxide produced by the reaction of baking soda with vinegar. Suggested equipment includes a plastic soft drink bottle, vinegar, baking soda, a balloon to cover the mouth of the bottle, and a teaspoon. One teaspoonful of baking soda is approximately 10 g and one teaspoonful of vinegar is approximately 4.9 mL. Vinegar is 5% acetic acid. Suggest that students use a constant amount of baking soda (one teaspoonful) and vary the amount of vinegar added. Ask students to find out if there is a point at which no more product is produced? Have students place their experimental designs and their results in their portfolios. L2 COOP LEARN P

Before reaction                          After reaction

3 Nitrogen molecules    3 Hydrogen molecules          2 Ammonia molecules    2 Nitrogen molecules
(6 Nitrogen atoms)      (6 Hydrogen atoms)                                   (4 Nitrogen atoms)

The calculations you did in Section 12.2 were based on having the reactants present in the ratio described by the balanced chemical equation. How can you calculate the amount of product formed when one reactant limits the amount of product and the other is in excess? The first thing you must do is determine which reactant is the limiting reactant.

Consider the reaction shown in **Figure 12-6** in which three molecules of nitrogen ($N_2$) and three molecules of hydrogen ($H_2$) react to form ammonia ($NH_3$). You can visualize that in the first step of the reaction, all the nitrogen molecules and hydrogen molecules are separated into individual atoms. These are the atoms available for reassembling into ammonia molecules just like the tools in **Figure 12-5** before they were assembled into tool kits. How many molecules of ammonia will be produced from the available atoms? Four tool kits could be assembled from the tools because only four hammers were available. Two ammonia molecules can be assembled from the hydrogen and nitrogen atoms because only six hydrogen atoms are available, three for each ammonia molecule. When the hydrogen is gone, two molecules of nitrogen remain unreacted. Thus, hydrogen is the limiting reactant and nitrogen is the excess reactant. It's important to know which reactant is the limiting reactant because, as you have just learned, the amount of product formed depends upon this reactant.

## Calculating the Product When a Reactant Is Limited

How can you determine which reactant is limited? As an example, consider the formation of disulfur dichloride ($S_2Cl_2$). Disulfur dichloride is used to vulcanize rubber, a process that makes rubber harder, stronger, and less likely to become soft when hot or brittle when cold. In the production of disulfur dichloride, molten sulfur reacts with chlorine gas according to this equation.

$$S_8(l) + 4Cl_2(g) \longrightarrow 4S_2Cl_2(l)$$

If 200.0 g of sulfur reacts with 100.0 g of chlorine, what mass of disulfur dichloride is produced?

Masses of both reactants are given. You must first determine which one is the limiting reactant because the reaction will stop producing product when the limiting reactant is used up. Identifying the limiting reactant involves finding the number of moles of each reactant. This is done by converting the masses of chlorine and sulfur to moles. Multiply each mass by the conversion factor that relates moles and mass, the inverse of the molar mass.

$$100.0 \ g \ Cl_2 \times \frac{1 \ mol \ Cl_2}{70.91 \ g \ Cl_2} = 1.410 \ mol \ Cl_2$$

$$200.0 \ g \ S_8 \times \frac{1 \ mol \ S_8}{256.5 \ g \ S_8} = 0.7797 \ mol \ S_8$$

**Figure 12-6**

Refer to **Table C-1** in Appendix C for a key to atom color conventions. Check to see whether all the atoms present before the reaction are present after the reaction. Some nitrogen molecules were unchanged in the reaction. Which reactant is in excess?

**Chemistry Online**

**Topic: Limiting Reactants**
To learn more about limiting reactants, visit the Chemistry Web site at **chemistrymc.com**

**Activity:** Research and explain how nutrients in soil can be depleted when crops are grown on a plot of land year after year. What is the limiting reactant in this case? How may the soil be enriched?

12.3 Limiting Reactants **365**

---

---

**DIFFERENTIATED INSTRUCTION**

## Gifted

**Interpersonal** Have capable students divide into groups and tell them they are to form their own cookie company. They have the following ingredients available for making the cookies described in the Assessment on this page.

1000 c flour            1.00 L salt
1.00 L baking soda      40 sticks butter
500 c granulated sugar  500 c brown sugar
10 doz eggs             1.00 L vanilla
100 oz chocolate chips
(One teaspoon = 4.9 mL)
Which of the ingredients is the limiting ingredient? butter
How many dozen cookies can be made? 80 dozen If a dozen cookies sells for $4.00, how much money would the company gross? $320.00 **L3** **COOP LEARN**

**365**

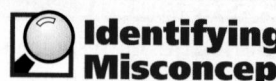
## Identifying Misconceptions

Students often have difficulty determining the limiting reactant when given the mass of more than one reactant.

### Uncover the Misconception
Ask how much magnesium oxide is produced when 48.6 g of magnesium reacts with 64.0 g of oxygen according to this equation: $2Mg + O_2 \rightarrow 2MgO$. Have students determine the moles of each of the reactants given in the problem. 2.00 mol Mg, 2.00 mol $O_2$ Ask which is the limiting reactant. Mg Ask what is the mass of magnesium oxide produced. 80.6g

### Demonstrate the Concept
Use nuts and bolts to represent moles of atoms. Represent 2 mol Mg by 2 bolts and 2 mol $O_2$ by 4 nuts. Have students identify the mole ratio between $O_2$ molecules and Mg atoms. 1 mol $O_2$ molecules (2 nuts)/2 mol Mg atoms (2 bolts) Ask what is in excess. 2 nuts or 1 mol $O_2$ Represent a mole of magnesium oxide using 1 bolt and 1 nut. Ask how many MgO formula units can be formed. 2 units of 1 nut and 1 bolt with 2 nuts left over

### Assess New Knowledge
Give students this problem. A 54.0-g sample of aluminum reacts with 508 g of iodine according to this equation: $2Al + 3I_2 \rightarrow 2AlI_3$. Have them determine the number of moles of each reactant. 2.00 mol Al, 2.00 mol $I_2$ Ask which is the limiting reactant. $I_2$ Ask how many moles of $AlI_3$ are formed. 1.33 mol

## Biology
### CONNECTION

Vitamins and minerals are needed in small amounts in your daily diet. These substances are essential to the reactions in normal metabolism, growth and development, and regulation of the functioning of your body's cells.

Vitamin B-12 is necessary for red blood cells to mature properly in the bone marrow. People with pernicious anemia lose their ability to make intrinsic factor, a substance secreted by the stomach's membrane lining that enables vitamin B-12 to be absorbed from the intestine. Without an adequate amount of vitamin B-12, the body is unable to synthesize DNA properly, which affects red blood cell production.

The next step involves determining whether the two reactants are in the correct mole ratio as given in the balanced chemical equation. The coefficients in the balanced chemical equation indicate that four moles of chlorine are needed to react with one mole of sulfur. This 4:1 ratio from the equation must be compared with the actual ratio of the moles of available reactants just calculated above. To determine the actual ratio of moles, divide the available moles of chlorine by the available moles of sulfur.

$$\frac{1.410 \text{ mol Cl}_2 \text{ available}}{0.7797 \text{ mol S}_8 \text{ available}} = \frac{1.808 \text{ mol Cl}_2 \text{ available}}{1 \text{ mol S}_8 \text{ available}}$$

Only 1.808 mol of chlorine is actually available for every 1 mol of sulfur instead of the 4 mol of chlorine required by the balanced chemical equation. Therefore, chlorine is the limiting reactant.

After the limiting reactant has been determined, the amount of product in moles can be calculated by multiplying the given number of moles of the limiting reactant (1.410 mol $Cl_2$) by the mole ratio that relates disulfur dichloride and chlorine.

$$1.410 \text{ mol Cl}_2 \times \frac{4 \text{ mol S}_2\text{Cl}_2}{4 \text{ mol Cl}_2} = 1.410 \text{ mol S}_2\text{Cl}_2$$

Then, moles of $S_2Cl_2$ is converted to grams of $S_2Cl_2$ by multiplying by the conversion factor that relates mass and moles, molar mass.

$$1.410 \text{ mol S}_2\text{Cl}_2 \times \frac{135.0 \text{ g S}_2\text{Cl}_2}{1 \text{ mol S}_2\text{Cl}_2} = 190.4 \text{ g S}_2\text{Cl}_2$$

These two calculations can be combined into one like this.

$$1.410 \text{ mol Cl}_2 \times \frac{4 \text{ mol S}_2\text{Cl}_2}{4 \text{ mol Cl}_2} \times \frac{135.0 \text{ g S}_2\text{Cl}_2}{1 \text{ mol S}_2\text{Cl}_2} = 190.4 \text{ g S}_2\text{Cl}_2$$

Now you know that 190.4 g $S_2Cl_2$ is produced when 1.410 mol $Cl_2$ reacts with an excess of $S_8$.

What about the reactant sulfur, which you know is in excess? How much of it actually reacted? You can calculate the mass of sulfur needed to react completely with 1.410 mol of chlorine using a mole-to-mass calculation. The first step is to multiply the moles of chlorine by the mole ratio of sulfur to chlorine to obtain the number of moles of sulfur. Remember, the unknown is the numerator and the known is the denominator.

$$1.410 \text{ mol Cl}_2 \times \frac{1 \text{ mol S}_8}{4 \text{ mol Cl}_2} = 0.3525 \text{ mol S}_8$$

Now, to obtain the mass of sulfur needed, 0.3525 mol $S_8$ is multiplied by the conversion factor that relates mass and moles, molar mass.

$$0.3525 \text{ mol S}_8 \times \frac{256.5 \text{ g S}_8}{1 \text{ mol S}_8} = 90.42 \text{ g S}_8 \text{ needed}$$

Knowing that 90.42 g $S_8$ is needed, you can calculate the amount of sulfur left unreacted when the reaction ends. Because 200.0 g of sulfur is available and only 90.42 g is needed, the mass in excess is

200.0 g $S_8$ available − 90.42 g $S_8$ needed = 109.6 g $S_8$ in excess.

## Demonstration

### Limiting Reactants

#### Purpose
Students will observe the effect of a limiting reactant on a chemical reaction.

#### Materials
burets (2); metric ruler; 25-mL graduated cylinder; stirring rods; 18 × 150-mm test

tubes (8); test-tube rack; 0.10$M$ $CuSO_4$; 0.20$M$ KOH; centrifuge; distilled water; See page 352C for preparation of solutions.

#### Safety Precautions

**Disposal** $CuSO_4$ and KOH solutions may be evaporated to dryness in a fume hood. The solid can be disposed of at an approved waste facility.

#### Procedure
Fill one buret with 0.20$M$ KOH and the other with 0.10$M$ $CuSO_4$. Label eight test tubes according to the amount of KOH to be added: 2.0 mL, 4.0 mL, 6.0 mL, 8.0 mL, 10.0 mL, 12.0 mL, 14.0 mL, and 16.0 mL. Dispense 10.0 mL $CuSO_4$ into all eight labeled test tubes. Add KOH according to the volume on the test tube label. Add enough water to each test tube so that each will have 26.0 mL. Stir and

## EXAMPLE PROBLEM 12-5

### Determining the Limiting Reactant

The reaction between solid white phosphorus and oxygen produces solid tetraphosphorus decoxide ($P_4O_{10}$). This compound is often called diphosphorus pentoxide because its empirical formula is $P_2O_5$.

**a.** Determine the mass of tetraphosphorus decoxide formed if 25.0 g of phosphorus ($P_4$) and 50.0 g of oxygen are combined.

**b.** How much of the excess reactant remains after the reaction stops?

### 1. Analyze the Problem

You are given the masses of both reactants so the limiting reactant must be identified and used for finding the mass of product. From moles of limiting reactant, the moles of the excess reactant used in the reaction can be determined. The number of moles of excess reactant that actually reacted can be converted to mass and subtracted from the given mass to find the amount in excess.

**Known**

mass of phosphorus = 25.0 g $P_4$
mass of oxygen = 50.0 g $O_2$

**Unknown**

mass of tetraphosphorus decoxide = ? g $P_4O_{10}$
mass of excess reactant = ? g excess reactant

### 2. Solve for the Unknown

**a.** Write the balanced chemical equation and identify the knowns and the unknown.

$$
\begin{array}{ccc}
25.0 \text{ g} & 50.0 \text{ g} & \text{? g} \\
P_4(s) + & 5O_2(g) \rightarrow & P_4O_{10}(s)
\end{array}
$$

Determine the number of moles of the reactants by multiplying each mass by the conversion factor that relates moles and mass, the inverse of molar mass.

$$25.0 \text{ g } P_4 \times \frac{1 \text{ mol } P_4}{123.9 \text{ g } P_4} = 0.202 \text{ mol } P_4$$

$$50.0 \text{ g } O_2 \times \frac{1 \text{ mol } O_2}{32.00 \text{ g } O_2} = 1.56 \text{ mol } O_2$$

Calculate the actual ratio of available moles of $O_2$ and available moles of $P_4$.

$$\frac{1.56 \text{ mol } O_2}{0.202 \text{ mol } P_4} = \frac{7.72 \text{ mol } O_2}{1 \text{ mol } P_4}$$

Determine the mole ratio of the two reactants from the balanced chemical equation.

$$\frac{5 \text{ mol } O_2}{1 \text{ mol } P_4}$$

Because 7.72 mol $O_2$ is available but only 5 mol is needed to react with 1 mol $P_4$, $O_2$ is in excess and $P_4$ is the limiting reactant. Use the moles of $P_4$ to determine the moles of $P_4O_{10}$ that will be produced.

Multiply the number of moles of $P_4$ by the mole ratio of $P_4O_{10}$ (the unknown) to $P_4$ (the known).

$$0.202 \text{ mol } P_4 \times \frac{1 \text{ mol } P_4O_{10}}{1 \text{ mol } P_4} = 0.202 \text{ mol } P_4O_{10}$$

*Continued on next page*

Tiny pieces of white phosphorus deposited on filter paper burst into flame on contact with air. That's why white phosphorus is never found free in nature. Phosphorus is an essential element in living systems; for example, phosphate groups occur regularly along strands of DNA.

12.3 Limiting Reactants **367**

---

✔ **Assessment**

**Portfolio** Have students write the equation for the reaction of lithium with bromine to produce lithium bromide. Have them determine the following given that 25.0 g of lithium and 25.0 g of bromine are present at the beginning of the reaction: the limiting reactant, the mass of lithium bromide produced, the excess reactant, the mass of the excess reactant. The students' work can be placed in their portfolios. Bromine is the limiting reactant. 27.1 g LiBr; Lithium is the excess reactant. 22.8 g excess **L2** **P**

National Science Content Standards

Pages 366–367
UCP.1, UCP.3; B.3

---

place each test tube in the centrifuge for about one minute. Remove each test tube from the centrifuge. Measure the height of the precipitate and note the color of the supernatant in each tube.

**Results**

Test tubes labeled 2, 4, 6, 8 have blue supernatant and increasing amounts of precipitate. Test tubes labeled 10, 12, 14, 16 have the same amount of precipitate and clear colorless supernatant.

**Analysis**

1. What is the balanced equation for the reaction between KOH and $CuSO_4$? $2KOH(aq) + CuSO_4(aq) \rightarrow Cu(OH)_2(s) + K_2SO_4(aq)$.

2. Explain the blue color of the supernatant in some test tubes. $CuSO_4$ is in excess in these tubes.

3. In which test tube(s) did the maximum amount of precipitate occur? in those

with 10, 12, 14, and 16 mL of potassium hydroxide

✔ **Assessment**

**Knowledge** Explain why the amount of precipitate levels off in the test tubes that have 10.0 mL or more of KOH. KOH is in excess and $CuSO_4$ is the limiting reactant.

**367**

Have students refer to Appendix
D for complete solutions to
Practice Problems.

20. a. $Fe_2O_3$
   b. Na
   c. 69.92 g Fe
   d. 13.6 g Na
21. a. $CO_2$
   b. $H_2O$, 28.0 g
   c. 60.0 g

# 3 Assess

## Check for Understanding

**Logical-Mathematical** On
the overhead or chalkboard,
write the equation for coal gasifica-
tion, a process that converts coal
into methane gas.
$2C + 2H_2O \rightarrow CH_4 + CO_2$
Have students determine the yield
of methane if 2000 g of carbon and
2000 g of water are used. 900 g

**Practice!** For more practice determining the limiting
reactant in a chemical
reaction, go to
Supplemental Practice
Problems in Appendix A.

To calculate the mass of $P_4O_{10}$, multiply moles of $P_4O_{10}$ by the conversion factor that relates mass and moles, molar mass.

$$0.202 \ \text{mol} \ P_4O_{10} \times \frac{283.9 \ \text{g} \ P_4O_{10}}{1 \ \text{mol} \ P_4O_{10}} = 57.3 \ \text{g} \ P_4O_{10}$$

**b.** Because $O_2$ is in excess, only part of the available $O_2$ is consumed.
Use the limiting reactant, $P_4$, to determine the moles and mass of
$O_2$ used.

$$0.202 \ \text{mol} \ P_4 \times \frac{5 \ \text{mol} \ O_2}{1 \ \text{mol} \ P_4} = 1.01 \ \text{mol} \ O_2 \ (\text{moles needed})$$

Multiply moles of $O_2$ by the conversion factor that relates mass and
moles, molar mass.

$$1.01 \ \text{mol} \ O_2 \times \frac{32.00 \ \text{g} \ O_2}{1 \ \text{mol} \ O_2} = 32.3 \ \text{g} \ O_2 \ (\text{mass needed})$$

Subtract the mass of $O_2$ needed from the mass available to calculate excess $O_2$.

50.0 g $O_2$ available − 32.3 g $O_2$ needed = 17.7 g $O_2$ in excess

**3. Evaluate the Answer**

All values have a minimum of three significant figures, so the mass
of $P_4O_{10}$ is correctly stated with three digits. The mass of excess $O_2$
(17.7 g) is found by subtracting two numbers that are accurate to the
first decimal place. Therefore, the mass of excess $O_2$ correctly shows
one decimal place. The sum of the oxygen that was consumed (32.3 g)
and the given mass of phosphorus (25.0 g) is 57.3 g, the calculated
mass of the product phosphorus decoxide.

## PRACTICE PROBLEMS

**20.** The reaction between solid sodium and iron(III) oxide is one in a
series of reactions that inflates an automobile airbag.

$6Na(s) + Fe_2O_3(s) \rightarrow 3Na_2O(s) + 2Fe(s)$

If 100.0 g Na and 100.0 g $Fe_2O_3$ are used in this reaction, determine

**a.** the limiting reactant.

**b.** the reactant in excess.

**c.** the mass of solid iron produced.

**d.** the mass of excess reactant that remains after the reaction is
complete.

**21.** Photosynthesis reactions in green plants use carbon dioxide and
water to produce glucose ($C_6H_{12}O_6$) and oxygen. Write the balanced
chemical equation for the reaction. If a plant has 88.0 g carbon dioxide and 64.0 g water available for photosynthesis, determine

**a.** the limiting reactant.

**b.** the excess reactant and the mass in excess.

**c.** the mass of glucose produced.

**Why use an excess of a reactant?** Why are reactions usually not carried
out using amounts of reactants in the exact mole ratios given in the balanced
equation? Some reactions do not continue until all the reactants are used up.
Instead, they appear to stop while portions of the reactants are still present in
the reaction mixture. Because this is inefficient and wasteful, chemists have
found that by using an excess of one reactant—often the least expensive

## CHEMISTRY JOURNAL

### Stoichiometric Steps

**Linguistic** In their chemistry journals, have students list the steps
needed for calculating the amounts of
products formed when the masses of all
reactants are given. Students should
explain the purpose for each step. **L2**

**National Science Content Standards**

**Pages 368–369**
UCP.1, UCP.3; B.3; E.1

one—reactions can be driven to continue until all of the limiting reactant is used up. Using an excess of one reactant can also speed up a reaction.

In **Figure 12-7,** you can see an example of how controlling the amount of a reactant can increase efficiency. Your school laboratory may have the kind of Bunsen burner shown in the figure. If so, you probably know that this type of burner has a control that can vary the amount of air (oxygen) that mixes with the gas. How efficiently the burner operates depends upon the ratio of oxygen to methane gas in the fuel mixture. When the amount of air is limited, the resulting flame is yellow because of glowing bits of unburned fuel, which deposit on glassware as soot (carbon). Fuel is wasted because the amount of energy released is less than the amount that could have been produced if enough oxygen were available. When sufficient oxygen is present in the combustion mixture, the burner produces a hot, intense blue flame. No soot is deposited because the fuel is completely converted to carbon dioxide and water vapor.

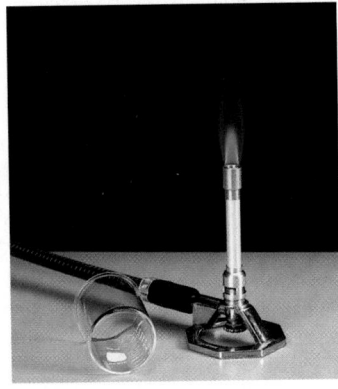

**Figure 12-7**

With insufficient oxygen, the burner on the left burns with a yellow, sooty flame. The burner on the right burns hot and clean because an excess of oxygen is available to react completely with the methane gas.

## Section 12.3 Assessment

**22.** What is meant by the limiting reactant? Why is it necessary to identify the limiting reactant when you want to know how much product will form in a chemical reaction?

**23.** Describe how the mass of the product can be calculated when one reactant is in excess.

**24.** Are limiting reactants present in all reactions? Explain.

**25. Thinking Critically** For the following reactions, identify the limiting reactant and the excess reactant. Give reasons for your choices.

  **a.** wood burning in a campfire

  **b.** sulfur in the air reacting with silver flatware to produce tarnish, or silver sulfide

  **c.** baking powder in cake batter decomposing to produce carbon dioxide, which makes the cake rise

**26. Analyze and Conclude** The equation representing the production of tetraphosphorus trisulfide ($P_4S_3$), a substance used in some match heads, is

$$8P_4 + 3S_8 \rightarrow 8P_4S_3$$

Determine if each of the following statements is correct. If the statement is incorrect, rewrite it to make it correct.

  **a.** To produce 4 mol $P_4S_3$, 4 mol $P_4$ must react with 1.5 mol $S_8$.

  **b.** When 4 mol $P_4$ reacts with 4 mol $S_8$, sulfur is the limiting reactant.

  **c.** When 6 mol $P_4$ and 6 mol $S_8$ react, 1320 g $P_4S_3$ is produced.

## Section 12.3 Assessment

**22.** the reactant that is completely consumed during a chemical reaction The limiting reactant determines the amount of product.

**23.** Determine which reactant is limiting and base the calculation on the limiting reactant.

**24.** Reactions with two or more reactants will often have a limiting reactant

**25. a.** The wood limits. The fire will burn only while wood is present.

  **b.** Silver is the limiting reactant. When a layer of tarnish covers the silver surface, it prevents the sulfur in the air from reacting.

  **c.** A decomposition reaction usually has only one reactant. The reaction is limited by the amount of baking powder present.

**26. a.** correct

  **b.** Phosphorus is the limiting reactant.

  **c.** correct

**369**

# 1 Focus

## FOCUS TRANSPARENCY

Before presenting the lesson, display **Section Focus Transparency 46** on the overhead projector. Have students answer the accompanying questions using **Section Focus Transparency Master 46.** **L1** **ELL**

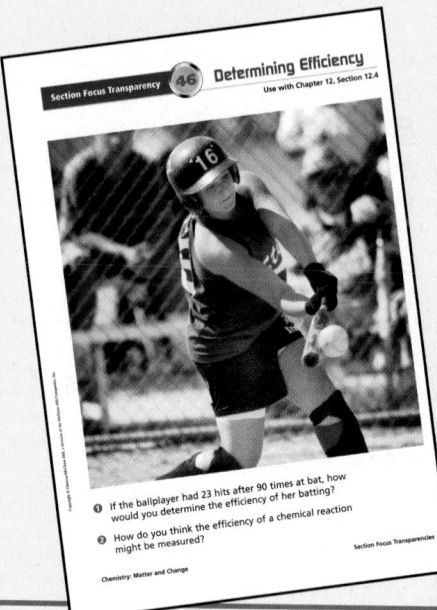

## 2 Teach
### Concept Development

Students may have learned that to obtain a percent, they should divide the part by the whole and multiply by 100. Help them to see that when they divide the part by the whole, they are finding out the fraction of the whole that the part is, or part per one. When they multiply by 100, they are finding the parts per 100, or percent. Ask what they would do to find parts per million.
Multiply part per one by $10^6$.

### Objectives

• **Calculate** the theoretical yield of a chemical reaction from data.

• **Determine** the percent yield for a chemical reaction.

### Vocabulary

theoretical yield
actual yield
percent yield

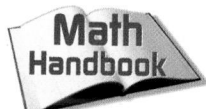

Review the meaning and calculation of percents in the **Math Handbook** on page 907 in this text.

Suppose you were determined to improve your jump shot and took time each afternoon to practice. One afternoon, you succeeded in getting the ball through the hoop 49 times out of a total of 75 tries. Theoretically, you could have been successful 75 times, but in actuality that usually doesn't happen. (That's why you practice.) But how successful were you? You could calculate your efficiency as a percent by dividing the number of successful tries by the total number of tries and multiplying by 100.

$$\frac{49 \text{ actual successes}}{75 \text{ theoretical successes}} \times 100 = 65\% \text{ successful shots}$$

Sixty-five percent successful jump shots means that you could expect to get the ball into the basket 65 times if you made 100 attempts.

Similar calculations are made to determine the success of chemical reactions because most reactions never succeed in producing the predicted amount of product. Although your work with stoichiometric problems so far may have led you to think that chemical reactions proceed according to the balanced equation without any difficulties and always produce the calculated amount of product, this is not the case! Not every reaction goes cleanly or completely. Many reactions stop before all of the reactants are used up, so the actual amount of product is less than expected. Liquid reactants or products may adhere to the surfaces of containers or evaporate, and solid product is always left behind on filter paper or lost in the purification process. In some instances, products other than the intended ones may be formed by competing reactions, thus reducing the yield of the desired product.

## How much product?

In many of the calculations you have been practicing, you have been asked to calculate the amount of product that can be produced from a given amount of reactant. The answer you obtained is called the theoretical yield of the reaction. The **theoretical yield** is the maximum amount of product that can be produced from a given amount of reactant. A chemical reaction rarely produces the theoretical yield of product. A chemist determines the actual yield of a reaction through a careful experiment in which the mass of the product is measured. The **actual yield** is the amount of product actually produced when the chemical reaction is carried out in an experiment.

Chemists need to know how efficient a reaction is in producing the desired product. One way of measuring efficiency is by means of percent yield. Just as you calculated your percent of successful jump shots, a chemist can calculate what percent of the amount of product that could theoretically be produced was actually produced. **Percent yield** of product is the ratio of the actual yield to the theoretical yield expressed as a percent.

$$\text{Percent yield} = \frac{\text{actual yield (from an experiment)}}{\text{theoretical yield (from stoichiometric calculations)}} \times 100$$

The **problem-solving LAB** on page 372 will help you understand the importance of percent yield in chemical reactions and the kind of factors that may determine the size of the percent yield.

## CHEMISTRY JOURNAL

### Batting Averages

If students don't know what is meant by a baseball batting average, have them research this subject and write in their journals how a batting average is similar to percent yield. **L1** **ELL**

## Portfolio

### Writing Questions

Have students develop six multiple-choice questions with four answer choices, one being the correct answer. These questions, with the correct answers, can be placed in their portfolios and used in a class game with a format similar to "Who Wants to Be a Millionaire?" **L2** **P**

## Calculating Percent Yield

When potassium chromate ($K_2CrO_4$) is added to a solution containing 0.500 g silver nitrate ($AgNO_3$), solid silver chromate ($Ag_2CrO_4$) is formed.

**a.** Determine the theoretical yield of the silver chromate precipitate.

**b.** If 0.455 g of silver chromate is obtained, calculate the percent yield.

### 1. Analyze the Problem

You are given the mass of the reactant $AgNO_3$ and the actual yield of the product $Ag_2CrO_4$. You need to write the balanced chemical equation and calculate the theoretical yield by making these conversions: grams of silver nitrate to moles of silver nitrate, moles of silver nitrate to moles of silver chromate, moles of silver chromate to grams of silver chromate. The percent yield can be calculated from the actual yield of product and the calculated theoretical yield.

**Known**

mass of silver nitrate = 0.500 g $AgNO_3$

actual yield = 0.455 g $Ag_2CrO_4$

**Unknown**

theoretical yield = ? g $Ag_2CrO_4$

percent yield = ? % $Ag_2CrO_4$

### 2. Solve for the Unknown

Write the balanced chemical equation and indicate the known and unknown quantities.

$$\overset{0.500 \text{ g}}{2AgNO_3(aq)} + K_2CrO_4(aq) \rightarrow \overset{? \text{ g}}{Ag_2CrO_4(s)} + 2KNO_3(aq)$$

Convert grams of $AgNO_3$ to moles of $AgNO_3$ using the inverse of molar mass.

$$0.500 \text{ g AgNO}_3 \times \frac{1 \text{ mol AgNO}_3}{169.9 \text{ g AgNO}_3} = 2.94 \times 10^{-3} \text{ mol AgNO}_3$$

Use the appropriate mole ratio to convert mol $AgNO_3$ to mol $Ag_2CrO_4$.

$$2.94 \times 10^{-3} \text{ mol AgNO}_3 \times \frac{1 \text{ mol Ag}_2CrO_4}{2 \text{ mol AgNO}_3} = 1.47 \times 10^{-3} \text{ mol Ag}_2CrO_4$$

Calculate the mass of $Ag_2CrO_4$ (the theoretical yield) by multiplying mol $Ag_2CrO_4$ by the molar mass.

$$1.47 \times 10^{-3} \text{ mol Ag}_2CrO_4 \times \frac{331.7 \text{ g Ag}_2CrO_4}{1 \text{ mol Ag}_2CrO_4} = 0.488 \text{ g Ag}_2CrO_4$$

Divide the actual yield by the theoretical yield and multiply by 100.

$$\frac{0.455 \text{ g Ag}_2CrO_4}{0.488 \text{ g Ag}_2CrO_4} \times 100 = 93.2\% \text{ Ag}_2CrO_4$$

### 3. Evaluate the Answer

All quantities have three significant figures so the percent is correctly stated with three digits. The molar mass of $Ag_2CrO_4$ is about twice the molar mass of $AgNO_3$, and the ratio of mol $AgNO_3$ to mol $Ag_2CrO_4$ in the equation is 2:1. Therefore, 0.500 g $AgNO_3$ should produce about the same mass of $Ag_2CrO_4$. The actual yield of $Ag_2CrO_4$ is close to 0.500 g, so a percent yield of 93.2% is reasonable.

Like silver chromate, all chromium compounds are colored. Although silver chromate is insoluble in water, potassium chromate ($K_2CrO_4$, yellow) and potassium dichromate ($K_2Cr_2O_7$, orange) are soluble.

### Quick Demo

Add 5.0 mL of cooking oil to a flask. Place 20 kernels of popcorn in the flask and cover with a piece of aluminum foil with holes punched in the top. Place the flask on a hot plate and pop the popcorn. Pour out the popcorn and count the number of kernels that popped, the actual yield. The theoretical yield is 20 kernels. Ask students to determine the percent yield using the results. Answers will vary depending on the data collected.

### Resource Manager

**Study Guide for Content Mastery,** p. 72 **L2**
**Solving Problems: A Chemistry Handbook,** Section 12.4 **L2**
**Section Focus Transparency 46 and Master L1 ELL**

## DIFFERENTIATED INSTRUCTION

### Gifted

 **Logical-Mathematical** Have capable students design a spreadsheet that can be used to determine the theoretical yield of a product from a given mass of reactant, and the percent yield of the reaction when given the actual yield. First, they must determine the theoretical yield of the reaction when given a mass of one of the reactants. Second, they must be able to enter an actual yield and calculate the percent yield of the reactions. The spreadsheet can be used as a tutorial for other students. **L3**

**National Science Content Standards**

Pages 370–371
UCP.1, UCP.3; B.3; E.1

Have students refer to Appendix D for complete solutions to Practice Problems.

27. 92.1% yield $AlCl_3$

28. $Cu + 2AgNO_3 \rightarrow 2Ag + Cu(NO_3)_2$, 68.0 g Ag, 88.2% yield Ag

29. $Zn + I_2 \rightarrow ZnI_2$, 610.3 g $ZnI_2$, 84.48% yield $ZnI_2$

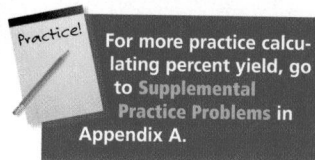

Practice! For more practice calculating percent yield, go to **Supplemental Practice Problems** in Appendix A.

27. Aluminum hydroxide is often present in antacids to neutralize stomach acid (HCl). If 14.0 g aluminum hydroxide is present in an antacid tablet, determine the theoretical yield of aluminum chloride produced when the tablet reacts with stomach acid. If the actual yield of aluminum chloride from this tablet is 22.0 g, what is the percent yield?

$$Al(OH)_3(s) + 3HCl(aq) \rightarrow AlCl_3(aq) + 3H_2O(l)$$

28. When copper wire is placed into a silver nitrate solution, silver crystals and copper(II) nitrate solution form. Write the balanced chemical equation for the reaction. If a 20.0-g sample of copper is used, determine the theoretical yield of silver. If 60.0 g silver is actually recovered from the reaction, determine the percent yield of the reaction.

29. Zinc reacts with iodine in a synthesis reaction. Write the balanced chemical equation for the reaction. Determine the theoretical yield if a 125.0-g sample of zinc was used. Determine the percent yield if 515.6 g product is recovered.

# problem-solving LAB

## Purpose

Students will design an experiment to explore how surface area affects percent yield.

## Process Skills

Designing an experiment, thinking critically, applying concepts, hypothesizing, predicting

## Teaching Strategies

- Have students explore how volume and surface area increase for a unit cube when the dimensions are doubled, tripled, etc. Then, have them relate what they learned to the amount of reactant present if a reactant were a cube.
- Discuss the importance of designing an experiment that explores the relationship between just two quantities.

## Thinking Critically

1. The amount of oxygen that reacts with the steel wool can be related to the diameter or gauge of the steel wool strands. The diameter of the strands can be obtained using a magnifying glass or dissection microscope. The change in mass (from Fe to $Fe_2O_3$) will yield the mass of oxygen. A stoichiometric calculation based upon the mass of oxygen provides the theoretical value to use in calculating the percent yield.

2. the mass of the steel wool sample used

3. By means of a graph with gauge as the independent variable and percent yield as the dependent variable

# problem-solving LAB

## How does the surface area of a solid reactant affect percent yield?

**Designing an Experiment** The cost of every manufactured item you buy is based largely on the cost of producing the item. Manufacturers compete to reduce costs and increase profits. This means increasing the percent yield of the manufacturing process by producing the most product for the amount of reactant used. If you were going to produce iron oxide ($Fe_2O_3$) from steel wool, how could you design an experiment to determine what gauge (diameter) steel wool will produce the highest yield? Write the equation for the reaction upon which you will base your experiment.

## Analysis

In the first photo, different gauges of steel wool are shown. The second photo shows the combustion of a sample of steel wool using a Bunsen burner.

## Thinking Critically

1. What quantities must be used to calculate the percent yield of $Fe_2O_3$ when iron is burned? How will these quantities be measured and how many measurements should be made?

2. What quantities should be kept constant in the experiment?

3. How will the resulting data be analyzed?

4. Are there any obvious errors in the design that could significantly affect the results? If so, how could they be avoided?

4. If there are any oils on the steel wool, they could be removed with a solvent. If the steel wool is an alloy, the percent yield will not be entirely accurate. If the reaction is hot enough, it could produce a gaseous component. Carry out the experiment in a covered crucible.

✓ **Assessment**

**Skill** Have students plot, on a single graph, the area vs the dimension and the volume vs the dimension of three different cubes. Have them determine the slopes of the lines and write a statement comparing how volume and area change as the dimension of a cube changes. **L2**

**Percent yield in the marketplace** You learned in the **problem-solving LAB** that in order to compete, manufacturers must reduce the cost of making their products to the lowest level possible. Percent yield is important in the calculation of overall cost effectiveness in industrial processes. For example, sulfuric acid ($H_2SO_4$) is made using mined sulfur, **Figure 12-8.** Sulfuric acid is an important chemical because it is a raw material for products such as fertilizers, detergents, pigments, and textiles. The cost of sulfuric acid affects the cost of many of the consumer items you use every day.

A two-step process called the contact process is often used for the manufacture of sulfuric acid. Over time, the process has been improved by chemical engineers to produce the maximum yield of product and, at the same time, comply with environmental standards for clean air. The two steps in the contact process are

$$S_8(s) + 8O_2(g) \rightarrow 8SO_2(g)$$

$$2SO_2(g) + O_2(g) \rightarrow 2SO_3(g)$$

A final step, the combination of $SO_3$ with water, produces the product, $H_2SO_4$.

$$SO_3(g) + H_2O(l) \rightarrow H_2SO_4(aq)$$

The first step, the combustion of sulfur, produces almost 100% yield. The second step also produces a high yield if a catalyst is used at the relatively low temperature of 400°C. A catalyst is a substance that speeds a reaction but does not appear in the chemical equation. Under these conditions, the reaction is slow. Raising the temperature speeds up the reaction but the yield decreases.

To maximize yield and minimize time in the second step, engineers have devised a system in which the reactants, $O_2$ and $SO_2$, are passed over a catalyst at 400°C. Because the reaction releases a great deal of heat, the temperature gradually increases with an accompanying decrease in yield. Thus, when the temperature reaches approximately 600°C, the mixture is cooled and then passed over the catalyst again. A total of four passes over the catalyst with cooling between passes results in a yield greater than 98%. This four-pass procedure maximizes the yield at temperatures near 400°C, and uses the modest increase in temperature to increase the rate and minimize the time.

**Figure 12-8**

The large tonnage of sulfur needed to make sulfuric acid and other products is often obtained by forcing hot water into underground deposits to melt the sulfur and then pumping the liquid sulfur to the surface.

---

## Section 12.4 Assessment

**30.** Distinguish between the theoretical yield and the actual yield of a chemical reaction.

**31.** Give several reasons why the actual yield is not usually equal to the theoretical yield.

**32.** Explain how percent yield is calculated.

**33. Thinking Critically** In an experiment, you are to combine iron with an excess of sulfur and heat the mixture to obtain iron(III) sulfide.

$$2Fe(s) + 3S(s) \rightarrow Fe_2S_3(s)$$

What experimental information must you collect in order to calculate the percent yield of this reaction?

**34. Interpreting Data** Use the data to determine the percent yield of the following reaction.
$$2Mg(s) + O_2(g) \rightarrow 2MgO(s)$$
Oxygen is in excess.

| Reaction Data | |
|---|---|
| Mass of crucible | 35.67 g |
| Mass of crucible + Mg | 38.06 g |
| Mass of Mg | |
| Mass of crucible + MgO | 39.15 g |
| Mass of MgO | |

chemistrymc.com/self_check_quiz

12.4 Percent Yield **373**

Write the equation $CH_4 + 2O_2 \rightarrow CO_2 + 2H_2O$ on the chalkboard. Ask students to determine the percent yield if 10.0 g of methane is burned producing 19.5 g of water. 86.7% yield

## Reteach

Discuss the burning of gasoline in an internal combustion engine.
$$2C_8H_{18} + 25O_2 \rightarrow 16CO_2 + 18H_2O$$
Ask students to determine the percent yield of carbon dioxide if 700.0 g of octane produces 1800.0 g of carbon dioxide. Have students explain each step of the calculation. 83.4% yield $CO_2$ **L2**

## Extension

**Intrapersonal** Have students research internal combustion engines and what is being done to increase the efficiency of automobiles and reduce air pollution. **L2**

## Assessment

**Performance** Have each student write four multiple choice questions involving percent yield calculations. Have them exchange their questions with a classmate and each answer the other's questions. Have them resolve any disagreements about the correct answer. Use the Performance Task Assessment List for Asking Questions in **PASC,** p. 19.

**National Science Content Standards**

**Pages 372–373**
UCP.1, UCP.3; B.3, B.6; E.1; F.4, F.6

---

## Section 12.4 Assessment

**30.** Theoretical yield is the maximum amount of product that can be produced from the available reactants. The actual yield is the amount of product actually produced from the same reactants.

**31.** Not all reactions go to completion. Some of the reactants or products stick to the surface of the container and are not massed or transferred. Other unexpected products form from competing reactions.

**32.** Percent yield equals the actual yield divided by the theoretical yield and the quotient multiplied by 100.

**33.** You must know the initial mass of iron and the final mass of iron(III) sulfide.

**34.** mass of Mg = 2.39 g Mg
mass of MgO = 3.48 g MgO
3.96 g MgO (theoretical yield), 87.9% yield

**373**

# CHEMLAB

## Preparation

### Time Allotment
One laboratory period

### Process Skills
Observing and inferring, measuring, collecting data, interpreting data, using numbers, comparing and contrasting, applying concepts

### Safety Precautions
Copper(II) sulfate is toxic. Be sure students wear aprons and goggles. Advise students to wash their hands with soap after the lab.

### Disposal
The copper(II) sulfate and iron(II) sulfate solutions can be evaporated to dryness in the fume hood. The solid can then be disposed of at a facility designated to receive solid waste.

### Preparation of Solutions
See page 352C for preparation of all solutions.

## Pre-Lab

3. It is not important to use hydrated copper(II) sulfate rather than anhydrous copper(II) sulfate because, in this experiment, iron is the limiting reactant. As long as the number of moles of copper sulfate exceeds the number of moles of iron (ratio $Cu^{2+}$ to Fe is 1:1), either form of the compound could be used.

## Procedure

- Decanting may be a new lab technique for students. Show them how to slowly pour the liquid from the beaker down the stirring rod and into another beaker.
- Tell students that the copper metal will not stick to the stirring rod when it is completely dry.
- **Troubleshooting** For best results, use iron filings that are free of oxidation.

**374**

# A Mole Ratio

Iron reacts with copper(II) sulfate in a single replacement reaction. By measuring the mass of iron that reacts and the mass of copper metal produced, you can calculate the ratio of moles of reactant to moles of product. This mole ratio can be compared to the ratio found in the balanced chemical equation.

### Problem
Which reactant is the limiting reactant? How does the experimental mole ratio of Fe to Cu compare with the mole ratio in the balanced chemical equation? What is the percent yield?

### Objectives
- **Observe** a single replacement reaction.
- **Measure** the masses of iron and copper.
- **Calculate** the moles of each metal and the mole ratio.

### Materials
iron metal filings, 20 mesh
copper(II) sulfate pentahydrate ($CuSO_4 \cdot 5H_2O$)
distilled water
stirring rod
150-mL beaker

400-mL beaker
100-mL graduated cylinder
weighing paper
balance
hot plate
beaker tongs

### Safety Precautions

- Always wear safety glasses and a lab apron.
- Hot objects will not appear to be hot.
- Do not heat broken, chipped, or cracked glassware.
- Turn off the hot plate when not in use.

### Pre-Lab

1. Read the entire **CHEMLAB**.
2. Prepare all written materials that you will take into the laboratory. Be sure to include safety precautions, procedure notes, and a data table.
3. Is it important that you know you are using the hydrated form of copper(II) sulfate? Would it be possible to use the anhydrous form? Why or why not?

| Data for the Reaction of Copper(II) Sulfate and Iron | |
|---|---|
| Mass of empty 150-mL beaker | |
| Mass of 150-mL beaker + $CuSO_4 \cdot 5H_2O$ | |
| Mass of $CuSO_4 \cdot 5H_2O$ | |
| Mass of iron filings | |
| Mass of 150-mL beaker and dried copper | |
| Mass of dried copper | |
| Observations | |

### Procedure

1. Measure and record the mass of a clean, dry 150-mL beaker.
2. Place approximately 12 g of copper(II) sulfate pentahydrate into the 150-mL beaker and measure and record the combined mass.
3. Add 50 mL of distilled water to the copper(II) sulfate pentahydrate and heat the mixture on the hot plate at a medium setting. Stir until all of the solid is dissolved, but do not boil. Using tongs, remove the beaker from the hot plate.
4. Measure approximately 2 g of iron metal filings onto a piece of weighing paper. Measure and record the exact mass of the filings.
5. While stirring, slowly add the iron filings to the hot copper(II) sulfate solution.
6. Allow the reaction mixture to stand, without stirring, for five minutes to ensure complete reaction. The solid copper metal will settle to the bottom of the beaker.
7. Use the stirring rod to decant (pour off) the liquid into a 400-mL beaker. Be careful to decant only the liquid.

**374    Chapter 12 Stoichiometry**

## Expected Results

See the data table at right.

### Reaction Between Copper(II) Sulfate and Iron

| | |
|---|---|
| Mass of empty 150-mL beaker | 69.87 g |
| Mass of 150-mL beaker + $CuSO_4 \cdot 5H_2O$ | 81.92 g |
| Mass of $CuSO_4 \cdot 5H_2O$ | 12.05 g |
| Mass of iron filings | 2.02 g |
| Mass of 150-mL beaker and dried copper | 72.13 g |
| Mass of dried copper | 2.26 g |

8. Add 15 mL of distilled water to the copper solid and carefully swirl the beaker to wash the copper. Decant the liquid into the 400-mL beaker.

9. Repeat step 8 two more times.

10. Place the 150-mL beaker containing the wet copper on the hot plate. Use low heat to dry the copper.

11. Remove the beaker from the hot plate and allow it to cool.

12. Measure and record the mass of the cooled 150-mL beaker and the copper.

## Cleanup and Disposal

1. Make sure the hot plate is off.

2. The dry copper can be placed in a waste container. Wet any residue that sticks to the beaker and wipe it out using a paper towel. Pour the unreacted copper(II) sulfate and iron(II) sulfate solutions into a large beaker in the fume hood.

3. Return all lab equipment to its proper place.

4. Wash your hands thoroughly after all lab work and cleanup is complete.

## Analyze and Conclude

1. **Observing and Inferring** What evidence did you observe that confirms that a chemical reaction occurred?

2. **Applying Concepts** Write a balanced chemical equation for the single-replacement reaction that occurred.

3. **Interpreting Data** From your data, determine the mass of copper produced.

4. **Using Numbers** Use the mass of copper to calculate the moles of copper produced.

5. **Using Numbers** Calculate the moles of iron used in the reaction.

6. **Using Numbers** Determine the whole number ratio of moles of iron to moles of copper.

7. **Comparing and Contrasting** Compare the ratio of moles of iron to moles of copper from the balanced chemical equation to the mole ratio calculated using your data.

8. **Evaluating Results** Use the balanced chemical equation to calculate the mass of copper that should have been produced from the sample of iron you used. Use this number and the mass of copper you actually obtained to calculate the percent yield.

9. **Error Analysis** What was the source of any deviation from the mole ratio calculated from the chemical equation? How could you improve your results?

10. **Drawing a Conclusion** Which reactant is the limiting reactant? Explain.

## Real-World Chemistry

1. A furnace that provides heat by burning methane gas ($CH_4$) must have the correct mixture of air and fuel to operate efficiently. What is the mole ratio of air to methane gas in the combustion of methane? Hint: Air is 20% oxygen.

2. Automobile air bags inflate on impact because a series of gas-producing chemical reactions are triggered. To be effective in saving lives, the bags must not overinflate or underinflate. What factors must automotive engineers take into account in the design of air bags?

## Analyze and Conclude

1. The solution changed color and the copper precipitated.

2. $Fe(s) + CuSO_4(aq) \rightarrow Cu(s) + FeSO_4(aq)$

3. $72.13\ g - 69.87\ g = 2.26\ g\ Cu$

4. $2.26\ g\ Cu \times 1\ mol\ Cu/63.55\ g\ Cu = 0.0356\ mol\ Cu$

5. $2.02\ g\ Fe \times 1\ mol\ Fe/55.85\ g\ Fe = 0.0362\ mol\ Fe$

6. mol Fe/mole Cu = $0.0362/0.0356 = 1.02$

7. The ratio of Fe to Cu in the equation is 1:1, almost the same as the experimental ratio.

8. $0.0362\ mol\ Fe \times 1\ mol\ Cu/1\ mol\ Fe \times 63.55\ g/1\ mol\ Cu = 2.30\ g\ Cu$
   Percent yield = $2.26\ g/2.30\ g \times 100 = 98.3\%$

9. The copper was not completely dry. Some copper could have oxidized if heated too hot. Copper also could have been lost. Use lower heat for a longer time. Use extra care in decanting.

10. Iron is the limiting reactant. All the iron was used up.

## Real-World Chemistry

1. $CH_4 + 2O_2 \rightarrow CO_2 + 2H_2O$
   1 mole of methane requires 2 moles of pure oxygen or 10 moles of air (20% $O_2$). This ratio shows that a large volume of air goes up the chimney.

2. the size of the bag and the amounts of the reactants; Just the right amount of product must form to inflate the bag but not overinflate it.

---

**Assessment**

**Knowledge** Have students solve this problem. If 12.0 g of $CuSO_4 \cdot 5H_2O$ (molar mass = 249.72 g/mol) reacted completely with an excess of iron metal, what mass of copper metal would be produced? 3.05 g

# How It Works

Students will learn how stoichiometry is critically important in the functioning of air bags.

## Background

The first proposal to equip automobiles with air bags was made in the early 1950s, but it was not until the late 1980s that reliable and safe air bags were offered to the public as an option.

Full deployment of an air bag takes about 40 milliseconds. The bag's velocity as it deploys is approximately 200 mph (322 kph).

Air bags begin to deflate by the time they make contact with a person. This helps to provide a cushioning effect by allowing a controlled deceleration of the person's body rather than an abrupt stop. The deflation is controlled by carefully designed vents in the bag.

The mechanism used for the air bag on the passenger side is shaped differently from the one used on the driver side, but the chemistry is the same.

## Visual Learning

Refer students to the illustration of the inflating bag. Ask under what circumstances the air bag could be a danger to the driver.

## Teaching Strategies

- Have students research statistics on the number of lives saved by air bags.
- Ask students to comment on the stability of sodium azide at high temperatures.
- Have students recall the properties of the alkali metals. Ask why the air bag design includes the reaction of sodium and potassium with sand.

## Thinking Critically

1. Students should predict that the sand ($SiO_2$) is the least important and that it does not

# How It Works
## Air Bags

Air bags fill with nitrogen gas as they deploy in automobile crashes. The source of the nitrogen gas is the chemical compound sodium azide ($NaN_3$). Hazardous sodium metal is produced along with the nitrogen, so potassium nitrate is added to convert the sodium into less hazardous sodium oxide ($Na_2O$). Stoichiometric calculations are needed to determine the precise quantity of sodium azide that will produce the volume of nitrogen gas required to inflate the air bag. If too much gas is produced, the air bag may be so rigid that hitting it would be the same as hitting a solid wall.

① Crash sensor detects rapid deceleration and sends signal to air bag module.

② Igniter explodes, heating sodium azide in the inflator.

③ High temperature decomposes sodium azide into sodium and nitrogen gas. Sodium and potassium nitrate react releasing more nitrogen gas.

④ Silicon dioxide (sand), sodium oxide, and potassium oxide formed in the inflator fuse into glass.

⑤ Nitrogen gas inflates air bag.

Air bag module
Inflator/igniter
Filters
Nitrogen gas
③ ④
① Electrical signal
② Igniter
Sodium azide, potassium nitrate, and silicon dioxide

### Thinking Critically

1. **Predicting** Which starting material used in the air bag inflator is the least important for the proper inflation of the air bag? Would it be necessary to have it present in a precise stoichiometric ratio? Why or why not?

2. **Analyze and Conclude** What is the correct stoichiometric ratio between $NaN_3$ and $KNO_3$ to ensure no sodium is unreacted? What would be the consequences of an excess of $KNO_3$ to the operation of an air bag?

need to be present in a precise stoichiometric ratio. It has no effect on the quantity of nitrogen gas generated, so the air bag would inflate correctly without it. The purpose for its inclusion is to convert harmful reaction byproducts ($Na_2O$ and $K_2O$) to a more harmless form (glass).

2. Students should find that the ratio is 5 mol $NaN_3$ to 1 mol $KNO_3$. $10Na(s) + 2KNO_3(s) \rightarrow 5Na_2O(s) + K_2O(s) + N_2(g)$. They should correctly conclude that an excess of $KNO_3$ would not be detrimental to the operation of the air bag. Any excess would not react because there would be nothing for it to react with.

## Summary

### 12.1 What is stoichiometry?

- Balanced chemical equations can be interpreted in terms of representative particles (atoms, molecules, formula units), moles, and mass.

- The law of conservation of mass, as applied to chemical reactions, means that the total mass of the reactants is equal to the total mass of the products.

- Mole ratios are central to stoichiometric calculations. They are derived from the coefficients in a balanced chemical equation. To write mole ratios, the number of moles of each reactant and product is placed, in turn, in the numerator of the ratio with the moles of each other reactant and product placed in the denominator.

### 12.2 Stoichiometric Calculations

- Stoichiometric calculations allow a chemist to predict the amount of product that can be obtained from a given amount of reactant or to determine how much of two or more reactants must be used to produce a specified amount of product.

- The four steps in stoichiometric calculations begin with the balanced chemical equation.

- Mole ratios used in the calculations are determined from the balanced chemical equation.

- The mass of the given substance is converted to moles of the given substance. Then, moles of the given substance are converted by means of a mole ratio to moles of the unknown substance. Finally, moles of the unknown substance are converted to the mass of the unknown substance.

### 12.3 Limiting Reactants

- The limiting reactant is the reactant that is completely consumed during a chemical reaction. Reactants that remain after the reaction stops are called excess reactants.

- To determine the limiting reactant, the actual mole ratio of the available reactants must be compared with the ratio of the reactants obtained from the coefficients in the balanced chemical equation.

- Stoichiometric calculations must be based on the given amount of the limiting reactant.

### 12.4 Percent Yield

- The theoretical yield of a chemical reaction is the maximum amount of product that can be produced from a given amount of reactant. Theoretical yield is calculated from the balanced chemical equation.

- The actual yield is the amount of product actually produced. Actual yield must be obtained through experimentation.

- Percent yield is the ratio of actual yield to theoretical yield expressed as a percent. High percent yield is important in reducing the cost of every product produced through chemical processes.

## Key Equations and Relationships

- $\text{moles of known} \times \dfrac{\text{moles of unknown}}{\text{moles of known}} = \text{moles of unknown}$
  (p. 358)

- $\dfrac{\text{actual yield (from experiment)}}{\text{theoretical yield (from stoichiometric calculations)}} \times 100 = \text{percent yield}$
  (p. 370)

## Vocabulary

- actual yield (p. 370)
- excess reactant (p. 364)
- limiting reactant (p. 364)
- mole ratio (p. 356)
- percent yield (p. 370 )
- stoichiometry (p. 354 )
- theoretical yield (p. 370 )

chemistrymc.com/vocabulary_puzzlemaker

Study Guide **377**

## Using the Vocabulary

To reinforce chapter vocabulary, have students write a sentence using each term. **L2** **ELL**

## Review Strategies

- Have students explain why a balanced equation is necessary in stoichiometry. **L2**
- Have students summarize the steps involved in stoichiometric calculations. **L2**
- Have students explain what is meant by a limiting reactant and why it is necessary to identify this reactant when solving a stoichiometric problem. **L2**
- Have students explain the percent yield of a reaction. **L2**
- Problems from Appendix A or the **Supplemental Problems** booklet can be used for review. **L2**

VOCABULARY
PuzzleMaker

For additional help with vocabulary, have students access the Vocabulary PuzzleMaker online.
chemistrymc.com/
vocabulary_puzzlemaker

Chemistry online

### EXAM*VIEW*® PRO

## Use Exam*View*® Pro Testmaker CD-ROM to:

- Create **multiple versions** of tests.
- Create **modified** tests with one mouse click for struggling students.
- **Edit** existing questions and add your own questions.
- **Build** tests based on national curriculum standards.

National Science Content Standards
Pages 376–377
UCP.1, UCP.3; B.3, B.6; E.1; F.5; G.1

## Concept Mapping

**35.** 1. balanced chemical equation; 2. molar mass; 3. mole ratio; 4. theoretical yield; 5. actual yield; 6. percent yield

## Mastering Concepts

**36.** The relationships among particles, moles, and mass for all reactants and products.

**37.** The mass of the reactants will always equal the mass of the products.

**38.** Mole ratios allow for the conversion from moles of one substance in a balanced chemical equation to moles of another substance in the same equation.

**39.** number of moles B/number of moles A

**40.** Write a balanced chemical equation for the reaction.

**41.** Molar mass is a conversion factor for converting moles of a given substance to mass or mass of a given substance to moles.

**42.** You must have the balanced chemical equation and know the quantity of one substance in the reaction other than the product you are to determine.

**43.** The limiting reactant is a reactant that is completely consumed during a chemical reaction. The excess reactant is a reactant that is not completely consumed.

**44.** The actual mole ratio of reactants from the chemical equation is compared to the mole ratio determined from the given quantities.

**45.** Actual yield is the amount of product actually obtained experimentally. Theoretical yield is the amount of product predicted by a stoichiometric calculation.

**46.** Actual yield is determined through experimentation.

**378**

## Chemistry Online

Go to the Chemistry Web site at **chemistrymc.com** for additional Chapter 12 Assessment.

## Concept Mapping

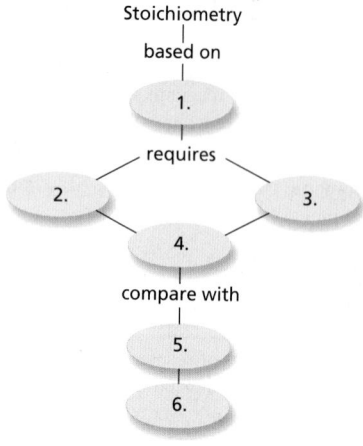

**35.** Fill in the ovals with the following terms to create a concept map: actual yield, balanced chemical equation, molar mass, mole ratio, percent yield, and theoretical yield.

## Mastering Concepts

**36.** What relationships can be determined from a balanced chemical equation? (12.1)

**37.** Explain how the law of conservation of mass allows you to interpret a balanced chemical equation in terms of mass. (12.1)

**38.** Explain why mole ratios are central to stoichiometric calculations. (12.1)

**39.** What is the mole ratio that can convert from moles of A to moles of B? (12.1)

**40.** What is the first step in all stoichiometric calculations? (12.2)

**41.** How is molar mass used in some stoichiometric calculations? (12.2)

**42.** What information must you have in order to calculate the mass of product formed in a chemical reaction? (12.2)

**43.** What is meant by limiting reactant? Excess reactant? (12.3)

**44.** How are mole ratios used in finding the limiting reactant in a reaction? (12.3)

**45.** What is the difference between actual yield and theoretical yield? (12.4)

**46.** How are actual yield and theoretical yield determined? (12.4)

**47.** Can the percent yield of a chemical reaction be more than 100%? Explain your answer. (12.4)

**48.** What relationship is used to determine the percent yield of a chemical reaction? (12.4)

**49.** What experimental information do you need in order to calculate both the theoretical and percent yield of any chemical reaction? (12.4)

**50.** A metal oxide reacts with water to produce a metal hydroxide. What additional information would you need to determine the percent yield of metal hydroxide from this reaction? (12.4)

## Mastering Problems
### Interpreting Equations (12.1)

**51.** Interpret the following equation in terms of particles, moles, and mass.
$$4Al(s) + 3O_2(g) \rightarrow 2Al_2O_3(s)$$

**52.** When tin(IV) oxide is heated with carbon in a process called smelting, the element tin can be extracted.
$$SnO_2(s) + 2C(s) \rightarrow Sn(l) + 2CO(g)$$
Interpret the equation in terms of particles, moles, and mass.

**53.** When hydrochloric acid solution reacts with lead(II) nitrate solution, lead(II) chloride precipitates and a solution of nitric acid is produced.
   **a.** Write the balanced chemical equation for the reaction.
   **b.** Interpret the equation in terms of molecules and formula units, moles, and mass.

### Mole Ratios (12.1)

**54.** When solid copper is added to nitric acid, copper(II) nitrate, nitrogen dioxide, and water are produced. Write the balanced chemical equation for the reaction. List six mole ratios for the reaction.

**55.** When aluminum is mixed with iron(III) oxide, iron metal and aluminum oxide are produced along with a large quantity of heat. What mole ratio would you use to determine mol Fe if mol $Fe_2O_3$ is known?
$$Fe_2O_3(s) + 2Al(s) \rightarrow 2Fe(s) + Al_2O_3(s) + heat$$

Theoretical yield is calculated from a given reactant or the limiting reactant.

## Resource Manager

**Chapter Assessment,** pp. 67–72
**Supplemental Problems,** Ch. 12
**ExamView® Pro CD-ROM**
**MindJogger Videoquizzes DVD/VHS**
**Solutions Manual,** Ch. 12
**Chemistry Interactive CD-ROM,**
   Ch. 12 quiz

**56.** Solid silicon dioxide, often called silica, reacts with hydrofluoric acid (HF) solution to produce the gas silicon tetrafluoride and water.

    **a.** Write the balanced chemical equation for the reaction.

    **b.** List three mole ratios and explain how you would use them in stoichiometric calculations.

**57.** Determine the mole ratio necessary to convert moles of aluminum to moles of aluminum chloride when aluminum reacts with chlorine.

**58.** Chromite ($FeCr_2O_4$) is the most important commercial ore of chromium. One of the steps in the process used to extract chromium from the ore is the reaction of chromite with coke (carbon) to produce ferrochrome ($FeCr_2$).

    $2C(s) + FeCr_2O_4(s) \rightarrow FeCr_2(s) + 2CO_2(g)$

    What mole ratio would you use to convert from moles of chromite to moles of ferrochrome?

**59.** The air pollutant $SO_2$ is removed from the air by means of a reaction among sulfur dioxide, calcium carbonate, and oxygen. The products of this reaction are calcium sulfate and carbon dioxide. Determine the mole ratio you would use to convert mol $SO_2$ to mol $CaSO_4$.

| Reaction Data | | | |
|---|---|---|---|
| **Moles of reactants** | | **Moles of products** | |
| **W** | **X** | **Y** | **Z** |
| 0.90 | 0.30 | 0.60 | 1.20 |

**60.** Two substances, W and X, react to form the products Y and Z. The table shows the numbers of moles of the reactants and products involved when the reaction was carried out in one experiment. Use the data to determine the coefficients that will balance the equation W + X → Y + Z.

## Stoichiometric Mole-to-Mole Conversions (12.2)

**61.** If 5.50 mol calcium carbide ($CaC_2$) reacts with an excess of water, how many moles of acetylene ($C_2H_2$) will be produced?

    $CaC_2(s) + 2H_2O(l) \rightarrow Ca(OH)_2(aq) + C_2H_2(g)$

**62.** When an antacid tablet dissolves in water, the fizz is due to a reaction between sodium hydrogen carbonate (sodium bicarbonate, $NaHCO_3$) and citric acid ($H_3C_6H_5O_7$).

    $3NaHCO_3(aq) + H_3C_6H_5O_7(aq) \rightarrow$
    $3CO_2(g) + 3H_2O(l) + Na_3C_6H_5O_7(aq)$

How many moles of carbon dioxide can be produced if one tablet containing 0.0119 mol $NaHCO_3$ is dissolved?

**63.** One of the main components of pearls is calcium carbonate. If pearls are put in acidic solution, they dissolve.

    $CaCO_3(s) + 2HCl(aq) \rightarrow CaCl_2(aq) + H_2O(l) + CO_2(g)$.

    How many mol $CaCO_3$ can be dissolved in 0.0250 mol HCl?

## Stoichiometric Mole-to-Mass Conversions (12.2)

**64.** Citric acid ($H_3C_6H_5O_7$) is a product of the fermentation of sucrose ($C_{12}H_{22}O_{11}$) in air.

    $C_{12}H_{22}O_{11}(aq) + 3O_2(g) \rightarrow 2H_3C_6H_5O_7(aq) + 3H_2O(l)$

    Determine the mass of citric acid produced when 2.50 mol $C_{12}H_{22}O_{11}$ is used.

**65.** Esterification is a reaction between an organic acid and an alcohol that forms as ester and water. The ester ethyl butanoate ($C_3H_7COOC_2H_5$), which is responsible for the fragrance of pineapples, is formed when the alcohol ethanol ($C_2H_5OH$) and butanoic acid ($C_3H_7COOH$) are heated in the presence of sulfuric acid.

    $C_2H_5OH(l) + C_3H_7COOH(l) \rightarrow$
    $C_3H_7COOC_2H_5(l) + H_2O(l)$

    Determine the mass of ethyl butanoate produced if 4.50 mol ethanol is used.

**66.** Carbon dioxide is released into the atmosphere through the combustion of octane ($C_8H_{18}$) in gasoline. Write the balanced chemical equation for the combustion of octane and calculate the mass of octane needed to release 5.00 mol $CO_2$.

**67.** A solution of potassium chromate reacts with a solution of lead(II) nitrate to produce a yellow precipitate of lead(II) chromate and a solution of potassium nitrate.

    **a.** Write the balanced chemical equation.

    **b.** Starting with 0.250 mol potassium chromate, determine the mass of lead chromate that can be obtained.

**68.** The exothermic reaction between liquid hydrazine ($N_2H_2$) and liquid hydrogen peroxide ($H_2O_2$) is used to fuel rockets. The products of this reaction are nitrogen gas and water.

    **a.** Write the balanced chemical equation.

    **b.** How many grams of hydrazine are needed to produce 10.0 mol nitrogen gas?

**47.** No, you cannot produce more product than the theoretical yield, which is determined from the starting reactants.

**48.** (actual yield/theoretical yield) × 100 = percent yield

**49.** the actual yield of the product

**50.** the mass of one substance in the reaction and the actual mass of metal hydroxide produced

## Mastering Problems

Complete solutions to Chapter Assessment problems can be found in the **Solutions Manual.**

### Interpreting Equations (12.1)

**Level 1**

**51.** 4 atoms Al + 3 molecules $O_2 \rightarrow$ 2 formula units $Al_2O_3$
4 mol Al + 3 mol $O_2 \rightarrow$ 2 mol $Al_2O_3$
107.92 g Al + 96.00 g $O_2 \rightarrow$ 203.92 g $Al_2O_3$

**52.** 1 formula unit $SnO_2$ + 2 atoms C → 1 atom Sn + 2 molecules CO
1 mol $SnO_2$ + 2 mol C → 1 mol Sn + 2 mol CO
150.71 g $SnO_2$ + 24.02 g C → 118.71 g Sn + 56.01 g CO

**Level 2**

**53. a.** $2HCl(aq) + Pb(NO_3)_2(aq) \rightarrow PbCl_2(s) + 2HNO_3(aq)$

    **b.** 2 molecules HCl + 1 formula unit $Pb(NO_3)_2 \rightarrow$ 1 formula unit $PbCl_2$ + 2 molecules $HNO_3$
2 mol HCl + 1 mol $Pb(NO_3)_2 \rightarrow$ 1 mol $PbCl_2$ + 2 mol $HNO_3$
72.92 g HCl + 331.2 g $Pb(NO_3)_2 \rightarrow$ 278.1 g $PbCl_2$ + 126.04 g $HNO_3$

## Mole Ratios (12.1)

### Level 1

**54.** $Cu(s) + 4HNO_3(aq) \rightarrow Cu(NO_3)_2(aq) + 2NO_2(g) + 2H_2O(l)$; answers may include 1 mol Cu/4mol $HNO_3$, 1 mol Cu/1mol $Cu(NO_3)_2$, 1 mol Cu/2mol $NO_2$, 1mol Cu/2 mol $H_2O$, 4 mol $HNO_3$/1 mol Cu, 4 mol $HNO_3$/1 mol $Cu(NO_3)_2$, 4 mol $HNO_3$/2 mol $NO_2$, 4 mol $HNO_3$/ 2 mol

$H_2O$, 1 mol $Cu(NO_3)_2$/1 mol Cu, 1 mol $Cu(NO_3)_2$/4 mol $HNO_3$, 1 mol $Cu(NO_3)_2$/2 mol $NO_2$, 1 mol $Cu(NO_3)_2$/ 2 mol $H_2O$, 2 mol $NO_2$/ 1 mol Cu, 2 mol $NO_2$/4 mol $HNO_3$, 2 mol $NO_2$/1 mol $Cu(NO_3)_2$, 2 mol $NO_2$/2 mol $H_2O$, 2 mol $H_2O$/1 mol Cu, 2 mol $H_2O$/4 mol $HNO_3$, 2 mol $H_2O$/1 mol $Cu(NO_3)_2$, 2 mol $H_2O$/2 mol $NO_2$

# CHAPTER 12 ASSESSMENT

**55.** 2 mol Fe/1 mol $Fe_2O_3$

**56. a.** $SiO_2(s) + 4HF(aq) \rightarrow$ $SiF_4(g) + 2H_2O(l)$

  **b.** Students may write any of 12 ratios. Examples might be the following. 4 mol HF/1 mol $SiO_2$; used to find the amount of HF that will react with a known amount of $SiO_2$
  1 mol $SiF_4$/1 mol $SiO_2$; used to find the amount of $SiF_4$ that can be formed from a known amount of $SiO_2$.
  2 mol $H_2O$/1 mol $SiF_4$; used to find the amount of $H_2O$ that will be produced with the $SiF_4$

## Level 2

**57.** $2Al + 3Cl_2 \rightarrow 2AlCl_3$
  2 mol $AlCl_3$/2 mol Al

**58.** 1 mol $FeCr_2$/1 mol $FeCr_2O_4$

**59.** $2SO_2 + 2CaCO_3 + O_2 \rightarrow$ $2CaSO_4 + 2CO_2$
  2 mol $CaSO_4$/2 mol $SO_2$

**60.** $3W + X \rightarrow 2Y + 4Z$

## Stoichiometric Mole-to-Mole Conversions (12.2)

### Level 1

**61.** 5.50 mole $C_2H_2$

**62.** 0.0119 mol $CO_2$

### Level 2

**63.** 0.0125 mol $CaCO_3$

## Stoichiometric Mole-to-Mass Conversions (12.2)

### Level 1

**64.** 961 g citric acid

**65.** 523 g $C_3H_7COOC_2H_5$

**66.** $2C_8H_{18}(l) + 25O_2(g) \rightarrow$ $16CO_2(g) + 18H_2O(l)$; 71.4 g $C_8H_{18}$

### Level 2

**67. a.** $K_2CrO_4(aq) +$ $Pb(NO_3)_2(aq) \rightarrow$ $PbCrO_4(s) + 2KNO_3(aq)$

  **b.** 80.8 g $PbCrO_4$

**68. a.** $N_2H_2(l) + H_2O_2(l) \rightarrow N_2(g) + 2H_2O(g)$

  **b.** $3.00 \times 10^2$ g $N_2H_2$

---

## Stoichiometric Mass-to-Mass Conversions (12.2)

**69.** Chloroform ($CHCl_3$), an important solvent, is produced by a reaction between methane and chlorine.

$CH_4(g) + 3Cl_2(g) \rightarrow CHCl_3(g) + 3HCl(g)$

How many g $CH_4$ is needed to produce 50.0 g $CHCl_3$?

**70.** Gasohol is a mixture of ethanol and gasoline. Balance the equation and determine the mass of $CO_2$ produced from the combustion of 100.0 g ethanol.

____$C_2H_5OH(l)$ + ____$O_2(g) \rightarrow$____$CO_2(g)$ + ____$H_2O(g)$

**71.** When surface water dissolves carbon dioxide, carbonic acid ($H_2CO_3$) is formed. When the water moves underground through limestone formations, the limestone dissolves and caves are sometimes produced.

$CaCO_3(s) + H_2CO_3(aq) \rightarrow Ca(HCO_3)_2(aq)$

What mass of limestone must have dissolved if $3.05 \times 10^{10}$ kg of calcium hydrogen carbonate was produced?

**72.** Car batteries use solid lead and lead(IV) oxide with sulfuric acid solution to produce an electric current. The products of this reaction are lead(II) sulfate in solution and water.

  **a.** Write the balanced chemical equation for this reaction.

  **b.** Determine the mass of lead(II) sulfate produced when 25.0 g lead reacts with an excess of lead(IV) oxide and sulfuric acid.

**73.** The fuel methanol ($CH_3OH$) is made by the reaction of carbon monoxide and hydrogen.

  **a.** Write the balanced chemical equation.

  **b.** How many grams of hydrogen are needed to produce 45.0 grams of methanol?

**74.** To extract gold from its ore, the ore is treated with sodium cyanide solution in the presence of oxygen and water.

$4Au(s) + 8NaCN(aq) + O_2(g) + 2H_2O(l) \rightarrow$ $4NaAu(CN)_2(aq) + 4NaOH(aq)$

  **a.** Determine the mass of gold that can be extracted if 25.0 g sodium cyanide is used.

  **b.** If the mass of the ore from which the gold was extracted is 150.0 g, what percentage of the ore is gold?

**75.** Photographic film contains silver bromide in gelatin. Once exposed, some of the silver bromide decomposes producing fine grains of silver. The unexposed silver bromide is removed by treating the film with sodium thiosulfate. Soluble sodium silver thiosulfate ($Na_3Ag(S_2O_3)_2$) is produced.

---

$AgBr(s) + 2Na_2S_2O_3(aq) \rightarrow Na_3Ag(S_2O_3)_2(aq) +$ $NaBr(aq)$
Determine the mass of $Na_3Ag(S_2O_3)_2$ produced if 0.275 g AgBr is removed.

## Limiting Reactants (12.3)

Ethyne    Hydrogen         Ethane    Ethyne

**76.** The illustration shows the reaction between ethyne (acetylene, $C_2H_2$) and hydrogen. The product is ethane ($C_2H_6$). Which is the limiting reactant? Which is the excess reactant? Explain.

**77.** This reaction takes place in a nickel-iron battery.

$Fe(s) + 2NiO(OH)(s) + 2H_2O(l) \rightarrow$ $Fe(OH)_2(s) + 2Ni(OH)_2(aq)$

Determine the number of moles of iron(II) hydroxide ($Fe(OH)_2$) produced if 5.00 mol Fe and 8.00 mol NiO(OH) react.

**78.** How many moles of cesium xenon heptafluoride ($CsXeF_7$) can be produced from the reaction of 12.5 mol cesium fluoride with 10.0 mol xenon hexafluoride?

$CsF(s) + XeF_6(s) \rightarrow CsXeF_7(s)$.

**79.** Iron is obtained commercially by the reaction of hematite ($Fe_2O_3$) with carbon monoxide. How many grams of iron are produced if 25.0 moles of hematite react with 30.0 moles of carbon monoxide?

$Fe_2O_3(s) + 3CO(g) \rightarrow 2Fe(s) + 3CO_2(g)$

**80.** Under certain conditions of temperature and pressure, hydrogen and nitrogen react to produce ammonia ($NH_3$). Write the balanced chemical equation and determine the mass of ammonia produced if 3.50 mol $H_2$ reacts with 5.00 mol $N_2$.

**81.** The reaction of chlorine gas with solid phosphorus ($P_4$) produces solid phosphorus pentachloride. When 16.0 g chlorine reacts with 23.0 g $P_4$, which reactant limits the amount of phosphorus pentachloride produced? Which reactant is in excess?

**82.** An alkaline battery produces electrical energy according to this equation.

$Zn(s) + 2MnO_2(s) + H_2O(l) \rightarrow$ $Zn(OH)_2(s) + Mn_2O_3(s)$

  **a.** Determine the limiting reactant if 25.0 g Zn and 30.0 g $MnO_2$ are used.

  **b.** Determine the mass of $Zn(OH)_2$ produced.

---

## Stoichiometric Mass-to-Mass Conversions (12.2)

### Level 1

**69.** 6.72 g $CH_4$

**70.** $C_2H_5OH(l) + 3O_2(g) \rightarrow 2CO_2(g) +$ $3H_2O(l)$; 191.0 g $CO_2$

### Level 2

**71.** $1.88 \times 10^{13}$ g or $1.88 \times 10^{10}$ kg $CaCO_3$

**72. a.** $Pb(s) + PbO_2(s) + 2H_2SO_4(aq) \rightarrow$ $2PbSO_4(aq) + 2H_2O(l)$

  **b.** 73.2 g $PbSO_4$

**73. a.** $CO(g) + 2H_2(s) \rightarrow CH_3OH(l)$

  **b.** 5.67 g $H_2$

**74. a.** 50.2 g Au

  **b.** 33.5 % gold in ore

**75.** 0.587 g $Na_3Ag(S_2O_3)_2$

**83.** Lithium reacts spontaneously with bromine to produce lithium bromide. Write the balanced chemical equation for the reaction. If 25.0 g of lithium and 25.0 g of bromine are present at the beginning of the reaction, determine

**a.** the limiting reactant
**b.** the mass of lithium bromide produced
**c.** the excess reactant and the mass in excess.

## Percent Yield (12.4)

**84.** Ethanol ($C_2H_5OH$) is produced from the fermentation of sucrose in the presence of enzymes.

$$C_{12}H_{22}O_{11}(aq) + H_2O(g) \rightarrow 4C_2H_5OH(l) + 4CO_2(g)$$

Determine the theoretical and percent yields of ethanol if 684 g sucrose undergoes fermentation and 349 g ethanol is obtained.

**85.** Lead(II) oxide is obtained by roasting galena, lead(II) sulfide, in air.

$$\_\_\_\_ \ PbS(s) + \_\_\_\_ \ O_2(g) \rightarrow$$
$$\_\_\_\_ \ PbO(s) + \_\_\_\_ \ SO_2(g)$$

**a.** Balance the equation and determine the theoretical yield of PbO if 200.0 g PbS is heated.
**b.** What is the percent yield if 170.0 g of PbO is obtained?

**86.** Upon heating, calcium carbonate decomposes to produce calcium oxide and carbon dioxide.

**a.** Determine the theoretical yield of $CO_2$ if 235.0 g $CaCO_3$ is heated.
**b.** What is the percent yield of $CO_2$ if 97.5 g $CO_2$ is collected?

**87.** Hydrofluoric acid solutions cannot be stored in glass containers because HF reacts readily with silica in glass to produce hexafluorosilicic acid ($H_2SiF_6$).

$$SiO_2(s) + 6HF(aq) \rightarrow H_2SiF_6(aq) + 2H_2O(l).$$

If 40.0 g $SiO_2$ and 40.0 g of HF react

**a.** determine the limiting reactant.
**b.** determine the mass of the excess reactant.
**c.** determine the theoretical yield of $H_2SiF_6$.
**d.** determine the percent yield if the actual yield is 45.8 g $H_2SiF_6$.

**88.** Pure zirconium is obtained using the two-step Van Arkel process. In the first step, impure zirconium and iodine are heated to produce zirconium iodide ($ZrI_4$). In the second step, $ZrI_4$ is decomposed to produce pure zirconium.

$$ZrI_4(s) \rightarrow Zr(s) + 2I_2(g)$$

Determine the percent yield of zirconium if 45.0 g $ZrI_4$ is decomposed and 5.00 g pure Zr is obtained.

**89.** Phosphorus is commercially prepared by heating a mixture of calcium phosphate, sand, and coke in an electric furnace. The process involves two reactions.

$$2Ca_3(PO_4)_2(s) + 6SiO_2(s) \rightarrow 6CaSiO_3(l) + P_4O_{10}(g)$$
$$P_4O_{10}(g) + 10C(s) \rightarrow P_4(g) + 10CO(g)$$

The $P_4O_{10}$ produced in the first reaction reacts with an excess of coke (C) in the second reaction. Determine the theoretical yield of $P_4$ if 250.0 g $Ca_3(PO_4)_2$ and 400.0 g $SiO_2$ are heated. If the actual yield of $P_4$ is 45.0 g, determine the percent yield of $P_4$.

**90.** Chlorine can be prepared by the reaction of manganese(IV) oxide with hydrochloric acid.

$$\_\_\_\_ \ MnO_2(s) + \_\_\_\_ \ HCl(aq) \rightarrow$$
$$\_\_\_\_ \ MnCl_2(aq) + \_\_\_\_ \ Cl_2(g) + \_\_\_\_ \ H_2O(l)$$

Balance the equation and determine the theoretical and percent yields of chlorine if 86.0 g $MnO_2$ and 50.0 g HCl react. The actual yield of chlorine is 20.0 g.

## Mixed Review

*Sharpen your problem-solving skills by answering the following.*

**91.** Ammonium sulfide reacts with copper(II) nitrate in a double replacement reaction. What mole ratio would you use to determine the moles of $NH_4NO_3$ produced if the moles of CuS are known?

**92.** One method for producing nitrogen in the laboratory is to react ammonia with copper(II) oxide.

$$\_\_\_\_ \ NH_3(g) + \_\_\_\_ \ CuO(s) \rightarrow$$
$$\_\_\_\_ \ Cu(s) + \_\_\_\_ \ H_2O(l) + \_\_\_\_ \ N_2(g)$$

**a.** Balance the equation.
**b.** If 40.0 g $NH_3$ is reacted with 80.0 g CuO, determine the limiting reactant.
**c.** Determine the mass of $N_2$ produced by this reaction.
**d.** Which reactant is in excess? How much remains after the reaction?

**93.** The compound calcium cyanamide (CaNCN) can be used as a fertilizer. To obtain this compound, calcium carbide is reacted with nitrogen at high temperatures.

$$CaC_2(s) + N_2(g) \rightarrow CaNCN(s) + C(s)$$

What mass of CaNCN can be produced if 7.50 mol $CaC_2$ reacts with 5.00 mol $N_2$?

**94.** When copper(II) oxide is heated in the presence of hydrogen gas, elemental copper and water are produced. What mass of copper can be obtained if 32.0 g copper(II) oxide is used?

---

## Limiting Reactants (12.3)

### Level 1

**76.** Hydrogen is limiting; ethyne is the excess reactant. One mol of ethyne is left over.
**77.** 4.0 mol $Fe(OH)_2$
**78.** 10.0 mol $CsXeF_7$
**79.** 1120 g Fe
**80.** $3H_2(g) + N_2(g) \rightarrow 2NH_3(g)$, 39.8 g $NH_3$

### Level 2

**81.** $Cl_2$ is the limiting reactant; phosphorus is in excess.
**82. a.** $MnO_2$ is the limiting reactant.
    **b.** 17.1 g $Zn(OH)_2$
**83.** $2Li(s) + Br_2(l) \rightarrow 2LiBr(s)$
    **a.** $Br_2$ is limiting.
    **b.** 27.1 g LiBr
    **c.** Li is the excess reactant, 22.8 g

## Percent Yield (12.4)

### Level 1

**84.** theoretical yield = 369 g $C_2H_5OH$, 94.6% yield $C_2H_5OH$
**85. a.** $2PbS + 3O_2 \rightarrow 2PbO + 2SO_2$; theoretical yield = 186.6 g PbO
    **b.** 91.10% yield PbO
**86. a.** theoretical yield = 103 g $CO_2$
    **b.** 94.7% yield $CO_2$

### Level 2

**87. a.** HF is the limiting reactant.
    **b.** $SiO_2$ is the excess reactant, 20.0 g.
    **c.** theoretical yield = 48.0 g $H_2SiF_6$
    **d.** percent yield = 95.4%
**88.** 73.0% yield Zr
**89.** theoretical yield = 49.92 g $P_4$; 90.1% yield $P_4$
**90.** $MnO_2(s) + 4HCl(aq) \rightarrow MnCl_2(aq) + Cl_2(g) + 2H_2O(l)$ theoretical yield = 24.3 g $Cl_2$; 82.3% yield $Cl_2$

**National Science Content Standards**

**Pages 380–381**
UCP.1, UCP.3; B.3; E.1

---

## Mixed Review

**91.** 2 mol $NH_4NO_3$/1 mol CuS
**92. a.** $2NH_3(g) + 3CuO(s) \rightarrow 3Cu(s) + 3H_2O(l) + N_2(g)$
    **b.** CuO is the limiting reactant.
    **c.** 9.43 g $N_2$
    **d.** Ammonia is the excess reactant. 28.6 g $NH_3$ in excess
**93.** 401 g CaNCN
**94.** 25.6 g Cu
**95. a.** $2NO(g) + O_2(g) \rightarrow 2NO_2(g)$
    **b.** 2 mol $NO_2$/2 mol NO
**96.** theoretical yield = 4.04 g $H_2$; 94.1% yield $H_2$
**97.** 1 mol $Cl_2$/2 mol NaCl, 2.43 mol $Cl_2$, 172 g $Cl_2$
**98.** 94.4% yield $Al_2O_3$

## Thinking Critically

**99.** No, percent yields cannot be greater than 100%. High results could mean the product was not completely dry, or it was contaminated.

**100. a.** no, because there is only one reactant

**b.** yes, because there are two reactants; Not enough information is given to identify which is the limiting reactant.

**c.** yes, because there are two reactants; Oxygen is in excess, so the limiting reactant is propane.

**101.** Obtain and record the mass of an empty evaporating dish. Add 2.00 g of copper(II) sulfate penta-hydrate and obtain and record the mass of the hydrate and evaporating dish. Heat the dish gently for 5 minutes, then strongly for 5 minutes to drive off the water. Cool the dish and remass. Record. Determine the mass of the anhydrous copper sulfate. Using the equation $CuSO_4 \cdot 5H_2O \rightarrow CuSO_4 + 5H_2O$ and the initial mass of the copper(II) sulfate pentahydrate, determine the theoretical yield of copper(II) sulfate. Determine the actual yield of copper(II) sulfate. Divide the actual yield by the theoretical yield and multiply by 100 to determine percent yield of copper(II) sulfate.

**102.** Drawing should show eight copper atoms and six diatomic chlorine molecules as reactants. The products should be represented as six formula units of $CuCl_2$ with two copper atoms in excess.

**103.** When you fan the flame, additional oxygen is added and the remaining coals can burn.

**95.** Nitrogen oxide is present in urban pollution but it is immediately converted to nitrogen dioxide as it reacts with oxygen.

**a.** Write the balanced chemical equation for the formation of nitrogen dioxide from nitrogen oxide.

**b.** What mole ratio would you use to convert from moles of nitrogen oxide to moles of nitrogen dioxide?

**96.** Determine the theoretical and percent yield of hydrogen gas if 36.0 g water undergoes electrolysis to produce hydrogen and oxygen and 3.80 g hydrogen is collected.

**97.** The Swedish chemist Karl Wilhellm was first to produce chlorine in the laboratory.

$2NaCl(s) + 2H_2SO_4(aq) + MnO_2(aq) \rightarrow Na_2SO_4(aq) + MnSO_4(aq) + 2H_2O(l) + Cl_2(g).$

What mole ratio could be used to find the moles of chlorine produced from 4.85 moles of sodium chloride? Determine the moles of chlorine produced. Determine the mass of chlorine produced.

**98.** The solid booster rockets of the space shuttle contain ammonium perchlorate ($NH_4ClO_4$) and powdered aluminum as the propellant.

$8Al + 3NH_4ClO_4 \rightarrow 4Al_2O_3 + 3NH_4Cl.$

Determine the percent yield if $6.00 \times 10^5$ kg $NH_4ClO_4$ produces $6.56 \times 10^5$ kg aluminum oxide.

## Thinking Critically

**99. Analyze and Conclude** In an experiment, you obtain a percent yield of product of 108%. Is such a percent yield possible? Explain. Assuming that your calculation is correct, what reasons might explain such a result?

**100. Observing and Inferring** Determine whether the following reactions depend upon a limiting reactant. Explain why or why not and identify the limiting reactant.

**a.** Potassium chlorate decomposes to form potassium chloride and oxygen.

**b.** Silver nitrate and hydrochloric acid react to produce silver chloride and nitric acid.

**c.** Propane ($C_3H_8$) burns in excess oxygen to produce carbon dioxide and water.

**101. Designing an Experiment** Design an experiment that can be used to determine the percent yield of anhydrous copper(II) sulfate when copper(II) sulfate pentahydrate is heated to remove water.

**102. Formulating Models** Copper reacts with chlorine to produce copper(II) chloride. Draw a diagram that represents eight atoms of copper reacting with six molecules of chlorine. Make sure you include the particles before the reaction and after the reaction. Include any excess reactants.

**103. Applying Concepts** When your campfire begins to die down and smolder, it helps to fan it. Explain in terms of stoichiometry why the fire begins to flare up again.

## Writing in Chemistry

**104.** Research the air pollutants produced by using gasoline in internal combustion engines. Discuss the common pollutants and the reaction that produces them. Show, through the use of stoichiometry, how each pollutant could be reduced if more people used mass transit.

**105.** The percent yield of ammonia produced when hydrogen and nitrogen are combined under ordinary conditions is extremely small. However, the Haber Process combines the two gases under a set of conditions designed to maximize yield. Research the conditions used in the Haber Process and find out why the development of the process was of great importance.

## Cumulative Review

*Refresh your understanding of previous chapters by answering the following.*

**106.** You observe that sugar dissolves more quickly in hot tea than in iced tea. You state that higher temperatures increase the rate at which sugar dissolves in water. Is this statement a hypothesis or theory and why? (Chapter 1)

**107.** Write the electron configuration for each of the following atoms. (Chapter 5)

**a.** fluorine
**b.** aluminum
**c.** titanium
**d.** radon

**108.** Explain why the gaseous nonmetals exist as diatomic molecules, but other gaseous elements exist as single atoms. (Chapter 9)

**109.** Write a balanced equation for the reaction of potassium with oxygen. (Chapter 10)

**110.** What is the molecular mass of $UF_6$? What is the molar mass of $UF_6$? (Chapter 11)

*Use these questions and the test-taking tip to prepare for your standardized test.*

**Interpreting Graphs**  Use the graph below to answer questions 1–4.

### Supply of Various Chemicals in Dr. Raitano's Laboratory

NaCl 700.0 g
Na$_2$CO$_3$ 500.0 g
Ca(OH)$_2$ 300.0 g
NaH$_2$PO$_4$ 350.0 g
KClO$_3$ 200.0 g
AgNO$_3$ 100.0 g

**1.** Pure silver metal can be made using the reaction shown below:

$$Cu(s) + 2AgNO_3(aq) \rightarrow 2Ag(s) + Cu(NO_3)_2(aq)$$

How many grams of copper metal will be needed to use up all of the AgNO$_3$ in Dr. Raitano's laboratory?

**a.** 18.70 g          **c.** 74.7 g
**b.** 37.3 g           **d.** 100 g

**2.** $Na_2CO_3(aq) + Ca(OH)_2(aq) \rightarrow 2NaOH(aq) + CaCO_3(s)$

The LeBlanc process, shown above, is the traditional method of manufacturing sodium hydroxide. Using the amounts of chemicals available in Dr. Raitano's lab, what is the maximum number of moles of NaOH that can be produced?

**a.** 4.05 mol          **c.** 8.097 mol
**b.** 4.72 mol          **d.** 9.43 mol

**3.** Pure O$_2$ gas can be generated from the decomposition of potassium chlorate (KClO$_3$):

$$2KClO_3(s) \rightarrow 2KCl(s) + 3O_2(g)$$

If half of the KClO$_3$ in the lab is used and 12.8 g of oxygen gas are produced, what is the percent yield of this reaction?

**a.** 12.8%          **c.** 65.6%
**b.** 32.7%          **d.** 98.0%

**4.** Sodium dihydrogen pyrophosphate (Na$_2$H$_2$P$_2$O$_7$), more commonly known as baking powder, is manufactured by heating NaH$_2$PO$_4$ at high temperatures:

$$2NaH_2PO_4(s) \rightarrow Na_2H_2P_2O_7(s) + H_2O(g)$$

If 444.0 g of Na$_2$H$_2$P$_2$O$_7$ are needed, how much more NaH$_2$PO$_4$ will Dr. Raitano have to buy to make enough Na$_2$H$_2$P$_2$O$_7$?

**a.** 94.0 g
**b.** 130.0 g
**c.** 480 g
**d.** none—the lab already has enough

**5.** Stoichiometry is based on the law of

**a.** constant mole ratios.
**b.** Avogadro's constant.
**c.** conservation of energy.
**d.** conservation of mass.

**6.** Red mercury(II) oxide decomposes at high temperatures to form mercury metal and oxygen gas:

$$2HgO(s) \rightarrow 2Hg(l) + O_2(g)$$

If 3.55 moles of HgO decompose to form 1.54 moles of O$_2$ and 618 g of Hg, what is the percent yield of this reaction?

**a.** 13.2%          **c.** 56.6%
**b.** 42.5%          **d.** 86.8%

**7.** Dimethyl hydrazine (CH$_3$)$_2$N$_2$H$_2$ ignites spontaneously upon contact with dinitrogen tetroxide (N$_2$O$_4$):

$$(CH_3)_2N_2H_2(l) + 2N_2O_4(l) \rightarrow 3N_2(g) + 4H_2O(g) + 2CO_2(g)$$

Because this reaction produces an enormous amount of energy from a small amount of reactants, it was used to drive the rockets on the Lunar Excursion Modules (LEMs) of the Apollo space program. If 2.0 moles of dimethyl hydrazine are mixed with 4.0 moles of dinitrogen tetroxide, and the reaction achieves an 85% yield, how many moles of N$_2$, H$_2$O, and CO$_2$ will be formed?

**a.** 0.57 mol N$_2$, 0.43 mol H$_2$O, 0.85 mol CO$_2$
**b.** 2.6 mol N$_2$, 3.4 mol H$_2$O, 1.7 mol CO$_2$
**c.** 5.1 mol N$_2$, 6.8 mol H$_2$O, 3.4 mol CO$_2$
**d.** 6.0 mol N$_2$, 8.0 mol H$_2$O, 4.0 mol CO$_2$

---

### TEST-TAKING TIP

**Calculators Are Only Machines**  If your test allows you to use a calculator, use it wisely. The calculator can't figure out what the question is asking. That's still *your* job. Figure out which numbers are relevant, and determine the best way to solve the problem before you start punching keys.

## Cumulative Review

**106.** a hypothesis, because it is based only on observation, not on data
**107.** **a.** [He]$2s^2 2p^5$
  **b.** [Ne]$3s^2 3p^1$
  **c.** [Ar]$4s^2 3d^2$
  **d.** [Xe]$6s^2 4f^{14} 5d^{10} 6p^6$
**108.** Diatomic molecules achieve a noble gas electron configuration by forming covalent bonds. The monoatomic gases already have noble gas electron configurations.
**109.** $4K(s) + O_2(g) \rightarrow 2K_2O(s)$
**110.** 352.02 amu, 352.02 g/mol

## Standardized Test Practice

**1.** a      **3.** b      **5.** d      **7.** c
**2.** c      **4.** b      **6.** d

**National Science Content Standards**
Page 382–383
UCP.1, UCP.3; B.3, B.6; E.2; F.4

# Resource Manager

| Section | Objectives | Activities/Features |
|---|---|---|
| **Section 13.1**<br>**Gases**<br>1 session<br>½ block | **1. Use** the kinetic-molecular theory to explain the behavior of gases.<br>**2. Describe** how mass affects the rates of diffusion and effusion.<br>**3. Explain** how gas pressure is measured and **calculate** the partial pressure of a gas. | **Discovery Lab:** Defying Density, p. 385<br>**Problem-Solving Lab:** How are the depth of a dive and pressure related?, p. 390 |
| **Section 13.2**<br>**Forces of Attraction**<br>1½ sessions<br>1 block | **4. Describe** and **compare** intramolecular and intermolecular forces.<br>**5. Distinguish** among intermolecular forces. | |
| **Section 13.3**<br>**Liquids and Solids**<br>1 session<br>½ block | **6. Apply** kinetic-molecular theory to the behavior of liquids and solids.<br>**7. Relate** properties such as viscosity, surface tension, and capillary action to intermolecular forces.<br>**8. Compare** the structures and properties of different types of solids. | **MiniLab:** Crystal Unit Cell Models, p. 401<br>**Careers Using Chemistry:** Materials Engineer, p. 403 |
| **Section 13.4**<br>**Phase Changes**<br>2½ sessions<br>1½ blocks | **9. Explain** how the addition and removal of energy can cause a phase change.<br>**10. Interpret** a phase diagram. | **Earth Science Connection,** p. 408<br>**ChemLab Small Scale:** Comparing Rates of Evaporation, pp. 410–411<br>**Everyday Chemistry:** Metals With a Memory, p. 412 |

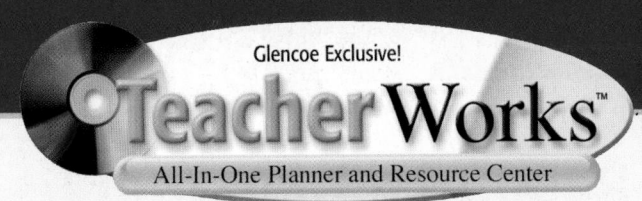

Glencoe Exclusive!

**TeacherWorks™**

All-In-One Planner and Resource Center

| National Science Content Standards | State/Local Standards | Reproducible Masters | Transparencies |
|---|---|---|---|
| UCP.1, UCP.2, UCP.3; A.1; B.2, B.4, B.5, B.6; E.2; G.3 | | **Study Guide for Content Mastery,** pp. 73–74 **L2** | **Section Focus Transparency 47 L1 ELL** <br> **Teaching Transparency 40 L2 ELL** |
| UCP.1, UCP.2, UCP.3; B.2, B.4 | | **Study Guide for Content Mastery,** p. 75 **L2** | **Section Focus Transparency 48 L1 ELL** |
| UCP.1, UCP.2, UCP.3; B.2, B.4, B.5 | | **Study Guide for Content Mastery,** p. 76 **L2** <br> **ChemLab and MiniLab Worksheets,** p. 49 **L2** <br> **Challenge Problems,** p. 13 **L3** | **Section Focus Transparency 49 L1 ELL** <br> **Math Skills Transparency 18 L2 ELL** |
| UCP.1, UCP.2, UCP.3; A.1; B.2, B.4, B.5, B.6; E.2; F.6 | | **Study Guide for Content Mastery,** pp. 77–78 **L2** <br> **ChemLab and MiniLab Worksheets,** pp. 50–52 **L2** <br> **Laboratory Manual,** pp. 97–104 **L2** <br> **Small-Scale Laboratory Manual,** pp. 33–36 **L2** <br> **CBL Laboratory Manual,** pp. 9–12 **L2** | **Section Focus Transparency 50 L1 ELL** <br> **Teaching Transparency 41 L2 ELL** |

**Key to National Science Content Standards:** UCP = Unifying Concepts and Processes, A = Science as Inquiry, B = Physical Science, C = Life Science, D = Earth and Space Sciences, E = Science and Technology, F = Science in Personal and Social Perspectives, G = History and Nature of Science

Refer to pages 4T–5T of the Teacher Guide for an explanation of the National Science Content Standards correlations.

# Resource Manager

## Materials List

### ChemLab (pages 410–411)
distilled water, ethanol, isopropyl alcohol, acetone, household ammonia, droppers (5), small plastic cups (5), grease pencil or masking tape and marking pen, paper towel, waxed paper, stopwatch

### Discovery Lab (page 385)
600-mL beaker, detergent, dropper, pin, water

### MiniLab (page 401)
plastic or paper soda straws (12), 22- or 26-gauge wire, scissors

### Demonstration (pages 398–399)
1-pint canning jar with ring lid, wire screen, distilled water, food coloring, card stock

## Preparation of Solutions

For a review of solution preparation, see page 46T of the Teacher Guide.

There are no solutions to be prepared for the activities in this chapter.

## Assessment Resources

**Chapter Assessment,** pp. 73–78
**MindJogger Videoquizzes DVD/VHS**
**Alternate Assessment in the Science Classroom**
**ExamView® Pro CD-ROM**
**Solutions Manual,** Chapter 13
**Supplemental Problems,** Chapter 13
**Performance Assessment in the Science Classroom**
**Chemistry Interactive CD-ROM,** Chapter 13 quiz

## Additional Resources

**Spanish Resources** ELL
**Guided Reading Audio Program,** Chapter 13 ELL
**Cooperative Learning in the Science Classroom**
**Lab and Safety Skills in the Science Classroom**
**Lesson Plans**
**Block Scheduling Lesson Plans**
**Chemistrymc.com**

## Glencoe Technology

The following multimedia for this chapter are available from Glencoe.

**VIDEOTAPE/DVD**
MindJogger Videoquizzes,
Chapter 13

**CD-ROM**
**Chemistry: Matter and Change**
*Three States of Matter,* Animation
*Surface Tension,* Demonstration
*Phase Changes,* Experiment
*Changes of State,* Video
*Superheated Steam,* Demonstration

**CD-ROM**
**ExamView® Pro
Testmaker**

**CD-ROM**
**Interactive Chalkboard**

**CD-ROM**
**TeacherWorks™**

## Multiple Learning Styles

Look for the following icons for strategies that emphasize different learning modalities.

*Kinesthetic*
Differentiated Instruction, pp. 389, 393; Building a
Model, p. 396

*Visual-Spatial*
Reteach, p. 403, Visual Learning, p. 412

*Intrapersonal*
Differentiated Instruction, pp. 396, 405; Portfolio,
p. 407

*Linguistic*
Chemistry Journal, pp. 386, 389, 394, 397, 404;
Portfolio, p. 388; Extension, p. 407

*Logical-Mathematical*
Enrichment, p. 387

## Key to Teaching Strategies

 **L1** Level 1 activities should be appropriate for students with
learning difficulties.

**L2** Level 2 activities should be within the ability range of
all students.

**L3** Level 3 activities are designed for above-average students.

**ELL** ELL activities should be within the ability range of
English Language Learners.

**COOP LEARN** Cooperative Learning activities are designed
for small group work.

 **P** These strategies represent student products that can be
placed into a best-work portfolio.

These strategies are useful in a block scheduling format.

## Assessment Planner

**Portfolio Assessment**
Portfolio, TWE, pp. 388, 406,
407, 413
Problem-Solving Lab, TWE,
p. 390

**Performance Assessment**
Discovery Lab, SE, p. 385
Assessment, TWE, pp. 403,
405, 409
Demonstration, TWE, p. 399
MiniLab, SE, p. 401
ChemLab, SE, pp. 410–411
ChemLab, TWE, p. 411

**Knowledge Assessment**
Assessment, TWE, pp. 388,
391, 403
Section Assessment, SE,
pp. 392, 395, 403, 409
MiniLab, TWE, p. 401
Chapter Assessment, SE,
pp. 414–417

**Skill Assessment**
Assessment, TWE, pp. 392,
394, 395

## Tying to Previous Knowledge

Have students review the following concepts before studying this chapter.
Chapter 2: density
Chapter 3: physical properties

## Using the Photo

Ask students what is happening to the particles in dry ice that form the "fog" on the stage. If possible, use dry ice to demonstrate this process in the classroom as well. The solid carbon dioxide particles in dry ice sublimate as they warm up, cooling water vapor in the air. The water vapor condenses to form fog.

**PowerPoint® Presentations**
This CD-ROM is an editable Microsoft® PowerPoint® presentation that includes:
- Section presentations
- Section checks
- Image bank
- Links to Chemistry Online
- All transparencies
- Animations
- Audio

---

# States of Matter

## What You'll Learn

▶ You will use the kinetic-molecular theory to explain the physical properties of gases, liquids, and solids.
▶ You will compare types of intermolecular forces.
▶ You will explain how kinetic energy and inter-molecular forces combine to determine the state of a substance.
▶ You will describe the role of energy in phase changes.

## Why It's Important

Water collects on a bathroom mirror as you shower, a full bottle of water shatters in a freezer, and a glass object breaks when it is dropped. You will be able to explain such familiar events after you learn more about the different states of matter.

Visit the Chemistry Web site at **chemistrymc.com** to find links about the states of matter.

Solid carbon dioxide is called dry ice. At room temperature, dry ice is used to create the illusion of fog on stage.

**384** Chapter 13

---

## DISCOVERY LAB

### Purpose
Students will observe the effect of surface tension in water.

### Safety and Disposal
Pins have sharp points.

### Teaching Strategies
Encourage students to be patient in floating the pins, as it takes practice. The

material and width of the container do not matter. Students could pour off some water if they are having trouble retrieving the pin.

### Expected Results
After the pin floats on the water, adding the detergent solution will cause it to sink.

## Defying Density

**Y**ou know that an object sinks or floats in water based on its density. In this activity, you will explore an exception to this rule.

### Safety Precautions

Be careful handling the pin, which has a sharp point.

### Procedure

1. Pour about 400 mL of water into a 600-mL beaker. Float the pin on the surface of the water.

2. Use a dropper to add one drop of water containing detergent to the beaker. Place the drop on the water surface near the wall of the beaker. Observe what happens.

### Analysis

Is a metal pin likely to be more or less dense than water? How does the shape of the pin help it to float? Hypothesize about the reason for the pin's behavior before and after you added the detergent.

**Materials**

pin
600-mL beaker
400 mL water
detergent
dropper

---

**Section 13.1**

# Gases

## Objectives

- **Use** the kinetic-molecular theory to explain the behavior of gases.

- **Describe** how mass affects the rates of diffusion and effusion.

- **Explain** how gas pressure is measured and **calculate** the partial pressure of a gas.

## Vocabulary

kinetic-molecular theory
elastic collision
temperature
diffusion
Graham's law of effusion
pressure
barometer
pascal
atmosphere
Dalton's law of partial
    pressures

You have learned that the types of atoms present (composition) and their arrangement (structure) determine the chemical properties of matter. Composition and structure also affect the physical properties of liquids and solids. Based solely on physical appearance, you can distinguish water from mercury or gold from graphite. By contrast, substances that are gases at room temperature usually display similar physical properties despite their different compositions. Why is there so little variation in behavior among gases? Why are the physical properties of gases different from those of liquids and solids?

### The Kinetic-Molecular Theory

Flemish physician Jan Baptista Van Helmont (1577–1644) used the Greek word *chaos*, which means without order, to describe those products of reactions that had no fixed shape or volume. From the word *chaos* came the term *gas*. By the eighteenth century, scientists knew how to collect gaseous products by displacing water. Now they could observe and measure properties of individual gases. About 1860, Ludwig Boltzmann and James Maxwell, who were working in different countries, each proposed a model to explain the properties of gases. That model is the kinetic-molecular theory. Because all of the gases known to Boltzmann and Maxwell contained molecules, the name of the model refers to molecules. The word *kinetic* comes from a Greek word meaning "to move." Objects in motion have energy called kinetic energy. The **kinetic-molecular theory** describes the behavior of gases in terms of particles in motion. The model makes several assumptions about the size, motion, and energy of gas particles.

13.1 Gases    **385**

---

# 1 Focus

**Focus Transparency**

Before presenting the lesson, display **Section Focus Transparency 47** on the overhead projector. Have students answer the accompanying questions using **Section Focus Transparency Master 47.** L1 ELL

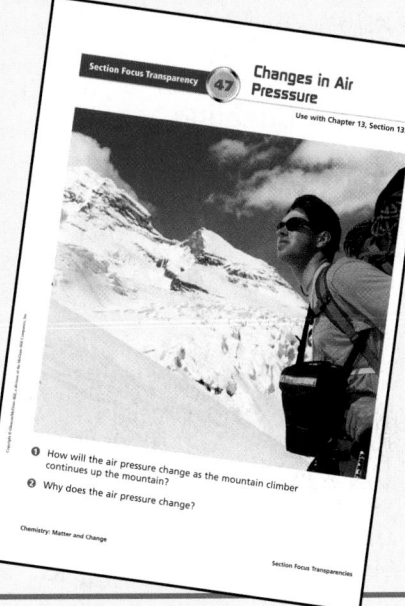

Section Focus Transparency **47** Changes in Air Presssure
Use with Chapter 13, Section 13.1

❶ How will the air pressure change as the mountain climber continues up the mountain?
❷ Why does the air pressure change?

Chemistry: Matter and Change

Section Focus Transparencies

## Chapter Themes

The following themes from the National Science Education Standards are covered in this chapter. Refer to page 4T of the Teacher Guide for an explanation of the correlations.

Systems, order, and organization (UCP.1)
Evidence, models, and explanation (UCP.2)
Change, constancy, and measurement (UCP.3)

---

## Analysis

Although the metal pin is likely to be denser than water, the pin floats because the surface tension of the water creates a force that pushes up against the pin. Since the pin is long and thin, it has a large surface area for the water's surface tension to act against. The detergent breaks the surface tension.

---

## GLENCOE
### TECHNOLOGY

CD-ROM
**Chemistry: Matter and Change**
Animation: *Three States of Matter*

---

## Resource Manager

**Study Guide for Content Mastery,** pp. 73–74 L2
**Solving Problems: A Chemistry Handbook,** Section 13.1 L2
**Section Focus Transparency 47 and Master** L1 ELL

**385**

**Figure 13-1a** Kinetic energy may be transferred between gas particles during an elastic collision. What influence do gas particles have on each other between collisions? Between collisions, the particles have no influence on each other.

**Figure 13-1b** What happens to the path of a gas particle after a collision? Gas particles travel in straight lines until they collide with each other or with the walls of their container. When gas particles collide, they immediately bounce apart.

## In-Text Question

**Page 386** What property of gases makes it possible for an air-filled flotation device to work? Gases are much less dense than liquids or solids.

**Figure 13-1**

**ⓐ** Kinetic energy may be transferred between gas particles during an elastic collision. What influence do gas particles have on each other between collisions?

**ⓑ** What happens to the path of a gas particle after a collision?

 **ⓐ**

 **ⓑ**

**Particle size** Gases consist of small particles that are separated from one another by empty space. The volume of the particles is small compared with the volume of the empty space. Because gas particles are far apart, there are no significant attractive or repulsive forces among them.

**Particle motion** Gas particles are in constant, random motion. Particles move in a straight line until they collide with other particles or with the walls of their container, as shown in **Figure 13-1.** Collisions between gas particles are elastic. An **elastic collision** is one in which no kinetic energy is lost. Kinetic energy may be transferred between colliding particles, but the total kinetic energy of the two particles does not change.

**Particle energy** Two factors determine the kinetic energy of a particle: mass and velocity. The kinetic energy of a particle can be represented by the equation

$$KE = \frac{1}{2}mv^2$$

**Figure 13-2**

The air in a life jacket allows the person wearing the jacket to float on the water.

in which *KE* is kinetic energy, *m* is the mass of the particle, and *v* is its velocity. Velocity reflects both the speed and the direction of motion. In a sample of a single gas, all particles have the same mass but all particles do not have the same velocity. Therefore, all particles do not have the same kinetic energy. Kinetic energy and temperature are related. **Temperature** is a measure of the average kinetic energy of the particles in a sample of matter. At a given temperature, all gases have the same average kinetic energy.

## Explaining the Behavior of Gases

Kinetic-molecular theory can help explain the behavior of gases. For example, the constant motion of gas particles allows a gas to expand until it fills its container, such as the flotation device in **Figure 13-2.** What property of gases makes it possible for an air-filled flotation device to work?

**Low density** Remember that density is mass per unit volume. The density of chlorine gas is $2.95 \times 10^{-3}$ g/mL at 20°C; the density of solid gold is 19.3 g/mL. Gold is more than 6500 times as dense as chlorine. This large difference cannot be due only to the difference in mass between gold atoms and chlorine molecules

386

**CHEMISTRY JOURNAL**

### Boltzmann and Maxwell

*Linguistic* Ask students to research Ludwig Boltzmann and James Maxwell, whose work on gases led to the kinetic-molecular theory. Ask them to include in their chemistry journals a synopsis of the contributions of both men and an evaluation of which scientist's work made a stronger contribution to the theory. **L2** (about 3:1). As the kinetic-molecular theory states, a great deal of space exists between gas particles. Thus, there are fewer chlorine molecules than gold atoms in the same volume.

**Compression and expansion** If you squeeze a pillow made of foam, you can compress it; that is, you can reduce its volume. The foam contains air pockets. The large amount of empty space between the air particles in those pockets allows the air to be easily pushed into a smaller volume. When you stop squeezing, the random motion of air particles fills the available space and the pillow expands to its original shape. **Figure 13-3** illustrates what happens to the density of a gas in a container as it is compressed and as it is allowed to expand.

**Diffusion and effusion** According to the kinetic-molecular theory, there are no significant forces of attraction between gas particles. Thus, gas particles can flow easily past each other. Often, the space into which a gas flows is already occupied by another gas. The random motion of the gas particles causes the gases to mix until they are evenly distributed. **Diffusion** is the term used to describe the movement of one material through another. The term may be new, but you are probably familiar with the process. If you are in the den, can you tell when someone sprays perfume in the bedroom? Perfume particles released in the bedroom diffuse through the air until they reach the den. Particles diffuse from an area of high concentration (the bedroom) to one of low concentration (the den).

The rate of diffusion depends mainly on the mass of the particles involved. Lighter particles diffuse more rapidly than heavier particles. Recall that different gases at the same temperature have the same average kinetic energy as described by the equation $KE = 1/2mv^2$. However, the mass of gas particles varies from gas to gas. For lighter particles to have the same average kinetic energy as heavier particles, they must, on average, have a greater velocity.

Effusion is a process related to diffusion. During effusion, a gas escapes through a tiny opening. What happens when you puncture a container such as a balloon or a tire? In 1846, Thomas Graham did experiments to measure the rates of effusion for different gases at the same temperature. Graham designed his experiment so that the gases effused into a vacuum—a space containing no matter. He discovered an inverse relationship between effusion rates and molar mass. **Graham's law of effusion** states that the rate of effusion for a gas is inversely proportional to the square root of its molar mass.

$$\text{Rate of effusion} \propto \frac{1}{\sqrt{\text{molar mass}}}$$

Graham's law also applies to rates of diffusion, which is logical because heavier particles diffuse more slowly than lighter particles at the same temperature. Using Graham's law, you can set up a proportion to compare the diffusion rates for two gases.

$$\frac{\text{Rate}_A}{\text{Rate}_B} = \sqrt{\frac{\text{molar mass}_B}{\text{molar mass}_A}}$$

For example, consider the gases ammonia ($NH_3$) and hydrogen chloride (HCl). Which gas diffuses faster? Example Problem 13-1 and the photograph on the next page provide quantitative and visual comparisons of the diffusion rates for ammonia and hydrogen chloride.

**Compression**

**Expansion**

**Figure 13-3**
The volume of the top cylinder is half that of the middle cylinder. The volume of the bottom cylinder is twice that of the middle cylinder. Compare the density of the gas in the top cylinder with its density in the bottom cylinder.

13.1 Gases    **387**

## Practice PROBLEMS

Have students refer to Appendix D for complete solutions to Practice Problems.

1. $R_{nitrogen}/R_{neon} = 0.849$
2. 1.25
3. 2.5 mol/min

---

## Math in Chemistry

When students use Graham's law to solve problems involving the relationship between the molar masses of gases and their rates of effusion, remind them that square roots are involved. Many students make the common mistakes of ignoring the square root symbol and treat the equation like a direct proportion.

## In-Text Question

**Page 388** How do the size and style of shoe you wear affect the force you exert on a surface? A flat shoe allows the mass to be distributed over a larger area than a high-heeled shoe, thus exerting less force on a surface than the high-heeled shoe.

---

## Assessment

**Knowledge** Ask students to write a test question on the material in this section. Then, collect students' questions and have the class discuss the answers, or have students exchange their questions and quiz each other. **L2**

---

When molecules of gaseous HCl (from a bottle of hydrochloric acid) and NH₃ (from a bottle of aqueous ammonia) meet, they react to form the white solid ammonium chloride, NH₄Cl.

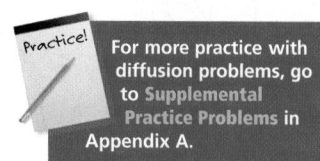

**Practice!** For more practice with diffusion problems, go to **Supplemental Practice Problems** in Appendix A.

---

## EXAMPLE PROBLEM 13-1

### Finding a Ratio of Diffusion Rates

Ammonia has a molar mass of 17.0 g/mol; hydrogen chloride has a molar mass of 36.5 g/mol. What is the ratio of their diffusion rates?

#### 1. Analyze the Problem

You are given the molar masses for ammonia and hydrogen chloride. To find the ratio of the diffusion rates for ammonia and hydrogen chloride, use the equation for Graham's law of effusion.

**Known**

molar mass$_{HCl}$ = 36.5 g/mol

molar mass$_{NH_3}$ = 17.0 g/mol

**Unknown**

ratio of diffusion rates = ?

#### 2. Solve for the Unknown

Substitute the known values into Graham's equation and solve.

$$\frac{Rate_{NH_3}}{Rate_{HCl}} = \sqrt{\frac{molar\ mass_{HCL}}{molar\ mass_{NH_3}}}$$

$$= \sqrt{\frac{36.5\ g/mol}{17.0\ g/mol}} = \sqrt{2.15} = 1.47$$

The ratio of diffusion rates is 1.47.

#### 3. Evaluate the Answer

Ammonia molecules diffuse about 1.5 times as fast as hydrogen chloride molecules. This ratio is logical because molecules of ammonia are about half as massive as molecules of hydrogen chloride. Because the molar masses have three significant figures, the answer does, too.

---

## PRACTICE PROBLEMS

1. Calculate the ratio of effusion rates for nitrogen (N₂) and neon (Ne).
2. Calculate the ratio of diffusion rates for carbon monoxide (CO) and carbon dioxide (CO₂).
3. What is the rate of effusion for a gas that has a molar mass twice that of a gas that effuses at a rate of 3.6 mol/min?

---

## Gas Pressure

If you were to walk across deep snow in boots, you would probably sink into the snow with each step. With a pair of snowshoes like those in **Figure 13-4**, you would be less likely to sink. In each case, the force with which you press down on the snow is related to your mass. With snowshoes, the force would be spread out over a larger area. Therefore, the pressure on any given area of snow would be reduced. **Pressure** is defined as force per unit area. How do the size and style of shoes you wear affect the force you exert on a surface?

Gas particles exert pressure when they collide with the walls of their container. Because an individual gas particle has little mass, it can exert little pressure. However, there are about $10^{22}$ gas particles in a liter container. With this many particles colliding, the pressure can be substantial. In Chapter 14, you will learn how temperature, volume, and number of moles affect the pressure that a gas exerts.

---

## Portfolio

### Applying Pressure

**Linguistic** Have students write these questions in their portfolios and answer them from their study of Section 13.1. **1.** Why is stepping on a nail more painful than lying on a bed of nails? When lying on a bed of nails, the force exerted by your mass is spread out over a larger area than when you step on a nail, so you feel less pressure, and thus less pain at any given point. **2.** Why can you ski over deep snow, whereas you would sink into it wearing boots? With skis, the force exerted is spread out over a larger area, so the pressure on any given area of the snow is reduced. **L2** **P**

Earth is surrounded by an atmosphere that extends into space for hundreds of kilometers. Because the particles in air move in every direction, they exert pressure in all directions. This pressure is called atmospheric pressure, or air pressure. At the surface of Earth, air pressure is approximately equal to the pressure exerted by a 1-kilogram mass on a square centimeter. Air pressure varies at different points on Earth. At the top of a mountain, the mass of the air column pressing down on a square centimeter of Earth is less than the mass of the air column at sea level. Thus, the air pressure at higher altitudes is slightly lower than at sea level.

**Measuring air pressure** Italian physicist Evangelista Torricelli (1608–1647) was the first to demonstrate that air exerted pressure. He had noticed that water pumps were unable to pump water higher than about ten meters. He hypothesized that the height of a column of liquid would vary with the density of the liquid. To test this idea, Torricelli designed the equipment shown in **Figure 13-5a.** He filled a thin glass tube that was closed at one end with mercury. While covering the open end so that air could not enter, he inverted the tube and placed it (open end down) in a dish of mercury. The open end was below the surface of the mercury in the dish. The height of the mercury in the tube fell to about 75 cm. Mercury is about 13.6 times denser than water. Did the results of his experiment support Torricelli's hypothesis?

The device that Torricelli invented is called a barometer. A **barometer** is an instrument used to measure atmospheric pressure. As Torricelli showed, the height of the mercury in a barometer is always about 760 mm. The exact height of the mercury is determined by two forces. Gravity exerts a constant downward force on the mercury. This force is opposed by an upward force exerted by air pressing down on the surface of the mercury. Changes in air temperature or humidity cause air pressure to vary. An increase in air pressure causes the mercury to rise; a decrease causes the mercury to fall.

A manometer is an instrument used to measure gas pressure in a closed container. In a manometer, a flask is connected to a U-tube that contains mercury. In **Figure 13-5b,** there is no gas in the flask. The mercury is at the same height in each arm of the U-tube. In **Figure 13-5c,** there is gas in the flask. When the valve between the flask and the U-tube is opened, gas particles diffuse out of the flask into the U-tube. The released gas particles push down on the mercury in the tube. What happens to the height of the mercury in each arm of the U-tube? The difference in the height of the mercury in the two arms is used to calculate the pressure of the gas in the flask.

**Figure 13-4**

Snowshoes reduce the force on a given area. What devices other than snowshoes can people use to travel across deep snow?

**Figure 13-5**

**ⓐ** A barometer measures air pressure. **ⓑ** A manometer measures the pressure of an enclosed gas. Before gas is released into the U-tube, the mercury is at the same height in each arm. **ⓒ** After gas is released into the U-tube, the heights in the two arms are no longer equal.

ⓐ Vacuum
Pressure exerted by mercury column
760 mm
Atmospheric pressure

ⓑ Closed end
Vacuum
Levels equal
Vacuum

ⓒ Difference in levels

13.1 Gases **389**

---

## Using Science Terms

Have students write definitions of the terms *temperature* and *pressure*; then, have them write sentences that include the terms. **L2** **ELL**

## Content Background

**Measuring Air Pressure** Ask students if they think that, by changing the diameter or length of the tube in Torricelli's apparatus, the level of mercury in the column would vary. Explain that Torricelli found that no matter what diameter or length of tube he used, the mercury always fell to a height of about 760 mm. Review with students the two forces that determine the exact height of the mercury. *gravity and air pressure*

## Figure Caption Question

**Figure 13-4** What devices other than snowshoes can people use to travel across deep snow? *skis*

## In-Text Question

**Page 389** What happens to the height of the mercury in each arm of the U-tube? *The mercury level in the first arm is lowered, and it is raised in the second arm of the tube.*

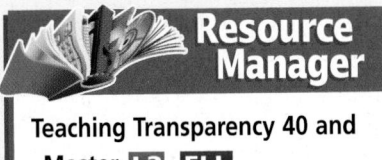

**Resource Manager**

Teaching Transparency 40 and Master **L2** **ELL**

---

**DIFFERENTIATED INSTRUCTION**

### Gifted

*Kinesthetic* Ask interested students to design, build, and test their own barometers. **L3**

**CHEMISTRY JOURNAL**

### Torricelli

*Linguistic* Ask students to write an epitaph for Evangelista Torricelli that briefly describes the major events in his life and work. **L2**

**National Science Content Standards**

Pages 388–389
UCP.1, UCP.2, UCP.3; B.2, B.4; G.3

## Purpose

Students will study the mathematical relationship between pressure and depth.

## Process Skills

Making and using graphs, recognizing cause and effect, applying concepts, predicting

## Background

Records dating to 4500 B.C. in Mesopotamia reveal that people were making single-breath, deep dives into the sea in search of the precious mother of pearl. These "free-dives" have recently become a competition of who can dive the deepest. On January 18, 2000, Cuban diver Francisco 'Pipin' Ferreras dove to a new record depth of 162 meters and returned to the surface 3.2 minutes later! At these depths, the pressure of the water pushing down on the body is the same as the weight of a full-grown elephant standing on one foot.

## Teaching Strategies

• Review the graphical features that are commonly encountered in the lab and the corresponding mathematical expressions that express these relationships. In particular, focus on the linear and inverse graphs.

• Ask students if they understand the concept of pressure and how fluids, such as water and air, exert pressure. Explain the basis for the unit of pressure, the atmosphere. *the pressure exerted by the atmosphere at sea level at a temperature of 0°C*

• Review with students that weight is a measure of the force of gravity on an object, and that pressure equals force per unit area.

• Water gets denser the deeper you descend into the sea because of compression from the water above, the lower temperature of deeper water, and the increased salinity of deeper water. Pressure is directly proportional to density. Therefore, the increase in density increases the pressure even more. Ask students how this would affect the graph of pressure

**390**

Table 13-1

| Comparison of Pressure Units | | |
|---|---|---|
| Unit | Compared with 1 atm | Compared with 1 kPa |
| kilopascal (kPa) | 1 atm = 101.3 kPa | |
| millimeters of mercury (mm Hg) | 1 atm = 760 mm Hg | 1 kPa = 7.501 mm Hg |
| torr | 1 atm = 760 torr | 1 kPa = 7.501 torr |
| pounds per square inch (psi or lb/in²) | 1 atm = 14.7 psi | 1 kPa = 0.145 psi |
| atmosphere (atm) | | 1 kPa = 0.009 869 atm |

**Units of pressure** The SI unit of pressure is the pascal (Pa). It is named for Blaise Pascal, a French mathematician and philosopher. The pascal is derived from the SI unit of force, the newton (N), which is derived from three SI base units: the kilogram, the meter, and the second. One **pascal** is equal to a force of one newton per square meter: $1 \text{ Pa} = 1 \text{ N/m}^2$. Many fields of science still use more traditional units of pressure. For example, engineers often report pressure as pounds per square inch (psi). The pressures measured by barometers and manometers can be reported in millimeters of mercury (mm Hg). There also is a unit called the torr, which is named to honor Torricelli. One torr is equal to one mm Hg.

At sea level, the average air pressure is 760 mm Hg when the temperature is 0°C. Air pressure often is reported in a unit called an atmosphere (atm). One **atmosphere** is equal to 760 mm Hg or 760 torr or 101.3 kilopascals (kPa). **Table 13-1** compares different units of pressure. Because the units 1 atm, 760 mm Hg, and 760 torr are defined units, they have as many significant figures as needed when used in calculations. Do the **problem-solving LAB** to see how the combined pressure of air and water affects divers.

## problem-solving LAB

### How are the depth of a dive and pressure related?

**Making and Using Graphs** For centuries, people have dived deep into the sea to collect items such as pearls. Nowadays, single-breath diving has become competitive. On January 18, 2000, Francisco "Pipin" Ferreras from Cuba set a new record with a dive of 162 meters. He was underwater for 3.2 minutes.

### Analysis

Use the data in the table to make a graph of pressure versus depth.

1. How are pressure and depth related?
2. What would the pressure be at the surface of the water? What does this value represent?
3. What was the pressure on Francisco at 162 m?

| Pressure Versus Depth | |
|---|---|
| Depth of dive (m) | Pressure (atm) |
| 10 | 2.0 |
| 20 | 3.0 |
| 30 | 4.0 |
| 40 | 5.0 |
| 50 | 6.0 |
| 60 | 7.0 |

### Thinking Critically

4. Using the equation for slope, calculate the slope of your graph. Then write an equation to express the relationship between pressure and depth. $\left(\text{slope} = \dfrac{\Delta y}{\Delta x} = \dfrac{y_2 - y_1}{x_2 - x_1}\right)$

versus depth. The shape of the graph would curve upward. See Solutions Manual.

### Analysis

1. Pressure varies directly with depth. With increasing depth, the weight of the water increases, causing greater pressure.
2. Extrapolating to D = 0 meters, P = 1.0 atm. This is the pressure of the atmosphere on the surface of the ocean.
3. At a depth of 162 meters, he would experience a pressure of 17.2 atm.

### Thinking Critically

Slope = 0.1 atm/m; pressure = (0.10 atm/m)(depth) + 1.0 atm

### ✓ Assessment

**Portfolio** Have students research how marine animals can withstand the huge pressures that are present under the sea and explain their findings in a written report. **L2** **P**

1 mol He
$P_1$

1 mol $N_2$
$P_2$

1 mol He + 1 mol $N_2$
$P_{Total}$

**Figure 13-6**

How do the partial pressures of nitrogen gas and helium gas compare when a mole of nitrogen gas and a mole of helium gas are in the same closed container? Refer to **Table C-1** in Appendix C for a key to atom color conventions.

**Dalton's law of partial pressures** When Dalton studied the properties of gases, he found that each gas in a mixture exerts pressure independently of the other gases present. **Dalton's law of partial pressures** states that the total pressure of a mixture of gases is equal to the sum of the pressures of all the gases in the mixture. The portion of the total pressure contributed by a single gas is called its partial pressure. The partial pressure of a gas depends on the number of moles of gas, the size of the container, and the temperature of the mixture. It does not depend on the identity of the gas. At a given temperature and pressure, the partial pressure of one mole of any gas is the same. Dalton's law of partial pressures can be summarized as

$$P_{total} = P_1 + P_2 + P_3 + ... P_n$$

$P_{total}$ represents the total pressure of a mixture of gases. $P_1$, $P_2$, and so on represent the partial pressures of each gas in the mixture. **Figure 13-6** shows what happens when one mole of helium and one mole of nitrogen are combined in a single closed container.

### EXAMPLE PROBLEM 13-2

**Finding the Partial Pressure of a Gas**

A mixture of oxygen ($O_2$), carbon dioxide ($CO_2$), and nitrogen ($N_2$) has a total pressure of 0.97 atm. What is the partial pressure of $O_2$, if the partial pressure of $CO_2$ is 0.70 atm and the partial pressure of $N_2$ is 0.12 atm?

**1. Analyze the Problem**

You are given the total pressure of a mixture and the partial pressure of two gases in the mixture. To find the partial pressure of the third gas, use the equation that relates partial pressures to total pressure.

| Known | Unknown |
|---|---|
| $P_{N_2}$ = 0.12 atm | $P_{O_2}$ = ? atm |
| $P_{CO_2}$ = 0.70 atm | |
| $P_{total}$ = 0.97 atm | |

**2. Solve for the Unknown**

Rearrange the equation to solve for the unknown value, $P_{O_2}$.

$P_{O_2} = P_{total} - P_{CO_2} - P_{N_2}$

$P_{O_2}$ = 0.97 atm − 0.70 atm − 0.12 atm

$P_{O_2}$ = 0.15 atm

**3. Evaluate the Answer**

Adding the calculated value for the partial pressure of oxygen to the known partial pressures gives the total pressure 0.97 atm. The answer has two significant figures to match the data.

13.1 Gases    **391**

### Internet Address Book

Note Internet addresses that you find useful in the space below for quick reference.

**National Science Content Standards**

Pages 390–391
UCP.1, UCP.2, UCP.3; B.2, B.4; E.2

## Practice PROBLEMS

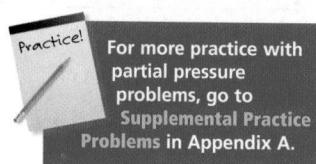

Have students refer to Appendix D for complete solutions to Practice Problems.

**4.** 161 mm Hg

**5.** 13.78 kPa

**6.** 10.2 kPa

### In-Text Question

**Page 392** If the total pressure of the hydrogen and water vapor mixture is 95.0 kPa, what is the partial pressure of the hydrogen at 20°C? 92.7 kPa

### Reteach

To emphasize that pressure depends on the force per unit area (not just the total force exerted by an object) ask students: Which will cause more wear and tear on a carpeted floor over a set length of time: a 125-pound person who walks back and forth on the carpet wearing shoes with spike heels, or a 125-pound person who makes the same number of trips wearing flat-soled shoes? The shoes with spike heels will place more pressure on the carpet because all of the person's mass will be focused on just two small areas. The flat shoes allow the mass to be distributed over a larger area so they exert less pressure per unit area.

### Extension

Ask students to use the definition of pressure to explain how people doing karate can break thick boards with the sides of their hands. They are exerting a large force over a small area, placing enough pressure on the board to break it.

✔ **Assessment**

**Skill** Ask students to design an experiment to compare the rates of diffusion of substances found in different perfumes. Suggest a format for students to follow with the problem, objectives, materials, safety precautions, procedure, and data collection. **L2**

392

---

For more practice with partial pressure problems, go to **Supplemental Practice Problems** in Appendix A.

**4.** What is the partial pressure of hydrogen gas in a mixture of hydrogen and helium if the total pressure is 600 mm Hg and the partial pressure of helium is 439 mm Hg?

**5.** Find the total pressure for a mixture that contains four gases with partial pressures of 5.00 kPa, 4.56 kPa, 3.02 kPa, and 1.20 kPa.

**6.** Find the partial pressure of carbon dioxide in a gas mixture with a total pressure of 30.4 kPa if the partial pressures of the other two gases in the mixture are 16.5 kPa and 3.7 kPa.

Dalton's law of partial pressures can be used to determine the amount of gas produced by a reaction. The gas produced is bubbled into an inverted container of water, as shown in **Figure 13-7.** As the gas collects, it displaces the water. The gas collected in the container will be a mixture of hydrogen and water vapor. Therefore, the total pressure inside the container will be the sum of the partial pressures of hydrogen and water vapor.

The partial pressures of gases at the same temperature are related to their concentration. The partial pressure of water vapor has a fixed value at a given temperature. You can look up the value in a reference table. At 20°C, the partial pressure of water vapor is 2.3 kPa. You can calculate the partial pressure of hydrogen by subtracting the partial pressure of water vapor from the total pressure. If the total pressure of the hydrogen and water mixture is 95.0 kPa, what is the partial pressure of hydrogen at 20°C?

As you will learn in Chapter 14, knowing the pressure, volume, and temperature of a gas allows you to calculate the number of moles of the gas. Temperature and volume can be measured during an experiment. Once the temperature is known, the partial pressure of water vapor is used to calculate the pressure of the gas. The known values for volume, temperature, and pressure are then used to find the number of moles.

**Figure 13-7**

In the flask, sulfuric acid ($H_2SO_4$) reacts with zinc to produce hydrogen gas. The hydrogen is collected at 20°C.

## Section 13.1 Assessment

**7.** What assumption of the kinetic-molecular theory explains why a gas can expand to fill a container?

**8.** How does the mass of a gas particle affect its rate of effusion?

**9.** Suppose two gases in a container have a total pressure of 1.20 atm. What is the pressure of gas B if the partial pressure of gas A is 0.75 atm?

**10.** Explain how changes in atmospheric pressure affect the height of the column of mercury in a barometer.

**11. Recognizing Cause and Effect** Explain why a tire or balloon expands when air is added.

**12. Thinking Critically** Explain why the container of water must be inverted when a gas is collected by displacement of water.

chemistrymc.com/self_check_quiz

---

## Section 13.1 Assessment

**7.** the assumption that gas particles are in constant and random motion

**8.** The rate of effusion decreases as mass increases.

**9.** 0.45 atm

**10.** An increase in atmospheric pressure increases the pressure on the surface of mercury and the column rises; a decrease in atmospheric pressure

decreases the pressure on the surface of the mercury and the column drops.

**11.** When air is added, there are more collisions between air particles and the walls, exerting greater pressure inside the balloon or tire and expanding the walls.

**12.** If the container is not inverted, the gas, which is less dense than water, will rise through the water and escape from

If all particles of matter at room temperature have the same average kinetic energy, why are some materials gases while others are liquids or solids? The answer lies with the attractive forces within and between particles. The attractive forces that hold particles together in ionic, covalent, and metallic bonds are called intramolecular forces. The prefix *intra-* means "within." For example, intramural sports are competitions among teams from within a single school. The term *molecular* can refer to atoms, ions, or molecules. **Table 13-2** summarizes what you learned about intramolecular forces in Chapters 8 and 9.

## Intermolecular Forces

Intramolecular forces do not account for all attractions between particles. There are forces of attraction called intermolecular forces. The prefix *inter-* means "between" or "among." For example, an interview is a conversation between two people. Intermolecular forces can hold together identical particles, such as water molecules in a drop of water, or two different types of particles, such as carbon atoms in graphite and the cellulose particles in paper. The three intermolecular forces that will be discussed in this section are dispersion forces, dipole–dipole forces, and hydrogen bonds. Although some intermolecular forces are stronger than others, all intermolecular forces are weaker than intramolecular, or bonding, forces.

**Dispersion forces** Recall that oxygen molecules are nonpolar because electrons are evenly distributed between the equally electronegative oxygen atoms. Under the right conditions, however, oxygen molecules can be compressed into a liquid. For oxygen to be compressed, there must be some force of attraction between its molecules. The force of attraction between oxygen molecules is called a dispersion force. **Dispersion forces** are weak forces that result from temporary shifts in the density of electrons in electron clouds. Dispersion forces are sometimes called London forces after the German-American physicist who first described them, Fritz London.

Remember that the electrons in an electron cloud are in constant motion. When two nonpolar molecules are in close contact, especially when they collide, the

### Objectives

- **Describe** and **compare** intramolecular and intermolecular forces.
- **Distinguish** among intermolecular forces.

### Vocabulary

dispersion force
dipole–dipole force
hydrogen bond

## 1 Focus

### Focus Transparency

Before presenting the lesson, display **Section Focus Transparency 48** on the overhead projector. Have students answer the accompanying questions using **Section Focus Transparency Master 48.** **L1** **ELL**

## 2 Teach

### Quick Demo

Use Velcro to model how the strength of intermolecular attractions is affected by the size of molecules. After students have observed you separate double strips of Velcro that are of different lengths, ask them whether it is easier to separate longer or shorter molecules.

**Table 13-2**

| Comparison of Intramolecular Forces | | | |
|---|---|---|---|
| **Force** | **Model** | **Basis of attraction** | **Example** |
| Ionic | | cations and anions | NaCl |
| Covalent | | positive nuclei and shared electrons | $H_2$ |
| Metallic | | metal cations and mobile electrons | Fe |

13.2 Forces of Attraction **393**

---

## DIFFERENTIATED INSTRUCTION

### Learning Disabled

*Kinesthetic* Students who have trouble understanding the additive nature of interparticle forces may benefit from making their own models of small and large molecules using cutouts of adhesive-backed shelf paper. Have students cut out different sized circles of the shelf paper, remove the backing, and stick them together. Then, students should try to separate the circles, comparing how long it takes to separate circles of different sizes. **L1** **ELL**

**National Science Content Standards**

Pages 392–393
UCP.1, UCP.2, UCP.3; A.1; B.2, B.4

## Applying Chemistry

**TECH PREP**

How well different fabrics absorb or repel water depends on their chemical structure. Cotton is formed from cellulose, a polymer of glucose. Each glucose molecule contains multiple hydroxyl (−OH) groups, each of which can hydrogen bond to more than one water molecule. Therefore, cotton absorbs water well and is often used to make towels. In hot weather, cotton clothing can be cooling, because the body's heat energy is used to evaporate water (from sweat) that is bonded to the cotton. Nylon's structure includes only a few groups that can hydrogen bond to water, and most of the nylon polymer is made of −CH₂ groups that can form only weaker dispersion forces. Therefore, nylon repels water and is used in rainjackets and umbrellas.

---

### ✔ Assessment

**Skill** Have students make a table of dispersion forces, dipole-dipole forces, and hydrogen bonds, listing their relative strength, how each force forms, and examples of the types of molecules in which they form. **L2**

---

### Figure Caption Questions

**Figure 13-8** What do the δ− and δ+ signs on a temporary dipole represent? They represent a partial negative and partial positive charge, respectively.

**Figure 13-9** What are the electronegativity values for hydrogen and chlorine? H: 2.20; Cl: 3.16

---

## 3 Assess

### Check for Understanding

Ask students what kind(s) of interparticle forces must be overcome to: **a.** melt ice? **b.** boil water? **c.** melt NaCl? **d.** sublime I₂? a. hydrogen bonds b. hydrogen bonds c. ionic bonds d. dispersion forces **L2**

---

electron cloud of one molecule repels the electron cloud of the other molecule. The electron density around each nucleus is, for a moment, greater in one region of each cloud. Each molecule forms a temporary dipole.

**Figure 13-8**

What do the δ− and δ+ signs on a temporary dipole represent?

Temporary dipole          Temporary dipole

When temporary dipoles are close together, a weak dispersion force exists between oppositely charged regions of the dipoles, as shown in **Figure 13-8.**

Due to the temporary nature of the dipoles, dispersion forces are the weakest intermolecular force. Dispersion forces exist between all particles, but they play a significant role only when there are no stronger forces of attraction acting on particles. Dispersion forces are the dominant force of attraction between identical nonpolar molecules. These forces can have a noticeable effect as the number of electrons involved increases. For example, fluorine, chlorine, bromine, and iodine exist as diatomic molecules. Recall that the number of nonvalence electrons increases from fluorine to chlorine to bromine to iodine. Because the larger halogen molecules have more electrons, there can be a greater difference between the positive and negative regions of their temporary dipoles and, thus, stronger dispersion forces. This difference in dispersion forces explains why fluorine and chlorine are gases, bromine is a liquid, and iodine is a solid at room temperature.

**Dipole–dipole forces** Polar molecules contain permanent dipoles; that is, some regions of a polar molecule are always partially negative and some regions of the molecule are always partially positive. Attractions between oppositely charged regions of polar molecules are called **dipole–dipole forces.** Neighboring polar molecules orient themselves so that oppositely charged regions line up. When hydrogen chloride gas molecules approach, the partially positive hydrogen atom in one molecule is attracted to the partially negative chlorine atom in another molecule. **Figure 13-9** shows multiple attractions among hydrogen chloride molecules.

**Figure 13-9**

The degree of polarity in a polar molecule depends on the relative electronegativity values of the elements in the molecule. What are the electronegativity values for hydrogen and chlorine?

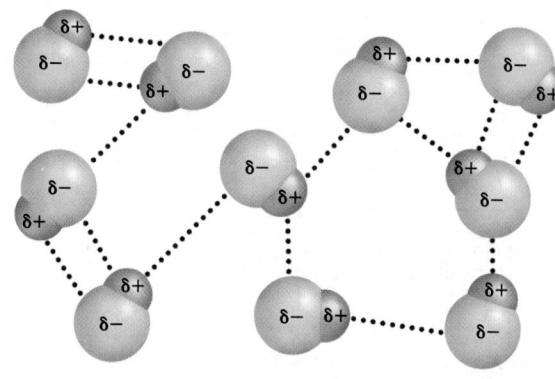

Because the dipoles are permanent, you might expect dipole–dipole forces to be stronger than dispersion forces. This prediction will hold true as long as the molecules being compared have approximately the same mass.

---

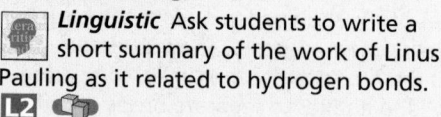

### CHEMISTRY JOURNAL

**Linus Pauling**

*Linguistic* Ask students to write a short summary of the work of Linus Pauling as it related to hydrogen bonds. **L2** 🖉

---

### Resource Manager

**Study Guide for Content Mastery,** p. 75 **L2**

**Solving Problems: A Chemistry Handbook,** Section 13.2 **L2**

**Section Focus Transparency 48 and Master L1 ELL**

**Hydrogen bonds** One special type of dipole–dipole attraction is called a hydrogen bond. A **hydrogen bond** is a dipole–dipole attraction that occurs between molecules containing a hydrogen atom bonded to a small, highly electronegative atom with at least one lone electron pair. For a hydrogen bond to form, hydrogen must be bonded to either a fluorine, oxygen, or nitrogen atom. These atoms are electronegative enough to cause a large partial positive charge on the hydrogen atom, yet small enough that their lone pairs of electrons can come close to hydrogen atoms. Consider, for example, a water molecule. In a water molecule, the hydrogen atoms have a large partial positive charge and the oxygen atom has a large partial negative charge. When water molecules approach, a hydrogen atom on one molecule is attracted to the oxygen atom on the other molecule, as shown in **Figure 13-10**.

Hydrogen bond

Hydrogen bonds explain why water is a liquid at room temperature while compounds of comparable mass are gases. Look at the data in **Table 13-3**. The difference between methane and water is easy to explain. Because methane molecules are nonpolar, the only forces holding the molecules together are relatively weak dispersion forces. The difference between ammonia and water is not as obvious. Molecules of both compounds can form hydrogen bonds. Yet, ammonia is a gas at room temperature, which indicates that the attractive forces between ammonia molecules are not as strong. Because oxygen atoms are more electronegative than nitrogen atoms, the O–H bonds in water are more polar than the N–H bonds in ammonia. As a result, the hydrogen bonds between water molecules are stronger than those between ammonia molecules.

**Table 13-3**

| Properties of Three Molecular Compounds | | |
|---|---|---|
| Compound | Molar mass (g) | Boiling point (°C) |
| Water ($H_2O$) | 18.0 | 100 |
| Methane ($CH_4$) | 16.0 | −164 |
| Ammonia ($NH_3$) | 17.0 | −33.4 |

**Figure 13-10**

The hydrogen bonds between water molecules are stronger than typical dipole–dipole attractions because the bond between hydrogen and oxygen is highly polar.

**Reteach**

Ask students to rank the intermolecular forces in order of increasing strength. dispersion forces → dipole-dipole forces → hydrogen bonds

**Extension**

Ask students which of the following compounds can form dipole-dipole forces.
**a.** $Cl_2$  **b.** CO  **c.** NO  **d.** $CH_4$
b, c

✔ **Assessment**

**Skill** Ask students to research the chemical structures of several different types of fabrics. Students should use the structures to rank the fabrics in terms of the number of hydrogen bonds that the molecules of each fabric should form with water, and then test their rankings by carrying out an absorbency test with water. **L2**

## Section 13.2 Assessment

**13.** Why are dipole–dipole forces stronger than dispersion forces for molecules of comparable mass?

**14.** Which of the molecules listed below can form hydrogen bonds? For which of the molecules would dispersion forces be the only intermolecular force? Give reasons for your answers.
  **a.** $H_2$
  **b.** $NH_3$
  **c.** HCl
  **d.** HF

**15. Predicting** Make a prediction about the relative boiling points of the noble gases. Give a reason for your answer.

**16. Thinking Critically** In a methane molecule ($CH_4$), there are 4 single covalent bonds. In an octane molecule ($C_8H_{18}$), there are 25 single covalent bonds. How does the number of bonds affect the dispersion forces in samples of methane and octane? Which compound is a gas at room temperature? Which is a liquid?

chemistrymc.com/self_check_quiz

13.2 Forces of Attraction    **395**

**National Science Content Standards**

**Pages 394–395**
UCP.1, UCP.2, UCP.3; B.2, B.4

## Section 13.2 Assessment

**13.** Dipole-dipole forces exist between permanent dipoles; dispersion forces exist between temporary dipoles.

**14.** hydrogen bonds: b, d; only dispersion forces: a; b and d are polar molecules with a highly electronegative atom bonded to hydrogen. a is nonpolar.

**15.** The boiling points will increase from helium to xenon because larger noble gas atoms have more electrons, making the dispersion forces between those atoms stronger. It takes more energy to overcome those forces.

**16.** More bonds mean more electrons to form temporary dipoles, which means greater dispersion forces. Methane is a gas; octane is a liquid.

# 1 Focus

Before presenting the lesson, display **Section Focus Transparency 49** on the overhead projector. Have students answer the accompanying questions using **Section Focus Transparency Master 49. L1 ELL**

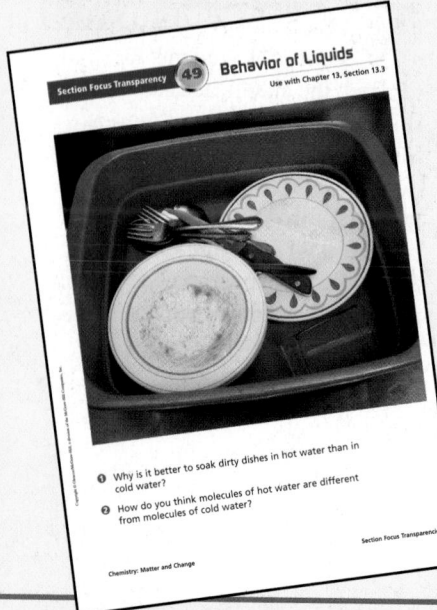

# 2 Teach

## Building a Model

**Kinesthetic** Assign students to create a model, collage, poster, or diagrammed chart of the three phases of a substance, such as water. Ask students to display their work in the classroom. **L2 ELL**

## Figure Caption Question

**Figure 13-11** How much time do you think it took for the food coloring to completely mix with the water? The length of time varies depending on the temperature of the water. It may take hours.

**National Science Content Standards**

Pages 396–397
UCP.1, UCP.2, UCP.3; B.2, B.4

---

Section **13.3** **Liquids and Solids**

## Objectives

- **Apply** kinetic-molecular theory to the behavior of liquids and solids.

- **Relate** properties such as viscosity, surface tension, and capillary action to intermolecular forces.

- **Compare** the structures and properties of different types of solids.

## Vocabulary

viscosity
surface tension
surfactant
crystalline solid
unit cell
amorphous solid

Although the kinetic-molecular theory was developed to explain the behavior of gases, the model can be applied to liquids and solids. When applying the kinetic-molecular theory to these states of matter, you must consider the forces of attraction between particles as well as their energy of motion.

## Liquids

In Chapter 3, you learned that a liquid can take the shape of its container but that its volume is fixed. In other words, the particles in a liquid can flow to adjust to the shape of a container, but the liquid cannot expand to fill its container. Kinetic-molecular theory predicts the constant motion of the liquid particles. Individual liquid molecules do not have fixed positions in the liquid. However, forces of attraction between liquid particles limit their range of motion so that the particles remain closely packed in a fixed volume.

**Density and compression** At 25°C and one atmosphere of air pressure, liquids are much denser than gases. The density of a liquid is much greater than that of its vapor at the same conditions. For example, liquid water is about 1250 times denser than water vapor at 25°C and one atmosphere of pressure. Because they are at the same temperature, both gas and liquid particles have the same average kinetic energy. Thus, the higher density of liquids must be traced to the intermolecular forces that hold particles together.

Like gases, liquids can be compressed. But the change in volume for liquids is much smaller because liquid particles are already tightly packed together. An enormous amount of pressure must be applied to reduce the volume of a liquid by even a few percent.

**Fluidity** Fluidity is the ability to flow. Gases and liquids are classified as fluids because they can flow. A liquid can diffuse through another liquid as shown in **Figure 13-11.** A liquid diffuses more slowly than a gas at the same

**Figure 13-11**

How much time do you think it took for the food coloring to completely mix with the water?

**396** Chapter 13 States of Matter

---

**DIFFERENTIATED INSTRUCTION**

## Gifted

**Intrapersonal** Ask interested students to design an apparatus or an experiment to test their predictions about the relative viscosities of several different liquids. Challenge them further by asking them to include in their designs a study of the effect of temperature on viscosity. **L3**

**Resource Manager**

**Study Guide for Content Mastery,** p. 76 **L2**

**Solving Problems: A Chemistry Handbook,** Section 13.3 **L2**

**Section Focus Transparency 49 and Master L1 ELL**

temperature, however, because intermolecular attractions interfere with the flow. Thus, liquids are less fluid than gases. A comparison between water and natural gas can illustrate this difference. When there is a leak in a basement water pipe, the water remains in the basement unless the amount of water released exceeds the volume of the basement. Damage can be limited if the water supply is shut off quickly.

Natural gas, or methane, is the fuel burned in gas furnaces, gas hot-water heaters, and gas stoves. Gas that leaks from a gas pipe can diffuse throughout a house. Because natural gas is odorless, companies that supply the fuel include a compound with a distinct odor to warn customers of a leak. If the gas is effusing through a small hole in a pipe, the customer has time to shut off the gas supply, open windows to allow the gas to diffuse, and call the gas company to report the leak. If there is a break in a gas line, the customer must leave the house immediately because natural gas can explode when it comes in contact with an open flame or spark.

**Viscosity** Do you know the meaning of the phrase "slow as molasses"? Have you ever tried to get ketchup to flow out of a bottle? If so, you are already familiar with the concept of viscosity. **Viscosity** is a measure of the resistance of a liquid to flow. The particles in a liquid are close enough for attractive forces to slow their movement as they flow past one another. The viscosity of a liquid is determined by the type of intermolecular forces involved, the shape of the particles, and the temperature.

The stronger the attractive forces, the higher the viscosity. If you have used glycerol in the laboratory to help insert a glass tube into a rubber stopper, you know that glycerol is a viscous liquid. **Figure 13-12** uses structural formulas to show the hydrogen bonding that makes glycerol so viscous. Because it has three hydrogen atoms attached to oxygen atoms, a glycerol molecule can form three hydrogen bonds with other glycerol molecules.

The size and shape of particles affect viscosity. Recall that the overall kinetic energy of a particle is determined by its mass and velocity. Suppose the attractive forces between molecules in liquid A and liquid B are similar. If the molecules in liquid A are more massive than the molecules in liquid B, liquid A will have a greater viscosity. Liquid A's molecules will, on average, move more slowly than the molecules in liquid B. Molecules with long chains have a higher viscosity than shorter, more compact molecules, assuming the molecules exert the same type of attractive forces. Within the long chains, there is less distance between atoms on neighboring molecules and, thus, a greater chance for attractions between atoms. The long molecules in cooking oils and motor oils make these liquids thick and slow to pour.

**Viscosity and temperature** Viscosity decreases with temperature. When you pour a tablespoon of cooking oil into a frying pan, the oil tends not to spread across the bottom of the pan until you heat the oil. With the increase in temperature, there is an increase in the average kinetic energy of the oil molecules. The added energy makes it easier for the molecules to overcome the intermolecular forces that keep the molecules from flowing.

In **Figure 13-13,** the motor oil that keeps the moving parts of an internal combustion engine lubricated is being replaced.

**Figure 13-12**

How many hydrogen bonds can a glycerol molecule form?

**Figure 13-13**

The viscosity of motor oil increases in summer because additives in the oil change their shape as the temperature rises.

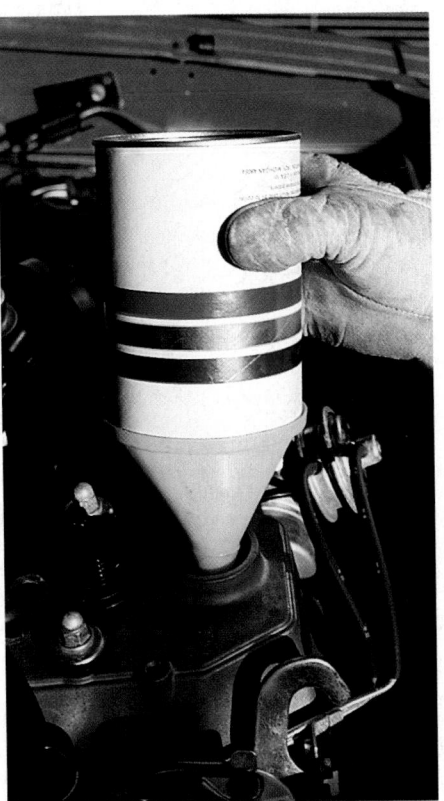

**Figure Caption Question**
**Figure 13-12** How many hydrogen bonds can a glycerol molecule form? 3

**Applying Chemistry**

**TECH PREP**

Supercritical fluid extraction is a relatively new technique for separating compounds and mixtures. A supercritical fluid is a substance that, at its critical temperature and pressure, has some properties of liquids and some of gases. Supercritical fluids can dissolve as much solute as a good liquid solvent, yet they can be more easily removed than most liquid solvents once the process is finished. Because it is inexpensive and nontoxic and usually has good selectivity and capacity, carbon dioxide is one of the most widely used supercritical fluids. Supercritical carbon dioxide is now used to extract caffeine from coffee beans when making decaffeinated coffee, replacing previously used toxic liquid solvents such as dichloromethane.

## GLENCOE TECHNOLOGY

CD-ROM
**Chemistry: Matter and Change**
Demonstration: *Surface Tension*

## CHEMISTRY JOURNAL

### Viscosity

*Linguistic* Have students observe everyday examples of viscosity. They should record a description of each situation and provide an explanation of what is occurring. Then, they should summarize what is common to the events and connect this information to what they have learned about intermolecular forces. **L2**

## Quick Demo

Fill a beaker with water until it is very full, but not overflowing. Ask students to predict how many pennies you can add to the beaker without causing the water to flow out. Students may predict a low number, but you should actually be able to add 25-35 pennies. Then, carefully add pennies, one at a time, into the water, dropping them in edge down. Ask students to explain why all the pennies don't cause the water to flow out. Surface tension causes the surface of the water to bulge as if it were a stretched membrane rather than to flow out. Repeat this demonstration using a different liquid, such as rubbing alcohol, and ask students to predict how the results will differ from those observed using water.

## In-Text Questions

**Page 398** What could happen to an engine if there was no motor oil to lubricate its parts? There would be increased friction between the moving parts of the engine, hampering performance.

**Page 398** What happened when you added a drop of detergent to your beaker in the Discovery Lab? The pin sank.

## Figure Caption Question

**Figure 13-14b** How does the spider's structure help it stay afloat on water? The spider's legs and appendages are long and thin, providing a large surface area for the water's surface tension to act against.

## Using Science Terms

Have students write statements explaining the meaning of the terms *viscosity* and *surfactant*.

**National Science Content Standards**

Pages 398–399
UCP.1, UCP.2, UCP.3; B.2, B.4, B.5

**398**

---

**Try at Home LAB**

See page 958 in Appendix E for
**Viscosity Race**

What could happen to an engine if there were no motor oil to lubricate its parts? Because temperature changes affect the viscosity of motor oil, people often used different motor oil blends in winter and summer. The motor oil used in winter was designed to keep flowing at low temperatures. The motor oil used in summer was more viscous so that it would maintain sufficient viscosity on extremely hot days or during long trips. Today, additives in motor oil can help adjust the viscosity so that the same oil blend can be used all year. Molecules in the additives are compact spheres with relatively low viscosity at cool temperatures. At high temperatures, the shape of the additive molecules changes to long strands. These strands get tangled with the oil molecules, which increases the viscosity of the oil.

**Surface tension** Intermolecular forces do not have an equal effect on all particles in a liquid, as shown in **Figure 13-14a.** Particles in the middle of the liquid can be attracted to particles above them, below them, and to either side. For particles at the surface of the liquid, there are no attractions from above to balance the attractions from below. Thus, there is a net attractive force pulling down on particles at the surface. The surface tends to have the smallest possible area and to act as though it is stretched tight like the head of a drum. For the surface area to increase, particles from the interior must move to the surface. It takes energy to overcome the attractions holding these particles in the interior. The energy required to increase the surface area of a liquid by a given amount is called **surface tension.** Surface tension is a measure of the inward pull by particles in the interior.

In general, the stronger the attractions between particles, the greater the surface tension. Water has a high surface tension because its molecules can form multiple hydrogen bonds. Drops of water are shaped like spheres because the surface area of a sphere is smaller than the surface area of any other shape of similar volume. Water's high surface tension is what allows the spider in **Figure 13-14b** to walk on the surface of a pond.

It is difficult to remove dirt from skin or clothing using only water. Because dirt particles cannot penetrate the surface of the water drops, the water cannot remove the dirt. What happened when you added a drop of detergent to the beaker in the **DISCOVERY LAB?** Soaps and detergents decrease the surface tension of water by disrupting the hydrogen bonds between water molecules. When the bonds are broken, the water spreads out. Compounds that lower the surface tension of water are called surface active agents or **surfactants.**

**Figure 13-14**

ⓐ Particles at the surface are drawn toward the interior of a liquid until attractive and repulsive forces are balanced.
ⓑ How does the spider's structure help it stay afloat on water?

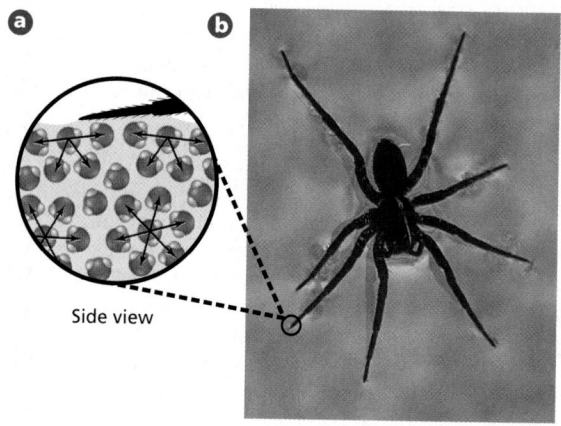

Side view

**398** Chapter 13 States of Matter

---

**Demonstration**

### Surface Tension

**Purpose**
Students will observe surface tension.

**Materials**
1-pint canning jar with ring lid; wire screen; distilled water with food coloring added (1 L); card stock (1 piece)

**Safety Precautions**
**Disposal** Items can be cleaned and reused.

**Procedure**
Cut a piece of wire window screen to fit inside the ring lid of a 1-pint canning jar. Screw on the lid with the wire-screen in place. Pour the colored water through the screen to fill the canning jar to overflowing. Have students predict what will happen when the jar is inverted. Cover the top of the jar with a piece of card stock. Turn the jar upside down over a

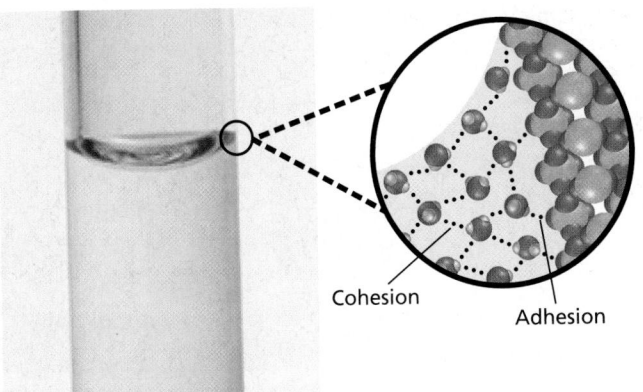

Cohesion

Adhesion

**Figure 13-15**

The surface of the water in a graduated cylinder is concave because water molecules are more strongly attracted to the silicon dioxide in glass than to other water molecules.

**Capillary action** When water is placed in a narrow container such as a graduated cylinder, you can see that the surface of the water is not straight. The surface forms a concave meniscus; that is, the surface dips in the center. **Figure 13-15** models what is happening to the water at the molecular level. There are two types of forces at work: cohesion and adhesion. Cohesion describes the force of attraction between identical molecules. Adhesion describes the force of attraction between molecules that are different. Because the adhesive forces between water molecules and the silicon dioxide in glass are greater than the cohesive forces between water molecules, the water rises along the inner walls of the cylinder.

If the cylinder is extremely narrow, a thin film of water will be drawn upward. Narrow tubes are called capillary tubes. This movement of a liquid such as water is called capillary action, or capillarity. Capillary action helps explain how paper towels can absorb large amounts of water. The water is drawn into the narrow spaces between the cellulose fibers in paper towels by capillary action. In addition, the water molecules form hydrogen bonds with cellulose molecules. These same factors account for the absorbent properties of disposable diapers. Water is drawn from the surface of the diaper to the interior by capillary action. The diaper can absorb about 200 times its mass in fluid.

## Solids

According to the kinetic-molecular theory, a mole of solid particles has as much kinetic energy as a mole of liquid particles at the same temperature. By definition, the particles in a solid must be in constant motion. So why do solids have a definite shape and volume? For a substance to be a solid rather than a liquid at a given temperature, there must be strong attractive forces acting between particles in the solid. These forces limit the motion of the particles to vibrations around fixed locations in the solid. Thus, there is more order in a solid than in a liquid. Because of this order, solids are much less fluid than liquids and gases. In fact, solids are not classified as fluids.

**Density of solids** In general, the particles in a solid are more closely packed than those in a liquid. Thus, most solids are more dense than most liquids. When the liquid and solid states of a substance coexist, the solid almost always sinks in the liquid. In **Figure 13-16,** solid cubes of benzene sink in liquid benzene because solid benzene is more dense than liquid benzene. There is about a 10% difference in density between the solid and

**Figure 13-16**

Ice cubes float in water. Benzene cubes sink in liquid benzene because solid benzene is more dense than liquid benzene.

13.3 Liquids and Solids    **399**

---

sink. Remove the card stock by sliding it off to the side. Have a student look up into the jar and report what he or she observes. While holding the inverted jar over the sink, slowly tip the jar sideways until the water flows through the wire screen into the sink.

**Results**
The surface tension is sufficient to form a film that holds the water in the jar when it is inverted.

**Analysis**
1. Why does the water remain in the inverted jar? The surface tension of the water forms a film that covers the holes in the window screen.
2. Why does water flow out of the jar when it is tilted? As air enters the jar, it displaces the water and pushes it out of the jar.

**Figure 13-17**

An iceberg can float because the rigid, three-dimensional structure of ice keeps water molecules farther apart than they are in liquid water.

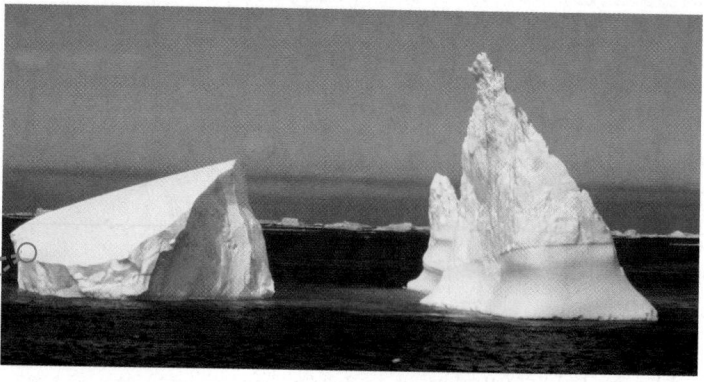

liquid states of most substances. Because the particles in a solid are closely packed, ordinary amounts of pressure will not change the volume of a solid.

You cannot predict the relative densities of ice and liquid water based on benzene. Ice cubes and icebergs float because water is less dense as a solid than it is as a liquid. **Figure 13-17** shows the reason for the exception. The water molecules in ice are less closely packed together than in liquid water; that is, there is more space between the molecules in ice. As a result, there are more particles per unit volume in liquid water than in solid water.

**Crystalline solids** Although ice is unusual in its density, ice is typical of most solids in that its molecules are packed together in a predictable way. A **crystalline solid** is a solid whose atoms, ions, or molecules are arranged in an orderly, geometric, three-dimensional structure. The individual pieces of a crystalline solid are called crystals. In Chapter 8, you learned that the locations of ions in an ionic solid can be represented as points on a framework called a crystal lattice. A **unit cell** is the smallest arrangement of connected points that can be repeated in three directions to form the lattice. The relationship of a unit cell to a crystal lattice is similar to that of a formula unit to an ionic compound. Both the unit cell and the formula unit are small, representative parts of a much larger whole. **Figure 13-18** shows three ways that atoms or ions can be arranged in a cubic unit cell.

The shape of a crystalline solid is determined by the type of unit cell from which its lattice is built. **Figure 13-19** shows seven categories of crystals based on shape. Crystal shapes differ because the surfaces, or faces, of unit cells do not always meet at right angles and the edges of the faces vary in length. In **Figure 13-19,** the edges are labeled a, b, and c; the angles at which the faces meet are labeled $\alpha$, $\beta$, and $\gamma$. Use the drawing as you model crystal shapes in the **miniLAB.**

**Figure 13-18**

These drawings show three of the ways particles are arranged in crystal lattices. Each sphere represents a particle. ⓐ Particles are arranged only at the corners of the cube. ⓑ There is a particle in the center of the cube. ⓒ There are particles in the center of each of the six cubic faces, but no particle in the center of the cube itself.

Simple cubic unit cell

Body-centered cubic unit cell

Face-centered cubic unit cell

**400** Chapter 13 States of Matter

## Internet Address Book

 Note Internet addresses that you find useful in the space below for quick reference.

_____

_____

_____

_____

**Fluorite**

$a = b = c$
$\alpha = \beta = \gamma = 90°$
**Cubic**

**Rutile**

$a = b \neq c$
$\alpha = \beta = \gamma = 90°$
**Tetragonal**

**Barite**

$a \neq b \neq c$
$\alpha = \beta = \gamma = 90°$
**Orthorhombic**

**Figure 13-19**
Crystals are classified into seven categories based on their overall shapes.

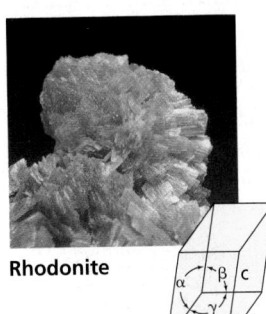
**Rhodonite**

$a \neq b \neq c$
$\alpha \neq \beta \neq \gamma \neq 90°$
**Triclinic**

**Corundum**

$a = b \neq c$
$\alpha = \beta = 90°, \gamma = 120°$
**Hexagonal**

**Iceland spar (calcite)**

$a = b = c$
$\alpha = \beta = \gamma \neq 90°$
**Rhombohedral**

**Borax**

$a \neq b \neq c$
$\alpha = \gamma = 90° \neq \beta$
**Monoclinic**

# miniLAB

## Crystal Unit Cell Models

**Formulating Models** You can make physical models that illustrate the structures of crystals.

**Materials** 12 plastic or paper soda straws, 22- or 26-gauge wire, scissors

### Procedure

1. Cut four soda straws into thirds. Wire the pieces to make a cube. All angles are 90°.
2. To model a rhombohedral crystal, deform the cube from step 1 until no angles are 90°.
3. To model a hexagonal crystal, flatten the model from step 2 until it looks like a pie with six slices.
4. To model a tetragonal crystal, cut four straws in half. Cut four of the pieces in half again. Wire the eight shorter pieces to make four

square ends. Use the longer pieces to connect the square ends.
5. To model the orthorhombic crystal, cut four straws in half. Cut 1/3 off four of the halves. Connect the four long, four medium, and four short pieces so that each side is a rectangle.
6. To model the monoclinic crystal, deform the model from step 5 along one axis. To model the triclinic crystal, deform the model from step 5 until it has no 90° angles.

### Analysis

1. Which two models have three axes of equal length? How do these models differ?
2. Which model includes a square and rectangle?
3. Which models have three unequal axes?
4. Do you think crystals are perfect or do they have defects? Explain your answer.

2. the tetragonal crystal model
3. The three crystal models that have three axes of unequal length are orthorhombic, monoclinic and triclinic.
4. They are not perfectly uniform, as they can be affected by external forces and conditions.

### ✓ Assessment

**Knowledge** Have students research the career field of gemology by interviewing a local jeweler and preparing a brief report of their findings. You could also invite a certified gemologist to speak to the class about gems—their structure, characteristic features, and qualities. **L2**

# miniLAB

## Purpose

Students will formulate and construct crystal cell unit models and classify and name them according to the length of their axes and the angles that the axes intersect. They will compare and contrast similar crystal structures with different angles between the axes, but the same length of axes.

## Process Skills

Classifying, comparing and contrasting, formulating models

## Safety Precautions

Wear apron and goggles. Be careful using scissors. The end of the wire is sharp.

## Disposal

Have students place the crystal models into a designated container.

## Teaching Strategies

- Students should refer to Figure 13-19 while constructing their crystals.
- You may wish to have students make the crystal models at home. Give each student four straws and a length of fine wire or string. Students could also work in teams.
- Collect all of the cubic unit cells and demonstrate how they fit together to make a large crystal lattice.
- Remind students that they have learned about only seven basic unit cells. There are more types to learn about in advanced courses.

## Expected Results

Students will construct the seven unit cells shown in Figure 13-19.

## Analysis

1. The two crystal models that have all three axes of equal length are cubic and rhombohedral. They differ in that the cubic has only 90-degree angles; the rhombohedral has no 90-degree angles.

**National Science Content Standards**

Pages 400–401
UCP.1, UCP.2, UCP.3; B.2, B.4

## Content Background

**Crystalline solids** Students may be intrigued by the very narrow range (just a few degrees Celsius) that separates the melting point and boiling points of the noble gases. Explain to students that Table 13-4 describes the solid phases of substances that may exist as gases or liquids at room temperature.

## In-Text Question

**Page 402** Based on its structure, will quartz have properties similar to diamond or to graphite? Quartz will be more like diamond because its structure is a three-dimensional covalent network in which all atoms are interlinked, like atoms in diamond, rather than arranged in parallel sheets like those in graphite.

**Table 13-4**

| | | Types of Crystalline Solids | |
|---|---|---|---|
| Type | Unit particles | Characteristics of solid phase | Examples |
| atomic | atoms | soft to very soft; very low melting points; poor conductivity | group 8A elements |
| molecular | molecules | fairly soft; low to moderately high melting points; poor conductivity | $I_2$, $H_2O$, $NH_3$, $CO_2$, $C_{12}H_{22}O_{11}$ (table sugar) |
| covalent network | atoms connected by covalent bonds | very hard; very high melting points; often poor conductivity | diamond (C) and quartz ($SiO_2$) |
| ionic | ions | hard; brittle; high melting points; poor conductivity | NaCl, KBr, $CaCO_3$ |
| metallic | atoms surrounded by mobile valence electrons | soft to hard; low to very high melting points; malleable and ductile; excellent conductivity | all metallic elements |

**Figure 13-20**

The most common kind of quartz has a hexagonal crystal structure.

Crystalline solids can be classified into five categories based on the types of particles they contain: atomic solids, molecular solids, covalent network solids, ionic solids, and metallic solids. **Table 13-4** summarizes the general characteristics of each category and provides examples. The only atomic solids are noble gases. Their properties reflect the weak dispersion forces between the atoms.

**Molecular solids** In molecular solids, the molecules are held together by dispersion forces, dipole–dipole forces, or hydrogen bonds. Most molecular compounds are not solids at room temperature. Even water, which can form strong hydrogen bonds, is a liquid at room temperature. Molecular compounds such as sugar are solids at room temperature because of their large molar masses. With larger molecules, many weak attractions can combine to hold the molecules together. Because they contain no ions, molecular solids are poor conductors of heat and electricity.

**Covalent network solids** Atoms such as carbon and silicon, which can form multiple covalent bonds, are able to form covalent network solids. In Chapter 7, you learned how the structures of graphite and diamond give those solid allotropes of carbon different properties. **Figure 13-20** shows the covalent network structure of quartz. Based on its structure, will quartz have properties similar to diamond or graphite?

**Ionic solids** Remember that each ion in an ionic solid is surrounded by ions of opposite charge. The type of ions and the ratio of ions determine the structure of the lattice and the shape of the crystal. The network of attractions that extends throughout an ionic crystal gives these compounds their high melting points and hardness. Ionic crystals are strong, but brittle. When ionic crystals are struck, the cations and anions are shifted from their fixed positions. Repulsions between ions of like charge cause the crystal to shatter.

### CULTURAL DIVERSITY

### The Agony of the Feet

Every year, firewalkers tread barefoot across glowing coals to open and close the three-day celebrations for the May 21 feast day of Saints Constantine and Helen in Aghia Eleni, Greece. This Greek Orthodox rite has never been fully sanctioned by the church, but references to firewalking can be traced back to Dionysus, the Greek god of revelry. How can firewalkers walk on hot coals for several minutes without burning their feet? The low thermal conductivity of the mostly molecular solids found in wood and charcoal makes them transfer heat so slowly that if you walk across the burning embers quickly you won't be injured. This is the same reason a wooden boardwalk is not as hot as sand, which contains compounds with a higher thermal conductivity.

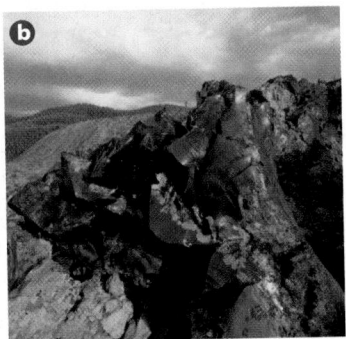

**Figure 13-21**

ⓐ The material a wire is made from, its thickness, and its length are variables that affect the flow of electrons through the wire. ⓑ Native Americans used the obsidian that forms when lava cools to make arrowheads and knives.

**Metallic solids** Recall from Chapter 8 that metallic solids consist of positive metal ions surrounded by a sea of mobile electrons. The strength of the metallic bonds between cations and electrons varies among metals and accounts for their wide range of physical properties. For example, tin melts at 232°C, but nickel melts at 1455°C. The mobile electrons make metals malleable—easily hammered into shapes—and ductile—easily drawn into wires. When force is applied to a metal, the electrons shift and thereby keep the metal ions bonded in their new positions. Read **Everyday Chemistry** at the end of the chapter to learn about shape-memory metals. Mobile electrons make metals good conductors of heat and electricity. Power lines carry electricity from power plants to homes and businesses and to the electric train shown in **Figure 13-21a.**

**Amorphous solids** Not all solids contain crystals. An **amorphous solid** is one in which the particles are not arranged in a regular, repeating pattern. The term amorphous is derived from a Greek word that means "without shape." An amorphous solid often forms when a molten material cools too quickly to allow enough time for crystals to form. **Figure 13-21b** shows an example of an amorphous solid.

Glass, rubber, and many plastics are amorphous solids. Recent studies have shown that glass may have some structure. When X-ray diffraction is used to study glass, there appears to be no pattern to the distribution of atoms. When neutrons are used instead, an orderly pattern of silicate units can be detected in some regions. Researchers hope to use this new information to control the structure of glass for optical applications and to produce glass that can conduct electricity.

**Careers Using Chemistry**

**Materials Engineer**

*Would you like to change the atomic and molecular structure of substances to create products ranging from computer chips to skis? If so, consider a career as a materials engineer.*

Materials engineers specialize in metals or ceramics. They create new materials to meet certain mechanical, electrical, or chemical standards. They also evaluate existing materials for new applications. Materials engineers work for the government and in the aviation, metal processing, electronics, automotive, and other industries in which materials play key roles.

---

**Section 13.3 Assessment**

**17.** Explain how hydrogen bonds affect the viscosity of a liquid. How does a change in temperature affect viscosity?

**18.** What effect does soap have on the surface tension of water?

**19.** How are a unit cell and a crystal lattice related?

**20.** Explain why solids are not classified as fluids.

**21.** What is the difference between a molecular solid and a covalent network solid?

**22.** Explain why most solids are denser than most liquids at the same temperature.

**23. Thinking Critically** Hypothesize why the surface of mercury in a thermometer is convex; that is, the surface is higher at the center.

chemistrymc.com/self_check_quiz

13.3 Liquids and Solids    **403**

---

## 3 Assess
### Check for Understanding

Ask the students to describe how a liquid with high viscosity differs in appearance from one with low viscosity. A viscous liquid often appears thick and moves very slowly when poured. A nonviscous liquid appears thinner and moves rapidly when poured.

### Reteach

**Visual-Spatial** Demonstrate surface tension using a beaker of water and a thumbtack. Ask students to draw a diagram showing how the molecules of water are arranged around the thumbtack so that the tack stays on the surface. See Figure 13-14. **L2** **ELL**

**Assessment**
**Performance** Assign groups of two to three students to build models of one of the three types of cubic unit cells. Have each group share its models with the class. Quiz students to see if they can label the models correctly. Use the Performance Task Assessment List for Model in **PASC**, p. 51. **L2** **COOP LEARN**

---

**Section 13.3 Assessment**

**17.** Hydrogen bonds increase viscosity because they increase the liquid's intermolecular forces, making it more resistant to flow. Viscosity decreases with temperature.

**18.** Soaps and detergents decrease the surface tension of water.

**19.** Unit cells are the building blocks of the crystal lattice.

**20.** The particles in a solid only vibrate around fixed locations.

**21.** A molecular solid is formed from molecules held together by intermolecular forces that are weaker than covalent bonds; covalent network solids are formed from molecules held together by covalent bonds.

**22.** Solids are usually denser than liquids because their particles are held more closely together by intermolecular attractions.

**23.** The cohesion between mercury atoms is stronger than the adhesion between mercury and glass.

**403**

Before presenting the lesson, display **Section Focus Transparency 50** on the overhead projector. Have students answer the accompanying questions using **Section Focus Transparency Master 50**. **L1**

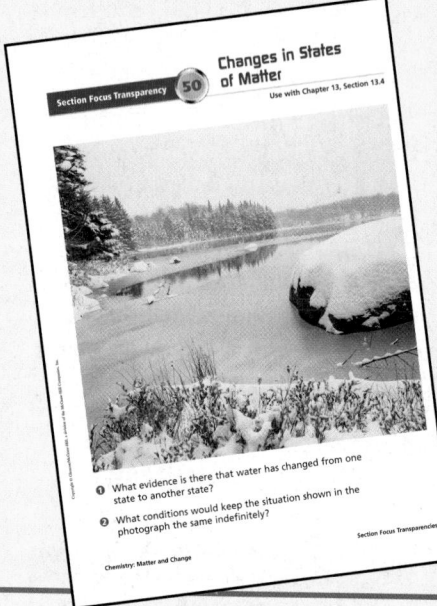

Section Focus Transparency **50**
Changes in States of Matter

Use with Chapter 13, Section 13.4

❶ What evidence is there that water has changed from one state to another state?

❷ What conditions would keep the situation shown in the photograph the same indefinitely?

*Chemistry: Matter and Change*

Section Focus Transparencies

# 2 Teach
### In-Text Questions

**Page 404** Can you use the kinetic-molecular theory to explain what happened to your drink? As water warmed, ice molecules moved faster until their kinetic energy overcame the forces holding them in the solid phase, and they entered the liquid phase. Liquid water disappeared because it warmed up and vaporized.

**Page 404** If a tray of ice cubes is left on a counter, where does the energy to melt the cubes come from? Energy radiates from light sources by convection or currents, or is transferred from the countertop to the ice.

### Figure Caption Question

**Figure 13-22** What phase changes can occur between solids and liquids? melting, freezing

### Objectives

- **Explain** how the addition and removal of energy can cause a phase change.
- **Interpret** a phase diagram.

### Vocabulary

melting point
vaporization
evaporation
vapor pressure
boiling point
sublimation
condensation
deposition
freezing point
phase diagram
triple point

Suppose you take a glass of ice water outside on a hot day. You set it down and rush inside to answer the phone. When you return much later, you find that the ice cubes have melted and there is less water in your glass. Can you use the kinetic-molecular theory to explain what happened to your drink?

Most substances can exist in three states depending on the temperature and pressure. A few substances, such as water, exist in all three states under ordinary conditions. States of a substance are referred to as phases when they coexist as physically distinct parts of a mixture. Ice water is a heterogeneous mixture with two phases, solid ice and liquid water. When energy is added or removed from a system, one phase can change into another. As you read this section, use what you know about the kinetic-molecular theory to help explain the phase changes summarized in **Figure 13-22**.

## Phase Changes That Require Energy

Because you are familiar with the phases of water—ice, liquid water, and water vapor—and have observed changes between those phases, we can use water as the primary example in the discussion of phase changes.

**Melting** What does happen to ice cubes in a glass of ice water? When ice cubes are placed in water, the water is at a higher temperature than the ice. Heat flows from the water to the ice. Heat is the transfer of energy from an object at a higher temperature to an object at a lower temperature. The energy absorbed by the ice is not used to raise the temperature of the ice. Instead, it disrupts the hydrogen bonds holding the water molecules together in the ice crystal. When molecules on the surface of the ice absorb enough energy to break the hydrogen bonds, they move apart and enter the liquid phase. As molecules are removed, the ice cube shrinks. The process continues until all of the ice melts. If a tray of ice cubes is left on a counter, where does the energy to melt the cubes come from?

The amount of energy required to melt one mole of a solid depends on the strength of the forces keeping the particles together in the solid. Because hydrogen bonds between water molecules are strong, a relatively large amount of energy is required. However, the energy required to melt ice is much less than the energy required to melt table salt because the ionic bonds in sodium chloride are much stronger than the hydrogen bonds in ice.

**Figure 13-22**

The six possible transitions between phases. What phase changes can occur between solids and liquids?

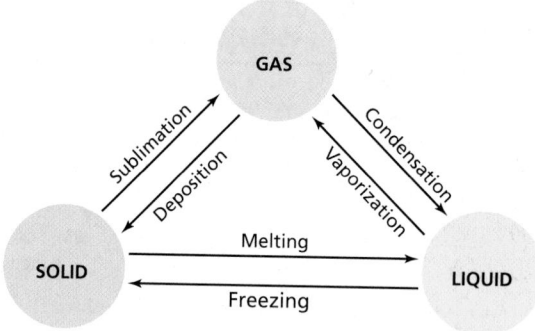

## CHEMISTRY JOURNAL

### Observing Phase Changes

*Linguistic* Ask students to keep a daily listing in their journals for one week in which they describe their observations of phase changes taking place. They should also name each phase change process that they observe. **L2**

### Melting Points

*Linguistic* Ask students to research the melting points of ten compounds for which the data are not included in their textbook. Tell students to summarize their findings in a table for their journals. **L2**

**Energy Distribution of Molecules in a Liquid**

Minimum kinetic energy required for vaporization

**Figure 13-23**

This graph shows a typical distribution of kinetic energies for a liquid at 25°C. The most probable kinetic energy lies at the peak of the curve. How would the curve look for the same liquid at 30°C?

The temperature at which the liquid phase and the solid phase of a given substance can coexist is a characteristic physical property of many solids. The **melting point** of a crystalline solid is the temperature at which the forces holding its crystal lattice together are broken and it becomes a liquid. It is difficult to specify an exact melting point for an amorphous solid because these solids tend to act like liquids when they are still in the solid state.

**Vaporization** While ice melts, the temperature of the ice–water mixture remains constant. Once all of the ice has melted, additional energy added to the system increases the kinetic energy of the liquid molecules. The temperature of the system begins to rise. In liquid water, some molecules will have more kinetic energy than other molecules. **Figure 13-23** shows how energy is distributed among the molecules in a liquid at 25°C. The shaded portion indicates those molecules that have the energy required to overcome the forces of attraction holding the molecules together in the liquid.

Particles that escape from the liquid enter the gas phase. For a substance that is ordinarily a liquid at room temperature, the gas phase is called a vapor. **Vaporization** is the process by which a liquid changes to a gas or vapor. If the input of energy is gradual, the molecules tend to escape from the surface of the liquid. Remember that molecules at the surface are attracted to fewer other molecules than are molecules in the interior. When vaporization occurs only at the surface of a liquid, the process is called **evaporation.** Even at cold temperatures, some water molecules have enough energy to evaporate. As the temperature rises, more and more molecules achieve the minimum energy required to escape from the liquid.

Evaporation, which requires energy, is the method by which your body controls its temperature. When you sit outside on a hot day or when you exercise, your body releases an aqueous solution called sweat from glands in your skin. Water molecules in sweat can absorb heat energy from your skin and evaporate. Excess heat is carried from all parts of your body to your skin by your blood. Evaporation of water also explains why a swim in cool ocean water is so refreshing. Not only is heat transferred from you to the cooler water while you are in the water, but water molecules left on your skin continue to cool you by evaporation once you come out of the water. The salts that remain when sea water evaporates often leave a white residue on your skin. To compare the rates of evaporation for different liquids, do the **CHEMLAB** at the end of the chapter.

13.4 Phase Changes    **405**

**Figure Caption Question**

**Figure 13-23** How would the curve look for the same liquid at 30°C? The peak of the graph would shift to the right.

## Identifying Misconceptions

Students may have misconceptions about the activity of molecules during phase changes.

**Uncover the Misconception**
Ask students what happens to molecules in a solid as it melts. They may respond that the molecules themselves break apart. They may also describe boiling and sublimation in the same way.

**Demonstrate the Concept**
Use drawings and models to show how intermolecular forces, rather than intramolecular bonds break as a substance is heated.

**Assess New Knowledge**
Ask students to draw several water molecules, using solid lines for intramolecular bonds and dashed lines for intermolecular forces. Then ask them to re-draw the molecules as the water is heated. Intermolecular forces are overcome; the intramolecular bonds remain intact.

## CHEMLAB

ChemLab 13, located at the end of the chapter, can be used at this point in the lesson.

## Assessment

**Performance** Have students demonstrate their lab skills by carefully melting an assigned substance and determining its melting-point range. Remind students to wear lab aprons and goggles, and to use proper protection when handling hot objects. Use the Performance Task Assessment List for Carrying Out a Strategy and Collecting Data in **PASC**, p. 25. **L2** **ELL**

## Resource Manager

**Study Guide for Content Mastery,** pp. 77–78 **L2**
**Solving Problems: A Chemistry Handbook,** Section 13.4 **L2**
**Section Focus Transparency 50 and Master L1** **ELL**
**Lab Manual,** pp. 97–100, 101–104 **L2**
**CBL Lab Manual,** pp. 9–12 **L2**

## DIFFERENTIATED INSTRUCTION

### Gifted

*Intrapersonal* Ask interested students to research the mechanisms by which the human body regulates its temperature and the health consequences when these mechanisms fail. **L3**

**Page 406** How does temperature affect the rate of evaporation? *The higher the temperature, the greater the rate of evaporation.*

**Page 406** How would a rise in temperature affect vapor pressure? *The vapor pressure would increase.*

## Quick Demo

Place a small lump of solid air freshener in the bottom of a beaker. Put a watch glass full of ice on top of the beaker, and place this setup in a shallow pan of warm water. Ask students to observe what happens and name the process that takes place. *The heat from the warm water causes the solid air freshener to undergo sublimation, and the cold surface of the watch glass causes the vaporized air freshener to condense into a solid again. If the air freshener is colored, ask students to explain why the material that sublimes is white. The dye is a separate compound from the air freshener and does not undergo sublimation itself.*

## ✔ Assessment

**Portfolio** Ask students to create a poster showing the movement of the particles of a substance among its three phases. In their drawings, students should show the relative spacing of particles in all phases and indicate whether energy is absorbed or released during each transition. Students should add their drawings to their portfolios after you have checked them. **L2 ELL P**

## Reinforcement

Explain that the average kinetic energy of particles determines their temperature. So even at temperatures below 100°C, water in an open container will evaporate. Liquids do not have to reach a full boil to be converted to gases.

**Figure 13-24**

Evaporation occurs in both open and closed containers.
**a** In an open container, water molecules that evaporate can escape from the container.
**b** Water vapor collects above the liquid in a closed container.

H$_2$O(g) molecules (water vapor)

H$_2$O(l) molecules

**Figure 13-24** compares evaporation in an open container with evaporation in a closed container. If water is in an open container, all the molecules will eventually evaporate. The time it takes for them to evaporate depends on the amount of water and the available energy. How does temperature affect the rate of evaporation? In a partially filled, closed container, the situation is different. Water vapor collects above the liquid and exerts pressure on the surface of the liquid. The pressure exerted by a vapor over a liquid is called **vapor pressure.** How would a rise in temperature affect vapor pressure?

The temperature at which the vapor pressure of a liquid equals the external or atmospheric pressure is called the **boiling point.** Use **Figure 13-25** to compare what happens to a liquid at temperatures below its boiling point with what happens to a liquid at its boiling point. At the boiling point, molecules throughout the liquid have enough energy to vaporize. Bubbles of vapor collect below the surface of the liquid and rise to the surface. If a container has smooth walls and there are no dust particles to provide a site for bubble formation, a liquid can be heated to a temperature above its boiling point. When the liquid finally boils, the eruption of bubbles can cause the liquid to spatter. This problem can be avoided if a stone or ceramic chip is added to the liquid.

**Figure 13-25**

**a** As temperature increases, water molecules gain kinetic energy. Vapor pressure increases (black arrows) but is less than atmospheric pressure (red arrows). **b** A liquid has reached its boiling point when its vapor pressure is equal to atmospheric pressure. At sea level, the boiling point of water is 100°C.

101.3 kPa (1 atm)     70° C

101.3 kPa (1 atm)     100°C

**a**     **b**

**406    Chapter 13** States of Matter

## GLENCOE TECHNOLOGY

**CD-ROM**
**Chemistry: Matter and Change**
Experiment: *Phase Changes*
Video: *Changes of State*
Demonstration: *Superheated Steam*

## Resource Manager

**Small-Scale Lab Manual,**
pp. 33–36 **L2**

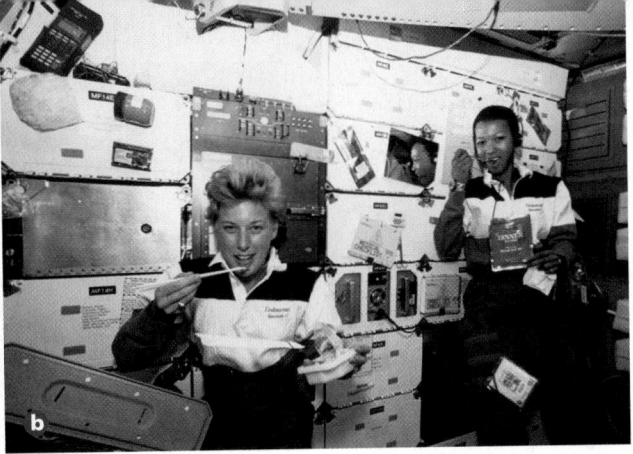

**Figure 13-26**

ⓐ Less flavor is lost when water is removed by freeze drying than when water is removed by evaporation. ⓑ These astronauts mix their freeze-dried food with water before eating.

**Sublimation** Many substances have the ability to change directly from the solid phase to the gas phase. **Sublimation** is the process by which a solid changes directly to a gas without first becoming a liquid. Solid iodine and solid carbon dioxide (dry ice) sublime at room temperature. The special effect shown in the chapter opener is caused when dry ice sublimes and cools water vapor in the air. Dry ice keeps objects that could be damaged by melting water cold during shipping. Moth balls, which contain the compounds napthalene or *p*-dichlorobenzene, sublime. So do solid air fresheners.

If ice cubes are left in a freezer for a long time, they shrink because the ice sublimes. At extremely low pressures, ice sublimes in a much shorter time period. This property of ice is used in a process called freeze drying. **Figure 13-26a** shows equipment used to produce freeze-dried food. Fresh food is frozen and placed in a container that is attached to a vacuum pump. As the pressure in the container is reduced, the ice sublimes and is removed from the container. The mass of the food is greatly reduced when water is removed. Backpackers often use freeze-dried foods because they want to carry as light a load as possible on a long hike. The astronauts shown in **Figure 13-26b** also have concerns about the mass of their cargo. More importantly, freeze-dried foods contain no water to support the growth of bacteria. They can be stored for a long time without refrigeration.

## Phase Changes That Release Energy

Have you ever awakened on a chilly morning to see dew on the grass or frost on your windows? When you set a glass of ice water on a picnic table, do you notice beads of water on the outside of the glass? These events are examples of phase changes that release energy into the surroundings.

**Condensation** When a water vapor molecule loses energy, its velocity is reduced. The vapor molecule is more likely to interact and form a hydrogen bond when it collides with another water molecule. The formation of hydrogen bonds signals the change from the vapor phase to the liquid phase. Because liquids are more dense than vapors, the process by which a gas or a vapor becomes a liquid is called **condensation.** Condensation is the reverse of vaporization. When hydrogen bonds form in liquid water, energy is released.

There are different causes for the condensation of water vapor. All involve a transfer of energy. The vapor molecules can come in contact with a cold surface such as the outside of a glass containing ice water. Heat from the vapor

### Extension

🧠 *Linguistic* When poets want to evoke the essence of the morning, they often make a reference to dew—the moisture on grass that disappears as the sun and the temperature rise. But what is dew due to? On a warm day with high humidity, the air becomes saturated with moisture. There is only so much water the air can hold at any given temperature, and that amount decreases when the temperature drops. The coolest nighttime temperatures tend to be in the hours just before sunrise. When the temperature drops, the air cannot hold as much moisture as it did earlier in the night. Excess moisture then condenses on anything the air touches, typically on the grass. Eventually, warmth from the rising sun's rays evaporates this moisture, and the dew is gone. Have students write a poem or song about dew, including scientific information in their creations. **L2**

✔ **Portfolio**

### Museum Specimens

🧑 *Intrapersonal* Ask interested students to research and present a report comparing the newer freeze-drying process to older taxidermy methods used to preserve animal specimens for museums. If possible, ask students to bring in specimens that have been preserved by both methods.

**L2** **P**

**National Science Content Standards**
Pages 404–407
UCP.1, UCP.2, UCP.3; B.2, B.4, B.6

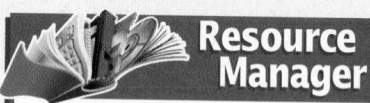
**Figure 13-27**

As water vapor cools, it can condense on a car or it can be deposited as six-sided snow crystals.

## Earth Science
### CONNECTION

Sometimes, too much rain falls in one location and too little rain falls in another. People have been trying to produce rain on demand for centuries. Because most clouds exist at temperatures below the freezing point of water, rain often begins when water vapor deposits on ice crystals. (When ice crystals approach the surface of Earth, they melt and fall as rain if the temperature of the air near the surface is above freezing.) Rainmakers focus on the crucial role played by ice crystals. For example, dry ice pellets can be dropped into a cloud. The cold dry ice cools the water vapor in the cloud and ice crystals form. Sometimes tiny silver iodide crystals are sprayed into a cloud to serve as artificial "ice pellets."

molecules is transferred to the glass as the water vapor condenses. The water vapor that condenses on blades of grass or the car shown in **Figure 13-27** forms liquid droplets called dew. When a layer of air near the ground cools, water vapor in the air condenses and produces fog. Dew and fog evaporate when exposed to sunlight. Clouds form when layers of air high above the surface of Earth cool. Clouds are made entirely of water droplets. When the drops grow large enough, they fall to the ground as rain.

**Deposition** Some substances can change directly into a solid without first forming a liquid. When water vapor comes in contact with a cold window in winter, it forms a solid deposit on the window called frost. **Deposition** is the process by which a substance changes from a gas or vapor to a solid without first becoming a liquid. Deposition is the reverse of sublimation. The snowflakes shown in **Figure 13-27** form when water vapor high up in the atmosphere changes directly into solid ice crystals. Energy is released as the crystals form.

**Freezing** Suppose you place liquid water in an ice tray in a freezer. As heat is removed from the water, the molecules lose kinetic energy and their velocity decreases. The molecules are less likely to flow past one another. When enough energy has been removed, the hydrogen bonds between water molecules keep the molecules fixed, or frozen, into set positions. Freezing is the reverse of melting. The **freezing point** is the temperature at which a liquid is converted into a crystalline solid. How do the melting point and freezing point of a given substance compare?

## Phase Diagrams

There are two variables that combine to control the phase of a substance: temperature and pressure. These variables can have opposite effects on a substance. For example, a temperature increase causes more liquid to vaporize, but an increase in pressure causes more vapor to condense. A **phase diagram** is a graph of pressure versus temperature that shows in which phase a substance exists under different conditions of temperature and pressure.

Figure 13-28a shows the phase diagram for water. You can use this graph to predict what phase water will be in for any combination of temperature and pressure. Note that there are three regions representing the solid, liquid, and vapor phases of water and three curves that separate the regions from one another. At points that fall along the curves, two phases of water can coexist. At what point on the graph do liquid water and water vapor exist at

**408** Chapter 13 States of Matter

---

**DIFFERENTIATED INSTRUCTION**

### Learning Disabled

Some students may have difficulty interpreting phase diagrams. Suggest that they interpret the diagrams one axis at a time. To identify the solid, liquid, and gas phases, students should first consider temperature. For example, students have learned that water is a solid at temperatures below 0°C, and as the temperature increases, it first becomes a liquid, then a gas. So, except for certain substances with unusual properties, the section on the left of the diagram represents the solid phase, the middle section the liquid phase, and the right section the gas phase. When they consider the pressure axis, they should make the same conclusion, knowing that at very high pressures, materials compress into solids. The section at the highest pressure represents the solid phase, the next section the liquid phase, and at the lowest pressure, the gas phase.

**Phase Diagram for H₂O**

217.75 — Critical point
B

LIQUID

Normal
freezing
point

1.00 —

Normal
boiling
point

SOLID  A

Triple point

VAPOR

Pressure (atm)

0.00    100.00    373.99

Temperature (C°)

ⓑ  **Phase Diagram for CO₂**

SOLID    LIQUID

1.0 —

GAS

−78    31

Pressure (atm)

Temperature (C°)

**Figure 13-28**

Compare the temperature and pressure values at the triple point for water and carbon dioxide.

1.00 atm and 100.00°C? The short, yellow curve shows the temperature and pressure conditions under which solid water and water vapor can coexist. The long, blue curve shows the temperature and pressure conditions under which liquid water and water vapor can coexist. The red curve shows the temperature and pressure conditions under which solid water and liquid water can coexist. What is the normal freezing point of water?

Point A on the phase diagram of water is the triple point for water. The **triple point** is the point on a phase diagram that represents the temperature and pressure at which three phases of a substance can coexist. All six phase changes can occur at the triple point: freezing and melting; evaporation and condensation; sublimation and deposition. Point B is called the critical point. This point indicates the critical pressure and critical temperature above which water cannot exist as a liquid. If water vapor is at the critical temperature, an increase in pressure will not change the vapor into a liquid.

The phase diagram for each substance is different because the normal boiling and freezing points of substances are different. However, each diagram will supply the same type of data for the phases, including a triple point. Of course, the range of temperatures chosen will vary to reflect the physical properties of the substance. Consider the phase diagram for carbon dioxide, which is shown in **Figure 13-28b.** If this diagram used the same temperature range chosen for water, there would be no solid region and an extrmely small liquid region. Find the triple point for carbon dioxide. Estimate the pressure and temperature conditions at the triple point.

**Extension**

Ask students to use Figure 13-28b to determine one temperature and pressure combination at which carbon dioxide is in the solid phase, one combination for the liquid phase, and one for the gas phase. Answers will vary but should agree with the figure.

**✓ Assessment**

**Performance** Ask students to design an experiment (including the setup) to measure the amount of gas produced by the sublimation of a solid air freshener. Students' designs should incorporate a sealed apparatus with tubing running from the air freshener container into an inverted graduated cylinder in a dish of water. Use the Performance Task Assessment List for Designing an Experiment in **PASC**, p. 23. **L2**

**Figure Caption Question**

**Figure 13-28** Compare the temperature and pressure values at the triple point for water and carbon dioxide. water: 0.01°C, 6.03 × 10⁻³ atm; carbon dioxide: −57°C, 5 atm

**In-Text Questions**

**Pages 408–409** At what point on the graph do liquid water and water vapor exist at 1.00 atm and 100.00°C? normal boiling point
**Page 409** What is the normal freezing point of water? 0.0°C
**Page 409** Find the triple point for carbon dioxide. Estimate the pressure and temperature conditions at the triple point. −57°C and 5 atm

## Section 13.4 Assessment

**24.** What information does a phase diagram supply?

**25.** What is the major difference between the processes of melting and freezing?

**26.** Explain what the triple point and the critical point on a phase diagram represent.

**27. Comparing and Contrasting** Compare what happens to the energy, order, and spacing of

particles when a solid other than ice changes to a liquid with what happens to the energy, order, and spacing of particles when a gas changes to a liquid.

**28. Thinking Critically** Aerosol cans contain compressed gases that, when released, help propel the contents out of the can. Why is it important to keep aerosol cans from overheating?

## Section 13.4 Assessment

**24.** the combinations of temperature and pressure under which a given substance exists as a solid, liquid, and gas

**25.** Freezing occurs when a liquid becomes a solid and energy is released. Melting requires an input of energy to convert a solid to a liquid.

**26.** triple point: the temperature at which the three phases of a substance can coexist; critical point: the pressure and temperature above which a substance cannot exist as a liquid

**27.** When a solid changes to a liquid, the particles gain kinetic energy, become less ordered, and are spaced

farther apart. When a gas changes to a liquid, the particles lose kinetic energy, become more ordered, and are spaced closer together.

**28.** Upon heating, the kinetic energy of the gas particles increases, raising the pressure. The can will explode.

**409**

## Preparation ⟨⟩

### Time Allotment
One laboratory period

### Process Skills
Acquiring and analyzing information, applying concepts, classifying, comparing and contrasting, drawing a conclusion, measuring, observing and inferring, recognizing cause and effect, thinking critically, using numbers

### Safety Precautions
Acetone, ethanol, and isopropyl alcohol are flammable. Keep open flames away from the vapors of these liquids. These liquids can also dry the skin or irritate the eyes.

### Disposal
Instruct students to return each unused liquid to the proper container for reuse.

### Alternative Materials
• You can use liquids other than those listed for the experiment, but these liquids are easy to obtain and relatively safe. Avoid liquids such as gasoline, benzene, and carbon tetrachloride because they are **not** approved chemicals for secondary schools.

### Pre-Lab

**2.** Evaporation is the process by which the surface of a liquid changes to a gas or a vapor. As liquid molecules acquire kinetic energy, they reach the minimum required energy to overcome the forces of attraction holding them together.

**3.** dispersion forces, dipole-dipole forces, hydrogen bonds; weakest force: dispersion forces; strongest: hydrogen bonds.

**4.** Students should predict that organic liquids will evaporate more quickly than $H_2O$ or $NH_3$ because there are fewer forces between the particles of liquid.

### National Science Content Standards
Pages 410–411
UCP.1, UCP.2, UCP.3; A.1; B.4, B.6

---

# Comparing Rates of Evaporation

**S**everal factors determine how fast a sample of liquid will evaporate. The volume of the sample is a key factor. A drop of water takes less time to evaporate than a liter of water. The amount of energy supplied to the sample is another factor. In this lab, you will investigate how the type of liquid and temperature affect the rate of evaporation.

### Problem
How do intermolecular forces affect the evaporation rates of liquids?

### Objectives
• **Measure** and **compare** the rates of evaporation for different liquids.
• **Classify** liquids based on their rates of evaporation.
• **Predict** which intermolecular forces exist between the particles of each liquid.

### Materials
distilled water
ethanol
isopropyl alcohol
acetone
household ammonia
5 droppers
5 small plastic cups

grease pencil or masking tape and a marking pen
paper towel
square of waxed paper
stopwatch

### Safety Precautions

• Always wear safety goggles and a lab apron.
• Wear gloves because some of the liquids can dry out your skin.
• Avoid inhaling any of the vapors, especially ammonia.
• There should be no open flames in the lab; some of the liquids are flammable.

### Pre-Lab

**1.** Read the entire **CHEMLAB.** Prepare a data table similar to the one shown.

**2.** What is evaporation? Describe what happens at the molecular level during evaporation.

**3.** List the three possible intermolecular forces. Which force is the weakest? Which force is the strongest?

**4.** Look at the materials list for this lab. Consider the five liquids you will test. Predict which liquids will evaporate quickly and which will take longer to evaporate. Give reasons for your predictions.

**5.** To calculate an evaporation rate, you would divide the evaporation time by the quantity of liquid used. Explain why it is possible to use the evaporation times from this lab as evaporation rates.

**6.** Make sure you know how to use the stopwatch provided. Will you need to convert the reading on the stopwatch to seconds?

| Evaporation Data | | |
|---|---|---|
| Liquid | Evaporation time (s) | Shape of liquid drop |
| distilled water | | |
| ethanol | | |
| warm ethanol | | |
| isopropyl alcohol | | |
| acetone | | |
| household ammonia | | |

### Procedure

**1.** Use a grease pencil or masking tape to label each of 5 small plastic cups. Use A for distilled water, B for ethanol, C for isopropyl alcohol, D for acetone, and E for household ammonia.

**2.** Place the plastic cups on a paper towel.

---

**5.** Evaporation times can be used as rates because the same quantity (a drop) was used for each liquid.

## Procedure
• Tell students if the drop of liquid is still visible after 5 minutes, they should record the data as > 300 seconds.
• Ethanol can be warmed in a warm water bath on a hot plate.

## Expected Results

| Liquid | Evap. time (s) | Obs.: Shape of liquid drop (top, side views) |
|---|---|---|
| Dist. water | >300 | Top: spherical; Side: domed |
| Ethanol | 140 | Top: jagged circular; Side: flat |
| Ethanol (warm) | <140 | Top: jagged circular; Side: flat |
| Isopropyl alcohol | 146 | Same as ethanol |
| Acetone | 8.4 | Top: small circular; Side: flat |
| Ammonia | >300 | Same as water |

3. Use a dropper to collect about 1 mL of distilled water and place the water in the cup labeled A. Place the dropper on the paper towel directly in front of the cup. Repeat with the other liquids.

4. Place a square of waxed paper on your lab surface. Plan where on the waxed paper you will place each of the 5 drops that you will test to avoid mixing.

5. Have your stopwatch ready. Collect some water in your water dropper and place a single drop on the waxed paper. Begin timing. Time how long it takes for the drop to completely evaporate. While you wait, make two drawings of the drop. One drawing should show the shape of the drop as viewed from above. The other drawing should be a side view at eye level. If the drop takes longer than 5 minutes to evaporate, record > 300 in your data table.

6. Repeat step 5 with the four other liquids.

7. Use the above procedure to design an experiment in which you can observe the effect of temperature on the rate of evaporation of ethanol. Your teacher will provide a sample of warm ethanol.

## Cleanup and Disposal

1. Crumple up the waxed paper and place it in the container assigned by your teacher.

2. Place unused liquids in the containers specified by your teacher.

3. Wash out all droppers and test tubes except those used for distilled water.

4. Wash your hands thoroughly.

## Analyze and Conclude

1. **Classifying** Which liquids evaporated quickly? Which liquids were slow to evaporate?

2. **Drawing a Conclusion** Based on your data, in which liquid(s) are the attractive forces between molecules most likely to be dispersion forces?

3. **Interpreting Data** Make a generalization about the shape of a liquid drop and the evaporation rate of the liquid.

4. **Recognizing Cause and Effect** What is the relationship between surface tension and the shape of a liquid drop? What are the attractive forces that increase surface tension?

5. **Applying Concepts** The isopropyl alcohol you used is a mixture of isopropyl alcohol and water. Would pure isopropyl alcohol evaporate more quickly or more slowly compared to the alcohol and water mixture? Give a reason for your answer.

6. **Thinking Critically** Household ammonia is a mixture of ammonia and water. Based on the data you collected, is there more ammonia or more water in the mixture? Use what you learned about the relative strengths of the attractive forces in ammonia and water to support your conclusion.

7. **Drawing a Conclusion** How does the rate of evaporation of warm ethanol compare to ethanol at room temperature? Use kinetic-molecular theory to explain your observations.

8. **Error Analysis** How could you change the procedure to make it more precise?

## Real-World Chemistry

1. The vapor phases of liquids such as acetone and alcohol are more flammable than their liquid phases. For flammable liquids, what is the relationship between evaporation rate and the likelihood that the liquid will burn?

2. Suggest why a person who has a higher than normal temperature might be given a rubdown with rubbing alcohol (70% isopropyl alcohol).

3. Table salt can be collected from salt water by evaporation. The water is placed in large shallow containers. What advantage do these shallow containers have over deep containers with the same overall volume?

CHEMLAB    411

## Analyze and Conclude

1. Acetone evaporates the fastest; the water and ammonia evaporate the slowest.

2. in the liquid that is nonpolar and that evaporates the fastest (acetone)

3. The more spread out the liquid drop, the higher the evaporation rate; the more spherical or dome-shaped the drop, the lower the rate.

4. The greater the surface tension, the more spherical or dome-shaped the drop. Intermolecular forces increase surface tension.

5. Because of less hydrogen bonding, pure alcohol would evaporate more quickly than a mixture of alcohol and water.

6. more water; the evaporation rate is more similar to that of water. (The hydrogen bonds in ammonia are weaker than those in water; thus, ammonia is a gas at room temperature.)

7. Warm ethanol evaporates faster than ethanol at room temperature. The average kinetic energy of the ethanol molecules increases at the higher temperature. Thus, a larger number of ethanol molecules have the energy needed to escape the surface of the liquid and evaporate.

8. by determining the exact volume of each liquid tested

## Real-World Chemistry

1. The higher the evaporation rate, the more likely the liquid will burn.

2. Rubbing alcohol has a high evaporation rate. Since evaporation requires energy, applying it to the skin can cause absorption of heat energy and a lowering of body temperature.

3. They provide greater surface area for evaporation.

## Resource Manager

**ChemLab and MiniLab Worksheets,** pp. 50–52 **L2**

## ✓ Assessment

**Performance** Have students determine how long it takes water and ammonia to evaporate. Depending on the humidity level of the room, it could take several hours. Ask students how they would determine and record the rates of evaporation of these liquids. (For example, they could use graduated cylinders to measure and record the amount of liquid every 15 to 30 minutes.) Use the Performance Task Assessment List for Analyzing the Data in **PASC,** p. 27. **L2**

# Everyday Chemistry

## Purpose

Students will learn about the chemical properties of shape-memory alloys.

## Background

Nitinol is an example of a shape-memory alloy. Its name is an acronym for *Nickel Titanium Naval Ordnance Laboratory*. It was developed at the Naval Ordnance Laboratory in White Oak, Maryland, by William J. Buehler. Buehler was studying alloys for use in missile nose cones. At a routine meeting, a strip of nitinol was folded accordion-style and then unfolded repeatedly to show that it resisted fatigue. One of the participants heated the folded nitinol with a lighter, and the strip unfolded spontaneously.

## Visual Learning

*Visual-Spatial* Have students research the molecular arrangements in the two phases, then use Styrofoam balls or gumdrops to make models of the austentite and martensite phases. Point out that both types of structures can be accommodated within the same array of atoms. **L2** **ELL**

## Teaching Strategies

- Explain that the wire converts to the martensite phase only after it is heated above the transition temperature and then cooled below the transition temperature. Heating can reverse any shape assumed by the metal below the transition temperature.
- The properties and uses of nitinol vary with its composition. The transition temperature varies from −50°C to 166°C. For example, a 3-millimeter diameter nitinol device is used to capture blood clots

### National Science Content Standards

**Pages 412–413**
UCP.1, UCP.2, UCP.3; B.2, B.4, B.5, B.6; E.2; F.6

**412**

## Metals with a Memory

How can the eyeglass frames shown in the photo "remember" their original shape? How do braces move your teeth? These items may be made of a shape-memory alloy that has a remarkable property. It reverts to its previous shape when heated or when the stress that caused its shape is removed.

### Two solid phases?

Melting is the transition of a material from a solid to a liquid. Transitions from one phase to another also can take place within a solid. A solid can have two phases if it has two possible crystal structures. It is the ability to undergo these changes in crystalline structure that gives shape-memory alloys their properties.

For example, an alloy that contains equal amounts of two metals may have phases called austentite and martensite. In the austentite phase, the metal ions are arranged in a rigid crystalline cubic structure. In the martensite phase, the metal ions are arranged in a more flexible structure. When the internal organization changes, the properties of the alloy change.

The austentite phase can be changed into the martensite phase if the alloy is cooled below the transition temperature under controlled conditions. Copper-aluminum-nickel, nickel-titanium, and copper-zinc-aluminum are the most common shape-memory alloys.

### Nitinol

Nitinol is an alloy of nickel and titanium that has the austentite phase structure. Each nickel atom is at the center of a cube of titanium, and a titanium atom is at the center of each cube of nickel atoms. If nitinol is shaped into a straight wire, heated, and cooled past the transition temperature, it converts into the martensite phase. Now its structure allows the nitinol to be bent by an external stress. If the wire is heated, the stress is released and it reverts back to its initial shape.

### Applications of nitinol

Nitinol is a corrosion resistant, light-weight material that generates a large force when it returns to its original shape. It also is safe to use inside the body, that is, nitinol is biocompatible. You may need fewer trips to the orthodontist because the nitinol wires in your braces need to be tightened and adjusted less frequently. Staples to repair human bones, devices that trap blood clots, and anchors used to reattach tendons to bone in an injured shoulder may be made of nitinol. Nitinol is used in a variety of military, safety, and robotics applications. Life-saving devices such as antiscalding valves that automatically shut off water flow and fire sprinklers that respond more quickly to heat rely on shape-memory alloys. So do vibration-control devices in buildings and bridges.

### Testing Your Knowledge

1. **Inferring** Twisted nitinol-wire eyeglass frames unbend at room temperature. Is the transition temperature of the frames above or below room temperature?

2. **Applying** Design a simple lever that could be raised and lowered smoothly using nitinol wires.

within veins. After insertion into a vein, the device unfolds into an opened, umbrella shape measuring approximately 28 mm in diameter. Ask students why this device must be bathed in cold saline solution as it is inserted into a vein. Human body temperature (37°C) is within the transition temperature range. Therefore, the device must be kept cool.

### Testing Your Knowledge

1. The transition temperature is below room temperature.
2. Accept any reasonable answer in which the lever is raised and lowered by opposing sets of wires so that they shorten or elongate when heated.

## Summary

### 13.1 Gases

- The kinetic-molecular theory explains the properties of gases in terms of the size, motion, and energy of their particles.

- Because of the space between gas particles, the density of gases is low and gases can be compressed.

- Because there are no significant forces of attraction between gas particles, gases can diffuse and effuse at rates determined by the mass of the particles.

- A barometer measures the pressure gas particles in Earth's atmosphere exert against Earth's surface.

- The total pressure of a gas mixture is the sum of the partial pressures of each gas in the mixture.

### 13.2 Forces of Attraction

- The intramolecular forces that hold together ionic, covalent, and metallic bonds are stronger than intermolecular forces.

- Dispersion forces are weak intermolecular forces between temporary dipoles of nonpolar molecules.

- Dipole–dipole forces occur between polar molecules. A hydrogen bond is a strong dipole–dipole force between molecules in which hydrogen atoms are bonded to highly electronegative atoms.

### 13.3 Liquids and Solids

- Particles are in motion in liquids and solids, but the range of motion is limited by intermolecular forces. Because liquids and solids are denser than gases, they are not easily compressed.

- In general, viscosity increases as the temperature decreases and as intermolecular forces increase.

- Surface tension results from an uneven distribution of attractive forces. A liquid displays capillarity when adhesive forces are stronger than cohesive forces.

- Except for amorphous solids, solids are more ordered than liquids. Crystalline solids can be classified by shape and composition.

### 13.4 Phase Changes

- Melting, vaporization, and sublimation are changes that require energy. Freezing, condensation, and deposition are changes that release energy. The temperature of a system remains constant during a phase change.

- Evaporation happens at the surface of a liquid. Boiling occurs when a liquid's vapor pressure is equal to atmospheric pressure.

- Phase diagrams show how different temperatures and pressures affect the phase of a substance.

## Key Equations and Relationships

Kinetic energy: $KE = 1/2mv^2$
(p. 386)

Dalton's law of partial pressures: $P_{total} = P_1 + P_2 + P_3 + ...P_n$
(p. 391)

Graham's law of effusion: $\dfrac{Rate_A}{Rate_B} = \sqrt{\dfrac{molar\ mass_B}{molar\ mass_A}}$
(p. 387)

## Vocabulary

- amorphous solid (p. 403)
- atmosphere (p. 390)
- barometer (p. 389)
- boiling point (p. 406)
- condensation (p. 407)
- crystalline solid (p. 400)
- Dalton's law of partial pressures (p. 391)
- deposition (p. 408)
- diffusion (p. 387)
- dipole–dipole forces (p. 394)

- dispersion forces (p. 393)
- elastic collision (p. 386)
- evaporation (p. 405)
- freezing point (p. 408)
- Graham's law of effusion (p. 387)
- hydrogen bond (p. 395)
- kinetic-molecular theory (p. 385)
- melting point (p. 405)
- pascal (p. 390)
- phase diagram (p. 408)

- pressure (p. 388)
- sublimation (p. 407)
- surface tension (p. 398)
- surfactant (p. 398)
- temperature (p. 386)
- triple point (p. 409)
- unit cell (p. 400)
- vaporization (p. 405)
- vapor pressure (p. 406)
- viscosity (p. 397)

## Using the Vocabulary

To reinforce chapter vocabulary, have students write a sentence using each term. **L2** **ELL**

## Review Strategies

- Have students make a chart comparing the characteristics of solids, liquids, and gases. **L2**

- Have students learn these pairs of terms that have opposite meanings: *vaporization/condensation, sublimation/deposition,* and *melting/freezing.* **L2**

- Problems from Appendix A or the **Supplemental Problems** booklet can be used for review. **L2**

## VOCABULARY PuzzleMaker CHEMISTRY

For additional help with vocabulary, have students access the Vocabulary PuzzleMaker online.

chemistrymc.com/
vocabulary_puzzlemaker

Chemistry Online

## EXAMVIEW® PRO

### Use ExamView® Pro Testmaker CD-ROM to:

- Create **multiple versions** of tests.
- Create **modified** tests with one mouse click for struggling students.
- **Edit** existing questions and add your own questions.
- **Build** tests based on national curriculum standards.

## Concept Mapping

**29.** 1. solid; 2. molecular solid; 3. covalent network solid; 4. ionic solid; 5. metallic solid

## Mastering Concepts

**30.** one in which no kinetic energy is lost

**31.** It is directly proportional to their temperature.

**32.** Because of the space between gas particles, gases are easily compressed when pushed into a smaller volume. When the pressure is removed, their random motion enables gases to expand.

**33.** Both involve the movement of particles. Diffusion is the movement of one substance through another; effusion is when a substance under pressure escapes through a tiny opening. Effusion and diffusion rates are inversely related to molecular mass of a gas.

**34.** Density decreases because the gas particles occupy more volume per unit mass.

**35.** because of the variation in air pressure with elevation; At high elevations, reduced air pressure results in a lower boiling point for water and cooking time is longer.

**36.** A temporary dipole forms when electrons move toward the near side of one nonpolar particle and the far side of another to avoid repelling each other. A permanent dipole is found only in polar molecules in which the difference in electronegativity between two atoms causes the electron orbits to shift toward the most electronegative atom.

**37.** Dispersion forces are between temporary

---

## Chemistry Online

Go to the Chemistry Web site at chemistrymc.com *for additional Chapter 13 Assessment.*

## Concept Mapping

**29.** Complete the concept map using the following terms: covalent network solid, molecular solid, metallic solid, ionic solid, solid.

Substances with definite shape and volume

1.

Molecules held by intermolecular forces

2.

Atoms held by a sea of electrons

5.

Atoms held by covalent bonds

3.

Atoms held by ionic bonds

4.

## Mastering Concepts

**30.** What is an elastic collision? (13.1)

**31.** How does the kinetic energy of particles vary as a function of temperature? (13.1)

**32.** Use the kinetic-molecular theory to explain the compression and expansion of gases. (13.1)

**33.** Compare diffusion and effusion. Explain the relationship between the rates of these processes and the molar mass of a gas. (13.1)

**34.** What happens to the density of gas particles in a cylinder as the piston is raised? (13.1)

**35.** Explain why the baking instructions on a box of cake mix are different for high and low elevations. Would you expect to have a longer or shorter cooking time at a high elevation? (13.1)

**36.** Explain the difference between a temporary dipole and a permanent dipole. (13.2)

**37.** Why are dispersion forces weaker than dipole–dipole forces? (13.2)

**38.** Explain why hydrogen bonds are stronger than most dipole–dipole forces. (13.2)

---

**39.** Use relative differences in electronegativity to label the ends of the polar molecules listed as partially positive or partially negative. (13.2)
   a. HF
   b. NO
   c. HBr
   d. CO

**40.** Draw the structure of the dipole–dipole interaction between two molecules of carbon monoxide. (13.2)

**41.** Decide which of the substances listed can form hydrogen bonds. (13.2)
   a. $H_2O$
   b. HF
   c. NaF
   d. NO
   e. $H_2O_2$
   f. $NH_3$
   g. $H_2$
   h. $CH_4$

**42.** Hypothesize why long, nonpolar molecules would interact more strongly with one another than spherical nonpolar molecules of similar composition. (13.2)

**43.** What is surface tension and what conditions must exist for it to occur? (13.3)

**44.** Explain why the surface of water in a graduated cylinder is curved. (13.3)

**45.** Which liquid is more viscous at room temperature, water or molasses? Explain. (13.3)

**46.** Use these drawings to compare the cubic, monoclinic, and hexagonal crystal systems. (13.3)

a = b = c
α = β = γ = 90°
**Cubic**

a ≠ b ≠ c
α = γ = 90° ≠ β
**Monoclinic**

a = b ≠ c
α = β = 90°, γ = 120°
**Hexagonal**

**47.** What is the difference between a network solid and an ionic solid? (13.3)

**48.** Explain why most metals bend when struck but most ionic solids shatter. (13.3)

**49.** What is an amorphous solid? Under what conditions is such a solid likely to form? (13.3)

**50.** List the types of crystalline solids that are usually good conductors of heat and electricity. (13.3)

**51.** How does the strength of a liquid's intermolecular forces affect its viscosity? (13.3)

chemistrymc.com/chapter_test

---

dipoles; dipole-dipole forces between permanent dipoles.

**38.** A hydrogen bond involves a large difference in electronegativity between the hydrogen atom and the atom it is attached to (O, N, or F), making the bond extremely polar.

---

## Resource Manager

Chapter Assessment, pp. 73–78 **L2**
Supplemental Problems, Ch. 13
ExamView® Pro CD-ROM
MindJogger Videoquizzes DVD/VHS
Solutions Manual, Ch. 13
Chemistry Interactive CD-ROM, Ch. 13 quiz

**52.** Explain why water has a higher surface tension than benzene, whose molecules are nonpolar. (13.3)

**53.** How does sublimation differ from deposition? (13.4)

**54.** Compare boiling and evaporation. (13.4)

**55.** Define melting point. (13.4)

**56.** Explain the relationships among vapor pressure, atmospheric pressure, and boiling point. (13.4)

**57.** Explain why dew forms on cool mornings. (13.4)

**58.** Label the solid, liquid, and gas phases, triple point, and critical point on the phase diagram shown. (13.4)

**Phase Diagram**

**59.** Why does it take more energy to boil 10 g of liquid water than to melt an equivalent mass of ice? (13.4)

**60.** Why does a pile of snow slowly shrink even on days when the temperature never rises above the freezing point of water? (13.4)

**61.** Examine the phase diagram for carbon dioxide in **Figure 13-28.** Notice that at 1 atm pressure, the solid sublimes to a gas. What happens to the solid at much higher pressures? (13.4)

## Mastering Problems

### Graham's Law of Effusion (13.1)

**62.** What is the molar mass of a gas that takes three times longer to effuse than helium?

**63.** What is the ratio of effusion rates of krypton and neon at the same temperature and pressure?

**64.** Calculate the molar mass of a gas that diffuses three times faster than oxygen under similar conditions.

### Dalton's Law of Partial Pressures (13.1)

**65.** What is the partial pressure of water vapor in an air sample when the total pressure is 1.00 atm, the partial pressure of nitrogen is 0.79 atm, the partial pressure of oxygen is 0.20 atm, and the partial pressure of all other gases in air is 0.0044 atm?

**66.** What is the total gas pressure in a sealed flask that contains oxygen at a partial pressure of 0.41 atm and water vapor at a partial pressure of 0.58 atm?

**67.** Find the partial pressure of oxygen in a sealed vessel that has a total pressure of 2.6 atm and also contains carbon dioxide at 1.3 atm and helium at 0.22 atm.

### Converting Pressure Units (13.1)

**68.** What is the total pressure in atmospheres of a mixture of three gases with partial pressures of 12.0 kPa, 35.6 kPa, and 22.2 kPa?

**69.** The pressure atop the world's highest mountain, Mount Everest, is usually about 33.6 kPa. Convert the pressure to atmospheres. How does the pressure compare with the pressure at sea level?

**70.** The atmospheric pressure in Denver, Colorado, is usually about 84.0 kPa. What is this pressure in atm and torr units?

**71.** At an ocean depth of 250 feet, the pressure is about 8.4 atm. Convert the pressure to mm Hg and kPa units.

## Mixed Review

*Sharpen your problem solving skills by answering the following.*

**72.** Use the kinetic-molecular theory to explain why both gases and liquids are fluids.

**73.** Use intermolecular forces to explain why oxygen is a gas at room temperature and water is a liquid.

**74.** Use the kinetic-molecular theory to explain why gases are easier to compress than liquids or solids.

**75.** The density of mercury at 25°C and a pressure of 760 mm Hg is 13.5 g/mL; water at the same temperature and pressure has a density of 1.00 g/mL. Explain this difference in terms of intermolecular forces and the kinetic-molecular theory.

**76.** Two flasks of equal size are connected by a narrow tube that is closed in the middle with a stopcock. One flask has no gas particles; the other flask contains 0.1 mol of hydrogen gas at a pressure of 2.0 atm.
 **a.** Describe what happens to the gas molecules after the stopcock is opened.
 **b.** What will happen to the gas pressure after the stopcock is opened?

**39. a.** $\overset{+}{H}—\overset{-}{F}$  **c.** $\overset{+}{H}—\overset{-}{Br}$
 **b.** $\overset{+}{N}—\overset{-}{O}$  **d.** $\overset{+}{C}—\overset{-}{O}$

**40.** See Figure 13-8. The drawing should show two CO molecules, with the C partially positive and the O partially negative. The C of each molecule should be bonded to the O of the other.

**41.** a, b, e, f

**42.** Because long molecules have greater surface areas, more intermolecular forces can exist.

**43.** the energy needed to increase the surface area of a liquid by a given amount; strong interparticle forces exist between the liquid particles

**44.** Adhesion between water and glass is greater than cohesion between water molecules.

**45.** Molasses; stronger intermolecular forces keep molasses from flowing.

**46.** See Figure 13-19.

**47.** Network solid is held together by covalent bonds; ionic solid by ionic bonds.

**48.** The sea of electrons that holds metal ions together can easily move to accommodate outside forces; in ionic solids a strong force can separate the solid along the plane bonding groups of atoms together.

**49.** one that lacks a regularly repeating structure; it can form when a liquid solidifies too quickly for crystal formation to occur.

**50.** metallic solids; ionic solids when molten or dissolved in an aqueous solution

**51.** Stronger intermolecular forces result in higher viscosity because the forces hold the particles together too tightly for them to flow easily.

**52.** Surface tension increases with strength of interparticle forces. Water molecules are held together by strong hydrogen bonds, resulting in higher surface tension; the weaker dispersion forces between benzene molecules result in lower surface tension.

**53.** Sublimation occurs when a solid is converted to a gas; deposition occurs when a gas is converted to a solid.

**54.** Evaporation: conversion of a liquid to a gas at the liquid's surface; boiling: when vapor pressure is equal to external atmospheric pressure; it occurs at and below the surface where bubbles form.

**55.** the temperature at which the crystal lattice of a solid disintegrates and it becomes a liquid

**National Science Content Standards**

**Pages 414—415**
UCP.1, UCP.2, UCP.3; B.2, B.4, B.5, B.6

**56.** Boiling point is the temperature at which vapor pressure exerted by liquid molecules escaping from the surface of a sample equals the atmospheric pressure on the surface of the liquid.

**57.** When water vapor in the air comes in contact with a cool object such as a windshield, it condenses on the object.

**58.** See Figure 13-28.

**59.** Melting does not require as much energy because the particles in a solid do not have to move far apart or gain much movement to form a liquid. Gas particles are much further apart and move much more rapidly than liquid particles.

**60.** Some of the snow sublimes.

**61.** At pressures much higher than 1 atm, solid $CO_2$ melts to form a liquid rather than sublimating to a gas.

## Mastering Problems

Complete solutions to Chapter Assessment problems can be found in the **Solutions Manual.**

### Graham's Law of Effusion (13.1)
**Level 1**
**62.** 36.0 g/mol

**Level 2**
**63.** $R_{krypton}/R_{neon}$ = 0.4931
**64.** 3.56 g/mol

### Dalton's Law of Partial Pressures (13.1)
**Level 1**
**65.** 0.01 atm
**66.** 0.99 atm
**67.** 1.1 atm

### Converting Pressure Units (13.1)
**Level 1**
**68.** 0.689 atm
**69.** 0.332 atm; It is about one-third of the 1-atm pressure at sea level.

**416**

## Thinking Critically

**77. Interpreting Graphs** Examine the graph below, which plots vapor pressure versus temperature for water and ethyl alcohol.
  **a.** What is the boiling point of water at 1 atm?
  **b.** What is the boiling point of ethyl alcohol at 1 atm?
  **c.** Describe the relationship between temperature and vapor pressure for water and alcohol.
  **d.** Estimate the temperature at which water will boil when the atmospheric pressure is 0.80 atm.

**78. Applying Concepts** A solid being heated stays at a constant temperature until it is completely melted. What happens to the heat energy put into the system during that time?

**79. Comparing and Contrasting** An air compressor uses energy to squeeze air particles together. When the air is released, it expands, allowing the energy to be used for purposes such as gently cleaning surfaces without using a more abrasive liquid or solid. Hydraulic systems essentially work the same way, but involve compression of liquid water rather than air. What do you think are some advantages and disadvantages of these two types of technology?

**80. Hypothesizing** What type of crystalline solid do you predict would best suit the following needs?
  **a.** a material that can be melted and reformed at a low temperature
  **b.** a material that can be drawn into long, thin wires
  **c.** a material that conducts electricity when molten
  **d.** an extremely hard material that is non-conductive

**81. Communicating** Which process is responsible for your being able to smell perfume from an open bottle that is located across the room from you, effusion or diffusion? Explain.

**82. Inferring** A laboratory demonstration involves pouring bromine vapors, which are a deep red color, into a flask of air and then tightly sealing the top of the flask. The bromine is observed to first sink to the bottom of the beaker. After several hours have passed, the red color is distributed equally throughout the flask.
  **a.** Is bromine gas more or less dense than air?
  **b.** Would liquid bromine diffuse more or less quickly than gaseous bromine after you pour it into another liquid?

## Writing in Chemistry

**83.** Propane gas is a commonly used heating fuel for gas grills and homes. It is not packaged as a gas, however. It is liquefied and referred to as liquid propane or "LP gas." What advantages are there to storing and transporting propane as a liquid rather than a gas? Are there any disadvantages?

**84.** Find out what your birthstone is if you don't already know, and write a brief report about the chemistry of that gem. Find out its chemical composition, which category its unit cell is in, how hard and durable it is, and its approximate cost at the present time.

**85.** What would happen to life on Earth if ice were denser than liquid water? Would life be possible? Write an essay on this topic.

## Cumulative Review

*Refresh your understanding of the previous chapters by answering the following.*

**86.** Identify the following as an element, compound, homogeneous mixture, or heterogeneous mixture. (Chapter 3)
  **a.** air        **e.** ammonia
  **b.** blood      **f.** mustard
  **c.** antimony   **g.** water
  **d.** brass      **h.** tin

**87.** Use the periodic table to separate these ten elements into five pairs of elements having similar properties. (Chapter 7)

  S, Ne, Li, O, Mg, Ag, Sr, Kr, Cu, Na

**88.** You are given two clear, colorless aqueous solutions. You are told that one solution contains an ionic compound and one contains a covalent compound. How could you determine which is an ionic solution and which is a covalent solution? (Chapter 9)

**89.** Determine the number of atoms in 56.1 g Al. (Chapter 11)

**Level 2**
**70.** 84.0 kPa = 0.829 atm and 6.30 × $10^2$ torr
**71.** 8.4 atm = 8.5 × $10^2$ kPa and 6.4 × $10^3$ mm Hg

## Mixed Review

**72.** Because their particles are held together by fewer attractive forces than in solids, the particles can flow.

**73.** Oxygen molecules are nonpolar and held together by dispersion forces, making them easy to separate. Water molecules are held together by stronger hydrogen bonds, making them harder to separate. As a result, water has a higher boiling point.

**74.** Because particles in gases are farther apart than particles in liquids or solids, there is more space for the particles to be compressed.

*Use these questions and the test-taking tip to prepare for your standardized test.*

**1.** Water has an extremely high boiling point compared to other compounds of similar molar mass because of

a. hydrogen bonding.
b. adhesive forces.
c. covalent bonding.
d. dispersion forces.

**2.** What is the ratio of effusion rates for nitric oxide (NO) and nitrogen tetroxide ($N_2O_4$)?

a. 0.326          c. 1.751
b. 0.571          d. 3.066

**3.** Which of the following is NOT an assumption of the kinetic-molecular theory?

a. Collisions between gas particles are elastic.
b. All the gas particles in a sample have the same velocity.
c. A gas particle is not significantly attracted or repelled by other gas particles.
d. All gases at a given temperature have the same average kinetic energy.

**4.** Which of the following statements does NOT describe what happens as a liquid boils?

a. The temperature of the system rises.
b. Energy is absorbed by the system.
c. The vapor pressure of the liquid is equal to atmospheric pressure.
d. The liquid is entering the gas phase.

**5.** The solid phase of a compound has a definite shape and volume because its particles

a. are not in constant motion.
b. are always packed more tightly than particles in the compound's liquid phase.
c. can only vibrate around fixed points.
d. are held together by strong intramolecular forces.

**6.** A sealed flask contains neon, argon, and krypton gas. If the total pressure in the flask is 3.782 atm, the partial pressure of Ne is 0.435 atm, and the partial pressure of Kr is 1.613 atm, what is the partial pressure of Ar?

a. 2.048 torr          c. 1556 torr
b. 1.734 torr          d. 1318 torr

**7.** Which of the following does not affect the viscosity of a liquid?

a. intermolecular attractive forces
b. size and shape of molecules
c. temperature of the liquid
d. capillary action

**Interpreting Graphs** Use the graph to answer the following questions.

**Phase Diagram of Carbon**

**8.** Diamond is most likely to form at

a. temperatures > 5000 K and pressures < 100 GPa.
b. temperatures > 6000 K and pressures > 25 GPa.
c. temperatures < 4000 K and pressures > 25 GPa.
d. temperatures < 4500 K and pressures < 10 GPa.

**9.** Find the point on the graph at which carbon exists in three phases: solid graphite, solid diamond, and liquid carbon. What are the temperature and pressure at that point?

a. 4700 K and 15 GPa
b. 3000 K and 10 GPa
c. 5100 K and 50 GPa
d. 14500 K and 5 GPa

**10.** In what form or forms does carbon exist at 6000 K and 75 GPa?

a. diamond only
b. liquid carbon only
c. diamond and liquid carbon
d. liquid carbon and graphite

### TEST-TAKING TIP

**Focus** When you take a test, pay no attention to anyone other than the proctor. If students near you are talking, move to a different seat. If someone other than the proctor talks to you during a test, don't respond. Not only is talking a distraction, but the proctor may think that you are cheating. Don't take the chance. Focus on the test, and nothing else.

**75.** Metallic bonds holding mercury atoms together are stronger than hydrogen bonds holding water molecules together, so the mercury atoms are more closely packed, resulting in greater mass per unit volume.

**76.** **a.** Gas will diffuse from the flask on the right into the evacuated flask until an equal number of molecules is in each flask.
**b.** It will decrease in the flask that contained $H_2$ and increase in the empty flask until pressure is equalized at 1 atm.

## Thinking Critically

**77.** **a.** 100°C; **b.** 78.5°C; **c.** the higher the temperature, the higher the vapor pressure; **d.** 94°C

**78.** The energy is used to break the intermolecular forces holding the particles of the solid together.

**79.** Air compressors produce rapid outputs of a large amount of energy because gases can be greatly compressed. Hydraulic systems involve liquid water, which cannot be compressed as much, and are more useful for a slow, steady output of energy.

**80.** **a.** molecular solid; **b.** metallic solid; **c.** ionic solid; **d.** covalent network solid

**81.** diffusion; gas particles in the perfume are mixing with air particles

**82.** **a.** more dense; **b.** less quickly

## Cumulative Review

**86.** **a.** homogeneous mixture;
**b.** heterogeneous mixture;
**c.** element; **d.** homogeneous mixture;
**e.** compound; **f.** heterogeneous mixture; **g.** compound; **h.** element

**87.** S and O, Ne and Kr, Li and Na, Mg and Sr, Ag and Cu

**88.** They could be tested for conductivity. The ionic compound in solution should conduct electricity; the covalent compound should not.

**89.** $1.25 \times 10^{24}$ atoms Al

## Standardized Test Practice

| 1. | a | 5. | c | 8. | c |
| 2. | c | 6. | b | 9. | a |
| 3. | b | 7. | d | 10. | b |
| 4. | a | | | | |

**National Science Content Standards**

**Pages 416–417**
UCP.1, UCP.2, UCP.3; B.2, B.4, B.6

# Resource Manager

| Section | Objectives | Activities/Features |
|---|---|---|
| **Section 14.1**<br>**The Gas Laws**<br>1½ sessions<br>⬛ 1 block | 1. **State** Boyle's law, Charles's law, and Gay-Lussac's law.<br>2. **Apply** the three gas laws to problems involving the pressure, temperature, and volume of a gas. | **Discovery Lab:** More Than Just Hot Air, p. 419<br>**Careers Using Chemistry:** Meteorologist, p. 421<br>**History Connection,** p. 423<br>**Problem-Solving Lab:** How is turbocharging in a car engine maximized? p. 424 |
| **Section 14.2**<br>**The Combined Gas Law and Avogadro's Principle**<br>1½ sessions<br>⬛ 1 block | 3. **State** the relationship among temperature, volume, and pressure as the combined gas law.<br>4. **Apply** the combined gas law to problems involving the pressure, temperature, and volume of a gas.<br>5. **Relate** numbers of particles and volumes by using Avogadro's principle. | |
| **Section 14.3**<br>**The Ideal Gas Law**<br>1 session<br>⬛ ½ block | 6. **Relate** the amount of gas present to its pressure, temperature, and volume by using the ideal gas law.<br>7. **Compare** the properties of real and ideal gases. | **MiniLab:** The Density of Carbon Dioxide, p. 439<br>**ChemLab:** Using the Ideal Gas Law, pp. 444–445 |
| **Section 14.4**<br>**Gas Stoichiometry**<br>3 sessions<br>⬛ 2 blocks | 8. **Determine** volume ratios for gaseous reactants and products by using coefficients from a chemical equation.<br>9. **Calculate** amounts of gaseous reactants and products in a chemical reaction using the gas laws. | **Chemistry and Technology:** Giving a Lift to Cargo, p. 446 |

Glencoe Exclusive!

**TeacherWorks™**

All-In-One Planner and Resource Center

| National Science Content Standards | State/Local Standards | Reproducible Masters | Transparencies |
|---|---|---|---|
| UCP.2, UCP.3; A.1; B.2, B.4, B.6; E.2; G.1, G.3 | | **Study Guide for Content Mastery,** p. 79 **L2**<br>**Laboratory Manual,** pp. 105–112 **L2**<br>**CBL Laboratory Manual,** pp. 13–20 **L2**<br>**Challenge Problems,** p. 14 **L3**<br>**Small-Scale Laboratory Manual,** pp. 37–40 **L2** | **Section Focus Transparency 51 L1 ELL**<br>**Teaching Transparencies 42, 43 L2 ELL**<br>**Math Skills Transparency 19 L2 ELL** |
| UCP.2, UCP.3; B.2, B.4, B.6 | | **Study Guide for Content Mastery,** pp. 80–81 **L2** | **Section Focus Transparency 52 L1 ELL**<br>**Math Skills Transparency 20 L2 ELL** |
| UCP.2, UCP.3; A.1; B.2, B.4, B.6; G.2 | | **Study Guide for Content Mastery,** pp. 82–83 **L2**<br>**ChemLab and MiniLab Worksheets,** pp. 53–56 **L2** | **Section Focus Transparency 53 L1 ELL**<br>**Math Skills Transparency 21 L2 ELL** |
| UCP.2, UCP.3; A.1; B.2, B.3, B.4, B.6; E.1, E.2; F.6 | | **Study Guide for Content Mastery,** p. 84 **L2** | **Section Focus Transparency 54 L1 ELL**<br>**Teaching Transparency 44 L2 ELL** |

**Key to National Science Content Standards:** UCP = Unifying Concepts and Processes, A = Science as Inquiry, B = Physical Science, C = Life Science, D = Earth and Space Sciences, E = Science and Technology, F = Science in Personal and Social Perspectives, G = History and Nature of Science

Refer to pages 4T–5T of the Teacher Guide for an explanation of the National Science Content Standards correlations.

# Resource Manager

## Materials List

**ChemLab** (pages 444–445)
aerosol can of duster, 600-mL beaker with graduations, 4-L bucket, thermometer, barometer, plastic microtip pipette, latex tubing, glass tubing, scissors, electrical or duct tape, balance

**Discovery Lab** (page 419)
5-gallon bucket, round balloon, ice, string

**MiniLab** (page 439)
masking tape, aluminum foil, metric ruler, 1-L beaker, candle, matches, thermometer, barometer, baking soda ($NaHCO_3$), vinegar (5% $CH_3COOH$)

**Demonstration** (pages 420–421)
2-L colorless plastic soft drink bottle with cap, dropper, food coloring, water

## Preparation of Solutions

For a review of solution preparation, see page 46T of the Teacher Guide.

Quantities are for a class of 30 students.

**MiniLab** (page 438)
**5% $CH_3COOH$** Add 50 mL glacial (17 M) acetic acid to 950 mL water while stirring.
CAUTION: Do NOT add the water to the acid.

## Assessment Resources

**Chapter Assessment,** pp. 79–84
**MindJogger Videoquizzes DVD/VHS**
**Alternate Assessment in the Science Classroom**
**ExamView® Pro CD-ROM**
**Solutions Manual,** Chapter 14
**Supplemental Problems,** Chapter 14
**Performance Assessment in the Science Classroom**
**Chemistry Interactive CD-ROM,** Chapter 14 quiz

## Additional Resources

**Spanish Resources** ELL
**Guided Reading Audio Program,** Chapter 14 ELL
**Cooperative Learning in the Science Classroom**
**Lab and Safety Skills in the Science Classroom**
**Lesson Plans**
**Block Scheduling Lesson Plans**
Chemistrymc.com

## Glencoe Technology

The following multimedia for this chapter are available from Glencoe.

**VIDEOTAPE/DVD**
MindJogger Videoquizzes,
Chapter 14

**CD-ROM**
**Chemistry: Matter and Change**
*Demonstrating Boyle's Law,* Demonstration
*Charles's Law,* Video
*Gas Volume and the Mole,* Demonstration
*Ideal Gas Laws,* Experiment
*Using the Gas Laws,* Exploration

**CD-ROM**
**ExamView® Pro**
**Testmaker**

**CD-ROM**
**Interactive Chalkboard**

**CD-ROM**
**TeacherWorks™**

## Multiple Learning Styles

Look for the following icons for strategies that emphasize different learning modalities.

***Kinesthetic***
Building a Model, pp. 426, 435; Quick Demo,
p. 435

***Visual-Spatial***
Differentiated Instruction, pp. 431, 440; Visual
Learning, p. 436

***Interpersonal***
Enrichment, p. 422; Differentiated Instruction,
p. 430; Reteach, p. 432

***Intrapersonal***
Portfolio, pp. 422, 436; Chemistry Journal, p. 430;
Differentiated Instruction, p. 435

***Linguistic***
Chemistry Journal, pp. 423, 432, 435; Check for
Understanding, p. 427; Using Science Terms, p. 430;
Portfolio, p. 441

***Logical-Mathematical***
Differentiated Instruction, p. 424

## Key to Teaching Strategies

**L1** Level 1 activities should be appropriate for students with
learning difficulties.

**L2** Level 2 activities should be within the ability range of
all students.

**L3** Level 3 activities are designed for above-average students.

**ELL** ELL activities should be within the ability range of
English Language Learners.

**COOP LEARN** Cooperative Learning activities are designed
for small group work.

 These strategies represent student products that can be
placed into a best-work portfolio.

 These strategies are useful in a block scheduling format.

## Assessment Planner

**Portfolio Assessment**
Portfolio, TWE, pp. 422, 436,
 441
ChemLab, TWE, p. 445
Assessment, TWE, p. 439

**Performance Assessment**
Assessment, TWE, pp. 420,
 441
MiniLab, SE, p. 439
ChemLab, SE, pp. 444–445
MiniLab, TWE, p. 438
Discovery Lab, SE, p. 419

**Knowledge Assessment**
Demonstration, TWE, p. 421
Assessment, TWE, pp. 423,
 427, 435, 443
Section Assessment, SE,
 pp. 427, 433, 439, 443
Chapter Assessment, SE,
 pp. 448–451

**Skill Assessment**
Problem-Solving Lab, TWE,
 p. 424
Assessment, TWE, pp. 430,
 433, 437

## Tying to Previous Knowledge

Have students review the following concepts before studying this chapter.

Chapter 2: density

Chapter 10: balancing equations

Chapter 12: stoichiometry of reactions

Chapter 13: kinetic-molecular theory, gas pressure

## Using the Photo

Ask students why the firefighters in the photo need to carry air tanks. A fire raises the temperature of all the gases in the immediate vicinity and reduces the amount of oxygen available for breathing.

## Chapter Themes

The following themes from the National Science Education Standards are covered in this chapter. Refer to page 4T of the Teacher Guide for an explanation of the correlations.

Systems, order, and organization (UCP.1)

Evidence, models, and explanation (UCP.2)

Change, constancy, and measurement (UCP.3)

**PowerPoint® Presentations**
This CD-ROM is an editable Microsoft® PowerPoint® presentation that includes:
- Section presentations
- Section checks
- Image bank
- Links to Chemistry Online
- All transparencies
- Animations
- Audio

# Gases

### What You'll Learn

▶ You will use gas laws to calculate how pressure, temperature, volume, and number of moles of a gas will change when one or more of these variables is altered.

▶ You will compare properties of real and ideal gases.

▶ You will apply the gas laws and Avogadro's principle to chemical equations.

### Why It's Important

From barbecuing on a gas grill to taking a ride in a hot-air balloon, many activities involve gases. It is important to be able to predict what effect changes in pressure, temperature, volume, or amount, will have on the properties and behavior of a gas.

Visit the Glencoe Chemistry Web site at **chemistrymc.com** to find links about gases.

Firefighters breathe air that has been compressed into tanks that they can wear on their backs.

**418     Chapter 14**

## DISCOVERY LAB

### Purpose
Students will demonstrate the relationship between temperature and volume of a gas in a closed system.

### Safety and Disposal
Remind students to wear goggles and not to shoot the balloons around the room.

### Teaching Strategies
- You may have one ice bath for the entire class.
- Remind students to measure around the widest part of the balloon. Students may use a marker to note where the initial circumference was measured.

### More Than Just Hot Air

How does a temperature change affect the air in a balloon?

**Safety Precautions**

 Always wear goggles to protect eyes from broken balloons.

**Procedure**

1. Inflate a round balloon and tie it closed.
2. Fill the bucket about half full of cold water and add ice.
3. Use a string to measure the circumference of the balloon.
4. Stir the water in the bucket to equalize the temperature. Submerge the balloon in the ice water for 15 minutes.
5. Remove the balloon from the water. Measure the circumference.

**Analysis**

What happens to the size of the balloon when its temperature is lowered? What might you expect to happen to its size if the temperature is raised?

**Materials**
5-gal bucket
round balloon
ice
string

## 1 Focus

### Focus Transparency

Before presenting the lesson, display **Section Focus Transparency 51** on the overhead projector. Have students answer the accompanying questions using **Section Focus Transparency Master 51.** L1 ELL

Section Focus Transparency 51 **Hot Gases**

Use with Chapter 14, Section 14.1

❶ What is coming out of the tail of this rocket?
❷ How do the rocket fuels enable this rocket to blast off?

Chemistry: Matter and Change

Section Focus Transparencies

---

## Section 14.1

# The Gas Laws

### Objectives

- **State** Boyle's law, Charles's law, and Gay-Lussac's law.
- **Apply** the three gas laws to problems involving the pressure, temperature, and volume of a gas.

### Vocabulary

Boyle's law
Charles's law
Gay-Lussac's law

The manufacturer of the air tank in the photo on the opposite page had to understand the nature of the gases the tank contains. Understanding gases did not happen accidentally. The work of many scientists over many years has contributed to our present knowledge of the nature of gases. The work of three scientists in particular was valuable enough that laws describing gas behavior were named in their honor. In this section, you'll study three important gas laws: Boyle's law, Charles's law, and Gay-Lussac's law. Each of these laws relates two of the variables that determine the behavior of gases—pressure, temperature, volume, and amount of gas present.

### Kinetic Theory

You can't understand gases without understanding the movement of gas particles. Remember from your study of the kinetic-molecular theory in Chapter 13 that gas particles behave differently than those of liquids and solids. The kinetic theory provides a model that is used to explain the properties of solids, liquids, and gases in terms of particles that are always in motion and the forces that exist between them. The kinetic theory assumes the following concepts about gases are true.

- *Gas particles do not attract or repel each other.* Gases are free to move within their containers without interference from other particles.
- *Gas particles are much smaller than the distances between them.* You saw in the **DISCOVERY LAB** that gas has volume. However, the kinetic theory assumes that gas particles themselves have virtually no volume.

14.1 The Gas Laws **419**

## 2 Teach
### Concept Development

Remind students that most of gas is empty space. The volume of a sample of gas is much greater than the total volume of its particles.

### Resource Manager

**Study Guide for Content Mastery,** p. 79 L2
**Solving Problems: A Chemistry Handbook,** Section 14.1 L2
**Section Focus Transparency 51 and Master** L1 ELL
**Lab Manual,** pp. 105–108 L2

---

- The circumference of the cold balloon must be measured as soon as it is taken from the bucket. Do not allow the balloon to warm up.

**Expected Results**
The circumference of the cold balloon will be smaller than the balloon at room temperature.

**Analysis**
The size of the balloon is smaller when it is cold than when it is room temperature. Because a decrease in temperature caused a decrease in circumference, the volume of the balloon is directly related to temperature. You would expect the volume to increase if the temperature is increased.

**National Science Content Standards**

Pages 418–419
UCP.2, UCP.3; A.1; B.2

### Figure 14-1

The kinetic theory relates pressure and the number of collisions per unit time for a gas.
**ⓐ** When the bicycle pump is pulled out as far as it will go, the pressure of the air inside the pump equals that of the atmosphere.
**ⓑ** If the piston is pushed down half the length of the pump, the air particles are squeezed into a space half the original size. Pressure doubles because the frequency of collisions between the gas particles and the inner wall of the pump has doubled.

**Try at Home** | **LAB**

See page 958 in Appendix E for
**Under Pressure**

Almost all the volume of a gas is empty space. Gases can be compressed by moving gas particles closer together because of this low density of particles.

• *Gas particles are in constant, random motion.* Gas particles spread out and mix with each other because of this motion. The particles move in straight lines until they collide with each other or with the walls of their container.

• *No kinetic energy is lost when gas particles collide with each other or with the walls of their container.* Such collisions are completely elastic. As long as the temperature stays the same, the total kinetic energy of the system remains constant.

• *All gases have the same average kinetic energy at a given temperature.* As temperature increases, the total energy of the gas system increases. As temperature decreases, the total energy of the gas system decreases.

**The nature of gases** Actual gases don't obey all the assumptions made by the kinetic theory. But for many gases, their behavior approximates the behavior assumed by the kinetic theory. You will learn more about real gases and how they vary from these assumptions in Section 14.3.

Notice how all the assumptions of the kinetic theory are based on the four factors previously mentioned—the number of gas particles present and the temperature, the pressure, and the volume of the gas sample. These four variables all work together to determine the behavior of gases. When one variable changes, it affects the other three. Look at the following example of how a change in one variable affects at least one other variable.

What happens to the gas in a plastic balloon if you squeeze it, decreasing its volume? Because the balloon is closed, the amount of gas is constant. Assume the temperature is held constant. Decreasing the volume pushes the gas particles closer together. Recall from the kinetic-molecular theory that as gas particles are pushed closer together, the number of collisions between particles themselves and between the particles and the walls of their container increases. As the number of collisions per unit time increases, so does the observed pressure. Therefore, as the volume of a gas decreases, its pressure increases. Similarly, if the balloon is no longer squeezed, the volume increases and the pressure decreases. You can see another example of this principle in **Figure 14-1**. The interdependence of the variables of volume, pressure, temperature, and amount of gas is the basis for the following gas laws.

**420** Chapter 14 Gases

---

## Boyle's Law

Robert Boyle (1627–1691), an Irish chemist, did experiments like the one shown in **Figure 14-2** to study the relationship between the pressure and the volume of a gas. By taking careful quantitative measurements, he showed that if the temperature is constant, doubling the pressure of a fixed amount of gas decreases its volume by one-half. On the other hand, reducing the pressure by half results in a doubling of the volume. A relationship in which one variable increases as the other variable decreases is referred to as an inversely proportional relationship. For help with understanding inverse relationships, see the **Math Handbook** page 905.

**Boyle's law** states that the volume of a given amount of gas held at a constant temperature varies inversely with the pressure. Look at the graph in **Figure 14-2** in which pressure versus volume is plotted for a gas. The plot of an inversely proportional relationship results in a downward curve. If you choose any two points along the curve and multiply the pressure times the volume at each point, how do your two answers compare? Note that the product of the pressure and the volume for each of points 1, 2, and 3 is 10 atm·L. From the graph, what would the volume be if the pressure is 2.5 atm? What would be the pressure if the volume is 2 L?

The products of pressure times volume for any two sets of conditions are equal, so Boyle's law can be expressed mathematically as follows.

$$P_1V_1 = P_2V_2$$

$P_1$ and $V_1$ represent a set of initial conditions for a gas and $P_2$ and $V_2$ represent a set of new conditions. If you know any three of these four values for a gas at constant temperature, you can solve for the fourth by rearranging the equation. For example, if $P_1$, $V_1$, and $P_2$ are known, dividing both sides of the equation by $P_2$ will isolate the unknown variable $V_2$.

Use the equation for Boyle's law to calculate the volume that corresponds to a pressure of 2.5 atm, assuming that the amount of gas and temperature are constant. Then find what pressure corresponds to a volume of 2.0 L. Use 2.0 atm for $P_1$ and 5 L for $V_1$. How do these answers compare to those you found using the graph in **Figure 14-2**?

### Figure 14-2

The gas particles in this cylinder take up a given volume at a given pressure. As pressure increases, volume decreases. The graph shows that pressure and volume have an inverse relationship, which means that as pressure increases, volume decreases. This relationship is illustrated by a downward curve in the line from condition 1 to condition 2 to condition 3.

Condition 1:
$k = P_1V_1$
$k = (1\ \text{atm})(10\ \text{L})$
$k = 10\ \text{atm·L}$

Condition 2:
$k = P_2V_2$
$k = (2\ \text{atm})(5\ \text{L})$
$k = 10\ \text{atm·L}$

Condition 3:
$k = P_3V_3$
$k = (4\ \text{atm})(2.5\ \text{L})$
$k = 10\ \text{atm·L}$

**Pressure–Volume Changes**

1 (1.0 atm, 10 L)
2 (2.0 atm, 5 L)
3 (4.0 atm, 2.5 L)

14.1 The Gas Laws **421**

dropper into the 2-L bottle and screw the cap on tight. Squeeze the sides of the bottle firmly until the dropper descends.

### Results
When the bottle is squeezed, the air in the dropper is compressed and displaced by water. The level of the colored water in the dropper rises, the dropper has more mass, and it descends.

### Analysis
Ask these questions.
**1.** As the pressure is increased on the air in the dropper, does the volume increase or decrease? The volume decreases.
**2.** Is the relationship between gas volume and pressure an inverse or direct relationship? inverse

## Content Background

**Discovery of Helium** The element helium was observed in the sun using spectroscopy in 1868, 23 years before it was found in uranium ore on Earth. Its discovery in the sun is why its name comes from the Greek word for the sun, *helios*. In 1900, helium was still quite rare, but the 1905 analysis of gas from a natural gas well in Kansas that wouldn't burn showed that it contained about 2% helium, and the rest was mostly nitrogen. Today, most of the world's helium comes from wells in the Texas panhandle near Amarillo.

## Enrichment

 *Interpersonal* Ask groups of three or four students to research the properties of an element that is a gas at normal atmospheric pressure and room temperature. Have student groups prepare classroom presentations about their findings. **L2**
**COOP LEARN**

## Practice PROBLEMS

Have students refer to Appendix D for complete solutions to Practice Problems.

**1.** 158 mL
**2.** 0.494 atm
**3.** 0.110 L
**4.** 78.4 atm
**5.** 0.657 L

## GLENCOE TECHNOLOGY

**CD-ROM**
**Chemistry: Matter and Change**
Video: *Charles's Law*
Animation: *Pumping Gas*

---

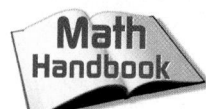
**Math Handbook**

Review using inverse relationships in the **Math Handbook** on page 905 of your textbook.

**Practice!** For more practice with Boyle's law problems, go to **Supplemental Practice Problems** in Appendix A.

---

**EXAMPLE** PROBLEM 14-1

### Boyle's Law

A sample of helium gas in a balloon is compressed from 4.0 L to 2.5 L at a constant temperature. If the pressure of the gas in the 4.0-L volume is 210 kPa, what will the pressure be at 2.5 L?

**1.** **Analyze the Problem**

You are given the initial and final volumes and the initial pressure of a sample of helium. Boyle's law states that as volume decreases, pressure increases if temperature remains constant. Because the volume in this problem is decreasing, the pressure will increase. So the initial pressure should be multiplied by a volume ratio greater than one.

| **Known** | **Unknown** |
|---|---|
| $V_1 = 4.0$ L | $P_2 = ?$ kPa |
| $V_2 = 2.5$ L | |
| $P_1 = 210$ kPa | |

**2.** **Solve for the Unknown**

Divide both sides of the equation for Boyle's law by $V_2$ to solve for $P_2$.

$$P_1V_1 = P_2V_2$$

$$P_2 = P_1\left(\frac{V_1}{V_2}\right)$$

Substitute the known values into the rearranged equation.

$$P_2 = 210 \text{ kPa}\left(\frac{4.0 \text{ L}}{2.5 \text{ L}}\right)$$

Multiply and divide numbers and units to solve for $P_2$.

$$P_2 = 210 \text{ kPa}\left(\frac{4.0 \text{ L}}{2.5 \text{ L}}\right) = 340 \text{ kPa}$$

**3.** **Evaluate the Answer**

When the volume is decreased by almost half, the pressure is expected to almost double. The calculated value of 340 kPa is reasonable. The unit in the answer is kPa, a pressure unit.

---

**PRACTICE** PROBLEMS

Assume that the temperature and the amount of gas present are constant in the following problems.

**1.** The volume of a gas at 99.0 kPa is 300.0 mL. If the pressure is increased to 188 kPa, what will be the new volume?

**2.** The pressure of a sample of helium in a 1.00-L container is 0.988 atm. What is the new pressure if the sample is placed in a 2.00-L container?

**3.** Air trapped in a cylinder fitted with a piston occupies 145.7 mL at 1.08 atm pressure. What is the new volume of air when the pressure is increased to 1.43 atm by applying force to the piston?

**4.** If it takes 0.0500 L of oxygen gas kept in a cylinder under pressure to fill an evacuated 4.00-L reaction vessel in which the pressure is 0.980 atm, what was the initial pressure of the gas in the cylinder?

**5.** A sample of neon gas occupies 0.220 L at 0.860 atm. What will be its volume at 29.2 kPa pressure?

---

**Portfolio** ✓

### Pressure Relationships

*Intrapersonal* Have students write the following questions in their portfolios and answer them as soon as they have learned enough from their study of Section 14.1.

**1.** Why do breads and muffins rise when baked? The yeast or baking powder in the dough produces carbon dioxide gas, which expands as it is heated.

**2.** Why do helium balloons rise? Helium is less dense than air.

**3.** Why do tennis balls come in pressurized cans? Tennis balls contain trapped gases that are inserted under pressure, which gives them greater bounce. Once the balls are out of the pressurized cans, the gas gradually escapes. **L2** **P** 🖼

## Charles's Law

Have you ever noticed that on a cold day, a tire on a car might look as if it's low on air? However, after driving the car for awhile, the tire warms up and looks less flat. What made the difference in the tire? When canning vegetables at home, why are they often packed hot in the jars and then sealed? These questions can be answered by applying another of the gas laws, Charles's law. Another example of how gases are affected by temperature is shown in the **problem-solving LAB.** If kelvin temperature is doubled, so is the volume.

**How are gas temperature and volume related?** The French physicist Jacques Charles (1746–1823) studied the relationship between volume and temperature. In his experiments, he observed that as temperature increases, so does the volume of a gas sample when the pressure is held constant. This property can be explained by the kinetic-molecular theory; at a higher temperature, gas particles move faster, striking each other and the walls of their container more frequently and with greater force. For the pressure to stay constant, volume must increase so that the particles have farther to travel before striking the walls. Having to travel farther decreases the frequency with which the particles strike the walls of the container.

Look at **Figure 14-3**, which includes a graph of volume versus temperature for a gas sample kept at a constant pressure. Note that the resulting plot is a straight line. Note also that you can predict the temperature at which the volume will reach a value of zero liters by extrapolating the line at temperatures below which values were actually measured. The temperature that corresponds to zero volume is $-273.15°C$, or 0 on the kelvin (K) temperature scale. This temperature is referred to as absolute zero, and it is the lowest possible theoretical temperature. Theoretically, at absolute zero, the kinetic energy of particles is zero, so all motion of gas particles at that point ceases.

Examine the relationship between temperature and volume shown by the cylinders in **Figure 14-3**. In the graph, note that 0°C does not correspond to zero volume. Although the relationship is linear, it is not direct. For example, you can see from the graph that increasing the temperature from 25°C to 50°C does not double the volume of the gas. If the kelvin temperature is plotted instead, a direct proportion is the result. See **Figure 14-4** on the next page.

## History
### CONNECTION

Jacques Charles's interest in the behavior of gases was sparked by his involvement in ballooning. He built the first balloon that was filled with hydrogen instead of hot air. Charles's investigations attracted the attention of King Louis XVI, who allowed Charles to establish a laboratory in the Louvre, which is a museum in Paris.

**Figure 14-3**

The gas particles in this cylinder take up a given volume at a given temperature. When the cylinder is heated, the kinetic energy of the particles increases. The volume of the gas increases, pushing the piston outward. Thus the distance that the piston moves is a measure of the increase in volume of the gas as it is heated. Note that the graph of volume versus temperature extrapolates to $-273.15°C$, or 0 K.

### In-Text Questions

**Page 423** What made the difference in the tire? The friction between the tire and the road causes the tire to heat up while the car is moving. As the air in the tire heats up, it expands because volume is directly proportional to temperature for a gas.

When canning vegetables at home, why are they often packed hot in the jars and then sealed? The air above the hot vegetables expands, and some of it leaves the jar. A partial vacuum forms as the jars cool, preventing growth of certain microorganisms.

### Content Background

**Industrial Production of Gases** Five of the top ten industrial chemicals in the United States are gases—oxygen, nitrogen, ethylene, propylene, and chlorine. The greatest use for oxygen is in the steel industry, where it reacts with impurities in crude iron. Nitrogen is extracted from air and then reacted with hydrogen to form ammonia, which is used in fertilizers and explosives. In a process called cracking, ethylene and propylene are produced by heating petroleum to approximately 500°C in the presence of a catalyst. Both gases are used in making plastics, particularly polyethylene and polypropylene. Chlorine is formed by the electrolysis of table salt (NaCl).

### ✓ Assessment

**Knowledge** Ask each student to write a question about either Boyle's law or Charles's law. Have students exchange questions and quiz each other. **L2**

Celsius Temperature vs. Volume

(75°C, 703 mL)
(0°C, 551 mL)
(−75° C, 400 mL)

Volume (mL): 800, 600, 400, 200, 0
Temperature (°C): −300 −250 −200 −150 −100 −50 0 50

## CHEMISTRY JOURNAL

### Practical Gases

 *Linguistic* Ask students to keep a daily listing in their journals for two weeks in which they record how they used a gas as part of their everyday activities. Ask them to note for each instance whether or not the gas was compressed. **L2**

**National Science Content Standards**

Pages 422–423
UCP.2, UCP.3; B.2, B.4, B.6; G.1, G.3

## Purpose

Students will study how the gas laws are applied to the workings of an engine.

## Process Skills

Recognizing cause and effect, analyzing and interpreting illustrations, applying concepts

## Teaching Strategies

- Explain to students how an automobile engine works. Essentially, air (oxygen supply) and vaporized gasoline are injected into the combustion chamber. These gases are compressed by the piston and then ignited by the spark plug, followed by the elimination of exhaust as the piston is retracted.
- Ask students how the four variables related to gases are applied in a gasoline engine. Intake: amount of gas and volume increase. Compression: temperature and pressure increase, volume decreases. Combustion: temperature and pressure increase. Exhaust: amount of gas, temperature, and pressure decrease; volume increases.

## Thinking Critically

1. The kinetic energy of gases as they leave the engine; energy is transferred from the gas to the turbine.
2. More gasoline must be supplied.
3. Pressure; if temperature and volume are constant, increased pressure means more gas is present.
4. When a gas is compressed, its temperature and pressure increase. Cooling decreases the pressure, allowing more air to be forced into the combustion chamber.

## Assessment

**Skill** Have students make a cycle concept map illustrating how the properties of a gas are affected in one turbocharging cycle. Encourage them to research internal combustion engines. **L2**

**424**

**Kelvin Temperature vs. Volume**

(348 K, 703 mL)
(273 K, 551 mL)
(198 K, 400 mL)

**Figure 14-4**

This graph illustrates the directly proportional relationship between the volume and the kelvin temperature of a gas held at constant pressure. When the kelvin temperature doubles, the volume doubles.

**Charles's law** states that the volume of a given mass of gas is directly proportional to its kelvin temperature at constant pressure. For help with understanding direct relationships, see the **Math Handbook,** page 905. So for any two sets of conditions, Charles's law can be expressed as

$$\frac{V_1}{T_1} = \frac{V_2}{T_2}$$

Here $V_1$ and $T_1$ represent any initial pair of conditions, while $V_2$ and $T_2$ are any new set of conditions. As with Boyle's law, if you know any three of the four values, you can calculate the fourth using the equation.

The temperature must be expressed in kelvin units when using the equation for Charles's law. The kelvin scale starts at absolute zero, which corresponds to −273.15°C and is 0 K. Because a Celsius degree and a kelvin unit are the same size, it is easy to convert a temperature in Celsius to kelvin units. Round 273.15 to 273, and add it to the Celsius temperature.

$$T_K = 273 + T_C$$

## How is turbocharging in a car engine maximized?

**Interpreting Scientific Illustrations** After gasoline and air are burned in the combustion chamber of an automobile, the resulting hot gases are exhausted out the tailpipe. The horsepower of an automobile engine can be significantly improved if the energy of these exhaust gases is used to operate a compressor that forces additional air into the combustion chamber. Outside air is then blown over this compressed air to cool it before it enters the engine. Increasing the power of an engine in this manner is known as turbocharging.

### Analysis

Examine the illustration of an engine fitted with a turbocharging system. The paths of the exhaust gas, entering combustion air, and the cooling air are shown.

### Thinking Critically

1. What property of the exhaust gas is being used to turn the turbine that runs the compressor? Explain.
2. If more power is to be gained from this design, what must also accompany the extra supply of oxygen to the combustion chamber?
3. What property does the compressor alter so that more air can be injected into the combustion chamber? Explain.
4. Why does the air in the compressor get hot, and why does cooling help to improve the power of the engine?

Turbocharger
Oil inlet
Turbine wheel
Compressor wheel
Charge-air cooler
Engine cylinder
Exhaust gas
Air inlet
Oil outlet

---

## DIFFERENTIATED INSTRUCTION

### Learning Disabled

*Logical-Mathematical* Some students will find solving gas law problems easier if they first predict what their answer will be, then solve the problem, and finally compare the calculated answer with the prediction. For example, if students are using Boyle's law to solve for the final pressure of a gas after being given the initial pressure and the initial and final volumes, ask them whether they think the pressure will increase or decrease *before* they try to do the calculation. If their prediction does not match their answer, they know to double check their calculation. **L1**

## EXAMPLE PROBLEM 14-2

### Charles's Law

A gas sample at 40.0°C occupies a volume of 2.32 L. If the temperature is raised to 75.0°C, what will the volume be, assuming the pressure remains constant?

**1.** **Analyze the Problem**

You are given the initial temperature and volume of a sample of gas. Charles's law states that as the temperature increases, so does the volume, assuming the pressure is constant. Because the temperature in this problem is increasing, the volume will increase. So the initial volume should be multiplied by a volume ratio greater than one.

| Known | Unknown |
|---|---|
| $T_1 = 40.0°C$ | $V_2 = ?$ L |
| $V_1 = 2.32$ L | |
| $T_2 = 75.0°C$ | |

**2.** **Solve for the Unknown**

Add 273 to the Celsius temperature to obtain the kelvin temperature.

$$T_K = 273 + T_C$$

Substitute the known Celsius temperatures for $T_1$ and $T_2$ to convert them to kelvin units.

$$T_1 = 273 + 40.0°C = 313 \text{ K}$$

$$T_2 = 273 + 75.0°C = 348 \text{ K}$$

Multiply both sides of the equation for Charles's law by $T_2$ to solve for $V_2$.

$$\frac{V_1}{T_1} = \frac{V_2}{T_2}$$

$$V_2 = V_1\left(\frac{T_2}{T_1}\right)$$

Substitute the known values into the rearranged equation.

$$V_2 = 2.32 \text{ L} \left(\frac{348 \text{ K}}{313 \text{ K}}\right)$$

Multiply and divide numbers and units to solve for $V_2$.

$$V_2 = 2.32 \text{ L} \left(\frac{348 \text{ K}}{313 \text{ K}}\right) = 2.58 \text{ L}$$

**3.** **Evaluate the Answer**

The increase in kelvin units is relatively small. Therefore, you expect the volume to show a small increase, which agrees with the answer. The unit of the answer is liters, a volume unit.

## PRACTICE PROBLEMS

Assume that the pressure and the amount of gas present remain constant in the following problems.

**6.** A gas at 89°C occupies a volume of 0.67 L. At what Celsius temperature will the volume increase to 1.12 L?

**7.** The Celsius temperature of a 3.00-L sample of gas is lowered from 80.0°C to 30.0°C. What will be the resulting volume of this gas?

**8.** What is the volume of the air in a balloon that occupies 0.620 L at 25°C if the temperature is lowered to 0.00°C?

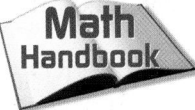

**Math Handbook**

Review using direct relationships in the **Math Handbook** on page 905 of this textbook.

**Practice!** For more practice with Charles's law problems, go to **Supplemental Practice Problems** in Appendix A.

---

**Practice** PROBLEMS

Have students refer to Appendix D for complete solutions to Practice Problems.

**6.** 330°C

**7.** 2.58 L

**8.** 0.57 L

### Quick Demo

Place three balloons, each containing an equal volume of air, in locations with three different temperatures, such as in a freezer or bucket of ice, on the lab bench, and on top of hot water in a bucket. Ask the students to predict what they will observe after the balloons remain at those temperatures for ten minutes. The hot balloon will expand, the balloon at room temperature will remain the same volume, and the cold balloon will shrink. Ask students to explain what happened. The volume of a gas is directly proportional to temperature, so heating causes expansion, and cooling causes compression.
**L2** **ELL**

### Reinforcement

Ask students why baking directions on cake mix boxes are different for high altitudes. The atmospheric pressure at high altitudes is less than it is at low altitudes, which makes the water in foods boil at a lower temperature. As a result, cooking time must be increased.

---

### Resource Manager

**Teaching Transparency 43 and Master**
**L2** **ELL**
**Laboratory Manual,** pp. 109–112 **L2**

**National Science Content Standards**

**Pages 424–425**
UCP.2, UCP.3; B.2, B.6; E.2

## Building a Model

 **_Kinesthetic_** Have students work in groups to build a model of Boyle's law, Charles's law, or Gay-Lussac's law. Ask each group to demonstrate their model to the class. **L2 COOP LEARN**

---

## Identifying Misconceptions

Students may think that something, such as air, fills in the space between gas particles.

**Uncover the Misconception**
Have students draw a picture of the inside of a balloon, representing all gas particles as circles. Be sure drawings show how many molecules are present and how far apart they are.

**Demonstrate the Concept**
Have each student use a finger to plug the end of a syringe. Have them use the plungers to try to compress the gas in the syringes. Have them repeat this procedure with water in the syringes. Students will observe the compressibility of air versus that of water. Discuss with students that empty space must exist between gas molecules or the gas could not be compressed.

**Assess New Knowledge**
**_Visual-Spatial_** Ask students to draw an illustration of what happens to the air molecules in the balloon as you squeeze it. The drawings should show molecules in the balloon starting out far apart but moving closer and closer together as the balloon is compressed. **L2**

---

**Kelvin Temperature vs. Pressure**

**Figure 14-5**

Compare the relationship between pressure and kelvin temperature as shown in this graph and the relationship between volume and kelvin temperature as shown in **Figure 14-4**. Notice that both show direct relationships.

This cooker is sealed so that the volume is constant. Pressure increases in the cooker as temperature increases.

---

## Gay-Lussac's Law

Boyle's law relates pressure and volume of a gas, and Charles's law states the relationship between a gas's temperature and volume. What is the relationship between pressure and temperature? Pressure is a result of collisions between gas particles and the walls of their container. An increase in temperature increases collision frequency and energy, so raising the temperature should also raise the pressure if the volume is not changed.

**How are temperature and pressure of a gas related?** Joseph Gay-Lussac explored the relationship between temperature and pressure of a contained gas at a fixed volume. He found that a direct proportion exists between the kelvin temperature and the pressure, such as that illustrated in **Figure 14-5**. **Gay-Lussac's law** states that the pressure of a given mass of gas varies directly with the kelvin temperature when the volume remains constant. It can be expressed mathematically.

$$\frac{P_1}{T_1} = \frac{P_2}{T_2}$$

As with Boyle's and Charles's laws, if you know any three of the four variables, you can calculate the fourth using this equation. Remember that temperature must be in kelvin units whenever it is used in a gas law equation.

---

### EXAMPLE PROBLEM 14-3

**Gay-Lussac's Law**
The pressure of a gas in a tank is 3.20 atm at 22.0°C. If the temperature rises to 60.0°C, what will be the gas pressure in the tank?

**1. Analyze the Problem**

You are given the initial pressure and the initial and final temperatures of a gas sample. Gay-Lussac's law states that if the temperature of a gas increases, so does its pressure. Because the temperature in this problem is increasing, the pressure will increase. So the initial pressure should be multiplied by a volume ratio greater than one.

**Known**                                  **Unknown**

$P_1$ = 3.20 atm                            $P_2$ = ? atm
$T_1$ = 22.0°C
$T_2$ = 60.0°C

**2. Solve for the Unknown**

Add 273 to the Celsius temperature to obtain the kelvin temperature.

$T_K = 273 + T_C$

Substitute the known Celsius temperatures for $T_1$ and $T_2$ to convert them to kelvin units.

$T_1 = 273 + 22.0°C = 295$ K

$T_2 = 273 + 60.0°C = 333$ K

Multiply both sides of the equation for Gay-Lussac's law by $T_2$ to solve for $P_2$.

$$\frac{P_1}{T_1} = \frac{P_2}{T_2}$$

$$P_2 = P_1\left(\frac{T_2}{T_1}\right)$$

---

**Resource Manager**

CBL Lab Manual, pp. 17–20 **L2**

Substitute the known values into the rearranged equation.

$$P_2 = 3.20 \text{ atm} \left(\frac{333 \text{ K}}{295 \text{ K}}\right)$$

Multiply and divide numbers and units to solve for $P_2$.

$$P_2 = 3.20 \text{ atm} \left(\frac{333 \text{ K}}{295 \text{ K}}\right) = 3.61 \text{ atm}$$

**3.** **Evaluate the Answer**

Gay-Lussac's law states that pressure and temperature are directly proportional. Kelvin temperature shows a small increase, so you expect the pressure to show a small increase, which agrees with the answer calculated. The unit is atm, a pressure unit.

## PRACTICE PROBLEMS

**Assume that the volume and the amount of gas are constant in the following problems.**

**9.** A gas in a sealed container has a pressure of 125 kPa at a temperature of 30.0°C. If the pressure in the container is increased to 201 kPa, what is the new temperature?

**10.** The pressure in an automobile tire is 1.88 atm at 25.0°C. What will be the pressure if the temperature warms up to 37.0°C?

**11.** Helium gas in a 2.00-L cylinder is under 1.12 atm pressure. At 36.5°C, that same gas sample has a pressure of 2.56 atm. What was the initial temperature of the gas in the cylinder?

**12.** If a gas sample has a pressure of 30.7 kPa at 0.00°C, by how much does the temperature have to decrease to lower the pressure to 28.4 kPa?

**13.** A rigid plastic container holds 1.00 L methane gas at 660 torr pressure when the temperature is 22.0°C. How much more pressure will the gas exert if the temperature is raised to 44.6°C?

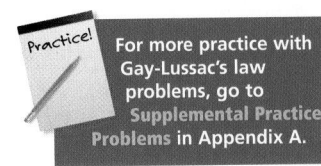

**Practice!** For more practice with Gay-Lussac's law problems, go to **Supplemental Practice Problems** in Appendix A.

You have seen how the variables of temperature, pressure, and volume affect a gas sample. The gas laws covered in this section each relate two of these three variables if the other variable remains constant. What happens when all three of these variables change? You'll investigate this situation in the next section.

## Section 14.1 Assessment

**14.** State Boyle's, Charles's, and Gay-Lussac's laws using sentences, then equations.

**15.** A weather balloon of known initial volume is released. The air pressures at its initial and final altitudes are known. Why can't you find its new volume by using these known values and Boyle's law?

**16.** Which of the three variables that apply to equal amounts of gases are directly proportional? Which are inversely proportional?

**17.** **Thinking Critically** Explain why gases such as the oxygen found in tanks used at hospitals are compressed. Why must care be taken to prevent compressed gases from reaching a high temperature?

**18.** **Concept Mapping** Draw a concept map that shows the relationship among pressure, volume, and temperature variables for gases and Boyle's, Charles's, and Gay-Lussac's laws.

chemistrymc.com/self_check_quiz

14.1 The Gas Laws **427**

# 1 Focus

Before presenting the lesson, display **Section Focus Transparency 52** on the overhead projector. Have students answer the accompanying questions using **Section Focus Transparency Master 52.** L1 ELL

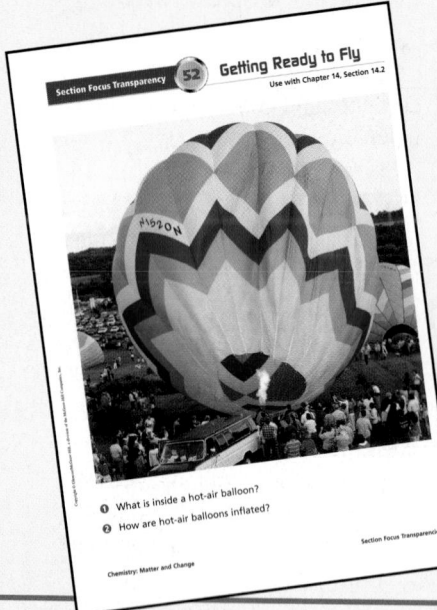

# 2 Teach
## Applying Chemistry

 Pump a bicycle tire up to the recommended pressure, and ask students to predict what will happen to the pressure as the temperature changes. Let them propose a method for testing their predictions and then run the tests. Students can test their predictions by placing the tire at locations with different temperatures and then measuring the pressure using the gauge. The pressure will increase as the temperature increases and decrease as the temperature decreases. L2 ELL

---

# The Combined Gas Law and Avogadro's Principle

### Objectives

- **State** the relationship among temperature, volume, and pressure as the combined gas law.

- **Apply** the combined gas law to problems involving the pressure, temperature, and volume of a gas.

- **Relate** numbers of particles and volumes by using Avogadro's principle.

### Vocabulary

combined gas law
Avogadro's principle
molar volume

In the previous section, you applied the three gas laws covered so far to problems in which either pressure, volume, or temperature of a gas sample was held constant as the other two changed. As illustrated in **Figure 14-6**, in a number of applications involving gases, all three variables change. If all three variables change, can you calculate what their new values will be? In this section you will see that Boyle's, Charles's, and Gay-Lussac's laws can be combined into a single equation that can be used for just that purpose.

## The Combined Gas Law

Boyle's, Charles's, and Gay-Lussac's laws can be combined into a single law. This **combined gas law** states the relationship among pressure, volume, and temperature of a fixed amount of gas. All three variables have the same relationship to each other as they have in the other gas laws: Pressure is inversely proportional to volume and directly proportional to temperature, and volume is directly proportional to temperature. The equation for the combined gas law can be expressed as

$$\frac{P_1V_1}{T_1} = \frac{P_2V_2}{T_2}$$

As with the other gas laws, this equation allows you to use known values for the variables under one set of conditions to find a value for a missing variable under another set of conditions. Whenever five of the six values from the two sets of conditions are known, the sixth can be calculated using this expression for the combined gas law.

This combined law lets you work out problems involving more variables that change, and it also provides a way for you to remember the other three laws without memorizing each equation. If you can write out the combined gas law equation, equations for the other laws can be derived from it by remembering which variable is held constant in each case.

For example, if temperature remains constant as pressure and volume vary, then $T_1 = T_2$. After simplifying the combined gas law under these conditions, you are left with

$$P_1V_1 = P_2V_2$$

You should recognize this equation as the equation for Boyle's law. See whether you can derive Charles's and Gay-Lussac's laws from the combined gas law.

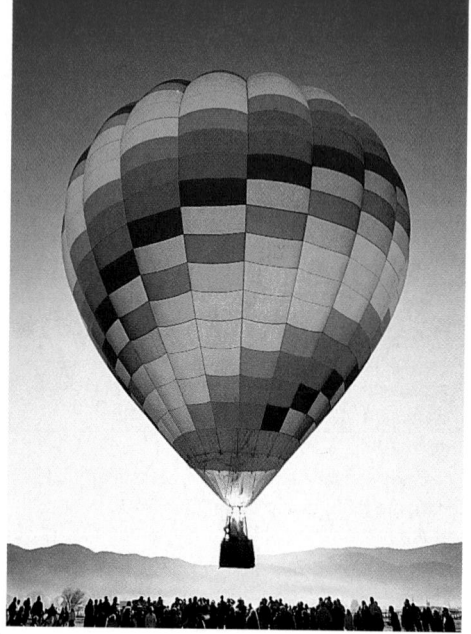

**Figure 14-6**

Constructing an apparatus that uses gases must take into account the changes in gas variables such as pressure, volume, and temperature that can take place. As a hot-air balloonist ascends in the sky, pressure and temperature both decrease, and the volume of the gas in the balloon is affected by those changes.

---

## High-Altitude Adaptations

Many populations of people throughout the world are native to high altitudes, including Andean peoples in South America and Himalayan Tibetans in Asia. The air at 17 500 feet at the Mount Everest Base Camp in the Himalayas has a partial pressure of oxygen about one-half that found at sea level. Many mountain climbers need to bring oxygen tanks along to reach the summit, while the Tibetan Sherpa guides often do without additional oxygen. For the past 100 years, scientists have been studying the genetic and phenotypical adaptations of these populations to determine how they differ from people adapted to living at lower altitudes. Many native highlanders have high hemoglobin

## EXAMPLE PROBLEM 14-4

### The Combined Gas Law

A gas at 110 kPa and 30.0°C fills a flexible container with an initial volume of 2.00 L. If the temperature is raised to 80.0°C and the pressure increased to 440 kPa, what is the new volume?

#### 1. Analyze the Problem

You are given the initial pressure, temperature, and volume of a gas sample as well as the final pressure and temperature. The volume of a gas is directly proportional to kelvin temperature, so volume increases as temperature increases. Therefore the volume should be multiplied by a temperature factor greater than one. Volume is inversely proportional to pressure, so as pressure increases, volume decreases. Therefore the volume should be multiplied by a pressure factor that is less than one.

**Known**

$P_1 = 110$ kPa
$T_1 = 30.0°C$
$V_1 = 2.00$ L
$T_2 = 80.0°C$
$P_2 = 440$ kPa

**Unknown**

$V_2 = ?$ L

#### 2. Solve for the Unknown

Add 273 to the Celsius temperature to obtain the kelvin temperature.

$$T_K = 273 + T_C$$

Substitute the known Celsius temperatures for $T_1$ and $T_2$ to convert them to kelvin units.

$$T_1 = 273 + 30.0°C = 303 \text{ K}$$

$$T_2 = 273 + 80.0°C = 353 \text{ K}$$

Multiply both sides of the equation for the combined gas law by $T_2$ and divide it by $P_2$ to solve for $V_2$.

$$\frac{P_1 V_1}{T_1} = \frac{P_2 V_2}{T_2}$$

$$V_2 = V_1 \left(\frac{P_1}{P_2}\right)\left(\frac{T_2}{T_1}\right)$$

Substitute the known values into the rearranged equation.

$$V_2 = 2.00 \text{ L} \left(\frac{110 \text{ kPa}}{440 \text{ kPa}}\right)\left(\frac{353 \text{ K}}{303 \text{ K}}\right)$$

Multiply and divide numbers and units to solve for $V_2$.

$$V_2 = 2.00 \text{ L} \left(\frac{110 \text{ kPa}}{440 \text{ kPa}}\right)\left(\frac{353 \text{ K}}{303 \text{ K}}\right) = 0.58 \text{ L}$$

#### 3. Evaluate the Answer

Increasing the temperature causes the volume to increase, but increasing the pressure causes the volume to decrease. Because the pressure change is much greater than the temperature change, the volume undergoes a net decrease. The calculated answer agrees with this. The unit is L, a volume unit.

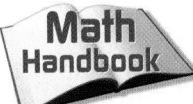

### Math Handbook

Review rearranging algebraic equations in the **Math Handbook** on page 897 of this textbook.

## Quick Demo

Record the mass of approximately 100 popcorn kernels. Pop the kernels in an air popper, and then record the mass of the resulting popcorn and unpopped kernels. Ask the students to explain how the difference in mass relates to the gas laws. The popcorn loses mass because water vapor escapes as the kernels break open during popping. Water trapped in the kernels vaporizes as it is heated; the pressure and volume of the trapped gases increase as more heat is added, resulting in the "popping" observed.

## Resource Manager

**Study Guide for Content Mastery**, pp. 80–81 L2
**Solving Problems: A Chemistry Handbook**, Section 14.2 L2
**Section Focus Transparency 52 and Master** L1 ELL
**Math Skills Transparency 20 and Master** L2 ELL

**National Science Content Standards**

Pages 428–429
UCP.2, UCP.3; B.2, B.4, B.6

concentrations in their blood, which enables them to carry what little oxygen there is more efficiently and gives them bright red lips and earlobes. Most people who adapt to a higher altitude before puberty have relatively large chest dimensions, which allow for large lung capacities. Alveoli in their lungs may increase in both number and size when compared with their sea-level counterparts. This knowledge may help in treating the chronic medical conditions often seen in these populations, such as pulmonary hypertension, swelling, and chronic mountain sickness. It may also help determine what medical intervention should be offered to mountain climbers, rescue workers, and other newcomers to high altitudes who may be experiencing difficulties.

## Using Science Terms

 *Linguistic* Have students write statements explaining the meanings of the terms *molar volume* and *combined gas law*.
**L1 ELL**

## ✓ Assessment

**Skill** Have students determine what additional information is needed to solve this problem. If a sample of gas at 12.0°C and 1.06 atm pressure is moved to a 2.30-L container at 24.9°C, what is the final pressure of the gas? To use the combined gas law to solve this problem, students need to know the initial volume of the gas. **L2**

## GLENCOE TECHNOLOGY

**CD-ROM**
**Chemistry: Matter and Change**
Demonstration: *Gas Volume and the Mole*

**430**

---

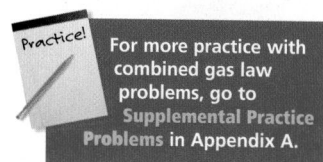

Practice! For more practice with combined gas law problems, go to **Supplemental Practice Problems** in Appendix A.

## PRACTICE PROBLEMS

**Assume that the amount of gas is constant in the following problems.**

**19.** A helium-filled balloon at sea level has a volume of 2.1 L at 0.998 atm and 36°C. If it is released and rises to an elevation at which the pressure is 0.900 atm and the temperature is 28°C, what will be the new volume of the balloon?

**20.** At 0.00°C and 1.00 atm pressure, a sample of gas occupies 30.0 mL. If the temperature is increased to 30.0°C and the entire gas sample is transferred to a 20.0-mL container, what will be the gas pressure inside the container?

**21.** A sample of air in a syringe exerts a pressure of 1.02 atm at a temperature of 22.0°C. The syringe is placed in a boiling water bath at 100.0°C. The pressure of the air is increased to 1.23 atm by pushing the plunger in, which reduces the volume to 0.224 mL. What was the original volume of the air?

**22.** An unopened, cold 2.00-L bottle of soda contains 46.0 mL of gas confined at a pressure of 1.30 atm at a temperature of 5.0°C. If the bottle is dropped into a lake and sinks to a depth at which the pressure is 1.52 atm and the temperature is 2.09°C, what will be the volume of gas in the bottle?

**23.** A sample of gas of unknown pressure occupies 0.766 L at a temperature of 298 K. The same sample of gas is then tested under known conditions and has a pressure of 32.6 kPa and occupies 0.644 L at 303 K. What was the original pressure of the gas?

## Avogadro's Principle

The particles making up different gases can vary greatly in size. However, according to the kinetic-molecular theory, the particles in a gas sample are usually far enough apart that size has a negligible influence on the volume occupied by a fixed number of particles, as shown in **Figure 14-7**. For example, 1000 relatively large krypton gas particles occupy the same volume as 1000 much smaller helium gas particles at the same temperature and pressure. It was Avogadro who first proposed this idea in 1811. Today, it is known as **Avogadro's principle**, which states that equal volumes of gases at the same temperature and pressure contain equal numbers of particles.

**Figure 14-7**

Compressed gas tanks of equal volume that are at the same pressure and temperature contain equal numbers of gas particles, regardless of which gas they contain. Refer to **Table C-1** in Appendix C for a key to atom color conventions.

---

Remember from Chapter 11 that the most convenient unit for counting numbers of atoms or molecules is the mole. One mole contains $6.02 \times 10^{23}$ particles. The **molar volume** for a gas is the volume that one mole occupies at 0.00°C and 1.00 atm pressure. These conditions of temperature and pressure are known as standard temperature and pressure (STP). Avogadro showed experimentally that one mole of any gas will occupy a volume of 22.4 L at STP. The fact that this value is the same for all gases greatly simplifies many gas law calculations. Because the volume of one mole of a gas at STP is 22.4 L, you can use the following conversion factor to find the number of moles, the mass, and even the number of particles in a gas sample.

$$\text{Conversion factor: } \frac{22.4 \text{ L}}{1 \text{ mol}}$$

Suppose you want to find the number of particles in a sample of gas that has a volume of 3.72 L at STP. First, find the number of moles of gas in the sample.

$$3.72 \text{ L} \times \frac{1 \text{ mol}}{22.4 \text{ L}} = 0.166 \text{ mol}$$

A mole of gas contains $6.02 \times 10^{23}$ gas particles. Use this definition to convert the number of moles to the number of particles.

$$0.166 \text{ mol} \times \frac{6.02 \times 10^{23} \text{ particles}}{1 \text{ mol}} = 9.99 \times 10^{22} \text{ particles}$$

The following example problems show you how to use molar volume in other ways.

## EXAMPLE PROBLEM 14-5

**Avogadro's Principle—Using Moles**

Calculate the volume that 0.881 mol of gas at standard temperature and pressure (STP) will occupy.

**1. Analyze the Problem**

You are given the temperature and pressure of a gas sample and the amount of gas the sample contains. According to Avogadro's principle, 1 mol of gas occupies 22.4 L at STP. The number of moles of gas should be multiplied by the conversion factor $\frac{22.4 \text{ L}}{1 \text{ mol}}$ to find the volume.

| Known | Unknown |
|---|---|
| $n = 0.881$ moles | $V = ? \text{ L}$ |
| $T = 0.00°C$ | |
| $P = 1.00$ atm | |

**2. Solve for the Unknown**

Because conditions are already at STP, multiply the known number of moles by the conversion factor that relates liters to moles to solve for the unknown volume.

$$V = 0.881 \text{ mol} \left( \frac{22.4 \text{ L}}{1 \text{ mol}} \right) = 19.7 \text{ L}$$

**3. Evaluate the Answer**

Because the amount of gas present is slightly less than one mole, you expect the answer to be slightly less than 22.4 L. The answer agrees with that prediction. The unit in the answer is L, a volume unit.

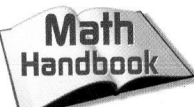

**Math Handbook**

Review unit conversion in the **Math Handbook** on page 901 of this textbook.

## DIFFERENTIATED INSTRUCTION

### Hearing Impaired

**Visual-Spatial** Students who learn visually will be able to understand the combined gas law better if they "discover" it themselves, step-by-step. Write the symbols $P_1$, $V_1$, $T_1$, $P_2$, $V_2$, $T_2$, and "=" on index cards and let students arrange the cards to form Boyle's, Charles's, and Gay-Lussac's laws. Then, ask them to arrange all of the cards into an equation that still keeps the relationships in all three gas laws correctly set up as direct or inverse proportions. **L2**

## Practice PROBLEMS

Have students refer to Appendix D for complete solutions to Practice Problems.

**24.** 54 L
**25.** 1.03 L
**26.** 22.8 L
**27.** 0.0893 mol
**28.** 0.0425 mol

# 3 Assess

## Check for Understanding

Put 1 L of several different gases such as hydrogen, methane, propane, and nitrogen in separate balloons and write the identifying elemental symbols on each. If the gases are unavailable, draw the balloons on the chalkboard. Ask students whether the volumes of the gases are equal. yes The number of molecules? yes The masses? no The number of moles? yes

## Reteach

 *Interpersonal* Have students work in groups to solve different combined gas law problems and ask each group to present their solution on the chalkboard to the rest of the class.
**L2 COOP LEARN**

**National Science Content Standards**

**Pages 432–433**
UCP.2, UCP.3; B.2, B.4, B.6

**432**

---

**Practice!** For more practice with Avogadro's principle problems that use moles, go to **Supplemental Practice Problems** in Appendix A.

## PRACTICE PROBLEMS

**24.** Determine the volume of a container that holds 2.4 mol of gas at STP.

**25.** What size container do you need to hold 0.0459 mol $N_2$ gas at STP?

**26.** What volume will 1.02 mol of carbon monoxide gas occupy at STP?

**27.** How many moles of nitrogen gas will be contained in a 2.00-L flask at STP?

**28.** If a balloon will rise off the ground when it contains 0.0226 mol of helium in a volume of 0.460 L, how many moles of helium are needed to make the balloon rise when its volume is 0.865 L? Assume that temperature and pressure stay constant.

---

Avogadro's principle is essential to manufacturers that use gases. This factory produces ammonia.

---

## EXAMPLE PROBLEM 14-6

### Avogadro's Principle—Using Mass

Calculate the volume that 2.0 kg of methane gas ($CH_4$) will occupy at STP.

**1. Analyze the Problem**

You are given the temperature and pressure of a gas sample and the mass of gas the sample contains. One mole of a gas occupies 22.4 L at STP. The number of moles can be calculated by dividing the mass of the sample, $m$, by its molar mass, M.

| Known | Unknown |
|---|---|
| $m = 2.00$ kg | $V = ?$ L |
| $T = 0.00°C$ | |
| $P = 1.00$ atm | |

**2. Solve for the Unknown**

Use atomic masses and numbers of each type of atom to determine molecular mass for methane. Express that molecular mass in grams per mole to determine molar mass.

$$M = \frac{1 \text{ C atom} \times 12.01 \text{ amu}}{\text{C atom}} + \frac{4 \text{ H atoms} \times 1.01 \text{ amu}}{\text{H atom}}$$

$$= 12.01 \text{ amu} + 4.04 \text{ amu} = 16.05 \text{ amu}; 16.05 \text{ g/mol}$$

Multiply the mass of methane by a conversion factor to change it from kg to g.

$$2.00 \text{ kg}\left(\frac{1000 \text{ g}}{1 \text{ kg}}\right) = 2.00 \times 10^3 \text{ g}$$

Divide the mass in grams of methane by its molar mass to find the number of moles.

$$\frac{m}{M} = \frac{2.00 \times 10^3 \text{ g}}{16.05 \text{ g/mol}} = 125 \text{ mol}$$

Because conditions are already at STP, multiply the known number of moles by the conversion factor of 22.4 L/1 mol to solve for the unknown volume.

$$V = 125 \text{ mol}\left(\frac{22.4 \text{ L}}{1 \text{ mol}}\right) = 2.80 \times 10^3 \text{ L}$$

**3. Evaluate the Answer**

The mass of methane present is much more than 1 mol, so you expect a large volume, which is in agreement with the answer. The units are L, a volume unit.

432    Chapter 14 Gases

---

## CHEMISTRY JOURNAL

### History of Chemistry

*Linguistic* Have students write a summary in their journals about their research on the work of the alchemists of the Middle Ages. Ask them to investigate how much the alchemists discovered about the nature of gases. Also ask them to include a drawing of an early experimental apparatus used by those early chemists. **L2**

## PRACTICE PROBLEMS

**29.** How many grams of carbon dioxide gas are in a 1.0-L balloon at STP?

**30.** What volume in milliliters will 0.00922 g $H_2$ gas occupy at STP?

**31.** What volume will 0.416 g of krypton gas occupy at STP?

**32.** A flexible plastic container contains 0.860 g of helium gas in a volume of 19.2 L. If 0.205 g of helium is removed without changing the pressure or temperature, what will be the new volume?

**33.** Calculate the volume that 4.5 kg of ethylene gas ($C_2H_4$) will occupy at STP.

 **Practice!** For more practice with Avogadro's principle problems that use mass, go to **Supplemental Practice Problems in Appendix A.**

Why aren't weather balloons completely inflated when they are released? How strong must the walls of a scuba tank be? Look at the example of the combined gas law and Avogadro's principle shown in **Figure 14-8.** Using the combined gas law and Avogadro's principle together will help you understand how gases are affected by pressure, temperature, and volume.

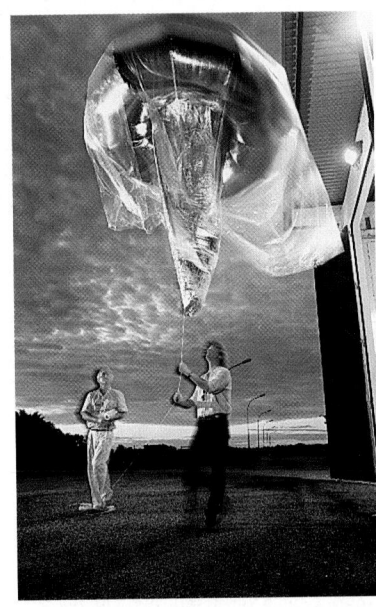

**Figure 14-8**
The combined gas law and Avogadro's principle have many practical applications that scientists and manufacturers must consider.

**34.** State the combined gas law using a sentence and then an equation.

**35.** What variable is assumed to be constant when using the combined gas law?

**36.** What three laws are used to make the combined gas law?

**37.** Explain why Avogadro's principle holds true for gases that have large particles and also for gases that have small particles.

**38.** Why must conditions of temperature and pressure be stated to do calculations involving molar volume?

**39.** **Thinking Critically** Think about what happens when a bottle of carbonated soft drink is shaken before being opened. Use the gas laws to explain whether the effect will be greater when the liquid is warm or cold.

**40.** **Applying Concepts** Imagine that you are going on an airplane trip in an unpressurized plane. You are bringing aboard an air-filled pillow that you have inflated fully. Predict what will happen when you try to use the pillow while the plane is at its cruising altitude.

 chemistrymc.com/self_check_quiz

14.2 The Combined Gas Law and Avogadro's Principle    **433**

## Extension

Ask a representative of a company that sells compressed gases to give a classroom presentation on their uses and how to handle compressed gas tanks.

### ✓ Assessment

**Skill** Write the combined gas law in words on the chalkboard, and ask students to use it to write the equation for the law. The pressure of a fixed amount of a gas is inversely proportional to its volume and directly proportional to its temperature, and its volume is directly proportional to its temperature. $P_1 \times V_1/T_1 = P_2 \times V_2/T_2$

### Practice PROBLEMS

Have students refer to Appendix D for complete solutions to Practice Problems.

**29.** 2.0 g

**30.** 102 mL

**31.** 0.111 L

**32.** 14.6 L

**33.** $3.6 \times 10^3$ L

## Section 14.2 Assessment

**34.** The pressure of a fixed amount of a gas is inversely proportional to volume and directly proportional to Kelvin temperature, and its volume is directly proportional to Kelvin temperature. $P_1 \times V_1/T_1 = P_2 \times V_2/T_2$

**35.** number of moles of gas

**36.** Boyle's law, Charles's law, and Gay-Lussac's law

**37.** The size of any gas particle is so small compared to the volume of the gas, it is assumed that no particle has any volume of its own.

**38.** Molar volume is accurate only for gases at STP. Any change from STP affects the volume.

**39.** Shaking soda bottles increases the motion of the gas particles inside,

raising the temperature and thus the pressure. Shaking a bottle before opening it results in the gas bubbles vigorously escaping. This effect will be greater when the soda is warm because the pressure is higher than when it is cold.

**40.** If the air in the plane is not fully pressurized, the air inside the pillow will expand as the plane ascends because volume is inversely proportional to pressure.

**433**

**Section** 14.3

# The Ideal Gas Law

## 1 Focus

### Focus Transparency

Before presenting the lesson, display **Section Focus Transparency 53** on the overhead projector. Have students answer the accompanying questions using **Section Focus Transparency Master 53.** L1 ELL

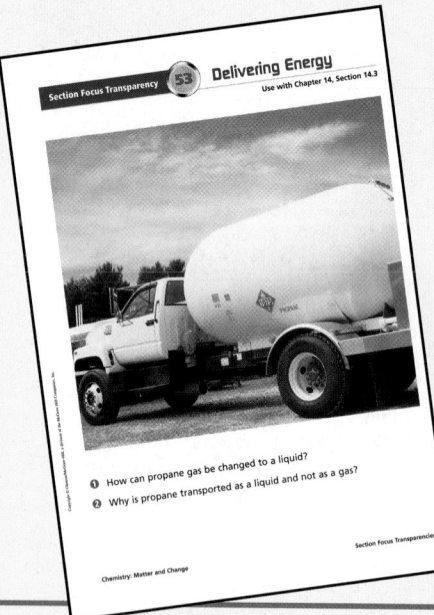

## 2 Teach

### Quick Demo

Place 5 mL of water in a balloon. Add a small piece of calcium carbide ($CaC_2$) to the balloon. Tie off the balloon and ask the students to explain what they observe in terms of the variables involved. The volume of the gas in the balloon increases because the amount of gas increases. Temperature and pressure stay constant.

### Objectives

- **Relate** the amount of gas present to its pressure, temperature, and volume by using the ideal gas law.

- **Compare** the properties of real and ideal gases.

### Vocabulary

ideal gas constant (R)
ideal gas law

**Figure 14-9**

The volume and temperature of this tire stay the same as air is added. However, the pressure in the tire increases as the amount of air present increases.

In the last section, you learned that Avogadro noted the importance of being able to calculate the number of moles of a gas present under a given set of conditions. The laws of Avogadro, Boyle, Charles, and Gay-Lussac can be combined into a single mathematical statement that describes the relationship among pressure, volume, temperature, and number of moles of a gas. This formula is called the ideal gas law because it works best when applied to problems involving gases contained under certain conditions. The particles in an ideal gas are far enough apart that they exert minimal attractive or repulsive forces on one another and occupy a negligible volume.

## The Ideal Gas Law

The number of moles is a fourth variable that can be added to pressure, volume, and temperature as a way to describe a gas sample. Recall that as the other gas laws were presented, care was taken to state that the relationships hold true for a "fixed mass" or a "given amount" of a gas sample. Changing the number of gas particles present will affect at least one of the other three variables.

As **Figure 14-9** illustrates, increasing the number of particles present in a sample will raise the pressure if the volume and temperature are kept constant. If the pressure and temperature are constant and more gas particles are added, the volume will increase.

Because pressure, volume, temperature, and the number of moles present are all interrelated, it would be helpful if one equation could describe their relationship. Remember that the combined gas law relates volume, temperature, and pressure of a sample of gas.

$$\frac{P_1 V_1}{T_1} = \frac{P_2 V_2}{T_2}$$

For a specific sample of gas, you can see that this relationship of pressure, volume, and temperature is always the same. You could say that

$$\frac{PV}{T} = k$$

where k is a constant based on the amount of gas present, $n$. Experiments using known values of $P$, $T$, $V$, and $n$ show that

$$k = nR$$

where **R** represents an experimentally determined constant that is referred to as the **ideal gas constant.** Therefore, the **ideal gas law**,

$$PV = nRT$$

describes the physical behavior of an ideal gas in terms of the pressure, volume, temperature, and number of moles of gas present. The ideal gas law is used in the **CHEMLAB** in this chapter.

**The ideal gas constant** In the ideal gas equation, the value of R depends on the units used for pressure. **Table 14-1** shows the numerical value of R for different units of pressure.

### Resource Manager

**Study Guide for Content Mastery,** pp. 82–83 L2
**Solving Problems: A Chemistry Handbook,** Section 14.3 L2
**Section Focus Transparency 53 and Master** L1 ELL

**Table 14-1**

| | Numerical Values of the Gas Constant, R | | | | |
|---|---|---|---|---|---|
| Units of R | Numerical value of R | Units of *P* | Units of *V* | Units of *T* | Units of *n* |
| $\frac{L \cdot atm}{mol \cdot K}$ | 0.0821 | atm | L | K | mol |
| $\frac{L \cdot kPa}{mol \cdot K}$ | 8.314 | kPa | L | K | mol |
| $\frac{L \cdot mm\ Hg}{mol \cdot K}$ | 62.4 | mm Hg | L | K | mol |

The R value you will probably find most useful is the first one listed in the table, $0.0821 \frac{L \cdot atm}{mol \cdot K}$. Use this R in problems in which the unit of volume is liters, the pressure is in atmospheres, and the temperature is in kelvins.

**Real versus ideal gases** What does the term *ideal gas* mean? An ideal gas is one whose particles take up no space and have no intermolecular attractive forces. An ideal gas follows the gas laws under all conditions of temperature and pressure.

In the real world, no gas is truly ideal. All gas particles have some volume, however small it may be, because of the sizes of their atoms and the lengths of their bonds. All gas particles also are subject to intermolecular interactions. Despite that, most gases will behave like ideal gases at many temperature and pressure levels. Under the right conditions of temperature and pressure, calculations made using the ideal gas law closely approximate actual experimental measurements.

When is the ideal gas law not likely to work for a real gas? Real gases deviate most from ideal gas behavior at extremely high pressures and low temperatures. As the amount of space between particles and the speed at which the particles move decrease, the effects of the volume of gas particles and intermolecular attractive forces become increasingly important. The gas behaves as a real gas in **Figure 14-10a**. Lowering the temperature of nitrogen gas results in less kinetic energy of the gas particles, which means their intermolecular attractive forces are strong enough to bond them more closely together. When the temperature is low enough, this real gas condenses to form a liquid. The gas in **Figure 14-10b** also behaves as a real gas. Increasing the pressure on a gas such as propane lowers the volume and forces the gas particles closer together until their volume is no longer negligible compared to the volume of the tank. Real gases such as propane will liquefy if enough pressure is applied.

**Figure 14-10**

Real gases deviate most from ideal gas behavior at low temperatures and high pressures.
**a** Liquid nitrogen is used to store biological tissue samples at low temperatures.
**b** Increased pressure allows a larger mass of propane to fit into a smaller volume for easier transport. Propane is sold as LP (liquid propane) for this reason, although it is actually burned for fuel as a gas.

14.3 The Ideal Gas Law **435**

**Figure 14-11**
In polar gas molecules, such as water vapor, oppositely charged poles attract each other through electrostatic forces.
A nonpolar gas, such as helium, is uncharged. Thus nonpolar gases are more likely to behave like ideal gases than are polar gases.

**Math Handbook**

Review fractions in the **Math Handbook** on page 907 of this textbook.

The nature of the particles making up a gas also affects how ideally the gas behaves. For example, polar gas molecules such as water vapor generally have larger attractive forces between their particles than nonpolar molecules such as chlorine gas. The oppositely charged ends of polar molecules are pulled together through electrostatic forces, as shown in **Figure 14-11**. Therefore polar gases do not behave as ideal gases. Also, the particles of gases composed of molecules such as butane ($C_4H_{10}$) occupy more actual volume than an equal number of gas particles of smaller molecules such as helium (He). Therefore, larger gas molecules tend to cause a greater departure from ideal behavior than do smaller gas molecules.

## Applying the Ideal Gas Law

Look again at the combined gas law on page 428. Notice that it cannot be used to find $n$, the number of moles of a gas. However, the ideal gas law can be used to solve for the value of any one of the four variables $P$, $V$, $T$, or $n$ if the values of the other three are known. Rearranging the $PV = nRT$ equation allows you to also calculate the molar mass and density of a gas sample if the mass of the sample is known.

To find the molar mass of a gas sample, the mass, temperature, pressure, and volume of the gas must be known. Remember from Chapter 12 that the number of moles of a gas ($n$) is equal to the mass ($m$) divided by the molar mass (M). Therefore, the $n$ in the equation can be replaced by $m/$M.

$$PV = \frac{mRT}{M} \text{ or } M = \frac{mRT}{PV}$$

### EXAMPLE PROBLEM 14-7

**The Ideal Gas Law—Using Moles**
Calculate the number of moles of gas contained in a 3.0-L vessel at $3.00 \times 10^2$ K with a pressure of 1.50 atm.

**1. Analyze the Problem**

You are given the volume, temperature, and pressure of a gas sample. When using the ideal gas law to solve for $n$, choose the value of R that contains the pressure and temperature units given in the problem.

**Known**

$V = 3.0$ L
$T = 3.00 \times 10^2$ K
$P = 1.50$ atm
$R = 0.0821 \frac{L \cdot atm}{mol \cdot K}$

**Unknown**

$n = ?$ mol

**436** Chapter 14 Gases

## Portfolio

### Joseph Priestley

**Intrapersonal** Ask interested students to research the work of the British scientist Joseph Priestley, who was given credit for the discovery of oxygen. Point out that Priestley, like many scientists, was active in politics. Because he was persecuted in Britain for his support for the American revolution, he came to America in 1794. **L2**

**P**

## 2. Solve for the Unknown

Divide both sides of the ideal gas law equation by $RT$ to solve for $n$.

$$PV = nRT$$

$$n = \frac{PV}{RT}$$

Substitute the known values into the rearranged equation.

$$n = \frac{(1.50 \text{ atm})(3.0 \text{ L})}{\left(0.0821 \frac{\text{L·atm}}{\text{mol·K}}\right)(3.00 \times 10^2 \text{ K})}$$

Multiply and divide numbers and units to solve for $n$.

$$n = \frac{(1.50 \cancel{\text{atm}})(3.0 \cancel{\text{L}})}{\left(0.0821 \frac{\cancel{\text{L·atm}}}{\text{mol·}\cancel{\text{K}}}\right)(3.00 \times 10^2 \cancel{\text{K}})} = 0.18 \text{ mol}$$

## 3. Evaluate the Answer

One mole of a gas at STP occupies 22.4 L. In this problem, the volume is much smaller than 22.4 L while the temperature and pressure values are not too different from those at STP. The answer agrees with the prediction that the number of moles present will be significantly less than one mole. The unit of the answer is the mole.

## PRACTICE PROBLEMS

**41.** If the pressure exerted by a gas at 25°C in a volume of 0.044 L is 3.81 atm, how many moles of gas are present?

**42.** Determine the Celsius temperature of 2.49 moles of gas contained in a 1.00-L vessel at a pressure of 143 kPa.

**43.** Calculate the volume that a 0.323-mol sample of a gas will occupy at 265 K and a pressure of 0.900 atm.

**44.** What is the pressure in atmospheres of a 0.108-mol sample of helium gas at a temperature of 20.0°C if its volume is 0.505 L?

**45.** Determine the kelvin temperature required for 0.0470 mol of gas to fill a balloon to 1.20 L under 0.988 atm pressure.

Practice! For more practice with ideal gas law problems that use moles, go to **Supplemental Practice Problems** in Appendix A.

Recall from Chapter 2 that density ($D$) is defined as mass ($m$) per unit volume ($V$). After rearranging the ideal gas equation to solve for molar mass, $D$ can be substituted for $m/V$.

$$M = \frac{mRT}{PV} = \frac{DRT}{P}$$

This equation can be rearranged to solve for the density of a gas.

$$D = \frac{MP}{RT}$$

Why might you need to know the density of a gas? Consider what requirements are necessary to fight a fire. One way to put out a fire is to remove its oxygen source by covering it with another gas that will neither burn nor support combustion. This gas must have a greater density than oxygen so that it will fall to the level of the fire. You can observe applications of density when you do the **miniLAB** later in this section and read the **Chemistry and Technology** feature.

14.3  The Ideal Gas Law    **437**

## Practice PROBLEMS

Have students refer to Appendix D for complete solutions to Practice Problems.

**41.** $6.9 \times 10^{-3}$ mol

**42.** −266°C

**43.** 7.81 L

**44.** 5.14 atm

**45.** 307 K

## ✓ Assessment

**Skill** Ask students to demonstrate their skill at reading a barometer. Check the pressure yourself first, explaining to the students how to read the instrument as you do so. Then ask each student to read the atmospheric pressure, recording each reading on a piece of paper. Assist the students who get incorrect readings in using the barometer. **L1** **ELL**

## GLENCOE TECHNOLOGY

**CD-ROM**
**Chemistry: Matter and Change**
Exploration: *Using the Gas Laws*

---

### CULTURAL DIVERSITY

## A Bit of Bubbly

The champagne that has launched thousands of ships had its start in the la Champagne region of northern France. Seventeenth-century monks, including cellarmaster Dom Perignon, tried for many years to get rid of bubbles that were considered a sign of poor wine-making. These tiny bubbles form because the conditions of the region result in a short growing season and a late grape harvest. The cool weather stops the fermentation process before the sugar in the wine has all been changed to alcohol. When spring comes, the fermentation starts again in the bottled wine, creating trapped carbon dioxide. Eventually the monks gave up trying to get rid of the bubbles and perfected the making of sparkling wines. By law, since 1927, only sparkling beverages produced in that region of France that is spread out over 312 villages can be labeled "Champagne."

Have students refer to Appendix D for complete solutions to Practice Problems.

**46.** 6.39 g
**47.** 0.694 g
**48.** 1.96 g/L
**49.** 26.1 g/mol
**50.** 1.78 g/L

# miniLAB

## Purpose
Students will use Avogadro's principle and the combined gas law to calculate and compare the density of three gases at room temperature and pressure.

## Process Skills
Using numbers, hypothesizing

## Safety Precautions
Have students wear aprons and goggles. Remind them to be careful around the candle flame.

## Disposal
Students should flush the contents of the beaker down the drain and properly dispose of burned matches.

## Teaching Strategies
• See page 418C for preparation of solutions.
• Use a weather radio to determine the local barometric pressure if you do not have a barometer.
• You may wish to have students calculate the volume of $CO_2$ gas needed to fill the cylinder.
$V = \pi r^2 h$; approximately 850 mL
• Remind students to be certain the end of the tube is positioned so that the gas will pour out directly onto the flame.

## Expected Results
The heavier-than-air $CO_2$ gas will flow down the foil cylinder and extinguish the candle flame.

National Science Content Standards
Pages 438–439
UCP.2, UCP.3; A.1; B.2, B.4, B.6

**438**

---

**EXAMPLE** PROBLEM 14-8

### The Ideal Gas Law—Using Molar Mass
What is the molar mass of a pure gas that has a density of 1.40 g/L at STP?

**1. Analyze the Problem**

You are given the density, temperature, and pressure of a sample of gas. Because density is known and mass and volume are not, use the form of the ideal gas equation that involves density.

**Known**

$D = 1.40\ \dfrac{g}{L}$

$T = 0.00°C$

$P = 1.00\ atm$

$R = 0.0821\ \dfrac{L \cdot atm}{mol \cdot K}$

**Unknown**

$M = ?\ \dfrac{g}{mol}$

**2. Solve for the Unknown**

Convert the standard $T$ to kelvin units.

$T_K = 273 + T_C$

$T_K = 273 + 0.00°C = 273\ K$

Use the form of the ideal gas law that includes density ($D$) and solves for $M$.

$$M = \frac{DRT}{P}$$

Substitute the known values into the equation.

$$M = \frac{\left(1.40\ \frac{g}{L}\right)\left(0.0821\ \frac{L \cdot atm}{mol \cdot K}\right)(273\ K)}{1\ atm}$$

Multiply and divide numbers and units to solve for $M$.

$$M = \frac{\left(1.40\ \frac{g}{\cancel{L}}\right)\left(0.0821\ \frac{\cancel{L} \cdot \cancel{atm}}{mol \cdot \cancel{K}}\right)(273\ \cancel{K})}{1\ \cancel{atm}} = 31.4\ g/mol$$

**3. Evaluate the Answer**

You would expect the molar mass of a gas to fall somewhere between that of one of the lightest gases under normal conditions, such as 2 g/mol for $H_2$, and that of a relatively heavy gas, such as 222 g/mol for Rn. The answer seems reasonable. The unit is g/mol, which is the molar mass unit.

The density of a gas can be used to identify it. This gas is denser than air and can be poured from one container to another.

Practice!
For more practice with ideal gas law problems that use molar mass, go to Supplemental Practice Problems in Appendix A.

**PRACTICE** PROBLEMS

**46.** How many grams of gas are present in a sample that has a molar mass of 70.0 g/mol and occupies a 2.00-L container at 117 kPa and 35.1°C?

**47.** Calculate the grams of $N_2$ gas present in a 0.600-L sample kept at 1.00 atm pressure and a temperature of 22.0°C.

**48.** What is the density of a gas at STP that has a molar mass of 44.0 g/mol?

**49.** What is the molar mass of a sample of gas that has a density of 1.09 g/L at 1.02 atm pressure and 25.0°C?

**50.** Calculate the density a gas will have at STP if its molar mass is 39.9 g/mol.

**438** Chapter 14 Gases

---

## Analysis
1. $CO_2$ gas is heavier than air.
2. Using $V_2 = P_1 V_1 T_2/(T_1 P_2)$ at 298 K and 98.6 kPa, the molar volume is 25.1 L.
3. $N_2$ 28.0 g/25.1 L = 1.12 g/L; $O_2$ 32.0 g/25.1 L = 1.27 g/L; $CO_2$ 44.0 g/25.1 L = 1.75 g/L
4. Yes, the heavier $CO_2$ gas moves down the cylinder, displacing the air and extinguishing the candle flame.

## ✓ Assessment
**Performance** Have students calculate the size of a cube that contains 22.4 L of a gas at STP. Students should then build such a box. Remind students that molar volume is also 22 400 $cm^3$. The box would be 28.2 cm on a side. Use the Performance Task Assessment List for Using Math in Science in **PASC**, p. 29. **L2** **ELL**

# miniLAB

## The Density of Carbon Dioxide

**Hypothesizing** Air is a mixture of mostly nitrogen and oxygen. Use observations to form a hypothesis about which has greater density, air or carbon dioxide.

**Materials** masking tape, aluminum foil, metric ruler, 1-L beaker, candle, matches, thermometer, barometer or weather radio, baking soda ($NaHCO_3$), vinegar (5% $CH_3COOH$)

**Procedure**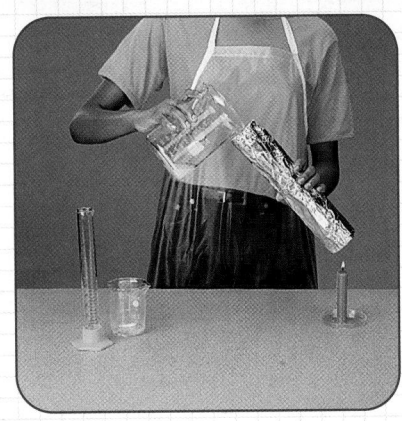

1. Record the temperature and the barometric pressure of the air in the classroom.
2. Roll a 23-cm × 30-cm piece of aluminum foil into a cylinder that is 6 cm × 30 cm. Tape the edges with masking tape.
3. Use matches to light a candle. **CAUTION:** *Run water over the extinguished match before throwing it away. Keep all hair and loose clothing away from the flame.*
4. Place 30 g of baking soda in the bottom of a large beaker. Add 40 mL of vinegar.
5. Quickly position the foil cylinder at approximately 45° up and away from the top of the candle flame.
6. While the reaction in the beaker is actively producing $CO_2$ gas, carefully pour the gas, but not the liquid, out of the beaker and into the top of the foil tube. Record your observations.

### Analysis

1. Based on your observations, state a hypothesis about whether $CO_2$ is heavier or lighter than air.
2. Use the combined gas law to calculate molar volume at room temperature and atmospheric pressure.
3. Carbon dioxide gas ($CO_2$) has a molar mass of 44 g/mol. The two major components of air, which are oxygen and nitrogen, have molar masses of 32 g/mol and 28 g/mol, respectively. Calculate the room-temperature densities in g/L of nitrogen ($N_2$), oxygen ($O_2$), and carbon dioxide ($CO_2$) gases.
4. Do these calculations confirm your hypothesis? Explain.

---

## Section 14.3 Assessment

51. Write the equation for the ideal gas law.
52. Use the kinetic-molecular theory to analyze and evaluate the ideal gas law's applicability to real gases.
53. List common units for each variable in the ideal gas law.
54. **Thinking Critically** Which of the following gases would you expect to behave most like an ideal gas at room temperature and atmospheric pressure: water vapor, carbon dioxide, helium, or hydrogen? Explain.

55. **Making and Using Graphs**  The accompanying data show the volume of hydrogen gas collected at a number of different temperatures. Illustrate these data with a graph and use them to determine the temperature at which the volume will reach a value of 0 mL. What is this temperature called? For more help, refer to **Drawing Line Graphs** in the **Math Handbook** on page 903 of this text.

| Volume of H₂ Collected at Different Temperatures | | | | | | |
|---|---|---|---|---|---|---|
| **Trial** | **1** | **2** | **3** | **4** | **5** | **6** |
| ***T* (°C)** | 300 | 175 | 110 | 0 | −100 | −150 |
| ***V* (mL)** | 48 | 37 | 32 | 22 | 15 | 11 |

---

## 3 Assess
### Check for Understanding

Ask groups of students to write and solve two ideal gas law problems.

### Reteach

Ask students to determine how to calculate how many moles of gas are contained in an inflated tire. Students can use the ideal gas law to do this calculation if they have a tire gauge, a thermometer, and a tape measure. **L2**

### Extension

Ask students to do research to identify noble gases that will react under extreme conditions and write the equations for the reactions that have taken place. **L3**

### ✔ Assessment

**Portfolio** Ask students to solve the following problem and place the solutions in their portfolios. A sample of helium gas occupies a spherical bulb that is 12.0 inches in diameter. The gas exerts a pressure of 6.80 atm at 15.0°C. What mass of helium is in the bulb? The volume of a sphere with radius $r$ is $V = \frac{4}{3}\pi r^3$. 17.0 g **L2** **P**

### Resource Manager

**ChemLab and MiniLab Worksheets, p. 53** **L2**

---

## Section 14.3 Assessment

51. $PV = nRT$
52. A real gas behaves most like an ideal gas under conditions that increase the distance and reduce the attractions among gas particles. The best conditions for that are high temperature and low pressure.
53. *P*: atm, mm Hg, torr, kPa; *V*: L, mL; *T*: K; *n*: mol
54. Helium; the intermolecular forces between its atoms are weaker than the forces between the molecules making up the other gases.
55. See the Solutions Manual. The graphs show a linear relationship in which temperature and volume are directly proportional to each other. Extrapolating the graph to a volume of 0 mL intersects the temperature axis at approximately −273°C, the temperature called absolute zero.

**439**

# 1 Focus

Before presenting the lesson, display **Section Focus Transparency 54** on the overhead projector. Have students answer the accompanying questions using **Section Focus Transparency Master 54.** L1 ELL

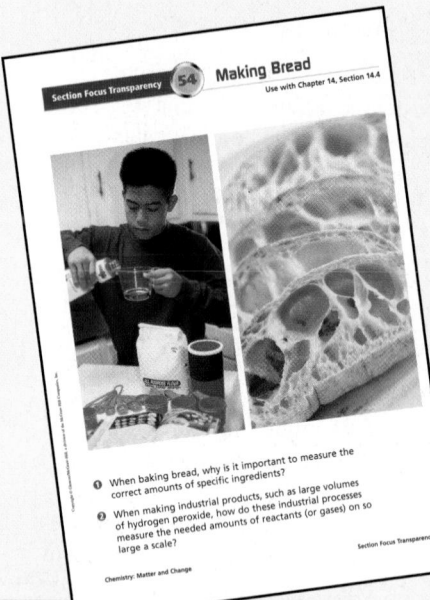

Section Focus Transparency **54** Making Bread
Use with Chapter 14, Section 14.4

❶ When baking bread, why is it important to measure the correct amounts of specific ingredients?

❷ When making industrial products, such as large volumes of hydrogen peroxide, how do these industrial processes measure the needed amounts of reactants (or gases) on so large a scale?

Chemistry: Matter and Change

Section Focus Transparencies

# 2 Teach

## Quick Demo

Light a candle, place it in a holder, and place an inverted beaker over the candle. Ask students to predict what will happen. Tell them to observe carefully for 5 to 10 minutes to see if their predictions were correct. The flame will burn for several minutes and then go out long before the candle has burned completely. Ask students to explain why their predictions were or were not correct. The flame goes out when oxygen in the air under the beaker is depleted because the flame is produced by a combustion reaction that requires oxygen.

---

  **Gas Stoichiometry**

## Objectives

• **Determine** volume ratios for gaseous reactants and products by using coefficients from a chemical equation.

• **Calculate** amounts of gaseous reactants and products in a chemical reaction using the gas laws.

All the laws you have learned so far involving gases can be applied to calculate the stoichiometry of reactions in which gases are reactants or products. Recall that the coefficients in chemical equations represent molar amounts of substances taking part in the reaction. For example, when butane gas burns, the reaction is represented by the following chemical equation.

$$2C_4H_{10}(g) + 13O_2(g) \rightarrow 8CO_2(g) + 10H_2O(g)$$

From the balanced chemical equation, you know that 2 mol of butane reacts with 13 mol of oxygen, producing 8 mol of carbon dioxide and 10 mol of water vapor. By examining this balanced equation, you are able to find mole ratios of substances in this reaction. Avogadro's principle states that equal volumes of gases at the same temperature and pressure contain equal numbers of particles. Thus, when gases are involved, the coefficients in a balanced chemical equation represent not only molar amounts but also relative volumes. For example, if 2 L of butane reacts, the reaction involves 13 L of oxygen and produces 8 L of carbon dioxide and 10 L of water vapor.

## Calculations Involving Only Volume

To find the volume of a gaseous reactant or product in a reaction, you must know the balanced chemical equation for the reaction and the volume of at least one other gas involved in the reaction. Examine the reaction showing the combustion of methane, which takes place every time you light a Bunsen burner.

$$CH_4(g) + 2O_2(g) \rightarrow CO_2(g) + 2H_2O(g)$$

Because the coefficients represent volume ratios for gases taking part in the reaction, you can determine that it takes 2 L of oxygen to react completely with 1 L of methane. The complete combustion of 1 L of methane will produce 1 L of carbon dioxide and 2 L of water vapor, as shown in **Figure 14-12**.

What volume of methane is needed to produce 26 L of water vapor? Because the volume ratio of methane and water vapor is 1:2, the volume of methane needed is half that of the water vapor. Thus, 13 L of methane is needed to produce 26 L of water vapor. What volume of oxygen is needed to produce 6.0 L of carbon dioxide?

Note that no conditions of temperature and pressure are listed. They are not needed as part of the calculation because after mixing, each gas is at the same temperature and pressure. The same temperature and pressure affect all gases in the same way, so these conditions don't need to be considered.

**Figure 14-12**

The coefficients in a balanced equation show the relationships among numbers of moles of all reactants and products. The coefficients also show the relationships among volumes of any gaseous reactants or products. From these coefficients, volume ratios can be set up for any pair of gases in the reaction.

Methane gas + Oxygen gas → Carbon dioxide gas + Water vapor
$CH_4(g)$  +  $2O_2(g)$  →  $CO_2(g)$  +  $2H_2O(g)$

1 mole    2 moles    1 mole    2 moles
1 volume    2 volumes    1 volume    2 volumes

---

## DIFFERENTIATED INSTRUCTION

### Learning Disabled

*Visual-Spatial* Some students understand stoichiometry problems better if they can visualize reactions using ball-and-stick models of reactants and products. Ask students to build models of the molecules involved in the combustion of methane, and use those models to find the mole ratio of: **a.** methane to oxygen, **b.** oxygen to carbon dioxide, **c.** methane to carbon dioxide, **d.** methane to water. Answers: **a.** 1:2, **b.** 2:1, **c.** 1:1, **d.** 1:2. L1 ELL

## EXAMPLE PROBLEM 14-9

### Volume-Volume Problems

What volume of oxygen gas is needed for the complete combustion of 4.00 L of propane gas ($C_3H_8$)? Assume constant pressure and temperature.

**1 Analyze the Problem**

You are given the volume of a gaseous reactant in a chemical reaction. Remember that the coefficients in a balanced chemical equation provide the volume relationships of gaseous reactants and products.

| Known | Unknown |
|---|---|
| $V_{C_3H_8}$ = 4.00 L | $V_{O_2}$ = ? L |

**2 Solve for the Unknown**

Write the balanced equation for the combustion of $C_3H_8$.

$$C_3H_8(g) + 5O_2(g) \longrightarrow 3CO_2(g) + 4H_2O(g)$$

Use the balanced equation to find the volume ratio for $O_2$ and $C_3H_8$.

$$\frac{5 \text{ volumes } O_2}{1 \text{ volume } C_3H_8}$$

Multiply the known volume of $C_3H_8$ by the volume ratio to find the volume of $O_2$.

$$(4.00 \text{ L } C_3H_8) \times \frac{5 \text{ volumes } O_2}{1 \text{ volume } C_3H_8} = 20.0 \text{ L } O_2$$

**3 Evaluate the Answer**

The coefficients in the combustion equation show that a much larger volume of $O_2$ than $C_3H_8$ is used up in the reaction, which is in agreement with the calculated answer. The unit of the answer is L, a unit of volume.

Correct proportions of gases are needed for many chemical reactions. The combustion of propane heats the air that inflates the balloon.

## PRACTICE PROBLEMS

56. What volume of oxygen is needed to react with solid sulfur to form 3.5 L $SO_2$?

57. Determine the volume of hydrogen gas needed to react completely with 5.00 L of oxygen gas to form water.

58. How many liters of propane gas ($C_3H_8$) will undergo complete combustion with 34.0 L of oxygen gas?

59. What volume of oxygen is needed to completely combust 2.36 L of methane gas ($CH_4$)?

Practice!

For more practice with volume-volume problems, go to **Supplemental Practice Problems** in Appendix A.

## Calculations Involving Volume and Mass

To do stoichiometric calculations that involve both gas volumes and masses, you must know the balanced equation for the reaction involved, at least one mass or volume value for a reactant or product, and the conditions under which the gas volumes have been measured. Then the ideal gas law can be used along with volume or mole ratios to complete the calculation.

In doing this type of problem, remember that the balanced chemical equation allows you to find ratios for moles and gas volumes only—not for masses. All masses given must be converted to moles or volumes before being used as part of a ratio. Also remember that the temperature units used must be kelvin.

14.4 Gas Stoichiometry    **441**

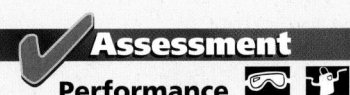

## Practice PROBLEMS

Have students refer to Appendix D for complete solutions to Practice Problems.

**56.** 3.5 L
**57.** 10.0 L
**58.** 6.80 L
**59.** 4.72 L

## ✔ Assessment

**Performance** 👓 🧪

Instruct students to set up a 250-mL flask containing warm water, sugar, and yeast with the opening of a balloon stretched over the top of the flask. Ask students to observe the flask and explain what happens. The yeast ferments to produce carbon dioxide, which expands the balloon. Have students remove the balloon carefully, trying not to lose any gas, and then use rubber tubing to release the gas deep under water in a beaker. Ask them to predict what happens to the water. The water becomes slightly acidic because carbon dioxide dissolves to form carbonic acid. This last step can be done with water that contains an indicator that has an end point of about pH 6 to test their predictions. Use the Performance Task Assessment List for Making Observations and Inferences in PASC, p. 17. **L2** 📦

## Resource Manager

**Study Guide for Content Mastery,** p. 84 **L2**
**Solving Problems: A Chemistry Handbook,** Section 14.4 **L2**
**Section Focus Transparency 54 and Master** **L1** **ELL**
**Teaching Transparency 44 and Master** **L2** **ELL**

## ✔ Portfolio

### Gas Law Application

**Linguistic** Ask interested students to watch the movie *Around the World in 80 Days* and write a brief review of the movie in which they focus on the way the gas laws are used in flying the balloon. Have students include the reviews in their portfolios. **L2** **P** 📦

**National Science Content Standards**

**Pages 440–441**
UCP.2, UCP.3; B.2, B.3

Have students refer to Appendix D for complete solutions to Practice Problems.

**60.** 0.357 g

**61.** 533 L

**62.** 0.541 mol

**63.** 15.6 L

**64.** $5.84 \times 10^{-2}$ L

# 3 Assess

## Check for Understanding

Place a 10.0-g wad of aluminum foil in concentrated hydrochloric acid in a well-ventilated area. Ask students to explain what they see. Bubbles of gas form as the acid reacts with the metal. Acids react with some metals to form hydrogen gas. Ask the students to write a balanced equation for this reaction and use it to predict how many liters of hydrogen gas will be produced at STP if the 10.0 g of aluminum reacts completely.

$2Al(s) + 6HCl(aq) \rightarrow 3H_2(g) + 2AlCl_3(aq)$; 12.5 L

For disposal, filter the product. Pour the liquid down the drain with plenty of water. Discard the solid in the trash can.

---

**EXAMPLE PROBLEM 14-10**

### Volume-Mass Problems

Ammonia is synthesized from hydrogen and nitrogen gases.

$$N_2(g) + 3H_2(g) \rightarrow 2NH_3(g)$$

If 5.00 L of nitrogen reacts completely by this reaction at a constant pressure and temperature of 3.00 atm and 298 K, how many grams of ammonia are produced?

#### 1. Analyze the Problem

You are given the volume, pressure, and temperature of a gas sample. The mole and volume ratios of gaseous reactants and products are given by the coefficients in the balanced chemical equation. Volume can be converted to moles and thus related to mass by using molar mass and the ideal gas law.

| Known | Unknown |
|---|---|
| $V_{N_2} = 5.00$ L | $m_{NH_3} = ?$ g |
| $P = 3.00$ atm | |
| $T = 298$ K | |

#### 2. Solve for the Unknown

Determine volume ratios from the balanced chemical equation.

$$\frac{1 \text{ volume } N_2}{2 \text{ volumes } NH_3}$$

Use this ratio to determine how many liters of gaseous ammonia will be made from 5.00 L of nitrogen gas.

$$5.00 \text{ L } N_2 \left( \frac{2 \text{ volumes } NH_3}{1 \text{ volume } N_2} \right) = 10.0 \text{ L } NH_3$$

Rearrange the equation for the ideal gas law to solve for $n$.

$$PV = nRT$$
$$n = \frac{PV}{RT}$$

Substitute the known values into the rearranged equation using the volume of $NH_3$ for $V$. Multiply and divide numbers and units to solve for the number of moles of $NH_3$.

$$n = \frac{(3.00 \text{ atm})(10.0 \text{ L})}{\left( 0.0821 \frac{\text{L·atm}}{\text{mol·K}} \right)(298 \text{ K})} = 1.23 \text{ mol } NH_3$$

Find the molar mass, M, of $NH_3$ by finding the molecular mass and expressing it in units of g/mol.

$$M = \left( \frac{1 \text{ N atom} \times 14.01 \text{ amu}}{\text{N atom}} \right) + \left( \frac{3 \text{ H atoms} \times 1.01 \text{ amu}}{\text{H atom}} \right)$$

$$= 17.04 \text{ amu}$$

$$M = 17.04 \frac{\text{g}}{\text{mol}}$$

Convert moles of ammonia to grams of ammonia using molar mass of ammonia as a conversion factor.

$$1.23 \text{ mol } NH_3 \times 17.04 \frac{\text{g}}{\text{mol}} = 21.0 \text{ g } NH_3$$

#### 3. Evaluate the Answer

To check your answer, calculate the volume of reactant nitrogen at STP. Then, use molar volume and the mole ratio between $N_2$ and $NH_3$ to determine how many moles of $NH_3$ were produced. You can convert the answer to grams using the molar mass of $NH_3$. All data was given in three significant digits as is the answer.

Ammonia is essential in the production of chemical fertilizers.

---

### Internet Address Book

Note Internet addresses that you find useful in the space below for quick reference.

_____

_____

_____

_____

_____

## PRACTICE PROBLEMS

**60.** Ammonium nitrate is a common ingredient in chemical fertilizers. Use the reaction shown to calculate the mass of solid ammonium nitrate that must be used to obtain 0.100 L of dinitrogen oxide gas at STP.

$NH_4NO_3(s) \rightarrow N_2O(g) + 2H_2O(g)$

**61.** Calcium carbonate forms limestone, one of the most common rocks on Earth. It also forms stalactites, stalagmites, and many other types of formations found in caves. When calcium carbonate is heated, it decomposes to form solid calcium oxide and carbon dioxide gas.

$CaCO_3(s) \rightarrow CaO(s) + CO_2(g)$

How many liters of carbon dioxide will be produced at STP if 2.38 kg of calcium carbonate reacts completely?

**62.** Determine how many moles of water vapor will be produced at 1.00 atm and 200°C by the complete combustion of 10.5 L of methane gas ($CH_4$).

**63.** When iron rusts, it undergoes a reaction with oxygen to form iron(III) oxide.

$4 Fe(s) + 3O_2(g) \rightarrow 2Fe_2O_3(s)$

Calculate the volume of oxygen gas at STP that is required to completely react with 52.0 g of iron.

**64.** Solid potassium metal will react with $Cl_2$ gas to form ionic potassium chloride. How many liters of $Cl_2$ gas are needed to completely react with 0.204 g of potassium at STP?

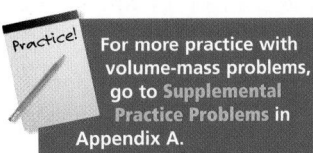

Practice! For more practice with volume-mass problems, go to **Supplemental Practice Problems** in Appendix A.

**Chemistry Online**

**Topic: Gases**
To learn more about gases, visit the Chemistry Web site at **chemistrymc.com**

**Activity:** Research how the gas laws are important to fish and scuba divers. Explain your answers using equations when possible.

Stoichiometric problems such as these are considered in industrial processes that involve gases. How much of a reactant should be purchased? How much of a product will be produced? What conditions of temperature and pressure are necessary? Answers to these questions are essential to effective production of a product.

## Section 14.4 Assessment

**65.** How do mole ratios compare to volume ratios for gaseous reactants and products in a balanced chemical equation?

**66.** Is the volume of a gas directly or inversely proportional to the number of moles of a gas at constant temperature and pressure? Explain.

**67.** Determine the volume ratio of ammonia to nitrogen in the reaction shown.

$3H_2 + N_2 \rightarrow 2NH_3$

Which will occupy a larger volume at a given temperature and pressure: one mole of $H_2$ or one mole of $NH_3$?

**68. Thinking Critically** One mole of a gas occupies a volume of 22.4 L at STP. Calculate the temperature and pressure conditions needed to fit two moles of a gas into a volume of 22.4 L.

**69. Predicting** Using what you have learned about gases, predict what will happen to the size of the reaction vessel you need to carry out a reaction involving gases if the temperature is doubled and the pressure is held constant.

chemistrymc.com/self_check_quiz

14.4 Gas Stoichiometry    **443**

## Section 14.4 Assessment

**65.** The molar and volume ratios are the same for reactants and products that are gases.

**66.** Directly proportional; as the amount of gas increases, so does volume.

**67.** 2 volumes $NH_3$:1 volume $N_2$; both will occupy the same volume.

**68.** Student answers may vary. Temperature can be halved or pressure doubled, or a combination of lowering temperature and increasing pressure can be used.

**69.** When the temperature is doubled, the volume will also double. The size of the reaction vessel should be doubled.

## Preparation

### Time Allotment
One laboratory period

### Process Skills
Measuring, using numbers

### Safety Precautions
Have students wear an apron and goggles. Have them use caution with the pressurized container and when placing the rubber tubing onto the piece of glass tubing.

### Disposal
Have students pour the water down the drain and properly dispose of empty cans according to directions on the label.

### Alternative Materials
A butane lighter can be used as a source of gas.

## Pre-Lab

**3.** Because the molar mass of water is likely to be less than that of the other gas present, it probably will lower the calculated molar mass of the other gas.

**4. a.** 44.11 g/mol
   **b.** 58.14 g/mol
   **c.** 120.91 g/mol
   **d.** 102.04 g/mol

**5.** M = mRT/PV = 0.810 g × 0.0821 L·atm/(mol·K) × 291 K/(0.954 atm × 0.461 L) = 44.0 g/mol

## Procedure

- Cut the tip from the plastic pipette so the pipette's stem will tightly fit on the long tip that comes with the can of duster.
- Have students hold the beaker down as it fills with gas or it will float up and some gas will be lost before it can be measured.
- If you wish to have students correct the gas pressure for the partial pressure of water vapor, they can subtract the water vapor pressure from the atmospheric pressure. The correction is small at room temperature, 3.2 kPa at 25°C.

---

# Using the Ideal Gas Law

The ideal gas law is a powerful tool that the chemist—and now you—can use to determine the molar mass of an unknown gas. By measuring the temperature, pressure, volume, and mass of a gas sample, you can calculate the molar mass of the gas.

### Problem
How can the equation for the ideal gas law be used to calculate the molar mass of a gas?

### Objectives
- **Measure** the mass, volume, temperature, and pressure of an insoluble gas collected over water.
- **Calculate** the molar mass of an unknown gas using the ideal gas equation.

### Materials
| | |
|---|---|
| aerosol can of duster | plastic microtip pipette |
| 600-mL graduated beaker | latex tubing |
| bucket or bowl | glass tubing |
| thermometer (°C) | scissors |
| barometer or weather radio | electrical or duct tape |
| | balance |

## Safety Precautions

- Read and observe all cautions listed on the aerosol can of office equipment duster.
- Do not have any open flames in the room.

## Pre-Lab

**1.** Read the entire **CHEMLAB**.

**2.** Prepare all written materials that you will take into the laboratory. Be sure to include safety precautions, procedure notes, and a data table.

**3.** Because you will collect the aerosol gas over water, the beaker contains both the aerosol gas and water vapor. Form a hypothesis about how the presence of water vapor will affect the calculated value of the molar mass of the gas. Explain.

**4.** The following gases are or have been used in aerosol cans, some as propellants. Use the gases' molecular formulas to calculate their molar masses.
   **a.** propane, $C_3H_8$
   **b.** butane, $C_4H_{10}$
   **c.** dichlorodifluoromethane, $CCl_2F_2$
   **d.** tetrafluoroethane, $C_2H_2F_4$

**5.** Given the following data for a gas, use the equation for the ideal gas law to calculate the molar mass.
   **a.** mass = 0.810 g
   **b.** pressure = 0.954 atm
   **c.** volume = 0.461 L
   **d.** temperature = 291 K

| Data and Calculations | |
|---|---|
| Mass of can before release of gas (g) | |
| Mass of can after release of gas (g) | |
| Mass of gas released (g) | |
| Air temperature (°C) | |
| Air temperature (K) | |
| Air pressure (list what unit was used) | |
| Air pressure (atm) | |
| Volume of gas collected (L) | |

## Procedure

**1.** Place the bucket in the sink and fill it with water.

**2.** Submerge the beaker in the water. Then, invert it in the bucket, being careful to keep it completely filled with water.

**3.** Measure the mass of an aerosol can of office equipment duster. Record the mass in the data table.

---

- The following conversions may be helpful: 29.9 inches of Hg = 760 mm = 101.3 kPa = 1 atm.
- **Troubleshooting** Remind students that the connections of glass tubing, latex tubing, plastic pipette stem, and the tip of the pressurized can must all fit together tightly to avoid losing the gas.

## Expected Results

| Sample Data and Calculations | |
|---|---|
| Mass of can before release of gas | 265.0 g |
| Mass of can after release of gas | 262.9 g |
| Mass of gas released | 2.1 g |
| Air temperature | 25°C |
| Air pressure in atmospheres | 1 atm |
| Volume of gas collected in L | 0.490 L |

4. Use scissors to cut the stem from a plastic microtip pipette.

5. Fit the pipette stem over the long plastic spray tip that comes with the aerosol can to extend the length of the tip and enlarge the diameter.

6. Connect one end of 30 cm of latex tubing to glass tubing that is 8 cm long.

7. Connect the other end to the pipette stem that is attached to the aerosol can. If necessary, tape any connections so that they don't leak.

8. Place the end of the glass tubing under the pour spout of the inverted beaker as shown in the photo.

9. Hold the beaker down while you slowly release the gas from the aerosol can. Collect between 400 and 500 mL of the gas by water displacement.

10. To equalize the air pressure, lift the beaker so that the water level inside and outside the beaker is the same.

11. Carefully read the volume of the gas collected using the graduations on the beaker.

12. Record this volume of the gas collected in the data table.

13. Remove the tubing from the aerosol can.

14. Measure the mass of the can and record it in the data table.

15. Using a barometer or weather radio, record the atmospheric pressure in the data table.

16. Using a thermometer, determine air temperature. Record it in the data table.

## Cleanup and Disposal

1. Dispose of the empty can according to the instructions on its label.

2. Pour the water down the drain.

3. Discard any tape and the pipettes in the trash can.

4. Return all lab equipment to its proper place.

## Analyze and Conclude

1. **Using Numbers** Fill in the remainder of the data table by calculating the mass of the gas that was released from the aerosol can, converting the atmospheric pressure from the units measured into atmospheres, and converting the air temperature into kelvins. Substitute your data from the table into the form of the ideal gas equation that solves for M. Calculate the molar mass of the gas in the can using the appropriate value for R.

2. **Using Numbers** Read the contents of the can and determine which of the gases from step 4 in the Pre-Lab is the most likely propellant.

3. **Error Analysis** Remember that you are collecting the gas after it has bubbled through water. What might happen to some of the gas as it goes through the water? What might be present in the gas in the beaker in addition to the gas from the can? Calculate the percent error using your calculated molar mass compared to the molar mass of the gas in the aerosol can.

4. **Interpreting Data** Were your data consistent with the ideal gas law? Evaluate the pressure and temperature at which your experiment was done, and the polarity of the gas. Would you expect the gas in your experiment to behave as an ideal gas or a real gas?

## Real-World Chemistry

1. Explain why the label on an aerosol can warns against exposing the can to high heat.

2. Use the ideal gas law to explain why the wind blows.

## Analyze and Conclude

1. Sample calculation: Subtract the mass after release from the mass before release. *2.1 g* Use °C + 273 = K to convert 25°C to 298 K.
M = mRT/PV = 105 g/mol

2. $C_2H_2F_4$ has a molar mass of 102 g/mol and is the most likely propellant.

3. Some of the gas might dissolve in the water. Water vapor might be present.
Sample calculation:
(105 − 102)/102 × 100% = 2.94% error

4. No; the gas would behave as a real gas.

## Real-World Chemistry

1. As temperature increases, pressure increases. If the pressure increases enough, the container might explode.

2. Assume the volume of air and the temperature are constant. Using the ideal gas equation, PV = nRT, as pressure increases, the amount of gas also increases, as all other values are constant. Thus, when air pressure drops, air moves (wind blows) from an area of high pressure to an area of low pressure.

✔ **Assessment**
**Portfolio** Have students place a copy of the lab report in their portfolios along with sketches that show what was done. **L2** **P**

CHEMLAB **445**

**Resource Manager**

**ChemLab and MiniLab Worksheets, pp. 54–56** **L2**

**National Science Content Standards**

**Pages 444–445**
UCP.2, UCP.3; A.1; B.2, B.6

## Purpose

Students will learn one way that the properties of gases are used for practical purposes.

## Background

The first airship in the CargoLifter fleet, the CL 160, will be the largest airship ever flown. It is 260 meters long and 65 meters wide, which is approximately the height of a 27-story building. It will contain enough helium to enable it to lift 160 metric tons. It will be able to cruise at 80 to 100 kph at a maximum altitude of approximately 1800 m for about 10 000 km. The outer skin will be made from multi-laminate material. The structure will be made of lightweight, super-strength polycarbon fiber.

## Teaching Strategies

• Ask students this question. The CargoLifter contains 450 000 m³ of helium gas at sea level. What volume would this gas occupy at the ship's flying altitude of 2000 m, where the air pressure is 79.5 kPa? Assume that temperature does not change. 573 000 m³

• Have students do research to answer the following questions. Where is Earth's supply of helium found? How was this helium produced? Why did the Hindenburg use flammable hydrogen instead of helium, which is chemically inert?

## Investigating the Technology

Because the airship contains a gas that is much lighter than air, its average density is less than that of air even though its structural materials are heavier than air.

# CHEMISTRY and
## Technology

## Giving a Lift to Cargo

Have you ever been caught in a traffic jam caused by a truck carrying an oversized piece of industrial equipment? The need to transport heavy loads more efficiently is one factor leading to the revival of a technology that most people considered to be dead—the airship, sometimes called a dirigible or zeppelin. The burning of the zeppelin *Hindenburg* in May 1937, followed closely by World War II, ended nearly all commercial use of these "lighter-than-air" ships. But by the 1990s, chemists and engineers had developed strong, lightweight alloys and tough, fiber-reinforced composite plastics. These materials, along with computerized control and satellite navigation systems are making commercial airships practical again.

### Modern airships

Modern airships use helium to provide lift. The *Hindenburg* used hydrogen gas, which provides about twice the lift of helium but is no longer used because it is extremely flammable. The helium is contained in bags made of a space-age, leakproof fabric called Tedlar, a type of plastic. The bags are loosely inflated so that the helium pressure is about the same as atmospheric pressure. The quantity of helium determines the lifting ability of the ship.

### Airships and Boyle's law

As the airship rises, atmospheric pressure decreases and the helium expands, as Boyle's law predicts. As the ship reaches the desired altitude, air is pumped into another bag called a *ballonet*. The pressure of the ballonet prevents the helium bags from expanding further, thus keeping the ship at that altitude. To descend, more air is pumped into the ballonet. This added pressure squeezes the helium bags, causing the volume to decrease and the density of the helium to increase. Also, the compressed air adds weight to the ship. The lifting power of the helium is reduced and the airship moves downward.

### Uses for modern airships

The old airships of 1900 to 1940 were used mostly for luxury passenger service. Among modern airships, the German Zeppelin-NT and a ship being

developed by the Hamilton Airship Company in South Africa are designed to carry passengers.

Probably the most interesting new airship is the huge CargoLifter from a German-American company. Its length is slightly less than the length of three football fields. CargoLifter's skeleton is constructed of a strong carbon fiber composite material that is much less dense than metals. At the mooring mast, it is as tall as a 27-story building and contains 450 000 m³ of helium. It is designed to carry loads up to 160 metric tons (352 000 pounds). It can pick up and deliver objects such as large turbines and entire locomotives. Because modern roads are not needed, equipment can be delivered to locations in developing countries that would otherwise be impossible to reach.

### Investigating the Technology

1. **Thinking Critically** No plastics, fabrics, or metals that are "lighter-than-air" exist. Yet these materials are used to make airships. Why is it possible to describe an airship as a lighter-than-air craft?

**Chemistry Online**

Visit the Chemistry Web site at chemistrymc.com to find links to more information about airships.

## Summary

### 14.1 The Gas Laws

- Boyle's law states that the pressure and volume of a contained gas are inversely proportional if temperature is constant.

- Charles's law states that the volume and kelvin temperature of a contained gas are directly proportional if pressure is constant.

- Gay-Lussac's law states that the pressure and kelvin temperature of a contained gas are directly proportional if volume is constant.

### 14.2 The Combined Gas Law and Avogadro's Principle

- Boyle's, Charles's, and Gay-Lussac's laws are brought together in the combined gas law, which permits calculations involving changes in the three gas variables of pressure, volume, and temperature.

- Avogadro's principle states that equal volumes of gases at the same temperature and pressure contain equal numbers of particles. The volume of one mole of a gas at STP is 22.4 L.

### 14.3 The Ideal Gas Law

- The combined gas law and Avogadro's principle are used together to form the ideal gas law. In the equation for the ideal gas law, R is the ideal gas constant.

- The ideal gas law allows you to determine the number of moles of a gas when its pressure, temperature, and volume are known.

- Real gases deviate from behavior predicted for ideal gases because the particles of a real gas occupy volume and are subject to intermolecular forces.

- The ideal gas law can be used to find molar mass if the mass of the gas is known, or the density of the gas if its molar mass is known.

### 14.4 Gas Stoichiometry

- The coefficients in a balanced chemical equation specify volume ratios for gaseous reactants and products.

- The gas laws can be used along with balanced chemical equations to calculate the amount of a gaseous reactant or product in a reaction.

## Key Equations and Relationships

- Boyle's law: $P_1V_1 = P_2V_2$, constant temperature (p. 421)

- Charles's law: $\dfrac{V_1}{T_1} = \dfrac{V_2}{T_2}$, constant pressure (p. 424)

- Gay-Lussac's law: $\dfrac{P_1}{T_1} = \dfrac{P_2}{T_2}$, constant volume (p. 426)

- Combined gas law: $\dfrac{P_1V_1}{T_1} = \dfrac{P_2V_2}{T_2}$ (p. 428)

- Ideal gas law: $PV = nRT$ (p. 434)

- Finding molar mass: $M = \dfrac{mRT}{PV}$ (p. 437)

- Finding density: $D = \dfrac{MP}{RT}$ (p. 437)

## Vocabulary

- Avogadro's principle (p. 430)
- Boyle's law (p. 421)
- Charles's law (p. 424)
- combined gas law (p. 428)
- Gay-Lussac's law (p. 426)
- ideal gas constant (R) (p. 434)
- ideal gas law (p. 434)
- molar volume (p. 431)

 chemistrymc.com/vocabulary_puzzlemaker

Study Guide    **447**

## Using the Vocabulary

To reinforce chapter vocabulary, have students write a sentence using each term. **L2** **ELL**

## Review Strategies

- Have students list the SI and one other common unit for volume, pressure, and temperature. **L2**
- Have students summarize the gas laws by listing the values that are held constant and those that vary for each law. **L2**
- Problems from Appendix A or the **Supplemental Problems** booklet can be used for review. **L2**

### VOCABULARY PuzzleMaker CHEMISTRY ONLINE

For additional help with vocabulary, have students access the Vocabulary PuzzleMaker online.

chemistrymc.com/
vocabulary_puzzlemaker

Chemistry Online

### EXAM*VIEW* PRO

## Use Exam*View*® Pro Testmaker CD-ROM to:

- Create **multiple versions** of tests.
- Create **modified** tests with one mouse click for struggling students.
- **Edit** existing questions and add your own questions.
- **Build** tests based on national curriculum standards.

National Science Content Standards

Pages 446–447
UCP.2, UCP.3; B.2, B.3, B.4, B.6; E.1; F.6

## Concept Mapping

**70.** 1. Charles's law; 2. Boyle's law; 3. Gay-Lussac's law

## Mastering Concepts

**71.** Boyle's Law: $P_1V_1 = P_2V_2$; Charles's Law: $V_1/T_1 = V_2/T_2$; Gay-Lussac's Law: $P_1/T_1 = P_2/T_2$

**72.** Pressure decreases.

**73.** Aerosol cans contain gases under pressure that can expand explosively if allowed to escape too rapidly.

**74.** The air trapped inside the bag expands as it gets hotter because volume is directly proportional to temperature.

**75.** One variable always decreases as the other increases.

**76.** One variable always increases as the other increases.

**77. a.** direct   **c.** inverse
**b.** direct

**78. a.** inverse   **c.** direct
**b.** direct

**79.** volume, pressure, temperature, and number of moles

**80.** $T = 0.00°C$ (273K) and $P = 1.00$ atm

**81.** $P_1V_1/T_1 = P_2V_2/T_2$. Units commonly used for the variables are atm for pressure, Kelvin for temperature, and L for volume.

**82.** At a fixed temperature and pressure, equal volumes of any ideal gas contain equal numbers of particles.

**83.** 22.4 L; 44.8 L

**84.** Kelvin units; $V$ is not directly proportional to Celsius temperature.

**85.** high pressure and low temperature

**86.** $R = 0.0821$ atm·L/(mol·K) and $R = 8.314$ L·kPa/(mol·K)

### Chemistry Online

*Go to the Glencoe Chemistry Web site at* chemistrymc.com *for additional Chapter 14 Assessment.*

## Concept Mapping

**70.** Complete the following concept map that shows how Boyle's law, Charles's law, and Gay-Lussac's law are derived from the combined gas law.

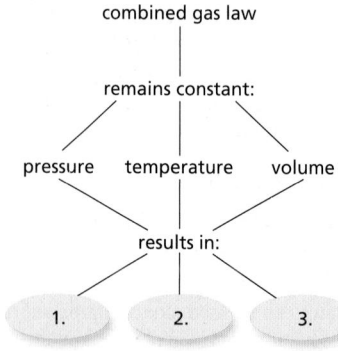

combined gas law

remains constant:

pressure    temperature    volume

results in:

1.    2.    3.

## Mastering Concepts

**71.** State the laws of Boyle, Charles, and Gay-Lussac as equations. (14.1)

**72.** What will happen to the pressure of a contained gas if its temperature is lowered? (14.1)

**73.** Why is it important not to puncture an aerosol can? (14.1)

**74.** Explain why an unopened bag of potato chips left in a hot car appears to become larger. (14.1)

**75.** If two variables have an inverse relationship, what happens to the value of one as the value of the other increases? (14.1)

**76.** If two variables have a direct relationship, what happens to the value of one as the value of the other is increased? (14.1)

**77.** Label the following examples as being generally representative of direct or inverse relationship. (14.1)

  **a.** popularity of a musical group versus how hard it is to get tickets for its concert
  **b.** number of carats a diamond weighs versus its cost
  **c.** number of people helping versus how long it takes to clean up after a party

**78.** Label the following examples as being representative of a direct or inverse relationship. (14.1)

  **a.** pressure versus volume of a gas
  **b.** volume versus temperature of a gas
  **c.** pressure versus temperature of a gas

**79.** What four variables are used to describe gases? (14.1)

**80.** List the standard conditions for gas measurements. (14.2)

**81.** Write the equation for the combined gas law. Identify the units most commonly used with each variable. (14.2)

**82.** State Avogadro's principle. (14.2)

**83.** What volume is occupied by one mole of a gas at STP? What volume do two moles occupy at STP? (14.2)

**84.** What units must be used to express the temperature in the equation for the ideal gas law? Explain. (14.3)

**85.** List two conditions under which a gas is least likely to behave ideally. (14.3)

**86.** Write the value and units for the gas constant R in two common forms. (14.3)

**87.** What information is needed to solve a volume-mass problem that involves gases? (14.4)

## Mastering Problems
### The Gas Laws (14.1)

**88.** Use Boyle's, Charles's, or Gay-Lussac's law to calculate the missing value in each of the following.

  **a.** $V_1 = 2.0$ L, $P_1 = 0.82$ atm, $V_2 = 1.0$ L, $P_2 = ?$
  **b.** $V_1 = 250$ mL, $T_1 = ?$, $V_2 = 400$ mL, $T_2 = 298$ K
  **c.** $V_1 = 0.55$ L, $P_1 = 740$ mm Hg, $V_2 = 0.80$ L, $P_2 = ?$
  **d.** $T_1 = 25°C$, $P_1 = ?$, $T_2 = 37°C$, $P_2 = 1.0$ atm

**89.** What is the pressure of a fixed volume of a gas at $30.0°C$ if it has a pressure of 1.11 atm at $15.0°C$?

**90.** A fixed amount of oxygen gas is held in a 1.00-L tank at a pressure of 3.50 atm. The tank is connected to an empty 2.00-L tank by a tube with a valve. After this valve has been opened and the oxygen is allowed to flow freely between the two tanks at a constant temperature, what is the final pressure in the system?

**91.** Hot-air balloons rise because the hot air inside the balloon is less dense than the cooler air outside. Calculate the volume an air sample will occupy inside a balloon at $43.0°C$ if it occupies 2.50 L at the outside air temperature of $22.0°C$, assuming the pressure is the same at both locations.

chemistrymc.com/chapter_test

**87.** balanced equation, at least one mass or volume value for a reactant or product, and $P$ and $T$ conditions under which gas volumes have been measured

### Resource Manager

**Chapter Assessment,** pp. 79–84 **L2**
**Supplemental Problems,** Ch. 14
**ExamView® Pro CD-ROM**
**MindJogger Videoquizzes DVD/VHS**
**Solutions Manual,** Ch. 14
**Chemistry Interactive CD-ROM,**
  Ch. 14 quiz

## The Combined Gas Law (14.2)

**92.** A sample of nitrogen gas is stored in a 500.0-mL flask at 108 kPa and 10.0°C. The gas is transferred to a 750.0-mL flask at 21.0°C. What is the pressure of nitrogen in the second flask?

**93.** The air in a dry, sealed 2-L soda bottle has a pressure of 0.998 atm at sea level at a temperature of 34.0°C. What will be its pressure if it is brought to a higher altitude where the temperature is only 23.0°C?

**94.** A weather balloon is filled with helium that occupies a volume of $5.00 \times 10^4$ L at 0.995 atm and 32.0°C. After it is released, it rises to a location where the pressure is 0.720 atm and the temperature is −12.0°C. What is the volume of the balloon at that new location?

## Avogadro's Principle (14.2)

**95.** Propane, $C_3H_8$, is a gas commonly used as a home fuel for cooking and heating.

    **a.** Calculate the volume that 0.540 mol of propane occupies at STP.

    **b.** Think about the size of this volume compared to the amount of propane that it contains. Why do you think propane is usually liquefied before it is transported?

**96.** Carbon monoxide, CO, is a product of incomplete combustion of fuels. Find the volume that 42 g of carbon monoxide gas occupies at STP.

## The Ideal Gas Law (14.3)

**97.** The lowest pressure achieved in a laboratory is about $1.0 \times 10^{-15}$ mm Hg. How many molecules of gas are present in a 1.00-L sample at that pressure and a temperature of 22.0°C?

**98.** Determine the density of chlorine gas at 22.0°C and 1.00 atm pressure.

**99.** Geraniol is a compound found in rose oil that is used in perfumes. What is the molar mass of geraniol if its vapor has a density of $0.480 \frac{g}{L}$ at a temperature of 260.0°C and a pressure of 0.140 atm?

**100.** A 2.00-L flask is filled with propane gas ($C_3H_8$) at 1.00 atm and −15.0°C. What is the mass of the propane in the flask?

## Gas Stoichiometry (14.4)

**101.** Ammonia is formed industrially by reacting nitrogen and hydrogen gases. How many liters of ammonia gas can be formed from 13.7 L of hydrogen gas at 93.0°C and a pressure of 40.0 kPa?

**102.** When 3.00 L of propane gas is completely combusted to form water vapor and carbon dioxide at a temperature of 350°C and a pressure of 0.990 atm, what mass of water vapor will result?

**103.** When heated, solid potassium chlorate ($KClO_3$) decomposes to form solid potassium chloride and oxygen gas. If 20.8 g of potassium chlorate decomposes, how many liters of oxygen gas will form at STP?

**104.** Use the reaction shown below to answer these questions.

$$CO(g) + NO(g) \rightarrow N_2(g) + CO_2(g)$$

    **a.** Balance the equation.

    **b.** What is the volume ratio of carbon monoxide to carbon dioxide in the balanced equation?

    **c.** If 42.7 g CO is reacted completely at STP, what volume of $N_2$ gas will be produced?

## Mixed Review

*Sharpen your problem-solving skills by answering the following.*

**105.** Gaseous methane ($CH_4$) undergoes complete combustion by reacting with oxygen gas to form carbon dioxide and water vapor.

    **a.** Write a balanced equation for this reaction.

    **b.** What is the volume ratio of methane to water in this reaction?

**106.** If 2.33 L of propane at 24°C and 67.2 kPa is completely burned in excess oxygen, how many moles of carbon dioxide will be produced?

**107.** Use Boyle's, Charles's, or Gay-Lussac's law to calculate the missing value in each of the following.

    **a.** $V_1 = 1.4$ L, $P_1 = ?$, $V_2 = 3.0$ L, $P_2 = 1.2$ atm

    **b.** $V_1 = 705$ mL, $T_1 = 273$ K, $V_2 = ?$, $T_2 = 323$ K

    **c.** $V_1 = 0.540$ L, $P_1 = ?$, $V_2 = 0.990$ L, $P_2 = 775$ mm Hg

    **d.** $T_1 = 37°C$, $P_1 = 5.0$ atm, $P_2 = 2.5$ atm, $T_2 = ?$

**108.** Determine the pressure inside a television picture tube with a volume of 3.50 L that contains $2.00 \times 10^{-5}$ g of nitrogen gas at 22.0°C.

**109.** Determine how many liters 8.80 g of carbon dioxide gas would occupy at:

    **a.** STP     **c.** 288 K and 118 kPa

    **b.** 160°C and 3.00 atm

**110.** If 5.00 L of hydrogen gas, measured at 20.0°C and 80.1 kPa is burned in excess oxygen to form water, what mass of oxygen (measured at the same temperature and pressure) will be consumed?

## Mastering Problems

Complete solutions to Chapter Assessment problems can be found in the **Solutions Manual.**

### The Gas Laws (14.1)
**Level 1**
**88. a.** 1.6 atm   **c.** 510 mm Hg
    **b.** 200 K   **d.** 0.96 atm
**89.** 1.17 atm

**Level 2**
**90.** 1.17 atm
**91.** 2.68 L

### The Combined Gas Law (14.2)
**Level 1**
**92.** 74.8 kPa
**93.** 0.962 atm

**Level 2**
**94.** $5.91 \times 10^4$ L

### Avogadro's Principle (14.2)
**Level 1**
**95. a.** 12.1 L
    **b.** It occupies a much smaller volume when liquefied.
**96.** 34 L

### The Ideal Gas Law (14.3)
**Level 1**
**97.** $3.3 \times 10^4$ molecules

**Level 2**
**98.** 2.93 g/L
**99.** $1.50 \times 10^2$ g/mol
**100.** 4.16 g

### Gas Stoichiometry (14.4)
**Level 1**
**101.** 9.13 L

**Level 2**
**102.** 4.2 g
**103.** 5.70 L

**104. a.** $2CO(g) + 2NO(g) \rightarrow N_2(g) + 2CO_2(g)$
    **b.** 1:1
    **c.** 17.1 L

## Mixed Review
**105. a.** $CH_4(g) + 2O_2(g) \rightarrow CO_2(g) + 2H_2O(g)$
    **b.** 1:2
**106.** 0.190 mol

**107. a.** 2.6 atm
    **b.** 834 mL
    **c.** 1420 mm Hg
    **d.** −118° C
**108.** $4.94 \times 10^{-6}$ atm
**109. a.** 4.48 L
    **b.** 2.37 L
    **c.** 4.06 L
**110.** 2.63 g

## Thinking Critically

**111.** Table: 30.0, 29.0, 28.0, 27.0, 26.0, 25.0 psi; Graph should show air pressure vs. temperature; the resulting plot will be a straight line showing a direct relationship between the variables. See the Solutions Manual.

**112.** $1.85 \times 10^3$ L

**113.** $8.314 \times 10^6$ Pa·cm³/(mol·K)

**114.** 20.4 atm

## Cumulative Review

**117. a.** 0.247 kg
   **b.** 53 000 kg
   **c.** $7.23 \times 10^{-9}$ kg
   **d.** $9.75 \times 10^{-4}$ kg

**118.** 5Ca, 10Mn, 40 O

**119.** $C_8H_6O_4$

**120.** c, b

## Thinking Critically —————

**111. Making and Using Graphs** Automobile tires become underinflated as temperatures drop during the winter months if no additional air is added to the tires at the start of the cold season. For every 10°F drop in temperature, the air pressure in a car's tires goes down by about 1 psi (14.7 psi equals 1.00 atm). Complete the following table. Then make a graph illustrating how the air pressure in a tire changes over the temperature range from 40°F to −10°F, assuming you start with a pressure of 30.0 psi at 40°F.

| Tire Inflation Based on Temperature | |
|---|---|
| Temperature (°F) | Pressure (psi) |
| 40 | |
| 30 | |
| 20 | |
| 10 | |
| 0 | |
| −10 | |

**112. Applying Concepts** When nitroglycerin $(C_3H_5N_3O_9)$ explodes, it decomposes into the following gases: $CO_2$, $N_2$, NO, and $H_2O$. If 239 g of nitroglycerin explodes, what volume will the mixture of gaseous products occupy at 1.00 atm pressure and 2678°C?

**113. Analyze and Conclude** What is the numerical value of the ideal gas constant (R) in

$$\frac{cm^3 \cdot Pa}{K \cdot mol}$$

**114. Applying Concepts** Calculate the pressure of a mixture of two gases that contains $4.67 \times 10^{22}$ molecules CO and $2.87 \times 10^{24}$ molecules of $N_2$ in a 6.00-L container at 34.8°C.

## Writing in Chemistry —————

**115.** It was the dream of many early balloonists to complete a trip around the world in a hot-air balloon, a goal not achieved until 1999. Write about what you imagine a trip in a balloon would be like, including a description of how manipulating air temperature would allow you to control altitude.

**116.** Investigate and explain the function of the regulators on the air tanks used by scuba divers.

## Cumulative Review —————

*Refresh your understanding of previous chapters by answering the following.*

**117.** Convert each of the following mass measurements to its equivalent in kilograms. (Chapter 2)

   **a.** 247 g
   **b.** 53 Mg
   **c.** 7.23 µg
   **d.** 975 mg

**118.** How many atoms of each element are present in five formula units of calcium permanganate? (Chapter 8)

**119.** Terephthalic acid is an organic compound used in the formation of polyesters. It contains 57.8 percent C, 3.64 percent H, and 38.5 percent O. The molar mass is known to be approximately 166 g/mol. What is the molecular formula of terephthalic acid? (Chapter 11)

**120.** The particles of which of the following gases have the highest average speed? The lowest average speed? (Chapter 13)

   **a.** carbon monoxide at 90°C
   **b.** nitrogen trifluoride at 30°C
   **c.** methane at 90°C
   **d.** carbon monoxide at 30°C

**450** Chapter 14 Gases

National Science Content Standards

Pages 450–451
UCP.2, UCP.3; B.2, B.3, B.4, B.6; E.2

*Use these questions and the test-taking tip to prepare for your standardized test.*

**1.** The kinetic-molecular theory describes the microscopic behavior of gases. One main point of the theory is that within a sample of gas, the frequency of collisions between individual gas particles and between the particles and the walls of their container increases if the sample is compressed. The gas law that states this relationship in mathematical terms is

  **a.** Gay-Lussac's Law.
  **b.** Charles's Law.
  **c.** Boyle's Law.
  **d.** Avogadro's Law.

**2.** Three 2.0-L containers are placed in a 50°C room. Samples of 0.5 mol $N_2$, 0.5 mol Xe, and 0.5 mol ethene ($C_2H_4$) are pumped into Containers 1, 2, and 3, respectively. Inside which container will the pressure, be greatest?

  **a.** Container 2
  **b.** Container 3
  **c.** Containers 2 and 3 have the same, higher pressure
  **d.** Containers 1, 2, and 3 have equal pressures

**Interpreting Graphs** Use the graph to answer questions 3–5.

**Pressures of Three Gases at Different Temperatures**

**3.** It can be seen from the graph that

  **a.** as temperature increases, pressure decreases.
  **b.** as pressure increases, volume decreases.
  **c.** as temperature decreases, moles decrease.
  **d.** as pressure decreases, temperature decreases.

**4.** Which of these gases is an ideal gas?
  **a.** Gas A      **c.** Gas C
  **b.** Gas B      **d.** none of the above

**5.** What is the predicted pressure of Gas B at 310 K?

  **a.** 260 kPa      **c.** 1000 kPa
  **b.** 620 kPa      **d.** 1200 kPa

**6.** What volume will 0.875 moles of $SF_4$ occupy at STP?

  **a.** 19.6 L      **c.** 22.4 L
  **b.** 21.4 L      **d.** 32.7 L

**7.** While it is on the ground, a blimp is filled with $5.66 \times 10^6$ L of He gas. The pressure inside the grounded blimp, where the temperature is 25°C, is 1.10 atm. Modern blimps are non-rigid, which means that their volume is changeable. If the pressure inside the blimp remains the same, what will be the volume of the blimp at a height of 2300 m, where the temperature is 12°C?

  **a.** $5.66 \times 10^6$ L      **c.** $5.4 \times 10^6$ L
  **b.** $2.72 \times 10^6$ L      **d.** $5.92 \times 10^6$ L

**8.** The reaction that provides blowtorches with their intense flame is the combustion of acetylene ($C_2H_2$) to form carbon dioxide and water vapor. Assuming that the pressure and temperature of the reactants are the same, what volume of oxygen gas is required to completely burn 5.60 L of acetylene?

  **a.** 2.24 L      **c.** 11.2 L
  **b.** 5.60 L      **d.** 14.0 L

**9.** A sample of argon gas is compressed into a volume of 0.712 L by a piston exerting 3.92 atm of pressure. The piston is slowly released until the pressure of the gas is 1.50 atm. What is the new volume of the gas?

  **a.** 0.272 L      **c.** 1.86 L
  **b.** 3.67 L      **d.** 4.19L

**10.** Assuming ideal behavior, how much pressure will 0.0468 g of ammonia ($NH_3$) gas exert on the walls of a 4.00-L container at 35.0°C?

  **a.** 0.0174 atm      **c.** 0.00198 atm
  **b.** 0.296 atm      **d.** 0.278 atm

---

**TEST-TAKING TIP**

**Ask Questions** If you've got a question about what will be on the test, the way the test is scored, the time limits placed on each section, or anything else. . .by all means ask! Will you be required to know the specific names of the gas laws, such as Boyle's law and Charles's law?

---

## Standardized Test Practice

**1.** c
**2.** d
**3.** d
**4.** d
**5.** b
**6.** a
**7.** c
**8.** d
**9.** c
**10.** a

# Resource Manager

| Section | Objectives | Activities/Features |
|---|---|---|
| **Section 15.1**<br>**What are solutions?**<br>1 session<br>½ block | **1. Describe** the characteristics of solutions and **identify** the various types.<br>**2. Relate** the intermolecular forces and the process of solvation.<br>**3. Define** solubility and **identify** factors affecting it. | **Discovery Lab:** Solution Formation, p. 453<br>**Earth Science Connection,** p. 457 |
| **Section 15.2**<br>**Solution Concentration**<br>2 sessions<br>1 block | **4. State** the concentrations of solutions in different ways.<br>**5. Calculate** the concentrations of solutions. | |
| **Section 15.3**<br>**Colligative Properties of Solutions**<br>2 sessions<br>1 block | **6. Explain** the nature of colligative properties.<br>**7. Describe** four colligative properties of solutions.<br>**8. Calculate** the boiling point elevation and the freezing point depression of a solution. | **MiniLab:** Freezing Point Depression, p. 473<br>**Careers Using Chemistry:** Renal Dialysis Technician, p. 475 |
| **Section 15.4**<br>**Heterogeneous Mixtures**<br>2 sessions<br>1 block | **9. Identify** the properties of suspensions and colloids.<br>**10. Describe** different types of colloids.<br>**11. Explain** the electrostatic forces in colloids. | **Problem-Solving Lab:** How can you measure the turbidity of a colloid? p. 478<br>**ChemLab CBL:** Beer's Law, pp. 480–481<br>**Chemistry and Society:** Sickle-Cell Disease, p. 482 |

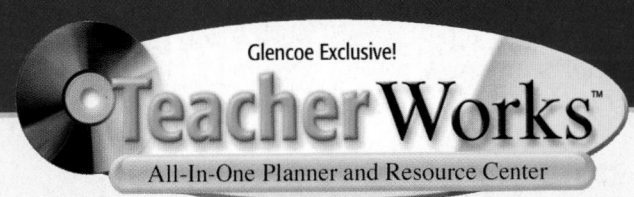

Glencoe Exclusive!
**TeacherWorks™**
All-In-One Planner and Resource Center

| National Science Content Standards | State/Local Standards | Reproducible Masters | Transparencies |
|---|---|---|---|
| UCP.1, UCP.2, UCP.4; B.2, B.4, B.5, B.6 | | **Study Guide for Content Mastery,** pp. 85–86 **L2** <br> **Laboratory Manual,** pp. 113–116 **L2** <br> **Small-Scale Laboratory Manual,** pp. 41–44 **L2** | **Section Focus** <br> **Transparency 55** **L1** **ELL** <br> **Teaching** <br> **Transparency 45** **L2** **ELL** |
| UCP.1, UCP.2, UCP.4; A.1, A.2; B.2 | | **Study Guide for Content Mastery,** pp. 87–88 <br> **ChemLab and MiniLab Worksheets,** pp. 58–60 **L2** | **Section Focus** <br> **Transparency 56** **L1** **ELL** <br> **Math Skills** <br> **Transparency 22** **L2** **ELL** |
| UCP.1, UCP.2, UCP.4; A.1; B.2, B.4, B.6 | | **Study Guide for Content Mastery,** p. 89 **L2** <br> **ChemLab and MiniLab Worksheets,** p. 57 **L2** <br> **CBL Laboratory Manual,** pp. 21–24 **L2** <br> **Challenge Problems,** p. 15 **L3** <br> **Laboratory Manual,** pp. 117–120 **L2** | **Section Focus** <br> **Transparency 57** **L1** **ELL** <br> **Teaching** <br> **Transparency 46** **L2** **ELL** <br> **Math Skills** <br> **Transparency 23** **L2** **ELL** |
| UCP.1, UCP.2, UCP.4; A.1, A.2; B.2, B.4, B.5, B.6; F.1, F.6 | | **Study Guide for Content Mastery,** p. 90 **L2** | **Section Focus** <br> **Transparency 58** **L1** **ELL** |

**Key to National Science Content Standards:** UCP = Unifying Concepts and Processes, A = Science as Inquiry, B = Physical Science, C = Life Science, D = Earth and Space Sciences, E = Science and Technology, F = Science in Personal and Social Perspectives, G = History and Nature of Science

Refer to pages 4T–5T of the Teacher Guide for an explanation of the National Science Content Standards correlations.

# Resource Manager

## Materials List

### ChemLab (pages 480–481)
CBL system, graphing calculator, Vernier colorimeter, DIN adaptor and cable, TI Graph-Link (optional), cuvette, cotton swabs, tissues, stock solution, unknown solution, distilled water, 50-mL graduated cylinder, 100-mL beakers (2), small test tubes (5), test-tube rack, pipette (2), pipette bulb, stirring rod

### Discovery Lab (page 453)
100-mL beakers (2), stirring rod, ammonium chloride ($NH_4Cl$), calcium chloride ($CaCl_2$), balance, 50-mL graduated cylinder, water

### MiniLab (page 473)
400-mL beakers (2), rock salt, water, stirring rods (2), 100-mL graduated cylinder, thermometers (2), balance, water, crushed ice

### Demonstration (pages 458–459)
20 g calcium acetate ($Ca(CH_3COO)_2$), 20 g potassium nitrate ($KNO_3$), stirring rods (2), hot plate, 125-mL Erlenmeyer flasks (2), water

## Preparation of Solutions

For a review of solution preparation, see page 46T of the Teacher Guide.

Quantities are for a class of 30 students.

### ChemLab (pages 480–481)
**stock blue dye solution** Prepare the stock blue dye solution by adding about six drops of blue food coloring to one liter of water. You may want to test the absorbance of the stock solution because poor results occur if the absorbance is greater than 0.6. It is important to use food coloring that is blue; other colors will not give the desired results in the exercise.

**unknown blue dye solution** Prepare the unknown solution by diluting the stock solution with water to an intermediate concentration. You may wish to prepare several unknowns and assign letters or numbers to each one.

## Assessment Resources

**Chapter Assessment,** pp. 85–90
**MindJogger Videoquizzes DVD/VHS**
**Alternate Assessment in the Science Classroom**
**ExamView® Pro CD-ROM**
**Solutions Manual,** Chapter 15
**Supplemental Problems,** Chapter 15
**Performance Assessment in the Science Classroom**
**Chemistry Interactive CD-ROM,** Chapter 15 quiz

## Additional Resources

**Spanish Resources** ELL
**Guided Reading Audio Program,** Chapter 15 ELL
**Cooperative Learning in the Science Classroom**
**Lab and Safety Skills in the Science Classroom**
**Lesson Plans**
**Block Scheduling Lesson Plans**
**Chemistrymc.com**

## Glencoe Technology

The following multimedia for this chapter are available from Glencoe.

**VIDEOTAPE/DVD**
MindJogger Videoquizzes,
Chapter 15

**CD-ROM**
**Chemistry: Matter and Change**
*Dissolving Table Salt,* Animation
*The Unique Properties of Water,* Video
*Spectrochemical Series,* Video

**CD-ROM**
**ExamView® Pro**
 **Testmaker**

**CD-ROM**
**Interactive Chalkboard**

**CD-ROM**
**TeacherWorks™**

## Multiple Learning Styles

Look for the following icons for strategies that emphasize different learning modalities.

**Kinesthetic**
Differentiated Instruction, pp. 465, 476;
Enrichment, p. 468

**Visual-Spatial**
Differentiated Instruction, p. 455; Extension,
p. 461; Quick Demo, p. 466

**Interpersonal**
Portfolio, p. 467

**Intrapersonal**
Portfolio, p. 456; Check for Understanding,
p. 461; Chemistry Journal, pp. 464, 474, 477

**Linguistic**
Chemistry Journal, pp. 457, 460; Differentiated
Instruction, p. 472

**Logical-Mathematical**
Quick Demo, p. 464; Math in Chemistry, p. 465;
Chemistry Journal, p. 466; Check for Understanding,
p. 469; Reteach, p. 470

## Key to Teaching Strategies

**L1** Level 1 activities should be appropriate for students with learning difficulties.

**L2** Level 2 activities should be within the ability range of all students.

**L3** Level 3 activities are designed for above-average students.

**ELL** ELL activities should be within the ability range of English Language Learners.

**COOP LEARN** Cooperative Learning activities are designed for small group work.

**P** These strategies represent student products that can be placed into a best-work portfolio.

These strategies are useful in a block scheduling format.

## ✔ Assessment Planner

**Portfolio Assessment**
Portfolio, TWE, pp. 456, 467, 483
Assessment, TWE, p. 475

**Performance Assessment**
Assessment, TWE, pp. 467, 479
ChemLab, SE, pp. 480–481
MiniLab, SE, p. 473
Discovery Lab, SE, p. 453

**Knowledge Assessment**
Assessment, TWE, pp. 455, 459, 461, 474
Section Assessment, SE, pp. 461, 470, 475, 479
Chapter Assessment, SE, pp. 484–487
Demonstration, TWE, p. 459
MiniLab, TWE, p. 473

**Skill Assessment**
Assessment, TWE, p. 470
ChemLab, TWE, p. 481
Problem-Solving Lab, TWE, p. 478

## Tying to Previous Knowledge

Have students review the following concepts before studying this chapter.
Chapter 3: classification of matter: solutions, alloys, heterogeneous and homogeneous mixtures
Chapter 8: ionic compounds
Chapter 9: covalent compounds
Chapter 11: determining moles and molar mass

## Using the Photo

Remind students that a solution is a homogeneous mixture. Ask them to explain how air, water, and steel each fulfill the definition of a solution.

## Chapter Themes

The following themes from the National Science Education Standards are covered in this chapter. Refer to page 4T of the Teacher Guide for an explanation of the correlations.
Systems, order, and organization (UCP.1)
Evidence, models, and explanation (UCP.2)
Change, constancy, and measurement (UCP.3)
Evolution and Equilibrium (UCP.4)
Form and function (UCP.5)

### Resource Manager

**Study Guide for Content Mastery,** pp. 85–86 L2
**Section Focus Transparency 55 and Master** L1 ELL
**Solving Problems: A Chemistry Handbook,** Section 15.1 L2
**Teaching Transparency 45 and Master** L2 ELL
**Lab Manual,** pp. 113–116 L2

# Solutions

## What You'll Learn

▶ You will describe and categorize solutions.
▶ You will calculate concentrations of solutions.
▶ You will analyze the colligative properties of solutions.
▶ You will compare and contrast heterogeneous mixtures.

## Why It's Important

The air you breathe, the fluids in your body, and some of the foods you ingest are solutions. Because solutions are so common, learning about their behavior is fundamental to understanding chemistry.

**Chemistry Online**

Visit the Chemistry Web site at chemistrymc.com to find links about solutions.

Though it isn't apparent, there are at least three different solutions in this photo; the air, the lake in the foreground, and the steel used in the construction of the buildings are all solutions.

452     Chapter 15

## DISCOVERY LAB

### Purpose
Students will investigate whether the dissolution of two different solids in water is an exothermic or endothermic process.

### Safety and Disposal
Dispose of solutions by rinsing them down the drain with excess water.

### Teaching Strategies
• After completing the lab, students may wish to experiment using other solids. Two other suggested solids to be dissolved are magnesium sulfate heptahydrate (Epsom salts) and anhydrous sodium borate (fused borax). Do not use plain borax, which is a decahydrate.

## DISCOVERY LAB

### Solution Formation

The intermolecular forces among dissolving particles and the attractive forces between solute and solvent particles result in an overall energy change. Can this change be observed?

### Safety Precautions

 Dispose of solutions by flushing them down a drain with excess water.

**Materials**

balance
50-mL graduated cylinder
100-mL beaker (2)
stirring rod
ammonium chloride (NH₄Cl)
calcium chloride (CaCl₂)
water

### Procedure

1. Measure 10 g of ammonium chloride ($NH_4Cl$) and place it in a 100-mL beaker.
2. Add 30 mL of water to the $NH_4Cl$, stirring with your stirring rod.
3. Feel the bottom of the beaker and record your observations.
4. Repeat the procedure with calcium chloride ($CaCl_2$).

### Analysis

Which dissolving process is exothermic? Endothermic? Suggest some practical applications for dissolving processes that are exothermic and for those that are endothermic.

---

# What are solutions?

## Objectives

- **Describe** the characteristics of solutions and **identify** the various types.
- **Relate** intermolecular forces and the process of solvation.
- **Define** solubility and **identify** factors affecting it.

## Vocabulary

soluble
insoluble
immiscible
miscible
solvation
heat of solution
solubility
saturated solution
unsaturated solution
supersaturated solution
Henry's law

Have you ever thought of the importance of solutions? Even if you haven't, the fact is that solutions are all around you. They are even inside you; you and all other organisms are composed of cells containing solutions that support life. You inhale a solution when you breathe. You are immersed in a solution whether standing in a room or swimming in a pool. Structures such as the ones shown in the photo on the previous page would not be possible without steel, yet another solution.

## Characteristics of Solutions

Cell solutions, ocean water, and steel may appear quite dissimilar, but they share certain characteristics. In Chapter 3, you learned that solutions are homogeneous mixtures containing two or more substances called the solute and the solvent. The solute is the substance that dissolves. The solvent is the dissolving medium. When you look at a solution, it is not possible to distinguish the solute from the solvent.

A solution may exist as a gas, liquid, or solid depending on the state of its solvent, as shown in **Figure 15-1** and **Table 15-1** on the next page. Air is a gaseous solution, and its solvent is nitrogen gas; braces may be made of nitinol, a solid solution of titanium in nickel. Most solutions, however, are liquids. You learned in Chapter 10 that reactions can take place in aqueous solutions, that is, solutions in which reactants and products are mixed in water. In fact, water is the most common solvent among liquid solutions.

15.1 What are solutions? **453**

---

# Section 15.1

## 1 Focus

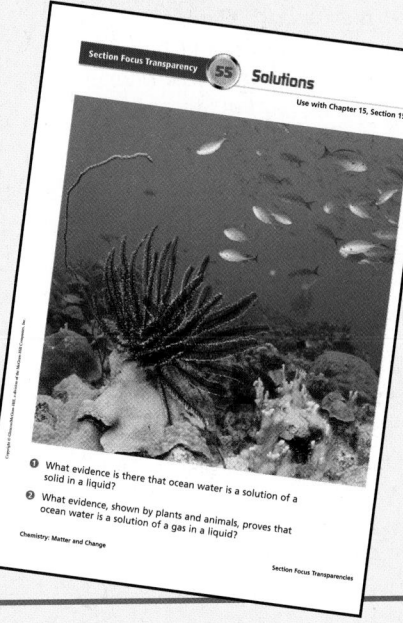

## 2 Teach

### Concept Development

Ask students to generate a list of solutions that they use regularly. Then, review the list in class to verify that students have correctly listed only solutions. **L2**

---

- For more precise results, students may use stirring rods and thermometers.

### Expected Results

calcium chloride: temperature increases
ammonium chloride: temperature decreases
(Optional solids)
Epsom salts: temperature decreases
Fused borax: temperature increases

### Analysis

Calcium chloride and fused borax dissolve exothermically. Ammonium chloride and Epsom salts dissolve endothermically. Suggestions about practical applications will vary, but might include hot packs and cold packs used for medical purposes.

**National Science Content Standards**

**Pages 452–453**
UCP.1, UCP.2, UCP.4; B.2, B.4, B.5, B.6

## In-Text Questions

**Page 454** Which solutions contain gaseous solutes? air, carbonated water, ocean water Which solutions are aqueous? carbonated water, ocean water, antifreeze, vinegar Are water and acetic acid miscible? yes

## Quick Demo

Fill three beakers with water. To the first beaker add 20 mL lemon juice, to the second beaker add 20 mL of vegetable oil, and to the third beaker add 20 mL of red or blue colored water. Stir each mixture thoroughly. Which mixtures appear to be solutions? Have students provide reasons for their responses. Ask which mixtures are miscible? Which are immiscible? 

**Figure 15-1**

**a** The air you breathe is a gas solution primarily containing oxygen, nitrogen, and argon. **b** The biological reactions necessary for life occur in aqueous solutions within cells. **c** A solid solution of titanium and nickel is commonly used for braces in orthodontia.

**Table 15-1** lists examples of different types of solutions. Note that the solutes in the solutions may be gases, liquids, or solids. Which solutions contain gaseous solutes? Which solutions are aqueous? Note also that solutions such as ocean water can contain more than one solute.

Some combinations of substances readily form solutions and others do not. A substance that dissolves in a solvent is said to be **soluble** in that solvent. For example, sugar is soluble in water, a fact you probably learned by dissolving sugar in flavored water to make a sweetened beverage such as tea, lemonade, or fruit punch. A substance that does not dissolve in a solvent is said to be **insoluble** in that solvent. Sand is insoluble in water. Have you ever shaken a bottle of oil and vinegar when making salad dressing? If so, what happens to the liquids shortly after you stop mixing them? You are correct if you answered that they separate, or cease to mix. Oil is insoluble in vinegar; and thus, oil and vinegar are said to be **immiscible**. Two liquids that are soluble in each other, such as those that form the antifreeze listed in **Table 15-1,** are said to be **miscible**. Are water and acetic acid miscible?

**Table 15-1**

| Types and Examples of Solutions | | | |
|---|---|---|---|
| **Type of solution** | **Example** | **Solvent** | **Solute** |
| **Gas** | | | |
| Gas in gas | Air | Nitrogen (gas) | Oxygen (gas) |
| **Liquid** | | | |
| Gas in liquid | Carbonated water | Water (liquid) | Carbon dioxide (gas) |
| Gas in liquid | Ocean water | Water (liquid) | Oxygen gas (gas) |
| Liquid in liquid | Antifreeze | Water (liquid) | Ethylene glycol (liquid) |
| Liquid in liquid | Vinegar | Water (liquid) | Acetic acid (liquid) |
| Solid in liquid | Ocean water | Water (liquid) | Sodium chloride (solid) |
| **Solid** | | | |
| Liquid in solid | Dental amalgam | Silver (solid) | Mercury (liquid) |
| Solid in solid | Steel | Iron (solid) | Carbon (solid) |

## Internet Address Book

**Chemistry Online** Note Internet addresses that you find useful in the space below for quick reference.

_____

_____

_____

_____

_____

**National Science Content Standards**

**Pages 454–455**
UCP.1, UCP.2, UCP.4; B.2, B.4, B.5

## Solvation in Aqueous Solutions

Why are some substances soluble in one another whereas others are not? To form a solution, solute particles must separate from one another and the solute and solvent particles must mix. Recall from Chapter 13 that attractive forces exist among the particles of all substances. Attractive forces exist between the pure solute particles, between the pure solvent particles, and between the solute and solvent particles. When a solid solute is placed in a solvent, the solvent particles completely surround the surface of the solid solute. If the attractive forces between the solvent and solute particles are greater than the attractive forces holding the solute particles together, the solvent particles pull the solute particles apart and surround them. These surrounded solute particles then move away from the solid solute, out into the solution. The process of surrounding solute particles with solvent particles to form a solution is called **solvation**. Solvation in water is called hydration.

"Like dissolves like" is the general rule used to determine whether solvation will occur in a specific solvent. To determine whether a solvent and solute are alike, you must examine the bonding and the polarity of the particles and the intermolecular forces between particles.

**Aqueous solutions of ionic compounds** Examine **Figure 15-2** to review the polar nature of water. Recall that water molecules are dipoles with partially positive and partially negative ends. Water molecules are in constant motion as described by the kinetic–molecular theory. When a crystal of an ionic compound, such as sodium chloride (NaCl), is placed in a beaker of water, the water molecules collide with the surface of the crystal. The charged ends of the water molecules attract the positive sodium ions and negative chloride ions. This attraction between the dipoles and the ions is greater than the attraction among the ions in the crystal, and so the ions break away from the surface. The water molecules surround the ions and the solvated ions move into solution, as shown in **Figure 15-3**. This exposes more ions on the surface of the crystal. Solvation continues until the entire crystal has dissolved and all ions are distributed throughout the solvent.

Gypsum is a compound composed of calcium ions and sulfate ions. It is mixed with water to make plaster. Plaster is a mixture, not a solution. Gypsum is insoluble in water because the attractive forces among the ions in calcium sulfate are so strong that they cannot be overcome by the attractive forces exerted by the water molecules. Solvation does not occur.

**Figure 15-2**

The bent shape of a water molecule results in dipoles that do not cancel each other out. The molecule has a net polarity, with the oxygen end being partially negative and the hydrogen ends being partially positive. Refer to **Table C-1** in Appendix C for a key to atom color conventions.

### Solvation Process of NaCl

Hydrated ions

Na⁺ ions

Cl⁻ ions

Water molecules

**Figure 15-3**

Solid sodium chloride dissolves as its ions are surrounded by solvent water molecules. Note how the polar water molecules orient themselves differently around the positive and negative ions.

15.1 What are solutions? **455**

## GLENCOE TECHNOLOGY

**CD-ROM**
**Chemistry: Matter and Change**
Animation: *Dissolving Table Salt*
Video: *The Unique Properties of Water*
Video: *Spectrochemical Series*

## DIFFERENTIATED INSTRUCTION

### English Language Learners

 ***Visual-Spatial*** Have students create a poster or diagram illustrating solvation. They should label the positive and negative ions and the polar ends of the water molecule. Have them share their posters or diagrams with the rest of the class and explain the process. **L2 ELL**

## Visual Learning

**Figure 15-2** Use the figure to review the polar nature of water. Remind students of the kinetic theory and stress that water molecules are constantly moving.

### Identifying Misconceptions

Students often think that water is the solvent in all solutions.

**Uncover the Misconception**
Provide the class with as many common solutions as possible. Solutions can include: window cleaning products; brass, steel, and pewter; rubbing alcohol; tincture of iodine; carbonated soda; and sport drinks. Ask groups of students to describe the composition of each solution, and if possible, state the solvent, the solute, and the states of matter in each.

**Demonstrate the Concept**
Write the column headings mixture, solute, and solvent on the board and have student groups list the components of the mixture. Help students label the components as solid, liquid, or gas. Students should start to realize that solutions are not just solids dissolved in liquids, and that water is not always the solvent.

**Assess New Knowledge**
Call on students to cite examples of different types of solution systems.

### Assessment

**Knowledge** Have students write an explanation of the general rule "like dissolves like" in their own words, citing examples from their own experiences. **L2**

## Visual Learning

**Figure 15-5** Ask students to study the figure and reason why oil spills in nature are difficult to clean up. Discuss the far-ranging environmental impact of an oil spill.

## Applying Chemistry

**TECH PREP**

Soaps and laundry detergents are an application of the rule "like dissolves like." Long hydrocarbon chains make up most soaps and detergents. These chains are nonpolar except for the carboxyl group at one end. The long nonpolar hydrocarbon chains are attracted to the grease, grime, and oil in clothing and tend to surround the stain particles. The polar ends of the soap molecule orient themselves toward the water molecules. As a result, the nonpolar stain that is surrounded by soap molecules can be washed out of the fabric.

## In-Text Question

**Page 456** Can you think of an example of how an increase in temperature affects the rate of dissolving? Examples will vary. One example is that sugar dissolves more quickly in hot tea than in iced tea.

**Resource Manager**

Small-Scale Laboratory Manual, pp. 41–44 **L2**

**National Science Content Standards**

Pages 456–457
UCP.1, UCP.2, UCP.4; B.2, B.4, B.6

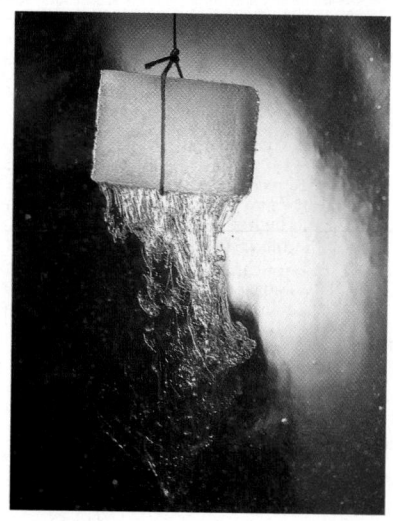

**Figure 15-4**

The solvation of a sugar cube (sucrose) can be seen in the above photo. Polar sucrose ($C_{12}H_{22}O_{11}$) molecules contain eight O–H bonds. Forces between polar water molecules and polar sucrose molecules break these O–H bonds and the sucrose dissolves.

**Figure 15-5**

Nonpolar oil molecules do not mix with polar water molecules. Because oil is less dense than water, it floats on the water's surface. For this reason, oil spills at sea often wash ashore.

**Aqueous solutions of molecular compounds** Water also is a good solvent for many molecular compounds. You know that table sugar dissolves in water. Table sugar is the molecular compound sucrose. See **Figure 15-4**. Note that its structure has a number of O–H bonds. Sucrose molecules are polar. When water is added to sucrose, each O–H bond becomes a site for hydrogen bonding with water. As soon as the sugar crystals contact the water, water molecules collide with the outer surface of the crystal. The attractive forces among sucrose molecules are overcome by the attractive forces between polar water molecules and polar sucrose molecules. Sugar molecules leave the crystal and become solvated by water molecules.

The oil in **Figure 15-5** is a substance made up of primarily carbon and hydrogen. It does not form a solution with water. Why are oil and water immiscible? There is little attraction between the polar water molecules and the nonpolar oil molecules. However, oil spills can be cleaned up with a nonpolar solvent. Nonpolar solutes are more readily dissolved in nonpolar solvents.

**Factors that affect rate of solvation** As you have just learned, solvation occurs only when and where the solute and solvent particles come in contact with each other. There are three common ways to increase the collisions between solute and solvent particles, and thus increase the rate at which the solute dissolves: agitating the mixture, increasing the surface area of the solute, and increasing the temperature of the solvent.

Agitating the mixture by stirring and shaking moves dissolved solute particles away from the contact surfaces more quickly and thereby allows new collisions between solute and solvent particles to occur. Without stirring or shaking, solvated particles move away from the contact areas slowly. Breaking the solute into small pieces increases its surface area. A greater surface area allows more collisions to occur. This is why a teaspoon of granulated sugar dissolves more quickly than an equal amount of sugar in a cube. Raising the temperature of the solvent increases the kinetic energy of its particles, resulting in more frequent collisions and collisions with greater energy than those that occur at lower temperatures. Can you think of an example of how an increase in temperature affects the rate of dissolving?

**456** **Chapter 15** Solutions

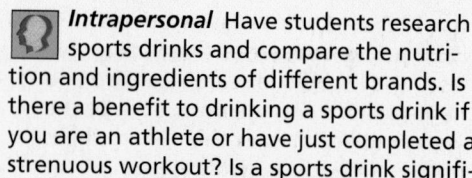

**Portfolio**

### Sport Drinks

*Intrapersonal* Have students research sports drinks and compare the nutrition and ingredients of different brands. Is there a benefit to drinking a sports drink if you are an athlete or have just completed a strenuous workout? Is a sports drink signifi- cantly different from other noncarbonated, flavored beverages? Have students compare the cost of various sports drinks to other flavored noncarbonated beverages. Have them place their findings in their portfolios. **L2**

**P**

**Heat of solution** During the process of solvation, the solute must separate into particles. Solvent particles also must move apart in order to allow solute particles to come between them. Energy is required to overcome the attractive forces within the solute and within the solvent, so both steps are endothermic. When solute and solvent particles mix, the particles attract each other and energy is released. This step in the solvation process is exothermic. The overall energy change that occurs during the solution formation process is called the **heat of solution.**

As you observed in the **DISCOVERY LAB** at the beginning of this chapter, some solutions release energy as they form, whereas others absorb energy during formation. For example, after ammonium nitrate dissolves in water, its container feels cool. In contrast, after calcium chloride dissolves in water, its container feels warm. You will learn more about the heat of solution in the next chapter.

## Solubility

If you have ever added so much sugar to a sweetened beverage that sugar crystals accumulated on the container's bottom, then you know that only a limited amount of solute can dissolve in a solvent at a given set of conditions. In fact, every solute has a characteristic solubility. **Solubility** refers to the maximum amount of solute that will dissolve in a given amount of solvent at a specified temperature and pressure. As you can see from **Table 15-2,** solubility is usually expressed in grams of solute per 100 g of solvent.

Table 15-2

| Solubilities of Some Solutes in Water at Various Temperatures | | | | | |
|---|---|---|---|---|---|
| Substance | Formula | Solubility (g/100 g $H_2O$)* | | | |
| | | 0°C | 20°C | 60°C | 100°C |
| Aluminum sulfate | $Al_2(SO_4)_3$ | 31.2 | 36.4 | 59.2 | 89.0 |
| Ammonium chloride | $NH_4Cl$ | 29.4 | 37.2 | 55.3 | 77.3 |
| Barium hydroxide | $Ba(OH)_2$ | 1.67 | 3.89 | 20.94 | — |
| Barium nitrate | $Ba(NO_3)_2$ | 4.95 | 9.02 | 20.4 | 34.4 |
| Calcium hydroxide | $Ca(OH)_2$ | 0.189 | 0.173 | 0.121 | 0.076 |
| Lead(II) chloride | $PbCl_2$ | 0.67 | 1.00 | 1.94 | 3.20 |
| Lithium sulfate | $Li_2SO_4$ | 36.1 | 34.8 | 32.6 | — |
| Potassium chloride | $KCl$ | 28.0 | 34.2 | 45.8 | 56.3 |
| Potassium sulfate | $K_2SO_4$ | 7.4 | 11.1 | 18.2 | 24.1 |
| Sodium chloride | $NaCl$ | 35.7 | 35.9 | 37.1 | 39.2 |
| Silver nitrate | $AgNO_3$ | 122 | 216 | 440 | 733 |
| Sucrose | $C_{12}H_{22}O_{11}$ | 179.2 | 203.9 | 287.3 | 487.2 |
| Ammonia* | $NH_3$ | 1130 | 680 | 200 | — |
| Carbon dioxide* | $CO_2$ | 1.713 | 0.878 | 0.359 | — |
| Oxygen* | $O_2$ | 0.048 | 0.031 | 0.019 | — |

\* L/1 L $H_2O$ of gas at standard pressure (101 kPa)
— No value available

## Earth Science
### CONNECTION

Water is the most abundant solvent on Earth. The amount of oxygen contained in water is called dissolved oxygen (DO). Dissolved oxygen is an indicator of water quality because oxygen is necessary for fish and other aquatic life. Oxygen enters a body of water by photosynthesis of aquatic plants and by transfer of oxygen across the air-water boundary.

Thermal pollution is a reduction in water quality due to an increase in water temperature. The discharge of heated water into a lake, river, or other body of water by factories or power plants causes the solubility of oxygen in water to decrease. In addition to not having enough oxygen to support life, as shown below, the lower oxygen level magnifies the effects of toxic and organic pollutants.

To reduce thermal pollution, measures must be taken before the heated water is released into the environment. The water can be discharged into holding lakes or canals and allowed to cool. In addition, many facilities use cooling towers to dissipate heat into the air.

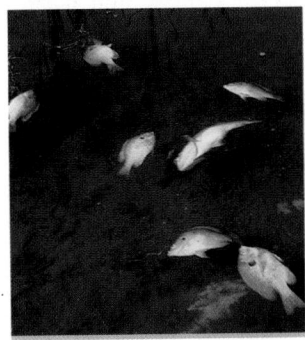

## Visual Learning

**Table 15-2** Ask students questions based on the data in the table. What happens to the solubility of aluminum sulfate as temperature increases? Ammonium chloride? Potassium chloride? Their solubilities increase. Is there a trend or pattern that can be suggested concerning solubility of a substance as temperature increases? The solubility of most non-gas substances increases with increasing temperature. Are there any exceptions? calcium hydroxide, ammonia, carbon dioxide, oxygen Have students note that with the exception of calcium hydroxide, the other three substances are gases that obey Henry's law.

## CHEMISTRY JOURNAL

### Making Solutions

*Linguistic* Have students write a paragraph explaining how a solubility graph can be used in making saturated, unsaturated, and supersaturated solutions. Then, have students exchange paragraphs and use them to make each type of solution. L2

**Page 458** According to Figure 15-7 and Table 15-2, what substances decrease in solubility as temperature increases? $Ce_2(SO_4)_3$, calcium hydroxide, lithium sulfate, ammonia, carbon dioxide, oxygen

## Figure Caption Question

**Figure 15-7** What is the solubility of $KClO_3$ at 60°C? 21 g of solute/100 g $H_2O$

## Concept Development

Use the following analogy to help students understand the terms *saturated, unsaturated,* and *supersaturated.* Suggest that the seats in the classroom represent the amount of solvent. Students represent the solute. If there are 20 students and 25 seats, there is still room to add more students; similarly, additional solute can be added to an unsaturated solution. With 25 students and 25 chairs, the classroom holds the maximum number of students it can accommodate; similarly, a saturated solution can accommodate no more solute. With 30 students squeezing into 25 chairs, the classroom holds more students than it normally can; similarly, a supersaturated solution contains more solute than the solution can normally hold. Have students note that students in the supersaturated class are not comfortable, just as a supersaturated solution is comparatively unstable. When the uncomfortable extra students get tired of being squeezed, they stand up and vacate the chairs. This is analogous to excess solute crystallizing out of a supersaturated solution. **L1** **ELL**

**Figure 15-6**

A dynamic equilibrium exists in a saturated solution. That is, the rate at which solute particles in the crystal are solvated is equal to the rate at which solvated solute particles rejoin the crystal.

**Figure 15-7**

This graph shows the solubility of several substances as a function of temperature. What is the solubility of $KClO_3$ at 60°C?

### Solubilities as a Function of Temperature

Just as solvation can be understood at the particle level, so can solubility. When a solute is added to a solvent, solvent particles collide with the solute's surface particles; solute particles begin to mix randomly among the solvent particles. At first, the solute particles are carried away from the crystal. However, as the number of solvated particles increases, the same random mixing results in increasingly frequent collisions between solvated solute particles and the remaining crystal. Some colliding solute particles rejoin the crystal, or crystallize as you can see in **Figure 15-6.** As solvation continues, the crystallization rate increases while the solvation rate remains constant. As long as the solvation rate is greater than the crystallization rate, the net effect is continuing solvation.

Depending on the amount of solute present, the rates of solvation and crystallization may eventually equalize: no more solute appears to dissolve and a state of dynamic equilibrium exists between crystallization and solvation (as long as the temperature remains constant). Although solute particles continue to dissolve and crystallize in solutions that reach equilibrium, the overall amount of dissolved solute in the solution remains constant. Such a solution is said to be a **saturated solution;** it contains the maximum amount of dissolved solute for a given amount of solvent at a specific temperature and pressure. An **unsaturated solution** is one that contains less dissolved solute for a given temperature and pressure than a saturated solution. In other words, more solute can be dissolved in an unsaturated solution.

## Factors That Affect Solubility

Pressure affects the solubility of gaseous solutes and gaseous solutions. The solubility of a solute also depends on the nature of the solute and solvent. Temperature affects the solubility of all substances. To learn how a blood disorder called sickle-cell disease can affect oxygen's solubility in blood, read the **Chemistry and Society** feature at the end of this chapter.

**Temperature and solubility** Many substances are more soluble at high temperatures than at low temperatures, as you can see by the data graphed in **Figure 15-7.** For example, calcium chloride ($CaCl_2$) has a solubility of about 64 g $CaCl_2$ per 100 g $H_2O$ at 10°C. Increasing the temperature to approximately 27°C increases the solubility by 50%, to 100 g $CaCl_2$ per 100 g $H_2O$. This fact also is illustrated by the data in **Table 15-2,** on the previous page. From the table you can see that at 20°C, 203.9 g of sucrose ($C_{12}H_{22}O_{11}$) dissolves in 100 g of water. At 100°C, 487.2 g of sucrose dissolves in 100 g of water, nearly a 140% increase in solubility over an 80°C temperature range. According to **Figure 15-7** and **Table 15-2,** what substances decrease in solubility as temperature increases?

---

## Demonstration

### Temperature and Solubility

**Purpose**
To demonstrate the effect of temperature on solubility

**Materials**
125-mL Erlenmeyer flasks (2); hot plate; stirring rods (2); $Ca(CH_3COO)_2$ (20 g); $KNO_3$ (20 g); water

**Safety Precautions**
**Disposal**
Rinse the chemicals down the drain with at least 100 times their volume in water.

**Procedure**
Measure out 20 g each of calcium acetate ($Ca(CH_3COO)_2$) and potassium nitrate ($KNO_3$). Place each solid in a separate 125-mL Erlenmeyer flask containing 50 mL of water. Have students note that the calcium acetate dissolves, whereas the $KNO_3$ is only partially soluble. Have students predict what will happen if the solutions are heated. Place both flasks on a hot plate and heat the solutions, stirring occasionally.

**Results**
The dissolved calcium acetate will crystallize and the undissolved $KNO_3$ will dissolve.

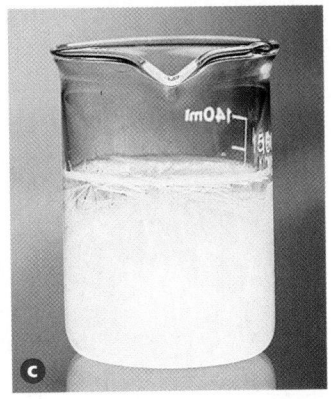

## Visual Learning

**Figure 15-9** Ask students to brainstorm other examples of supersaturated solutions. Point out the figure and the description in the text of cloud seeding to promote rainfall. An example of a supersaturated solution in cooking is the making of fudge.

**Figure 15-8**

Sodium acetate ($NaC_2H_3O_2$) is commonly used in the preparation of a supersaturated solution. When a seed crystal is added **a**, the excess sodium acetate quickly crystallizes out of the solution, **b** and **c**.

As you can see from **Table 15-2,** the gases oxygen and carbon dioxide are less soluble at higher temperatures than at lower temperatures. This is a predictable trend for all gaseous solutes in liquid solvents. Can you explain why? Recall from Chapter 13 that the kinetic energy of gas particles allows them to escape from a solution more readily at higher temperatures. Thus, as a solution's temperature increases, the solubility of a gaseous solute decreases.

The fact that solubility changes with temperature and that some substances become more soluble with increasing temperature, is the key to forming supersaturated solutions. A **supersaturated solution** contains more dissolved solute than a saturated solution at the same temperature. To make a supersaturated solution, a saturated solution is formed at a high temperature and then cooled slowly. The slow cooling allows the excess solute to remain dissolved in solution at the lower temperature, as shown in **Figure 15-8a.** Supersaturated solutions are unstable. If a tiny amount of solute, called a seed crystal, is added to a supersaturated solution, the excess solute precipitates quickly, as shown in **Figures 15-8b** and **15-8c.** Crystallization can also occur if the inside of the container is scratched or the supersaturated solution undergoes a physical shock such as stirring or tapping the container. Using crystals of silver iodide (AgI) to seed air supersaturated with water vapor causes the water particles to come together and form droplets that may fall to Earth as rain. This often-performed technique is called cloud seeding. The rock candy and mineral deposits at the edges of mineral springs, shown in **Figure 15-9,** are formed from supersaturated solutions.

**Figure 15-9**

Examples of crystals that formed from supersaturated solutions include rock candy and hot spring mineral deposits.

15.1 What are solutions?     **459**

### Quick Demo

Before class, prepare a supersaturated solution. To do this, slowly heat approximately 10 g of sodium acetate with about 8 mL of distilled water in a small Erlenmeyer flask until the solid is completely dissolved. Let the solution cool to room temperature, being careful not to disturb it while cooling. Add one or two crystals of sodium acetate to the solution and have students observe the sodium acetate crystals form. The sodium acetate may be reused after the water is allowed to evaporate.

### Assessment

**Knowledge** Ask students to write a paragraph describing what they would expect to observe when one or two crystals of a solute are added to unsaturated, saturated, and supersaturated solutions. **L2**

### National Science Content Standards

**Pages 458–459**
UCP.1, UCP.2, UCP.4; B.2, B.4, B.6

| Solubility in g/100 mL $H_2O$ | | |
|---|---|---|
| **Solid** | **0°C** | **100°C** |
| $Ca(CH_3COO)_2$ | 37.4 | 29.7 |
| $KNO_3$ | 13.3 | 24.7 |

Because the solubility of calcium acetate decreases as the temperature increases, it begins to crystallize out of solution at higher temperatures. The solubility of $KNO_3$ increases dramatically at higher temperatures.

**Analysis**

1. Do the observations agree with your predictions? Most students will predict that both substances will dissolve when heated.
2. Which substance has a positive enthalpy of solution? $KNO_3$
3. Is the slope of the calcium acetate's solubility curve positive or negative? negative

### Assessment

**Knowledge** Ask students to use this demonstration to review Le Châtelier's principle as it relates to solution equilibrium. Potassium nitrate has a positive enthalpy of solution (endothermic) and the graph of solubility versus temperature has a positive slope. The opposite is true for calcium acetate.

**459**

**Figure 15-10**

**ⓐ** When the cap on the soda bottle is closed, pressure above the solution keeps excess carbon dioxide ($CO_2$) from escaping the solution. **ⓑ** When the cap is removed, the decreased pressure above the solution results in the decreased solubility of the carbon dioxide—the carbon dioxide escapes the solution.

**Pressure and solubility** Pressure affects the solubility of gaseous solutes. The solubility of a gas in any solvent increases as its external pressure (the pressure above the solution) increases. Carbonated beverages depend on this fact. Carbonated beverages contain carbon dioxide gas dissolved in an aqueous solution. The dissolved gas gives the beverage its fizz. In bottling the beverage, carbon dioxide is dissolved in the solution at a pressure higher than atmospheric pressure. When the beverage container is opened, the pressure of the carbon dioxide gas in the space above the liquid (in the neck of the bottle) decreases. As a result, bubbles of carbon dioxide gas form in the solution, rise to the top, and escape. See **Figure 15-10.** Unless the cap is placed back on the bottle, the process will continue until the solution loses almost all of its carbon dioxide gas and goes flat.

**Henry's law** The decreased solubility of the carbon dioxide contained in the beverage after its cap is removed can be described by Henry's law. **Henry's law** states that at a given temperature, the solubility ($S$) of a gas in a liquid is directly proportional to the pressure ($P$) of the gas above the liquid. You can express this relationship in the following way

$$\frac{S_1}{P_1} = \frac{S_2}{P_2}$$

where $S_1$ is the solubility of a gas at a pressure $P_1$ and $S_2$ is the solubility of the gas at the new pressure $P_2$.

You often will solve Henry's law for the solubility $S_2$ at a new pressure $P_2$, where $P_2$ is known. The basic rules of algebra can be used to solve Henry's law for any one specific variable. To solve for $S_2$, begin with the standard form of Henry's law.

$$\frac{S_1}{P_1} = \frac{S_2}{P_2}$$

Cross-multiplying yields,

$$S_1P_2 = P_1S_2$$

Dividing both sides of the equation by $P_1$ yields the desired result, the equation solved for $S_2$.

$$\frac{S_1P_2}{P_1} = \frac{\cancel{P_1}S_2}{\cancel{P_1}} \qquad\qquad S_2 = \frac{S_1P_2}{P_1}$$

**National Science Content Standards**

**Pages 460–461**
UCP.1, UCP.2, UCP.4; B.2, B.4, B.6

## CHEMISTRY JOURNAL

### Air and Health

**Linguistic** Have students research the historical development of the composition of air used in scuba tanks and diving bells. They should include information about decompression sickness or the "bends" and discuss its cause and remedy. Have student use Henry's law to discuss the "bends." Another topic for research is the use of hyperbaric chambers in hospitals. The chambers use increased oxygen concentration in the air in order to increase the amount of oxygen that reaches a patient's blood and brain. The chambers are commonly used to promote healing of burn victims as the increased oxygen supply helps to regenerate cells. **L2**

## EXAMPLE PROBLEM 15-1

**Using Henry's Law**
If 0.85 g of a gas at 4.0 atm of pressure dissolves in 1.0 L of water at 25°C, how much will dissolve in 1.0 L of water at 1.0 atm of pressure and the same temperature?

### 1. Analyze the Problem

You are given the solubility of a gas at an initial pressure. The temperature of the gas remains constant as the pressure changes. Because decreasing pressure reduces a gas's solubility, less gas should dissolve at the lower pressure.

| Known | Unknown |
|---|---|
| $S_1 = 0.85$ g/L | $S_2 = ?$ g/L |
| $P_1 = 4.0$ atm | |
| $P_2 = 1.0$ atm | |

### 2. Solve for the Unknown

Rearrange Henry's law to solve for $S_2$.

$$\frac{S_1}{P_1} = \frac{S_2}{P_2}, \quad S_2 = S_1\left(\frac{P_2}{P_1}\right)$$

Substitute the known values into the equation and solve.

$$S_2 = (0.85 \text{g/L})\left(\frac{1.0 \text{ atm}}{4.0 \text{ atm}}\right) = 0.21 \text{g/L}$$

### 3. Evaluate the Answer

The answer is correctly expressed to two significant figures. The solubility decreased as expected. The pressure on the solution was reduced from 4.0 atm to 1.0 atm, so the solubility should be reduced to one-fourth its original value, which it is.

## PRACTICE PROBLEMS

1. If 0.55 g of a gas dissolves in 1.0 L of water at 20.0 kPa of pressure, how much will dissolve at 110.0 kPa of pressure?

2. A gas has a solubility of 0.66 g/L at 10.0 atm of pressure. What is the pressure on a 1.0-L sample that contains 1.5 g of gas?

*Practice!* For more practice with Henry's law problems, go to **Supplemental Practice Problems** in Appendix A.

---

## Section 15.1 Assessment

3. Describe the characteristics of a solution and identify the various types.

4. How do intermolecular forces affect solvation?

5. What is solubility? Describe two factors that affect solubility.

6. **Thinking Critically** If a seed crystal was added to a supersaturated solution, how would you characterize the resulting solution?

7. **Making and Using Graphs** Use the information in **Table 15-2** to graph the solubilities of aluminum sulfate, lithium sulfate, and potassium sulfate at 0°C, 20°C, 60°C, and 100°C. Which substance's solubility is most affected by increasing temperature?

---

## Section 15.1 Assessment

3. All solutions are homogeneous mixtures containing two or more substances. Solutions may be liquid, solid, or gas. Solution types are identified in Table 15-1.

4. The attractive forces between solute and solvent particles overcome the forces holding the solute particles together, thus pulling the solute particles apart.

5. Solubility refers to the maximum amount of solute that can dissolve in a given amount of solvent at a particular temperature and pressure. Surface area, temperature, and pressure affect solubility.

6. After the excess solute particles crystallize out of solution, the solution is saturated.

7. Aluminum sulfate shows the greatest change in solubility over the temperature range.

**461**

---

# 3 Assess
## Check for Understanding

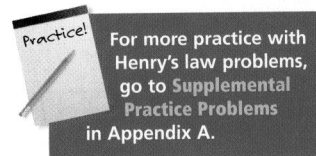

*Intrapersonal* Ask students to identify at least one solid solute and one gaseous solute in ocean water. Ask students to compare the degree of solubility of oxygen or carbon dioxide (two common gases dissolved in ocean water) in warmer regions (near the equator) with ocean water in colder regions of the world. Have students describe the difference in solubility using Henry's law. **L2**

## Reteach

Have students write the equation for Henry's law and explain the equation in their own words. **L2**

## Extension

*Visual-Spatial* Ask students to hypothesize about the oxygen needs of fish found in different regions of the world with different water temperatures. Discuss the terms *dissolved oxygen (DO)* and *biological oxygen demand (BOD)*. Make a connection about what happens to the amount of dissolved oxygen as the temperature increases. Have students draw a solubility graph for the amount of oxygen dissolved based on ocean water temperature. **L2**

## ✓ Assessment

**Knowledge** Ask students to explain why a carbonated soda, once opened, will go flat more quickly at room temperature than when placed in a refrigerator. **L2**

# 1 Focus

Before presenting the lesson, display **Section Focus Transparency 56** on the overhead projector. Have students answer the accompanying questions using **Section Focus Transparency Master 56.** **L1** **ELL**

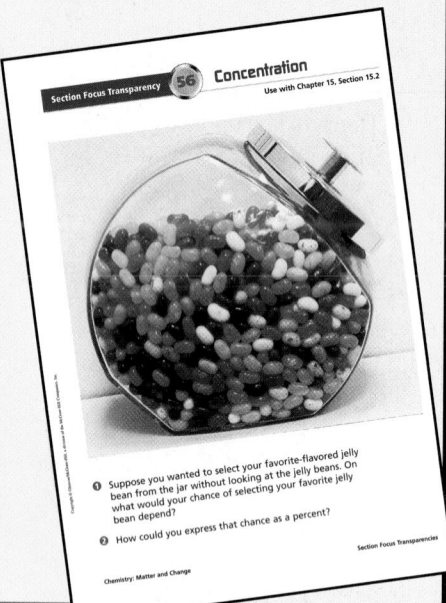

# 2 Teach
## In-Text Question

**Page 462** How do you know that the tea on the right in Figure 15-11 is a more dilute solution than the tea on the left? It has a very light color compared with the other cup of tea.

## Visual Learning

**Table 15-3** Refer to the table and introduce the different concentration ratios that will be described in this chapter. Emphasize that all are ratios expressing amount of solute per amount of solution and that different units are used for different concentration ratios. Have students match an equation or definition with the appropriate concentration ratio.

---

# Solution Concentration

## Objectives
- **State** the concentrations of solutions in different ways.
- **Calculate** the concentrations of solutions.

## Vocabulary
concentration
molarity
molality
mole fraction

You have learned about the process of solvation and the factors that affect solubility. The **concentration** of a solution is a measure of how much solute is dissolved in a specific amount of solvent or solution. How would you describe the concentration of the solutions in **Figure 15-11**? Concentration may be described qualitatively using the words *concentrated* or *dilute*. In general, a concentrated solution, as shown on the left in **Figure 15-11,** contains a large amount of solute. Conversely, a dilute solution contains a small amount of solute. How do you know that the tea on the right in **Figure 15-11** is a more dilute solution than the tea on the left?

## Expressing Concentration

Although qualitative descriptions of concentration can be useful, solutions are more often described quantitatively. Some commonly used quantitative descriptions are percent by either mass or volume, molarity, and molality. These descriptions express concentration as a ratio of measured amounts of solute and solvent or solution. **Table 15-3** lists each ratio's description.

You may be wondering if one description is preferable to another. The description used depends on the type of solution analyzed and the reason for describing it. For example, a chemist working with a reaction in an aqueous solution most likely refers to the molarity of the solution, because he or she needs to know the number of particles involved in the reaction.

**Table 15-3**

| Concentration Ratios | |
|---|---|
| **Concentration description** | **Ratio** |
| Percent by mass | $\dfrac{\text{mass of solute}}{\text{mass of solution}} \times 100$ |
| Percent by volume | $\dfrac{\text{volume of solute}}{\text{volume of solution}} \times 100$ |
| Molarity | $\dfrac{\text{moles of solute}}{\text{liter of solution}}$ |
| Molality | $\dfrac{\text{moles of solute}}{\text{kilogram of solvent}}$ |
| Mole fraction | $\dfrac{\text{moles of solute}}{\text{moles of solute} + \text{moles of solvent}}$ |

**Figure 15-11**

The strength of the tea corresponds to its concentration. The darker cup of tea is more concentrated than the lighter cup.

---

## Internet Address Book

**Chemistry Online**    Note Internet addresses that you find useful in the space below for quick reference.

_____

_____

_____

_____

# Using Percent to Describe Concentration

Concentration expressed as a percent is a ratio of a measured amount of solute to a measured amount of solution. Percent by mass usually describes solutions in which a solid is dissolved in a liquid, such as sodium chloride in water. The percent by mass is the ratio of the solute's mass to the solution's mass expressed as a percent. The mass of the solution equals the sum of the masses of the solute and the solvent.

$$\text{Percent by mass} = \frac{\text{mass of solute}}{\text{mass of solution}} \times 100$$

## EXAMPLE PROBLEM 15-2

### Calculating Percent by Mass

In order to maintain a sodium chloride (NaCl) concentration similar to ocean water, an aquarium must contain 3.6 g NaCl per 100.0 g of water. What is the percent by mass of NaCl in the solution?

**1. Analyze the Problem**

You are given the amount of sodium chloride dissolved in 100.0 g of water. The percent by mass of a solute is the ratio of the solute's mass to the solution's mass, which is the sum of the masses of the solute and the solvent.

| Known | Unknown |
|---|---|
| mass of solute = 3.6 g NaCl | percent by mass = ? |
| mass of solvent = 100.0 g $H_2O$ | |

**2. Solve for the Unknown**

Find the mass of the solution.

Mass of solution = grams of solute + grams of solvent

$= 3.6\ g + 100.0\ g$

$= 103.6\ g$

Substitute the known values into the percent by mass equation.

$$\text{Percent by mass} = \frac{\text{mass of solute}}{\text{mass of solution}} \times 100$$

$$= \frac{3.6\ \cancel{g}}{103.6\ \cancel{g}} \times 100$$

$$= 3.5\%$$

**3. Evaluate the Answer**

Because only a small mass of sodium chloride is dissolved per 100.0 g of water, the percent by mass should be a small value, which it is. The mass of sodium chloride was given with two significant figures, therefore, the answer also is expressed with two significant figures.

## PRACTICE PROBLEMS

**8.** What is the percent by mass of $NaHCO_3$ in a solution containing 20 g $NaHCO_3$ dissolved in 600 mL $H_2O$?

**9.** You have 1500.0 g of a bleach solution. The percent by mass of the solute sodium hypochlorite, NaOCl, is 3.62%. How many grams of NaOCl are in the solution?

**10.** In question 9, how many grams of solvent are in the solution?

Maintaining the proper saline (salt) concentration is important to the health of saltwater fish.

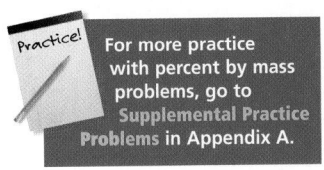
**Practice!** For more practice with percent by mass problems, go to **Supplemental Practice Problems** in Appendix A.

---

## Figure Caption Question

**Figure 15-12** What does each v in the expression 70% (v/v) refer to? The expression v/v refers to the ratio of the volume of solute to the volume of solvent.

## Concept Development

Review the two percentage-related equations on pages 463–464. Remind students that an important difference when solving percent by mass and percent by volume problems is that the unit used for the amount of solution is different.

### Quick Demo

**Logical-Mathematical** Demonstrate that two separate liquid volumes do not always add together mathematically to give the new solution volume. Mix 50.0 mL of water with 50.0 mL of isopropyl alcohol in a 100 mL graduated cylinder. Have students observe the volume of the resulting solution. Note that it is less than 100.0 mL. Have students calculate the percent by volume based on the volume of the solution measured after the two liquids were mixed together. When done with the demo, the solution may be flushed down the drain. **L2**

Percent by volume usually describes solutions in which both solute and solvent are liquids. The percent by volume is the ratio of the volume of the solute to the volume of the solution expressed as a percent. The volume of the solution is the sum of the volumes of the solute and the solvent. Calculations are similar to those involving percent by mass.

$$\text{Percent by volume} = \frac{\text{volume of solute}}{\text{volume of solution}} \times 100$$

Rubbing alcohol is an aqueous solution of liquid isopropyl alcohol. The label on a typical container, such as the one shown in **Figure 15-12**, usually states that the rubbing alcohol is 70% isopropyl alcohol. This value is a percent by volume. It tells you that 70 volumes of isopropyl alcohol are dissolved in every 100 volumes of solution. Because a solution's volume is the sum of the volumes of solute and solvent, there must be 30 volumes of water (solvent) in every 100 volumes of the rubbing alcohol.

## PRACTICE PROBLEMS

**11.** What is the percent by volume of ethanol in a solution that contains 35 mL of ethanol dissolved in 115 mL of water?

**12.** If you have 100.0 mL of a 30.0% aqueous solution of ethanol, what volumes of ethanol and water are in the solution?

**13.** What is the percent by volume of isopropyl alcohol in a solution that contains 24 mL of isopropyl alcohol in 1.1 L of water?

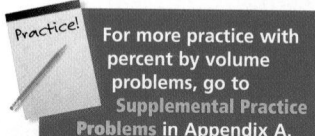

Practice! For more practice with percent by volume problems, go to Supplemental Practice Problems in Appendix A.

## Molarity

As you have learned, percent by volume and percent by mass are only two of the commonly used ways to quantitatively describe the concentrations of liquid solutions. One of the most common units of solution concentration is molarity. **Molarity** ($M$) is the number of moles of solute dissolved per liter of solution. Molarity also is known as molar concentration. The unit $M$ is read as molar. A liter of solution containing one mole of solute is a $1M$ solution, which is read as a one molar solution. A liter of solution containing 0.1 mole of solute is a $0.1M$ solution.

To calculate a solution's molarity, you must know the volume of the solution and the amount of dissolved solute.

$$\text{Molarity } (M) = \frac{\text{moles of solute}}{\text{liters of solution}}$$

For example, suppose you need to calculate the molarity of 100.0 mL of an aqueous solution containing 0.085 mole of dissolved potassium chloride (KCl). You would first convert the volume of the solution from milliliters to liters using the conversion factor 1 L = 1000 mL.

$$(100 \text{ mL}) \left( \frac{1 \text{ L}}{1000 \text{ mL}} \right) = 0.1000 \text{ L}$$

Then, to determine the molarity, you would divide the number of moles of solute by the solution volume in liters.

$$\frac{0.085 \text{ mol KCl}}{0.1000 \text{ L solution}} = \frac{0.85 \text{ mol}}{\text{L}} = 0.85M$$

**Figure 15-12**

The composition of this isopropyl alcohol is given in percent by volume, which is often expressed as % (v/v). What does each v in the expression 70% (v/v) refer to?

## CHEMISTRY JOURNAL

### Comparing Concentration

**Intrapersonal** Have students develop a list of concentration units related to household and daily situations. Examples might include medication dosages in mg/kg (compare adult and child dosages of cough syrup), percent hydrogen peroxide (compare antiseptic to hydrogen peroxide used to bleach hair), and concentrated orange juice or insecticides (compare concentrate and dilute forms). **L2**

Do the **CHEMLAB** at the end of this chapter to learn about an experimental technique for determining solution concentration.

## EXAMPLE PROBLEM 15-3

### Calculating Molarity

A 100.5-mL intravenous (IV) solution contains 5.10 g of glucose ($C_6H_{12}O_6$). What is the molarity of this solution? The molar mass of glucose is 180.16 g/mol.

#### 1. Analyze the Problem

You are given the mass of glucose dissolved in a volume of solution. The molarity of the solution is the ratio of moles of solute per liter of solution. Glucose is the solute and water is the solvent.

**Known**

mass of solute = 5.10 g $C_6H_{12}O_6$
molar mass of $C_6H_{12}O_6$ = 180.16 g/mol
volume of solution = 100.5 mL

**Unknown**

solution concentration = ?$M$

#### 2. Solve for the Unknown

Use the molar mass to calculate the number of moles of $C_6H_{12}O_6$.

$$(5.10 \text{ g } C_6H_{12}O_6)\frac{1 \text{ mol } C_6H_{12}O_6}{180.16 \text{ g } C_6H_{12}O_6} = 0.0283 \text{ mol } C_6H_{12}O_6$$

Use the conversion factor $\frac{1 \text{ L}}{1000 \text{ mL}}$ to convert the volume of $H_2O$ in milliliters to liters.

$$\left(100.5 \text{ mL solution}\right)\left(\frac{1 \text{ L}}{1000 \text{ mL}}\right) = 0.1005 \text{ L solution}$$

Substitute the known values into the equation for molarity and solve.

$$\text{molarity} = \frac{\text{moles of solute}}{\text{liters of solution}}$$

$$\text{molarity} = \frac{0.0283 \text{ mol } C_6H_{12}O_6}{0.1005 \text{ L solution}} = \frac{0.282 \text{ mol } C_6H_{12}O_6}{\text{L solution}} = 0.282M$$

#### 3. Evaluate the Answer

The molarity is a small value, which is expected because only a small mass of glucose was dissolved in the solution. The mass of glucose used in the problem contained three significant figures, and therefore, the value of the molarity also has three significant figures.

To prevent dehydration, intravenous (IV) drips are administered to many hospital patients. A solution containing sodium chloride and glucose is commonly used.

## PRACTICE PROBLEMS

**14.** What is the molarity of an aqueous solution containing 40.0 g of glucose ($C_6H_{12}O_6$) in 1.5 L of solution?

**15.** What is the molarity of a bleach solution containing 9.5 g of NaOCl per liter of bleach?

**16.** Calculate the molarity of 1.60 L of a solution containing 1.55 g of dissolved KBr.

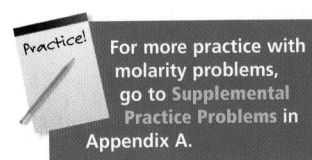

**Practice!** For more practice with molarity problems, go to **Supplemental Practice Problems** in Appendix A.

---

## CHEMLAB

ChemLab 15, located at the end of this chapter, can be used at this point in the lesson.

### Math in Chemistry

*Logical-Mathematical* Have students solve for the missing quantity in the following chart for a 0.149$M$ solution of $Na_2SO_4$.

| Mass (g) | Moles | Volume (mL) |
|----------|-------|-------------|
| 5.29 | | 250 |
| 11.1 | 0.0782 | |
| | 0.101 | 675 |
| 17.7 | 0.125 | |
| | 0.425 | 2850 |

Using a graphing calculator, enter the values for moles in one list and the values from volume in a second list. Graph moles versus volume. Find the best fit line and use the linear regression function of the calculator to determine the equation of the resulting straight line. Ask what the graph's slope means. The slope is equal to the molarity. **L2**

### Practice PROBLEMS

Have students refer to Appendix D for complete solutions to Practice Problems.
**14.** 0.148$M$
**15.** 0.128$M$
**16.** 8.13 × 10⁻³$M$

---

## DIFFERENTIATED INSTRUCTION

### Learning Disabled

*Kinesthetic* Have students role play solution concentration. Tape the perimeter of a large square on the floor. The square represents the amount of solvent. Have three students stand in the square. Add three more students and ask them to describe what happens to the numerical value of the concentration. Repeat the scenario with three students in the square, then decrease the size of the square. Ask what happens to the concentration value. **L1**
**ELL**

**National Science Content Standards**
**Pages 464–465**
UCP.1, UCP.2, UCP.4; A.1; B.2

**466**

## Practice PROBLEMS

Have students refer to Appendix D for complete solutions to Practice Problems.

**17.** 11 g $CaCl_2$
**18.** 80 g NaOH
**19.** 11 g $CaCl_2$
**20.** $3.0 \times 10^1$ g NaOH

### Figure 15-13

Accurately preparing a solution takes care. **a** In step 1, the mass of solute to be used is measured out. **b** In step 2, the solute is placed in a volumetric flask of the correct volume. **c** In step 3, distilled water is added to the flask to bring the solution level up to the calibration mark on the flask.

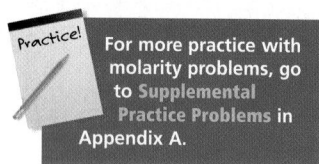

Practice! For more practice with molarity problems, go to Supplemental Practice Problems in Appendix A.

## Preparing Molar Solutions

Now that you know how to calculate the molarity of a solution, how do you think you would prepare 1 L of a 1.50$M$ aqueous solution of sucrose ($C_{12}H_{22}O_{11}$) for an experiment? A 1.50$M$ aqueous solution of sucrose contains 1.50 moles of sucrose dissolved in a liter of solution. The molar mass of sucrose is 342 g. Thus, 1.50 moles of sucrose has a mass of 513 g, an amount that you can measure on a balance.

$$\frac{1.50 \text{ mol } C_{12}H_{22}O_{11}}{1 \text{ L solution}} \times \frac{342 \text{ g } C_{12}H_{22}O_{11}}{1 \text{ mol } C_{12}H_{22}O_{11}} = \frac{513 \text{ g } C_{12}H_{22}O_{11}}{1 \text{ L solution}}$$

Unfortunately, you cannot simply add 513 g of sugar to one liter of water to make the 1.50$M$ solution. Do you know why? Like all substances, sugar takes up space and will add volume to the solution. Therefore, you must use slightly less than one liter of water to make one liter of solution. Follow the steps shown in **Figure 15-13** to learn how to prepare the correct volume of the solution.

You often will do experiments that call for only small quantities of solution. For example, you may need only 100 mL of a 1.50$M$ sucrose solution for an experiment. How do you determine the amount of sucrose to use? Look again at the definition of molarity. As calculated above, 1.50$M$ solution of sucrose contains 1.50 mol of sucrose per one liter of solution. Therefore, one liter of solution contains 513 g of sucrose.

This relationship can be used as a conversion factor to calculate how much solute you need for your experiment.

$$100 \text{ mL} \times \frac{1 \text{ L}}{1000 \text{ mL}} \times \frac{513 \text{ g } C_{12}H_{22}O_{11}}{1 \text{ L solution}} = 51.3 \text{ g } C_{12}H_{22}O_{11}$$

Thus, you would need to measure out 51.3 g of sucrose to make 100 mL of a 1.50$M$ solution.

### PRACTICE PROBLEMS

**17.** How many grams of $CaCl_2$ would be dissolved in 1.0 L of a 0.10$M$ solution of $CaCl_2$?

**18.** A liter of 2$M$ NaOH solution contains how many grams of NaOH?

**19.** How many grams of $CaCl_2$ should be dissolved in 500.0 mL of water to make a 0.20$M$ solution of $CaCl_2$?

**20.** How many grams of NaOH are in 250 mL of a 3.0$M$ NaOH solution?

---

## CHEMISTRY JOURNAL

### IV Solutions

*Logical-Mathematical* Intravenous solutions are important in medicine to help stabilize the fluid and electrolyte levels of patients. Solutions of sodium chloride and glucose are commonly used. Have students investigate why medical establishments typically use percent concentration instead of molarity. Also have them determine the molarity of glucose ($C_6H_{12}O_6$) that is labeled 5% by mass. If a 500.0 g bag of saline solution (NaCl) is 0.85% by mass, what is its molarity? Work should be placed in student portfolios. **L2** **P**

**Diluting solutions** In the laboratory, you may use concentrated solutions of standard molarities called stock solutions. For example, concentrated hydrochloric acid (HCl) is $12M$. Recall that a concentrated solution has a large amount of solute. You can prepare a less concentrated solution by diluting the stock solution with solvent. When you add solvent, you increase the number of solvent particles among which the solute particles move, as shown in **Figure 15-14**, thereby decreasing the solution's concentration. Would you still have the same number of moles of solute particles that were in the stock solution? Why?

How do you determine the volume of stock solution you must dilute? You know that

$$\text{Molarity } (M) = \frac{\text{moles of solute}}{\text{liters of solution}}$$

You can rearrange the expression of molarity to solve for moles of solute.

$$\text{Moles of solute} = \text{molarity} \times \text{liters of solution}$$

Because the total number of moles of solute does not change during dilution,

$$\text{Moles of solute in the stock solution} = \text{moles of solute after dilution}$$

You can write this relationship as the expression

$$M_1V_1 = M_2V_2$$

where $M_1$ and $V_1$ represent the molarity and volume of the stock solution and $M_2$ and $V_2$ represent the molarity and volume of the dilute solution.

**Figure 15-14**

The concentration of a solution can be diluted by adding additional solvent.

Solvent (water)

Solute

Add solvent

Concentrated solution
$M_1 V_1$

**a** Before dilution, this solution contains a fairly high ratio of solute particles to solvent particles (water molecules).

Dilute solution
$M_2 V_2$

**b** After adding additional solvent to the solution, the ratio of solute particles to solvent particles (water molecules) has decreased. This solution is less concentrated than the solution in **a**.

15.2 Solution Concentration    **467**

**In-Text Questions**

**Page 467** Would you still have the same number of moles of solute particles that were in the stock solution? Why? Yes. The number of solute particles is unchanged. Only the number of solvent particles has increased.

**Assessment**
**Performance**

Assign each student or pair of students a dilution to prepare from a stock solution. Give them a file card with the following information: solution name, stock solution concentration, final concentration, and final volume. Have students use simulated stock solutions prepared from food coloring and water. (Use a solution of yellow food coloring for $0.250M$ potassium chromate; use a solution of green food coloring for $0.355M$ nickel(II) nitrate; use a solution of blue food coloring for $0.175M$ copper(II) acetate; and use a solution of red and blue food coloring for $0.865M$ chromium(III) nitrate). Students may use volumetric flasks or graduated cylinders depending on their lab skill level. Provide each student an appropriate container in which to prepare the solution and have students provide a complete description of the calculations and steps used to prepare the solution. Use the Performance Task Assessment List for Using Math in Science in **PASC**, p. 29. **L2**

**Portfolio**

**Allowable Contaminants**

**Interpersonal** Have student groups investigate the EPA's allowable limits for various contaminants found in drinking water. Local, state, and national allowable limits may vary. Have groups compare different regions of the country and speculate why regulations may vary. Have students place their findings in their portfolios. **L2**

**National Science Content Standards**
**Pages 466–467**
UCP.1, UCP.2, UCP.4; A.1; B.2

## Enrichment

**Kinesthetic** Have students bring in water samples from their homes, nearby pond, or river, and provide them with test kits to test for the presence of dissolved ions such as calcium, nitrates, phosphates, chlorine, and dissolved oxygen. Have them organize their results in a chart or table and discuss their findings. **L1** **ELL**

### Practice PROBLEMS

Have students refer to Appendix D for complete solutions to Practice Problems.

**21.** 125 mL
**22.** 5.0 mL
**23.** 0.70*M*

## Extension

Compare the solution concentration units introduced in this section to a commonly used environmental unit, ppm, or parts per million. One ppm is the equivalent of one mg/liter. Compute the molarity and molality of a solution that is 5 ppm benzene ($C_6H_6$).

---

Knowing how to apply the equation $M_1V_1 = M_2V_2$ makes the preparation of dilute solutions easy.

---

### Diluting Stock Solutions

What volume, in milliliters of 2.00*M* calcium chloride ($CaCl_2$) stock solution would you use to make 0.50 L of 0.300*M* calcium chloride solution?

#### 1. Analyze the Problem

You are given the molarity of a stock solution of $CaCl_2$ and the volume and molarity of a dilute solution of $CaCl_2$. Use the relationship between molarities and volumes to find the volume, in liters, of the stock solution required. Then convert the volume to milliliters.

**Known**

$M_1 = 2.00M\ CaCl_2$
$M_2 = 0.300M$
$V_2 = 0.50\ L$

**Unknown**

$V_1 = ?\ L\ 2.00M\ CaCl_2$

#### 2. Solve for the Unknown

Solve the molarity–volume relationship for the volume of the stock solution, $V_1$.

$$M_1V_1 = M_2V_2$$

Dividing both sides of the equation yields,

$$V_1 = V_2\left(\frac{M_2}{M_1}\right)$$

Substitute the known values into the equation and solve.

$$V_1 = (0.50\ L)\left(\frac{0.300M}{2.000M}\right)$$

$$V_1 = 0.075\ L$$

Use the conversion factor $\frac{1000\ mL}{1\ L}$ to convert the volume from liters to milliliters.

$$V_1 = (0.075\ L)\left(\frac{1000\ mL}{1\ L}\right) = 75\ mL$$

To make the dilution, measure out 75 mL of the stock solution and dilute it with enough water to make the final volume 0.50 L.

#### 3. Evaluate the Answer

The volume $V_1$ was calculated and then its value was converted to milliliters. Of the given information, $V_2$ had the fewest number of significant figures with two. Thus, the volume $V_1$ should also have two significant figures, as it does.

---

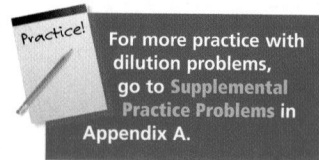

**Practice!** For more practice with dilution problems, go to Supplemental Practice Problems in Appendix A.

### PRACTICE PROBLEMS

**21.** What volume of a 3.00*M* KI stock solution would you use to make 0.300 L of a 1.25*M* KI solution?

**22.** How many milliliters of a 5.0*M* $H_2SO_4$ stock solution would you need to prepare 100.0 mL of 0.25*M* $H_2SO_4$?

**23.** If you dilute 20.0 mL of a 3.5*M* solution to make 100.0 mL of solution, what is the molarity of the dilute solution?

---

## CULTURAL DIVERSITY

### Fluoridated Water

Research has shown a link between the presence of fluoride ions in drinking water and a decrease in dental cavities. Cavities form in teeth when common sugars ferment in the mouth, forming lactic acid. This acid then reacts with the enamel on the tooth, causing a loss of enamel. Introducing fluorine levels as low as 5 ppm (5 mg fluoride/kg of water) in drinking water inhibits this enamel-decaying reaction in the mouth. Some regions of the world have this level of fluoride naturally contained in their drinking water. However, too much fluorine is not good; excess levels of fluoride in water can result in a condition known as fluorosis. Ask students why this condition might occur more frequently in

# Molality and Mole Fraction

The volume of a solution changes with temperature as it expands or contracts. This change in volume alters the molarity of the solution. Masses, however, do not change with temperature. Because of this, it is sometimes more useful to describe solutions in terms of how many moles of solute are dissolved in a specific mass of solvent. Such a description is called **molality**—the ratio of the number of moles of solute dissolved in one kilogram of solvent. The unit *m* is read as molal. A solution containing one mole of solute per kilogram of solvent is a one molal solution.

$$\text{Molality } (m) = \frac{\text{moles of solute}}{\text{kilogram of solvent}} = \frac{\text{moles of solute}}{1000 \text{ g of solvent}}$$

## EXAMPLE PROBLEM 15-5

### Calculating Molality

In the lab, a student adds 4.5 g of sodium chloride (NaCl) to 100.0 g of water. Calculate the molality of the solution.

**1. Analyze the Problem**

You are given the mass of solute and solvent. The molar mass of the solute can be used to determine the number of moles of solute in solution. Then, the molality can be calculated.

| Known | Unknown |
|---|---|
| mass of water ($H_2O$) = 100.0 g | $m = ?$ mol/kg |
| mass of sodium chloride (NaCl) = 4.5 g | |

**2. Solve for the Unknown**

Use molar mass to calculate the number of moles of NaCl.

$$4.5 \text{ g NaCl} \times \frac{1 \text{ mol NaCl}}{58.44 \text{ g NaCl}} = 0.077 \text{ mol NaCl}$$

Convert the mass of $H_2O$ from grams to kilograms.

$$100.0 \text{ g } H_2O \times \frac{1 \text{ kg } H_2O}{1000 \text{ g } H_2O} = 0.1000 \text{ kg } H_2O$$

Substitute the known values into the expression for molality and solve.

$$m = \frac{\text{moles of solute}}{\text{kilogram of solvent}} = \frac{0.077 \text{ mol NaCl}}{0.1000 \text{ kg } H_2O}$$

$$m = 0.77 \text{ mol/kg}$$

**3. Evaluate the Answer**

Because there was less than one-tenth mole of solute present in one-tenth kilogram of water, the molality should be less than one, as it is. The mass of sodium chloride was given with two significant figures; therefore the molality also is expressed with two significant figures.

The concentration of the resulting solution can be expressed in terms of moles of solute per volume (molarity) or moles of solute per mass (molality).

## PRACTICE PROBLEMS

**24.** What is the molality of a solution containing 10.0 g $Na_2SO_4$ dissolved in 1000.0 g of water?

**25.** What is the molality of a solution containing 30.0 g of naphthalene ($C_{10}H_8$) dissolved in 500.0 g of toluene?

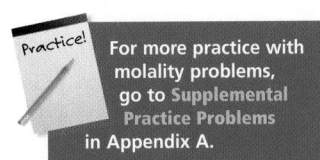

Practice! For more practice with molality problems, go to Supplemental Practice Problems in Appendix A.

15.2 Solution Concentration    **469**

regions of the world where the climate is very hot or where people consume more water.

The addition of fluoride to drinking water varies from one locale to another and from one country to another.

Adding low levels of fluoride to drinking water is a controversial issue in many countries. Some people think adding fluoride ions to public drinking water is a form of compulsory medication. Debate reasons why people might object to

adding fluoride in spite of the positive benefit of decreased tooth decay. Some reasons might include accidental overdose, individual toxicity and sensitivity, and exposure to fluoride through toothpastes and rinses.

Have students refer to Appendix D for complete solutions to Practice Problems.

**26.** 0.118

**27.** 86.5 g

## In-Text Question

**Page 470** Why must the sum of the mole fractions for all components in a solution equal one? Each mole fraction is basically a percent of the whole solution—100% of the solution must be accounted for by the fractions.

## Reteach

**Logical-Mathematical**
Have students create a chart that lists the steps needed to solve concentration problems for each of the solution types discussed in this section. Then, solve the following problem for at least two different measures of concentration (molarity, molality, percent volume, or percent mass). Use the following information: 115.0 grams of acetic acid ($HC_2H_3O_2$) in 1500.0 mL of water. Remember that for water, 1 mL equals 1 g. Remind students to pay careful attention to units.

## Assessment

**Skill** Assign each student a problem to solve from the problems at the end of the chapter or from the **Supplemental Practice Problems** in Appendix A. **L2**

---

### Hydrochloric Acid in Aqueous Solution

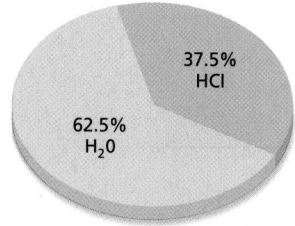

37.5% HCl

62.5% $H_2O$

$$X_{HCl} + X_{H_2O} = 1.000$$
$$0.229 + 0.771 = 1.000$$

**Figure 15-15**

The mole fraction expresses the number of moles of solvent and solute relative to the total number of moles of solution. Each mole fraction can be thought of as a percent. For example, the mole fraction of water ($X_{H_2O}$) is 0.771, which is equivalent to saying the solution contains 77.1% water (on a mole basis).

---

**Mole fraction** If you know the number of moles of solute and solvent, you can also express the concentration of a solution in what is known as a **mole fraction**—the ratio of the number of moles of solute in solution to the total number of moles of solute and solvent.

The symbol $X$ is commonly used for mole fraction, with a subscript to indicate the solvent or solute. The mole fraction for the solvent ($X_A$) and the mole fraction for the solute ($X_B$) can be expressed as follows

$$X_A = \frac{n_A}{n_A + n_B} \qquad X_B = \frac{n_B}{n_A + n_B}$$

where $n_A$ is the number of moles of solvent and $n_B$ is the number of moles of solute. Why must the sum of the mole fractions for all components in a solution equal one?

Consider as an example the mole fraction of hydrochloric acid (HCl) in the aqueous solution shown in **Figure 15-15**. For every 100 grams of solution, 37.5 g would be HCl and 62.5 g would be $H_2O$. To convert these masses to moles, you would use the molar masses as conversion factors.

$$n_{HCl} = 37.5 \text{ g HCl} \times \frac{1 \text{ mol HCl}}{36.5 \text{ g HCl}} = 1.03 \text{ mol HCl}$$

$$n_{H_2O} = 62.5 \text{ g } H_2O \times \frac{1 \text{ mol } H_2O}{18.0 \text{ g } H_2O} = 3.47 \text{ mol } H_2O$$

Thus, the mole fractions of hydrochloric acid and water can be expressed as

$$X_{HCl} = \frac{n_{HCl}}{n_{HCl} + n_{H_2O}} = \frac{1.03 \text{ mol HCl}}{1.03 \text{ mol HCl} + 3.47 \text{ mol } H_2O}$$

$$X_{HCl} = 0.229$$

$$X_{H_2O} = \frac{n_{H_2O}}{n_{HCl} + n_{H_2O}} = \frac{3.47 \text{ mol } H_2O}{1.03 \text{ mol HCl} + 3.47 \text{ mol } H_2O}$$

$$X_{H_2O} = 0.771$$

### PRACTICE PROBLEMS

Practice! For more practice with mole fraction problems, go to **Supplemental Problems in Appendix A.**

**26.** What is the mole fraction of NaOH in an aqueous solution that contains 22.8% NaOH by mass?

**27.** An aqueous solution of NaCl has a mole fraction of 0.21. What is the mass of NaCl dissolved in 100.0 mL of solution?

---

## Section 15.2 Assessment

**28.** Distinguish between a dilute solution and a concentrated solution.

**29.** Compare and contrast five quantitative ways to describe the composition of solutions.

**30.** Describe the laboratory procedure for preparing a specific volume of a dilute solution from a concentrated stock solution.

**31. Thinking Critically** Explain the similarities and differences between a $1M$ solution of NaOH and a $1m$ solution of NaOH.

**32. Using Numbers** A can of chicken broth contains 450 mg of sodium chloride in 240.0 g of broth. What is the percent by mass of sodium chloride in the broth?

 chemistrymc.com/self_check_quiz

---

## Section 15.2 Assessment

**28.** concentrated: large amount of solute relative to its solubility; dilute: small amount of solute relative to its solubility.

**29.** molarity, molality, and mole fraction are based on moles of solute per some other quantity; percent by volume and molarity are defined on a per volume of solution basis; molality and mole fraction are based on a per quantity of solvent basis; percent by mass and percent by volume are the only ratios involving percentages

**30.** Calculate the volume of stock solution needed and add it to a volu-metric flask. Add water up to the flask's calibration line.

**31.** Both solutions contain NaOH (solute) dissolved in water (solvent). The $1m$ solution contains 1 mole of NaOH per kilogram of water; the $1M$ solution contains 1 mole of NaOH per liter of solution.

**32.** 0.19%

# Colligative Properties of Solutions

Solutes affect some of the physical properties of their solvents. Early researchers were puzzled to discover that the effects of a solute on a solvent depended only on how many solute particles were in solution, not on the specific solute dissolved. Physical properties of solutions that are affected by the number of particles but not the identity of dissolved solute particles are called **colligative properties.** The word colligative means "depending on the collection." Colligative properties include vapor pressure lowering, boiling point elevation, freezing point depression, and osmotic pressure.

## Electrolytes and Colligative Properties

In Chapter 8, you learned that ionic compounds are called electrolytes because they dissociate in water to form a solution that conducts electric current. Some molecular compounds ionize in water and also are electrolytes. Electrolytes that produce many ions in solution are called strong electrolytes; those that produce only a few ions in solution are called weak electrolytes.

Sodium chloride is a strong electrolyte. It almost completely dissociates in solution, producing $Na^+$ and $Cl^-$ ions.

$$NaCl(s) \rightarrow Na^+(aq) + Cl^-(aq)$$

Dissolving one mole of NaCl in a kilogram of water does not yield a $1m$ solution of ions. Rather, there would be almost two moles of solute particles in solution—approximately one mole each of $Na^+$ and $Cl^-$ ions. How many moles of ions would you expect to find in a $1m$ aqueous solution of HCl?

**Nonelectrolytes in aqueous solution** Many molecular compounds dissolve in solvents but do not ionize. Such solutions do not conduct an electric current, and the solutes are called nonelectrolytes. Sucrose is an example of a nonelectrolyte. A $1m$ sucrose solution contains only one mole of sucrose particles. **Figure 15-16** compares the conductivity of a solution containing an electrolyte solute with one containing a nonelectrolyte solute. Which compound would have the greater effect on colligative properties, sodium chloride or sucrose?

### Objectives

- **Explain** the nature of colligative properties.
- **Describe** four colligative properties of solutions.
- **Calculate** the boiling point elevation and the freezing point depression of a solution.

### Vocabulary

colligative property
vapor pressure lowering
boiling point elevation
freezing point depression
osmosis
osmotic pressure

**Figure 15-16**

**a** Sodium chloride is a strong electrolyte and conducts electricity well. **b** Sucrose, while soluble in water, does not ionize and therefore does not conduct electricity. Which solute, sodium chloride or sucrose, produces more particles in solution per mole?

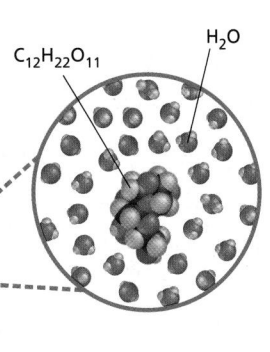

$Na^+$   $Cl^-$   $H_2O$   $C_{12}H_{22}O_{11}$   $H_2O$

**a**   **b**

15.3 Colligative Properties of Solutions   **471**

## 1 Focus

### Focus Transparency

Before presenting the lesson, display **Section Focus Transparency 57** on the overhead projector. Have students answer the accompanying questions using **Section Focus Transparency Master 57.** L1 ELL

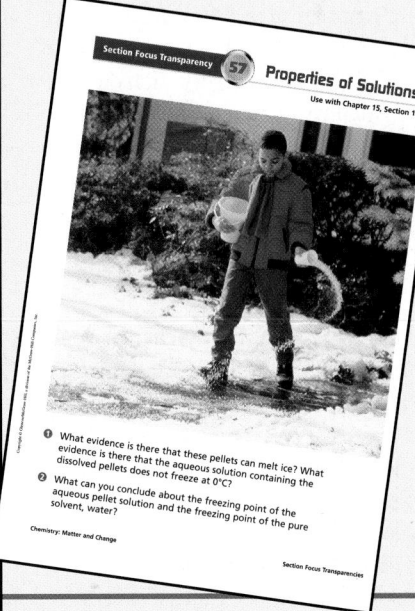

Section Focus Transparency **57** Properties of Solutions
Use with Chapter 15, Section 15.3

❶ What evidence is there that these pellets can melt ice? What evidence is there that the aqueous solution containing the dissolved pellets does not freeze at 0°C?

❷ What can you conclude about the freezing point of the aqueous pellet solution and the freezing point of the pure solvent, water?

Chemistry: Matter and Change

Section Focus Transparencies

## 2 Teach

### In-Text Questions

**Page 471** How many moles of ions would you expect to find in an aqueous solution of HCl? twice the number of moles of ions as moles HCl Which compound would have a greater effect on colligative properties, sodium chloride or sucrose? sodium chloride

### Figure Caption Question

**Figure 15-16** Which solute, sodium chloride or sucrose, produces more particles in solution per mole? sodium chloride

### Resource Manager

**Study Guide for Content Mastery,** p. 89 L2
**Section Focus Transparency 57 and Master** L1 ELL
**Solving Problems: A Chemistry Handbook,** Section 15.3 L2
**Teaching Transparency 46 and Master** L2 ELL

**National Science Content Standards**

Pages 470–471
UCP.1, UCP.2, UCP.4; A.2; B.2, B.4

Most students will think adding a solute will not change the normal boiling point or freezing point of a solution. Remind students that for a pure solvent, a substance's boiling and condensing points occur at the same temperature, and its freezing and melting points also occur at the same temperature (but at a temperature different from that of the boiling/condensation point).

### Uncover the Misconception

Ask students to brainstorm practical examples of situations in which a freezing point is lowered or a boiling point is increased. Examples might include adding salt to water when cooking, adding salt to ice on roadways in the winter, adding salt to water when making ice cream, and spraying a liquid such as ethylene glycol on planes to melt the ice before the plane takes off.

### Demonstrate the Concept

Put 100 mL of water in a clear plastic bottle, such as an empty soda container, and replace the cap. Repeat with a solution of rubbing alcohol that is 70% alcohol and 30% water. Label the plastic containers clearly and place them on their sides in a freezer at the beginning of the class period. At the end of the class period, retrieve the bottles and compare the extent of freezing of the two solutions. The water should show more evidence of freezing. Have students explain why.

### Assess New Knowledge

Have students describe the effect of vapor pressure on the normal boiling point and freezing point of a solvent when a solute is added. 📦

**National Science Content Standards**

**Pages 472–473**
UCP.1, UCP.2, UCP.4; B.2, B.4, B.6

**a**

Water

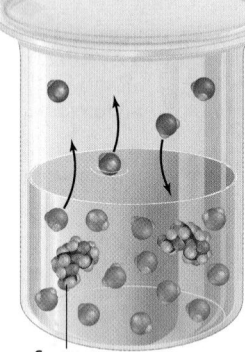

**b**

Sucrose

**Figure 15-17**

The vapor pressure of a pure solvent **a** is greater than the vapor pressure of a solution containing a nonvolatile solute **b**.

**Table 15-4**

| Molal Boiling-Point Elevation Constants ($K_b$) | | |
|---|---|---|
| Solvent | Boiling point (°C) | $K_b$ (°C/$m$) |
| Water | 100.0 | 0.512 |
| Benzene | 80.1 | 2.53 |
| Carbon tetrachloride | 76.7 | 5.03 |
| Ethanol | 78.5 | 1.22 |
| Chloroform | 61.7 | 3.63 |

## Vapor Pressure Lowering

In Chapter 13, you learned that vapor pressure is the pressure exerted in a closed container by liquid particles that have escaped the liquid's surface and entered the gaseous state. In a closed container at constant temperature and pressure, the solvent particles reach a state of dynamic equilibrium, escaping and reentering the liquid state at the same rate. The vapor pressure for a closed container of pure water is shown in **Figure 15-17a.**

Experiments show that adding a nonvolatile solute (one that has little tendency to become a gas) to a solvent lowers the solvent's vapor pressure. The particles that produce vapor pressure escape the liquid phase at its surface. When a solvent is pure, as shown in **Figure 15-17a,** its particles occupy the entire surface area. However, when the solvent contains solute, as shown in **Figure 15-17b,** a mix of solute and solvent particles occupies the surface area. With fewer solvent particles at the surface, fewer particles enter the gaseous state, and the vapor pressure is lowered. The greater the number of solute particles in a solvent, the lower the resulting vapor pressure. Thus, **vapor pressure lowering** is due to the number of solute particles in solution and is a colligative property of solutions.

You can predict the relative effect of a solute on vapor pressure based on whether the solute is an electrolyte or a nonelectrolyte. For example, one mole each of the solvated nonelectrolytes glucose, sucrose, and ethanol molecules has the same relative effect on the vapor pressure. However, one mole each of the solvated electrolytes sodium chloride, sodium sulfate, and aluminum chloride has an increasingly greater effect on vapor pressure because of the increasing number of ions each produces in solution.

## Boiling Point Elevation

Because a solute lowers a solvent's vapor pressure, it also affects the boiling point of the solvent. Recall from Chapter 13 that the liquid in a pot on your stove boils when its vapor pressure equals atmospheric pressure. When the temperature of a solution containing a nonvolatile solute is raised to the boiling point of the pure solvent, the resulting vapor pressure is still less than the atmospheric pressure and the solution will not boil. Thus, the solution must be heated to a higher temperature to supply the additional kinetic energy needed to raise the vapor pressure to atmospheric pressure. The temperature difference between a solution's boiling point and a pure solvent's boiling point is called the **boiling point elevation.**

For nonelectrolytes, the value of the boiling point elevation, which is symbolized $\Delta T_b$, is directly proportional to the solution's molality.

$$\Delta T_b = K_b m$$

The molal boiling point elevation constant, $K_b$, is the difference in boiling points between a $1m$ nonvolatile, nonelectrolyte solution and a pure solvent. It is expressed in units of °C/$m$ and varies for different solvents. Values of $K_b$ for several common solvents are found in **Table 15-4.** Note that water's $K_b$ value is 0.512°C/$m$. This means that a $1m$ aqueous solution containing a nonvolatile, nonelectrolyte solute boils at 100.512°C, a temperature 0.512°C higher than pure water's boiling point of 100.0°C.

Like vapor pressure lowering, boiling point elevation is a colligative property. The value of the boiling point elevation is directly proportional to the solution's solute molality, that is, the greater the number of solute particles in the solution, the greater the boiling point elevation.

### Gifted

*Linguistic* Have students research the kidney's role in the body as well as the medical process known as dialysis. Have them write a paragraph explaining how osmosis, a colligative property, is used in this medical procedure. **L3** 📦

# Freezing Point Depression

The freezing point depression of a solution is another colligative property of solutions. At a solvent's freezing point temperature, the particles no longer have sufficient kinetic energy to overcome the interparticle attractive forces; the particles form into a more organized structure in the solid state. In a solution, the solute particles interfere with the attractive forces among the solvent particles. This prevents the solvent from entering the solid state at its normal freezing point. The freezing point of a solution is always lower than that of a pure solvent. **Figure 15-18** shows the differences in boiling and melting points of pure water and an aqueous solution. By comparing the solid and dashed lines, you can see that the temperature range over which the aqueous solution exists as a liquid is greater than that of pure water. You can observe the effect of freezing point depression by doing the **miniLAB** on this page.

A solution's **freezing point depression**, $\triangle T_f$, is the difference in temperature between its freezing point and the freezing point of its pure solvent. For nonelectrolytes, the value of the freezing point depression, which is symbolized as $\triangle T_f$, is directly proportional to the solution's molality.

$$\triangle T_f = K_f m$$

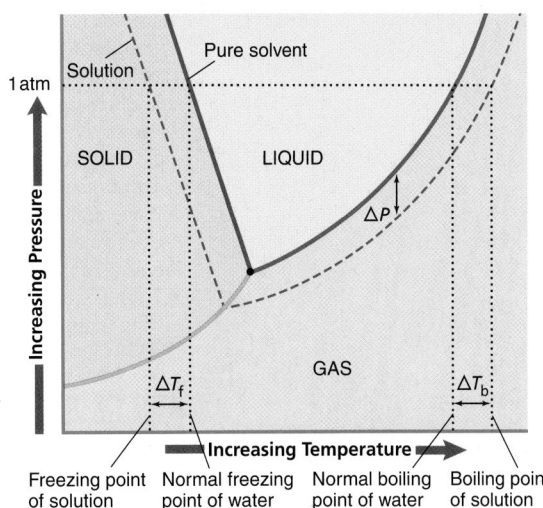

**Figure 15-18**

This phase diagram shows how temperature and pressure affect the solid, liquid, and gas phases of a pure solvent (solid lines) and a solution (dashed lines). The difference between the solid and dashed lines corresponds to vapor pressure lowering ($\triangle P$), boiling point elevation ($\triangle T_b$), and freezing point depression ($\triangle T_f$).

## miniLAB

### Freezing Point Depression

**Measuring** The colligative property of freezing point depression can be observed in a simple laboratory investigation. You will measure the temperatures of two beakers and their contents.

**Materials** 400-mL beakers (2), crushed ice, rock salt (NaCl), water, stirring rods (2), graduated cylinder, thermometers (2), balance

**Procedure**

1. Fill two 400-mL beakers with crushed ice. Add 50 mL of cold tap water to each beaker.

2. Stir the contents of each beaker with a stirring rod until both beakers are at a constant temperature, approximately one minute.

3. Measure the temperature of each beaker using a thermometer and record the readings.

4. Add 75 g of rock salt to one of the beakers. Continue stirring both beakers. Some of the salt will dissolve.

5. When the temperature in each beaker is constant, record the readings.

6. To clean up, flush the contents of each beaker down the drain with excess water.

**Analysis**

1. Compare your readings taken for the ice water and the salt water. How do you explain the observed temperature change?

2. Why was salt only added to one of the beakers?

3. Salt is a strong electrolyte that produces two ions, $Na^+$ and $Cl^-$, when it dissociates in water. Why is this important to consider when calculating the colligative property of freezing point depression?

4. Predict if it would it be better to use coarse rock salt or fine table salt when making homemade ice cream. Explain.

15.3 Colligative Properties of Solutions **473**

**✔ Assessment**

**Knowledge** Have students calculate the freezing point of a 2.5*M* aqueous solution of glucose (a nonelectrolyte). **L2**

Values of $K_f$ for several common solvents are found in **Table 15-5**. As with $K_b$ values, $K_f$ values are specific to their solvents. With water's $K_f$ value of 1.86°C/*m*, a 1*m* aqueous solution containing a nonvolatile, nonelectrolyte solute freezes at −1.86°C rather than at pure water's freezing point of 0.0°C.

However, in using the $\triangle T_b$ and $\triangle T_f$ relationships with electrolytes, you must make sure to use the effective molality of the solution. For example, one mole of the electrolyte sodium chloride (NaCl) forms one mole of $Na^+$ ions and one mole of $Cl^-$ ions in solution. Thus, a 1*m* aqueous NaCl solution produces two moles of solute particles in a kilogram of water—effectively acting as a 2*m* solution. Because of this, 2*m*, and not 1*m*, must be used in the $\triangle T_b$ and $\triangle T_f$ relationships for a 1*m* solution of sodium chloride. The following Example Problem illustrates this point.

**Table 15-5**

| Molal Freezing Point Depression Constants ($K_f$) | | |
|---|---|---|
| Solvent | Freezing point (°C) | $K_f$ (°C/*m*) |
| Water | 0.0 | 1.86 |
| Benzene | 5.5 | 5.12 |
| Carbon tetrachloride | −23 | 29.8 |
| Ethanol | −114.1 | 1.99 |
| Chloroform | −63.5 | 4.68 |

## EXAMPLE PROBLEM 15-6

### Changes in Boiling and Freezing Points

What are the boiling point and freezing point of a 0.029*m* aqueous solution of sodium chloride (NaCl)?

**1. Analyze the Problem**

You are given the molality of an aqueous sodium chloride solution. First, calculate $\Delta T_b$ and $\Delta T_f$ based on the number of particles in solution. Then, to determine the elevated boiling point and the depressed freezing point, add $\Delta T_b$ to the normal boiling point and subtract $\Delta T_f$ from the normal freezing point.

**Known**

solute = sodium chloride (NaCl)
molality of sodium chloride solution = 0.029*m*

**Unknown**

boiling point = ? °C
freezing point = ? °C

**2. Solve for the Unknown**

Each mole of the electrolyte sodium chloride dissociates in solution to produce two moles of particles. Calculate the effective number of solute particles in solution.

particle molality = 2 × 0.029*m* = 0.058*m*

Substitute the known values for $K_b$, $K_f$, and particle molality into the $\Delta T_b$ and $\Delta T_f$ equations and solve.

$\Delta T_b = K_b m$ = (0.512°C/*m*)(0.058*m*) = 0.030°C
$\Delta T_f = K_f m$ = (1.86°C/*m*)(0.058*m*) = 0.11°C

Add $\Delta T_b$ to the normal boiling point and subtract $\Delta T_f$ from the normal freezing point to determine the elevated boiling point and depressed freezing point of the solution.

boiling point = 100.0°C + 0.030°C = 100.030°C
freezing point = 0.0°C − 0.11°C = −0.11°C

**3. Evaluate the Answer**

The boiling point is higher and the freezing point is lower, as expected. Because the molality of the solution has two significant figures, both $\Delta T_b$ and $\Delta T_f$ also have two significant figures. Because the normal boiling point and freezing point are exact values, they do not affect the number of significant figures in the final answer.

## CHEMISTRY JOURNAL

### Salting Roads

*Intrapersonal* Rock salt is used extensively to melt the ice on roadways in the winter. Have students compare the positive factors (reducing accidents) and negative factors (corrosion of cars and bridges, the accelerated deterioration of roadways, and the killing of roadside plant life) of using salt. **L2**

## Resource Manager

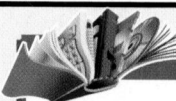

**ChemLab and MiniLab Worksheets,** p. 57 **L2**

**Challenge Problems,** p. 15 **L3**

**Math Skills Transparency 23 and Master, L2 ELL**

**CBL Lab Manual,** pp. 21–24 **L2**

**Laboratory Manual,** pp. 117–120 **L2**

## PRACTICE PROBLEMS

**33.** What are the boiling point and freezing point of a 0.625*m* aqueous solution of any nonvolatile, nonelectrolyte solute?

**34.** What are the boiling point and freezing point of a 0.40*m* solution of sucrose in ethanol?

**35.** A lab technician determines the boiling point elevation of an aqueous solution of a nonvolatile, nonelectrolyte to be 1.12°C. What is the solution's molality?

**36.** A student dissolves 0.500 mol of a nonvolatile, nonelectrolyte solute in one kilogram of benzene ($C_6H_6$). What is the boiling point elevation of the resulting solution?

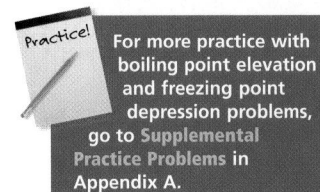

For more practice with boiling point elevation and freezing point depression problems, go to **Supplemental Practice Problems** in Appendix A.

## Osmosis and Osmotic Pressure

In Chapter 13, you learned that diffusion is the mixing of gases or liquids resulting from their random motions. **Osmosis** is the diffusion of solvent particles across a semipermeable membrane from an area of higher solvent concentration to an area of lower solvent concentration. Semipermeable membranes are barriers with tiny pores that allow some but not all kinds of particles to cross. The membranes surrounding all living cells are semipermeable membranes. Osmosis plays an important role in many biological systems such as kidney dialysis and the uptake of nutrients by plants.

Let's look at a simple system in which a sucrose-water solution is separated from its solvent—pure water—by a semipermeable membrane. During osmosis, water molecules move in both directions across the membrane, but the sugar molecules cannot cross it. Both water and sugar molecules contact the membrane on the solution side, but only water molecules contact the membrane on the pure solvent side. Thus, more water molecules cross the membrane from the pure solvent side than from the solution side.

The additional water molecules on the solution side of the membrane create pressure and push some water molecules back across the membrane. The amount of additional pressure caused by the water molecules that moved into the solution is called the **osmotic pressure.** Osmotic pressure depends upon the number of solute particles in a given volume of solution. Therefore, osmotic pressure is another colligative property of solutions.

## Section 15.3 Assessment

**37.** Explain the nature of colligative properties.

**38.** Describe four colligative properties of solutions.

**39.** Explain why a solution has a lower boiling point than the pure solvent.

**40. Thinking Critically** Explain why the colligative properties described in this section may not apply to solutions containing volatile solutes. Hint: Volatile solutes are able to leave the liquid phase and enter the gas phase.

**41. Using Numbers** Calculate the boiling point elevation and freezing point depression of a solution containing 50.0 g of glucose ($C_6H_{12}O_6$) dissolved in 500.0 g of water.

## Section 15.3 Assessment

**37.** Colligative properties depend on the number of solute particles.

**38.** vapor pressure lowering: the decrease in vapor pressure with increasing solute particles in solution; boiling point elevation: the increase in boiling point with increasing solute particles in solution; freezing point depression: the decrease in freezing point with increasing solute particles in solution; osmotic pressure: the change in osmotic pressure with increasing solute particles in solution

**39.** Solute particles in solution decrease the vapor pressure above the solution. Because a solution boils when its vapor pressure equals the external pressure, this decrease in vapor results in the need for a higher temperature in order for the solution to boil.

**40.** When volatile solute particles leave the solution, they are no longer a factor in affecting colligative properties.

**41.** $T_b = 100.285°C$; $T_f = -1.03°C$  **475**

# 1 Focus

Before presenting the lesson, display **Section Focus Transparency 58** on the overhead projector. Have students answer the accompanying questions using **Section Focus Transparency Master 58.** L1 ELL

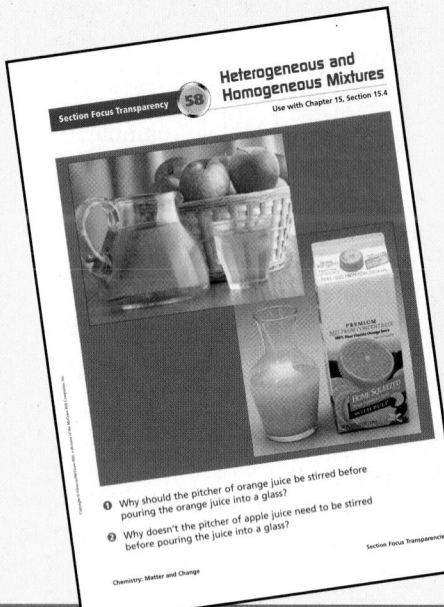

# 2 Teach
## Concept Development

After developing the concept that many mixtures are solutions, it is important to remind students that not all mixtures are solutions. Many important mixtures are suspensions and colloids.

**Resource Manager**

Study Guide for Content
 Mastery, p. 90 L2
Section Focus Transparency 58
 and Master L1 ELL
Solving Problems: A Chemistry
 Handbook, Section 15.4 L2

**Section** 15.4

# Heterogeneous Mixtures

## Objectives

- **Identify** the properties of suspensions and colloids.

- **Describe** different types of colloids.

- **Explain** the electrostatic forces in colloids.

## Vocabulary

suspension
colloid
Brownian motion
Tyndall effect

As you learned in Chapter 3, most of the forms of matter that you encounter are mixtures. A mixture is a combination of two or more substances that keep their basic identity. Components of a mixture come in contact with each other but do not undergo chemical change. You have been studying homogeneous mixtures called solutions so far in this chapter. Not all mixtures are solutions, however. Heterogeneous mixtures contain substances that exist in distinct phases. Two types of heterogeneous mixtures are suspensions and colloids.

## Suspensions

Look at the mixture shown in **Figure 15-19a.** Although it resembles milk, it is actually a freshly-made mixture of cornstarch stirred into water. If you let this mixture stand undisturbed for a while, it separates into two distinct layers: a thick, white, pastelike substance on the bottom and the water on top. Cornstarch in water is a **suspension,** a mixture containing particles that settle out if left undisturbed. As shown in **Figure 15-19b,** pouring a liquid suspension through a filter also separates out the suspended particles. Other examples of suspensions include fine sand in water and muddy water.

 Suspended particles are large compared to solvated particles, with diameters greater than 1000 nm ($10^{-6}$ m) compared to diameters less than 1 nm ($1^{-9}$ m) for solvated particles. Gravity acts on suspended particles in a short time, causing them to settle out of the mixture. Interestingly, the settled out cornstarch particles form a solidlike state on the bottom of the container. However, when stirred, the solidlike state quickly begins flowing like a liquid. Substances that behave this way are called thixotropic. One of the most common applications of a thixotropic mixture is house paint. The paint flows rather easily when applied with a brush, but quickly thickens to a solidlike state. The quickly thickening paint helps it stick to the house and prevents runs in the paint.

**Figure 15-19**

A suspension is a type of heterogeneous mixture. Suspension particles settle out over time **a**, and can be separated from the mixture by filtration **b**.

---

**DIFFERENTIATED INSTRUCTION**

## Visually Impaired

*Kinesthetic* Prepare several aqueous cornstarch solutions and let the cornstarch settle out so it forms a thick layer on the bottom of each container. Place a metal spoon or other unbreakable stirring device into each solution. Have students use the spoon to probe the bottom of the container

and note the solid feel of the cornstarch phase. Then have them stir the cornstarch and note how the cornstarch quickly breaks apart and becomes easy to stir. Discuss the thixotropic behavior of the cornstarch. L1 ELL

**Table 15-6**

| Types of Colloids | | | |
|---|---|---|---|
| Category | Dispersed particles | Dispersing medium | Example |
| Solid sol | Solid | Solid | Colored gems |
| Sol | Solid | Liquid | Blood, gelatin |
| Solid emulsion | Liquid | Solid | Butter, cheese |
| Emulsion | Liquid | Liquid | Milk, mayonnaise |
| Solid foam | Gas | Solid | Marshmallow, soaps that float |
| Foam | Gas | Liquid | Whipped cream, beaten egg white |
| Aerosol | Solid | Gas | Smoke, dust in air |
| Aerosol | Liquid | Gas | Spray deodorant, clouds |

## Colloids

Particles in a suspension are much larger than atoms. In contrast, particles in a solution are atomic-scale in size. A heterogeneous mixture of intermediate size particles (between the size of solution particles and suspension particles) is a **colloid.** Colloid particles are between 1 nm and 1000 nm in diameter. The most abundant substance in the mixture is the dispersion medium. Milk is a colloid. Although homogenized milk resembles the cornstarch mixture in **Figure 15-19a,** you cannot separate its components by settling or by filtration.

Colloids are categorized according to the phases of their dispersed particles and dispersing mediums. Milk is a colloidal emulsion because liquid particles are dispersed in a liquid medium. Other types of colloids are described in **Table 15-6** and shown in **Figure 15-20.** How many of them are familiar to you? Can you name others?

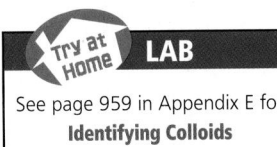

Try at Home **LAB**

See page 959 in Appendix E for
**Identifying Colloids**

**Figure 15-20**

All of the photos shown here are examples of colloids. **a** Fog, which is a liquid aerosol, is formed when small liquid particles are dispersed in a gas. **b** Many paints are sols, a fluid colloidal system of fine solid particles in a liquid medium. **c** The bagel has a coarse texure with lots of small holes throughout. These small holes are formed by a type of foam produced by yeast in the dough.

Many students will think that all mixtures are solutions.

**Uncover the Misconception**
Ask students to classify the following mixtures: blood, fog, paint, and mayonnaise. Point out the different kinds of mixture combinations in Table 15-7.

**Demonstrate the Concept**
Using three mixtures (carbonated orange drink, muddy water, and motor oil), have students produce a list of properties exhibited by these different mixtures. For example, the drink has color but is transparent, the muddy water is opaque, and the motor oil is somewhat cloudy and unclear. The muddy water begins to settle, but the solute particles in the motor oil and orange drink do not settle. Show that only the mud can be separated from the water by filtration. Discuss how particle size affects the classification of mixtures.

**Assess New Knowledge**
Have students draw three beakers containing three solutions. Have them illustrate how particle size would affect one or more of the properties of a solution, colloid, or suspension. Students should then explain their illustrations to other students in the classroom.

## Quick Demo

Pour some water into a beaker. Add several milliliters of milk and stir thoroughly. Darken the room. Use a laser pointer as a light source and point it so that the beam of light travels through the mixture. Have students look at the beaker through the side and note the cone of light. This is the Tyndall effect. **CAUTION:** *Remind students that laser pointers should not be aimed at a person's eyes.*

## CHEMISTRY JOURNAL

### Kitchen Chemistry

*Intrapersonal* Have students research cooking techniques and discuss how solution chemistry is applied in the kitchen. What kinds of ingredients are added to foods as emulsifiers to help keep them mixed? What ingredients are used as thickening agents? How do the thickening agents work? Have students place their findings in their portfolios. **L2** **P**

## Purpose 🗂

Students will design an experiment to measure the relationship between turbidity and visibility.

## Process Skills

Designing an experiment, identifying variables, thinking critically, analyzing and concluding

## Teaching Strategies

• Discuss the details of conducting an experiment that is designed to find the relationship between an independent variable (the one varied by the experimenter) and the dependent variable (the result that occurs when the independent variable is changed). Relate this discussion to the objective of this experiment. Ask students what other factors might affect the results and how these factors can be kept constant. Light intensity must be kept constant, the colloid must be uniform, and the same technique should be used for each measurement.

• When the Tyndall effect is used to monitor water clarity, the measurement is called turbidity. The transmittance of light through a given depth of water is measured and compared to the same reading for pure water.

• Suggest students use milk mixed in varying ratios with water as a basis for determining their turbidity scales. Discuss how the number of protein particles in the milk can be related to the turbidity of the solution.

## Thinking Critically

1. milk, water, a ruler, an eye dropper, and a graduated cylinder with a mark on its bottom (for determining the depth through which the mark can no longer be seen)

2. The amount of turbidity can be equated with the number of milk drops used to create the colloid and the distance at which the mark on the bottom of the graduated cylinder can just be seen.

3. To alter the turbidity, a fixed total volume to which

**Figure 15-21**

The dispersing medium particles form charged layers around the colloid particles. These charged layers repel each other and keep the particles from settling out.

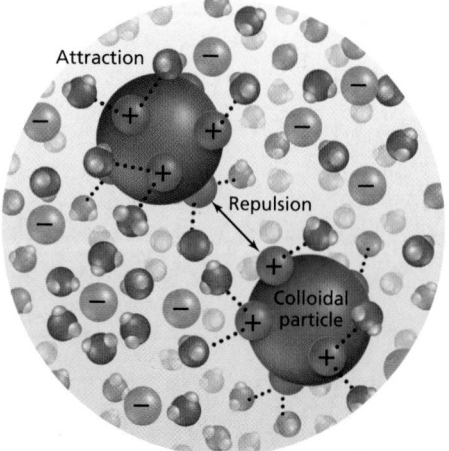

**Brownian motion** If you were to observe a liquid colloid under the magnification of a microscope, you would see that the dispersed particles make jerky, random movements. This erratic movement of colloid particles is called **Brownian motion.** It was first observed by and later named for the Scottish botanist Robert Brown, who noticed the random movements of pollen grains dispersed in water. Brownian motion results from collisions of particles of the dispersion medium with the dispersed particles. These collisions prevent the colloid particles from settling out of the mixture.

The reason the dispersed particles do not settle out is because they have polar or charged atomic groups on their surfaces. These areas on their surfaces attract the positively or negatively charged areas of the dispersing-medium particles. This results in the formation of electrostatic layers around the particles, as shown in **Figure 15-21.** The layers repel each other when the dispersed particles collide and, thus, the particles remain in the colloid. If you interfere with the electrostatic layering, colloid particles will settle out of the mixture. For example, if you stir an electrolyte into a colloid, the dispersed particles increase in size, destroying the colloid. Heating also destroys a colloid because it gives colliding particles enough kinetic energy to overcome the electrostatic forces and settle out.

## problem-solving LAB

### How can you measure the turbidity of a colloid?

**Designing an Experiment** The presence of cloudy water, or *turbidity*, in a lake or river results from the suspension of solids in the water. Most of these colloid particles come from erosion, industrial and human waste, algae blooms from fertilizers, and decaying organic matter. The degree of turbidity can greatly affect the health of a body of water in a number of ways, but its greatest impact is that it prevents light from reaching vegetation.

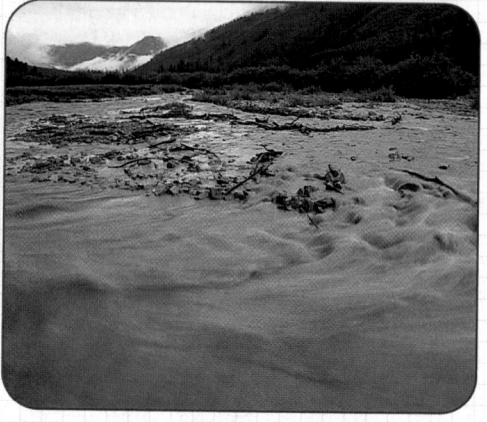

### Analysis

The Tyndall effect can be used to measure the turbidity of water. Your goal is to plan a procedure and develop a scale to interpret the data.

### Thinking Critically

Your plan should address the following.

1. What materials would you need to measure the Tyndall effect? Can you select CBLs, computers, or graphing calculators to collect or interpret data?

2. What variables can be used to relate the ability of light to pass through the liquid and the number of the colloid particles present?

3. How would you change the turbidity in the experiment?

4. What variable would change and by how much?

5. What will you use as a control?

6. How could you relate the variables used in the experiment to the actual number of colloid particles that are present?

7. Are there any safety precautions you must consider?

478   **Chapter 15** Solutions

different numbers of milk drops are added could be used.

4. The concentration of milk-water colloid is the independent variable. The concentration range should allow for 10 to 20 measurements to be made within the vertical column inside the graduated cylinder.

5. pure water

6. Through research, students could estimate the volume of protein molecules in a stan-

dard milk sample based on its composition. The colloid particles at each concentration could then be extrapolated from the standard sample.

7. Answers will vary.

## ✔ Assessment

**Skill** Have students use their results to determine the turbidity of an unknown sample.

**Figure 15-22**

Two examples of the Tyndall effect are shown here. **ⓐ** The scattering of light by fog greatly reduces visibility. **ⓑ** The beam of light is visible in the colloid because of light scattering.

**The Tyndall effect** Whereas concentrated colloids are often cloudy or opaque, dilute colloids sometimes appear as clear as solutions. Dilute colloids appear to be homogeneous because their dispersed particles are so small that they cannot be seen by the unaided eye. However, dispersed colloid particles are large enough to scatter light, a phenomenon known as the **Tyndall effect.** In **Figure 15-22b,** a beam of light is shone through two unknown mixtures. Which mixture is the colloid? Which is the solution? You can see that dispersed colloid particles scatter the light, unlike solvated particles in the solution. Solutions never exhibit the Tyndall effect. Suspensions, such as the cornstarch shown in Figure **15-19a,** also exhibit the Tyndall effect. You have observed the Tyndall effect if you have observed rays of sunlight passing through smoke-filled air, or viewed lights through fog at night, as shown in **Figure 15-22a.** Do the **problem-solving LAB** on the previous page to see how the Tyndall effect can be used to determine the amount of colloid particles in suspension.

## Section 15.4 Assessment

**42.** Distinguish between suspensions and colloids.

**43.** Describe different types of colloids.

**44.** Why do dispersed colloid particles stay dispersed?

**45. Thinking Critically** Use the Tyndall effect to explain why it is more difficult to drive through fog using high beams than using low beams.

**46. Comparing and Contrasting** Make a table that compares the properties of solutions, suspensions, and colloids.

---

# 3 Assess
## Check for Understanding

Ask students to compare the properties of a heterogeneous mixture and a colloid. How would they distinguish between them? **L2**

## Reteach

Have students collect pictures of the common household mixtures described in Table 15-7 and paste them on a poster board. Under each picture, have them describe the dispersed particles and dispersing medium for the mixture. Label the picture according to the proper mixture classification. If it is a colloid, label it as a sol, emulsion, or aerosol. **L1** **ELL**

## Extension

Have students classify various health and beauty products, such as liquid makeup, shampoos, and shaving creams, as to the type of colloid they are. **L2** **ELL**

### ✓ Assessment
**Performance** Assign each student or group of students a mixture and have them design an experiment that would allow them to classify the mixture as a solution, suspension, or a colloid. Use the Performance Task Assessment List for Designing an Experiment in **PASC,** p. 23. **L2**

**National Science Content Standards**

**Pages 476–479**
UCP.1, UCP.2, UCP.4; A.1, A.2; B.2, B.4

---

## Section 15.4 Assessment

**42.** Suspension particles are larger than colloidal particles. Suspension particles settle out of the mixture, whereas colloidal particles do not.

**43.** See Table 15-6 for descriptions of colloid types.

**44.** The particles do not settle out because they have polar or charged layers surrounding them.

These layers repel each other and prevent the particles from settling or separating.

**45.** High beams are aimed farther down the road than low beams. Because the fog scatters light, there is less light from the high beams to illuminate the road than from the low beams. Also, because the high

beams are aimed more directly into the fog, more of their light is reflected back toward the driver, making it more difficult to see.

**46.** Student tables will vary, but should include particle size, if the particles settle out, and if the particles display the Tyndall effect.

**479**

## Preparation

### Time Allotment
One laboratory period

### Process Skills
Acquiring and analyzing information, collecting and interpreting data, making and using graphs

### Safety Precautions
The food coloring solutions are safe, but they can stain clothes.

### Disposal
All solutions can be flushed down the drain with water.

### Preparation of Materials
- See page 452C for preparation of all solutions.
- Make sure all calculators have the ChemBio program loaded.
- Unknowns can be prepared by diluting the stock solution to many different concentrations. You may want to do several unknowns and assign numbers or letters to each.
- Review with students how the colorimeter works.
- Review with students the relationship between absorbance and % transmittance (%*T*). The relationship is inverse and logarithmic. $A = \log(1/T)$, but since %*T* is usually used, it can be written $A = \log(100/\%T)$.

## Pre-Lab

**2.** Each test tube contains 10mL. % by volume: 1, 20%; 2, 40%; 3, 60%; 4, 80%; 5, 100%

**3.** $A = \log(100/\%T)$

**4.** The colorimeter is being calibrated for red light. The cuvette of water is used as a measure of 100 %*T* because it contains no blue dye solution.

## Procedure

- Remind students to place the cuvette into the colorimeter the same way each time to reduce error. They may want to mark the cuvette so that it can be aligned consistently.
- Reduce error by using 1 cuvette.
- Do not fill cuvettes to the brim. Do not spill liquid in the colorimeter.

---

# Beer's Law

**F**inding the concentration of an unknown solution is an important procedure in laboratory work. One method commonly used to determine solution concentration is to measure how much of a single wavelength of light is absorbed by the solution and compare it to known values of concentration and wavelength. Light absorbance is directly related to the concentration of a solution. This relationship is called Beer's law.

### Problem
How is light absorbance used to find the concentration of a blue dye solution?

### Objectives
- **Prepare** solutions of known concentration from a blue dye stock solution.
- **Measure** the absorbance of known and unknown aqueous solutions.
- **Infer** the relationship between light absorbance and concentration of a solution.

### Materials
CBL system
graphing calculator
Vernier colorimeter
DIN adaptor and
  cable
TI Graph-Link
  (optional)
cuvette
cotton swabs
tissues for wiping
  cuvette

blue dye stock
  solution
unknown solution
distilled water
50-mL graduated
  cylinder
100-mL beaker (2)
small test tube (5)
test tube rack
pipette (2)
pipette bulb
stirring rod

### Safety Precautions

- Always wear safety goggles and a lab apron.
- The food-coloring solution can stain clothes.

### Pre-Lab

**1.** Read the entire **CHEMLAB** procedure.

**2.** What is the total volume of solution in each test tube? Calculate the percent by volume of the solutions in test tubes 1 through 5. Prepare a data table.

**3.** Review with your teacher how a colorimeter works. How are absorbance (*A*) and transmittance (%*T*) related?

| Known and Unknown Solutions Data | | | |
|---|---|---|---|
| **Test tube** | **Concentration (%)** | **%T** | **A** |
| 1 | | | |
| 2 | | | |
| 3 | | | |
| 4 | | | |
| 5 | | | |
| Unknown | | | |

**4.** What is occurring during step 3 of the procedure? Why is a cuvette of water used?

### Procedure

**1.** Transfer 30 mL of blue dye stock solution into a beaker. Transfer 30 mL of distilled water into another beaker.

**2.** Label five clean, dry test tubes 1 through 5.

**3.** Pipette 2 mL of blue dye stock solution from the beaker into test tube 1, 4 mL into test tube 2, 6 mL into test tube 3, and 8 mL into test tube 4. **CAUTION:** *Always pipette using a pipette bulb.*

**4.** With another pipette, transfer 8 mL of distilled water from the beaker into test tube 1, 6 mL into tube 2, 4 mL into tube 3, and 2 mL into tube 4.

**5.** Mix the solution in test tube 1 with a stirring rod. Rinse and dry the stirring rod. Repeat this procedure with each test tube.

## Expected Results

| Known and Unknown Solutions Data | | | |
|---|---|---|---|
| **Test tube** | **Concentration %** | **%T** | **A** |
| 1 | 20 | 88.888 | 0.05116 |
| 2 | 40 | 72.934 | 0.13707 |
| 3 | 60 | 61.253 | 0.21287 |
| 4 | 80 | 53.846 | 0.26885 |
| 5 | 100 | 44.729 | 0.34941 |
| Unknown | Depends on solution prepared by instructor. | | |

6. Pipette 10 mL of blue dye stock into test tube 5.

7. Load the ChemBio program into the calculator. Connect the CBL to the colorimeter using a DIN adaptor. Connect the CBL to the calculator using a link cable. Begin the ChemBio program on the calculator. Select "1" probe. Select 4: COLORIMETER. Enter Channel "1."

8. Fill a cuvette about three-fourths full with distilled water and dry its outside with a tissue. To calibrate the colorimeter, place the cuvette in the colorimeter and close the lid. Turn the wavelength knob to 0%T. Press TRIGGER on the CBL and enter 0 into the calculator. Turn the wavelength knob to Red (635 nm). Press TRIGGER on the CBL and enter 100 into the calculator. Leave the colorimeter set on Red for the rest of the lab. Remove the cuvette from the colorimeter. Empty the distilled water from the cuvette. Dry the inside of the cuvette with a clean cotton swab.

9. Select COLLECT DATA from the MAIN MENU. Select TRIGGER/PROMPT from the DATA COLLECTION menu. Fill the cuvette about three-fourths full with the solution from test tube 1. Dry the outside of the cuvette with a tissue and place the cuvette in the colorimeter. Close the lid. After 10 to 15 seconds, press TRIGGER and enter the concentration in percent from your data table into the calculator. Remove the cuvette and pour out the solution. Rinse the inside of the cuvette with distilled water and dry it with a clean cotton swab. Repeat this step for test tubes 2 through 5.

10. Select STOP AND GRAPH from the DATA COLLECTION menu when you have finished with data collection. Draw the graph, or use the TI Graph-Link to make a copy of the graph from the calculator screen. You also will want to copy the data from the STAT list into your data table (or you can print it from a screen print using Graph-Link).

11. Clean the cuvette with a cotton swab and fill it about three-fourths full with the unknown dye solution. Place the cuvette in the colorimeter and close the lid. From the MAIN MENU, select COLLECT DATA (do not select SET UP PROBES as this will erase your data lists). Select

MONITOR INPUT from the DATA COLLECTION MENU. Press ENTER to monitor the absorbance value of the colorimeter. After about 10-15 seconds, record the absorbance value and record it in your data table.

## Cleanup and Disposal

1. All of the blue dye solutions can be rinsed down the drain.

2. Turn off the colorimeter. Clean and dry the cuvette. Return all equipment to its proper place.

## Analyze and Conclude

1. **Analyzing Data** Evaluate how close your graph is to the direct relationship exhibited by Beer's law by doing a linear-regression line. Select FIT CURVE from the MAIN MENU (do not select SET UP PROBES as this will erase your data lists). Select LINEAR L1,L2. The calculator will give you an equation in the form of $y = ax + b$. One indicator of the fit of your graph is the size of $b$. A small value of $b$ means the graph passes close to the origin. The closer the correlation coefficient $r$ reported by the program is to 1.00, the better the fit of the graph.

2. **Drawing Conclusions** Use the graph of your absorbance and concentration data to determine the concentration of your unknown solution.

3. **Form a Hypothesis** Would you obtain the same data if red dye was used? Explain.

4. **Error Analysis** Analyze your $b$ and $r$ values. How closely do your results match Beer's law? Reexamine the procedure and suggest reasons why the correlation coefficient from your data does not equal 1.00.

## Real-World Chemistry

1. Explain how Beer's law can be applied in food, drug, and medical testing.

2. The reaction of alcohol with orange dichromate ions to produce blue-green chromium(III) ions is used in the Breathalyzer test, a test that measures the presence of alcohol in a person's breath. How could a colorimeter be used in this analysis?

## Analyze and Conclude

1. See sample graph in Solutions Manual. The sample data results in $b = -0.0146$ and $r = 0.998$. These values show a good correlation to Beer's law.

2. Answers will vary. A solution with an absorbance of 0.127 will have a concentration of 39%.

3. The color of the solution is due to reflected light. The blue dye solution reflects blue light and absorbs red. A red dye solution would absorb blue and reflect red. If the procedure were repeated with red dye solution, no red light would be absorbed. Absorbance readings would not be obtained.

4. Accurate results would not be obtained if the solutions were not prepared carefully, the cuvette was not cleaned and dried adequately between solutions, more than one cuvette was used, the cuvette was not consistently aligned in the colorimeter, or data was not entered correctly.

## Real-World Chemistry

1. This method can be used to find concentrations of colored solutions such as fruit juices or colored drug preparations.

2. A color scale relating the blue-green color and alcohol concentration could be used.

---

**Resource Manager**

ChemLab and MiniLab Worksheets, pp. 58–60 **L2**

**✔ Assessment**

**Skill** Have students repeat the experiment, but use a different colored solution. Have them research how they would determine the color of LED they would use with a colored dye solution.

**National Science Content Standards**

**Pages 480–481**
UCP.1, UCP.2, UCP.4; A.1, A.2; B.2

# CHEMISTRY and
## Society

## Purpose

Students will learn how the chemical hemoglobin functions in the body, and how abnormal hemoglobin can result in sickle cell disease.

## Background

Sickle cell disease is one of the most prevalent genetic diseases in the United States. Although there is a continuum in the severity of the symptoms caused, more than 50 000 Americans are affected by this condition. Inheriting the sickle cell gene from only one parent results in a condition called sickle cell trait. These individuals are carriers of the disease, but rarely suffer any health problems as a result. One in 12 African Americans in the United States has sickle cell trait. Symptoms of sickle cell disease include chronic anemia, stroke, spleen and kidney problems, and susceptibility to bacterial infections, conditions that can lead to early death.

## Teaching Strategies

- Ask students to describe how coping daily with the symptoms of sickle cell disease might change their lives.
- Have students diagram the path of a red blood cell from the lungs to some part of the body, indicating locations where oxygen and carbon dioxide are transferred to and from hemoglobin molecules.
- Ask students to research and diagram the shape of a normal red blood cell and the shape of a red blood cell in an individual with sickle cell disease.

## Investigating the Issue

1. Newborn screening, parent education, better medical care, and specific drugs have combined to result in a decrease in the death rate of individuals with sickle cell disease.

# Sickle Cell Disease

There are millions of red blood cells in a single drop of blood. Red blood cells play a crucial role, transporting oxygen throughout the body.

## Hemoglobin in Red Blood Cells

The cells pictured at the right appear red because they contain a bright red molecule—a protein called hemoglobin. One molecule of hemoglobin contains four iron(II) ions. Four oxygen molecules bind to each molecule of hemoglobin as blood passes through the lungs. As the blood circulates through the body, hemoglobin releases oxygen to the cells that make up various body tissues.

Healthy red blood cells are round and flexible, passing easily through narrow capillaries. But, hemoglobin in people with sickle cell disease differs from normal hemoglobin.

## What makes sickle cells different?

Each hemoglobin molecule consists of four chains. The entire molecule contains 574 amino acid groups. In people with sickle cell disease, two nonpolar amino acid groups are substituted for two polar amino acid groups. As a result, there is less repulsion between hemoglobin molecules, which allows abnormal hemoglobin molecules to clump together. This causes the abnormal hemoglobin molecules to be less soluble in the red blood cells, especially after oxygen has been absorbed through the lungs. The abnormal hemoglobin forces the red blood cells to become rigid and C-shaped, resembling the farming tool called a sickle.

These unusually shaped sickle cells clog the circulatory system, reducing blood flow. Therefore, oxygen supply to nearby tissues is reduced. Sickle cell disease causes pain, anemia, stroke, and susceptibility to infection.

## Searching for a Cure

While most individuals with sickle cell disease have Mediterranean or African ancestry, it is common practice to screen all newborns in the United States for the condition. Research shows that early intervention can reduce the risk of serious infection, the leading cause of death in children with sickle cell disease. Intensive chemotherapy and stem cell

transfusions are being studied as ways to treat and possibly cure sickle cell disease.

### Investigating the Issue

1. **Communicating Ideas** Learn about the latest advances in sickle cell disease research. Create a chart that shows major symptoms, their causes, and their treatment. Share your findings with other students in your class.

2. **Debating the Issue** The intensive chemotherapy required to treat sickle cell disease drastically weakens the immune system, leaving the patient vulnerable to overwhelming infection. Five to eight percent of the children who undergo this treatment do not survive. Should doctors be allowed to use this procedure to treat sickle cell disease?

Visit the Chemistry Web site at chemistrymc.com to find links to more information about sickle cell disease.

2. Opinions will vary widely on this issue. Some students will not feel that any procedure is worth the risk if 5% to 8% of those who undergo it will not survive. Other students may feel that living with the pain and other symptoms of this condition would make life unbearable, and that regaining good health would be worth the risk.

## Summary

### 15.1 What are solutions?
- A solute dissolves in a solvent during a process called solvation. When the solvent is water, the process also is called hydration.
- Every substance has a characteristic solubility in a given solvent.
- Factors that affect solubility include the nature of the solute and solvent, temperature, and pressure.
- Henry's law states that the solubility (*S*) of a gas in a liquid is directly proportional to the pressure (*P*) of the gas above the liquid at a given temperature.

### 15.2 Solution Concentration
- The concentration of a solution is a quantitative measure of the amount of solute in a given amount of solvent or solution.
- Measures of concentration include mass and volume percentages, molarity, molality, and mole fraction.

- A dilute solution can be prepared from a more concentrated standard stock solution.

### 15.3 Colligative Properties of Solutions
- Physical properties affected by the concentration of the solute but not the nature of the solute are called colligative properties.
- Colligative properties of solutions include vapor pressure lowering, boiling point elevation, freezing point depression, and osmotic pressure.

### 15.4 Heterogeneous Mixtures
- One of the key differences between solutions, colloids, and suspensions is particle size.
- The random motion of colloidal dispersions due to molecular collisions is called Brownian motion.
- The scattering of light by colloidal particles is called the Tyndall effect. The Tyndall effect can be used to distinguish colloids from solutions.

## Key Equations and Relationships

- Henry's law: $\dfrac{S_1}{P_1} = \dfrac{S_2}{P_2}$ (p. 460)
- Percent by mass = $\dfrac{\text{mass of solute}}{\text{mass of solution}} \times 100$ (p. 463)
- Percent by volume = $\dfrac{\text{volume of solute}}{\text{volume of solution}} \times 100$ (p. 464)
- Molarity (*M*) = $\dfrac{\text{moles of solute}}{\text{liters of solution}}$ (p. 464)

- Molarity-volume relationship: $M_1V_1 = M_2V_2$ (p. 467)
- Molality (*m*) = $\dfrac{\text{moles of solute}}{\text{kilogram of solvent}}$ (p. 469)
- Mole fractions: $X_A = \dfrac{n_A}{n_A + n_B}$ $X_B = \dfrac{n_B}{n_A + n_B}$ (p. 470)
- Boiling point elevation: $\Delta T_b = K_b m$ (p. 472)
- Freezing point depression: $\Delta T_f = K_f m$ (p. 473)

## Vocabulary

- boiling point elevation (p. 472)
- Brownian motion (p. 478)
- colligative property (p. 471)
- colloid (p. 477)
- concentration (p. 462)
- freezing point depression (p. 473)
- heat of solution (p. 457)
- Henry's law (p. 460)

- immiscible (p. 454)
- insoluble (p. 454)
- miscible (p. 454)
- molality (p. 469)
- molarity (p. 464)
- mole fraction (p. 470)
- osmosis (p. 475)
- osmotic pressure (p. 475)
- saturated solution (p. 458)

- solubility (p. 457)
- soluble (p. 454)
- solvation (p. 455)
- supersaturated solution (p. 459)
- suspension (p. 476)
- Tyndall effect (p. 479)
- unsaturated solution (p. 458)
- vapor pressure lowering (p. 472)

chemistrymc.com/self_check_quiz

Study Guide **483**

## Using the Vocabulary
To reinforce chapter vocabulary, have students write a sentence using each term. **L2** **ELL**

## Review Strategies
- Have students work in groups and explain to each other when a certain equation is used to solve a problem. **L2**
- Have students organize the terms in this chapter in groups. For example, students should think of supersaturated, saturated, and unsaturated solutions as a set and understand the similarities and differences among those three terms. Other sets would be dilute and concentrated; molarity and molality; percent by mass and percent by volume. **L2**
- Problems from Appendix A or the **Supplemental Problems** booklet can be used for review. **L2**

**VOCABULARY PuzzleMaker**

For additional help with vocabulary, have students access the Vocabulary PuzzleMaker online.
chemistrymc.com/ vocabulary_puzzlemaker

**Chemistry** online

**National Science Content Standards**

Pages 482–483
UCP.1, UCP.2, UCP.4; A.1, A.2; B.2, B.4, B.6; F.1, F.6

## Concept Mapping

**47.** 1. moles of solute;
2. molarity; 3. molality;
4. mole fraction

## Mastering Concepts

**48.** A solute is the substance being dissolved. The solvent is the substance in which the solute dissolves.

**49.** the polarity of the solute and solvent, temperature, and pressure

**50.** A saturated solution contains the maximum amount of solute under a given set of conditions. An unsaturated solution contains less than the maximum amount.

**51.** Two liquids are miscible when they are soluble in any proportion.

**52.** increase the temperature of the solvent, increase the surface area of the solute, agitation

**53.** An increase in temperature increases the kinetic energy of the gas particles. More gas particles escape the surface of the solution.

**54.** Percent by mass is a comparison between the mass of solute and the total mass of the solute. Percent by volume is a comparison between the volume of the solute and the total volume of the solution.

**55.** Molarity is solution concentration expressed as the moles of solute per volume of solution. Molality expresses concentration as moles of solute per kilogram of solvent. Molality does not depend upon the temperature of the solution.

**56.** When a solvent contains a solute, fewer solvent particles occupy the surface. Fewer particles escape into the gaseous state.

**Chemistry Online**

*Go to the Chemistry Web site at* chemistrymc.com *for additional Chapter 15 Assessment.*

## Concept Mapping

**47.** Complete the following concept map using the following terms: molarity, mole fraction, molality, moles of solute.

## Mastering Concepts

**48.** What is the difference between solute and solvent? (15.1)

**49.** What determines whether a solute will be soluble in a given solvent? (15.1)

**50.** Explain the difference between saturated and unsaturated solutions. (15.1)

**51.** What does it mean if two liquids are said to be miscible? (15.1)

**52.** What are three ways to increase the rate of solvation? (15.1)

**53.** Why are gases less soluble at higher temperatures? (15.1)

**54.** What is the difference between percent by mass and percent by volume? (15.2)

**55.** What is the difference between molarity and molality? (15.2)

**56.** Explain on a particle basis why the vapor pressure of a solution is lower than a pure solvent. (15.3)

**57.** How does a solute affect the boiling point of a solution? (15.3)

**58.** How does a solute affect the freezing point of a solution? (15.3)

**59.** Describe osmosis. (15.4)

**60.** What is a colligative property? (15.4)

**61.** What is a suspension and how does it differ from a colloid? (15.4)

**62.** Name a colloid formed from a gas dispersed in a liquid. (15.4)

**63.** How can the Tyndall effect be used to distinguish between a colloid and a solution? Why? (15.4)

## Mastering Problems

### Henry's Law (15.1)

**64.** The solubility of a gas in water is 0.22 g/L at 20.0 kPa of pressure. What is the solubility when the pressure is increased to 115 kPa?

**65.** The solubility of a gas in water is 0.66 g/L at 15 kPa of pressure. What is the solubility when the pressure is increased to 40.0 kPa?

**66.** The solubility of a gas is 2.0 g/L at 50.0 kPa of pressure. How much gas will dissolve in 1 L at a pressure of 10.0 kPa?

**67.** The solubility of a gas is 4.5 g/L at a pressure of 1.0 atm. At what pressure will there be 45 g of gas in 1.0 L of solution?

**68.** The partial pressure of $CO_2$ inside a bottle of soft drink is 4.0 atm at 25°C. The solubility of $CO_2$ is 0.12 mol/L. When the bottle is opened, the partial pressure drops to $3.0 \times 10^{-4}$ atm. What is the solubility of $CO_2$ in the open drink? Express your answer in grams per liter.

### Percent Solutions (15.2)

**69.** Calculate the percent by mass of 3.55 g NaCl dissolved in 88 g water.

**70.** Calculate the percent by mass of benzene in a solution containing 14.2 g of benzene in 28.0 g of carbon tetrachloride.

**71.** What is the percent by volume of 25 mL of methanol in 75 mL of water?

**72.** A solution is made by adding 1.23 mol KCl to 1000.0 g of water. What is the percent by mass of KCl in this solution?

**73.** What mass of water must be added to 255.0 g NaCl to make a 15.00 percent by mass aqueous solution?

**74.** The label on a 250-mL stock bottle reads "21.5% alcohol by volume." What volume of alcohol does it contain?

**75.** A 14.0 percent by mass solution of potassium iodide dissolved in water has a density of 1.208 g/mL. How many grams of KI are in 25.0 mL of the solution?

chemistrymc.com/self_check_quiz

**57.** A liquid boils when its vapor pressure equals atmospheric pressure. The vapor pressure of a solution is less than pure solvent. Thus, the boiling point is higher.

### Resource Manager

Chapter Assessment, pp. 85–90 **L2**
Supplemental Problems, Ch. 15
ExamView® Pro CD-ROM
MindJogger Videoquizzes DVD/VHS
Solutions Manual, Ch. 15
Chemistry Interactive CD-ROM,
Ch. 15 quiz

## Molarity (15.2)

**76.** What is the molarity of the following solutions?

   **a.** 2.5 mol KCl in 1.0 L of solution
   **b.** 1.35 mol $H_2SO_4$ in 245 mL of solution
   **c.** 0.875 mol of ammonia in 155 mL of solution

**77.** What is the molarity of the following solutions?

   **a.** 0.96 g $MgCl_2$ in 500 mL of solution
   **b.** 9.33 g $Na_2S$ in 450 mL solution
   **c.** 2.48 g $CaF_2$ in 375 mL of solution

**78.** How many moles of solute are contained in the following solutions?

   **a.** 15.25 mL 2.10$M$ $CaCl_2$
   **b.** 125 mL 0.0500$M$ $Ba(OH)_2$
   **c.** 53.1 mL 12.2$M$ HCl

**79.** How many grams of solute are contained in the following solutions?

   **a.** 64.3 mL 0.0238$M$ KOH
   **b.** 142 mL 1.40$M$ $K_2SO_4$
   **c.** 750.0 mL 0.225$M$ $NH_4OH$

## Molar Dilution (15.2)

**80.** How many milliliters of 2.55$M$ NaOH is needed to make 125 mL 0.75$M$ NaOH solution?

**81.** How many milliliters of 0.400$M$ HBr solution can be made from 50.0 mL of 8.00$M$ HBr solution?

**82.** What is the molarity of each resulting solution when the following mixtures are prepared?

   **a.** 500.0 mL $H_2O$ is added to 20.0 mL 6.00$M$ $HNO_3$
   **b.** 30.0 mL 1.75$M$ HCl is added to 80.0 mL 0.450$M$ HCl

## Molality and Mole Fraction (15.2)

**83.** Calculate the molality of the following solutions.

   **a.** 15.7 g NaCl in 100.0 g $H_2O$
   **b.** 20.0 g $CaCl_2$ in 700.0 g $H_2O$
   **c.** 3.76 g NaOH in 0.850 L $H_2O$

**84.** Calculate the mole fraction of NaCl, $CaCl_2$, and NaOH in the solutions listed in the previous problem.

**85.** What are the molality and mole fraction of solute in a 35.5 percent by mass aqueous solution of formic acid (HCOOH)?

## Colligative Properties (15.3)

**86.** Using the information in **Tables 15-4** and **15-5**, calculate the freezing point and boiling point of 12.0 g of glucose ($C_6H_{12}O_6$) in 50.0 g $H_2O$.

**87.** Using the information in **Tables 15-4** and **15-5**, calculate the freezing point and boiling point of each of the following solutions.

   **a.** 2.75$m$ NaOH in water
   **b.** 0.586$m$ of water in ethanol
   **c.** 1.26$m$ of naphthalene ($C_{10}H_8$) in benzene

**88.** A rock salt (NaCl), ice, and water mixture is used to cool milk and cream to make homemade ice cream. How many grams of rock salt must be added to water to lower the freezing point 10.0°C?

**89.** Calculate the freezing point and boiling point of a solution that contains 55.4 g NaCl and 42.3 g KBr dissolved in 750.3 mL $H_2O$.

## Mixed Review

*Sharpen your problem-solving skills by answering the following.*

**90.** If you prepared a saturated aqueous solution of potassium chloride at 25°C and then heated it to 50°C, would you describe the solution as unsaturated, saturated, or supersaturated? Explain.

**91.** Use the graph below to explain why a carbonated beverage does not go flat as quickly when it contains ice.

**Solubility of $CO_2$ in Water at 1 atm**

Solubility (mol/L) vs. Temperature (°C)

**92.** Which of the following substances will be soluble in the nonpolar solvent carbon tetrachloride ($CCl_4$): $Br_2$, $C_6H_{14}$, $NaNO_3$, HCl? Explain.

**93.** How many grams of calcium nitrate ($Ca(NO_3)_2$) would you need to prepare 3.00 L of a 0.500$M$ solution?

**94.** What would be the molality of the solution described in the previous problem?

**58.** A solute interferes with the attractive forces between solvent particles. The freezing point is lowered.

**59.** Osmosis is the diffusion of solvent particles across a semipermeable membrane.

**60.** A colligative property is a property of a solution that depends on concentration and not the identity of the solute.

**61.** A suspension is a heterogeneous mixture that settles out if left undisturbed. The particles dispersed in a colloid are much smaller than those in a suspension and do not settle out.

**62.** Student answers may include whipped cream or beaten egg whites.

**63.** A beam of light is visible in a colloid but not in a solution. Dispersed colloid particles are large enough to scatter light (Tyndall effect).

## Mastering Problems

Complete solutions to Chapter Assessment problems can be found in the **Solutions Manual.**

### Henry's Law (15.1)
**Level 1**
   **64.** 1.3 g/L
   **65.** 1.8 g/L

**Level 2**
   **66.** 0.40 g
   **67.** $1.0 \times 10^1$ atm
   **68.** $4.0 \times 10^{-4}$ g/L

### Percent Solutions (15.2)
**Level 1**
   **69.** 3.9%
   **70.** 33.6%
   **71.** 25%

**Level 2**
   **72.** 8.40%
   **73.** 1445 g
   **74.** 54 mL
   **75.** 4.23 g

### Molarity (15.2)
**Level 1**
   **76. a.** 2.5$M$
     **b.** 5.51$M$
     **c.** 5.64$M$

**Level 2**
   **77. a.** 0.02$M$
     **b.** 0.27$M$
     **c.** 0.0847$M$
   **78. a.** 0.0320 mol
     **b.** 0.00625 mol
     **c.** 0.648 mol
   **79. a.** 0.0859 g
     **b.** 34.6 g
     **c.** 5.91 g

**National Science Content Standards**

**Pages 484–485**
UCP.1, UCP.2, UCP.4; A.1; B.2, B.4, B.5

# CHAPTER 15 ASSESSMENT

## Molar Dilution (15.2)

### Level 1

**80.** $V_2 = 37$ mL

**81.** $V_2 = 1.00 \times 10^3$ mL

### Level 2

**82. a.** $0.240M$

 **b.** $0.805M$

## Molality and Mole Fraction (15.2)

### Level 1

**83. a.** $2.69m$

 **b.** $0.257m$

 **c.** $0.111m$

**84. a.** $0.0462$

 **b.** $0.00461$

 **c.** $0.00199$

### Level 2

**85.** $12.0m$; $0.177$

## Colligative Properties (15.3)

### Level 1

**86.** fp $= -2.47°C$; bp $= 100.681°C$

### Level 2

**87. a.** fp $= -10.2°C$; bp $= 102.8°C$

 **b.** fp $= -115.8°C$; bp $= 79.1°C$

 **c.** fp $= -1.0°C$; bp $= 83.3°C$

**88.** 157 g NaCl per 1 kg $H_2O$

**89.** fp $= -6.46°C$; bp $= 101.81°C$

## Mixed Review

**90.** unsaturated; the solubility of KCl in water increases with temperature. A solution at 50°C holds more solute than one at 25°C.

**91.** Ice keeps the drink at a temperature at which the carbon dioxide has greater solubility.

**92.** $Br_2$, $C_6H_{14}$; They are nonpolar molecules. Like dissolves like; therefore, they are soluble in non-polar solvents.

**93.** 246 g

**94.** $0.500m$

## Thinking Critically

**95. Inferring** Why not spread a nonelectrolyte on a road to help ice melt?

**96. Using Scientific Diagrams** Complete the diagram below using the following phrases: solution, separated solvent + solute, separated solvent + separated solute, solvent + solute. Is the process described exothermic or endothermic?

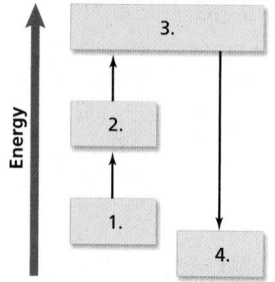

**97. Designing an Experiment** You are given a sample of a solid solute and three aqueous solutions containing that solute. How would you determine which solution is saturated, unsaturated, and supersaturated?

**98. Using Graphs** The following solubility data was collected in an experiment. Plot a graph of the molarity of KI versus temperature. What is the solubility of KI at 55°C?

**Table 15-7**

| Solubility of KI Data | |
|---|---|
| Temperature (°C) | Grams of KI per 100.0 g solution |
| 20 | 144 |
| 40 | 162 |
| 60 | 176 |
| 80 | 192 |
| 100 | 206 |

**99. Comparing** Which of the following solutions has the highest concentration? Rank the solutions from the greatest to the smallest boiling point depression. Explain your answer.

 **a.** 0.10 mol NaBr in 100.0 mL solution

 **b.** 2.1 mol KOH in 1.00 L solution

 **c.** 1.2 mol $KMnO_4$ in 3.00 L solution

## Writing in Chemistry

**100.** Investigate the total amount of salt used in the U.S. Construct a circle graph showing the different uses and amounts. Discuss each of these areas in detail. Salt was once used as a currency of high value. Find out why this was the case.

**101.** Look up the various electrolytes in the human blood stream and discuss the importance of each.

**102.** Research the contents of the tank scuba divers typically use. How does its composition differ from the air that you breathe? What is the condition known as the bends? How is it treated?

## Cumulative Review

*Refresh your understanding of previous chapters by answering the following.*

**103.** The radius of an argon atom is 94 pm. Assuming the atom is spherical, what is the volume of an argon atom in $nm^3$? $V = 4/3\pi r^3$ (Chapter 2)

**104.** Identify which of the following molecules is polar. (Chapter 9)

 **a.** $SiH_4$

 **b.** $NO_2$

 **c.** $H_2S$

 **d.** $NCl_3$

**105.** Name the following compounds. (Chapter 8)

 **a.** NaBr

 **b.** $Pb(CH_3COO)_2$

 **c.** $(NH_4)_2CO_3$

**106.** A 12.0-g sample of an element contains $5.94 \times 10^{22}$ atoms. What is the unknown element? (Chapter 11)

**107.** Pure bismuth can be produced by the reaction of bismuth oxide with carbon at high temperatures.

$$2Bi_2O_3 + 3C \rightarrow 4Bi + 3CO_2$$

How many moles of $Bi_2O_3$ reacted to produce 12.6 moles of $CO_2$? (Chapter 12)

**108.** A gaseous sample occupies 32.4 mL at $-23°C$ and 0.75 atm. What volume will it occupy at STP? (Chapter 14)

chemistrymc.com/chapter_test

## Thinking Critically

**95.** An electrolyte will dissociate and produce a greater freezing point depression.

**96.** 1. solvent + solute, 2. separated solvent + solute, 3. separated solvent + separated solute, 4. solution; exothermic

**97.** Add a pinch of solute to each container. If the solution is supersaturated, crystallization will occur; saturated, no solute will dissolve; unsaturated, solute will dissolve.

**98.** Molarity equals $8.67M$, $9.76M$, $10.6M$, $11.6M$, and $12.4M$ at 20°C, 40°C, 60°C, 80°C, and 100°C, respectively. The graph increases from left to right. The solubility of KI at 55°C is about $10.4M$.

**99.** The molarities are $1.0M$ NaBr, $2.1M$ KOH, and $0.40M$ $KMnO_4$. Because the KOH solution has the greatest concentration, it has the greatest

*Use these questions and the test-taking tip to prepare for your standardized test.*

**1.** How much water must be added to 6.0 mL of a 0.050*M* stock solution to dilute it to 0.020*M*?

  **a.** 15 mL          **c.** 6.0 mL
  **b.** 9.0 mL         **d.** 2.4 mL

**2.** At a pressure of 1.00 atm and a temperature of 20°C, 1.72 g $CO_2$ will dissolve in 1 L of water. How much $CO_2$ will dissolve if the pressure is raised to 1.35 atm and the temperature stays the same?

  **a.** 2.32 g/L       **c.** 0.785 g/L
  **b.** 1.27 g/L       **d.** 0.431 g/L

**3.** What is the molality of a solution containing 0.25 g of dichlorobenzene ($C_6H_4Cl_2$) dissolved in 10.0 g of cyclohexane ($C_6H_{12}$)?

  **a.** 0.17 mol/kg     **c.** 0.025 mol/kg
  **b.** 0.014 mol/kg    **d.** 0.00017 mol/kg

**4.** If 1 mole of each of the solutes listed below is dissolved in 1 L of water, which solute will have the greatest effect on the vapor pressure of its respective solution?

  **a.** KBr            **c.** $MgCl_2$
  **b.** $C_6H_{12}O_6$   **d.** $CaSO_4$

**5.** What volume of a 0.125*M* $NiCl_2$ solution contains 3.25 g $NiCl_2$?

  **a.** 406 mL         **c.** 38.5 mL
  **b.** 201 mL         **d.** 26.0 mL

**Interpreting Graphs**   Use the graph to answer questions 6–8.

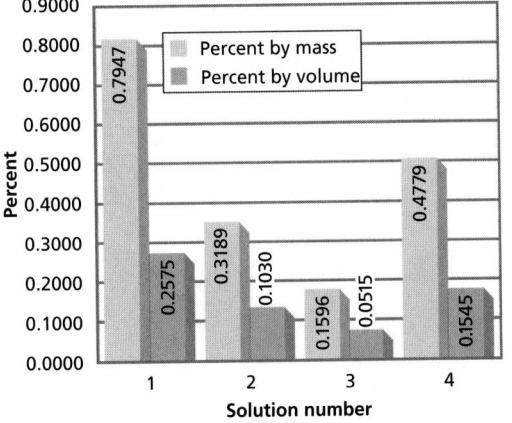

**Bromine ($Br_2$) Concentration of Four Aqueous Solutions**

**6.** What is the volume of bromine ($Br_2$) in 7.000 L of Solution 1?

  **a.** 55.63 mL
  **b.** 8.808 mL
  **c.** 18.03 mL
  **d.** 27.18 mL

**7.** How many grams of $Br_2$ are in 55.00 g of Solution 4?

  **a.** 3.560 g
  **b.** 0.084 98 g
  **c.** 1.151 g
  **d.** 0.2628 g

**8.** Which of the following relationships is true?

  **a.** 2 × Concentration of solution 2
              = Concentration of solution 3
  **b.** 0.5 × Concentration of solution 2
              = Concentration of solution 3
  **c.** Concentration of solution 2
              = 0.25 × Concentration of solution 3
  **d.** Concentration of solution 2
              = 3 × Concentration of solution 3

**9.** Which is NOT a colligative property?

  **a.** boiling point elevation
  **b.** freezing point depression
  **c.** vapor pressure increase
  **d.** osmotic pressure

**10.** How can colloids be distinguished from solutions?

  **a.** dilute colloids have particles that can be seen with the naked eye
  **b.** colloid particles are much smaller than solvated particles
  **c.** colloid particles that are dispersed will settle out of the mixture in time
  **d.** colloids will scatter light beams that are shone through them

chemistrymc.com/standardized_test

---

**TEST-TAKING TIP**

**Take a Break!**  If you have a chance to take a break or get up from your desk during a test, take it! Getting up and moving around will give you extra energy and help you clear your mind. During your stretch break, think about something other than the test so you'll be able to get back to the test with a fresh start.

---

boiling point elevation; $KMnO_4$ has the lowest concentration and the smallest boiling point depression. Boiling point elevation depends only upon concentration.

## Cumulative Review

**103.** $3.5 \times 10^{-3}$ nm³
**104. a.** nonpolar
     **b.** polar
     **c.** polar
     **d.** polar
**105. a.** sodium bromide
     **b.** lead acetate
     **c.** ammonium carbonate
**106.** The atomic mass is 122 amu. The element is antimony.
**107.** 8.40 mol $Bi_2O_3$
**108.** 26 mL

## Standardized Test Practice

| | |
|---|---|
| **1.** b | **6.** c |
| **2.** a | **7.** d |
| **3.** a | **8.** b |
| **4.** c | **9.** c |
| **5.** b | **10.** d |

# CHAPTER 16

## Resource Manager

| Section | Objectives | Activities/Features |
|---|---|---|
| **Section 16.1**<br>**Energy**<br>1 session<br>½ block | 1. **Explain** what energy is and **distinguish** between potential and kinetic energy.<br>2. **Relate** chemical potential energy to the heat lost or gained in chemical reactions.<br>3. **Calculate** the amount of heat absorbed or released by a substance as its temperature changes. | **Discovery Lab:** Temperature of a Reaction, p. 489 |
| **Section 16.2**<br>**Heat in Chemical Reactions and Processes**<br>1 session<br>½ block | 4. **Describe** how a calorimeter is used to measure energy absorbed or released.<br>5. **Explain** the meaning of enthalpy and enthalpy change in chemical reactions and processes. | **Careers Using Chemistry:** Heating and Cooling Specialist, p. 499<br>**ChemLab:** Calorimetry, pp. 520–521 |
| **Section 16.3**<br>**Thermochemical Equations**<br>2 sessions<br>1½ blocks | 6. **Write** thermochemical equations for chemical reactions and other processes.<br>7. **Describe** how energy is lost or gained during changes of state.<br>8. **Calculate** the heat absorbed or released in a chemical reaction. | **Problem-Solving Lab:** How much energy is needed to heat water from a solid to a vapor? p. 503<br>**MiniLab:** Enthalpy of Fusion for Ice, p. 505 |
| **Section 16.4**<br>**Calculating Enthalpy Change**<br>2 sessions<br>1½ blocks | 9. **Use** Hess's law of summation of enthalpies of reaction to calculate the enthalpy change for a reaction.<br>10. **Explain** the basis for the table of standard enthalpies of formation.<br>11. **Calculate** $\Delta H_{rxn}$ using thermochemical equations.<br>12. **Determine** the enthalpy change for a reaction using standard enthalpies of formation data. | |
| **Section 16.5**<br>**Reaction Spontaneity**<br>2 sessions<br>1 block | 13. **Differentiate** between spontaneous and nonspontaneous processes.<br>14. **Explain** how changes in entropy and free energy determine the spontaneity of chemical reactions and other processes. | **Earth Science Connection,** p. 517<br>**How It Works:** Refrigerator, p. 522 |

| National Science Content Standards | State/Local Standards | Reproducible Masters | Transparencies |
|---|---|---|---|
| UCP.1, UCP.3; A.1; B.3, B.4, B.5, B.6; F.4, F.6 | | **Study Guide for Content Mastery,** p. 91 **L2** | **Section Focus Transparency 59** **L1** **ELL** |
| UCP.1, UCP.3; B.3, B.5; E.1 | | **Study Guide for Content Mastery,** p. 92 **L2** **ChemLab and MiniLab Worksheets,** pp. 62–64 **L2** **CBL Laboratory Manual,** pp. 25–28 **L2** | **Section Focus Transparency 60** **L1** **ELL** **Teaching Transparency 47** **L2** **ELL** **Math Skills Transparency 24** **L2** **ELL** |
| UCP.1, UCP.3; A.1; B.3, B.5, B.6; E.2 | | **Study Guide for Content Mastery,** p. 93 **L2** **ChemLab and MiniLab Worksheets,** p. 61 **L2** **Laboratory Manual,** pp. 121–128 **L2** **CBL Laboratory Manual,** pp. 29–32 **L2** | **Section Focus Transparency 61** **L1** **ELL** **Teaching Transparency 48** **L2** **ELL** |
| UCP.1, UCP.3; B.3, B.5; E.2 | | **Study Guide for Content Mastery,** pp. 94–95 **L2** **Challenge Problems,** p. 16 **L3** | **Section Focus Transparency 62** **L1** **ELL** **Teaching Transparency 49** **L2** **ELL** **Math Skills Transparency 25** **L2** **ELL** |
| UCP.1, UCP.3; A.1, A.2; B.3, B.5, B.6; E.1, E.2 | | **Study Guide for Content Mastery,** p. 96 **L2** **Small-Scale Laboratory Manual,** pp. 49–51 **L2** | **Section Focus Transparency 63** **L1** **ELL** **Teaching Transparency 49** **L2** **ELL** **Math Skills Transparency 26** **L2** **ELL** |

# Resource Manager

## Materials List

### ChemLab (pages 520–521)
large potato chip, 250-mL beaker, 100-mL graduated cylinder, thermometer, ring stand with ring, wire gauze, evaporating dish, matches, stirring rod, balance, water

### Discovery Lab (page 489)
large test tubes (2), thermometer, 25-mL graduated cylinder, 5M HCl, 5M NaOH, test-tube rack, distilled water

### MiniLab (page 505)
foam cup, thermometer, stirring rod, ice, water, balance

### Demonstration (pages 492–493)
thermite mixture, thermite starter, round filter paper, crucible tongs, magnesium ribbon (8 cm), laboratory burner, hammer, bucket of dry sand, magnet

## Preparation of Solutions

For a review of solution preparation, see page 46T of the Teacher Guide.

Quantities are for a class of 30 students.

### Discovery Lab (page 489)
**5M hydrochloric acid** Add 85mL concentrated (12M) hydrochloric acid to 120 mL distilled water while stirring. **CAUTION:** Do NOT add the water to the acid.

**5M NaOH solution** Carefully add 40 g NaOH to 120 mL distilled water. Make up to 200 mL final volume with distilled water. **CAUTION:** Solution will become very hot. Solution should be allowed to cool to room temperature before using it in this activity.

### Demonstration (pages 492–493)
**thermite mixture** Mix 125 g iron(III) oxide ($Fe_2O_3$) with 50 g aluminum powder (100 mesh). Note: For best results, ensure that the mixing process is thorough.

**thermite starter** Potassium chlorate ($KClO_3$) may be used in place of commercially prepared thermite starter. Substitute potassium chlorate in the procedure given. **CAUTION:** Do NOT attempt to prepare thermite starter.

## Assessment Resources

**Chapter Assessment,** pp. 91–96
**MindJogger Videoquizzes DVD/VHS**
**Alternate Assessment in the Science Classroom**
**ExamView® Pro CD-ROM**
**Solutions Manual,** Chapter 16
**Supplemental Problems,** Chapter 16
**Performance Assessment in the Science Classroom**
**Chemistry Interactive CD-ROM,** Chapter 16 quiz

## Additional Resources

**Spanish Resources** ELL
**Guided Reading Audio Program,** Chapter 16 ELL
**Cooperative Learning in the Science Classroom**
**Lab and Safety Skills in the Science Classroom**
**Lesson Plans**
**Block Scheduling Lesson Plans**
**Chemistrymc.com**

## Glencoe Technology

The following multimedia for this chapter are available from Glencoe.

 **VIDEOTAPE/DVD**
MindJogger Videoquizzes,
Chapter 16

**CD-ROM**
**Chemistry: Matter and Change**
*A Thermite Reaction,* Demonstration
*Burning Calories,* Exploration
*Hess's Law,* Experiment
*Thermochemistry,* Video
*Entropy,* Video

 **CD-ROM**
**ExamView® Pro**
**Testmaker**

 **CD-ROM**
**Interactive Chalkboard**

 **CD-ROM**
**TeacherWorks**™

## Multiple Learning Styles

Look for the following icons for strategies that emphasize different learning modalities.

 *Visual-Spatial*
Portfolio, pp. 490, 499; Differentiated Instruction,
pp. 494, 498, 514; Chemistry Journal, p. 496;
Extension, p. 514

 *Intrapersonal*
Chemistry Journal, pp. 502, 517; Check for
Understanding, p. 505

 *Linguistic*
Chemistry Journal, pp. 491, 506; Using Science
Terms, pp. 502, 514

 *Logical-Mathematical*
Reinforcement, p. 497; Portfolio, pp. 501, 509;
Reteach, p. 505; Differentiated Instruction, p. 510;
Chemistry Journal, p. 511; Quick Demo, p. 515

## Key to Teaching Strategies

**L1** Level 1 activities should be appropriate for students with learning difficulties.

**L2** Level 2 activities should be within the ability range of all students.

**L3** Level 3 activities are designed for above-average students.

**ELL** ELL activities should be within the ability range of English Language Learners.

**COOP LEARN** Cooperative Learning activities are designed for small group work.

**P** These strategies represent student products that can be placed into a best-work portfolio.

These strategies are useful in a block scheduling format.

## Assessment Planner

**Portfolio Assessment**
Portfolio, TWE, pp. 490, 499,
501, 509
MiniLab, TWE, p. 504
Assessment, TWE, p. 519

**Performance Assessment**
Assessment, TWE, pp. 492,
510
MiniLab, SE, p. 504
ChemLab, SE, pp. 520–521
ChemLab, TWE, p. 521
Discovery Lab, SE, p. 489

**Knowledge Assessment**
Demonstration, TWE, p. 493
Assessment, TWE, pp. 495,
511
Section Assessment, SE,
pp. 495, 500, 505, 512, 519
Chapter Assessment, SE,
pp. 524–527

**Skill Assessment**
Assessment, TWE, pp. 497,
500, 505, 517
Problem-Solving Lab, TWE,
p. 503

## Tying to Previous Knowledge

Have students review the following concepts before studying this chapter.
Chapter 10: writing chemical equations
Chapter 11: mole concept
Chapter 13: kinetic theory

## Using the Photo

Ask students if they would associate the word *energy* with a roller coaster. yes Point out that the energy of the roller coaster changes from energy of motion (kinetic energy) to energy of position (potential energy) throughout the ride. Potential energy is greatest at the top of a hill and least at the bottom of a hill. Ask when the roller coaster's kinetic energy is least. when the roller coaster is at the top of a hill Ask when is it greatest. when it is at the bottom of a hill

**PowerPoint® Presentations**
This CD-ROM is an editable Microsoft® PowerPoint® presentation that includes:
• Section presentations
• Section checks
• Image bank
• Links to Chemistry Online
• All transparencies
• Animations
• Audio

 **Resource Manager**

**Study Guide for Content Mastery,** p. 91 L2
**Solving Problems: A Chemistry Handbook,** Section 16.1 L2
**Section Focus Transparency 59 and Master** L1 ELL

**488**

---

# Energy and Chemical Change

## What You'll Learn

▶ You will measure and calculate the energy involved in chemical changes.
▶ You will write thermochemical equations and use them to calculate changes in enthalpy.
▶ You will explain how changes in enthalpy, entropy, and free energy affect the spontaneity of chemical reactions and other processes.

## Why It's Important

Energy enables you to live, move from place to place, and stay comfortably warm or cool. Almost all of the energy you use comes from chemical reactions, including those that take place in your own body.

 **Chemistry Online**

Visit the Chemistry Web site at **chemistrymc.com** to find links about energy and chemical change.

Each time the roller coaster zooms up and down the track, its energy changes back and forth between kinetic energy of motion and potential energy of position.

**488    Chapter 16**

## DISCOVERY LAB

### Purpose
Students will observe an exothermic reaction by mixing solutions of HCl and NaOH.

### Safety and Disposal
Students should wear aprons, safety glasses, and gloves. The HCl and NaOH solutions can burn skin and clothing. Caution students to take care in pouring the HCl solution into the NaOH solution.

The solutions can be flushed down the drain with plenty of water.

### Teaching Strategies
• The two solutions should have the same temperature before mixing (room temperature). Because heat will be generated when the solutions are made, prepare the solutions far enough in advance so that they have time to cool to room temperature.

**Temperature of a Reaction**

**D**oes a temperature change occur when a chemical reaction takes place?

**Safety Precautions**

 Use care when handling HCl and NaOH solutions.

**Procedure**

1. Measure about 5 mL 5*M* NaOH solution and pour it into a large test tube. Determine the temperature of the solution.

2. Rinse the thermometer and the graduated cylinder with distilled water as directed by your teacher. Repeat step 1 using 5*M* HCl.

3. Pour the HCl solution into the NaOH solution. Immediately insert the thermometer and record the temperature of the mixture. How does it compare to the temperatures of NaOH and HCl solutions?

**Analysis**

What evidence do you have that a chemical reaction has occurred? Write the balanced chemical equation for the reaction between aqueous sodium hydroxide and aqueous hydrochloric acid.

**Materials**

test tubes (2)
thermometer
25-mL graduated cylinder
test tube rack
distilled water
5*M* HCl
5*M* NaOH

---

**Section** 16.1

# Energy

## Objectives

- **Explain** what energy is and distinguish between potential and kinetic energy.

- **Relate** chemical potential energy to the heat lost or gained in chemical reactions.

- **Calculate** the amount of heat absorbed or released by a substance as its temperature changes.

## Vocabulary

energy
law of conservation of energy
chemical potential energy
heat
calorie
joule
specific heat

You're familiar with the term *energy*. Perhaps you've heard someone say, "I just ran out of energy," after a strenuous game or a difficult day. Solar energy, nuclear energy, energy-efficient automobiles, and other energy-related topics are often discussed in the media. In the **DISCOVERY LAB**, you observed a temperature change associated with the release of energy during a chemical reaction. But does energy affect your everyday life?

## The Nature of Energy

Energy cooks the food you eat and propels the vehicles that transport you. If the day is especially hot or cold, energy from burning fuels helps keep your home and school comfortable. Electrical energy provides light and operates devices from computers and TV sets to cellular phones, wristwatches, and calculators. Energy helped manufacture and deliver every material and device in your home, including the clothes you wear. Your every movement and thought requires energy. In fact, you can think of each cell in your body as a miniature factory that runs on energy derived from the food you eat. These examples only begin to define the role that energy plays in your life.

What is energy? **Energy** is the ability to do work or produce heat. It exists in two basic forms, potential energy and kinetic energy. Potential energy is energy due to the composition or position of an object. A macroscopic example of potential energy of position is water stored behind a dam above the turbines of a hydroelectric generating plant. When the dam gates are opened,

16.1 Energy    **489**

---

# 1 Focus

**Focus Transparency**

Before presenting the lesson, display **Section Focus Transparency 59** on the overhead projector. Have students answer the accompanying questions using **Section Focus Transparency Master 59.** L1 ELL

Section Focus Transparency 59 **Heat**

Use with Chapter 16, Section 16.1

❶ What do you observe in the picture?
❷ Why do firefighters wear protective clothing?

Chemistry: Matter and Change

Section Focus Transparencies

## Chapter Themes

The following themes from the National Science Education Standards are covered in this chapter. Refer to page 4T of the Teacher Guide for an explanation of the correlations.

Systems, order, and organization (UCP.1)

Evidence, models, and explanation (UCP.2)

Change, constancy, and measurement (UCP.3)

Form and function (UCP.5)

---

- See page 488C for preparation of solutions.
- Students should observe a temperature increase. The actual amount of the increase is not important.
- Ask students to identify the kind of chemical reaction that occurs. double replacement

**Expected Results**

In a sample experiment, the temperature increased by 3°C.

**Analysis**

The temperature increased when the two solutions were mixed.

$$HCl(aq) + NaOH(aq) \rightarrow NaCl(aq) + H_2O(l)$$

**National Science Content Standards**

Pages 488–489
UCP.1, UCP.3; A.1; B.3, B.5, B.6

Measure 100 mL of water into each of two 250-mL beakers. Put a Celsius thermometer in each beaker and allow them to reach the water's temperature. Record the temperatures and remove the thermometers. Ask a student to assist you in the next step. While you add approximately one tablespoon of anhydrous borax to one beaker, your assistant adds approximately one tablespoon of Epsom salts to the second beaker. Use stirring rods to stir until the solids are dissolved. Read and record the temperatures of the solutions. Temperature increased with the dissolving of anhydrous borax and decreased with the dissolving of Epsom salts. Ask students which process is exothermic and which is endothermic. The dissolving of anhydrous borax is exothermic. The dissolving of Epsom salts is endothermic. Flush solutions down the drain with plenty of water.

## GLENCOE
### TECHNOLOGY

**CD-ROM**
**Chemistry: Matter and Change**
Demonstration: *A Thermite Reaction*
Exploration: *Burning Calories*

**Figure 16-1**

Energy is conserved in these energy transformations. In ⓐ, some of the potential energy of water stored behind Folsom Dam in California is converted to electrical energy. In ⓑ, the chemical potential energy stored in wood is converted to heat.

the water rushes down and does work by turning the turbines to produce electrical energy.

Kinetic energy is energy of motion. You can observe kinetic energy in the motion of people and objects all around you. The potential energy of the dammed water is converted to kinetic energy as the dam gates are opened and the water flows out.

Chemical systems contain both kinetic energy and potential energy. Recall from Chapter 13 that the kinetic energy of a substance is directly related to the constant random motion of its atoms or molecules and is proportional to temperature. As temperature increases, the motion of submicroscopic particles increases. The potential energy of a substance depends upon its composition: the type of atoms in the substance, the number and type of chemical bonds joining the atoms, and the particular way the atoms are arranged.

**Law of conservation of energy** When water rushes through turbines in the hydroelectric plant in **Figure 16-1a**, some of the water's potential energy is converted to electrical energy. When wood burns in a fireplace, as shown in **Figure 16-1b**, potential energy is liberated as heat. In both of these examples, energy changes from one form to another. But does the amount of energy change? No. As energy changes from one form to another, the total amount of energy remains constant. Energy is conserved. To better understand the conservation of energy, suppose you have money in two accounts at a bank and you transfer funds from one account to the other. Although the amount of money in each account has changed, the total amount of your money in the bank remains the same. When applied to energy, this analogy embodies the law of conservation of energy. The **law of conservation of energy** states that in any chemical reaction or physical process, energy can be converted from one form to another, but it is neither created nor destroyed.

**Chemical potential energy** The energy stored in a substance because of its composition is called **chemical potential energy.** Chemical potential energy plays an important role in chemical reactions. For example, consider octane ($C_8H_{18}$), one of the principal components of gasoline. The chemical potential energy of octane results from the arrangement of the carbon and

## ✓ Portfolio

### Energy Value of Foods

*Visual-Spatial* Have students look up the caloric content of at least ten food items including all the foods consumed in a single meal, such as a lunch or dinner. Then, have students make posters or construct a chalkboard table of class data. Students should include their individual results and either the poster or the class data table in their portfolios. **L2** **ELL** **P** hydrogen atoms and the strength of the bonds that join them. When gasoline burns in an automobile's engine, some of octane's stored energy is converted to work in moving the pistons, which ultimately move the wheels and propel the automobile and its occupants from place to place. However, much of the potential energy of octane is released as heat. **Heat,** which is represented by the symbol $q$, is energy that is in the process of flowing from a warmer object to a cooler object. When the warmer object loses heat, its temperature decreases. When the cooler object absorbs heat, its temperature rises.

**Measuring heat** The flow of energy and the resulting change in temperature are clues to how heat is measured. In the metric system of units, the amount of heat required to raise the temperature of one gram of pure water by one degree Celsius (1°C) is defined as a **calorie** (cal). You've heard much about the caloric content of various foods. When your body breaks down sugars and fats to form carbon dioxide and water, these exothermic reactions generate heat that can be measured in Calories. Note that the nutritional Calorie is capitalized. That's because one nutritional Calorie, also known as one kilocalorie (kcal), equals 1000 calories. Suppose you eat a tablespoon of butter. One tablespoon of butter "has" 100 Calories. That means that if the butter was burned completely to produce carbon dioxide and water, 100 kcal (100 000 cal) of heat would be released.

The SI unit of heat and energy is the **joule** (J). One joule is the equivalent of 0.2390 calories, or one calorie equals 4.184 joules. **Table 16-1** shows the relationships among calories, nutritional Calories, joules, and kilojoules (kJ) and the conversion factors you can use to convert from one unit to another.

**Table 16-1**

| Relationships Among Energy Units | |
|---|---|
| Relationship | Conversion factors |
| 1 J = 0.2390 cal | $\dfrac{1 \text{ J}}{0.2390 \text{ cal}}$ |
| | $\dfrac{0.2390 \text{ cal}}{1 \text{ J}}$ |
| 1 cal = 4.184 J | $\dfrac{1 \text{ cal}}{4.184 \text{ J}}$ |
| | $\dfrac{4.184 \text{ J}}{1 \text{ cal}}$ |
| 1 kJ = 1000 J | $\dfrac{1 \text{ kJ}}{1000 \text{ J}}$ |
| | $\dfrac{1000 \text{ J}}{1 \text{ kJ}}$ |
| 1 Calorie = 1 kcal | $\dfrac{1 \text{ Calorie}}{1000 \text{ cal}}$ |
| 1 kcal = 1000 cal | $\dfrac{1000 \text{ cal}}{1 \text{ kcal}}$ |

## EXAMPLE PROBLEM 16-1

### Converting Energy Units

The breakfast shown in the photograph contains 230 nutritional Calories. How much energy in joules will this healthy breakfast supply?

**1. Analyze the Problem**

You are given an amount of energy in nutritional Calories. You must convert nutritional Calories to calories and then calories to joules.

**Known**

amount of energy = 230 Calories

**Unknown**

amount of energy = ? J

**2. Solve for the Unknown**

Use a conversion factor from **Table 16-1** to convert nutritional Calories to calories.

$$230 \text{ Calories} \times \frac{1000 \text{ cal}}{1 \text{ Calorie}} = 2.3 \times 10^5 \text{ cal}$$

Use a conversion factor to convert calories to joules.

$$2.3 \times 10^5 \text{ cal} \times \frac{4.184 \text{ J}}{1 \text{ cal}} = 9.6 \times 10^5 \text{ J}$$

**3. Evaluate the Answer**

The minimum number of significant figures used in the conversion is two, so the answer correctly has two digits. A value of the order of $10^5$ or $10^6$ is expected because the given number of kilocalories is of the order of $10^2$ and it must be multiplied by $10^3$ to convert it to calories. Then, the calories must be multiplied by a factor of approximately 4. Therefore, the answer is reasonable.

It's important to eat the appropriate number of Calories. It's also important that the foods you select provide the nutrients your body needs.

16.1 Energy **491**

## Enrichment

Explain that even a well-tuned automobile is able to convert only about 25% of the chemical energy in gasoline to useful mechanical energy that actually moves the car and occupants. Point out that the remaining 75% of energy is lost to the surroundings as heat.

## Content Background

**Another Unit of Heat** Ask students how the heating and cooling capacities of most furnaces and air conditioners in the U.S. are rated. in BTU, British thermal units Explain that 1 BTU = 1055 J and is the energy required to raise the temperature of one pound of water one degree Fahrenheit, from 63°F to 64°F.

## CHEMISTRY JOURNAL

### Life Without Petroleum

*Linguistic* Ask students to write a short story in their journals describing what their lives might be like living without petroleum in the year 2040.

**National Science Content Standards**

**Pages 490–491**
UCP.1, UCP.3; B.4, B.5, B.6

## Practice PROBLEMS

Have students refer to Appendix D for complete solutions to Practice Problems.

**1.** 142 000 cal

**2.** 20.7 kcal

**3.** 0.0612 kcal

---

## Assessment

**Performance** Have students make a poster or chart that depicts U.S. energy use from approximately 1800 to the present in each of these categories: wood, coal, petroleum and natural gas, hydroelectric, and nuclear. Discuss the reasons for and consequences of trends shown by the chart. Use the Performance Task Assessment List for Poster in **PASC**, p. 73. **L2** **ELL**

## Demonstration

Commercially prepared thermite mixture and thermite starter are available from chemical-supply houses. If you wish to prepare your own mixture and starter, see page 488C for instructions.

**National Science Content Standards**

Pages 492–493
UCP.1, UCP.3; B.5, B.6; F.4

---

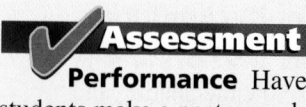

**Practice!** For more practice converting from one energy unit to another, go to Supplemental Practice Problems in Appendix A.

**Table 16-2**

| Specific Heats of Common Substances at 298 K (25°C) | |
|---|---|
| **Substance** | **Specific heat J/(g·°C)** |
| Water(l) (liquid) | 4.184 |
| Water(s) (ice) | 2.03 |
| Water(g) (steam) | 2.01 |
| Ethanol(l) (grain alcohol) | 2.44 |
| Aluminum(s) | 0.897 |
| Granite(s) | 0.803 |
| Iron(s) | 0.449 |
| Lead(s) | 0.129 |
| Silver(s) | 0.235 |
| Gold(s) | 0.129 |

**Figure 16-2**

Ocean and lake fronts are preferred places for growing fruit because the water absorbs heat during sunny days and releases heat when the air cools, thus moderating temperatures.

---

## PRACTICE PROBLEMS

**1.** A fruit and oatmeal bar contains 142 nutritional Calories. Convert this energy to calories.

**2.** An exothermic reaction releases 86.5 kJ. How many kilocalories of energy are released?

**3.** If an endothermic process absorbs 256 J, how many kilocalories are absorbed?

## Specific Heat

You've learned that one calorie, or 4.184 J, is required to raise the temperature of one gram of pure water by one degree Celsius (1°C). That quantity, 4.184 J/(g·°C), is defined as the specific heat ($c$) of water. The **specific heat** of any substance is the amount of heat required to raise the temperature of one gram of that substance by one degree Celsius. Because different substances have different compositions, each substance has its own specific heat. The specific heats of several common substances are listed in **Table 16-2**.

Note how different the specific heats of the various substances are. If the temperature of water is to rise by one degree, 4.184 joules must be absorbed by each gram of water. But only 0.129 joule is required to raise the temperature of an equal mass of gold by one degree. Because of its high specific heat, water can absorb and release large quantities of heat. Have you ever noticed that vineyards and orchards are often planted near large bodies of water, as shown in **Figure 16-2**? During hot weather, the water in the lake or ocean absorbs heat from the air and thereby cools the surrounding area. During a cold snap, the water releases heat, warming the air in the surrounding area so that fruit trees and fruit are less susceptible to frost damage.

The high specfic heat of water is also the basis for the use of water-filled plastic enclosures by gardeners in northern climates. Usually the planting of tender seedlings must wait until all danger of frost is past. However, the growing season can be extended into early spring if each plant is surrounded by a clear plastic enclosure filled with water. The water absorbs the heat of the Sun during the day. As the temperature drops at night, the water releases the absorbed

---

## Demonstration

### A Thermite Reaction

**Purpose** To demonstrate an exothermic reaction

**Materials** Thermite mixture; thermite starter; 11-cm round piece of filter paper; bucket of dry sand; crucible tongs; 8-cm length of Mg ribbon; burner; hammer; magnet

### Safety Precautions

A safety shield must be used. Do not allow students to come closer than 10 feet or to look directly at the burning Mg.

**Disposal** Reuse sand. Discard glass.

### Procedure

Fill a large bucket with dry sand and place it in a sink. Form a large, funnel-shaped depression in the sand. Use 11-cm filter

paper to form a paper cone. Place the paper cone in the sand near the center of the bucket at the bottom of the depression. There must be at least 10 cm of sand all around and under the cone. Place enough thermite mixture in the paper cone to almost fill it and mix in a teaspoonful of the starter. Make a slight depression in the center of the thermite mixture and fill with thermite starter. Insert 4 cm of an 8-cm length of Mg ribbon into the starter and thermite. Allow heat. The plant is kept warm even when the temperature of the air drops to 0°C.

**Calculating heat evolved and absorbed** If you've taken an early morning dive into a swimming pool similar to the one in **Figure 16-3**, you know that the water might be cold at that time of the day. Later in the day, especially if the Sun shines, the temperature of the water will be warmer. How much

**Figure 16-3**

The cold water of a swimming pool in the morning demonstrates that heat is lost by the water during the night.

warmer depends upon the specific heat of water, but other factors also are important. For example, suppose an architect designs a house that is to be partially heated by solar energy. Heat from the Sun will be stored in a solar pond similar to the swimming pool. The pond is to be made of 14 500 kg of granite rock and contain 22 500 kg of water. Both the granite and the water will absorb energy from the Sun during daylight hours. At night, the energy will not be released to the air, as happens with the swimming pool, but harnessed for use in the home. After conducting several experiments, the architect finds that the temperature of the water and granite increases an average of 22°C during the daylight hours and decreases the same amount during the night. Given these data, how much heat will the pond absorb and release during an average 24-hour period?

The specific heats of water and granite indicate how much heat one gram of each substance absorbs or releases when its temperature changes by 1°C. However, the pond contains much more than one gram of water and one gram of granite. And the temperatures of the two substances will increase and decrease an average of 22°C each day. How do mass and change in temperature affect the architect's calculations?

For the same change in temperature, 100 grams of water or granite absorb or release 100 times as much heat as one gram. Also, for the same 100 grams, increasing the temperature by 20 degrees Celsius requires 20 times as much heat as increasing the temperature by one degree Celsius. Therefore, the heat absorbed or released by a substance during a change in temperature depends not only upon the specific heat of the substance, but also upon the mass of the substance and the amount by which the temperature changes. You can express these relationships in an equation.

$$q = c \times m \times \Delta T$$

In the equation, $q$ = the heat absorbed or released, $c$ = the specific heat of the substance, $m$ = the mass of the sample in grams, and $\Delta T$ is the change in temperature in °C. $\Delta T$ is the difference between the final temperature and the initial temperature or, $T_{final} - T_{initial}$.

You can use this equation to calculate the total amount of heat the solar pond will absorb and release on a typical day. A mass of 22 500 kg of water equals $2.25 \times 10^7$ g and 14 500 kg of granite equals $1.45 \times 10^7$ g. The change in temperature for both the water and the granite is 22°C. The specific heat of water is 4.184 J/(g·°C) and the specific heat of granite is 0.803 J/(g·°C). Because each substance has its own specific heat, the amount of heat absorbed or released by water and granite must be calculated separately.

**Topic: Solar Heating**
To learn more about solar heating, visit the Chemistry Web site at **chemistrymc.com**

**Activity:** Research different ways that people capture solar energy, and what they use it for. Design a solar oven or other solar heat device. Explain how the energy is transferred from the sun through the device.

16.1 Energy **493**

**Identifying Misconceptions**

Students may think heat and temperature are the same thing.

**Uncover the Misconception**
Ask students which has a higher temperature, 100.0 g of ethanol at 25.0°C or 10.0 g of ethanol at 30.0°C. 10.0 g of ethanol at 30.0°C Then, ask which can transfer more heat as it cools by 10°C. 100.0 g of ethanol

**Demonstrate the Concept**
Demonstrate for students how to calculate the amounts of heat evolved in the previous example.

$q_1$ = 2.44 J/(g·°C) × 100.0 g × 10°C = 2440 J

$q_2$ = 2.44 J/(g·°C) × 10.0 g × 10°C = 244 J

**Assess New Knowledge**
Give students the following information: a 5.00-g piece of lead at 85.0°C and a 20.00-g piece of aluminum at 65.0°C are placed in a container of cold water. After the two metals have attained thermal equilibrium, a thermometer in the water reads 25.0°C. Ask students which metal had the higher initial temperature. lead Ask which had the greater $\Delta T$ as it cooled? lead Have students compare the heat lost by the two metals and explain the difference.

$q_{Pb}$ = 0.129 J/(g·°C) × 5.00 g × 60.0°C = 38.7 J

$q_{Al}$ = 0.897 J/(g·°C) × 5.00 g × 40.0°C = 179 J

Aluminum started at a lower temperature and had a smaller $\Delta T$, but it lost more heat because it has a higher specific heat.

the remaining 4 cm of ribbon to stick out to be used as a fuse. Place a safety shield between the class and the sink. **CAUTION:** *Wear safety goggles.* Darken the room. Bend the end of the Mg ribbon over to form a fuse and light it with a burner. Move students to the back of the room. Move away quickly. The heat generated produces white-hot molten iron and sparks. After the reaction stops, have students look at the molten sand and metal while the room is

dark. After about 15 min., use crucible tongs to hold the metal in a stream of water. When completely cooled, use a hammer to break off the melted sand around the iron core. Test the pieces with a magnet.

**Results**
Al reacted with $Fe_2O_3$ to produce Fe.

**Analysis**
**1.** Write the balanced chemical equation.
$Fe_2O_3 + 2Al \rightarrow Al_2O_3 + 2Fe + energy$

**2.** What was used to supply the high activation energy required for the reaction? the heat of the burning Mg ribbon

**Assessment**

**Knowledge** Have students explain how the thermite reaction can be used for practical applications. underwater welding is one example

**493**

Ask students to decide if each of the following changes is exothermic or endothermic. 1. Tea is warmed in a microwave oven. endothermic 2. Natural gas is burned in the furnace of a home. exothermic 3. Ice melts on the pond in the afternoon sunlight. endothermic **L2**

## Reteach

Ask students to explain the difference between temperature and heat. Temperature is the measure of the average kinetic energy of the particles that make up a substance. Heat is a form of energy that flows from a warmer substance to a cooler substance. **L2**

## Extension

Explain to students that the study of energy in chemical reactions is known as thermodynamics and that thermodynamics has its own specialized vocabulary. In their chemistry journals, ask them to keep a list of thermodynamic terms and definitions. **L2 ELL**

**National Science Content Standards**

**Pages 494–495**
UCP.1, UCP.3; B.6; F.4, F.6

**494**

$$q = c \times m \times \Delta T$$

$$q_{water} = 4.184 \text{ J/(g·°C)} \times (2.25 \times 10^7 \text{ g}) \times 22°C = 2.1 \times 10^9 \text{ J}$$

$$q_{granite} = 0.803 \text{ J/(g·°C)} \times (1.45 \times 10^7 \text{ g}) \times 22°C = 2.6 \times 10^8 \text{ J}$$

The total amount of heat absorbed or released by the pond is the sum of the two quantities.

$$q_{total} = q_{water} + q_{granite}$$

$$q_{total} = (2.1 \times 10^9 \text{ J}) + (2.6 \times 10^8 \text{ J}) = 2.4 \times 10^9 \text{ J} \text{ or } 2.4 \times 10^6 \text{ kJ}$$

The solar pond will absorb 2.4 million kJ of heat during a sunny day and release 2.4 million kJ during the night.

### EXAMPLE PROBLEM 16-2

**Calculating Specific Heat**

In the construction of bridges and skyscrapers, gaps must be left between adjoining steel beams to allow for the expansion and contraction of the metal due to heating and cooling. The temperature of a sample of iron with a mass of 10.0 g changed from 50.4°C to 25.0°C with the release of 114 J heat. What is the specific heat of iron?

**1. Analyze the Problem**

You are given the mass of the sample, the initial and final temperatures, and the quantity of heat released. The specific heat of iron is to be calculated. The equation that relates these variables can be rearranged to solve for $c$.

**Known**

joules of energy released = 114 J
$\Delta T = 50.4°C - 25.0°C = 25.4°C$
mass of iron = 10.0 g Fe

**Unknown**

specific heat of iron, $c = ? \text{ J/(g·°C)}$

**2. Solve for the Unknown**

Rearrange the equation $q = c \times m \times \Delta T$ to isolate $c$ by dividing each side of the equation by $m$ and $\Delta T$.

$$\frac{c \times m \times \Delta T}{m \times \Delta T} = \frac{q}{m \times \Delta T}$$

$$c = \frac{q}{m \times \Delta T}$$

Solve the equation using the known values.

$$c = \frac{114 \text{ J}}{(10.0 \text{ g})(25.4°C)} = 0.449 \text{ J/(g·°C)}$$

**3. Evaluate the Answer**

The values used in the calculation have three significant figures. Therefore, the answer is correctly stated with three digits. The value of the denominator of the equation is approximately two times the value of the numerator, so the final result (0.449), which is approximately 0.5, is reasonable. The calculated value is the same as that recorded for iron in **Table 16-2**.

Architects must make provision for the expansion and contraction of the steel frameworks of buildings because metals expand as they absorb heat and contract as they release heat.

### DIFFERENTIATED INSTRUCTION

**English Language Learners**

 *Visual-Spatial* Ask students to prepare flash cards for the vocabulary words and phrases in this section. Each card should have a word or phrase on one side and the definition on the reverse side. Then, have students work in pairs using the cards until they have mastered the terms. **L1 ELL**

**4.** If the temperature of 34.4 g of ethanol increases from 25.0°C to 78.8°C, how much heat has been absorbed by the ethanol?

**5.** A 4.50-g nugget of pure gold absorbed 276 J of heat. What was the final temperature of the gold if the initial temperature was 25.0°C? The specific heat of gold is 0.129 J/(g·°C).

**6.** A 155-g sample of an unknown substance was heated from 25.0°C to 40.0°C. In the process, the substance absorbed 5696 J of energy. What is the specific heat of the substance? Identify the substance among those listed in **Table 16-2**.

*Practice!* For more practice calculating and using specific heat, go to **Supplemental Practice Problems** in Appendix A.

**Using the Sun's energy** The Sun is a virtually inexhaustible source of energy. Radiation from the Sun could supply all the energy needs of the world and reduce or eliminate the use of carbon dioxide-producing fuels, but practical problems have delayed the development of solar energy. The Sun shines for only a fraction of the day. Clouds often reduce the amount of available radiation. Because of this variability, effective storage of energy is critical. Solar ponds, such as the one you have been reading about, take up large land areas and can lose heat to the atmosphere.

Another method for storage involves the use of hydrates such as sodium sulfate decahydrate ($Na_2SO_4 \cdot 10H_2O$), which you learned about in Chapter 11. When heated by the Sun, the hydrate undergoes an endothermic process in which the sodium sulfate dissolves in the water of hydration. When the temperature drops at night, the hydrate re-crystalizes with the release of the absorbed solar energy.

A more promising approach to the harnessing of solar energy is the development of photovoltaic cells. These electronic devices convert solar radiation directly to electricity. Photovoltaic cells are now being used to provide the energy needs of space vehicles, as shown in **Figure 16-4**. At present, the cost of supplying electricity by means of photovoltaic cells is high compared to the cost of burning coal and oil. Therefore, although photovoltaic cells are clean and efficient, they remain a choice for the future.

The specific heat of a substance is a measure of how efficiently that substance absorbs heat. Water is particularly efficient and, for this reason, plays an important role in calorimetry, an experimental procedure you will learn about in Section 16.2.

**Figure 16-4**

Photovoltaic cells, positioned to absorb energy from the Sun, are the source of energy for the operation of this artist's conception of a space station.

**Assessment**

**Knowledge** Ask students why more heat is required to raise the temperature of a given mass of water a given number of degrees than is needed to raise the same mass of ethanol by the same number of degrees. Water has a higher specific heat than ethanol. **L2**

**Practice PROBLEMS**

Have students refer to Appendix D for complete solutions to Practice Problems.

**4.** $4.52 \times 10^3$ J
**5.** $5.00 \times 10^2$°C
**6.** 2.45J/(g·°C), ethanol

## Section 16.1 Assessment

**7.** Explain what is meant by energy and list two units in which energy is measured.

**8.** Distinguish between kinetic and potential energy in the following examples: two separated magnets; an avalanche of snow; books on library shelves; a mountain stream; a stock car race; separation of charge in a battery.

**9.** What is the relationship between a calorie and a joule?

**10.** **Thinking Critically** One lawn chair is made of aluminum and another is made of iron. Both chairs are painted the same color. On a sunny day, which chair will be hottest to sit in? Explain why.

**11.** **Using Numbers** What is the specific heat of an unknown substance if a 2.50-g sample releases 12.0 cal as its temperature changes from 25.0°C to 20.0°C?

## Section 16.1 Assessment

**7.** Energy is the ability to do work or produce heat. Joules and calories are two common units of energy.

**8.** Two separated magnets illustrate potential energy. In a snow avalanche, positional potential energy is changing to kinetic energy. Books on a shelf illustrate positional potential energy. As water races down a mountain stream, positional potential energy is changing to kinetic energy. In a stock car race, chemical potential energy is being changed to kinetic energy. The separation of charge in a battery illustrates electrical potential energy.

**9.** 4.184 joules = one calorie

**10.** If the chairs are the same mass and absorb the same amount of heat, the iron chair will likely be hotter. Comparing the metals' specific heats, for the same mass and the same increase in temperature, aluminum would require twice as much heat as iron.

**11.** c = 4.02 J/(g·°C)

# Heat in Chemical Reactions and Processes

Before presenting the lesson, display **Section Focus Transparency 60** on the overhead projector. Have students answer the accompanying questions using **Section Focus Transparency Master 60. L1 ELL**

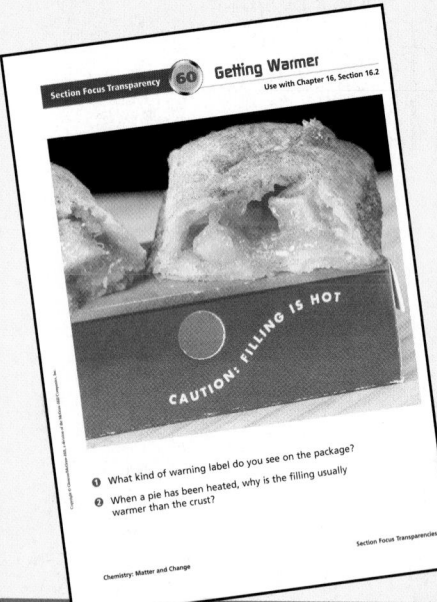

### Objectives

- **Describe** how a calorimeter is used to measure energy absorbed or released.

- **Explain** the meaning of enthalpy and enthalpy change in chemical reactions and processes.

### Vocabulary

calorimeter
thermochemistry
system
surroundings
universe
enthalpy
enthalpy (heat) of reaction

You have learned that some chemical reactions and processes must absorb energy in order to occur. These are called endothermic reactions. Others release energy and are called exothermic reactions. Whenever you cook food using methane or propane gas in your kitchen range, you utilize the heat released in the combustion of these fuels. But how do you measure the amount of heat released or absorbed when chemical reactions such as these occur?

## Measuring Heat

Heat changes that occur during chemical and physical processes can be measured accurately and precisely using a calorimeter. A **calorimeter** is an insulated device used for measuring the amount of heat absorbed or released during a chemical or physical process. A known mass of water is placed in an insulated chamber in the calorimeter to absorb the energy released from the reacting system or to provide the energy absorbed by the system. The data to be collected is the change in temperature of this mass of water. Good results can be obtained in your calorimetry experiments by using a calorimeter made from nested plastic foam cups similar to the one shown in **Figure 16-5**. Because the foam cup is not tightly sealed, it is, in effect, open to the atmosphere. Reactions carried out in this type of calorimeter, therefore, occur at constant pressure.

**Determining specific heat** You can use a calorimeter to determine the specific heat of an unknown metal. Suppose you put 125 g of water into a foam-cup calorimeter and find that its initial temperature is 25.6°C, as shown in **Figure 16-5a**. Then, you heat a 50.0-g sample of the unknown metal to a temperature of 115.0°C and put the metal sample into the water. Heat flows from the hot metal to the cooler water and the temperature of the water rises. The flow of heat stops only when the temperature of the metal and the water are equal. In **Figure 16-5b**, the temperature of the water is constant. Both water and metal have attained a final temperature of 29.3°C. Assuming no heat is lost to the surroundings, the heat gained by the water is equal to the heat lost by the metal. This quantity of heat can be calculated using the equation you learned in Section 16.1.

$$q = c \times m \times \Delta T$$

First, calculate the heat gained by the water. For this you need the specific heat of water, 4.184 J/(g·°C).

$$q_{water} = 4.184 \text{ J/(g·°C)} \times 125 \text{ g} \times (29.3°C - 25.6°C)$$

$$q_{water} = 4.184 \text{ J/(g·°C)} \times 125 \text{ g} \times 3.7°C$$

$$q_{water} = 1900 \text{ J}$$

The heat gained by the water, 1900 J, equals the heat lost by the metal, $q_{metal}$, so you can write this equation.

$$q_{metal} = 1900 \text{ J} = c_{metal} \times m \times \Delta T$$

$$1900 \text{ J} = c_{metal} \times m \times \Delta T$$

# 2 Teach
## Visual Learning

**Figure 16-5** Explain to students that not all the energy released in a reaction is absorbed by the water in the calorimeter. Some energy is absorbed by the calorimeter itself, the amount depending upon the materials used in the calorimeter and how it is constructed. Therefore, new calorimeters are calibrated individually to determine a calorimeter constant, which is then applied to all calculations made using that calorimeter.

**496   Chapter 16** Energy and Chemical Change

### CHEMISTRY JOURNAL

#### The Bomb Calorimeter

 **Visual-Spatial** Have students research how a bomb calorimeter is used to determine the caloric content of foods. Have them draw a diagram of the calorimeter and explain how it works. Students should include the diagram and written explanation in their chemistry journals. **L2 ELL**

(a)

(b)

**Figure 16-5**

In **a**, the measured mass of water has an initial temperature of 25.6°C. A piece of hot metal is added. The metal transfers heat to the water until metal and water attain the same temperature. That final temperature is shown in **b** as 29.3°C.

Now, solve the equation for the specific heat of the metal, $c_{metal}$, by dividing both sides of the equation by $m \times \Delta T$.

$$c_{(metal)} = \frac{1900 \text{ J}}{m \times \Delta T}$$

The change in temperature for the metal, $\Delta T$, is the difference between the final temperature of the water and the initial temperature of the metal (115.0°C − 29.3°C = 85.7°C). Substitute the known values of $m$ and $\Delta T$ (50.0 g and 85.7 °C) into the equation and solve.

$$c_{metal} = \frac{1900 \text{ J}}{(50.0 \text{ g})(85.7°C)} = 0.44 \text{ J/(g·°C)}$$

The unknown metal has a specific heat of 0.44 J/(g·°C). From **Table 16-2** on page 492, you can infer that the metal could be iron. The **CHEMLAB** at the end of this chapter will give you practice in calorimetry.

## EXAMPLE PROBLEM 16-3

### Using Data from Calorimetry

A piece of metal with a mass of 4.68 g absorbs 256 J of heat when its temperature increases by 182°C. What is the specific heat of the metal? Could the metal be one of the alkaline earth metals listed in **Table 16-3**?

**1. Analyze the Problem**

You are given the mass of the metal, the amount of heat it absorbs, and the temperature change. You must calculate the specific heat. The equation for $q$, the quantity of heat, should be used, but it must be solved for specific heat, $c$.

**Known**

mass of metal = 4.68 g metal
quantity of heat absorbed, $q$ = 256 J
$\Delta T$ = 182°C

**Unknown**

specific heat, $c$ = ? J/(g·°C)

*Continued on next page*

**Table 16-3**

| Periodic Trend in Specific Heats | |
| --- | --- |
| Alkaline earth elements | Specific heat (J/g·°C) |
| Beryllium | 1.825 |
| Magnesium | 1.023 |
| Calcium | 0.647 |
| Strontium | 0.301 |
| Barium | 0.204 |

## Assessment

**Skill** Have students devise a procedure to determine the specific heat of a metal object of unknown composition using a thermometer, beaker, hot plate, balance, water, graduated cylinder, and foam cup calorimeter. If time permits, give interested students a metal object and have them perform the experiment. **L3**

## Reinforcement

**Logical-Mathematical** Have students compare energy changes in chemical reactions to profits and losses in a business. Each month the business has receipts (positive dollar amounts) and expenses (negative dollar amounts). If receipts exceed expenditures, a positive dollar amount or profit occurs. If expenditures are greater than receipts, money is lost and a negative dollar amount results. **L2**

## CHEMLAB

ChemLab 16, located at the end of the chapter, can be used at this point in the lesson.

## Resource Manager

Study Guide for Content Mastery, p. 92 **L2**
Solving Problems: A Chemistry Handbook, Section 16.2 **L2**
Section Focus Transparency 60 and Master **L1** **ELL**
CBL Lab Manual, pp. 25–28
Math Skills Transparency 24 and Master **L2** **ELL**
Teaching Transparency 47 and Master **L2** **ELL**

## Internet Address Book

Note Internet addresses that you find useful in the space below for quick reference.

_____

_____

_____

_____

## Quick Demo

Place a beaker of crushed ice on a hot plate set on low. Explain to students that the system may be defined as the ice, and the surroundings may be defined as the beaker, hot plate, and remainder of the universe. Point out that the energy gained by the system as the ice melts equals the energy lost by the surroundings.

### 2. Solve for the Unknown

Solve for $c$ by dividing both sides of the equation by $m \times \Delta T$.

$$q = c \times m \times \Delta T$$

$$c = \frac{q}{m \times \Delta T}$$

Substitute the known values into the equation.

$$c = \frac{256 \text{ J}}{(4.68 \text{ g})(182°C)} = 0.301 \text{ J/(g·°C)}$$

**Table 16-3** indicates that the metal could be strontium.

### 3. Evaluate the Answer

The three quantities used in the calculation have three significant figures, so the answer is correctly stated with three digits. The calculations are correct and yield the expected unit. The calculated specific heat is the same as that of strontium.

**Practice!** For more practice using calorimetry data, go to **Supplemental Practice Problems** in Appendix A.

## PRACTICE PROBLEMS

**12.** If 335 g water at 65.5°C loses 9750 J of heat, what is the final temperature of the water?

**13.** The temperature of a sample of water increases from 20.0°C to 46.6°C as it absorbs 5650 J of heat. What is the mass of the sample?

**Figure 16-6**

The energy released in the reaction of iron with oxygen provides comforting warmth for cold hands.

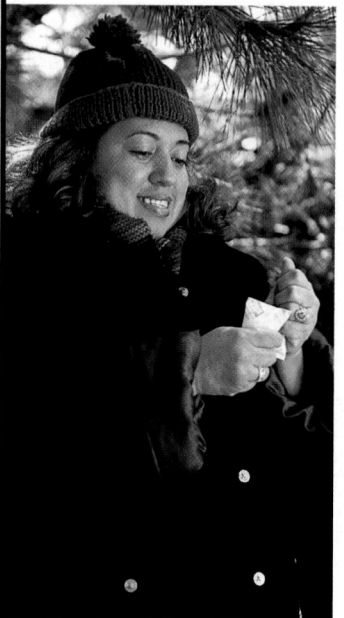

## Chemical Energy and the Universe

Virtually every chemical reaction and change of physical state either releases or absorbs heat. Recall that an exothermic reaction is one in which energy is released and an endothermic reaction is one in which energy is absorbed. What happens to the heat released by an exothermic chemical reaction? What is the source of the heat absorbed by an endothermic reaction? Thermochemistry provides answers to these questions. **Thermochemistry** is the study of heat changes that accompany chemical reactions and phase changes.

Think about what happens when you warm your hands on a cold day by using a heat pack similar to the one shown in **Figure 16-6**. When you remove the plastic wrap, oxygen from the air enters the pack. The oxygen reacts with iron in the pack in an exothermic reaction described by the following equation. Note that energy is shown as a product of the reaction, which means that heat is released.

$$4Fe(s) + 3O_2(g) \rightarrow 2Fe_2O_3(s) + 1625 \text{ kJ}$$

Because you are interested in the heat evolved by the chemical reaction going on inside the pack, it's convenient to think of the pack and its contents as the system. In thermochemistry, the **system** is the specific part of the universe that contains the reaction or process you wish to study. Everything in the universe other than the system is considered the **surroundings**. Therefore, the **universe** is defined as the system plus the surroundings.

$$\text{universe} = \text{system} + \text{surroundings}$$

What kind of energy transfer occurs during the exothermic heat-pack reaction? Heat produced by the reaction flows from the heat pack (the system) to your cold hands (part of the surroundings).

## DIFFERENTIATED INSTRUCTION

### Hearing Impaired

*Visual-Spatial* Use ball-and-stick molecular models to depict the exothermic reaction $2H_2(g) + O_2(g) \rightarrow 2H_2O(l)$. As you construct the reactant molecules, draw them on a chalkboard energy diagram at a high level. Then, construct the product molecules and draw them on the energy diagram at a lower energy level. Indicate how the energy changed by drawing an arrow pointing downward from reactants to products. **L2** **ELL**

What happens in an endothermic reaction or process? The flow of heat is reversed. Heat flows from the surroundings to the system. For example, if you dissolve ammonium nitrate ($NH_4NO_3$) in water, the temperature of the water decreases. This is the equation for that process. Note that energy is on the reactant side of the equation, which means energy is absorbed.

$$27 \text{ kJ} + NH_4NO_3(s) \rightarrow NH_4^+(aq) + NO_3^-(aq)$$

The athletic trainer in **Figure 16-7** can cause this reaction to occur in a cold pack by breaking a membrane in the pack and allowing ammonium nitrate to mix with water. When the cold pack is placed on an injured knee, heat flows from the knee (part of the surroundings) into the cold pack (the system).

**Enthalpy and enthalpy changes** The total amount of energy a substance contains depends upon many factors, some of which are not totally understood today. Therefore, it's impossible to know the total heat content of a substance. Fortunately, chemists are usually more interested in changes in energy during reactions than in the absolute amounts of energy contained in the reactants and products.

For many reactions, the amount of energy lost or gained can be measured conveniently in a calorimeter at constant pressure, as in the experiment illustrated in **Figure 16-5** on page 497. The foam cup is not sealed, so the pressure is constant. Many reactions of interest take place at constant atmospheric pressure; for example, those that occur in living organisms on Earth's surface, in lakes and oceans, and in open beakers and flasks in the laboratory. To more easily measure and study the energy changes that accompany such reactions, chemists have defined a property called enthalpy. **Enthalpy** ($H$) is the heat content of a system at constant pressure.

But why define a property if you can't know its absolute value? Although you can't measure the actual energy or enthalpy of a substance, you can measure the change in enthalpy, which is the heat absorbed or released in a chemical reaction. The change in enthalpy for a reaction is called the **enthalpy (heat) of reaction** ($\Delta H_{rxn}$). You have already learned that a symbol preceded by the Greek letter $\Delta$ means a change in the property. Thus, $\Delta H_{rxn}$ is the difference between the enthalpy of the substances that exist at the end of the reaction and the enthalpy of the substances present at the start.

$$\Delta H_{rxn} = H_{final} - H_{initial}$$

Because the reactants are present at the beginning of the reaction and the products are present at the end, $\Delta H_{rxn}$ is defined by this equation.

$$\Delta H_{rxn} = H_{products} - H_{reactants}$$

**The sign of the enthalpy of reaction** Recall the heat-pack reaction of iron with oxygen.

$$4Fe(s) + 3O_2(g) \rightarrow 2Fe_2O_3(s) + 1625 \text{ kJ}$$

According to the equation, the reactants in this exothermic reaction lose heat. Therefore, $H_{products} < H_{reactants}$. When $H_{reactants}$ is subtracted from the smaller $H_{products}$, a negative value for $\Delta H_{rxn}$ is obtained. Enthalpy changes for exothermic reactions are always negative. The equation for the heat-pack reaction and its enthalpy change are usually written like this.

$$4Fe(s) + 3O_2(g) \rightarrow 2Fe_2O_3(s) \quad \Delta H_{rxn} = -1625 \text{ kJ}$$

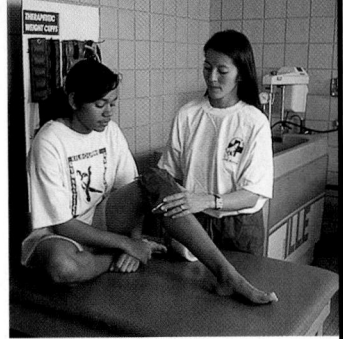

**Figure 16-7**

Heat is absorbed when ammonium nitrate dissolves in water in a cold pack. In this photograph, heat is transferred from the injured knee to the chemical process.

**Concept Development**

Explain that enthalpy is a state function—a property of a system that depends upon only its present state. Explain that an important characteristic of a state function, such as $H$, is that a change in $H$ ($\Delta H$) is independent of the pathway between the initial and final states.

$$\Delta H_{rxn} = H_{products} - H_{reactants}$$

**Math in Chemistry**

Help students understand the $+$ and $-$ signs assigned to changes in energy during a chemical reaction by pointing out that the sign always reflects the *system's point of view*. A $+$ sign for $\Delta H$ indicates that the energy of the system has increased while a $-$ sign indicates that the energy of the system has decreased.

**CAREERS USING CHEMISTRY**

**Career Path** A career as a heating and cooling specialist would include high school courses in chemistry, applied physics, computer science, electronics, math, and mechanical drawing. Mechanics might learn on the job or complete a six-month to two-year training program. Thirty states require these mechanics to be licensed.

**Career Issue** Have students find out why people who handle refrigerants must have special training.

**For More Information**
For more information about apprenticeship programs in heating and cooling mechanics, students can contact

Associated Builders and Contractors
1300 N. Seventeenth Street, Suite 800
Rosslyn, VA 22209

**Portfolio**

**Cataloging Everyday Reactions**

*Visual-Spatial* Ask students to think critically about two exothermic and two endothermic chemical reactions or processes they encounter in their daily lives. Ask them to make a table that includes the following information: a description of each reaction or process, the direction of heat flow between the system and surroundings, the change in enthalpy of the system, the change in enthalpy of the surroundings, and the sign (positive or negative) of $\Delta H_{rxn}$. Have students include the tables in their portfolios. **L2** **P**

# 3 Assess

## Check for Understanding

Give students the following oral assignment: Define the universe and give three examples. After some discussion, point out that, in thermodynamics, the universe is simply defined as the sum of the system and surroundings (universe = system + surroundings). Therefore, an example of the universe could be any combination of system and surroundings. **L2**

## Reteach

Ask students to define and compare energy, heat, and enthalpy. Energy is the ability to do work or produce heat. Heat is a form of energy that flows from a warmer object or material to a colder object or material. Enthalpy is the heat content of a system at constant pressure.

## Extension

Arrange a field trip to a nearby electrical power plant or ask a power company representative to make a class presentation on the processes involved in the production of electricity. Alternatively, an interested student might interview the representative and make a class presentation of his or her findings. **L2** **ELL**

## Assessment

**Skill** Have students write the thermochemical equation for a reaction between two solid substances, A and B, which yields two gaseous substances, C and D, and releases 128 kJ of heat. $A(s) + B(s) \rightarrow C(g) + D(g)$ $\Delta H = -128$ kJ

**Exothermic Reaction**
$\Delta H < 0$
**(a)**

**Endothermic Reaction**
$\Delta H > 0$
**(b)**

**Figure 16-8**

The downward arrow in **(a)** shows that 1625 kJ of heat is released to the surroundings in the reaction between Fe and $O_2$ to form $Fe_2O_3$. In contrast, the upward arrow in **(b)** indicates that 27 kJ of heat is absorbed from the surroundings in the process of dissolving $NH_4NO_3$.

**Table 16-4**

| Enthalpy Changes for Exothermic and Endothermic Reactions | |
|---|---|
| Type of reaction | Sign of $\Delta H_{rxn}$ |
| Exothermic | Negative |
| Endothermic | Positive |

**Figure 16-8a** is a diagram of the energy change for the exothermic reaction between iron and oxygen. You can see that the enthalpy of the product, $Fe_2O_3$, is 1625 kJ less than the enthalpy of the reactants Fe and $O_2$ because energy is released.

Similarly, recall the cold-pack reaction.

$$27 \text{ kJ} + NH_4NO_3(s) \rightarrow NH_4^+(aq) + NO_3^-(aq)$$

For this endothermic reaction, $\Delta H_{products} > \Delta H_{reactants}$. Therefore, when $\Delta H_{reactants}$ is subtracted from the larger $\Delta H_{products}$, a positive value for $\Delta H_{rxn}$ is obtained. Enthalpy changes for endothermic reactions are always positive. Chemists write the equation for the cold-pack reaction and its enthalpy change in this way.

$$NH_4NO_3(s) \rightarrow NH_4^+(aq) + NO_3^-(aq) \quad \Delta H_{rxn} = 27 \text{ kJ}$$

**Figure 16-8b** shows the energy change for the cold-pack reaction. In this endothermic reaction, the enthalpy of the products, aqueous $NH_4^+$ and $NO_3^-$ ions, is 27 kJ greater than the enthalpy of the reactant, $NH_4NO_3$ because energy is absorbed in the reaction. Compare **Figure 16-8a** and **Figure 16-8b** and then study **Table 16-4**, which shows the sign of $\Delta H_{rxn}$ for exothermic and endothermic reactions.

Recall that $q$ was defined as the heat gained or lost in a chemical reaction or process. When the reaction takes place at constant pressure, the subscript p is sometimes added to the symbol $q$. The enthalpy change, $\Delta H$, is equal to $q_p$, the heat gained or lost in a reaction or process carried out at constant pressure. Because all reactions presented in this textbook occur at constant pressure, you may assume that $q = \Delta H_{rxn}$.

## Section 16.2 Assessment

**14.** Describe how you would calculate the amount of heat absorbed or released by a substance when its temperature changes.

**15.** Why does $\Delta H$ for an exothermic reaction have a negative value?

**16.** Why is a measured volume of water an essential part of a calorimeter?

**17.** Explain the meaning of $\Delta H_{rxn}$. Why is $\Delta H_{rxn}$ sometimes positive and sometimes negative?

**18. Thinking Critically** Could another liquid be used just as effectively as water in a calorimeter? Why or why not?

**19. Designing an Experiment** Explain how you would design an experiment to determine the specific heat of a 45-g piece of metal.

chemistrymc.com/self_check_quiz

---

## Section 16.2 Assessment

**14.** The heat absorbed or released equals the specific heat of the substance times its mass times its change in temperature.

**15.** $\Delta H_{rxn} = H_{products} - H_{reactants}$ and $H_{products} < H_{reactants}$

**16.** The water absorbs the energy

released. The heat released equals the mass of water times the change in temperature times the specific heat.

**17.** $\Delta H_{rxn} = H_{products} - H_{reactants}$. If $H_{products} > H_{reactants}$, $\Delta H_{rxn}$ is positive. If $H_{products} < H_{reactants}$, $\Delta H_{rxn}$ is negative.

**18.** Yes, if its specific heat is known. However, most liquids have lower specific heats than water. Other

liquids may be more volatile and/or more reactive.

**19.** Put a known mass of water into a calorimeter and measure its temperature. Heat a 45-g metal sample to 100°C in boiling water. Put the heated metal sample into the water in the calorimeter and wait until the temperature of the

Chemical reactions either release energy (exothermic reactions) or absorb energy (endothermic reactions). The change in energy is an important part of chemical reactions so chemists include $\Delta H$ as part of the chemical equation.

## Writing Thermochemical Equations

The equations for the heat-pack and cold-pack reactions that you learned about in Section 16.2 are called thermochemical equations when they are written like this.

$$4Fe(s) + 3O_2(g) \rightarrow 2Fe_2O_3(s) \quad \Delta H = -1625 \text{ kJ}$$

$$NH_4NO_3(s) \rightarrow NH_4^+(aq) + NO_3^-(aq) \quad \Delta H = 27 \text{ kJ}$$

A **thermochemical equation** is a balanced chemical equation that includes the physical states of all reactants and products and the energy change, usually expressed as the change in enthalpy, $\Delta H$.

The nature of the reaction or process described by a thermochemical equation is often written as a subscript of $\Delta H$. For example, the highly exothermic combustion (comb) of glucose ($C_6H_{12}O_6$) occurs in the body as food is metabolized to produce energy for activities such as the one shown in **Figure 16-9.** The thermochemical equation for the combustion of glucose is

$$C_6H_{12}O_6(s) + 6O_2(g) \rightarrow 6CO_2(g) + 6H_2O(l) \quad \Delta H_{comb} = -2808 \text{ kJ}$$

The energy released ($-2808$ kJ) is the enthalpy of combustion. The **enthalpy (heat) of combustion** ($\Delta H_{comb}$) of a substance is the enthalpy change for the complete burning of one mole of the substance. Standard enthalpies of combustion for several common substances are given in **Table 16-5.** Standard enthalpy changes have the symbol $\Delta H°$. The zero superscript tells you that the reactions were carried out under standard conditions. Standard conditions are one atmosphere pressure and 298 K (25°C) and should not be confused with standard temperature and pressure (STP).

### Objectives

- **Write** thermochemical equations for chemical reactions and other processes.
- **Describe** how energy is lost or gained during changes of state.
- **Calculate** the heat absorbed or released in a chemical reaction.

### Vocabulary

thermochemical equation
enthalpy (heat) of combustion
molar enthalpy (heat) of vaporization
molar enthalpy (heat) of fusion

### Figure 16-9

The energy expended by both horse and rider is obtained through the exothermic combustion of glucose in cells.

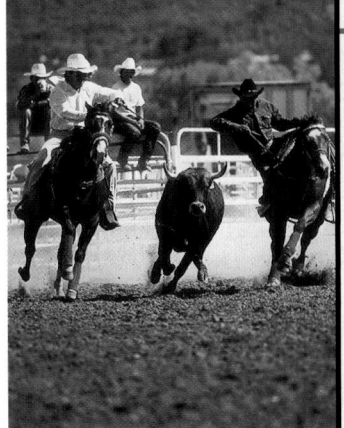

### Table 16-5

| Standard Enthalpies of Combustion | | |
|---|---|---|
| Substance | Formula | $\Delta H°_{comb}$ (kJ/mol) |
| Sucrose (table sugar) | $C_{12}H_{22}O_{11}(s)$ | −5644 |
| Octane (a component of gasoline) | $C_8H_{18}(l)$ | −5471 |
| Glucose (a simple sugar found in fruit) | $C_6H_{12}O_6(s)$ | −2808 |
| Propane | $C_3H_8(g)$ | −2219 |
| Ethanol | $C_2H_5OH(l)$ | −1367 |
| Methane (the major component of natural gas) | $CH_4(g)$ | −891 |
| Methanol (wood alcohol) | $CH_3OH(l)$ | −726 |
| Carbon (graphite) | $C(s)$ | −394 |
| Hydrogen | $H_2(g)$ | −286 |

16.3 Thermochemical Equations **501**

water is constant. Measure the final temperature of the water. Assume no heat is lost to the surroundings. Calculate the specific heat of the metal by equating the quantity of heat gained by the water to the quantity of heat lost by the metal.

## Figure Caption Question

**Figure 16-10** What would be the energy of the process called sublimation in which ice is converted directly to water vapor? 46.7 kJ **L2**

## In-Text Question

**Page 502** How would you summarize your observations? The same amount of energy is absorbed in the vaporization of water as is released in the condensation of water. The same amount of energy is absorbed in the melting of ice as is released in the freezing of water.

## Using Science Terms

*Linguistic* Have students use a dictionary to look up and explain the meanings of several key English words used in Sections 16.1, 16.2, and 16.3: potential, conservation, capacity, calorimetry, system, surroundings, universe, thermochemical, combustion, vaporization, fusion. **L1 ELL**

**Resource Manager**

**Study Guide for Content Mastery**, p. 93 **L2**

**Solving Problems: A Chemistry Handbook**, Section 16.3 **L2**

**Section Focus Transparency 61 and Master L1 ELL**

**National Science Content Standards**

**Pages 500–503**
UCP.1, UCP.3; B.3, B.5, B.6; E.2

**502**

## Changes of State

Many processes other than chemical reactions absorb or release heat. For example, think about what happens when you step out of a hot shower. You shiver as water evaporates from your skin. That's because your skin provides the heat needed to vaporize the water. As heat is taken from your skin to vaporize the water, you cool down. The heat required to vaporize one mole of a liquid is called its **molar enthalpy (heat) of vaporization** ($\Delta H_{vap}$). Similarly, if you want a glass of cold water, you might drop an ice cube into it. The water cools as it provides the heat to melt the ice. The heat required to melt one mole of a solid substance is called its **molar enthalpy (heat) of fusion** ($\Delta H_{fus}$). Because vaporizing a liquid and melting a solid are endothermic processes, their $\Delta H$ values are positive. Standard molar enthalpies of vaporization and fusion for four common compounds are shown in **Table 16-6**.

**Table 16-6**

| Standard Enthalpies of Vaporization and Fusion | | | |
|---|---|---|---|
| Substance | Formula | $\Delta H^{\circ}_{vap}$ (kJ/mol) | $\Delta H^{\circ}_{fus}$ (kJ/mol) |
| Water | $H_2O$ | 40.7 | 6.01 |
| Ethanol | $C_2H_5OH$ | 38.6 | 4.94 |
| Methanol | $CH_3OH$ | 35.2 | 3.22 |
| Ammonia | $NH_3$ | 23.3 | 5.66 |

**Thermochemical equations for changes of state** The vaporization of water and the melting of ice can be described by the following equations.

$$H_2O(l) \rightarrow H_2O(g) \quad \Delta H_{vap} = 40.7 \text{ kJ}$$
$$H_2O(s) \rightarrow H_2O(l) \quad \Delta H_{fus} = 6.01 \text{ kJ}$$

The first equation indicates that 40.7 kJ of energy is absorbed when one mole of water is converted to one mole of water vapor. The second equation shows that when one mole of ice melts to form one mole of liquid water, 6.01 kJ of energy is absorbed.

What happens in the reverse processes, when water vapor condenses to liquid water or liquid water freezes to ice? The same amounts of energy are released in these exothermic processes as are absorbed in the endothermic processes of vaporization and melting. Thus, the molar enthalpy (heat) of condensation ($\Delta H_{cond}$) and the molar enthalpy of vaporization have the same numerical value but opposite signs. Similarly, the molar enthalpy (heat) of solidification ($\Delta H_{solid}$) and the molar enthalpy of fusion have the same numerical value but differ in sign.

$$\Delta H_{vap} = -\Delta H_{cond}$$
$$\Delta H_{fus} = -\Delta H_{solid}$$

Compare the following equations for the condensation and freezing of water with the equations above for the vaporization and melting of water. How would you summarize your observations? The relationships are illustrated in **Figure 16-10**.

$$H_2O(g) \rightarrow H_2O(l) \quad \Delta H_{cond} = -40.7 \text{ kJ}$$
$$H_2O(l) \rightarrow H_2O(s) \quad \Delta H_{solid} = -6.01 \text{ kJ}$$

**Figure 16-10**

The left arrows show that the energy of the system increases as water melts and then vaporizes. The right arrows show that the energy of the system decreases as gaseous water condenses and then solidifies. What would be the energy of the process called sublimation in which ice is converted directly to water vapor?

$H_2O(g)$
$\Delta H_{vap} = +40.7 \text{ kJ}$
$\Delta H_{cond} = -40.7 \text{ kJ}$
$H_2O(l)$
$\Delta H_{fus} = +6.01 \text{ kJ}$
$\Delta H_{solid} = -6.01 \text{ kJ}$
$H_2O(s)$
Enthalpy

**CHEMISTRY JOURNAL**

## Gasoline Additives

*Intrapersonal* The requirement that gasoline in some areas of the country contain oxygenating compounds is under close scrutiny because of its added cost and some negative environmental effects. Have students research the effects—on mileage and on the environment—of adding oxygenating compounds such as ethanol and methyl tert-butyl ether (MTBE) to gasoline. Have them record their findings in their chemistry journals. **L2**

Some farmers make use of the heat of fusion of water to protect fruit from freezing. They flood their orchards or fields with water, as shown in **Figure 16-11.** The energy released as the water freezes ($\Delta H_{fus}$) often increases the temperature of the air enough to prevent frost damage to the fruit.

In the **problem-solving LAB,** you will interpret the heating curve of water using the heats of fusion and vaporization. The **How It Works** feature, at the end of the chapter, describes a practical application of the vaporization of a liquid.

**Figure 16-11**

If the temperature should drop to freezing, the water that floods this field will release heat ($\triangle H_{fus}$) as it freezes and warm the surrounding air.

## problem-solving LAB

### How much energy is needed to heat water from a solid to a vapor?

**Making and Using Heating Curves** Water molecules have a strong attraction for one another because they are polar. The polarity of water accounts for its high specific heat and relatively high enthalpies of fusion and vaporization. Water's high specific heat and the presence of an enormous amount of water on Earth's surface have a large influence on the weather.

**Analysis**

Use the data in the table to plot a heating curve of temperature versus time for a 180-g sample of water as it is heated at a constant rate from −20°C to 120°C. Draw a best-fit line through the points. Note the time required for water to pass through each segment of the graph.

**Thinking Critically**

1. For each of the five regions of the graph, indicate how the absorption of heat changes the energy (kinetic or potential) of the water molecules.

2. Calculate the amount of heat required to pass through each region of the graph (180 g H₂O = 10 mol H₂O, $\Delta H_{fus}$ = 6.01 kJ/mol, $\Delta H_{vap}$ = 40.7 kJ/mol, c = 4.184 J/g·°C). How does the length of time needed to pass through each region relate to the amount of heat absorbed?

3. What would the heating curve of ethanol look like? Make a rough sketch of ethanol's curve from −120°C to 90°C. Ethanol melts at −114°C and boils at 78°C. What factors determine the

| Time and Temperature Data for Water | | | |
|---|---|---|---|
| Time (min) | Temperature °C | Time (min) | Temperature °C |
| 0.0 | −20 | 13.0 | 100 |
| 0.5 | −11 | 13.5 | 100 |
| 1.0 | 0 | 14.0 | 100 |
| 1.5 | 0 | 14.5 | 100 |
| 2.0 | 0 | 15.0 | 100 |
| 2.5 | 0 | 15.5 | 100 |
| 3.0 | 9 | 16.0 | 100 |
| 3.5 | 18 | 16.5 | 100 |
| 4.0 | 26 | 17.0 | 100 |
| 4.5 | 34 | 17.5 | 100 |
| 5.0 | 42 | 18.0 | 100 |
| 5.5 | 51 | 18.5 | 100 |
| 6.0 | 58 | 19.0 | 100 |
| 6.5 | 65 | 19.5 | 100 |
| 7.0 | 71 | 20.0 | 100 |
| 7.5 | 77 | 20.5 | 100 |
| 8.0 | 83 | 21.0 | 100 |
| 8.5 | 88 | 21.5 | 100 |
| 9.0 | 92 | 22.0 | 100 |
| 9.5 | 95 | 22.5 | 100 |
| 10.0 | 98 | 23.0 | 100 |
| 10.5 | 100 | 23.5 | 100 |
| 11.0 | 100 | 24.0 | 100 |
| 11.5 | 100 | 24.5 | 108 |
| 12.0 | 100 | 25.0 | 120 |
| 12.5 | 100 | | |

lengths of the flat regions of the graph and the slope of the curve between the flat regions?

3. rising slope from −120°C to −114°C, plateau at −114°C, rising slope from −114°C to 78°C, plateau at 78°C, rising slope from 78°C to 90°C; length of plateaus: $\triangle H_{fus}$, $\triangle H_{vap}$, rate of heating; slope of rises: specific heat, rate of heating; see Solutions Manual.

### ✔ Assessment

**Skill** Have students refer to their sketches for question 3 and calculate the total energy required to heat 180 g of ethanol from −120°C to 90°C. 262 kJ **L2** **ELL**

## problem-solving LAB

**Purpose** 

Students will plot the heating curve of water and infer the internal energy changes that take place.

**Process Skills**

Making and using graphs, applying concepts, interpreting data, recognizing cause and effect

**Teaching Strategies**

• Review the relationship between temperature and the average kinetic energy of the molecules.

• Use magnets to model the potential energy associated with strong attractive dipole forces between water molecules.

• Students' graphs will have three steps. The first slope will increase from −20°C to 0°C and plateau at 0°C. The second slope increases from 0°C to 100°C and plateaus at 100°C. The third slope increases from 100°C to 120°C.

**Thinking Critically**

1. From −20°C to 0°C, kinetic energy increases. At the 0°C plateau, potential energy increases as particles gain more freedom of movement. From 0°C to 100°C, kinetic energy increases. At the 100°C plateau, potential energy increases as particles separate completely. From 100°C to 120°C, kinetic energy increases.

2. The more heat required, the longer the region. Changing water from a liquid to a gas requires the larger amount of energy.
   For −20°C to 0°C, q = 180 g × 20°C × 4.184 J/g·°C × 1 kJ/ 1000 J = 15 kJ
   Melting the ice, q = 6.01 kJ/mol × 10 mol = 60 kJ
   For 0°C to 100°C, q = 180 g × 100°C × 4.184 J/g·°C × 1 kJ/1000 J = 75 kJ
   Vaporizing the water, q = 40.7 kJ/mol × 10 mol = 410 kJ
   For 100°C to 120°C, q = 180 g × 20°C × 4.184 J/g·°C × 1 kJ/1000 J = 15 kJ

504

## Practice PROBLEMS

Have students refer to Appendix D for complete solutions to Practice Problems.

**20.** 2.58 kJ

**21.** 376 kJ

**22.** 232 g

## mini LAB

### Purpose

Students will use experimental data to calculate the enthalpy of fusion of ice.

### Process Skills

Applying concepts, collecting data, measuring, using numbers

### Teaching Strategies

- Crushed ice gives the best results. Small ice cubes are better than large.
- A large foam cup works best. The cup does not have to be covered because little heat is lost from the water surface.
- Be sure students understand that when ice melts, the temperature of the water that is produced is initially at 0.0°C. Heat will be transferred from the calorimeter water to the melted ice until the temperatures of the two masses of water are the same.

### Expected Results

Mass of cup = 3.97g

Mass of water + cup = 157.67 g

Mass of liquid water = 153.70 g

Mass of cup + water + melted ice = 172.43 g

Mass of melted ice = 14.76 g

$\triangle T$ (liquid water) = 21.0°C − 13.0°C = 8.0°C

$\triangle T$ (melted ice) = 13.0°C − 0.0°C = 13.0°C

### Analysis

**1.** $q_{water}$ = 4.184 J/(g·°C) × 153.70 g × 8.0°C = 5100 J

**2.** $q_{melted\ ice}$ = 4.184 J/(g·°C) × 14.76 g × 13.0°C = 803 J

**3.** (5100 J − 800 J)/14.76 g = 290 J/g

**4.** 290 J/g × 1 kJ/1000 J × 18.02 g/mol = 5.2 kJ/mol

**5.** ((6.01 − 5.2)/6.01) × 100 = 13% error

---

Thermometer

Ignition terminals

Stirrer

Water

Insulation

Sealed reaction chamber containing substance and oxygen

Inside the central chamber or bomb of a bomb calorimeter, reactions are carried out at constant volume. A sample of known mass is ignited by an electric spark and burned in an excess of oxygen. The heat released is transferred to a known mass of water in the well insulated outer chamber.

---

*Practice!* **For more practice calculating the energy released in a reaction, go to Supplemental Practice Problems in Appendix A.**

---

## EXAMPLE PROBLEM 16-4

### Calculating Energy Released in a Reaction

A bomb calorimeter is useful for measuring the energy released in combustion reactions. The reaction is carried out in a constant volume bomb with a high pressure of oxygen. How much heat is evolved when 54.0 g glucose ($C_6H_{12}O_6$) is burned according to this equation?

$C_6H_{12}O_6(s) + 6O_2(g) \rightarrow 6CO_2(g) + 6H_2O(l)$  $\Delta H_{comb} = -2808$ kJ

### 1. Analyze the Problem

You are given a mass of glucose, the equation for the combustion of glucose, and $\Delta H_{comb}$. Grams of glucose must be converted to moles of glucose. Because the molar mass of glucose is more than three times the given mass of glucose, you can predict that the energy evolved will be less than one-third $\Delta H_{comb}$.

| Known | Unknown |
|---|---|
| mass of glucose = 54.0 g $C_6H_{12}O_6$ | $q$ = ? kJ |
| $\Delta H_{comb}$ = −2808 kJ | |

### 2. Solve for the Unknown

Convert grams of $C_6H_{12}O_6$ to moles of $C_6H_{12}O_6$ by multiplying by the conversion factor that relates moles and mass, the inverse of molar mass.

$$54.0 \text{ g } C_6H_{12}O_6 \times \frac{1 \text{ mol } C_6H_{12}O_6}{180.18 \text{ g } C_6H_{12}O_6} = 0.300 \text{ mol } C_6H_{12}O_6$$

Multiply moles of $C_6H_{12}O_6$ by the conversion factor that relates kJ and moles, the enthalpy of combustion, $\Delta H_{comb}$.

$$\frac{\text{kJ released}}{1 \text{ mole substance burned}}$$

$$0.300 \text{ mol } C_6H_{12}O_6 \times \frac{2808 \text{ kJ}}{1 \text{ mol } C_6H_{12}O_6} = 842 \text{ kJ}$$

### 3. Evaluate the Answer

All values in the calculation have at least three significant figures, so the answer is correctly stated with three digits. As predicted, the released energy is less than one-third $\Delta H_{comb}$.

## PRACTICE PROBLEMS

**20.** Calculate the heat required to melt 25.7 g of solid methanol at its melting point.

**21.** How much heat is evolved when 275 g of ammonia gas condenses to a liquid at its boiling point?

**22.** What mass of methane must be burned in order to liberate 12 880 kJ of heat?

Example Problem 16-4 shows that when glucose is burned in a bomb calorimeter, a significant amount of energy is released. The same amount of energy is produced in your body when an equal mass of glucose is metabolized (converted to carbon dioxide and water). The reaction, which occurs in every cell of your body, may not occur in the same way as the combustion in Example Problem 16-4, but the overall result is the same. The metabolism of glucose and other sugars provides the energy you need to breathe, move, think, and grow.

---

 **Assessment**

**Portfolio** Have students write a lab report to be placed in their portfolios. Ask them to include an evaluation of their results and to suggest ways of improving the design of the experiment to reduce error. **L2** **P**

---

### Resource Manager

**ChemLab and MiniLab Worksheets,** p. 61 **L2**

**Teaching Transparency 48 and** **Master** **L2** **ELL**

**Lab Manual,** pp. 121–128 **L2**

## miniLAB

### Enthalpy of Fusion for Ice

**Applying Concepts** When ice is added to water at room temperature, the water provides the energy for two processes. The first process is the melting of the ice. The energy required to melt ice is the enthalpy of fusion ($\Delta H_{fus}$). The second process is raising the temperature of the melted ice from its initial temperature of 0.0°C to the final temperature of the liquid water. In this experiment, you will collect data to calculate the enthalpy of fusion for ice.

**Materials** foam cup, thermometer, stirring rod, ice, water, balance

**Procedure**

1. Measure the mass of an empty foam cup and record it in your data table.
2. Fill the foam cup about one-third full of water. Measure and record the mass.
3. Place the thermometer in the cup. Read and record the initial temperature of the water.
4. Quickly place a small quantity of ice in the plastic cup. Gently stir the water with a stirring rod until the ice melts. Record the lowest temperature reached as the final temperature.
5. Measure the mass of the cup and water.

**Analysis**

1. The heat lost by the liquid water equals the heat needed to melt the ice plus the heat needed to increase the temperature of the melted ice from 0.0°C to the final temperature. Calculate the heat lost by the water.
2. Calculate the heat gained by the melted ice as its temperature rose from 0.0°C to the final temperature.
3. The difference between the heat lost by the water and the heat gained by the melted ice equals the heat of fusion. Calculate the heat of fusion in joules per gram of ice.
4. Calculate $\Delta H_{fus}$ in kJ/mol.
5. Calculate the percent error of your experimental $\Delta H_{fus}$. Compare your value to the actual value 6.01 kJ/mol.

As in the **miniLAB** above, you can use calorimetry to measure the energy released or absorbed in a chemical reaction or change of state. However, sometimes carrying out an experiment is difficult or even impossible. In the next section, you'll see that there are ways to calculate energy changes.

## Section 16.3 Assessment

23. List the information contained in a thermochemical equation.
24. Which of the following processes are exothermic? Endothermic?
    a. $C_2H_5OH(l) \rightarrow C_2H_5OH(g)$
    b. $NH_3(g) \rightarrow NH_3(l)$
    c. $Br_2(l) \rightarrow Br_2(s)$
    d. $NaCl(s) \rightarrow NaCl(l)$
    e. $C_5H_{12}(g) + 8O_2(g) \rightarrow 5CO_2(g) + 6H_2O(l)$
25. Explain how you could calculate the heat released in freezing 0.250 mol water.
26. **Thinking Critically** The freezing of water at 0.0°C is an exothermic process. Explain how the positions and thus, the chemical potential energy of the water molecules change as water goes from

a liquid to a solid. Does the kinetic energy of the water molecules change?

27. **Interpreting Scientific Illustrations** The reaction A → C is shown in the enthalpy diagram. Is the reaction exothermic or endothermic? Explain your answer.

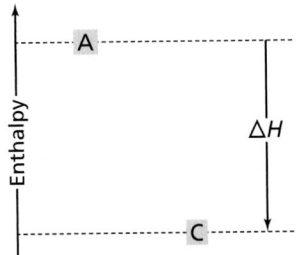

16.3 Thermochemical Equations **505**

# 3 Assess

## Check for Understanding

**Intrapersonal** Have students classify the following changes of state as exothermic or endothermic.
$C_3H_8(g) \rightarrow C_3H_8(l)$ exothermic
$CO_2(s) \rightarrow CO_2(g)$ endothermic
$C_{10}H_8(s) \rightarrow C_{10}H_8(l)$ endothermic
$H_2O(l) \rightarrow H_2O(s)$ exothermic

## Reteach

**Logical-Mathematical** Have students write and compare the chemical and thermochemical equations for the combustion of one mole of methane.
$CH_4 + 2O_2 \rightarrow CO_2 + 2H_2O$
$CH_4(g) + 2O_2(g) \rightarrow CO_2(g) + 2H_2O(l)$ $\Delta H = -891$ kJ
The thermochemical equation includes the physical state of the reactants and products and the change in enthalpy.

## Extension

Explain to students that some solid substances go directly from the solid state to the gas phase without becoming liquids. This process is called sublimation. Ask students how the energy involved in the sublimation of a mole of water compares to the energy required to melt and then vaporize a mole of the water. The same amount of energy would be needed.

### ✔ Assessment

**Skill** Ask students to write the thermochemical equation for the complete oxidation of sucrose ($C_{12}H_{22}O_{11}$) to gaseous carbon dioxide and liquid water.
$C_{12}H_{22}O_{11}(s) + 12O_2(g) \rightarrow 12CO_2(g) + 11H_2O(l)$ $\Delta H = -5644$ kJ

## Section 16.3 Assessment

23. A thermochemical equation is a balanced chemical equation that includes the enthalpy change and the physical states of the reactants and products.
24. Reactions b, c, and e are exothermic. Reactions a and d are endothermic.
25. multiply 0.250 mol times the molar heat of fusion of water, 6.01 kJ/mol.
26. Because energy is released, the total potential energy of the water molecules must decrease. The formation of hydrogen bonds between water molecules causes the process to be exothermic even

though the molecules are farther apart in the solid than in the liquid phase. The kinetic energy of the water molecules does not change.
27. The reaction is exothermic because the product (C) has a lower energy than the reactant (A).

**505**

# 1 Focus

## Focus Transparency

Before presenting the lesson, display **Section Focus Transparency 62** on the overhead projector. Have students answer the accompanying questions using **Section Focus Transparency Master 62.** **L1** **ELL**

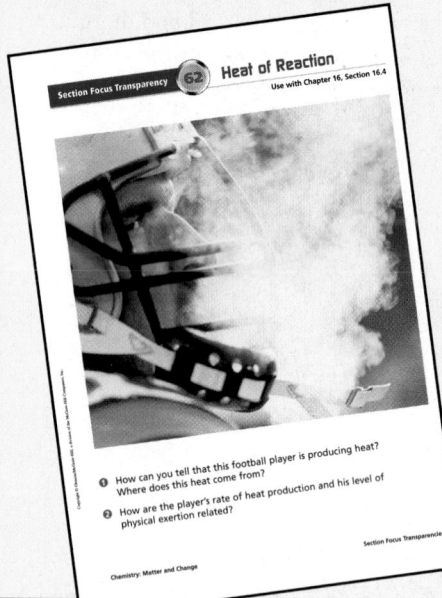

## Objectives

- **Use** Hess's law of summation of enthalpies of reaction to calculate the enthalpy change for a reaction.

- **Explain** the basis for the table of standard enthalpies of formation.

- **Calculate** $\Delta H_{rxn}$ using thermochemical equations.

- **Determine** the enthalpy change for a reaction using standard enthalpies of formation data.

## Vocabulary

Hess's law
standard enthalpy (heat) of formation

In principle, you can determine $\Delta H$ for any chemical reaction by using a calorimeter to measure the heat evolved or absorbed during the reaction. However, consider the reaction involving the conversion of carbon in its allotropic form diamond to carbon in its allotropic form graphite.

$$C(s, \text{diamond}) \rightarrow C(s, \text{graphite})$$

This reaction occurs over millions of years—so slowly that measuring the enthalpy change is virtually impossible. Other reactions occur under conditions difficult to duplicate in a laboratory. Still others don't occur cleanly; that is, products other than the desired ones may be formed. For reactions such as these, chemists use a theoretical way to determine $\Delta H$.

## Hess's Law

Suppose you are studying the formation of acid rain that results from the reaction of water in the atmosphere with sulfur trioxide expelled during a volcanic eruption such as the one shown in **Figure 16-12.** You would need to determine $\Delta H$ for this reaction.

$$2S(s) + 3O_2(g) \rightarrow 2SO_3(g) \qquad \Delta H = ?$$

Unfortunately, when you try to duplicate the reaction in the laboratory by burning sulfur in air, only small quantities of sulfur trioxide are formed. What results is a mixture containing mostly sulfur dioxide produced according to this equation.

$$S(s) + O_2(g) \rightarrow SO_2(g) \qquad \Delta H = -297 \text{ kJ}$$

In situations such as this, you can calculate $\Delta H$ for the formation of sulfur trioxide using Hess's law of heat summation. **Hess's law** states that if you can add two or more thermochemical equations to produce a final equation for a reaction, then the sum of the enthalpy changes for the individual reactions is the enthalpy change for the final reaction. Hess's law enables you to calculate enthalpy changes for an enormous number of chemical reactions by imagining that each reaction occurs through a series of steps for which the enthalpy changes are known.

**Applying Hess's law** How can Hess's law be used to calculate the energy change for the reaction that produces $SO_3$?

$$2S(s) + 3O_2(g) \rightarrow 2SO_3(g) \qquad \Delta H = ?$$

First, chemical equations are needed that contain the substances found in the desired equation and have known enthalpy changes. The following equations contain S, $O_2$, and $SO_3$.

**a.** $S(s) + O_2(g) \rightarrow SO_2(g)$ $\qquad\qquad \Delta H = -297 \text{ kJ}$

**b.** $2SO_3(g) \rightarrow 2SO_2(g) + O_2(g)$ $\qquad \Delta H = 198 \text{ kJ}$

The desired equation shows two moles of sulfur reacting, so Equation **a** must be rewritten for two moles of sulfur by multiplying the coefficients by 2. The enthalpy change, $\Delta H$, must also be doubled because twice the energy will be

# 2 Teach

## Concept Development

Help students understand Hess's law with this analogy. Suppose you are going on a long trip by automobile. If you drive 500 miles on day 1, 450 miles on day 2, 375 miles on day 3, and 425 miles on day 4, you can calculate your total trip mileage by adding the day totals (500 mi + 450 mi + 375 mi + 425 mi = 1750 mi). Explain that, if a reaction is the sum of two or more reactions, the sum of the enthalpy changes for the two or more reactions is the enthalpy change for the overall reaction.

### CHEMISTRY JOURNAL

## Balancing a Checkbook

**Linguistic** Have students describe the similarities between balancing a checkbook and calculating $\triangle H$ for a chemical reaction using Hess's law. If they don't have a checking account or don't know how to balance one, show them. Have them include their descriptions in their chemistry journals. **L2**

### GLENCOE TECHNOLOGY

**CD-ROM**
**Chemistry: Matter and Change**
Experiment: *Hess's Law*

released if two moles of sulfur react. When these changes are made, Equation **a** becomes the following (Equation **c**).

**c.** $2S(s) + 2O_2(g) \rightarrow 2SO_2(g)$  $\Delta H = 2(-297 \text{ kJ}) = -594 \text{ kJ}$

Because you want to determine $\Delta H$ for a reaction in which $SO_3$ is a product rather than a reactant, Equation **b** must be reversed. Recall that when you reverse an equation, the sign of $\Delta H$ changes. The reverse of Equation **b** is Equation **d**.

**d.** $2SO_2(g) + O_2(g) \rightarrow 2SO_3(g)$  $\Delta H = -198 \text{ kJ}$

Now, add Equations **c** and **d** to obtain the equation for the desired reaction. Add the $\Delta H$ values for the two equations to determine $\Delta H$ for the desired reaction. Any terms that are common to both sides of the combined equation should be canceled.

$$2S(s) + 2O_2(g) \rightarrow 2SO_2(g) \qquad \Delta H = -594 \text{ kJ}$$
$$\underline{2SO_2(g) + O_2(g) \rightarrow 2SO_3(g) \qquad \Delta H = -198 \text{ kJ}}$$
$$2SO_2(g) + 2S(s) + 3O_2(g) \rightarrow 2SO_2(g) + 2SO_3(g) \qquad \Delta H = -792 \text{ kJ}$$

The sum of the two equations is the equation for the burning of sulfur to form $SO_3$, and the sum of the $\Delta H$ values is the enthalpy change for the reaction.

$$2S(s) + 3O_2(g) \rightarrow 2SO_3(g) \quad \Delta H = -792 \text{ kJ}$$

The diagram in **Figure 16-13** will help you visualize the calculation.

Sometimes thermochemical equations are written with fractional coefficients because they are balanced for one mole of product. For example, the thermochemical equation for the reaction between sulfur and oxygen to form one mole of sulfur trioxide is the following.

$$S(s) + \frac{3}{2}O_2(g) \rightarrow SO_3(g) \quad \Delta H = -396 \text{ kJ}$$

What factor would you need to multiply this equation and its enthalpy change by to obtain the equation you worked with above?

**Figure 16-12**

A volcanic eruption releases solid materials, gases, and heat into the atmosphere. Carbon dioxide and water account for more than 90% of the gases emitted. An eruption can send as much as 20 million tons of sulfur dioxide and sulfur trioxide into the stratosphere.

**GLENCOE**
**TECHNOLOGY**

**CD-ROM**
**Chemistry: Matter and Change**
Video: *Thermochemistry*

## Concept Development

Illustrate the application of Hess's law by using these general equations.
$A + B \rightarrow C$
$C + D \rightarrow E + B$
Show how C and B can be eliminated from the overall equation because they are present in equal amounts on both sides. Show that the sum of the two reactions is $A + D \rightarrow E$

## Figure Caption Question

**Figure 16-13** What is the enthalpy change for the conversion of S and $O_2$ to $SO_3$? -792 kJ

**Figure 16-13**

The arrow on the left indicates the release of 594 kJ as S and $O_2$ react to form $SO_2$ (Reaction **c**). Then, $SO_2$ and $O_2$ react to form $SO_3$ (Reaction **d**) with the release of 198 kJ (middle arrow). The overall energy change (the sum of the two processes) is shown by the arrow on the right. What is the enthalpy change for the conversion of S and $O_2$ to $SO_3$?

16.4 Calculating Enthalpy Change  **507**

**Resource Manager**

**Study Guide for Content Mastery,**
pp. 94–95 L2
**Solving Problems: A Chemistry Handbook,** Section 16.4 L2
**Section Focus Transparency 62 and Master** L1 ELL

**National Science Content Standards**

**Pages 504–507**
UCP.1, UCP.3; A.1; B.3, B.5, B.6; E.2

Have students refer to Appendix D for complete solutions to Practice Problems.

28. $\triangle H = -746.6$ kJ
29. $\triangle H = -1789$ kJ

## Quick Demo

 Demonstrate the exothermic combustion of table sugar by first dabbing some fine ashes from a wood splint on a sugar cube. The wood ashes act as a catalyst for the combustion. Use tongs to hold the cube in a burner flame. The resulting carbon may be put in the trash when cool. Have students write the thermochemical equation for the combustion of sucrose to gaseous carbon dioxide and liquid water. $C_{12}H_{22}O_{11}(s) + 12O_2(g) \rightarrow 12CO_2(g) + 11H_2O(l)$ $\triangle H = -5644$ kJ

## Resource Manager

Teaching Transparency 49 and Master L2 ELL

The photo shows an X-15 rocket-powered aircraft used to test the effects of high-speed, high-altitude flight on humans and materials. The rocket engines, mounted under the wing of a B52 bomber, are powered by the reaction of $H_2$ and $O_2$. Data from 199 runs made by such aircraft were used in the development of the space shuttle.

Practice! For more practice using Hess's law, go to Supplemental Practice Problems in Appendix A.

## EXAMPLE PROBLEM 16-5

### Applying Hess's Law

Use thermochemical Equations **a** and **b** to determine $\Delta H$ for the decomposition of hydrogen peroxide ($H_2O_2$), a compound that has uses ranging from bleaching hair to energizing rocket engines.

$$2H_2O_2(l) \rightarrow 2H_2O(l) + O_2(g)$$

  **a.** $2H_2(g) + O_2(g) \rightarrow 2H_2O(l)$    $\Delta H = -572$ kJ
  **b.** $H_2(g) + O_2(g) \rightarrow H_2O_2(l)$    $\Delta H = -188$ kJ

### 1. Analyze the Problem

You have been given two chemical equations and their enthalpy changes. These two equations contain all the substances found in the desired equation.

**Known**

Equations **a** and **b** and their enthalpy changes

**Unknown**

$\Delta H$ = ? kJ

### 2. Solve for the Unknown

$H_2O_2$ is a reactant, so reverse Equation **b**.
$H_2O_2(aq) \rightarrow H_2(g) + O_2(g)$
Two moles of $H_2O_2$ are needed. Multiply the equation by 2 to obtain Equation **c**.
**c.** $2H_2O_2(aq) \rightarrow 2H_2(g) + 2O_2(g)$
When you reverse an equation, you must change the sign of $\Delta H$. When you double an equation, you must double $\Delta H$.
$\Delta H$ for Equation **c** = $-(\Delta H_{\text{Equation b}})(2)$
$\Delta H$ for Equation **c** = $-(-188 \text{ kJ})(2) = 376$ kJ
**c.** $2H_2O_2(aq) \rightarrow 2H_2(g) + 2O_2(g)$  $\Delta H = 376$ kJ
Add Equations **a** and **c** canceling any terms common to both sides of the combined equation. Add the enthalpies of Equations **a** and **c**.

| | | |
|---|---|---|
| **c.** $2H_2O_2(l) \rightarrow 2H_2(g) + 2O_2(g)$ | $\Delta H =$ | 376 kJ |
| **a.** $2H_2(g) + O_2(g) \rightarrow 2H_2O(l)$ | $\Delta H =$ | $-572$ kJ |
| $2H_2O_2(l) \rightarrow 2H_2O(l) + O_2(g)$ | $\Delta H =$ | $-196$ kJ |

### 3. Evaluate the Answer

All values are accurate to the units place, so $\Delta H$ is correctly stated. The two equations produce the desired equation.

## PRACTICE PROBLEMS

28. Use reactions **a** and **b** to determine $\Delta H$ for the following reaction.

   $2CO(g) + 2NO(g) \rightarrow 2CO_2(g) + N_2(g)$    $\Delta H = ?$
   **a.** $2CO(g) + O_2(g) \rightarrow 2CO_2(g)$    $\Delta H = -566.0$ kJ
   **b.** $N_2(g) + O_2(g) \rightarrow 2NO(g)$    $\Delta H = 180.6$ kJ

29. Use reactions **a** and **b** to determine $\Delta H$ for the following reaction.

   $4Al(s) + 3MnO_2(s) \rightarrow 2Al_2O_3(s) + 3Mn(s)$    $\Delta H = ?$
   **a.** $4Al(s) + 3O_2(g) \rightarrow 2Al_2O_3(s)$    $\Delta H = -3352$ kJ
   **b.** $Mn(s) + O_2(g) \rightarrow MnO_2(s)$    $\Delta H = -521$ kJ

## Internet Address Book

**Chemistry Online** Note Internet addresses that you find useful in the space below for quick reference.

_____
_____
_____
_____
_____

# Standard Enthalpy (Heat) of Formation

You have seen the usefulness of Hess's law in allowing you to calculate unknown $\Delta H$ values using known reactions and their experimentally determined $\Delta H$ values. However, recording and storing $\Delta H$ values for all known chemical reactions would be a huge and constantly evolving task. To avoid this problem, scientists have chosen to record and use enthalpy changes for one type of reaction—a reaction in which a compound is formed from its constituent elements in their standard states. The standard state of a substance means the normal physical state of the substance at one atmosphere pressure and 298 K (25°C). For example, in its standard state, iron is a solid, mercury is a liquid, and oxygen is a diatomic gas.

The $\Delta H$ value for such reactions is called the standard enthalpy (heat) of formation of the compound. The **standard enthalpy (heat) of formation** ($\Delta H_f^\circ$) is defined as the change in enthalpy that accompanies the formation of one mole of the compound in its standard state from its constituent elements in their standard states. A typical standard heat of formation reaction is the formation of one mole of $SO_3$ from its elements.

$$S(s) + \tfrac{3}{2}O_2(g) \rightarrow SO_3(g) \qquad \Delta H_f^\circ = -396 \text{ kJ}$$

**Where do standard heats of formation come from?** When you state the height of a mountain, you do so relative to some point of reference—usually sea level. In a similar way, standard enthalpies of formation are stated based on the following arbitrary standard: Every free element in its standard state is assigned a $\Delta H_f^\circ$ of exactly 0.0 kJ. With zero as the starting point, the experimentally determined enthalpies of formation of compounds can be placed on a scale above and below the elements in their standard states. Think of the zero of the enthalpy scale as being similar to the arbitrary assignment of 0.0°C to the freezing point of water. All substances warmer than freezing water have a temperature above zero. All substances colder than freezing water have a temperature below zero.

Standard enthalpies of formation of many compounds have been measured experimentally. For example, consider the equation for the formation of nitrogen dioxide.

$$\tfrac{1}{2}N_2(g) + O_2(g) \rightarrow NO_2(g)$$

The elements nitrogen and oxygen are diatomic gases in their standard states, so their standard enthalpies of formation are zero. When nitrogen and oxygen gases react to form one mole of nitrogen dioxide, the experimentally determined $\Delta H$ for the reaction is 33.2 kJ. That means that 33.2 kJ of energy is absorbed in this endothermic reaction. Thus, the energy content of the product, $NO_2$, is 33.2 kJ greater than the energy content of the reactants. On a scale on which the $\Delta H_f^\circ$ of reactants is defined as zero, $\Delta H_f^\circ$ of $NO_2(g)$ is +33.2 kJ. **Figure 16-14** shows that on the scale of standard enthalpies of formation, $NO_2$ is placed 33.2 kJ above the elements from which it was formed. Sulfur trioxide ($SO_3$) is placed 396 kJ below zero on the scale because the formation of $SO_3(g)$ is an exothermic reaction. The energy content of the product $SO_3(g)$ is 396 kJ less than the energy content of the elements from which it was formed.

**Table 16-7** on the next page lists standard enthalpies of formation for some common compounds. A more complete list is in Appendix C, **Table C-13.**

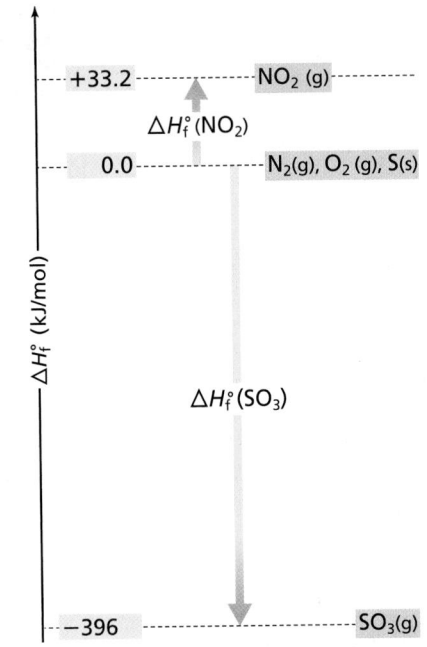

**Figure 16-14**

Note $\Delta H_f^\circ$ for the elements $N_2$, $O_2$, and S is 0.0 kJ. When $N_2$ and $O_2$ react to form 1 mole of $NO_2$, 33.2 kJ is absorbed. One mole of $NO_2$, has 33.2 kJ/mol more energy than the elements from which it is formed. Thus, $\Delta H_f^\circ$ for $NO_2$ is +33.2 kJ/mol. When S and $O_2$ react to form one mole of $SO_3$, 396 kJ is released. Thus, $\Delta H_f^\circ$ for $SO_3$ is −396 kJ/mol.

## Applying Chemistry

**TECH PREP** Explain that many U.S. homes are heated and cooled by heat pumps, which utilize the endothermic vaporization and exothermic condensation of coolant compounds—usually compounds called hydrochlorofluorocarbons (HCFCs), which are made up of the elements hydrogen, chlorine, fluorine, and carbon. HCFCs have high enthalpies of vaporization and condensation. Explain that a heat pump is like a refrigerator that can be run in two directions. In summer, the heat pump makes use of the endothermic vaporization of the coolant to absorb heat from the home and the exothermic condensation of the coolant to expel the heat into the outside air. In winter, the heat pump uses the endothermic vaporization of the coolant to absorb heat from the cold outside air and its exothermic condensation to transfer the heat into the home.

---

## Portfolio

### Thermochemical Formation Equations

**Logical-Mathematical** Have students write the thermochemical formation equations for the following compounds and place them in their portfolios: silver cyanide(s), $\Delta H_f^\circ = 146$ kJ/mol; magnesium hydroxide(s), $\Delta H_f^\circ = -925$ kJ/mol; phosphorus pentafluoride(g), $\Delta H_f^\circ = -1578$ kJ/mol; $CH_3COOH(l)$, $\Delta H_f^\circ = -484$ kJ/mol. **L2** **P**

**National Science Content Standards**

Pages 508–509
UCP.1, UCP.3; B.3, B.5

Table 16-7

| Standard Enthalpies of Formation for Selected Compounds | | |
|---|---|---|
| Compound | Formation equation | $\Delta H_f^\circ$ (kJ/mol) |
| $NO_2(g)$ | $\frac{1}{2}N_2(g) + O_2(g) \rightarrow NO_2(g)$ | 33 |
| $H_2S(g)$ | $H_2(g) + S(s) \rightarrow H_2S(g)$ | −21 |
| $NH_3(g)$ | $\frac{1}{2}N_2(g) + \frac{3}{2}H_2(g) \rightarrow NH_3(g)$ | −46 |
| $CH_4(g)$ | $C(s, graphite) + 2H_2(g) \rightarrow CH_4(g)$ | −75 |
| $HF(g)$ | $\frac{1}{2}H_2(g) + \frac{1}{2}F_2(g) \rightarrow HF(g)$ | −273 |
| $CCl_4(l)$ | $C(s, graphite) + 2Cl_2(g) \rightarrow CCl_4(l)$ | −128 |
| $H_2O(l)$ | $H_2(g) + \frac{1}{2}O_2(g) \rightarrow H_2O(l)$ | −286 |
| $SO_2(g)$ | $S(s) + O_2(g) \rightarrow SO_2(g)$ | −297 |
| $CO_2(g)$ | $C(s, graphite) + O_2(g) \rightarrow CO_2(g)$ | −394 |
| $Fe_2O_3(s)$ | $2Fe(s) + \frac{3}{2}O_2(g) \rightarrow Fe_2O_3(s)$ | −824 |
| $SF_6(g)$ | $S(s) + 3F_2(g) \rightarrow SF_6(g)$ | −1220 |
| $Al_2O_3(s)$ | $2Al(s) + \frac{3}{2}O_2(g) \rightarrow Al_2O_3(s)$ | −1680 |

## Assessment

**Performance** Have students form teams (pro and con) to research and debate the use of fossil fuels as a source of energy for generating electric power in the U.S. Be sure the teams include both economic and environmental considerations in their debate. Use the Performance Task Assessment List for Investigating an Issue Controversy in **PASC**, p. 65. **L2**

**COOP LEARN**

## Visual Learning

**Table 16-7** Have students pick three reactions, other than the formation of $NO_2(g)$, from the list in Table 16-7 and construct diagrams that show the energy changes involved. Have them use Figure 16-14 as a model for their diagrams. **L2**

**Figure 16-15**

Sulfur hexafluoride, one of the heaviest known gases, is used in this electrical substation to insulate circuit breakers, transformers, and other electrical equipment including high voltage transmission lines.

**Using standard enthalpies of formation** What is the significance of standard enthalpies of formation? How are they used? Standard enthalpies of formation provide useful data for calculating the enthalpies of reactions under standard conditions ($\Delta H_{rxn}^\circ$) using Hess's law. Suppose you want to calculate $\Delta H_{rxn}^\circ$ for this reaction, in which sulfur hexafluoride is produced. Sulfur hexafluoride is a stable, unreactive gas with some interesting applications, one of which is shown in **Figure 16-15**.

$$H_2S(g) + 4F_2(g) \rightarrow 2HF(g) + SF_6(g) \quad \Delta H_{rxn}^\circ = ?$$

Recall that Hess's law allows you to combine equations and their $\Delta H$ values to produce the desired equation and its $\Delta H$ value. To apply Hess's law using standard enthalpies of formation data, you must have one equation for the formation of each compound in the desired equation. You can find these in **Table 16-7**. Three compounds are in the equation, HF, $SF_6$, and $H_2S$, so the three equations are these.

**a.** $\frac{1}{2}H_2(g) + \frac{1}{2}F_2(g) \rightarrow HF(g) \qquad \Delta H_f^\circ = -273$ kJ

**b.** $S(s) + 3F_2(g) \rightarrow SF_6(g) \qquad \Delta H_f^\circ = -1220$ kJ

**c.** $H_2(g) + S(s) \rightarrow H_2S(g) \qquad \Delta H_f^\circ = -21$ kJ

Equations **a** and **b** are for the formation of the products HF and $SF_6$. Therefore, they can be used in the direction in which they are written. But because two moles of HF are required, Equation **a** and its enthalpy change must be multiplied by 2.

$$H_2(g) + F_2(g) \rightarrow 2HF(g) \qquad \Delta H_f^\circ = 2(-273) = -546 \text{ kJ}$$

Equation **b** can be used as it is.

$$S(s) + 3F_2(g) \rightarrow SF_6(g) \qquad \Delta H_f^\circ = -1220 \text{ kJ}$$

In the desired equation, $H_2S$ is a reactant rather than a product. Therefore, Equation **c** must be reversed. Recall that reversing a reaction changes the sign of $\Delta H$, so the sign of $\Delta H$ for Equation **c** becomes positive.

---

## DIFFERENTIATED INSTRUCTION

### Gifted

**Logical-Mathematical** Have students use the enthalpy of combustion of sucrose (−5644 kJ/mol) and the enthalpies of formation of gaseous carbon dioxide and liquid water to calculate $\Delta H_f^\circ$ for sucrose.
$C_{12}H_{22}O_{11}(s) + 12O_2(g) \rightarrow 12CO_2(g) + 11H_2O(l)$

$\Delta H_{rxn}^\circ = \Sigma \Delta H_f^\circ$ (products) $- \Sigma \Delta H_f^\circ$ (reactants)
$-5644$ kJ $= (12(-394$ kJ$) + 11(-286$ kJ$)) - \Delta H_f^\circ$ sucrose
$\Delta H_f^\circ$ sucrose $= -2230$ kJ **L3**

$$H_2S(g) \rightarrow H_2(g) + S(s) \quad \Delta H_f^\circ = 21 \text{ kJ}$$

The three equations and their enthalpy changes can now be added. The elements $H_2$ and S cancel.

| | |
|---|---|
| $\cancel{H_2(g)} + F_2(g) \rightarrow 2HF(g)$ | $\Delta H_f^\circ = \quad -546 \text{ kJ}$ |
| $\cancel{S(s)} + 3F_2(g) \rightarrow SF_6(g)$ | $\Delta H_f^\circ = \quad -1220 \text{ kJ}$ |
| $H_2S(g) \rightarrow \cancel{H_2(g)} + \cancel{S(s)}$ | $\Delta H_f^\circ = \qquad 21 \text{ kJ}$ |
| $H_2S(g) + 4F_2(g) \rightarrow 2HF(g) + SF_6(g)$ | $\Delta H_{rxn}^\circ = -1745 \text{ kJ}$ |

This example shows how standard heats of formation equations combine to produce the desired equation and its $\Delta H_{rxn}^\circ$. The entire procedure is summed up in the following formula.

$$\Delta H_{rxn}^\circ = \Sigma \Delta H_f^\circ(\text{products}) - \Sigma \Delta H_f^\circ(\text{reactants})$$

The symbol $\Sigma$ means "to take the sum of the terms." The formula says to subtract the sum of heats of formation of the reactants from the sum of the heats of formation of the products. You can see how this formula applies to the reaction between hydrogen sulfide and fluorine.

$$H_2S(g) + 4F_2(g) \rightarrow 2HF(g) + SF_6(g)$$
$$\Delta H_{rxn}^\circ = [(2)\Delta H_f^\circ(HF) + \Delta H_f^\circ(SF_6)] - [\Delta H_f^\circ(H_2S) + (4)\Delta H_f^\circ(F_2)]$$
$$\Delta H_{rxn}^\circ = [(2)(-273 \text{ kJ}) + (-1220 \text{ kJ})] - [-21 \text{ kJ} + (4)(0.0 \text{ kJ})]$$
$$\Delta H_{rxn}^\circ = -1745 \text{ kJ}$$

Note that the heat of formation of HF is multiplied by 2 because two moles of HF are formed. Also note that it is not necessary to change the sign of $\Delta H_f^\circ(H_2S)$ and that $\Delta H_f^\circ(F_2)$ is 0.0 kJ because the standard heat of formation of an element in its standard state is zero.

### EXAMPLE PROBLEM 16-6

**Enthalpy Change from Standard Enthalpies of Formation**

Use standard enthalpies of formation to calculate $\Delta H_{rxn}^\circ$ for the combustion of methane. Methane is found in the atmosphere of the planet Pluto.

$$CH_4(g) + 2O_2(g) \rightarrow CO_2(g) + 2H_2O(l)$$

**1. Analyze the Problem**

You are given an equation and asked to calculate the change in enthalpy. The formula $\Delta H_{rxn}^\circ = \Sigma \Delta H_f^\circ(\text{products}) - \Sigma \Delta H_f^\circ(\text{reactants})$ can be used with data from **Table 16-7**.

| Known | Unknown |
|---|---|
| $\Delta H_f^\circ(CO_2) = -394 \text{ kJ}$ | $\Delta H_{rxn}^\circ = ? \text{ kJ}$ |
| $\Delta H_f^\circ(H_2O) = -286 \text{ kJ}$ | |
| $\Delta H_f^\circ(CH_4) = -75 \text{ kJ}$ | |
| $\Delta H_f^\circ(O_2) = 0.0 \text{ kJ}$ | |

Pluto, the smallest of the Sun's planets and the farthest, on average, from the Sun, is shown with its moon Charon. Methane has been found in the thin atmosphere of Pluto.

**2. Solve for the Unknown**

Use the formula $\Delta H_{rxn}^\circ = \Sigma \Delta H_f^\circ(\text{products}) - \Sigma \Delta H_f^\circ(\text{reactants})$.

Expand the formula to include a term for each reactant and product. Multiply each term by the coefficient of the substance in the balanced chemical equation.

*Continued on next page*

## 3 Assess
### Check for Understanding

Ask students if elements in their standard states possess zero energy. no Ask, "If that's so, why are elements in their standard states assigned enthalpies of zero?" They are assigned enthalpies of zero in order to establish a standard value that can be compared with the enthalpies of compounds or the enthalpies of elements in nonstandard states.

### Reteach

Ask students how they might use enthalpy of formation data to calculate $\triangle H$ for a reaction they cannot perform. Write the equation for the reaction. Then, use the formula $\triangle H_{rxn}^\circ = \Sigma \triangle H_f^\circ$ (products) $- \Sigma \triangle H_f^\circ$ (reactants).

### Extension

Give students this data: $\triangle H_f^\circ$ (carbon, graphite) = 0.0 kJ/mol, $\triangle H_f^\circ$ (carbon, diamond) = 1.9 kJ/mol. Ask them to write the equation for the conversion of graphite to diamond and determine $\triangle H_{rxn}$. C(graphite) $\rightarrow$ C(diamond) $\triangle H_{rxn}$ = 1.9 kJ – 0.0 kJ = 1.9 kJ. Ask what is the standard state for carbon. graphite

### ✔ Assessment

**Knowledge** Have students write the formation equation for solid copper(II) nitrate. Cu(s) + $N_2(g)$ + 3$O_2(g)$ $\rightarrow$ Cu(NO$_3$)$_2$(s) Ask students what the enthalpy change for the equation is called. the enthalpy of formation of solid copper(II) nitrate **L2**

### CHEMISTRY JOURNAL

## Chemical to Thermochemical

**Logical-Mathematical** Have students choose five chemical equations from the Practice Problems in Chapter 10. Have them look up the enthalpies of formation of the reactants and products and calculate $\triangle H$ for each of the reactions. Finally, have students convert each chemical equation to a thermochemical equation. Students should summarize their results in tables and include the tables in their chemistry journals. **L2**

National Science Content Standards

Pages 510–511
UCP.1, UCP.3; B.3, B.5

Have students refer to Appendix D for complete solutions to Practice Problems.

**30. a.** $2(\frac{1}{2}N_2(g) + O_2(g) \rightarrow NO_2(g))$

$2(NO(g) \rightarrow \frac{1}{2}O_2(g) + \frac{1}{2}N_2(g))$

$\overline{2NO(g) + O_2(g) \rightarrow 2NO_2(g)}$

**b.** $H_2(g) + S(s) + 2O_2(g) \rightarrow H_2SO_4(l)$

$SO_3(g) \rightarrow S(s) + \frac{3}{2}O_2(g)$

$H_2O(l) \rightarrow H_2(g) + \frac{1}{2}O_2(g)$

$\overline{SO_3(g) + H_2O(l) \rightarrow H_2SO_4(l)}$

**31. a.** $\Delta H°_{rxn} = 178.3$ kJ

**b.** $\Delta H°_{rxn} = -53.4$ kJ

**c.** $\Delta H°_{rxn} = 66.36$ kJ

**d.** $\Delta H°_{rxn} = -196.1$ kJ

**e.** $\Delta H°_{rxn} = -1397.82$ kJ

---

$\Delta H°_{rxn} = [\Delta H°_f(CO_2) + (2)\Delta H°_f(H_2O)] - [\Delta H°_f(CH_4) + (2)\Delta H°_f(O_2)]$

Substitute the $\Delta H°_f$ values into the formula.

$\Delta H°_{rxn} = [(-394 \text{ kJ}) + (2)(-286 \text{ kJ})] - [(-75 \text{ kJ}) + (2)(0.0 \text{ kJ})]$

$\Delta H°_{rxn} = [-966 \text{ kJ}] - [-75 \text{ kJ}] = -966 \text{ kJ} + 75 \text{ kJ} = -891 \text{ kJ}$

The combustion of 1 mol $CH_4$ releases 891 kJ.

**3. Evaluate the Answer**

All values are accurate to the units place. Therefore, the answer is correct as stated. The calculated value is the same as that given in **Table 16-5** on page 501.

**PRACTICE PROBLEMS**

**30.** Show how the sum of enthalpy of formation equations produces each of the following reactions. You need not look up and include $\Delta H$ values.

**a.** $2NO(g) + O_2(g) \rightarrow 2NO_2(g)$

**b.** $SO_3(g) + H_2O(l) \rightarrow H_2SO_4(l)$

**31.** Use standard enthalpies of formation from Appendix C, **Table C-13** to calculate $\Delta H°_{rxn}$ for each of the following reactions.

**a.** $CaCO_3(s) \rightarrow CaO(s) + CO_2(g)$

**b.** $CH_4(g) + 2Cl_2(g) \rightarrow CCl_4(l) + 2H_2(g)$

**c.** $N_2(g) + 2O_2(g) \rightarrow 2NO_2(g)$

**d.** $2H_2O_2(l) \rightarrow 2H_2O(l) + O_2(g)$

**e.** $4NH_3(g) + 7O_2(g) \rightarrow 4NO_2(g) + 6H_2O(l)$

Practice! For more practice using standard enthalpies of formation, go to **Supplemental Practice Problems** in Appendix A.

You can see how valuable enthalpy of formation data are to a chemist. The $\Delta H°_{rxn}$ for any reaction can be calculated if $\Delta H°_f$ is known for all of the compounds among the reactants and products.

**Section** 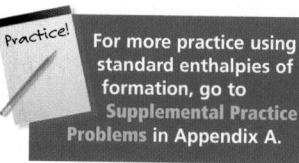 **16.4 Assessment**

**32.** Explain what is meant by Hess's law and how it is used.

**33.** What formula can be applied to determining $\Delta H°_{rxn}$ when using Hess's law? Explain the formula in words.

**34.** On the scale of standard enthalpies of formations, how are the elements in their standard states defined?

**35.** Low energy is associated with stability. Examine the data in **Table 16-7**. What conclusion can you draw about the stabilities of the compounds listed relative to the elements in their standard states?

**36. Thinking Critically** Could the absolute enthalpy or heat content of the elements at 298°C and one atmosphere pressure actually be 0.0 kJ? Explain why or why not.

**37. Interpreting Scientific Illustrations** Using the data below, draw a diagram similar to **Figure 16-14** and use the diagram to determine the heat of vaporization of water at 298 K.

Liquid water: $\Delta H°_f = -285.8$ kJ/mol

Gaseous water: $\Delta H°_f = -241.8$ kJ/mol

National Science Content Standards
Pages 512–513
UCP.1, UCP.3; B.3, B.5

chemistrymc.com/self_check_quiz

---

**Section 16.4 Assessment**

**32.** Hess's law enables you to calculate $\Delta H$ for a reaction by imagining that the reaction occurs through a series of reactions with known $\Delta H$ values. If you add two or more thermochemical equations and produce an equation for a reaction, you can add the enthalpy changes for the individual reactions to determine the enthalpy change for the final reaction.

**33.** $\Delta H°_{rxn} = \Sigma\Delta H°_f \text{(products)} - \Sigma\Delta H°_f \text{(reactants)}$

**34.** Elements in their standard states are assigned enthalpies of formation of zero.

**35.** All compounds listed, except $NO_2$, are more stable than their constituent elements.

**36.** No, the absolute enthalpy of an element consists of many types of energy, not all of which can be calculated.

**37.** 44.0 kJ/mol; see Solutions Manual

In **Figure 16-16**, you can see a familiar picture of what happens to an iron object when it's left outdoors in moist air. Iron rusts slowly according to the following equation. It's the same chemical reaction that occurs in the heat pack you learned about earlier in the chapter.

$$4Fe(s) + 3O_2(g) \rightarrow 2Fe_2O_3(s) \qquad \Delta H = -1625 \text{ kJ}$$

The heat pack goes into action the moment you activate it by ripping off the plastic covering. Similarly, unprotected iron objects rust whether you want them to or not.

## Spontaneous Processes

Rusting, like many other processes, is spontaneous. A **spontaneous process** is a physical or chemical change that occurs with no outside intervention. However, for many spontaneous processes, some energy must be supplied to get the process started. For example, you may have used a sparker or a match to light a Bunsen burner in your school lab. Or perhaps you are familiar with the continuously burning pilot lights that are used in gas stoves and furnaces to start these appliances immediately. Once the gas has been ignited, the combustion process can proceed spontaneously.

You saw in an earlier problem that the thermochemical equation for the combustion of methane, the major component of natural gas, is this

$$CH_4(g) + 2O_2(g) \rightarrow CO_2(g) + 2H_2O(l) \qquad \Delta H = -891 \text{ kJ}$$

Suppose you reverse the direction of this equation and the equation for the rusting of iron. Recall that when you change the direction of a reaction, the sign of $\Delta H$ changes. Both reactions become endothermic.

$$2Fe_2O_3(s) \rightarrow 4Fe(s) + 3O_2(g) \qquad \Delta H = 1625 \text{ kJ}$$
$$CO_2(g) + 2H_2O(l) \rightarrow CH_4(g) + 2O_2(g) \qquad \Delta H = 891 \text{ kJ}$$

Reversing the equation will not make rust decompose spontaneously into iron and oxygen under ordinary conditions. And carbon dioxide will not react with water to form methane and oxygen. These two equations represent reactions that are not spontaneous.

Do you notice a correlation? Iron rusting and methane burning are exothermic and spontaneous. The reverse reactions are endothermic and nonspontaneous. Based upon reactions such as these, some nineteenth-century scientists concluded that all exothermic processes are spontaneous and all endothermic processes are nonspontaneous. However, you need not look far for evidence that this conclusion is incorrect. For example, you know that ice melts at room temperature. That's a spontaneous, endothermic process.

$$H_2O(s) \rightarrow H_2O(l) \qquad \Delta H = 6.01 \text{ kJ}$$

It's evident that something other than $\Delta H$ plays a role in determining whether a chemical process occurs spontaneously under a given set of conditions. That something is called entropy.

### Objectives
- **Differentiate** between spontaneous and nonspontaneous processes.
- **Explain** how changes in entropy and free energy determine the spontaneity of chemical reactions and other processes.

### Vocabulary
spontaneous process
entropy
law of disorder
free energy

**Figure 16-16**

Year by year, the iron in this abandoned railroad equipment in the Alaskan tundra combines with oxygen to form rust, $Fe_2O_3$.

## 1 Focus

### Focus Transparency

Before presenting the lesson, display **Section Focus Transparency 63** on the overhead projector. Have students answer the accompanying questions using **Section Focus Transparency Master 63.** **L1** **ELL**

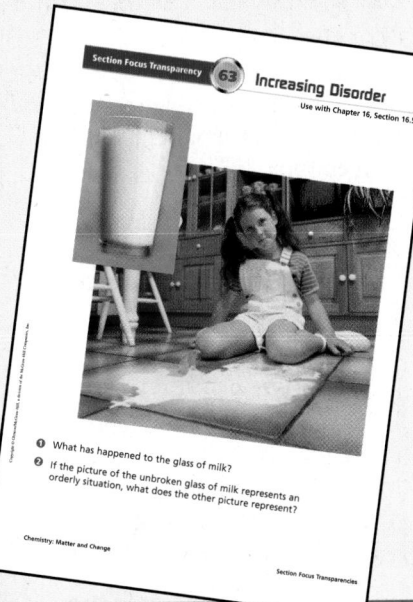

## 2 Teach
### Visual Learning

**Figure 16-16** Ask students if painting an iron object makes the rusting reaction shown in the photo nonspontaneous. no Ask how painting an iron object enables it to exist in wet conditions without rusting. A coat of paint prevents the iron from coming into contact with oxygen in the air.

---

### CULTURAL DIVERSITY

#### Energy and Humankind

Humans have been preoccupied with energy since their earliest conscious concerns about survival. Over the centuries, people have marveled at the heat released when dead tree limbs burned—heat that warmed their bodies, cooked their food, and protected them from hos-

tile creatures, real and imagined. Much later, the Greeks showed their fascination with energy, particularly with fire, when they proposed that matter consists of four elements—earth, air, fire, and water. Many centuries later, the alchemists of the Middle Ages were still perpetuating

the Greeks' view and continued to do so up until the sixteenth century. In fact, it has been only within the last 250 years that scientists have conducted a rigorous, scientific study of heat and its transformations, the branch of science known as thermodynamics.

After one hour

Chlorine gas | Nitrogen gas | Nitrogen and chlorine gas | Nitrogen and chlorine gas

**Extension**

**Visual-Spatial** Ask an interested student to make a poster that depicts the molecular arrangements and motions that result during the following changes, all of which result in higher entropy states: a solid melting, a solid dissolving in a liquid, a liquid evaporating, a gas at a lower temperature heated to a higher temperature at constant volume. Discuss each of the changes with the class. **L2** **ELL**

## Using Science Terms

**Linguistic** Have students write statements that describe several reactions and processes. Each statement should include the term entropy. **L2**

## Resource Manager

**Study Guide for Content Mastery,** p. 96 **L2**

**Solving Problems: A Chemistry Handbook,** Section 16.5 **L2**

**Section Focus Transparency 63 and Master** **L1** **ELL**

**Teaching Transparency 49 and Master** **L2** **ELL**

**Math Skills Transparency 26 and Master** **L2** **ELL**

**Figure 16-17**

At the beginning of the experiment, chlorine and nitrogen molecules occupy separate bulbs. But when the stopcock is opened, the gas molecules move back and forth between the two bulbs and become thoroughly mixed. Refer to **Table C-1** in Appendix C for a key to atom color conventions.

**What is entropy?** Think about what might happen when a glass bulb containing chlorine gas is connected to a similar glass bulb containing nitrogen gas, as shown in **Figure 16-17**. When the stopcock in the tube connecting the two bulbs is opened, the gases can pass freely from one bulb to the other. After an hour, you can see that the chlorine and nitrogen molecules are distributed uniformly between the two bulbs. You're probably not surprised at that result. After all, the delicious smell of brownies baking in the kitchen doesn't stay in the kitchen. It wafts to wherever you are. So, whether it's the aroma of brownies or the chlorine and nitrogen in the experiment, gases tend to mix. Why? The answer is that molecules are more likely to exist in a high state of disorder (mixed) than in a low state of disorder (unmixed). In thermodynamics, the term for disorder is *entropy*. **Entropy** (S) is a measure of the disorder or randomness of the particles that make up a system.

The tendency toward disorder or randomness is summarized in the **law of disorder**, which states that spontaneous processes always proceed in such a way that the entropy of the universe increases. This law also is called the second law of thermodynamics. You can observe the law of disorder in many everyday situations. For example, suppose you shuffle a deck of 52 playing cards thoroughly and lay them down one after another to form four rows of 13 cards each. The cards might form the highly ordered arrangement shown in **Figure 16-18a**. However, the probability that you will lay down this exact, low-entropy sequence is one chance in $8.07 \times 10^{67}$. In other words, it's nearly impossible. Because there are so many possible highly disordered arrangements, it's almost infinitely more likely that you'll produce a high-entropy sequence such as the one shown in **Figure 16-18b**.

**Predicting changes in entropy** Recall that the change in enthalpy for a reaction is equal to the enthalpy of the products minus the enthalpy of the reactants. The change in entropy ($\Delta S$) during a reaction or process is similar.

**Figure 16-18**

What are the chances that a shuffled deck of cards will lay out into four perfectly ordered rows as shown in  **a** ? Experience tells you that the chances for an orderly arrangement are almost negligible, and that a random arrangement like the one in **b** is far more likely.

---

## DIFFERENTIATED INSTRUCTION

### Learning Disabled

**Visual-Spatial** Illustrate the increase in entropy that occurs when sodium chloride dissolves in water by first showing students a model of the low-entropy, face-centered cubic NaCl crystal lattice. Then, draw a chalkboard diagram of a beaker of water showing the Na$^+$ and Cl$^-$ ions distrib-

uted randomly throughout the beaker. Explain that the highly disordered arrangement of the ions in solution represents a higher state of entropy than the rigidly organized ions in the solid state. **L1** **ELL**

$$\Delta S_{system} = S_{products} - S_{reactants}$$

Therefore, if the entropy of a system increases during a reaction or process, $S_{products} > S_{reactants}$ and $\Delta S_{system}$ is positive. Conversely, if the entropy of a system decreases during a reaction or process, $S_{products} < S_{reactants}$ and $\Delta S_{system}$ is negative.

Can you predict if $\Delta S_{system}$ is positive or negative by examining the equation for a reaction or process? In some cases you can.

**1.** *Entropy changes associated with changes in state, such as those shown for water in* **Figure 16-19,** *can be predicted.* In solids, molecules are tightly packed and have limited movement, but they have some freedom to move in liquids. In gases, molecules are unrestricted in their movements except by the container in which they are held. Therefore, entropy increases as a substance changes from a solid to a liquid and from a liquid to a gas. For example, the entropy of the system increases ($\Delta S_{system}$ is positive) as water vaporizes and as methanol melts.

$$H_2O(l) \rightarrow H_2O(g) \quad \Delta S_{system} > 0$$

$$CH_3OH(s) \rightarrow CH_3OH(l) \quad \Delta S_{system} > 0$$

**2.** *The dissolving of a gas in a solvent always results in a decrease in entropy.* Gas particles have more entropy when they can move freely in the gaseous state than when they are dissolved in a liquid or solid that limits their movements and randomness. For example, $\Delta S_{system}$ is negative for the dissolving of carbon dioxide in water.

$$CO_2(g) \rightarrow CO_2(aq) \quad \Delta S_{system} < 0$$

**3.** *Assuming no change in physical state, the entropy of a system usually increases when the number of gaseous product particles is greater than the number of gaseous reactant particles.* That's because the larger the number of gaseous particles, the more random arrangements are available. For the following reaction, $\Delta S_{system}$ is positive because two gaseous molecules react and three gaseous molecules are produced.

$$2SO_3(g) \rightarrow 2SO_2(g) + O_2(g) \quad \Delta S_{system} > 0$$

$$H_2O(s) \quad \rightarrow \quad H_2O(l) \quad \rightarrow \quad H_2O(g)$$

**Figure 16-19**

The molecules in an ice cube are in a rigid, orderly arrangement. The molecules in liquid water have some freedom to move and create different arrangements. Water molecules in the gas phase are completely separated and can create an almost infinite number of arrangements.

16.5 Reaction Spontaneity **515**

**GLENCOE** *TECHNOLOGY*

**CD-ROM**
**Chemistry: Matter and Change**
Video: *Entropy*

**National Science Content Standards**

**Pages 514–515**
UCP.1, UCP.3; B.3, B.5

516

# Enrichment

Explain to students that the tendencies of reactions to occur from states of high to low energy and from states of low disorder or entropy to high disorder or entropy are manifestations of the second law of thermodynamics, which is another name for the law of disorder. The second law of thermodynamics states that in any spontaneous process, the entropy of the universe always increases. Point out that the tendency from high to low energy exists because the energy lost by the system is gained by the surroundings, thereby increasing the thermal entropy of the surroundings.

## Practice PROBLEMS

Have students refer to Appendix D for complete solutions to Practice Problems.

**38. a.** $\Delta S_{system}$ is negative.
  **b.** $\Delta S_{system}$ is negative.
  **c.** $\Delta S_{system}$ is positive.
  **d.** $\Delta S_{system}$ is negative.

**Figure 16-20**

Sodium chloride and liquid water are pure substances each with a degree of orderliness. When sodium chloride dissolves in water, the entropy of the system increases because $Na^+$ and $Cl^-$ ions and water molecules mix together to create a large number of random arrangements.

$$NaCl\,(s) \quad + \quad H_2O\,(l) \quad \rightarrow \quad NaCl\,(aq)$$

**4.** *With some exceptions, you can predict the change in entropy when a solid or a liquid dissolves to form a solution.* The solute particles, which are separate and pure before dissolving, become dispersed throughout the solvent. Therefore, dissolution usually increases the randomness and disorder of the particles, as shown in **Figure 16-20**, and the entropy of the system increases. For the dissolving of sodium chloride in water, $\Delta S_{system}$ is positive.

$$NaCl(s) \rightarrow Na^+(aq) + Cl^-(aq) \qquad \Delta S_{system} > 0$$

**5.** *An increase in the temperature of a substance is always accompanied by an increase in the random motion of its particles.* Recall that the kinetic energy of molecules increases with temperature. Increased kinetic energy means faster movement, more possible arrangements, and increased disorder. Therefore, the entropy of any substance increases as its temperature increases, and $\Delta S_{system} > 0$.

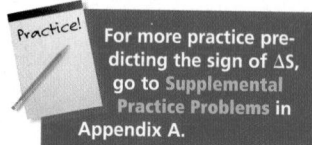

For more practice predicting the sign of $\Delta S$, go to **Supplemental Practice Problems** in Appendix A.

## PRACTICE PROBLEMS

**38.** Predict the sign of $\Delta S_{system}$ for each of the following changes.

  **a.** $ClF(g) + F_2(g) \rightarrow ClF_3(g)$
  **b.** $NH_3(g) \rightarrow NH_3(aq)$
  **c.** $CH_3OH(l) \rightarrow CH_3OH(aq)$
  **d.** $C_{10}H_8(l) \rightarrow C_{10}H_8(s)$

**Try at Home** **LAB**

See page 959 in Appendix E for **Observing Entropy**

## Entropy, the Universe, and Free Energy

You may be wondering whether entropy has an effect on reaction spontaneity. Recall that the law of disorder states that the entropy of the universe must increase as a result of a spontaneous reaction or process. Therefore, the following is true for any spontaneous process.

$$\Delta S_{universe} > 0$$

Because the universe equals the system plus the surroundings, any change in the entropy of the universe is the sum of changes occurring in the system and surroundings.

$$\Delta S_{universe} = \Delta S_{system} + \Delta S_{surroundings}$$

---

**DIFFERENTIATED INSTRUCTION**

### Gifted

The entropy of a system usually increases when a solid or liquid dissolves to form a solution. However, explain to capable students that some solutes form highly charged ions in solution, which may result in extensive clustering of water molecules in ordered patterns around the ions and a resulting decrease in entropy. **L3**

How do changes in a system's enthalpy and entropy affect $\Delta S_{universe}$? In nature, $\Delta S_{universe}$ tends to be positive for reactions and processes under the following conditions.

1. *The reaction or process is exothermic, which means $\Delta H_{system}$ is negative.* The heat released by an exothermic reaction raises the temperature of the surroundings and thereby increases the entropy of the surroundings. $\Delta S_{surroundings}$ is positive.

2. *The entropy of the system increases, so $\Delta S_{system}$ is positive.*

Thus, exothermic chemical reactions accompanied by an increase in entropy are all spontaneous.

**Free energy** Can you definitely determine if a reaction is spontaneous? In 1878, J. Willard Gibbs, a physicist at Yale University, defined a combined enthalpy-entropy function called Gibbs free energy that answers that question. For reactions or processes that take place at constant pressure and temperature, Gibbs free energy ($G_{system}$), commonly called **free energy**, is energy that is available to do work. Thus, free energy is useful energy. In contrast, some entropy is associated with energy that is spread out into the surroundings as, for example, random molecular motion and cannot be recovered to do useful work. The free energy change ($\Delta G_{system}$) is the difference between the system's change in enthalpy ($\Delta H_{system}$) and the product of the Kelvin temperature and the change in entropy ($T\Delta S_{system}$).

$$\Delta G_{system} = \Delta H_{system} - T\Delta S_{system}$$

When a reaction or process occurs under standard conditions (298 K and one atmosphere pressure) the standard free energy change can be expressed by this equation.

$$\Delta G^{\circ}_{system} = \Delta H^{\circ}_{system} - T\Delta S^{\circ}_{system}$$

The sign of the free energy change of the system, $\Delta G_{system}$, tells you whether or not a reaction or process is spontaneous at a constant specified temperature and pressure. If the sign of the free energy change of the system is negative, the reaction is spontaneous. If the sign of the free energy change is positive, the reaction is nonspontaneous. The relationship between $\Delta G_{system}$, $\Delta S_{universe}$, and reaction spontaneity is summarized in **Table 16-8**.

**Calculating free energy change** How do changes in enthalpy and entropy affect free energy change and spontaneity for the reaction between nitrogen and hydrogen to form ammonia?

$$N_2(g) + 3H_2(g) \rightarrow 2NH_3(g) \quad \Delta H^{\circ}_{system} = -91.8 \text{ kJ} \quad \Delta S^{\circ}_{system} = -197 \text{ J/K}$$

Note that the entropy of the system decreases because four moles of gaseous molecules react and only two moles of gaseous molecules are produced. Therefore, $\Delta S^{\circ}_{system}$ is negative. A decrease in the entropy of the system tends

**Table 16-8**

| $\Delta G_{system}$ and Reaction Spontaneity | | |
|---|---|---|
| **Type of reaction or process** | $\Delta G_{system}$ | $\Delta S_{universe}$ |
| Spontaneous | negative | positive |
| Nonspontaneous | positive | negative |

16.5 Reaction Spontaneity    **517**

## Earth Science
### CONNECTION

Volcanoes, fumaroles, hot springs, geysers, and boiling mud pools are manifestations of the great amount of geothermal energy in Earth's interior. Volcanoes are vents in Earth's crust from which flow molten rock (magma), steam, and other materials. When surface water moves downward through Earth's crust, it can interact with magma and/or hot rocks. Water that comes back to the surface in hot springs is heated to temperatures much higher than the surrounding air temperatures. Geysers are actually hot springs that spout hot water and steam into the air. Fumaroles emit steam and other gases such as hydrogen sulfide.

Geothermal energy provides an inexhaustible supply of energy that has been harnessed for a variety of applications. Buildings, homes, and greenhouses are warmed with energy from these sources. Geothermal energy also is used to warm soil to increase crop production in cooler climates. In several countries, electricity is generated by steam from geysers.

## CHEMISTRY JOURNAL

### The Work of J. Willard Gibbs

*Intrapersonal* Have students research the work of J. Willard Gibbs (1839–1903), an American scientist born in New Haven, Connecticut. In their chemistry journals, have them summarize Gibbs's contributions to our understanding of energy and entropy associated with processes and reactions. L2

**National Science Content Standards**

Pages 516–517
UCP.1, UCP.3; B.3, B.5

### Check for Understanding

Give students this equation for the formation of silicon carbide from sand and coke: 624.7 kJ + $SiO_2(s)$ + 3C(s) → SiC(s) + 2CO(g). Ask them to write the system's enthalpy change and predict the sign of the entropy change. $\Delta H°_{rxn}$ = 624.7 kJ, $\Delta S_{system}$ is positive.

### Reteach

Burn a wood splint and ask students how the entropies of the system and surroundings change. Both increase. The reaction is exothermic, increasing the thermal entropy of the surrounding. The ashes have more entropy than the wood.

## Resource Manager

**Small-Scale Laboratory Manual**, pp. 49–51 L2

---

to make the reaction nonspontaneous. But the reaction is exothermic ($\Delta H°_{system}$ is negative), which tends to make the reaction spontaneous. To determine which of the two conflicting tendencies predominates, you must calculate $\Delta G°_{system}$ for the reaction. First, convert $\Delta H°_{system}$ to joules.

$$\Delta H°_{system} = -91.8 \, kJ \times \frac{1000 \, J}{1 \, kJ} = -91\,800 \, J$$

Now, substitute $\Delta H°_{system}$, $T$, and $\Delta S°_{system}$ into the defining equation for $\Delta G°_{system}$.

$$\Delta G°_{system} = \Delta H°_{system} - T\Delta S°_{system}$$
$$\Delta G°_{system} = -91\,800 \, J - (298 \, K)(-197 \, J/K)$$
$$\Delta G°_{system} = -91\,800 \, J + 58\,700 \, J = -33\,100 \, J$$

Because $\Delta G°_{system}$ for this reaction is negative, the reaction is spontaneous under standard conditions.

The reaction between nitrogen and hydrogen demonstrates that the entropy of a system may actually decrease during a spontaneous process. However, it can do so only if the entropy of the surroundings increases more than the entropy of the system decreases. The situation is analogous to that of a company that manufactures two products, A and B. The company can operate profitably if it loses money on product A, but only if it earns more money on product B than it loses on product A. **Table 16-9** shows how reaction spontaneity depends on the signs of $\Delta H_{system}$ and $\Delta S_{system}$.

If $\Delta G°_{system} = 0$, both reactants and products are present in a state known as chemical equilibrium. Chemical equilibrium describes a state in which the rate of the forward reaction equals the rate of the reverse reaction. You will learn more about chemical equilibrium in Chapter 18.

**Table 16-9**

| How $\Delta H_{system}$ and $\Delta S_{system}$ Affect Reaction Spontaneity | | |
|---|---|---|
| | $-\Delta H_{system}$ | $+\Delta H_{system}$ |
| $+\Delta S_{system}$ | Always spontaneous | Spontaneity depends upon temperature |
| $-\Delta S_{system}$ | Spontaneity depends upon temperature | Never spontaneous |

### Math Handbook

Review solving algebraic equations in the **Math Handbook** on page 897 of this text.

### EXAMPLE PROBLEM 16-7

**Determining Reaction Spontaneity**

For a process, $\Delta H_{system}$ = 145 kJ and $\Delta S_{system}$ = 322 J/K. Is the process spontaneous at 382 K?

**1. Analyze the Problem**

You are given $\Delta H_{system}$ and $\Delta S_{system}$ for a process and must calculate $\Delta G_{system}$ to determine its sign.

**Known**

$T$ = 382 K
$\Delta H_{system}$ = 145 kJ
$\Delta S_{system}$ = 322 J/K

**Unknown**

sign of $\Delta G_{system}$ = ?

---

## Internet Address Book

**Chemistry Online**     Note Internet addresses that you find useful in the space below for quick reference.

_____

_____

_____

_____

_____

## 2. Solve for the Unknown

Convert $\Delta H_{system}$, given in kJ, to joules.

$$145 \text{ kJ} \times \frac{1000 \text{ J}}{1 \text{ kJ}} = 145\,000 \text{ J}$$

Solve the free energy equation using the known values.

$\Delta G_{system} = \Delta H_{system} - T\Delta S_{system}$

$\Delta G_{system} = 145\,000 \text{ J} - (382 \text{ K})(322 \text{ J/K})$

$\Delta G_{system} = 145\,000 \text{ J} - 123\,000 \text{ J} = 22\,000 \text{ J}$

Because $\Delta G_{system}$ is positive, the reaction is nonspontaneous.

## 3. Evaluate the Answer

The given data have three significant figures. When $\Delta H_{system}$ and $\Delta S_{system}$ are expressed in joules, they are accurate to the nearest 1000. Therefore, $\Delta G_{system}$ is also accurate to the nearest 1000, so the answer is correctly stated. When both $\Delta H_{system}$ and $\Delta S_{system}$ are positive, $\Delta G_{system}$ is positive only if the temperature is low enough. The temperature (109°C) is not high enough to make the second term of the equation greater than the first and so $\Delta G_{system}$ is positive.

### PRACTICE PROBLEMS

**39.** Given $\Delta H_{system}$, $T$, and $\Delta S_{system}$, determine if each of the following processes or reactions is spontaneous or nonspontaneous.

   **a.** $\Delta H_{system} = -75.9$ kJ, $T = 273$ K, $\Delta S_{system} = 138$ J/K

   **b.** $\Delta H_{system} = -27.6$ kJ, $T = 535$ K, $\Delta S_{system} = -55.2$ J/K

   **c.** $\Delta H_{system} = 365$ kJ, $T = 388$ K, $\Delta S_{system} = -55.2$ J/K

*Practice!* For more practice predicting the spontaneity of a reaction, go to **Supplemental Practice Problems** in Appendix A.

**Coupled reactions** Many of the chemical reactions that enable plants and animals to live and grow are nonspontaneous, that is, $\Delta G_{system}$ is positive. Based on that information, you might ask why these nonspontaneous reactions occur so readily in nature. In living systems, nonspontaneous reactions often occur in conjunction with other reactions that are spontaneous (reactions for which $\Delta G_{system}$ is negative). Reactions of this type that occur together are called coupled reactions. In coupled reactions, free energy released by one or more spontaneous reactions is used to drive a nonspontaneous reaction.

## Section 16.5 Assessment

**40.** In terms of energy, explain the difference between a spontaneous and a nonspontaneous reaction.

**41.** If a system becomes more disordered during a process, how does the system's entropy change?

**42.** When you dissolve a teaspoonful of sugar in a cup of tea, does the entropy of the system increase or decrease? Define the system and explain your answer.

**43. Thinking Critically** Evaluate the following statement and explain why it is true or false: The law of disorder means that the entropy of a system can never decrease during a spontaneous reaction or process.

**44. Predicting** Predict the sign of $\Delta S_{system}$ for the following reaction. Explain the basis for your prediction.

$$2H_2(g) + O_2(g) \rightarrow 2H_2O(g)$$

---

## Section 16.5 Assessment

**40.** A reaction occurs spontaneously only when the temperature, entropy change within the system, and energy exchanged between the system and surroundings cause the entropy of the universe to increase.

**41.** The system's entropy increases.

**42.** The system's entropy increases. The system consists of the sugar and tea. Randomness or disorder increases as sugar molecules disperse throughout the tea.

**43.** The statement is false. A system's entropy may decrease during a spontaneous process if the entropy of the surroundings increases more than the entropy of the system decreases.

**44.** $\Delta S_{system}$ is probably negative. The smaller number of gaseous product particles (two mol $H_2O$) have fewer random arrangements and thus less entropy than the larger number of gaseous reactant particles (two mol $H_2$ and one mol $O_2$).

**519**

### Extension

Explain that the third law of thermodynamics states that the entropy of a perfect crystal at 0 K is zero. A perfect crystal is one in which the particles are aligned in perfect order in the crystal structure. Ask students whether the entropy increases or decreases as temperature increases. Increases, because the added energy allows for some movement that may break the perfect alignment of the particles.

### ✓ Assessment

**Portfolio** Ask students to define the circumstances under which an exothermic reaction with a negative $\Delta S_{system}$ is spontaneous. Answers can be placed in student portfolios. The reaction is spontaneous only if the sum of $\Delta H_{system}$ and $-T\Delta S_{system}$ yields a negative value. **L2** **P**

### Practice PROBLEMS

Have students refer to Appendix D for complete solutions to Practice Problems.

**39. a.** spontaneous

    **b.** nonspontaneous

    **c.** nonspontaneous

## CHEMLAB  16

### Preparation

**Time Allotment**
One laboratory period

**Process Skills**
Observing, measuring, inferring

**Safety Precautions**
Students should wear aprons and goggles. The exothermic reaction produces flames. Students with long hair should tie their hair back.

**Disposal**
The ash can be placed in a receptacle for solid waste. The soot can be washed from the beaker with soap and water.

**Alternative Materials**
Similar snack products, such as corn chips, can be used instead of potato chips. Sample data is from a low-fat chip.

### Pre-Lab

3. The quantity of heat produced by the reaction will exceed the quantity of heat absorbed by the water.
4. $q = c \times m \times \triangle T$
5. carbon dioxide and water vapor

| Observations of the Burning of a Potato Chip | |
|---|---|
| Mass of beaker and 50 mL of water | 148.26 g |
| Mass of empty beaker | 98.00 g |
| Mass of water in beaker | 50.26 g |
| Mass of potato chip | 1.63 g |
| Highest temperature of water | 37.4°C |
| Initial temperature of water | 22.1°C |
| Change in temperature | 15.3°C |

## CHEMLAB 16

# Calorimetry

In this laboratory investigation, you will use the methods of calorimetry to approximate the amount of energy contained in a potato chip. The burning of a potato chip releases heat stored in the substances contained in the chip. The heat will be absorbed by a mass of water.

**Problem**

How many Calories of energy does the potato chip contain? How can the experiment be improved to provide a more accurate answer?

**Objectives**

• **Identify** the reactants and products in the reaction.
• **Measure** mass and temperature in order to calculate the amount of heat released in the reaction.
• **Propose** changes in the procedure and design of the equipment to decrease the percent error.

**Materials**

large potato chip
250-mL beaker
100-mL graduated cylinder
evaporating dish
thermometer
ring stand with ring
wire gauze
matches
stirring rod
balance

**Safety Precautions**

• Always wear safety goggles and a lab apron.
• Tie back long hair.
• Hot objects may not appear to be hot.
• Do not heat broken, chipped, or cracked glassware.
• Do not eat any items used in the lab.

**Pre-Lab**

1. Read the entire **CHEMLAB**.
2. Prepare all written materials that you will take into the laboratory. Be sure to include safety precautions, procedure notes, and a data table.

| Observations of the Burning of a Potato Chip | |
|---|---|
| Mass of beaker and 50 mL of water | |
| Mass of empty beaker | |
| Mass of water in beaker | |
| Mass of potato chip | |
| Highest temperature of water | |
| Initial temperature of water | |
| Change in temperature | |

3. Form a hypothesis about how the quantity of heat produced by the combustion reaction will compare with the quantity of heat absorbed by the water.
4. What formula will you use to calculate the quantity of heat absorbed by the water?
5. Assuming that the potato chip contains compounds made up of carbon and hydrogen, what gases will be produced in the combustion reaction?

520    **Chapter 16** Energy and Chemical Change

## Procedure

• Point out to students that the soot on the beaker is unburned carbon. It accounts for a large percent error.
• **Troubleshooting** Flames will rise 10 cm above the top of the potato chip.

## Expected Results

See the data table.

520

## Procedure

1. Measure the mass of a potato chip and record it in the data table.
2. Place the potato chip in an evaporating dish on the metal base of the ring stand. Position the ring and wire gauze so that they will be 10 cm above the top of the potato chip.
3. Measure the mass of an empty 250-mL beaker and record it in the data table.
4. Using the graduated cylinder, measure 50 mL of water and pour it into the beaker. Measure the mass of the beaker and water and record it in the data table.
5. Place the beaker on the wire gauze on the ring stand.
6. Measure and record the initial temperature of the water.
7. Use a match to ignite the bottom of the potato chip.
8. With a stirring rod, stir the water in the beaker while the chip burns. Measure the highest temperature of the water and record it in the data table.

### Cleanup and Disposal

1. Clean all lab equipment and return it to its proper place.
2. Wash your hands thoroughly after all lab work and cleanup is complete.

### Analyze and Conclude

1. **Classifying** Is the reaction exothermic or endothermic? Explain how you know.
2. **Observing and Inferring** Describe the reactant and products of the chemical reaction. Was the reactant (potato chip) completely consumed? What evidence supports your answer?
3. **Using Numbers** Calculate the mass of water in the beaker and the temperature change of the water. Use $q = c \times m \times \Delta T$ to calculate how much heat in joules was transferred to the water in the beaker by the burning of one chip.
4. **Using Numbers** Convert the quantity of heat in joules/chip to Calories/chip.

5. **Using Numbers** From the information on the chip's container, determine the mass in grams of one serving. Using your data, calculate the number of Calories that would be released by the combustion of one serving of chips.
6. **Error Analysis** Use the chip's container to determine how many Calories are contained in one serving. Compare your calculated Calories per serving with the value on the chip's container. Calculate the percent error.
7. **Observing and Inferring** Was all of the heat that was released collected by the water in the beaker? How can the experimental equipment be improved to decrease the percent error?

### Real-World Chemistry

1. From the ingredients identified on the potato chip container, list the actual substances that burned to produce energy. Are there any ingredients that did not produce energy? Explain.
2. You have discovered that potato chips provide a significant number of Calories per serving. Would it be advisable to make potato chips a substantial part of your diet? Explain.

CHEMLAB **521**

## Analyze and Conclude

1. The reaction is exothermic because heat and light were visible and the temperature of the water increased.
2. The potato chip burns in oxygen from the air to produce carbon dioxide gas, water vapor, and unburned carbon. The chip was not completely consumed as indicated by the presence of soot and ash.
3. 50.26 g water, 15.3 °C
$q = c \times m \times \Delta T$
$q = 4.184$ J/(g·°C) $\times$ 50.26 g $\times$ 15.3°C = 3220 J/chip
4. 3220 J/chip $\times$ 1 cal/4.184 J $\times$ 1 Calorie/1000 cal = 0.770 Calories
5. 28 g per serving
0.770 Calories/1.63 g $\times$ 28 g/1 serving = 13.2 Calories
6. 75 Calories per serving, but answers will vary according to the snack used (75 Calories − 13.2 Calories)/75 Calories $\times$ 100 = 82% error.
7. No, the air, glass beaker, and wire gauze absorbed heat from the flame, contributing to the high percent error. An insulated container would improve the experimental design.

## Real-World Chemistry

1. A potato chip is mostly the carbohydrate contained in potatoes and fats. These are the substances that burned. If the potato chip was salted, the salt would not burn to produce energy.
2. The contents of potato chips are too limited to provide a healthy diet if made a substantial part of a diet.

### Resource Manager

ChemLab and MiniLab Worksheets, pp. 62–64 **L2**

### ✓ Assessment

**Performance** Have students put their ideas for improved results into action by repeating the investigation using their redesigned equipment. Use the Performance Task Assessment List for Assessing a Whole Experiment and Planning the Next Experiment in **PASC**, p. 33.

**National Science Content Standards**

Pages 520–523
UCP.1, UCP.3; A.1, A.2; B.3, B.5, B.6; E.1

# How It Works

## Refrigerator

## Purpose

Students will learn that a refrigerator makes use of the enthalpy of vaporization and the enthalpy of condensation of a substance called a coolant or refrigerant.

## Background

In some modern refrigerators, the condenser coils are placed at the bottom or top. This allows the refrigerator to be placed in a closed-in area where coils in the rear would not work well because of lack of air circulation. Most refrigerators use a fan inside to circulate the cold air and thus improve the efficiency of heat transfer.

## Visual Learning

Have students trace the circuit of the liquid coolant from the point at which it enters the cooling coils inside the refrigerator. Have them note the change in color that indicates the relative temperatures of the coolant.

## Teaching Strategies

- Point out that the refrigerant should vaporize at the required temperature and pressure, condense to a liquid at a temperature close to room temperature, and have low toxicity, in case of a leak. Two refrigerants that are not highly toxic but very unpleasant are sulfur dioxide and ammonia. Ammonia is still used in industrial ice-making plants.

- Most refrigerators are powered by electricity, but some use natural gas or propane. Ask students why a gas refrigerator might be preferable to an electric refrigerator. Gas may be cheaper. Electricity may not be available in a remote area.

## Thinking Critically

1. Students should correctly predict that the refrigerator will not work properly in

**522**

# How It Works

## Refrigerator

When you put soft drinks into a cooler containing ice, heat is absorbed from the soft drinks to melt the ice. The energy involved in the phase change from solid water to liquid water is responsible for cooling the soft drinks.

A refrigerator also uses the phase changes (evaporation and condensation) of a substance to move heat from the inside of the refrigerator to the outside. A liquid called a refrigerant circulates through coils within the refrigerator and absorbs heat from the interior. The absorbed heat changes the refrigerant from a liquid to a gas. The gas is then compressed and circulated in condenser coils outside the refrigerator where it releases heat to the environment and is converted to a liquid.

❶ Liquid refrigerant enters the cooling coils inside the refrigerator at a temperature lower than the temperature of the air in the refrigerator.

❷ The refrigerant absorbs heat from the air in the refrigerator and is converted from a liquid to a gas.

❸ The gaseous refrigerant leaves the refrigerator and enters a compressor, which squeezes the gas molecules together increasing their temperature and pressure.

Expansion valve

❺ The liquid refrigerant passes through an expansion valve which lowers its pressure and increases its volume. The refrigerant is now ready to re-enter the refrigerator.

❹ The hot, dense gas enters the condenser coils outside the refrigerator. Heat is released to the environment and the refrigerant condenses to a liquid.

Compressor

### Thinking Critically

1. **Predicting** What would happen if too much refrigerant was present in the system? Too little? Use phase changes to explain your predictions.

2. **Hypothesizing** A heat pump is a device that can either heat or cool a house. It is constructed in a fashion similar to a refrigerator. Explain how you think a heat pump works.

**522** Chapter 16 Energy and Chemical Change

either case. When there is too much refrigerant, the pressure in the system may be so high that evaporation is not possible. This could damage the compressor because liquids are not easily compressed. In the case of too little refrigerant, the pressure may be so low that the liquid phase cannot be achieved. In either case, there will be no phase changes or diminished ones; thus, heat transfer through the system will be hampered.

2. Students should correctly reason that some method of reversing the roles of the condenser and the evaporator will be required. This could be accomplished by valves that reverse the flow of refrigerant through the system. Condenser inside = heating. Evaporator inside = cooling.

## Summary

### 16.1 Energy

- Energy is the capacity to do work or to produce heat. Energy may change from one form to another, but the amount of energy does not change.

- Chemical potential energy is energy stored in chemical bonds of a substance by virtue of the arrangement of the atoms and molecules.

- Chemical potential energy is released or absorbed as heat during chemical processes or reactions.

### 16.2 Heat in Chemical Reactions and Processes

- In thermochemistry, the universe is defined as the system plus the surroundings. The system is the reaction or process that is being studied, and the surroundings include everything in the universe except the system.

- The heat lost or gained by a system during a reaction or process carried out at constant pressure is called the change in enthalpy ($\Delta H$).

- When $\Delta H$ is positive, the reaction is endothermic. When $\Delta H$ is negative, the reaction is exothermic.

### 16.3 Thermochemical Equations

- A thermochemical equation includes the physical states of the reactants and products and specifies the change in enthalpy.

- The molar enthalpy (heat) of vaporization, $\Delta H_{vap}$, is the amount of energy required to evaporate one mole of a liquid.

- The molar enthalpy (heat) of fusion, $\Delta H_{fus}$, is the amount of energy needed to melt one mole of a solid.

### 16.4 Calculating Enthalpy Change

- Using Hess's law, the enthalpy change for a reaction can be calculated by adding two or more thermochemical equations and their enthalpy changes.

- Standard enthalpies of formation are based upon assigning a standard enthalpy of 0.0 kJ to all elements in their standard states.

### 16.5 Reaction Spontaneity

- Exothermic reactions tend to be spontaneous because they increase the entropy of the surroundings.

- Entropy is a measure of the disorder or randomness of the particles of a system. Spontaneous processes always result in an increase in the entropy of the universe.

- Free energy is the energy available to do work.

- If the change in a system's free energy is negative, the reaction is spontaneous. If the change in free energy is positive, the reaction is nonspontaneous.

## Key Equations and Relationships

- $q = c \times m \times \Delta T$
  (p. 493)

- $\Delta H_{rxn}^{o} = \Sigma \Delta H_{f}^{o}(\text{products}) - \Sigma \Delta H_{f}^{o}(\text{reactants})$
  (p. 511)

- $\Delta G_{system} = \Delta H_{system} - T\Delta S_{system}$
  (p. 517)

## Vocabulary

- calorie (p. 491)
- calorimeter (p. 496)
- chemical potential energy (p. 490)
- energy (p. 489)
- enthalpy (p. 499)
- enthalpy (heat) of combustion (p. 501)
- enthalpy (heat) of reaction (p. 499)
- entropy (p. 514)

- free energy (p. 517)
- heat (p. 491)
- Hess's law (p. 506)
- joule (p. 491)
- law of conservation of energy (p. 490)
- law of disorder (p. 514)
- molar enthalpy (heat) of fusion (p. 502)
- molar enthalpy (heat) of vaporization (p. 502)

- specific heat (p. 492)
- spontaneous process (p. 513)
- standard enthalpy (heat) of formation (p. 509)
- surroundings (p. 498)
- system (p. 498)
- thermochemical equation (p. 501)
- thermochemistry (p. 498)
- universe (p. 498)

## Using the Vocabulary

To reinforce chapter vocabulary, have students write a sentence using each term. **L2** **ELL**

## Review Strategies

- Ask students to relate chemical potential energy to exothermic and endothermic chemical reactions. **L2**

- Have students describe the steps involved in writing thermochemical equations. **L2**

- Ask students to relate the sign of $\Delta H_{vap}$ to the vaporization and condensation of water. **L2**

- Have students explain the significance and use of Hess's law in determining the enthalpies of chemical reactions. **L2**

- Ask students to explain why endothermic reactions tend to be nonspontaneous. **L2**

- Have students explain how $\Delta G_{system}$ relates to the spontaneity of a reaction or process. **L2**

- Problems from Appendix A or the **Supplemental Problems** booklet can be used for review. **L2**

VOCABULARY
PuzzleMaker CHEMISTRY ONLINE

For additional help with vocabulary, have students access the Vocabulary PuzzleMaker online.

chemistrymc.com/ vocabulary_puzzlemaker

Chemistry Online

---

**EXAMVIEW® PRO**

## Use ExamView® Pro Testmaker CD-ROM to:

- Create **multiple versions** of tests.
- Create **modified** tests with one mouse click for struggling students.
- **Edit** existing questions and add your own questions.
- **Build** tests based on national curriculum standards.

## Concept Mapping

**45.** 1. joule; 2. calorie;
3. calorimeter; 4. thermochemical equation

## Mastering Concepts

**46.** Potential energy is energy related to composition or position, and kinetic energy is energy related to motion.

**47.** It increases.

**48.** One nutritional Calorie equals 1000 calories.

**49.** specific heat

**50.** Student answers will vary. A typical answer is: During an avalanche, the potential energy of snow at a higher altitude is converted to kinetic energy as the snow cascades down a mountain.

**51.** The system is the specific part of the universe that is the reaction or process being studied. The surroundings include everything in the universe other than the system.

**52.** at constant pressure

**53.** The system's chemical potential energy is less after the reaction than before the reaction.

**54.** The enthalpy of the products is lower for an exothermic reaction and higher for an endothermic reaction.

**55.** $\triangle H$ is negative for an exothermic reaction and positive for an endothermic reaction.

**56.** Heat is calculated using the equation $q = c \times m \times \triangle T$, which includes the specific heat of the substance.

**57.** They are equal.

**58.** A thermochemical equation includes the physical states of the reactants and products, and the enthalpy change for the reaction.

**59.** a mole of liquid water

## Chemistry Online

*Go to the Chemistry Web site at* chemistrymc.com *for additional Chapter 16 Assessment.*

## Concept Mapping

**45.** Fill in the boxes with the following terms: calorimeter, calorie, thermochemical equation, joule.

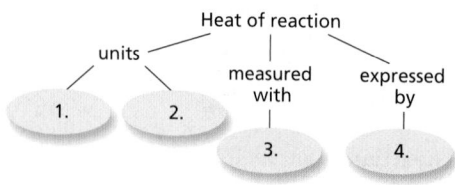

## Mastering Concepts

**46.** Compare and contrast temperature and heat. (16.1)

**47.** How does the chemical potential energy of a system change during an endothermic reaction? (16.1)

**48.** How does the nutritional Calorie compare with the calorie? (16.1)

**49.** What quantity has the units J/(g · °C)? (16.1)

**50.** Describe a situation that illustrates potential energy changing to kinetic energy. (16.1)

**51.** In describing a chemical reaction, what is meant by the system? The surroundings? (16.2)

**52.** Under what condition is the heat ($q$) evolved or absorbed in a chemical reaction equal to a change in enthalpy ($\triangle H$)? (16.2)

**53.** The enthalpy change for a reaction, $\triangle H$, is negative. What does this indicate about the chemical potential energy of the system before and after the reaction? (16.2)

**54.** How does the enthalpy of the products compare with the enthalpy of the reactants in an exothermic reaction? An endothermic reaction? (16.2)

**55.** What is the sign of $\triangle H$ for an exothermic reaction? An endothermic reaction? (16.2)

**56.** Explain why you need to know the specific heat of a substance in order to calculate how much heat is gained or lost by the substance as a result of a temperature change. (16.2)

**57.** How is the quantity of heat lost by the system related to the quantity of heat gained by the surroundings during an exothermic process? (16.2)

**58.** How is a thermochemical equation different from a balanced chemical equation? (16.3)

**59.** Which has the higher heat content, a mole of liquid water or a mole of ice? (16.3)

**60.** Write the correct sign of $\triangle H_{system}$ for each of the following changes in physical state. (16.3)

  **a.** $C_2H_5OH(s) \rightarrow C_2H_5OH(l)$
  **b.** $H_2O(g) \rightarrow H_2O(l)$
  **c.** $CH_3OH(l) \rightarrow CH_3OH(g)$
  **d.** $NH_3(l) \rightarrow NH_3(s)$

**61.** How are the chemical elements in their standard states used as references for standard enthalpies of formation? (16.4)

**62.** Write the formula that can be used to calculate the enthalpy of a reaction from the enthalpies of formation of the reactants and products. (16.4)

**63.** Compare and contrast enthalpy and entropy. (16.5)

**64.** What does the entropy of a substance measure? (16.5)

**65.** What must happen to the entropy of the universe during a spontaneous reaction or process? (16.5)

**66.** From each pair, pick the one with the greater entropy. (16.5)

  **a.** $NH_3(g)$ and $NH_3(l)$
  **b.** $NH_3(g)$ and $NH_3(aq)$
  **c.** $CO_2(s)$ and $CO_2(g)$
  **d.** $KBr(s)$ and $KBr(l)$

**67.** What is meant by the free energy of a system? (16.5)

**68.** What is the equation that defines free energy? (16.5)

**69.** How is the free energy change for a reaction related to its spontaneity? (16.5)

**70.** Explain how an exothermic reaction changes the entropy of the surroundings. Does the enthalpy change for such a reaction increase or decrease $\triangle G_{system}$? Explain your answer. (16.5)

**71.** Explain how an endothermic reaction changes the entropy of the surroundings. How does the enthalpy change for such a reaction affect $\triangle G_{system}$? (16.5)

**72.** Under what circumstance might a nonspontaneous reaction become spontaneous when the temperature increases? Decreases? (16.5)

chemistrymc.com/chapter_test

**60. a.** $\triangle H_{system}$ is +.
   **b.** $\triangle H_{system}$ is −.
   **c.** $\triangle H_{system}$ is +.
   **d.** $\triangle H_{system}$ is −.

**61.** Every free element in its standard state is assigned a $\triangle H_f°$ of exactly zero.

## Resource Manager

Chapter Assessment, pp. 91–96 **L2**
Supplemental Problems, Ch. 16
ExamView® Pro CD-ROM
MindJogger Videoquizzes DVD/VHS
Solutions Manual, Ch. 16
Chemistry Interactive CD-ROM,
  Ch. 16 quiz

**73.** Explain why the gaseous state of a substance has a greater entropy than the liquid state of the same substance. (16.5)

**74.** Predict the sign of $\Delta S_{system}$ for each of these chemical reactions. Explain your predictions. (16.5)

a. $2SO_3(g) + CO_2(g) \rightarrow CS_2(g) + 4O_2(g)$
b. $PCl_5(g) \rightarrow PCl_3(g) + Cl_2(g)$
c. $2CO(g) + O_2(g) \rightarrow 2CO_2(g)$
d. $C_6H_{12}O_6(s) \rightarrow 2C_2H_5OH(l) + 2CO_2(g)$
e. $H_2SO_4(l) \rightarrow H_2O(l) + SO_3(g)$

# Mastering Problems
## Energy (16.1)

**75.** A fast-food item contains 544 nutritional Calories. Convert this energy to calories and to joules.

**76.** An endothermic process absorbs 138 kJ. How many calories of heat are absorbed?

**77.** An exothermic reaction releases 325 000 calories. Convert this energy to kJ.

## Measuring Heat (16.2)

**78.** How many joules of heat are lost by 3580 kg granite as it cools from 41.2°C to −12.9°C?

**79.** How much heat is absorbed by a 2000 kg granite boulder as energy from the sun causes its temperature to change from 10°C to 29°C?

**80.** A sample of silver with a mass of 63.3 g is heated to a temperature of 384.4 K and placed in a container of water at 290.0 K. The final temperature of the silver and water is 292.4 K. Assuming no heat loss, what mass of water was in the container? The specific heat of water is 4.184 J/(g·°C) and of silver, 0.24 J/(g·°C).

**81.** A swimming pool, 20.0 m × 12.5 m, is filled with water to a depth of 3.75 m. If the initial temperature of the water is 18.4°C, how much heat must be added to the water to raise its temperature to 29.0°C? Assume that the density of water is 1.000 g/mL.

## Calculating Energy Change (16.3)

**82.** How much heat is required to vaporize 343 g of liquid ethanol at its boiling point? $\Delta H_{vap} = 38.6$ kJ/mol

**83.** How much heat is evolved when 1255 g of water condenses to a liquid at 100°C? $\Delta H_{cond} = -40.7$ kJ/mol

**84.** How much heat is liberated by the combustion of 206 g of hydrogen? $\Delta H_{comb} = -286$ kJ/mol

**85.** A sample of ammonia liberates 5.66 kJ of heat as it solidifies at its melting point. What is the mass of the sample? $\Delta H_{solid} = -5.66$ kJ/mol.

**86.** How much heat is required to warm 225 g of ice from −46.8°C to 0.0°C, melt the ice, warm the water from 0.0°C to 100.0°C, boil the water, and heat the steam to 173.0°C?

**87.** How much energy is involved in the dissolving of sodium hydroxide in water? The table shows data from an experiment in which a measured amount of NaOH is dissolved in water in a foam cup calorimeter. Calculate $\Delta H$ for the process in kJ/mol. If the enthalpy change for the solution of NaOH is −44.51 kJ/mol, what is the percent error of the experiment?

**Table 16-10**

| Data for the Dissolving of NaOH | |
|---|---|
| Mass of NaOH + weighing paper | 4.71 g |
| Mass of weighing paper | 0.70 g |
| Mass of NaOH | |
| Mass of foam cup + water | 109.85 g |
| Mass of foam cup | 10.25 g |
| Mass of water | |
| Final temperature of water | 35.9°C |
| Initial temperature of water | 25.5°C |
| Change in temperature, $\Delta T$ | |

## Using Hess's Law (16.4)

**88.** You are given these two equations.

$Sn(s) + Cl_2(g) \rightarrow SnCl_2(s) \quad \Delta H = -325$ kJ
$SnCl_2(s) + Cl_2(g) \rightarrow SnCl_4(l) \quad \Delta H = -186$ kJ

Calculate $\Delta H$ for this reaction.
$Sn(s) + 2Cl_2(g) \rightarrow SnCl_4(l)$

**89.** Use standard enthalpies of formation from **Table C-13** in Appendix C to calculate $\Delta H^\circ_{rxn}$ for each of these reactions.

a. $2NaHCO_3(s) \rightarrow Na_2CO_3(s) + CO_2(g) + H_2O(g)$
b. $H_2(g) + O_2(g) \rightarrow H_2O_2(l)$
c. $NH_3(g) + HCl(g) \rightarrow NH_4Cl(s)$
d. $2H_2S(g) + 3O_2(g) \rightarrow 2H_2O(g) + 2SO_2(g)$
e. $4FeS(s) + 7O_2(g) \rightarrow 2Fe_2O_3(s) + 4SO_2(g)$

**62.** $\Delta H^\circ_{rxn} = \Sigma \Delta H_f^\circ$ (products) $- \Sigma \Delta H_f^\circ$ (reactants)

**63.** Enthalpy is a measure of a system's heat content at constant pressure. Entropy is a measure of the disorder or randomness of the particles that make up the system.

**64.** The entropy of a substance is a measure of the disorder of its particles.

**65.** The entropy of the universe must increase.

**66. a.** $NH_3(g)$
 **b.** $NH_3(g)$
 **c.** $CO_2(g)$
 **d.** $KBr(l)$

**67.** Free energy—a combined enthalpy-entropy function—is energy available to do work.

**68.** $\Delta G^\circ_{system} = \Delta H^\circ_{system} - T\Delta S^\circ_{system}$

**69.** The reaction is spontaneous if $\Delta G_{system}$ is negative and nonspontaneous if $\Delta G_{system}$ is positive.

**70.** The heat released by an exothermic reaction increases the entropy of the surroundings. Such a reaction decreases $\Delta G_{system}$ because $\Delta H_{system}$ is negative in the equation $\Delta G^\circ_{system} = \Delta H^\circ_{system} - T\Delta S^\circ_{system}$.

**71.** The heat absorbed by an endothermic reaction decreases the entropy of the surroundings. Such a reaction increases $\Delta G^\circ_{system}$ because $\Delta H^\circ_{system}$ is positive in the equation $\Delta G^\circ_{system} = \Delta H^\circ_{system} - T\Delta S^\circ_{system}$.

**72.** Temperature increases: an endothermic reaction for which the entropy of the system increases. Temperature decreases: an exothermic reaction for

which the entropy of the system decreases.

**73.** The particles of a gas are farther apart and able to move in a more random manner than the particles of a liquid.

**74. a.** $\Delta S_{system}$ is positive. The products are made up of more gaseous particles than the reactants.
 **b.** $\Delta S_{system}$ is positive. The products are made up of more gaseous particles than the reactants.

**c.** $\Delta S_{system}$ is negative. The products are made up of fewer gaseous particles than the reactants.

**d.** $\Delta S_{system}$ is positive. The products are made up of liquid and gaseous particles; the reactant is made up of solid particles.

**e.** $\Delta S_{system}$ is positive. The products are made up of liquid and gaseous particles; the reactant is made up of liquid particles.

**National Science Content Standards**

Pages 524–525
UCP.1, UCP.3; B.3, B.5, B.6

## Mastering Problems

Complete solutions to Chapter Assessment problems can be found in the **Solutions Manual.**

### Energy (16.1)
**Level 1**
**75.** 544 000 cal, $2.28 \times 10^6$ J
**76.** $3.30 \times 10^4$ cal
**77.** 1360 kJ

### Measuring Heat (16.2)
**Level 1**
**78.** $1.56 \times 10^8$ J
**79.** 30 000 kJ

**Level 2**
**80.** 140 g of water
**81.** $4.16 \times 10^{10}$ J

### Calculating Energy Change (16.3)
**Level 1**
**82.** 287 kJ
**83.** 2830 kJ
**84.** 29 200 kJ
**85.** 17.0 g

**Level 2**
**86.** 732 kJ
**87.** 43.3 kJ/mol, 2.72% error

### Using Hess's Law (16.4)
**Level 1**
**88.** $\triangle H°_{rxn} = -511$ kJ

**Level 2**
**89. a.** $\triangle H°_{rxn} = 135.6$ kJ
**b.** $\triangle H°_{rxn} = -187.8$ kJ
**c.** $\triangle H°_{rxn} = -176.0$ kJ
**d.** $\triangle H°_{rxn} = -1036.04$ kJ
**e.** $\triangle H°_{rxn} = -2435.7$ kJ

### Reaction Spontaneity (16.5)
**Level 1**
**90. a.** $\triangle G°_{system} = 87\ 800$ J, nonspontaneous
**b.** $\triangle G°_{system} = -2.70 \times 10^5$ J, spontaneous
**c.** $\triangle G°_{system} = 84\ 100$ J, nonspontaneous

**Level 2**
**91.** 266 K
**92.** $\triangle G°_{system} = -3.20 \times 10^4$ J
$\triangle G°_{system}$ is negative, which means that the entropy of

## Reaction Spontaneity (16.5)
**90.** Calculate $\Delta G_{system}$ for each process and state if the process is spontaneous or nonspontaneous.

**a.** $\Delta H_{system} = 145$ kJ, $T = 293$ K, $\Delta S_{system} = 195$ J/K
**b.** $\Delta H_{system} = -232$ kJ, $T = 273$ K, $\Delta S_{system} = 138$ J/K
**c.** $\Delta H_{system} = -15.9$ kJ, $T = 373$ K, $\Delta S_{system} = -268$ J/K

**91.** Calculate the temperature at which $\Delta G_{system} = -34.7$ kJ if $\Delta H_{system} = -28.8$ kJ and $\Delta S_{system} = 22.2$ J/K?

**92.** Under certain conditions, iron ore ($Fe_3O_4$) can be converted to iron by the following reaction.

$Fe_3O_4(s) + 4H_2(g) \rightarrow 3Fe(s) + 4H_2O(g)$

$\Delta H_{system} = 149.8$ kJ

$\Delta S_{system} = 610.0$ J/K

Is the reaction spontaneous at 298 K? Explain why or why not based upon how the entropy of the system, surroundings, and universe change as a result of the reaction.

## Mixed Review

*Sharpen your problem-solving skills by answering the following.*

**93.** What mass of octane must be burned in order to liberate 5340 kJ of heat? $\Delta H_{comb} = -5471$ kJ/mol.

**94.** How much heat is released to the surroundings when 200 g of water at 96.0°C cools to 25.0°C? The specific heat of water is 4.184 J/(g·°C).

**95.** What is the final temperature of 1280 g of water, originally at 20.0°C, if it absorbs 47.6 kJ of heat?

**96.** Is the following reaction spontaneous at 456 K? If not, is it spontaneous at some other temperature? Explain your answer.

$N_2(g) + 2O_2(g) \rightarrow 2NO_2(g)$

$\Delta H_{system} = 68$ kJ

$\Delta S_{system} = -122$ J/K

**97.** Use Hess's law to determine ΔH for the reaction

$NO(g) + O(g) \rightarrow NO_2(g) \quad \Delta H = ?$

given the following reactions. Show your work.

$O_2(g) \rightarrow 2O(g) \quad \Delta H = +495$ kJ
$2O_3(g) \rightarrow 3O_2(g) \quad \Delta H = -427$ kJ
$NO(g) + O_3(g) \rightarrow NO_2(g) + O_2(g) \quad \Delta H = -199$ kJ

## Thinking Critically

**98. Using Numbers** A 133-g piece of granite rock is heated to 65.0°C, then placed in 643 g ethanol at 12.7°C. Assuming no heat loss, what is the final temperature of the granite and ethanol? See **Table 16-2**.

**99. Applying Concepts** Write the thermochemical equation for the decomposition of liquid hydrogen peroxide ($H_2O_2$) to water vapor and oxygen gas. Calculate $\Delta H_{system}$ for the reaction using standard enthalpies of formation. Analyze the reaction and explain why NASA found this reaction suitable for providing thrust in the control jets of some space vehicles.

**100. Recognizing Cause and Effect** Explain why the equation $\Delta G_{system} = \Delta H_{system} - T\Delta S_{system}$ is especially valuable in recognizing how reactions and processes affect the entropy of the universe.

## Writing in Chemistry

**101.** Research and explain how hydrogen might be produced, transported, and used as a fuel for automobiles. Summarize the benefits and drawbacks of using hydrogen as an alternative fuel for internal combustion engines.

**102.** Research the use of wind as a source of electrical power. Explain the possible benefits, disadvantages, and limitations of its use.

## Cumulative Review

*Refresh your understanding of previous chapters by answering the following.*

**103.** Why is it necessary to perform repeated experiments in order to support a hypothesis? (Chapter 1)

**104.** Phosphorus has the atomic number 15 and an atomic mass of 31 amu. How many protons, neutrons, and electrons are in a neutral phosphorus atom? (Chapter 4)

**105.** What element has the electron configuration $[Ar]4s^13d^5$? (Chapter 5)

**106.** Name the following molecular compounds. (Chapter 8)
**a.** $S_2Cl_2$
**b.** $CS_2$
**c.** $SO_3$
**d.** $P_4O_{10}$

**107.** Determine the molar mass for the following compounds. (Chapter 11)
**a.** $Co(NO_3)_2 \cdot 6H_2O$
**b.** $Fe(OH)_3$

the universe increases and the reaction is spontaneous. The increase in the entropy of the system is greater than the decrease in the entropy of the surroundings.

## Mixed Review
**93.** 112 g
**94.** 60 000 J
**95.** 28.9°C

**96.** $\triangle G°_{system} = 124\ 000$ J
$\triangle G°_{system}$ is positive, which means that the entropy of the universe would decrease if the reaction occurred. Therefore, the reaction is nonspontaneous. Because the entropy of both the system and the surroundings decreases, the reaction is not spontaneous at any temperature.
**97.** −233 kJ

*Use these questions and the test-taking tip to prepare for your standardized test.*

**1.** The specific heat of ethanol is 2.44 J/g·°C. How many kilojoules of energy are required to heat 50.0 g of ethanol from −20.0°C to 68.0°C?
**a.** 10.7 kJ  **c.** 2.44 kJ
**b.** 8.30 kJ  **d.** 1.22 kJ

**2.** When a reaction takes place at constant pressure, what is $q$ for the reaction?
**a.** $\triangle S_{rxn}$.  **c.** $\triangle G_{rxn}$.
**b.** $\triangle H_{rxn}$.  **d.** $c_{rxn}$.

**3.** Determine $\triangle H$ for the reaction of aluminum and sulfur dioxide.

$4Al(s) + 3SO_2(g) \rightarrow 2Al_2O_3(s) + 3S(s)$

Use the following equations:

$4Al(s) + 3O_2(g) \rightarrow 2Al_2O_3(s) \triangle H = -3352$ kJ/mol
$S(s) + O_2(g) \rightarrow SO_2(g)$    $\triangle H = -297$ kJ/mol

**a.** −4243 kJ  **c.** −3055 kJ
**b.** −3649 kJ  **d.** −2461 kJ

**Interpreting Graphs** Use the graph to answer questions 4–6.

### $\triangle G$ for the Vaporization of Cyclohexane as a Function of Temperature

**4.** In the range of temperatures shown, the vaporization of cyclohexane
**a.** does not occur at all.
**b.** will occur spontaneously.
**c.** is not spontaneous.
**d.** occurs only at high temperatures.

chemistrymc.com/standardized_test

**5.** The standard free energy, enthalpy, and entropy of vaporization are often written with the subscript *vap* to indicate that they are associated with a vaporization reaction. What is the $\triangle G^{\circ}_{vap}$ of cyclohexane at 300 K?
**a.** 5.00 kJ/mol  **c.** 3.00 kJ/mol
**b.** 4.00 kJ/mol  **d.** 2.00 kJ/mol

**6.** When $\triangle G^{\circ}_{vap}$ is plotted as a function of temperature, the slope of the line equals $\triangle S^{\circ}_{vap}$ and the *y*-intercept of the line equals $\triangle H^{\circ}_{vap}$. What is the approximate standard entropy of vaporization of cyclohexane.
**a.** 50.0 J/mol·K.  **c.** 5.0 J/mol·K.
**b.** 10.0 J/mol·K.  **d.** 100 J/mol·K.

**7.** 3.00 g of aluminum foil is placed in an oven and heated from 20.0°C to 662.0°C. If it absorbs 1728 J of heat, what is the specific heat of aluminum?
**a.** 0.131 J/g·°C  **c.** 0.897 J/g·°C
**b.** 0.870 J/g·°C  **d.** 2.61 J/g·°C

**8.** $AB(s) + C_2(l) \rightarrow AC(g) + BC(g)$

Which cannot be predicted about this reaction?
**a.** the entropy of the system decreases
**b.** the entropy of the products is higher than that of the reactants
**c.** the change in entropy for this reaction, $\triangle S_{rxn}$, is positive
**d.** the disorder of the system increases

**9.** $Co(s) + S(s) + 2O_2(g) \rightarrow CoSO_4(s)$
$\triangle H^{\circ}_f = -888.3$ kJ/mol, $\triangle S^{\circ}_f = 118.0$ J/mol·K

Given the above thermochemical data for the formation of cobalt(II) sulfate from its elements, what is $\triangle G^{\circ}_f$ for $CoSO_4$ at 25°C?

**a.** −853.1 kJ/mol  **c.** −891.3 kJ/mol
**b.** −885.4 kJ/mol  **d.** −923.5 kJ/mol

---

**TEST-TAKING TIP**

**Stock Up On Supplies** Bring all your test-taking tools: number two pencils, black and blue pens, erasers, correction fluid, a sharpener, a ruler, a calculator, and a protractor. Bring munchies, too. You might not be able to eat them in the testing room, but they come in handy for the break, if you're allowed to go outside.

## Standardized Test Practice
**1.** a    **6.** d
**2.** b    **7.** c
**3.** d    **8.** a
**4.** c    **9.** d
**5.** a

## Thinking Critically
**98.** 16.0°C
**99.** $2H_2O_2(l) \rightarrow 2H_2O(g) + O_2(g)$   $\triangle H^{\circ}_{rxn} = -108.0$ kJ
The reaction produces gases that provide thrust as they exit the control jets. The heat produced by the reaction causes the gases to expand and leave the control jets at higher velocities, increasing the thrust.
**100.** For reactions or processes that take place at constant pressure and temperature, $\triangle G_{system}$ is related to $\triangle S_{universe}$ in the following way: If $\triangle G_{system}$ is negative, the entropy of the universe increases ($\triangle S_{universe}$ is positive) and the reaction or process is spontaneous. If $\triangle G_{system}$ is positive, the entropy of the universe decreases ($\triangle S_{universe}$ is negative) and the reaction or process is nonspontaneous.

## Cumulative Review
**103.** Experiments must be repeated to be sure that they yield similar results each time.
**104.** number of protons = 15; number of electrons = 15; number of neutrons = mass number − number of protons = 16
**105.** chromium
**106.** **a.** disulfur dichloride
**b.** carbon disulfide
**c.** sulfur trioxide
**d.** tetraphosphorus decoxide
**107.** **a.** molar mass = 291.07 g/mol $Co(NO_3)_2 \cdot 6H_2O$
**b.** molar mass = 106.88 g/mol $Fe(OH)_3$

**National Science Content Standards**

Pages 526–527
UCP.1, UCP.3; B.3, B.5, B.6; E.2

# Resource Manager

| Section | Objectives | Activities/Features |
|---|---|---|
| **Section 17.1** <br> **A Model for Reaction Rates** <br> 1 session <br> 🔲 ¹/₂ block | **1. Calculate** average rates of chemical reactions from experimental data. <br> **2. Relate** rates of chemical reactions to collisions between reacting particles. | **Discovery Lab:** Speeding Reactions, p. 529 <br> **Problem-Solving Lab:** Speed and Energy of Collision, p. 533 |
| **Section 17.2** <br> **Factors Affecting Reaction Rates** <br> 1 session <br> 🔲 ¹/₂ block | **3. Identify** factors that affect the rates of chemical reactions. <br> **4. Explain** the role of a catalyst. | **MiniLab:** Examining Reaction Rate and Temperature, p. 539 |
| **Section 17.3** <br> **Reaction Rate Laws** <br> 2 sessions <br> 🔲 1¹/₂ blocks | **5. Express** the relationship between reaction rate and concentration. <br> **6. Determine** reaction orders using the method of initial rates. | **Physics Connection,** p. 544 <br> **ChemLab:** Concentration and Reaction Rate, pp. 550–551 |
| **Section 17.4** <br> **Instantaneous Reaction Rates and Reaction Mechanisms** <br> 3 sessions <br> 🔲 1¹/₂ blocks | **7. Calculate** instantaneous rates of chemical reactions. <br> **8. Understand** that many chemical reactions occur in steps. <br> **9. Relate** the instantaneous rate of a complex reaction to its reaction mechanism. | **Careers Using Chemistry:** Food Technologist, p. 548 <br> **How It Works:** Catalytic Converter, p. 552 |

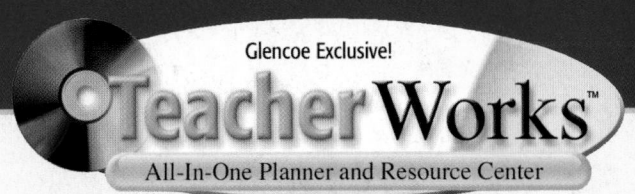

Glencoe Exclusive!

## TeacherWorks™
All-In-One Planner and Resource Center

| National Science Content Standards | State/Local Standards | Reproducible Masters | Transparencies |
|---|---|---|---|
| UCP.2, UCP.3; A.1; B.3, B.4, B.5, B.6; E.2; F.1 | | **Study Guide for Content Mastery,** pp. 97–98 **L2**<br>**Challenge Problems,** p. 17 **L3** | **Section Focus**<br>**Transparency 64** **L1** **ELL** |
| UCP.2, UCP.3; A.1; B.2, B.3, B.4, B.6; F.1, F.4, F.6 | | **Study Guide for Content Mastery,** p. 99 **L2**<br>**ChemLab and MiniLab Worksheets,** pp. 65–68 **L2**<br>**Laboratory Manual,** pp. 129–132 **L2** | **Section Focus**<br>**Transparency 65** **L1** **ELL**<br>**Teaching**<br>**Transparency 50** **L2** **ELL** |
| UCP.2, UCP.3; A.1; B.3 | | **Study Guide for Content Mastery,** p. 100 **L2**<br>**ChemLab and MiniLab Worksheets,** pp. 66–68 **L2**<br>**Small-Scale Laboratory Manual,** pp. 53–56 **L2** | **Section Focus**<br>**Transparency 66** **L1** **ELL**<br>**Teaching**<br>**Transparency 51** **L2** **ELL**<br>**Math Skills**<br>**Transparency 27** **L2** **ELL** |
| UCP.2, UCP.3; A.1; B.2, B.3, B.4, B.6; E.2; F.4, F.5, F.6 | | **Study Guide for Content Mastery,** pp. 101–102 **L2**<br>**Laboratory Manual,** pp. 133–136 **L2** | **Section Focus**<br>**Transparency 67** **L1** **ELL**<br>**Teaching**<br>**Transparency 52** **L2** **ELL** |

**Key to National Science Content Standards:** UCP = Unifying Concepts and Processes, A = Science as Inquiry, B = Physical Science, C = Life Science, D = Earth and Space Sciences, E = Science and Technology, F = Science in Personal and Social Perspectives, G = History and Nature of Science

Refer to pages 4T–5T of the Teacher Guide for an explanation of the National Science Content Standards correlations.

# Resource Manager

## Materials List

### ChemLab (pages 550–551)
10-mL graduated pipette, pipette filler, 6*M* hydrochloric acid, labels, test tubes(4), test-tube rack, magnesium ribbon, metric ruler, fine sandpaper, tongs, stopwatch, stirring rod

### Discovery Lab (page 529)
3% hydrogen peroxide, 100-mL beaker, active dry yeast, toothpick

### MiniLab (page 539)
100-mL beaker, 250-mL beaker, thermometer, balance, hot plate, water, bicarbonate antacid tablet (Alka-Seltzer®), stopwatch

### Demonstration (pages 536–537)
lycopodium powder, Bunsen burner, ceramic pad

## Preparation of Solutions

For a review of solution preparation, see page 46T of the Teacher Guide.

Quantities are for a class of 30 students.

**ChemLab (pages 550–551)**
   **6*M* hydrochloric acid** Add 250 mL concentrated (12*M*) hydrochloric acid to 250 mL distilled water while stirring. **CAUTION:** Do NOT add the water to the acid.

**Discovery Lab (page 529)**
   **3% hydrogen peroxide** Add 30 mL 30% hydrogen peroxide to 270 mL of distilled water. Store in a tightly-sealed brown glass bottle. **CAUTION:** Avoid skin contact with 30% hydrogen peroxide.

## Assessment Resources

**Chapter Assessment,** pp. 97–102
**MindJogger Videoquizzes DVD/VHS**
**Alternate Assessment in the Science Classroom**
**ExamView® Pro CD-ROM**
**Solutions Manual,** Chapter 17
**Supplemental Problems,** Chapter 17
**Performance Assessment in the Science Classroom**
**Chemistry Interactive CD-ROM,** Chapter 17 quiz

## Additional Resources

**Spanish Resources** ELL
**Guided Reading Audio Program,** Chapter 17 ELL
**Cooperative Learning in the Science Classroom**
**Lab and Safety Skills in the Science Classroom**
**Lesson Plans**
**Block Scheduling Lesson Plans**
Chemistrymc.com

## Glencoe Technology

The following multimedia for this chapter are available from Glencoe.

**VIDEOTAPE/DVD**
MindJogger Videoquizzes,
Chapter 17

**CD-ROM**
**Chemistry: Matter and Change**
*Chemical Kinetics,* Experiment
*Exothermic and Endothermic Reactions,*
Animation
*Surface Area Affects Reactions,*
Demonstration

**CD-ROM**
**ExamView® Pro**
**Testmaker**

**CD-ROM**
**Interactive Chalkboard**

**CD-ROM**
**TeacherWorks™**

## Multiple Learning Styles

Look for the following icons for strategies that emphasize different learning modalities.

**Kinesthetic**
Differentiated Instruction, p. 540; Extension,
p. 545

**Visual-Spatial**
Differentiated Instruction, pp. 533, 534; Extension,
p. 535; Portfolio, p. 538

**Interpersonal**
Extension, p. 541

**Intrapersonal**
Differentiated Instruction, p. 543; Chemistry
Journal, p. 544; Extension, p. 547

**Linguistic**
Chemistry Journal, pp. 530, 538, 546;
Differentiated Instruction, p. 548

**Logical-Mathematical**
Chemistry Journal, p. 531

## Key to Teaching Strategies

 **L1** Level 1 activities should be appropriate for students with
learning difficulties.

**L2** Level 2 activities should be within the ability range of
all students.

**L3** Level 3 activities are designed for above-average students.

**ELL** ELL activities should be within the ability range of
English Language Learners.

**COOP LEARN** Cooperative Learning activities are designed
for small group work.

 **P** These strategies represent student products that can be
placed into a best-work portfolio.

 These strategies are useful in a block scheduling format.

## Assessment Planner

**Portfolio Assessment**
Assessment, TWE, p. 541
Demonstration, TWE, p. 537
Portfolio, TWE, pp. 538, 553

**Performance Assessment**
Assessment, TWE, pp. 534,
542, 549
Discovery Lab, SE, p. 529
MiniLab, SE, p. 539
ChemLab, SE, pp. 550–551

**Knowledge Assessment**
Assessment, TWE, pp. 531,
532, 535, 537, 545

**Section Assessment, SE,**
pp. 535, 541, 545, 549
**Chapter Assessment, SE,**
pp. 554–557

**Skill Assessment**
MiniLab, TWE, p. 539
ChemLab, TWE, p. 551
Problem-Solving Lab, TWE,
p. 533

## Tying to Previous Knowledge

Have students review the following concepts before studying this chapter.
Chapter 10: chemical reactions, equations for chemical reactions
Chapter 14: gas laws
Chapter 15: molarity

## Using the Photo

Ask students why NASA engineers use liquid rather than gaseous reactants (hydrogen and oxygen) to power the space shuttle's booster rockets. The two elements are much denser in the liquid state than in the gaseous state. Therefore, many more reacting $H_2$ and $O_2$ molecules come into contact per unit time, greatly increasing the rate at which energy is released to propel the shuttle into orbit.

**with Image Bank**

### PowerPoint® Presentations

This CD-ROM is an editable Microsoft® PowerPoint® presentation that includes:
• Section presentations
• Section checks
• Image bank
• Links to Chemistry Online
• All transparencies
• Animations
• Audio

**National Science Content Standards**

**Pages 528–529**
UCP.2, UCP.3; A.1; B.3; E.2

# Reaction Rates

## What You'll Learn

▶ You will investigate a model describing how chemical reactions occur as a result of collisions.
▶ You will compare the rates of chemical reactions under varying conditions.
▶ You will calculate the rates of chemical reactions.

## Why It's Important

Perhaps someday you'll be involved with the space program. Rockets, along with their crews and cargo, are propelled into space by the result of a chemical reaction. An understanding of reaction rates is the tool that allows us to control chemical reactions and use them effectively.

**Chemistry Online**

Visit the Chemistry Web site at **chemistrymc.com** to find links about reaction rates.

This launch of the Mars Exploration Rover *Spirit* in June 2003 propelled the robot to its successful touchdown on Mars in January 2004.

## DISCOVERY LAB

### Purpose

Students will observe how an enzyme increases the rate of a chemical reaction.

### Safety and Disposal

The spent hydrogen peroxide/yeast mixture can be flushed down the drain with water.

### Teaching Strategies

• Describe yeast metabolism and explain how yeast cause bread to rise.
• Continue to develop the concept of enzymes acting as catalysts in biological functions. Also discuss chemical catalysts in other every-day situations.
• See page 528C for preparation of solutions.

## DISCOVERY LAB

### Speeding Reactions

**M**any chemical reactions occur so slowly that you don't even know they are happening. For some reactions, it is possible to alter the reaction speed using another substance.

#### Safety Precautions

 Always use safety goggles and an apron in the lab.

#### Procedure

1. Create a "before and after" table and record your observations.
2. Pour about 10 mL of hydrogen peroxide into a small beaker or cup. Observe the hydrogen peroxide.
3. Add a "pinch" (1/8 tsp) of yeast to the hydrogen peroxide. Stir gently with a toothpick and observe the mixture again.

#### Analysis

Into what two products does hydrogen peroxide decompose? Why aren't bubbles produced in step 1? What is the function of the yeast?

**Materials**
hydrogen peroxide
beaker or cup
baker's yeast
toothpicks

---

# A Model for Reaction Rates

## Objectives

- **Calculate** average rates of chemical reactions from experimental data.
- **Relate** rates of chemical reactions to collisions between reacting particles.

## Vocabulary

reaction rate
collision theory
activated complex
transition state
activation energy

One of the most spectacular chemical reactions, the one between liquid hydrogen and liquid oxygen, provides the energy to launch rockets into space as shown on the opposite page. This reaction is fast and exothermic. Yet other reactions and processes you're familiar with, such as the hardening of concrete or the formation of fossil fuels, occur at considerably slower rates. The **DISCOVERY LAB** for this chapter emphasized that the speed at which a reaction occurs can vary if other substances are introduced into the reaction. In this section, you'll learn about a model that scientists use to describe and calculate the rates at which chemical reactions occur.

## Expressing Reaction Rates

As you know, some chemical reactions are fast and others are slow; however, *fast* and *slow* are inexact, relative terms. Chemists, engineers, medical researchers, and others often need to be more specific.

Think about how you express speed or rate in the situations shown in **Figure 17-1** on the next page. The speed of the sprinter on the track team may be expressed as meters per second. The speed at which the hiker moves might be expressed differently, perhaps as meters per minute. We generally define the average rate of an action or process to be the change in a given quantity during a specific period of time. Recall from your study of math that the Greek letter delta ($\Delta$) before a quantity indicates a change in the quantity. In equation form, average rate or speed is written as

$$\text{Average rate} = \frac{\Delta \text{quantity}}{\Delta t}$$

17.1 A Model for Reaction Rates **529**

---

### Focus Transparency

Before presenting the lesson, display **Section Focus Transparency 64** on the overhead projector. Have students answer the accompanying questions using **Section Focus Transparency Master 64.** **L1** **ELL**

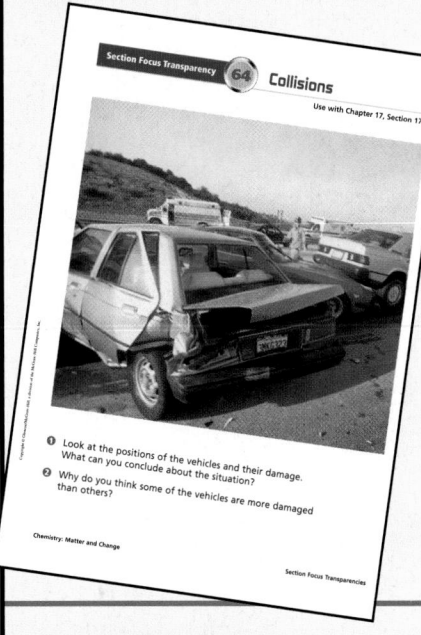

### Chapter Themes

The following themes from the National Science Education Standards are covered in this chapter. Refer to page 4T of the Teacher Guide for an explanation of the correlations.
Systems, order, and organization (UCP.1)
Evidence, models, and explanation (UCP.2)
Change, constancy, and measurement (UCP.3)
Form and function (UCP.5)

### Resource Manager

**Study Guide for Content Mastery,** pp. 97–98 **L2**
**Solving Problems: A Chemistry Handbook,** Section 17.1 **L2**
**Section Focus Transparency 64 and Master** **L1** **ELL**

---

### Expected Results
The hydrogen peroxide is clear and colorless. When yeast is added, bubbles form. After a short while, the mixture also starts to foam.

### Analysis
Hydrogen peroxide decomposes into water and oxygen. Even though the hydrogen peroxide is decomposing in step 1, decomposition is occurring so slowly that oxygen bubbles cannot be seen. The yeast contain an enzyme that speeds up the decomposition of hydrogen peroxide.

Bring a portable microwave oven and a bag of uncooked, unopened microwave popcorn into the classroom. (If you cannot bring a microwave oven into the classroom to perform the demonstration, bring a bag of popped corn and give students the popping time.) Following the instructions on the oven and on the bag of popcorn, pop the corn and have students time the process from the first "pop" to the last. After the popped corn has cooled, help students understand the nature of reaction rates by having them open the bag, count the number of popped kernels, and calculate the average popping rate expressed in kernels per second.

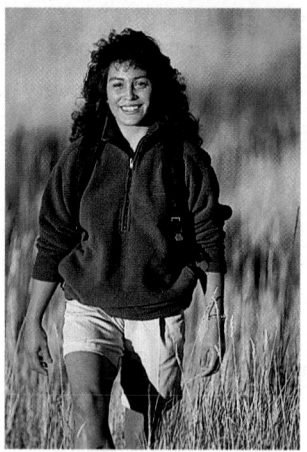

**Figure 17-1**

The average rate of travel for these activities is based on the change in distance over time. Similarly, the reaction rate is based on the change in concentration over time.

For chemical reactions, this equation defines the average rate at which reactants produce products, which is the amount of change of a reactant in a given period of time. Most often, chemists are concerned with changes in the molar concentration (mol/L, $M$) of a reactant or product during a reaction. Therefore, the **reaction rate** of a chemical reaction is stated as the change in concentration of a reactant or product per unit time, expressed as mol/(L·s). Brackets around the formula for a substance denote the molar concentration. For example, $[NO_2]$ represents the molar concentration of $NO_2$.

It's important to understand that reaction rates are determined experimentally by measuring the concentrations of reactants and/or products in an actual chemical reaction. Reaction rates cannot be calculated from balanced equations as stoichiometric amounts can.

Suppose you wish to express the average rate of the reaction

$$CO(g) + NO_2(g) \rightarrow CO_2(g) + NO(g)$$

during the time period beginning at time $t_1$ and ending at time $t_2$. Calculating the rate at which the products of the reaction are produced results in a reaction rate having a positive value. The rate calculation based on the production of NO will have the form

$$\text{Average reaction rate} = \frac{[NO] \text{ at time } t_2 - [NO] \text{ at time } t_1}{t_2 - t_1} = \frac{\Delta[NO]}{\Delta t}$$

For example, if the concentration of NO is $0.00M$ at time $t_1 = 0.00$ s and $0.010M$ two seconds after the reaction begins, the following calculation gives the average rate of the reaction expressed as moles of NO produced per liter per second.

$$\text{Average reaction rate} = \frac{0.010M - 0.000M}{2.00 \text{ s} - 0.00 \text{ s}}$$

$$= \frac{0.010M}{2.00 \text{ s}} = 0.0050 \text{ mol/(L·s)}$$

Notice how the units calculate:

$$\frac{M}{s} = \frac{\text{mol/L}}{s} = \frac{\text{mol}}{L} \cdot \frac{1}{s} = \frac{\text{mol}}{(L \cdot s)}$$

Although mol/L = $M$, chemists typically reserve $M$ to express concentration and mol/(L·s) to express rate.

Alternatively, you can choose to state the rate of the reaction as the rate at which CO is consumed, as shown below:

$$\text{Average reaction rate} = \frac{[CO] \text{ at time } t_2 - [CO] \text{ at time } t_1}{t_2 - t_1} = \frac{\Delta[CO]}{\Delta t}$$

Do you predict a positive or negative value for this reaction? In this case, a negative value indicates that the concentration of CO decreases as the reaction proceeds.

Actually, reaction rates must always be positive. When the rate is measured by the consumption of a reactant, scientists commonly apply a negative sign to the calculation to get a positive reaction rate. Therefore, the following form of the average rate equation is used to calculate the rate of consumption:

$$\text{Average reaction rate} = -\frac{\Delta \text{quantity}}{\Delta t}$$

### Fast and Slow

*Linguistic* Ask students to list in their chemistry journals at least five fast reactions or processes and five slow reactions or processes that they encounter in their daily lives. Have students list reactants and products for at least one of the reactions or processes. If possible, have them obtain information about one reaction or process sufficient to calculate and express an average reaction rate. **L2**

## Calculating Average Reaction Rates

Reaction data for the reaction between butyl chloride ($C_4H_9Cl$) and water ($H_2O$) is given in **Table 17-1**. Calculate the average reaction rate over this time period expressed as moles of $C_4H_9Cl$ consumed per liter per second.

**Table 17-1**

| Molar Concentration of $C_4H_9Cl$ | |
|---|---|
| [$C_4H_9Cl$] at $t = 0.00$ s | [$C_4H_9Cl$] at $t = 4.00$ s |
| 0.220M | 0.100M |

### 1. Analyze the Problem

You are given the initial and final concentrations of $C_4H_9Cl$ and the initial and final times. You can calculate the average reaction rate of the chemical reaction using the change in concentration of butyl chloride in four seconds. In this problem, the reactant butyl chloride is consumed.

**Known**

$t_1 = 0.00$ s
$t_2 = 4.00$ s
[$C_4H_9Cl$] at $t_1 = 0.220M$
[$C_4H_9Cl$] at $t_2 = 0.100M$

**Unknown**

Average reaction rate = ? mol/(L·s)

### 2. Solve for the Unknown

Write the equation for the average reaction rate, insert the known quantities, and perform the calculation.

$$\text{Average reaction rate} = -\frac{[C_4H_9Cl] \text{ at time } t_2 - [C_4H_9Cl] \text{ at time } t_1}{t_2 - t_1}$$

$$= -\frac{0.100M - 0.220M}{4.00 \text{ s} - 0.00 \text{ s}}$$

$$(\text{Substitute units}) = -\frac{0.100 \text{ mol/L} - 0.220 \text{ mol/L}}{4.00 \text{ s} - 0.00 \text{ s}}$$

$$= -\frac{-0.120 \text{ mol/L}}{4.00 \text{ s}}$$

$$= 0.0300 \text{ mol/(L·s)}$$

### 3. Evaluate the Answer

The average reaction rate of 0.0300 moles $C_4H_9Cl$ consumed per liter per second seems reasonable based on start and end amounts. The answer is correctly expressed in three significant figures.

## PRACTICE PROBLEMS

Use the data in the following table to calculate the average reaction rates.

| Experimental Data for $H_2 + Cl_2 \rightarrow 2HCl$ | | | |
|---|---|---|---|
| Time (s) | [$H_2$] (*M*) | [$Cl_2$] (*M*) | [HCl] (*M*) |
| 0.00 | 0.030 | 0.050 | 0.000 |
| 4.00 | 0.020 | 0.040 | 0.020 |

**1.** Calculate the average reaction rate expressed in moles $H_2$ consumed per liter per second.

**2.** Calculate the average reaction rate expressed in moles $Cl_2$ consumed per liter per second.

**3.** Calculate the average reaction rate expressed in moles HCl produced per liter per second.

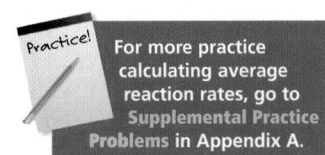

Practice! For more practice calculating average reaction rates, go to **Supplemental Practice Problems** in Appendix A.

---

## Assessment

**Knowledge** For the reaction A + 2B → 3C at time = 0, [A] = 2.00 mol/L, [B] = 4.00 mol/L, and [C] = 0.00 mol/L. At time = 3.00 minutes, [A] has dropped to 0.50 mol/L. Have students calculate and express the rate of the reaction over the 3.00-minute time interval in mol A consumed/(L·min), mol B consumed/(L·min), and mol C produced/(L·min). Rate = 0.500 mol A/(L·min); Rate = 1.00 mol B/(L·min); Rate = 1.50 mol C/(L·min) **L2**

## Practice PROBLEMS

Have students refer to Appendix D for complete solutions to Practice Problems.

**1.** 0.0025 mol/(L·s)
**2.** 0.0025 mol/(L·s)
**3.** 0.0050 mol/(L·s)

---

## CHEMISTRY JOURNAL

### Miles per Gallon and Miles per Dollar

*Logical-Mathematical* To give students experience in stating the change of one quantity in proportion to the change of another, ask them to keep track of the miles driven, gallons of gasoline consumed, and cost of gasoline for an automobile for one week. Then, have them calculate the automobile's mileage in miles driven per gallon consumed and cost to drive in miles driven per dollar spent (gasoline only). If a student's family has more than one automobile, ask him or her to keep records for all the vehicles and compare the mileage and cost-to-drive figures. Data and calculations may be placed in students' portfolios. **L2 P**

National Science Content Standards
Pages 530–531
UCP.2, UCP.3; B.3

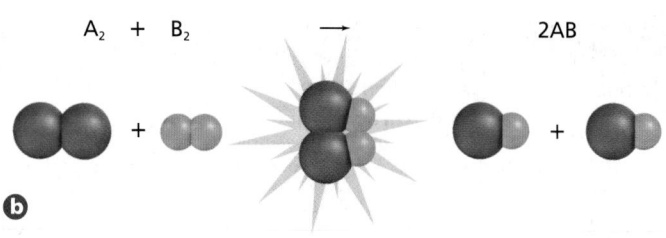

$$A_2 + B_2 \longrightarrow 2AB$$

**ⓑ**

**Figure 17-2**

**ⓐ** The product of a demolition derby, the crunch of metal, is the result of collisions between the cars. **ⓑ** The product of a chemical reaction is the result of collisions between atoms, ions, and molecules. Refer to **Table C-1** in Appendix C for a key to atom color conventions.

**Table 17-2**

| Collision Theory Summary |
|---|
| 1. Reacting substances (atoms, ions, or molecules) must collide. |
| 2. Reacting substances must collide with the correct orientation. |
| 3. Reacting substances must collide with sufficient energy to form the activated complex. |

## The Collision Theory

You have learned that reaction rates are calculated from experimental data. But what are we actually measuring with these calculations? Looking at chemical reactions from the molecular level will provide a clearer picture of exactly what reaction rates measure.

Have you ever seen a demolition derby in which the competing vehicles are constantly colliding? Each collision may result in the demolition of one or more vehicles as shown in **Figure 17-2a**. The reactants in a chemical reaction must also come together in order to form products, as shown in **Figure 17-2b**. The **collision theory** states that atoms, ions, and molecules must collide in order to react. The collision theory, summarized in **Table 17-2**, explains why reactions occur and how the rates of chemical reactions can be modified.

Consider the reaction between hydrogen gas ($H_2$) and oxygen gas ($O_2$).

$$2H_2 + O_2 \rightarrow 2H_2O$$

According to the collision theory, $H_2$ and $O_2$ molecules must collide in order to react and produce $H_2O$. Now look at the reaction between carbon monoxide (CO) gas and nitrogen dioxide ($NO_2$) gas at a temperature above 500 K.

$$CO(g) + NO_2(g) \rightarrow CO_2(g) + NO(g)$$

These molecules collide to produce carbon dioxide ($CO_2$) gas and nitrogen monoxide (NO) gas. However, detailed calculations of the number of molecular collisions per second yield a puzzling result—only a small fraction of collisions produce reactions. In this case, other factors must be considered.

**Orientation and the activated complex** Why don't the $NO_2$ and CO molecules shown in **Figure 17-3a** and **b** react when they collide? Analysis of this example indicates that in order for a collision to lead to a reaction, the carbon atom in a CO molecule must contact an oxygen atom in an $NO_2$ molecule at the instant of impact. Only in that way can a temporary bond between the carbon atom and an oxygen atom form. The collisions shown in **Figure 17-3a** and **b** do not lead to reactions because the molecules collide with unfavorable orientations. That is, because a carbon atom does not contact an oxygen atom at the instant of impact, the molecules simply rebound.

When the orientation of colliding molecules is correct, as **Figure 17-3c** illustrates, a reaction occurs as an oxygen atom is transferred from an $NO_2$ molecule to a CO molecule. A short-lived, intermediate substance is formed. The intermediate substance, in this case OCONO, is called an activated complex. An **activated complex** is a temporary, unstable arrangement of atoms that may form products or may break apart to re-form the reactants. Because the activated complex is as likely to form reactants as it is to form products, it is sometimes referred to as the **transition state**. An activated complex is the first step leading to the resulting chemical reaction.

---

**CULTURAL DIVERSITY**

## Ultrafast Reaction Rates

Ahmed Zewail, an Egyptian-born professor of chemistry and physics at California Institute of Technology, won the 1999 Nobel Prize in chemistry for his development of laser techniques that enable scientists to measure the rates of ultrafast reactions and see the movements of atoms. Zewail uses ultrafast laser pulses that, acting like a strobe light, capture changes in molecular structure at intervals just under ten femtoseconds. With this technique, scientists can directly observe phenomena such as bond breaking, bond making, short-lived intermediates, and transition states.

Zewail's techniques can be applied to gases, liquids, solids, clusters of atoms and molecules, surfaces, catalysts, polymers, and biological systems such as proteins and DNA.

Collision — Rebound
**Incorrect orientation**

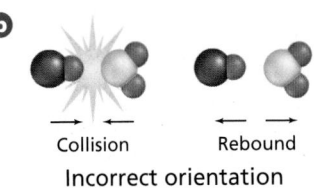

Collision — Rebound
**Incorrect orientation**

Collision — Activated complex — Products
**Correct orientation**

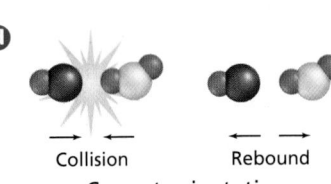

Collision — Rebound
**Correct orientation**
**Insufficient energy**

**Figure 17-3**

The collisions in ⓐ and ⓑ do not result in a reaction because the molecules are not in position to form bonds. The molecules in ⓒ are in the correct orientation when they collide, and a reaction occurs. The molecules in ⓓ are also in the correct positions on collision, but insufficient energy at the point of collision prevents a chemical reaction.

**Activation energy and reaction** The collision depicted in **Figure 17-3d** does not lead to a reaction for a different reason. Although the CO and $NO_2$ molecules collide with a favorable orientation, no reaction occurs because they collide with insufficient energy to form the activated complex. The minimum amount of energy that reacting particles must have to form the activated complex and lead to a reaction is called the **activation energy**, $E_a$.

Activation energy has a direct influence on the rate of a reaction. A high $E_a$ means that relatively few collisions will have the required energy to produce the activated complex and the reaction rate will be low. On the other hand, a low $E_a$ means that more collisions will have sufficient energy to react, and the reaction rate will be higher. The **problem-solving LAB** below emphasizes this fact. It might be helpful to think of this relationship in terms of a person pushing a heavy cart up a hill. If the hill is high, a substantial amount of energy and effort will be required to move the cart and it will take a long time to get it to the top. If the hill is low, less energy will be required and the task will be accomplished faster.

# problem-solving LAB

## Speed and Energy of Collision

**Designing an Experiment** Controlling the rate of a reaction is common in your everyday experience. Consider two of the major appliances in your kitchen: a refrigerator slows down chemical processes that cause food to spoil and an oven speeds up chemical processes that cause foods to cook. Petroleum and natural gases require a spark to run your car's engine and heat your home.

## Analysis

According to collision theory, reactants must collide with enough energy in order to react. Recall from the kinetic-molecular theory that mass and velocity determine the kinetic energy of a parti-

cle. In addition, temperature is a measure of the average kinetic energy of the particles in a sample of matter. According to kinetic-molecular theory, how are the frequency and energy of collisions between gas particles related to temperature?

## Thinking Critically

How would you design an experiment with a handful of marbles and a shoe box lid to simulate the range of speeds among a group of particles at a given temperature? How would you model an increase in temperature? Describe how your marble model would demonstrate the relationship between temperature and the frequency and energy of the collisions among a group of particles.

**Figure 17-4** Point out to students that the energy diagram shown in Figure 17-5 is simply the reverse of the reaction described in Figure 17-4 written in the forward direction. The higher energy barrier in Figure 17-5 indicates that the reverse reaction's activation energy is greater than that of the forward reaction. Explain that this factor favors the forward reaction (17-4) over the reverse reaction. Remind them also that the forward reaction is exothermic, which, as they learned in Chapter 16, also favors the forward reaction.

## Assessment

**Performance** Have students draw a general energy diagram for an endothermic reaction, being sure to include an activation energy barrier. Ask them which reaction (forward or reverse) has the greater activation energy. The forward reaction has the greater activation energy. Use the Performance Task Assessment List for Scientific Drawing in **PASC**, p. 55.

## GLENCOE TECHNOLOGY

**CD-ROM**
**Chemistry: Matter and Change**
Animation: *Exothermic and Endothermic Reactions*

National Science Content Standards

Pages 534–535
UCP.2, UCP.3; B.3, B.4, B.5, B.6

**Figure 17-4**

In an exothermic reaction, molecules collide with enough energy to overcome the activation energy barrier, form an activated complex, then release energy and form products at a lower energy level.

**Figure 17-4** shows the energy diagram for the progress of the reaction between carbon monoxide and nitrogen dioxide. Does this energy diagram look somewhat different from those you studied in Chapter 16? Why? In addition to the energies of the reactants and products, this diagram shows the activation energy of the reaction. Activation energy can be thought of as a barrier the reactants must overcome in order to form the products. In this case, the CO and $NO_2$ molecules collide with enough energy to overcome the barrier, and the products formed lie at a lower energy level. Do you recall that reactions that lose energy, such as this example, are called exothermic reactions?

For many reactions, the process from reactants to products is reversible. **Figure 17-5** shows the reverse endothermic reaction between $CO_2$ and NO to reform CO and $NO_2$. In this reverse reaction, the reactants, which are the molecules that were formed in the exothermic forward reaction, lie at a low energy level and must overcome a significant activation energy to reform CO and $NO_2$. This requires an input of energy. If this reverse reaction is achieved, CO and $NO_2$ again lie at a high energy level.

**Figure 17-5**

In the reverse endothermic reaction, the reactant molecules lying at a low energy level must absorb energy to overcome the activation energy barrier and form high-energy products.

## DIFFERENTIATED INSTRUCTION

### Hearing Impaired

*Visual-Spatial* Have hearing impaired students use molecular models to depict the reactants, activated complex, and products for the favorable collision orientation between a carbon monoxide molecule and a nitrogen dioxide molecule. Also, have them correlate the models of reactants, activated complex, and products with the appropriate locations on a chalkboard version of the reaction's energy diagram, such as the one shown in Figure 17-4. **L2** **ELL**

**The influence of spontaneity** Recall from Chapter 16 that reaction spontaneity is related to change in free energy, $\Delta G$. If $\Delta G$ is negative, the reaction is spontaneous under the conditions specified. If $\Delta G$ is positive, the reaction is not spontaneous. Let's now consider whether spontaneity has any effect on reaction rates. Are more spontaneous reactions faster than less spontaneous ones?

To investigate the relationship between spontaneity and reaction rate, consider the following gas-phase reaction between hydrogen and oxygen.

$$2H_2(g) + O_2(g) \rightarrow 2H_2O(g)$$

Here, $\Delta G = -458$ kJ at 298 K (25°C) and 1 atm pressure. Because $\Delta G$ is negative, the reaction is spontaneous. For the same reaction, $\Delta H = -484$ kJ, which means that the reaction is highly exothermic. You can examine the speed of this reaction by filling a tape-wrapped soda bottle with stoichiometric quantities of the two gases—two volumes hydrogen and one volume oxygen. A thermometer in the stopper allows you to monitor the temperature inside the bottle. As you watch for evidence of a reaction, the temperature remains constant for hours. Have the gases escaped? Or have they simply failed to react? If you remove the stopper and hold a burning splint to the mouth of the bottle, a reaction occurs explosively. Clearly, the hydrogen and oxygen gases have not escaped from the bottle. Yet they did not react noticeably until you supplied additional energy in the form of a lighted splint. The example shown in **Figure 17-6** illustrates this same phenomenon. The soap bubbles you see billowing from the bowl are filled with hydrogen. When the lighted splint introduces additional energy, an explosive reaction occurs between the hydrogen that was contained in the bubbles and oxygen in the air.

As these examples show, reaction spontaneity in the form of $\Delta G$ implies *absolutely nothing* about the speed of the reaction; $\Delta G$ merely indicates the natural tendency for a reaction or process to proceed. Factors other than spontaneity, however, do affect the rate of a chemical reaction. These factors are keys in controlling and using the power of chemistry.

**Figure 17-6**

ⓐ Although the reaction of hydrogen and oxygen is spontaneous, the combination does not produce an obvious reaction when mixed.
ⓑ If an additional form of energy is introduced to the same spontaneous reaction, the reaction rate increases significantly.

## 3 Assess
### Check for Understanding
Ask students to identify which condition of the collision theory is related to the reaction's activation energy and relate how that condition explains why $H_2$ and $O_2$ molecules may not react. Activation energy is related to the fact that the molecules may collide with insufficient energy to form the activated complex.

### Reteach
Have students relate the following three reasons why a dart thrown at a target board may not score a 10 (by analogy) to the three reasons that $H_2$ and $O_2$ molecules may not react.
1) The dart misses the 10 area on the target. The molecules may not collide.
2) The fins of the dart (rather than the point) hit the target. The molecules may collide with an incorrect orientation.
3) The dart's speed is so low that it bounces off the target. The molecules may collide with insufficient energy to form the activated complex.

### Extension
**Visual-Spatial** Ask a group of students to devise a setup that demonstrates activation energy using small model cars and a flexible track. L2 ELL

✔ **Assessment**
**Knowledge** Ask students to use the following data to calculate the average speed of an automobile using the equation for average rate. The automobile travels 129 km in 3.5 hours. 37 km/h

## Section 17.1 Assessment

4. What does the reaction rate indicate about a particular chemical reaction?

5. How is the rate of a chemical reaction usually expressed?

6. What is the collision theory, and how does it relate to reaction rates?

7. According to the collision theory, what must happen in order for two molecules to react?

8. How is the speed of a chemical reaction related to the spontaneity of the reaction?

9. **Thinking Critically** How would the rate of the reaction $2H_2(g) + O_2(g) \rightarrow 2H_2O(g)$ stated as the consumption of hydrogen compare with the rate stated as the consumption of oxygen?

10. **Interpreting Scientific Illustrations** Based on your analysis of **Figures 17-4** and **5**, how does $E_a$ for the reaction $CO + NO_2 \leftarrow CO_2 + NO$ (the reverse reaction) compare with that of the reaction $CO + NO_2 \rightarrow CO_2 + NO$ (the forward reaction)?

 chemistrymc.com/self_check_quiz

17.1 A Model for Reaction Rates    **535**

## Section 17.1 Assessment

4. The reaction rate tells how fast or slowly the reaction occurs.
5. The rate of a chemical reaction is usually expressed as change in concentration of a reactant or product per unit time.
6. The collision theory states that atoms, ions, and molecules must collide in order to react. The theory explains why reactions occur and how reaction rates can be modified.
7. The molecules must collide, collide with the correct orientation, and collide with sufficient energy to form the activated complex.
8. The speed of a chemical reaction is unrelated to the spontaneity of the reaction.
9. The rate stated as the consumption of hydrogen would be twice the rate stated as the consumption of oxygen.
10. $E_a$ for the reverse reaction is greater than $E_a$ for the forward reaction.

# Factors Affecting Reaction Rates

### Focus Transparency

Before presenting the lesson, display **Section Focus Transparency 65** on the overhead projector. Have students answer the accompanying questions using **Section Focus Transparency Master 65. L1 ELL**

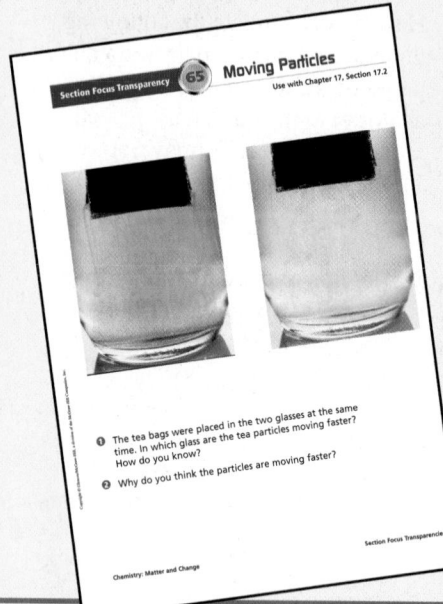

### Objectives

- **Identify** factors that affect the rates of chemical reactions.

- **Explain** the role of a catalyst.

### Vocabulary

catalyst
inhibitor
heterogeneous catalyst
homogeneous catalyst

According to the collision theory, chemical reactions occur when molecules collide in a particular orientation and with sufficient energy to achieve activation energy. You can probably identify chemical reactions that occur fast, such as gasoline combustion, and others that occur more slowly, such as iron rusting. But can the reaction rate of any single reaction vary, or is the reaction rate constant regardless of the conditions? In this section you will learn that the reaction rate for almost any chemical reaction can be modified by varying the conditions of the reaction.

## The Nature of Reactants

An important factor that affects the rate of a chemical reaction is the reactive nature of the reactants. As you know, some substances react more readily than others. For example, calcium and sodium are both reactive metals; however, what happens when each metal is added to water is distinctly different. When a small piece of calcium is placed in cold water, as shown in **Figure 17-7a**, the calcium and water react slowly to form hydrogen gas and aqueous calcium hydroxide.

$$Ca(s) + 2H_2O(l) \rightarrow H_2(g) + Ca(OH)_2(aq)$$

When a small piece of sodium is placed in cold water, the sodium and water react quickly to form hydrogen gas and aqueous sodium hydroxide, as shown in **Figure 17-7b.**

$$2Na(s) + 2H_2O(l) \rightarrow H_2(g) + 2NaOH(aq)$$

Comparing the two equations, it's evident that the reactions are similar. However, the reaction between sodium and water occurs much faster because sodium is more reactive with water than calcium is. In fact, the reaction releases so much heat so quickly that the hydrogen gas ignites as it is formed.

# 2 Teach

### Reinforcement

Remind students that, in general, an element's reactivity is related to its electron configuration. For example, elements whose atoms have one electron in their outermost orbitals and elements whose atoms lack a single electron tend to be extremely reactive.

**Figure 17-7**

The tendency of a substance to react influences the rate of a reaction involving the substance. The more reactive a substance is, the faster the reaction rate.

**536    Chapter 17** Reaction Rates

**536**

### Demonstration

## Surface Area and Reaction Rate

### Purpose

To demonstrate that increasing the surface area of a reactant increases the rate of a chemical reaction

### Materials

lycopodium powder (2 g); ceramic pad; laboratory burner or butane lighter

## Safety Precautions 🔥 🚫 🥽 🧤

**Disposal**  Throw the product in the trash.

### Procedure

Dim the room lights. Using a burner or lighter, attempt to ignite about 2 g of lycopodium powder placed in a small pile on a ceramic pad. Have students observe that there is no reaction. Then lift the pad containing the powder about 40 cm above the burner flame and turn the pad over. **CAUTION:** *The falling*

**Figure 17-8**

**ⓐ** The concentration of oxygen in the air surrounding the steel wool is much less than that of the pure oxygen in the flask.
**ⓑ** The higher oxygen concentration accounts for the faster reaction.

## Quick Demo

Pour 25 mL of household vinegar into each of two petri dishes and set the dishes on an overhead projector. With the projector on, simultaneously add 0.1 g of magnesium turnings to one dish and 0.1 g of 20-mesh granular magnesium to the other dish. Because the granular magnesium presents a greater surface area than the magnesium turnings, the granular magnesium's bubbling reaction occurs at a higher rate. The residue from this reaction can be flushed down the drain.

## Concentration

Reactions speed up when the concentrations of reacting particles are increased. One of the fundamental principles of the collision theory is that particles must collide to react. The number of particles in a reaction makes a difference in the rate at which the reaction takes place. Think about a reaction where reactant A combines with reactant B. At a given concentration of A and B, the molecules of A collide with B to produce AB at a particular rate. What happens if the amount of B is increased? Increasing the concentration of B makes more molecules available with which A can collide. Reactant A "finds" reactant B more easily because there are more B molecules in the area, which increases probability of collision, and ultimately increases the rate of reaction between A and B.

Look at the two reactions shown in **Figure 17-8**. Steel wool is first heated over a burner until it is red hot. In **Figure 17-8a**, the hot steel wool reacts with oxygen in the air. How does this reaction compare with the one in **Figure 17-8b**, in which the hot steel wool is lowered immediately into a flask containing nearly 100 percent oxygen—approximately five times the concentration of oxygen in air? Applying the collision theory to this reaction, the higher concentration of oxygen increases the collision frequency between iron atoms and oxygen molecules, which increases the rate of the reaction.

If you have ever been near a person using bottled oxygen or seen an oxygen generator, you may have noticed a sign cautioning against smoking or using open flames. Can you now explain the reason for the caution notice? The high concentration of oxygen could cause a combustion reaction to occur at an explosive rate. The **CHEMLAB** at the end of this chapter gives you an opportunity to further investigate the effect of concentration on reaction rates.

## Surface Area

Now suppose you were to lower a red-hot chunk of steel instead of steel wool into a flask of oxygen gas. The oxygen would react with the steel much more slowly than it would with the steel wool. Using what you know about the collision theory, can you explain why? You are correct if you said that, for the same mass of iron, steel wool has much more surface area than the chunk of steel. The greater surface area of the steel wool allows the oxygen molecules to collide with many more iron atoms per unit of time.

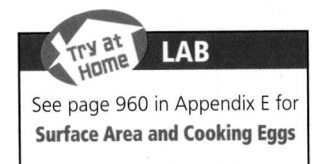

Try at Home **LAB**

See page 960 in Appendix E for **Surface Area and Cooking Eggs**

## Assessment

**Knowledge** Ask students to think of at least one (each) highly reactive and at least one (each) relatively unreactive solid, liquid, and gas. Highly reactive materials: solids—TNT, dynamite, gunpowder; liquids—nitroglycerin, gasoline; gases—hydrogen, methane, propane. Relatively unreactive materials: solids—teflon, treated wood; liquids—water, liquid nitrogen; gases—helium, neon, nitrogen.

## Resource Manager

**Study Guide for Content Mastery, p. 99** L2
**Solving Problems: A Chemistry Handbook, Section 17.2** L2
**Section Focus Transparency 65 and Master** L1 ELL
**Teaching Transparency 50 and Master** L2 ELL

---

*dust will produce a roaring flame.* Have students discuss the effect of increased surface area on reaction rate. Relate this to dust explosions in grain elevators.

**Results**
The lycopodium powder does not ignite until dispersed above the flame. The falling dust ignites explosively.

**Analysis**
**1.** Write a summary statement describing this demonstration. Reaction rate increases when surface area increases.

**2.** Predict which would dissolve first, a sugar cube or the same mass of granulated sugar. the granulated sugar

**3.** What do you believe happens to the collision rate between oxygen molecules and dust particles as the surface area increases? The collision rate increases as surface area increases.

## Assessment

**Portfolio** Have interested students photograph the demonstration. They can add the developed photographs to their portfolios with a written summary of the demonstration. L2 ELL P

ChemLab 17, located at the end of the chapter, can be used at this point in the lesson.

## Identifying Misconceptions

Students often confuse catalysts and intermediates in reaction mechanisms.

**Uncover the Misconception**
Have students examine the three elementary reactions that comprise the mechanism for the complex reaction shown on page 549. Ask if $N_2O_2$ and $N_2O$ are catalysts or intermediates. Both are intermediates because they are produced in one elementary step and consumed in a subsequent step.

**Demonstrate the Concept**
Have students examine the following general reaction mechanism and identify catalysts and intermediates.
$A + B + C \rightarrow X$
$X + D \rightarrow Y + A$
$Y \rightarrow E$
X and Y are intermediates. A is a catalyst.

**Assess New Knowledge**
Have students write the overall reaction for the previous reaction. $B + C + D \rightarrow E$. Ask students to explain why A is a catalyst whereas B and C are reactants. A is a catalyst because it reacts in step 1 of the reaction mechanism and is reformed in step 2. However, B and C are also reactants because they are rearranged into different molecules in the first elementary step and are not reformed.

**Figure 17-9**

Increasing the surface area of reactants provides more opportunity for collisions with other reactants, thereby increasing the reaction rate.

**Figure 17-10**

ⓐ Increasing the temperature of a reaction increases the frequency of collisions and therefore the rate of reaction.
ⓑ Increasing the temperature also raises the kinetic energy of the particles, thus more of the collisions at high temperatures have enough energy to overcome the activation energy barrier and react.

Pulverizing (or grinding) a substance is one way to increase its rate of reaction. This is because, for the same mass, many small particles possess more total surface area than one large particle. So, a spoonful of granulated sugar placed in a cup of water dissolves faster than the same mass of sugar in a single chunk, which has less surface area, as shown in **Figure 17-9**. This example illustrates that increasing the surface area of a reactant does not change its concentration, but it does increase the rate of reaction by increasing the collision rate between reacting particles.

## Temperature

Generally, increasing the temperature at which a reaction occurs increases the reaction rate. For example, you know that the reactions that cause foods to spoil occur much faster at room temperature than when the foods are refrigerated. The graph in **Figure 17-10a** illustrates that increasing the temperature by 10 K can approximately double the rate of a reaction. How can a small increase in temperature have such a significant effect?

As you learned in Chapter 13, increasing the temperature of a substance increases the average kinetic energy of the particles that make up the substance. For that reason, reacting particles collide more frequently at higher temperatures than at lower temperatures. However, that fact alone doesn't account for the increase in reaction rate with increasing temperature. To better understand how reaction rate varies with temperature, examine the graph shown in **Figure 17-10b**. This graph compares the numbers of particles having sufficient energy to react at temperatures $T_1$ and $T_2$, where $T_2$ is greater than $T_1$. The shaded area under each curve represents the number of collisions having energy equal to or greater than the activation energy. The dotted line indicates the activation energy ($E_a$) for the reaction. How do the shaded areas compare? The number of high-energy collisions at the higher temperature, $T_2$, is much greater than at the lower temperature, $T_1$. Therefore, as the temperature increases more collisions result in a reaction.

As you can see, increasing the temperature of the reactants increases the reaction rate because raising the kinetic energy of the reacting particles raises both the collision frequency and the collision energy. You can investigate the relationship between reaction rate and temperature by performing the **miniLAB** for this chapter.

**Reaction Rate and Temperature**

(graph, a) showing Relative reaction rate vs Temperature (K), with points (290 K, 2), (310 K, 8), (320 K, 16), (330 K, 32)

**Particle Energy and Temperature**

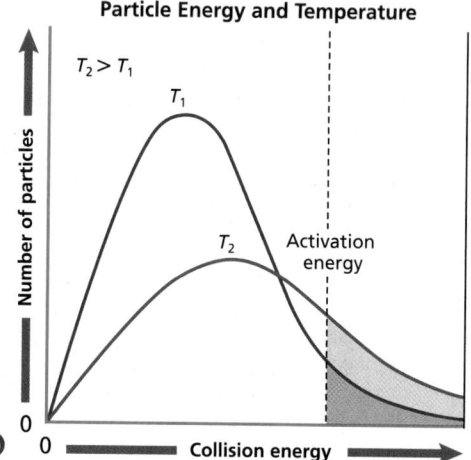

$T_2 > T_1$, curves labeled $T_1$ and $T_2$, Number of particles vs Collision energy, Activation energy

---

## GLENCOE TECHNOLOGY

**CD-ROM**
**Chemistry: Matter and Change**
Demonstration: *Surface Area Affects Reactions*

**538**

---

### CHEMISTRY JOURNAL

**Kitchen Reaction Rates**

*Linguistic* Ask students to keep notes while they watch or assist in the preparation of at least five meals. Their notes should describe ways in which conditions in their kitchens are varied or controlled to influence the rates of reactions during food storage and preparation. Have them include their notes in their chemistry journals. **L2** **ELL**

---

### Portfolio

**Reaction Pathways**

*Visual-Spatial* Have students make general energy diagrams for one of each of the following types of chemical reactions: exothermic, endothermic, and thermoneutral (neither exothermic nor endothermic). The diagrams should show both uncatalyzed and catalyzed reaction pathways. Have students include the diagrams in their portfolios. **L2** **P**

## Examining Reaction Rate and Temperature

**Recognizing Cause and Effect** Several factors affect the rate of a chemical reaction. This lab allows you to examine the effect of temperature on a common chemical reaction.

**Materials** small beaker, thermometer, hot plate, 250-mL beaker, balance, water, effervescent (bicarbonate) tablet, stopwatch or clock with second hand

### Procedure

1. Take a single effervescent tablet and break it into four roughly equal pieces.
2. Measure the mass of one piece of the tablet. Measure 50 mL of room-temperature water (approximately 20°C) into a small cup or beaker. Measure the temperature of the water.
3. With a stopwatch ready, add the piece of tablet to the water. Record the amount of time elapsed between when the tablet hits the water and when you see that all of the piece of tablet has dissolved in the water.
4. Repeat steps 2 and 3 twice more, except use water temperatures of about 50°C and 65°C. Be sure to raise the temperature gradually and maintain the desired temperature (equilibrate) throughout the run.

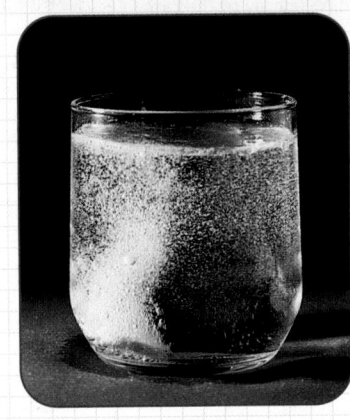

### Analysis

1. Calculate the reaction rate by finding the mass/time for each run.
2. Graph the reaction rate (mass/time) versus temperature for the runs.
3. What is the relationship between reaction rate and temperature for this reaction?
4. Using your graphed data, predict the reaction rate for the reaction carried out at 40°C. Heat and equilibrate the water to 40°C and use the last piece of tablet to test your prediction.
5. How did your prediction for the reaction rate at 40°C compare to the actual reaction rate?

## Catalysts

You've seen that increasing the temperature and/or the concentration of reactants can dramatically increase the rate of a reaction. However, an increase in temperature is not always the best (or most practical) thing to do. For example, suppose that you want to increase the rate of a reaction such as the decomposition of glucose in a living cell. Increasing the temperature and/or the concentration of reactants is not a viable alternative because it might harm or kill the cell.

It is a fact that many chemical reactions in living organisms would not occur quickly enough to sustain life at normal living temperatures if it were not for the presence of enzymes. An enzyme is a type of **catalyst**, a substance that increases the rate of a chemical reaction without itself being consumed in the reaction. Although catalysts are important substances in a chemical reaction, a catalyst does not yield more product and is not included in the product(s) of the reaction. In fact, catalysts are not included in the chemical equation.

How does a catalyst increase the reaction rate? **Figure 17-11** on the next page shows the energy diagram for an exothermic chemical reaction. The red line represents the uncatalyzed reaction pathway—the reaction pathway with no catalyst present. The blue line represents the catalyzed reaction pathway.

17.2 Factors Affecting Reaction Rates **539**

### Purpose

Students will determine the effect of temperature on the rate of a chemical reaction.

### Process Skills

Collecting and interpreting data, making and using graphs, observing, predicting, recognizing cause and effect

### Safety Precautions

Hot plate surface will be hot.

### Teaching Strategies

- Use an effervescent tablet that contains sodium hydrogen carbonate and citric acid or another weak acid.
- Describe the chemical reaction for the tablet: acetyl salicylic acid (aspirin) + citric acid + sodium hydrogen carbonate → sodium citrate + sodium acetyl salicylate + water + carbon dioxide (produces the bubbles).

### Expected Results

See table below.

### Analysis

1. See data table below.
2. 

3. As temperature increases, the reaction rate increases.
4. Answers will vary; however, prediction is about 0.047 g/s.
5. Answers will vary. The value may not be as predicted due to experimental errors.

| Mass of tablet (g) | Reaction time (s) | Reaction rate (g/s) | Temperature (°C) |
| --- | --- | --- | --- |
| 0.92 | 27.56 | 0.033 | 23.6 |
| 0.79 | 13.22 | 0.060 | 53.4 |
| 0.89 | 13.77 | 0.065 | 64.0 |
| 0.54 (Analysis 4 trial) | 11.38 | 0.047 | 40.0 |

### ✓ Assessment

**Skill** Instead of using paper for graphing, have students analyze the data using a graphing calculator or a computer graphing program and submit the results with their reports.

## Applying Chemistry

Explain to students that in the future, automobiles and air conditioners may actually purify our air, consuming ozone and carbon dioxide as they operate! Engelhard Corporation, a New Jersey company that manufactures catalytic converters for automobiles, has developed a catalyst that catalyzes the conversion of ozone ($O_3$) to diatomic oxygen ($O_2$) and the conversion of carbon monoxide (CO) to carbon dioxide ($CO_2$). Because the catalyst works well at warm temperatures, it's possible that it can be painted on automobile radiators, air conditioner compressors, and other devices in which fans move large volumes of air for cooling purposes.

## Using Science Terms

Have students explain the meanings of the terms homogeneous and heterogeneous and give example of homogeneous and heterogeneous systems.

**Resource Manager**

ChemLab and MiniLab
  Worksheets, p. 65 **L2**
Lab Manual, pp. 129–132 **L2**

---

**Figure 17-11**

This energy diagram shows how the activation energy of the catalyzed reaction is lower and therefore the reaction produces the products at a faster rate than the uncatalyzed reaction does.

Note that the activation energy for the catalyzed reaction is much lower than for the uncatalyzed reaction. The lower activation energy for the catalyzed reaction means that more collisions have sufficient energy to initiate reaction. It might help you to visualize this relationship by thinking of the reaction's activation energy as a mountain range to be crossed, as shown in **Figure 17-12**. In this analogy, the tunnel, representing the catalyzed pathway, provides an easier and therefore quicker route to the other side of the mountains.

Another type of substance that affects reaction rates is called an inhibitor. Unlike a catalyst, which speeds up reaction rates, an **inhibitor** is a substance that slows down, or inhibits, reaction rates. Some inhibitors, in fact, actually prevent a reaction from happening at all.

In our fast-paced world, it might seem unlikely that it would be desirable to slow a reaction. But if you think about your environment, you can probably come up with several uses for inhibitors. One of the primary applications for inhibitors is in the food industry, where inhibitors are called preservatives. **Figure 17-13** shows how a commercially available fruit freshener

**Figure 17-12**

Compare the amount of time it would take this train to travel over or around the barrier with the time it takes to travel through the barrier. Obviously, travel is faster through the mountain with the aid of the tunnel.

---

**DIFFERENTIATED INSTRUCTION**

### Visually Impaired

*Kinesthetic* Help visually impaired students understand the effect of a catalyst on activation energy. Have them simulate an exothermic reaction with a large activation energy by first rolling a ball up an incline until it reaches the top and falls or rolls down to a lower level (such as a ramp or hill on school property). Explain that the incline represents the activation energy (an energy barrier that must be overcome to initiate the reaction). The high point on the incline represents the reactants' energy, and the low point represents the products' energy. Then, to simulate the lower activation energy resulting from a catalyst, have students perform the same activity with a lower incline. **L1** **ELL**

**Figure 17-13**

The preservative that was applied to the apple on the left is an inhibitor that reacted with substances in the apple to slow the chemical reactions that cause the apple to brown.

inhibits fruit from browning once it is cut. These preservatives are safe to eat and give food a longer shelf-life. Another inhibitor is the compound maleic hydrazide ($C_4N_2H_4O_2$), which is used as a plant growth inhibitor and weed killer. Inhibitors also are important in biology. For example, a class of inhibitors called monoamine oxidase inhibitors blocks a chemical reaction that can cause depression.

**Heterogeneous and homogeneous catalysts** In order to reduce harmful engine emissions, automobiles manufactured today must have catalytic converters similar to the one described in **How It Works** at the end of the chapter. The most effective catalysts for this application are transition metal oxides and metals such as palladium and platinum. These substances catalyze reactions that convert nitrogen monoxide to nitrogen and oxygen, carbon monoxide to carbon dioxide, and unburned gasoline to carbon dioxide and water. Because the catalysts in a catalytic converter are solids and the reactions they catalyze are gaseous, the catalysts are called heterogeneous catalysts. A **heterogeneous catalyst** exists in a physical state different than that of the reaction it catalyzes. A catalyst that exists in the same physical state as the reaction it catalyzes is called a **homogeneous catalyst**. For example, if both an enzyme and the reaction it catalyzes are in aqueous solution, the enzyme is a homogeneous catalyst.

**Chemistry Online**

**Topic: Industrial Catalysts**
To learn more about industrial catalysts, visit the Chemistry Web site at chemistrymc.com

**Activity:** Research how catalysts help reactions to occur in industry that would not otherwise be able to proceed. Explain how scientists have been able to design materials that will only use catalysts at a certain time.

## Section 17.2 Assessment

**11.** How do temperature, concentration, and surface area affect the rate of a chemical reaction?

**12.** How does the collision model explain the effect of concentration on the reaction rate?

**13.** How does the activation energy of an uncatalyzed reaction compare with that of the catalyzed reaction?

**14. Thinking Critically** For a reaction of A and B that proceeds at a specific rate, $x$ mol/(L·s), what is the effect of decreasing the amount of one of the reactants?

**15. Using the Internet** Conduct Internet research on how catalysts are used in industry, in agriculture, or in the treatment of contaminated soil, waste, or water. Write a short report summarizing your findings about one use of catalysts.

## Section 17.2 Assessment

**11.** The rate of a chemical reaction increases with increasing temperature, increasing concentration, and increasing surface area.

**12.** Increasing reactant concentration increases collision frequency between reactant particles.

**13.** The uncatalyzed reaction has the greater activation energy.

**14.** Decreasing the amount of one or more reactants will decrease the reaction rate.

**15.** Student answers will vary, but they should describe the process and the catalyst chemistry.

## 3 Assess
### Check for Understanding

Provide students with a general energy curve for an endothermic reaction—both catalyzed and uncatalyzed. Check for understanding by asking them to label the following: products, reactants, activated complex, catalyzed reaction pathway, and uncatalyzed reaction pathway.

### Reteach

Ask students to explain the two factors that cause the rate of a chemical reaction to increase with increasing temperature. Increasing the temperature increases both the reacting particles' collision frequency and collision energy.

### Extension

**Interpersonal** Ask students to investigate the reactions used to develop and print photographic film. Have them pay particular attention to how photographers control the rates of these reactions. You may want to have a student or a group of students make a class presentation of their findings. **L2**
**COOP LEARN**

### ✓ Assessment

**Portfolio** Ask students to create a table that summarizes the effects of the following factors on the rates of chemical reactions: reactivity, concentration, surface area, temperature, and catalysts. Have them include the table in their portfolios. **L2** **P**

**National Science Content Standards**

**Pages 538–541**
UCP.2, UCP.3; A.1; B.2, B.3, B.4, B.6; F.1, F.4, F.6

**Section** 17.3   **Reaction Rate Laws**

# 1 Focus

## Focus Transparency

Before presenting the lesson, display **Section Focus Transparency 66** on the overhead projector. Have students answer the accompanying questions using **Section Focus Transparency Master 66.** L1 ELL

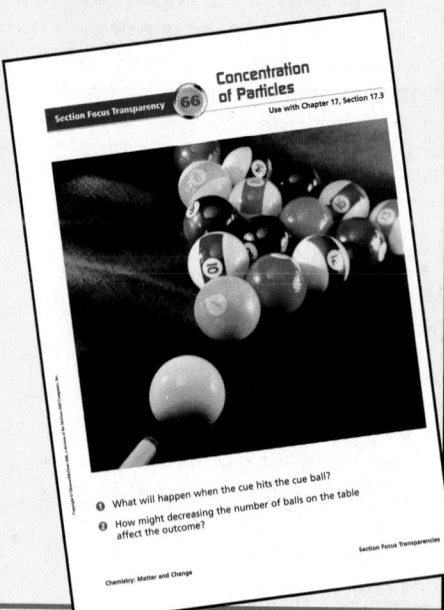

Section Focus Transparency  **66**
Concentration of Particles
Use with Chapter 17, Section 17.3

❶ What will happen when the cue hits the cue ball?

❷ How might decreasing the number of balls on the table affect the outcome?

Chemistry: Matter and Change

Section Focus Transparencies

# 2 Teach

## ✓ Assessment

### Performance

Have students design and carry out an experiment in which they evaluate the effect of vinegar concentration on the rate of the reaction between vinegar, $CH_3COOH(aq)$, and baking soda, $NaHCO_3(s)$. Student experiments may involve diluting vinegar and comparing the rates at which $CO_2(g)$ is produced from given concentrations of vinegar for a given mass of baking soda. Use the Performance Task Assessment List for Designing an Experiment in **PASC**, p. 23.

---

## Objectives

- **Express** the relationship between reaction rate and concentration.

- **Determine** reaction orders using the method of initial rates.

## Vocabulary

rate law
specific rate constant
reaction order
method of initial rates

---

# Reaction Rate Laws

In Section 17.1, you learned how to calculate the average rate of a chemical reaction given the initial and final times and concentrations. The word *average* is important because most chemical reactions slow down as the reactants are consumed. To understand why most reaction rates slow over time, recall that the collision theory states that chemical reactions can occur only when the reacting particles collide and that reaction rate depends upon reactant concentration. As reactants are consumed, fewer particles collide and the reaction slows. Chemists use the concept of rate laws to quantify the results of the collision theory in terms of a mathematical relationship between the rate of a chemical reaction and the reactant concentration.

## Reaction Rate Laws

The equation that expresses the mathematical relationship between the rate of a chemical reaction and the concentration of reactants is called a **rate law**. For example, the reaction $A \rightarrow B$, which is a one-step reaction, has only one activated complex between reactants and products. The rate law for this reaction is expressed as

$$\text{Rate} = k[A]$$

where $k$ is the **specific rate constant**, or a numerical value that relates reaction rate and concentration of reactants at a given temperature. Units for the rate constant include $L/(mol \cdot s)$, $L^2/(mol^2 \cdot s)$, and $s^{-1}$. Depending on the reaction conditions, especially temperature, $k$ is unique for every reaction.

The rate law means that the reaction rate is directly proportional to the molar concentration of A. Thus, doubling the concentration of A will double the reaction rate. Increasing the concentration of A by a factor of 5 will increase the reaction rate by a factor of 5. The specific rate constant, $k$, does not change with concentration; however, $k$ does change with temperature. A large value of $k$ means that A reacts rapidly to form B. What does a small value of $k$ mean?

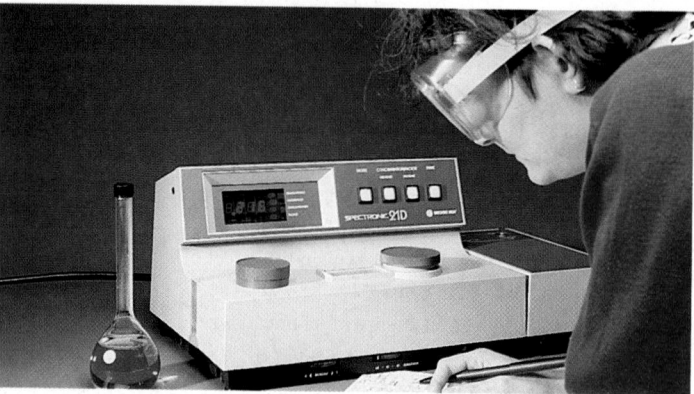

**Figure 17-14**

Specific rate constants are determined experimentally. Scientists have a number of methods at their disposal that can be used to establish $k$ for a given reaction.

ⓐ A spectrophotometer measures the absorption of specific wavelengths of light by a reactant or product as a reaction progresses to determine the specific rate constant for the reaction.

**542     Chapter 17** Reaction Rates

---

## Internet Address Book

**Chemistry Online**

Note Internet addresses that you find useful in the space below for quick reference.

_____

_____

_____

_____

_____

**Reaction order** In the expression Rate = $k$[A], it is understood that the notation [A] means the same as [A]$^1$. In other words, for reactant A, the understood exponent 1 is called the reaction order. The **reaction order** for a reactant defines how the rate is affected by the concentration of that reactant. For example, the rate law for the decomposition of $H_2O_2$ is expressed by the following equation.

$$Rate = k[H_2O_2]$$

Because the reaction rate is directly proportional to the concentration of $H_2O_2$ raised to the first power, $[H_2O_2]^1$, the decomposition of $H_2O_2$ is said to be first order in $H_2O_2$. Because the reaction is first order in $H_2O_2$, the reaction rate changes in the same proportion that the concentration of $H_2O_2$ changes. So if the $H_2O_2$ concentration decreases to one-half its original value, the reaction rate is halved as well.

Recall from Section 17.1 that reaction rates are determined from experimental data. Because reaction order is based on reaction rates, it follows that reaction order also is determined experimentally. Finally, because the rate constant describes the reaction rate, $k$, too, must be determined experimentally. **Figure 17-14** illustrates two of several experimental methods that are commonly used to measure reaction rates.

**Other reaction orders** The overall reaction order of a chemical reaction is the sum of the orders for the individual reactants in the rate law. Many chemical reactions, particularly those having more than one reactant, are not first order. Consider the general form for a chemical reaction with two reactants. In this chemical equation, $a$ and $b$ are coefficients.

$$aA + bB \rightarrow products$$

The general rate law for such a reaction is

$$Rate = k[A]^m[B]^n$$

where $m$ and $n$ are the reaction orders for A and B, respectively. Only if the reaction between A and B occurs in a single step (and with a single activated complex) does $m = a$ and $n = b$. That's unlikely, however, because single-step reactions are uncommon.

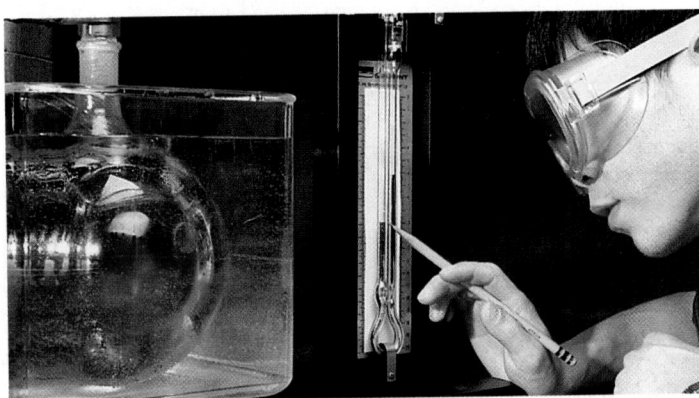

**ⓑ** A manometer measures pressure changes that result from the production of gas as a reaction progresses. The reaction rate is directly proportional to the rate at which the pressure increases.

---

**Math Handbook**

Review direct and inverse relationships in the **Math Handbook** on page 905 of this text.

---

---

---

**DIFFERENTIATED INSTRUCTION**

**Gifted**

*Intrapersonal* Have gifted students create a data table showing initial molar concentrations of substances A and B for three trials in the reaction A + B → C. Give them the rate law Rate = $k$[A]$^2$[B]$^3$ and have them express the reaction rate as moles C produced per liter per second. Data should show that when [A] is doubled, the rate increases by a factor of four; when [B] is doubled, the rate increases by a factor of eight. L3

Lead students through several examples of mathematical operations to be sure they understand how to use exponents in rate laws. Use 0.10 for the rate constant $k$ and initial [A] = 0.50 in the following examples. In each example, [A] is doubled in trial 2.

- Rate = $k$[A] (understood exponent is 1)
  Trial 1: Rate = 0.10(0.50) = 0.050
  Trial 2: Rate = 0.10(1.00) = 0.10
  Point out that doubling [A] doubled the rate because $2^1 = 2$.
- Rate = $k$[A]$^2$
  Trial 1: Rate = 0.10(0.50)$^2$ = 0.025
  Trial 2: Rate = 0.10(1.00)$^2$ = 0.10
  Point out that doubling [A] increased the rate by a factor of four because $2^2 = 4$.
- Rate = $k$[A]$^3$
  Trial 1: Rate = 0.10(0.50)$^3$ = 0.0125
  Trial 2: Rate = 0.10(1.00)$^3$ = 0.10
  Point out that doubling [A] increased the rate by a factor of eight because $2^3 = 8$.

### Practice PROBLEMS

Have students refer to Appendix D for complete solutions to Practice Problems.

**16.** Rate = $k$[A]$^3$
**17.** Rate = $k$[A]$^0$[B] = $k$[B]
**18.** Rate = $k$[CH$_3$CHO]$^2$

The time it takes for bonds to form and break during a chemical reaction is measured in femtoseconds. A femtosecond is one thousandth of a trillionth of a second. Until recently, scientists could only calculate and imagine the actual atomic activity of chemical bonding. In 1999, Dr. Ahmed Zewail of the California Institute of Technology won a Nobel Prize for his achievements in the field of femtochemistry. Zewail has developed an ultrafast laser device that can monitor and record chemical reactions in real time. Zewail's laser "flashes" every ten femtoseconds, allowing chemists to record changes in the wavelengths (colors) that vibrating molecules emitted during the course of a reaction. The changes correspond to bond formation and breakage and are mapped to the various intermediates and products that are formed during a reaction and that were previously impossible to witness.

For example, the reaction between nitrogen monoxide (NO) and hydrogen (H$_2$) is described by the following equation.

$$2NO(g) + 2H_2(g) \rightarrow N_2(g) + 2H_2O(g)$$

This reaction, which occurs in more than one step, has the following rate law.

$$\text{Rate} = k[NO]^2[H_2]$$

This rate law was determined experimentally. The data tell that the rate depends on the concentration of the reactants as follows. If [NO] doubles, the rate quadruples; if [H$_2$] doubles, the rate doubles. The reaction is described as second order in NO, first order in H$_2$, and third order overall because the sum of the orders for the individual reactants (the sum of the exponents) is (2 + 1), or 3.

## Determining Reaction Order

One common experimental method of evaluating reaction order is called the method of initial rates. The **method of initial rates** determines reaction order by comparing the initial rates of a reaction carried out with varying reactant concentrations. To understand how this method works, let's use the general reaction $aA + bB \rightarrow$ products. Suppose that this reaction is carried out with varying concentrations of A and B and yields the initial reaction rates shown in **Table 17-3**.

**Table 17-3**

| | Experimental Initial Rates for $aA + bB \rightarrow$ products | | |
|---|---|---|---|
| Trial | Initial [A] (M) | Initial [B] (M) | Initial Rate (mol/(L·s)) |
| 1 | 0.100 | 0.100 | 2.00 × 10$^{-3}$ |
| 2 | 0.200 | 0.100 | 4.00 × 10$^{-3}$ |
| 3 | 0.200 | 0.200 | 16.0 × 10$^{-3}$ |

Recall that the general rate law for this type of reaction is

$$\text{Rate} = k[A]^m[B]^n$$

To determine $m$, the concentrations and reaction rates in Trials 1 and 2 are compared. As you can see from the data, while the concentration of B remains constant, the concentration of A in Trial 2 is twice that of Trial 1. Note that the initial rate in Trial 2 is twice that of Trial 1. Because doubling [A] doubles the rate, the reaction must be first order in A. That is, because $2^m = 2$, $m$ must equal 1. The same method is used to determine $n$, only this time Trials 2 and 3 are compared. Doubling the concentration of B causes the rate to increase by four times. Because $2^n = 4$, $n$ must equal 2. This information suggests that the reaction is second order in B, giving the following overall rate law.

$$\text{Rate} = k[A]^1[B]^2$$

The overall reaction order is third order (sum of exponents 2 + 1 = 3).

## CHEMISTRY JOURNAL

### Reaction Rate Laws

*Intrapersonal* Have students create a table in their journals in which they describe the effect of doubling, tripling, and quadrupling [A] on the overall rate of chemical reactions having the following rate laws: Rate = $k$[A]$^0$; Rate = $k$[A]; Rate = $k$[A]$^2$; Rate = $k$[A]$^3$. **L2**

## Resource Manager

Teaching Transparency 51 and Master **L2 ELL**
Math Skills Transparency 27 and Master **L2 ELL**
Small-Scale Laboratory Manual, pp. 53–56 **L2**

# PRACTICE PROBLEMS

**16.** Write the rate law for the reaction $aA \rightarrow bB$ if the reaction is third order in A. [B] is not part of the rate law.

**17.** Given the following experimental data, use the method of initial rates to determine the rate law for the reaction $aA + bB \rightarrow$ products. Hint: Any number to the zero power equals one. For example, $(0.22)^0 = 1$ and $(55.6)^0 = 1$.

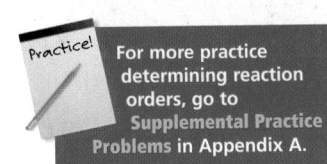

Practice! **For more practice determining reaction orders, go to Supplemental Practice Problems in Appendix A.**

### Practice Problem 17 Experimental Data

| Trial | Initial [A] (M) | Initial [B] (M) | Initial Rate (mol/(L·s)) |
|---|---|---|---|
| 1 | 0.100 | 0.100 | $2.00 \times 10^{-3}$ |
| 2 | 0.200 | 0.100 | $2.00 \times 10^{-3}$ |
| 3 | 0.200 | 0.200 | $4.00 \times 10^{-3}$ |

**18.** Given the following experimental data, use the method of initial rates to determine the rate law for the reaction $CH_3CHO(g) \rightarrow CH_4(g) + CO(g)$.

### Practice Problem 18 Experimental Data

| Trial | Initial [CH₃CHO] (M) | Initial rate (mol/(L·s)) |
|---|---|---|
| 1 | $2.00 \times 10^{-3}$ | $2.70 \times 10^{-11}$ |
| 2 | $4.00 \times 10^{-3}$ | $10.8 \times 10^{-11}$ |
| 3 | $8.00 \times 10^{-3}$ | $43.2 \times 10^{-11}$ |

In summary, the rate law for a reaction relates reaction rate, the rate constant $k$, and the concentration of the reactants. Although the equation for a reaction conveys a great deal of information, it is important to remember that the actual rate law and order of a complex reaction can be determined only by experiment.

## Section 17.3 Assessment

**19.** What does the rate law for a chemical reaction tell you about the reaction?

**20.** Use the rate law equations to show the difference between a first-order reaction having a single reactant and a second-order reaction having a single reactant.

**21.** What relationship is expressed by the specific rate constant for a chemical reaction?

**22. Thinking Critically** When giving the rate of a chemical reaction, explain why it is significant to know that the reaction rate is an average reaction rate.

**23. Designing an Experiment** Explain how you would design an experiment to determine the rate law for the general reaction $aA + bB \rightarrow$ products using the method of initial rates.

chemistrymc.com/self_check_quiz

17.3 Reaction Rate Laws    **545**

---

---

## Section 17.3 Assessment

**19.** The rate law expresses the mathematical relationship between the reaction's rate and the concentrations of reactants.

**20.** First-order reaction: Rate = $k[A]$. Second-order reaction: Rate = $k[A]^2$.

**21.** The specific rate constant, $k$, relates reaction rate and concen-

tration at a specific temperature.

**22.** The rate of a reaction decreases over time as reactant concentrations decrease. Therefore, the rate is an average over time rather than the rate at a given instant.

**23.** Determine the order of reactant A by measuring the reaction rate for

several trials in which [A] is varied while [B] remains constant. Determine the order of reactant B by measuring the reaction rate for several trials in which [B] is varied while [A] remains constant.

**545**

# 1 Focus

## Focus Transparency

Before presenting the lesson, display **Section Focus Transparency 67** on the overhead projector. Have students answer the accompanying questions using **Section Focus Transparency Master 67.** [L1] [ELL]

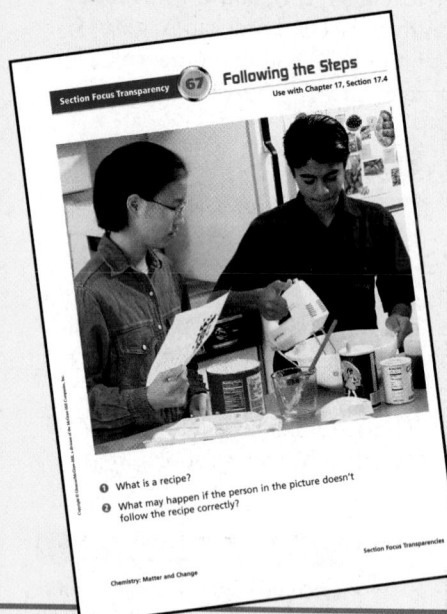

Section Focus Transparency **67**  Following the Steps
Use with Chapter 17, Section 17.4

❶ What is a recipe?

❷ What may happen if the person in the picture doesn't follow the recipe correctly?

Chemistry: Matter and Change                    Section Focus Transparencies

# 2 Teach
## Visual Learning

**Figure 17-15** Review with students how to determine the slope of a straight line, which is constant. That is, $\triangle y/\triangle x$ (in the case of reaction rate, $\triangle[A]/\triangle t$) is the same for any line segment. However, the plot of concentration of a reactant or product over an appreciable time interval will be a curve. Point out that, because the slope of the curve varies, the reaction rate varies. Students can determine the instantaneous reaction rate at any point on the curve by drawing a straight line tangent to the curve at that point and determining the slope of the line.

---

# Instantaneous Reaction Rates and Reaction Mechanisms

## Objectives

- **Calculate** instantaneous rates of chemical reactions.

- **Understand** that many chemical reactions occur in steps.

- **Relate** the instantaneous rate of a complex reaction to its reaction mechanism.

## Vocabulary

instantaneous rate
complex reaction
reaction mechanism
intermediate
rate-determining step

The average reaction rate you learned to calculate in Section 17.3 gives important information about the reaction over a period of time. However, chemists also may need to know at what rate the reaction is proceeding at a specific time. A pharmacist developing a new drug treatment might need to know the progress of a reaction at an exact instant. This information makes it possible to adjust the product for maximum performance. Can you think of other situations where it might be critical to know the specific reaction rate at a given time?

## Instantaneous Reaction Rates

The decomposition of hydrogen peroxide ($H_2O_2$) is represented as follows.

$$2H_2O_2(aq) \rightarrow 2H_2O(l) + O_2(g)$$

For this reaction, the decrease in $H_2O_2$ concentration over time is shown in **Figure 17-15**. The curved line shows how the reaction rate decreases as the reaction proceeds. The **instantaneous rate**, or the rate of decomposition at a specific time, can be determined by finding the slope of the straight line tangent to the curve at that instant. This is because the slope of the tangent to the curve at a particular point is $\Delta[H_2O_2]/\Delta t$, which is one way to express the reaction rate. In other words, the rate of change in $H_2O_2$ concentration relates to one specific point (or instant) on the graph.

Another way to determine the instantaneous rate for a chemical reaction is to use the experimentally determined rate law, given the reactant concentrations and the specific rate constant for the temperature at which the reaction occurs. For example, the decomposition of dinitrogen pentoxide ($N_2O_5$) into nitrogen dioxide ($NO_2$) and oxygen ($O_2$) is given by the following equation.

$$2N_2O_5(g) \rightarrow 4NO_2(g) + O_2(g)$$

**Figure 17-15**

The instantaneous rate for a specific point in the reaction progress can be determined from the tangent to the curve that passes through that point. The equation for the slope of the line ($\Delta y/\Delta x$) is the equation for instantaneous rate in terms of $\Delta[H_2O_2]$ and $\Delta t$:

instantaneous rate $= \dfrac{\Delta[H_2O_2]}{\Delta t}$

**Change in [H₂O₂] with Time**

Instantaneous rate $= \dfrac{\Delta[H_2O_2]}{\Delta t}$

[H₂O₂] (mol/L)

$\Delta[H_2O_2]$

$\Delta t$

Relative time

---

## CHEMISTRY JOURNAL

### Reaction Rates—How Poetic

*Linguistic* Have a contest in which students write creative, multistanza poems that incorporate several facets of reaction rates. For example, you could require that the first stanza begin with the line: Reaction rates, reaction rates... . Have students include the poems in their chemistry journals. Ask a colleague to help you judge the poems and choose winners. After awarding prizes, read the best poems to the class. [L2]

The experimentally determined rate law for this reaction is

$$\text{Rate} = k[N_2O_5]$$

where $k = 1.0 \times 10^{-5} \text{ s}^{-1}$. If $[N_2O_5] = 0.350M$, the instantaneous reaction rate would be calculated as

$$\text{Rate} = (1.0 \times 10^{-5} \text{ s}^{-1})(0.350 \text{ mol/L})$$
$$= 3.5 \times 10^{-6} \text{ mol/(L·s)}$$

## EXAMPLE PROBLEM 17-2

### Calculating Instantaneous Reaction Rates

The following equation is first order in $H_2$ and second order in NO with a rate constant of $2.90 \times 10^2$ (L²/(mol²·s)).

$$2NO(g) + H_2(g) \rightarrow N_2O(g) + H_2O(g)$$

Calculate the instantaneous rate when the reactant concentrations are [NO] = 0.00200$M$ and [$H_2$] = 0.00400$M$.

**1. Analyze the Problem**

The rate law can be expressed by Rate = $k[NO]^2[H_2]$. Therefore, the instantaneous reaction rate can be determined by inserting reactant concentrations and the specific rate constant into the rate law equation.

**Known**

[NO] = 0.00200$M$
[$H_2$] = 0.00400$M$
$k = 2.90 \times 10^2$ (L²/(mol²·s))

**Unknown**

Rate = ? mol/(L·s)

**2. Solve for the Unknown**

Insert the known quantities into the rate law equation.

Rate = $k[NO]^2[H_2]$

Rate = $2.90 \times 10^2$ (L²/(mol²·s))(0.00200 mol/L)²(0.00400 mol/L)

Rate = $4.64 \times 10^{-6}$ mol/(L·s)

**3. Evaluate the Answer**

Are the units correct? Units in the calculation cancel to give mol/(L·s), which is the common unit for the expression of reaction rates. Is the magnitude reasonable? A magnitude of approximately $10^{-6}$ mol/(L·s) fits with the quantities given and the rate law equation.

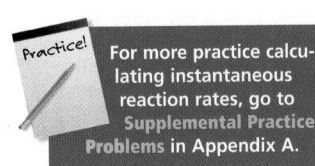

Review solving algebraic equations in the **Math Handbook** on page 897 of this text.

## PRACTICE PROBLEMS

Use the rate law in Example Problem 17-2 and the concentrations given in each practice problem to calculate the instantaneous rate for the reaction between NO and $H_2$.

**24.** [NO] = 0.00500$M$ and [$H_2$] = 0.00200$M$

**25.** [NO] = 0.0100$M$ and [$H_2$] = 0.00125$M$

**26.** [NO] = 0.00446$M$ and [$H_2$] = 0.00282$M$

 For more practice calculating instantaneous reaction rates, go to **Supplemental Practice Problems** in Appendix A.

## Extension

*Intrapersonal* Many reaction rates are determined experimentally using spectrometric, conductometric, or manometric methods. Ask interested students to research these methods and make a class presentation explaining their use.

### Practice PROBLEMS

Have students refer to Appendix D for complete solutions to Practice Problems.

**24.** Rate = $1.45 \times 10^{-5}$ mol/(L·s)

**25.** Rate = $3.63 \times 10^{-5}$ mol/(L·s)

**26.** Rate = $1.63 \times 10^{-5}$ mol/(L·s)

### In-Text Question

**Page 546** Can you think of other situations where it might be critical to know the specific reaction rate at a given time? Possible examples include production situations in which instantaneous rates and manufacturing procedure may affect the product, and cooking where the result and success of the dish may depend on exact cooking time.

### Resource Manager

**Study Guide for Content Mastery**, pp. 101–102 [L2]
**Solving Problems: A Chemistry Handbook**, Section 17.4 [L2]
**Section Focus Transparency 67 and Master** [L1] [ELL]
**Teaching Transparency 52 and Master** [L2] [ELL]
**Lab Manual**, pp. 133–136 [L2]

## Internet Address Book

Note Internet addresses that you find useful in the space below for quick reference.

Chemistry Online

**National Science Content Standards**

Pages 546–547
UCP. 2, UCP.3; B.3

## Careers Using Chemistry

### Food Technologist

*Everyone needs to eat, and in today's fast-paced world, we've become accustomed to having safe, convenient, and nutritious food at our fingertips, ready to toss in the microwave. Food technologists help make nutrition in our fast-paced lifestyle more convenient by developing new ways to process, preserve, package, and store food.*

Food technologists are also called food chemists, food scientists, and food engineers. They find ways to make food products more healthful, more convenient, and better tasting. Part of their job is searching for ways to stop or slow chemical reactions and lengthen the shelf life of food. Food technologists might find careers in the food industry, universities, or the federal government.

**Figure 17-16**

In an automobile assembly plant, the process that is most time consuming limits the production rate. For example, because it takes longer to install the onboard computer system than it takes to attach the hood assembly, the computer installation is a rate-determining step.

# Reaction Mechanisms

Most chemical reactions consist of a sequence of two or more simpler reactions. For example, recent evidence indicates that the reaction $2O_3 \rightarrow 3O_2$ occurs in three steps after intense ultraviolet radiation from the sun liberates chlorine atoms from certain compounds in Earth's stratosphere. Steps 1 and 2 in this reaction may occur simultaneously or in reverse order.

**1.** Chlorine atoms decompose ozone according to the equation
$Cl + O_3 \rightarrow O_2 + ClO$.

**2.** Ultraviolet radiation causes the decomposition reaction $O_3 \rightarrow O_2 + O$.

**3.** ClO produced in the reaction in step 1 reacts with O produced in step 2 according to the equation $ClO + O \rightarrow Cl + O_2$.

Each of the reactions described in steps 1 through 3 is called an elementary step. These three elementary steps comprise the complex reaction $2O_3 \rightarrow 3O_2$. A **complex reaction** is one that consists of two or more elementary steps. The complete sequence of elementary steps that make up a complex reaction is called a **reaction mechanism**. Adding the elementary steps in steps 1 through 3 and canceling formulas that occur in equal amounts on both sides of the reaction arrow produce the net equation for the complex reaction as shown below:

Elementary step: $\cancel{Cl} + O_3 \rightarrow O_2 + \cancel{ClO}$
Elementary step: $O_3 \rightarrow O_2 + \cancel{O}$
Elementary step: $\cancel{ClO} + \cancel{O} \rightarrow \cancel{Cl} + O_2$
Complex reaction: $2O_3 \rightarrow 3O_2$

Because chlorine atoms react in step 1 of the reaction mechanism and are re-formed in step 3, chlorine is said to catalyze the decomposition of ozone. Do you know why? Because ClO and O are formed in the reactions in steps 1 and 2, respectively, and are consumed in the reaction in step 3, they are called intermediates. In a complex reaction, an **intermediate** is a substance produced in one elementary step and consumed in a subsequent elementary step. Catalysts and intermediates do not appear in the net chemical equation.

**Rate-determining step** You have probably heard the expression, "A chain is no stronger than its weakest link." Chemical reactions, too, have a "weakest link" in that a complex reaction can proceed no faster than the slowest of its elementary steps. In other words, the slowest elementary step in a reaction mechanism limits the instantaneous rate of the overall reaction.

## Section 17.4 Assessment

**27.** Insert actual experimental rate constant and reactant concentrations into the rate law, then calculate.

**28.** An elementary reaction occurs in a single step. A complex reaction consists of two or more elementary steps.

**Figure 17-17**

The three peaks in this energy diagram correspond to activation energies for the intermediate steps of the reaction. The middle hump represents the highest energy barrier to overcome; therefore, the reaction involving $N_2O_2 + 2H_2$ is the rate-determining step.

For that reason, the slowest of the elementary steps in a complex reaction is called the **rate-determining step**. **Figure 17-16** illustrates this concept in a manufacturing plant.

To see how the rate-determining step affects reaction rate, again consider the gas-phase reaction between hydrogen and nitrogen monoxide discussed earlier in the chapter.

$$2NO(g) + 2H_2(g) \rightarrow N_2(g) + 2H_2O(g)$$

A proposed mechanism for this reaction consists of the following elementary steps.

$$2NO \rightarrow N_2O_2 \qquad \text{(fast)}$$
$$N_2O_2 + H_2 \rightarrow N_2O + H_2O \quad \text{(slow)}$$
$$N_2O + H_2 \rightarrow N_2 + H_2O \quad \text{(fast)}$$

Although the first and third elementary steps occur relatively fast, the middle step is the slowest, and it limits the overall reaction rate. It is the rate-determining step. The relative energy levels of reactants, intermediates, products, and activated complex are illustrated in **Figure 17-17**.

Chemists can make use of instantaneous reaction rates, reaction orders, and rate-determining steps to develop efficient ways to manufacture products such as pharmaceuticals. By knowing which step of the reaction is slowest, a chemist can work to speed up that rate-determining step and thereby increase the rate of the overall reaction.

## Section 17.4 Assessment

**27.** How can the rate law for a chemical reaction be used to determine an instantaneous reaction rate?

**28.** Compare and contrast an elementary chemical reaction with a complex chemical reaction.

**29.** What is a reaction mechanism? An intermediate?

**30. Thinking Critically** How can you determine whether a product of one of the elementary steps in a complex reaction is an intermediate?

**31. Communicating** How would you explain the significance of the rate-determining step in a chemical reaction?

chemistrymc.com/self_check_quiz 17.4 Instantaneous Reaction Rates and Reaction Mechanisms **549**

**29.** A reaction mechanism is the complete sequence of elementary steps that make up a complex reaction. An intermediate is a substance produced in one elementary step and consumed in a subsequent step.

**30.** The product is consumed in a subsequent elementary step.

**31.** Answers will vary but may include a description of how the rate-determining step limits the reaction rate, an analogy such as the "weakest link," and/or a real-world example.

---

**Performance** Have students use ball-and-stick molecular models to simulate the three-step reaction between monatomic chlorine and ozone. Ask students to demonstrate and explain why Cl is said to catalyze the reaction and why ClO and O are said to be reaction intermediates. Use the Performance Task Assessment List for Model in **PASC**, p. 51. **L1** **ELL**

## 3 Assess
### Check for Understanding

Ask students to explain why the rate of a chemical reaction generally decreases over time. The rate decreases because the reactant concentration(s) decreases.

### Reteach

Reinforce the concept that most reactions occur in a series of steps called a reaction mechanism. Point out that a reaction may have several different mechanisms. In particular, explain that the mechanism for a complex, catalyzed reaction always differs from that of the uncatalyzed reaction.

### Extension

Physicians and other healthcare personnel must have a good understanding of metabolic reactions and the conditions that affect them. Ask a healthcare professional to make a class presentation on this topic.

**Knowledge** Ask students to differentiate between an elementary reaction and a complex reaction and to give one example of each. An elementary reaction occurs in a single step; a complex reaction in two or more elementary steps. Examples will vary.

## Preparation

**Time Allotment**
One laboratory period

**Process Skills**
Observing and inferring, sequencing, collecting data, interpreting data, hypothesizing

**Safety Precautions**
Remind students: Wear an apron and goggles. Never pipette any chemical by mouth. Use a safety pipette filler.

**Disposal**
Neutralize the acid from the test tubes with baking soda ($NaHCO_3$) before rinsing it down the drain with water. $MgCl_2$ solution can be flushed down the drain.

**Preparation of Solutions**
Concentrated hydrochloric acid (HCl (aq)) is $12M$. Dilute it with an equal volume of distilled water to produce approximately $6M$ HCl. See page 528C for preparation of solutions.

## Pre-Lab

4. Students' hypotheses should reflect that the reaction rate is faster with higher concentration; slower with lower concentration.
5. The amount of Mg is the constant. [HCl] is the independent variable. Time is the dependent variable.
6. hydrogen gas; $Mg(s) + 2HCl(aq) \rightarrow MgCl_2(s) + H_2(g)$
7. Cleaning removes any deposits on the metal and exposes the entire magnesium surface for reaction. If a piece of magnesium is not clean, the reaction rate will be slower.

| Test tube | [HCl] (M) | Reaction time (s) |
|---|---|---|
| 1 | 6.0 | 5 |
| 2 | 3.0 | 25 |
| 3 | 1.5 | 40 |
| 4 | 0.75 | 110 |

## Procedure

• Clean the Mg metal with emery cloth or sandpaper until it shines.

**550**

---

# CHEMLAB 17

# Concentration and Reaction Rate

The collision theory describes how the change in concentration of one reactant affects the rate of chemical reactions. In this laboratory experiment you will observe how concentration affects the reaction rate.

### Problem

How does the concentration of a reactant affect the reaction rate?

### Objectives

• **Sequence** the acid concentrations from the most to the least concentrated.
• **Observe** which concentration results in the fastest reaction rate.

### Materials

graduated pipette 10-mL
safety pipette filler
$6M$ hydrochloric acid
distilled water
25 mm × 150 mm test tubes (4)
test-tube rack

magnesium ribbon
emery cloth or fine sandpaper
scissors
plastic ruler
tongs
watch with second hand
stirring rod

### Safety Precautions

• Always wear safety goggles and an apron in the lab.
• Never pipette any chemical by mouth.
• No open flame.

### Pre-Lab

1. Read the entire **CHEMLAB**. Prepare all written materials that you will take into the laboratory. Be sure to include safety precautions, procedure notes, and a data table.

| Reaction Time Data | | |
|---|---|---|
| **Test tube** | **[HCl] (M)** | **Time (s)** |
| 1 | | |
| 2 | | |
| 3 | | |
| 4 | | |

2. Use emery paper or sand paper to polish the magnesium ribbon until it is shiny. Use scissors to cut the magnesium into four 1-cm pieces.

3. Place the four test tubes in the test-tube rack. Label the test tubes #1 (6.0M HCl), #2 (3M HCl), #3 (1.5M HCl), and #4 (0.75M HCl).

4. Form a hypothesis about how the chemical reaction rate is related to reactant concentration.

5. What reactant quantity is held constant? What are the independent and dependent variables?

6. What gas is produced in the reaction between magnesium and hydrochloric acid? Write the balanced formula equation for the reaction.

7. Why is it important to clean the magnesium ribbon? If one of the four pieces is not thoroughly polished, how will the rate of the reaction involving that piece be affected?

### Procedure

1. Use a safety pipette to draw 10 mL of $6.0M$ hydrochloric acid (HCl) into a 10-mL graduated pipette.

2. Dispense the 10 mL of $6.0M$ HCl into test tube #1.

3. Draw 5.0 mL of the $6.0M$ HCl from test tube #1 with the empty pipette. Dispense this acid into test tube #2 and use the pipette to add an additional

---

• Remind students to carefully measure the volume of the acid and water that is transferred from each test tube.

### Expected Results

See the data table for this lab.

### Analyze and Conclude

1. The volume in each test tube must be the same, 5.0 mL.

2. Reaction Time vs Concentration

Concentration (M)

3. nonlinear; Reaction time and concentration are inversely related.

4. Because the acid concentration is inversely related to the reaction time, reaction time decreases as concentration increases.

5.0 mL of distilled water to the acid. Use the stirring rod to mix thoroughly. This solution is 3.0*M* HCl.

4. Draw 5.0 mL of the 3.0*M* HCl from test tube #2 with the empty pipette. Dispense this acid into test tube #3 and use the pipette to add an additional 5.0 mL of distilled water to the acid. Use the stirring rod to mix thoroughly. This solution is 1.5*M* HCl.

5. Draw 5.0 mL of the 1.5*M* HCl from test tube #3 with the empty pipette. Dispense this acid into test tube #4 and use the pipette to add an additional 5.0 mL of distilled water to the acid. Use the stirring rod to mix thoroughly. This solution is 0.75*M* HCl.

6. Draw 5.0 mL of the 0.75*M* HCl from test tube #4 with the empty pipette. Neutralize and discard it in the sink.

7. Using the tongs, place a 1-cm length of magnesium ribbon into test tube #1. Record the time in seconds that it takes for the bubbling to stop.

8. Repeat step 7 using the remaining three test tubes of HCl and the three remaining pieces of magnesium ribbon. Record in your data table the time (in seconds) it takes for the bubbling to stop.

## Cleanup and Disposal

1. Place acid solutions in an acid discard container. Your teacher will neutralize the acid for proper disposal.

2. Wash thoroughly all test tubes and lab equipment.

3. Discard other materials as directed by your teacher.

4. Return all lab equipment to its proper place.

## Analyze and Conclude

1. **Analyzing** In step 6, why is 5.0 mL HCl discarded?

2. **Making and Using Graphs** Plot the concentration of the acid on the *x*-axis and time it takes for the bubbling to stop on the *y*-axis. Draw a smooth curve through the data points.

3. **Interpreting Graphs** Is the curve in question 2 linear or nonlinear? What does the slope tell you?

4. **Drawing a Conclusion** Based on your graph, what do you conclude about the relationship between the acid concentration and the reaction rate?

5. **Hypothesizing** Write a hypothesis using the collision theory, reaction rate, and reactant concentration to explain your results.

6. **Designing an Experiment** Write a brief statement of how you would set up an experiment to test your hypothesis.

7. Error Analysis Compare your experimental results with those of several other students in the laboratory. Explain the differences.

## Real-World Chemistry

1. Describe a situation that may occur in your daily life that exemplifies the effect of concentration on the rate of a reaction.

2. Some hair-care products, such as hot-oil treatments, must be heated before application. Explain in terms of factors affecting reaction rates why heat is required.

CHEMLAB **551**

5. As the concentration of the HCl reactant increases in the test tube, the probability of an effective collision with the Mg metal increases. These collisions displace $H_2$ gas from the acid, increasing the rate of the reaction as is evidenced by increased bubbling.

6. Student answers will vary. An example is an experiment to perform a combustion reaction with increasing concentrations of oxygen to verify the increased rate of combustion.

7. Errors may arise from differences in measuring and/or inaccurate pipetting in the series from test tubes 1–4. Students may also record variances in the time they first see bubbles.

## Real-World Chemistry

1. Answers will vary. For example, students might relate the concentration of chlorine in a pool to control algae growth, or they might describe how the concentration of powdered drink mix affects the solution.

2. Heat increases the kinetic activity of the molecules, which in turn increases the number of high-energy collisions that will overcome the activation energy barrier and form the desired products (and effects). If the reactants remained unheated, the desired product would not form.

 **Resource Manager**

**ChemLab and MiniLab Worksheets,** pp. 66–68

✓ **Assessment**

**Skill** Have the students use their graphs to predict how many seconds the bubbling will last if the acid concentration is 4.0*M*. **L2**

**National Science Content Standards**

**Pages 550–551**
UCP.2, UCP.3; A.1; B.3

# How It Works

## Purpose

Students will recognize the purpose of a catalytic converter in an automobile and learn the specific chemistry and design of the device.

## Background

The Clean Air Act of 1970 was essentially the beginning of the move to more efficient and cleaner running automobiles in the United States. One of the first devices to be used for emissions control was a charcoal-containing canister that was used to collect hydrocarbon vapors. Gasoline recirculation valves were also used to reduce the emission of nitrogen oxides. The first "real" catalytic converters came into production in the mid 70s, and since that time, catalytic converters have become increasingly more efficient in reducing air pollution from exhausts. However, over the years, the number of miles we drive has increased dramatically, which leads many to believe that the increase in travel has offset the benefits of reduced emissions.

## Teaching Strategies

- Contact an auto repair shop or parts dealer and ask if they can provide an actual catalytic converter to show the students.
- Provide a diagram of a car's exhaust system and point out the relative location of the catalytic converter in the system.
- Discuss why the change from leaded to unleaded gasoline was an important step in reducing automobile emissions. Explain that the lead in leaded gasoline coats the catalyst in the converter and prevents the chemical reactions that take place in the converter.

## Thinking Critically

1. The air provides a source of oxygen for the reactions that convert CO to $CO_2$ and the burning of the hydrocarbon

552

# How It Works
## Catalytic Converter

Concerns for our environment have made a huge impact in the products and processes we use every day. The catalytic converter is one of those impacts.

When a combustion engine converts fuel into energy, the reactions of the combustion process are incomplete. Incomplete combustion results in the production of poisonous carbon monoxide and undesirable nitrogen oxides. Since 1975, catalytic converters have reduced the exhaust emissions that contribute to air pollution by approximately 90%.

**1** Gases from the engine and the air pass through the exhaust system to the catalytic converter. Oxygen intake into the engine at this point is critical for the reactions of the catalysts.

**2** Inside the catalytic converter is a porous ceramic structure with a surface coating of platinum and rhodium particles.

**3** In many models of catalytic converters, this inner structure resembles tubes in a honeycomb arrangement, which provides significant surface area to accommodate the catalysts.

Rhodium

Platinum

**5** At the rhodium catalyst surface, nitric oxide is converted to nitrogen and oxygen.

Nitrogen gas   Oxygen gas

Nitric oxide          Nitric oxide

Hot (500°C) rhodium particle
$2\ NO \rightarrow N_2 + O_2$

Carbon monoxide   Carbon dioxide

Hydro-carbon          Water

Oxygen

Hot (500°C) platinum particle
$2\ CO + O_2 \rightarrow 2\ CO_2$
$C_xH_y + O_2 \rightarrow CO_2 + H_2O$

**4** At high temperatures (300–500°C) on the platinum catalyst surface, the dangerous carbon monoxide and hydrocarbons react with oxygen to form the compounds carbon dioxide and water.

### Thinking Critically

**1. Inferring** Why is it necessary to have additional air in exhaust before it enters the catalytic converter?

**2. Hypothesizing** A catalytic converter is not effective when cold. Use the concept of activation energy to explain why.

552    **Chapter 17 Reaction Rates**

fragments to $CO_2$ and $H_2O$. Both of these are present in relatively large quantities and the amount of oxygen liberated from the reduction of the nitrogen oxides is insufficient.

2. If the starting temperature of the reactants is not high enough, the catalyst is not effective even though it lowers the activation energy of the reaction. The energy available at lower temperatures is

not sufficient to allow the reaction to occur even in the presence of the catalyst.

## Summary

### 17.1 A Model for Reaction Rates

- The rate of a chemical reaction is expressed as the rate at which a reactant is consumed or the rate at which a product is formed.

- Reaction rates are generally calculated and expressed in moles per liter per second (mol/(L·s)).

- In order to react, the particles in a chemical reaction must collide in a correct orientation and with sufficient energy to form the activated complex.

- The rate of a chemical reaction is unrelated to the spontaneity of the reaction.

### 17.2 Factors Affecting Reaction Rates

- Key factors that influence the rate of chemical reactions include reactivity, concentration, surface area, temperature, and catalysts.

- Catalysts increase the rates of chemical reactions by lowering activation energies.

- Raising the temperature of a reaction increases the rate of the reaction by increasing the collision frequency and the number of collisions forming the activated complex.

### 17.3 Reaction Rate Laws

- The mathematical relationship between the rate of a chemical reaction at a given temperature and the concentrations of reactants is called the rate law.

- The rate law for a chemical reaction is determined experimentally using the method of initial rates.

### 17.4 Instantaneous Reaction Rates and Reaction Mechanisms

- The instantaneous rate for a chemical reaction is calculated from the rate law, the specific rate constant, and the concentrations of all reactants.

- Most chemical reactions are complex reactions consisting of two or more elementary steps.

- A reaction mechanism is the complete sequence of elementary steps that make up a complex reaction.

- For a complex reaction, the rate-determining step limits the instantaneous rate of the overall reaction.

## Key Equations and Relationships

- Average rate = $\dfrac{\Delta\text{quantity}}{\Delta t}$
  (p. 529)

- Rate = $k[A]$
  (p. 542)

- Rate = $k[A]^m[B]^n$
  (p. 543)

## Vocabulary

- activated complex (p. 532)
- activation energy (p. 533)
- catalyst (p. 539)
- collision theory (p. 532)
- complex reaction (p. 548)
- heterogeneous catalyst (p. 541)
- homogeneous catalyst (p. 541)
- inhibitor (p. 540)
- instantaneous rate (p. 546)
- intermediate (p. 548)
- method of initial rates (p. 544)
- rate-determining step (p. 549)
- rate law (p. 542)
- reaction mechanism (p. 548)
- reaction order (p. 543)
- reaction rate (p. 530)
- specific rate constant (p. 542)
- transition state (p. 532)

## Using the Vocabulary

To reinforce chapter vocabulary, have students write a sentence using each term. **L2** **ELL**

## Review Strategies

- Have students summarize how reaction rates are expressed and explain how the collision model relates to reaction rates. **L2**
- Have students list and explain the conditions and factors that affect reaction rates. **L2**
- Have students give an example of a reaction rate law. **L2**
- Have students explain the difference between an average reaction rate and an instantaneous reaction rate. **L2**
- Problems from Appendix A or the **Supplemental Problems** booklet can be used for review. **L2**

**VOCABULARY PuzzleMaker** ONLINE CHEMISTRY

For additional help with vocabulary, have students access the Vocabulary PuzzleMaker online.

chemistrymc.com/ vocabulary_puzzlemaker

Chemistry Online

**EXAM*VIEW*® PRO**

## Use Exam*View*® Pro Testmaker CD-ROM to:

- Create **multiple versions** of tests.
- Create **modified** tests with one mouse click for struggling students.
- **Edit** existing questions and add your own questions.
- **Build** tests based on national curriculum standards.

**National Science Content Standards**

**Pages 552–553**
UCP.2, UCP.3; B.2, B.3, B.4, B.6; F.4, F.6

## Concept Mapping

**32.** 1. reaction rates; 2. collision theory; 3–7. surface area, temperature, concentration, reactivity, catalyst

## Mastering Concepts

**33.** Although this information tells you the reaction is spontaneous under the specified conditions, it tells you nothing about the reaction rate.

**34.** The rate may be expressed as the decrease in [A] per unit time: Rate $= \frac{\Delta[A]}{\Delta t}$. Numerically, the two rates would be equal; however, $\frac{\Delta[A]}{\Delta t}$ would be negative and $\frac{\Delta[B]}{\Delta t}$ would be positive.

**35.** Activation energy represents the minimum amount of energy that reacting particles must have to form the activated complex.

**36.** The activated complex is a transition state between reactants and products.

**37.** The molecules do not react if they collide with insufficient energy or lack favorable orientations at the instant of impact.

**38.** The activation energy defines the minimum energy particles must have in order for collisions to result in the formation of the activated complex.

**39.** Reactant bonds are being broken and product bonds are being formed.

**40.** The activation energy for the forward reaction is less than the activation energy for the reverse reaction.

**41.** Generally, the greater the reactivity of the reactants, the faster the reaction.

**42.** The finely divided solid presents a larger surface area than the large chunk.

**43.** a catalyst

*Go to the Chemistry Web site at* chemistrymc.com *for additional Chapter 17 Assessment.*

## Concept Mapping

**32.** Complete the following concept map using the following terms: surface area, collision theory, temperature, reaction rates, concentration, reactivity, catalyst.

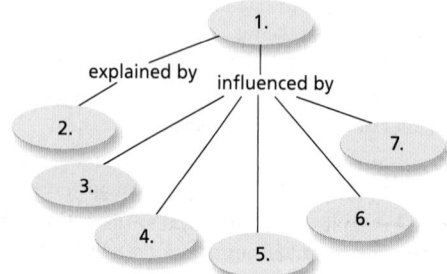

## Mastering Concepts

**33.** For a specific chemical reaction, assume that the change in free energy ($\Delta G$) is negative. What does this information tell you about the rate of the reaction? (17.1)

**34.** How would you express the rate of the chemical reaction A $\longrightarrow$ B based on the concentration of reactant A? How would that rate compare with the reaction rate based on the product B? (17.1)

**35.** What does the activation energy for a chemical reaction represent? (17.1)

**36.** What is the role of the activated complex in a chemical reaction? (17.1)

**37.** Suppose two molecules that can react collide. Under what circumstances do the colliding molecules not react? (17.1)

**38.** How is the activation energy for a chemical reaction related to whether or not a collision between molecules initiates a reaction? (17.1)

**39.** In the activated complex for a chemical reaction, what bonds are broken and what bonds are formed? (17.1)

**40.** If A $\longrightarrow$ B is exothermic, how does the activation energy for the forward reaction compare with the activation energy for the reverse reaction (A $\longleftarrow$ B)? (17.1)

**41.** What role does the reactivity of the reactants play in determining the rate of a chemical reaction? (17.2)

**42.** Explain why a crushed solid reacts with a gas more quickly than a large chunk of the same solid. (17.2)

**43.** What do you call a substance that increases the rate of a chemical reaction without being consumed in the reaction? (17.2)

**44.** In general, what is the relationship between reaction rate and reactant concentration? (17.2)

**45.** In general, what is the relationship between reaction rate and temperature? (17.2)

**46.** Distinguish between a homogeneous catalyst and a heterogeneous catalyst. (17.2)

**47.** Explain how a catalyst affects the activation energy for a chemical reaction. (17.2)

**48.** Use the collision theory to explain why increasing the concentration of a reactant usually increases the reaction rate. (17.2)

**49.** Use the collision theory to explain why increasing the temperature usually increases the reaction rate. (17.2)

**50.** In a chemical reaction, what relationship does the rate law describe? (17.3)

**51.** What is the name of the proportionality constant in the mathematical expression that relates reaction rate and reactant concentration? (17.3)

**52.** What does the order of a reactant tell you about the way the concentration of that reactant appears in the rate law? (17.3)

**53.** Why does the specific rate constant for a chemical reaction often double for each increase of 10 K? (17.3)

**54.** Explain why the rates of most chemical reactions decrease over time. (17.3)

**55.** In the method of initial rates used to determine the rate law for a chemical reaction, what is the significance of the word *initial*? (17.3)

**56.** If a reaction has three reactants and is first order in one, second order in another, and third order in the third, what is the overall order of the reaction? (17.3)

**57.** What do you call the slowest of the elementary steps that make up a complex reaction? (17.4)

**58.** What is an intermediate in a complex reaction? (17.4)

**59.** Distinguish between an elementary step, a complex reaction, and a reaction mechanism. (17.4)

**60.** Under what circumstances is the rate law for the reaction 2A + 3B $\longrightarrow$ products correctly written as Rate $= k[A]^2[B]^3$? (17.3)

chemistrymc.com/chapter_test

**44.** Increasing the concentration increases the rate, and decreasing the concentration decreases the rate.

### Resource Manager

Chapter Assessment, pp. 97–102 **L2**
Supplemental Problems, Ch. 17
ExamView® Pro CD-ROM
MindJogger Videoquizzes DVD/VHS
Solutions Manual, Ch. 17
Chemistry Interactive CD-ROM,
 Ch. 17 quiz

**61.** How does the activation energy of the rate-determining step in a complex reaction compare with the activation energies of the other elementary steps? (17.4)

## Mastering Problems

### A Model for Reaction Rates (17.1)

**62.** In the gas-phase reaction $I_2 + Cl_2 \rightarrow 2ICl$, the $[I_2]$ changes from $0.400M$ at time $= 0$ to $0.300M$ at time $= 4.00$ min. Calculate the average reaction rate in moles $I_2$ consumed per liter per minute.

**63.** If a chemical reaction occurs at a rate of $2.25 \times 10^{-2}$ moles per liter per second at 322 K, what is the rate expressed in moles per liter per minute?

**64.** On the accompanying energy level diagram, match the appropriate number with the quantity it represents.

**a.** reactants  **c.** products
**b.** activated complex  **d.** activation energy

**65.** Given the following data for the decomposition of hydrogen peroxide, calculate the average reaction rate in moles $H_2O_2$ consumed per liter per minute for each time interval.

| Decomposition of $H_2O_2$ | |
|---|---|
| Time (min) | $[H_2O_2]$ (M) |
| 0 | 2.50 |
| 2 | 2.12 |
| 5 | 1.82 |
| 10 | 1.48 |
| 20 | 1.00 |

**66.** At a given temperature and for a specific time interval, the average rate of the following reaction is $1.88 \times 10^{-4}$ moles $N_2$ consumed per liter per second.

$$N_2 + 3H_2 \rightarrow 2NH_3$$

Express the reaction rate in moles $H_2$ consumed per liter per second and in moles $NH_3$ produced per liter per second.

### Factors Affecting Reaction Rates (17.2)

**67.** Estimate the rate of the reaction described in problem 63 at 332 K. Express the rate in moles per liter per second.

**68.** Estimate the rate of the reaction described in problem 63 at 352 K and with $[I_2]$ doubled (assume the reaction is first order in $I_2$).

### Reaction Rate Laws (17.3)

**69.** Nitrogen monoxide gas and chlorine gas react according to the equation $2NO + Cl_2 \rightarrow 2NOCl$. Use the following data to determine the rate law for the reaction by the method of initial rates. Also, calculate the value of the specific rate constant.

| $2NO + Cl_2$ Reaction Data | | |
|---|---|---|
| Initial [NO] (M) | Initial [Cl$_2$] (M) | Initial rate (mol/(L·min)) |
| 0.50 | 0.50 | $1.90 \times 10^{-2}$ |
| 1.00 | 0.50 | $7.60 \times 10^{-2}$ |
| 1.00 | 1.00 | $15.20 \times 10^{-2}$ |

**70.** Use the following data to determine the rate law and specific rate constant for the reaction $2ClO_2(aq) + 2OH^-(aq) \rightarrow ClO_3^-(aq) + ClO_2^-(aq) + H_2O(l)$.

| $2ClO_2(aq) + 2OH^-(aq)$ Reaction Data | | |
|---|---|---|
| Initial [ClO$_2$] (M) | Initial [OH$^-$] (M) | Initial rate (mol/(L·min)) |
| 0.0500 | 0.200 | 6.90 |
| 0.100 | 0.200 | 27.6 |
| 0.100 | 0.100 | 13.8 |

### Instantaneous Reaction Rates and Reaction Mechanisms (17.4)

**71.** The gas-phase reaction $2HBr + NO_2 \rightarrow H_2O + NO + Br_2$ is thought to occur by the following mechanism.

$HBr + NO_2 \rightarrow HOBr + NO \quad \Delta H = 4.2$ kJ (slow)

$HBr + HOBr \rightarrow H_2O + Br_2 \quad \Delta H = -86.2$ kJ (fast)

Draw the energy diagram that depicts this reaction mechanism. On the diagram, show the energy of the reactants, energy of the products, and relative activation energies of the two elementary steps.

Assessment  **555**

**45.** Increasing the temperature increases the rate, and decreasing the temperature decreases the rate.

**46.** A homogeneous catalyst exists in the same physical state as the reaction it catalyzes; a heterogeneous catalyst exists in a different physical state from the reaction it catalyzes.

**47.** A catalyst lowers the activation energy.

**48.** Increasing the concentration of a reactant increases the frequency of collisions between reacting particles.

**49.** Increasing the temperature increases collision frequency and collision energy.

**50.** The rate law defines the mathematical relationship between the reaction rate and the concentration of the reactants.

**51.** the specific rate constant

**52.** The reactant's order defines the exponent to which the reactant's concentration is raised in the rate law.

**53.** For many reactions, an increase of 10 K approximately doubles the number of collisions having sufficient energy to initiate reaction.

**54.** As reactants are consumed, their concentrations decrease over time.

**55.** The initial rate is the instantaneous rate at the stated concentrations; however, the rate begins to decrease the instant the reaction starts.

**56.** sixth order

**57.** the rate-determining step or rate-limiting step

**58.** An intermediate is a substance produced in one elementary step and consumed in a subsequent elementary step.

**59.** A simple reaction occurs in a single step; a complex reaction is made up of two or more elementary steps; a reaction mechanism consists of the complete sequence of elementary steps that make up a complex reaction.

**60.** The rate law is correct if the reaction occurs in a single step. The rate law is possible, but unlikely, if the reaction occurs in multiple steps.

**61.** The rate-determining step has the highest activation energy.

National Science Content Standards

Pages 554–555
UCP.2, UCP.3; B.2, B.3, B.4, B.6

## Mastering Problems

Complete solutions for Chapter Assessment problems can be found in the **Solutions Manual.**

### A Model for Reaction Rates (17.1)
#### Level 1
**62.** 0.0250 mol/(L·min)
**63.** 1.35 mol/(L·min)

#### Level 2
**64. a.** 2    **c.** 4
   **b.** 3    **d.** 1
**65.** First: 0.2 mol/(L·min)
Second: 0.1 mol/(L·min)
Third: 0.07 mol/(L·min)
Fourth: 0.05 mol/(L·min)
**66.** Rate = $5.64 \times 10^{-4}$
mol $H_2$/(L·s)
Rate = $3.76 \times 10^{-4}$
mol $NH_3$/(L·s)

### Factors Affecting Reaction Rates (17.2)
#### Level 1
**67.** approximate rate at 332 K
= ($4.50 \times 10^{-2}$ mol/(L·s))

#### Level 2
**68.** approximate rate at 352 K
= 0.360 mol/(L·s)

### Reaction Rate Laws (17.3)
#### Level 1
**69.** Examining the first two trials, doubling [NO] increases the rate by a factor of four; therefore, the reaction is second order in NO. Examining the second and third trials, doubling [$Cl_2$] doubles the rate; therefore, the reaction is first order in $Cl_2$.
Rate = $k[NO]^2[Cl_2]$.
$k$ = 0.152 L²/(mol²·min)

#### Level 2
**70.** Examining the first two trials, doubling [$ClO_2$] increases the rate by a factor of four; therefore, the reaction is second order in $ClO_2$. Examining the second and third trials, halving [$OH^-$] halves the rate; therefore, the reaction is first order in $OH^-$. Rate = $k[ClO_2]^2[OH^-]$.
$k$ = $1.38 \times 10^4$ L²/(mol²·min)

**72.** Are there any intermediates in the complex reaction described in problem 71? Explain why or why not. If any intermediates exist, what are their formulas?

**73.** Given the rate law Rate = $k[A][B]^2$ for the generic reaction A + B → products, the value for the specific rate constant ($4.75 \times 10^{-7}$ L²/(mol²·s)), the concentration of A (0.355$M$), and the concentration of B (0.0122$M$), calculate the instantaneous reaction rate.

## Mixed Review

*Sharpen your problem-solving skills by answering the following.*

**74.** Use the method of initial rates and the following data to determine and express the rate law for the reaction A + B → 2C.

| A + B → 2C Reaction Data | | |
|---|---|---|
| Initial [A] (*M*) | Initial [B] (*M*) | Initial rate (mol C/(L·s)) |
| 0.010 | 0.010 | 0.0060 |
| 0.020 | 0.010 | 0.0240 |
| 0.020 | 0.020 | 0.0960 |

**75.** The concentration of reactant A decreases from 0.400 mol/L at time = 0 to 0.384 mol/L at time = 4.00 min. Calculate the average reaction rate during this time period. Express the rate in mol/(L·min).

**76.** It is believed that the following two elementary steps make up the mechanism for the reaction between nitrogen monoxide and chlorine:

$$NO(g) + Cl_2(g) \rightarrow NOCl_2(g)$$
$$NOCl_2(g) + NO(g) \rightarrow 2NOCl(g)$$

Write the equation for the overall reaction and identify any intermediates in the reaction mechanism.

**77.** One reaction that takes place in an automobile's engine and exhaust system is described by the equation $NO_2(g) + CO(g) \rightarrow NO(g) + CO_2(g)$. This reaction's rate law at a particular temperature is given by the relationship rate = 0.50 L/(mol·s)[$NO_2$]². What is the reaction's initial, instantaneous rate at [$NO_2$] = 0.0048 mol/L?

**78.** At 232 K, the rate of a certain chemical reaction is $3.20 \times 10^{-2}$ mol/(L·min). Predict the reaction's approximate rate at 252 K.

## Thinking Critically

**79. Using Numbers** Draw a diagram that shows all of the possible collision combinations between two molecules of reactant A and two molecules of reactant B. Now, increase the number of molecules of A from two to four and sketch each possible A–B collision combination. By what factor did the number of collision combinations increase? What does this imply about the reaction rate?

**80. Applying Concepts** Use the collision theory to explain two reasons why increasing the temperature of a reaction by 10 K often doubles the reaction rate.

**81. Formulating Models** Create a table of concentrations, starting with 0.100$M$ concentrations of all reactants, that you would propose in order to establish the rate law for the reaction $a$A + $b$B + $c$D → products using the method of initial rates.

## Writing in Chemistry

**82.** Research the way manufacturers in the United States produce nitric acid from ammonia. Write the reaction mechanism for the complex reaction. If catalysts are used in the process, explain how they are used and how they affect any of the elementary steps.

**83.** Write an advertisement that explains why Company A's lawn care product (fertilizer or weed killer) works better than the competition's because of the smaller sized granules. Include applicable diagrams.

## Cumulative Review

*Refresh your understanding of previous chapters by answering the following.*

**84.** Classify each of the following elements as a metal, nonmetal, or metalloid. (Chapter 6)
   **a.** molybdenum
   **b.** bromine
   **c.** arsenic
   **d.** neon
   **e.** cerium

**85.** Balance the following equations. (Chapter 10)
   **a.** $Sn(s) + NaOH(aq) \rightarrow Na_2SnO_2 + H_2$
   **b.** $C_8H_{18}(l) + O_2(g) \rightarrow CO_2(g) + H_2O(l)$
   **c.** $Al(s) + H_2SO_4(aq) \rightarrow Al_2(SO_4)_3(aq) + H_2(g)$

**86.** What mass of iron(III) chloride is needed to prepare 1.00 L of a 0.255$M$ solution? (Chapter 15)

**87.** $\Delta H$ for a reaction is negative. Compare the energy of the products and the reactants. Is the reaction endothermic or exothermic? (Chapter 16)

### Instantaneous Reaction Rates and Reaction Mechanisms (17.4)
#### Level 1
**71.**

**National Science Content Standards**
Pages 556–557
UCP.2, UCP.3; B.2, B.3, B.4, B.6; E.2

*Use these questions and the test-taking tip to prepare for your standardized test.*

**1.** The rate of a chemical reaction is all of the following EXCEPT

**a.** the speed at which a reaction takes place.
**b.** the change in concentration of a reactant per unit time.
**c.** the change in concentration of a product per unit time.
**d.** the amount of product formed in a certain period of time.

**2.** The complete dissociation of acid $H_3A$ takes place in three steps:

$H_3A(aq) \rightarrow H_2A^-(aq) + H^+(aq)$
   Rate $= k_1[H_3A]$   $k_1 = 3.2 \times 10^2$ s$^{-1}$

$H_2A^-(aq) \rightarrow HA^{2-}(aq) + H+(aq)$
   Rate $= k_2[H_2A^-]$   $k_2 = 1.5 \times 10^2$ s$^{-1}$

$HA^{2-}(aq) \rightarrow A^{3-}(aq) + H+(aq)$
   Rate $= k_3[HA^{2-}]$   $k_3 = 0.8 \times 10^2$ s$^{-1}$

overall reaction:   $H_3A(aq) \rightarrow A^{3-}(aq) + 3H^+(aq)$

When the reactant concentrations are $[H_3A] = 0.100M$, $[H_2A^-] = 0.500M$, and $[HA^{2-}] = 0.200M$, which reaction is the rate-determining step?

**a.** $H_3A(aq) \rightarrow H_2A^-(aq) + H^+(aq)$
**b.** $H_2A^-(aq) \rightarrow HA^{2-}(aq) + H^+(aq)$
**c.** $HA^{2-}(aq) \rightarrow A^{3-}(aq) + H^+(aq)$
**d.** $H_3A(aq) \rightarrow A^{3-}(aq) + 3H^+(aq)$

**3.** Which of the following is NOT an acceptable unit for expressing a reaction rate?

**a.** $M$/min
**b.** L/s
**c.** mol/(mL·h)
**d.** mol/(L·min)

**Interpreting Tables** Use the table to answer questions 4–6.

Reaction: $SO_2Cl_2(g) \rightarrow SO_2(g) + Cl_2(g)$

| Experimental Data Collected for Reaction | | | |
|---|---|---|---|
| Time (min) | [SO$_2$Cl$_2$] ($M$) | [SO$_2$] ($M$) | [Cl$_2$] ($M$) |
| 0.0 | 1.00 | 0.00 | 0.00 |
| 100.0 | 0.87 | 0.13 | 0.13 |
| 200.0 | 0.74 | ? | ? |

**4.** What is the average reaction rate for this reaction, expressed in moles $SO_2Cl_2$ consumed per liter per minute?

**a.** $1.30 \times 10^{-3}$ mol/(L·min)
**b.** $2.60 \times 10^{-1}$ mol/(L·min)
**c.** $7.40 \times 10^{-3}$ mol/(L·min)
**d.** $8.70 \times 10^{-3}$ mol/(L·min)

**5.** On the basis of the average reaction rate, what will the concentrations of $SO_2$ and $Cl_2$ be at 200.0 min?

**a.** 0.130$M$
**b.** 0.260$M$
**c.** 0.39$M$
**d.** 0.52$M$

**6.** How long will it take for half of the original amount of $SO_2Cl_2$ to decompose at the average reaction rate?

**a.** 285 min
**b.** 335 min
**c.** 385 min
**d.** 500 min

**7.** Which of the following does NOT affect reaction rate?

**a.** catalysts
**b.** surface area of reactants
**c.** concentration of reactants
**d.** reactivity of products

**8.** The reaction between persulfate ($S_2O_8^{2-}$) and iodide ($I^-$) ions is often studied in student laboratories because it occurs slowly enough for its rate to be measured:

$S_2O_8^{2-}(aq) + 2I^-(aq) \rightarrow 2SO_4^{2-}(aq) + I_2(aq)$

This reaction has been experimentally determined to be first order in $S_2O_8^{2-}$ and first order in $I^-$. Therefore, what is the overall rate law for this reaction?

**a.** Rate $= k[S_2O_8^{2-}]^2[I^-]$
**b.** Rate $= k[S_2O_8^{2-}][I^-]$
**c.** Rate $= k[S_2O_8^{2-}][I^-]^2$
**d.** Rate $= k[S_2O_8^{2-}]^2[I^-]^2$

**9.** The rate law for the reaction $A + B + C \rightarrow$ products is:   Rate $= k[A]^2[C]$

If $k = 6.92 \times 10^{-5}$ L$^2$/(mol$^2$·s), $[A] = 0.175M$, $[B] = 0.230M$, and $[C] = 0.315M$, what is the instantaneous reaction rate?

**a.** $6.68 \times 10^{-7}$ mol/(L·s)
**b.** $8.77 \times 10^{-7}$ mol/(L·s)
**c.** $1.20 \times 10^{-6}$ mol/(L·s)
**d.** $3.81 \times 10^{-6}$ mol/(L·s)

### TEST-TAKING TIP

**Watch the Little Words** Underline words like *least, not,* and *except* when you see them in test questions. They change the meaning of the question!

Standardized Test Practice   **557**

## Level 2
**72.** Yes. HOBr is an intermediate because it is formed in the first reaction and consumed in the second reaction. The NO formed in the first reaction is a final product; therefore, HOBr is the only intermediate.
**73.** Rate $= k[A][B]^2 = 4.75 \times 10^{-7}$ L$^2$/(mol$^2$·s)(0.355)(0.0122)$^2 = 2.51 \times 10^{-11}$

## Mixed Review
**74.** Rate $= k[A]^2[B]^2$.
**75.** Average rate $= 4.00 \times 10^{-3}$ mol/(L·min).
**76.** $2NO(g) + Cl_2(g) \rightarrow 2NOCl$ and $NOCl_2$ is a reaction intermediate.
**77.** Rate $= 1.2 \times 10^{-5}$ mol/(L·s).
**78.** Predicted rate $= 0.128$ mol/(L·min).

## Thinking Critically
**79.** The number of A–B collision combinations increased from four to eight, a factor of two. Because the reaction rate depends upon the number of molecular collisions, the rate probably doubles.

Two Molecules of A and Two Molecules of B

Four collision combinations

**80.** Increasing the temperature by 10 K increases the average speed of the reacting particles. Therefore, the collision frequency increases. In addition, the number of collisions possessing sufficient energy to form the activated complex increases, often by a factor of approximately two.

**81.** The table should include sets of trials in which the concentrations of two reactants are held constant while that of the third reactant is varied.

**b.** $2C_8H_{18} + 25O_2 \rightarrow 16CO_2 + 18H_2O$
**c.** $2Al + 3H_2SO_4 \rightarrow Al_2(SO_4)_3 + 3H_2$
**86.** 41.4 g
**87.** $H_{products} < H_{reactants}$; exothermic

## Cumulative Review
**84. a.** metal; **b.** nonmetal; **c.** metalloid; **d.** nonmetal; **e.** metal
**85. a.** $Sn(s) + 2NaOH(aq) \rightarrow Na_2SnO_2 + H_2$

## Standardized Test Practice

| | | |
|---|---|---|
| **1.** d | **4.** a | **7.** d |
| **2.** c | **5.** b | **8.** b |
| **3.** b | **6.** c | **9.** a |

# Resource Manager

| Section | Objectives | Activities/Features |
|---|---|---|
| **Section 18.1**<br>**Equilibrium: A State of Dynamic Balance**<br>1½ sessions<br>🔲 ½ block | 1. **Recognize** the characteristics of chemical equilibrium.<br>2. **Write** equilibrium expressions for systems that are at equilibrium.<br>3. **Calculate** equilibrium constants from concentration data. | **Discovery Lab:** What's equal about equilibrium?, p. 559<br>**Physics Connection,** p. 563 |
| **Section 18.2**<br>**Factors Affecting Chemical Equilibrium**<br>1½ sessions<br>🔲 ½ block | 4. **Describe** how various factors affect chemical equilibrium.<br>5. **Explain** how Le Châtelier's principle applies to equilibrium systems. | **Careers Using Chemistry:** Nurse Anesthetist, p. 569<br>**MiniLab:** Shifts in Equilibrium, p. 573 |
| **Section 18.3**<br>**Using Equilibrium Constants**<br>3 sessions<br>🔲 2 blocks | 6. **Determine** equilibrium concentrations of reactants and products.<br>7. **Calculate** the solubility of a compound from its solubility product constant.<br>8. **Explain** the common ion effect. | **Problem-Solving Lab:** How does fluoride prevent tooth decay? p. 583<br>**ChemLab Small Scale:** Comparing Two Solubility Product Constants, pp. 586–587<br>**Chemistry and Technology:** The Haber Process, p. 588 |

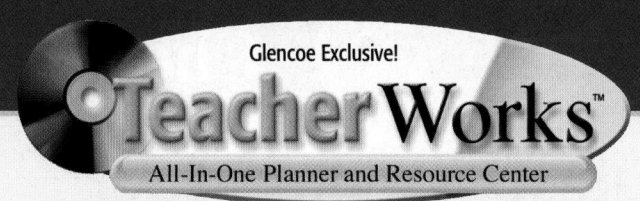

Glencoe Exclusive!
TeacherWorks™
All-In-One Planner and Resource Center

| National Science Content Standards | State/Local Standards | Reproducible Masters | Transparencies |
|---|---|---|---|
| UCP.3, UCP.4; A.1; B.3, B.4; E.2; G.3 | | **Study Guide for Content Mastery,** pp. 103–104 L2<br>**Challenge Problems,** p. 18 L3<br>**Small-Scale Laboratory Manual,** pp. 57–60 L2 | **Section Focus Transparency 68** L1 ELL<br>**Teaching Transparency 53** L2 ELL<br>**Math Skills Transparency 28** L2 ELL |
| UCP.3, UCP.4; A.1; B.3, B.4, B.6; E.2; G.3 | | **Study Guide for Content Mastery,** pp. 105–106 L2<br>**ChemLab and MiniLab Worksheets,** pp. 69–72 L2<br>**Laboratory Manual,** pp. 137–140 L2<br>**Small-Scale Laboratory Manual,** pp. 61–64 L2 | **Section Focus Transparency 69** L1 ELL<br>**Teaching Transparency 54** L2 ELL |
| UCP.3, UCP.4; A.1, A.2; B.2, B.3, B.4, B.6; E.1, E.2; F.1, F.6 | | **Study Guide for Content Mastery,** pp. 107–108 L2<br>**ChemLab and MiniLab Worksheets,** pp. 70–72 L2<br>**Laboratory Manual,** pp. 141–144 L2 | **Section Focus Transparency 70** L1 ELL<br>**Math Skills Transparency 29** L2 ELL |

**Key to National Science Content Standards:** UCP = Unifying Concepts and Processes, A = Science as Inquiry, B = Physical Science, C = Life Science, D = Earth and Space Sciences, E = Science and Technology, F = Science in Personal and Social Perspectives, G = History and Nature of Science

Refer to pages 4T–5T of the Teacher Guide for an explanation of the National Science Content Standards correlations.

# Resource Manager

## Materials List

**ChemLab** (pages 586–587)
$AgNO_3$ solution, NaCl solution, $Na_2S$ solution, 24-well microplate, thin-stem pipettes, wash bottle

**Discovery Lab** (page 559)
100-mL beaker, 100-mL graduated cylinder, glass tubes, equal diameter, open at both ends (2)

**MiniLab** (page 573)
test tubes (2), 10-mL graduated cylinder, 250-mL beaker, concentrated hydrochloric acid, $0.1M$ $CoCl_2$ solution, ice bath, table salt, hot plate

**Demonstration** (pages 570–571)
1.4 g $CoCl_2 \cdot 2H_2O$, 60 mL acetone, 100-mL graduated cylinder, 30 mL water

## Preparation of Solutions

For a review of solution preparation, see page 46T of the Teacher Guide.

Quantities are for a class of 30 students.

**ChemLab** (pages 586–587)
  **$AgNO_3$ solution** Dissolve 4 g $AgNO_3$ in 100 mL distilled water.
    **CAUTION:** Silver nitrate is toxic and will stain skin and clothing.
  **NaCl solution** Dissolve 4 g NaCl in 100 mL distilled water.
  **$Na_2S$ solution** Dissolve 6 g sodium sulfide ($Na_2S \cdot 9H_2O$) in 50 mL distilled water.
**MiniLab** (page 573)
  **$0.1M$ $CoCl_2$ solution** Dissolve 2.4 g cobalt(II) chloride hexahydrate ($CoCl_2 \cdot 6H_2O$) in 100 mL distilled water.

## Assessment Resources

**Chapter Assessment,** pp. 103–108
**MindJogger Videoquizzes DVD/VHS**
**Alternate Assessment in the Science Classroom**
**ExamView® Pro CD-Rom**
**Solutions Manual,** Chapter 18
**Supplemental Problems,** Chapter 18
**Performance Assessment in the Science Classroom**
**Chemistry Interactive CD-ROM,** Chapter 18 quiz

## Additional Resources

**Spanish Resources** ELL
**Guided Reading Audio Program,** Chapter 18 ELL
**Cooperative Learning in the Science Classroom**
**Lab and Safety Skills in the Science Classroom**
**Lesson Plans**
**Block Scheduling Lesson Plans**
**Chemistrymc.com**

## Glencoe Technology

The following multimedia for this chapter are available from Glencoe.

**VIDEOTAPE/DVD**
MindJogger Videoquizzes,
Chapter 18

**CD-ROM**
**Chemistry: Matter and Change**
*Equilibrium,* Animation
*Chemical Equilibrium,* Video
*Hydrogen Bonding,* Demonstration

**CD-ROM**
**ExamView® Pro**
**Testmaker**

**CD-ROM**
**Interactive Chalkboard**

**CD-ROM**
**TeacherWorks**™

## Multiple Learning Styles

Look for the following icons for strategies that emphasize different learning modalities.

**Kinesthetic**
Differentiated Instruction, p. 562; Portfolio, p. 578

**Intrapersonal**
Chemistry Journal, pp. 563, 582; Portfolio, p. 566

**Linguistic**
Chemistry Journal, pp. 560, 572, 577, 583;
Differentiated Instruction, p. 565

**Logical-Mathematical**
Differentiated Instructions, pp. 567, 579, 584;
Reteach, p. 567; Extension, p. 568; Portfolio, p. 580

## Key to Teaching Strategies

**L1** Level 1 activities should be appropriate for students with learning difficulties.

**L2** Level 2 activities should be within the ability range of all students.

**L3** Level 3 activities are designed for above-average students.

**ELL** ELL activities should be within the ability range of English Language Learners.

**COOP LEARN** Cooperative Learning activities are designed for small group work.

**P** These strategies represent student products that can be placed into a best-work portfolio.

 These strategies are useful in a block scheduling format.

## Assessment Planner

**Portfolio Assessment**
Portfolio, TWE, pp. 566, 578, 580
Assessment, TWE, p. 574
MiniLab, TWE, p. 573
Problem-Solving Lab, TWE, p. 583

**Performance Assessment**
Assessment, TWE, p. 571
ChemLab, SE, pp. 586–587
MiniLab, SE, p. 573
Discovery Lab, SE, p. 559

**Knowledge Assessment**
Assessment, TWE, pp. 563, 568, 584
Section Assessment, SE, pp. 568, 574, 585
Demonstration, TWE, p. 571
Chapter Assessment, SE, pp. 590–593

**Skill Assessment**
Assessment, TWE, pp. 581, 585
ChemLab, TWE, p. 587

## Tying to Previous Knowledge

Have students review the following concepts before studying this chapter.
Chapter 10: chemical reactions, equations for chemical reactions
Chapter 17: reaction rates, reaction rate laws

## Using the Photo

Ask students if they know the name and formula of the most common form of high-nitrogen fertilizer sprayed directly into the soil. ammonia, $NH_3$ Explain that ammonia is produced by the reaction between nitrogen and hydrogen, $N_2(g) + 3H_2(g) \rightleftharpoons 2NH_3(g)$. Point out that the reaction can occur in both directions, which poses special problems in producing large amounts of ammonia. Explain that in this chapter, they'll learn how the reaction can be managed for maximum production of ammonia.

## PowerPoint® Presentations

This CD-ROM is an editable Microsoft® PowerPoint® presentation that includes:
• Section presentations
• Section checks
• Image bank
• Links to Chemistry Online
• All transparencies
• Animations
• Audio

# Chemical Equilibrium

## What You'll Learn

▶ You will discover that many reactions and processes reach a state of equilibrium.
▶ You will use Le Châtelier's principle to explain how various factors affect chemical equilibria.
▶ You will calculate equilibrium concentrations of reactants and products using the equilibrium constant expression.
▶ You will determine the solubilities of sparingly soluble ionic compounds.

## Why It's Important

The concentrations of substances called acids and bases in your blood are crucial to your health. These substances continuously enter and leave your bloodstream, but the chemical equilibria among them maintain the balance needed for good health.

Visit the Chemistry Web site at chemistrymc.com to find links about chemical equilibrium.

One of the most important of ammonia's many uses is as a fertilizer.

**558    Chapter 18**

## DISCOVERY LAB

### Purpose
Students will discover that equilibrium does not mean equal amounts of reactant and product.

### Teaching Strategies
• The two glass tubes should be longer than the graduated cylinder is tall and have the same internal diameters.
• Demonstrate how to transfer the water from the beaker to the graduated cylinder and vice versa. Pairs of students can make simultaneous transfers.
• Have students stop and write their observations.

### Expected Results
Initially, the height of the 20 mL of water in the graduated cylinder is greater than the height of the 20 mL of water in the

### What's equal about equilibrium?

**D**oes equilibrium mean that the amounts of reactants and products are equal?

**Safety Precautions**

 Always wear safety goggles and a lab apron.

**Procedure**

1. Measure 20 mL of water in a graduated cylinder and pour it into a 100-mL beaker. Fill the graduated cylinder to the 20-mL mark. Place a glass tube in the graduated cylinder and another glass tube in the beaker. The tubes should reach the bottoms of the containers.

2. Cover the open ends of both glass tubes with your index fingers. Simultaneously, transfer the water from the cylinder to the beaker, and from the beaker to the cylinder.

3. Repeat the transfer process about 25 times. Record your observations.

**Analysis**

How can you explain your observations during the transfer process? What does this tell you about the concept of equilibrium?

**Materials**

100-mL beaker
graduated cylinder
glass tubes, equal diameter,
    open at both ends (2)

## 1 Focus

### Focus Transparency

Before presenting the lesson, display **Section Focus Transparency 68** on the overhead projector. Have students answer the accompanying questions using **Section Focus Transparency Master 68.** [L1] [ELL]

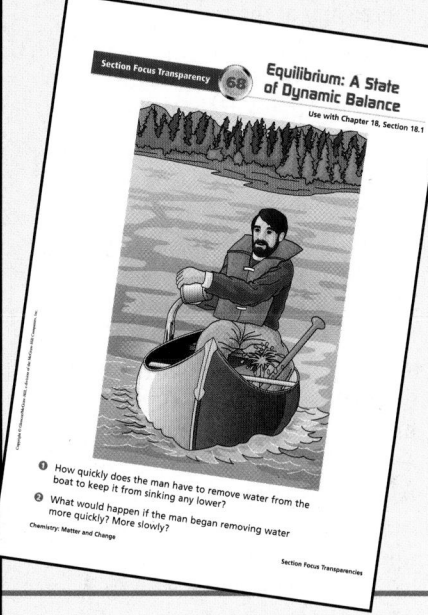

---

# Equilibrium: A State of Dynamic Balance

### Objectives

- **Recognize** the characteristics of chemical equilibrium.

- **Write** equilibrium expressions for systems that are at equilibrium.

- **Calculate** equilibrium constants from concentration data.

### Vocabulary

reversible reaction
chemical equilibrium
law of chemical equilibrium
equilibrium constant
homogeneous equilibrium
heterogeneous equilibrium

When you get off a whirling amusement park ride, you probably pause a minute to "get your equilibrium." If so, you are talking about getting your balance back after the ride exerted rapidly changing forces on you. But soon you are balanced steadily on your feet once more. Often, chemical reactions also reach a point of balance or equilibrium. The **DISCOVERY LAB** is an analogy for chemical equilibrium. You found that a point of balance was reached in the transfer of water from the beaker to the graduated cylinder and from the graduated cylinder to the beaker.

### What is equilibrium?

Consider the reaction for the formation of ammonia from nitrogen and hydrogen that you learned about in Chapter 16.

$$N_2(g) + 3H_2(g) \rightarrow 2NH_3(g) \qquad \triangle G° = -33.1 \text{ kJ}$$

This reaction is important to agriculture because ammonia is used widely as a source of nitrogen for fertilizing corn and other farm crops. The photo on the opposite page shows ammonia being "knifed" into the soil.

Note that the equation for the production of ammonia has a negative standard free energy, $\triangle G°$. Recall that a negative sign for $\triangle G°$ indicates that the

18.1 Equilibrium: A State of Dynamic Balance    **559**

### Chapter Themes

The following themes from the National Science Education Standards are covered in this chapter. Refer to page 4T of the Teacher Guide for an explanation of the correlations.
Systems, order, and organization (UCP.1)
Evidence, models, and explanation (UCP.2)
Change, constancy, and measurement (UCP.3)
Evolution and Equilibrium (UCP.4)
Form and function (UCP.5)

---

beaker. Therefore, water will reach a higher level in the glass tube placed in the graduated cylinder than it will in the tube placed in the beaker. As time passes, the heights of water in the tubes will even out. At the end, 30 mL is in the beaker and 10 mL is in the graduated cylinder.

**Analysis**
After a period of time, the rate at which water goes into the beaker is equal to the rate at which water goes into the graduated cylinder. The amounts of water in the beaker and graduated cylinder are not equal.

### National Science Content Standards

**Pages 558–559**
UCP.3, UCP.4; A.1; B.3; E.2

## Visual Learning

**Figure 18-1** Help students appreciate how the graph relates to the equation for the production of ammonia and use it to introduce the idea of reversible reactions. Ask students to look at the labeling of the *x*- and *y*-axes. Ask what is changing with time. the concentrations of the reactants and products Ask which quantities are decreasing and which is increasing. $H_2$ and $N_2$ are decreasing and $NH_3$ is increasing. Ask if, on the left side of the graph, $H_2$ and $N_2$ are decreasing at the same rate. $H_2$ is decreasing faster than $N_2$. Write the equation for the reaction on the chalkboard. Ask if the equation confirms their answer. Yes, in the equation, three moles of $H_2$ react for every mole of $N_2$, so three moles of $H_2$ are used up for every one mole of $N_2$. Ask students what is happening to the concentration of $NH_3$. The concentration of $NH_3$ is increasing. Ask what happens on the right side of the vertical dashed line. The concentrations of $H_2$, $N_2$, and $NH_3$ don't change anymore. Ask them to draw an inference from that observation. The reaction has stopped. Ask if all the $H_2$ and $N_2$ have been used up. No, the concentration of the two reactants are not zero.

**560**

---

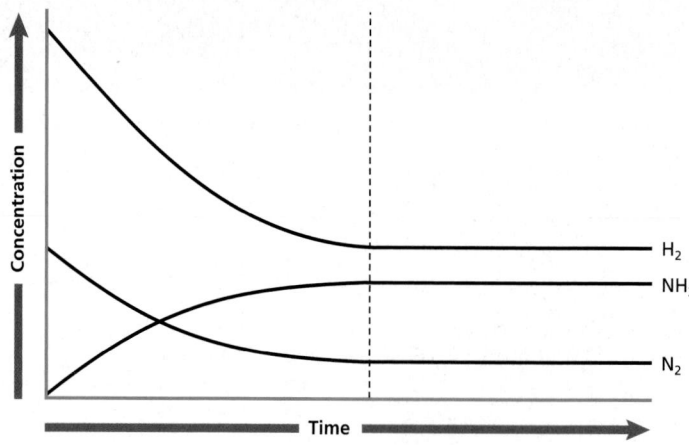

reaction is spontaneous under standard conditions. Standard conditions are defined as 298 K and one atmosphere pressure. But spontaneous reactions are not always fast. When carried out under standard conditions, this ammonia-forming reaction is much too slow. To produce ammonia at a rate that is practical, the reaction must be carried out at a much higher temperature than 298 K and a higher pressure than one atmosphere.

What happens when one mole of nitrogen and three moles of hydrogen, the amounts shown in the equation, are placed in a closed reaction vessel at 723 K? Because the reaction is spontaneous, nitrogen and hydrogen begin to react. **Figure 18-1** illustrates the progress of the reaction. Note that the concentration of the product, $NH_3$, is zero at the start and gradually increases with time. The reactants, $H_2$ and $N_2$, are consumed in the reaction, so their concentrations gradually decrease. After a period of time, however, the concentrations of $H_2$, $N_2$, and $NH_3$ no longer change. All concentrations become constant, as shown by the horizontal lines on the right side of the diagram. The concentrations of $H_2$ and $N_2$ are not zero, so not all of the reactants were converted to product even though $\triangle G°$ for this reaction is negative.

**Reversible reactions** When a reaction results in almost complete conversion of reactants to products, chemists say that the reaction goes to completion. But most reactions, including the ammonia-forming reaction, do not go to completion. They appear to stop. The reason is that these reactions are reversible. A **reversible reaction** is one that can occur in both the forward and the reverse directions.

$$\text{Forward: } N_2(g) + 3H_2(g) \rightarrow 2NH_3(g)$$
$$\text{Reverse: } N_2(g) + 3H_2(g) \leftarrow 2NH_3(g)$$

Chemists combine these two equations into a single equation that uses a double arrow to show that both reactions occur.

$$N_2(g) + 3H_2(g) \rightleftharpoons 2NH_3(g)$$

When you read the equation, the reactants in the forward reaction are on the left. In the reverse reaction, the reactants are on the right. In the forward reaction, hydrogen and nitrogen combine to form the product ammonia. In the reverse

---

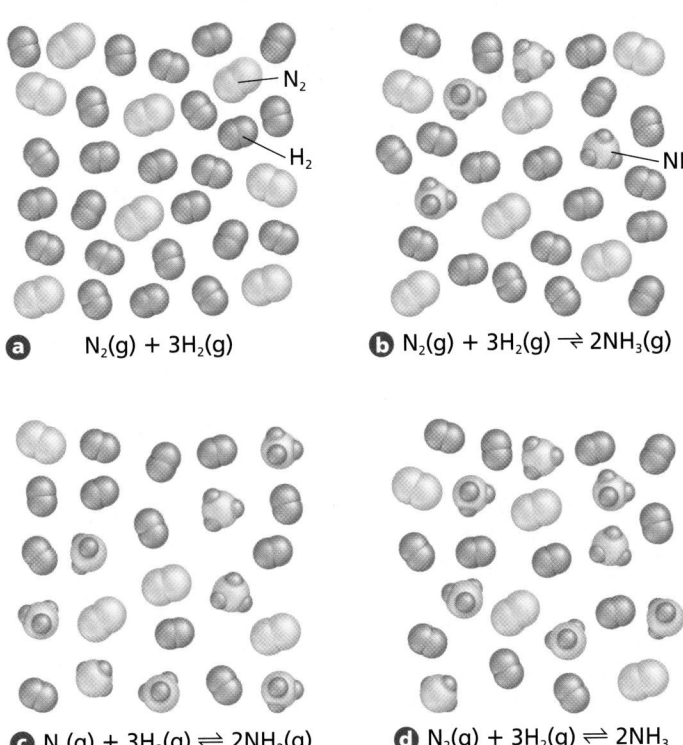

**a** $N_2(g) + 3H_2(g)$

**b** $N_2(g) + 3H_2(g) \rightleftharpoons 2NH_3(g)$

**c** $N_2(g) + 3H_2(g) \rightleftharpoons 2NH_3(g)$

**d** $N_2(g) + 3H_2(g) \rightleftharpoons 2NH_3$

**Figure 18-2**

Only the forward reaction can occur in **a** because only the reactants are present. In **b**, the product, ammonia, is present and the reverse reaction begins. Compare **c** and **d**. Has equilibrium been established? Refer to **Table C-1** in Appendix C for a key to atom color correlations.

reaction, ammonia decomposes into the products hydrogen and nitrogen. How does the reversibility of this reaction affect the production of ammonia?

**Figure 18-2a** shows a mixture of nitrogen and hydrogen just as the reaction begins at a definite, initial rate. No ammonia is present so only the forward reaction can occur.

$$N_2(g) + 3H_2(g) \rightarrow 2NH_3(g)$$

As hydrogen and nitrogen combine to form ammonia, their concentrations decrease, as shown in **Figure 18-2b.** Recall from Chapter 17 that the rate of a reaction depends upon the concentration of the reactants. The decrease in the concentration of the reactants causes the rate of the forward reaction to decrease. As soon as ammonia is present, the reverse reaction can occur, slowly at first, but at an increasing rate as the concentration of ammonia increases.

$$N_2(g) + 3H_2(g) \leftarrow 2NH_3(g)$$

As the reaction proceeds, the rate of the forward reaction continues to decrease and the rate of the reverse reaction continues to increase until the two rates are equal. At that point, ammonia is being produced as fast as it is being decomposed, so the concentrations of nitrogen, hydrogen, and ammonia remain constant, as shown in **Figures 18-2c** and **18-2d.** The system has reached a state of balance or equilibrium. The word *equilibrium* means that opposing processes are in balance. **Chemical equilibrium** is a state in which the forward and reverse reactions balance each other because they take place at equal rates.

$$\text{Rate}_{\text{forward reaction}} = \text{Rate}_{\text{reverse reaction}}$$

18.1 Equilibrium: A State of Dynamic Balance **561**

## Visual Learning

**Figure 18-4** At first, students may not fully appreciate the significance of this figure. Explain that in order for radioactive I-131 atoms in the molecules in the flask on the right to become part of molecules in the flask on the left, dynamic, solid-vapor equilibria must exist in both flasks.

## Enrichment

Explain that the radioactivity of I-131 is used to diagnose thyroid-gland abnormalities. Patients drink a solution containing a very small amount of NaI consisting of stable sodium atoms and radioactive I-131 atoms. A scanning monitor follows the thyroid gland's uptake of the radioactive iodine atoms, enabling physicians to evaluate thyroid function.

## Figure Caption Question

**Figure 18-3** Will the same vehicles always be in the same city? No, the vehicles, moving back and forth, will be in different cities at different times, but the numbers in each city will be the same.

**Figure 18-3**

If the only way in or out of San Francisco and Sausalito is across the Golden Gate Bridge, which joins the two cities, then the number of vehicles in the two cities will remain constant if the number of vehicles per hour crossing the bridge in one direction equals the number of vehicles crossing in the opposite direction. Will the same vehicles always be in the same city?

You can recognize that the ammonia-forming reaction reaches a state of chemical equilbrium because its chemical equation is written with a double arrow like this.

$$N_2(g) + 3H_2(g) \rightleftharpoons 2NH_3(g)$$

At equilibrium, the concentrations of reactants and products are constant, as you saw in **Figures 18-2c** and **18-2d.** However, that doesn't mean that the amounts or concentrations of reactants and products are equal. That is seldom the case. In fact, it's not unusual for the equilibrium concentrations of a reactant and product to differ by a factor of one million or more.

**The dynamic nature of equilibrium** Equilibrium is a state of action, not inaction. For example, consider this analogy. The Golden Gate Bridge, shown in **Figure 18-3,** connects two California cities, San Francisco and Sausalito. Suppose that all roads leading into and out of the two cities are closed for a day—except the Golden Gate Bridge. In addition, suppose that the number of vehicles per hour crossing the bridge in one direction equals the number of vehicles per hour traveling in the opposite direction. Given these circumstances, the number of vehicles in each of the two cities remains constant even though vehicles continue to cross the bridge. In this analogy, note that the total numbers of vehicles in the two cities do not have to be equal. Equilibrium requires only that the number of vehicles crossing the bridge in one direction is equal to the number crossing in the opposite direction.

The dynamic nature of chemical equilibrium can be illustrated by placing equal masses of iodine crystals in two interconnected flasks, as shown in **Figure 18-4a.** The crystals in the flask on the left contain iodine molecules made up entirely of the nonradioactive isotope I-127. The crystals in the flask on the right contain iodine molecules made up of the radioactive isotope I-131. The Geiger counters indicate the radioactivity within each flask.

**Figure 18-4**

Radioactive iodine molecules from the solid in the flask on the right could not appear in the solid in the flask on the left unless iodine molecules were changing back and forth between the solid and gaseous phases.

---

## DIFFERENTIATED INSTRUCTION

### Visually Impaired

*Kinesthetic* Have two students sit on opposite sides of a table, rest their right (or left) elbows on the table, and lock hands palm-to-palm. Have them push gently with equal force so that their hands do not move. Ask them if the lack of movement means that no forces are being exerted. no

Point out that opposing forces cancel each other, and make the analogy with the equilibrium state. Equilibrium is a state in which the concentrations of reactants and products do not change because two opposing processes are occurring at equal rates. **L1** **ELL**

Each flask is a closed system. No reactant or product can enter or leave. At 298 K and one atmosphere pressure, this equilibrium is established in both flasks.

$$I_2(s) \rightleftharpoons I_2(g)$$

In the forward process, called sublimation, iodine molecules change directly from the solid phase to the gas phase. In the reverse process, gaseous iodine molecules return to the solid phase. A solid-vapor equilibrium is established in each flask.

When the stopcock in the tube connecting the two flasks is opened, iodine vapor can travel back and forth between the two flasks. After a period of time, the readings on the Geiger counters indicate that the flask on the left contains as many radioactive I-131 molecules as the flask on the right *in both the vapor and the solid phases.* See **Figure 18-4b.** How could radioactive I-131 molecules that were originally in the crystals in the flask on the right become part of the crystals in the flask on the left? The evidence suggests that iodine molecules constantly change from the solid phase to the gas phase according to the forward process, and that gaseous iodine molecules convert back to the solid phase according to the reverse process.

## Equilibrium Expressions and Constants

You have learned that some chemical systems have little tendency to react and others go readily to completion. In between these two extremes are the majority of reactions that reach a state of equilibrium with varying amounts of reactants unconsumed. If the reactants are not consumed, then not all the product predicted by the balanced chemical equation will be produced. According to the equation for the ammonia-producing reaction, two moles of ammonia should be produced when one mole of nitrogen and three moles of hydrogen react. Because the reaction reaches a state of equilibrium, however, fewer than two moles of ammonia will actually be obtained. Chemists need to be able to predict the yield of a reaction.

In 1864, the Norwegian chemists Cato Maximilian Guldberg and Peter Waage proposed the **law of chemical equilibrium,** which states that at a given temperature, a chemical system may reach a state in which a particular ratio of reactant and product concentrations has a constant value. For example, the general equation for a reaction at equilibrium can be written as follows.

$$a\text{A} + b\text{B} \rightleftharpoons c\text{C} + d\text{D}$$

A and B are the reactants; C and D the products. The coefficients in the balanced equation are $a$, $b$, $c$, and $d$. If the law of chemical equilibrium is applied to this reaction, the following ratio is obtained.

$$K_{eq} = \frac{[\text{C}]^c[\text{D}]^d}{[\text{A}]^a[\text{B}]^b}$$

This ratio is called the equilibrium constant expression. The square brackets indicate the molar concentrations of the reactants and products at equilibrium in mol/L. The **equilibrium constant,** $K_{eq}$, is the numerical value of the ratio of product concentrations to reactant concentrations, with each concentration raised to the power corresponding to its coefficient in the balanced equation. The value of $K_{eq}$ is constant only at a specified temperature.

How can you interpret the size of the equilibrium constant? Recall that ratios, or fractions, with large numerators are larger numbers than fractions

## Physics
### CONNECTION

In physics, a push or pull on an object is known as a force. Whenever someone pushes on a door, pulls on a dog's leash, or throws a ball, that person exerts a force. When two or more forces are exerted on the same object they add together. If the forces are exerted in opposite directions, one is essentially subtracted from the other. Thus, in a game of tug of war when two teams pull on a rope with equal force, the resulting force has a magnitude of zero. As a result, the object does not move and the system is said to be in equilibrium. Similarly, the acrobats below represent a system in equilibrium. Equal and opposite forces are called balanced forces. If, instead, one force is greater in magnitude than the other, the resulting force is greater than zero when the smaller force is subtracted from the greater one. The resulting force is called an unbalanced force, and an unbalanced force will cause an object to move.

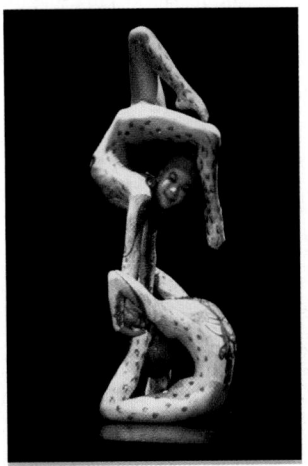

18.1 Equilibrium: A State of Dynamic Balance **563**

---

Students may think that equilibrium systems must contain equal amounts of reactants and products.

### Uncover the Misconception
Ask students to describe the relative amounts of reactants and products in a system at equilibrium. If they answer 50% reactants and 50% products, they display the misconception.

### Demonstrate the Concept
Have students estimate the relative equilibrium concentrations of $N_2$, $H_2$, and $NH_3$ shown in Figure 18-1. Ask if they are equal. approximately $1N_2$: $4H_2$: $3NH_3$; They are not equal.

### Assess New Knowledge
Remind students that the value of the equilibrium constant for the equilibrium system $H_2 + I_2 \rightleftharpoons 2HI$ at 731 K is given on this page as 49.7. Ask them what the value of $K_{eq}$ would be if all concentrations were 1.0$M$. $K_{eq} = 1.0$ Point out that the $K_{eq}$ value of 49.7 clearly shows that the equilibrium system contains more products than reactants.

---

### In-Text Question

**Page 564** Considering the size of $K_{eq}$, are there more products than reactants present at equilibrium? $K_{eq}$ is greater than 1, so there are more products than reactants.

## Resource Manager

Small-Scale Lab Manual, pp. 57–60 **L2**
Challenge Problems, p. 18 **L3**

---

with large denominators. For example, compare the ratio 5/1 with 1/5. Five is a larger number than one-fifth. Because the product concentrations are in the numerator of the equilibrium expression, a numerically large $K_{eq}$ means that the equilibrium mixture contains more products than reactants. Similarly, a numerically small $K_{eq}$ means that the equilibrium mixture contains more reactants than products.

$$K_{eq} > 1: \text{More products than reactants at equilibrium.}$$
$$K_{eq} < 1: \text{More reactants than products at equilibrium.}$$

**Constants for homogeneous equilibria** How would you write the equilibrium constant expression for this reaction in which hydrogen and iodine react to form hydrogen iodide?

$$H_2(g) + I_2(g) \rightleftharpoons 2HI(g)$$

This reaction is a **homogeneous equilibrium,** which means that all the reactants and products are in the same physical state. All participants are gases. To begin writing the equilibrium constant expression, place the product concentration in the numerator and the reactant concentrations in the denominator.

$$\frac{[HI]}{[H_2][I_2]}$$

The expression becomes equal to $K_{eq}$ when you add the coefficients from the balanced chemical equation as exponents.

$$K_{eq} = \frac{[HI]^2}{[H_2][I_2]}$$

$K_{eq}$ for this homogeneous equilibrium at 731 K is 49.7. Note that 49.7 has no units. In writing equilibrium constant expressions, it's customary to omit units. Considering the size of $K_{eq}$, are there more products than reactants present at equilibrium?

### EXAMPLE PROBLEM 18-1

**Equilibrium Constant Expressions for Homogeneous Equilibria**

Write the equilibrium constant expression for the reaction in which ammonia gas is produced from hydrogen and nitrogen.

$$N_2(g) + 3H_2(g) \rightleftharpoons 2NH_3(g)$$

**1. Analyze the Problem**

You have been given the equation for the reaction, which provides the information needed to write the equilibrium constant expression. The equilibrium is homogeneous because the reactants and product are in the same physical state. The form of the equilibrium constant expression is $K_{eq} = \frac{[C]^c}{[A]^a[B]^b}$.

**Known**

| | |
|---|---|
| $[C] = [NH_3]$ | coefficient $NH_3 = 2$ |
| $[A] = [N_2]$ | coefficient $N_2 = 1$ |
| $[B] = [H_2]$ | coefficient $H_2 = 3$ |

**Unknown**

$K_{eq} = ?$

This plant for the manufacture of ammonia employs the Haber process, which maximizes the yield of ammonia by adjusting the temperature and pressure of the reaction.

---

## Internet Address Book

**Chemistry Online**    Note Internet addresses that you find useful in the space below for quick reference.

_____

_____

_____

_____

_____

## 2. Solve for the Unknown

Place the product concentration in the numerator and the reactant concentrations in the denominator.

$$\frac{[NH_3]}{[N_2][H_2]}$$

Raise the concentration of each reactant and product to a power equal to its coefficient in the balanced chemical equation and set the ratio equal to $K_{eq}$.

$$K_{eq} = \frac{[NH_3]^2}{[N_2][H_2]^3}$$

## 3. Evaluate the Answer

The product concentration is in the numerator and the reactant concentrations are in the denominator. Product and reactant concentrations are raised to powers equal to their coefficients.

## PRACTICE PROBLEMS

**1.** Write equilibrium constant expressions for these equilibria.
  **a.** $N_2O_4(g) \rightleftharpoons 2NO_2(g)$
  **b.** $CO(g) + 3H_2(g) \rightleftharpoons CH_4(g) + H_2O(g)$
  **c.** $2H_2S(g) \rightleftharpoons 2H_2(g) + S_2(g)$

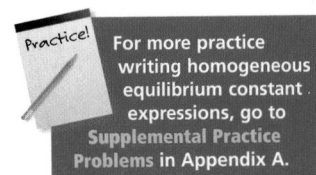

Practice! For more practice writing homogeneous equilibrium constant expressions, go to **Supplemental Practice Problems in Appendix A.**

**Constants for heterogeneous equilibria** You have learned to write $K_{eq}$ expressions for homogeneous equilibria, those in which all reactants and products are in the same physical state. When the reactants and products of a reaction are present in more than one physical state, the equilibrium is called a **heterogeneous equilibrium.**

When ethanol is placed in a closed flask, a liquid-vapor equilibrium is established, as illustrated in **Figure 18-5.**

$$C_2H_5OH(l) \rightleftharpoons C_2H_5OH(g)$$

To write the equilibrium constant expression for this process, you would form a ratio of the product to the reactant. At a given temperature, the ratio would have a constant value $K$.

$$K = \frac{[C_2H_5OH(g)]}{[C_2H_5OH(l)]}$$

Note that the term in the denominator is the concentration of liquid ethanol. Because liquid ethanol is a pure substance, its concentration is constant at a given temperature. That's because the concentration of a pure substance is its density in moles per liter. At any given temperature, density does not change. No matter how much or how little $C_2H_5OH$ is present, its concentration remains constant. Therefore, the term in the denominator is a constant and can be combined with $K$.

$$K[C_2H_5OH(l)] = [C_2H_5OH(g)] = K_{eq}$$

The equilibrium constant expression for this phase change is

$$K_{eq} = [C_2H_5OH(g)]$$

$C_2H_5OH(g)$

$C_2H_5OH(l)$

**Figure 18-5**

The rate of evaporation of ethanol equals the rate of condensation. This two-phase equilibrium is called a heterogeneous equilibrium. $K_{eq}$ depends only on $[C_2H_5OH(g)]$.

18.1 Equilibrium: A State of Dynamic Balance    **565**

## Practice PROBLEMS

Have students refer to Appendix D for complete solutions to Practice Problems.

**1. a.** $K_{eq} = \frac{[NO_2]^2}{[N_2O_4]}$

  **b.** $K_{eq} = \frac{[CH_4][H_2O]}{[CO][H_2]^3}$

  **c.** $K_{eq} = \frac{[H_2]^2[S_2]}{[H_2S]^2}$

## Concept Development

Lead students through the process of calculating the molar concentration of liquid ethanol. 1000 mL $CH_3CH_2OH$/1 L $CH_3CH_2OH$ × 0.789 g $CH_3CH_2OH$/1 mL $CH_3CH_2OH$ × 1 mol $CH_3CH_2OH$/46.07 g $CH_3CH_2OH$ = 17.1 mol/L Point out that unless the density of liquid ethanol changes due to a change in temperature, 17.1 mol/L may be considered a constant for the substance.

## DIFFERENTIATED INSTRUCTION

### English Language Learners

*Linguistic* Have English language learners look up and then explain the meanings of several key English words used in this section: *reversible, equilibrium, homogeneous, heterogeneous.* Have them use each word in a sentence or write a paragraph using all of the words. **L1**
**ELL**

**National Science Content Standards**

**Pages 564–565**
UCP.3, UCP.4; B.3, B.4

Fill a small flask about half-full of water. Stopper the flask securely and show it to students. The next day, ask if the amount of water in the flask is changing. no Then ask if that means that no reactions or processes are occurring in the flask. no Point out that the amount of liquid water remains constant even though two opposing processes are in equilibrium. Ask students to write the chemical equation and equilibrium constant expression for the heterogeneous equilibrium inside the flask. $H_2O(l) \rightleftharpoons H_2O(g)$, $K_{eq} = [H_2O(g)]$

Obtain a bottle of smelling salts and pass it around the classroom for students to smell. Explain that smelling salts are primarily ammonium carbonate, which decomposes to ammonium hydrogen carbonate and ammonia according to the equation $(NH_4)_2CO_3(s) \rightarrow NH_4HCO_3(s) + NH_3(g)$. The ammonia produced in the reaction acts as a heart stimulant when used as smelling salts. Ask students to write the equilibrium constant expression for the heterogeneous chemical equilibrium that exists inside the closed bottle of smelling salts. $K_{eq} = [NH_3(g)]$

Solids also are pure substances with unchanging concentrations, so equilibria involving solids can be simplified in the same way. For example, recall the experiment involving the sublimation of iodine crystals in **Figure 18-4** on page 562.

$$I_2(s) \rightleftharpoons I_2(g)$$

$$K_{eq} = [I_2(g)]$$

The equilibrium depends only on the concentration of gaseous iodine in the system.

## EXAMPLE PROBLEM 18-2

### Equilibrium Constant Expressions for Heterogeneous Equilibria

Write the equilibrium constant expression for the decomposition of baking soda (sodium hydrogen carbonate).

$$2NaHCO_3(s) \rightleftharpoons Na_2CO_3(s) + CO_2(g) + H_2O(g)$$

**1. Analyze the Problem**

You are given a heterogeneous equilibrium involving gases and solids. The general form of the equilibrium constant expression for this reaction is

$$K_{eq} = \frac{[C]^c[D]^d[E]^e}{[A]^a[B]^b}.$$

Because the reactant and one of the products are solids with constant concentrations, they can be omitted from the equilibrium constant expression.

**Known**

| | |
|---|---|
| $[C] = [Na_2CO_3]$ | coefficient $Na_2CO_3 = 1$ |
| $[D] = [CO_2]$ | coefficient $CO_2 = 1$ |
| $[E] = [H_2O]$ | coefficient $H_2O = 1$ |
| $[A] = [NaHCO_3]$ | coefficient $NaHCO_3 = 2$ |

**Unknown**

equilibrium constant expression = ?

**2. Solve for the Unknown**

Write a ratio with the concentrations of the products in the numerator and the concentration of the reactant in the denominator.

$$\frac{[Na_2CO_3][CO_2][H_2O]}{[NaHCO_3]}$$

Leave out $[NaHCO_3]$ and $[Na_2CO_3]$ because they are solids.

$$[CO_2][H_2O]$$

Because the coefficients of $[CO_2]$ and $[H_2O]$ are 1, the expression is complete.

$$K_{eq} = [CO_2][H_2O]$$

**3. Evaluate the Answer**

The expression correctly applies the law of chemical equilibrium to the equation.

Baking soda, or sodium hydrogen carbonate, makes this Irish soda bread light and airy. Baking soda is also useful as an antacid, a cleaner, and a deodorizer.

**566** Chapter 18 Chemical Equilibrium

## Portfolio

### Concentrations of Solids and Liquids

**Intrapersonal** Ask students to explain why concentrations of solids and liquids are omitted from the equilibrium constant expressions for heterogeneous equilibria. Have them write the chemical equations and equilibrium constant expres- sions for two heterogeneous equilibria that involve solids and two that involve liquids. Have them put their explanation, equations, and expressions in their portfolios. **L2** **P**

**2.** Write equilibrium constant expressions for these heterogeneous equilibria.
  **a.** $C_{10}H_8(s) \rightleftharpoons C_{10}H_8(g)$
  **b.** $CaCO_3(s) \rightleftharpoons CaO(s) + CO_2(g)$
  **c.** $H_2O(l) \rightleftharpoons H_2O(g)$
  **d.** $C(s) + H_2O(g) \rightleftharpoons CO(g) + H_2(g)$
  **e.** $FeO(s) + CO(g) \rightleftharpoons Fe(s) + CO_2(g)$

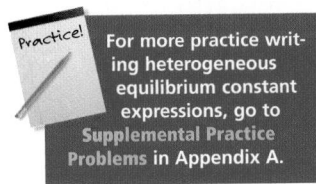

Practice! For more practice writing heterogeneous equilibrium constant expressions, go to **Supplemental Practice Problems in Appendix A.**

## Determining the Value of Equilibrium Constants

For a given reaction at a given temperature, $K_{eq}$ will always be the same regardless of the initial concentrations of reactants and products. To test the truth of this statement, three experiments were carried out to investigate this reaction.

$$H_2(g) + I_2(g) \rightleftharpoons 2HI(g)$$

The results are summarized in **Table 18-1.** In trial 1, 1.0000 mol $H_2$ and 2.0000 mol $I_2$ are placed in a 1.0000-L vessel. These initial concentrations have the symbols $[H_2]_0$ and $[I_2]_0$. No HI is present at the beginning of trial 1. In trial 2, only HI is present at the start of the experiment. In trial 3, each of the three participants has the same initial concentration.

When equilibrium is established, the concentration of each substance is determined experimentally. In **Table 18-1,** the symbol $[HI]_{eq}$ represents the concentration of HI at equilibrium. Note that the equilibrium concentrations are not the same in the three trials, yet when each set of equilibrium concentrations is put into the equilibrium constant expression, the value of $K_{eq}$ is the same. Each set of equilibrium concentrations represents an equilibrium position. Although an equilibrium system has only one value for $K_{eq}$ at a particular temperature, it has an unlimited number of equilibrium positions. Equilibrium positions depend upon the initial concentrations of the reactants and products.

The large value of $K_{eq}$ for the reaction $H_2(g) + I_2(g) \rightleftharpoons 2HI(g)$ means that at equilibrium the product is present in larger amount than the reactants. Many equilibria, however, have small $K_{eq}$ values. Do you remember what this means? $K_{eq}$ for the equilibrium $N_2(g) + O_2(g) \rightleftharpoons 2NO(g)$ equals $4.6 \times 10^{-31}$ at 298 K. A $K_{eq}$ this small means that the product, NO, is practically nonexistent at equilibrium.

**Table 18-1**

| Three Experiments for an Equilibrium System | | | | | | |
|---|---|---|---|---|---|---|
| $H_2(g) + I_2(g) \rightleftharpoons 2HI(g)$ at 731 K | | | | | | |
| Trial | $[H_2]_0$ (M) | $[I_2]_0$ (M) | $[HI]_0$ (M) | $[H_2]_{eq}$ (M) | $[I_2]_{eq}$ (M) | $[HI]_{eq}$ (M) | $K_{eq} = \dfrac{[HI]^2}{[H_2][I_2]}$ |
| 1 | 1.0000 | 2.0000 | 0.0 | 0.06587 | 1.0659 | 1.8682 | $\dfrac{[1.8682]^2}{[0.06587][1.0659]} = 49.70$ |
| 2 | 0.0 | 0.0 | 5.0000 | 0.5525 | 0.5525 | 3.8950 | $\dfrac{[3.8950]^2}{[0.5525][0.5525]} = 49.70$ |
| 3 | 1.0000 | 1.0000 | 1.0000 | 0.2485 | 0.2485 | 1.7515 | $\dfrac{[1.7515]^2}{[0.2485][0.2485]} = 49.70$ |

18.1 Equilibrium: A State of Dynamic Balance    **567**

Have students refer to Appendix D for complete solutions to Practice Problems.

**2. a.** $K_{eq} = [C_{10}H_8(g)]$
  **b.** $K_{eq} = [CO_2(g)]$
  **c.** $K_{eq} = [H_2O(g)]$
  **d.** $K_{eq} = \dfrac{[CO][H_2]}{[H_2O]}$
  **e.** $K_{eq} = \dfrac{[CO_2]}{[CO]}$

# 3 Assess
## Check for Understanding

Ask students if a liquid-vapor equilibrium can be established over a liquid in a container open to the atmosphere. generally, no However, an equilibrium can be established if the atmosphere is saturated or becomes saturated with the vapor.

## Reteach

**Logical-Mathematical** Ask students to use the density of water at 277 K (1.000 g/mL) to calculate the molar concentration of liquid water at that temperature. 55.5 mol/L **L2**

---

## Gifted

**Logical-Mathematical** Have capable students use algebra to determine the number of molecules of each substance present at equilibrium for the reaction $A_3(g) + AB(g) \rightleftharpoons A_2(g) + A_2B(g)$, $K_{eq} = 16$. Initially, the system contains nine $A_3$ molecules and 12 AB molecules. $16 = \dfrac{(x)A_2 \times (x)A_2B}{(9-x)A_3 \times (12-x)AB}$

Solving the equation for $x$ gives a value of 8. Therefore, the equilibrium mixture contains 1 molecule of $A_3$, 4 molecules of AB, 8 molecules of $A_2$, and 8 molecules of $A_2B$. **L3**

National Science Content Standards

Pages 566–567
UCP.3, UCP.4; B.3, B.4; E.2

## Extension

**Logical-Mathematical**
Have interested students use the ideal gas law ($PV = nRT$) to work out the relationship between $K_{eq}$ and $K_p$, the equilibrium constant expressed in partial pressures of gases rather than molar concentrations. $K_{eq} = K_p(1/RT)^{\Delta n}$ where $\Delta n$ = moles of gaseous products − moles of gaseous reactants. **L3**

## ✓ Assessment

**Knowledge** Ask students to write equilibrium constant expressions for the following equilibria.

$2SO_2(g) + O_2(g) \rightleftharpoons 2SO_3(g)$

$K_{eq} = \dfrac{[SO_3]^2}{[SO_2]^2[O_2]}$

$Ni(OH)_2(s) \rightleftharpoons NiO(s) + H_2O(g)$

$K_{eq} = [H_2O]$

## Practice PROBLEMS

Have students refer to Appendix D for complete solutions to Practice Problems.

**3.** $K_{eq} = 0.213$
**4.** $K_{eq} = 3.93$

## CAREERS USING CHEMISTRY

**Career Path** High school courses should include chemistry, biology, other sciences, computer science, and math. Nurse anesthetists complete two to three years of graduate work beyond a bachelor's degree in nursing. They must also be licensed and certified.

**Career Issue** Ask students if they consider the job of nurse anesthetist to be a step into the future or the past. (These nurses have been administering anesthesia for more than 100 years.)

**For More Information**
For more information about a career as a nurse anesthetist, students can contact:
American Association of
  Nurse Anesthetists
222 South Prospect Avenue
Park Ridge, IL 60068

---

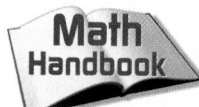

Review solving algebraic equations in the **Math Handbook** on page 897 of this text.

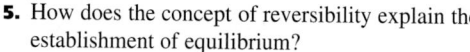

**For more practice** evaluating quotients, go to **Supplemental Practice Problems** in Appendix A.

---

**EXAMPLE** PROBLEM 18-3

### Calculating the Value of Equilibrium Constants

Calculate the value of $K_{eq}$ for the equilibrium constant expression $K_{eq} = \dfrac{[NH_3]^2}{[N_2][H_2]^3}$ given concentration data at one equilibrium position: $[NH_3]$ = 0.933 mol/L, $[N_2]$ = 0.533 mol/L, $[H_2]$ = 1.600 mol/L.

**1. Analyze the Problem**

You have been given the equilibrium constant expression and the concentration of each reactant and product. You must calculate the equilibrium constant. Because the reactant, $H_2$, has the largest concentration and is raised to the third power in the denominator, $K_{eq}$ is likely to be less than 1.

| Known | Unknown |
|---|---|
| $K_{eq} = \dfrac{[NH_3]^2}{[N_2][H_2]^3}$ | $K_{eq} = ?$ |
| $[NH_3]$ = 0.933 mol/L | |
| $[N_2]$ = 0.533 mol/L | |
| $[H_2]$ = 1.600 mol/L | |

**2. Solve for the Unknown**

Substitute the known values into the equilibrium constant expression and calculate its value.

$$K_{eq} = \dfrac{[0.933]^2}{[0.533][1.600]^3} = 0.399$$

**3. Evaluate the Answer**

The smallest number of significant figures in the given data is three. Therefore, the answer is correctly stated with three digits. The calculation is correct and, as predicted, the value of $K_{eq}$ is less than 1.

**PRACTICE** PROBLEMS

**3.** Calculate $K_{eq}$ for the equilibrium in Practice Problem 1a on page 565 using the data $[N_2O_4]$ = 0.0185 mol/L and $[NO_2]$ = 0.0627 mol/L.

**4.** Calculate $K_{eq}$ for the equilibrium in Practice Problem 1b on page 565 using the data $[CO]$ = 0.0613 mol/L, $[H_2]$ = 0.1839 mol/L, $[CH_4]$ = 0.0387 mol/L, and $[H_2O]$ = 0.0387 mol/L.

---

## Section 18.1 Assessment

**5.** How does the concept of reversibility explain the establishment of equilibrium?

**6.** What characteristics define a system at equilibrium?

**7** When you write an equilibrium constant expression, how do you decide what goes in the numerator and in the denominator?

**8. Thinking Critically** Determine whether the following statement is correct: When chemical equilibrium exists, the reactant and product concentrations remain constant and the forward and reverse reactions cease. Explain your answer.

**9. Using Numbers** Determine the value of $K_{eq}$ at 400 K for the decomposition of phosphorus pentachloride if $[PCl_5]$ = 0.135 mol/L, $[PCl_3]$ = 0.550 mol/L, and $[Cl_2]$ = 0.550 mol/L. The equation for the reaction is: $PCl_5(g) \rightleftharpoons PCl_3(g) + Cl_2(g)$

chemistrymc.com/self_check_quiz

---

## Section 18.1 Assessment

**5.** A reversible reaction leads to equilibrium because two opposing reactions may occur at equal rates.

**6.** The concentrations of reactants and products remain constant and the forward and reverse reactions take place at equal rates.

**7.** The concentrations of the products go in the numerator, and the concentrations of the reactants go in the denominator.

**8.** The reactant and product concentrations remain constant; however, the forward and reverse reactions do not cease. Rather, they occur at equal rates.

**9.** $K_{eq}$ = 2.24 See Solutions Manual.

Manufacturers are aware that it makes good sense to minimize waste by finding ways of using leftover materials. Manufacturing new products from byproducts adds to profits and eliminates the problem of disposing of waste without causing environmental damage. What part does equilibrium play in promoting cost-cutting efficiency?

### Le Châtelier's Principle

Suppose that the byproducts of an industrial process are the gases carbon monoxide and hydrogen and a company chemist believes these gases can be combined to produce the fuel methane ($CH_4$) using this reaction.

$$CO(g) + 3H_2(g) \rightarrow CH_4(g) + H_2O(g) \quad \triangle H° = -206.5 \text{ kJ}$$

When the industrial chemist places CO and $H_2$ in a closed reaction vessel at 1200 K, the reaction establishes this equilibrium position (equilibrium position 1).

$$CO(g) \quad + \quad 3H_2(g) \quad \rightleftharpoons \quad CH_4(g) \quad + \quad H_2O(g)$$
$$0.30000M \quad\quad 0.10000M \quad\quad 0.05900M \quad\quad\quad 0.02000M$$

Inserting these concentrations into the equilibrium expression gives an equilibrium constant equal to 3.933.

$$K_{eq} = \frac{[CH_4][H_2O]}{[CO][H_2]^3} = \frac{(0.05900)(0.02000)}{(0.30000)(0.10000)^3} = 3.933$$

Unfortunately, a methane concentration of 0.05900 mol/L in the equilibrium mixture is too low to be of any practical use. Can the chemist change the equilibrium position and thereby increase the amount of methane?

In 1888, the French chemist Henri-Louis Le Châtelier discovered that there are ways to control equilibria to make reactions, including this one, more productive. He proposed what is now called **Le Châtelier's principle:** If a stress is applied to a system at equilibrium, the system shifts in the direction that relieves the stress. A stress is any kind of change in a system at equilibrium that upsets the equilibrium. You can use Le Châtelier's principle to predict how changes in concentration, volume (pressure), and temperature affect equilibrium. Changes in volume and pressure are interrelated because decreasing the volume of a reaction vessel at constant temperature increases the pressure inside. Conversely, increasing the volume decreases the pressure.

**Changes in concentration** What happens if the industrial chemist injects additional carbon monoxide into the reaction vessel, raising the concentration of carbon monoxide from 0.30000*M* to 1.00000*M*? The higher carbon monoxide concentration immediately increases the number of effective collisions between CO and $H_2$ molecules and unbalances the equilibrium. The rate of the forward reaction increases, as indicated by the longer arrow to the right.

$$CO(g) + 3H_2(g) \rightleftharpoons CH_4(g) + H_2O(g)$$

### Objectives
- **Describe** how various factors affect chemical equilibrium.
- **Explain** how Le Châtelier's principle applies to equilibrium systems.

### Vocabulary
Le Châtelier's principle

## Section **18.2**

### 1 Focus

**Focus Transparency**

Before presenting the lesson, display **Section Focus Transparency 69** on the overhead projector. Have students answer the accompanying questions using **Section Focus Transparency Master 69**. **L1** **ELL**

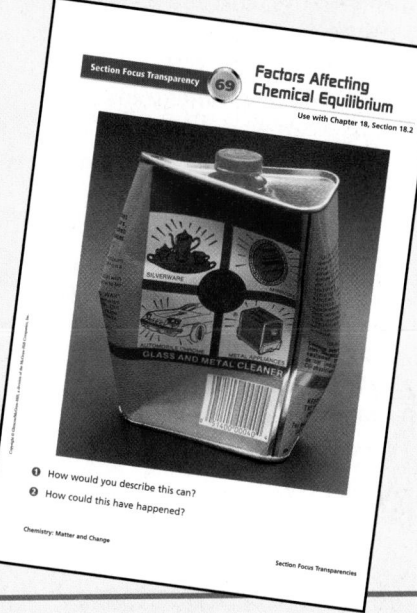

Section Focus Transparency **69**

Factors Affecting Chemical Equilibrium
Use with Chapter 18, Section 18.2

GLASS AND METAL CLEANER

❶ How would you describe this can?
❷ How could this have happened?

Chemistry: Matter and Change

Section Focus Transparencies

### 2 Teach
#### Reinforcement

Emphasize that although Le Châtelier's principle is useful in determining how changes in conditions affect many chemical reactions, it can be applied only to systems at equilibrium.

#### Concept Development

Explain that heat can be thought of as a reactant in an endothermic reaction and a product in an exothermic reaction.

**Resource Manager**

Section Focus Transparency 69 and
  Master **L1** **ELL**
Solving Problems: A Chemistry
  Handbook, Section 18.2 **L2**
Study Guide for Content Mastery,
  pp. 105–106 **L2**

**DIFFERENTIATED INSTRUCTION**

### Learning Disabled

Help students visualize Le Châtelier's principle with this analogy. Hens lay eggs in order to incubate and hatch them. If their eggs are removed after laying, hens lay more eggs in order to fulfill their purpose. Farmers encourage hens to lay more eggs (the reaction) by removing the eggs (product) as soon as they are laid. **L1**

**National Science Content Standards**

Pages 568–569
UCP.3, UCP.4; B.3, B.4; E.2; G.3

Tell students that chemical equilibrium will help simulate the changing of seasons in this Quick Demo. Place a few crystals, about 0.3 g, of crushed $CoCl_2 \cdot 6H_2O$ in a test tube. **CAUTION:** *There should be no open flames in the room.* Add 10 mL ethanol and shake or stir vigorously until most of the solid has dissolved. If the solution is not pink, add water dropwise until the solution just turns light pink. Make a simple painting of a winter scene on a piece of white construction paper, painting the snow with the cobalt chloride solution. To simulate a change in seasons, warm the painting over a hot plate or hot-air register. Explain that the snow turns bluish-green because of the stress of added heat on the equilibrium, which is described in this section.

**GLENCOE TECHNOLOGY**

CD-ROM
**Chemistry: Matter and Change**
Demonstration:
*Hydrogen Bonding*

National Science Content Standards
Pages 570–571
UCP.3, UCP.4; B.3, B.4

In time, the rate of the forward reaction slows down as the concentrations of CO and $H_2$ decrease. Simultaneously, the rate of the reverse reaction increases as more and more $CH_4$ and $H_2O$ molecules are produced. Eventually, a new equilibrium position (position 2) is established with these concentrations.

$$CO(g) + 3H_2(g) \rightleftharpoons CH_4(g) + H_2O(g)$$
$$0.99254M \quad 0.07762M \quad 0.06648M \quad 0.02746M$$

$$K_{eq} = \frac{[CH_4][H_2O]}{[CO][H_2]^3} = \frac{(0.06648)(0.02746)}{(0.99254)(0.07762)^3} = 3.933$$

Note that although $K_{eq}$ has not changed, the new equilibrium position results in the desired effect—an increased concentration of methane. The results of this experiment are summarized in **Table 18-2.**

**Table 18-2**

| Two Equilibrium Positions for the Equilibrium | | | | | |
|---|---|---|---|---|---|
| $CO(g) + 3H_2(g) \rightleftharpoons CH_4(g) + H_2O(g)$ | | | | | |
| Equilibrium position | $[CO]_{eq}$ M | $[H_2]_{eq}$ M | $[CH_4]_{eq}$ M | $[H_2O]_{eq}$ M | $K_{eq}$ M |
| 1 | 0.30000 | 0.10000 | 0.05900 | 0.02000 | 3.933 |
| 2 | 0.99254 | 0.07762 | 0.06648 | 0.02746 | 3.933 |

Could you have predicted this result using Le Châtelier's principle? Yes. Think of the increased concentration of CO as a stress on the equilibrium. The equilibrium system reacts to the stress by consuming CO at an increased rate. This response, called a shift to the right, forms more $CH_4$ and $H_2O$. Any increase in the concentration of a reactant results in a shift to the right and additional product.

Suppose that rather than injecting more reactant, the chemist decides to remove a product ($H_2O$) by adding a desiccant to the reaction vessel. Recall from Chapter 11 that a desiccant is a substance that absorbs water. What does Le Châtelier's principle predict the equilibrium will do in response to a decrease in the concentration of water (the stress)? You are correct if you said that the equilibrium shifts in the direction that will tend to bring the concentration of water back up. That is, the equilibrium shifts to the right and results in additional product.

It might be helpful to think about the produce vendor in **Figure 18-6** who wants to keep a display of vegetables looking neat and tempting. The vendor must constantly add new vegetables to fill the empty spaces created when customers buy the vegetables. Similarly, the equilibrium reaction attempts to restore the lost water by producing more water. As a result, more water and more methane are produced. In any equilibrium, the removal of a product results in a shift to the right and the production of more product.

The equilibrium position also can be shifted to the left, toward the reactants. Do you have an idea how? Le Châtelier's principle predicts that if additional product is added to a reaction at equilibrium, the reaction will shift to the left. The stress is relieved by converting products to reactants. If one of the reactants is removed, a similar shift to the left will occur.

When predicting the results of a stress on an equilibrium using Le Châtelier's principle, it is important to have the equation for the reaction in

**Figure 18-6**

A neat arrangement of produce can be thought of as being at equilibrium—nothing is changing. But when a customer buys some of the vegetables, the equilibrium is disturbed. The produce vendor then restores equilibrium by filling the empty spots.

## Demonstration

### Hydrogen Bonding

#### Purpose
To demonstrate hydrogen bonding in the context of equilibrium

#### Materials
$CoCl_2 \cdot 2H_2O$ (1.4 g); acetone (60 mL); 100-mL graduated cylinder; $H_2O$ (30 mL)

#### Safety Precautions

#### Disposal Solutions can be rinsed down the drain.

#### Procedure
Dissolve 1.4 g of $CoCl_2 \cdot 2H_2O$ in 30 mL of $H_2O$. Place this solution in a 100-mL graduated cylinder. Slowly pour 60 mL of acetone down the inside of the graduated

cylinder. **CAUTION:** *The cobalt chloride solution is toxic and acetone is flammable.* Have students observe the blue layer on top.

#### Results
The acetone forms hydrogen bonds with water and decreases the effective concentration of water in the top layer of the solution. The equilibrium shifts to the right to form the blue chloro complex in the following reaction.

$$CO(g) + 3H_2(g) \rightleftharpoons CH_4(g) + H_2O(g)$$

**❶** $CO(g) + 3H_2(g) \rightleftharpoons CH_4(g) + H_2O(g)$

$\text{⟨CO(g)⟩}$

**❷** $CO(g) + 3H_2(g) \rightleftharpoons CH_4(g) + \text{⟨}H_2O(g)\text{⟩}$

**❸** $\text{⟨CO(g)⟩} + 3H_2(g) \rightleftharpoons CH_4(g) + H_2O(g)$

**❹** $CO(g) + 3H_2(g) \rightleftharpoons CH_4(g) + H_2O(g)$

$\text{⟨}H_2O(g)\text{⟩}$

**Figure 18-7**

The addition or removal of a reactant or product shifts the equilibrium in the direction that relieves the stress. Note the unequal arrows, which indicate the direction of the shift. How would the reaction shift if you added $H_2$? Removed $CH_4$?

view. The effects of changing concentration are summarized in **Figure 18-7.** Refer to this figure as you practice applying Le Châtelier's principle.

**Changes in volume** Consider again the reaction for making methane from byproduct gases.

$$CO(g) + 3H_2(g) \rightleftharpoons CH_4(g) + H_2O(g)$$

Can this reaction be forced to produce more methane by changing the volume of the reaction vessel? Suppose the vessel's volume can be changed using a piston-like device similar to the one shown in **Figure 18-8.** If the piston is forced downward, the volume of the system decreases. You have learned that Boyle's law says that decreasing the volume at constant temperature increases the pressure. The increased pressure is a stress on the reaction at equilibrium. How does the equilibrium respond to the disturbance and relieve the stress?

Recall that the pressure exerted by an ideal gas depends upon the number of gas particles that collide with the walls of the vessel. The more gas particles contained in the vessel, the greater the pressure. If the number of gas particles is increased at constant temperature, the pressure of the gas increases. Similarly, if the number of gas particles is decreased, the pressure also decreases. How does this relationship between numbers of gas particles and pressure apply to the reaction for making methane? Compare the number of moles of gaseous reactants in the equation with the number of moles of gaseous products. For every two moles of gaseous products (1 mol $CH_4$ and 1 mol $H_2O$), four moles of gaseous reactants are consumed (1 mol CO and 3 mol $H_2$), a net decrease of two moles. If you apply Le Châtelier's principle, you can see that the equilibrium can relieve the stress of increased pressure by shifting to the right. This shift decreases the total number of moles of gas and thus, the pressure inside the reaction vessel decreases. Although the shift to the right does not reduce the pressure to its original value, it has the desired effect—the equilibrium produces more methane. See **Figure 18-8.**

**Figure 18-8**

In **ⓐ**, the reaction between CO and $H_2$ is at equilibrium. In **ⓑ**, the piston has been lowered decreasing the volume and increasing the pressure. The outcome is seen in **ⓒ**. More molecules of the products have formed. Their formation helped relieve the stress on the system. How do the numbers of particles in **ⓐ** and **ⓒ** compare?

CO — H₂

CH₄ — H₂O

ⓐ    ⓑ    ⓒ

18.2 Factors Affecting Chemical Equilibrium    **571**

**✓ Assessment**

**Performance** The equilibrium between $NO_2$ and $N_2O_4$ is described by the equation $2NO_2(g) \rightleftharpoons N_2O_4(g) + 57.2$ kJ (brown)    (colorless).
Have students make a poster that illustrates how the relative numbers of molecules of $NO_2$ and $N_2O_4$ in a closed container change and how the color of the equilibrium mixture changes when the system is subjected to two stresses: (1) the volume of the container is increased; (2) the temperature is lowered. When the container's volume is increased, the number of $NO_2$ molecules increases and the color becomes darker. When the temperature is decreased, the number of $N_2O_4$ molecules increases and the color lightens. Use the Performance Task Assessment List for Poster in **PASC,** p. 73.

**Visual Learning**

**Figure 18-7** Explain that a longer equilibrium arrow to the left or right means that one reaction occurs faster than the other *temporarily.* Emphasize that once a new equilibrium position is established, the two reactions again occur at equal rates.

**Figure Caption Questions**

**Figure 18-7** How would the reaction shift if you added $H_2$? to the right Removed $CH_4$? to the right
**Figure 18-8** How do the numbers of particles in **a** and **c** compare? There are fewer particles in **c** than in **a**.

---

$$Co(H_2O)_6{}^{2+} + 4Cl^- \rightleftharpoons CoCl_4{}^{2-} + 6H_2O$$
  (pink)                (blue)

**Analysis**

1. Why does the acetone layer form on top of the water? Acetone is less dense than water.
2. What do chemists call the formation of an attractive force between the

hydrogen atoms of one water molecule and the oxygen atom of another water molecule? hydrogen bonding
3. Using the chemical equation for the equilibrium, which direction is favored when the water is attracted to the acetone and its effective concentration is thereby lowered? the right, favoring the formation of the blue, $CoCl_4{}^{2-}$

**✓ Assessment**

**Knowledge** Ask students to explain the difference between a hydrogen bond and a covalent bond. A covalent bond is the sharing of one or more pairs of electrons. A hydrogen bond is an attractive force between a hydrogen atom and an electronegative element having unshared electrons.

## Applying Chemistry

**TECH PREP** Le Châtelier's principle helped Fritz Haber, a German research chemist, become the first person to synthesize large amounts of ammonia from hydrogen and nitrogen in 1909. The reaction is $3H_2(g) + N_2(g) \rightleftharpoons 2NH_3(g) +$ heat.

The Haber process produces high yields of ammonia partly by adjusting two factors that shift the equilibrium to the right. Increasing the pressure in the reaction vessel shifts the equilibrium to the right because two gaseous molecules ($NH_3$) exert less pressure than four gaseous molecules ($3H_2 + N_2$). To take advantage of this tendency, Haber carried out the reaction at a total pressure of about $2 \times 10^5$ kPa. Although a low temperature favors the products, Haber was forced to raise the temperature to approximately 600°C in order to provide the necessary activation energy. At that temperature, the molecular collisions between hydrogen and nitrogen molecules had sufficient energy to achieve a reasonable reaction rate.

Changing the volume (and pressure) of an equilibrium system shifts the equilibrium only if the number of moles of gaseous reactants is different from the number of moles of gaseous products. Changing the volume of a reaction vessel containing the equilibrium $H_2(g) + I_2(g) \rightleftharpoons 2HI(g)$ would cause no shift in the equilibrium because the number of moles of gas is the same on both sides of the equation.

**Changes in temperature** You have now learned that changes in concentration and volume change the equilibrium position by causing shifts to the right or left, but they do not change the equilibrium constant. A change in temperature, however, alters both the equilibrium position and the equilibrium constant. To understand how a change in temperature affects an equilibrium, recall that virtually every chemical reaction is either endothermic or exothermic. For example, the reaction for making methane has a negative $\triangle H°$, which means that the forward reaction is exothermic and the reverse reaction is endothermic.

$$CO(g) + 3H_2(g) \rightleftharpoons CH_4(g) + H_2O(g) \quad \triangle H° = -206.5 \text{ kJ}$$

Heat can be thought of as a product in the forward reaction and a reactant in the reverse reaction. You can see this by reading the equation forward and backward.

$$CO(g) + 3H_2(g) \rightleftharpoons CH_4(g) + H_2O(g) + \text{heat}$$

How could an industrial chemist regulate the temperature to increase the amount of methane in the equilibrium mixture? According to Le Châtelier's principle, if heat is added, the reaction shifts in the direction in which heat is used up; that is, the reaction shifts to the left. A shift to the left means a decrease in the concentration of methane because methane is a reactant in the reverse reaction. However, lowering the temperature shifts the equilibrium to the right because the forward reaction liberates heat and relieves the stress. In shifting to the right, the equilibrium produces more methane.

Any change in temperature results in a change in $K_{eq}$. Recall that the larger the value of $K_{eq}$, the more product is found in the equilibrium mixture. Thus, for the methane-producing reaction, $K_{eq}$ increases in value when the temperature is lowered and decreases when the temperature is raised.

**Figure 18-9** shows how another equilibrium responds to changes in temperature. The endothermic equilibrium is described by this equation.

$$\text{heat} + Co(H_2O)_6^{2+}(aq) + 4Cl^-(aq) \rightleftharpoons CoCl_4^{2-}(aq) + 6H_2O(l)$$
$$\quad\quad\quad\quad \text{pink} \quad\quad\quad\quad\quad\quad\quad\quad\quad\quad\quad \text{blue}$$

**Figure 18-9**

At room temperature, the solution in **a** is an equilibrium mixture of pink reactants and blue products. When the temperature is lowered in **b**, this endothermic reaction shifts toward the pink reactants. In **c**, the stress of higher temperature causes the reaction to shift toward the blue products.

**National Science Content Standards**

Pages 572–573
UCP.3, UCP.4; A.1; B.3, B.6

## CHEMISTRY JOURNAL

### Le Châtelier in Verse

*Linguistic* Have a contest in which students write creative stories or poems that illustrate Le Châtelier's principle. Have students include the stories or poems in their chemistry journals. Ask a colleague to help you choose winners, and award prizes. Read the best stories or poems to the class. **L2**

## Resource Manager

Small-Scale Lab Manual, pp. 61–64
**L2**

Lab Manual, pp. 137–140 **L2**

$$CO(g) + 3H_2(g) \rightleftharpoons CH_4(g) + H_2O(g) + \text{heat}$$

$$CO(g) + 3H_2(g) \rightleftharpoons CH_4(g) + H_2O(g) + \boxed{\text{heat}}$$

$$\text{heat} + Co(H_2O)_6^{2+}(aq) + 4Cl^-(aq) \rightleftharpoons CoCl_4^{2-}(aq) + 6H_2O(l)$$

$$\boxed{\text{heat}} + Co(H_2O)_6^{2+}(aq) + 4Cl^-(aq) \rightleftharpoons CoCl_4^{2-}(aq) + 6H_2O(l)$$

**Figure 18-10**

For the exothermic reaction between CO and $H_2$, raising the temperature shifts the equilibrium to the left (top equation). Lowering the temperature results in a shift to the right (second equation). The opposite is true for the endothermic reaction involving cobalt and chloride ions (third and last equations).

At room temperature, this mixture of aqueous ions appears violet because it contains significant amounts of pink $Co(H_2O)_6^{2+}(aq)$ and blue $CoCl_4^{2-}(aq)$. When cooled in an ice bath, the equilibrium mixture turns pink. The removal of heat is a stress on the equilibrium. The stress is relieved by an equilibrium shift to the left, generating more heat and producing more pink $Co(H_2O)_6^{2+}$ ions. When heat is added, the equilibrium mixture appears blue because the equilibrium shifts to the right to absorb the additional heat. As a result, more blue $CoCl_4^{2-}$ ions are created. You can investigate this equilibrium system further in the **miniLAB** below. The diagram in **Figure 18-10** shows the effect of heating and cooling on exothermic and endothermic reactions.

Changes in concentration, volume, and temperature make a difference in the amount of product formed in a reaction. Can a catalyst also affect product concentration? A catalyst speeds up a reaction, but it does so equally in both directions. Therefore, a catalyzed reaction reaches equilibrium more quickly, but with no change in the amount of product formed. Read the **Chemistry and Technology** feature at the end of this chapter to learn how Le Châtelier's principle is applied to an important industrial process.

# miniLAB

## Shifts in Equilibrium

**Observing and Inferring** Le Châtelier's principle states that if a stress is placed on a reaction at equilibrium, the system will shift in a way that will relieve the stress. In this experiment, you will witness an equilibrium shift in a colorful way.

**Materials** test tubes (2); 10-mL graduated cylinder; 250-mL beaker; concentrated hydrochloric acid; 0.1$M$ CoCl$_2$ solution; ice bath; table salt; hot plate

**Procedures**

1. Place about 2 mL of 0.1$M$ CoCl$_2$ solution in a test tube. Record the color of the solution.

2. Add about 3 mL of concentrated HCl to the test tube. Record the color of the solution. **CAUTION:** *HCl can burn skin and clothing.*

3. Add enough water to the test tube to make a color change occur. Record the color.

4. Add about 2 mL of 0.1$M$ CoCl$_2$ to another test tube. Add concentrated HCl dropwise until the solution turns purple. If the solution becomes blue, add water until it turns purple.

5. Place the test tube in an ice bath that has had some salt sprinkled into the ice water. Record the color of the solution in the test tube.

6. Place the test tube in a hot water bath that is at least 70°C. Record the color of the solution.

### Analysis

1. The equation for the reversible reaction in this experiment is

$$Co(H_2O)_6^{2+} + 4Cl^- \rightleftharpoons CoCl_4^{2-} + 6H_2O$$
$$\quad\text{pink}\qquad\qquad\qquad\text{blue}$$

Use the equation to explain your observations of color in steps 1–3.

2. Explain how the equilibrium shifts when energy is added or removed.

# miniLAB

## Purpose

Students will observe visible evidence of shifts in equilibrium when stresses are placed on a reaction at equilibrium.

## Process Skills

Analyzing, comparing and contrasting, drawing a conclusion, observing and inferring, recognizing cause and effect

## Safety Precautions

Have students wear gloves, aprons, and goggles. Concentrated HCl is very corrosive to skin and eyes.

## Disposal

Because the solutions produced are acidic, neutralize them with sodium hydrogen carbonate before flushing down the drain.

## Teaching Strategies

- See page 558C for preparation of solutions.
- Reinforce the idea that complex ions are responsible for the colored solutions. The geometry of the pink complex is octahedral; the geometry of the blue complex is tetrahedral.
- Provide HCl in dropper bottles. You may want to use HCl in a fume hood.

## Expected Results

Addition of HCl to the pink solution produces a blue solution. When water is added to the blue solution, it turns pink. The purple solution will turn pink in the ice bath, but turns blue in the hot water bath.

## Analysis

1. The addition of excess chloride ions from the HCl pushes the equilibrium toward the blue ion. Addition of water pushes it back toward the pink ion.

2. Because the blue ion formed when heat was added, the formation of the blue ion is endothermic. The formation of the pink ion is exothermic.

**Resource Manager**

ChemLab and MiniLab Worksheets, p. 69 **L2**
Teaching Transparency 54 and Master **L2** **ELL**

**Assessment**

**Portfolio** Students can write a lab report and include it in their portfolios. **L2**
**P**

# 3 Assess

## Check for Understanding

Ask students to explain why the addition of a catalyst does not change an equilibrium position. A catalyst speeds up the forward and reverse reactions equally.

## Reteach

Summarize the factors that may cause a change in equilibrium position: concentration; volume (pressure); temperature. Ask student volunteers to explain how equilibria may shift in response to each stress.

## Extension

Explain that adding a noble gas to an equilibrium system does not cause the equilibrium to shift to the right or left because, although the total pressure in the container increases, the partial pressures or concentrations of the reactants and products do not change.

## ✓ Assessment

**Portfolio** Ask students to explain how the following stresses affect the equilibrium system.
$PF_3(g) + F_2(g) \rightleftharpoons PF_5(g) + heat$
(1) Volume is decreased. The equilibrium shifts to the right.
(2) Temperature is increased. The equilibrium shifts to the left.
Answers can be placed in students' portfolios. [L2] [P]

## Figure Caption Question

**Figure 18-11** Do you think Sherpas would experience a period of adjustment if they moved to sea level? Yes, the adjustment would be the reverse of that described in the text.

---

**Figure 18-11**

The equilibrium in the blood of Sherpas is adjusted to the lower level of oxygen in the air at high altitudes. Do you think Sherpas would experience a period of adjustment if they moved to sea level?

**A biological equilibrium** If you have ever traveled to the mountains for a strenuous activity such as skiing, hiking, or mountain climbing, it is likely that you have felt tired and lightheaded for a time. This feeling is a result of the fact that at high altitudes, the air is thinner and contains fewer oxygen molecules. An important equilibrium in your body is disturbed. That equilibrium is represented by the following equation.

$$Hgb(aq) + O_2(g) \rightleftharpoons Hgb(O_2)(aq)$$

Hgb and $Hgb(O_2)$ are greatly simplified formulas for hemoglobin and oxygenated hemoglobin, respectively. Hemoglobin is the blood protein that transports oxygen from your lungs to your muscles and other tissues where it is used in the metabolic processes that produce energy. What happens to this equilibrium at an altitude where both the atmospheric pressure and oxygen concentration are lower than normal for your body? Applying Le Châtelier's principle, the equilibrium shifts to the left to produce more oxygen. This shift reduces the amount of $Hgb(O_2)$ in your blood and, therefore, the supply of oxygen to your muscles and other tissues.

After spending some time in the mountains, you probably noticed that your fatigue lessened. That's because your body adapted to the reduced oxygen concentration by producing more Hgb, which shifts the equilibrium back to the right and increases the amount of $Hgb(O_2)$ in your blood. The Sherpas in **Figure 18-11,** who live and work in the mountains, do not experience discomfort because the equilibrium systems in their blood are adapted to high-altitude conditions.

---

## Section 18.2 Assessment

**10.** How does a system at equilibrium respond to a stress? What factors are considered to be stresses on an equilibrium system?

**11.** Use Le Châtelier's principle to predict how each of these changes would affect the ammonia equilibrium system.

$$N_2(g) + 3H_2(g) \rightleftharpoons 2NH_3(g)$$

   **a.** removing hydrogen from the system
   **b.** adding ammonia to the system
   **c.** adding hydrogen to the system

**12.** How would decreasing the volume of the reaction vessel affect each of these equilibria?

   **a.** $2SO_2(g) + O_2(g) \rightleftharpoons 2SO_3(g)$
   **b.** $H_2(g) + Cl_2(g) \rightleftharpoons 2HCl(g)$
   **c.** $2NOBr(g) \rightleftharpoons 2NO(g) + Br_2(g)$

**13.** In the following equilibrium, would you raise or lower the temperature to obtain these results?

$$C_2H_2(g) + H_2O(g) \rightleftharpoons CH_3CHO(g)$$
$$\triangle H° = -151 \text{ kJ}$$

   **a.** an increase in the amount of $CH_3CHO$
   **b.** a decrease in the amount of $C_2H_2$
   **c.** an increase in the amount of $H_2O$

**14. Thinking Critically** Why does changing the volume of the reaction vessel have no effect on this equilibrium?

$$CO(g) + Fe_3O_4(s) \rightleftharpoons CO_2(g) + 3FeO(s)$$

**15. Predicting** Predict how this equilibrium would respond to a simultaneous increase in both temperature and pressure.

$$CO(g) + Cl_2(g) \rightleftharpoons COCl_2(g) \quad \triangle H° = -220 \text{ kJ}$$

chemistrymc.com/self_check_quiz

---

## Section 18.2 Assessment

**10.** If possible, the equilibrium shifts in the direction that relieves the stress. changes in concentration, pressure (volume), and temperature

**11. a.** The equilibrium shifts to the left.
   **b.** The equilibrium shifts to the left.
   **c.** The equilibrium shifts to the right.

**12. a.** The equilibrium shifts to the right.
   **b.** The stress has no effect on the equilibrium.
   **c.** The equilibrium shifts to the left.

**13. a.** Lower the temperature.
   **b.** Lower the temperature.
   **c.** Raise the temperature.

**14.** The number of gaseous particles reacting equals the number of gaseous particles produced.

**15.** Given only this information, the response cannot be predicted because an increase in temperature favors a shift to the left, while an increase in pressure favors a shift to the right.

When a reaction has a large $K_{eq}$, the products are favored at equilibrium. That means that the equilibrium mixture contains more products than reactants. Conversely, when a reaction has a small $K_{eq}$, the reactants are favored at equilibrium, which means that the equilibrium mixture contains more reactants than products. Knowing the size of the equilibrium constant can help a chemist decide whether a reaction is practical for making a particular product.

## Calculating Equilibrium Concentrations

The equilibrium constant expression can be useful in another way. Knowing the equilibrium constant expression, a chemist can calculate the equilibrium concentration of any substance involved in a reaction if the concentrations of all other reactants and products are known.

Suppose the industrial chemist that you read about earlier knows that at 1200 K, $K_{eq}$ equals 3.933 for the reaction that forms methane from $H_2$ and CO. How much methane would actually be produced? If the concentrations of $H_2$, CO, and $H_2O$ are known, the concentration of $CH_4$ can be calculated.

$$CO(g) \quad + \quad 3H_2(g) \quad \rightleftharpoons \quad CH_4(g) \quad + \quad H_2O(g)$$

$$0.850M \qquad 1.333\,M \qquad\quad ?M \qquad\quad 0.286M$$

The first thing the chemist would do is write the equilibrium constant expression.

$$K_{eq} = \frac{[CH_4][H_2O]}{[CO][H_2]^3}$$

The equation can be solved for the unknown $[CH_4]$ by multiplying both sides of the equation by $[CO][H_2]^3$ and dividing both sides by $[H_2O]$.

$$[CH_4] = K_{eq} \times \frac{[CO][H_2]^3}{[H_2O]}$$

All the known concentrations and the value of $K_{eq}$ (3.933) can now be substituted into the equilibrium constant expression.

$$[CH_4] = 3.933 \times \frac{(0.850)(1.333)^3}{(0.286)} = 27.7 \text{ mol/L}$$

The equilibrium concentration of $CH_4$ is 27.7 mol/L.

At this point an industrial chemist would evaluate whether an equilibrium concentration of 27.7 mol/L was sufficient to make the conversion of waste CO and $H_2$ to methane practical. Methane is becoming the fuel of choice for heating homes and cooking food. It is also the raw material for the manufacture of many products including acetylene and formic acid. Increasingly, it is being used as the energy source of fuel cells. At present, methane is relatively inexpensive but as demand grows, the cost will increase. Can the cost of a process which produces 27.7 mol/L $CH_4$ compete with the cost of obtaining methane from underground deposits? This is an important question for the manufacturer. **Figure 18-12** shows a surprising source of methane in the atmosphere.

## Objectives

- **Determine** equilibrium concentrations of reactants and products.

- **Calculate** the solubility of a compound from its solubility product constant.

- **Explain** the common ion effect.

## Vocabulary

solubility product constant
common ion
common ion effect

**Figure 18-12**

As termites relentlessly digest cellulose (wood) throughout the world, they produce methane gas, which enters the atmosphere. Although now present in comparatively small amounts, methane is counted as one of the greenhouse gases.

18.3 Using Equilibrium Constants **575**

# 1 Focus

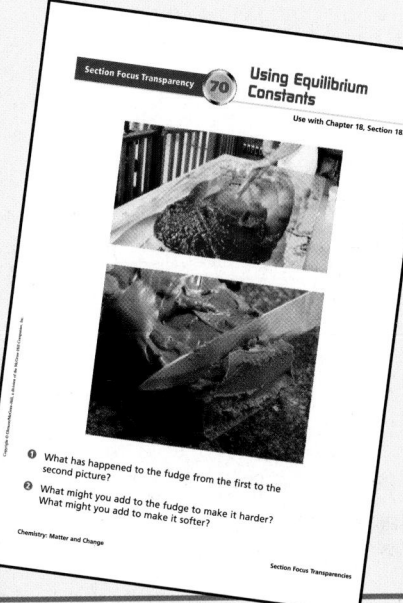

# 2 Teach
### Content Background

**Using Stresses** An industrial chemist might apply Le Châtelier's principle to the reaction between $H_2$ and CO by removing one or both of the product gases as they are formed and simultaneously replenishing the reactants. Both are stresses on the equilibrium that produce more product.

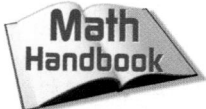

Review solving algebraic equations in the **Math Handbook** on page 897 of this text.

# EXAMPLE PROBLEM 18-4

## Calculating Equilibrium Concentrations

At 1405 K, hydrogen sulfide, also called rotten egg gas because of its bad odor, decomposes to form hydrogen and a diatomic sulfur molecule, $S_2$. The equilibrium constant for the reaction is $2.27 \times 10^{-3}$.

$$2H_2S(g) \rightleftharpoons 2H_2(g) + S_2(g)$$

What is the concentration of hydrogen gas if $[S_2] = 0.0540$ mol/L and $[H_2S] = 0.184$ mol/L?

**1. Analyze the Problem**

You have been given $K_{eq}$ and two of the three variables in the equilibrium constant expression. The equilibrium expression can be solved for $[H_2]$. $K_{eq}$ is less than one, so more reactants than products are in the equilibrium mixture. Thus, you can predict that $[H_2]$ will be less than 0.184 mol/L, the concentration of the reactant $H_2S$.

| Known | Unknown |
|---|---|
| $K_{eq} = 2.27 \times 10^{-3}$ | $[H_2] = ?$ mol/L |
| $[S_2] = 0.0540$ mol/L | |
| $[H_2S] = 0.184$ mol/L | |

**2. Solve for the Unknown**

Write the equilibrium constant expression.

$$\frac{[H_2]^2[S_2]}{[H_2S]^2} = K_{eq}$$

Solve the equation for $[H_2]^2$ by dividing both sides of the equation by $[S_2]$ and multiplying both sides by $[H_2S]^2$.

$$[H_2]^2 = K_{eq} \times \frac{[H_2S]^2}{[S_2]}$$

Substitute the known quantities into the expression and solve for $[H_2]$.

$$[H_2]^2 = 2.27 \times 10^{-3} \times \frac{(0.184)^2}{(0.0540)} = 1.42 \times 10^{-3}$$

$$[H_2] = \sqrt{1.42 \times 10^{-3}} = 0.0377 \text{ mol/L}$$

The equilibrium concentration of $H_2$ is 0.0377 mol/L.

**3. Evaluate the Answer**

All of the data for the problem have three significant figures, so the answer is correctly stated with three digits. As predicted, the equilibrium concentration of $H_2$ is less than 0.184 mol/L.

## PRACTICE PROBLEMS

**16.** At a certain temperature, $K_{eq} = 10.5$ for the equilibrium

$$CO(g) + 2H_2(g) \rightleftharpoons CH_3OH(g)$$

Calculate these concentrations:

**a.** $[CO]$ in an equilibrium mixture containing 0.933mol/L $H_2$ and 1.32 mol/L $CH_3OH$

**b.** $[H_2]$ in an equilibrium mixture containing 1.09 mol/L CO and 0.325 mol/L $CH_3OH$

**c.** $[CH_3OH]$ in an equilibrium mixture containing 0.0661 mol/L $H_2$ and 3.85 mol/L CO.

## Internet Address Book

 Note Internet addresses that you find useful in the space below for quick reference.

_____

_____

_____

_____

## Solubility Equilibria

Some ionic compounds dissolve readily in water and some barely dissolve at all. Sodium chloride, or table salt, is typical of the soluble ionic compounds. On dissolving, all ionic compounds dissociate into ions.

$$NaCl(s) \rightarrow Na^+(aq) + Cl^-(aq)$$

Approximately 36 g NaCl dissolves in 100 mL of water at 273 K. Without this high solubility, sodium chloride couldn't flavor and preserve foods like the pickles shown in **Figure 18-13.** Sodium chloride's vital role as an electrolyte in blood chemistry also depends upon its high solubility.

Although high solubility in water is often beneficial, low solubility also is important in many applications. For example, although barium ions are toxic to humans, patients are required to ingest barium sulfate prior to having an X ray of the digestive tract taken. X rays taken without barium sulfate in the digestive system are not well defined. Why can patients safely ingest barium sulfate?

In water solution, barium sulfate dissociates according to this equation.

$$BaSO_4(s) \rightarrow Ba^{2+}(aq) + SO_4^{2-}(aq)$$

As soon as the first product ions form, the reverse reaction begins to re-form the reactants according to this equation.

$$BaSO_4(s) \leftarrow Ba^{2+}(aq) + SO_4^{2-}(aq)$$

With time, the rate of the reverse reaction becomes equal to the rate of the forward reaction and equilibrium is established.

$$BaSO_4(s) \rightleftharpoons Ba^{2+}(aq) + SO_4^{2-}(aq)$$

For sparingly soluble compounds, such as $BaSO_4$, the rates become equal when the concentrations of the aqueous ions are exceedingly small. Nevertheless, the solution at equilibrium is a saturated solution. The equilibrium constant expression for the dissolving of $BaSO_4$ is

$$K_{eq} = \frac{[Ba^{2+}][SO_4^{2-}]}{[BaSO_4]}$$

In the equilibrium expression, $[BaSO_4]$ is constant because barium sulfate is a solid. This constant value is combined with $K_{eq}$ by multiplying both sides of the equation by $[BaSO_4]$.

18.3 Using Equilibrium Constants    **577**

## Reinforcement

Ask students to explain how adding additional sulfate ions to a saturated solution of barium sulfate would affect the concentration of barium ions. According to Le Châtelier's principle, the equilibrium would shift to lower the sulfate ion concentration. Such a shift would lower the concentration of barium ions as well.

## Concept Development

Some students may have difficulty comparing numerical values expressed in scientific notation. Help them clarify their understanding by asking them to rank the following quantities from largest to smallest: (a) $5.55 \times 10^{-10}$; (b) $8.40 \times 10^{-5}$; (c) $1.43 \times 10^{-25}$; (d) $2.76 \times 10^4$; (e) $3.44 \times 10^{-3}$; (f) $9.81 \times 10^{-33}$; (g) $9.81 \times 10^{-10}$; (h) $2.50 \times 10^{-10}$. d, e, b, g, a, h, c, f

## Figure Caption Question

**Figure 18-13** Can you think of other foods that are preserved by salting? cabbage (sauerkraut), fish, ham

---

### Electrolytes

**Linguistic** Have students research the ions present in human blood plasma. Explain that these ions are called electrolytes. Also, have students research the effects of unusually high or low electrolyte concentrations in the blood and how the body normally maintains appropriate levels of these ions. Ask them to summarize their findings in their chemistry journals. **L2**

**National Science Content Standards**

Pages 576–577
UCP.3, UCP.4; B.2, B.3, B.4; E.2

Point out that, as with solubility product constants, incorporating constant concentrations into equilibrium constants is not unusual. Remind students that in Section 18.1, concentrations of solids and liquids were similarly incorporated when writing equilibrium constant expressions for heterogeneous equilibria.

**Concept Development**

Emphasize to students that when writing chemical equations for solubility equilibria, the solid is always written as the reactant—to the left of the equilibrium arrows—and the ions are always written as the products—to the right of the arrows.

## Resource Manager

**Math Skills Transparency 29 and Master** L2 ELL
**Lab Manual,** pp. 141–144 L2

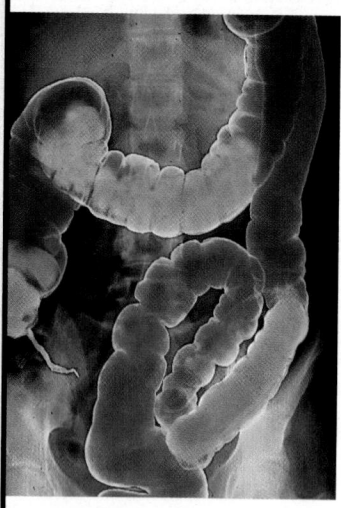

**Figure 18-14**

The presence of barium ions in the gastrointestinal system made the sharp definition of this X ray possible.

$$K_{eq} \times [BaSO_4] = [Ba^{2+}][SO_4^{2-}]$$

The product of $K_{eq}$ and the concentration of the undissolved solid creates a new constant called the solubility product constant, $K_{sp}$. The **solubility product constant** is an equilibrium constant for the dissolving of a sparingly soluble ionic compound in water. The solubility product constant expression is

$$K_{sp} = [Ba^{2+}][SO_4^{2-}] = 1.1 \times 10^{-10} \text{ at } 298 \text{ K}$$

The solubility product constant expression is the product of the concentrations of the ions each raised to the power equal to the coefficient of the ion in the chemical equation. The small value of $K_{sp}$ indicates that products are not favored at equilibrium. Thus, few barium ions are present at equilibrium ($1.0 \times 10^{-5} M$) and a patient can safely ingest a barium sulfate solution to obtain a clear X ray like the one shown in **Figure 18-14.**

Here is another example.

$$Mg(OH)_2(s) \rightleftharpoons Mg^{2+}(aq) + 2OH^-(aq)$$
$$K_{sp} = [Mg^{2+}][OH^-]^2$$

$K_{sp}$ depends only on the concentrations of the ions in the saturated solution. However, to establish an equilibrium system, some undissolved solid, no matter how small the amount, must be present in the equilibrium mixture.

The solubility product constants for some ionic compounds are listed in **Table 18-3.** Note that they are all small numbers. Solubility product constants are measured and recorded only for sparingly soluble compounds.

**Using solubility product constants** The solubility product constants in **Table 18-3** have been determined through careful experiments. $K_{sp}$ values are important because they can be used to determine the solubility of a sparingly soluble compound. Recall that the solubility of a compound in water is the amount of the substance that will dissolve in a given volume of water.

**Table 18-3**

| Solubility Product Constants at 298 K | | | | | |
|---|---|---|---|---|---|
| Compound | $K_{sp}$ | Compound | $K_{sp}$ | Compound | $K_{sp}$ |
| **Carbonates** | | **Halides** | | **Hydroxides** | |
| $BaCO_3$ | $2.6 \times 10^{-9}$ | $CaF_2$ | $3.5 \times 10^{-11}$ | $Al(OH)_3$ | $4.6 \times 10^{-33}$ |
| $CaCO_3$ | $3.4 \times 10^{-9}$ | $PbBr_2$ | $6.6 \times 10^{-6}$ | $Ca(OH)_2$ | $5.0 \times 10^{-6}$ |
| $CuCO_3$ | $2.5 \times 10^{-10}$ | $PbCl_2$ | $1.7 \times 10^{-5}$ | $Cu(OH)_2$ | $2.2 \times 10^{-20}$ |
| $PbCO_3$ | $7.4 \times 10^{-14}$ | $PbF_2$ | $3.3 \times 10^{-8}$ | $Fe(OH)_2$ | $4.9 \times 10^{-17}$ |
| $MgCO_3$ | $6.8 \times 10^{-6}$ | $PbI_2$ | $9.8 \times 10^{-9}$ | $Fe(OH)_3$ | $2.8 \times 10^{-39}$ |
| $Ag_2CO_3$ | $8.5 \times 10^{-12}$ | $AgCl$ | $1.8 \times 10^{-10}$ | $Mg(OH)_2$ | $5.6 \times 10^{-12}$ |
| $ZnCO_3$ | $1.5 \times 10^{-10}$ | $AgBr$ | $5.4 \times 10^{-13}$ | $Zn(OH)_2$ | $3 \times 10^{-17}$ |
| $Hg_2CO_3$ | $3.6 \times 10^{-17}$ | $AgI$ | $8.5 \times 10^{-17}$ | **Sulfates** | |
| **Chromates** | | **Phosphates** | | $BaSO_4$ | $1.1 \times 10^{-10}$ |
| $BaCrO_4$ | $1.2 \times 10^{-10}$ | $AlPO_4$ | $9.8 \times 10^{-21}$ | $CaSO_4$ | $4.9 \times 10^{-5}$ |
| $PbCrO_4$ | $2.3 \times 10^{-13}$ | $Ca_3(PO_4)_2$ | $2.1 \times 10^{-33}$ | $PbSO_4$ | $2.5 \times 10^{-8}$ |
| $Ag_2CrO_4$ | $1.1 \times 10^{-12}$ | $Mg_3(PO_4)_2$ | $1.0 \times 10^{-24}$ | $Ag_2SO_4$ | $1.2 \times 10^{-5}$ |

## Portfolio

### Lead-Based Paints

**Kinesthetic** Have students research the insoluble lead compounds that were used as paint pigments for many years until it was discovered that people—mostly children—were being poisoned by exposure to the lead in these paints. You may decide to have an interested student illustrate the brilliant colors of these compounds on poster paper. L2 COOP LEARN P

Suppose you wish to determine the solubility of silver iodide (AgI) in mol/L at 298 K. The equilibrium equation and solubility product constant expression are

$$AgI(s) \rightleftharpoons Ag^+(aq) + I^-(aq)$$

$$K_{sp} = [Ag^+][I^-] = 8.5 \times 10^{-17} \text{ at } 298 \text{ K}$$

The first thing you should do is let the symbol $s$ represent the solubility of AgI; that is, the number of moles of AgI that dissolves in a liter of solution. The equation indicates that for every mole of AgI that dissolves, an equal number of moles of $Ag^+$ ions forms in solution. Therefore, $[Ag^+]$ equals $s$. Every $Ag^+$ has an accompanying $I^-$ ion, so $[I^-]$ also equals $s$. Substituting $s$ for $[Ag^+]$ and $[I^-]$, the $K_{sp}$ expression becomes

$$[Ag^+][I^-] = (s)(s) = s^2 = 8.5 \times 10^{-17}$$

$$s = \sqrt{8.5 \times 10^{-17}} = 9.2 \times 10^{-9} \text{ mol/L}.$$

The solubility of AgI is $9.2 \times 10^{-9}$ mol/L at 298 K.

---

**EXAMPLE** PROBLEM 18-5

### Calculating Molar Solubility from $K_{sp}$

Use the $K_{sp}$ value from **Table 18-3** to calculate the solubility in mol/L of copper(II) carbonate ($CuCO_3$) at 298 K.

**1. Analyze the Problem**

You have been given the solubility product constant for $CuCO_3$. The copper and carbonate ion concentrations are in a one-to-one relationship with the molar solubility of $CuCO_3$. Use the solubility product constant expression to solve for the solubility. Because $K_{sp}$ is of the order of $10^{-10}$, you can predict that the solubility will be the square root of $K_{sp}$, or about $10^{-5}$.

| Known | Unknown |
|---|---|
| $K_{sp}$ ( $CuCO_3$) = $2.5 \times 10^{-10}$ | solubility of $CuCO_3$ = ? mol/L |

**2. Solve for the Unknown**

Write the balanced chemical equation for the solubility equilibrium and the solubility product constant expression.

$$CuCO_3(s) \rightleftharpoons Cu^{2+}(aq) + CO_3^{2-}(aq)$$

$$K_{sp} = [Cu^{2+}][CO_3^{2-}] = 2.5 \times 10^{-10}$$

Relate the solubility to $[Cu^{2+}]$ and $[CO_3^{2-}]$.

$$s = [Cu^{2+}] = [CO_3^{2-}]$$

Substitute $s$ for $[Cu^{2+}]$ and $[CO_3^{2-}]$ and solve for $s$.

$$(s)(s) = s^2 = 2.5 \times 10^{-10}$$

$$s = \sqrt{2.5 \times 10^{-10}} = 1.6 \times 10^{-5} \text{ mol/L}$$

The molar solubility of $CuCO_3$ in water at 298 K is $1.6 \times 10^{-5}$ mol/L.

Finely ground copper carbonate is added to cattle and poultry feed to supply the necessary element, copper, to animal diets.

**3. Evaluate the Answer**

The $K_{sp}$ value has two significant figures, so the answer is correctly expressed with two digits. As predicted, the molar solubility of $CuCO_3$ is approximately $10^{-5}$ mol/L.

## Reinforcement

At first, students may need help in class with the calculations for Practice Problems 17 and 18.

---

### Practice PROBLEMS

Have students refer to Appendix D for complete solutions to Practice Problems.

**17. a.** $4.8 \times 10^{-7}$ mol/L
 **b.** $1.3 \times 10^{-5}$ mol/L
 **c.** $5.8 \times 10^{-5}$ mol/L
 **d.** $7.0 \times 10^{-3}$ mol/L

---

## CHEMLAB

ChemLab 18, located at the end of the chapter, can be used at this point in the lesson.

---

## Example Problem Question

Can you explain that statement using Le Châtelier's principle?
Solid $Mg(OH)_2$ is in equilibrium with its ions in solution. As $OH^-$ ions are neutralized by stomach acid, the equilibrium shifts to the right to produce more ions.

---

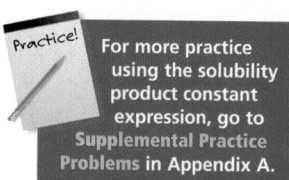

**Practice!** **For more practice using the solubility product constant expression, go to Supplemental Practice Problems in Appendix A.**

This thick white suspension of magnesium hydroxide ($Mg(OH)_2$) is the antacid milk of magnesia. Because $Mg(OH)_2$ is only sparingly soluble, few formula units are in solution. These will be neutralized by stomach acid and then others will dissolve. Can you explain that statement using Le Châtelier's principle?

---

### PRACTICE PROBLEMS

**17.** Use the data in **Table 18-3** to calculate the solubility in mol/L of these ionic compounds at 298 K.
 **a.** $PbCrO_4$      **c.** $CaCO_3$
 **b.** $AgCl$      **d.** $CaSO_4$

You have learned that the solubility product constant can be used to determine the molar solubility of an ionic compound. You can apply this information as you do the **CHEMLAB** at the end of this chapter. $K_{sp}$ also can be used to find the concentrations of the ions in a saturated solution.

### EXAMPLE PROBLEM 18-6

**Calculating Ion Concentration from $K_{sp}$**

Magnesium hydroxide is a white solid that is processed from seawater. Determine the hydroxide ion concentration at 298 K in a saturated solution of $Mg(OH)_2$ if the $K_{sp}$ equals $5.6 \times 10^{-12}$.

**1.  Analyze the Problem**

You have been given the $K_{sp}$ for $Mg(OH)_2$. The moles of $Mg^{2+}$ ions in solution equal the moles of $Mg(OH)_2$ that dissolved, but the moles of $OH^-$ ions in solution are two times the moles of $Mg(OH)_2$ that dissolved. You can use these relationships to write the solubility product constant expression in terms of one unknown. Because the equilibrium expression is a third power equation, you can predict that $[OH^-]$ will be approximately the cube root of $10^{-12}$, or approximately $10^{-4}$.

| Known | Unknown |
|---|---|
| $K_{sp} = 5.6 \times 10^{-12}$ | $[OH^-] = ?$ mol/L |

**2.  Solve for the Unknown**

Write the equation for the solubility equilibrium and the $K_{sp}$ expression.

$$Mg(OH)_2(s) \rightleftharpoons Mg^{2+}(aq) + 2OH^-(aq)$$

$$K_{sp} = [Mg^{2+}][OH^-]^2 = 5.6 \times 10^{-12}$$

Let $x$ equal $[Mg^{2+}]$. Because there are two $OH^-$ ions for every $Mg^{2+}$ ion, $[OH^-] = 2x$. Substitute these terms into the $K_{sp}$ expression and solve for $x$.

$$(x)(2x)^2 = 5.6 \times 10^{-12}$$

$$(x)(4)(x)^2 = 5.6 \times 10^{-12}$$

$$4x^3 = 5.6 \times 10^{-12}$$

$$x^3 = \frac{5.6 \times 10^{-12}}{4} = 1.4 \times 10^{-12}$$

$$x = [Mg^{2+}] = \sqrt[3]{1.4 \times 10^{-12}} = 1.1 \times 10^{-4} \text{ mol/L}$$

Multiply $[Mg^{2+}]$ by 2 to obtain $[OH^-]$.

$$[OH^-] = 2[Mg^{2+}] = 2(1.1 \times 10^{-4} \text{ mol/L}) = 2.2 \times 10^{-4} \text{ mol/L}$$

**3.  Evaluate the Answer**

The given $K_{sp}$ has two significant figures, so the answer is correctly stated with two digits. As predicted, $[OH^-]$ is about $10^{-4}$ mol/L.

---

---

## ✓ Portfolio

### Molar Solubility from $K_{sp}$

**Logical-Mathematical** Have students write the equation for the solubility equilibrium for silver carbonate. Then have them calculate the compound's molar solubility in water at 298 K. Have them include their equations and calculations in their portfolios. **L2** **P** 

$$Ag_2CO_3(s) \rightleftharpoons 2Ag^+(aq) + CO_3^{2-}(aq)$$
$s = $ mol/L $Ag_2CO_3$ that dissolves
$[CO_3^{2-}] = s$ mol/L, $[Ag^+] = 2s$ mol/L
$K_{sp} = [Ag^+]^2[CO_3^{2-}]$
$8.5 \times 10^{-12} = (2s)^2(s) = 4s^3$
$s = 1.3 \times 10^{-4}$ mol/L

---

**National Science Content Standards**
Pages 580–581
UCP.3, UCP.4; B.2, B.3; E.2

**18.** Use $K_{sp}$ values from **Table 18-3** to calculate the following.
   **a.** $[Ag^+]$ in a solution of AgBr at equilibrium
   **b.** $[F^-]$ in a saturated solution of $CaF_2$
   **c.** $[Ag^+]$ in a solution of $Ag_2CrO_4$ at equilibrium
   **d.** the solubility of $PbI_2$

Practice! For more practice using the solubility product constant expression, go to **Supplemental Practice Problems in Appendix A.**

**Predicting precipitates** You have seen that solubility product constants are useful for finding the solubility of an ionic compound and for calculating the concentrations of ions in a saturated solution. You also can use $K_{sp}$ to predict whether a precipitate will form when two ionic solutions are mixed. For example, will a precipitate form when equal volumes of $0.10M$ aqueous solutions of iron(III) chloride ($FeCl_3$) and potassium hexacyanoferrate(II) ($K_4Fe(CN)_6$) are poured together? A double-replacement reaction might occur according to this equation.

$$4FeCl_3 + 3K_4Fe(CN)_6 \rightarrow 12KCl + Fe_4(Fe(CN)_6)_3$$

A precipitate is likely to form only if either product, KCl or $Fe_4(Fe(CN)_6)_3$, has low solubility. You are probably aware that KCl is a soluble compound and would be unlikely to precipitate. However, the $K_{sp}$ for $Fe_4(Fe(CN)_6)_3$ is a very small number, $3.3 \times 10^{-41}$, which suggests that $Fe_4(Fe(CN)_6)_3$ might be expected to precipitate if the concentrations of its ions are large enough. Perhaps you are wondering how large is large enough.

The following equilibrium is possible between solid $Fe_4(Fe(CN)_6)_3$ (a precipitate) and its ions in solution, $Fe^{3+}$ and $Fe(CN)_6^{4-}$.

$$Fe_4(Fe(CN)_6)_3(s) \rightleftharpoons 4Fe^{3+}(aq) + 3Fe(CN)_6^{4-}(aq)$$

When the two solutions are mixed, if the concentrations of the ions $Fe^{3+}$ and $Fe(CN)_6^{4-}$ are greater than those that can exist in a saturated solution of $Fe_4(Fe(CN)_6)_3$, the equilibrium will shift to the left and $Fe_4(Fe(CN)_6)_3(s)$ will precipitate. To make a prediction, then, the ion concentrations must be calculated.

**Table 18-4** shows the concentrations of the ions of reactants and products in the original solutions ($0.10M$ $FeCl_3$ and $0.10M$ $K_4Fe(CN)_6$) and in the mixture immediately after equal volumes of the two solutions were mixed. Note that $[Cl^-]$ is three times as large as $[Fe^{3+}]$ because the ratio of $Cl^-$ to $Fe^{3+}$ in $FeCl_3$ is 3:1. Also note that $[K^+]$ is four times as large as $[Fe(CN)_6^{4-}]$ because the ratio of $K^+$ to $Fe(CN)_6^{4-}$ in $K_4Fe(CN)_6$ is 4:1. In addition, note that the concentration of each ion in the mixture is one-half its original concentration. This is because when equal volumes of two solutions are mixed, the same number of ions are dissolved in twice as much solution, so the concentration is reduced by one-half.

You can now use the data in the table to make a trial to see if the concentrations of $Fe^{3+}$ and $Fe(CN)_6^{4-}$ in the mixed solution exceed the value of $K_{sp}$ when substituted into the solubility product constant expression.

$$K_{sp} = [Fe^{3+}]^4[Fe(CN)_6^{4-}]^3$$

But first, remember that you have not determined whether the solution is saturated. When you make this substitution, it will not necessarily give the solubility product constant. Instead, it provides a number called the ion product, $Q_{sp}$. $Q_{sp}$ is a trial value that can be compared with $K_{sp}$.

**Table 18-4**

| Ion Concentrations in Original and Mixed Solutions | |
|---|---|
| Original solutions (mol/L) | Mixture (mol/L) |
| $[Fe^{3+}] = 0.10$ | $[Fe^{3+}] = 0.050$ |
| $[Cl^-] = 0.30$ | $[Cl^-] = 0.15$ |
| $[K^+] = 0.40$ | $[K^+] = 0.20$ |
| $[Fe(CN)_6^{4-}] = 0.10$ | $[Fe(CN)_6^{4-}] = 0.050$ |

---

Have students refer to Appendix D for complete solutions to Practice Problems.

**18. a.** $[Ag^+] = 7.3 \times 10^{-7}$ mol/L
   **b.** $[F^-] = 4.2 \times 10^{-4}$ mol/L
   **c.** $[Ag^+] = 1.3 \times 10^{-4}$ mol/L
   **d.** $s = 1.3 \times 10^{-3}$ mol/L

✓ **Assessment**

**Skill** Have students look up five compounds that have widely varying $K_{sp}$ values. Have them use the $K_{sp}$ values to calculate the molar solubilities of the compounds and the solubilities in grams per liter of solution. Students can put their data and calculations in their portfolios.
**L2** **P**

✓ **Assessment**

**Skill** To assess how well students understand how to calculate ion concentrations when solutions are mixed, ask them to determine all final ion concentrations in the solution that results from mixing equal volumes of $0.100M$ NaCl solution and $0.100M$ $BaCl_2$ solution. $[Na^+] = 0.050M$, $[Ba^{2+}] = 0.050M$, $[Cl^-] = 0.150M$
**L2**

---

## CULTURAL DIVERSITY

### Prussian Blue

The common name for highly insoluble, deep blue potassium ferrocyanide ($K_4(Fe(CN)_6)_3 \cdot xH_2O$) is Prussian blue. The compound's original name came from its use as a dye in German army uniforms.

A German color maker and dyer in Berlin named Diesbach accidentally discovered Prussian blue's deep blue color in 1704, mistakenly thinking—because it was made from cattle blood—that the pigment would be red.

Prussian blue was the earliest of the modern synthetic colors. After its discovery in 1704, the manufacturing process of this pigment was passed to Diesbach's pupil, de Pierre, who in turn began manufacturing Prussian blue in Paris. Simon Eikenlenberg, a Dutch painter, wrote on the knowledge of Prussian blue in his Notes on Paint and Painting in 1722. By 1724, the manufacturing process of the pigment had spread to England and appeared in an artists' manual by Woodard.

## Precipitate Colors and Qualitative Analysis

Explain to students that precipitate colors are often characteristic of particular compounds and can be used to confirm the presence of a particular ion in solution. For example, as a test for the presence of iron(III) ions, the addition of several drops of aqueous potassium hexacyanoferrate(II) solution to a solution containing iron(III) produces a deep blue precipitate of iron(III) hexacyanoferrate(II).

### Practice PROBLEMS

Have students refer to Appendix D for complete solutions to Practice Problems.

**19. a.** A precipitate of $PbF_2$ forms.

**b.** No precipitate forms.

**c.** A precipitate of $Mg(OH)_2$ forms.

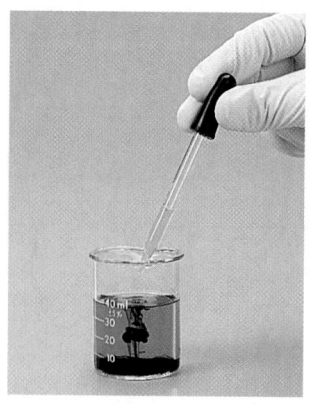

**Figure 18-15**

Because the ion product constant ($Q_{sp}$) is greater than $K_{sp}$, you could predict that this precipitate of $Fe_4(Fe(CN)_6)_3$ would form.

The peeling lead-based paint on this building is a hazard to small children who sometimes ingest small pieces of paint. Lead can build up in the body and cause many physical symptoms as well as brain damage and mental retardation.

$$Q_{sp} = [Fe^{3+}]^4[Fe(CN)_6^{4-}]^3 = (0.050)^4(0.050)^3 = 7.8 \times 10^{-10}$$

You can now compare $Q_{sp}$ and $K_{sp}$. This comparison can have one of three outcomes: $Q_{sp}$ can be less than $K_{sp}$, equal to $K_{sp}$, or greater than $K_{sp}$.

**1.** If $Q_{sp} < K_{sp}$, the solution is unsaturated. No precipitate will form.

**2.** If $Q_{sp} = K_{sp}$, the solution is saturated and no change will occur.

**3.** If $Q_{sp} > K_{sp}$, a precipitate will form reducing the concentrations of the ions in the solution until the product of their concentrations in the $K_{sp}$ expression equals the numerical value of $K_{sp}$. Then the system is in equilibrium and the solution is saturated.

In the case of the $Fe_4(Fe(CN)_6)_3$ equilibrium, $Q_{sp}$ ($7.8 \times 10^{-10}$) is larger than $K_{sp}$ ($3.3 \times 10^{-41}$) so a deeply colored blue precipitate of $Fe_4(Fe(CN)_6)_3$ forms, as you can see in **Figure 18-15**. Example Problem 18-7 and the **problem-solving LAB** on the following page will give you practice in calculating $Q_{sp}$ to predict precipitates.

### EXAMPLE PROBLEM 18-7

**Predicting a Precipitate**

Predict whether a precipitate of $PbCl_2$ will form if 100 mL of 0.0100M NaCl is added to 100 mL of 0.0200M $Pb(NO_3)_2$.

**1. Analyze the Problem**

You have been given equal volumes of two solutions with known concentrations. The concentrations of the initial solutions allow you to calculate the concentrations of $Pb^{2+}$ and $Cl^-$ ions in the mixed solution. The initial concentrations, when multiplied together in the solubility product constant expression, give an ion product of the order of $10^{-6}$, so it is probable that after dilution, $Q_{sp}$ will be less than $K_{sp}$ ($1.7 \times 10^{-5}$) and $PbCl_2$ will not precipitate.

| Known | Unknown |
|---|---|
| 100 mL 0.0100M NaCl | $Q_{sp} > K_{sp}$? |
| 100 mL 0.0200M $Pb(NO_3)_2$ | |
| $K_{sp} = 1.7 \times 10^{-5}$ | |

**2. Solve for the Unknown**

Write the equation for the dissolving of $PbCl_2$ and the ion product expression, $Q_{sp}$.

$$PbCl_2(s) \rightleftharpoons Pb^{2+}(aq) + 2Cl^-(aq)$$

$$Q_{sp} = [Pb^{2+}][Cl^-]^2$$

Divide the concentrations of $Cl^-$ and $Pb^{2+}$ in half because on mixing, the volume doubles.

$$[Cl^-] = \frac{0.0100M}{2} = 0.00500M$$

$$[Pb^{2+}] = \frac{0.0200M}{2} = 0.0100M$$

Substitute these values into the ion product expression.

$$Q_{sp} = (0.0100)(0.00500)^2 = 2.5 \times 10^{-7}$$

Compare $Q_{sp}$ with $K_{sp}$.

$$Q_{sp} (2.5 \times 10^{-7}) < K_{sp} (1.7 \times 10^{-5})$$

A precipitate will not form.

### CHEMISTRY JOURNAL

#### Spectator Ions and Activity

*Intrapersonal* Have interested and capable students research the effects of spectator ions on solubility. Spectator ions increase the solubilities of ionic compounds in aqueous solutions. Have them explain how activities take these electro-static interactions into account and replace concentrations in the $K_{sp}$, thus providing a more accurate equilibrium constant. Have students put their findings in their chemistry journals. **L3**

## 3. Evaluate the Answer

As predicted, $Q_{sp}$ is less than $K_{sp}$. The $Pb^{2+}$ and $Cl^-$ ions are not present in high enough concentrations in the mixed solution to cause precipitation to occur.

## PRACTICE PROBLEMS

19. Use $K_{sp}$ values from **Table 18-3** to predict whether a precipitate will form when equal volumes of the following aqueous solutions are mixed.
    a. 0.10$M$ $Pb(NO_3)_2$ and 0.030$M$ NaF
    b. 0.25$M$ $K_2SO_4$ and 0.010$M$ $AgNO_3$
    c. 0.20$M$ $MgCl_2$ and 0.0025$M$ NaOH

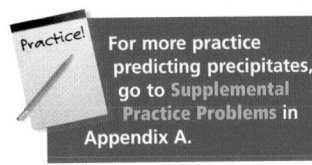

For more practice predicting precipitates, go to Supplemental Practice Problems in Appendix A.

## Common Ion Effect

The solubility of lead chromate ($PbCrO_4$) in water is $4.8 \times 10^{-7}$ mol/L at 298 K. That means you can dissolve $4.8 \times 10^{-7}$ mol $PbCrO_4$ in 1.00 L of pure water. However, you can't dissolve $4.8 \times 10^{-7}$ mol $PbCrO_4$ in 1.00 L of 0.10$M$ aqueous potassium chromate ($K_2CrO_4$) solution at that temperature. Why is $PbCrO_4$ less soluble in an aqueous $K_2CrO_4$ solution than in pure water?

## problem-solving LAB

### How does fluoride prevent tooth decay?

**Using Numbers** During the last half century, tooth decay has decreased significantly because minute quantities of fluoride ion ($6 \times 10^{-5}M$) are being added to most public drinking water and many people are using toothpastes containing sodium fluoride or tin(II) fluoride. Use what you know about the solubility of ionic compounds and reversible reactions to explore the role of the fluoride ion in maintaining cavity-free teeth.

### Analysis

Tooth enamel, the hard, protective outer layer of the tooth, is 98% hydroxyapatite ($Ca_5(PO_4)_3OH$). Although quite insoluble ($K_{sp} = 6.8 \times 10^{-37}$ in water), demineralization, which is the dissolving of hydroxyapatite, does occur especially when the saliva contains acids. The reverse reaction, remineralization, also occurs. Remineralization is the re-depositing of tooth enamel. When hydroxyapatite is in solution with fluoride ions, a double-replacement reaction can occur. Fluoride ion replaces the hydroxide ion to form fluoroapatite ($Ca_5(PO_4)_3F$, $K_{sp} = 1 \times 10^{-60}$). Fluoroapatite remineralizes the tooth enamel, thus partially displacing hydroxyapatite. Because fluoroapatite is less soluble than hydroxyapatite, destructive demineralization is reduced.

### Thinking Critically

1. Write the equation for the dissolving of hydroxyapatite and its equilibrium constant expression. How do the conditions in the mouth differ from those of a true equilibrium?

2. Write the equation for the double-replacement reaction that occurs between hydroxyapatite and sodium fluoride.

3. Calculate the solubility of hydroxyapatite and fluoroapatite in water. Compare the solubilities.

4. What is the ion product constant ($Q_{sp}$) for the reaction if 0.00050$M$ NaF is mixed with an equal volume of 0.000015$M$ $Ca_5(PO_4)_3OH$? Will a precipitate form (re-mineralization)?

18.3 Using Equilibrium Constants    **583**

---

## problem-solving LAB

### Purpose

Students will use solubility product calculations to explore the effectiveness of fluoride in preventing tooth decay.

### Process Skills

Using numbers, drawing conclusions, thinking critically, applying concepts

### Teaching Strategies

- Tell students how the effects of fluoride were discovered when people in areas having high concentrations of fluoride in their drinking water were found to have a low incidence of cavities. Many communities now add fluoride to public water supplies.
- Explain that if saliva were static and microbe free, solid hydroxyapatite would establish an equilibrium with its ions in solution and there would be no net loss of enamel. The flow of saliva prevents a true equilibrium from being achieved; however, remineralizing does take place.

### Thinking Critically

1. $Ca_5(PO_4)_3OH(s) \rightleftharpoons 5Ca^{2+}(aq) + 3PO_4^{3-}(aq) + OH^-(aq)$
   $K_{sp} = [Ca^{2+}]^5[PO_4^{3-}]^3[OH^-]$
   The mouth is not a closed system. Saliva is being produced and swallowed regularly.

2. $Ca_5(PO_4)_3OH + NaF \rightleftharpoons NaOH + Ca_5(PO_4)_3F$

3. For hydroxyapatite, let $[OH^-] = s$ (the solubility). Then, $[Ca^{2+}] = 5s$ and $[PO_4^{3-}] = 3s$.
   $K_{sp} = [Ca^{2+}]^5[PO_4^{3-}]^3[OH^-] = 6.8 \times 10^{-37}$
   Solubility ($Ca_5(PO_4)_3OH$) = $(5s)^5(3s)^3(s)$; $s = 2.7 \times 10^{-5}$ $M$
   For fluoroapatite, $(5s)^5(3s)^3(s) = 1 \times 10^{-60}$
   Solubility ($Ca_5(PO_4)_3F$) = $s = 6 \times 10^{-8}M$
   The solubility of hydroxyapatite is 450 times greater than the solubility of fluoroapatite.

4. $Q_{sp} = [5(\frac{1}{2})(0.000015)]^5 [3(\frac{1}{2})(0.000015)]^3[(\frac{1}{2})0.00050] = 2.5 \times 10^{-40}$. The product will precipitate, remineralizing the tooth enamel.

---

## CHEMISTRY JOURNAL

### Solubility and Qualitative Analysis

*Linguistic* Have students research the way that solubility is used in qualitative analysis to separate the group II cations such as $Zn^{2+}$, and group III cations such as $Fe^{3+}$ and $Cu^{2+}$. Have students put their explanations, including relevant equations, in their chemistry journals. **L2**

## ✓ Assessment

**Portfolio** Have students research the fluoridation of drinking water. Have them look more closely into the effect of salivary acid on hydroxyapatite and apply what they learn to the question of fluoridation. Students can write reports to be added to their portfolios. **L2** **P**

## Assessment

**Knowledge** Ask students to explain two ways in which they could use the common ion effect to lower the solubility of silver iodide in an aqueous solution. Increase the concentration of silver ions by adding a soluble silver compound or increase the concentration of iodide ions by adding a soluble iodide compound.

## Figure Caption Questions

**Figure 18-18** Which reactions are separations? the reactions with HCl, hot water, and NH$_3$ Which reactions confirm the presence of an ion? The reaction of Pb$^{2+}$ with K$_2$CrO$_4$ confirms Pb$^{2+}$, the reaction of Ag$^+$ and Hg$_2^{2+}$ with ammonia confirms Hg$_2^{2+}$, and the reaction of Ag(NH$_3$)$^+$ with HNO$_3$ confirms Ag$^+$.

# 3 Assess

## Check for Understanding

Ask students how a solid compound's molar concentration is used in calculating the compound's molar solubility in water. It is not used.

**National Science Content Standards**

**Pages 584–585**
UCP.3, UCP.4; A.2; B.2, B.4

---

**Figure 18-16**

In a solution of PbCrO$_4$ in pure water, [Pb$^{2+}$] and [CrO$_4^{2-}$] are equal. But in a solution with a common CrO$_4^{2-}$ ion, [Pb$^{2+}$] is much less than [CrO$_4^{2-}$]. In each case, however, the product of the two ions equals $K_{sp}$ and the solubility of PbCrO$_4$ equals [Pb$^{2+}$].

**Figure 18-17**

In **a**, PbCrO$_4$(s) is in equilibrium with its ions in solution. Then, in **b**, the equilibrium is stressed by the addition of Pb(NO$_3$)$_2$ and more PbCrO$_4$ precipitate forms. Use the equation and Le Châtelier's principle to convince yourself that a shift to the left occurred. Then write the $K_{sp}$ for this reaction as in **Figure 18-16**.

a

b

---

$$[Pb^{2+}][CrO_4^{2-}] = 2.3 \times 10^{-13} \text{ (in water)}$$

$$[Pb^{2+}]\left[CrO_4^{2-}\right] = 2.3 \times 10^{-13} \text{ (in } 0.10M \text{ K}_2\text{CrO}_4)$$

The equation for the PbCrO$_4$ solubility equilibrium and the solubility product constant expression are

$$PbCrO_4(s) \rightleftharpoons Pb^{2+}(aq) + CrO_4^{2-}(aq).$$

$$K_{sp} = [Pb^{2+}][CrO_4^{2-}] = 2.3 \times 10^{-13}$$

Recall that $K_{sp}$ is a constant at any given temperature, so if the concentration of either Pb$^{2+}$ or CrO$_4^{2-}$ increases when the system is at equilibrium, the concentration of the other ion must decrease. The product of the concentrations of the two ions must always equal $K_{sp}$. The K$_2$CrO$_4$ solution contains CrO$_4^{2-}$ ions before any PbCrO$_4$ dissolves. In this example, the CrO$_4^{2-}$ ion is called a common ion because it is part of both PbCrO$_4$ and K$_2$CrO$_4$. A **common ion** is an ion that is common to two or more ionic compounds. The lowering of the solubility of a substance by the presence of a common ion is called the **common ion effect.**

**Figure 18-16** illustrates how the balance between the ion concentrations differs in a solution of PbCrO$_4$ in pure water and in a 0.10$M$ solution of K$_2$CrO$_4$. In each case, [Pb$^{2+}$] represents the solubility of PbCrO$_4$.

**The common ion effect and Le Châtelier's principle** A saturated solution of lead chromate (PbCrO$_4$) is shown in **Figure 18-17a**. Note the solid yellow PbCrO$_4$ in the bottom of the test tube. The solution and solid are in equilibrium according to this equation.

$$PbCrO_4(s) \rightleftharpoons Pb^{2+}(aq) + CrO_4^{2-}(aq)$$

When a solution of Pb(NO$_3$) is added to the saturated PbCrO$_4$ solution, more solid PbCrO$_4$ precipitates, as you can see in **Figure 18-17b**. The Pb$^{2+}$ ion, common to both Pb(NO$_3$)$_2$ and PbCrO$_4$, reduces the solubility of PbCrO$_4$. Can this precipitation of PbCrO$_4$ be explained by Le Châtelier's principle? Adding Pb$^{2+}$ ion to the solubility equilibrium stresses the equilibrium. To relieve the stress, the equilibrium shifts to the left to form more solid PbCrO$_4$.

The common ion effect also plays a role in the use of barium sulfate (BaSO$_4$) when X rays are taken of the digestive system. Recall that patients who need such X rays must drink a mixture containing BaSO$_4$. The low solubility of BaSO$_4$ helps ensure that the amount of the toxic barium ion absorbed into patient's system is small enough to be harmless. The procedure is further safeguarded by the addition of sodium sulfate (Na$_2$SO$_4$), a soluble ionic compound that provides a common ion, SO$_4^{2-}$. How does the additional SO$_4^{2-}$ affect the concentration of barium ion in the mixture that patients must drink?

---

**DIFFERENTIATED INSTRUCTION**

### Gifted

*Logical-Mathematical* Have capable students calculate the molar solubility of lead(II) iodide in 0.422$M$ potassium iodide at 298 K. Students can calculate the solubility based on the concentration of Pb$^{2+}$. Have them tabulate initial ion concentrations before the addition of PbI$_2$, the change in concentration as the result of adding PbI$_2$, and the equilibrium ion concentrations. The equilibrium concentrations then can be substituted into the ion product to calculate $Q_{sp}$, but to avoid solving a quadratic equation, a simplifying assumption can be made. Have students identify the assumption and justify its use. The assumption is that 2s is negligible compared to 0.422$M$. s = 2.3 × 10$^{-4}$ mol/L **L3**

$$BaSO_4(s) \rightleftharpoons Ba^{2+}(aq) + SO_4^{2-}(aq)$$

Le Châtelier's principle predicts that additional $SO_4^{2-}$ from the $Na_2SO_4$ will shift the equilibrium to the left to produce more solid $BaSO_4$ and reduce the number of harmful $Ba^{2+}$ ions in solution.

## Solubility Equilibria in the Laboratory

Suppose you are given a clear aqueous solution and told that it could contain almost any of the ions formed by the common metallic elements. Your job is to find out which ions the solution contains. It seems an impossible task, but chemists have worked out a scheme that allows you to separate and identify many common metal ions. The scheme is based upon the differing solubilities of the ions. For example, only three ions form insoluble chlorides—$Ag^+$, $Pb^{2+}$, and $Hg_2^{2+}$. That may give you an idea of how you could proceed. If you add HCl to your solution, those three ions will precipitate as a white solid that would contain $AgCl(s)$, $PbCl_2(s)$, and $Hg_2Cl_2(s)$ if all three of the metal ions are present. The ions that do not form insoluble chlorides will be left in the clear solution, which can be separated from the white solid.

Is $PbCl_2$ present in the white solid? To find out, you can use the fact that $PbCl_2$ is soluble in hot water but AgCl and $Hg_2Cl_2$ are not. After adding water and heating the mixture of chlorides, you can separate the liquid (that could contain dissolved $PbCl_2$) from AgCl and $Hg_2Cl_2$, which are still in solid form. What test could you use to show that the separated liquid contains $Pb^{2+}$? Remember that $PbCrO_4$ is a sparingly compound. You could add $K_2CrO_4$. If a yellow precipitate of $PbCrO_4$ forms, you have proof of the presence of $Pb^{2+}$.

Are $Hg_2Cl_2$, or AgCl, or both compounds present in the remaining precipitate? Silver chloride is soluble in ammonia; mercury(I) chloride forms a black precipitate with ammonia. Suppose you add ammonia and get a black precipitate. You can conclude that $Hg_2^{2+}$ is present. But did AgCl dissolve in ammonia, or was all the white precipitate $Hg_2Cl_2$? To find out, you can add HCl to the solution. HCl will interact with the ammonia in the solution and cause AgCl to precipitate again.

The procedure you have been reading is just one step in the complete analysis of the initial solution of ions. **Figure 18-18** is a flow chart of the steps in the procedure. Follow the chart step by step through each identification. Note that as each reactant is added (HCl, hot water, $NH_3$), a separation is made between those ions that are soluble and those that are not.

**Figure 18-18**

Follow the process down the chart. The reactants added at each step are written on the downward arrows. Which reactions are separations? Which reactions confirm the presence of an ion?

**LAB** Try at Home

See page 960 in Appendix E for **Cornstarch Solubility**

chemistrymc.com/self_check_quiz

18.3 Using Equilibrium Constants    **585**

## Reteach

Lead students through writing the solubility product constant expressions for iron(III) hydroxide and calcium phosphate. $K_{sp} = [Fe^{3+}][OH^-]^3$; $K_{sp} = [Ca^{2+}]^3[PO_4^{3-}]^2$.

## Extension

Students may be surprised to learn that spectator ions increase the solubility of an ionic compound in an aqueous solution. Explain that ions in solution can exert significant forces on each other, in effect increasing $K_{sp}$ as ion concentration increases.

### ✔ Assessment

**Skill** Ask students to use Table 18-3 to predict the formulas of precipitates that might form when aqueous solutions of the following compounds are mixed: (a) copper(II) chloride and sodium carbonate $CuCO_3$; (b) magnesium sulfate and phosphoric acid $Mg_3(PO_4)_2$; (c) lead(II) nitrate and lithium fluoride $PbF_2$. **L2**

---

## Section 18.3 Assessment

**20.** List the information you would need in order to calculate the concentration of a product in a reaction mixture at equilibrium.

**21.** How can you use the solubility product constant to calculate the solubility of a sparingly soluble ionic compound?

**22.** What is a common ion? Explain how a common ion reduces the solubility of an ionic compound.

**23. Thinking Critically** When aqueous solutions of two ionic compounds are mixed, how does $Q_{sp}$ relate to $K_{sp}$ for a possible precipitate?

**24. Designing an Experiment** An aqueous solution is known to contain either $Mg^{2+}$ or $Pb^{2+}$. Design an experiment based on solubilities that would help you determine which of the two ions is present. The solubilities of many ionic compounds are given in **Table C-10** in Appendix C.

**23.** If $Q_{sp} > K_{sp}$, a precipitate forms. If $Q_{sp} = K_{sp}$, no precipitate forms and the solution is saturated. If $Q_{sp} < K_{sp}$, no precipitate forms and the solution is unsaturated.

**24.** Because magnesium chromate is soluble and lead(II) chromate is insoluble, add 10.0 mL of 0.10$M$ aqueous potassium chromate solution to 100.0 mL of the unknown aqueous solution. If the unknown solution contains magnesium ion, no precipitate of $MgCrO_4$ will be produced. However, if the unknown solution contains lead(II) ion, solid, yellow $PbCrO_4$ will precipitate.

---

## Section 18.3 Assessment

**20.** the concentrations of the reactants and all other products and $K_{eq}$

**21.** Write the equation for the solubility equilibrium and the solubility product constant expression. Let $s$ equal the compound's molar solubility. Substitute the appropriate multiples of $s$ into the $K_{sp}$ expression and solve the expression for $s$.

**22.** an ion that is common to two or more ionic compounds; the presence of a common ion reduces solubility by shifting the solubility equilibrium in the direction of the solid.

**585**

# CHEMLAB 18 Small Scale

## Preparation

### Time Allotment
One laboratory period

### Process Skills
Observing and inferring, comparing and contrasting, drawing a conclusion, using numbers

### Safety Precautions
Students should wear aprons and goggles and wash their hands after completing the laboratory investigation.

### Disposal
Use a wash bottle to transfer the contents of the microplate into a large waste beaker. Evaporate the contents of the beaker to dryness. Dispose of the solid at a facility that is licensed to receive hazardous waste and recover silver.

### Preparation of Solutions
See page 558C for preparation of all solutions.

## Pre-Lab

**3.** Le Châtelier's principle states that if a stress is applied to a system at equilibrium, the system shifts in the direction that relieves the stress.

**4.** The control is the solution prepared in well A1 by mixing 10 drops of silver nitrate solution and 10 drops of sodium chloride solution. The independent variable is the 10 drops of ammonium sulfide added to the solution in well A2.

**5.** molar solubility $s = \sqrt{K_{sp}}$

## Procedure

• Place small amounts of each solution in labeled containers throughout the laboratory.
• **Troubleshooting** Pipettes should be used for one solution only. Contamination of the solutions results in precipitation.

## Expected Results

When the first two solutions are mixed, a white precipitate of AgCl forms. The color of the precipitate

# Comparing Two Solubility Product Constants

**L**e Châtelier's principle is a powerful tool for explaining how a reaction at equilibrium shifts when a stress is placed on the system. In this experiment, you can use Le Châtelier's principle to evaluate the relative solubilities of two precipitates. By observing the formation of two precipitates in the same system, you can infer the relationship between the solubilities of the two ionic compounds and the numerical values of their solubility product constants ($K_{sp}$). You will be able to verify your own experimental results by calculating the molar solubilities of the two compounds using the $K_{sp}$ for each compound.

### Problem
How can a saturated solution of one ionic compound react with another ionic compound to form another precipitate? What is the relationship between solubility and the $K_{sp}$ value of a saturated solution?

### Objectives
• **Observe** evidence that a precipitate is in equilibrium with its ions in solution.
• **Infer** the relative solubilities of two sparingly soluble ionic compounds.
• **Compare** the values of the $K_{sp}$ for two different compounds and relate them to your observations.
• **Explain** your observations of the two precipitates by using Le Châtelier's principle.
• **Calculate** the molar solubilities of the two ionic compounds from their $K_{sp}$ values.

### Materials
AgNO$_3$ solution
NaCl solution
Na$_2$S solution
24-well microplate
thin-stem pipettes (3)
wash bottle

### Safety Precautions

• Always wear safety goggles, gloves, and a lab apron.
• Silver nitrate is highly toxic and will stain skin and clothing.

### Pre-Lab

**1.** Read the entire **CHEMLAB**.

**2.** Prepare all written materials that you will take into the laboratory. Be sure to include safety precautions, procedure notes, and a data table in which to record your observations.

| Precipitate Formation | |
|---|---|
| | Observations |
| Step 3 | |
| Step 5 | |
| Step 6 | |

**3.** State Le Châtelier's principle.

**4.** Identify the control and the independent variable in the experiment.

**5.** When a solid dissolves to form two ions and the solid's $K_{sp}$ is known, what is the mathematical formula you can use to calculate the molar solubility?

### Procedure

**1.** Place 10 drops of AgNO$_3$ solution in well A1 of a 24-well microplate. Place 10 drops of the same solution in well A2.

**2.** Add 10 drops of NaCl solution to well A1 and 10 drops to well A2.

changes from white to black when the sodium sulfide solution is added, producing the Ag$_2$S precipitate.

### Resource Manager

**ChemLab and MiniLab Worksheets,** pp. 70–72 **L2**

**3.** Allow the precipitate to form in each well. Record your observations.

**4.** To well A2, add 10 drops of $Na_2S$ solution.

**5.** Allow the precipitate to form. Record your observations of the precipitate.

**6.** Compare the contents of wells A1 and A2 and record your observations in your table.

## Cleanup and Disposal

**1.** Use a wash bottle to transfer the contents of the well plate into a large waste beaker.

**2.** Wash your hands thoroughly after all lab work and cleanup are complete.

## Analyze and Conclude

**1. Analyzing Information** Write the complete equation for the double-replacement reaction that occurred when NaCl and $AgNO_3$ were mixed in wells A1 and A2 in step 2. Write the net ionic equation.

**2. Analyzing Information** Write the solubility product constant expression for the equilibrium established in wells A1 and A2 in step 2. $K_{sp}$ (AgCl) = $1.8 \times 10^{-10}$.

**3. Analyzing Information** Write the equation for the equilibrium that was established in well A2 when you added $Na_2S$. $K_{sp}$ ($Ag_2S$) = $8 \times 10^{-48}$

**4. Inferring** Identify the two precipitates by color.

**5. Comparing and Contrasting** Compare the $K_{sp}$ values for the two precipitates. Infer which of the two ionic compounds is more soluble.

**6. Recognizing Cause and Effect** Use Le Châtelier's principle to explain how the addition of $Na_2S$ in procedure step 4 affected the equilibrium established in well A2.

**7. Using Numbers** Calculate the molar solubilities of the two precipitates using the $K_{sp}$ values. Which of the precipitates is more soluble?

**8. Thinking Critically** What evidence from this experiment supports your answer to question 7? Explain.

**9.** Error Analysis Did you observe the well plate from the side as well as from the top? What did you notice?

**10. Developing General Rules** The solubility of an ionic compound depends upon the nature of the cations and anions that make up the compound. The reactants you used in this **CHEMLAB** are all soluble ionic compounds, whereas, the precipitates are insoluble. How does soluble $Na_2S$ differ from insoluble $Ag_2S$? How does soluble NaCl differ from insoluble AgCl? Use this information and $K_{sp}$ data from **Table 18-3** and the *Handbook of Chemistry and Physics* to develop general rules for solubility. What group of metal ions is not found in sparingly soluble compounds? What polyatomic ions, positive and negative, form only soluble ionic compounds? How does $K_{sp}$ relate to a compound's relative solubility?

## Real-World Chemistry

**1.** Research how industries use precipitation to remove hazardous chemicals from wastewater before returning it to the water cycle.

**2.** *Hard water* is the name given to water supplies that contain significant concentrations of $Mg^{2+}$ and $Ca^{2+}$ ions. Check on the solubility of ionic compounds formed with these ions and predict what problems they may cause.

**3.** Explain what would happen if you lost the stopper for a bottle of a saturated solution of lead sulfate ($PbSO_4$) and the bottle stood open to the air for a week. Would your answer be different if it were an unsaturated solution? Explain.

CHEMLAB **587**

## Analyze and Conclude

**1.** $AgNO_3(aq) + NaCl(aq) \rightarrow$
$AgCl(s) + NaNO_3(aq)$
$AgCl(s) \rightleftarrows Ag^+(aq) + Cl^-(aq)$

**2.** $K_{sp} = [Ag^+][Cl^-] = 1.8 \times 10^{-10}$

**3.** $2AgCl(s) + Na_2S(aq) \rightarrow Ag_2S(s) + 2NaCl(aq)$
$Ag_2S(s) \rightleftarrows 2Ag^+(aq) + S^{2-}(aq)$

**4.** AgCl: white
$Ag_2S$: black

**5.** $K_{sp}(AgCl) = 1.8 \times 10^{-10}$
$K_{sp}(Ag_2S) = 8 \times 10^{-48}$
AgCl is more soluble.

**6.** Silver ions are in equilibrium with solid white AgCl. On the addition of $Na_2S$, $S^{2-}$ ions combine with $Ag^+$ ions to form solid, black $Ag_2S$. According to Le Châtelier's principle, the removal of the $Ag^+$ ions shifts the AgCl equilibrium to the right, thus dissolving AgCl as $Ag_2S$ forms.

**7.** Solubility AgCl = $1.3 \times 10^{-5}M$
Solubility $Ag_2S$ = $1 \times 10^{-16}M$
AgCl is more soluble.

**8.** The concentration of $Ag^+$ ions that could exist in equilibrium with solid AgCl was larger than the $Ag^+$ concentration that could exist in equilibrium with solid $Ag_2S$. If that were not the case, there would have been no precipitate of $Ag_2S$.

**9.** After standing undisturbed for a time, the solid layers are on the bottom with the black on top of the white layer and a clear layer of solution above.

**10.** By examining the ionic compounds used and formed in this activity, students can conclude that the $Na^+$ ion forms soluble compounds. Students should find that all the compounds formed by the Group 1A metals are soluble. Compounds formed with the acetate, ammonium, and nitrate ions are soluble. If you compare compounds with the same number of ions, the smaller the value of $K_{sp}$, the lower the molar solubility of the ionic compound.

## Real-World Chemistry

**1.** Toxic heavy metals in waste water are often precipitated in large holding ponds. The water is then released and the sludge is removed to a hazardous waste facility.

**2.** Ca and Mg ions form many insoluble compounds that deposit in water pipes and precipitate as soap scum.

**3.** A precipitate would form as the water evaporated. For an unsaturated solution, the process would take longer.

## ✔ Assessment

**Skill** Refer students to Table 18-3 and have them predict what might happen when solutions of $Pb(NO_3)_2$ and $Na_2SO_4$ are mixed. Ask what might happen if a solution of NaI is added. Have them write equations and solubility product constant expressions for the equilibria involved. **L2**

## Purpose

Students will learn about the development of the Haber–Bosch process for ammonia production.

## Background

Haber and Bosch were each awarded the Nobel Prize in Chemistry, Haber in 1918 and Bosch in 1931. Prior to the synthetic production of ammonia, farmers relied on animal manure, the planting of nitrogen-fixing plants such as peas and beans, and natural sources of sodium nitrate to keep their fields fertile. Today more than 100 million tons of ammonia is used worldwide.

## Teaching Strategies

- Almost eight of every ten molecules in Earth's atmosphere are nitrogen molecules, so nitrogen is a cheap raw material.
- Point out to students that the reaction of 6 g of hydrogen gas and 28 g of nitrogen gas produces about 92 kJ of heat.
- Ask students how cooling the reactant-product mixture will affect the equilibrium of the reaction between nitrogen and hydrogen. The cooling will favor the production of ammonia because it would lessen the stress (heat).
- In the modern commercial process, the synthesis reaction takes place at temperatures around 400°C and at a pressure of 70-100 ×10³ kPa. The catalysts are usually mixtures of iron, aluminum oxide, and potassium oxides, which were originally developed by Bosch.

**National Science Content Standards**

**Pages 586–589**
UCP.3, UCP.4; A.1; B.2, B.3, B.4, B.6; E.1; F.6

## The Haber Process

Diatomic nitrogen makes up about 79 percent of Earth's atmosphere. A few species of soil bacteria can use atmospheric nitrogen to produce ammonia ($NH_3$). Other species of bacteria then convert the ammonia into nitrite and nitrate ions, which can be absorbed and used by plants. Ammonia also can be synthesized.

### Applying Le Châtelier's Principle

The process of synthesizing large amounts of ammonia from nitrogen and hydrogen gases was first demonstrated in 1909 by Fritz Haber, a German research chemist, and his English research assistant, Robert LeRossignol. The Haber process involves this reaction.

$$N_2(g) + 3H_2(g) \rightleftharpoons 2NH_3(g) + heat$$

The process produces high yields of ammonia by manipulating three factors that influence the reaction—pressure, temperature, and catalytic action.

During the synthesis of ammonia, four molecules of reactant produce two molecules of product. According to Le Châtelier's principle, if the pressure on this reaction is increased, the forward reaction will speed up to reduce the stress because two molecules exert less pressure than four molecules. Increased pressure will also cause the reactants to collide more frequently, thus increasing the reaction rate. Haber's apparatus used a pressure of $2 \times 10^5$ kPa.

The forward reaction is favored by a low temperature because the stress caused by the heat generated by the reaction is reduced. But low temperature decreases the number of collisions between reactants, thus decreasing the rate of reaction. Haber compromised by using an intermediate temperature of about 450°C.

A catalyst is used to decrease the activation energy and thus, increase the rate at which equilibrium is reached. Haber used iron as a catalyst in his process.

### The Industrial Process

Haber's process incorporated several operations that increased the yield of ammonia. The reactant

**Haber Process**

Nitrogen → Compressor ← Hydrogen
Compressor → Catalyst chamber
Catalyst chamber → Cooler
Cooler → Liquid ammonia
Return pump → Compressor

gases entering the chamber were warmed by heat produced by the reaction. The reactant-product mixture was allowed to cool slowly after reacting over the catalyst. Ammonia gas was removed from the process by liquefication, and the unreacted nitrogen and hydrogen were recycled back into the process.

Carl Bosch, a German industrial chemist improved Haber's process by designing new reaction chambers, improving pressurizing pumps, and finding inexpensive catalysts. By 1913, Bosch had built the first plant for synthesizing ammonia in Oppau, Germany.

### Investigating the Technology

1. **Thinking Critically** How does removing ammonia from the process affect equilibrium?
2. **Using Resources** Research how ammonia is used in the production of many agricultural fertilizers and other products.

## Chemistry Online

Visit the Chemistry Web site at **chemistrymc.com** to find links to more information about the Haber process and ammonia.

## Investigating the Technology

1. The removal of ammonia will decrease the reverse reaction and shift the equilibrium to the production of ammonia.
2. Ammonia is applied directly as a fertilizer. It is processed in acidic water to produce the ammonium ion which forms ammo- nium nitrate in water containing nitric acid. It forms ammonium sulfate if the water contains sulfuric acid. Both are components of agricultural fertilizers. Ammonia is also used in the production of explosives, nylon, household cleaners, and refrigerants.

## Summary

### 18.1 Equilibrium: A State of Dynamic Balance

- A reversible reaction is one that can take place in both the forward and reverse directions.

- A reversible reaction leads to an equilibrium state in which the forward and reverse reactions take place at equal rates and the concentrations of reactants and products remain constant.

- You can write the equilibrium constant expression for an equilibrium system using the law of chemical equilibrium.

- The equilibrium constant expression is a ratio of the molar concentrations of the products divided by the molar concentrations of the reactants with all concentrations in the ratio raised to a power equal to their coefficients in the balanced chemical equation.

- The value of the equilibrium constant expression, $K_{eq}$, is a constant for a given temperature.

- A large value for $K_{eq}$ means that the products are favored at equilibrium; a small $K_{eq}$ value means that the reactants are favored.

- You can calculate $K_{eq}$ by substituting known equilibrium concentrations into the equilibrium constant expression.

### 18.2 Factors Affecting Chemical Equilibrium

- Le Châtelier's principle describes how an equilibrium system shifts in response to a stress or disturbance. A stress is any change in the system at equilibrium.

- An equilibrium can be forced in the direction of the products by adding a reactant or by removing a product. It can be forced in the direction of the reactants by adding a product or removing a reactant.

- When an equilibrium shifts in response to a change in concentration or volume, the equilibrium position changes but $K_{eq}$ remains constant. A change in temperature, however, alters both the equilibrium position and the value of $K_{eq}$.

### 18.3 Using Equilibrium Constants

- Given $K_{eq}$, the equilibrium concentration of a substance can be calculated if you know the equilibrium concentrations of all other reactants and products.

- The solubility product constant expression, $K_{sp}$, describes the equilibrium between a sparingly soluble ionic compound and its ions in solution.

- You can calculate the molar solubility of an ionic compound using the solubility product constant expression.

- The ion product, $Q_{sp}$, can be calculated from the molar concentrations of the ions in a solution and compared with the $K_{sp}$ to determine whether a precipitate will form when two solutions are mixed.

- The solubility of a substance is lower when the substance is dissolved in a solution containing a common ion. This is called the common ion effect.

## Key Equations and Relationships

- $K_{eq} = \dfrac{[C]^c[D]^d}{[A]^a[B]^b}$  (p. 563)

## Vocabulary

- chemical equilibrium ( p. 561)
- common ion ( p. 584)
- common ion effect ( p. 584)
- equilibrium constant ( p. 563)
- heterogeneous equilibrium ( p. 565)
- homogeneous equilibrium ( p. 564)
- law of chemical equilibrium ( p. 563)
- Le Châtelier's principle ( p. 569)
- reversible reaction ( p. 560)
- solubility product constant ( p. 578)

chemistrymc.com/vocabulary_puzzlemaker

Study Guide **589**

## Using the Vocabulary

To reinforce chapter vocabulary, have students write a sentence using each term. L2 ELL

## Review Strategies

- Ask students to write the chemical equations and equilibrium constant expressions for three homogeneous equilibria. L2
- Ask students to explain Le Châtelier's principle in their own words. L2
- Ask students to write the chemical equations and solubility product constant expressions for three compounds listed in Table 18-3. L2
- Have students write the equations they would use to calculate the molar solubilities of AgCl and $CaF_2$. L2
- Ask students to explain the difference between $Q_{sp}$ and $K_{sp}$. L2
- Problems from Appendix A or the **Supplemental Problems** booklet can be used for review. L2

 For additional help with vocabulary, have students access the Vocabulary PuzzleMaker online.

chemistrymc.com/ vocabulary_puzzlemaker

## EXAMVIEW® PRO

### Use ExamView® Pro Testmaker CD-ROM to:

- Create **multiple versions** of tests.
- Create **modified** tests with one mouse click for struggling students.
- **Edit** existing questions and add your own questions.
- **Build** tests based on national curriculum standards.

## Concept Mapping

**25.** 1. reversible reactions;
2. chemical equilibria;
3. homogeneous equilibria;
4. heterogeneous equilibria; 5. equilibrium constant expressions

## Mastering Concepts

**26.** situations such as vehicle traffic across a bridge

**27.** Reactants are continuing to form products and products are continuing to form reactants.

**28.** Use double arrows.

**29.** The equation should have double arrows.

**30.** homogeneous equilibrium: all reactants and products are in the same physical state; heterogeneous equilibrium system: reactants and products exist in more than one physical state.

**31.** a particular set of equilibrium concentrations

**32.** the ratio of product concentrations to reactant concentrations, with each concentration raised to the power corresponding to its coefficient in the balanced equation

**33.** A numerically large $K_{eq}$ means that product concentrations, which are in the numerator, are greater than reactant concentrations, which are in the denominator.

**34.** The concentrations of pure liquids or solids are omitted from the equilibrium constant expression.

**35.** Such an equilibrium can exist if the small amounts of products react so quickly that the rate of the reverse reaction is quickly equal to the rate of the forward reaction. $K_{eq}$ must have a small numerical value.

**36.** the evaporation and condensation of ethanol

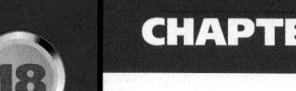

### Chemistry Online

*Go to the Chemistry Web site at* chemistrymc.com *for additional Chapter 18 Assessment.*

## Concept Mapping

**25.** Fill in the spaces on the concept map with the following phrases: equilibrium constant expressions, reversible reactions, heterogeneous equilibria, homogeneous equilibria, chemical equilibria.

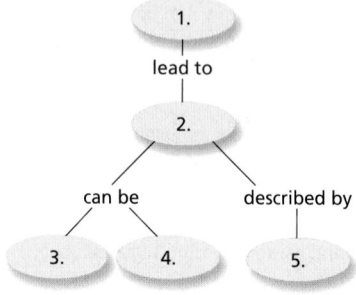

## Mastering Concepts

**26.** Describe an equilibrium in everyday life that illustrates a state of balance between two opposing processes. (18.1)

**27.** Given the fact that the concentrations of reactants and products are not changing, why is the word *dynamic* used for describing chemical equilibrium? (18.1)

**28.** How can you indicate in a chemical equation that a reaction is reversible? (18.1)

**29.** Although the general equation for a chemical reaction is reactants → products, explain why this equation is not complete for a system at equilibrium. (18.1)

**30.** Explain the difference between a homogeneous equilibrium and a heterogeneous equilibrium. (18.1)

**31.** What is an equilibrium position? (18.1)

**32.** Explain how to use the law of chemical equilibrium in writing an equilibrium constant expression. (18.1)

**33.** Why does a numerically large $K_{eq}$ mean that the products are favored in an equilibrium system? (18.1)

**34.** Why should you pay attention to the physical states of all reactants and products when writing equilibrium constant expressions? (18.1)

**35.** How can an equilibrium system contain small and unchanging amounts of products yet have large amounts of reactants? What can you say about the relative size of $K_{eq}$ for such an equilibrium? (18.1)

**36.** Describe the opposing processes in the physical equilibrium that exists in a closed container half-filled with liquid ethanol. (18.1)

**37.** What is meant by a stress on a reaction at equilibrium? (18.2)

**38.** How does Le Châtelier's principle describe an equilibrium's response to a stress? (18.2)

**39.** Why does removing a product cause an equilibrium to shift in the direction of the products? (18.2)

**40.** When an equilibrium shifts toward the reactants in response to a stress, how is the equilibrium position changed? (18.2)

**41.** Use Le Châtelier's principle to explain how a shift in the equilibrium $H_2CO_3(aq) \rightleftharpoons H_2O(l) + CO_2(g)$ causes a soft drink to go flat when its container is left open to the atmosphere. (18.2)

**42.** How is $K_{eq}$ changed when heat is added to an equilibrium in which the forward reaction is exothermic? Explain using Le Châtelier's principle. (18.2)

**43.** Changing the volume of the system alters the equilibrium position of this equilibrium.

$$N_2(g) + 3H_2(g) \rightleftharpoons 2NH_3(g)$$

But a similar change has no effect on this equilibrium.

$$H_2(g) + Cl_2(g) \rightleftharpoons 2HCl(g)$$

Explain. (18.2)

**44.** How might the addition of a noble gas to the reaction vessel affect this equilibrium?

$$2N_2H_4(g) + 2NO_2(g) \rightleftharpoons 3N_2(g) + 4H_2O(g)$$

Assume that the volume of the reaction vessel does not change. (18.2)

**45.** When an equilibrium shifts to the right, what happens to the following? (18.2)

   **a.** the concentrations of the reactants
   **b.** the concentrations of the products

**46.** How would each of the following changes affect the equilibrium position of the system used to produce methanol from carbon monoxide and hydrogen? (18.2)

$$CO(g) + 2H_2(g) \rightleftharpoons CH_3OH(g) + heat$$

   **a.** adding CO to the system
   **b.** cooling the system
   **c.** adding a catalyst to the system
   **d.** removing $CH_3OH$ from the system
   **e.** decreasing the volume of the system

chemistrymc.com/chapter_test

**37.** any change in concentration, volume (pressure), or temperature which causes the equilibrium to shift.

**38.** It will shift in the direction that relieves the stress.

### Resource Manager

Chapter Assessment, pp. 103–108
Supplemental Problems, Ch. 18
ExamView® Pro CD-ROM
MindJogger Videoquizzes DVD/VHS
Solutions Manual, Ch. 18
Chemistry Interactive CD-ROM,
   Ch. 18 quiz

**47.** Why is the concentration of a solid not included as part of the solubility product constant? (18.3)

**48.** What does it mean to say that two solutions have a common ion? Give an example that supports your answer. (18.3)

**49.** Explain the difference between $Q_{sp}$ and $K_{sp}$. (18.3)

**50.** Explain why a common ion lowers the solubility of an ionic compound. (18.3)

**51.** Describe the solution that results when two solutions are mixed and $Q_{sp}$ is found to equal $K_{sp}$. Does a precipitate form?

## Mastering Problems

### The Equilibrium Constant Expression (18.1)

**52.** Write equilibrium constant expressions for these homogeneous equilibria.

  **a.** $2N_2H_4(g) + 2NO_2(g) \rightleftharpoons 3N_2(g) + 4H_2O(g)$
  **b.** $2NbCl_4(g) \rightleftharpoons NbCl_3(g) + NbCl_5(g)$
  **c.** $I_2(g) \rightleftharpoons 2I(g)$
  **d.** $2SO_3(g) + CO_2(g) \rightleftharpoons CS_2(g) + 4O_2(g)$

**53.** Write equilibrium constant expressions for these heterogeneous equilibria.

  **a.** $2NaHCO_3(s) \rightleftharpoons Na_2CO_3(s) + H_2O(g) + CO_2(g)$
  **b.** $C_6H_6(l) \rightleftharpoons C_6H_6(g)$
  **c.** $Fe_3O_4(s) + 4H_2(g) \rightleftharpoons 3Fe(s) + 4H_2O(g)$

**54.** Pure water has a density of 1.00 g/mL at 297 K. Calculate the molar concentration of pure water at this temperature.

**55.** Calculate $K_{eq}$ for the following equilibrium when $[SO_3] = 0.0160$ mol/L, $[SO_2] = 0.00560$ mol/L, and $[O_2] = 0.00210$ mol/L.

  $$2SO_3(g) \rightleftharpoons 2SO_2(g) + O_2(g)$$

**56.** $K_{eq}$ for this reaction is 3.63.

  $$A + 2B \rightleftharpoons C$$

  The data in the table shows the concentrations of the reactants and product in two different reaction mixtures at the same temperature. Does the data provide evidence that both reactions are at equilibrium?

**Table 18-5**

| Concentrations of A, B, and C | | |
|---|---|---|
| A (mol/L) | B (mol/L) | C (mol/L) |
| 0.500 | 0.621 | 0.700 |
| 0.250 | 0.525 | 0.250 |

**57.** When solid ammonium chloride is put in a reaction vessel at 323 K, the equilibrium concentrations of both ammonia and hydrogen chloride are found to be 0.0660 mol/L. $NH_4Cl(s) \rightleftharpoons NH_3(g) + HCl(g)$. Calculate $K_{eq}$.

**58.** Suppose you have a cube of pure manganese metal measuring 5.25 cm on each side. You find that the mass of the cube is 1076.6 g. What is the molar concentration of manganese in the cube?

### Le Châtelier's Principle (18.2)

**59.** Use Le Châtelier's principle to predict how each of the following changes would affect this equilibrium. $H_2(g) + CO_2(g) \rightleftharpoons H_2O(g) + CO(g)$

  **a.** adding $H_2O(g)$ to the system
  **b.** removing $CO(g)$ from the system
  **c.** adding $H_2(g)$ to the system
  **d.** adding something to the system to absorb $CO_2(g)$

**60.** How would increasing the volume of the reaction vessel affect these equilibria?

  **a.** $NH_4Cl(s) \rightleftharpoons NH_3(g) + HCl(g)$
  **b.** $N_2(g) + O_2(g) \rightleftharpoons 2NO(g)$

**61.** How would decreasing the volume of the reaction vessel affect these equilibria?

  **a.** $2N_2H_4(g) + 2NO_2(g) \rightleftharpoons 3N_2(g) + 4H_2O(g)$
  **b.** $2H_2O(g) \rightleftharpoons 2H_2(g) + O_2(g)$

**62.** How would these equilibria be affected by increasing the temperature?

  **a.** $4NH_3(g) + 5O_2(g) \rightleftharpoons 4NO(g) + 6H_2O(g) + heat$
  **b.** $heat + NaCl(s) \rightleftharpoons Na^+(aq) + Cl^-(aq)$

**63.** Ethylene ($C_2H_4$) reacts with hydrogen to form ethane ($C_2H_6$).
  $C_2H_4(g) + H_2(g) \rightleftharpoons C_2H_6(g) + heat$
  How would you regulate the temperature of this equilibrium in order to do the following?

  **a.** increase the yield of ethane
  **b.** decrease the concentration of ethylene
  **c.** increase the amount of hydrogen in the system

**64.** How would simultaneously decreasing the temperature and volume of the system affect these equilibria?

  **a.** $heat + CaCO_3(s) \rightleftharpoons CaO(s) + CO_2(g)$
  **b.** $4NH_3(g) + 5O_2(g) \rightleftharpoons 4NO(g) + 6H_2O(g) + heat$

### Calculations Using $K_{eq}$ (18.3)

**65.** $K_{eq}$ is 1.60 at 933 K for this reaction.
  $H_2(g) + CO_2(g) \rightleftharpoons H_2O(g) + CO(g)$

  Calculate the equilibrium concentration of hydrogen when $[CO_2] = 0.320$ mol/L, $[H_2O] = 0.240$ mol/L, and $[CO] = 0.280$ mol/L.

**39.** In order to restore the equilibrium amount of product, the equilibrium shifts to produce more product.

**40.** The equilibrium position shifts to the left.

**41.** Because $CO_2(g)$ continually escapes from the open container, the equilibrium shifts to the right until $H_2CO_3(aq)$ is depleted.

**42.** $K_{eq}$ is lowered. Adding heat increases the rate of the heat-absorbing reaction, which is the direction of the reactants.

**43.** The number of gaseous particles reacting in the first equilibrium is different from the number of gaseous particles produced; therefore, the system can shift in response to a change in volume (pressure). The second equilibrium cannot shift in response to a change in volume because the number of gaseous particles reacting equals the number produced.

**44.** Addition of a noble gas does not change the partial pressures or concentrations of the reactants or products, so the equilibrium is not affected.

**45. a.** decrease **b.** increase

**46. a.** The equilibrium shifts to the right.
  **b.** The equilibrium shifts to the right.
  **c.** The equilibrium does not shift.
  **d.** The equilibrium shifts to the right.
  **e.** The equilibrium shifts to the right.

**47.** The concentration of a solid is a constant value.

**48.** They both contain the

same ion. NaCl(aq) and KCl(aq) both contain $Cl^-(aq)$.

**49.** $K_{sp}$ describes a saturated solution. $Q_{sp}$ describes a solution with any concentrations of ions.

**50.** If the concentration of either ion produced by the dissolving compound is increased by a common ion present in the solution, the concentration of the compound's other ion must decrease.

**51.** The new solution is saturated. No precipitate will form.

National Science Content Standards

Pages 590–591
UCP.3, UCP.4; B.2, B.3, B.4, B.6

• Ion concentrations in compound B's solubility product constant expression have lower-value exponents.

## Mastering Problems

Complete solutions to Chapter Assessment problems can be found in the **Solutions Manual**.

### The Equilibrium Constant Expression (18.1)

**Level 1**

**52. a.** $K_{eq} = \dfrac{[N_2]^3[H_2O]^4}{[N_2H_4]^2[NO_2]^2}$

  **b.** $K_{eq} = \dfrac{[NbCl_3][NbCl_5]}{[NbCl_4]^2}$

  **c.** $K_{eq} = \dfrac{[I]^2}{[I_2]}$

  **d.** $K_{eq} = \dfrac{[CS_2][O_2]^4}{[SO_3]^2[CO_2]}$

**53. a.** $K_{eq} = [H_2O][CO_2]$

  **b.** $K_{eq} = [C_6H_6 \,(g)]$

  **c.** $K_{eq} = \dfrac{[H_2O]^4}{[H_2]^4}$

**54.** 55.5 mol/L

**Level 2**

**55.** $K_{eq} = 2.57 \times 10^{-4}$

**56.** No. The data give different $K_{eq}$ values.

**57.** $K_{eq} = 0.00436$

**58.** 135 mol/L

### Le Châtelier's Principle (18.2)

**Level 1**

**59. a.** shift to the left
  **b.** shift to the right
  **c.** shift to the right
  **d.** shift to the left

**60. a.** shift to the right
  **b.** no shift

**61. a.** shift to the left
  **b.** shift to the left

**62. a.** shift to the left, decreasing $K_{eq}$
  **b.** shift to the right, increasing $K_{eq}$

**Level 2**

**63. a.** lower the temperature
  **b.** lower the temperature
  **c.** raise the temperature

**64. a.** shift to the left
  **b.** Decreasing the temperature causes a shift to the right and

**66.** At 2273 K, $K_{eq} = 6.2 \times 10^{-4}$ for the reaction

$$N_2(g) + O_2(g) \rightleftharpoons 2NO(g)$$

If $[N_2] = 0.05200$ mol/L and $[O_2] = 0.00120$ mol/L, what is the concentration of NO at equilibrium?

## Calculations Using $K_{sp}$ (18.3)

**67.** Calculate the ion product to determine if a precipitate will form when 125 mL 0.00500$M$ sodium chloride is mixed with 125 mL 0.00100$M$ silver nitrate solution.

**68.** Calculate the molar solubility of strontium chromate in water at 298 K if $K_{sp} = 3.5 \times 10^{-5}$.

**69.** Will a precipitate form when 1.00 L of 0.150$M$ iron(II) chloride solution is mixed with 2.00 L of 0.0333$M$ sodium hydroxide solution? Explain your reasoning and show your calculations.

## Mixed Review

*Sharpen your problem-solving skills by answering the following.*

**70.** How many moles per liter of silver chloride will be in a saturated solution of AgCl? $K_{sp} = 1.8 \times 10^{-10}$

**71.** A 6.00-L vessel contains an equilibrium mixture of 0.0222 mol $PCl_3$, 0.0189 mol $PCl_5$, and 0.1044 mol $Cl_2$. Calculate $K_{eq}$ for the following reaction.

$$PCl_5(g) \rightleftharpoons PCl_3(g) + Cl_2(g)$$

**72.** How would simultaneously increasing the temperature and volume of the system affect these equilibria?

  **a.** $2O_3(g) \rightleftharpoons 3O_2(g) + \text{heat}$
  **b.** $\text{heat} + N_2(g) + O_2(g) \rightleftharpoons 2NO(g)$

**73.** The solubility product constant for lead(II) arsenate $(Pb_3(AsO_4)_2)$, is $4.0 \times 10^{-36}$ at 298 K. Calculate the molar solubility of the compound at this temperature.

**74.** How would these equilibria be affected by decreasing the temperature?

  **a.** $2O_3(g) \rightleftharpoons 3O_2(g) + \text{heat}$
  **b.** $\text{heat} + H_2(g) + F_2(g) \rightleftharpoons 2HF(g)$

## Thinking Critically

**75. Predicting** Suppose you're thinking about using the following reaction to produce hydrogen from hydrogen sulfide.

$$2H_2S(g) + \text{heat} \rightleftharpoons 2H_2(g) + S_2(g)$$

Given that $K_{eq}$ for the equilibrium is $2.27 \times 10^{-4}$, would you expect a high yield of hydrogen? Explain how you could regulate the volume of the reaction vessel and the temperature to increase the yield.

**76. Applying Concepts** Smelling salts, sometimes used to revive a groggy or unconscious person, are made of ammonium carbonate. The equation for the endothermic decomposition of ammonium carbonate is

$$(NH_4)_2CO_3(s) \rightleftharpoons 2NH_3(g) + CO_2(g) + H_2O(g)$$

Would you expect smelling salts to work as well on a cold winter day as on a warm summer day? Explain your answer.

**77. Comparing and Contrasting** Which of the two solids, calcium phosphate or iron(III) phosphate, has the greater molar solubility? $K_{sp}$ $(Ca_3(PO_4)_2) = 1.2 \times 10^{-29}$; $K_{sp}$ $(FePO_4) = 1.0 \times 10^{-22}$. Which compound has the greater solubility expressed in grams per liter?

**78. Recognizing Cause and Effect** You have 12.56 g of a mixture made up of sodium chloride and barium chloride. Explain how you could use a precipitation reaction to determine how much of each compound the mixture contains.

## Writing in Chemistry

**79.** Research the role that solubility plays in the formation of kidney stones. Find out what compounds are found in kidney stones and their $K_{sp}$ values. Summarize your findings in a report.

**80.** The presence of magnesium and calcium ions in water makes the water "hard." Explain in terms of solubility why the presence of these ions is often undesirable. Find out what measures can be taken to eliminate them.

## Cumulative Review

*Refresh your understanding of previous chapters by answering the following.*

**81.** How are electrons shared differently in $H_2$, $O_2$, and $N_2$? (Chapter 9)

**82.** How can you tell if a chemical equation is balanced? (Chapter 10)

**83.** What mass of carbon must burn to produce 4.56 L $CO_2$ gas at STP? (Chapter 14)

$$C(s) + O_2(g) \rightarrow CO_2(g)$$

**84.** When you reverse a thermochemical equation, why must you change the sign of $\Delta H$? (Chapter 16)

---

decreasing the volume causes a shift to the left.

## Calculations Using $K_{eq}$ (18.3)

**Level 1**

**65.** $[H_2] = 0.131M$
**66.** $[NO] = 2.0 \times 10^{-4}M$

## Calculations Using $K_{sp}$ (18.3)

**Level 1**

**67.** $Q_{sp} = 1.25 \times 10^{-6}$,

$K_{sp} = 1.8 \times 10^{-10}$
Because $Q_{sp} > K_{sp}$, a precipitate forms.
**68.** $s = 5.9 \times 10^{-3}$ mol/L

**Level 2**

**69.** $Q_{sp} = 2.46 \times 10^{-5}$, $K_{sp} = 4.9 \times 10^{-17}$
$Q_{sp} > K_{sp}$, so a precipitate forms.

## Mixed Review

**70.** $1.3 \times 10^{-5}$ mol/L
**71.** $K_{eq} = 2.04 \times 10^{-2}$

*Use these questions and the test-taking tip to prepare for your standardized test.*

**1.** A system reaches chemical equilibrium when

  **a.** no new product is formed by the forward reaction.
  **b.** the reverse reaction no longer occurs in the system.
  **c.** the concentration of reactants in the system is equal to the concentration of products.
  **d.** the rate at which the forward reaction occurs equals the rate of the reverse reaction.

**2.** What does a value of $K_{eq}$ greater than 1 mean?

  **a.** more reactants than products exist at equilibrium
  **b.** more products than reactants exist at equilibrium
  **c.** the rate of the forward reaction is high at equilibrium
  **d.** the rate of the reverse reaction is high at equilibrium

**3.** The hydrogen sulfide produced as a byproduct of petroleum refinement can be used to produce elemental sulfur: $2H_2S(g) + SO_2(g) \rightarrow 3S(l) + 2H_2O(g)$

What is the equilibrium constant expression for this reaction?

  **a.** $K_{eq} = \dfrac{[H_2O]}{[H_2S][SO_2]}$    **c.** $K_{eq} = \dfrac{[H_2O]^2}{[H_2S]^2[SO_2]}$

  **b.** $K_{eq} = \dfrac{[H_2S]^2[SO_2]}{[H_2S]^2}$    **d.** $K_{eq} = \dfrac{[S]^3[H_2O]^2}{[H_2S]^2[SO_2]}$

**4.** The following system is in equilibrium:

$2S(s) + 5F_2(g) \rightleftharpoons SF_4(g) + SF_6(g)$

The equilibrium will shift to the right if _____ .

  **a.** the concentration of $SF_4$ is increased
  **b.** the concentration of $SF_6$ is increased
  **c.** the pressure on the system is increased
  **d.** the pressure on the system is decreased

**Interpreting Tables** Use the table to answer questions 5–7.

**5.** What is the $K_{sp}$ for $MnCO_3$?

  **a.** $2.24 \times 10^{-11}$    **c.** $1.12 \times 10^{-9}$
  **b.** $4.00 \times 10^{-11}$    **d.** $5.60 \times 10^{-9}$

**6.** What is the molar solubility of $MnCO_3$ at 298 K?

  **a.** $4.73 \times 10^{-6}M$    **c.** $7.48 \times 10^{-5}M$
  **b.** $6.32 \times 10^{-2}M$    **d.** $3.35 \times 10^{-5}M$

**7.** A 50.0-mL volume of $3.00 \times 10^{-6}M$ $K_2CO_3$ is mixed with 50.0 mL of $MnCl_2$. A precipitate of $MnCO_3$ will form only when the concentration of the $MnCl_2$ solution is greater than _____ .

  **a.** $7.47 \times 10^{-6}M$    **c.** $2.99 \times 10^{-5}M$
  **b.** $1.49 \times 10^{-5}M$    **d.** $1.02 \times 10^{-5}M$

 chemistrymc.com/standardized_test

| Concentration Data for the Equilibrium System $MnCO_3(s) \rightleftharpoons Mn^{2+}(aq) + CO_3^{2-}(aq)$ at 298 K | | | | |
|---|---|---|---|---|
| Trial | $[Mn^{2+}]_0$ (M) | $[CO_3^{2-}]_0$ (M) | $[Mn^{2+}]_{eq}$ (M) | $[CO_3^{2-}]_{eq}$ (M) |
| 1 | 0.0000 | 0.00400 | $5.60 \times 10^{-9}$ | $4.00 \times 10^{-3}$ |
| 2 | 0.0100 | 0.0000 | $1.00 \times 10^{-2}$ | $2.24 \times 10^{-9}$ |
| 3 | 0.0000 | 0.0200 | $1.12 \times 10^{-9}$ | $2.00 \times 10^{-2}$ |

**8.** Which of the following statements about the common ion effect is NOT true?

  **a.** The effects of common ions on an equilibrium system can be explained by Le Châtelier's principle.
  **b.** The decreased solubility of an ionic compound due to the presence of a common ion is called the common ion effect.
  **c.** The addition of NaCl to a saturated solution of AgCl will produce the common ion effect.
  **d.** The common ion effect is due to a shift in equilibrium towards the aqueous products of a system.

**9.** If the forward reaction of a system in equilibrium is endothermic, increasing the temperature of the system will _____ .

  **a.** shift the equilibrium to the left
  **b.** shift the equilibrium to the right
  **c.** decrease the rate of the forward reaction
  **d.** decrease the rate of the reverse reaction

**10.** $Cl_2(g) + 3O_2(g) + F_2(g) \rightleftharpoons 2ClO_3F(g)$

The formation of perchloryl fluoride ($ClO_3F$) from its elements has an equilibrium constant of $3.42 \times 10^{-9}$ at 298 K. If $[Cl_2] = 0.563M$, $[O_2] = 1.01M$, and $[ClO_3F] = 1.47 \times 10^{-5}M$ at equilibrium, what is the concentration of $F_2$?

  **a.** $9.18 \times 10^0 M$    **c.** $1.09 \times 10^{-1}M$
  **b.** $3.73 \times 10^{-10}M$    **d.** $6.32 \times 10^{-2}M$

---

### TEST-TAKING TIP

**Maximize Your Score** If possible, find out how your standardized test will be scored. In order to do your best, you need to know if there is a penalty for guessing, and if so, what the penalty is. If there is no random-guessing penalty at all, you should always fill in an answer, even if you haven't read the question!

---

**72. a.** Increasing the temperature would tend to cause a shift to the left; increasing the volume would tend to cause a shift to the right.
  **b.** The equilibrium would shift to the right.
**73.** $s = 3.3 \times 10^{-8}$ mol/L
**74. a.** shift to the right
  **b.** shift to the left

## Thinking Critically

**75.** You would not expect a high yield of hydrogen. You could increase the hydrogen yield by increasing the volume of the reaction vessel and by increasing the temperature.
**76.** No, because the decomposition of ammonium carbonate is endothermic, the compound decomposes most readily at higher temperatures.
**77.** $s$ ($Ca_3(PO_4)_2$) = $1.1 \times 10^{-7}$ mol/L, $s$ ($FePO_4$) = $1.1 \times 10^{-11}$ mol/L; $Ca_3(PO_4)_2$ has the greater molar solubility. Mass solubility of $Ca_3(PO_4)_2$ = $3.4 \times 10^{-5}$ g/L; mass solubility of $FePO_4$ = $1.7 \times 10^{-9}$ g/L; $Ca_3(PO_4)_2$ has a greater mass solubility than $FePO_4$.
**78.** 1. Dissolve the mixture in distilled water. 2. Add an excess of a solution containing an anion such as carbonate, chromate, or sulfate that will precipitate essentially all the barium ions. 3. Filter, dry, and mass the precipitate. 4. Calculate the moles of barium compound formed, which equal the moles of barium chloride in the original mixture. 5. Calculate the

---

mass of barium chloride in the original mixture. The remainder of the original mixture is sodium chloride.

## Cumulative Review

**81.** In $H_2$, one pair of electrons is shared; in $O_2$, two pairs; in $N_2$, three pairs.
**82.** The numbers and kinds of atoms are the same on both sides of the equations and the coefficients are in the smallest possible integer ratio.

**83.** 2.44 g C
**84.** A reaction that is exothermic in one direction is endothermic in the opposite direction.

## Standardized Test Practice

| | | | | |
|---|---|---|---|---|
| **1.** d | **3.** c | **5.** a | **7.** c | **9.** b |
| **2.** b | **4.** c | **6.** a | **8.** d | **10.** c |

**National Science Content Standards**

Pages 592–593
UCP.3, UCP.4; B.2, B.3, B.4, B.6

**593**

# Resource Manager

| Section | Objectives | Activities/Features |
|---|---|---|
| **Section 19.1**<br>**Acids and Bases: An Introduction**<br>1 session<br>🔲 ¹/₂ block | **1. Identify** the physical and chemical properties of acids and bases.<br>**2. Classify** solutions as acidic, basic, or neutral.<br>**3. Compare** the Arrhenius and Brønsted-Lowry models of acids and bases. | **Discovery Lab:** Investigating What's in Your Cupboards, p. 595<br>**Careers Using Chemistry:** Agricultural Technician, p. 599<br>**Earth Science Connection,** p. 600 |
| **Section 19.2**<br>**Strengths of Acids and Bases**<br>1¹/₂ sessions<br>🔲 1 block | **4. Relate** the strength of an acid or base to its degree of ionization.<br>**5. Compare** the strength of a weak acid with the strength of its conjugate base and the strength of a weak base with the strength of its conjugate acid.<br>**6. Explain** the relationship between the strengths of acids and bases and the values of their ionization constants. | **MiniLab:** Acid Strength, p. 604 |
| **Section 19.3**<br>**What is pH?**<br>1¹/₂ sessions<br>🔲 1 block | **7. Explain** the meaning of pH and pOH.<br>**8. Relate** pH and pOH to the ion product constant for water.<br>**9. Calculate** the pH and pOH of aqueous solutions. | |
| **Section 19.4**<br>**Neutralization**<br>3 sessions<br>🔲 2 blocks | **10. Write** chemical equations for neutralization reactions.<br>**11. Explain** how neutralization reactions are used in acid-base titrations.<br>**12. Compare** the properties of buffered and unbuffered solutions. | **Problem-Solving Lab:** How does your blood maintain its pH? p. 624<br>**ChemLab:** Standardizing a Base Solution by Titration, pp. 626–627<br>**How It Works:** Antacids, p. 628 |

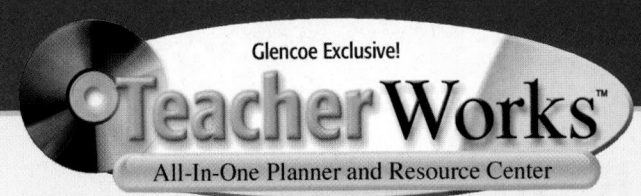

| National Science Content Standards | State/Local Standards | Reproducible Masters | Transparencies |
|---|---|---|---|
| UCP.2, UCP.3, UCP.4; A.1; B.2, B.3, B.4 | | **Study Guide for Content Mastery,** p. 109 L2 | **Section Focus** Transparency 71 L1 ELL  **Teaching** Transparency 55 L2 ELL |
| UCP.2, UCP.3, UCP.4; A.1; B.2, B.4 | | **Study Guide for Content Mastery,** p. 110 L2  **ChemLab and MiniLab Worksheets,** p. 73 L2  **Challenge Problems,** p. 19 L3 | **Section Focus** Transparency 72 L1 ELL  **Teaching** Transparency 56 L2 ELL  **Math Skills** Transparency 30 L2 ELL |
| UCP.2, UCP.3, UCP.4; A.1; B.2, B.4; E.2 | | **Study Guide for Content Mastery,** pp. 111–112 L2  **Forensics Laboratory Manual,** pp. 13–24 L2  **Small-Scale Laboratory Manual,** pp. 65–68 L2 | **Section Focus** Transparency 73 L1 ELL  **Teaching** Transparency 57 L2 ELL  **Math Skills** Transparency 31 L2 ELL |
| UCP.2, UCP.3, UCP.4; A.1; B.2, B.3, B.4; E.2; F.1 | | **Study Guide for Content Mastery,** pp. 113–114 L2  **ChemLab and MiniLab Worksheets,** pp. 74–76 L2  **Laboratory Manual,** pp. 145–152 L2  **CBL Laboratory Manual,** pp. 33–36 L2  **Small-Scale Laboratory Manual,** pp. 69–72 L2 | **Section Focus** Transparency 74 L1 ELL  **Teaching** Transparency 58 L2 ELL |

**Key to National Science Content Standards:** UCP = Unifying Concepts and Processes, A = Science as Inquiry, B = Physical Science, C = Life Science, D = Earth and Space Sciences, E = Science and Technology, F = Science in Personal and Social Perspectives, G = History and Nature of Science

Refer to pages 4T–5T of the Teacher Guide for an explanation of the National Science Content Standards correlations.

# Resource Manager

## Materials List

### ChemLab (pages 626–627)
50-mL buret, buret clamp, ring stand, weighing bottle, 250-mL Erlenmeyer flask, 500-mL Florence flask with rubber stopper, 250-mL beaker, balance, wash bottle, dropper, 400 mL distilled water, sodium hydroxide pellets (NaOH), potassium hydrogen phthalate ($KHC_8H_4O_4$), phenolphthalein solution, spatula

### Discovery Lab (page 595)
red litmus paper, blue litmus paper, phenolphthalein, microplate, household products (6–8)

### MiniLab (page 604)
glacial acetic acid, distilled water, 10-mL graduated cylinder, dropping pipette, 50-mL beaker, 24-well micro plate, stirring rod, battery-powered conductivity tester

### Demonstration (pages 622–623)
1 mL glacial acetic acid, 100-mL beakers (3), 60 mL distilled water, 4 g sodium acetate ($NaC_2H_3O_2$), large test tubes (3), universal indicator, stirring rods (3), 50 mL 4.0$M$ NaOH, dropper

## Preparation of Solutions

For a review of solution preparation, see page 46T of the Teacher Guide.

Quantities are for a class of 30 students.

### Discovery Lab (page 595) and ChemLab (pages 626–627)
**Phenolphthalein solution** Dissolve 0.1 g phenolphthalein powder in 70 mL 95% ethanol. Make up to 100 mL final volume with distilled water.

### Demonstration (pages 622–623)
**4.0$M$ NaOH solution** Carefully add 16 g NaOH to 75 mL distilled water. Make up to 100 mL final volume with distilled water. **CAUTION:** Solution will become hot.

## Assessment Resources

**Chapter Assessment,** pp. 109–114
**MindJogger Videoquizzes DVD/VHS**
**Alternate Assessment in the Science Classroom**
**ExamView® Pro CD-ROM**
**Solutions Manual,** Chapter 19
**Supplemental Problems,** Chapter 19
**Performance Assessment in the Science Classroom**
**Chemistry Interactive CD-ROM,** Chapter 19 quiz

## Additional Resources

**Spanish Resources** ELL
**Guided Reading Audio Program,** Chapter 19 ELL
**Cooperative Learning in the Science Classroom**
**Lab and Safety Skills in the Science Classroom**
**Lesson Plans**
**Block Scheduling Lesson Plans**
**Chemistrymc.com**

## Glencoe Technology

The following multimedia for this chapter are available from Glencoe.

**VIDEOTAPE/DVD**
MindJogger Videoquizzes,
Chapter 19

**CD-ROM**
**Chemistry: Matter and Change**
*Chemical Properties; The Actions of Acids and Bases*, Video
*Acids and Bases*, Video
*Forming a Basic Anhydride*, Demonstration
*Ionization of a Weak Acid*, Demonstration
*Forming a Salt*, Demonstration
*An Acid Base Reaction*, Animation

*An Acid Base Titration*, Video
*Acid Base Titrations*, Experiment
*Using a Buffer*, Demonstration

**CD-ROM**
**ExamView® Pro Testmaker**

**CD-ROM**
**Interactive Chalkboard**

**CD-ROM**
**TeacherWorks™**

## Multiple Learning Styles

Look for the following icons for strategies that emphasize different learning modalities.

*Kinesthetic*
Differentiated Instruction, p. 598; Extension, p. 611; Quick Demo, p. 613; Chemistry Journal, p. 620

*Visual-Spatial*
Extension, p. 620

*Interpersonal*
Differentiated Instruction, pp. 602, 624; Portfolio, p. 614

*Intrapersonal*
Chemistry Journal, pp. 596, 605; Differentiated Instruction, pp. 599, 603

*Linguistic*
Differentiated Instruction, p. 597; Chemistry Journal, pp. 609, 611, 617, 618

*Logical-Mathematical*
Differentiated Instruction, pp. 610, 615; Reteach, p. 615

## Key to Teaching Strategies

**L1** Level 1 activities should be appropriate for students with learning difficulties.

**L2** Level 2 activities should be within the ability range of all students.

**L3** Level 3 activities are designed for above-average students.

**ELL** ELL activities should be within the ability range of English Language Learners.

**COOP LEARN** Cooperative Learning activities are designed for small group work.

**P** These strategies represent student products that can be placed into a best-work portfolio.

 These strategies are useful in a block scheduling format.

## Assessment Planner

**Portfolio Assessment**
Portfolio, TWE, pp. 614, 629
Assessment, TWE. p. 618
ChemLab, TWE, p. 627

**Performance Assessment**
Assessment, TWE, pp. 599, 619
MiniLab, SE, p. 604
Problem-Solving Lab, TWE, p. 624
ChemLab, SE, pp. 626–627
Discovery Lab, SE, p. 595

**Knowledge Assessment**
Section Assessment, SE, pp. 601, 607, 616, 625
MiniLab, TWE, p. 604
Assessment, TWE, pp. 605, 612, 616, 623, 625
Demonstration, TWE, p. 623
Chapter Assessment, SE, pp. 630–633

**Skill Assessment**
Assessment, TWE, pp. 601, 607

## Tying to Previous Knowledge

Have students review the following concepts before studying this chapter.

Chapter 10: chemical reactions, equations for chemical reactions

Chapter 17: reaction rates, reaction rate laws

Chapter 18: chemical equilibrium

## Using the Photo

Ask students what is meant by sour soil and sweet soil. *Sour soil is soil that is acid. Sweet soil is neutral or alkaline.* Explain that hydrangeas can be made to produce blue or pink blossoms depending upon the amount of acid in the soil.

## PowerPoint® Presentations

This CD-ROM is an editable Microsoft® PowerPoint® presentation that includes:

• Section presentations
• Section checks
• Image bank
• Links to Chemistry Online
• All transparencies
• Animations
• Audio

---

# CHAPTER  19

# Acids and Bases

## What You'll Learn

▶ You will compare acids and bases and understand why their strengths vary.

▶ You will define pH and pOH and calculate the pH and pOH of aqueous solutions.

▶ You will calculate acid and base concentrations and determine concentrations experimentally.

▶ You will explain how buffers resist changes in pH.

## Why It's Important

Acids and bases are present in the soil of Earth, the foods you eat, the products you buy. Amino acids make up the fabric of every organ in your body and are crucial to your existence.

Visit the Chemistry Web site at chemistrymc.com to find links about acids and bases.

The color of the big-leaf hydrangea can vary from pink to blue depending upon the acidity of the soil in which it is grown.

---

## DISCOVERY LAB

### Purpose
Students will use two indicators to distinguish between household products that are acidic and basic.

### Safety and Disposal
The products can be washed down the drain with plenty of water.

### Teaching Strategies
• Distribute six to eight products to students in small labeled beakers with droppers.
• Suggested acids: white vinegar, white apple juice, colorless soft drink; suggested bases: household ammonia, colorless liquid soap, a solution of baking soda

### Expected Results
Acids turn blue litmus red; bases turn red litmus blue. Phenolphthalein turns pink in bases.

### Analysis
One group reacts to litmus only. The other reacts to both litmus and phenolphthalein. Household products can be grouped by their reactions to litmus and phenolphthalein.

## DISCOVERY LAB

### Investigating What's in Your Cupboards

You can learn something about the properties of products in your household by testing them with strips of paper called litmus paper. Can you separate household products into two groups?

### Safety Precautions

 **Always wear safety goggles and an apron.**

### Procedure

1. Place three or four drops of each liquid into separate wells of a microplate. Draw a chart to show the position of each liquid.

2. Test each product with litmus paper. Place 2 drops of phenolphthalein in each sample. Record your observations.

### Analysis

Separate the products into two groups based upon your observations. How do the groups differ? What can you conclude?

**Materials**

red litmus paper
blue litmus paper
microplate
household products (6-8)
phenolphthalein

---

## Section 19.1

# Acids and Bases: An Introduction

### Objectives

- **Identify** the physical and chemical properties of acids and bases.

- **Classify** solutions as acidic, basic, or neutral.

- **Compare** the Arrhenius and Brønsted-Lowry models of acids and bases.

### Vocabulary

acidic solution
basic solution
Arrhenius model
Brønsted-Lowry model
conjugate acid
conjugate base
conjugate acid-base pair
amphoteric

When ants sense danger to the ant colony, they emit a substance called formic acid that alerts the entire colony. Acids in rainwater hollow out enormous limestone caverns and destroy valuable buildings and statues. Acids flavor many of the beverages and foods you like, and it's an acid in your stomach that helps digest what you eat. Bases also play a role in your life. The soap you use and the antacid tablet you may take for an upset stomach are bases. Perhaps you have already concluded that the household products you used in the **DISCOVERY LAB** are acids and bases.

### Properties of Acids and Bases

Acids and bases are some of the most important industrial compounds on Earth. In the U.S. alone, industries use 30 to 40 billion kilograms of sulfuric acid each year in the manufacture of products such as plastics, detergents, batteries, and metals.

You are probably already familiar with some of the physical properties of acids and bases. For example, you may know that acidic solutions taste sour. Carbonic and phosphoric acids give many carbonated beverages their sharp taste; citric and ascorbic acids give lemons and grapefruit their mouth-puckering tartness; and acetic acid makes vinegar taste sour. You may also know that basic solutions taste bitter and feel slippery. Just think about the bar of soap that slips from your hand in the shower. **CAUTION:** *You should never attempt to identify an acid or base (or any other substance in the laboratory) by its taste or feel.* The photo on the opposite page shows how the color of a hydrangea depends upon the presence of acids in the soil.

19.1 Acids and Bases: An Introduction    **595**

---

# 1 Focus

## Focus Transparency

Before presenting the lesson, display **Section Focus Transparency 71** on the overhead projector. Have students answer the accompanying questions using **Section Focus Transparency Master 71.** L1 ELL

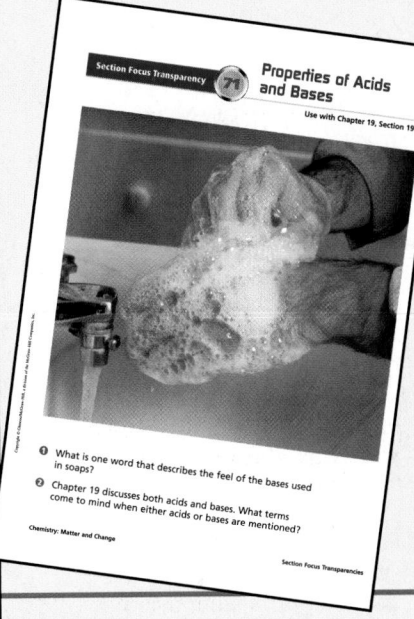

## Chapter Themes

The following themes from the National Science Education Standards are covered in this chapter. Refer to page 4T of the Teacher Guide for an explanation of the correlations.
Systems, order, and organization (UCP.1)
Evidence, models, and explanation (UCP.2)
Change, constancy, and measurement (UCP.3)
Evolution and Equilibrium (UCP.4)
Form and function (UCP.5)

---

## Resource Manager

Section Focus Transparency 71 and Master L1 ELL
Solving Problems: A Chemistry Handbook, Section 19.1 L2
Study Guide for Content Mastery, p. 109 L2

---

**National Science Content Standards**

**Pages 594–595**
UCP.2, UCP.3, UCP.4; A.1; B.2, B.3

**1. a.** $Mg(s) + 2HNO_3(aq) \rightarrow$
   $Mg(NO_3)_2(aq) + H_2(g)$

   **b.** $2Al(s) + 3H_2SO_4(aq) \rightarrow$
   $Al_2(SO_4)_3(aq) + 3H_2(g)$

   **c.** $CaCO_3(s) + 2HBr(aq) \rightarrow$
   $CaBr_2(aq) + H_2O(l) +$
   $CO_2(g)$

   **d.** $KHCO_3(s) + HCl(aq) \rightarrow$
   $KCl(aq) + H_2O(l) +$
   $CO_2(g)$

**Figure 19-1**

The blue litmus paper turned pink when it was dipped into the HCl solution, confirming that HCl is an acid. The red litmus paper turned blue after being dipped into the NaOH solution, so NaOH is a base.

Acids can also be identified by their reaction with some metals. Aluminum, magnesium, and zinc react with aqueous solutions of acids to produce hydrogen gas. The reaction between zinc and hydrochloric acid is described by the following equation.

$$Zn(s) + 2HCl(aq) \rightarrow ZnCl_2(aq) + H_2(g)$$

Metal carbonates and hydrogen carbonates also react with aqueous solutions of acids to produce carbon dioxide gas. When vinegar is added to baking soda, a foaming, effervescent reaction occurs between acetic acid ($HC_2H_3O_2$) dissolved in the vinegar solution, and sodium hydrogen carbonate ($NaHCO_3$). The production of $CO_2$ gas accounts for the effervescence.

$$NaHCO_3(s) + HC_2H_3O_2(aq) \rightarrow NaC_2H_3O_2(aq) + H_2O(l) + CO_2(g)$$

Geologists identify rocks as limestone ($CaCO_3$) by using an HCl solution. If a few drops of the acid produce bubbles of carbon dioxide, the rock is limestone.

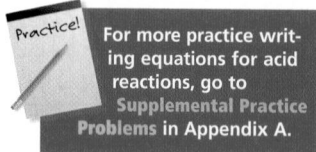

For more practice writing equations for acid reactions, go to **Supplemental Practice Problems** in Appendix A.

### PRACTICE PROBLEMS

**1.** Write a balanced formula equation for the reaction that occurs between each of the following pairs of reactants.
   **a.** magnesium and nitric acid
   **b.** aluminum and sulfuric acid
   **c.** calcium carbonate and hydrobromic acid
   **d.** potassium hydrogen carbonate and hydrochloric acid

The litmus in litmus paper is one of the dyes commonly used to distinguish solutions of acids and bases, as shown in **Figure 19-1.** Aqueous solutions of acids cause blue litmus paper to turn pink. Aqueous solutions of bases cause red litmus paper to turn blue. With this information you can now identify the two groups of household products you used in the **DISCOVERY LAB.**

Another property of acid and base solutions is their ability to conduct electricity. Pure water is a nonconductor of electricity, but the addition of an acid or base to water causes the resulting solution to become a conductor.

**Ions in solution** Why are some aqueous solutions acidic, others basic, and still others neutral? Neutral solutions are neither acidic nor basic. Scientists have learned that all water (aqueous) solutions contain hydrogen ions ($H^+$)

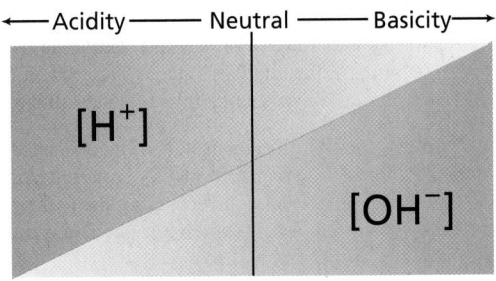

←——Acidity——— Neutral ——— Basicity——→

[H⁺]

[OH⁻]

**Figure 19-2**

Note how [H⁺] and [OH⁻] change simultaneously. As [H⁺] decreases to the right, [OH⁻] increases to the right. At what point in the diagram are the two ion concentrations equal?

and hydroxide ions (OH⁻). The relative amounts of the two ions determine whether an aqueous solution is acidic, basic, or neutral.

An **acidic solution** contains more hydrogen ions than hydroxide ions. A **basic solution** contains more hydroxide ions than hydrogen ions. What do you think a neutral solution contains? You are correct if you said a neutral solution contains equal concentrations of hydrogen ions and hydroxide ions. These relationships are illustrated in **Figure 19-2.**

The usual solvent for acids and bases is water. Water produces equal numbers of H⁺ ions and OH⁻ ions in a process known as self-ionization. In self-ionization, two water molecules react to form a hydronium ion ($H_3O^+$) and a hydroxide ion according to this equilibrium.

$$H_2O(l) + H_2O(l) \rightleftharpoons H_3O^+(aq) + OH^-(aq)$$
Water molecules      Hydronium      Hydroxide
ion            ion

The hydronium ion is a hydrated hydrogen ion, which means that a water molecule is attached to a hydrogen ion by a covalent bond. However, the symbols H⁺ and $H_3O^+$ can be used interchangeably in chemical equations to represent a hydrogen ion in aqueous solution. Thus, a simplified version of the equation for the self-ionization of water is

$$H_2O(l) \rightleftharpoons H^+(aq) + OH^-(aq)$$

From the equation, you can infer that pure water is neutral because equal numbers of H⁺ ions and OH⁻ ions are always present.

**The Arrhenius model of acids and bases** If pure water itself is neutral, how does an aqueous solution become acidic or basic? The first person to answer this question was the Swedish chemist Svante Arrhenius, who in 1883 proposed what is now called the Arrhenius model of acids and bases. The **Arrhenius model** states that an acid is a substance that contains hydrogen and ionizes to produce hydrogen ions in aqueous solution. A base is a substance that contains a hydroxide group and dissociates to produce a hydroxide ion in aqueous solution. Some household acids and bases are shown in **Figure 19-3.**

As an example of the Arrhenius model of acids and bases, consider what happens when hydrogen chloride gas dissolves in water. HCl molecules ionize to form H⁺ ions, which make the solution acidic.

$$HCl(g) \rightarrow H^+(aq) + Cl^-(aq)$$

When the ionic compound NaOH dissolves in water, it dissociates to produce OH⁻ ions, which make the solution basic.

$$NaOH(s) \rightarrow Na^+(aq) + OH^-(aq)$$

**Figure 19-3**

You probably have some of these products in your home. Examine their labels and the labels of other household products and list the acids and bases you find.

19.1 Acids and Bases: An Introduction      **597**

**Reinforcement**

Ask students to distinguish between HCl(g) and HCl(aq). HCl(g) is gaseous hydrogen chloride; HCl(aq) is hydrogen chloride gas dissolved in water and is called hydrochloric acid. Because the names of acids will be used often in this chapter, review with students what they learned earlier about naming binary acids and oxyacids. **L1**

**Extension**

Students may assume that any metallic hydroxide will produce a basic aqueous solution. Explain that dissolving highly charged metal-ion hydroxides, such as $Al(OH)_3$, in water actually results in acidic solutions because the positively charged metal ions attract electrons from the O–H bond, which weakens it and enables the hydrogen atom to ionize.

**Quick Demo**

CAUTION: *Perform this demo in a well-ventilated area or under a hood. Wet a piece of red litmus paper with distilled water and hold the litmus paper with forceps over the mouth of a bottle of concentrated ammonia solution. The litmus color changes from red to blue. Ask students what this indicates regarding the interaction of ammonia with the water in the paper. A basic solution is produced.*

**Figure Caption Question**

**Figure 19-2** At what point in the diagram are the two ion concentrations equal? At the vertical line marked "neutral."

**DIFFERENTIATED INSTRUCTION**

**English Language Learners**

*Linguistic* Have English language learners look up and then explain the meanings of several key English prefixes and words used in this section: mono-, di-, tri-, poly-, conjugate, polyprotic. **L1** **ELL**

**National Science Content Standards**

**Pages 596–597**
UCP.2, UCP.3, UCP.4; B.2, B.3

### Figure Caption Questions

**Figure 19-4** If the footbag is a hydrogen ion, which person is an acid? the person with the footbag If the footbag is passed to another person, which person is the acid? the person to whom the footbag was passed Is the other person a conjugate base or a conjugate acid? a conjugate base

Although the Arrhenius model is useful in explaining many acidic and basic solutions, it has some shortcomings. For example, ammonia ($NH_3$) does not contain a hydroxide group, yet ammonia produces hydroxide ions in solution and is a well known base. Clearly, a model that includes all bases is needed.

**The Brønsted-Lowry model** The Danish chemist Johannes Brønsted and the English chemist Thomas Lowry independently proposed a more inclusive model of acids and bases—a model that focuses on the hydrogen ion ($H^+$). In the **Brønsted-Lowry model** of acids and bases, an acid is a hydrogen-ion donor and a base is a hydrogen-ion acceptor.

What does it mean to be a hydrogen-ion donor or a hydrogen-ion acceptor? The symbols X and Y may be used to represent nonmetallic elements or negative polyatomic ions. Thus the general formula for an acid can be written as HX or HY. When a molecule of acid, HX, dissolves in water, it donates a $H^+$ ion to a water molecule. The water molecule acts as a base and accepts the $H^+$ ion.

$$HX(aq) + H_2O(l) \rightleftharpoons H_3O^+(aq) + X^-(aq)$$

On accepting the $H^+$ ion, the water molecule becomes an acid $H_3O^+$. The hydronium ion ($H_3O^+$) is an acid because it has an extra $H^+$ ion that it can donate. On donating its $H^+$ ion, the acid HX becomes a base, $X^-$. Why? You are correct if you said $X^-$ is a base because it has a negative charge and can readily accept a positive hydrogen ion. Thus, an acid-base reaction in the reverse direction can occur. The acid $H_3O^+$ can react with the base $X^-$ to form water and HX and the following equilibrium is established.

$$HX(aq) + H_2O(l) \rightleftharpoons H_3O^+(aq) + X^-(aq)$$

| Acid | Base | Conjugate acid | Conjugate base |

The forward reaction is the reaction of an acid and a base. The reverse reaction also is the reaction of an acid and a base. The acid and base that react in the reverse reaction are identified under the equation as a conjugate acid and a conjugate base. A **conjugate acid** is the species produced when a base accepts a hydrogen ion from an acid. The base $H_2O$ accepts a hydrogen ion from the acid HX and becomes the conjugate acid, $H_3O^+$. A **conjugate base** is the species that results when an acid donates a hydrogen ion to a base. The acid HX donates its hydrogen ion and becomes the conjugate base $X^-$. In the reaction above, the hydronium ion ($H_3O^+$) is the conjugate acid of the base $H_2O$. The $X^-$ ion is the conjugate base of the acid HX. Every Brønsted-Lowry interaction involves conjugate acid-base pairs. A **conjugate acid-base pair** consists of two substances related to each other by the donating and accepting of a single hydrogen ion.

An analogy for conjugate acid-base pairs is shown in **Figure 19-4.** When you have the footbag (Hacky Sack), you are an acid. You pass the footbag (hydrogen ion) to your friend. Now your friend is an acid because she has the footbag (hydrogen ion) to give away and you are a base because you are able to accept the footbag (hydrogen ion). You, with the footbag, and your friend are the acid and base in the forward reaction. In the reverse reaction, your friend with the footbag is the conjugate acid and you are the conjugate base.

**Figure 19-4**

In a game of freestyle footbag, the players stand in a circle. If the footbag is a hydrogen ion, which person is an acid? If the footbag is passed to another person, which person is the acid? Is the other person a conjugate base or a conjugate acid?

**598     Chapter 19** Acids and Bases

---

## DIFFERENTIATED INSTRUCTION

### Learning Disabled

*Kinesthetic* Have students make paper cutouts to represent the atoms of hydrogen, oxygen, and chlorine in the reaction between hydrogen chloride and water. They can use thumbtacks to attach the cutouts to a poster board or bulletin board, then physically transfer the $H^+$ from HCl to $H_2O$ to create $H_3O^+$ and $Cl^-$. **L1**

**ELL**

Now, consider the equation for the ionization of hydrogen fluoride in water. According to the Brønsted-Lowry definition, the equation is written this way.

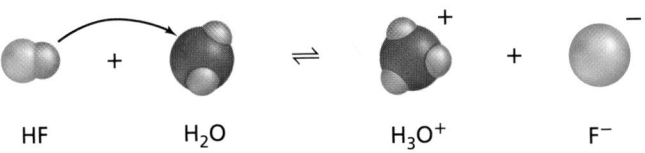

HF      H₂O      H₃O⁺      F⁻

What are the conjugate acid-base pairs? Hydrogen fluoride (HF), the acid in the forward reaction, produces its conjugate base $F^-$, the base in the reverse reaction. Water, the base in the forward reaction, produces its conjugate acid $H_3O^+$, the acid in the reverse reaction.

Hydrogen fluoride is an acid according to both the Arrhenius and Brønsted-Lowry definitions. All of the acids and bases that fit the Arrhenius definition of acids and bases also fit the Brønsted-Lowry definition. But what about bases such as ammonia, that cannot be considered bases according to the Arrhenius definition because they lack a hydroxide group? Does the Brønsted-Lowry model explain why they are bases?

When ammonia dissolves in water, water is a Brønsted-Lowry acid in the forward reaction. Because the $NH_3$ molecule accepts a $H^+$ ion to form the ammonium ion ($NH_4^+$), ammonia is a Brønsted-Lowry base in the forward reaction.

$$NH_3(aq) + H_2O(l) \rightleftharpoons NH_4^+(aq) + OH^-(aq)$$
Base      Acid      Conjugate      Conjugate
                       acid           base

Now look at the reverse reaction. The ammonium ion gives up a $H^+$ ion to form the molecule ammonia and thus acts as a Brønsted-Lowry acid. The ammonium ion is the conjugate acid of the base ammonia. The hydroxide ion accepts a $H^+$ ion to form a water molecule and is thus a Brønsted-Lowry base. The hydroxide ion is the conjugate base of the acid water.

Recall that when HF dissolves in water, water acts a base; when $NH_3$ dissolves in water, water acts as an acid. Depending upon what other substances are in the solution, water can act as either an acid or a base. Water and other substances that can act as both acids and bases are said to be **amphoteric.**

Compare what you have learned about the Arrhenius model and the Brønsted-Lowry model of acids and bases. It should be clear to you that all substances classified as acids and bases by the Arrhenius model are classified as acids and bases by the Brønsted-Lowry model. In addition, some substances *not* classified as bases by the Arrhenius model *are* classified as bases by the Brønsted-Lowry model.

## PRACTICE PROBLEMS

**2.** Identify the conjugate acid-base pairs in the following reactions.
 **a.** $NH_4^+(aq) + OH^-(aq) \rightleftharpoons NH_3(aq) + H_2O(l)$
 **b.** $HBr(aq) + H_2O(l) \rightleftharpoons H_3O^+(aq) + Br^-(aq)$
 **c.** $CO_3^{2-}(aq) + H_2O(l) \rightleftharpoons HCO_3^-(aq) + OH^-(aq)$
 **d.** $HSO_4^-(aq) + H_2O(l) \rightleftharpoons H_3O^+(aq) + SO_4^{2-}(aq)$

Practice! For more practice identifying conjugate acid-base pairs, go to **Supplemental Practice Problems** in Appendix A.

19.1 Acids and Bases: An Introduction    **599**

## Careers Using Chemistry
### Agricultural Technician

*Would you like to work on a large farm, checking soil pH and deciding when to use fertilizers and pesticides? If so, become an agricultural technician.*

Agricultural technicians also work for the government, research groups, and companies that produce fertilizers and other farm chemicals. They know how to modify soil conditions, increase crop yields, help crops resist disease and insects, and store produce. Some agricultural technicians help keep farm animals healthy and productive.

## Chemistry Online

**Topic: Food Chemistry**
To learn more about acids and bases that affect food chemistry, visit the Chemistry Web site at **chemistrymc.com**

**Activity:** As a class, compile tips for using acids and bases properly in cooking and any chemical equations you can find for the processes that occur in cooking, marinating, and baking.

## ✓ Assessment

**Performance** Have two student volunteers plan and perform a debate involving the Arrhenius and Brønsted-Lowry models of acids and bases. Have one student assume the role of Svante Arrhenius and advocate his model while the other student plays Johannes Brønsted and supports his model. Use the Performance Task Assessment List for Skit in **PASC**, p. 75.

## Practice PROBLEMS

Have students refer to Appendix D for complete solutions to Practice Problems.

**2. a.** $NH_4^+$ (acid) and $NH_3$ (conjugate base), $OH^-$ (base) and $H_2O$ (conjugate acid)

 **b.** HBr (acid) and $Br^-$ (conjugate base), $H_2O$ (base) and $H_3O^+$ (conjugate acid)

 **c.** $CO_3^{2-}$ (base) and $HCO_3^-$ (conjugate acid), $H_2O$ (acid) and $OH^-$ (conjugate base)

 **d.** $HSO_4^-$ (acid) and $SO_4^{2-}$ (conjugate base), $H_2O$ (base) and $H_3O^+$ (conjugate acid)

## GLENCOE TECHNOLOGY

**CD-ROM**
**Chemistry: Matter and Change**
Video: *Chemical Properties; The Actions of Acids and Bases*
Video: *Acids and Bases*
Demonstration: *Forming a Basic Anhydride*

**National Science Content Standards**
**Pages 598–599**
UCP.2, UCP.3, UCP.4; B.2, B.4

## DIFFERENTIATED INSTRUCTION

### Gifted

**Intrapersonal** Have interested and capable students research the Lewis model of acids and bases. Have them summarize their findings and include equations that illustrate and compare the Arrhenius, Brønsted-Lowry, and Lewis models. If time and class interest permit, have them make a class presentation. **L3**

## Applying Chemistry

If possible, bring in a nineteenth century book with badly decomposed pages. Explain that in the nineteenth century, paper was often sized, a process in which microscopic holes were filled with alum (aluminum sulfate) to lower absorption of moisture and reduce spreading of inks. The alum formed $Al(H_2O)_6^{3+}$ ions, which are acidic. Over time, the $Al(H_2O)_6^{3+}$ ions reacted with the wood fibers in paper, causing the paper to disintegrate and the books to fall apart. Explain that books older than the nineteenth century are generally in better condition because alum was not used for sizing at that time.

# 3 Assess

## Check for Understanding

Ask students why hydrogen sulfide ($H_2S$) is generally considered an acid while methane ($CH_4$) is not. Although hydrogen atoms are bonded to nonmetallic elements in both compounds, $H_2S$ ionizes in aqueous solution to produce $H^+$ ions. $CH_4$ does not.

## Reteach

Ask students whether the reaction $H_2O(l) + CH_3NH_2(aq) \rightarrow OH^-(aq) + CH_3NH_3^+(aq)$ is an acid-base reaction according to the Arrhenius model. no Ask if it is an acid-base reaction according to the Brønsted-Lowry model. yes Have them identify the Brønsted-Lowry acid in the forward reaction. $H_2O$
L2

## In-Text Question

**Page 601** What acid will form from $N_2O_5$? $HNO_3$

**National Science Content Standards**

**Pages 600–601**
UCP.2, UCP.3, UCP.4; B.2, B.4

**600**

---

**Figure 19-5**

A partial separation of charge is shown in **a** for the O—H bond and in **b** for the H—F bond. These bonds are polar. In water solution, the $H^+$ ionizes, so solutions of HF and ethanoic acid are acidic. The benzene molecule in **c** contains no polar bonds so benzene is not an acid.

**a** Ethanoic acid  **b** Hydrogen fluoride  **c** Benzene

## Earth Science
### CONNECTION

As rain falls, carbon dioxide gas in the air dissolves in the falling water to form a weak acid called carbonic acid. When the acidic rainwater reaches the ground, some water sinks into the pores of the soil to become groundwater. If that groundwater reaches bedrock consisting of limestone, the carbonic acid will slowly dissolve the limestone. Over the course of thousands of years, the limestone is dissolved to the point that huge underground tunnels known as caverns are produced. In many places throughout the cavern, groundwater may drip from the ceiling. As it does so, it deposits some of the dissolved limestone. Thin deposits shaped like icicles on the ceiling are called stalactites. Rounded masses on the floor are called stalagmites. In some cases, stalactites and stalagmites eventually meet in a column or pillar.

## Monoprotic and Polyprotic Acids

You now know that HCl and HF are acids because they can donate a hydrogen ion in an acid-base reaction. From their chemical formulas, you can see that each acid can donate only one hydrogen ion per molecule. An acid that can donate only one hydrogen ion is called a monoprotic acid. Other monoprotic acids are perchloric acid ($HClO_4$), nitric acid ($HNO_3$), hydrobromic acid (HBr), and acetic acid ($CH_3COOH$). The formula for acetic acid is sometimes written $HC_2H_3O_2$ and the compound is often called ethanoic acid.

In **Figure 19-5a,** you can see that each ethanoic acid molecule contains four hydrogen atoms. Can ethanoic acid donate more than one hydrogen ion? No; each $CH_3COOH$ molecule contains only one ionizable hydrogen atom.

$$CH_3COOH(aq) + H_2O(l) \rightleftharpoons H_3O^+(aq) + CH_3COO^-(aq)$$

Only one of the four hydrogen atoms in the $CH_3COOH$ molecule can be donated because only those hydrogen atoms bonded to electronegative elements by polar bonds are ionizable.

In an HF molecule, the hydrogen atom is bonded to a fluorine atom, which has the highest electronegativity of all the elements. In **Figure 19-5b,** you can see that the bond linking hydrogen and fluorine is polar; in solution, water facilitates the release of the $H^+$ ion. In the $CH_3COOH$ molecule shown in **Figure 19-5a,** three of the four hydrogen atoms are joined to a carbon atom by covalent bonds that are nonpolar because carbon and hydrogen have almost equal electronegativities. Only the hydrogen atom bonded to the electronegative oxygen atom can be released as a $H^+$ ion in water. Although a molecule of benzene ($C_6H_6$) contains six hydrogen atoms, it is not an acid at all. As **Figure 19-5c** shows, none of the hydrogen atoms are ionizable because they are all joined to carbon atoms by nonpolar bonds.

Some acids, however, do donate more than one hydrogen ion. For example, sulfuric acid ($H_2SO_4$) and carbonic acid ($H_2CO_3$) can donate two hydrogen ions. In each compound, both hydrogen atoms are attached to oxygen atoms by polar bonds. Acids that contain two ionizable hydrogen atoms per molecule are called diprotic acids. In a similar way, phosphoric acid ($H_3PO_4$) and boric acid ($H_3BO_3$) contain three ionizable hydrogen atoms per molecule. Acids with three hydrogen ions to donate are called triprotic acids. The term polyprotic acid can be used for any acid that has more than one ionizable hydrogen atom. **Figure 19-6** shows models of two polyprotic acids.

All polyprotic acids ionize in steps. The three ionizations of phosphoric acid are described by these equations.

$$H_3PO_4(aq) + H_2O(l) \rightleftharpoons H_3O^+(aq) + H_2PO_4^-(aq)$$
$$H_2PO_4^-(aq) + H_2O(l) \rightleftharpoons H_3O^+(aq) + HPO_4^{2-}(aq)$$
$$HPO_4^{2-}(aq) + H_2O(l) \rightleftharpoons H_3O^+(aq) + PO_4^{3-}(aq)$$

---

## Internet Address Book

 Note Internet addresses that you find useful in the space below for quick reference.

$H_2SO_4$
Sulfuric acid

$H_3PO_4$
Phosphoric acid

**Figure 19-6**

Refer to **Table C-1** in Appendix C for a key to atom color conventions. Then, identify the two hydrogen atoms bonded to oxygen atoms in the sulfuric acid model and the three hydrogen atoms bonded to oxygen atoms in the phosphoric acid model.

## PRACTICE PROBLEMS

**3.** Write the steps in the complete ionization of the following polyprotic acids.
  **a.** $H_2Se$
  **b.** $H_3AsO_4$
  **c.** $H_2SO_3$

*Practice!* For more practice writing ionization equations for polyprotic acids, go to **Supplemental Practice Problems** in Appendix A.

**Anhydrides** Some oxides can become acids or bases by adding the elements contained in water. These compounds are called anhydrides. Oxides of nonmetallic elements, such as carbon, sulfur, or nitrogen, produce an acid in aqueous solution. Oxides of metallic elements usually form basic solutions. For example, carbon dioxide, an oxide of a nonmetal, forms a solution of carbonic acid, whereas, calcium oxide (CaO) forms a basic solution of calcium hydroxide.

$$CO_2(g) + H_2O(l) \rightarrow H_2CO_3(aq)$$

$$CaO(s) + H_2O(l) \rightarrow Ca^{2+}(aq) + 2OH^-(l)$$

Similarly, $SO_3$ is the anhydride of $H_2SO_4$ and MgO is the anhydride of $Mg(OH)_2$. What acid will form from $N_2O_5$?

## Section 19.1 Assessment

**4.** Compare the properties of acidic solutions and basic solutions.

**5.** How do the concentrations of hydrogen ion and hydroxide ion determine whether a solution is acidic, basic, or neutral?

**6.** Based on their formulas, which of the following compounds *may* be Arrhenius acids: $CH_4$, $SO_2$, $H_2S$, $Ca_3(PO_4)_2$? Explain your reasoning.

**7.** Identify the conjugate acid-base pairs in the following equation.

$$HNO_2 + H_2O \rightleftharpoons NO_2^- + H_3O^+$$

**8. Thinking Critically** Methylamine ($CH_3NH_2$) forms hydroxide ions in aqueous solution. Why is methylamine a Brønsted-Lowry base but not an Arrhenius base?

**9. Interpreting Scientific Illustrations** In the accompanying structural formula, identify any hydrogen atoms that are likely to be ionizable.

**Extension**

Have students write the chemical equation for the acidic reaction of $Al(H_2O)_6^{3+}$ with water.
$Al(H_2O)_6^{3+}(aq) + H_2O(l) \rightleftharpoons$
$H_3O^+(aq) + Al(H_2O)_5OH^{2+}(aq)$

## Assessment

**Skill** Ask students to write the equations for the three ionizations of boric acid ($H_3BO_3$).
$H_3BO_3(aq) + H_2O(l) \rightleftharpoons H_3O^+(aq) + H_2BO_3^-(aq)$, $H_2BO_3^-(aq) + H_2O(l) \rightleftharpoons H_3O^+(aq) + HBO_3^{2-}(aq)$, $HBO_3^{2-}(aq) + H_2O(l) \rightleftharpoons H_3O^+(aq) + BO_3^{3-}(aq)$.

## Practice PROBLEMS

Have students refer to Appendix D for complete solutions to Practice Problems.

**3. a.** $H_2Se(aq) + H_2O(l) \rightleftharpoons H_3O^+(aq) + HSe^-(aq)$
$HSe^-(aq) + H_2O(l) \rightleftharpoons H_3O^+(aq) + Se^{2-}(aq)$

**b.** $H_3AsO_4(aq) + H_2O(l) \rightleftharpoons H_3O^+(aq) + H_2AsO_4^-(aq)$
$H_2AsO_4^-(aq) + H_2O(l) \rightleftharpoons H_3O^+(aq) + HAsO_4^{2-}(aq)$
$HAsO_4^{2-}(aq) + H_2O(l) \rightleftharpoons H_3O^+(aq) + AsO_4^{3-}(aq)$

**c.** $H_2SO_3(aq) + H_2O(l) \rightleftharpoons H_3O^+(aq) + HSO_3^-(aq)$
$HSO_3^-(aq) + H_2O(l) \rightleftharpoons H_3O^+(aq) + SO_3^{2-}(aq)$

**Resource Manager**

Teaching Transparency 55 and Master **L2** **ELL**

## Section 19.1 Assessment

**4.** Acidic solutions taste sour, turn blue litmus red, produce solutions that conduct electricity, react with certain metals to produce hydrogen gas, and react with carbonates to produce carbon dioxide. Basic solutions taste bitter and feel slippery, turn red litmus blue, and produce solutions that conduct electricity.

**5.** In an acidic solution, $[H^+] > [OH^-]$; in a neutral solution, $[H^+] = [OH^-]$; in a basic solution, $[H^+] < [OH^-]$.

**6.** Because they contain hydrogen, $CH_4$ and $H_2S$ may be Arrhenius acids.

**7.** $HNO_2$ (acid) and $NO_2^-$ (conjugate base), $H_2O$ (base) and $H_3O^+$ (conjugate acid)

**8.** The $CH_3NH_2$ molecule is a hydrogen-ion acceptor; however, the molecule does not contain an OH group.

**9.** the two hydrogen atoms attached to oxygen atoms

**601**

# 1 Focus

**Section 19.2**    **Strengths of Acids and Bases**

## Focus Transparency

Before presenting the lesson, display **Section Focus Transparency 72** on the overhead projector. Have students answer the accompanying questions using **Section Focus Transparency Master 72.** L1 ELL

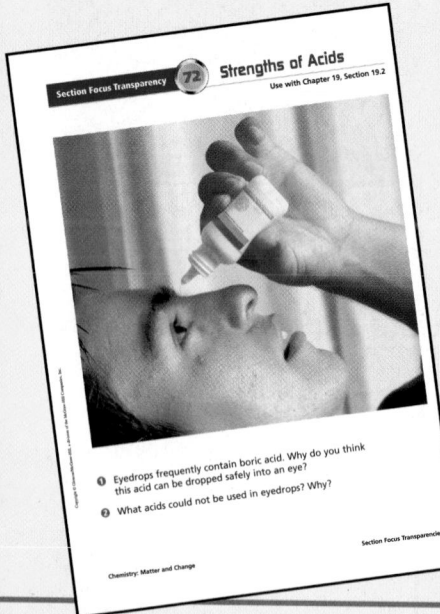

## Objectives

- **Relate** the strength of an acid or base to its degree of ionization.

- **Compare** the strength of a weak acid with the strength of its conjugate base and the strength of a weak base with the strength of its conjugate acid.

- **Explain** the relationship between the strengths of acids and bases and the values of their ionization constants.

## Vocabulary

strong acid
weak acid
acid ionization constant
strong base
weak base
base ionization constant

# Strengths of Acids and Bases

In the previous section, you learned that one of the properties of acidic and basic solutions is that they conduct electricity. What can electrical conductivity tell you about the hydrogen ions and hydroxide ions in these aqueous solutions?

## Strengths of Acids

To answer this question, suppose you test the electrical conductivities of $0.10M$ aqueous solutions of hydrochloric acid and acetic acid using a conductivity apparatus similar to the one shown in **Figure 19-7.** When the electrodes are placed in the solutions, both bulbs glow, indicating that both solutions conduct electricity. However, if you compare the brightness of the bulb connected to the hydrochloric acid solution with that of the bulb connected to the acetic acid solution, you can't help but notice a significant difference. The $0.10M$ HCl solution conducts electricity better than the $0.10M$ $HC_2H_3O_2$ solution. Why is this true if the concentrations of the two acids are both $0.10M$?

The answer is that it is ions that carry electricity through the solution and all the HCl molecules that make up the solution are in the form of hydrogen ions and chloride ions. Acids that ionize completely are called **strong acids.** Because strong acids produce the maximum number of ions, they are good conductors of electricity. Other strong acids include perchloric acid ($HClO_4$), nitric acid ($HNO_3$), hydroiodic acid (HI), sulfuric acid ($H_2SO_4$), and hydrobromic acid (HBr). The ionization of hydrochloric acid in water may be represented by the following equation, which has a single arrow pointing to the right. What does a single arrow to the right mean?

$$HCl(aq) + H_2O(l) \rightarrow H_3O^+(aq) + Cl^-(aq)$$

Because hydrochloric acid is virtually 100% ionized, you can consider that the reaction goes to completion and essentially no reaction occurs in the reverse direction.

If the brightly lit bulb of the hydrochloric acid apparatus is due to the large number of ions in solution, then the weakly lit bulb of the acetic acid apparatus must mean that the acetic acid solution has fewer ions. Because the two solutions have the same molar concentrations, you can conclude that acetic acid

**Figure 19-7**

Both solutions have the same molar concentration, yet HCl produces a brighter light than $HC_2H_3O_2$. Because the amount of electrical current depends upon the number of ions in solution, the HCl solution must contain more ions.

# 2 Teach

## Content Background

**Acid Strength and Bonding**
Explain that an acid's strength relates to the strength and polarity of its H–X bond, where X represents a nonmetallic element or, in some instances, a negatively charged polyatomic ion. Point out that bond strength depends primarily upon the relative electronegativities of H and X or, for a negatively charged polyatomic ion, the electronegativities of H, X, and other elements bonded to X. In general, the weaker the H–X bond, the stronger the acid.

**National Science Content Standards**

Pages 602–603
UCP.2, UCP.3, UCP.4; A.1; B.2, B.4

## DIFFERENTIATED INSTRUCTION

### Visually Impaired

*Interpersonal* Have students, parents, or school personnel prepare an "acid-base buffet" made up of food items that contain acids and/or bases. Arrange the "buffet" in the school cafeteria or the school's home economics classroom. Organize an in-school field trip in which students sample these items and report on their distinctive tastes. L1 ELL

## Resource Manager

**Section Focus Transparency 72 and Master** L1 ELL
**Solving Problems: A Chemistry Handbook,** Section 19.2 L2
**Study Guide for Content Mastery,** p. 110 L2

HCl            $HC_2H_3O_2$

Hydronium ion

Chloride ion

Acetic acid molecule

Acetate ion

Hydronium ion

**Figure 19-8**

All of the HCl molecules have ionized to hydronium and chloride ions, but only one $HC_2H_3O_2$ molecule has ionized to a hydronium ion and acetate ion. It's no wonder, then, that the strong acid HCl causes the light to burn brighter than the weak acid $HC_2H_3O_2$.

does not ionize completely. Some of the acetic acid remains in molecular form in solution. An acid that ionizes only partially in dilute aqueous solution is defined as a **weak acid.** Weak acid produce fewer ions and thus cannot conduct electricity as efficiently as strong acids. Some common weak acids are acetic acid ($HC_2H_3O_2$), hydrofluoric acid (HF), hydrocyanic acid (HCN), carbonic acid ($H_2CO_3$), and boric acid ($H_3BO_3$).

Recall from Chapter 18 that some reactions reach a state of equilibrium in which the forward and reverse reactions occur at equal rates and all reactants and products are present in the equilibrium mixture. The ionization of a weak acid is such a reaction. The ionization of acetic acid is described by this equilibrium equation.

$$HC_2H_3O_2(aq) + H_2O(l) \rightleftharpoons H_3O^+(aq) + C_2H_3O_2^-(aq)$$

The relative degrees of ionization for HCl and $HC_2H_3O_2$ in aqueous solution are illustrated in **Figure 19-8**. Ionization equations for several common acids are also shown in **Table 19-1**. For simplicity, water is not included in the equations. The **miniLAB** on the next page demonstrates the relationship between electrical conductivity and ion concentration.

**Acid strength and the Brønsted-Lowry model** Can the Brønsted-Lowry model explain why HCl ionizes completely but $HC_2H_3O_2$ forms only a few ions? Consider again the ionization of a strong acid, HX. Remember that the acid on the reactant side of the equation produces a conjugate base on the product side. Similarly, the base on the reactant side produces a conjugate acid.

$$HX(aq) + H_2O(l) \rightarrow H_3O^+(aq) + X^-(aq)$$
Acid    Base    Conjugate acid    Conjugate base

Because HX is a strong acid, its conjugate base is weak. That is, HX is nearly 100% ionized because $H_2O$ is a stronger base (in the forward reaction) than is the conjugate base $X^-$ (in the reverse reaction). In other words, the ionization equilibrium lies almost completely to the right because the base $H_2O$ has a much greater attraction for the $H^+$ ion than does the base $X^-$. You can think of this as the battle of the bases: Which of the two ($H_2O$ or $X^-$) has a

**Table 19-1**

| Ionization Equations | |
|---|---|
| **Strong Acids** | |
| **Name** | **Ionization equation** |
| Hydrochloric | HCl → $H^+$ + $Cl^-$ |
| Hydrobromic | HBr → $H^+$ + $Br^-$ |
| Hydroiodic | HI → $H^+$ + $I^-$ |
| Perchloric | $HClO_4$ → $H^+$ + $ClO_4^-$ |
| Nitric | $HNO_3$ → $H^+$ + $NO_3^-$ |
| Sulfuric | $H_2SO_4$ → $H^+$ + $HSO_4^-$ |
| **Weak Acids** | |
| Hydrofluoric | HF $\rightleftharpoons$ $H^+$ + $F^-$ |
| Hydrocyanic | HCN $\rightleftharpoons$ $H^+$ + $CN^-$ |
| Acetic | $HC_2H_3O_2 \rightleftharpoons$ $H^+$ + $C_2H_3O_2^-$ |
| Hydrosulfuric | $H_2S \rightleftharpoons H^+$ + $HS^-$ |
| Carbonic | $H_2CO_3 \rightleftharpoons$ $H^+$ + $HCO_3^-$ |
| Hypochlorous | HClO $\rightleftharpoons$ $H^+$ + $ClO^-$ |

---

**DIFFERENTIATED INSTRUCTION**

**Gifted**

**Intrapersonal** Ask gifted students to research and explain the relative strengths of the oxyacids of chlorine (HOCl, $HClO_2$, and $HClO_4$). Hypochlorous acid (HOCl) is the weakest because the chlorine draws very little of the electron density and strength from the H–O bond.

Perchloric acid, which can be written $HOClO_3$, is the strongest because the three oxygen atoms that are bonded to the chlorine atom draw a great deal of the electron density and strength from the Cl–O–H bond. **L3**

### Purpose

Students will observe the electrical conductivity of acetic acid solutions of varying concentrations and infer the relative numbers of ions in the solutions.

### Process Skills

Observing and inferring, recognizing cause and effect, hypothesizing

### Safety Precautions

Be sure students wear lab aprons and goggles. Acetic acid is corrosive. Use a battery-operated conductivity tester to avoid electrical shock. The Flinn conductivity meter AP1493 is recommended.

### Disposal

Dilute all acid solutions twenty-fold and wash down the drain.

### Teaching Strategies

- Have students read Section 19.2 before performing the investigation.
- Use the results of the investigation to initiate a discussion of proper first aid treatment if acid splashes in eyes or on skin.

### Expected Results

The glacial acetic acid does not conduct electricity, so neither the red nor the green LED glows. For all of the dilutions, the red LED on the tester glows brightly. For the 6.0$M$ acetic acid solution, the green LED is dim; for 1.0$M$ acid, the green LED is bright; for 0.1$M$ acid, the green LED is dimmer than for the 6.0$M$.

### Analysis

1. $CH_3COOH(aq) + H_2O(l) \rightleftharpoons H_3O^+(aq) + CH_3COO^-(aq)$

   $K_a = \frac{[CH_3COO^-][H^+]}{[CH_3COOH]} = 1.8 \times 10^{-5}$;
   Very little acetic acid is ionized.

2. Yes, comparing 6.0$M$ and 1.0$M$ solutions, the 1.0$M$ solution has a higher percent of ionization. The larger fraction of ions results in increased conductivity. However, continued dilution reduces the overall concentration of ions enough so that the conductivity of the 0.1$M$ solution decreases.

---

greater attraction for the hydrogen ion? In the case of all strong acids, water is the stronger base. How does the situation differ for the weak acid, HY?

$$HY(aq) + H_2O(l) \rightleftharpoons H_3O^+(aq) + Y^-(aq)$$
Acid — Base — Conjugate acid — Conjugate base

The ionization equilibrium for a weak acid lies far to the left because the conjugate base $Y^-$ has a greater attraction for the $H^+$ ion than does the base $H_2O$. In the battle of the bases, the conjugate base $Y^-$ (in the reverse reaction) proves stronger than the base $H_2O$ (in the forward reaction) and essentially manages to capture the hydrogen ion.

Although the Brønsted-Lowry model helps explain acid strength, the model does not provide a quantitative way to express the strength of an acid or to compare the strengths of various acids. The equilibrium constant expression provides the quantitative measure of acid strength.

## miniLAB

### Acid Strength

**Observing and inferring** The electrical conductivities of solutions of weak acids, such as acetic acid, are related to the degree of ionization of the acid.

**Materials** glacial acetic acid; distilled water; 10-mL graduated cylinder; dropping pipette; 50-mL beaker; 24-well micro plate; conductivity tester with battery; stirring rod

### Procedure

1. Use a 10-mL graduated cylinder to measure 3 mL of glacial acetic acid. Use a dropping pipette to transfer the 3 mL of glacial acetic acid into well A1 of a 24-well micro plate.

2. Lower the electrodes of a conductivity tester into the glacial acetic acid in well A1. Record your results.

3. Rinse the graduated cylinder with water. Prepare a 6.0$M$ solution of acetic acid by adding 3.4 mL of glacial acetic acid to 6.6 mL of distilled water in the 10-mL graduated cylinder.

4. Empty the 10 mL of diluted acid into a 50-mL beaker. After mixing, transfer 3 mL of the 6.0$M$ acetic acid into well A2. Save the remaining 6.0$M$ acetic acid for procedure step 5. Test and record the conductivity of the solution.

5. Prepare a 1.0$M$ acetic acid solution by adding 1.7 mL of 6.0$M$ acetic acid to 8.3 mL of distilled water in the 10-mL graduated cylinder. Empty

the 10 mL of diluted acid into the rinsed 50-mL beaker. After mixing, transfer 3 mL of the 1.0$M$ acetic acid into well A3. Save the remaining 1.0$M$ acetic acid for procedure step 6. Test and record the conductivity of the solution.

6. Prepare a 0.1$M$ acetic acid solution by adding 1.0 mL of 1.0$M$ acetic acid to 9.0 mL of distilled water in the rinsed 10-mL graduated cylinder. Empty the 10 mL of diluted acid into the rinsed 50-mL beaker. After mixing, transfer 3 mL of the 0.1$M$ acetic acid into well A4. Test and record the conductivity of the solution.

### Analysis

1. Write the equation for the ionization of acetic acid in water and the equilibrium constant expression. ($K_{eq} = 1.8 \times 10^{-5}$) What does the size of $K_{eq}$ indicate about the degree of ionization of acetic acid?

2. Do the following approximate percents ionization fit your laboratory results: glacial acetic acid, 0.1%; 6.0$M$ acetic acid, 0.2%; 1.0$M$ acetic acid, 0.4%; 0.1$M$ acetic acid, 1.3%? Explain.

3. State a hypothesis that will explain your observations and incorporate your answer to Question 2.

4. Based on your hypothesis, what can you conclude about the need to use large amounts of water for rinsing when acid spills on living tissue?

---

3. The more dilute the weak acid becomes, the better it conducts electricity because there is a higher degree of ionization. The water acts to increase the percent of ionization. Eventually, the acid is so dilute that the conductivity decreases because there is relatively little acetic acid present.

4. A small amount of water can actually increase the acid's apparent strength and resulting tissue damage. For acid spills, large amounts of water should be used to quickly dilute the acid and flush it away.

### ✓ Assessment

**Knowledge** Ask students to predict the conductivity of 6.0$M$, 1.0$M$, and 0.1$M$ solutions of the strong acid HCl.

**Acid ionization constants** As you have learned, a weak acid produces an equilibrium mixture of molecules and ions in aqueous solution. Thus, the equilibrium constant, $K_{eq}$, provides a quantitative measure of the degree of ionization of the acid. Consider hydrocyanic acid (HCN), a deadly poison with applications in the steel industry and in the processing of metal ores. See **Figure 19-9.** The ionization equation and equilibrium constant expression for hydrocyanic acid are

$$HCN(aq) + H_2O(l) \rightleftharpoons H_3O^+(aq) + CN^-(aq)$$

$$K_{eq} = \frac{[H_3O^+][CN^-]}{[HCN][H_2O]}$$

The concentration of liquid water in the denominator of the expression is considered to be constant in dilute aqueous solutions, so it can be combined with $K_{eq}$ to give a new equilibrium constant, $K_a$.

$$K_{eq}\,[H_2O] = K_a = \frac{[H_3O^+][CN^-]}{[HCN]} = 6.2 \times 10^{-10}$$

$K_a$ is called the acid ionization constant. The **acid ionization constant** is the value of the equilibrium constant expression for the ionization of a weak acid. Like all equilibrium constants, the value of $K_a$ indicates whether reactants or products are favored at equilibrium. For weak acids, the concentrations of the ions (products) in the numerator tend to be small compared to the concentration of un-ionized molecules (reactant) in the denominator. The weakest acids have the smallest $K_a$ values because their solutions have the lowest concentrations of ions and the highest concentrations of un-ionized acid molecules. $K_a$ values and ionization equations for several weak acids are listed in **Table 19-2.** Note that for polyprotic acids there is a $K_a$ value for each ionization and the values decrease for each successive ionization.

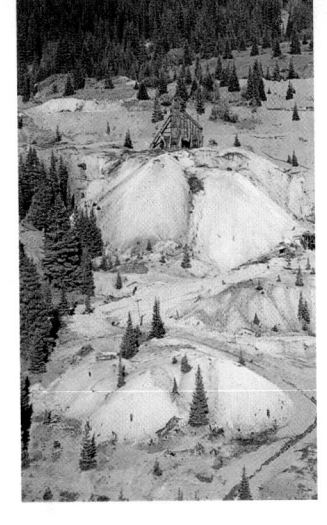

**Figure 19-9**

Mine tailings are crushed rock discarded as waste. Hydrocyanic acid and its compounds can be used to extract useable materials from mine tailings.

**Table 19-2**

| Ionization Constants for Weak Acids at 25°C | | |
|---|---|---|
| **Acid** | **Ionization equation** | $K_a$ **(298 K)** |
| Hydrosulfuric | $H_2S \rightleftharpoons H^+ + HS^-$ | $8.9 \times 10^{-8}$ |
| | $HS^- \rightleftharpoons H^+ + S^{2-}$ | $1 \times 10^{-19}$ |
| Hydrofluoric | $HF \rightleftharpoons H^+ + F^-$ | $6.3 \times 10^{-4}$ |
| Methanoic (Formic) | $HCOOH \rightleftharpoons H^+ + HCOO^-$ | $1.8 \times 10^{-4}$ |
| Ethanoic (Acetic) | $CH_3COOH \rightleftharpoons H^+ + CH_3COO^-$ | $1.8 \times 10^{-5}$ |
| Carbonic | $H_2CO_3 \rightleftharpoons H^+ + HCO_3^-$ | $4.5 \times 10^{-7}$ |
| | $HCO_3^- \rightleftharpoons H^+ + CO_3^{2-}$ | $4.7 \times 10^{-11}$ |
| Hypochlorous | $HClO \rightleftharpoons H^+ + ClO^-$ | $4.0 \times 10^{-8}$ |

## PRACTICE PROBLEMS

**10.** Write ionization equations and acid ionization constant expressions for the following acids.
- **a.** $HClO_2$
- **b.** $HNO_2$
- **c.** $HIO$

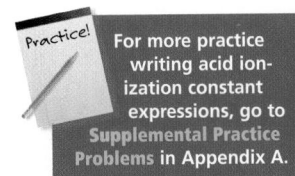

Practice! For more practice writing acid ionization constant expressions, go to **Supplemental Practice Problems** in Appendix A.

19.2 Strengths of Acids and Bases    **605**

## Resource Manager

**Teaching Transparency 56 and Master**
L2 ELL
**ChemLab and MiniLab Worksheets,**
p. 73 L2
**Challenge Problems, p. 19** L3
**Math Skills Transparency 30 and**
Master L2 ELL

## CHEMISTRY JOURNAL

### Acids in Foods

*Intrapersonal* Have students evaluate the strengths of acids in foods and explain why acids such as hydrochloric acid and sulfuric acid are not used to preserve or increase the tartness of foods. Have them record their findings in their journals. L2

Have students refer to Appendix D for complete solutions to Practice Problems.

**11. a.** $K_b = \dfrac{[C_6H_{13}NH_3{}^+][OH^-]}{[C_6H_{13}NH_2]}$

**b.** $K_b = \dfrac{[C_3H_7NH_3{}^+][OH^-]}{[C_3H_7NH_2]}$

**c.** $K_b = \dfrac{[HCO_3{}^-][OH^-]}{[CO_3^{2-}]}$

**d.** $K_b = \dfrac{[H_2SO_3][OH^-]}{[HSO_3{}^-]}$

## Figure Caption Questions

**Figure 19-10** Can you distinguish them? Which of the acids is more concentrated? Which is stronger? Which of the bases is more concentrated? Which is stronger?
They can be distinguished by their concentrations. $6M$ $HC_2H_3O_2$ is the more concentrated acid; $0.01M$ HCl is stronger. $6M$ NaOH is the more concentrated base. It is stronger than $NH_3$.

# Strengths of Bases

What you have learned about acids can be applied to bases except that $OH^-$ ions rather than $H^+$ ions are involved. For example, the conductivity of a base depends upon the extent to which the base produces hydroxide ions in aqueous solution. **Strong bases** dissociate entirely into metal ions and hydroxide ions. Therefore, metallic hydroxides, such as sodium hydroxide, are strong bases.

$$NaOH(s) \rightarrow Na^+(aq) + OH^-(aq)$$

Some metallic hydroxides such as calcium hydroxide have low solubility and thus are poor sources of $OH^-$ ions. Note that the solubility product constant, $K_{sp}$, for $Ca(OH)_2$ is small, indicating that few hydroxide ions are present in a saturated solution.

$$Ca(OH)_2(s) \rightleftharpoons Ca^{2+}(aq) + 2OH^-(aq) \quad K_{sp} = 6.5 \times 10^{-6}$$

Nevertheless, calcium hydroxide and other slightly soluble metallic hydroxides are considered strong bases because all of the compound that dissolves is completely dissociated. The dissociation equations for several strong bases are listed in **Table 19-3**.

In contrast to strong bases, a **weak base** ionizes only partially in dilute aqueous solution to form the conjugate acid of the base and hydroxide ion. The weak base methylamine ($CH_3NH_2$) reacts with water to produce an equilibrium mixture of $CH_3NH_2$ molecules, $CH_3NH_3{}^+$ ions, and $OH^-$ ions.

$$CH_3NH_2(aq) + H_2O(l) \rightleftharpoons CH_3NH_3{}^+(aq) + OH^-(aq)$$

| Base | Acid | Conjugate acid | Conjugate base |

This equilibrium lies far to the left because the base, $CH_3NH_2$, is weak and the conjugate base, $OH^-$ ion, is strong. The hydroxide ion has a much greater attraction for a hydrogen ion than a molecule of methyl amine has.

**Base ionization constants** You won't be surprised to learn that like weak acids, weak bases also form equilibrium mixtures of molecules and ions in aqueous solution. Therefore, the equilibrium constant provides a measure of the extent of the base's ionization. The equilibrium constant for the ionization of methylamine in water is defined by this equilibrium constant expression.

$$K_b = \dfrac{[CH_3NH_3{}^+][OH^-]}{[CH_3NH_2]}$$

The constant $K_b$ is called the base ionization constant. The **base ionization constant** is the value of the equilibrium constant expression for the ionization of a base. The smaller the value of $K_b$, the weaker the base. $K_b$ values and ionization equations for several weak bases are listed in **Table 19-4**.

**Table 19-3**

| Common Strong Bases |
| --- |
| $NaOH(s) \rightarrow Na^+(aq) + OH^-(aq)$ |
| $KOH(s) \rightarrow K^+(aq) + OH^-(aq)$ |
| $RbOH(s) \rightarrow Rb^+(aq) + OH^-(aq)$ |
| $CsOH(s) \rightarrow Cs^+(aq) + OH^-(aq)$ |
| $Ca(OH)_2(s) \rightarrow Ca^{2+}(aq) + 2OH^-(aq)$ |
| $Ba(OH)_2(s) \rightarrow Ba^{2+}(aq) + 2OH^-(aq)$ |

**Practice!** For more practice writing base ionization constant expressions, go to Supplemental Practice Problems in Appendix A.

## PRACTICE PROBLEMS

**11.** Write ionization equations and base ionization constant expressions for the following bases.
   **a.** hexylamine ($C_6H_{13}NH_2$)   **c.** carbonate ion ($CO_3^{2-}$)
   **b.** propylamine ($C_3H_7NH_2$)   **d.** hydrogen sulfite ion ($HSO_3{}^-$)

**National Science Content Standards**
**Pages 604–607**
UCP.2, UCP.3, UCP.4; B.2, B.4

**Table 19-4**

| Ionization Constants of Weak Bases | | |
|---|---|---|
| **Base** | **Ionization equation** | **$K_b$ (298 K)** |
| Ethylamine | $C_2H_5NH_2(aq) + H_2O(l) \rightleftharpoons$ $C_2H_5NH_3^+(aq) + OH^-(aq)$ | $5.0 \times 10^{-4}$ |
| Methylamine | $CH_3NH_2(aq) + H_2O(l) \rightleftharpoons$ $CH_3NH_3^+(aq) + OH^-(aq)$ | $4.3 \times 10^{-4}$ |
| Ammonia | $NH_3(aq) + H_2O(l) \rightleftharpoons$ $NH_4^+(aq) + OH^-(aq)$ | $2.5 \times 10^{-5}$ |
| Aniline | $C_6H_5NH_2(aq) + H_2O(l) \rightleftharpoons$ $C_6H_5NH_3^+(aq) + OH^-(aq)$ | $4.3 \times 10^{-10}$ |

**Figure 19-10**

The photos show a strong acid and a weak acid, a strong base and a weak base. Can you distinguish them? Which of the acids is more concentrated? Which is stronger? Which of the bases is more concentrated? Which is stronger?

**Strong or weak, concentrated or dilute** You have been learning about acids and bases that are often described as weak or strong. When you use the words, weak and strong, do they mean the same as when you describe your cup of tea as being weak or strong? No, there is a difference. When talking about your tea, you could substitute the words *dilute* and *concentrated* for weak and strong. But in talking about acids and bases, the words *weak* and *dilute* have different meanings. Similarly, the words *strong* and *concentrated* are not interchangeable. The terms *dilute* and *concentrated* refer to the number of the acid or base molecules dissolved in a volume of solution. The molarity of the solution is a measure of how dilute or concentrated a solution is. The words *weak* or *strong* refer to the degree to which the acid or base separates into ions. You have already learned that solutions of weak acids and bases contain few ions because few of the molecules are ionized. Solutions of strong acids and bases are completely separated into ions. It's possible to have a dilute solution of a strong acid such as hydrochloric acid, or a concentrated solution of a weak acid such as acetic acid. Which is strong, which is more concentrated, a solution of 0.6*M* hydrochloric acid or a solution of 6*M* acetic acid? See **Figure 19-10.**

**12.** An acid is highly ionized in aqueous solution. Is the acid strong or weak? Explain your reasoning.

**13.** How is the strength of a weak acid related to the strength of its conjugate base?

**14.** Identify the acid-base pairs in the following.
   **a.** $HCOOH(aq) + H_2O(l) \rightleftharpoons HCOO^-(aq) + H_3O^+(aq)$
   **b.** $NH_3(aq) + H_2O(l) \rightleftharpoons NH_4^+(aq) + OH^-(aq)$

**15.** $K_b$ for aniline is $4.3 \times 10^{-10}$. Explain what this tells you about aniline.

**16. Thinking Critically** Why is a strong base such as sodium hydroxide generally not considered to have a conjugate acid?

**17. Predicting** Use **Table 19-2** to predict which aqueous solution would have the greater electrical conductivity: 0.1*M* HClO or 0.1*M* HF. Explain.

---

**Page 607** Which is strong, which is more concentrated, a solution of 0.6*M* hydrochloric acid or a solution of 6*M* acetic acid? 0.6*M* hydrochloric acid is strong. 6*M* acetic acid is more concentrated.

# 3 Assess
## Check for Understanding
Ask students to use $K_a$ values to rank the electrical conductivities of 0.10*M* solutions of $H_2S$, HClO, and HI. HI > $H_2S$ > HClO

## Reteach
Write on the chalkboard: 0.1*M* HCl and 1.0*M* HClO. Ask which solution is more concentrated. 1.0*M* HClO Ask which is stronger. 0.1*M* HCl

## Extension
Have interested and capable students use a college text to investigate the leveling effect of water on the strengths of strong acids and bases. Have them explain this effect in terms of this analogy. Suppose that the five strongest persons in the world were asked to lift a 100-lb weight to determine who was strongest. **L3**

### Assessment
**Skill** Ask students to write the ionization equation and ionization constant expression for bromous acid ($HBrO_2$). $HBrO_2(aq) + H_2O(l) \rightleftharpoons H_3O^+(aq) + BrO_2^-(aq)$ or $HBrO_2(aq) \rightleftharpoons H^+(aq) + BrO_2^-(aq)$
$$K_a = \frac{[H^+][BrO_2^-]}{[HBrO_2]}$$

---

**12.** The acid is strong. Strong acids ionize completely in dilute aqueous solution.

**13.** The stronger the acid, the weaker its conjugate base. The weaker the acid, the stronger its conjugate base.

**14. a.** acid: HCOOH; conjugate base: $HCOO^-$; conjugate acid: $H_3O^+$; base: $H_2O$
   **b.** acid: $H_2O$; conjugate base: $OH^-$; conjugate acid: $NH_4^+$, base: $NH_3$

**15.** Aniline is a weak base.

**16.** Strong bases dissociate completely in aqueous solution. There is no reaction in the reverse direction involving a conjugate acid.

**17.** The 0.1*M* HF solution would have the greater electrical conductivity. The acid ionization constant for HF is greater than the acid ionization constant for HClO. Therefore, HF forms more ions in equimolar solutions of the two acids.

**607**

# 1 Focus

Before presenting the lesson, display **Section Focus Transparency 73** on the overhead projector. Have students answer the accompanying questions using **Section Focus Transparency Master 73.** **L1** **ELL**

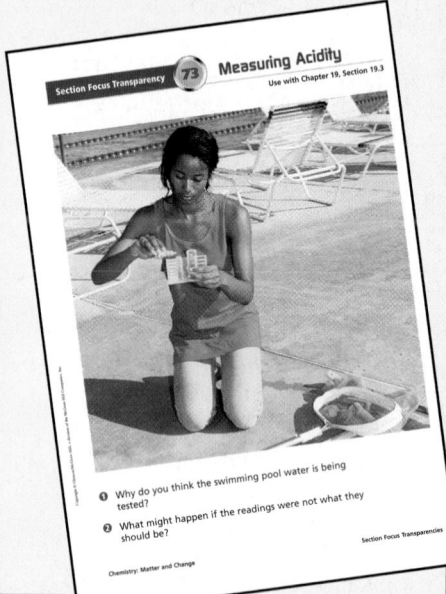

# 2 Teach

**Math in Chemistry**

Remind students that a change of one unit in an exponent of 10 reflects a ten-fold change in the number. For example, $10^4$ is ten times larger than $10^3$, and $10^{-7}$ is ten times smaller than $10^{-6}$.

**National Science Content Standards**

Pages 608–609
UCP.2, UCP.3, UCP.4; B.2, B.4; E.2

---

## Section 19.3 | What is pH?

**Objectives**

• **Explain** the meaning of pH and pOH.

• **Relate** pH and pOH to the ion product constant for water.

• **Calculate** the pH and pOH of aqueous solutions.

**Vocabulary**

ion product constant for water
pH
pOH

Water not only serves as the solvent in solutions of acids and bases, it also plays a role in the formation of the ions. In aqueous solutions of acids and bases, water sometimes acts as an acid and sometimes as a base. You can think of the self-ionization of water as an example of water assuming the role of an acid and a base in the same reaction.

## Ion Product Constant for Water

Recall from Section 19.1 that pure water contains equal concentrations of $H^+$ and $OH^-$ ions produced by self-ionization. One molecule of water acts as a Brønsted-Lowry acid and donates a hydrogen ion to a second water molecule. The second molecule of water accepts the hydrogen ion and becomes a hydronium ion. The 1:1 ratio between the products means that equal numbers of hydronium ions and hydroxide ions are formed.

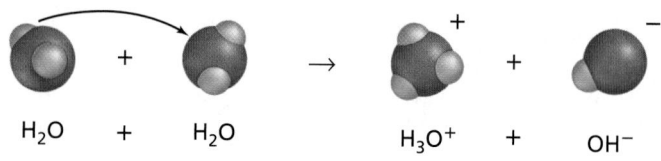

$$H_2O \quad + \quad H_2O \quad \rightarrow \quad H_3O^+ \quad + \quad OH^-$$

The equation for the equilibrium can be simplified in this way.

$$H_2O(l) \rightleftharpoons H^+(aq) + OH^-(aq)$$

The double arrow indicates that this is an equilibrium. Recall that the equilibrium constant expression is written by placing the concentrations of the products in the numerator and the concentrations of the reactants in the denominator. In this example, all terms are to the first power because all the coefficients are 1.

$$K_{eq} = \frac{[H^+][OH^-]}{[H_2O]}$$

The concentration of pure water is constant so it can be combined with $K_{eq}$ by multiplying both sides of the equation by $[H_2O]$.

$$K_{eq}[H_2O] = K_w = [H^+][OH^-]$$

The result is a special equilibrium constant expression that applies only to the self-ionization of water. The constant, $K_w$, is called the ion product constant for water. The **ion product constant for water** is the value of the equilibrium constant expression for the self-ionization of water. Experiments show that in pure water at 298 K, $[H^+]$ and $[OH^-]$ are both equal to $1.0 \times 10^{-7}M$. Therefore, at 298 K, the value of $K_w$ is $1.0 \times 10^{-14}$.

$$K_w = [H^+][OH^-] = (1.0 \times 10^{-7})(1.0 \times 10^{-7})$$
$$K_w = 1.0 \times 10^{-14}$$

---

**DIFFERENTIATED INSTRUCTION**

**English Language Learners**

Explain that testing acidic and basic solutions with litmus paper is so well known that related terminology is often used in the English language to describe any definitive test. Point out that such a test might be applied to determine the validity of a proposition or the ability of a person to accomplish a certain goal or successfully complete an activity. For example, one might say, "The big soccer game will be a *litmus test* of her goal-tending ability." **ELL**

The product of [H⁺] and [OH⁻] always equals $1.0 \times 10^{-14}$ at 298 K. This means that if the concentration of H⁺ ion increases, the concentration of OH⁻ ion must decrease. Similarly, an increase in the concentration of OH⁻ ion causes a decrease in the concentration of H⁺ ion. You can think about these changes in terms of Le Châtelier's principle, which you learned about in Chapter 18. Adding extra hydrogen ions to the self-ionization of water at equilibrium is a stress on the system. The system reacts in a way to relieve the stress. The added H⁺ ions react with OH⁻ ions to form more water molecules. Thus, the concentration of OH⁻ ion decreases. Example Problem 19-1 shows how you can use $K_w$ to calculate the concentration of either the hydrogen ion or the hydroxide ion if you know the concentration of the other ion.

## EXAMPLE PROBLEM 19-1

### Using $K_w$ to Calculate [H⁺] and [OH⁻]

At 298 K, the H⁺ ion concentration of an aqueous solution is $1.0 \times 10^{-5}M$. What is the OH⁻ ion concentration in the solution? Is the solution acidic, basic, or neutral?

**1. Analyze the Problem**

You are given the concentration of H⁺ ion and you know that $K_w$ equals $1.0 \times 10^{-14}$. You can use the ion product constant expression to solve for [OH⁻]. Because [H⁺] is greater than $1.0 \times 10^{-7}$, you can predict that [OH⁻] will be less than $1.0 \times 10^{-7}$.

| Known | Unknown |
|---|---|
| $[H^+] = 1.0 \times 10^{-5}M$ | $[OH^-] = ?$ mol/L |
| $K_w = 1.0 \times 10^{-14}$ | |

**2. Solve for the Unknown**

Write the ion product constant expression.

$$K_w = [H^+][OH^-] = 1.0 \times 10^{-14}$$

Isolate [OH⁻] by dividing both sides of the equation by [H⁺].

$$[OH^-] = \frac{K_w}{[H^+]}$$

Substitute $K_w$ and [H⁺] into the expression and solve.

$$[OH^-] = \frac{1.0 \times 10^{-14}}{1.0 \times 10^{-5}} = 1.0 \times 10^{-9} \text{ mol/L}$$

Because [H⁺] > [OH⁻], the solution is acidic.

**3. Evaluate the Answer**

The answer is correctly stated with two signifigant figures because [H⁺] and $K_w$ each have two. As predicted, the hydroxide ion concentration, [OH⁻], is less than $1.0 \times 10^{-7}$ mol/L.

The hydrogen ion and hydroxide ion concentrations of these familiar vegetables are the same as the concentrations calculated in this Example Problem.

## PRACTICE PROBLEMS

**18.** The concentration of either the H⁺ ion or the OH⁻ ion is given for three aqueous solutions at 298 K. For each solution, calculate [H⁺] or [OH⁻]. State whether the solution is acidic, basic, or neutral.
   **a.** $[H^+] = 1.0 \times 10^{-13}M$
   **b.** $[OH^-] = 1.0 \times 10^{-7}M$
   **c.** $[OH^-] = 1.0 \times 10^{-3}M$

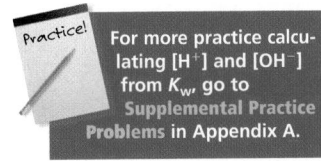

*Practice!* For more practice calculating [H⁺] and [OH⁻] from $K_w$, go to **Supplemental Practice Problems** in Appendix A.

## Practice PROBLEMS

Have students refer to Appendix D for complete solutions to Practice Problems.

**18. a.** $[OH^-] = 1.0 \times 10^{-1}$ *M*, basic

   **b.** $[H^+] = 1.0 \times 10^{-7}$ *M*, neutral

   **c.** $[H^+] = 1.0 \times 10^{-11}$ *M*, basic

## Reinforcement

To emphasize for students that the concentration of a liquid or solid is essentially constant, lead them through the process of calculating the molar concentration of liquid water at 4°C. 1000 mL $H_2O$/1 L $H_2O$ × 1.00 g $H_2O$/1 mL $H_2O$ × 1 mol $H_2O$/18.0 g $H_2O$ = 55.6 mol/L. Point out that unless the density of water changes because of a change in temperature, 55.6 mol/L may be considered a constant for the concentration of water.

**Resource Manager**

**Section Focus Transparency 73 and Master** L1 ELL
**Solving Problems: A Chemistry Handbook**, Section 19.3 L2
**Study Guide for Content Mastery**, pp. 111–112 L2
**Math Skills Transparency 31 and Master** L2 ELL
**Teaching Transparency 57 and Master** L2 ELL

---

## CHEMISTRY JOURNAL

### Soil pH and Plants

**Linguistic** Have interested students research plants that grow best in acidic soil and those that grow best in basic soil. Have them find out how soils can be made more acidic (sour) or more basic (sweet).

Good sources of information are books on gardening, seed catalogs, florists, and people who work in plant nurserys. Students can summarize their findings in their chemistry journals. L2

Explain that a common log is an exponent of 10, which is why a common log is called a log to the base 10. Point out, for example, that the common log of 2 is 0.3010 because $2 = 10^{0.3010}$.

## Figure Caption Questions

**Figure 9-11** Which has the higher concentration of hydrogen ions, seawater or detergent? How many times higher? Seawater has the higher concentration of hydrogen ions—100 times higher.

## Concept Development

Help students learn to use their calculators in determining pH. Based on the relationship pH = $-\log$ [H$^+$], calculating pH on most calculators involves the following steps.
1. Enter the [H$^+$].
2. Take the log of [H$^+$] by pressing the key marked "log".
3. Change the sign by pressing the [+/−] key.

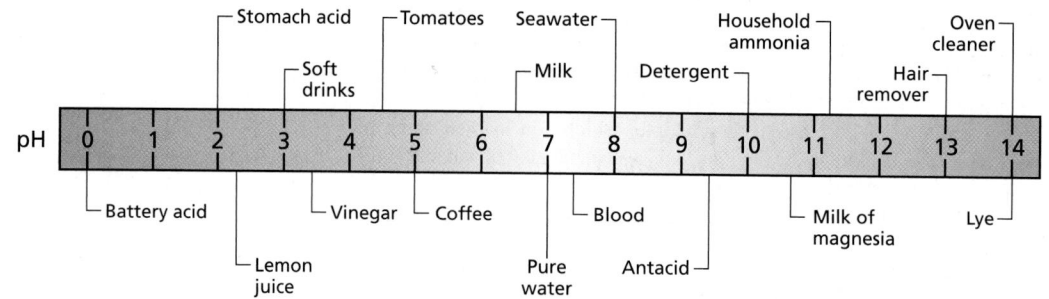

**Figure 19-11**

Which has the higher concentration of hydrogen ion, sea water or detergent? How many times higher?

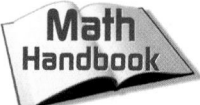

Review logarithms in the **Math Handbook** on page 910 of this text.

## pH and pOH

As you have probably noted, concentrations of H$^+$ ions are often small numbers expressed in exponential notation. Because these numbers are cumbersome, chemists adopted an easier way to express H$^+$ ion concentrations using a pH scale based on common logarithms. The **pH** of a solution is the negative logarithm of the hydrogen ion concentration.

$$pH = -\log [H^+]$$

At 298 K, acidic solutions have pH values below 7. Basic solutions have pH values above 7. Thus, a solution having a pH of 0.0 is strongly acidic; a solution having a pH of 14.0 is strongly basic; and a solution with pH = 7.0 is neutral. The logarithmic nature of the pH scale means that a change of one pH unit represents a tenfold change in ion concentration. A solution having a pH of 3.0 has ten times the hydrogen ion concentration of a solution with a pH of 4.0. The pH scale and pH values of some common substances are shown in **Figure 19-11**.

### EXAMPLE PROBLEM 19-2

**Calculating pH from [H$^+$]**
What is the pH of a neutral solution at 298 K?

**1. Analyze the Problem**

You know that in a neutral solution at 298 K, [H$^+$] = $1.0 \times 10^{-7}$ M. You need to find the negative log of [H$^+$]. Because the solution is neutral, you can predict that the pH will be 7.00. You will need a log table or a calculator with a log function.

| Known | Unknown |
| --- | --- |
| [H$^+$] = $1.0 \times 10^{-7}$ M | pH = ? |

**2. Solve for the Unknown**

pH = $-\log$ [H$^+$]

Substitute $1.0 \times 10^{-7}$M for [H$^+$] in the equation.

pH = $-\log (1.0 \times 10^{-7})$

pH = $-$ (log 1.0 + log 10$^{-7}$)

A log table or calculator shows that log 1.0 = 0 and log 10$^{-7}$ = $-7$. Substitute these numbers in the pH equation.

pH = $-[0 + (-7)]$ = 7.00

The pH of the neutral solution at 298 K is 7.00.

### DIFFERENTIATED INSTRUCTION

**Gifted**

 *Logical-Mathematical* Explain to capable students that the ion product constant of water increases with increasing temperature. For example, $K_w = 9.25 \times 10^{-14}$ at 60°C. Have students calculate the hydrogen-ion concentration and pH of pure water at this temperature. [H$^+$] = $3.04 \times 10^{-7}$M, pH = 6.52 **L3**

### Resource Manager

**Small-Scale Lab Manual**, pp. 65–68 **L2**

**Forensics Lab Manual**, pp. 13–24 **L2**

## 3. Evaluate the Answer

Values for pH are expressed with as many decimal places as the number of significant figures in the $H^+$ ion concentration. Thus, the pH is correctly stated with two decimal places. As predicted, the pH value is 7.00.

## PRACTICE PROBLEMS

**19.** Calculate the pH of solutions having the following ion concentrations at 298 K.
   **a.** $[H^+] = 1.0 \times 10^{-2}\ M$
   **b.** $[H^+] = 3.0 \times 10^{-6}\ M$
   **c.** $[OH^-] = 8.2 \times 10^{-6}\ M$

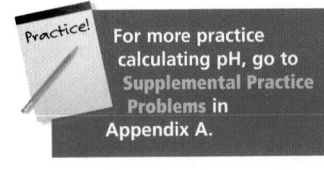

Practice! For more practice calculating pH, go to **Supplemental Practice Problems** in **Appendix A.**

**Using pOH** Sometimes chemists find it convenient to express the basicity, or alkalinity, of a solution on a pOH scale that mirrors the relationship between pH and $[H^+]$. The **pOH** of a solution is the negative logarithm of the hydroxide ion concentration.

$$pOH = -\log [OH^-]$$

At 298 K, a solution having a pOH less than 7.0 is basic; a solution having a pOH of 7.0 is neutral; and a solution having a pOH greater than 7.0 is acidic. As with the pH scale, a change of one pOH unit expresses a tenfold change in ion concentration. For example, a solution with a pOH of 2.0 has 100 times the hydroxide ion concentration of a solution with a pOH of 4.0.

A simple relationship between pH and pOH makes it easy to calculate either quantity if the other is known.

$$pH + pOH = 14.00$$

**Figure 19-12** illustrates the relationship between pH and $[H^+]$ and the relationship between pOH and $[OH^-]$ at 298 K. Use this diagram as a reference until you become thoroughly familiar with these relationships.

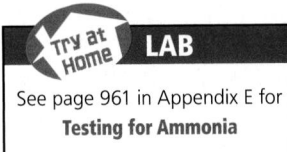

See page 961 in Appendix E for **Testing for Ammonia**

**Figure 19-12**

Study this diagram to sharpen your understanding of pH and pOH. Note that at each vertical position, the sum of pH (above the arrow) and pOH (below the arrow) equals 14. Also note that at every position the product of $[H^+]$ and $[OH^-]$ equals $10^{-14}$.

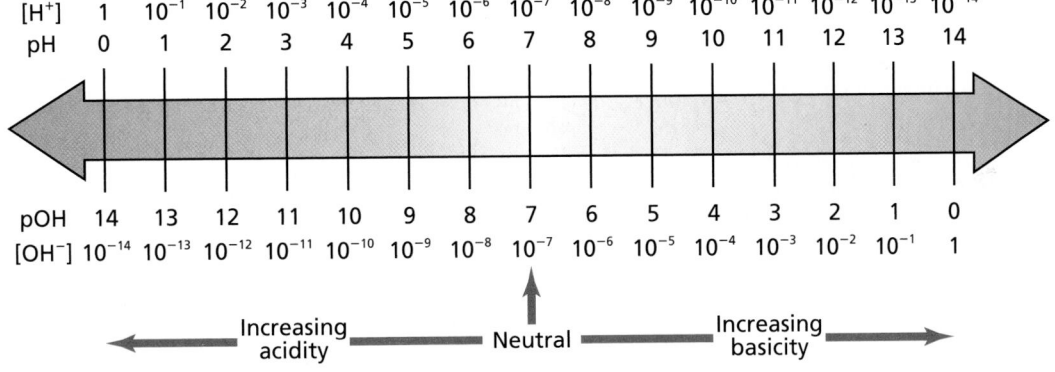

19.3 What is pH? **611**

## Extension

*Kinesthetic* Have interested students investigate the natural indicators present in the leaves of colored plants and vegetables, such as purple cabbage. Have students boil the leaves of various plants to extract the pigments, then add small amounts of the resulting solutions to solutions of known pH. Ask them to make charts of pH colors for an extracted pigment and share their results with the class. **L2 ELL**

## Enrichment

Although practically all students have heard of the term *pH*, they may wonder how the term originated. Explain that pH is derived from the French *pouvoir hydrogene*, which means hydrogen power.

## Practice PROBLEMS

Have students refer to Appendix D for complete solutions to Practice Problems.

**19. a.** pH = 2.00
   **b.** pH = 5.52
   **c.** pH = 8.92

## CHEMISTRY JOURNAL

### pH and Skin

*Linguistic* Have students research the pH of skin and how various products—particularly basic soaps—can interact with substances that protect the skin. Have them include their findings in their journals. **L2**

**National Science Content Standards**

**Pages 610–611**
UCP.2, UCP.3, UCP.4; B.2; E.2

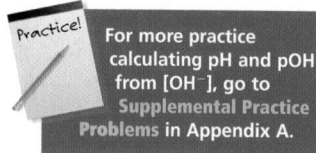

The pH paper shows that this common cleaner containing ammonia has a pH greater than 11.

**Practice!** For more practice calculating pH and pOH from [OH⁻], go to **Supplemental Practice Problems** in Appendix A.

## EXAMPLE PROBLEM 19-3

### Calculating pOH and pH from [$OH^-$]

An ordinary household ammonia cleaner is an aqueous solution of ammonia gas with a hydroxide-ion concentration of $4.0 \times 10^{-3}M$. Calculate pOH and pH of a typical cleaner at 298 K.

**1. Analyze the Problem**

You have been given the concentration of hydroxide ion and must calculate pOH and pH. First, you must calculate pOH using the definition of pOH. Then, pH can be calculated using the relationship pH + pOH = 14.00. The negative log of $10^{-3}$ (the power of 10 of the hydroxide ion concentration) is 3. Therefore, pOH should be close to 3 and pH should be close to 11 or 12.

| Known | Unknown |
|---|---|
| $[OH^-] = 4.0 \times 10^{-3}M$ | pOH = ? |
| | pH = ? |

**2. Solve for the Unknown**

$$pOH = -\log [OH^-]$$

Substitute $4.0 \times 10^{-3}M$ for $[OH^-]$ in the equation.
$$pOH = -\log (4.0 \times 10^{-3})$$

$$pOH = -(\log 4.0 + \log 10^{-3})$$

Log tables or your calculator indicate log 4.0 = 0.60 and log $10^{-3}$ = -3. Substitute these values in the equation.

$$pOH = -[0.60 + (-3)] = -(0.60 - 3) = 2.40$$

The pOH of the solution is 2.40.
Solve the equation pH + pOH = 14.00 for pH by subtracting pOH from both sides of the equation.

$$pH = 14.00 - pOH$$

Substitute the value of pOH.
$$pH = 14.00 - 2.40 = 11.60$$

The pH of the solution is 11.60.

**3. Evaluate the Answer**

The values of pH and pOH are correctly expressed with two decimal places because the given concentration has two significant figures. As predicted, pOH is close to 3 and pH is close to 12.

## PRACTICE PROBLEMS

**20.** Calculate the pH and pOH of aqueous solutions having the following ion concentrations.
   **a.** $[OH^-] = 1.0 \times 10^{-6}M$     **c.** $[H^+] = 3.6 \times 10^{-9}M$
   **b.** $[OH^-] = 6.5 \times 10^{-4}M$     **d.** $[H^+] = 0.025M$

**Calculating ion concentrations from pH** Suppose the pH of a solution is 3.50 and you must determine the concentrations of $H^+$ and $OH^-$. The definition of pH relates pH and $H^+$ ion concentration and can be solved for $[H^+]$.

$$pH = -\log [H^+]$$

## Internet Address Book

**Chemistry Online**     Note Internet addresses that you find useful in the space below for quick reference.

_____
_____
_____
_____
_____

First you need to multiply both sides of the equation by $-1$.

$$-\text{pH} = \log [\text{H}^+]$$

To calculate $[\text{H}^+]$ using this equation you must take the antilog of both sides of the equation.

$$\text{antilog} (-\text{pH}) = [\text{H}^+]$$

To calculate $[\text{H}^+]$, substitute 3.50 for pH in the equation.

$$\text{antilog} (-3.50) = [\text{H}^+]$$

Use a log table or your calculator to determine the antilog of $-3.50$. The antilog is $3.2 \times 10^{-4}$.

$$[\text{H}^+] = 3.2 \times 10^{-4} \text{ mol/L}$$

You can calculate $[\text{OH}^-]$ using the relationship $[\text{OH}^-] = \text{antilog} (-\text{pOH})$.

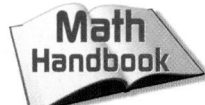

Math Handbook

Review antilogs in the **Math Handbook** on page 910 of this text.

## EXAMPLE PROBLEM 19-4

### Calculating [H⁺] and [OH⁻] from pH

What are $[\text{H}^+]$ and $[\text{OH}^-]$ in a healthy person's blood that has a pH of 7.40? Assume that the temperature is 298 K.

**1. Analyze the Problem**

You have been given the pH of a solution and must calculate $[\text{H}^+]$ and $[\text{OH}^-]$. You can obtain $[\text{H}^+]$ using the equation that defines pH. Then, subtract the pH from 14.00 to obtain pOH. The pH is close to 7 but greater than 7, so $[\text{H}^+]$ should be slightly less than $10^{-7}$ and $[\text{OH}^-]$ should be greater than $10^{-7}$.

**Known**

pH = 7.40

**Unknown**

$[\text{H}^+] = ?$ mol/L
$[\text{OH}^-] = ?$ mol/L

**2. Solve for the Unknown**

Write the equation that defines pH and solve for $[\text{H}^+]$.

$\text{pH} = -\log [\text{H}^+]$

$[\text{H}^+] = \text{antilog} (-\text{pH})$

Substitute the known value of pH.

$[\text{H}^+] = \text{antilog} (-7.40)$

Use a log table or your calculator to find the antilog. The antilog of $-7.40$ is $4.0 \times 10^{-8}$.

$[\text{H}^+] = 4.0 \times 10^{-8}M$

The concentration of hydrogen ion in blood is $4.0 \times 10^{-8}M$.
To determine $[\text{OH}^-]$, calculate pOH using the equation
$\text{pH} + \text{pOH} = 14.00$.
Solve for pOH by subtracting pH from both sides of the equation.
$\text{pOH} = 14.00 - \text{pH}$

Substitute the known value of pH.
$\text{pOH} = 14.00 - 7.40 = 6.60$

Substitute 6.60 for pOH in the equation $[\text{OH}^-] = \text{antilog} (-\text{pOH})$
$[\text{OH}^-] = \text{antilog} (-6.60)$

*Continued on next page*

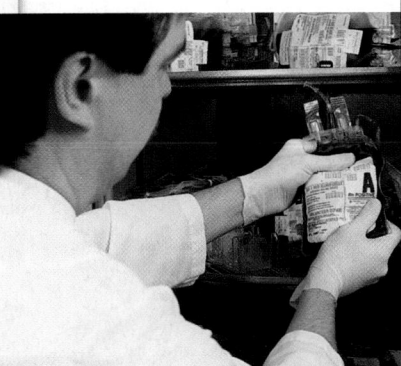

Blood banks collect blood from healthy people to hold in reserve for persons who need tranfusions.

## Quick Demo

**Kinesthetic**

Put about 250 mL of 95% ethanol into a 500-mL flask. **CAUTION:** *Have no open flames in the room.* Add 5 or 6 drops of thymolphthalein indicator solution and sufficient 0.1$M$ sodium hydroxide solution to produce a blue color. Stopper the flask until ready for the demo. Pass the flask around the class and ask each student in turn to remove the stopper, politely ask the solution to turn color, re-stopper the flask, and give the liquid a gentle swirl. At some point, enough $CO_2$ will have dissolved in the solution to lower the pH sufficiently that the thymolphthalein will change from blue to yellow. Ask students if they know what was special about the person's voice that caused the color to change. Some of the exhaled $CO_2$ dissolved, producing a weak carbonic acid solution, lowering the pH and changing the color of the indicator. **L2**

19.3  What is pH?    **613**

**National Science Content Standards**

Pages 612–613
UCP.2, UCP.3, UCP.4; B.2

Use a log table or your calculator to find the antilog. The antilog of −6.60 is $2.5 \times 10^{-7}$.

$[OH^-] = 2.5 \times 10^{-7}M$.

The concentration of hydroxide ion in blood is $2.5 \times 10^{-7}M$.

**3. Evaluate the Answer**

The concentrations of the hydrogen ion and hydroxide ion are correctly stated with two significant figures because the given pH has two decimal places. As predicted, [H⁺] is less than $10^{-7}$ and [OH⁻] is greater than $10^{-7}$.

### PRACTICE PROBLEMS

**21.** The pH is given for three solutions. Calculate [H⁺] and [OH⁻] in each solution.

    **a.** pH = 2.37        **c.** pH = 6.50

    **b.** pH = 11.05

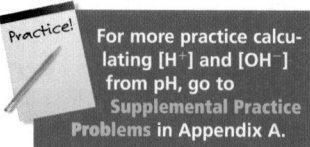

For more practice calculating [H⁺] and [OH⁻] from pH, go to **Supplemental Practice Problems** in Appendix A.

**Calculating the pH of solutions of strong acids and strong bases**

Look at the bottles of acid and base solutions in **Figure 19-13.** They are labeled with the number of moles of molecules or formula units that were dissolved in a liter of water (*M*) when the solutions were made. Each of the bottles contains a strong acid or base. Recall from Section 19.2 that strong acids and bases are essentially 100% ionized. That means that this reaction for the ionization of HCl goes to completion.

$$HCl(aq) \rightarrow H^+(aq) + Cl^-(aq)$$

Every HCl molecule produces one H⁺ ion. The bottle labeled 0.1*M* HCl contains 0.1 mole of H⁺ ions per liter and 0.1 mole of Cl⁻ ions per liter. For all strong monoprotic acids, the concentration of the acid is the concentration of H⁺ ion. Thus, you can use the concentration of the acid for calculating pH.

Similarly, the 0.1*M* solution of the strong base NaOH in **Figure 19-13** is fully ionized.

$$NaOH(aq) \rightarrow Na^+(aq) + OH^-(aq)$$

One formula unit of NaOH produces one OH⁻ ion. Thus, the concentration of the hydroxide ion is the same as the concentration of the solution, 0.1*M*.

Some strong bases contain two or more hydroxide ions in each formula unit. Calcium hydroxide ($Ca(OH)_2$) is an example. The concentration of hydroxide ion in a solution of $Ca(OH)_2$ is twice the concentration of the ionic compound. Thus, the concentration of OH⁻ in a $7.5 \times 10^{-4}M$ solution of $Ca(OH)_2$ is $7.5 \times 10^{-4}M \times 2 = 1.5 \times 10^{-3}M$.

**Figure 19-13**

The label on a bottle of a strong acid or a strong base tells you immediately the concentration of hydrogen ions or hydroxide ions in the solution. That's because, in solution, strong acids and bases exist entirely as ions. What is [H⁺] in 0.1*M* HCl? What is [OH⁻] in 0.1*M* NaOH?

### PRACTICE PROBLEMS

**22.** Calculate the pH of the following solutions.

    **a.** 1.0*M* HI        **c.** 1.0*M* KOH

    **b.** 0.050*M* HNO₃     **d.** $2.4 \times 10^{-5}M$ Mg(OH)₂

**Using pH to calculate $K_a$** Suppose you measured the pH of a $0.100M$ solution of the weak acid HF and found it to be 3.20. Would you have enough information to calculate $K_a$ for HF?

$$HF(aq) \rightleftharpoons H^+(aq) + F^-(aq)$$

$$K_a = \frac{[H^+][F^-]}{[HF]}$$

From the pH, you could calculate $[H^+]$. Then, remember that for every mole per liter of $H^+$ ion there must be an equal concentration of $F^-$ ion. That means that you know two of the variables in the $K_a$ expression. What about the third, $[HF]$? The concentration of HF at equilibrium is equal to the initial concentration of the acid ($0.100M$) minus the moles per liter of HF that dissociated ($[H^+]$). Example Problem 19-5 illustrates a similar calculation for formic acid.

## EXAMPLE PROBLEM 19-5

### Calculating $K_a$ from pH

The pH of a $0.100M$ solution of formic acid is 2.38. What is $K_a$ for HCOOH?

**1. Analyze the Problem**

You are given the pH of the solution which allows you to calculate the concentration of the hydrogen ion. You know that the concentration of $HCOO^-$ equals the concentration of $H^+$. The concentration of un-ionized HCOOH is the difference between the initial concentration of the acid and $[H^+]$.

| Known | Unknown |
|---|---|
| pH = 2.38 | $K_a = ?$ |
| concentration of the solution = $0.100M$ | |

**2. Solve for the Unknown**

Write the acid ionization constant expression.

$$K_a = \frac{[H^+][HCOO^-]}{[HCOOH]}$$

Use the pH to calculate $[H^+]$.

$$pH = -\log[H^+]$$

$$[H^+] = \text{antilog} (-pH)$$

Substitute the known value of pH.

$$[H^+] = \text{antilog} (-2.38)$$

Use a log table or calculator to find the antilog. The antilog of $-2.38$ is $4.2 \times 10^{-3}$.

$$[H^+] = 4.2 \times 10^{-3}M$$

$$[HCOO^-] = [H^+] = 4.2 \times 10^{-3}M$$

$[HCOOH]$ equals the initial concentration minus $[H^+]$.

$$[HCOOH] = 0.100M - 4.2 \times 10^{-3}M = 0.096M$$

Substitute the known values into the $K_a$ expression.

$$K_a = \frac{(4.2 \times 10^{-3})(4.2 \times 10^{-3})}{(0.096)} = 1.8 \times 10^{-4}$$

The acid ionization constant for HCOOH is $1.8 \times 10^{-4}$.

*Continued on next page*

Natural rubber is an important agricultural export in Southeast Asia. Formic acid is used during the process that converts the milky latex fluid tapped from rubber trees into natural rubber.

19.3 What is pH? **615**

# 3 Assess
## Check for Understanding

Have students compare the $[H^+]$ and the acidity of three solutions: solution 1 with pH = 6.00, solution 2 with pH = 3.00, solution 3 with pH = 1.00. Solution 1 is least acidic, $[H^+] = 1 \times 10^{-6}$. In solution 2, $[H^+] = 1 \times 10^{-3}$; therefore, solution 2 is 1000 times more acidic than solution 1. In solution 3, $[H^+] = 1 \times 10^{-1}$; therefore, solution 3 is 100 times more acidic than solution 2.

## Reteach

**Logical-Mathematical** Have students use the relationship between pH and pOH and the ion product constant for water to calculate $[OH^-]$ in a solution having pH = 2.5. $[OH^-] = 3.16 \times 10^{-12}$ **L2**

---

## DIFFERENTIATED INSTRUCTION

### Gifted

**Logical-Mathematical** Capable students will want to know how to calculate the pH of solutions of weak acids and weak bases. Tell them that this type of calculation involves solving the acid or base dissociation constant expression for $[H^+]$ or $[OH^-]$. To simplify the calculations, one or more assumptions can be made that must be evaluated after solving the problem. For example, in calculating the pH of $1.00M$ acetic acid solution, where $x = $ mol/L of acid that ionizes, two assumptions can be made.
1. $x$ is insignificant compared with $1.00M$.
2. $10^{-7}$ is insignificant compared with $x$. If either of these assumptions is invalid, the problem must be solved using the quadratic formula. pH = 2.37 **L3**

**615**

## Extension

Advise students that it's possible for solutions to have pH values less than 0 and greater than 14. Have students calculate the pH of 1.5$M$ HCl solution. pH = -0.18

### ✓ Assessment

**Knowledge** Ask students why S. P. L. Sørensen, the Dutch biochemist who designed the pH scale, created a scale from 1 to 14, with 7 being neutral. Because of the autoionization of water ($2H_2O(l) \rightleftharpoons H_3O^+(aq) + OH^-(aq)$), the concentrations of both hydronium and hydroxide ions are $10^{-7}M$ at 25°C. Logically, Sørensen related the pH of a solution to the exponent of the hydronium-ion concentration. **L2**

### Practice PROBLEMS

Have students refer to Appendix D for complete solutions to Practice Problems.

**23. a.** $5.4 \times 10^{-3}$
 **b.** $1.1 \times 10^{-2}$

---

**3. Evaluate the Answer**

The calculations are correct and the answer is correctly reported with two sinigicant figures. The $K_a$ is in the range of reasonably weak acids.

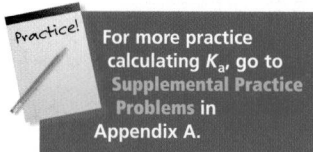

For more practice calculating $K_a$, go to **Supplemental Practice Problems** in Appendix A.

### PRACTICE PROBLEMS

**23.** Calculate the $K_a$ for the following acids using the given information.
  **a.** 0.220$M$ solution of $H_3AsO_4$, pH = 1.50
  **b.** 0.0400$M$ solution of $HClO_2$, pH = 1.80

**Measuring pH** Perhaps in an earlier science course, you used indicator paper to measure the pH of a solution. All pH paper is impregnated with one or more substances called indicators that change color depending upon the concentration of hydrogen ion in a solution. When a strip of pH paper is dipped into an acidic or basic solution, the color of the paper changes. To determine the pH, the new color of the paper is compared with standard pH colors on a chart, as shown in **Figure 19-14a**. The pH meter in **Figure 19-14b** provides a more accurate measure of pH. When electrodes are placed in a solution, the meter gives a direct analog or digital readout of pH.

**Figure 19-14**

The approximate pH of a solution can be obtained by wetting a piece of pH paper with the solution and comparing the color of the wet paper with a set of standard colors as shown in **ⓐ**. The pH meter in **ⓑ** provides a more accurate measurment in the form of a digital display of the pH.

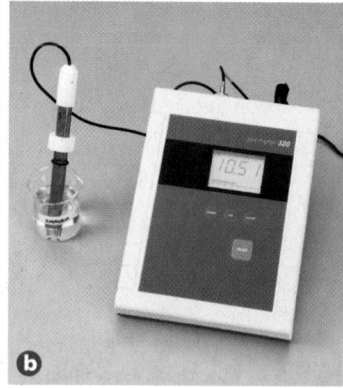

---

### Section 19.3 Assessment

**24.** What is the relationship between the pH of a solution and the concentration of hydrogen ions in the solution?

**25.** If you know the pOH of a solution, how can you determine its pH?

**26.** How does the ion product constant for water relate to the concentrations of $H^+$ and $OH^-$ in aqueous solutions?

**27. Thinking Critically** Why is it logical to assume that the hydrogen ion concentration in an aqueous solution of a strong monoprotic acid equals the molarity of the acid?

**28. Applying Concepts** Would it be possible to calculate the pH of a weak acid solution if you knew the molarity of the solution and its $K_a$? Explain.

---

### Section 19.3 Assessment

**24.** pH = $-\log[H^+]$
**25.** Subtract the pOH from 14.00.
**26.** At 298 K, the product of the $H^+$ and $OH^-$ concentrations equals $1.00 \times 10^{-14}$.

**27.** Strong acids are virtually 100% ionized in dilute aqueous solution.
**28.** Yes, you can use the acid's ionization constant expression and $K_a$ to determine $[H^+]$. Then, use $[H^+]$ to calculate pH.

If you were to experience heartburn or indigestion, you might take an antacid to relieve your discomfort. What kind of reaction occurs when magnesium hydroxide, the active ingredient in the common antacid called milk of magnesia, contacts hydrochloric acid produced by the stomach?

## The Reaction Between Acids and Bases

When magnesium hydroxide and hydrochloric acid react, the resulting solution has properties characteristic of neither an acid nor a base. This type of reaction is called a neutralization reaction. A **neutralization reaction** is a reaction in which an acid and a base react in aqueous solution to produce a salt and water. A **salt** is an ionic compound made up of a cation from a base and an anion from an acid. Neutralization is a double-replacement reaction. In the reaction between magnesium hydroxide and hydrochloric acid, magnesium replaces hydrogen in HCl and hydrogen replaces magnesium in $Mg(OH)_2$. The reaction may be described by this balanced formula equation.

$$Mg(OH)_2(aq) + 2HCl(aq) \rightarrow MgCl_2(aq) + 2H_2O(l)$$
$$\text{base} \quad + \quad \text{acid} \quad \rightarrow \text{a salt} \quad + \quad \text{water}$$

Note that the cation from the base ($Mg^{2+}$) is combined with the anion from the acid ($Cl^-$) in the salt $MgCl_2$.

### PRACTICE PROBLEMS

**29.** Write balanced formula equations for the following acid-base neutralization reactions.
  **a.** nitric acid and cesium hydroxide
  **b.** hydrobromic acid and calcium hydroxide
  **c.** sulfuric acid and potassium hydroxide
  **d.** acetic acid and ammonium hydroxide

*Practice!* **For more practice writing neutralization equations, go to Supplemental Practice Problems in Appendix A.**

When considering neutralization reactions, it is important to determine whether all of the reactants and products exist in solution as molecules or formula units. For example, examine the formula equation and complete ionic equation for the reaction between hydrochloric acid and sodium hydroxide.

$$HCl(aq) + NaOH(aq) \rightarrow NaCl(aq) + H_2O(l)$$

Because HCl is a strong acid, NaOH a strong base, and NaCl a soluble salt, all three compounds exist as ions in aqueous solution.

$$H^+(aq) + Cl^-(aq) + Na^+(aq) + OH^-(aq) \rightarrow Na^+(aq) + Cl^-(aq) + H_2O(l)$$

The chloride ion and the sodium ion appear on both sides of the equation so they are spectator ions. They can be eliminated to obtain the net ionic equation for the neutralization of a strong acid by a strong base.

$$H^+(aq) + OH^-(aq) \rightarrow H_2O(l)$$

## Objectives

- **Write** chemical equations for neutralization reactions.
- **Explain** how neutralization reactions are used in acid-base titrations.
- **Compare** the properties of buffered and unbuffered solutions.

## Vocabulary

neutralization reaction
salt
titration
equivalence point
acid-base indicator
end point
salt hydrolysis
buffer
buffer capacity

## 1 Focus

### Focus Transparency

Before presenting the lesson, display **Section Focus Transparency 74** on the overhead projector. Have students answer the accompanying questions using **Section Focus Transparency Master 74.** **L1** **ELL**

Section Focus Transparency **74**   Neutralizing Soil
Use with Chapter 19, Section 19.4

❶ Lime is added to soil that has a low pH to bring the pH back to nearly neutral. Infer what type of compound lime is.

❷ What do you think might happen to the soil if too much lime is added?

Chemistry: Matter and Change

Section Focus Transparencies

## 2 Teach

### Practice PROBLEMS

Have students refer to Appendix D for complete solutions to Practice Problems.

**29. a.** $HNO_3(aq) + CsOH(aq) \rightarrow CsNO_3(aq) + H_2O(l)$

   **b.** $2HBr(aq) + Ca(OH)_2(aq) \rightarrow CaBr_2(aq) + 2H_2O(l)$

   **c.** $H_2SO_4(aq) + 2KOH(aq) \rightarrow K_2SO_4(aq) + 2H_2O(l)$

   **d.** $CH_3COOH(aq) + NH_4OH(aq) \rightarrow NH_4CH_3COO(aq) + H_2O(l)$

### National Science Content Standards

Pages 616–617
UCP.2, UCP.3, UCP.4; A.1; B.2, B.3

### Resource Manager

**Section Focus Transparency 74 and Master** **L1** **ELL**
**Solving Problems: A Chemistry Handbook,** Section 19.4 **L2**
**Study Guide for Content Mastery,** pp. 113–114 **L2**

### CHEMISTRY JOURNAL

#### Antacids

*Linguistic* Have students examine the labels of several brands of antacids, identify the substances that neutralize acids, and investigate the possible hazards and side effects of taking these products. Have them summarize their findings in their chemistry journals. **L2**

**Portfolio** Have interested students design an experiment to test the efficacy of various over-the-counter antacids. After you okay their procedure, ask them to carry out the experiment in the laboratory. Have students include a description of their experiment and their results in their portfolios. **L2** **P**

## Applying Chemistry

Point out that the low solubilities of aluminum hydroxide and magnesium hydroxide make these compounds useful as antacids. If they were highly soluble, the high concentrations of hydroxide ions produced as the compounds dissolved would harm the tissues of the mouth, esophagus, and stomach.

## Concept Development

Explain to students that because a weak acid is only partially ionized in aqueous solution, the net ionic equation for a weak acid-strong base neutralization reaction is different from the net ionic equation for a strong acid-strong base reaction. For example, the net ionic equation for the reaction between aqueous HClO and NaOH solutions is HClO(aq) + OH⁻(aq) → H₂O(l) + ClO⁻(aq), whereas, the net ionic equation for the reaction between aqueous HCl and NaOH solutions is H⁺(aq) + OH⁻(aq) → H₂O(l).

## GLENCOE
### TECHNOLOGY

**CD-ROM**
**Chemistry: Matter and Change**
Demonstration:
*Forming a Salt*
Animation: *An Acid Base Reaction*

**618**

---

**Figure 19-15**

A hydronium ion transfers a hydrogen ion to a hydroxide ion. The loss of the hydrogen ion by H₃O⁺ results in a water molecule. The gain of a hydrogen ion by OH⁻ also results in a water molecule.

$$H_3O^+(aq) \quad OH^-(aq) \rightarrow \quad 2H_2O(l)$$

Recall that in an aqueous solution, a $H^+$ ion exists as a $H_3O^+$ ion, so the net ionic equation for an acid-base neutralization reaction is

$$H_3O^+(aq) + OH^-(aq) \rightarrow 2H_2O(l)$$

This neutralization reaction is illustrated in **Figure 19-15.** The **How It Works** feature at the end of this chapter shows that this equation does not apply to the neutralization of a strong acid by a weak base.

**Acid-base titration** The stoichiometry of an acid-base neutralization reaction is the same as that of any other reaction that occurs in solution. In the antacid reaction you just read about, one mole of magnesium hydroxide neutralizes two moles of hydrochloric acid.

$$Mg(OH)_2(aq) + 2HCl(aq) \rightarrow MgCl_2(aq) + 2H_2O(l)$$

In the reaction of sodium hydroxide and hydrogen chloride, one mole of sodium hydroxide neutralizes one mole of hydrogen chloride.

$$NaOH(aq) + HCl(aq) \rightarrow NaCl(aq) + H_2O(l)$$

Stoichiometry provides the basis for a procedure called titration, which is used to determine the concentrations of acidic and basic solutions. **Titration** is a method for determining the concentration of a solution by reacting a known volume of the solution with a solution of known concentration. If you wished to find the concentration of an acid solution, you would titrate the acid solution with a solution of a base of known concentration. You also could titrate a base of unknown concentration with an acid of known concentration. How is an acid-base titration carried out? **Figure 19-16** illustrates the equipment used for the following titration procedure using a pH meter.

**1.** A measured volume of an acidic or basic solution of unknown concentration is placed in a beaker. The electrodes of a pH meter are immersed in this solution and the initial pH of the solution is read and recorded.

**2.** A buret is filled with the titrating solution of known concentration. This solution is called the standard solution.

**3.** Measured volumes of the standard solution are added slowly and mixed into the solution in the beaker. The pH is read and recorded after each addition. This process continues until the reaction reaches the stoichiometric point, which is the point at which moles of $H^+$ ion from the acid equal moles of $OH^-$ ion from the base. The stoichiometric point is known as the **equivalence point** of the titration.

**Figure 19-17** shows how the pH of the solution changes during the titration of 50.0 mL of 0.100*M* HCl, a strong acid, with 0.100*M* NaOH, a strong base. The initial pH of the 0.100*M* HCl is 1.00. As NaOH is added, the acid is neutralized and the solution's pH increases gradually. However, when nearly all of the $H^+$ ions from the acid have been used up, the pH increases dramatically with the addition of an exceedingly small volume of NaOH. This

**Figure 19-16**

In the titration of an acid by a base, the pH meter measures the pH of the acid solution in the beaker as a solution of base with a known concentration is added from the buret.

---

---

## CHEMISTRY JOURNAL

### What happens to hydrogen?

 *Linguistic* Have students write creative essays that trace a hydrogen atom in a molecule of hydrogen chloride as the molecule dissolves in water and produces hydrochloric acid, which is then neutralized by an aqueous sodium hydroxide solution. **L2**

## DIFFERENTIATED INSTRUCTION

### English Language Learners

Have English language learners describe in their native languages and in English a Quick Demo or another classroom activity relating to this section. **ELL** **P** abrupt increase in pH occurs at the equivalence point of the titration. Beyond the equivalence point, the addition of more NaOH again results in a gradual increase in pH.

For convenience, chemists often use a chemical dye rather than a pH meter to detect the equivalence point of an acid-base titration. Chemical dyes whose colors are affected by acidic and basic solutions are called **acid-base indicators.** The chart in **Figure 19-18** shows the colors of several common acid-base indicators at various positions on the pH scale. The point at which the indicator used in a titration changes color is called the **end point** of the titration. The color change of the indicator selected for an acid-base titration should coincide closely with the equivalence point of the titration because the role of the indicator is to indicate to you, by means of a color change, that just enough of the titrating solution has been added to neutralize the unknown solution. In **Figure 19-18** you can see that bromthymol blue is an excellent choice for an equivalence point near pH 7. Bromthymol blue turns from yellow to blue as the pH of the solution changes from acidic to basic. Thus, the indicator's green transition color can mark an equivalence point near pH 7. What indicator might you choose for a titration that has its equivalence point at pH 5?

You might think that all titrations must have an equivalence point at pH 7 because that's the point at which concentrations of hydrogen ions and hydroxide ions are equal and the solution is neutral. This is not the case, however. Some titrations have equivalence points at pH < 7 and some have equivalence

50.0 mL 0.100*M* HCl Titrated with 0.100*M* NaOH

pH

Equivalence point

Volume NaOH added (mL)

**Figure 19-17**

A steep rise in the pH of the acid solution indicates that all the $H^+$ ions from the acid have been neutralized by the $OH^-$ ions of the base. The point at which the curve flexes (at its intersection with the dashed line) is the equivalence point of the titration. What is equivalent at this point?

**Figure 19-18**

Choosing the right indicator is important. The indicator must change color at the equivalence point of the titration and the equivalance point is not always at pH 7. Would methyl red be a good choice for the titration graphed in **Figure 19-17?**

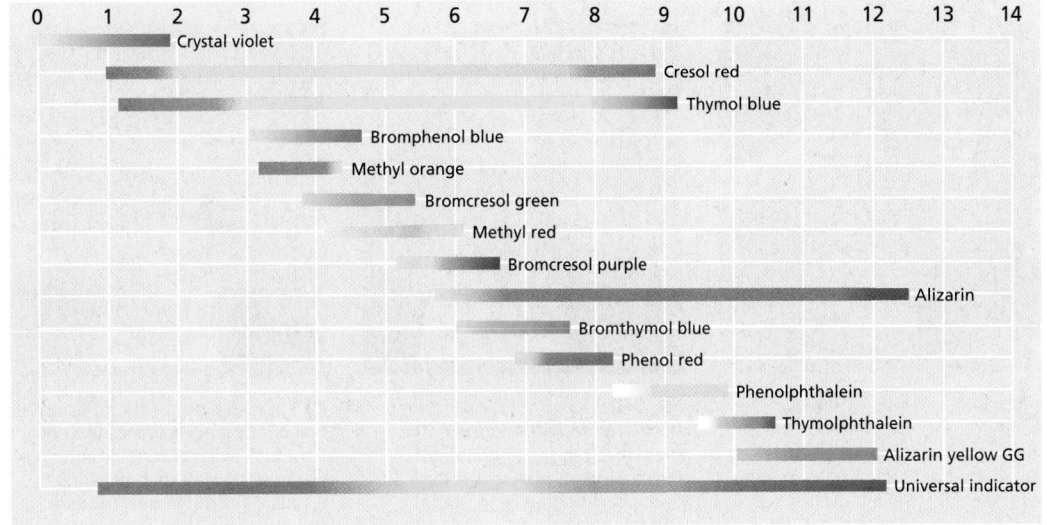

19.4 Neutralization **619**

---

## CULTURAL DIVERSITY

### For a Headache, Find a Willow Tree

Native Americans discovered that they could relieve pain by chewing on willow bark. However, it wasn't until the 1800s that scientists isolated the bark's active ingredient and identified it as salicylic acid. Although salicylic acid is effective, many people do not tolerate it well—and some have allergic reactions to the compound. Fortunately, a German chemist named Felix Hoffman, who worked for the

Bayer Company in the late 1800s, discovered how to modify salicylic acid so that it was less acidic, but still effective. The compound Hoffman synthesized, acetylsalicylic acid, is analgesic (anti-pain), antipyretic (anti-fever), and anti-inflammatory. Acetylsalicylic acid was first marketed as a powder called aspirin in packets and capsules in 1899.

---

## Concept Development

Explain to students that titration is a form of volumetric analysis, a laboratory procedure that can be applied to reactions other than acid-base neutralization. Point out, for example, that environmental chemists often determine the concentration of oxygen in surface waters using a titration in which a sodium thiosulfate solution is the titrant and a starch solution is the indicator.

## ✓ Assessment

**Performance** Have students make drawings of a titration setup. Have them label and describe the function of each part of the setup, including the titrant and the solution to be titrated. Ask them to place their drawings and descriptions in their portfolios. Use the Performance Task Assessment List for Scientific Drawing in **PASC**, p. 55. L2 P

## In-Text Question

**Page 619** What indicator might you choose for a titration that has its equivalence point at pH 5? Bromcresol green or methyl red because their color changes occur in the range that includes pH 5.

## Figure Caption Questions

**Figure 19-17** What is equivalent at this point? the moles of $H^+$ ions and the moles of $OH^-$ ions in the two solutions

**Figure 19-18** Would methyl red be a good choice for the titration graphed in Figure 19-17? No, methyl red does not change color at pH 7.

## Resource Manager

**Lab Manual,** pp. 145–148, 149–152 L2
**Teaching Transparency 58 and Master** L2 ELL

**Figure 19-19** Use this figure to drive home an important point about titrations—that the equivalence point does not always occur at pH 7.

## Extension

*Visual-Spatial* Use the chalkboard or an overhead transparency to illustrate the pH vs. volume-of-acid curve for the titration of a polyprotic acid with sodium hydroxide. A college chemistry textbook is a good source for such a titration curve. Guide students as they write the equation for the neutralization reaction occurring during each plateau. For example, during the first plateau of the titration of $H_3PO_4$ with NaOH, the reaction $H_3PO_4(aq) + OH^-(aq) \rightarrow H_2PO_4^-(aq) + H_2O(l)$ occurs. During the second plateau, the reaction $H_2PO_4^-(aq) + OH^-(aq) \rightarrow HPO_4^{2-}(aq) + H_2O(l)$ occurs, and during the third plateau, the reaction $HPO_4^{2-}(aq) + OH^-(aq) \rightarrow PO_4^{3-}(aq) + H_2O(l)$ occurs.

## Figure Caption Questions

**Figure 19-19** Check Figure 19-18. Do you agree that phenolphthalein is the best choice for this titration? Why? Yes, phenolphthalein changes color at the equivalence point of this titration.

---

**Figure 19-19**

In this titration of a weak acid (HCOOH) by a strong base (NaOH), the equivalence point is not at pH 7. Check **Figure 19-18.** Do you agree that phenolphthalein is the best choice of indicator for this titration? Why?

50.00 mL 0.1000*M* HCOOH Titrated with 0.1000*M* NaOH

**Figure 19-20**

Titration is a precise procedure requiring practice. The white paper under the flask provides a background for viewing the indicator color change.

**a** The buret contains the standard solution (0.1000*M* NaOH) and the flask contains 25.00 mL HCOOH solution along with a small amount of phenolphthalein indicator.

**b** The standard solution is added slowly to the acid solution in the flask. Although the phenolphthalein indicator turns pink, the color disappears upon mixing until the end point is reached.

**c** The end point of the titration is marked by a permanent but very light pink color. A careful reading of the buret reveals that 18.28 mL 0.1000*M* NaOH has been added.

---

points at pH values $> 7$. The pH at the equivalence point of a titration depends upon the relative strengths of the reacting acid and base. **Figure 19-19** shows that the equivalence point for the titration of methanoic acid (a weak acid) with sodium hydroxide (a strong base) lies between pH 8 and pH 9. Therefore, phenolphthalein is a good indicator for this titration. **Figure 19-20** illustrates and describes the titration of a solution of methanoic acid (HCOOH) of unknown concentration with 0.1000*M* sodium hydroxide solution.

**Calculating molarity** From the experimental data, the molarity of the unknown HCOOH solution can be calculated by following these steps.

**1.** Write the balanced formula equation for the acid-base reaction.

$$HCOOH(aq) + NaOH(aq) \rightarrow HCOONa (aq) + H_2O(l)$$

**2.** Calculate the number of moles of NaOH contained in the volume of standard solution added. First, convert milliliters of NaOH to liters by multiplying the volume by a conversion factor that relates milliliters and liters.

$$18.28 \text{ mL NaOH} \times \frac{1 \text{ L NaOH}}{1000 \text{ mL NaOH}} = 0.01828 \text{ L NaOH}$$

Determine the moles of NaOH used by multiplying the volume by a conversion factor that relates moles and liters, the molarity of the solution.

$$0.01828 \text{ L NaOH} \times \frac{0.1000 \text{ mol NaOH}}{1 \text{ L NaOH}} = 1.828 \times 10^{-3} \text{ mol NaOH}$$

---

**CHEMISTRY JOURNAL**

## Measuring pH

*Kinesthetic* Have students use pH meters or acid-base indicators to investigate the pH of soil, rain, lake water, and stream water in their local area. Ask them if they can explain the pH levels that they find. Have them include their results and explanations in their journals. **L2**

**GLENCOE** TECHNOLOGY

**CD-ROM**
**Chemistry: Matter and Change**
Video: *An Acid Base Titration*
Experiment: *Acid Base Titrations*

**3.** Use the mole ratio in the balanced equation to calculate the moles of reactant in the unknown solution.

$$1.828 \times 10^{-3} \text{ mol NaOH} \times \frac{1 \text{ mol HCOOH}}{1 \text{ mol NaOH}} =$$
$$1.828 \times 10^{-3} \text{ mol HCOOH}$$

**4.** Because molarity is defined as moles of solute per liter of solution, calculate the molarity of the unknown solution by dividing the moles of unknown (HCOOH) by the volume of the unknown solution expressed in liters. (25.00 mL = 0.02500 L)

$$M_{\text{HCOOH}} = \frac{1.828 \times 10^{-3} \text{ mol HCOOH}}{0.02500 \text{ L HCOOH}} = 7.312 \times 10^{-2} M$$

The molarity of the HCOOH solution is $7.312 \times 10^{-2} M$, or $0.07312 M$. In the **CHEMLAB** at the end of this chapter, you will use titration to standardize a base.

### PRACTICE PROBLEMS

**30.** What is the molarity of a CsOH solution if 30.0 mL of the solution is neutralized by 26.4 mL 0.250$M$ HBr solution?

**31.** What is the molarity of a nitric acid solution if 43.33 mL 0.1000$M$ KOH solution is needed to neutralize 20.00 mL of unknown solution?

**32.** What is the concentration of a household ammonia cleaning solution if 49.90 mL 0.5900$M$ HCl is required to neutralize 25.00 mL solution?

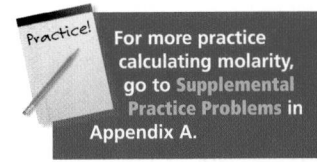

*Practice!* **For more practice calculating molarity, go to Supplemental Practice Problems in Appendix A.**

### Salt Hydrolysis

You just learned that a salt is an ionic compound made up of a cation from a base and an anion from an acid. What reaction, if any, occurs when a salt is dissolved in pure water? In **Figure 19-21,** several drops of bromthymol blue indicator solution have been added to 0.10$M$ aqueous solutions of the salts ammonium chloride ($NH_4Cl$), sodium nitrate ($NaNO_3$), and potassium fluoride (KF). Sodium nitrate turns the indicator green, which means that a solution of sodium nitrate is neutral. However, the blue color of the KF solution means that a solution of potassium fluoride is basic, and the yellow color of the ammonium chloride solution indicates that the $NH_4Cl$ solution is acidic. Why are some aqueous salt solutions neutral, some basic, and some acidic?

The answer is that many salts react with water in a process known as salt hydrolysis. In **salt hydrolysis,** the anions of the dissociated salt accept hydrogen ions from water or the cations of the dissociated salt donate hydrogen ions to water. Does a reaction occur when potassium fluoride dissolves in water? Potassium fluoride is the salt of a strong base (KOH) and a weak acid (HF) and dissociates into potassium ions and fluoride ions.

$$KF(s) \rightarrow K^+(aq) + F^-(aq)$$

Some fluoride ions react with water molecules to establish this equilibrium.

$$F^-(aq) + H_2O(l) \rightleftharpoons HF(aq) + OH^-(aq)$$

Note that the fluoride ion acts as a Brønsted-Lowry base and accepts a hydrogen ion from $H_2O$. Hydrogen fluoride molecules and $OH^-$ ions are produced. Although the resulting equilibrium lies far to the left, the potassium fluoride solution is basic because some $OH^-$ ions were produced

**Figure 19-21**

The indicator bromthymol blue provides surprising results when added to three solutions of ionic salts. An ammonium chloride solution is acidic, a sodium nitrate solution is neutral, and a potassium fluoride solution is basic. The explanation has to do with the strengths of the acid and base from which each salt was formed.

### Practice PROBLEMS

Have students refer to Appendix D for complete solutions to Practice Problems.

**30.** 0.220$M$

**31.** 0.2167$M$

**32.** 1.178$M$

### Concept Development

Help students with the process of determining a salt's "acid parent" and "base parent" by adding sufficient numbers of $H^+$ ions to the salt's negative ion and $OH^-$ ions to the salt's positive ion. For example, help students work out that the parent acid and parent base of $MgSO_4$ are $H_2SO_4$ and $Mg(OH)_2$, respectively.

### Reinforcement

Reinforce the concept that the $H_3O^+$ or $OH^-$ ions formed during salt hydrolysis do not come from the salt itself. Rather, water molecules react with either the negative or positive ions of the salt and produce additional $H_3O^+$ or $OH^-$ ions.

### CHEMLAB

ChemLab 19, located at the end of the chapter, can be used at this point in the lesson.

 **Resource Manager**

**Small-Scale Lab Manual,** pp. 69–72
**L2**

 **GLENCOE** *TECHNOLOGY*

**CD-ROM**
**Chemistry: Matter and Change**
Demonstration: *Using a Buffer*

making the concentration of $OH^-$ ions greater than the concentration of $H^+$ ions.

What about ammonium chloride? $NH_4Cl$ is the salt of a weak base ($NH_3$) and a strong acid (HCl). When dissolved in water, the salt dissociates into ammonium ions and chloride ions.

$$NH_4Cl(s) \rightarrow NH_4^+(aq) + Cl^-(aq)$$

The ammonium ions then react with water molecules to establish this equilibrium.

$$NH_4^+(aq) + H_2O(l) \rightleftharpoons NH_3(aq) + H_3O^+(aq)$$

The ammonium ion is a Brønsted-Lowry acid in the forward reaction, which produces $NH_3$ molecules and hydronium ions. This equilibrium also lies far to the left. However, an ammonium chloride solution is acidic because the solution contains more hydronium ions than hydroxide ions.

The hydrolysis of KF produces a basic solution; the hydrolysis of $NH_4Cl$ produces an acidic solution. What about sodium nitrate ($NaNO_3$)? Sodium nitrate is the salt of a strong acid (nitric acid) and a strong base (sodium hydroxide). Little or no salt hydrolysis occurs and a solution of sodium nitrate is neutral.

**Practice!** For more practice writing equations for salt hydrolysis reactions, go to **Supplemental Practice Problems** in Appendix A.

**PRACTICE** PROBLEMS

**33.** Write equations for the salt hydrolysis reactions that occur when the following salts are dissolved in water. Classify each solution as acidic, basic, or neutral.
**a.** ammonium nitrate
**b.** rubidium acetate
**c.** potassium sulfate
**d.** calcium carbonate

## Buffered Solutions

If you maintain a tropical-fish aquarium similar to the one shown in **Figure 19-22,** you know that the pH of the water must be kept relatively constant if the fish are to survive. Control of pH is important in your body, too. The pH of your blood must be maintained at an average of 7.4. A potentially fatal problem will develop if the pH rises or falls as much as 0.3 pH unit. The gastric juices in your stomach must have a pH between 1.6 and 1.8 to promote digestion of certain foods. How does your body maintain pH values within such narrow limits? It does so by producing buffers.

**Figure 19-22**

This freshwater aquarium is home to a variety of cichlid. To provide a healthy environment for this fish, it's necessary to know whether it is an African cichlid or a South American cichlid. The African cichlid requires water at a pH of 8.0 to 9.2; the South American cichlid requires a pH of 6.4 to 7.0. What would happen if you put a South American cichlid and some plants into a tank with water at pH of 8.5?

**Buffers** are solutions that resist changes in pH when limited amounts of acid or base are added. For example, adding 0.01 mole of HCl to 1 L of pure water lowers the pH by 5.0 units, from 7.0 to 2.0. Similarly, adding 0.01 mole of NaOH to 1 L of pure water increases the pH from 7.0 to 12.0. But if you add the same amount of either HCl or NaOH to 1 L of a buffered solution, the pH might change by no more than 0.1 unit.

**How do buffers work?** A buffer is a mixture of a weak acid and its conjugate base or a weak base and its conjugate acid. The mixture of ions and molecules in a buffer solution resists changes in pH by reacting with any hydrogen ions or hydroxide ions added to the buffered solution.

Suppose that a buffer solution contains 0.1$M$ concentrations of hydrofluoric acid, and 0.1$M$ fluoride ion (NaF). See **Figure 19-23**. HF is the acid and $F^-$ is its conjugate base. The following equilibrium would be established.

$$HF(aq) \rightleftharpoons H^+(aq) + F^-(aq)$$

When an acid is added to this buffered solution, the equilibrium shifts to the left. The added $H^+$ ions react with $F^-$ ions to form additional HF molecules.

$$HF(aq) \overset{\curvearrowleft}{\rightleftharpoons} H^+(aq) + F^-(aq)$$

The pH of the solution remains fairly constant because the additional HF molecules do not ionize appreciably.

When a base is added to the hydrofluoric acid/fluoride ion buffer system, the added $OH^-$ ions react with $H^+$ ions to form water. This decreases the concentration of hydrogen ions and the equilibrium shifts to the right to replace the $H^+$ ions.

$$HF(aq) \overset{\curvearrowright}{\rightleftharpoons} H^+(aq) + F^-(aq)$$

Although the shift to the right consumes HF molecules and produces additional $F^-$ ions, the pH remains fairly constant because the $H^+$ ion concentration has not changed appreciably.

A buffer solution's capacity to resist pH change can be exceeded by the addition of too much acid or base. Excessive acid overwhelms the hydrofluoric acid/fluoride ion buffer system by using up almost all of the $F^-$ ions. Similarly, too much base overwhelms the same system by using up almost all of the HF molecules. The amount of acid or base a buffer solution can absorb without a significant change in pH is called the **buffer capacity** of the solution. The greater the concentrations of the buffering molecules and ions in the solution, the greater the solution's buffer capacity. Do the **problem-solving LAB** on the next page to find out how buffers work in your blood.

**Choosing a buffer** A buffer can best resist both increases and decreases in pH when the concentrations of the conjugate acid-base pair are equal or nearly equal. Consider the $H_2PO_4^-/HPO_4^{2-}$ buffer system made by mixing equal molar amounts of $NaH_2PO_4$ and $Na_2HPO_4$.

$$H_2PO_4^- \rightleftharpoons H^+ + HPO_4^{2-}$$

What is the pH of such a buffer solution? The acid ionization constant expression for the equilibrium can provide the answer.

$$K_a = 6.2 \times 10^{-8} = \frac{[H^+][HPO_4^{2-}]}{[H_2PO_4^-]}$$

**Figure 19-23**

Hydrofluoric acid is used to etch decorative designs on glass. Beeswax is coated on the glass and the design is drawn in the wax with a metal stylus. When the glass is dipped into hydrofluoric acid solution, the acid etches the glass in the grooves left by the stylus.

19.4 Neutralization    **623**

**National Science Content Standards**

Pages 622–623
UCP.2, UCP.3, UCP.4; B.2; E.2

**Reinforcement**

Remind students that members of a conjugate acid-base pair are related by the presence or absence of a hydrogen ion. The acid form contains the $H^+$ ion; the base form does not. Explain that a buffer has its maximum buffering capacity in both directions when it contains equal quantities of an acid and its conjugate base or a base and its conjugate acid.

✓ **Assessment**

**Knowledge** Ask students which combinations of compounds could be used to produce buffer solutions. 1. $HC_2H_3O_2$ and NaCl no 2. HCl and NaCl no 3. HClO and KClO yes 4. NaOH and $HNO_3$ no 5. $NH_3$ and $NH_4I$ yes **L2**

**Figure Caption Questions**

**Figure 19-22** What would happen if you put a South American cichlid and some plants into a tank with water at pH of 8.5? The cichlid would eventually die. Plants requiring an acid environment would die, and plants requiring a basic environment could thrive. Over time, the ecosystem may become unbalanced.

---

ately labeled test tubes. Add a few drops of universal indicator to each test tube. Place a stirring rod in each test tube. Add a filled dropper of 4$M$ NaOH to each solution. **CAUTION:** *NaOH is caustic.* Stir and observe the color. Fill the dropper, repeat many times, and record your observations.

**Results**

The buffered test tube does not change color as rapidly as do the other two test tubes.

**Analysis**

1. Which of the three test tubes served as a control in this experiment? The control was the distilled water.

2. How was the definition of a buffer verified? The indicator's color did not change as several measures of base were added.

✓ **Assessment**

**Knowledge** Ask students if they think buffered aspirin would be better for their stomachs than unbuffered aspirin. Yes, buffered aspirin would neutralize the acid in aspirin.

**Table 19-5**

| Buffer Systems with Equimolar Components | | |
|---|---|---|
| **Buffer equilibrium** | **Conjugate acid-base pair in buffered solution** | **Buffer pH** |
| $HF(aq) \rightleftharpoons H^+(aq) + F^-(aq)$ | $HF/F^-$ | 3.20 |
| $CH_3COOH(aq) \rightleftharpoons H^+(aq) + CH_3COO^-(aq)$ | $CH_3COOH/CH_3COO^-$ | 4.76 |
| $H_2CO_3(aq) \rightleftharpoons H^+(aq) + HCO_3^-(aq)$ | $H_2CO_3/HCO_3^-$ | 6.35 |
| $H_2PO_4^-(aq) \rightleftharpoons H^+(aq) + HPO_4^{2-}(aq)$ | $H_2PO_4^-/HPO_4^{2-}$ | 7.21 |
| $NH_3(aq) + H_2O(l) \rightleftharpoons NH_4^+(aq) + OH^-(aq)$ | $NH_4^+/NH_3$ | 9.4 |
| $C_2H_5NH_2(aq) + H_2O(l) \rightleftharpoons C_2H_5NH_3^+(aq) + OH^-(aq)$ | $C_2H_5NH_3^+/C_2H_5NH_2$ | 10.70 |

Because the solution has been made up with equal molar amounts of $Na_2HPO_4$ and $NaH_2PO_4$, $[HPO_4^{2-}]$ is equal to $[H_2PO_4^-]$. Thus, the two terms in the acid ionization expression cancel.

$$6.2 \times 10^{-8} = \frac{[H^+][\cancel{HPO_4^{2-}}]}{[\cancel{H_2PO_4^-}]}$$

$$6.2 \times 10^{-8} = [H^+]$$

Recall that $pH = -\log[H^+]$.

## problem-solving LAB

### Purpose
Students will use Le Châtelier's principle to explain what occurs when the components of a buffer system are changed in human blood.

### Process Skills
Drawing conclusions, recognizing cause and effect, applying concepts, predicting

### Teaching Strategies
- Relate the carbonic acid-hydrogen carbonate buffer condition to the Brønsted-Lowry model. Show the action of carbon dioxide as an acid anhydride and the hydrogen carbonate ion as the conjugate base.
- Show how a buffer minimizes the effect of the addition of an acid or base as required by Le Châtelier's principle.

### Thinking Critically
1. pH 7.4 corresponds to $[H^+] = 4.0 \times 10^{-8}M$; pH 7.1 corresponds to $[H^+] = 7.9 \times 10^{-8}M$. The $H^+$ concentration has doubled.
2. A healthy body will dump acid into the blood through increased activity. The excess hydrogen carbonate is available to neutralize the acid, thus driving the reaction toward the production of carbon dioxide.
3. **a.** Vomit is acidic and will raise the pH. The buffer reaction shifts to the right. The kidneys can respond by removing hydrogen carbonate and the person should be kept quiet to retain $CO_2$.
   **b.** The pH rises as the hydrogen carbonate levels increase. This shifts the buffer reaction to the left forming more $CO_2$. The kidneys can respond by removing hydrogen carbonate and the person can breathe more rapidly to expel $CO_2$.

**National Science Content Standards**

**Pages 624–625**
UCP.2, UCP.3, UCP.4; B.2; E.2; F.1

## problem-solving LAB

### How does your blood maintain its pH?

The pH of human blood must be kept within the narrow range of 7.1 to 7.7. Outside this range, proteins in the body lose their structure and ability to function. Fortunately, a number of buffers maintain the necessary acid/base balance. The carbonic acid/hydrogen carbonate buffer is the most important.

$$CO_2(g) + H_2O(l) \rightleftharpoons H_2CO_3(aq) \rightleftharpoons H^+(aq) + HCO_3^-(aq)$$

As acids and bases are dumped into the bloodstream as a result of normal activity, the blood's buffer systems shift to effectively maintain a healthy pH.

### Analysis

Depending upon the body's metabolic rate and other factors, the $H_2CO_3/HCO_3^-$ equilibrium will shift according to Le Châtelier's principle. In addition, the lungs can alter the rate at which $CO_2$ is expelled from the body by breathing and the kidneys can alter the rate of removal of hydrogen carbonate ion.

### Thinking Critically
1. Calculate the molarity of $H^+$ in blood at a normal pH = 7.4 and at pH = 7.1, the lower limit of a healthy pH range. If the blood's pH changes from 7.4 to 7.1, how many times greater is the concentration of hydrogen ion?
2. The ratio of $HCO_3^-$ to $CO_2$ is 20:1. Why is this imbalance favorable for maintaining a healthy pH?
3. In the following situations, predict whether the pH of the blood will rise or fall, and which way the $H_2CO_3/HCO_3^-$ equilibrium will shift.
   **a.** A person with severe stomach flu vomits many times during a 24-hour period.
   **b.** To combat heartburn, a person foolishly takes a large amount of sodium hydrogen carbonate.

**624**   Chapter 19   Acids and Bases

### ✓ Assessment

**Performance** Ask students to describe the buffer's response if someone who has difficulty breathing overexerts; or ask students why a person could lose consciousness if he or she breathed in and out rapidly about 20 times, then held his or her breath. Use the Performance Task Assessment List for Analyzing the Data in **PASC**, p. 27. **L2**

### DIFFERENTIATED INSTRUCTION

#### Gifted

*Interpersonal* Have capable students investigate the use of equivalents and normality in describing the concentrations of acidic and basic solution. Have them show other students how the equation $V_A N_A = V_B N_B$ can be used in titration calculations. **L3**

$$pH = -\log (6.2 \times 10^{-8}) = 7.21$$

Thus, when equimolar amounts of each of the components are present in the $H_2PO_4^-/HPO_4^{2-}$ buffer system, the system can maintain a pH close to 7.21. Note that the pH is the negative log of $K_a$. **Table 19-5** lists several buffer systems with the pH at which each is effective. The pH values were calculated as the pH for the $H_2PO_4^-/HPO_4^{2-}$ buffer system was calculated above.

**Buffers in Blood**   Your blood is a slightly alkaline solution with a pH of approximately 7.4. To be healthy, that pH must be maintained within narrow limits. A condition called acidosis occurs if the pH falls more than 0.3 units below 7.4. An equally serious condition called alkalosis exists if the pH rises 0.3 units. You may have experienced a mild case of acidosis if you have overexerted and developed a cramp in your leg. Cramping results from the formation of lactic acid in muscle tissue.

Your body employs three principle strategies for maintaining proper blood pH. The first is excretion of excess acid or base in the urine. The second is the elimination of $CO_2$, the anhydride of carbonic acid, by breathing. The third involves a number of buffer systems. You have already learned about the $H_2CO_3/HCO_3^-$ buffer in the **problem-solving LAB**.

$$CO_2(g) + H_2O(l) \rightleftharpoons H_2CO_3(aq) \rightleftharpoons H^+(aq) + HCO_3^-(aq)$$

The $H_2PO_4^-/HPO_4^{2-}$ buffer system described above is also present in blood. Because the concentration of phosphates in the blood is not as high as the concentration of carbonates, the phosphate buffer plays a lesser role in maintaining blood pH even though it is a more efficient buffer. Other buffer systems, including some associated with the hemoglobin molecule work together with the carbonate and phosphate buffers to maintain pH.

Recall that if acid levels begin to rise, the $H_2CO_3/HCO_3^-$ equilibrium shifts to the left to consume the added $H^+$. At the same time, the respiratory system is signaled to increase the rate of breathing to eliminate the higher level of $CO_2$. If levels of base begin to rise, the equilibrium shifts to the right as $H^+$ neutralizes the base and the respiratory system slows the removal of $CO_2$ by depressing the breathing rate. Can you explain why?

Suppose that during a concert a fan becomes overexcited and begins to hyperventilate. Excessive loss of $CO_2$ shifts the $H_2CO_3/HCO_3^-$ equilibrium to the left and increases the pH. The situation can be controlled by helping the person calm down and breathe into a paper bag to recover exhaled $CO_2$ as shown in **Figure 19-24**.

**Figure 19-24**

Look at the equation for the carbonate buffer as you think about this situation. As $CO_2$ is eliminated through rapid breathing, the equilibrium shifts to the left. The $[H^+]$ decreases and pH increases. Re-breathing $CO_2$ from a paper bag helps restore the pH balance.

---

## Section 19.4 Assessment

**34.** Write the formula equation and the net ionic equation for the neutralization reaction between hydroiodic acid and potassium hydroxide.

**35.** Explain the difference between the equivalence point and the end point of a titration.

**36.** Predict the results of two experiments: A small amount of base is added to an unbuffered solution with a pH of 7 and the same amount of base is added to a buffered solution with a pH of 7.

**37. Thinking Critically**   When a salt is dissolved in water, how can you predict whether or not a salt hydrolysis reaction occurs?

**38. Designing an Experiment**   Describe how you would design and carry out a titration in which you use 0.250$M$ $HNO_3$ to determine the molarity of a cesium hydroxide solution.

---

## 3 Assess
### Check for Understanding

Ask students to write the formula equation, complete ionic equation, and net ionic equation for the neutralization reaction between perchloric acid and sodium hydroxide. $HClO_4(aq) + NaOH(aq) \rightarrow H_2O(l) + NaClO_4(aq)$; $H^+(aq) + ClO_4^-(aq) + Na^+(aq) + OH^- \rightarrow H_2O(l) + Na^+(aq) + ClO_4^-(aq)$; $H^+(aq) + OH^-(aq) \rightarrow H_2O(l)$.

### Reteach

Have students choose from Table 19-5 a conjugate acid-base pair that could be used to produce a buffer solution of pH 9 with capacity sufficient to neutralize both added acids and bases. $NH_3$ (base) and $NH_4^+$ (conjugate acid) **L2**

### Assessment

**Knowledge**  Ask students to write the chemical equations for the reaction of both added hydrogen ion and hydroxide ion with a carbonic acid/hydrogen carbonate ion buffer solution. $H^+(aq) + HCO_3^-(aq) \rightleftharpoons H_2CO_3(aq)$ and $OH^-(aq) + H_2CO_3(aq) \rightleftharpoons H_2O(l) + HCO_3^-(aq)$

### In-Text Question

**Page 625**  If levels of base begin to rise, the equilibrium shifts to the right as $H^+$ neutralizes the base and the respiratory system slows the removal of $CO_2$ by depressing the breathing rate. Can you explain why? When base reacts with $H^+$, it removes $H^+$ from the right side of the equation. Le Châtelier's principle predicts that the equilibrium will shift to the right to produce more $H^+$. This shift is aided by decreasing the loss of $CO_2$ by slower breathing.

---

## Section 19.4 Assessment

**34.** $HI(aq) + KOH(aq) \rightarrow KI(aq) + H_2O(l)$; $H^+(aq) + OH^-(aq) \rightarrow H_2O(l)$

**35.** Equivalence point is the pH at which the moles of $H^+$ ions from the acid equal the moles of $OH^-$ ions from the base. The end point is the point at which the indicator used in a titration changes color.

**36.** The pH of the unbuffered solution increases more than the pH of the buffered solution.

**37.** If the salt has a weak acid parent and/or a weak base parent, hydrolysis occurs.

**38.** Place a measured volume of CsOH solution into a flask. Add an indicator. Fill a buret with the 0.250$M$ $HNO_3$ solution. Record the initial buret reading. Add $HNO_3$ solution slowly to the CsOH solution until the end point. Record the final buret reading. Calculate the volume of $HNO_3$ added. Use the volume and molarity of $HNO_3$ and the volume of CsOH to calculate the molarity of the CsOH solution.

**625**

# CHEMLAB 19

## Preparation

### Time Allotment
Three laboratory periods

### Process Skills
Observing and inferring, collecting data, interpreting data, using numbers

### Safety Precautions
Students should wear safety goggles and lab aprons and wash their hands after each laboratory period.

### Disposal
The neutralized solutions can be washed down the drain with plenty of water.

### Preparation of Solutions
See page 594C for preparation of all solutions.

### Alternative Materials
• Potassium hydroxide could be used instead of sodium hydroxide.
• For the Real-World Chemistry question, students could use their standardized base. The water samples will have relatively low concentrations of acid, so the standardized base should be diluted quantitatively.

## Pre-Lab

1. the point in a titration when the number of moles of H⁺ ions from the acid equals the number of moles of OH⁻ ions from the base
3. independent variable, the mass of acid; dependent variable, the volume of base; constants, the drops of indicator and amounts of water.
4. one mole of H⁺ ions for each mole of acid used
5. molarity = moles of solute per liter of solution
7. Wear goggles, apron, and gloves. Handle glassware carefully. Do not allow chemicals to contact skin.

## Procedure

• The NaOH solution can be prepared in advance. For a $0.25M$

# Standardizing a Base Solution by Titration

The procedure called titration can be used to standardize a solution of a base, which means determine its molar concentration. To standardize a base, a solution of the base with unknown molarity is gradually added to a solution containing a known mass of an acid. The procedure enables you to determine when the number of moles of added OH⁻ ions from the base equals the number of moles of H⁺ion from the acid.

### Problem
How can you determine the molar concentration of a base solution? How do you know when the neutralization reaction has reached the equivalence point?

### Objectives
• **Recognize** the color change of the indicator that shows that the equivalence point has been reached.
• **Measure** the mass of the acid and the volume of the base solution used.
• **Calculate** the molar concentration of the base solution.

### Materials
50-mL buret
buret clamp
ring stand
sodium hydroxide pellets (NaOH)
potassium hydrogen phthalate ($KHC_8H_4O_4$)
distilled water
weighing bottle
spatula

250-mL Erlenmeyer flask
500-mL Florence flask and rubber stopper
250-mL beaker
centigram balance
wash bottle
phenolphthalein solution
dropper

### Safety Precautions

• **Always wear safety goggles and a lab apron.**

### Pre-Lab

1. What is the equivalence point of a titration?
2. Read the entire **CHEMLAB**.
3. What is the independent variable? The dependent variable? Constant?
4. When the solid acid dissolves to form ions, how many moles of H⁺ ions are produced for every mole of acid used?
5. What is the formula used to calculate molarity?
6. Prepare a data table that will accomodate multiple titration trials.
7. List safety precautions that must be taken.

| Titration Data | |
|---|---|
| | Trial 1 |
| mass of weighing bottle and acid | |
| mass of weighing bottle | |
| mass of solid acid | |
| moles of acid | |
| moles of base required | |
| final reading of base buret | |
| initial reading of base buret | |
| volume of base used in mL | |
| molarity of base | |

solution, dissolve 10 g NaOH in 1 L of distilled water.
• The amount of potassium hydrogen phthalate for each trial can vary from 0.3 g to 0.5 g.
• An empty plastic 35-mm film container works well as a weighing bottle.
• Demonstrate a complete titration and use the data to review the calculations.
• Remind students that their success depends upon the careful reading of the buret.

• **Troubleshooting** Students often forget to add indicator to their acid solutions.
• Have students stopper their flasks between lab periods because NaOH reacts with carbon dioxide in the air to form sodium carbonate.

### Expected Results
See the data table on page 627.

## Procedure

1. Place approximately 4 g NaOH in a 500-mL Florence flask. Add enough water to dissolve the pellets and bring the volume of the NaOH solution to about 400 mL. **CAUTION:** *The solution will get hot.* Keep the stopper in the flask.

2. Use the weighing bottle to mass by difference about 0.40 g of potassium hydrogen phthalate (molar mass = 204.32 g/mol) into a 250-mL Erlenmeyer flask. Record this data.

3. Using a wash bottle, rinse down the insides of the flask and add enough water to make about 50 mL of solution. Add two drops of phenolphthalein indicator solution.

4. Set up the buret as shown. Rinse the buret with about 10 mL of your base solution. Discard the rinse solution in a discard beaker.

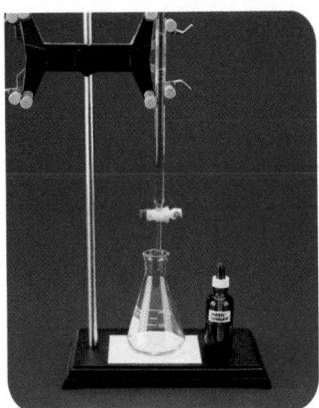

5. Fill the buret with NaOH solution. To remove any air trapped in the tip, allow a small amount of the base to flow from the tip of the buret into the discard beaker. Read the buret to the nearest 0.02 mL and record this initial reading. The meniscus of the solution in the buret should be at eye level when you make a reading.

6. Place a piece of white paper under the buret. Allow the NaOH solution to flow slowly from the buret into the flask containing the acid. Control the flow of the base solution with your left hand, and gently swirl the flask with your right hand.

7. The NaOH solution may be added in a rapid stream of drops until the pink color begins to last

longer as the flask is swirled. At this stage, begin adding the base drop by drop.

8. The equivalence point is reached when one additional drop of base turns the acid in the flask pink. The pink color should persist as the flask is swirled. Record the final volume in the buret.

9. Calculate the molarity of your base using steps 2–5 below.

10. Refill your buret with base. Rinse your Erlenmeyer flask with water. Repeat the titration with additional samples of acid until you get three trials that show close agreement between the calculated values of the molarity.

## Cleanup and Disposal

1. The neutralized solutions can be washed down the sink using plenty of water.

## Analyze and Conclude

1. **Observing and Inferring** Identify the characteristics of this neutralization reaction.

2. **Collecting and Interpreting Data** Complete the data table. Calculate the number of moles of acid used in each trial by dividing the mass of the sample by the molar mass of the acid.

3. **Using Numbers** How many moles of base are required to react with the moles of acid you used?

4. **Using Numbers** Convert the volume of base used from milliliters to liters.

5. **Analyze and Conclude** For each trial, calculate the molar concentration of the base by dividing the moles of base by the volume of base in liters.

6. **Error Analysis** How well did your calculated molarities agree? Explain any irregularities.

## Real-World Chemistry

1. Use what you have learned about titration to design a field investigation to determine whether your area is affected by acid rain. Research the factors that affect the pH of rain, such as location, prevailing winds, and industries. Form a hypothesis about the pH of rain in your area. What equipment will you need to collect samples? To perform the titration? What indicator will you use?

## Analyze and Conclude

1. An acid and a base reacted to form a salt and water.

2. See data table.
   0.39 g $KHC_8H_4O_4$ × 1 mol $KHC_8H_4O_4$/204.23 g $KHC_8H_4O_4$ = 0.00191 mol $KHC_8H_4O_4$

3. The mole ratio is 1:1, so the number of moles of NaOH and $KHC_8H_4O_4$ are the same.

4. 7.64 mL × 1 L/1000 mL = 0.00764 L

5. 0.00191 mol/0.00764 L = 0.250$M$

6. Student results will vary. inaccurate buret readings or mass determinations, overshooting the end point, spillage, bubbles in the buret

| Titration Data | |
|---|---|
| mass of weighing bottle and acid | 12.88 g |
| mass of empty weighing bottle | 12.49 g |
| mass of solid acid | 0.39 g |
| moles of acid used | 0.00191 mol |
| final reading of base buret | 8.80 mL |
| initial reading of base buret | 1.16 mL |
| volume of base used in mL | 7.64 mL |
| moles of base required | 0.00191 mol |

## Real-World Chemistry

1. Student designs should include the selection of a standard solution for titration and the use of **Figure 19-18** to choose an indicator. Students may want to form a hypothesis about sources of acid rain and attempt to verify their hypothesis by analyzing samples from various locations. Students could begin their study by

## Resource Manager

**ChemLab and MiniLab Worksheets,** pp. 74–76 **L2**

collecting samples and testing them with pH paper. Students should outline the steps in a titration of an acid by a strong base similar to the procedure in the ChemLab.

## Assessment

**Portfolio** Students can write a complete report for the lab and place it in their portfolios. **L2** **P**

**National Science Content Standards**

**Pages 626–627**
UCP.2, UCP.3, UCP.4; A.1; B.3; E.2

# How It Works

To learn how an antacid reacts in the stomach

### Background

Explain to students that digestion starts with chewing. When pieces of food mix with saliva in the mouth, the process of breaking the food down into a form useable by the body begins. When food is swallowed, it travels through the esophagus to the stomach where the major part of the digestion process goes on. After food leaves the stomach, the process continues in the small intestine.

An ulcer can form if the mucous membrane breaks down and stomach acid attacks the stomach wall. Ulcers are thought to form because of weakness in the stomach lining or because of excess stomach acid. Recent studies show that bacteria also can form ulcers.

### Visual Learning

Refer students to the illustration. Note that the stomach is lined with a mucous membrane but the esophagus is not. Ask what would happen if stomach fluids move up the esophagus. Stomach acid would attack the unprotected walls of the esophagus, causing the burning pain associated with heartburn.

### Teaching Strategies

- Ask students why the terms acid indigestion and acid stomach are misleading. A stomach must contain acid in order to be healthy. Have the students discuss what they know about the pH of various foods. Ask which might cause excess acid in the stomach. Answers may include orange juice, tomato products, and lemonade.

- Remind students that reactions in aqueous solutions are double-replacement reactions that form a precipitate, a gas, or water. Ask

# How It Works
## Antacids

Your stomach is a hollow organ where the food you eat is broken down into a usable form. The stomach contains powerful enzymes and hydrochloric acid, which are responsible for the breakdown process. Once the food is processed, it is released into the small intestine.

The pain and discomfort of indigestion is an indication that normal digestion has been interrupted. Heartburn is an irritation of the esophagus that is caused by stomach acid. Millions of people use antacids to treat indigestion and heartburn. Antacids are bases that neutralize digestive acids.

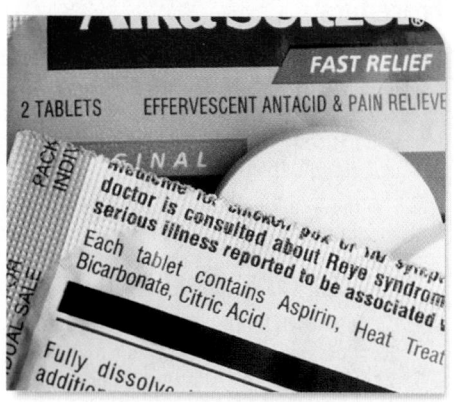

**❶** Acids and enzymes in the stomach help digest food. The pH in the stomach is about 2.5.

**❷** A basic mucous membrane lines the stomach and protects it from corrosion.

Esophagus

Mucous membrane

$CO_2$

Stomach

$H^+$     $HCO_3^-$

$H_2CO_3$

$Na^+$     $Cl^-$

$H_2O$

Carbonic acid

Small intestine

Stomach contents

**❹** Carbonic acid decomposes into carbon dioxide gas and water.

$$H_2CO_3(aq) \rightarrow H_2O(l) + CO_2(g)$$

**❸** A sodium hydrogen carbonate (sodium bicarbonate) antacid reacts with hydrochloric acid in the stomach and forms carbonic acid.

$$NaHCO_3(s) + HCl(aq) \rightarrow NaCl(aq) + H_2CO_3(aq)$$

### Thinking Critically

1. **Applying** Milk of magnesia is a suspension of magnesium hydroxide in water. Write the net ionic equation for the neutralization reaction between magnesium hydroxide and hydrochloric acid.

2. **Comparing and Contrasting** Why is sodium hydrogen carbonate an effective antacid but sodium hydroxide is not?

**Chapter 19** Acids and Bases

what is formed during the neutralization of stomach acid by sodium hydrogen carbonate. a gas, $CO_2$ Ask what is the net ionic equation for the reaction between sodium hydrogen carbonate and hydrochloric acid.

$$H^+(aq) + HCO_3^- \rightarrow H_2O(l) + CO_2(g)$$

### Thinking Critically

1. $OH^-(aq) + H^+(aq) \rightarrow H_2O(l)$
2. NaOH is a strong base that is highly reactive, corrosive, and toxic. It would damage tissue in the mouth and esophagus.

## Summary

### 19.1 Acids and Bases: An Introduction

- Acidic solutions contain more hydrogen ions than hydroxide ions; neutral solutions contain equal concentrations of hydrogen ions and hydroxide ions; basic solutions contain more hydroxide ions than hydrogen ions.

- In the Arrhenius model, an acid is a substance that contains hydrogen and ionizes in aqueous solution to produce hydrogen ions. An Arrhenius base is a substance that contains a OH group and dissociates in aqueous solution to produce hydroxide ions.

- According to the Brønsted-Lowry model, an acid is a hydrogen ion donor and a base is a hydrogen ion acceptor.

- When a Brønsted-Lowry acid donates a hydrogen ion, a conjugate base is formed; when a Brønsted-Lowry base accepts a hydrogen ion, a conjugate acid is formed.

### 19.2 Strengths of Acids and Bases

- Strong acids and strong bases are completely ionized in dilute aqueous solution. Weak acids and weak bases are partially ionized.

- For weak acids and weak bases, the value of the acid or base ionization constant is a measure of the strength of the acid or base.

### 19.3 What is pH?

- The pH of a solution is the negative log of the hydrogen ion concentration and the pOH is the negative log of the hydroxide ion concentration.

- A neutral solution has a pH of 7.0 and a pOH of 7.0 because the concentrations of hydrogen ion and hydroxide ion are equal. The pH of a solution decreases as the solution becomes more acidic and increases as the solution becomes more basic. The pOH of a solution decreases as the solution becomes more basic and increases as the solution becomes more acidic.

- The ion product constant for water, $K_w$, equals the product of the hydrogen ion concentration and the hydroxide ion concentration.

### 19.4 Neutralization

- The general equation for an acid-base neutralization reaction is acid + base → salt + water.

- The net ionic equation for the neutralization of a strong acid by a strong base is $H^+(aq) + OH^-(aq) \rightarrow H_2O(l)$.

- Titration is the process in which an acid-base neutralization reaction is used to determine the concentration of a solution of unknown concentration.

- Buffered solutions contain mixtures of molecules and ions that resist changes in pH.

## Key Equations and Relationships

- $pH = -\log [H^+]$ (p. 610)
- $pOH = -\log [OH^-]$ (p. 611)
- $pH + pOH = 14.00$ (p. 611)
- $K_w = [H^+][OH^-]$ (p. 608)

## Vocabulary

- acid-base indicator (p. 619)
- acid ionization constant (p. 605)
- acidic solution (p. 597)
- amphoteric (p. 599)
- Arrhenius model (p. 597)
- base ionization constant (p. 606)
- basic solution (p. 597)
- Brønsted-Lowry model (p. 598)
- buffer (p. 623)
- buffer capacity (p. 623)
- conjugate acid (p. 598)
- conjugate acid-base pair (p. 598)
- conjugate base (p. 598)
- end point (p. 619)
- equivalence point (p. 618)
- ion product constant for water (p. 608)
- neutralization reaction (p. 617)
- pH (p. 610)
- pOH (p. 611)
- salt (p. 617)
- salt hydrolysis (p. 621)
- strong acid (p. 602)
- strong base (p. 606)
- titration (p. 618)
- weak acid (p. 603)
- weak base (p. 606)

chemistrymc.com/vocabulary_puzzlemaker

## Using the Vocabulary

To reinforce chapter vocabulary, have students write a sentence using each term. **L2** **ELL**

## Review Strategies

- Ask students to compare the concentrations of hydrogen ions and hydroxide ions in acidic, neutral, and basic solutions. **L2**
- Ask students to distinguish between Arrhenius and Brønsted-Lowry acids and bases and identify conjugate acid-base pairs. **L2**
- Ask students to distinguish between strong and weak acids. **L2**
- Ask students to define pH and pOH and compare the pH and pOH values in acidic, neutral, and basic solutions. **L2**
- Problems from Appendix A or the **Supplemental Problems** booklet can be used for review. **L2**

## VOCABULARY PuzzleMaker CHEMISTRY ONLINE

For additional help with vocabulary, have students access the Vocabulary PuzzleMaker online.

**chemistrymc.com/ vocabulary_puzzlemaker**

Chemistry Online

## Use ExamView® Pro Testmaker CD-ROM to:

- Create **multiple versions** of tests.
- Create **modified** tests with one mouse click for struggling students.
- **Edit** existing questions and add your own questions.
- **Build** tests based on national curriculum standards.

**National Science Content Standards**

**Pages 628–629**
UCP.2, UCP.3, UCP.4; B.2, B.3, B.4; E.2; F.1

## Concept Mapping

**39.** 1. acids; 2. Arrhenius model; 3. Brønsted-Lowry model; 4. acidic solutions; 5. pH < 7; 6. bases; 7. a salt plus water

## Mastering Concepts

**40.** The solution is basic.

**41.** The formula is $CO_2$.

**42.** acidic, $[H^+] > [OH^-]$; neutral, $[H^+] = [OH^-]$; basic, $[H^+] < [OH^-]$

**43.** $H_2O(l) + H_2O(l) \rightleftharpoons H_3O^+(aq) + OH^-(aq)$

**44.** An acid contains hydrogen and ionizes to produce $H^+$ in aqueous solution. A base contains an OH group and dissociates to produce $OH^-$ in aqueous solution.

**45.** No, none of the hydrogens ionize to produce $H^+$.

**46. a.** acid    **c.** base
**b.** base    **d.** acid

**47.** a monoprotic acid: can donate one $H^+$ (HCl); a diprotic acid: can donate two $H^+$ ($H_2SO_4$); a triprotic acid: can donate three $H^+$ ($H_3PO_4$)

**48.** Acidic solutions react with and dissolve carbonates. $H_2SO_4(aq) + CaCO_3(s) \rightarrow CaSO_4(aq) + H_2O(l) + CO_2(g)$

**49.** $NH_3$ accepts a hydrogen ion to form the ammonium ion.

**50.** acid: $HC_2H_3O_2$; conjugate base: $C_2H_3O_2^-$; base: $H_2O$; conjugate acid: $H_3O^+$

**51.** It is a Brønsted-Lowry acid-base reaction because HCl donates a hydrogen ion to $NH_3$. This reaction does not occur in water. Thus, it does not follow the Arrhenius model.

**52.** In dilute aqueous solution, a strong acid ionizes completely; a weak acid ionizes slightly.

**53.** Because strong acids and bases ionize completely, the large number of ions

---

# CHAPTER 19 ASSESSMENT

## Chemistry Online

Go to the Chemistry Web site at chemistrymc.com *for additional Chapter 19 Assessment.*

## Concept Mapping

**39.** Use the following words and phrases to complete the concept map: acidic solutions, acids, bases, Arrhenius model, pH < 7, a salt plus water, Brønsted-Lowry model.

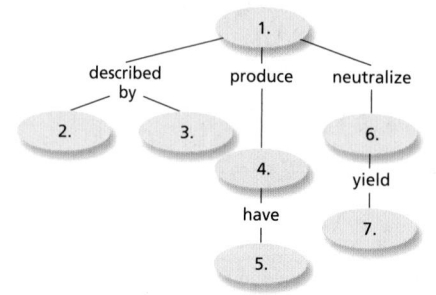

## Mastering Concepts

**40.** An aqueous solution tastes bitter and turns litmus blue. Is the solution acidic or basic? (19.1)

**41.** An acidic solution reacts with magnesium carbonate to produce a gas. What is the formula for the gas? (19.1)

**42.** In terms of ion concentrations, distinguish between acidic, neutral, and basic solutions. (19.1)

**43.** Write a balanced chemical equation that represents the self-ionization of water. (19.1)

**44.** How did Arrhenius describe acids and bases? Why was his description important? (19.1)

**45.** Table sugar ($C_{12}H_{22}O_{11}$) contains 22 hydrogen atoms per molecule. Does this make table sugar an Arrhenius acid? Explain your answer. (19.1)

**46.** Classify each of the following compounds as an Arrhenius acid or an Arrhenius base. (19.1)
**a.** $H_2S$    **c.** $Mg(OH)_2$
**b.** RbOH    **d.** $H_3PO_4$

**47.** Explain the difference between a monoprotic acid, a diprotic acid, and a triprotic acid. Give an example of each. (19.1)

---

**48.** Why does acid rain dissolve statues made of marble ($CaCO_3$)? Write the formula equation for the reaction between sulfuric acid and calcium carbonate. (19.1)

**49.** Ammonia contains three hydrogen atoms per molecule. However, an aqueous ammonia solution is basic. Explain using the Brønsted-Lowry model of acids and bases. (19.1)

**50.** Identify the conjugate acid-base pairs in the equilibrium equation.
$HC_2H_3O_2 + H_2O \rightleftharpoons H_3O^+ + C_2H_3O_2^-$ (19.1)

**51.** Gaseous HCl molecules interact with gaseous $NH_3$ molecules to form a white smoke made up of solid $NH_4Cl$ particles. Explain whether or not this is an acid-base reaction according to both the Arrhenius model and the Brønsted-Lowry model. (19.1)

**52.** Explain the difference between a strong acid and a weak acid. (19.2)

**53.** Why are strong acids and bases also strong electrolytes? (19.2)

**54.** State whether each of the following acids is strong or weak. (19.2)
**a.** acetic acid    **c.** hydrofluoric acid
**b.** hydroiodic acid    **d.** phosphoric acid

**55.** State whether each of the following bases is strong or weak. (19.2)
**a.** rubidium hydroxide    **c.** ammonia
**b.** methylamine    **d.** sodium hydroxide

**56.** How would you compare the strengths of two weak acids (19.2)
**a.** experimentally?
**b.** by looking up information in a table or a handbook?

**57. Figure 19-7** shows the conductivity of two acids. Explain how you could distinguish between solutions of two bases, one containing NaOH and the other $NH_3$. (19.2)

**58.** Explain why the base ionization constant ($K_b$) is a measure of the strength of a base. (19.2)

**59.** Explain why a weak acid has a strong conjugate base. Give an equation that illustrates your answer. (19.2)

**60.** Explain why a weak base has a strong conjugate acid. Give an equation that illustrates your answer. (19.2)

**61.** Explain how you can calculate $K_a$ for a weak acid if you know the concentration of the acid and its pH. (19.2)

**62.** What is the relationship between the pOH and the hydroxide-ion concentration of a solution? (19.3)

chemistrymc.com/chapter_test

---

produced causes the solution to have a high electrical conductivity.

**54. a.** weak    **c.** weak
**b.** strong    **d.** weak

**55. a.** strong    **c.** weak
**b.** weak    **d.** strong

## Resource Manager

**Chapter Assessment,** pp. 109–114
**Supplemental Problems,** Ch. 19
**ExamView® Pro CD-ROM**
**MindJogger Videoquizzes DVD/VHS**
**Solutions Manual,** Ch. 19
**Chemistry Interactive CD-ROM,**
  Ch. 19 quiz

**63.** Solution A has a pH of 2.0. Solution B has a pH of 5.0. Which solution is more acidic? Based on the hydrogen-ion concentrations in the two solutions, how many times more acidic? (19.3)

**64.** If the concentration of hydrogen ions in an aqueous solution decreases, what must happen to the concentration of hydroxide ions? Why? (19.3)

**65.** Explain why pure water has a very slight electrical conductivity. (19.3)

**66.** Why is the pH of pure water 7.0 at 298 K? (19.3)

**67.** What is a standard solution in an acid-base titration? (19.4)

**68.** How do you recognize the end point in an acid-base titration? (19.4)

**69.** Give the name and formula of the acid and the base from which each salt was formed. (19.4)
  **a.** NaCl
  **b.** $KClO_3$
  **c.** $NH_4NO_2$
  **d.** CaS

**70.** How does buffering a solution change the solution's behavior when a base is added? When an acid is added? (19.4)

**71.** Why are some aqueous salt solutions acidic or basic? (19.4)

**72.** How does knowing the equivalence point in an acid-base titration help you choose an indicator for the titration? (19.4)

**73.** An aqueous solution causes bromthymol blue to turn blue and phenolphthalein to turn colorless. What is the approximate pH of the solution? (19.4)

**74.** In the net ionic equation for the neutralization reaction between nitric acid and magnesium hydroxide, what ions are left out of the equation? (19.4)

**75.** Describe two ways you might detect the end point of an acid-base titration experimentally. (19.4)

**76.** What is the approximate pH of the equivalence point in the titration pH curve? (19.4)

**Titration Curve for a Base**
Volume of acid added

**77.** Define both the equivalence point and the end point of an acid-base titration. Why should you choose an indicator so that the two points are nearly the same pH? (19.4)

**78.** Explain how you can predict whether an aqueous salt solution is acidic, basic, or neutral by evaluating the strengths of the salt's acid and base parents. (19.4)

**79.** In a hypochlorous acid/hypochlorite-ion buffer, what chemical species reacts when an acid is added to the solution? (19.4)

**80.** Arrange the three buffers in order of increasing pH values. In order of increasing buffer capacity.
  **a.** $1.0M$ $HClO/1.0M$ $NaClO$
  **b.** $0.10M$ $HClO/0.10M$ $NaClO$
  **c.** $0.010M$ $HClO/0.010M$ $NaClO$

## Mastering Problems

### Equations for Acid and Base Reactions (19.1)

**81.** Write a balanced formula equation for the reaction between sulfuric acid and calcium metal.

**82.** Write a balanced formula equation for the reaction between potassium hydrogen carbonate and chlorous acid ($HClO_2$).

**83.** Write the balanced chemical equation for the ionization of perchloric acid ($HClO_4$) in water.

**84.** Write the balanced chemical equation for the dissociation of solid magnesium hydroxide in water.

### Weak Acids and Bases (19.2)

**85.** Write the equation for the ionization reaction and the acid ionization constant expression for the $HS^-$ ion in water.

**86.** Write the equation for the ionization reaction and the acid ionization constant expression for the third ionization of phosphoric acid in water.

### $K_w$, pH, and pOH (19.3)

**87.** Given the concentration of either hydrogen ion or hydroxide ion, use the ion product constant of water to calculate the concentration of the other ion at 298 K.
  **a.** $[H^+] = 1.0 \times 10^{-4}M$
  **b.** $[OH^-] = 1.3 \times 10^{-2}M$

**88.** Calculate the pH at 298 K of solutions having the following ion concentrations.
  **a.** $[H^+] = 1.0 \times 10^{-4}M$
  **b.** $[H^+] = 5.8 \times 10^{-11}M$

**56. a.** Compare the conductivities of equimolar solutions of the acids.
  **b.** Compare acid ionization constants of the two acids.

**57.** The conductivity of the strong base NaOH is greater than the conductivity of the weak base $NH_3$.

**58.** The greater the value of $K_b$, the greater the $[OH^-]$.

**59.** $HF(aq) + H_2O(l) \rightleftharpoons H_3O^+(aq) + F^-(aq)$ HF has little tendency to donate a $H^+$ to $H_2O$ (weak acid). Therefore, $F^-$ has a strong tendency to accept a $H^+$ from $H_3O^+$ (strong base).

**60.** $CH_3NH_2(aq) + H_2O(l) \rightleftharpoons CH_3NH_3^+(aq) + OH^-(aq)$ $CH_3NH_2$ has little tendency to accept a $H^+$ from $H_2O$. Therefore, $CH_3NH_3^+$ has a strong tendency to donate a $H^+$ to $OH^-$.

**61.** Obtain $[H^+]$ from the pH. $[X^-] = [H^+]$. $[HX] =$ the initial concentration minus $[H^+]$. Use the acid's ionization constant expression to calculate $K_a$.

**62.** $pOH = -\log [OH^-]$

**63.** Solution A is $10^3$, or 1000 times more acidic than B.

**64.** $[OH^-]$ increases. $[H^+][OH^-] = K_w$

**65.** Pure water ionizes to a slight degree producing $H_3O^+$ and $OH^-$ ions.

**66.** $pH = -\log [H^+]$, and $[H^+]$ in pure water at 298 K is $1.0 \times 10^{-7}M$.

**67.** the solution of known concentration

**68.** the color of the acid-base indicator changes

**69. a.** hydrochloric acid, HCl; sodium hydroxide, NaOH
  **b.** chloric acid, $HClO_3$;

  potassium hydroxide, KOH
  **c.** nitrous acid, $HNO_2$; ammonium hydroxide, $NH_4OH$
  **d.** hydrosulfuric acid, $H_2S$; calcium hydroxide, $Ca(OH)_2$

**70.** Buffering minimizes the pH change in both instances.

**71.** Cations of some salts donate $H^+$ to water, forming acidic solutions. Anions of other salts accept $H^+$ from water, producing basic solutions.

**72.** The color change should occur at a pH near the equivalence point.

**73.** between 7.6 and 8.5

**74.** nitrate and magnesium ions

**75.** Use a pH meter or an acid-base indicator.

**76.** approximately pH 5

**77.** The equivalence point is the point at which mol $H^+$ ions equals mol $OH^-$ ions. The end point is the point at which the indicator changes color. An

**National Science Content Standards**

Pages 630–631
UCP.2, UCP.3, UCP.4; B.2, B.3, B.4

indicator detects the equivalence point, so the two
should occur at the same
pH.

**78.** An aqueous salt solution
is acidic if the salt's acid
parent is strong and its base
parent is weak, basic if the
salt's acid parent is weak
and its base parent is
strong, neutral if both the
acid parent and base parent
are strong.

**79.** hypochlorite ion

**80.** All three solutions have the
same pH. the buffer
capacity: c, b, a

## Mastering Problems

Complete solutions to Chapter
Assessment problems can be found
in the **Solutions Manual.**

### Equations for Acid and Base Reactions (19.1)
#### Level 1

**81.** $H_2SO_4(aq) + Ca(s) \rightarrow$
$CaSO_4(aq) + H_2(g)$

**82.** $KHCO_3(s) + HClO_2(aq) \rightarrow$
$KClO_2(aq) + H_2O(l) + CO_2(g)$

**83.** $HClO_4(aq) + H_2O(l) \rightarrow$
$H_3O^+(aq) + ClO_4^-(aq)$

**84.** $Mg(OH)_2(s) \rightleftharpoons Mg^{2+}(aq) +$
$2OH^-(aq)$

### Weak Acids and Bases (19.2)
#### Level 1

**85.** $HS^-(aq) + H_2O(l) \rightleftharpoons$
$H_3O^+(aq) + S^{2-}(aq)$
$K_a = \frac{[H_3O^+][S^{2-}]}{[HS^-]}$

#### Level 2

**86.** $HPO_4^{2-}(aq) + H_2O(l) \rightleftharpoons$
$H_3O^+(aq) + PO_4^{3-}(aq)$
$K_a = \frac{[H_3O^+][PO_4^{3-}]}{[HPO_4^{2-}]}$

### $K_w$, pH, and pOH (19.3)
#### Level 1

**87. a.** $[OH^-] = 1.0 \times 10^{-10}M$
**b.** $[H^+] = 7.7 \times 10^{-13}M$

**88. a.** pH = 4.00
**b.** pH = 10.24

#### Level 2

**89. a.** pOH = 12.00; pH = 2.00
**b.** pOH = 1.89; pH = 12.11

**89.** Calculate the pOH and pH at 298 K of solutions having the following ion concentrations.

   **a.** $[OH^-] = 1.0 \times 10^{-12}M$
   **b.** $[OH^-] = 1.3 \times 10^{-2}M$

**90.** Calculate the pH of each of the following strong acid
or strong base solutions at 298 K.

   **a.** $2.6 \times 10^{-2}M$ HCl
   **b.** $0.28M$ $HNO_3$
   **c.** $7.5 \times 10^{-3}M$ NaOH
   **d.** $0.44M$ KOH

### Calculations Using $K_a$ (19.3)

**91.** A $8.6 \times 10^{-3}M$ solution of $H_3PO_4$ has a pH = 2.30.
What is $K_a$ for $H_3PO_4$?

**92.** What is $K_a$ for a solution of chloroacetic acid
($C_2H_3ClO_2$) which has a concentration of $0.112M$ and
a pH of 1.92?

### Neutralization Reactions (19.4)

**93.** Write formula equations for the following acid-base
neutralization reactions.

   **a.** sulfuric acid + sodium hydroxide
   **b.** methanoic acid + potassium hydroxide

**94.** Write formula equations and net ionic equations for
the hydrolysis of the following salts in water.

   **a.** sodium carbonate
   **b.** ammonium bromide

**95.** In a titration, 33.21 mL $0.3020M$ rubidium hydroxide
solution is required to exactly neutralize 20.00 mL
hydrofluoric acid solution. What is the molarity of the
hydrofluoric acid solution?

**96.** A 35.00 mL-sample of NaOH solution is titrated to an
endpoint by 14.76 mL $0.4122M$ HBr solution. What is
the molarity of the NaOH solution?

### Mixed Review

*Sharpen your problem-solving skills by answering the
following.*

**97.** Calculate $[H^+]$ and $[OH^-]$ in each of the following
solutions at 298 K.
   **a.** pH = 3.00    **b.** pH = 5.24

**98.** Write the equation for the ionization reaction and the
base ionization constant expression for ethylamine
($C_2H_5NH_2$) in water.

**99.** Write net ionic equations for the three ionizations of
boric acid ($H_3BO_3$) in water. Include $H_2O$ in the three
equations. Identify the conjugate acid-base pairs.

**100.** How many milliliters of $0.225M$ HCl would be
required to titrate 6.00 g KOH?

**101.** What is the pH of a $0.200M$ solution of hypobro-
mous acid (HBrO), $K_a = 2.8 \times 10^{-9}$.

## Thinking Critically

**102. Analyzing and Concluding** Is it possible that an
acid according to the Arrhenius model is not a
Brønsted-Lowry acid? Is it possible that an acid
according to the Brønsted-Lowry model is not an
Arrhenius acid? Explain and give examples.

**103. Applying Concepts** Use the ion product constant of
water at 298 K to explain why a solution with a pH
of 3.0 must have a pOH of 11.0.

**104. Using Numbers** The ion product constant of water
rises with temperature. What is the pH of pure water
at 313 K if $K_w$ at that temperature is $2.917 \times 10^{-14}$?

**105. Interpreting Scientific Illustrations** Sketch the
shape of the approximate pH vs. volume curve that
would result from titrating a diprotic acid with a
$0.10M$ NaOH solution.

**106. Recognizing Cause and Effect** Illustrate how a
buffer works using the $C_2H_5NH_3^+/C_2H_5NH_2$ buffer
system. Show with equations how the weak
base/conjugate acid system is affected when small
amounts of acid and base are added to a solution
containing this buffer system.

## Writing in Chemistry

**107.** Examine the labels of at least two brands of shampoo
and record any information regarding pH. Research
the pH of skin, hair, and the pH ranges of various
shampoos. Write a report summarizing your findings.

**108.** The twenty amino acids combine to form proteins in
living systems. Research the structures and $K_a$ values
for five amino acids. Compare the strengths of these
acids with the weak acids in **Table 19-2.**

## Cumulative Review

*Refresh your understanding of previous chapters by
answering the following.*

**109.** What factors determine whether a molecule is polar
or nonpolar? (Chapter 9)

**110.** When 5.00 g of a compound was burned in a calorimeter, the temperature of 2.00 kg of water increased
from 24.5°C to 40.5°C. How much heat would be
released by the combustion of 1.00 mol of the compound (molar mass = 46.1 g/mol)? (Chapter 16)

**90. a.** pH = 1.59
   **b.** pH = 0.55
   **c.** pH = 11.87
   **d.** pH = 13.64

### Calculations Using $K_a$ (19.3)
#### Level 1

**91.** $K_a = 6.9 \times 10^{-3}$
**92.** $K_a = 1.4 \times 10^{-3}$

### Neutralization Reactions (19.4)
#### Level 1

**93. a.** $H_2SO_4(aq) + 2NaOH(aq) \rightarrow$
$Na_2SO_4(aq) + 2H_2O(l)$
   **b.** $HCOOH(aq) + KOH(aq) \rightarrow$
$KHCOO(aq) + H_2O(l)$

**94. a.** $Na_2CO_3(s) + H_2O(l) \rightarrow NaHCO_3(aq)$
$+ NaOH(aq); CO_3^{2-}(aq) + H_2O(l) \rightarrow$
$HCO_3^-(aq) + OH^-(aq)$
   **b.** $NH_4Br(s) + H_2O(l) \rightarrow HBr(aq) +$

*Use these questions and the test-taking tip to prepare for your standardized test.*

**1.** A carbonated soft drink has a pH of 2.5. What is the concentration of $H^+$ ions in the soft drink?
   **a.** $3 \times 10^{-12} M$
   **b.** $3 \times 10^{-3} M$
   **c.** $4.0 \times 10^{-1} M$
   **d.** $1.1 \times 10^{1} M$

**2.** At the equivalence point of a strong acid-strong base titration, what is the approximate pH?
   **a.** 3          **c.** 7
   **b.** 5          **d.** 9

**3.** Hydrogen bromide (HBr) is a strong, highly corrosive acid. What is the pOH of a $0.0375 M$ HBr solution?
   **a.** 12.57       **b.** 12.27
   **c.** 1.73        **d.** 1.43

**4.** A compound that accepts $H^+$ ions is
   **a.** an Arrhenius acid.
   **b.** an Arrhenius base.
   **c.** a Brønsted-Lowry acid.
   **d.** a Brønsted-Lowry base.

**Interpreting Tables** Use the table to answer questions 5–7.

**5.** Which of the following acids is the strongest?
   **a.** formic acid
   **b.** cyanoacetic acid
   **c.** lutidinic acid
   **d.** barbituric acid

**6.** What is the acid dissociation constant of propanoic acid?
   **a.** $1.4 \times 10^{-5}$
   **b.** $2.43 \times 10^{0}$
   **c.** $3.72 \times 10^{-3}$
   **d.** $7.3 \times 10^{4}$

**7.** What is the pH of a $0.400 M$ solution of cyanoacetic acid?
   **a.** 2.059       **c.** 2.45
   **b.** 1.22        **d.** 1.42

**8.** Which of the following is NOT a characteristic of a base?
   **a.** bitter taste
   **b.** ability to conduct electricity
   **c.** reactivity with some metals
   **d.** slippery feel

**9.** Diprotic succinic acid ($H_2C_4H_4O_4$) is an important part of the process that converts glucose to energy in the human body. What is the $K_a$ expression for the second ionization of succinic acid?

   **a.** $K_a = \dfrac{[H_3O^+][HC_4H_4O_4^-]}{[H_2C_4H_4O_4]}$

   **b.** $K_a = \dfrac{[H_3O^+][C_4H_4O_4^{2-}]}{[HC_4H_4O_4^-]}$

   **c.** $K_a = \dfrac{[H_2C_4H_4O_4]}{[H_3O^+][HC_4H_4O_4^-]}$

   **d.** $K_a = \dfrac{[H_2C_4H_4O_4]}{[H_3O^+][C_4H_4O_4^{2-}]}$

**10.** A solution of $0.600 M$ HCl is used to titrate 15.00 mL of KOH solution. The endpoint of the titration is reached after the addition of 27.13 mL of HCl. What is the concentration of the KOH solution?
   **a.** $9.000 M$
   **b.** $1.09 M$
   **c.** $0.332 M$
   **d.** $0.0163 M$

---

### TEST-TAKING TIP

**Slow Down!** Check to make sure you're answering the question that each problem is posing. Read the questions and every answer choice very carefully. Remember that doing most of the problems and getting them right is always preferable to doing all the problems and getting lots of them wrong.

---

| Ionization Constants and pH Data for Several Weak Organic Acids | | | |
|---|---|---|---|
| **Acid** | **Ionization equation** | **pH of 1.000M solution** | **$K_a$** |
| Formic | $HCHO_2 \rightleftharpoons H^+ + CHO_2^-$ | 1.87 | $1.78 \times 10^{-4}$ |
| Cyanoacetic | $HC_3H_2NO_2 \rightleftharpoons H^+ + C_3H_2NO_2^-$ | ? | $3.55 \times 10^{-3}$ |
| Propanoic | $HC_3H_5O_2 \rightleftharpoons H^+ + C_3H_5O_2^-$ | 2.43 | ? |
| Lutidinic | $H_2C_7H_3NO_4 \rightleftharpoons H^+ + C_7H_4NO_4^-$ | 1.09 | $7.08 \times 10^{-3}$ |
| Barbituric | $HC_4H_3N_2O_3 \rightleftharpoons H^+ + C_4H_3N_2O_3^-$ | 2.01 | $9.77 \times 10^{-5}$ |

chemistrymc.com/standardized_test

Standardized Test Practice  **633**

---

$NH_4OH(aq); NH_4^+(aq) + H_2O(l) \rightarrow NH_3(aq) + H_3O^+(aq)$

## Level 2
**95.** $M_{HF} = 0.5015 M$
**96.** $M_{NaOH} = 0.1738 M$

## Mixed Review
**97. a.** $[H^+] = 1.0 \times 10^{-3} M$; $[OH^-] = 1.0 \times 10^{-11} M$
   **b.** $[H^+] = 5.8 \times 10^{-6} M$; $[OH^-] = 1.7 \times 10^{-9} M$

**98.** $C_2H_5NH_2(aq) + H_2O(l) \rightleftharpoons C_2H_5NH_3^+(aq) + OH^-(aq)$
$K_b = \dfrac{[C_2H_5NH_3^+][OH^-]}{[C_2H_5NH_2]}$

**99.** $H_3BO_3(aq) + H_2O(l) \rightleftharpoons H_3O^+(aq) + H_2BO_3^-(aq)$
Acid: $H_3BO_3$; Conjugate base: $H_2BO_3^-$; Base: $H_2O$; Conjugate acid: $H_3O^+$
$H_2BO_3^-(aq) + H_2O(l) \rightleftharpoons H_3O^+(aq) + HBO_3^{2-}(aq)$
Acid: $H_2BO_3^-$; Conjugate base: $HBO_3^{2-}$; Base: $H_2O$; Conjugate acid: $H_3O^+$
$HBO_3^{2-}(aq) + H_2O(l) \rightleftharpoons H_3O^+(aq) + BO_3^{3-}(aq)$
Acid: $HBO_3^{2-}$; Conjugate base: $BO_3^{3-}$; Base: $H_2O$; Conjugate acid: $H_3O^+$
**100.** 475 mL
**101.** pH = 4.63

## Thinking Critically
**102.** All Arrhenius acids are Brønsted-Lowry acids and all Brønsted-Lowry acids are Arrhenius acids when in aqueous solution.
**103.** A solution having a pH of 3.0 has a hydrogen-ion concentration of $1.00 \times 10^{-3} M$. Substitute $1.00 \times 10^{-3} M$ for $[H^+]$ in the expression $K_w = [H^+][OH^-]$. $[OH^-] = 1.00 \times 10^{-11} M$; pOH = 11.
**104.** pH = 6.7675
**105.** See the Solutions Manual.

---

**106.** $C_2H_5NH_3^+(aq) \rightleftharpoons H^+(aq) + C_2H_5NH_2(aq)$
When an acid is added, the buffer equilibrium shifts to the left. When a base is added, the added $OH^-$ ions react with $H^+$ ions and the reaction shifts to the right

## Cumulative Review
**109.** bond polarity and molecular shape
**110.** 1240 kJ/mol

## Standardized Test Practice
**1.** b     **6.** a
**2.** c     **7.** d
**3.** a     **8.** c
**4.** d     **9.** b
**5.** c     **10.** b

**National Science Content Standards**
**Pages 632–633**
UCP.2, UCP.3, UCP.4; B.2, B.3, B.4

# Resource Manager

| Section | Objectives | Activities/Features |
|---|---|---|
| **Section 20.1**<br>**Oxidation and Reduction**<br>1 session<br>🎞 1/2 block | **1. Describe** the processes of oxidation and reduction.<br>**2. Identify** oxidizing and reducing agents.<br>**3. Determine** the oxidation number of an element in a compound.<br>**4. Interpret** redox reactions in terms of change in oxidation state. | **Discovery Lab:** Observing an Oxidation-Reduction Reaction, p. 635<br>**Biology Connection,** p. 637<br>**MiniLab:** Cleaning by Redox, p. 638<br>**Careers Using Chemistry:** Photochemical Etching Artist, p. 641 |
| **Section 20.2**<br>**Balancing Redox Equations**<br>1 1/2 sessions<br>🎞 1 block | **5. Relate** changes in oxidation numbers to the transfer of electrons.<br>**6. Use** changes in oxidation number to balance redox equations.<br>**7. Balance** net ionic redox equations by the oxidation-number method. | **Problem-Solving Lab:** How does redox lift a space shuttle? p. 647 |
| **Section 20.3**<br>**Half-Reactions**<br>2 1/2 sessions<br>🎞 1 1/2 blocks | **8. Recognize** the interdependence of oxidation and reduction processes.<br>**9. Derive** oxidation and reduction half-reactions from a redox equation.<br>**10. Balance** redox equations by the half-reaction method. | **ChemLab:** Redox Reactions, pp. 654–655<br>**How It Works:** Photographic Film, p. 656 |

# CHAPTER 20 RESOURCE MANAGER

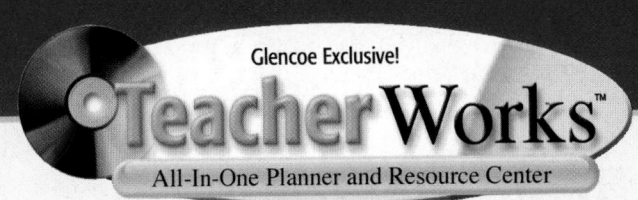

Glencoe Exclusive!
**TeacherWorks**™
All-In-One Planner and Resource Center

| National Science Content Standards | State/Local Standards | Reproducible Masters | Transparencies |
|---|---|---|---|
| UCP.1, UCP.3; A.1; B.1, B.2, B.3; E.2; G.2 | | **Study Guide for Content Mastery,** pp. 115–116 L2<br>**ChemLab and MiniLab Worksheets,** p. 77 L2<br>**Laboratory Manual,** pp. 153–156 L2<br>**CBL Laboratory Manual,** pp. 37–40 L2 | **Section Focus** Transparency 75 L1 ELL<br>**Teaching** Transparencies 59, 60 L2 ELL |
| UCP.1, UCP.3; A.1; B.2, B.3; E.1, E.2; F.6 | | **Study Guide for Content Mastery,** pp. 117–118 L2<br>**Laboratory Manual,** pp. 157–160 L2<br>**Small-Scale Laboratory Manual,** pp. 73–76 L2 | **Section Focus** Transparency 76 L1 ELL<br>**Teaching** Transparency 61 L2 ELL |
| UCP.1, UCP.3; A.1; B.1, B.2, B.3, B.6; E.2 | | **Study Guide for Content Mastery,** pp. 119–120 L2<br>**ChemLab and MiniLab Worksheets,** pp. 78–80 L2<br>**Challenge Problems,** p. 20 L3 | **Section Focus** Transparency 77 L1 ELL<br>**Teaching** Transparency 62 L2 ELL |

**Key to National Science Content Standards:** UCP = Unifying Concepts and Processes, A = Science as Inquiry, B = Physical Science, C = Life Science, D = Earth and Space Sciences, E = Science and Technology, F = Science in Personal and Social Perspectives, G = History and Nature of Science

Refer to pages 4T–5T of the Teacher Guide for an explanation of the National Science Content Standards correlations.

# Resource Manager

## Materials List

### ChemLab (pages 654–655)
copper metal, 6$M$ nitric acid ($HNO_3$), evaporating dish, forceps, distilled water, dropping pipette, household ammonia, crystal drain cleaner, thermometer, 250-mL beaker, watchglass, spoon

### Discovery Lab (page 635)
test tube, iron nail, steel wool, 1$M$ copper(II) sulfate ($CuSO_4$)

### MiniLab (page 638)
aluminum foil, steel wool, small tarnished silver object, 400-mL beaker, baking soda ($NaHCO_3$), table salt ($NaCl$), hot plate, wood splint, beaker tongs, spoon, water

### Demonstration (pages 636–637)
$AgNO_3$ (12.8 g), KOH (3.4 g), dextrose (2.3 g), 15$M$ $NH_3$(aq), concentrated (16$M$) $HNO_3$ (50 mL), 600-mL beaker, dropper, 250-mL graduated cylinder, stirring rod, 1.5 L distilled water, 1-L Erlenmeyer flask with stopper

## Preparation of Solutions

For a review of solution preparation, see page 46T of the Teacher Guide.

Quantities are for a class of 30 students.

### ChemLab (pages 654–655)
**6$M$ nitric acid** Slowly add 380 mL concentrated (16$M$) $HNO_3$ to 500 mL distilled water. Make up to 1 L final volume with distilled water. **CAUTION:** Do NOT add the water to the acid.

### Discovery Lab (page 635)
**1$M$ copper(II) sulfate** Dissolve 25 g copper(II) sulfate pentahydrate ($CuSO_4 \cdot 5H_2O$) in 70 mL distilled water. Make up to 100 mL final volume with distilled water.

### Demonstration (pages 636–637)
**CAUTION:** Prepare fresh solutions for each demonstration. To dispose, dilute mixed solution with large quantities of water and flush immediately. The leftover mixed solution forms an explosive precipitate if allowed to stand for several hours.

**Solution A** Dissolve 12.8 g silver nitrate ($AgNO_3$) in 150 mL distilled water. **CAUTION:** This solution is toxic.

**Solution B** Dissolve 3.4 g potassium hydroxide (KOH) in 75 mL distilled water.

**Solution C** Dissolve 2.3 g dextrose in 50 mL distilled water.

## Assessment Resources

**Chapter Assessment,** pp. 115–120
**MindJogger Videoquizzes** DVD/VHS
**Alternate Assessment in the Science Classroom**
**ExamView® Pro CD-ROM**
**Solutions Manual,** Chapter 20
**Supplemental Problems,** Chapter 20
**Performance Assessment in the Science Classroom**
**Chemistry Interactive CD-ROM,** Chapter 20 quiz

## Additional Resources

**Spanish Resources** ELL
**Guided Reading Audio Program,** Chapter 20 ELL
**Cooperative Learning in the Science Classroom**
**Lab and Safety Skills in the Science Classroom**
**Lesson Plans**
**Block Scheduling Lesson Plans**
**Chemistrymc.com**

## Glencoe Technology

The following multimedia for this chapter are available from Glencoe.

**VIDEOTAPE/DVD**
MindJogger Videoquizzes,
Chapter 20

**CD-ROM**
**Chemistry: Matter and Change**
*An Oxidation–Reduction Reaction,*
  Animation
*Titrate Using Redox,* Experiment
*Forming Crystals by Redox,* Demonstration
*Tollen's Silver Mirror Test,* Demonstration
*Iron Smelting,* Video
*Chemistry of Photography,* Video

**CD-ROM**
**ExamView® Pro**
**Testmaker**

**CD-ROM**
**Interactive Chalkboard**

**CD-ROM**
**TeacherWorks™**

## Multiple Learning Styles

Look for the following icons for strategies that emphasize different learning modalities.

**Visual-Spatial**
Chemistry Journal, p. 638; Reteach, p. 643;
Extension, p. 643; Differentiated Instruction, p. 644;
Cultural Diversity, p. 651

**Interpersonal**
Identifying Misconceptions, p. 636

**Intrapersonal**
Differentiated Instruction, pp. 639, 642;
Reinforcement, p. 641; Check for Understanding,
p. 649; Chemistry Journal, p. 652

**Linguistic**
Chemistry Journal, pp. 640, 646; Quick Demo,
p. 650; Check for Understanding, p. 653

## Key to Teaching Strategies

**L1** Level 1 activities should be appropriate for students with
learning difficulties.

**L2** Level 2 activities should be within the ability range of
all students.

**L3** Level 3 activities are designed for above-average students.

**ELL** ELL activities should be within the ability range of
English Language Learners.

**COOP LEARN** Cooperative Learning activities are designed
for small group work.

**P** These strategies represent student products that can be
placed into a best-work portfolio.

These strategies are useful in a block scheduling format.

## Assessment Planner

**Portfolio Assessment**
Assessment, TWE, pp. 648,
  649, 657
ChemLab, TWE, p. 655

**Performance Assessment**
Assessment, TWE, p. 639
Discovery Lab, SE, p. 635
MiniLab, SE, p. 638
ChemLab, SE, pp. 654–655

**Knowledge Assessment**
Assessment, TWE, p. 651
MiniLab, TWE, p. 638
Problem-Solving Lab, TWE,
  p. 647
Section Assessment, SE,
  pp. 643, 649, 653
Chapter Assessment, SE,
  pp. 658–661

**Skill Assessment**
Assessment, TWE, pp. 643,
  648, 653
Demonstration, TWE, p. 637

## Tying to Previous Knowledge

Have students review the following concepts before studying this chapter.
Chapter 9: electronegativity
Chapter 10: chemical reactions and types of reactions

## Using the Photo

This bombardier beetle's defense mechanism involves combining two chemicals that undergo a redox reaction, resulting in a chemical "sting" that wards off predators. Chemistry plays a key role in defending nature's creatures. Discuss with students some other organisms that may have a chemical defense mechanism. Among others, examples might include venomous snakes, deadly tree frogs, and skunks.

## PowerPoint® Presentations

This CD-ROM is an editable Microsoft® PowerPoint® presentation that includes:
• Section presentations
• Section checks
• Image bank
• Links to Chemistry Online
• All transparencies
• Animations
• Audio

---

# Redox Reactions

## What You'll Learn

▶ You will examine the processes of oxidation and reduction in electron-transfer reactions.

▶ You will discover how oxidation numbers of elements in compounds are determined and how they relate to electron transfer.

▶ You will separate redox reactions into their oxidation and reduction processes.

▶ You will use two different methods to balance oxidation–reduction equations.

## Why It's Important

Oxidation and reduction reactions are among the most prevalent in chemistry. From natural phenomena to commercial manufacturing, redox reactions play a major role in your daily life.

Visit the Chemistry Web site at chemistrymc.com to find links about redox reactions.

When threatened, the bombardier beetle sprays chemicals from its abdomen that, when combined, undergo an oxidation–reduction reaction. The result is a boiling-hot, foul-smelling "bomb" that allows the beetle to escape predators.

---

## DISCOVERY LAB

### Purpose
Students will observe a redox reaction.

### Safety and Disposal
Solutions can be rinsed down the drain with large amounts of water. Dispose of solutions separately; do not mix solutions in the drain. If your school is on a septic system, do not dispose of chemicals down the drain. Check with local EPA authorities for proper disposal methods.
The copper-coated nails can be thrown in the trash.

### Teaching Strategies
• Prepare $CaSO_4$ in advance. See page 634C for preparation of all solutions.
• Remind students that the reaction is also a single replacement reaction. Ask them to explain why.

### Expected Results
The iron replaces the copper ions in solution, allowing copper metal to form on the nail. The blue copper(II) sulfate solution will turn colorless.

### Analysis
Copper metal is found on the nail. The solution turns from blue to colorless. $Fe + CuSO_4 \rightarrow Cu + FeSO_4$. The iron loses electrons and becomes iron ions in solution.

## DISCOVERY LAB

### Observing an Oxidation–Reduction Reaction

Rust is the result of a reaction of iron and oxygen. Iron nails can also react with substances other than oxygen, as you will find out in this experiment.

**Safety Precautions**

 Always wear safety goggles and an apron in the laboratory.

**Procedure**

1. Use a piece of steel wool to polish the end of an iron nail.
2. Add about 3 mL 1.0$M$ CuSO$_4$ to a test tube. Place the polished end of the nail into the CuSO$_4$ solution. Let stand and observe for about 10 minutes. Record your observations.

**Analysis**

What is the substance found clinging to the nail? What happened to the color of the copper(II) sulfate solution? Write the balanced chemical equation for the reaction you observed.

**Materials**
test tube
iron nail
steel wool or sandpaper
1$M$ copper(II) sulfate (CuSO$_4$)

---

Before presenting the lesson, display **Section Focus Transparency 75** on the overhead projector. Have students answer the accompanying questions using **Section Focus Transparency Master 75.** **L1** **ELL**

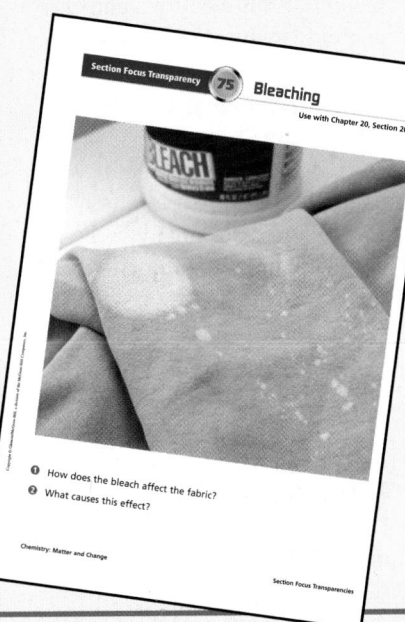

Section Focus Transparency **75** Bleaching
Use with Chapter 20, Section 20.1

❶ How does the bleach affect the fabric?
❷ What causes this effect?

Chemistry: Matter and Change

Section Focus Transparencies

---

**Section** 20.1

# Oxidation and Reduction

## Objectives

- **Describe** the processes of oxidation and reduction.
- **Identify** oxidizing and reducing agents.
- **Determine** the oxidation number of an element in a compound.
- **Interpret** redox reactions in terms of change in oxidation state.

## Vocabulary

oxidation–reduction reaction
redox reaction
oxidation
reduction
oxidizing agent
reducing agent

In Chapter 10, you learned that a chemical reaction can usually be classified as one of five types—synthesis, decomposition, combustion, single-replacement, or double-replacement. In this chapter, you'll investigate a special characteristic of many of these reactions—the ability of elements to gain or lose electrons when they react with other elements. You experimented with this characteristic when you did the **DISCOVERY LAB**.

## Electron Transfer and Redox Reactions

One of the defining characteristics of single-replacement and combustion reactions is that they always involve the transfer of electrons from one atom to another. So do many, but not all, synthesis and decomposition reactions. For example, you studied the synthesis reaction in which sodium and chlorine react to form the ionic compound sodium chloride.

Complete chemical equation: $2Na(s) + Cl_2(g) \rightarrow 2NaCl(s)$

Net ionic equation: $2Na(s) + Cl_2(g) \rightarrow 2Na^+ + 2Cl^-$ (ions in crystal)

In this reaction, an electron from each of two sodium atoms is transferred to the Cl$_2$ molecule to form two Cl$^-$ ions. An example of a combustion reaction is the burning of magnesium in air.

Complete chemical equation: $2Mg(s) + O_2(g) \rightarrow 2MgO(s)$

Net ionic equation: $2Mg(s) + O_2(g) \rightarrow 2Mg^{2+} + 2O^{2-}$ (ions in crystal)

20.1 Oxidation and Reduction **635**

## Chapter Themes

The following themes from the National Science Education Standards are covered in this chapter. Refer to page 4T of the Teacher Guide for an explanation of the correlations.
Evidence, models, and explanation (UCP. 2)
Change, constancy, and measurement (UCP. 3)
Form and function (UCP. 5)

---

### Resource Manager

**Study Guide for Content Mastery,** pp. 115–116 **L2**
**Solving Problems: A Chemistry Handbook,** Section 20.1 **L2**
**Section Focus Transparency 75 and Master** **L1** **ELL**
**Teaching Transparency 59 and Master** **L2** **ELL**

**National Science Content Standards**

**Pages 634–635**
UCP.1, UCP.3; A.1; B.1, B.3

One of the most common mistakes students make is to confuse oxidation and reduction definitions.

### Uncover the Misconception
Students tend to think that reduction involves a loss of electrons because students lose weight when they reduce. Remind them that the oxidation number increases when an element loses electrons and decreases when an element gains electrons.

### Demonstrate the Concept
Be sure to reinforce this concept early by providing students with examples of half-reactions. Have them determine which atom's oxidation number has increased or decreased, whether electrons are lost or gained during the process, and correctly label the half-reaction as an oxidation or reduction process.

### Assess New Knowledge
*Interpersonal* Have small groups of students develop an analogy that illustrates each of the following terms: oxidation, reduction, oxidizing agent, and reducing agent. Have them present their analogies to the class.

**National Science Content Standards**

Pages 636–637
UCP.1, UCP.3; B.1, B.3; G.2

**Figure 20-1**

The reaction of magnesium and oxygen involves a transfer of electrons from magnesium to oxygen. Therefore, this reaction is an oxidation–reduction reaction. Using the classifications given in Chapter 10, this redox reaction also is classified as a combustion reaction.

**Figure 20-2**

Like the reaction shown in **Figure 20-1**, this reaction of chlorine and bromine in an aqueous solution is also a redox reaction. Here, electrons are transferred from bromide ions to chlorine.

When magnesium reacts with oxygen, as illustrated in **Figure 20-1**, each magnesium atom transfers two electrons to each oxygen atom. What is the result of this electron transfer? The two magnesium atoms become $Mg^{2+}$ ions and the two oxygen atoms become $O^{2-}$ ions (oxide ions). If you compare this reaction with the reaction of sodium and chlorine, you will see that they are alike in that both involve the transfer of electrons between atoms. A reaction in which electrons are transferred from one atom to another is called an **oxidation–reduction reaction**. For simplicity, chemists often refer to oxidation–reduction reactions as **redox reactions**.

Now consider the single-replacement reaction in which chlorine in an aqueous solution replaces bromine from an aqueous solution of potassium bromide, which is shown in **Figure 20-2**.

Complete chemical equation: $2KBr(aq) + Cl_2(aq) \rightarrow 2KCl(aq) + Br_2(aq)$

Net ionic equation: $2Br^-(aq) + Cl_2(aq) \rightarrow Br_2(aq) + 2Cl^-(aq)$

Note that chlorine "steals" electrons from bromide ions to become chloride ions. When the bromide ions lose their extra electrons, the two bromine atoms form a covalent bond with each other to produce $Br_2$ molecules. The result of this reaction, the characteristic color of elemental bromine in solution, is shown in **Figure 20-2**. The formation of the covalent bond by sharing of electrons also is an oxidation–reduction reaction.

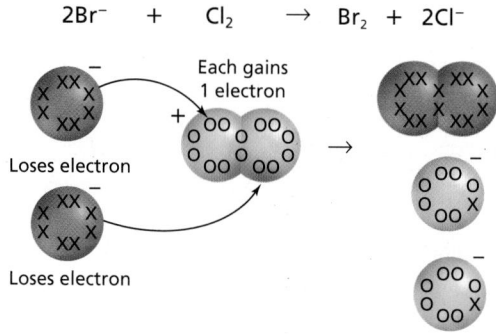

---

### Demonstration

## Tollen's Silver Mirror Test

### Purpose
Students will see how a reducing sugar changes the $Ag^+$ ion into an Ag metal mirror.

### Materials
(A) $AgNO_3$ (12.8 g); (B) KOH (3.4 g);
(C) dextrose (D-glucose $C_6H_{12}O_6$, 2.3g); $15M$ $NH_3(aq)$; concentrated nitric acid (50 mL); beaker (600-mL); dropper; stoppered container to be silvered (1- to 2-L); graduated cylinder; stirring rod; distilled water (1.5 L)
See p. 634C for preparation of all solutions.

### Safety Precautions 🥽 🔥 🧪 ☠ 🧤 ✋
Always wear goggles in the laboratory.

Nitric acid is corrosive. Use caution.

**Disposal** Remove Ag from inside of container with 50 mL of $1M$ $HNO_3$; recover $AgNO_3$ by evaporation.

### Procedure
Place 150 mL of A into a 600-mL beaker. Add 75 mL of B to the beaker. Slowly add enough $15M$ $NH_3(aq)$ with stirring to just dissolve the precipitate. The container to be silvered must be very clean. Rinse it with

**How do oxidation and reduction differ?** Originally, the word *oxidation* referred only to reactions in which a substance combined with oxygen, such as the burning of magnesium in air or the burning of natural gas (methane, $CH_4$) in air. Today, **oxidation** is defined as the loss of electrons from atoms of a substance. Look again at the net ionic equation for the reaction of sodium and chlorine. Sodium is oxidized because it loses an electron. To state this reaction more clearly,

$$Na \rightarrow Na^+ + e^-$$

For oxidation to take place, the electrons lost by the substance that is oxidized must be accepted by atoms or ions of another substance. In other words, there must be an accompanying process that involves the gain of electrons. **Reduction** is defined as the gain of electrons by atoms of a substance. Following our sodium chloride example further, the reduction reaction that accompanies the oxidation of sodium is the reduction of chlorine.

$$Cl_2 + 2e^- \rightarrow 2Cl^-$$

Can oxidation occur without reduction? By our definitions, oxidation and reduction are complementary processes; oxidation cannot occur unless reduction also occurs.

It is important to recognize and distinguish between oxidation and reduction. The following memory aid may help.

**LEO** the lion says **GER** or, for short, **LEO GER**

This phrase will help you remember that **L**oss of **E**lectrons is **O**xidation, and **G**ain of **E**lectrons is **R**eduction.

**Changes in oxidation number** You may recall from previous chapters that the *oxidation number* of an atom in an ionic compound is the number of electrons lost or gained by the atom when it forms ions. For example, look at the following equation for the redox reaction of potassium metal with bromine vapor.

Complete chemical equation: $2K(s) + Br_2(g) \rightarrow 2KBr(s)$

Net ionic equation: $2K(s) + Br_2(g) \rightarrow 2K^+(s) + 2Br^-(s)$

Potassium, a group 1A element that tends to lose one electron in reactions because of its low electronegativity, is assigned an oxidation number of $+1$. On the other hand, bromine, a group 7A element that tends to gain one electron in reactions because of its high electronegativity, is assigned an oxidation number of $-1$. In redox terms, you would say that potassium atoms are oxidized from 0 to the $+1$ state because each loses an electron, and bromine atoms are reduced from 0 to the $-1$ state because each gains an electron. Can you see why the term reduction is used? When an atom or ion is reduced, the numerical value of its oxidation number is lowered.

Oxidation numbers are tools that scientists use in written chemical equations to help them keep track of the movement of electrons in a redox reaction. Like some of the other tools you have learned about in chemistry, oxidation numbers have a specific notation. Oxidation numbers are written with the positive or negative sign before the number ($+3$, $+2$), whereas ionic charge is written with the sign after the number ($3+$, $2+$).

Oxidation number: $+3$     Ionic charge: $3+$

50 mL conc. nitric acid and then rinse thoroughly with distilled water. Pour 50 mL of C and the entire contents of the beaker ($AgNO_3$ + KOH + $NH_3$) into the vessel to be silvered. Rotate and tilt the stoppered container to keep all of the surfaces wet. After a minute or two, a silver mirror will begin to form. Continue to rotate and tilt until the mirror completely covers the inside surface. Pour out the reaction mixture and rinse the inside of the

container two times with tap water.

**Results**
$Ag^+$ is reduced to $Ag^0$, which is deposited on the inside of the reaction vessel.

**Analysis**
What is the complementary oxidation reaction? The aldehyde group from the dextrose is oxidized to a carboxylic acid.

## miniLAB

### Purpose

Students will use a redox reaction to clean tarnish from a silver spoon or other silver object.

### Process Skills

Applying concepts, comparing and contrasting, observing and inferring

### Safety Precautions

Use care when boiling the water on the hotplate. Do not let the water boil away. Add water if needed.

### Disposal

If your school participates in a local recycling program, the aluminum foil can be deposited in the aluminum collection bin. Otherwise, it can be disposed of in the regular trash.

### Teaching Strategies

• If you do not have a tarnished silver object, spread mayonnaise or mustard, both of which contain sulfides, on a silver or a silver-plated object and leave it overnight. Rinse the object with water and wipe off all residues of the mayonnaise or mustard.

• Explain that the tarnishing compound in the environment is primarily hydrogen sulfide. It is formed from the decay of plant and animal material, and from industrial processes.

### Expected Results

The tarnish is removed from the entire object, not just the part contacting the aluminum.

### Analysis

1. $2Ag + H_2S \rightarrow Ag_2S + H_2$
2. $3Ag_2S + 2Al \rightarrow 6Ag + Al_2S_3$
3. Aluminum has the greater oxidation potential because it is oxidized in the reaction while silver is reduced.
4. The aluminum pan would deteriorate.

### ✔ Assessment

**Knowledge** Consider the knowledge gained by this lab and investigate how cleaning by oxidation–reduction might apply to objects other than tarnished silver.

**638**

---

**Figure 20-3**

A redox reaction involving silver and environmental sulfides deposited tarnish on the discolored cup. Another redox reaction, essentially the reverse of the first, reduces silver ions in the tarnish to silver atoms that can be rinsed away, leaving the shiny silver cup.

See page 961 in Appendix E for **Kitchen Oxidation**

## miniLAB

### Cleaning by Redox

**Applying Concepts** The tarnish on silver is silver sulfide, which is formed when the silver reacts with sulfide compounds in the environment. In this miniLAB you will use an oxidation–reduction reaction to remove the tarnish from silver or a silver-plated object.

**Materials** aluminum foil, steel wool, small tarnished silver object, 400-mL beaker (or size large enough to hold the tarnished object), baking soda, table salt, hot plate, beaker tongs

### Procedure

1. Buff a piece of aluminum foil lightly with steel wool to remove any oxide coating.
2. Wrap the tarnished object in the aluminum foil, making sure that the tarnished area makes firm contact with the foil.
3. Place the wrapped object in the beaker and add sufficient tap water to cover.
4. Add about 1 spoonful of baking soda and about 1 spoonful of table salt.
5. Set the beaker and contents on a hot plate and heat until the water is nearly boiling. Maintain the heat approximately 15 min until the tarnish disappears.

### Analysis

1. Write the equation for the reaction of silver with hydrogen sulfide, yielding silver sulfide and hydrogen.
2. Write the equation for the reaction of the tarnish (silver sulfide) with the aluminum foil, yielding aluminum sulfide and silver.
3. Which metal, aluminum or silver, is more reactive? How do you know this from your results?
4. Why should you not use an aluminum pan to clean silver objects by this method?

**638** Chapter 20 Redox Reactions

---

## Oxidizing and Reducing Agents

Chemists also describe the potassium–bromine reaction in another way by saying that "potassium is oxidized by bromine." This description is useful because it clearly identifies both the substance that is oxidized and the substance that does the oxidizing. The substance that oxidizes another substance by accepting its electrons is called an **oxidizing agent**. This term is another way of saying "the substance that is reduced." The substance that reduces another substance by losing electrons is called a **reducing agent**. A reducing agent supplies electrons to the substance getting reduced (gaining electrons), and is itself oxidized because it loses electrons. By this definition, the reducing agent in the potassium–bromine reaction is potassium, the substance that is oxidized.

$$\overbrace{2K(s) + Br_2(g)}^{\text{oxidized}} \rightarrow 2KBr(s)$$
$$\underbrace{\qquad\qquad}_{\text{reduced}}$$

A common application of redox chemistry is to remove tarnish from metal objects, such as the silver cups in **Figure 20-3**. The **miniLAB** below describes this tarnish removal technique. Other oxidizing and reducing agents such as those shown in **Figure 20-4** play significant roles in your daily life. For example, when you add chlorine bleach to your laundry to whiten clothes, you are using an aqueous solution of sodium hypochlorite (NaClO), an oxidizing agent. It oxidizes dyes, stains, and other materials that discolor clothes. Hydrogen peroxide ($H_2O_2$) can be used as an antiseptic because it oxidizes some of the vital biomolecules of germs, or as an agent to lighten hair because it oxidizes the dark pigment of the hair.

---

## CHEMISTRY JOURNAL

### Chemistry in Cartoons

 **Visual-Spatial** Have students draw a cartoon or brief comic strip story of an atom losing an electron to another atom. Have them include in their story captions describing which atom is oxidized and which atom is reduced. **L2** **ELL**

---

## Resource Manager

ChemLab and MiniLab Worksheets, p. 77 **L2**
Lab Manual, pp. 153–156 **L2**
CBL Lab Manual, pp. 37–40 **L2**

Figure 20-4

Each of these images illustrates a common use of redox chemistry. **a** Hydrogen peroxide sanitizes wounds by a redox reaction that kills germs and bacteria. **b** Photography also uses a series of redox reactions in the image capture and development processes. The feature **How It Works** at the end of this chapter describes how redox reactions are used in photography. **c** Chlorine is a strong oxidizer that is used in chlorine bleach to whiten laundry.

## Redox and Electronegativity

The chemistry of oxidation–reduction reactions is not limited to atoms of an element changing to ions or the reverse. Some redox reactions involve changes in molecular substances or polyatomic ions in which atoms are covalently bonded to other atoms. For example, the following equation represents the redox reaction used to manufacture ammonia.

$$N_2(g) + 3H_2(g) \rightarrow 2NH_3(g)$$

This process involves neither ions nor any obvious transfer of electrons. The reactants and products are all molecular compounds. Still, it is a redox reaction in which nitrogen is the oxidizing agent and hydrogen is the reducing agent.

In situations such as the formation of $NH_3$ where two atoms share electrons, how is it possible to say that one atom lost electrons and was oxidized while the other atom gained electrons and was reduced? The answer is that you have to know which atom attracts electrons more strongly, or, in other words, which atom is more electronegative. You might find it helpful to review the discussion of electronegativity trends in Chapters 6 and 8. **Table 20-1** gives the specific electronegativities for hydrogen and nitrogen.

**Table 20-1**

| Electronegativity of Hydrogen and Nitrogen | |
|---|---|
| Hydrogen | 2.20 |
| Nitrogen | 3.04 |

Reduced (partial gain of e⁻)

$$N_2(g) + 3H_2(g) \rightarrow 2NH_3(g)$$

Oxidized (partial loss of e⁻)

For the purpose of studying oxidation–reduction reactions, the more electronegative atom (nitrogen) is treated as if it had been reduced by gaining electrons from the other atom. The less electronegative atom (hydrogen) is treated as if it had been oxidized by losing electrons.

20.1 Oxidation and Reduction **639**

## Tying to Previous Knowledge

Review with students the concept of electronegativity from Chapter 9. Pick several polyatomic ions with which your students are familiar, have them look up the electronegativity values, and remind them that the atom with the higher electronegativity value will be the more negative element when assigning oxidation numbers. **L2**

## ✓ Assessment

**Performance** Have students choose a metal to investigate. Have them research its primary ore and how the metal is extracted and purified from the ore. Oxidizing and reducing agents in each reaction should be identified. Students can give oral reports to the class. Use the Performance Task Assessment List for Oral Presentation in **PASC**, p. 71. **L2**

## GLENCOE TECHNOLOGY

**CD-ROM**
**Chemistry: Matter and Change**
Experiment: *Titrate Using Redox*
Demonstration: *Forming Crystals by Redox*
Demonstration: *Tollen's Silver Mirror Test*
Video: *Iron Smelting*
Video: *Chemistry of Photography*

**EXAMPLE PROBLEM 20-1**

### Identifying Oxidation–Reduction Reactions

The following equation represents the redox reaction of aluminum and iron.

$$2Al + 2Fe^{3+} + 3O^{2-} \rightarrow 2Fe + 2Al^{3+} + 3O^{2-}$$

Identify what is oxidized and what is reduced in this reaction. Identify the oxidizing agent and the reducing agent.

**1. Analyze the Problem**

You are given the ions in the reaction. Using this information, you must determine the electron transfers that take place. Then you can apply the definitions of oxidizing agent and reducing agent to answer the question.

**2. Solve for the Unknown**

Identify the oxidation process and the reduction process by evaluating the electron transfer. In this case, aluminum loses three electrons and becomes an aluminum ion in the oxidation process. The iron ion accepts the three electrons lost from aluminum in the reduction process.

$Al \rightarrow Al^{3+} + 3e^-$ (loss of $e^-$ is oxidation)

$Fe^{3+} + 3e^- \rightarrow Fe$ (gain of $e^-$ is reduction)

Aluminum is oxidized and therefore is the reducing agent. Iron is reduced and therefore is the oxidizing agent.

**3. Evaluate the Answer**

In this process aluminum lost electrons and is oxidized, whereas iron gained electrons and is reduced. The definitions of oxidation and reduction and oxidizing agent and reducing agent apply. Note that the oxidation number of oxygen is unchanged in this reaction; therefore, oxygen is not a key factor in this problem.

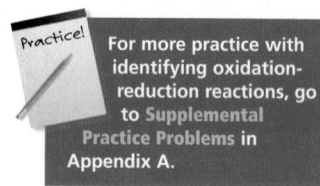

For more practice with identifying oxidation-reduction reactions, go to **Supplemental Practice Problems** in Appendix A.

**PRACTICE PROBLEMS**

**1.** Identify each of the following changes as either oxidation or reduction. Recall that $e^-$ is the symbol for an electron.

   **a.** $I_2 + 2e^- \rightarrow 2I^-$
   **b.** $K \rightarrow K^+ + e^-$
   **c.** $Fe^{2+} \rightarrow Fe^{3+} + e^-$
   **d.** $Ag^+ + e^- \rightarrow Ag$

**2.** Identify what is oxidized and what is reduced in the following processes.

   **a.** $2Br^- + Cl_2 \rightarrow Br_2 + 2Cl^-$
   **b.** $2Ce + 3Cu^{2+} \rightarrow 3Cu + 2Ce^{3+}$
   **c.** $2Zn + O_2 \rightarrow 2ZnO$

**3.** Identify the oxidizing agent and the reducing agent in each of the following reactions.

   **a.** $Mg + I_2 \rightarrow MgI_2$
   **b.** $2Na + 2H^+ \rightarrow 2Na^+ + H_2$
   **c.** $H_2S + Cl_2 \rightarrow S + 2HCl$

# Determining Oxidation Numbers

In order to understand all kinds of redox reactions, you must have a way to determine the oxidation number of the atoms involved in the reaction. Chemists use a set of rules to make this determination easier.

### Rules for determining oxidation numbers

1. *The oxidation number of an uncombined atom is zero.* This is true for elements that exist as polyatomic molecules such as $O_2$, $Cl_2$, $H_2$, $N_2$, $S_8$.

2. *The oxidation number of a monatomic ion is equal to the charge on the ion.* For example, the oxidation number of a $Ca^{2+}$ ion is $+2$, and the oxidation number of a $Br^-$ ion is $-1$.

3. *The oxidation number of the more electronegative atom in a molecule or a complex ion is the same as the charge it would have if it were an ion.* In ammonia ($NH_3$), for example, nitrogen is more electronegative than hydrogen, meaning that it attracts electrons more strongly than does hydrogen. So nitrogen is assigned an oxidation number of $-3$, as if it had gained three electrons to complete an octet. In the compound silicon tetrachloride ($SiCl_4$), chlorine is more electronegative than silicon, so each chlorine has an oxidation number of $-1$ as if it had taken an electron from silicon. The silicon atom is given an oxidation number of $+4$ as if it had lost electrons to the four chlorine atoms.

4. *The most electronegative element, fluorine, always has an oxidation number of $-1$ when it is bonded to another element.*

5. *The oxidation number of oxygen in compounds is always $-2$, except in peroxides, such as hydrogen peroxide ($H_2O_2$), where it is $-1$. When it is bonded to fluorine, the only element more electronegative than oxygen, the oxidation number of oxygen is $+2$.*

6. *The oxidation number of hydrogen in most of its compounds is $+1$.* The exception to this rule occurs when hydrogen is bonded to less electronegative metals to form hydrides such as LiH, NaH, $CaH_2$, and $AlH_3$. In these compounds, hydrogen's oxidation number is $-1$ because it attracts electrons more strongly than does the metal atom.

7. *The metals of groups 1A and 2A and aluminum in group 3A form compounds in which the metal atom always has a positive oxidation number equal to the number of its valence electrons ($+1$, $+2$, and $+3$, respectively).*

8. *The sum of the oxidation numbers in a neutral compound is zero.* Notice how the oxidation numbers add up to zero in the following examples.

$$(+1) + (-1) = 0 \qquad (+2) + 2(-1) = 0 \qquad 2(+1) + (-2) = 0 \qquad (+4) + 4(-1) = 0$$
$$\text{NaCl} \qquad\qquad \text{CaBr}_2 \qquad\qquad \text{H}_2\text{S} \qquad\qquad \text{CCl}_4$$

9. *The sum of the oxidation numbers of the atoms in a polyatomic ion is equal to the charge on the ion.* The following examples illustrate.

$$(-3) + 4(+1) = +1 \qquad\qquad (+4) + 3(-2) = -2$$
$$\text{NH}_4{}^+ \qquad\qquad\qquad \text{SO}_3{}^{2-}$$

Many elements other than those specified in the rules above, including most of the transition metals, metalloids, and nonmetals, can be found with different oxidation numbers in different compounds. For example, the two copper compounds and the two chromium compounds shown in **Figure 20-5 a** and **b**, respectively, have different oxidation numbers.

**Figure 20-5**

The difference in oxidation number gives compounds different chemical and physical properties.
**a** The oxidation number of copper in copper(I) oxide (orange color) is +1, whereas the oxidation number of copper in copper(II) oxide (black color) is +2.
**b** Likewise, the oxidation number of chromium in chromium(II) chloride tetrahydrate (blue solution) differs from that in chromium(III) chloride hexahydrate (green solution).

**a**

**b**

20.1 Oxidation and Reduction **641**

---

## Internet Address Book

Note Internet addresses that you find useful in the space below for quick reference.

_____

_____

_____

_____

642

## Practice PROBLEMS

Have students refer to Appendix D for complete solutions to Practice Problems.

4. **a.** +7
   **b.** +5
   **c.** +3
5. **a.** −3
   **b.** +5
   **c.** +6

## In-Text Question

**Page 643** How would the reaction differ if you used zinc bromide instead of potassium bromide? There would be no significant change in the reaction if zinc bromide was substituted for potassium bromide because the zinc ion will function as a spectator ion just like the potassium ion did.

# 3 Assess

## Check for Understanding

Give students the following equation: $4Fe + 3O_2 \rightarrow 2Fe_2O_3$. Have them assign oxidation numbers and determine the oxidizing and reducing agents. Fe goes from 0 to +3. Oxygen goes from 0 to −2. Oxygen is the oxidizing agent and is reduced. Iron is the reducing agent and is oxidized. **L2**

**National Science Content Standards**

**Pages 642–643**
UCP.1, UCP.3; B.2, B.3

**642**

## EXAMPLE PROBLEM 20-2

### Determining Oxidation Numbers

Determine the oxidation number of each element in the following compounds or ions.
**a.** $KClO_3$ (potassium chlorate)
**b.** $SO_3^{2-}$ (sulfite ion)

### 1. Analyze the Problem

From the rules for determining oxidation numbers, you are given the oxidation number of oxygen (−2) and potassium (group 1 metal, +1). You are also given the overall charge of the compound or ion. Using this information and applying the rules, you can determine the oxidation numbers of chlorine and sulfur.

### 2. Solve for the Unknown

**Strategy**

Assign the known oxidation numbers to their elements, set the sum of all oxidation numbers to zero or to the ion charge, and solve for the unknown oxidation number. (Let $n_{element}$ = oxidation number of the element in question.)

**Solution**

**a.** Potassium chlorate is a neutral salt, so oxidation numbers must add up to zero. According to rule 5, the oxidation number of oxygen in compounds is −2. Rule 7 states that Group 1 metals have a +1 oxidation number in compounds.

$$(+1) + (n_{Cl}) + 3(-2) = 0$$
$$KClO_3$$
$$1 + n_{Cl} + (-6) = 0$$
$$n_{Cl} = +5$$

**b.** Sulfite ion has a charge of 2−, so oxidation numbers must add up to −2. According to rule 5, the oxidation number of oxygen in compounds is −2.

$$(n_S) + 3(-2) = -2$$
$$SO_3^{2-}$$
$$n_S + (-6) = -2$$
$$n_S = +4$$

### 3. Evaluate the Answer

The rules for determining oxidation numbers have been correctly applied. All of the oxidation numbers in each substance add up to the proper value.

Among other applications, potassium chlorate is used in explosives, fireworks, and matches.

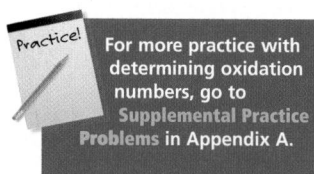

Practice! For more practice with determining oxidation numbers, go to **Supplemental Practice Problems** in Appendix A.

## PRACTICE PROBLEMS

4. Determine the oxidation number of the boldface element in the following formulas for compounds.

   **a.** Na**Cl**O$_4$    **b.** Al**P**O$_4$    **c.** H**N**O$_2$

5. Determine the oxidation number of the boldface element in the following formulas for ions.

   **a.** **N**H$_4^+$    **b.** **As**O$_4^{3-}$    **c.** **Cr**O$_4^{2-}$

## DIFFERENTIATED INSTRUCTION

### Learning Disabled

 *Intrapersonal* For students having difficulty with Practice Problems 4 and 5, have them write the number of the rule for determining oxidation numbers (as given in the text) and state the reason why they chose that rule. This helps students focus on the task at hand and provides them with a more concrete method to help in answering the question. **L1**

# Oxidation Number in Redox Reactions

Having studied oxidation numbers, you are now able to relate oxidation–reduction reactions to changes in oxidation number. Look again at the equation for a reaction that you saw at the beginning of this section, the replacement of bromine in aqueous KBr by $Cl_2$.

$$2KBr(aq) + Cl_2(aq) \rightarrow 2KCl(aq) + Br_2(aq)$$

To see how oxidation numbers change, start by assigning numbers, shown in **Table 20-2,** to all elements in the balanced equation. Then review the changes as shown in the accompanying diagram.

As you can see, the oxidation number of bromine changed from $-1$ to $0$, an increase of 1. At the same time, the oxidation number of chlorine changed from $0$ to $-1$, a decrease of 1. Therefore, chlorine is reduced and bromine is oxidized. All redox reactions follow the same pattern. When an atom is oxidized, its oxidation number increases. When an atom is reduced, its oxidation number decreases. Note that there is no change in the oxidation number of potassium. The potassium ion takes no part in the reaction and is called a spectator ion. How would the reaction differ if you used zinc bromide ($ZnBr_2$) instead of potassium bromide?

**Table 20-2**

| Oxidation Number Assignment | | |
|---|---|---|
| **Element** | **Oxidation number** | **Rule** |
| K in KBr | +1 | 7 |
| Br in KBr | −1 | 8 |
| Cl in $Cl_2$ | 0 | 1 |
| K in KCl | +1 | 7 |
| Cl in KCl | −1 | 8 |
| Br in $Br_2$ | 0 | 1 |

## Section 20.1 Assessment

6. Describe the processes of oxidation and reduction.

7. Explain the roles of oxidizing agents and reducing agents in a redox reaction. How is each changed in the reaction?

8. Determine the oxidation number of the boldface element in these compounds.
   - **a.** $\mathbf{Sb_2}O_5$
   - **b.** $H\mathbf{N}O_3$
   - **c.** $Ca\mathbf{N_2}$
   - **d.** $Cu\mathbf{W}O_4$ (copper(II) tungstate)

9. Determine the oxidation number of the boldface element in these ions.
   - **a.** $\mathbf{I}O_4^-$
   - **b.** $\mathbf{Mn}O_4^-$
   - **c.** $\mathbf{B_4}O_7^{2-}$
   - **d.** $\mathbf{N}H_2^-$

10. **Thinking Critically** Write the equation for the reaction of iron metal with hydrobromic acid to form iron(III) bromide and hydrogen gas. Determine which element is reduced and which element is oxidized in this reaction.

11. **Making Predictions** Alkali metals are strong reducing agents. Would you predict that their reducing ability would increase or decrease as you move down the family from sodium to francium? Give reasons for your prediction.

## Section 20.1 Assessment

6. The process in which an element loses electrons is called oxidation. The process in which an element gains electrons is reduction.

7. An oxidizing agent causes another species to be oxidized by gaining the electrons from it. A reducing agent causes another species to be reduced by losing electrons to that element.

8. **a.** +5; **b.** +5; **c.** −3; **d.** +6

9. **a.** +7; **b.** +7; **c.** +3; **d.** −3

10. $2Fe + 6HBr \rightarrow 2FeBr_3 + 3H_2$
    Fe is oxidized; H is reduced.

11. In general, as you move down the periodic table within a family, the tendency to lose electrons increases so the reducing ability increases. *Note: lithium does not follow the pattern of increasing reducing power in the series.*

## Reteach

*Visual-Spatial* Have students make a chart with two columns. One column should be labeled oxidation and the other column should be labeled reduction. Have the students complete the chart for the following questions.
**a.** What happens to the electrons when oxidation occurs? Reduction?
**b.** What happens to the charge of the atom that undergoes oxidation? Reduction?
**c.** Which process provides the oxidizing agent? Reducing agent? **L2**

## Extension

*Visual-Spatial* Have students research the oxidation–reduction reactions that take place in a blast furnace and make a poster outlining the process. Students should point out the oxidizing and reducing agents in each reaction. **L2 ELL**

## Assessment

**Skill** Provide students with ten compounds in sealed, clear containers. The containers should be labeled with the formula of the compound. Have the students determine the oxidation number of each element in each compound. Try to include compounds that are colored solids. Compounds could include $CuSO_4$, $K_2Cr_2O_7$, $NaNO_3$, $Co(NO_3)_3$, etc. Caution the students that they are not to open the sealed bottles. **L2 ELL**

**643**

# 1 Focus

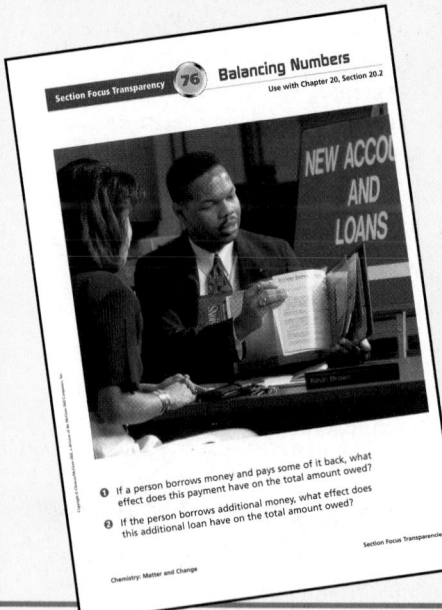

Section Focus Transparency 76 Balancing Numbers
Use with Chapter 20, Section 20.2

NEW ACCOU AND LOANS

① If a person borrows money and pays some of it back, what effect does this payment have on the total amount owed?

② If the person borrows additional money, what effect does this additional loan have on the total amount owed?

Chemistry: Matter and Change

Section Focus Transparencies

# 2 Teach

### Quick Demo

Clean a piece of copper with sandpaper and drop it into several milliliters of 0.1*M* silver nitrate solution in a test tube. Wait several minutes and have the students observe the formation of silver on the copper surface. Write the reaction on the board and ask the students to determine which atom was oxidized, which atom was reduced, which substance was the oxidizing agent, and which was the reducing agent. Silver can be precipitated as AgCl using a solution of NaCl, or check your local school policy for disposal methods of silver nitrate solution.

---

## Objectives

- **Relate** changes in oxidation numbers to the transfer of electrons.
- **Use** changes in oxidation number to balance redox equations.
- **Balance** net ionic redox equations by the oxidation-number method.

## Vocabulary

oxidation-number method

**Figure 20-6**

Some chemical equations for redox reactions, such as this reaction between copper and nitric acid, can be difficult to balance because one or more elements may appear several times on both sides of the equation. The oxidation-number method makes it easier to balance the equation for this redox reaction.

# Balancing Redox Equations

You already know that chemical equations are written to represent chemical reactions by showing what substances react and what products are formed. You also know that chemical equations must be balanced to show the correct quantities of reactants and products. Equations for oxidation–reduction reactions are no different. In this section, you'll learn a specific method to balance redox equations.

## The Oxidation-Number Method

Many equations for redox reactions are easy to balance. For example, try to balance the following unbalanced equation for the redox reaction that occurs when potassium chlorate is heated and decomposes to produce potassium chloride and oxygen gas.

$$\text{Unbalanced equation: } KClO_3(s) \rightarrow KCl(s) + O_2(g)$$

Did you get the correct result shown below?

$$\text{Balanced equation: } 2KClO_3(s) \rightarrow 2KCl(s) + 3O_2(g)$$

Equations for other redox reactions are not as easy to balance. Study the following unbalanced equation for the reaction that occurs when copper metal is placed in concentrated nitric acid. This reaction is shown in **Figure 20-6.** The brown gas you see is nitrogen dioxide ($NO_2$), produced by the reduction of nitrate ions ($NO_3^-$), and the blue solution is the result of the oxidation of copper to copper(II) ions.

$$Cu(s) + HNO_3(aq) \rightarrow Cu(NO_3)_2(aq) + NO_2(g) + H_2O(l)$$

Note that oxygen appears in only one reactant, $HNO_3$, but in all three products. Nitrogen appears in $HNO_3$ and in two of the products. Redox equations such as this one, in which the same element appears in several reactants and products, can be hard to balance by the conventional method. For this reason, you need to learn a different balancing technique for redox equations that is based on the fact that the number of electrons transferred from atoms must equal the number of electrons accepted by other atoms.

As you know, when an atom loses electrons, its oxidation number increases; when an atom gains electrons, its oxidation number decreases. Therefore, the total increase in oxidation numbers (oxidation) must equal the total decrease in oxidation numbers (reduction) of the atoms involved in the reaction. The balancing technique called the **oxidation-number method** is based on these principles. The **CHEMLAB** at the end of this chapter gives you the opportunity to perform and balance the copper–nitric acid redox reaction.

### Steps for balancing redox equations by the oxidation-number method

1. Assign oxidation numbers to all atoms in the equation.
2. Identify the atoms that are oxidized and the atoms that are reduced.
3. Determine the change in oxidation number for the atoms that are oxidized and for the atoms that are reduced.
4. Make the change in oxidation numbers equal in magnitude by adjusting coefficients in the equation.

---

### DIFFERENTIATED INSTRUCTION

#### English Language Learners

*Visual-Spatial* Have students collect pictures from advertisements for various processes that involve redox reactions or that are products of a redox reaction. Examples might include ads showing household bleach and detergents containing bleach, paints, and waxes that prevent rusting, antioxidants found in foods, or cameras and film. Have them name and describe these items in their native language and in English. Also have them look up the derivation of the words *oxidation* and *reduction*. To emphasize the universal language of chemistry, provide the chemical names and symbols for some of the items and point out how they do not change with local language. **L2 ELL**

**5.** If necessary, use the conventional method to balance the remainder of the equation.

You can see these steps clearly by following Example Problem 20-3.

## EXAMPLE PROBLEM 20-3

### Balancing a Redox Equation by the Oxidation-Number Method

Balance the redox equation shown here for the reaction that produces copper nitrate.

$$Cu + HNO_3 \rightarrow Cu(NO_3)_2 + NO_2 + H_2O$$

**1. Analyze the Problem**

You are given the formulas for the reactants and products, and you have the rules for determining oxidation number. You also know that the increase in oxidation number of the oxidized atoms must equal the decrease in oxidation number of the reduced atoms. With this information you can adjust the coefficients to balance the equation.

**2. Solve for the Unknown**

*Step 1.* Apply the appropriate rules on page 641 to assign oxidation numbers to all atoms in the equation.

$$\overset{0}{Cu} + \overset{+1\ +5\ -2}{HNO_3} \rightarrow \overset{+2\ +5\ -2}{Cu(NO_3)_2} + \overset{+4\ -2}{NO_2} + \overset{+1\ -2}{H_2O}$$

*Step 2.* Identify which atoms are oxidized and which are reduced.

$$\overset{0}{Cu} + \overset{+1\ +5\ -2}{HNO_3} \rightarrow \overset{+2\ +5\ -2}{Cu(NO_3)_2} + \overset{+4\ -2}{NO_2} + \overset{+1\ -2}{H_2O}$$

The oxidation number of copper increases from 0 to +2 as it is oxidized in the reaction. The oxidation number of nitrogen decreases from +5 to +4 as it is reduced in the formation of $NO_2$. The oxidation numbers of hydrogen and oxygen do not change. Note that the nitrogen atoms remain unchanged in the nitrate ion ($NO_3^-$), which appears on both sides of the equation. It is neither oxidized nor reduced.

*Step 3.* Draw a line connecting the atoms involved in oxidation and another line connecting the atoms involved in reduction. Write the net change in oxidation number above or below each line.

$$\overset{+2}{Cu + HNO_3 \rightarrow Cu(NO_3)_2 + NO_2 + H_2O}$$
$$_{-1}$$

*Step 4.* Make the changes in oxidation number equal in magnitude by placing the appropriate coefficients in front of the formulas in the equation. Because the oxidation number for nitrogen is $-1$, you must add a coefficient 2 to balance. This coefficient applies to $HNO_3$ on the left and $NO_2$ on the right.

$$\overset{+2}{Cu + 2HNO_3 \rightarrow Cu(NO_3)_2 + 2NO_2 + H_2O}$$
$$_{2(-1) = -2}$$

*Continued on next page*

Copper nitrate ($Cu(NO_3)_2$) is used in light-sensitive paper.

20.2 Balancing Redox Equations     **645**

## CHEMLAB

ChemLab 20, located at the end of the chapter, can be used at this point in the lesson.

### Identifying Misconceptions

Students often want to think about redox in its simplest terms: what is oxidized and what is reduced.

**Uncover the Misconception**
Students may think that when you balance the reactions using hydrogen ions, hydroxide ions, and water, you are inventing these substances for convenience. Remind them that many redox reactions take place in aqueous environments and in the presence of either an acid ($H^+$) or a base ($OH^-$).

**Demonstrate the Concept**
For the first several reactions that you do with the students, write the complete, original reaction that contains the acid/base conditions and water before simplifying the reaction in its net ionic form. Then, show them how to use the net ionic reaction to complete the balancing step. Finally, help them see the connection between the final balanced reaction using the method learned in this section and the original reaction.

**Assess New Knowledge**
Give the students a reaction and have them explain why water and hydrogen ions or hydroxide ions are necessary to balance a redox reaction.

### Resource Manager

**Study Guide for Content Mastery,** pp. 117–118 **L2**
**Solving Problems: A Chemistry Handbook,** Section 20.2 **L2**
**Section Focus Transparency 76 and Master L1 ELL**
**Teaching Transparency 61 and Master L2 ELL**

**National Science Content Standards**

**Pages 644–645**
UCP.1, UCP.3; A.1; B.2, B.3; E.2

**Liftoff** The space shuttle consists of the orbiter, where the astronauts reside; the external tank, which holds approximately two million liters of liquid hydrogen and oxygen; and two solid rocket boosters (SRBs) that each contain 495 000 kg of fuel. The entire system weighs approximately two million kg on the launch pad. The ammonium perchlorate–aluminum reaction is very exothermic, and the products are much more massive than the water reaction taking place in the external tank. When these heavier molecules are expelled, they provide the majority of the lift that propels the shuttle into space.

## Practice PROBLEMS

Have students refer to Appendix D for complete solutions to Practice Problems.

**12.** $3HCl + 2HNO_3 \rightarrow 3HOCl + 2NO + H_2O$
oxidation number of Cl increases from $-1$ to $+1$; oxidation number of N decreases from $+5$ to $+2$

**13.** $3SnCl_4 + 2Fe \rightarrow 3SnCl_2 + 2FeCl_3$
oxidation number of Fe increases from 0 to $+3$; oxidation number of Sn decreases from $+4$ to $+2$

**14.** $8NH_3(g) + 6NO_2(g) \rightarrow 7N_2(g) + 12H_2O(l)$
oxidation number of N increases from $-3$ to 0; oxidation number of N decreases from $+4$ to 0

**National Science Content Standards**

**Pages 646–647**
UCP.1, UCP.3; B.3; E.1, E.2; F.6

---

*Step 5.* Use the conventional method to balance the number of atoms and the charges in the remainder of the equation. This equation shows no charged species, so charge balance need not be considered here.

$$Cu + 2HNO_3 \rightarrow Cu(NO_3)_2 + 2NO_2 + H_2O$$

The coefficient of $HNO_3$ must be increased from 2 to 4 to balance the four nitrogen atoms in the products.

$$Cu + 4HNO_3 \rightarrow Cu(NO_3)_2 + 2NO_2 + H_2O$$

Add a coefficient of 2 to $H_2O$ to balance the four hydrogen atoms on the left.

$$Cu(s) + 4HNO_3(aq) \rightarrow Cu(NO_3)_2(aq) + 2NO_2(g) + 2H_2O(l)$$

**3. Evaluate the Answer**

The number of atoms of each element is equal on both sides of the equation. No subscripts have been changed.

## PRACTICE PROBLEMS

*Practice!* For more practice balancing redox reactions, go to **Supplemental Practice Problems** in Appendix A.

Use the oxidation-number method to balance these redox equations.

**12.** $HCl + HNO_3 \rightarrow HOCl + NO + H_2O$

**13.** $SnCl_4 + Fe \rightarrow SnCl_2 + FeCl_3$

**14.** $NH_3(g) + NO_2(g) \rightarrow N_2(g) + H_2O(l)$

## Balancing Net Ionic Redox Equations

Sometimes chemists prefer to express redox reactions in the simplest possible terms—as an equation showing only the oxidation and reduction processes and nothing else. Look again at the balanced equation for the oxidation of copper by nitric acid.

$$Cu(s) + 4HNO_3(aq) \rightarrow Cu(NO_3)_2(aq) + 2NO_2(g) + 2H_2O(l)$$

Note that the reaction takes place in aqueous solution, so $HNO_3$, which is a strong acid, will be ionized. Likewise, copper(II) nitrate ($Cu(NO_3)_2$) will be dissociated into ions. Therefore, the equation can also be written in ionic form.

$$Cu(s) + 4H^+(aq) + 4NO_3^-(aq) \rightarrow$$
$$Cu^{2+}(aq) + 2NO_3^-(aq) + 2NO_2(g) + 2H_2O(l)$$

You can see that there are four nitrate ions among the reactants, but only two of them undergo change to form two nitrogen dioxide molecules. What is the role of the other nitrate ions? The other two are only spectator ions and can be eliminated from the equation. To simplify things when writing redox equations in ionic form, chemists usually indicate hydrogen ions by $H^+$ with the understanding that they exist in hydrated form as hydronium ions ($H_3O^+$). The equation can then be rewritten showing only the substances that undergo change.

$$Cu(s) + 4H^+(aq) + 2NO_3^-(aq) \rightarrow Cu^{2+}(aq) + 2NO_2(g) + 2H_2O(l)$$

Now look at the equation in unbalanced form.

$$Cu(s) + H^+(aq) + NO_3^-(aq) \rightarrow Cu^{2+}(aq) + NO_2(g) + H_2O(l)$$

## CHEMISTRY JOURNAL

### The Balance of Life

*Linguistic* Have students do a free writing assignment in which they describe the tendency of our environment to be balanced. Students might make a list of things around them that appear balanced or they may write an essay on the importance of balance in our world. Have students describe the consequences of imbalance. **L2**

You might even see this same reaction expressed in a way that shows only the substances that are oxidized and reduced.

$$Cu(s) + NO_3^-(aq) \rightarrow Cu^{2+}(aq) + NO_2(g) \text{ (in acid solution)}$$

In this case, the hydrogen ion and the water molecule are eliminated because neither is oxidized nor reduced. The only additional information needed is that the reaction takes place in acid solution. In acid solution, hydrogen ions ($H^+$) and water molecules are abundant and free to participate in redox reactions as either reactants or products. Some redox reactions can occur only in basic solution. When you balance equations for these reactions, you may add hydroxide ions ($OH^-$) and water molecules to either side of the equation. Basic solutions have an abundance of $OH^-$ ions instead of $H_3O^+$ ions.

If you try to balance the equation given above, you will see that it appears impossible. Net ionic equations can still be balanced, though, by applying the oxidation-number method, as you will see in Example Problem 20-4. The **problem-solving LAB** below shows how the oxidation-number method can be used for a real-world application.

## problem-solving LAB

### How does redox lift a space shuttle?

**Using Numbers** The space shuttle gains nearly 72% of its lift from its solid rocket boosters (SRBs) during the first two minutes of launch. The two pencil-shaped SRB tanks are attached to both sides of the liquid hydrogen and oxygen fuel tank. Each SRB contains 495 000 kg of an explosive mixture of ammonium perchlorate and aluminum. The unbalanced equation for the reaction is given below.

$$NH_4ClO_4(s) + Al(s) \rightarrow$$
$$Al_2O_3(g) + HCl(g) + N_2(g) + H_2O(g)$$

Use the oxidation-number method to balance this redox equation.

### Analysis

The SRB reaction can be balanced using the rules for assigning oxidation numbers. In this way, you can ensure that the oxidation reaction balances the reduction reaction. Write the oxidation number above each element in the equation. Which elements are reduced and which are oxidized? What coefficients are required to balance the reaction?

### Thinking Critically

What are some of the benefits of using SRBs for the first two minutes of launch?

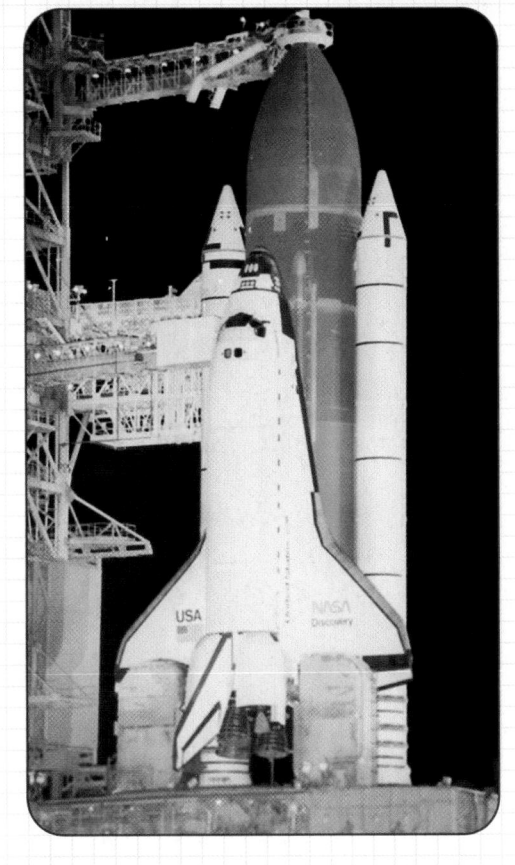

## problem-solving LAB

### Purpose
Students will apply the rules for balancing redox reactions to a challenging and realistic example.

### Process Skills
Using numbers, applying concepts, drawing conclusions, analyzing and concluding

### Teaching Strategies
• Review the gas laws as they apply to volume and temperature and to explosions. Also, explain the action–reaction in the rocket engine. Gases expand with temperature. When the gas hits an upper surface, it forces the shuttle upward (action) while the surface deflects the gas particles downward (reaction). The hotter the gas, the greater the force.

### Analysis

$$\overset{-3\ +1\ +7\ -2}{NH_4ClO_4}(s) + \overset{0}{Al}(s) \rightarrow \overset{+3\ -2}{Al_2O_3}(g) +$$
$$\overset{+1-1}{HCl}(g) + \overset{0}{N_2}(g) + \overset{+1\ -2}{H_2O}(g)$$

The nitrogen and aluminum are oxidized and the chlorine is reduced.

These are the equations for the oxidation and reduction reactions.

$$\overset{-3}{2N} \rightarrow \overset{0}{N_2} + 6e^-$$
$$\overset{-3}{6N} \rightarrow 3\overset{0}{N_2} + 18e^-$$
$$\overset{0}{2Al} \rightarrow \overset{+3}{Al_2} + 6e^-$$
$$\overset{0}{10Al} \rightarrow 5\overset{+3}{Al_2} + 30e^-$$
$$\overset{+7}{Cl} + 8e^- \rightarrow \overset{-1}{Cl}$$
$$\overset{+7}{6Cl} + 48e^- \rightarrow 6\overset{-1}{Cl}$$

Because the chlorine and nitrogen are in the same equation, the coefficient will apply to both. If 6 is used for the ammonium perchlorate and 10 for aluminum, this will balance with 48 electrons making a move in the redox reaction.

Cl and N appear equally in $NH_4ClO_4$, so the coefficient in front of HCl must be the same (6) and is half as much in front of $N_2$ (3). Also, the coefficient in front of Al must be twice as large as the coefficient in front of $Al_2O_3$. The water molecules can be balanced last.

$$6NH_4ClO_4(s) + 10Al(s) \rightarrow 5Al_2O_3(g)$$
$$+ 6HCl(g) + 3N_2(g) + 9H_2O(g)$$

### Thinking Critically
Solid fuel has the densest arrangement of particles; therefore, the tanks can hold more solid fuel than fuel in another state (i.e., liquid). After the enormous amount of solid fuel is burned, the heavy containment vessels are jettisoned, making the shuttle much lighter.

### ✔ Assessment
**Knowledge** Have students balance the following spontaneous propulsion reaction that the shuttle uses in orbit. The propellant is monomethylhydrazine and the oxidizer is dinitrogen tetroxide.
$$N_2O_4 + CH_3N_2H_3 \rightarrow H_2O + N_2 + CO_2$$
In $CH_3N_2H_3$, the oxidation numbers for carbon and nitrogen are –4 and –1, respectively. **L3**

**✓ Skill** Have the students analyze each of these half-reactions and find and correct each mistake.

**a.** $14H^+ + 12e^- + Cr_2O_7{}^{2-} \rightarrow$
$Cr^{3+} + 7H_2O$

**b.** $H_2O + ClO^- + e^- \rightarrow Cl^- + OH^-$

**c.** $4H_2O + Mn^{2+} + 5e^- \rightarrow MnO_4{}^- + 8H^+$

**d.** $I^- \rightarrow I_2 + e^-$

**a.** $14H^+ + 6e^- + Cr_2O_7{}^{2-} \rightarrow 2Cr^{3+} + 7H_2O$

**b.** $H_2O + ClO^- + 2e^- \rightarrow Cl^- + 2OH^-$

**c.** $4H_2O + Mn^{2+} \rightarrow MnO_4{}^- + 5e^- + 8H^+$

**d.** $2I^- \rightarrow I_2 + 2e^-$

## Practice PROBLEMS

Have students refer to Appendix D for complete solutions to Practice Problems.

**15.** $2H^+(aq) + 3H_2S(g) + 2NO_3{}^-(aq) \rightarrow 3S(s) + 2NO(g) + 4H_2O(l)$
oxidation number of S increases from $-2$ to $0$; oxidation number of N decreases from $+5$ to $+2$

**16.** $14H^+(aq) + Cr_2O_7{}^{2-}(aq) + 6I^-(aq) \rightarrow 2Cr^{3+}(aq) + 3I_2(s) + 7H_2O(l)$
oxidation number of I increases from $-1$ to $0$; oxidation number of Cr decreases from $+6$ to $+3$

**17.** $6I^-(aq) + 2MnO_4{}^-(aq) + 4H_2O(l) \rightarrow 3I_2(s) + 2MnO_2(s) + 8OH^-(aq)$
oxidation number of I increases from $-1$ to $0$; oxidation number of Mn decreases from $+7$ to $+4$

Examine the substance.

Element — Monatomic ion

Molecule or polyatomic ion

Oxidation number equals zero. — Oxidation number equals the charge.

Oxidation number of the most electronegative element is the same as the charge it would have as an ion.

Molecule — Polyatomic ion

The sum of the oxidation numbers equals zero. — The sum of the oxidation numbers equals the charge on the ion.

Use this flow chart to review the rules for assigning oxidation numbers listed on page 641.

---

## EXAMPLE PROBLEM 20-4

### Balancing a Net Ionic Redox Equation

Use the oxidation-number method to balance this net ionic redox equation for the reaction between the perchlorate ion and the bromide ion in acid solution.

$$ClO_4{}^-(aq) + Br^-(aq) \rightarrow Cl^-(aq) + Br_2(g) \text{ (in acid solution)}$$

#### 1. Analyze the Problem

You are given the formulas for the reactants and products, and you have the rules for determining oxidation number. You also know that the increase in oxidation number of the oxidized atoms must equal the decrease in oxidation number of the reduced atoms. You are told that the reaction takes place under acidic conditions. With this information you can adjust the coefficients to balance the equation.

#### 2. Solve for the Unknown

*Step 1.* Apply rules to assign oxidation numbers to all atoms in the equation using the flow chart on the left.

$$\overset{+7\ -2}{ClO_4{}^-}(aq) + \overset{-1}{Br^-}(aq) \rightarrow \overset{-1}{Cl^-}(aq) + \overset{0}{Br_2}(g) \text{ (in acid solution)}$$

*Step 2.* Identify which atoms are oxidized and which are reduced.

$$\overset{+7\ -2}{ClO_4{}^-}(aq) + \overset{-1}{Br^-}(aq) \rightarrow \overset{-1}{Cl^-}(aq) + \overset{0}{Br_2}(g) \text{ (in acid solution)}$$
↑      ↑      ↑      ↑

The oxidation number of bromine increases from $-1$ to $0$ as it is oxidized. The oxidation number of chlorine decreases from $+7$ to $-1$ as it is reduced. Note that no oxygen atoms appear in the products. This deficiency will be fixed shortly.

*Step 3.* Draw a line connecting the atoms involved in oxidation and another line connecting the atoms involved in reduction. Write the net change in oxidation number above or below each line.

$$\underset{-8}{ClO_4{}^-(aq) + \overset{+1}{Br^-}(aq) \rightarrow Cl^-(aq) + Br_2(g)} \text{ (in acid solution)}$$

*Step 4.* Make the changes in oxidation number equal in magnitude by placing the appropriate coefficients in front of the formulas in the equation.

$$\underset{-8}{ClO_4{}^-(aq) + \overset{8(+1)=+8}{8Br^-}(aq) \rightarrow Cl^-(aq) + 4Br_2(g)} \text{ (in acid solution)}$$

Note that $4Br_2$ represents eight bromine atoms to balance the $8Br^-$ on the left side.

*Step 5.* Add enough hydrogen ions and water molecules to the equation to balance the oxygen atoms on both sides. This is the reason that you must know the conditions of the reaction.

$$ClO_4{}^-(aq) + 8Br^-(aq) + 8H^+(aq) \rightarrow Cl^-(aq) + 4Br_2(g) + 4H_2O(l)$$

---

## ✓ Portfolio

### Redox around the House

**Linguistic** Cleaning cloths that are treated to prevent tarnishing of metal are available in household goods sections in many stores. Have students research these types of cloths and learn how they prevent tarnish. Then ask them to write an advertisement for the product.

---

### Resource Manager

**Lab Manual,** pp. 157–160 **L2**
**Small-Scale Laboratory Manual,**
pp. 73–76 **L2**

Four oxygen atoms are present in one $ClO_4^-$ ion, enough to form four $H_2O$ molecules. Therefore, a total of $8H^+$ ions will also be needed to form the four water molecules.

**3.** **Evaluate the Answer**

Review the balanced equation, counting the number of atoms to be sure there are equal numbers of each element. As with any ionic equation, you must also check to see if the net charge on the right equals the net charge on the left. Check to be sure that you did not change any subscripts in the equation.

## PRACTICE PROBLEMS

Use the oxidation-number method to balance the following net ionic redox equations.

**15.** $H_2S(g) + NO_3^-(aq) \rightarrow S(s) + NO(g)$ (in acid solution)

**16.** $Cr_2O_7^{2-}(aq) + I^-(aq) \rightarrow Cr^{3+}(aq) + I_2(s)$ (in acid solution)

**17.** $I^-(aq) + MnO_4^-(aq) \rightarrow I_2(s) + MnO_2(s)$ (in basic solution) Hint: Hydroxide ions will appear on the right, and water molecules on the left.

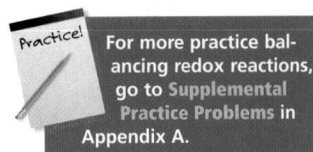

For more practice balancing redox reactions, go to Supplemental Practice Problems in Appendix A.

The oxidation-number method is convenient for balancing most redox equations, but you will see in the next section that there are occasions when you must balance the net ionic charge on both sides of the equation in addition to balancing the atoms.

 **Section 20.2 Assessment**

**18.** A reactant in an oxidation–reduction reaction loses four electrons when it is oxidized. How many electrons must be gained by the reactant that is reduced?

**19.** Why is it important to know the conditions under which an aqueous redox reaction takes place in order to balance the ionic equation for the reaction?

**20.** Balance these equations for redox reactions by using the oxidation-number method.

**a.** $HClO_3(aq) \rightarrow ClO_2(g) + HClO_4(aq) + H_2O(l)$

**b.** $H_2O_2(aq) + H_2SO_4(aq) + FeSO_4(aq) \rightarrow Fe_2(SO_4)_3(aq) + H_2O(l)$
(Hint: Review rule 5 to learn how to determine the oxidation numbers in $H_2O_2$.)

**c.** $H_2SeO_3(aq) + HClO_3(aq) \rightarrow H_2SeO_4(aq) + Cl_2(g) + H_2O(l)$

**21.** Balance these net ionic equations for redox reactions.

**a.** $Cr_2O_7^{2-}(aq) + Fe^{2+}(aq) \rightarrow Cr^{3+}(aq) + Fe^{3+}(aq)$ (in acid solution)

**b.** $Zn(s) + V_2O_5(aq) \rightarrow Zn^{2+}(aq) + V_2O_4(aq)$ (in acid solution)

**c.** $N_2O(g) + ClO^-(aq) \rightarrow Cl^-(aq) + NO_2^-(aq)$ (in basic solution)

**22.** **Thinking Critically** Explain how changes in oxidation number are related to the electrons transferred in a redox reaction. How are the changes related to the processes of oxidation and reduction?

**23.** **Applying Concepts** The processes used to remove metals from their ores usually involve a reduction process. For example, mercury may be obtained by roasting the ore mercury(II) sulfide with calcium oxide to produce mercury metal, calcium sulfide, and calcium sulfate. Write and balance the redox equation for this process.

 chemistrymc.com/self_check_quiz

20.2 Balancing Redox Equations **649**

**Section 20.2 Assessment**

**18.** four
**19.** It is important to know that $H^+$ or $OH^-$ are available to balance the equation.
**20. a.** $3HClO_3 \rightarrow 2ClO_2 + HClO_4 + H_2O$
**b.** $H_2O_2 + H_2SO_4 + 2FeSO_4 \rightarrow Fe_2(SO_4)_3 + 2H_2O$
**c.** $5H_2SeO_3 + 2HClO_3 \rightarrow 5H_2SeO_4 + Cl_2 + H_2O$

**21. a.** $Cr_2O_7^{2-} + 6Fe^{2+} + 14H^+ \rightarrow 2Cr^{3+} + 6Fe^{3+} + 7H_2O$
**b.** $Zn + 2H^+ + V_2O_5 \rightarrow Zn^{2+} + V_2O_4 + H_2O$
Oxidation number of Zn increases from 0 to +2.
Oxidation number of V decreases from +5 to +4.

## 3 Assess
### Check for Understanding

*Intrapersonal* Organize the class into groups of two. Prepare enough file cards with a reaction written on them to give one to each group. Have each student balance the reaction individually and then have team members discuss and compare their answers. **L2** **COOP LEARN**

### Reteach

Provide students with the steps for balancing a redox reaction by the oxidation number method. Have them explain in their own words what is happening in each step. **L2**

### Assessment

**Portfolio** Have students investigate and report on one of the following oxidation reduction topics: breathalyzer test, black and white photography, use of bleach in the laundry room, hydrogen peroxide as an antiseptic, or bioluminescence. Have them explain the principles of oxidation and reduction in the context of the selected topic, and have them write the redox reaction. **L2** **P**

**c.** $N_2O + 2ClO^- + 2OH^- \rightarrow 2Cl^- + 2NO_2^- + H_2O$

**22.** Because the nucleus (specifically, number of protons) never changes during this type of reaction, whenever there is a transfer of electrons from one atom to another atom, there is a change in the net charge of that species.

**23.** skeleton equation: $HgS + CaO \rightarrow CaS + Hg + CaSO_4$
Oxidation number of S increases from −2 to +6; oxidation number of Hg decreases from +2 to 0.
balanced equation: $4HgS + 4CaO \rightarrow 3CaS + 4Hg + CaSO_4$

# 1 Focus

## Focus Transparency

Before presenting the lesson, display **Section Focus Transparency 77** on the overhead projector. Have students answer the accompanying questions using **Section Focus Transparency Master 77**. **L1** **ELL**

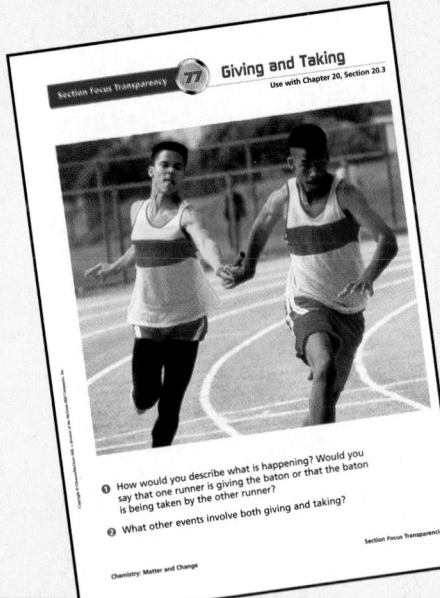

# 2 Teach

## Quick Demo

*Linguistic* The flameless ration heater (FRH) is a good visual to show students that redox reactions are useful; in this case, redox provides heat to cook food in a situation where there is no appliance or fire for that purpose.

Demonstrate the FRH and have the students describe their observations in their chemistry journals. One of the reactions occurring in the FRH is $Mg + H_2O \rightarrow Mg(OH)_2 + H_2 +$ heat. Have the students balance this reaction by the half-reaction method. **L2**

---

## Section 20.3

# Half-Reactions

### Objectives

- **Recognize** the interdependence of oxidation and reduction processes.
- **Derive** oxidation and reduction half-reactions from a redox equation.
- **Balance** redox equations by the half-reaction method.

### Vocabulary

species
half-reaction

Throughout this chapter, you have read about oxidation–reduction reactions. You know that redox reactions involve the loss and gain of electrons. Thus, the "pairing" or complementary nature of redox reactions is probably apparent to you. So, let's consider the two halves of redox reactions.

## Identifying Half-Reactions

As you know, oxidation–reduction reactions can involve molecules, ions, free atoms, or combinations of all three. To make it easier to discuss redox reactions without constantly specifying the kind of particle involved, chemists use the term species. In chemistry, a **species** is any kind of chemical unit involved in a process. For example, a solution of sugar in water contains two major species. In the equilibrium equation $NH_3 + H_2O \rightleftharpoons NH_4^+ + OH^-$, there are four species: the two molecules $NH_3$ and $H_2O$ and the two ions $NH_4^+$ and $OH^-$.

Oxidation–reduction reactions take place whenever a species that can give up electrons (reducing agent) comes in contact with another species that can accept them (oxidizing agent). In a sense, the species being reduced doesn't "care" where the electrons are coming from as long as they are readily available. Likewise, the species undergoing oxidation doesn't "care" where its electrons go as long as a willing receiver is available. The cartoon electron donor/acceptor machine shown in **Figure 20-7** illustrates this principle.

For example, active metals can be oxidized by a variety of oxidizing agents. When iron rusts, it is oxidized by oxygen. You can also say that iron reduces oxygen because iron acts as a reducing agent.

$$4Fe + 3O_2 \rightarrow 2Fe_2O_3$$

But iron can reduce many other oxidizing agents, including chlorine.

$$2Fe + 3Cl_2 \rightarrow 2FeCl_3$$

In this reaction, each iron atom is oxidized by losing three electrons to become an $Fe^{3+}$ ion. This is the oxidation half of the oxidation–reduction reaction. Recall that $e^-$ represents one electron.

$$Fe \rightarrow Fe^{3+} + 3e^-$$

At the same time, each chlorine atom in $Cl_2$ is reduced by accepting one electron to become a $Cl^-$ ion. This is the reduction half of the oxidation–reduction reaction.

$$Cl_2 + 2e^- \rightarrow 2Cl^-$$

### Figure 20-7

This imaginary electron machine illustrates the point that the electrons that are involved in redox reactions can come from any source, as long as they are available to transfer. It also points out that reduction, the complimentary process of oxidation, requires something to accept the electrons. These two processes can be identified and separated to help understand redox reactions and balance redox equations.

Oxidation

Reduction

## Internet Address Book

**Chemistry Online**

Note Internet addresses that you find useful in the space below for quick reference.

Table 20-3

**Various Oxidation–Reduction Reactions in which Iron Is Oxidized**

| Overall reaction (unbalanced) | Oxidation half-reaction | Reduction half-reaction |
|---|---|---|
| $Fe + O_2 \rightarrow Fe_2O_3$ | $Fe \rightarrow Fe^{3+} + 3e^-$ | $O_2 + 4e^- \rightarrow 2O^{2-}$ |
| $Fe + Cl_2 \rightarrow FeCl_3$ | $Fe \rightarrow Fe^{3+} + 3e^-$ | $Cl_2 + 2e^- \rightarrow 2Cl^-$ |
| $Fe + F_2 \rightarrow FeF_3$ | $Fe \rightarrow Fe^{3+} + 3e^-$ | $F_2 + 2e^- \rightarrow 2F^-$ |
| $Fe + HBr \rightarrow H_2 + FeBr_3$ | $Fe \rightarrow Fe^{3+} + 3e^-$ | $2H^+ + 2e^- \rightarrow H_2$ |
| $Fe + AgNO_3 \rightarrow Ag + Fe(NO_3)_3$ | $Fe \rightarrow Fe^{3+} + 3e^-$ | $Ag^+ + e^- \rightarrow Ag$ |
| $Fe + CuSO_4 \rightarrow Cu + Fe_2(SO_4)_3$ | $Fe \rightarrow Fe^{3+} + 3e^-$ | $Cu^{2+} + 2e^- \rightarrow Cu$ |

Equations such as these represent half-reactions. A **half-reaction** is one of the two parts of a redox reaction—the oxidation half alone or the reduction half alone. **Table 20-3** shows a variety of reduction half-reactions that can accept electrons from iron, oxidizing it from Fe to $Fe^{3+}$.

## Balancing Redox Equations by Half-Reactions

You will learn more about the importance of half-reactions when you study electrochemistry in Chapter 21. For now, however, you can learn to use half-reactions to balance a redox equation. First, look at an unbalanced equation taken from **Table 20-3** to see how to separate a redox equation into half-reactions. For example, the following unbalanced equation represents the reaction that occurs when you put an iron nail into a solution of copper(II) sulfate, as shown in **Figure 20-8.** Iron atoms are oxidized as they lose electrons to the copper(II) ions.

$$Fe(s) + CuSO_4(aq) \rightarrow Cu(s) + Fe_2(SO_4)_3(aq)$$

### Steps for balancing by half-reactions

**1.** Write the net ionic equation for the reaction, omitting spectator ions.

$Fe + Cu^{2+} + \cancel{SO_4^{2-}} \rightarrow Cu + 2Fe^{3+} + 3\cancel{SO_4^{2-}}$

$Fe + Cu^{2+} \rightarrow Cu + 2Fe^{3+}$

**2.** Write the oxidation and reduction half-reactions for the net ionic equation.

$Fe \rightarrow 2Fe^{3+} + 6e^-$

$Cu^{2+} + 2e^- \rightarrow Cu$

**3.** Balance the atoms and charges in each half-reaction.

$2Fe \rightarrow 2Fe^{3+} + 6e^-$

$Cu^{2+} + 2e^- \rightarrow Cu$

**4.** Adjust the coefficients so that the number of electrons lost in oxidation equals the number of electrons gained in reduction.

$2Fe \rightarrow 2Fe^{3+} + \cancel{6e^-}$

$3Cu^{2+} + \cancel{6e^-} \rightarrow 3Cu$

**5.** Add the balanced half-reactions and return spectator ions.

$2Fe + 3Cu^{2+} \rightarrow 3Cu + 2Fe^{3+}$

$2Fe(s) + 3CuSO_4(aq) \rightarrow 3Cu(s) + Fe_2(SO_4)_3(aq)$

**Figure 20-8**

As a result of this redox reaction between iron and copper sulfate solution, solid copper metal is deposited on the iron nail. To balance the equation given in the text for this reaction you could use the method of half-reactions.

20.3 Half-Reactions **651**

**Math in Chemistry**

When balancing redox reactions by the half-reaction method, note the step (step 4) that is essentially solving a simultaneous equation. In this case, you are making sure that the total number of electrons lost during the oxidation half-reaction is the same as the total number of electrons gained in the reduction half-reaction by finding the least common multiple for the two half-reactions and multiplying all substances in the half-reaction by that number. When you are ready to add the two half-reactions back together, the number of electrons lost and gained will be equal.

**✔ Assessment**

**Knowledge** Organize the students in groups of two. Assign each group two problems from the text that they have completed for homework. Have the first student explain to the second student how he or she solved the first problem. For the second problem, have the students reverse roles. **L2**

**Resource Manager**

**Study Guide for Content Mastery,** pp. 119–120 **L2**
**Challenge Problems,** p. 20 **L3**
**Solving Problems: A Chemistry Handbook,** Section 20.3 **L2**
**Section Focus Transparency 77 and Master** **L1** **ELL**

**CULTURAL DIVERSITY**

## Redox Shapes History

*Visual-Spatial* Have the students recall various historical time periods, such as the copper age, bronze age, and iron age. Several of these early time periods centered in the Middle East. In each case, the discovery of a new material by a particular cultural group or nation allowed that group to con-trol the region for a period of time. Have students locate these key regions on a world map. What are several chemical and physical properties of copper, bronze, and iron that would allow a nation a significant advantage over neighboring countries? What is the role of redox chemistry in history? **L2**

**National Science Content Standards**

**Pages 650–651**
UCP.1, UCP.3; B.3; E.2

### Practice PROBLEMS

Have students refer to Appendix D for complete solutions to Practice Problems.

**24.** $14H^+(aq) + Cr_2O_7^{2-}(aq) + 6I^-(aq) \rightarrow 3I_2(s) + 2Cr^{3+}(aq) + 7H_2O(l)$

**25.** $3Mn^{2+}(aq) + 5BiO_3^-(aq) + 6H^+(aq) \rightarrow 3MnO_4^-(aq) + 5Bi^{2+}(aq) + 3H_2O(l)$

**26.** $N_2O(g) + 2ClO^-(aq) + 2OH^-(aq) \rightarrow 2NO_2^-(aq) + 2Cl^-(aq) + H_2O(l)$

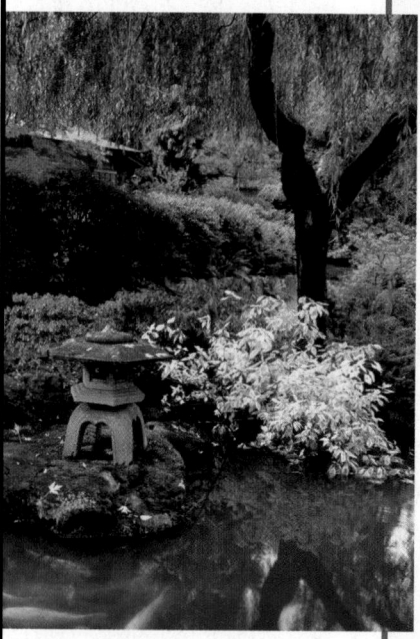

Potassium permanganate ($KMnO_4$) is used to disinfect decorative fish ponds and the water in fish hatcheries.

**EXAMPLE** PROBLEM 20-5

### Balancing a Redox Equation by Half-Reactions

The permanganate ion ($MnO_4^-$) is widely used in the chemistry laboratory as a strong oxidizing agent. Permanganate is usually sold as potassium salt $KMnO_4$. When sulfur dioxide gas is bubbled into an acidic solution of potassium permanganate, it reacts to form sulfate ions. Balance the redox equation for this reaction using half-reactions.

$$KMnO_4(aq) + SO_2(g) \rightarrow MnSO_4(aq) + K_2SO_4(aq)$$

**1.** **Analyze the Problem**

You are given the skeleton equation for the reaction of permanganate and sulfur dioxide. You also know that the reaction takes place in an acid solution. With this information, the rules for determining oxidation numbers, and the steps for balancing by half-reactions, you can write a complete balanced equation.

**2.** **Solve for the Unknown**

*Step 1.* Write the net ionic equation for the reaction. You can eliminate coefficients, spectator ions, and state symbols.

$$MnO_4^- + SO_2 \rightarrow Mn^{2+} + SO_4^{2-}$$

*Step 2.* Write the oxidation and reduction half-reactions for the net ionic equation, including oxidation numbers. Recall the rules for assigning oxidation numbers from page 641.

$$\overset{+4}{S}O_2 \rightarrow \overset{+6}{S}O_4^{2-} + 2e^- \text{ (oxidation)}$$

$$\overset{+7}{Mn}O_4^- + 5e^- \rightarrow \overset{+2}{Mn}^{2+} \text{ (reduction)}$$

*Step 3.* Balance the atoms and charges in the half-reactions.

**a.** In this case, the sulfur atoms are balanced on both sides of the equation and the manganese atoms are balanced on both sides of the equation. Recall that in acid solution, $H_2O$ molecules are available in abundance and can be used to balance oxygen atoms in the half-reactions.

$$SO_2 + 2H_2O \rightarrow SO_4^{2-} + 2e^- \text{ (oxidation)}$$

$$MnO_4^- + 5e^- \rightarrow Mn^{2+} + 4H_2O \text{ (reduction)}$$

**b.** Recall also that in acid solution, $H^+$ ions are readily available and can be used to balance the charge in the half-reactions.

$$SO_2 + 2H_2O \rightarrow SO_4^{2-} + 2e^- + 4H^+ \text{ (oxidation)}$$

$$MnO_4^- + 5e^- + 8H^+ \rightarrow Mn^{2+} + 4H_2O \text{ (reduction)}$$

*Step 4.* Adjust the coefficients so that the number of electrons lost in oxidation (2) equals the number of electrons gained in reduction (5). In this case, the least common multiple of 2 and 5 is 10. Cross-multiplying gives the balanced oxidation and reduction half-reactions.

$$5SO_2 + 10H_2O \rightarrow 5SO_4^{2-} + 20H^+ + 10e^- \text{ (oxidation)}$$

$$2MnO_4^- + 16H^+ + 10e^- \rightarrow 2Mn^{2+} + 8H_2O \text{ (reduction)}$$

*Step 5.* Add the balanced half-reactions and simplify by canceling or reducing like terms on both sides of the equation.

$$5SO_2 + 2H_2O + 2MnO_4^- \rightarrow 5SO_4^{2-} + 4H^+ + 2Mn^{2+}$$

Finally, return spectator ions ($K^+$) and restore the state descriptions. In this case, two $K^+$ ions go with the two $MnO_4^-$ anions on the left side of the equation. Therefore, you can add only two $K^+$ ions to the right side, which will form $K_2SO_4$. The remaining $SO_4^{2-}$ ions recombine with $Mn^{2+}$ and $H^+$ to form two molecules of $MnSO_4$ and $H_2SO_4$, respectively.

$$5SO_2(g) + 2H_2O(l) + 2KMnO_4(aq) \rightarrow K_2SO_4(aq) + 2H_2SO_4(aq) + 2MnSO_4(aq)$$

**3. Evaluate the Answer**

A review of the balanced equation indicates that the number of atoms of each element is equal on both sides of the equation. No subscripts have been changed.

## PRACTICE PROBLEMS

Use the half-reaction method to balance the following redox equations. Begin with step 2 of Example Problem 20-5, and leave the balanced equation in ionic form.

**24.** $Cr_2O_7^{2-}(aq) + I^-(aq) \rightarrow Cr^{3+}(aq) + I_2(s)$ (in acid solution)

**25.** $Mn^{2+}(aq) + BiO_3^-(aq) \rightarrow MnO_4^-(aq) + Bi^{2+}(aq)$ (in acid solution)

**26.** $N_2O(g) + ClO^-(aq) \rightarrow NO_2^-(aq) + Cl^-(aq)$ (in basic solution). Hint: Add O and H in the form of $OH^-$ ions and $H_2O$ molecules.

*Practice!* **For more practice solving problems using the half-reaction method, go to Supplemental Practice Problems in Appendix A.**

You have learned two methods by which redox equations can be balanced. Both methods will provide the same results; however, the half-reaction method may be more useful to your study of electrochemistry.

## Section 20.3 Assessment

**27.** Explain why an oxidation process must always accompany a reduction process.

**28.** Write the oxidation and reduction half-reactions for this redox equation.

$$Pb(s) + Pd(NO_3)_2(aq) \rightarrow Pb(NO_3)_2(aq) + Pd(s)$$

**29.** Use the half-reaction method to balance this redox equation. Begin with step 2 of Example Problem 20-5, and leave the balanced equation in ionic form.

$$AsO_4^{3-}(aq) + Zn(s) \rightarrow AsH_3(g) + Zn^{2+}(aq)$$
(in acid solution)

**30. Thinking Critically** The oxidation half-reaction of a redox reaction is $Sn^{2+} \rightarrow Sn^{4+} + 2e^-$ and the reduction half-reaction is $Au^{3+} + 3e^- \rightarrow Au$. What minimum numbers of tin(II) ions and

gold(III) ions would have to react in order to have no electrons left over?

**31. Calculating** The concentration of thallium(I) ions in solution may be determined by oxidizing to thallium(III) ions with an aqueous solution of potassium permanganate ($KMnO_4$) under acidic conditions. Suppose that a 100.00 mL sample of a solution of unknown $Tl^+$ concentration is titrated to the endpoint with 28.23 mL of a $0.0560M$ solution of potassium permanganate. What is the concentration of $Tl^+$ ions in the sample? You must first balance the redox equation for the reaction to determine its stoichiometry.

$$Tl^+(aq) + MnO_4^-(aq) \rightarrow Tl^{3+}(aq) + Mn^{2+}(aq)$$

20.3 Half-Reactions     **653**

*Linguistic* Have students explain in their own words the process of balancing a redox reaction by both the oxidation number method and the half-reaction method.

### Reteach

One of the problems students have is organizing and keeping their work neat and orderly when balancing redox reactions by the half-reaction method. Encourage students to use plenty of space on their papers to write, check, and recheck each redox equation that they are balancing. Guide them into the habit of writing the problem correctly and including all appropriate charges.

### Extension

Invite a person in your community who sells or tests water in swimming pools or hot tubs to describe the oxidation–reduction chemistry involved in maintaining the water in pools and hot tubs. **L2**

### Assessment

**Skill** Have students complete this reaction in which elemental phosphorus reacts with water to form a compound that smells like decaying fish (phosphine). **L2**

$$P_4 + H_2O \rightarrow PH_3 + H_2PO_2$$

$$5P_4 + 24H_2O \rightarrow 8PH_3 + 12H_2PO_2$$

## Section 20.3 Assessment

**27.** To lose an electron (oxidation), there must be another species willing to accept that electron (reduction).

**28.** oxidation: $Pb \rightarrow Pb^{2+} + 2e^-$
reduction: $Pd^{2+} + 2e^- \rightarrow Pd$

**29.** $11H^+ + AsO_4^{3-} + 4Zn \rightarrow AsH_3 + 4H_2O + 4Zn^{2+}$

**30.** Three $Sn^{2+}$ ions; two $Au^{3+}$ ions

**31.** $0.0395M$ $Tl^{1+}$

**National Science Content Standards**

**Pages 652–653**
UCP.1, UCP.3; B.2, B.3; E.2

**653**

## Preparation

### Time Allotment
One laboratory period

### Process Skills
Classifying, comparing and contrasting, measuring, using numbers

### Safety Precautions
- The reaction of copper with nitric acid should be done in a ventilation hood. Do not breathe the fumes from this reaction.
- Nitric acid, ammonia, and hydrochloric acid can cause burns. Avoid contact with skin and eyes.

### Disposal
- After step 2 is finished, students should pour the solution down the drain and flush with copious amounts of water.
- After step 5 is finished, students should pour the solution down the drain and flush with lots of water.

### Pre-Lab

2. Student tables should look like the table shown in the Pre-Lab section of the student textbook.

3. A redox reaction is a reaction in which electrons are transferred from one atom to another.

4. Aluminum is oxidized, due to the loss of three electrons, to form $Al^{3+}$. Hydrogen is reduced to a zero oxidation number due to the gain of one electron.

### Preparation of Materials
- Drano crystals are available in hardware and grocery stores.
- See page 634C for preparation of all solutions.

### Procedure
- Make sure that the reaction of copper and nitric acid is performed in a ventilation hood. All other reactions can be done outside the hood.

**654**

# Redox Reactions

In Section 20.2, a redox reaction involving copper and nitric acid is discussed. This reaction is balanced by a method called the oxidation-number method. In this lab, you will carry out this reaction, along with another redox reaction that involves a common household substance. You will practice balancing various redox reactions using both the oxidation-number method (from Section 20.2) and the half-reaction method (from Section 20.3).

### Problem
What are some examples of redox reactions and how can the equations describing them be balanced?

### Objectives
- **Observe** various redox reactions.
- **Balance** redox reactions using the oxidation-number method.
- **Balance** redox reactions using the half-reaction method.

### Materials
copper metal
6M nitric acid
evaporating dish
forceps
distilled water
dropper pipette
spoon

household ammonia
crystal drain cleaner
thermometer
250-mL beaker

### Safety Precautions

- The reaction of copper with nitric acid should be done in a ventilation hood. Do not breathe the fumes from this reaction.
- Nitric acid and ammonia can cause burns. Avoid contact with skin and eyes.

### Pre-Lab

1. Read the entire **CHEMLAB**.
2. Prepare all written materials that you will take into the laboratory. Be sure to include safety precautions, procedure notes, and a data table.

| Data Table | |
|---|---|
| Step 1 | |
| Step 2 | |
| Step 3 | |
| Step 4 | |
| Step 5 | |

3. Review what a redox reaction is.
4. Read the label of the crystal drain cleaner package. Understand that the compound is solid sodium hydroxide that contains aluminum. When the material is added to water, sodium hydroxide dissolves rapidly, producing heat. Aluminum reacts with water in the basic solution to produce $Al(OH)_4^-$ ions

and hydrogen gas. Is aluminum oxidized or reduced in the reaction? Is hydrogen oxidized or reduced in the reaction? Explain your answers.

### Procedure

1. In a ventilation hood, place a piece of copper metal in a clean, dry evaporating dish. Add enough 6M nitric acid to cover the metal. **CAUTION:** *Nitric acid can cause burns. The reaction of nitric acid with copper generates dangerous fumes. Use a ventilation hood.* Observe what happens and record your observations in the data table.

2. Pour about 2 mL of the solution from the evaporating dish into a test tube that contains about 2 mL of distilled water. Add ammonia until a change occurs. Record your observation in the data table.

3. Add about 50 mL of tap water to a 250-mL beaker. Use a thermometer to measure the temperature of the water. Record your observations in the data table.

- Have some students start with step 4 if there is not enough hood space to start with step 1.

### Expected Results

Step 1: Students should observe bubbles and a blue solution.
Step 2: Students should observe a dark blue solution.

Step 3: The water temperature should be approximately 25°C.
Step 4: Students should observe white and green particles, bits of metal.
Step 5: Students should note the maximum temperature reached—approximately 40°C.

4. Pour approximately 1 cm³ of dry drain cleaner onto a watchglass. **CAUTION:** *Drain cleaner is caustic and will burn skin. Use forceps to move the crystals and observe their composition.* Record your observations in the data table.

5. Carefully pour about one-half spoonful of the crystals into the water in the beaker. As the crystals react with the water, watch the thermometer in the water for a few minutes and record in the data table the highest temperature reached and any other observations you make.

## Cleanup and Disposal

1. After step 1 is completed, use forceps to remove any excess pieces of copper metal. Rinse the copper metal with tap water and dispose of the metal as your teacher instructs.

2. After step 2 is finished, pour the solution down the drain and flush with a lot of water.

3. After step 5 is finished, pour the solution down the drain and flush with a lot of water.

## Analyze and Conclude

1. **Applying Concepts** The reaction between copper and nitric acid is discussed in Section 20.2. Write the half-reaction for the substance that is oxidized.

2. **Applying Concepts** Write the half-reaction for the substance that is reduced.

3. **Thinking Critically** In step 2, a deep blue copper–ammonia complex is formed according to the following reaction.

$$Cu^{2+} + NH_3 \rightarrow Cu(NH_3)_4^{2+}$$

Is this a redox reaction? Why or why not?

4. **Using Numbers** The following side reaction occurs from the reaction of copper with nitric acid.

$$Cu + HNO_3 \rightarrow Cu(NO_3)_2 + NO + H_2O$$

Balance this redox reaction using both the oxidation-number method and the half-reaction method.

5. **Using Numbers** Write and balance the redox reaction of sodium hydroxide with aluminum and water.

6. **Error Analysis** Give possible reasons why you might not have been able to balance the equation for the redox reaction you performed in this experiment.

## Real-World Chemistry

1. Using your observations in this lab, how do drain cleaning crystals remove clogs?

2. Ammonia and bleach are two common household chemicals that should never be mixed. One product of this reaction is chloramine, a poisonous, volatile compound. The reaction is as follows.

$$NH_3 + ClO^- \rightarrow NH_2Cl + OH^-$$

What is the balanced redox reaction?

3. One type of breathalyzer detects whether ethanol is in the breath of a person. Ethanol is oxidized to acetaldehyde by dichromate ions in acidic solution. The dichromate ion in solution is orange, while the $Cr^{3+}$ aqueous ion is green. The appearance of a green color in the breathalyzer test shows that the breath exceeds the legal limit of alcohol. The equation is

$$H^+ + Cr_2O_7^{2-} + C_2H_5OH \rightarrow$$
$$Cr^{3+} + C_2H_4O + H_2O$$

Balance this redox reaction.

4. Diluted hydrochloric acid can be used to remove limestone (calcium carbonate) surrounding phosphate and silicate fossils. The reaction produces carbon dioxide, water, and aqueous calcium chloride. Write the balanced chemical equation. Is it a redox reaction? Explain.

## Analyze and Conclude

1. $Cu \rightarrow Cu^{2+}$
2. $NO_3^- \rightarrow NO_2$
3. It is not a redox reaction because none of the atoms change oxidation number.
4. $3Cu + 8HNO_3 \rightarrow 3Cu(NO_3)_2 + 2NO + 4H_2O$
5. $2NaOH + 6H_2O + 2Al \rightarrow 2Na[Al(OH)_4] + 3H_2$
6. Answers will vary. Incorrect half-reactions will make it difficult or impossible to balance the redox equation.

## Real-World Chemistry

1. The sodium hydroxide reacts with hair and grease. The reaction gets hot, which helps loosen hair and grease.
2. The reaction is balanced as given.
3. $8H^+ + Cr_2O_7^{2-} + 3C_2H_5OH \rightarrow 2Cr^{3+} + 3C_2H_4O + 7H_2O$
4. $CaCO_3(aq) + 2HCl(aq) \rightarrow CO_2(g) + H_2O(l) + CaCl_2$
This is not a redox reaction. None of the oxidation numbers change.

### ✓ Assessment

**Portfolio** Ask the students to find out what ingredients are found in liquid drain cleaners. Also, have them research the ingredients in the new foaming drain cleaners and how they work. Reports can be placed in students' portfolios. **L2** **P**

CHEMLAB **655**

## Resource Manager

**ChemLab and MiniLab Worksheets,** pp. 78–80 **L2**

**National Science Content Standards**

**Pages 654–655**
UCP.1, UCP.3; A.1; B.3

# How It Works

## Purpose

Students will learn how photographic images are the result of redox reactions.

## Background

The process described is for black and white film and has been essentially the same for the last one hundred years. All silver halides darken on exposure to light, but only the bromide, chloride, and iodide are used in photography. Each halide has different light sensitivity characteristics.

Color photography is based on a similar set of reactions. The color comes from dyes produced by reactions between chemicals added to the film and others added to the processing solutions. The redox reaction that forms the silver image acts as a catalyst for these dye-forming reactions.

## Visual Learning

You can demonstrate the reduction of silver halides to metallic silver upon exposure to light by exposing a piece of photographic film to bright light. Tape an opaque object or a photographic negative to the emulsion side of a piece of undeveloped photographic film (or paper). Place the film in sunlight or under a high-intensity light source for about 5 minutes. Remove the object from the film and allow students to observe that the film has darkened in the areas where it was exposed to light. The darkened areas contain large numbers of metallic silver particles whereas the unexposed areas have very few. Remind students that the amount of light received by the film in a camera is not enough to create a visible image.

## Teaching Strategies

- Emphasize that only the silver bromide grains that have received sufficient light are capable of being reduced to metallic silver.

**656**

---

# How It Works
## Photographic Film

Black and white photography is a popular art form. The spectacular images that are captured on and printed from black and white film are the product of a series of redox reactions. The first redox reaction captures the image on the film inside the camera. The second is a reaction to produce a negative image of the exposed film. The third redox reaction creates the positive print from the negative film image.

1. Photographic film contains small grains of silver bromide (AgBr) suspended in a gelatinous emulsion that is spread onto a flexible backing material.

2. When a camera shutter opens, incoming light energizes the silver bromide grains, causing some of the bromide ions to lose an electron and reduce some of the silver ions to silver atoms. These are called activated grains.

3. In a darkroom, a reducing chemical, such as hydroquinone or pyrogallol, reduces all of the silver ions in any activated AgBr grain to silver atoms. (The silver atoms that were created in step 2 act as catalysts in this reduction.) The reducing agent does not react with silver ions in AgBr grains that are not activated.

4. Now the remaining silver bromide must be removed to keep the film from darkening. Sodium thiosulfate reacts with the silver bromide to form bromide ions and a water-soluble complex ion. The film is washed to remove the processing chemicals and the soluble reaction products. The resulting image is a negative image of the original subject.

5. A positive image is created by virtually an identical series of reactions after light is shown through the negative film onto light-sensitive photographic paper.

### Thinking Critically

1. **Predicting** Time, temperature, and solution concentration are all important factors in the developing process. What would be the consequence of leaving the film too long in the hydroquinone developer? *(Hint: the developer is a reducing agent.)*

2. **Hypothesizing** Color photographs are composed of dyes formed during the development of the silver image. The silver metal must be removed because it is opaque. Use the redox principle to explain how the silver could be removed from the color photo.

656  Chapter 20  Redox Reactions

---

- Remind students that reduction is always accompanied by oxidation. Ask students to identify the oxidation reaction that takes place when the silver ion is reduced by exposure to light. The bromide ion is oxidized to bromine.
- Ask students to identify both the oxidation and reduction reactions during the developing process. The silver ions are reduced and the developer (hydroquinone) is oxidized.

## Thinking Critically

1. Answers will vary, but students should correctly predict that a prolonged development time will cause unexposed silver bromide grains to be reduced to silver metal.

2. Answers will vary. Students should propose that the silver is removed by some reaction that oxidizes the silver metal, creating soluble ions that can be washed away.

## Summary

### 20.1 Oxidation and Reduction

- An oxidation–reduction (redox) reaction is any chemical reaction in which electrons are transferred from one atom to another. Most chemical reactions other than double replacement reactions are oxidation–reduction reactions.

- Oxidation occurs when an atom loses electrons. Reduction occurs when an atom gains electrons.

- Oxidation increases an atom's oxidation number and reduction decreases an atom's oxidation number.

- Oxidation and reduction must always occur together because the reduction process requires a supply of electrons available only from the oxidation process. At the same time, the oxidation process must have a receiver for lost electrons.

- The species that is oxidized in a redox reaction is the reducing agent and loses electrons. The species that is reduced is the oxidizing agent and gains electrons.

- The oxidation number of an element in a compound can be determined by applying a series of rules to the atoms in the compound.

### Summary of Oxidation and Reduction Processes

| Process | Oxidation | Reduction |
|---|---|---|
| Examples | $Na \rightarrow Na^+ + e^-$<br>$Fe^{2+} \rightarrow Fe^{3+} + e^-$ | $Cl_2 + 2e^- \rightarrow Cl^-$<br>$Sn^{4+} + 2e^- \rightarrow Sn^{2+}$ |
| Electron transfer | Atom loses electrons | Atom gains electrons |
| Change in oxidation number | Increases | Decreases |
| Function | Reducing agent | Oxidizing agent |

### 20.2 Balancing Redox Equations

- Many simple redox equations may be balanced by inspection. The oxidation-number method can be used to balance more difficult reactions.

- Redox equations are often balanced by examining the change in oxidation number that occurs in the oxidized and reduced species. The following principle is then applied.

$$e^- \text{ lost in oxidation} = e^- \text{ gained in reduction}$$

Therefore, the total increase in oxidation numbers equals the total decrease in oxidation numbers.

- Redox reactions that take place in acidic solution often use water molecules and hydrogen ions in the process. Redox reactions that take place in basic solution often use water molecules and hydroxide ions in the process. Therefore, it is appropriate to add these species to the equation in order to balance the numbers of oxygen and/or hydrogen atoms.

- Redox reactions involving ionic species may be represented by net ionic equations, leaving out spectator ions.

### 20.3 Half-Reactions

- The oxidation and reduction processes of a redox reaction can be represented as half-reactions.

- An oxidation half-reaction shows the number of electrons lost when a species is oxidized. A reduction half-reaction shows the number of electrons gained when a species is reduced.

- The fact that an oxidation process must always be coupled with a reduction process provides a basis for using half-reactions to balance redox equations.

## Vocabulary

- half-reaction (p. 651)
- oxidation (p. 637)
- oxidation-number method (p. 644)
- oxidation–reduction reaction (p. 636)
- oxidizing agent (p. 638)
- redox reaction (p. 636)
- reducing agent (p. 638)
- reduction (p. 637)
- species (p. 650)

## Using the Vocabulary

To reinforce chapter vocabulary, have students write a sentence using each term. **L2** **ELL**

## Review Strategies

- Have students give an example for each of the rules for determining oxidation numbers. **L2**

- Have students create a chart or table to compare the two different methods used for balancing oxidation-reduction reactions. **L2**

- Problems from Appendix A or the **Supplemental Problems** booklet can be used for review. **L2**

- Have students summarize in their own words the steps for balancing oxidation-reduction reactions by the oxidation number method and by the method of half-reactions. **L2**

For additional help with vocabulary, have students access the Vocabulary PuzzleMaker online.

chemistrymc.com/
vocabulary_puzzlemaker

## EXAM*VIEW*® PRO

### Use Exam*View*® Pro Testmaker CD-ROM to:

- Create **multiple versions** of tests.
- Create **modified** tests with one mouse click for struggling students.
- **Edit** existing questions and add your own questions.
- **Build** tests based on national curriculum standards.

**National Science Content Standards**
Pages 656–657
UCP.1, UCP.3; B.1, B.3, B.6; E.2

## Concept Mapping

**32.** 1. redox reaction; 2. half-reactions; 3. oxidation; 4. reduction; 5. lose electrons; 6. gain electrons; 7. increases; 8. decreases

## Mastering Concepts

**33.** All oxidation–reduction reactions involve the transfer of electrons.

**34.** Electrons are lost; electrons are gained.

**35.** alkaline earth metals = +2; alkali metals = +1

**36.** Oxidation number increases; oxidation number decreases.

**37.** If an atom loses an electron, some other species must gain the electron.

**38.** oxidizing agent, $Ag^+$; reducing agent, Fe; $Ag^+$ is reduced; Fe is oxidized.

**39.** The total charge on the left-hand side does not equal the total charge on the right-hand side.

**40.** The change in oxidation number equals the number of electrons lost in oxidation, gained in reduction.

**41.** The type of solution provides the $H^+$ and $OH^-$ ions needed to balance the redox equation because they are readily available.

**42.** reduction; Electrons are gained and the oxidation number for Zn decreases.

**43.** half-reaction

## Mastering Problems

Complete solutions to Chapter Assessment problems can be found in the **Solutions Manual.**

### Oxidation and Reduction (20.1)
#### Level 1

**44. a.** Ga is oxidized, Br is reduced.
   **b.** Zn is oxidized, H is reduced.
   **c.** Mg is oxidized, N is reduced.

**658**

---

**Chemistry Online**

*Go to the Chemistry Web site at* **chemistrymc.com** *for additional Chapter 20 Assessment.*

## Concept Mapping

**32.** Complete the concept map using the following terms: decreases, half-reactions, gain electrons, reduction, lose electrons, redox reaction, oxidation, increases.

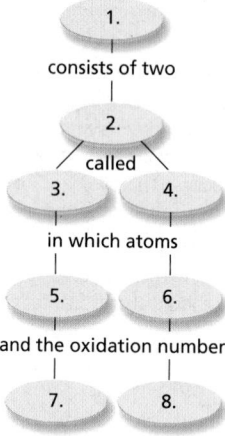

## Mastering Concepts

**33.** What is the main characteristic of oxidation–reduction reactions? (20.1)

**34.** In terms of electrons, what happens when an atom is oxidized? When an atom is reduced? (20.1)

**35.** What is the oxidation number of alkaline earth metals in their compounds? Of alkali metals? (20.1)

**36.** How does the oxidation number change when an element is oxidized? When it is reduced? (20.1)

**37.** Explain why oxidation and reduction must occur simultaneously. (20.1)

**38.** Identify the oxidizing agent and the reducing agent in the following equation. Explain your answer. (20.2)

$$Fe(s) + Ag^+(aq) \rightarrow Fe^{2+}(aq) + Ag(s)$$

---

**39.** How can you tell that the redox equation in question 38 is not balanced? (20.2)

**40.** How does the change in oxidation number in an oxidation process relate to the number of electrons lost? How does the change in oxidation number in a reduction process relate to the number of electrons gained? (20.2)

**41.** Before you attempt to balance the equation for a redox reaction, why do you need to know whether the reaction takes place in acidic or basic solution? (20.3)

**42.** Does the following equation represent a reduction or an oxidation process? Explain your answer. (20.3)

$$Zn^{2+} + 2e^- \rightarrow Zn$$

**43.** What term is used for the type of reaction represented in question 42? (20.3)

## Mastering Problems
### Oxidation and Reduction (20.1)

**44.** Identify the species oxidized and the species reduced in each of these redox equations.

   **a.** $3Br_2 + 2Ga \rightarrow 2GaBr_3$
   **b.** $HCl + Zn \rightarrow ZnCl_2 + H_2$
   **c.** $Mg + N_2 \rightarrow Mg_3N_2$

**45.** Identify the oxidizing agent and the reducing agent in each of these redox equations.

   **a.** $H_2S + Cl_2 \rightarrow 2HCl + S$
   **b.** $N_2 + 3H_2 \rightarrow 2NH_3$
   **c.** $2Na + I_2 \rightarrow 2NaI$

**46.** Identify each of these half-reactions as either oxidation or reduction.

   **a.** $Al \rightarrow Al^{3+} + 3e^-$
   **b.** $NO_2 \rightarrow NO_3^- + e^-$
   **c.** $Cu^{2+} + e^- \rightarrow Cu^+$

**47.** Determine the oxidation number of the bold element in these substances and ions.

   **a.** $Ca\mathbf{Cr}O_4$    **c.** $\mathbf{N}O_2^-$
   **b.** $Na\mathbf{H}SO_4$    **d.** $\mathbf{Br}O_3^-$

**48.** Determine the net change of oxidation number of each of the elements in these redox equations.

   **a.** $C + O_2 \rightarrow CO_2$
   **b.** $Cl_2 + ZnI_2 \rightarrow ZnCl_2 + I_2$
   **c.** $CdO + CO \rightarrow Cd + CO_2$

**49.** Which of these equations does **not** represent a redox reaction? Explain your answer.

   **a.** $LiOH + HNO_3 \rightarrow LiNO_3 + H_2O$
   **b.** $Ag + S \rightarrow Ag_2S$
   **c.** $MgI_2 + Br_2 \rightarrow MgBr_2 + I_2$

**chemistrymc.com/chapter_test**

---

**45. a.** $Cl_2$ is the oxidizing agent, $H_2S$ is the reducing agent.
   **b.** $N_2$ is the oxidizing agent, $H_2$ is the reducing agent.
   **c.** $I_2$ is the oxidizing agent, Na is the reducing agent.

### Resource Manager

**Chapter Assessment,** pp. 115–120 **L2**
**Supplemental Problems,** Ch. 20
**ExamView® Pro CD-ROM**
**MindJogger Videoquizzes DVD/VHS**
**Solutions Manual,** Ch. 20
**Chemistry Interactive CD-ROM,**
  Ch. 20 quiz

**50.** Identify each of these half-reactions as either oxidation or reduction.

  **a.** $Fe^{3+} \rightarrow Fe^{2+}$
  **b.** $HPO_3^{2-} \rightarrow HPO_4^{2-}$
  **c.** $BCl_3 \rightarrow B_2Cl_4$

**51.** Determine the oxidation number of nitrogen in each of these molecules or ions.

  **a.** $NH_3$    **c.** $N_2H_4$    **e.** $N_2O$
  **b.** $KCN$    **d.** $NO_3^-$    **f.** $NF_3$

**52.** Determine the oxidation number of each element in these compounds or ions.

  **a.** $FeCr_2O_4$ (iron(II) chromite)
  **b.** $Au_2(SeO_4)_3$ (gold(III) selenate)
  **c.** $Ni(CN)_2$ (nickel(II) cyanide)

**53.** Explain how the sulfite ion ($SO_3^{2-}$) differs from sulfur trioxide ($SO_3$).

## Balancing Redox Equations (20.2)

**54.** Use the oxidation-number method to balance these redox equations.

  **a.** $CO + I_2O_5 \rightarrow I_2 + CO_2$
  **b.** $Cl_2 + NaOH \rightarrow NaCl + HOCl$
  **c.** $SO_2 + Br_2 + H_2O \rightarrow HBr + H_2SO_4$
  **d.** $HBrO_3 \rightarrow Br_2 + H_2O + O_2$

**55.** Use the oxidation-number method to balance the following ionic redox equations.

  **a.** $Al + I_2 \rightarrow Al^{3+} + I^-$
  **b.** $MnO_2 + Br^- \rightarrow Mn^{2+} + Br_2$ (in acid solution)
  **c.** $Cu + NO_3^- \rightarrow Cu^{2+} + NO$ (in acid solution)
  **d.** $Zn + NO_3^- \rightarrow Zn^{2+} + NO_2$ (in acid solution)

**56.** Use the oxidation-number method to balance these redox equations.

  **a.** $PbS + O_2 \rightarrow PbO + SO_2$
  **b.** $NaWO_3 + NaOH + O_2 \rightarrow Na_2WO_4 + H_2O$
  **c.** $NH_3 + CuO \rightarrow Cu + N_2 + H_2O$
  **d.** $Al_2O_3 + C + Cl_2 \rightarrow AlCl_3 + CO$

**57.** Use the oxidation-number method to balance these ionic redox equations.

  **a.** $MoCl_5 + S^{2-} \rightarrow MoS_2 + Cl^- + S$
  **b.** $Al + OH^- + H_2O \rightarrow H_2 + AlO_2^-$
  **c.** $TiCl_6^{2-} + Zn \rightarrow Ti^{3+} + Cl^- + Zn^{2+}$

## Half-Reactions (20.3)

**58.** Write the oxidation and reduction half-reactions represented in each of these redox equations. Write the half-reactions in net ionic form if they occur in aqueous solution.

  **a.** $PbO(s) + NH_3(g) \rightarrow N_2(g) + H_2O(l) + Pb(s)$

  **b.** $I_2(s) + Na_2S_2O_3(aq) \rightarrow Na_2S_2O_4(aq) + NaI(aq)$
  **c.** $Sn(s) + 2HCl(aq) \rightarrow SnCl_2(aq) + H_2(g)$

**59.** Use the half-reaction method to balance these equations. Add water molecules and hydrogen ions (in acid solutions) or hydroxide ions (in basic solutions) as needed. Keep balanced equations in net ionic form.

  **a.** $Cl^-(aq) + NO_3^-(aq) \rightarrow ClO^-(aq) + NO(g)$ (in acid solution)
  **b.** $IO_3^-(aq) + Br^-(aq) \rightarrow Br_2(l) + IBr(s)$ (in acid solution)
  **c.** $I_2(s) + Na_2S_2O_3(aq) \rightarrow Na_2S_2O_4(aq) + NaI(aq)$ (in acid solution)

**60.** Use the half-reaction method to balance these equations for redox reactions. Add water molecules and hydrogen ions (in acid solutions) or hydroxide ions (in basic solutions) as needed.

  **a.** $NH_3(g) + NO_2(g) \rightarrow N_2(g) + H_2O(l)$
  **b.** $Mn^{2+}(aq) + BiO_3^-(aq) \rightarrow Bi^{2+}(aq) + MnO_4^-(aq)$ (in acid solution)
  **c.** $Br_2 \rightarrow Br^- + BrO_3^-$ (in basic solution)

**61.** Balance the following redox chemical equation. Rewrite the equation in full ionic form, then derive the net ionic equation and balance by the half-reaction method. Give the final answer as it is shown below but with the balancing coefficients.

  $KMnO_4(aq) + FeSO_4(aq) + H_2SO_4(aq) \rightarrow$
  $Fe_2(SO_4)_3(aq) + MnSO_4(aq) + K_2SO_4(aq) + H_2O(l)$

**62.** Balance this equation in the same manner as in question 61 above.

  $HNO_3(aq) + K_2Cr_2O_4(aq) + Fe(NO_3)_2(aq) \rightarrow$
  $KNO_3(aq) + Fe(NO_3)_3(aq) + Cr(NO_3)_2(aq) + H_2O(l)$

## Mixed Review

*Sharpen your problem-solving skills by answering the following.*

**63.** Determine the oxidation number of the bold element in each of the following examples.

  **a.** $OF_2$    **c.** $RuO_4$
  **b.** $UO_2^{2+}$    **d.** $Fe_2O_3$

**64.** Identify the reducing agents in these equations.

  **a.** $4NH_3 + 5O_2 \rightarrow 4NO + 6H_2O$
  **b.** $Na_2SO_4 + 4C \rightarrow Na_2S + 4CO$
  **c.** $4IrF_5 + Ir \rightarrow 5IrF_4$

**46. a.** oxidation
  **b.** oxidation
  **c.** reduction

**47. a.** $+6$
  **b.** $+6$
  **c.** $+3$
  **d.** $+5$

**48. a.** C, $+4$; O, $-2$
  **b.** I $+1$, Cl, $-1$; Zn, no change
  **c.** C, $+2$; Cd, $-2$; O, no change

**49.** Choice **a** is not redox because none of the atoms in the reaction undergo a change in oxidation number.

**50. a.** reduction
  **b.** oxidation
  **c.** reduction

**51. a.** $-3$    **d.** $+5$
  **b.** $-3$    **e.** $+1$
  **c.** $-2$    **f.** $+3$

**52. a.** Fe, $+2$; Cr, $+3$; O, $-2$
  **b.** Au, $+3$; Se, $+6$; O, $-2$
  **c.** Ni, $+2$; C, $+2$; N, $-3$

**53.** $SO_3^{2-}$ is a polyatomic ion and the oxidation number of sulfur is $+4$. $SO_3$ is a compound and the oxidation number of S in this compound is $+6$.

## Balancing Redox Equations (20.2)

### Level 1

**54. a.** $5CO + I_2O_5 \rightarrow I_2 + 5CO_2$
  **b.** $Cl_2 + NaOH \rightarrow NaCl + HOCl$
  **c.** $SO_2 + Br_2 + 2H_2O \rightarrow 2HBr + H_2SO_4$
  **d.** $4HBrO_3 \rightarrow 2Br_2 + 2H_2O + 5O_2$

**55. a.** $2Al + 3I_2 \rightarrow 2Al^{3+} + 6I^-$
  **b.** $MnO_2 + 2Br^- + 4H^+ \rightarrow Mn^{2+} + Br_2 + 2H_2O$
  **c.** $3Cu + 2NO_3^- + 8H^+ \rightarrow 3Cu^{2+} + 2NO + 4H_2O$
  **d.** $Zn + 2NO_3^- + 4H^+ \rightarrow Zn^{2+} + 2NO_2 + 2H_2O$

### Level 2

**56. a.** $2PbS + 3O_2 \rightarrow 2PbO + 2SO_2$
  **b.** $4NaWO_3 + 4NaOH + O_2 \rightarrow 4Na_2WO_4 + 2H_2O$
  **c.** $2NH_3 + 3CuO \rightarrow 3Cu + N_2 + 3H_2O$
  **d.** $Al_2O_3 + 3Cl_2 + 3C \rightarrow 2AlCl_3 + 3CO$

**57. a.** $2MoCl_5 + 5S^{2-} \rightarrow 2MoS_2 + 10Cl^- + S$
  **b.** $2Al + 2OH^- + 2H_2O \rightarrow 3H_2 + 2AlO_2^-$
  **c.** $2TiCl_6^{2-} + Zn \rightarrow 2Ti^{3+} + 12Cl^- + Zn^{2+}$

## Half-Reactions (20.3)

### Level 1

**58. a.** $NH_3(g) \rightarrow N_2(g) + 3e^-$ oxidation
  $PbO(s) + 2e^- \rightarrow Pb(s)$ reduction
  **b.** $I_2(s) + 2e^- \rightarrow 2I^-(aq)$ reduction
  $2S_2O_3^{2-}(aq) \rightarrow 2S_2O_4^{2-}(aq) + 2e^-$ oxidation

**659**

**c.** $Sn(s) \rightarrow Sn^{2+}(aq) + 2e^-$ (oxidation)
$2H^+(aq) + 2e^- \rightarrow H_2(g)$ reduction

**59. a.** $3Cl^- + 2NO_3^- + 2H^+ \rightarrow 3ClO^- + 2NO + H_2O$

**b.** $6H^+ + 5Br^- + IO_3^- \rightarrow 2Br_2 + IBr + 3H_2O$

**c.** $S_2O_3^{-2}(aq) + H_2O(l) + I_2(s) \rightarrow S_2O_4^{-2}(aq) + 2H^+(aq) + 2I^-(aq)$

## Level 2

**60. a.** $8NH_3 + 6NO_2 \rightarrow 7N_2 + 12H_2O$

**b.** $3Mn^{2+} + 5BiO_3^- + 6H^+ \rightarrow 5Bi^{2+} + 3MnO_4^- + 3H_2O$

**c.** $3Br_2 + 6OH^- \rightarrow 5Br^- + BrO_3^- + 3H_2O$

**61.** $2KMnO_4 + 10FeSO_4 + 8H_2SO_4 \rightarrow 5Fe_2(SO_4)_3 + 2MnSO_4 + K_2SO_4 + 8H_2O$

**62.** $2Fe(NO_3)_2(aq) + 8HNO_3(aq) + K_2Cr_2O_4(aq) \rightarrow 2KNO_3(aq) + 2Fe(NO_3)_3(aq) + 2Cr(NO_3)_2(aq) + 4H_2O(l)$

## Mixed Review

**63. a.** O, +2
**b.** U, +6
**c.** Ru, +8
**d.** Fe, +3

**64. a.** $NH_3$
**b.** C
**c.** Ir

**65. a.** $Fe + Te^{2+} \rightarrow Fe^{2+} + Te$
**b.** $3IO_4^- + 2Al + 6H^+ \rightarrow 3IO_3^- + 2Al^{3+} + 3H_2O$
**c.** $4I_2 + N_2O + 5H_2O \rightarrow 8I^- + 2NO_3^- + 10H^+$

**66. a.** $3P + 2H_2O + 5HNO_3 \rightarrow 3H_3PO_4 + 5NO$
**b.** $4HCl + 2KClO_3 \rightarrow Cl_2 + 2ClO_2 + 2KCl + 2H_2O$

**67. a.** $12H_2O + 5Sb^{3+} + 2MnO_4^- \rightarrow 5SbO_4^{3-} + 2Mn^{2+} + 24H^+$
**b.** $N_2O + 2ClO^- + 2OH^- \rightarrow 2NO_2^- + 2Cl^- + H_2O$

**68. a.** $3Mg + 2Fe^{3+} \rightarrow 3Mg^{2+} + 2Fe$
**b.** $ClO_3^- + 3SO_2 + 3H_2O \rightarrow Cl^- + 3SO_4^{2-} + 6H^+$

**660**

---

**65.** Write a balanced ionic redox equation using the following pairs of redox half-reactions.
**a.** $Fe \rightarrow Fe^{2+} + 2e^-$
$Te^{2+} + 2e^- \rightarrow Te$
**b.** $IO_4^- + 2e^- \rightarrow IO_3^-$
$Al \rightarrow Al^{3+} + 3e^-$ (in acid solution)
**c.** $I_2 + 2e^- \rightarrow 2I^-$
$N_2O \rightarrow NO_3^- + 4e^-$ (in acid solution)

**66.** Balance these redox equations by any method.
**a.** $P + H_2O + HNO_3 \rightarrow H_3PO_4 + NO$
**b.** $KClO_3 + HCl \rightarrow Cl_2 + ClO_2 + H_2O + KCl$

**67.** Balance these ionic redox equations by any method.
**a.** $Sb^{3+} + MnO_4^- \rightarrow SbO_4^{3-} + Mn^{2+}$ in acid solution
**b.** $N_2O + ClO^- \rightarrow Cl^- + NO_2^-$ in basic solution

**68.** Balance these ionic redox equations by any method.
**a.** $Mg + Fe^{3+} \rightarrow Mg^{2+} + Fe$
**b.** $ClO_3^- + SO_2 \rightarrow Cl^- + SO_4^{2-}$ (in acid solution)

## Thinking Critically

**69. Applying Concepts** The following equations show redox reactions that are sometimes used in the laboratory to generate pure nitrogen gas and pure dinitrogen monoxide gas (nitrous oxide, $N_2O$).

$NH_4NO_2(s) \rightarrow N_2(g) + 2H_2O(l)$
$NH_4NO_3(s) \rightarrow N_2O(g) + 2H_2O(l)$

**a.** Determine the oxidation number of each element in the two equations and then make diagrams as in Example Problem 20-2 showing the changes in oxidation numbers that occur in each reaction.
**b.** Identify the atom that is oxidized and the atom that is reduced in each of the two reactions.
**c.** Identify the oxidizing and reducing agents in each of the two reactions.
**d.** Write a sentence telling how the electron transfer taking place in these two reactions differs from that taking place here.
$2AgNO_3 + Zn \rightarrow Zn(NO_3)_2 + 2Ag$

**70. Comparing and Contrasting** All redox reactions involve a transfer of electrons, but this transfer can take place between different types of atoms as illustrated by the two equations below. How does electron transfer in the first reaction differ from electron transfer in the second reaction?

$3Pb^{2+}(aq) + 2Cr(s) \rightarrow 2Cr^{3+}(aq) + 3Pb(s)$
$ClO_3^-(aq) + NO_2^-(aq) \rightarrow ClO_2^-(aq) + NO_3^-(aq)$

**71. Using Numbers** Examine the net ionic equation below for the reaction that occurs when the thiosulfate ion ($S_2O_3^{2-}$) is oxidized to the tetrathionate ion

---

($S_4O_6^{2-}$). Balance the equation using the half-reaction method. The structures of the two ions will help you to determine the oxidation numbers to use.

$S_2O_3^{2-} + I_2 \rightarrow I^- + S_4O_6^{2-}$ (in acid solution)

Thiosulfate ion ($S_2O_3^{2-}$)  Tetrathionate ion ($S_4O_6^{2-}$)

**72. Predicting** Consider the fact that all of the following are stable compounds. What can you infer about the oxidation state of phosphorus in its compounds?

$PH_3, PCl_3, P_2H_4, PCl_5, H_3PO_4, Na_3PO_3$

## Writing in Chemistry

**73.** Research the role of oxidation–reduction reactions in the manufacture of steel. Write a summary of your findings, including appropriate diagrams and equations representing the reactions.

**74.** Practice your technical writing skills by writing (in your own words) a procedure for cleaning tarnished silverware by a redox chemical process. Be sure to include background information describing the process as well as logical steps that would enable anyone to accomplish the task.

## Cumulative Review

*Refresh your understanding of previous chapters by answering the following.*

**75.** How do the following characteristics apply to the electron configurations of transition metals? (Chapter 7)
**a.** Ions vary in charge.
**b.** Many elements have high melting points.
**c.** Many of their solids are colored.
**d.** Some elements are hard solids.

**76.** When iron(III) chloride reacts in an atmosphere of pure oxygen the following occurs:
$4FeCl_3(s) + 3O_2(g) \rightarrow 2Fe_2O_3(s) + 6Cl_2(g)$
If 45.0 g of iron(III) chloride reacts and 20.5 g of iron(III) oxide is recovered, determine the percent yield. (Chapter 12)

---

**69. a.**

$$\overset{+3e^-}{\overbrace{\phantom{xxxxxxxxxx}}}$$
$\underset{-3+1}{N}\underset{+3-2}{H_4} \underset{}{N}\underset{}{O_2}(s) \rightarrow \underset{0}{N_2}(g) + \underset{+1 -2}{2H_2O}(l)$
$$\underset{-3e^-}{\underbrace{\phantom{xxxxxxxxxx}}}$$

$$\overset{+4e^-}{\overbrace{\phantom{xxxxxxxxxx}}}$$
$\underset{-3+1}{N}\underset{+5-2}{H_4} \underset{}{N}\underset{}{O_3}(s) \rightarrow \underset{+1 -2}{N_2O}(g) + \underset{+1 -2}{2H_2O}(l)$
$$\underset{-4e^-}{\underbrace{\phantom{xxxxxxxxxx}}}$$

**b.** $N^{-3}$ to $N_2$ loses 3 e$^-$ (oxidized); $N^{+3}$ to $N_2$ gains 3 e$^-$ (reduced)
$N^{-3}$ to $N^{+1}$ loses 4 e$^-$ (oxidized); $N^{+5}$ to $N^{+1}$ gains 4 e$^-$ (reduced)
**c.** $NO_2^-$ and $NO_3^-$ (oxidizing agents); $NH_4^+$ (reducing agent)
**d.** In the first two reactions, nitrogen is oxidized and reduced. The third reaction involves redox between two different elements.

*Use these questions and the test-taking tip to prepare for your standardized test.*

**1.** The reducing agent in a redox reaction is all of the following EXCEPT

 **a.** the substance oxidized.
 **b.** the electron acceptor.
 **c.** the reducer of another substance.
 **d.** the electron donor.

**2.** What are the oxidation numbers of the elements in $CuSO_4$?

 **a.** $Cu = +2$, $S = +6$, $O = -2$
 **b.** $Cu = +3$, $S = +5$, $O = -2$
 **c.** $Cu = +2$, $S = +2$, $O = -1$
 **d.** $Cu = +2$, $S = 0$, $O = -2$

**3.** For the reaction $X + Y \rightarrow XY$, the element that will be reduced is the one that is

 **a.** more reactive.     **c.** more electronegative.
 **b.** more massive.      **d.** more radioactive.

**4.** The net ionic reaction between iodine and lead(IV) oxide is shown below:
$$I_2(s) + PbO_2(s) \rightarrow IO_3^-(aq) + Pb^{2+}(aq)$$
If the reaction takes place in acidic solution, which is the balanced equation?

 **a.** $I_2(s) + 5PbO_2(s) + 4H_2O(l) \rightarrow 2IO_3^-(aq) + 5Pb^{2+}(aq) + 8OH^-(aq)$
 **b.** $I_2(s) + 5PbO_2(s) + H^+(aq) \rightarrow 2IO_3^-(aq) + 5Pb^{2+}(aq) + H_2O(l)$
 **c.** $I_2(s) + 5PbO_2(s) + 4H_2O(l) \rightarrow 2IO_3^-(aq) + 5Pb^{2+}(aq) + 8H^+(aq)$
 **d.** $I_2(s) + 5PbO_2(s) + 8H^+(aq) \rightarrow 2IO_3^-(aq) + 5Pb^{2+}(aq) + 4H_2O(l)$

**5.** The reaction between sodium iodide and chlorine is shown below:
$$2NaI(aq) + Cl_2(aq) \rightarrow 2NaCl(aq) + I_2(aq)$$
The oxidation state of Na remains unchanged for which reason?

 **a.** $Na^+$ is a spectator ion
 **b.** $Na^+$ cannot be reduced
 **c.** Na is an uncombined element
 **d.** $Na^+$ is a monatomic ion

**6.** The reaction between nickel and copper(II) chloride is shown below:
$$Ni(s) + CuCl_2(aq) \rightarrow Cu(s) + NiCl_2(aq)$$
What are the half-reactions for this redox reaction?

 **a.** $Ni \rightarrow Ni^{2+} + 2e^-$, $Cl_2 \rightarrow 2Cl^- + 2e^-$

 **b.** $Ni \rightarrow Ni^+ + e^-$, $Cu^+ + e^- \rightarrow Cu$
 **c.** $Ni \rightarrow Ni^{2+} + 2e^-$, $Cu^{2+} + 2e^- \rightarrow Cu$
 **d.** $Ni \rightarrow Ni^{2+} + 2e^-$, $2Cu^+ + 2e^- \rightarrow Cu$

**Interpreting Tables** Use the table to answer questions 7–9.

| Data for Elements in the Redox Reaction $Zn + HNO_3 \rightarrow Zn(NO_3)_2 + NO_2 + H_2O$ | | |
|---|---|---|
| **Element** | **Oxidation Number** | **Complex ion of which element is a part** |
| Zn | 0 | none |
| Zn in $Zn(NO_3)_2$ | +2 | none |
| H in $HNO_3$ | +1 | none |
| H in $H_2O$ | ? | none |
| N in $HNO_3$ | ? | $NO_3^-$ |
| N in $NO_2$ | +4 | none |
| N in $Zn(NO_3)_2$ | ? | $NO_3^-$ |
| O in $HNO_3$ | -2 | $NO_3^-$ |
| O in $NO_2$ | ? | none |
| O in $Zn(NO_3)_2$ | ? | $NO_3^-$ |
| O in $H_2O$ | -2 | none |

**7.** Which of these elements forms a monatomic ion that is a spectator in the redox reaction?

 **a.** Zn     **c.** N
 **b.** O      **d.** H

**8.** What is the oxidation number of N in $Zn(NO_3)_2$?

 **a.** +3     **c.** +1
 **b.** +5     **d.** +6

**9.** What is the element that is oxidized in this reaction?

 **a.** Zn     **c.** N
 **b.** O      **d.** H

---

### TEST-TAKING TIP

**Write It Down!** Most tests ask you a large number of questions in a small amount of time. Write down your work wherever possible. Write out the half-reactions for a redox problem, and make sure they add up. Do math on paper, not in your head. Underline and reread important facts in passages and diagrams—don't try to memorize them.

**70.** The first reaction shows oxidation and reduction of a metal and a metal ion. The second shows oxidation and reduction of nonmetals within polyatomic ions.

**71. a.** $2S_2O_3^{2-} + I_2 \rightarrow 2I^- + S_4O_6^{2-}$ (in acid solution)

**72.** Phosphorus has several oxidation states ($-3$, $+2$, $+3$, $+5$) that make phosphorus very flexible when combining with nonmetals.

## Cumulative Review

**75. a.** Transition metals can lose $ns^2$ outer electrons, forming 2+ ions. They can also move inner d electrons to the outer energy level and form ions of 3+ or higher.
 **b.** High melting points are due to unpaired electrons in the d sublevel.
 **c.** Electrons in the d sublevel can absorb visible light of specific wavelengths as they move to an excited state.
 **d.** Hardness is a property determined by the number of unpaired d electrons. The more unpaired d electrons, the harder the solid.

**76.** $45.0 \text{ g FeCl}_3 \times \dfrac{1 \text{ mol FeCl}_3}{162.20 \text{ g FeCl}_3} \times \dfrac{2 \text{ mol Fe}_2O_3}{4 \text{ mol FeCl}_3} \times \dfrac{159.69 \text{ g Fe}_2O_3}{1 \text{ mol Fe}_2O_3} =$

$22.15 \text{ g Fe}_2O_3$

$\dfrac{20.5 \text{ g Fe}_2O_3}{22.15 \text{ g Fe}_2O_3} \times 100 =$

$92.5\%$ yield

---

## Standardized Test Practice

**1.** b      **6.** c
**2.** a      **7.** d
**3.** c      **8.** b
**4.** d      **9.** a
**5.** a

# Resource Manager

| Section | Objectives | Activities/Features |
|---|---|---|
| **Section 21.1**<br>**Voltaic Cells**<br>2 sessions<br>1 block | **1. Describe** a way to obtain electrical energy from a redox reaction.<br>**2. Identify** the parts of a voltaic cell, and **explain** how each part operates.<br>**3. Calculate** cell potentials and **determine** the spontaneity of redox reactions. | **Discovery Lab:** A Lemon Battery? p. 663<br>**ChemLab CBL:** Voltaic Cell Potentials, pp. 688–689 |
| **Section 21.2**<br>**Types of Batteries**<br>1 session<br>1/2 block | **4. Describe** the structure, composition, and operation of the typical carbon-zinc dry cell battery.<br>**5. Distinguish** between primary and secondary batteries and give two examples of each type.<br>**6. Explain** the structure and operation of the hydrogen-oxygen fuel cell.<br>**7. Describe** the process of corrosion of iron and methods to prevent corrosion. | **Careers Using Chemistry:** Electrochemist, p. 677<br>**Problem-Solving Lab:** Can the simplest atom power a car? p. 679<br>**MiniLab:** Corrosion, p. 681 |
| **Section 21.3**<br>**Electrolysis**<br>2 sessions<br>1 1/2 blocks | **8. Describe** how it is possible to reverse a spontaneous redox reaction in an electrochemical cell.<br>**9. Compare** the reactions involved in the electrolysis of molten sodium chloride with those in the electrolysis of brine.<br>**10. Discuss** the importance of electrolysis in the smelting and purification of metals. | **History Connection,** p. 684<br>**Chemistry and Technology:** Fuel Cells, p. 690 |

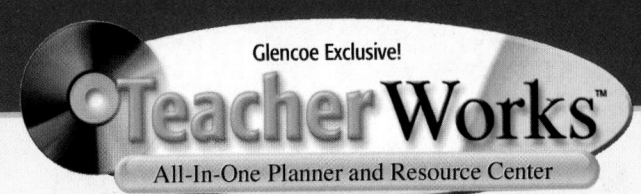

Glencoe Exclusive!
**TeacherWorks™**
All-In-One Planner and Resource Center

| National Science Content Standards | State/Local Standards | Reproducible Masters | Transparencies |
|---|---|---|---|
| UCP.1, UCP.3; B.3, B.6; E.2; G.3 | | **Study Guide for Content Mastery,** pp. 121–123 **L2** <br> **ChemLab and MiniLab Worksheets,** pp. 82–84 **L2** <br> **Challenge Problems,** p. 21 **L3** <br> **Forensics Laboratory Manual,** pp. 25–35 **L2** | **Section Focus** <br> Transparency 78 **L1** **ELL** <br> **Teaching** <br> Transparency 63 **L2** **ELL** <br> **Math Skills** <br> Transparency 32 **L2** **ELL** |
| UCP.1, UCP.3; A.1; B.3, B.6; E.1, E.2; F.6; G.1, G.3 | | **Study Guide for Content Mastery,** pp. 124–125 **L2** <br> **ChemLab and MiniLab Worksheets,** p. 81 **L2** | **Section Focus** <br> Transparency 79 **L1** **ELL** <br> **Teaching** <br> Transparency 64 **L2** **ELL** <br> **Math Skills** <br> Transparency 33 **L2** **ELL** |
| UCP.1, UCP.3; A.1, A.2; B.3, B.6; E.2; F.3, F.4, F.6; G.1, G.3 | | **Study Guide for Content Mastery,** p. 126 **L2** <br> **Laboratory Manual,** pp. 161–168 **L2** | **Section Focus** <br> Transparency 80 **L1** **ELL** <br> **Teaching** <br> Transparency 65 **L2** **ELL** |

**Key to National Science Content Standards:** UCP = Unifying Concepts and Processes, A = Science as Inquiry, B = Physical Science, C = Life Science, D = Earth and Space Sciences, E = Science and Technology, F = Science in Personal and Social Perspectives, G = History and Nature of Science

Refer to pages 4T–5T of the Teacher Guide for an explanation of the National Science Content Standards correlations.

# Resource Manager

## Materials List

### ChemLab (pages 688–689)
copper strip, aluminum strip, magnesium strip, zinc strip, $1M$ copper(II) nitrate, $1M$ aluminum nitrate, $1M$ magnesium nitrate, $1M$ zinc nitrate, $1M$ potassium nitrate, Beral-type pipette (5), filter paper, forceps, steel wool, 24-well microplate, CBL system, voltage probe

### Discovery Lab (page 663)
lemon pieces, zinc metal strip, copper metal strip, voltmeter with leads

### MiniLab (page 681)
iron nails (4), magnesium ribbon (10 cm), copper metal (10 cm), 150-mL beakers (4), sandpaper, distilled water, saltwater solution

### Demonstration (pages 670–671)
flashbulb or flashcube, steel wool, 14-gauge copper wire (15 cm), magnesium ribbon (20 cm), $6M$ HCl, 150-mL beaker, ring stand and clamp, connecting leads with alligator clips at each end (2)

## Preparation of Solutions

Quantities are for a class of 30 students.

### ChemLab (pages 688–689)
**$1M$ aluminum nitrate ($Al(NO_3)_3$)** Dissolve 37.5 g $Al(NO_3)_3 \cdot 9H_2O$ in 60 mL distilled water. Make up to 100 mL final volume with distilled water.

**$1M$ copper(II) nitrate ($Cu(NO_3)_2$)** Dissolve 24.2 g $Cu(NO_3)_2 \cdot 3H_2O$ in 60 mL distilled water. Make up to 100 mL final volume with distilled water.

**$1M$ magnesium nitrate ($Mg(NO_3)_2$)** Dissolve 14.8 g $Mg(NO_3)_2$ in 60 mL distilled water. Make up to 100 mL final volume with distilled water.

**$1M$ potassium nitrate ($KNO_3$)** Dissolve 10.1 g $KNO_3$ in 60 mL distilled water. Make up to 100 mL final volume with distilled water.

**$1M$ zinc nitrate ($Zn(NO_3)_2$)** Dissolve 29.7 g $Zn(NO_3)_2 \cdot 6H_2O$ in 60 mL distilled water. Make up to 100 mL final volume with distilled water.

### MiniLab (page 681)
**saltwater solution** Dissolve 60 g sodium chloride (NaCl) in 2 L water.

### Demonstration (pages 670–671)
**$6M$ hydrochloric acid** Add 50 mL concentrated ($12M$) hydrochloric acid to 50 mL distilled water while stirring. **CAUTION:** Do NOT add the water to the acid.

## Assessment Resources

**Chapter Assessment,** pp. 121–126
**MindJogger Videoquizzes** DVD/VHS
**Alternate Assessment in the Science Classroom**
**ExamView® Pro CD-ROM**
**Solutions Manual,** Chapter 21
**Supplemental Problems,** Chapter 21
**Performance Assessment in the Science Classroom**
**Chemistry Interactive CD-ROM,** Chapter 21 quiz

## Additional Resources

**Spanish Resources** ELL
**Guided Reading Audio Program,** Chapter 21 ELL
**Cooperative Learning in the Science Classroom**
**Lab and Safety Skills in the Science Classroom**
**Lesson Plans**
**Block Scheduling Lesson Plans**
**Chemistrymc.com**

## Glencoe Technology

The following multimedia for this chapter are available from Glencoe.

**VIDEOTAPE/DVD**
MindJogger Videoquizzes,
Chapter 21

**CD-ROM**
**Chemistry: Matter and Change**
*Build an Electrochemical Cell,* Experiment
*Electrochemistry,* Video
*An Electrochemical Flash,* Demonstration
*Galvanic Cell,* Animation
*Building a Battery,* Exploration
*Electrolysis of KI,* Demonstration
*Chromium Electroplating,* Video

**CD-ROM**
**ExamView® Pro**
**Testmaker**

**CD-ROM**
**Interactive Chalkboard**

**CD-ROM**
**TeacherWorks**™

## Multiple Learning Styles

Look for the following icons for strategies that emphasize different learning modalities.

**Kinesthetic**
Reinforcement, p. 676; Differentiated Instruction, p. 677

**Visual-Spatial**
Differentiated Instruction, pp. 665, 668, 680; Chemistry Journal, p. 667; Check for Understanding, p. 672

**Interpersonal**
Reinforcement, p. 665; Reteach, p. 672; Chemistry Journal, p. 681

**Intrapersonal**
Concept Development, p. 673; Extension, pp. 675, 684; Portfolio, p. 675; Differentiated Instruction, p. 683

**Linguistic**
Extension, p. 669; Chemistry Journal, p. 684

## Key to Teaching Strategies

 **L1** Level 1 activities should be appropriate for students with learning difficulties.

**L2** Level 2 activities should be within the ability range of all students.

**L3** Level 3 activities are designed for above-average students.

**ELL** ELL activities should be within the ability range of English Language Learners.

**COOP LEARN** Cooperative Learning activities are designed for small group work.

**P** These strategies represent student products that can be placed into a best-work portfolio.

 These strategies are useful in a block scheduling format.

## ✔ Assessment Planner

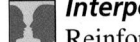

**Portfolio Assessment**
Portfolio, TWE, pp. 675, 691
Problem-Solving Lab, TWE, p. 679

**Performance Assessment**
Assessment, TWE, pp. 669, 671
Demonstration, TWE, p. 671
Discovery Lab, SE, p. 663
MiniLab, SE, TWE, p. 681
ChemLab, SE, TWE, pp. 688–689

**Knowledge Assessment**
Assessment, TWE, pp. 666, 674, 680, 682, 685, 687
Section Assessment, SE, pp. 672, 682, 687
Chapter Assessment, SE, pp. 692–695

**Skill Assessment**
Assessment, TWE, p. 672

## Tying to Previous Knowledge

Have students review the following concepts before studying this chapter.

Chapter 10: types of reactions, activity series of elements

Chapter 16: energy, chemical potential energy, spontaneous process

Chapter 20: oxidation, reduction half-reactions

## Using the Photo

Ask students to brainstorm a list of items that require some type of battery, such as the TV remote control in the photo. Students should be able to list items such as radios and CD players, calculators, toys, smoke detectors, clocks, cell phones, video cameras, computers, flashlights, car and lawn mower batteries.

Ask them to propose reasons why certain battery types are used in some household items but not others. Some expected responses could include size of the battery, how long the battery is used at any one time, cost, whether the battery produces enough voltage to power the object.

### PowerPoint® Presentations

This CD-ROM is an editable Microsoft® PowerPoint® presentation that includes:

• Section presentations
• Section checks
• Image bank
• Links to Chemistry Online
• All transparencies
• Animations
• Audio

# Electrochemistry

## What You'll Learn

▶ You will learn how oxidation–reduction reactions produce electric current.
▶ You will determine the voltage of the current produced by pairs of redox half-reactions.
▶ You will determine the direction of current flow for a particular pair of redox half-reactions.
▶ You will investigate how electric current can be used to carry out redox reactions.

## Why It's Important

You've probably used aluminum foil to cover food, and most kids have hidden under a blanket to read by flashlight. The manufacturing process for aluminum and the light from your flashlight involve electrochemistry.

### Chemistry Online

Visit the Chemistry Web site at chemistrymc.com to find links about electrochemistry.

You can look around you to see how important electricity is, from the lights in the room to the batteries that power the remote control, to the manufacturing processes that produce consumer goods. Electrochemistry is one method by which electricity can be generated for use.

## DISCOVERY LAB

### Purpose
Students will examine how a battery works.

### Safety and Disposal
Use the lemon pieces for several classes. Throw them in the trash at the end of the day. Clean and reuse the zinc and copper metal pieces.

### Teaching Strategies
• Introduce the concept by connecting a battery to the voltmeter and explaining the reading.
• You can use metals other than zinc and copper. Magnesium and iron are also good choices.

### Expected Results
Using zinc and copper, the voltmeter will read about 1.1 V. When one of the metals is removed from the lemon, the voltmeter

## DISCOVERY LAB

### A Lemon Battery?

**Y**ou can purchase a handy package of portable power at any convenience store—a battery. You also can craft a working battery from a lemon. How are these power sources alike?

#### Safety Precautions

 Always wear an apron and safety goggles in the lab. Use caution with electricity.

#### Procedure

1. Insert the zinc and copper strips into the lemon, about 2 cm apart from each other.
2. Attach the black lead from a voltmeter to the zinc and the red lead to the copper. Read and record the potential difference (voltage) from the voltmeter.
3. Remove one of the metals from the lemon and observe what happens to the potential difference on the voltmeter.

#### Analysis

What is the purpose of the zinc and copper metals? What is the purpose of the lemon?

**Materials**

lemon pieces
zinc metal strip
copper metal strip
voltmeter with leads

---

Section **21.1**

# Voltaic Cells

### Objectives

- **Describe** a way to obtain electrical energy from a redox reaction.
- **Identify** the parts of a voltaic cell and explain how each part operates.
- **Calculate** cell potentials and **determine** the spontaneity of redox reactions.

### Vocabulary

salt bridge
electrochemical cell
voltaic cell
half-cell
anode
cathode
reduction potential
standard hydrogen
 electrode
battery

You now know much of the basic chemistry on which advanced chemistry is based. This chapter introduces an important branch of chemistry called electrochemistry. Electrochemistry is the study of the process by which chemical energy is converted to electrical energy and vice versa.

## Redox in Electrochemistry

In Chapter 20, you learned that all redox reactions involve a transfer of electrons from the species that is oxidized to the species that is reduced. The **DISCOVERY LAB** illustrates the simple redox reaction in which zinc atoms are oxidized to form $Zn^{2+}$ ions. The two electrons donated from each zinc atom are accepted by a $Cu^{2+}$ ion, which changes to an atom of copper metal. The following net ionic equation illustrates the electron transfer that occurs.

$$\overset{\overset{\displaystyle 2e^-}{\frown}}{Zn(s) + Cu^{2+}(aq)} \rightarrow Zn^{2+}(aq) + Cu(s)$$

Two half-reactions make up this redox process:

$$Zn \rightarrow Zn^{2+} + 2e^- \text{ (oxidation half-reaction: electrons lost)}$$
$$Cu^{2+} + 2e^- \rightarrow Cu \text{ (reduction half-reaction: electrons gained)}$$

21.1 Voltaic Cells **663**

---

# 1 Focus

### Focus Transparency

Before presenting the lesson, display **Section Focus Transparency 78** on the overhead projector. Have students answer the accompanying questions using **Section Focus Transparency Master 78. L1 ELL**

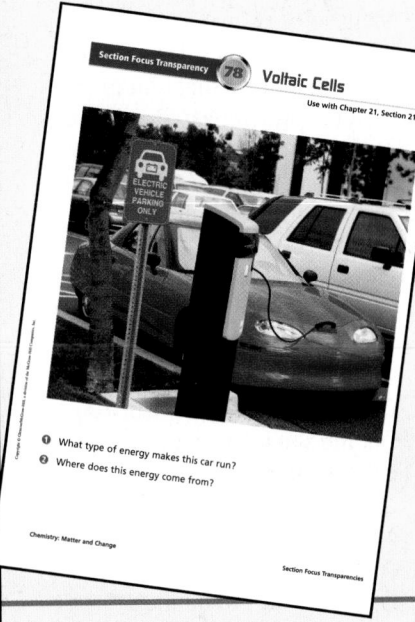

Section Focus Transparency 78 — Voltaic Cells
Use with Chapter 21, Section 21.1

❶ What type of energy makes this car run?
❷ Where does this energy come from?

Chemistry: Matter and Change
Section Focus Transparencies

### Chapter Themes

The following themes from the National Science Education Standards are covered in this chapter. Refer to page 4T of the Teacher Guide for an explanation of the correlations.
Systems, order, and organization (UCP.1)
Evidence, models, and explanation (UCP.2)
Change, constancy, and measurement (UCP.3)
Form and function (UCP.5)

---

will read 0 V, or whatever the default zero reading is. (The CBL multimeter setting will read about 2 V for its default reading.)

### Analysis

The two metals provide a potential that is measured in volts. The lemon acts as an electrolyte solution for ions and electrons to travel from metal to metal.

### Resource Manager

**Study Guide for Content Mastery,** pp. 121–123 **L2**
**Solving Problems: A Chemistry Handbook,** Section 21.1 **L2**
**Section Focus Transparency 78 and Master L1 ELL**

**National Science Content Standards**

Pages 662–663
UCP.1, UCP.3; B.3, B.6

What do you think would happen if you separated the oxidation half-reaction from the reduction half-reaction? Can redox occur? Consider **Figure 21-1a** in which a zinc strip is immersed in a solution of zinc sulfate and a copper strip is immersed in a solution of copper(II) sulfate. Two problems prohibit a redox reaction in this situation. First, with this setup there is no way for zinc atoms to transfer electrons to copper(II) ions. This problem can be solved by connecting a metal wire between the zinc and copper strips, as shown in **Figure 21-1b.** The wire serves as a pathway for electrons to flow from the zinc strip to the copper strip.

Even with the conducting wire, another problem exists that prohibits the redox reaction. A positive charge builds up in one solution and a negative charge builds up in the other. The buildup of positive zinc ions on the left prohibits the oxidation of zinc atoms. On the other side, the buildup of negative ions prohibits the reduction of copper ions. To solve this problem a salt bridge must be built into the system. A **salt bridge** is a pathway constructed to allow the passage of ions from one side to another, as shown in **Figure 21-1c.** A salt bridge consists of a tube containing a conducting solution of a soluble salt, such as KCl, held in place by an agar gel or other form of plug. The ions can move through the plug but the solutions in the two beakers cannot mix.

When the metal wire and the salt bridge are in place, electrons flow through the wire from the oxidation half-reaction to the reduction half-reaction while positive and negative ions move through the salt bridge. A flow of charged particles, such as electrons, is called an electric current. Take a minute to identify the electric current in **Figure 21-1.** The flow of electrons through the wire and the flow of ions through the salt bridge make up the electric current. The energy

### Figure 21-1

**a** These containers are constructed and arranged so that zinc is oxidized on one side while copper ions are reduced on the other. **b** A wire connected between the zinc and copper strips provides a pathway for the flow of electrons. **c** However, it takes a salt bridge to complete the system and allow the redox reaction to produce an electric current.

$$Zn \rightarrow Zn^{2+} + 2e^- \qquad Cu^{2+} + 2e^- \rightarrow Cu$$

of the flowing electrons can be put to use in lighting a bulb or running an electric motor.

The completed device shown in **Figure 21-1c** is an electrochemical cell. An **electrochemical cell** is an apparatus that uses a redox reaction to produce electrical energy or uses electrical energy to cause a chemical reaction. A **voltaic cell** is a type of electrochemical cell that converts chemical energy to electrical energy by a spontaneous redox reaction. **Figure 21-2** shows a version of the original voltaic cell as devised by its inventor Alessandro Volta.

## Chemistry of Voltaic Cells

An electrochemical cell consists of two parts, called **half-cells,** in which the separate oxidation and reduction reactions take place. Each half-cell contains an electrode, which is the object that conducts electrons to or from another substance, usually a solution of ions. In **Figure 21-1**, the beaker with the zinc electrode is where the oxidation part of the redox reaction takes place. The beaker with the copper electrode is where the reduction part of the reaction takes place. The reaction that takes place in each half-cell is the half-reaction, sometimes called half-cell reaction, that you studied in Chapter 20. The electrode where oxidation takes place is called the **anode** of the cell. The electrode where reduction takes place is called the **cathode** of the cell. Which beaker in **Figure 21-1** contains the anode and which contains the cathode?

Recall from Chapter 16 that an object's potential energy is due to its position or composition. In electrochemistry, electrical potential energy is a measure of the amount of current that can be generated from a voltaic cell to do work. Electric charge can flow between two points only when a difference in electrical potential energy exists between the two points. In an electrochemical cell, these two points are the two electrodes. The potential difference of a voltaic cell is an indication of the energy that is available to move electrons from the anode to the cathode.

To better understand this concept, consider the analogy illustrated in **Figure 21-3.** A golf ball that lands on a hillside will roll downhill into a low spot because a difference in gravitational potential energy exists between the two points. The kinetic energy attained by a golf ball rolling down a hill is determined by the difference in height (potential energy) between the high point and the low point. Similarly, the energy of the electrons flowing from anode to cathode in a voltaic cell is determined by the

**Figure 21-2**

The voltaic cell is named for Alessandro Volta (1745–1827), the Italian physicist who is credited with its invention in 1800.

**Figure 21-3**

In this illustration of gravitational potential, we can say that the golf ball has potential energy relative to the bottom of the hill because there is a difference in the height position of the ball from the top of the hill to the bottom. Similarly, an electrochemical cell has potential energy to produce a current because there is a difference in the ability of the electrodes to move electrons from the anode to the cathode.

**Content Background**

**Salt Bridges** Explain that salt bridges can take various forms such as a U tube filled with salt and connecting two separate beakers containing solutions, a porous cup containing one solution and placed inside another container containing the second solution, or a simple paper towel soaked in an electrolyte such as salt water and draped over two individual beakers, thereby connecting the two solutions.

**Reinforcement**

*Interpersonal* Have students assemble in small groups and quiz each other using the vocabulary in this section. **L2**

Rolls to lower potential

Remains stationary

Difference in gravitational potential energy

21.1 Voltaic Cells **665**

---

**DIFFERENTIATED INSTRUCTION**

**Learning Disabled**

*Visual-Spatial* Make a visual aid to help students define and label the anode, cathode, and direction of electric current in an electrochemical cell. Draw pictures of a cell, such as one of the systems described in the text, on poster board, cut out, and attach flexible magnets to the back

of the appropriate solution (ion). Now that you have defined the electrodes and solutions in each half-cell, have student volunteers label the anode and cathode, place electrons into the diagram to complete the circuit, and label the direction of the electron flow using an arrow. **L2 ELL**

**National Science Content Standards**

Pages 664–665
UCP.1, UCP.3; B.3, B.6; G.3

**Figure 21-3** In groups of two, have students study the figure and explain the analogy. Have one student explain the analogy to the second and then have the second student describe how this analogy helps better understand how a zinc–copper cell works. Then have both students illustrate the zinc–copper cell, overlaying the analogy of the downward hill and the golf ball into the illustration.
**L2** COOP LEARN

## Assessment

**Knowledge** Have students determine which species in each of the following pairs is the reactant and which is the product. **L2**

**a.** $Zn|Zn^{2+} \| Cu^{2+}|Cu$
**b.** $Zn|Zn^{2+} \| Pb^{2+}|Pb$
**c.** $Pb|Pb^{2+} \| Cu^{2+}|Cu$
**d.** $Cu|Cu^{2+} \| Ag^+|Ag$

Reactants:
**a.** Zn, $Cu^{2+}$
**b.** Zn, $Pb^{2+}$
**c.** Pb, $Cu^{2+}$
**d.** Cu, $Ag^+$

## Reinforcement

Have students determine which of the following pairs represent spontaneous and which represent nonspontaneous reactions.
**a.** $Ni + Zn^{2+}$  not spontaneous
**b.** $Fe + Cu^{2+}$  spontaneous
**c.** $Fe^{2+} + Cu^{2+}$  not spontaneous

## GLENCOE
### TECHNOLOGY

**CD-ROM**
**Chemistry: Matter and Change**
Video: *Electrochemistry*

---

difference in electrical potential between the two electrodes. In redox terms, the voltage of a cell is determined by the difference in the tendency of the electrode material to accept electrons.

Thinking again of the golf ball analogy, the force of gravity causes the ball always to roll downhill to a lower energy state, not uphill to a higher energy state. In other words, the golf ball rolling process occurs spontaneously only in the downhill direction. In the zinc–copper cell under standard conditions, copper(II) ions at the cathode accept electrons more readily than the zinc ions at the anode. In other words, the redox reaction occurs spontaneously only when the electrons flow from the zinc to the copper.

## Calculating Electrochemical Cell Potential

You know from the previous chapter that the gain of electrons is called reduction. Building on this fact, we can call the tendency of a substance to gain electrons its **reduction potential.** The reduction potential of an electrode, measured in volts, cannot be determined directly because the reduction half-reaction must be coupled with an oxidation half-reaction. When these half-reactions are coupled, the voltage corresponds to the *difference* in potential between the half-reactions. The electrical potential difference between two points is expressed in volts (V). Long ago, chemists decided to measure the reduction potential of all electrodes against one standard electrode, the standard hydrogen electrode. The **standard hydrogen electrode** consists of a small sheet of platinum immersed in an HCl solution that has a hydrogen ion concentration of $1M$. Hydrogen gas at a pressure of 1 atm is bubbled in and the temperature is maintained at 25°C, as shown in **Figure 21-4.** The potential (also called the standard reduction potential) of this standard hydrogen electrode is defined as 0 V. This electrode can act as an oxidation half-reaction or a reduction half-reaction, depending upon the half-cell to which it is connected. The reactions at the hydrogen electrode are

$$2H^+(aq) + 2e^- \underset{\text{Oxidation}}{\overset{\text{Reduction}}{\rightleftharpoons}} H_2(g) \qquad E^0 = 0.000 \text{ V}$$

**Figure 21-4**

A standard hydrogen electrode consists of a platinum electrode with hydrogen gas at 1 atm pressure bubbling into an acidic solution that is $1M$ in hydrogen ions. The reduction potential for this configuration is 0 V.

Salt bridge
$H_2(g)$ (at 1 atm)
$1M$ acid solution
$H_2$ bubbles
Platinum electrode

---

## Internet Address Book

Chemistry Online

Note Internet addresses that you find useful in the space below for quick reference.

_____
_____
_____
_____
_____

Over the years, chemists have measured and recorded the standard reduction potentials, abbreviated $E^0$, of many different half-cells. **Table 21-1** lists some common half-cell reactions in order of increasing reduction potential. The values in the table are based on using the half-cell reaction that is being measured as the cathode and the standard hydrogen electrode as the anode. All of the half-reactions in **Table 21-1** are written as reductions. However, in any voltaic cell, which always contains two half-reactions, the half-reaction with the lower reduction potential will proceed in the opposite direction and will be an oxidation reaction. In other words, the half-reaction that is more positive will proceed as a reduction and the half-reaction that is more negative will proceed as an oxidation.

**Table 21-1**

| Standard Reduction Potentials at 25°C, 1 atm, and 1*M* Ion Concentration | | | |
|---|---|---|---|
| **Half-reaction** | $E^0$ (V) | **Half-reaction** | $E^0$ (V) |
| $Li^+ + e^- \rightarrow Li$ | $-3.0401$ | $Sn^{4+} + 2e^- \rightarrow Sn^{2+}$ | $0.151$ |
| $Cs^+ + e^- \rightarrow Cs$ | $-3.026$ | $Cu^{2+} + e^- \rightarrow Cu^+$ | $0.153$ |
| $K^+ + e^- \rightarrow K$ | $-2.931$ | $SO_4^{2-} + 4H^+ + 2e^- \rightarrow H_2SO_3 + H_2O$ | $0.172$ |
| $Ba^{2+} + 2e^- \rightarrow Ba$ | $-2.912$ | $Bi^{3+} + 3e^- \rightarrow Bi$ | $0.308$ |
| $Ca^{2+} + 2e^- \rightarrow Ca$ | $-2.868$ | $Cu^{2+} + 2e^- \rightarrow Cu$ | $0.3419$ |
| $Na^+ + e^- \rightarrow Na$ | $-2.71$ | $O_2 + 2H_2O + 4e^- \rightarrow 4OH^-$ | $0.401$ |
| $Mg^{2+} + 2e^- \rightarrow Mg$ | $-2.372$ | $Cu^+ + e^- \rightarrow Cu$ | $0.521$ |
| $Ce^{3+} + 3e^- \rightarrow Ce$ | $-2.336$ | $I_2 + 2e^- \rightarrow 2I^-$ | $0.5355$ |
| $H_2 + 2e^- \rightarrow 2H^-$ | $-2.323$ | $O_2 + 2H^+ + 2e^- \rightarrow H_2O_2$ | $0.695$ |
| $Nd^{3+} + 3e^- \rightarrow Nd$ | $-2.1$ | $Fe^{3+} + e^- \rightarrow Fe^{2+}$ | $0.771$ |
| $Be^{2+} + 2e^- \rightarrow Be$ | $-1.847$ | $NO_3^- + 2H^+ + e^- \rightarrow NO_2 + H_2O$ | $0.775$ |
| $Al^{3+} + 3e^- \rightarrow Al$ | $-1.662$ | $Hg_2^{2+} + 2e^- \rightarrow 2Hg$ | $0.7973$ |
| $Mn^{2+} + 2e^- \rightarrow Mn$ | $-1.185$ | $Ag^+ + e^- \rightarrow Ag$ | $0.7996$ |
| $Cr^{2+} + 2e^- \rightarrow Cr$ | $-0.913$ | $Hg^{2+} + 2e^- \rightarrow Hg$ | $0.851$ |
| $2H_2O + 2e^- \rightarrow H_2 + 2OH^-$ | $-0.8277$ | $2Hg^{2+} + 2e^- \rightarrow Hg_2^{2+}$ | $0.920$ |
| $Zn^{2+} + 2e^- \rightarrow Zn$ | $-0.7618$ | $Pd^{2+} + 2e^- \rightarrow Pd$ | $0.951$ |
| $Cr^{3+} + 3e^- \rightarrow Cr$ | $-0.744$ | $NO_3^- + 4H^+ + 3e^- \rightarrow NO + 2H_2O$ | $0.957$ |
| $Ga^{3+} + 3e^- \rightarrow Ga$ | $-0.549$ | $Br_2(l) + 2e^- \rightarrow 2Br^-$ | $1.066$ |
| $2CO_2 + 2H^+ + 2e^- \rightarrow H_2C_2O_4$ | $-0.49$ | $Ir^{3+} + 3e^- \rightarrow Ir$ | $1.156$ |
| $S + 2e^- \rightarrow S^{2-}$ | $-0.47627$ | $Pt^{2+} + 2e^- \rightarrow Pt$ | $1.18$ |
| $Fe^{2+} + 2e^- \rightarrow Fe$ | $-0.447$ | $O_2 + 4H^+ + 4e^- \rightarrow 2H_2O$ | $1.229$ |
| $Cr^{3+} + e^- \rightarrow Cr^{2+}$ | $-0.407$ | $Cl_2 + 2e^- \rightarrow 2Cl^-$ | $1.35827$ |
| $Cd^{2+} + 2e^- \rightarrow Cd$ | $-0.4030$ | $Au^{3+} + 2e^- \rightarrow Au^+$ | $1.401$ |
| $PbI_2 + 2e^- \rightarrow Pb + 2I^-$ | $-0.365$ | $Au^{3+} + 3e^- \rightarrow Au$ | $1.498$ |
| $PbSO_4 + 2e^- \rightarrow Pb + SO_4^{2-}$ | $-0.3588$ | $MnO_4^- + 8H^+ + 5e^- \rightarrow Mn^{2+} + 4H_2O$ | $1.507$ |
| $Co^{2+} + 2e^- \rightarrow Co$ | $-0.28$ | $Au^+ + e^- \rightarrow Au$ | $1.692$ |
| $Ni^{2+} + 2e^- \rightarrow Ni$ | $-0.257$ | $H_2O_2 + 2H^+ + 2e^- \rightarrow 2H_2O$ | $1.776$ |
| $Sn^{2+} + 2e^- \rightarrow Sn$ | $-0.1375$ | $Co^{3+} + e^- \rightarrow Co^{2+}$ | $1.92$ |
| $Pb^{2+} + 2e^- \rightarrow Pb$ | $-0.1262$ | $S_2O_8^{2-} + 2e^- \rightarrow 2SO_4^{2-}$ | $2.010$ |
| $Fe^{3+} + 3e^- \rightarrow Fe$ | $-0.037$ | $O_3 + 2H^+ + 2e^- \rightarrow O_2 + H_2O$ | $2.076$ |
| $2H^+ + 2e^- \rightarrow H_2$ | $0.0000$ | $F_2 + 2e^- \rightarrow 2F^-$ | $2.866$ |

**Figure 21-5**

**ⓐ** When a Cu|Cu²⁺ electrode is connected to the hydrogen electrode, electrons flow toward the copper strip and reduce Cu²⁺ ions to Cu atoms. The voltage of this reaction is +0.342 V.
**ⓑ** When a Zn|Zn²⁺ electrode is connected to the hydrogen electrode, electrons flow away from the zinc strip and zinc atoms are oxidized to Zn²⁺ ions. The voltage of this reaction is −0.762 V.

The electrode being measured also must be under standard conditions; that is, immersed in a $1M$ solution of its ions at 25°C and 1 atm pressure. The superscript zero in the notation $E^0$ is a shorthand way of indicating "measured under standard conditions."

With **Table 21-1**, it is possible to calculate the electrical potential of a voltaic cell having a copper electrode and a zinc electrode under standard conditions. The first step is to determine the standard reduction potential for the copper half-cell ($E^0_{Cu}$). When the copper electrode is attached to a standard hydrogen electrode, as in **Figure 21-5a**, electrons flow *from* the hydrogen electrode *to* the copper electrode, and copper ions are reduced to copper metal. The $E^0$, measured by a voltmeter, is +0.342 V. The positive voltage indicates that $Cu^{2+}$ ions at the copper electrode being measured accept electrons more readily than do $H^+$ ions at the standard hydrogen electrode. From this information, you can determine where oxidation and reduction take place. In this case, oxidation takes place at the hydrogen electrode, and reduction takes place at the copper electrode. The oxidation and reduction half-cell reactions and the overall reaction are

$$H_2(g) \rightarrow 2H^+(aq) + 2e^- \text{ (oxidation half-cell reaction)}$$
$$\underline{Cu^{2+}(aq) + 2e^- \rightarrow Cu(s) \text{ (reduction half-cell reaction)}}$$
$$H_2(g) + Cu^{2+}(aq) \rightarrow 2H^+(aq) + Cu(s) \text{ (overall reduction reaction)}$$

This reaction can be written in a form called cell notation to clearly describe the copper reduction reaction.

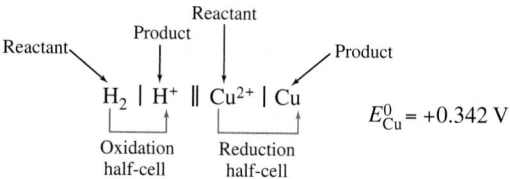

Note that the two participants in the oxidation reaction are written first and in the order they appear in the oxidation half-reaction—*reactant | product*.

**668** Chapter 21 Electrochemistry

They are followed by a double vertical line (∥) indicating the wire and salt bridge connecting the half-cells. Then, the two participants in the reduction reaction are written in the same *reactant | product* order. Note in this example that it is customary to place a plus sign before a positive voltage to avoid confusion.

The next step is to determine the standard reduction potential for the zinc half-cell ($E_{Zn}^0$). When the zinc electrode is measured against the standard hydrogen electrode under standard conditions, as in **Figure 21-5b**, electrons flow from the zinc electrode to the hydrogen electrode. The $E^0$ of the zinc half-cell, measured by a voltmeter, is $-0.762$ V. This means that the $H^+$ ions at the hydrogen electrode accept electrons more readily than do the zinc ions, and thus the hydrogen ions have a *higher* reduction potential than the zinc ions. If you remember that the hydrogen electrode is assigned a zero potential, you will realize that the reduction potential of the zinc electrode must have a negative value. Electrodes at which oxidation is carried out when connected to a hydrogen electrode have negative standard reduction potentials. How would you write the oxidation and reduction reactions and the overall zinc oxidation reaction? The reactions are written as follows.

$$Zn(s) \rightarrow Zn^{2+}(aq) + 2e^- \quad \text{(oxidation half-cell reaction)}$$

$$2H^+(aq) + 2e^- \rightarrow H_2(g) \quad \text{(reduction half-cell reaction)}$$

$$Zn(s) + 2H^+(aq) \rightarrow Zn^{2+}(aq) + H_2(g) \quad \text{(overall oxidation cell reaction)}$$

This reaction can be written in cell notation to clearly describe the zinc oxidation reaction.

$$E_{Zn}^0 = -0.762 \text{ V}$$

The final step is to combine the Cu and Zn half-cells as a voltaic cell, which means calculating the voltaic cell's standard potential using the following formula

$$E_{cell}^0 = E_{reduction}^0 - E_{oxidation}^0$$

Because reduction occurred at the copper electrode and oxidation occurred at the zinc electrode, the $E^0$ values are substituted as follows.

$$E_{cell}^0 = E_{Cu^{2+}|Cu}^0 - E_{Zn^{2+}|Zn}^0$$
$$= 0.342 \text{ V} - (-0.762 \text{ V})$$
$$= +1.104 \text{ V}$$

**Figure 21-6** describes this potential calculation. The graph shows the zinc half-cell with the lower reduction potential (the oxidation half-reaction) and the copper half-cell with the higher reduction potential (the reduction half-reaction). You can see that the space between the two ($E_{cell}^0$) is the difference between the potentials of the individual half-cells. The Example Problem that follows gives a step-by-step description of calculating cell potentials.

**Figure 21-6**

This simple graph illustrates how the overall cell potential is derived from the difference in reduction potential of two electrodes.

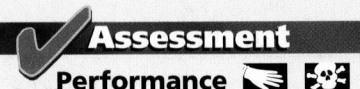

**National Science Content Standards**

**Pages 668–669**
UCP.1, UCP.3; B.3, B.6; E.2

Have students refer to Appendix D for complete solutions to Practice Problems.

**1.** $Pt^{2+}(aq) + Sn(s) \rightarrow Pt(s) + Sn^{2+}(aq)$

$E^0_{cell} = 1.18\ V - (-0.1375\ V)$

$E^0_{cell} = 1.32\ V$

$Sn|Sn^{2+}||Pt^{2+}|Pt$

**2.** $3Co^{2+}(aq) + 2Cr(s) \rightarrow 3Co(s) + 2Cr^{3+}(aq)$

$E^0_{cell} = (-0.28\ V) - (-0.744\ V)$

$E^0_{cell} = 0.46\ V$

$Cr|Cr^{3+}||Co^{2+}|Co$

**3.** $Hg^{2+}(aq) + Cr(s) \rightarrow Hg(l) + Cr^{2+}(aq)$

$E^0_{cell} = 0.851\ V - (-0.913\ V)$

$E^0_{cell} = 1.764\ V$

$Cr|Cr^{2+}||\ Hg^{2+}|Hg$

## CHEMLAB

ChemLab 21, located at the end of the chapter, can be used at this point in the lesson.

## GLENCOE TECHNOLOGY

**CD-ROM**

**Chemistry: Matter and Change**

Demonstration: *An Electrochemical Flash*

---

Cloud seeding using iodine compounds to promote precipitation may be one way to ease severe drought conditions.

---

**EXAMPLE** PROBLEM 21-1

### Calculating Cell Potential

The two reduction half-reactions in this example represent the half-cells of a voltaic cell.

$I_2(s) + 2e^- \rightarrow 2I^-(aq)$

$Fe^{2+}(aq) + 2e^- \rightarrow Fe(s)$

Determine the overall cell reaction and the standard cell potential. Write the cell chemistry using cell notation with vertical lines separating components.

**1. Analyze the Problem**

You are given the half-cell descriptions for a voltaic cell and standard reduction potentials in **Table 21-1**. In any voltaic cell, the half-reaction with the lower reduction potential will proceed as an oxidation. With this information, you can write the overall cell reaction and calculate the standard cell potential.

**Known**

Standard reduction potentials for the half-cells

$E^0_{cell} = E^0_{reduction} - E^0_{oxidation}$

**Unknown**

$E^0_{cell} = ?$

**2. Solve for the Unknown**

Find the standard reduction potentials of each half-reaction in a reference source such as **Table 21-1**.

$I_2(s) + 2e^- \rightarrow 2I^-(aq)$      $E^0_{I_2|I^-} = +0.536\ V$

$Fe^{2+}(aq) + 2e^- \rightarrow Fe(s)$      $E^0_{Fe^{2+}|Fe} = -0.447\ V$

Note that reduction of iodine has the higher reduction potential. This half-reaction will proceed in the forward direction as a reduction. The iron half-reaction will proceed in the reverse direction as an oxidation. Rewrite the half-reactions in the correct direction.

$I_2(s) + 2e^- \rightarrow 2I^-(aq)$ (reduction half-cell reaction)

$Fe(s) \rightarrow Fe^{2+}(aq) + 2e^-$ (oxidation half-cell reaction)

$I_2(s) + Fe(s) \rightarrow Fe^{2+}(aq) + 2I^-(aq)$ (overall cell reaction)

Balance the reaction if necessary. Note that this reaction is balanced as written.

Calculate cell standard potential.

$E^0_{cell} = E^0_{reduction} - E^0_{oxidation}$

$E^0_{cell} = E^0_{I_2|I^-} - E^0_{Fe^{2+}|Fe}$

$E^0_{cell} = +0.536\ V - (-0.447\ V)$

$E^0_{cell} = +0.983\ V$

Write the reaction using cell notation. When representing a reaction in cell notation, the species in the oxidation half-reaction are written first in the following order: reactant | product, or in this case, $Fe\ |\ Fe^{2+}$. The species in the reduction half-reaction are written next in the order reactant | product, or in this case, $I_2\ |\ I^-$. Therefore, the complete cell is represented as

$Fe\ |\ Fe^{2+}\ ||\ I_2\ |\ I^-$

---

## An Electrochemical Flash

**Purpose**

Students will see that a voltaic cell produces a current.

**Materials**

Flashbulb (flashcube); small piece of steel wool; 14-gauge copper wire (15-cm length); Mg ribbon (20-cm length); 12*M* HCl (50 mL); beaker (150 mL); ring stand and clamp; connection leads with alligator clips at each end (2)

**Safety Precautions**

**Disposal** Neutralize the acid with sodium bicarbonate and rinse down the sink with large quantities of water.

**Procedure**

In advance, prepare 100 mL of 6*M* HCl. See page 662C for preparation of all solutions. **CAUTION:** *Hydrochloric acid is corrosive.* Use steel wool to clean a 15-cm length of 14-gauge copper wire and a 20-cm length of magnesium ribbon. Wrap the magnesium ribbon and the copper wire around a pencil to form coils. Remove the coils from the pencil. Attach the magnesium to one of the electrodes of the flash-

The standard potential for this voltaic cell seems reasonable given the reduction potentials of the half-cells that comprise it. The mathematical operations with negative numbers are correct and the answer is correct to the thousandths place.

## PRACTICE PROBLEMS

For each of these pairs of half-reactions, write the balanced equation for the overall cell reaction and calculate the standard cell potential. Express the reaction using cell notation. You may wish to refer to Chapter 20 to review writing and balancing redox equations.

**1.** $Pt^{2+}(aq) + 2e^- \rightarrow Pt(s)$

$Sn^{2+}(aq) + 2e^- \rightarrow Sn(s)$

**2.** $Co^{2+}(aq) + 2e^- \rightarrow Co(s)$

$Cr^{3+}(aq) + 3e^- \rightarrow Cr(s)$

**3.** $Hg^{2+}(aq) + 2e^- \rightarrow Hg(l)$

$Cr^{2+}(aq) + 2e^- \rightarrow Cr(s)$

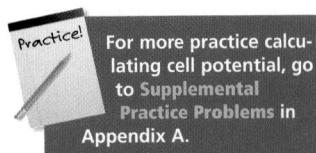

Practice! For more practice calculating cell potential, go to **Supplemental Practice Problems** in Appendix A.

The **CHEMLAB** at the end of this chapter offers an opportunity to create voltaic cells and calculate cell potentials.

## Using Standard Reduction Potentials

You just practiced using the data from **Table 21-1** to calculate the standard potential (voltage) of voltaic cells by determining the difference in reduction potential of the half-cell reactions. Another important use of standard reduction potentials is to determine if a proposed reaction under standard conditions will be spontaneous. How can standard reduction potentials indicate spontaneity? Electrons in a voltaic cell always flow from the half-cell with the lower standard reduction potential to the half-cell with higher reduction potential, giving a positive cell voltage. To predict whether any proposed redox reaction will occur spontaneously, simply write the process in the form of half-reactions and look up the reduction potential of each. Use the values to calculate the potential of a voltaic cell operating with these two half-cell reactions. If the calculated potential is positive, the reaction is spontaneous. If the value is negative, the reaction is not spontaneous. However, the reverse reaction will occur because it will give a positive cell voltage and, therefore, the reverse reaction is spontaneous.

For example, use the standard reduction potentials in **Table 21-1** to calculate the potential of the cell Li| Li$^+$ ‖ Ag$^+$| Ag.

$$E^0_{cell} = E^0_{Ag^+|Ag} - E^0_{Li^+|Li}$$

$$= 0.7996 \text{ V} - (-3.0401 \text{ V})$$

$$= 3.8397 \text{ V}$$

The calculated potential for the cell Li| Li$^+$ ‖ Ag$^+$| Ag is a positive number. Thus, the redox reaction in this cell will proceed spontaneously if the system is at 25°C, 1 atm, and $1M$ concentration.

---

Have students refer to Appendix D for complete solutions to Practice Problems.

**4.** $E^0_{cell} > 0$  Spontaneous

**5.** $E^0_{cell} > 0$  Spontaneous

**6.** $E^0_{cell} < 0$  Not spontaneous

**7.** $E^0_{cell} < 0$  Not spontaneous

### ✓ Assessment

**Performance** Using Table 21-1, have students design at least one electrochemical cell that would have a voltage output that you specify. Have students explain the reasons for their design and why they selected their solutions and electrodes. Use the Performance Task Assessment List for Invention in **PASC**, p. 45. **L2** **ELL**

**National Science Content Standards**

**Pages 670–671**
UCP.1, UCP.3; B.3, B.6

---

bulb using a connecting lead. Use a second connecting lead to attach the copper wire to the other electrode of the flashbulb. Clamp the flashbulb to a ring stand. Lower the clamp until the Cu and Mg electrodes are simultaneously immersed in the HCl in the beaker.

**Results**

The flashbulb or flashcube will fire when the two electrodes are immersed in the HCl solution.

**Analysis**

**1.** Using the half-reactions listed in Table 21-1, predict which metal is the anode (oxidation) and which metal is the cathode (reduction). Mg|Mg$^{2+}$ is the anode and Cu$^{2+}$|Cu is the cathode.

**2.** The Mg–Cu cell is capable of producing 12.7 volts. Most cameras use how many AA-size batteries, and how much voltage can they produce? Two 1.5-V batteries produce 3 V.

### ✓ Assessment

**Performance** Repeat the demonstration using different metals to see how those metals compare with copper and magnesium. Use the Performance Task Assessment List for Carrying Out a Strategy and Collecting Data in **PASC**, p. 25.

## Check for Understanding

**Visual-Spatial** Provide the students with an electrochemical diagram and have them label the half-cell, anode, cathode, and use an arrow to indicate the direction of the reaction. **L2** **ELL**

## Reteach

**Interpersonal** Allow students to work in small groups. Have them write on index cards any questions that they still have related to Section 21.1. Label the file cards with a group number, then collect the questions, shuffle the cards, and redistribute them to different groups. Ask students to attempt to answer the questions they were dealt. Near the end of the class period, return the questions and answers to the originating group so that they can review the answers. **L2** **COOP LEARN**

## Extension

Have students explain in their own words the difference between standard reduction potentials and standard hydrogen electrodes.

## ✔ Assessment

**Skill** Obtain a two-potato clock. (These are available from a variety of scientific supply stores or retail science stores.) Identify the two different electrodes as zinc and copper. Have the students diagram the two-potato clock and label the anode and cathode of the electrochemical cell. Also ask them to label the part of the clock that is functioning as the electrolyte. **L2** **ELL**

---

**Practice!** For more practice determining if redox reactions are spontaneous, go to Supplemental Practice Problems in Appendix A.

---

### PRACTICE PROBLEMS

Calculate the cell potential to determine if each of the following balanced redox reactions is spontaneous as written. Examining the reactions in **Table 21-1** can help you determine the correct half-reactions.

**4.** $Sn(s) + 2Cu^+(aq) \rightarrow Sn^{2+}(aq) + 2Cu(s)$

**5.** $Mg(s) + Pb^{2+}(aq) \rightarrow Pb(s) + Mg^{2+}(aq)$

**6.** $2Mn^{2+}(aq) + 8H_2O(l) + 10Hg^{2+}(aq) \rightarrow 2MnO_4^-(aq) + 16H^+(aq) + 5Hg_2^{2+}(aq)$

**7.** $2SO_4^{2-}(aq) + Co^{2+}(aq) \rightarrow Co(s) + S_2O_8^{2-}(aq)$

---

Now that you know the chemistry of voltaic cells, you may begin to see their value as a power source. It turns out that Alessandro Volta also realized the value of this chemistry. From his experimentation, Volta deduced that if one cell generates a current, several cells connected together should produce a larger current. Volta connected a series of cells by making a pile of alternating zinc plates serving as anodes and silver plates serving as cathodes separated by layers of cloth soaked with salt solution. The cloth had the same function as the salt bridge. This arrangement became known as a "voltaic pile" and was literally a "pile", as you saw in **Figure 21-2**. Volta's pile was the first battery. A **battery** consists of one or more electrochemical cells in a single package that generates electrical current. You'll learn more about batteries in the next section of this chapter.

---

## Section 21.1 Assessment

**8.** Under what conditions can a redox reaction be used to cause an electric current to flow through a wire?

**9.** What are the components of a voltaic cell? What is the role of each component in the operation of the cell?

**10.** Write the balanced equation for the spontaneous cell reaction that will occur in a cell with these reduction half-reactions.

**a.** $Ag^+(aq) + e^- \rightarrow Ag(s)$
$Ni^{2+} + 2e^- \rightarrow Ni(s)$

**b.** $Mg^{2+}(aq) + 2e^- \rightarrow Mg(s)$
$2H^+(aq) + 2e^- \rightarrow H_2(g)$

**c.** $Sn^{4+}(aq) + 2e^- \rightarrow Sn^{2+}(aq)$
$Cr^{3+}(aq) + 3e^- \rightarrow Cr(s)$

**11.** These equations represent overall cell reactions. Determine the standard potential for each cell and identify the reactions as spontaneous or nonspontaneous as written.

**a.** $2Al^{3+}(aq) + 3Cu(s) \rightarrow 3Cu^{2+}(aq) + 2Al(s)$

**b.** $Hg^{2+}(aq) + 2Cu^+(aq) \rightarrow 2Cu^{2+}(aq) + Hg$

**c.** $Cd(s) + 2NO_3^-(aq) + 4H^+(aq) \rightarrow$
$Cd^{2+}(aq) + 2NO_2(g) + 2H_2O(l)$

**12. Thinking Critically** The reduction half-reaction $I_2 + 2e^- \rightarrow 2I^-$ has a lower standard reduction potential than the reduction half-reaction $Cl_2 + 2e^- \rightarrow 2Cl^-$. In terms of electron transfer, what is the significance of this difference in reduction potentials? Which of these reactions would produce the higher voltage in a cell in which the oxidation half-reaction is $Zn \rightarrow Zn^{2+} + 2e^-$? Explain your choice.

**13. Predicting** Suppose you have a half-cell of unknown composition, but you know the cell is at standard conditions. You connect it to a copper–copper(II) sulfate half-cell, also at standard conditions, and the voltmeter in the circuit reads 0.869 V. Is it possible to predict the probable composition of the unknown half-cell? Explain your answer.

chemistrymc.com/self_check_quiz

---

## Section 21.1 Assessment

**8.** An electrochemical cell in which an oxidation half-reaction and a reduction half-reaction are connected by a salt bridge results in a flow of electrons (electric current) through a conducting wire.

**9.** A voltaic cell consists of an anode, a cathode, and a salt bridge. Oxidation takes place at the anode, reduction takes place at the cathode, and the salt bridge allows movement of ions from one solution to the other.

**10. a.** $2Ag^+ + Ni \rightarrow 2Ag + Ni^{2+}$
**b.** $Mg + 2H^+ \rightarrow Mg^{2+} + H_2$
**c.** $3Sn^{4+} + 2Cr \rightarrow 2Cr^{3+} + 3Sn^{2+}$

**11. a.** $E^0_{cell} = -2.004$ V; nonspontaneous
**b.** $E^0_{cell} = +0.698$ V; spontaneous
**c.** $E^0_{cell} = +1.178$ V; spontaneous

**12.** The $Cl_2 + 2e^- \rightarrow 2Cl^-$ reaction has a greater tendency to gain electrons. The $E^0_{cell}$ is greater with $Cl_2 + 2e^- \rightarrow 2Cl^-$ and therefore produces more voltage.

How many different uses of batteries can you identify? Batteries power flashlights, remote controls, calculators, hearing aids, portable CD players, heart pacemakers, smoke and carbon monoxide detectors, and video cameras, to name a few. Batteries in cars and trucks provide electric energy to start the engine and power the vehicle's many electric lights, sound system, and other accessories, even when the engine is not running.

## Dry Cells

In Section 21.1, you learned that the simplest form of a battery is a single voltaic cell. The word *battery* once referred only to a group of single cells in one package, such as the 9 V battery. Today, however, the word *battery* refers to both single cells and packages of several cells, such as the batteries shown in **Figure 21-7**. From the time of its invention in the 1860s until recently, the most commonly used voltaic cell was the zinc–carbon dry cell, shown in **Figure 21-8** on the next page. A **dry cell** is an electrochemical cell in which the electrolyte is a moist paste. The paste in a zinc–carbon dry cell consists of zinc chloride, manganese(IV) oxide, ammonium chloride, and a small amount of water inside a zinc case. The zinc shell is the cell's anode, where the oxidation of zinc metal occurs. The following equation describes the oxidation half-cell reaction for this dry cell.

$$Zn(s) \rightarrow Zn^{2+}(aq) + 2e^-$$

A carbon (graphite) rod in the center of the dry cell serves as the cathode, but the reduction half-cell reaction takes place in the paste. An electrode made of a material that does not participate in the redox reaction is called an inactive electrode. The carbon rod in this type of dry cell is an inactive cathode. (Contrast this with the zinc case, which is an active anode because the zinc is oxidized.) The reduction half-cell reaction for this dry cell follows.

$$2NH_4^+(aq) + 2MnO_2(s) + 2e^- \rightarrow Mn_2O_3(s) + 2NH_3(aq) + H_2O(l)$$

Chemists know that the reduction reaction is more complex than this equation shows, but they still do not know precisely what happens in the reaction. A spacer, made of a porous material and damp from the liquid in the paste, separates the paste from the zinc anode. The spacer acts as a salt bridge to

### Objectives

- **Describe** the structure, composition, and operation of the typical carbon–zinc dry cell battery.

- **Distinguish** between primary and secondary batteries and give two examples of each type.

- **Explain** the structure and operation of the hydrogen–oxygen fuel cell.

- **Describe** the process of corrosion of iron and methods to prevent corrosion.

### Vocabulary

dry cell
primary battery
secondary battery
fuel cell
corrosion
galvanizing

**Figure 21-7**

The small batteries (AA, AAA, C, and D) that power household appliances and small electrical devices consist of single electrochemical cells. The large battery of a car, however, consists of six electrochemical cells connected together.

**Section** (21.2)

## 1 Focus

### Focus Transparency

Before presenting the lesson, display **Section Focus Transparency 79** on the overhead projector. Have students answer the accompanying questions using **Section Focus Transparency Master 79.** L1 ELL

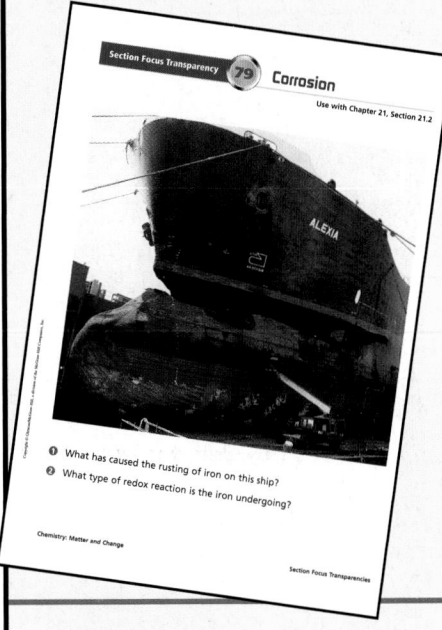

Section Focus Transparency **79** Corrosion
Use with Chapter 21, Section 21.2

ALEXIA

❶ What has caused the rusting of iron on this ship?
❷ What type of redox reaction is the iron undergoing?

Chemistry: Matter and Change

Section Focus Transparencies

## 2 Teach

### Concept Development

*Intrapersonal* Have students list all of the different kinds of batteries that they find in their households and their applications. Such a list will include: common dry cell, alkaline batteries (another type of dry cell), lithium batteries, NiCd batteries, and lead–acid batteries. Students may also include on their lists disposable and rechargeable batteries, AA, AAA, C, D, and 9-volt and 6-volt dry cell batteries. Have students compare the cost of the different types of batteries. L2

**National Science Content Standards**

Pages 672–673
UCP.1, UCP.3; B.3, B.6; E.1; G.3

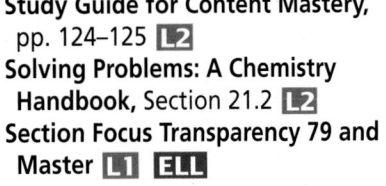

### Resource Manager

**Study Guide for Content Mastery,**
pp. 124–125 L2
**Solving Problems: A Chemistry
Handbook,** Section 21.2 L2
**Section Focus Transparency 79 and
Master** L1 ELL

**13.** Yes. By substituting the known values of $E^0_{cell}$ and the standard reduction potential value of the copper/copper(II) sulfate half-cell, you can solve for the standard reduction potential of the unknown half-cell and deduce its composition from a table of standard reduction potentials.

Using a screw driver, dismantle a 9-volt battery to use as a display so that students can see the inside makeup of a battery. Point out the carbon and zinc electrodes. Have students count the cells in a 9-volt battery and ask them why there are more than one. **CAUTION:** *Do not get the paste wet. Intense heat will result.* Students should realize that to produce a particular voltage the battery must contain the number of electrochemical cells that, when multiplied by the voltage per cell, equals the total voltage. A 9-volt battery has six cells, each producing 1.5 volts, totaling 9 volts.

## ✓ Assessment

**Knowledge** Ask students to determine the voltage output of a flashlight containing four D-size batteries. Each D battery produces 1.5 V; therefore, four D batteries produce 6 volts. **L2**

# GLENCOE
## TECHNOLOGY

**CD-ROM**
**Chemistry: Matter and Change**
Animation: *Galvanic Cell*

**Figure 21-8**

The so-called dry cell actually contains a moist paste in which the cathode half-reaction takes place. **ⓐ** In the zinc–carbon dry cell, the zinc case acts as the anode. **ⓑ** The alkaline battery uses powdered zinc and is contained in a steel case. **ⓒ** Although it looks different, the mercury battery is much like the alkaline battery, except that the mercury battery uses mercury(II) oxide (HgO) in the cathode instead of manganese(IV) oxide ($MnO_2$).

allow the transfer of ions, much like the model voltaic cell you studied in Section 21.1. The zinc–carbon dry cell produces a voltage of 1.5 V, until the reduction product ammonia comes out of its aqueous solution as a gas. At that point, the voltage drops to a level that makes the battery useless.

As new research and development bring about newer and more efficient products, the standard zinc–carbon dry cell has begun to give way to the alkaline dry cell, also shown in **Figure 21-8b.** The alkaline cell oxidizes zinc, but the zinc is in a powdered form. Why might the powdered zinc be an advantage? The powdered form, as you learned in Chapter 17, provides more surface area for reaction. The zinc is mixed in a paste with potassium hydroxide, a strong alkali base, and the paste is contained in a steel case. The cathode mixture is manganese(IV) oxide, also mixed with potassium hydroxide. The zinc anode half-cell reaction is

$$Zn(s) + 2OH^-(aq) \rightarrow ZnO(s) + H_2O(l) + 2e^-$$

The cathode half-cell reaction is

$$MnO_2(s) + 2H_2O(s) + 2e^- \rightarrow Mn(OH)_2(s) + 2OH^-(aq)$$

Alkaline batteries do not need the carbon rod cathode and are, therefore, smaller and more compatible with smaller devices.

The mercury battery shown in **Figure 21-8c** is smaller yet and is used to power devices such as hearing aids and calculators. The mercury battery uses the same anode half-reaction as the alkaline battery, with this cathode half-reaction.

$$HgO(s) + H_2O(l) + 2e^- \rightarrow Hg(l) + 2OH^-(aq)$$

## DIFFERENTIATED INSTRUCTION

### Hearing Impaired

Many brand-name battery packages give an Internet site address for consumer and product information. Have students access one or more of these sites and present what these sites report about the chemistry and performance of their products. **L2** **ELL**

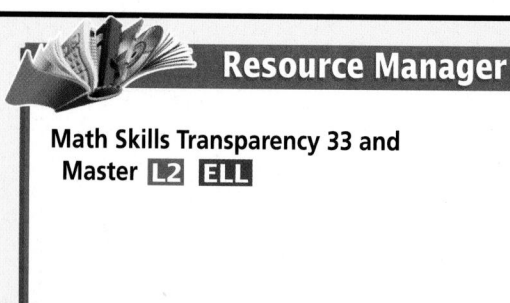

## Resource Manager

**Math Skills Transparency 33 and Master** **L2** **ELL**

## Primary and secondary batteries

Batteries are divided into two types depending on their chemical processes. The zinc–carbon, alkaline–zinc, and mercury cells are classified as primary batteries. **Primary batteries** produce electric energy by means of redox reactions that are not easily reversed. These cells deliver current until the reactants are gone, and then the battery is discarded. Batteries that are rechargeable depend on reversible redox reactions. They are called **secondary batteries.** What devices can you identify that use secondary batteries? A car battery and the battery in a laptop computer are examples of secondary batteries, sometimes called *storage batteries*.

The storage batteries that power devices such as cordless drills and screwdrivers, shavers, and camcorders are usually nickel–cadmium rechargeable batteries, sometimes called NiCad batteries, as shown in **Figure 21-9**. For maximum efficiency, the anode and cathode are long, thin ribbons of material separated by a layer that ions can pass through. The ribbons are wound into a tight coil and packaged into a steel case. The anode reaction that occurs when the battery is used to generate electric current is the oxidation of cadmium in the presence of a base.

$$Cd(s) + 2OH^-(aq) \rightarrow Cd(OH)_2(s) + 2e^-$$

The cathode reaction is the reduction of nickel from the +3 to the +2 oxidation state.

$$NiO(OH)(s) + H_2O(l) + e^- \rightarrow Ni(OH)_2(s) + OH^-(aq)$$

When the battery is recharged, these reactions are reversed.

## Lead–Acid Storage Battery

Another common storage battery is the lead–acid battery. The standard automobile battery is an example of a lead–acid battery. Most auto batteries of this type contain six cells that generate about 2 V each for a total output of 12 V. The anode of each cell consists of two or more grids of porous lead, and the cathode consists of lead grids filled with lead(IV) oxide. This type of battery probably should be called a lead–lead(IV) oxide battery, but the term *lead–acid* is commonly used because the battery's electrolyte is a solution of sulfuric acid.

The following equation represents the oxidation half-cell reaction at the anode where lead is oxidized from the zero oxidation state to the +2 oxidation state.

$$Pb(s) + SO_4^{2-}(aq) \rightarrow PbSO_4(s) + 2e^-$$

The reduction of lead from the +4 to the +2 oxidation state takes place at the cathode. The half-cell reaction for the cathode is

$$PbO_2(s) + 4H^+(aq) + SO_4^{2-}(aq) + 2e^- \rightarrow PbSO_4(s) + 2H_2O(l)$$

**Figure 21-9**

Cordless tools and phones often use rechargeable batteries, such as the NiCad type, for power. The battery pack in the phone is recharged when the handset is replaced on the base. In this case, the base is plugged into an electrical outlet, which supplies the power to drive the nonspontaneous recharge reaction.

21.2 Types of Batteries   **675**

## Extension

*Intrapersonal* Remind students that many batteries contain toxic metals, such as cadmium, mercury, nickel, and lead. Ask them to research some of the environmental problems that can occur if these metals are disposed improperly. Have students investigate how car batteries are disposed of in their own community. Do other types of batteries require special disposal in their community according to local regulations and policies?

### GLENCOE TECHNOLOGY

**CD-ROM**
**Chemistry: Matter and Change**
Exploration: *Building a Battery*

## Portfolio

### Fuel Cells

*Intrapersonal* Ask students to list some of the current applications of fuel cells. Have them research future applications of fuel cells, limitations, and benefits. Reports can be placed in students' portfolios. **L2**  **P**

**National Science Content Standards**
Pages 674–675
UCP.1, UCP.3; B.3, B.6; E.1, E.2

**Kinesthetic** Ask students how they can tell when a battery is used up. Investigate recent packaging efforts by manufacturers that allow the consumer to test the amount of charge left in a battery. Help students discover how this test method works. Have a few batteries on hand for students to test. **L2** **ELL**

---

### CAREERS USING CHEMISTRY

**TECH PREP** **Career Path** A career in electrochemistry would include high school courses in chemistry, physics, computer science, electronics, and math. Electrochemists must earn at least a bachelor's degree in natural science, engineering, or a related field. People with advanced degrees are more likely to conduct and direct research.

**Career Issue** Ask students if they would like to conduct research in order to make a profit for their employer.

#### For More Information
For more information about careers in electrochemistry, students can contact:

The Electrochemical Society, Inc.
65 South Main Street
Pennington, NJ 08534-2839

**Figure 21-10**

**ⓐ** Lead–acid batteries contain lead plates and lead(IV) oxide plates. The electrolyte is a solution of sulfuric acid. When the battery is in use, the sulfuric acid is depleted and the electrolyte becomes less dense. **ⓑ** The condition of the battery can be checked by measuring the density of the electrolyte solution.

---

### Chemistry Online

**Topic: History of Batteries**
To learn more about the history of batteries, visit the Chemistry Web site at **chemistrymc.com**

**Activity:** Draw a timeline showing improvements in batteries over time. List at least five improvements that industry has made to increase the power and life of batteries.

The overall reaction is

$$Pb(s) + PbO_2(s) + 4H^+(aq) + 2SO_4^{2-}(aq) \rightarrow 2PbSO_4(s) + 2H_2O(l)$$

By looking at the half-cell reactions, you can see that lead(II) sulfate ($PbSO_4$) is the reaction product in both oxidation and reduction. Also, Pb, $PbO_2$, and $PbSO_4$ are solid substances, so they stay in place where they are formed. Thus, whether the battery is discharging or charging, the reactants are available where they are needed. Sulfuric acid serves as the electrolyte in the battery, but, as the overall cell equation shows, it is depleted as the battery generates electric current. For this reason, it is possible to measure a battery's state of charge by measuring the density of the electrolyte. Sulfuric acid ($H_2SO_4$) has almost twice the density of water. As the $H_2SO_4$ is used up, the solution becomes less dense. What happens when the battery is recharging? In this case, the reactions reverse, forming lead and lead(IV) oxide and releasing sulfuric acid, shown as $4H^+ + 2SO_4^{2-}$ in the equation.

The lead-storage battery shown in **Figure 21-10** is a good choice for motor vehicles because it provides a large initial supply of energy to start the engine, has a long shelf-life, and is reliable at low temperatures.

### Lithium Batteries

Although lead–acid batteries are reliable and suitable for many applications, the recent trend has been, and continues to be, the development of batteries with less mass and higher capacity to power devices from wristwatches to electric cars. For applications where a battery is the key component and must provide a significant amount of power, such as for the operation of electric cars, lead–acid batteries are too heavy to be feasible.

The solution is to develop lightweight batteries that store a large amount of energy for their size. Scientists and engineers have focused a lot of attention on the element lithium for two main reasons: lithium is the lightest

---

### Internet Address Book

 Note Internet addresses that you find useful in the space below for quick reference.

known metal and lithium has the lowest standard reduction potential of the metallic elements, $-3.04$ V (see **Table 21-1**). This means that a battery that oxidizes lithium at the anode can generate almost 2.3 volts more than a similar battery in which zinc is oxidized. Compare the two oxidation half-reactions and their standard reduction potentials.

$$Zn \rightarrow Zn^{2+} + 2e^- \qquad (E^0_{Zn^{2+}|Zn} = -0.762 \text{ V})$$

$$Li \rightarrow Li^+ + e^- \qquad (E^0_{Li^+|Li} = -3.04 \text{ V})$$

$$E^0_{Zn^{2+}|Zn} - E^0_{Li^+|Li} = +2.28 \text{ V}$$

Lithium batteries can be either primary or secondary, depending on which reduction reactions are coupled to the oxidation of lithium. For example, some lithium batteries use the same cathode reaction as zinc–carbon dry cells, the reduction of manganese(IV) oxide ($MnO_2$) to manganese(III) oxide ($Mn_2O_3$). These batteries produce electric current at about 3 V compared to 1.5 V for zinc–carbon cells. Lithium batteries last much longer than other kinds of batteries. As a result, they are often used in watches, computers, and cameras to maintain time, date, memory, and personal settings—even when the device is turned off.

## Fuel Cells

The dynamic reaction in which a fuel, such as hydrogen gas or methane, burns may seem quite different from the relatively calm redox reactions that take place in batteries. However, the burning of fuel shown in **Figure 21-11** also is an oxidation–reduction reaction. What happens when hydrogen burns in air?

$$2H_2(g) + O_2(g) \rightarrow 2H_2O(l)$$

In this reaction, hydrogen is oxidized from zero oxidation state in $H_2$ to a $+1$ oxidation state in water. Oxygen is reduced from zero oxidation state in $O_2$ to $-2$ in water. When hydrogen burns in air, hydrogen atoms form polar covalent bonds with oxygen, in effect sharing electrons directly with the highly electronegative oxygen atom. This reaction is analogous to the reaction that occurs when a zinc strip is immersed in a solution of copper(II) sulfate. Electrons from the oxidation of zinc transfer directly to copper(II) ions, reducing them to atoms of copper metal. Because the zinc atoms and copper ions are in close contact, there is no reason for electrons to flow through an external circuit.

You saw in Section 21.1 how the oxidation and reduction processes can be separated to cause electrons to flow through a wire. The same can be done so that a fuel "burns" in a highly controlled way while generating electric current. A **fuel cell** is a voltaic cell in which the oxidation of a fuel is used to produce electric energy. Although many people believe the fuel cell to be a modern invention, the first one was demonstrated in 1839 by William Grove (1811–1896), a British electrochemist. He called his cell a "gas battery." It was not until the 1950s, when scientists began working earnestly on the space program, that efficient, practical fuel cells were developed. As in other voltaic

## Careers Using Chemistry

### Electrochemist

*Do you like to experiment with batteries and other devices that generate electric current? Then consider becoming an electrochemist.*

Electrochemists study electrons. The presence, absence, and movement of electrons often determine whether a chemical reaction will take place. Electrochemists work with semiconductors, medical sensors, metal plating, and anti-corrosion technology in the automobile, medical, and computer industries and in other fields.

**Figure 21-11**

This oxyhydrogen torch uses hydrogen as its fuel and oxidizes hydrogen to water in a vigorous combustion reaction. Like the torch, fuel cells also oxidize hydrogen to water, but fuel cells operate at a much more controlled rate.

## Identifying Misconceptions

Many students may think that a dry cell is dry.

**Uncover the Misconception**
Ask students to describe how they envision the inside of a dry cell battery. What do they think is the consistency of the center substance?

**Demonstrate the Concept**
Show students a cross section of a battery that you have dismantled. A 9-volt battery can be dismantled using a screw driver and pliers. Enlist the help of an industrial technology teacher to cut the cross section. Cover the exposed interior of the dry cell with plastic wrap so that the paste does not dry and students will not come into contact with the substances. **Do not** cut a cross section of an alkaline dry cell battery due to the corrosiveness of the substances that make up this type of battery. An alternative would be to refer to Figure 21-8a and b if you do not have access to cross sections of common dry cell or 9-volt batteries.

**Assess New Knowledge**
Ask students to explain why a dry cell is not dry. The dry cell contains an electrolytic paste made up of zinc chloride, manganese(IV) oxide, ammonium chloride, and a little water. **L1** **ELL**

## DIFFERENTIATED INSTRUCTION

### English Language Learners

*Kinesthetic* Have students build models of cross sections of the batteries shown in the diagrams in the text or from the research that they conducted. Refer to the various figures of batteries in the text. Have students label all of the parts of the batteries in English and in the students' native languages. **L1** **ELL**

**National Science Content Standards**

Pages 676–677
UCP.1, UCP.3; B.3, B.6; E.2; G.1, G.3

Ask students if copper would make a good cathodic protector to prevent the corrosion of iron. No, because iron oxidizes easier than copper.

Ask a representative of a local gas or oil company to discuss with the class the use of sacrificial metal as a method of preventing the corrosion of pipeline metal. One of the questions to ask might be what elements are commonly used as cathodic protectors or sacrificial metals.

## Extension

Have students read news accounts or watch video of the Apollo 13 mission, during which an oxygen tank exploded and damaged the fuel cells on the space capsule. Point out how creative problem solving was key to the safe return of the astronauts.

**National Science Content Standards**

**Pages 678–679**
UCP.1, UCP.3; B.3, B.6; E.1, E.2

**678**

cells, an electrolyte is required so that ions can migrate between electrodes. In the case of the fuel cell, a common electrolyte is an alkaline solution of potassium hydroxide.

In a fuel cell, each electrode is a hollow chamber of porous carbon walls that allow contact between the inner chamber and the electrolyte surrounding it. The walls of the chamber also contain catalysts, such as powdered platinum or palladium, which speed up the reactions. These catalysts are similar to those in an automobile's catalytic converter, which you read about in Chapter 17. The following oxidation half-reaction takes place at the anode.

$$2H_2(g) + 4OH^-(aq) \rightarrow 4H_2O(l) + 4e^-$$

The reaction uses the hydroxide ions abundant in the alkaline electrolyte and releases electrons to the anode. Electrons from the oxidation of hydrogen flow through the external circuit to the cathode where the following reduction half-reaction takes place

$$O_2(g) + 2H_2O(l) + 4e^- \rightarrow 4OH^-(aq)$$

The electrons allow the reduction of oxygen in the presence of water to form four hydroxide ions, which replenish the hydroxide ions used up at the anode. By combining the two half-reactions, the overall cell reaction is determined. As you can see, it is the same as the equation for the burning of hydrogen in oxygen.

$$2H_2(g) + O_2(g) \rightarrow 2H_2O(l)$$

The hydrogen–oxygen fuel cell also burns hydrogen in a sense, but the burning is controlled so that most of the chemical energy is converted to electrical energy, not to heat.

In understanding fuel cells, it might be helpful to think of them as reaction chambers into which oxygen and hydrogen are fed from outside sources and from which the reaction product, water, is removed. Because the fuel for the cell is provided from an outside source, fuel cells never "run down." They keep on producing electricity as long as fuel is fed to them.

Newer fuel cells, such as the cell in the **problem-solving LAB** and the cell shown in **Figure 21-12,** use a plastic sheet called a proton-exchange membrane,

**Figure 21-12**

**ⓐ** In this fuel cell, hydrogen is the fuel. The half-reactions are separated by a proton-exchange membrane so that the electrons lost in oxidation flow through an external circuit to reach the site of reduction. As electrons travel through the external circuit, they can do useful work, such as running electric motors. The byproduct of this redox reaction is water, a harmless substance. **ⓑ** A "stack" of PEM-type cells can generate enough energy to power an electric car.

---

## CULTURAL DIVERSITY

### Preserving National Treasures

Remind students that bridges and cars are not the only objects subject to corrosion. Many art objects are also vulnerable to corrosion. One of the best publicized restorations was that of the Statue of Liberty. Another art object that was recently restored was *The Thinker,* a bronze cast statue by Rodin that has been in Philadelphia since 1925.

Have students research other works of art that are important to cultures around the world and that are exposed to the elements and in danger of corrosion. Have students describe the chemistry of the corrosion problem and steps that have been taken (or could be taken) to restore the treasures.

### Interpreting Scientific Illustrations

**Can the simplest atom power a car?**

Daimler–Chrysler's NECAR IV may be a preview of the future of automobiles. The NECAR IV is a compact car that is powered by a hydrogen fuel cell (HFC). This model can reach speeds of 90 mph (145 km/h), carry up to five passengers and cargo, and travel 280 miles (450 km) before refueling. It runs on oxygen from the air and pure hydrogen supplied in a tank. Its exhaust is water, making it pollution free.

**Analysis**

To power a 1200-kg automobile, a hydrogen fuel cell must produce about 144 volts. Although the cell potential for a hydrogen fuel cell is 1.229 V, approximately 43% of that voltage is lost to the production of heat, meaning that each cell's actual potential is closer to 0.7 V. To generate enough voltage to power a car, the HFCs must be stacked, similar to the stack shown in **Figure 21-12b**. When the electrodes are connected to a device, such as an electric motor, the electrons, which cannot travel through the PEM, travel through the external circuit and turn the motor.

**Thinking Critically**

1. How many cells would be needed to power a 1200-kg automobile? What would be the length of the stack if one cell is 1.2 mm thick? Is it small enough to fit under the hood?

2. Compare and contrast a stack of cells with a voltaic pile.

or PEM, instead of a liquid electrode to separate the reactions. PEMs are not corrosive and they are safer and lighter in weight than liquid electrodes. Hydrogen ions ($H^+$) are protons, and they can pass directly through the membrane from the anode (where hydrogen is oxidized) to the cathode. There, they combine with oxygen molecules and electrons returning from the external circuit to form water molecules, which are released as steam.

One potential application for fuel cells is as an alternative power source for automobiles. However, as the **Chemistry and Technology** feature at the end of this chapter explains, scientists must resolve some fundamental challenges before fuel cells power the cars we drive.

## Corrosion

So far in this chapter, you have examined the spontaneous redox reactions in voltaic cells. Spontaneous redox reactions also occur in nature. A prime example is corrosion, usually called rusting, of iron. **Corrosion** is the loss of metal resulting from an oxidation–reduction reaction of the metal with substances in the environment. Although rusting is usually thought of as a reaction between iron and oxygen, it is more complex. Can you recall ever seeing or reading about corrosion happening in perfectly dry air or in water that contains no dissolved oxygen? Probably not because both water and oxygen must be present for rusting to take place. For this reason, the steel hulls of ships, such as that shown in **Figure 21-13,** are especially susceptible to corrosion in the form of rust.

Rusting usually begins where there is a pit or small break in the surface of the iron. This

**Figure 21-13**

The steel hull of oceangoing ships offers strength, reliability, and durability, but steel is susceptible to corrosion. Ships such as this one in St. John Harbour, New Brunswick, Canada, often show the telltale sign of corrosion, which is rust.

### Resource Manager

**Teaching Transparency 64 and Master**
L2  ELL

### ✓ Assessment

**Portfolio** Have students give a number of reasons why this technology would be beneficial to the quality of life on the planet. Write-ups can be placed in students' portfolios. L2  P

**Purpose**

Students will discover the effect that multiple cells and surface area have on the production of current and voltage.

**Process Skills**

Interpreting scientific illustrations, using numbers, drawing conclusions, applying concepts, predicting

**Background**

The hydrogen fuel cell was invented at DuPont and was immediately put to use by NASA to provide power for the Apollo command module. Fuel cells contain an organic polymer that has long chains of hydrocarbons with Teflon-like properties that provide strength and durability. At the side chains, water is absorbed and $SO_3H$ molecules dissociate to form $SO_3^-$ and $H^+$. The $H^+$ is free to roam in solution while the $SO_3^-$ remains attached to the polymer. This allows the $H^+$ ions that are formed at the anode to traverse this "salt bridge" to the cathode. The benefits are enormous: there are no caustic chemicals, it is extremely thin and lightweight, and the byproduct of the reaction is water.

**Teaching Strategy**

• Ask students how an acid acts as an electrolyte and what would happen if one of the ions were restricted from moving? Charge could flow only in one direction through the solution, making it semipermeable.

**Thinking Critically**

1. 144 volts/0.7 volts = 206 cells. At about 1.2 mm per cell, the length of the stack is about 25 cm long, which does not take up much space.

2. The voltaic pile and stack are similar in design, with alternating layers, and in their ability to increase voltage by the number of repeating layers. They differ in that the voltaic pile eventually expires when all of the electrolytes are consumed. The stack runs as long as it is supplied with fuel.

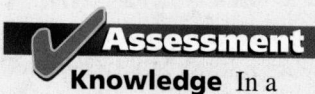
**Knowledge** In a nickel–cadmium battery, the two half-reactions are

$$Cd + OH^- \rightarrow CdO + H_2O + e^-$$
and
$$NiO + H_2O + e^- \rightarrow Ni + OH^-$$

Have students balance the reactions using the half-reaction method from Chapter 20. Identify what is oxidized, what is reduced, which element functions as the anode, and which element functions as the cathode. If an external source is applied during the recharging process, which element becomes the anode? The cathode? Also have students draw a diagram of the electrochemical cell and label all of the parts.

**Resource Manager**

**ChemLab and MiniLab Worksheets, p. 81** L2

**Figure 21-14**

Corrosion occurs when air, water, and iron set up a voltaic cell similar to the conditions shown at the surface of this iron I-beam.

Air

$O_2$

Water

Rust

$Fe^{2+}$
$Fe^{3+}$

$e^-$

Iron

Anode
$Fe(s) \rightarrow Fe^{2+}(aq) + 2e^-$
$Fe^{2+}(aq) \rightarrow Fe^{3+}(aq) + e^-$

Cathode
$O_2(g) + 4H^+(aq) + 4e^- \rightarrow 2H_2O(l)$

region becomes the anode of the cell as iron atoms begin to lose electrons, as illustrated in **Figure 21-14.**

$$Fe(s) \rightarrow Fe^{2+}(aq) + 2e^-$$

The iron(II) ions become part of the water solution while the electrons move through the iron to the cathode region. In effect, the piece of iron becomes the external circuit as well as the anode. The cathode is usually located at the edge of the water drop where water, iron, and air come in contact. Here, the electrons reduce oxygen from the air in this half-reaction.

$$O_2(g) + 4H^+(aq) + 4e^- \rightarrow 2H_2O(l)$$

The supply of $H^+$ ions is probably furnished by carbonic acid formed when $CO_2$ from the air dissolves in water.

Next, the $Fe^{2+}$ ions in solution are oxidized to $Fe^{3+}$ ions by reaction with oxygen dissolved in the water. The $Fe^{3+}$ ions combine with oxygen to form insoluble $Fe_2O_3$, rust.

$$4Fe^{2+}(aq) + 2O_2(g) + 2H_2O(l) + 4e^- \rightarrow 2Fe_2O_3(s) + 4H^+(aq)$$

Combining the three equations yields the overall cell reaction for the corrosion of iron.

$$4Fe(s) + 3O_2(g) \rightarrow 2Fe_2O_3(s)$$

You can observe the process of corrosion first-hand by performing the **miniLAB** that results in the corrosion of an iron nail.

**(a)**

**Figure 21-15**

Because corrosion can cause considerable damage, it is important to investigate ways to prevent rust and deterioration.
**(a)** Paint or another protective coating is one way to protect steel structures from corrosion.
**(b)** Sacrificial anodes of magnesium or other active metals are also used to prevent corrosion.

Moist soil

Underground iron pipe

Magnesium rod

$e^-$

Oxidation: $Mg(s) \rightarrow Mg^{2+}(aq) + 2e^-$
Reduction: $O_2(g) + 4H^+(aq) + 4e^- \rightarrow 2H_2O(l)$

**(b)**

**680** Chapter 21 Electrochemistry

---

**DIFFERENTIATED INSTRUCTION**

## Hearing Impaired

*Visual-Spatial* Assign to each student a pair of reactions that make an electrochemical cell. Have students create a poster on which they will draw and label the electrochemical reaction, incorporating as many of the vocabulary terms and concepts from this chapter as possible. This poster or a picture of it may be included in the students' portfolios. L2 **ELL** P

**National Science Content Standards**

**Pages 680–681**
UCP.1, UCP.3; A.1; B.3, B.6; E.1; F.6

Rusting is a rather slow process because water droplets have few ions and therefore are not good electrolytes. However, if the water contains abundant ions, as in seawater or in regions where roads are salted in winter, corrosion occurs much faster because the solutions are excellent electrolytes.

It has been estimated that corrosion of cars, bridges, ships, the structures of buildings, and other metallic objects costs more than 100 billion dollars a year in the U.S. alone. For this reason, people have devised several means to minimize corrosion. One is simply to apply a coat of paint to seal out both air and moisture, but, because paint deteriorates, objects such as the ship's hull shown in **Figure 21-15a** must be repainted often.

The steel hulls of ships are constantly in contact with saltwater, so the prevention of corrosion is vital. Although the hull may be painted, another method is used to minimize corrosion. Blocks of metals, such as magnesium, aluminum, or titanium, that oxidize more easily than iron are placed in contact with the steel hull. These blocks rather than the iron in the hull become the anode of the corrosion cell. As a result, these blocks, called sacrificial anodes, are corroded while the iron in the hull is spared. Of course, the sacrificial anodes must be replaced before they corrode away completely, leaving the ship's hull unprotected. A similar technique is used to protect iron pipes that are run underground. Magnesium bars are attached to the pipe by wires, and these bars corrode instead of the pipe, as shown in **Figure 21-15b**.

Another approach to preventing corrosion is to coat iron with another metal that is more resistant to corrosion. In the **galvanizing** process, iron is

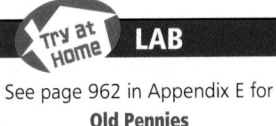
**Try at Home** **LAB**
See page 962 in Appendix E for
**Old Pennies**

## miniLAB

### Corrosion

**Comparing and Contrasting** A lot of money is spent every year correcting and preventing the effects of corrosion. Corrosion is a real-world concern of which everyone needs to be aware.

**Materials** iron nails (4); magnesium ribbon (2 pieces, each about 5 cm long); copper metal (2 pieces, each about 5 cm long); 150-mL beakers (4); distilled water; saltwater solution; sandpaper.

**Procedures**

1. Use the sandpaper to buff the surfaces of each nail. Wrap two nails with the magnesium ribbon and two nails with the copper. Wrap the metals tightly enough so that the nails do not slip out.

2. Place each of the nails in a separate beaker. Add distilled water to one of the beakers containing a copper-wrapped nail and one of the beakers containing a magnesium-wrapped nail. Add enough distilled water to just cover the wrapped nails. Add saltwater to the other two beakers. Record your observations for each of the beakers.

3. Let the beakers stand overnight in the warmest place available. Examine the nails and solutions the next day and record your observations.

### Analysis

1. Describe the difference between copper-wrapped nails in the distilled water and saltwater after standing overnight.

2. Describe the difference between the magnesium-wrapped nails in the distilled water and saltwater.

3. In general, what is the difference between a copper-wrapped nail and a magnesium-wrapped nail?

21.2 Types of Batteries **681**

# 3 Assess

## Check for Understanding

Have the students construct a chart comparing the major types of batteries (dry cell or primary battery, lead–acid storage battery, and fuel cells) described in this chapter. Compare size, voltage produced, and lifetime of the battery. **L2**

## Reteach

Make sure students understand the difference between a primary battery and a secondary battery. Using the information illustrated in Figures 21-8 through 21-10, have them classify the different batteries illustrated as primary or secondary and explain their reasons for the classification. **L2**

## Assessment

**Knowledge** Ask what are some reasons why there would be a difference in the type of battery selected to supply energy to a toy compared to a battery that supplies energy to a pacemaker that is surgically implanted. The most important reason is the length of time before the battery would have to be replaced, which requires another surgical procedure. Size is a second consideration. Another concern is durability in the body and that the battery would resist corrosion and deterioration inside the human body. Cost differences are probably of least importance.

**a** Galvanized object with zinc coating intact

**b** Galvanized object with zinc coating broken

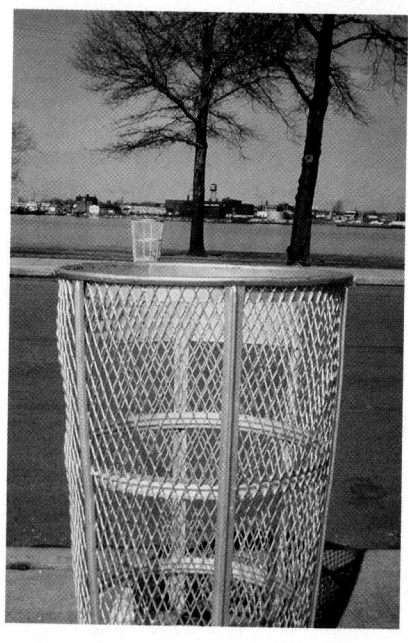

**c**

**Figure 21-16**

Galvanizing helps prevent corrosion in two ways. **a** The zinc coating seals the iron from air and water by forming a barrier of zinc oxide that repels water and oxygen. **b** If the zinc coating breaks, the zinc acts as a sacrificial anode. **c** Metal objects that are left outside are often galvanized to prevent rust and corrosion caused by the elements.

coated with a layer of zinc by either dipping the iron object into molten zinc or by electroplating the zinc onto it. Although zinc is more readily oxidized than iron, it is one of the *self-protecting metals*, a group that also includes aluminum and chromium. When exposed to air, these metals oxidize at the surface, but the thin metal oxide coating clings tightly to the metal and seals it from further oxidation.

Galvanizing protects iron in two ways. As long as the zinc layer is intact, water and oxygen cannot reach the iron's surface. Inevitably, though, the zinc coating cracks. When this happens, zinc protects iron from rapid corrosion by becoming the anode of the voltaic cell set up when water and oxygen contact iron and zinc at the same time. **Figure 21-16** illustrates how these two forms of corrosion protection work.

## Section 21.2 Assessment

**14.** What is reduced and what is oxidized in the ordinary zinc–carbon dry cell battery? What features make the alkaline dry cell an improvement over the earlier type of dry cell battery?

**15.** Explain how primary and secondary batteries differ. Give an example of each type.

**16.** Explain why a fuel cell does not run down like other batteries.

**17.** What is a sacrificial anode? How is one used?

**18. Thinking Critically** Standard dry cell batteries have a relatively short shelf life. Explain why older dry-cell batteries may not have the same power output as newer batteries. How can the shelf life of these batteries be extended?

**19. Calculating** Use data from **Table 21-1** to calculate the cell potential of the hydrogen–oxygen fuel cell described in this section.

chemistrymc.com/self_check_quiz

## Section 21.2 Assessment

**14.** Zinc is oxidized; manganese oxide is reduced in the electrolytic paste. Alkaline cells use zinc in a powdered form, which provides more surface area for reaction, thus more power in the package. Alkaline cells also eliminate the inactive carbon rod cathode.

**15.** A primary battery (zinc–carbon dry cell) cannot be recharged, and a secondary battery (nickel–cadmium) can.

**16.** A fuel cell is fueled by an outside source and can produce power without running down as long as the external fuel source exists.

**17.** A sacrificial anode is a piece of metal attached to another metal

that will protect from corrosion. The sacrificial anode is more active than the metal it protects and corrodes instead of the protected metal.

**18.** The zinc anode reacts with $NH_4^+$ ions in the electrolyte. Batteries can be stored in a cool place to slow the reaction rate.

**19.** $E^0_{cell} = +1.229$ V

# Electrolysis

In Section 21.2, you learned that rechargeable batteries can regain their electrical potential and be reused. You learned that a current can be introduced to cause the reverse reaction, which is not spontaneous, to happen. This aspect of electrochemistry—the use of an external force, usually in the form of electricity, to drive a chemical reaction—is important and has many practical applications.

## Reversing Redox Reactions

When a battery generates electricity, electrons given up at the anode flow through an external circuit to the cathode where they are used in a reduction reaction. A secondary battery is one that can be recharged by passing a current through it in the opposite direction. The current source can be a generator or even another battery. The energy of this current reverses the cell redox reaction and regenerates the battery's original substances.

To understand this process, look at **Figure 21-17,** which shows an electrochemical cell powering a light bulb by a spontaneous redox reaction. The beakers on the left contain a zinc strip in a solution of zinc ions. The beakers on the right contain a copper strip in a solution of copper ions. You saw in Section 21.1 how electrons in this system flow from the zinc side to the copper side, creating an electric current. As the reaction continues, the zinc strip deteriorates, while copper from the copper ion solution is deposited as copper metal on the copper strip. Over time, the flow of electrons decreases and the strength of the electrical output diminishes to the point that the bulb will not light. However, the cell can be regenerated if current is applied in the reverse direction using an external voltage source. The reverse reaction is nonspontaneous, which is why the voltage source is required. If the voltage source remains long enough, eventually the cell will return to near its original strength and can again produce electrical energy to light the bulb.

The use of electrical energy to bring about a chemical reaction is called **electrolysis.** An electrochemical cell in which electrolysis occurs is called an **electrolytic cell.** For example, when a secondary battery is recharged, it is acting as an electrolytic cell.

## Objectives

- **Describe** how it is possible to reverse a spontaneous redox reaction in an electrochemical cell.

- **Compare** the reactions involved in the electrolysis of molten sodium chloride with those in the electrolysis of brine.

- **Discuss** the importance of electrolysis in the smelting and purification of metals.

## Vocabulary

electrolysis
electrolytic cell

**Figure 21-17**

ⓐ Electrons in this zinc–copper electrochemical cell flow from the zinc strip to the copper strip, causing an electric current that powers the light bulb. As the spontaneous reaction continues, much of the zinc strip is oxidized to zinc ions and the copper ions are reduced to copper metal, which is deposited on the copper strip. ⓑ If an outside voltage source is applied to reverse the flow of electrons, the original conditions of the cell are restored.

# 1 Focus

## Focus Transparency

Before presenting the lesson, display **Section Focus Transparency 80** on the overhead projector. Have students answer the accompanying questions using **Section Focus Transparency Master 80.** [L1] [ELL]

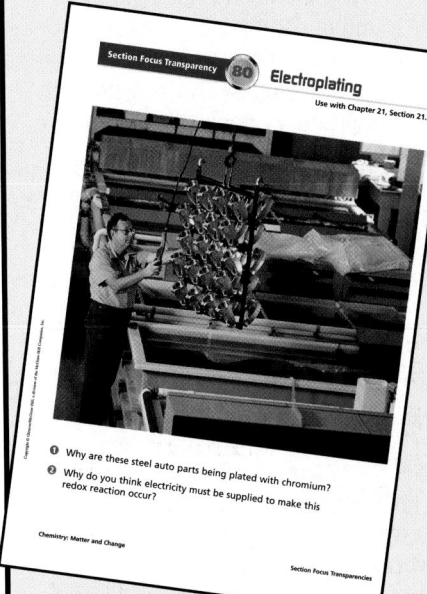

Section Focus Transparency 80 — Electroplating
Use with Chapter 21, Section 21.3

❶ Why are these steel auto parts being plated with chromium?
❷ Why do you think electricity must be supplied to make this redox reaction occur?

Chemistry: Matter and Change

Section Focus Transparencies

# 2 Teach

## Concept Development

Students do not always realize that reactions are reversible. Refer to the analogy developed earlier in the chapter with the golf ball rolling down the hill. Ask the students what must happen to get the ball back up the hill. They will need to use energy to push it back up the hill. By adding energy (external electricity) to the reaction, the reaction can be forced in the opposite direction.

## Resource Manager

**Study Guide for Content Mastery,** p. 126 [L2]
**Solving Problems: A Chemistry Handbook,** Section 21.3 [L2]
**Section Focus Transparency 80 and Master** [L1] [ELL]

## DIFFERENTIATED INSTRUCTION

### Visually Impaired

*Intrapersonal* Ask students to describe orally why the addition of an electrolyte to water would help with the process of electrolysis. Students should explain that water is a polar molecule and, therefore, a poor conductor of electricity. [L2]

## National Science Content Standards

**Pages 682–683**
UCP.1, UCP.3; B.3, B.6; E.1, E.2; F.6

**Figure 21-18**

In a Down's cell, electrons supplied by a generator are used to reduce sodium ions. As electrons are removed from the anode, chloride ions are oxidized to chlorine gas.

## Applications of Electrolysis

Recall that the voltaic cells convert chemical energy to electrical energy as a result of a spontaneous redox reaction. Electrolytic cells do just the opposite: they use electrical energy to drive a nonspontaneous reaction. A common example is the electrolysis of water. In this case, an electric current decomposes water into hydrogen and oxygen.

$$2H_2O(l) \xrightarrow{\text{electric current}} 2H_2(g) + O_2(g)$$

The electrolysis of water is one method by which hydrogen gas can be generated for commercial use. Aside from the decomposition of water, electrolysis has many other practical applications.

**Electrolysis of molten NaCl** Just as electrolysis can decompose water into its elements, it also can separate molten sodium chloride into sodium metal and chlorine gas. This process, the only practical way to obtain elemental sodium, is carried out in a chamber called a Down's cell, as shown in **Figure 21-18.** The electrolyte in the cell is the molten sodium chloride itself. Remember that ionic compounds can conduct electricity only when their ions are free to move, such as when they are dissolved in water or are in the molten state.

The anode reaction of the Down's cell is the oxidation of chloride ions.

$$2Cl^-(l) \rightarrow Cl_2(g) + 2e^-$$

At the cathode, sodium ions are reduced to atoms of sodium metal.

$$Na^+(l) + e^- \rightarrow Na(l)$$

The net cell reaction is

$$2Na^+(l) + 2Cl^-(l) \rightarrow 2Na(l) + Cl_2(g)$$

**a**

Anode (+)  Cathode (−)

Ion-permeable membrane

Depleted brine

$Cl_2$  $H_2$  Water

$Cl^-$ →  $Na^+$ →

Brine

$H_2O$  $H_2O$  $OH^-$  NaOH(aq)

**Figure 21-19**

**a** Commercial facilities use an electrolytic process to derive hydrogen gas, chlorine gas, and sodium hydroxide from brine. **b** Chlorine gas is used to manufacture polyvinyl chloride products such as these irrigation pipes. **c** Sodium hydroxide is the key ingredient in drain cleaners.

**b**

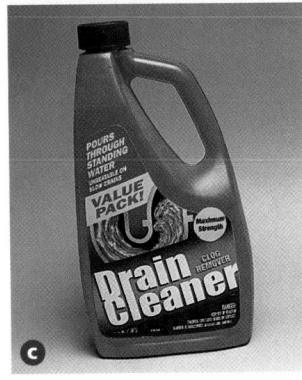

**c**

**Electrolysis of brine** The decomposition of brine, an aqueous solution of sodium chloride, is another process that is accomplished by electrolysis. **Figure 21-19** illustrates the electrolytic cell and products of the electrolysis of brine. Two reactions are possible at the cathode, the reduction of sodium ions and the reduction of hydrogen in water molecules.

$$Na^+(aq) + e^- \rightarrow Na(s)$$

$$2H_2O(l) + 2e^- \rightarrow H_2(g) + 2OH^-(aq)$$

Here, a key product of reduction is hydrogen gas.

Two reactions are possible at the anode, the oxidation of chloride ions and the oxidation of oxygen in water molecules.

$$2Cl^-(aq) \rightarrow Cl_2(g) + 2e^-$$

$$2H_2O(l) \rightarrow O_2(g) + 4H^+(aq) + 4e^-$$

When the concentration of chloride ions is high, the primary product of oxidation is chlorine gas. However, as the brine solution becomes dilute, oxygen gas becomes the primary product.

To appreciate the commercial importance of this process, look at the overall cell reaction.

$$2H_2O(l) + 2NaCl(aq) \rightarrow H_2(g) + Cl_2(g) + 2NaOH(aq)$$

All three products of the electrolysis of brine—hydrogen gas, chlorine gas, and sodium hydroxide—are substances that are commercially important to industry.

**Aluminum manufacture** Aluminum is the most abundant metallic element in Earth's crust, but until the late nineteenth century, aluminum metal was more precious than gold. Aluminum was expensive because no one knew how to purify it in large quantities. Instead, it was produced by a tedious and expensive small-scale process in which metallic sodium was used to reduce aluminum ions in molten aluminum fluoride to metallic aluminum.

$$3Na(l) + AlF_3(l) \rightarrow Al(l) + 3NaF(l)$$

In 1886, 22-year-old Charles Martin Hall (1863–1914) developed a process to produce aluminum by electrolysis using heat from a blacksmith

Carbon anode: $C(s) + 2O^{2-}(l) \rightarrow CO_2 + 4e^-$

Power source

Carbon-lining cathode: $Al^{3+}(l) + 3e^- \rightarrow Al(l)$

$Al_2O_3$ in $Na_3AlF_6(l)$

Electrolyte

Al outlet

Molten Al

**a**

**b**

### Figure 21-20

**a** Aluminum is produced by the Hall–Héroult process in cells similar to this one. Note that the cathode is the carbon (graphite) lining of the cell itself. **b** Every ton of aluminum that is recycled saves huge quantities of electrical energy that would be spent to produce new aluminum from ore.

forge, electricity from home-made batteries, and his mother's iron skillets as electrodes. At almost the same time, one of Le Châtelier's students, Paul L. T. Héroult (1863–1914), also 22 years old, discovered the same process. Today, it is called the Hall–Héroult process, which is illustrated in **Figure 21-20**.

In the modern version of this process, aluminum metal is obtained by electrolysis of aluminum oxide, which is refined from bauxite ore ($Al_2O_3 \cdot 2H_2O$). The aluminum oxide is dissolved at 1000°C in molten synthetic cryolite ($Na_3AlF_6$), another aluminum compound. The cell is lined with graphite, which forms the cathode for the reaction. Another set of graphite rods is immersed in the molten solution as an anode. The following half-reaction occurs at the cathode.

$$Al^{3+} + 3e^- \rightarrow Al(l)$$

The molten aluminum settles to the bottom of the cell and is drawn off periodically. Oxide ions are oxidized at the cathode in this half-reaction.

$$2O^{2-} \rightarrow O_2(g) + 4e^-$$

Because temperatures are high, the liberated oxygen reacts with the carbon of the anode to form carbon monoxide.

$$2C(s) + O_2(g) \rightarrow 2CO(g)$$

The Hall–Héroult process uses huge amounts of electric energy. For this reason, aluminum often is produced in plants built close to large hydroelectric power stations, where electric energy is abundant and less expensive. The vast amount of electricity needed to produce aluminum from ore is the prime reason that it is especially important to recycle aluminum. Recycled aluminum already has undergone electrolysis, so the only energy required to make it usable again is the heat used to melt it in a furnace.

**Purification of ores** Another application of electrolysis is in the purification of metals such as copper. Most copper is mined in the form of the ores chalcopyrite ($CuFeS_2$), chalcocite ($Cu_2S$), and malachite ($Cu_2CO_3(OH)_2$). The sulfides are most abundant and yield copper metal when heated strongly in the presence of oxygen.

$$Cu_2S(s) + O_2(g) \rightarrow 2Cu(l) + SO_2(g)$$

The copper from this process contains many impurities and must be refined, so the molten copper is cast into large, thick plates. These plates are then used as an anode in an electrolytic cell containing a solution of copper(II) sulfate. The cathode of the cell is a thin sheet of pure copper. As current is passed through the cell, copper atoms in the impure anode are oxidized to copper(II) ions, which migrate through the solution to the cathode where they are reduced to copper atoms. These atoms become part of the cathode while impurities fall to the bottom of the cell.

**Electroplating** Objects can be electroplated with a metal such as silver in a method similar to that used to refine copper. The object to be silver plated is the cathode of an electrolytic cell that has a silver anode, as shown in **Figure 21-21.** At the cathode, silver ions present in the electrolyte solution are reduced to silver metal by electrons from an external power source. The silver forms a thin coating over the object being plated. The anode consists of a silver bar or sheet, which is oxidized to silver ions as electrons are removed by the power source. Current passing through the cell must be carefully controlled in order to get a smooth, even metal coating.

$e^-$ flow

$Ag^+ + e^- \rightarrow Ag$

Anode

Cathode

$Ag \rightarrow Ag^+ + e^-$

$NO_3^-$

Ag    Ag

$Ag^+$

Battery

**Figure 21-21**

In an electrolytic cell used for silver plating, the object to be plated is the cathode where silver ions in the electrolyte solution are reduced to silver metal and deposited on the object.

# Section 21.3 Assessment

**20.** Define electrolysis and relate the definition to spontaneity of redox reactions.

**21.** What are the products of the electrolysis of brine? Of the electrolysis of molten sodium chloride? Explain why the reaction products differ.

**22.** Describe the process by which the copper that results from smelting of ore is purified by electrolysis.

**23. Thinking Critically** Suppose you want to plate an object with gold by electrolysis. What sort of substances would you need to have in the electrolyte solution? What would you use as the cathode and the anode of the cell?

**24. Inferring** Producing a kilogram of silver from its ions by electrolysis requires much less electrical energy than producing a kilogram of aluminum from its ions. Give a reason for this difference.

# 3 Assess
## Check for Understanding

Ask students which of the following metals is the most active and thus the most difficult to refine from its ore: silver, gold, iron, or copper? copper

## Reteach

Take time to make sure that students recognize that many of the examples in this section relate to previous chapters, such as Chapter 20 (redox reactions) and Chapter 10 (types of reactions).

### ✓ Assessment

**Knowledge** Organize the class into small groups and ask students to explain the significance of the chemical reactions that are discussed in this section. Have students focus on one of the reactions described in Section 21.3 and explain how the reaction impacts their lives. Students should respond that the reactions require energy to proceed or that the reactions are not spontaneous without an outside energy source. Many commercial products could not be manufactured without knowledge of these specific reactions. **L2 COOP LEARN**

# Section 21.3 Assessment

**20.** Electrolysis is the process of using electrical energy to produce a chemical reaction. The chemical reactions in an electrolytic process are not spontaneous.

**21.** brine: hydrogen gas, chlorine gas, and sodium hydroxide; molten NaCl: sodium metal and chlorine gas. Electrolysis of brine involves an aqueous solution, which affects the products.

**22.** Electrolysis of the product of copper smelting involves copper atoms being oxidized to $Cu^{2+}$, which are subsequently reduced to pure Cu atoms, with the impurities falling away.

**23.** The electrolyte should be a solution containing gold ions. The cathode should be the object to be plated, and the anode should be gold.

**24.** Aluminum is more active and has a tendency to lose electrons more readily; therefore, it would require more electricity to reverse that tendency.

**687**

## Preparation

**Time Allotment**
One laboratory period

**Process Skills**
Analyze and conclude, classifying, comparing and contrasting, using numbers, measuring, sequencing

**Safety Precautions**
Remind students not to use the CBL and voltage probe on sources of higher current and potential difference, such as AC outlets. Doing so can be dangerous. Lab solutions are irritants. If students get solutions on their skin, they should wash the area thoroughly.

**Disposal**
Rinse solutions down the sink with lots of water. Reuse metals.

**Preparation of Solutions**
See page 662C for preparation of all solutions.

**Alternative Materials**
• Voltmeters can be used in place of the CBL. Tell the students which metals are anodes and cathodes because a negative voltage on some types of voltmeters can damage them. The CBL voltage range is ±10 volts.

### Pre-Lab

4. A voltaic cell is a device that converts chemical energy to electrical energy.
5. A salt bridge allows positive and negative ions to travel from one solution to the other.
6. $E^0_{cell} = E^0_{red} - E^0_{oxid}$
7. Mg is anode; Hg is cathode; Mg is oxidized; Hg is reduced $E^0_{cell} = 3.223$ V
8. [(theoretical potential − actual potential)/theoretical potential] × 100%

# Voltaic Cell Potentials

**A** voltaic cell converts chemical energy into electrical energy. It consists of two parts called half-cells. When two different metals, one in each half-cell, are used in the voltaic cell, a potential difference is produced. In this experiment, you will measure the potential difference of various combinations of metals used in voltaic cells and compare these values to the values found in the standard reduction potentials table.

**Problem**

How can you measure the potential of voltaic cells?

**Objectives**

• **Construct** voltaic cells using various combinations of metals for electrodes.
• **Design** the arrangement of the voltaic cells in a microplate in such a way as to use materials efficiently.
• **Determine** which metals are the anode and cathode in voltaic cells.
• **Compare** the experimental cell potential to the theoretical value found in **Table 21-1**.

**Materials**

metal strips (approximately 0.6 cm by 1.3 cm) of copper, aluminum, zinc, and magnesium
1*M* copper(II) nitrate
1*M* aluminum nitrate
1*M* zinc nitrate
1*M* magnesium nitrate
24-well microplate
Beral-type pipette (5)

CBL System
voltage probe
filter paper (6 pieces size 0.6 cm by 2.5 cm)
1*M* potassium nitrate
forceps
steel wool or sandpaper
table of standard reduction potentials

## Safety Precautions

• Always wear goggles and an apron in the lab.
• The chemicals used in this experiment are eye and skin irritants. Wash thoroughly if they are spilled on the skin.

### Pre-Lab

1. Read the entire **CHEMLAB**.
2. Plan and organize how you will arrange voltaic cells in the 24-well microplate using the four metal combinations so that your time and materials will be used in the most efficient manner possible. Have your instructor approve your plan before you begin the experiment.
3. Prepare all written materials that you will take into the laboratory. Be sure to include safety precautions, procedure notes, and a data table similar to the example below in which to record your observations.
4. Review the definition of a voltaic cell.

| Voltaic Cell Potential Data | | | | | | |
|---|---|---|---|---|---|---|
| Anode metal (black) | Cathode metal (red) | Actual cell potential (V) | Anode half-reaction and theoretical potential | Cathode half-reaction and theoretical potential | Theoretical cell potential | % Error |
| | | | | | | |
| | | | | | | |
| | | | | | | |

**688**    Chapter 21 Electrochemistry

## Procedure

• To create voltaic cells, place the four different solutions in wells A1, A2, B1, and B2. The metals should be put in the wells with matching ion. Complete the cell with a salt bridge (filter paper saturated with potassium nitrate) to connect wells A1 and A2. After the potential for this cell is measured,

remove the salt bridge and use a new salt bridge to connect A1 and B1. Continue for A1–B2, B2–A1, B1–B2, A2–B1, and A2–B2. This will allow students to test all four metals efficiently.
• You may want different lab groups to use different metals so that more metals can be tested and more data collected.

**5.** Review the purpose of a salt bridge in the voltaic cell. In this experiment, the filter paper strips soaked in potassium nitrate are the salt bridges.

**6.** Review the equation to calculate cell potential.

**7.** For the voltaic cell $Mg\,|\,Mg^{2+}\,\|\,Hg^{2+}\,|\,Hg$, identify which metal is the anode and which metal is the cathode. Which metal is being oxidized and which metal is being reduced? What is the theoretical potential for this voltaic cell?

**8.** Review the equation to calculate percent error.

### Procedure

**1.** Prepare the CBL to read potential differences (voltage). Plug the voltage probe into Channel 1. Turn the CBL on. Push the MODE button once to activate the voltmeter function.

**2.** Soak the strips of filter paper in 2 mL of potassium nitrate solution. These are the salt bridges for the experiment. Use forceps to handle the salt bridges.

**3.** Using the plan from your Pre-Lab, construct voltaic cells using the four metals and 1 mL of each of the solutions. Remember to minimize the use of solutions. Put the metals in the wells that contain the appropriate solution (for example, put the zinc metal in the solution with zinc nitrate). Use a different salt bridge for each voltaic cell. If you get a negative value for potential difference, switch the leads of the probe on the metals.

**4.** Record which metals are the anode and cathode in each cell in the data table. The black lead of the probe will be attached to the metal that acts as the anode. The red lead will be attached to the cathode.

**5.** Record the cell potential of each cell.

### Cleanup and Disposal

**1.** Use forceps to remove the metals from the microplate.

**2.** Rinse the solution off the metal pieces with water, then use steel wool or sandpaper to clean them.

**3.** Rinse the wells of the microplate.

**4.** Return each metal to its correct container.

### Analyze and Conclude

**1. Applying Concepts** Write the half-reactions for the anode and cathode in each of the voltaic cells in the data table. Look up the half-reaction potentials from the standard reduction potentials table (**Table 21-1**) and record these in the data table.

**2. Using Numbers** Calculate the theoretical potential for each voltaic cell and record it in the data table.

**3. Predicting** Using your data, rank the metals you used in order of most active to least active.

**4. Using Models** Calculate the percent error of the voltaic cell potential.

**5. Error Analysis** Why is the percent error calculated in step 4 large for some voltaic cells and small for others?

### Real-World Chemistry

**1.** Why is lithium metal becoming a popular electrode in modern batteries? Use the standard reduction potentials table to help you answer this question.

**2.** What type of battery is used in pacemakers to regulate a patient's heartbeat? What are some of the benefits of this battery?

- **Troubleshooting** The CBL will read about 2 V as a default, even when nothing is being tested. This is normal.

### Expected Results

See the data table below.

### Analyze and Conclude

**1–4.** See the data table.

**5.** It is hard to get ideal conditions for each cell; therefore, some cells will get better results than others.

### Real-World Chemistry

**1.** Lithium is the highest on the standard reduction potentials chart. If another metal is combined with this in a battery, it will provide a large cell potential. Lithium is also the lightest metal, so it will help reduce the weight.

**2.** Lithium batteries are commonly used in pacemakers because they are lightweight, durable, and long-lasting.

**✓ Assessment**

**Performance** Students can test other metal combinations in voltaic cells. Use the Performance Task Assessment List for Carrying Out a Strategy and Collecting Data in **PASC**, p. 25. **L2**

**Resource Manager**

ChemLab and MiniLab Worksheets, pp. 82–84 **L2**

## Data Table

| | Anode metal (black) | Cathode metal (red) | Cell potential (volts) | Anode half-reaction and theoretical potential | Cathode half-reaction and theoretical potential | Theoretical cell potential | % Error |
|---|---|---|---|---|---|---|---|
| 1 | Al | Cu | +0.703 | $Al \rightarrow Al^{3+} + 3e^-$ (+1.662 V) | $Cu^{2+} + 2e^- \rightarrow Cu$ (+0.3419 V) | +2.004 V | 64.9% |
| 2 | Al | Zn | +0.425 | $Al \rightarrow Al^{3+} + 3e^-$ (+1.662 V) | $Zn^{2+} + 2e^- \rightarrow Zn$ (−0.7618 V) | +0.900 V | 53.8% |
| 3 | Mg | Al | +0.461 | $Mg \rightarrow Mg^{2+} + 2e^-$ (+2.372 V) | $Al^{3+} + 3e^- \rightarrow Al$ (−1.662 V) | +0.710 V | 35.1% |
| 4 | Zn | Cu | +0.942 | $Zn \rightarrow Zn^{2+} + 2e^-$ (+0.7618 V) | $Cu^{2+} + 2e^- \rightarrow Cu$ (+0.3419 V) | +1.104 V | 14.7% |
| 5 | Mg | Cu | +1.65 | $Mg \rightarrow Mg^{2+} + 2e^-$ (+2.372 V) | $Cu^{2+} + 2e^- \rightarrow Cu$ (+0.3419 V) | +2.714 V | 39.2% |
| 6 | Mg | Zn | +1.07 | $Mg \rightarrow Mg^{2+} + 2e^-$ (+2.372 V) | $Zn^{2+} + 2e^- \rightarrow Zn$ (−0.7618 V) | +1.610 V | 33.5% |

## Purpose

Students will learn the technology of fuel cells, specifically hydrogen fuel cells, and recognize the drawbacks and challenges to overcome before fuel cells can be practical for everyday usage.

## Background

Although the fuel cell may seem to be new technology, its history began in 1839 when Sir William Grove (1811–1896), an English physicist, built the first fuel cell, which he called a "gas battery." In 1932, the Allis-Chalmers Company demonstrated a fuel cell powered tractor. Still, early fuel cells had little commercial value because they were inefficient and extremely expensive. In 1959, a fledgling government agency, the National Aeronautics and Space Administration (NASA), began looking for a small and lightweight power source to use for its future manned space missions. They decided that fuel cells could be the answer if they could be made reliable and more efficient. NASA's insight caused a wave of research to perfect the fuel cell. Despite the fact that fuel cells have been used in the space program for more than 40 years, they still remain too expensive to use in everyday consumer products.

## Teaching Strategies

- Discuss the origins of fossil fuels and how they are refined for various uses in our society. Include in the discussion facts pertaining to the finite supply of fossil fuels and the need to develop alternative energy sources for the future.
- Locate or make a model fuel cell of the variety that uses a PEM and demonstrate the chemistry and technology behind energy production.

# CHEMISTRY and Technology

## Fuel Cells

An important consideration for auto manufacturers today is fuel economy and pollution reduction. Fuel cells represent one option to achieve these goals. Like a battery, a fuel cell produces electricity from a redox reaction. Unlike a battery, a fuel cell can generate electric current indefinitely because it oxidizes a continuous stream of fuel from an outside source.

### Fuel Cell Basics

Fuel cells can use several kinds of fuel, including natural gas and petroleum products. However, these are fossil fuels that produce carbon dioxide, an undesirable byproduct, when oxidized. Another drawback of common fuel cells is that they operate at temperatures from 200°C to 1000°C, and some contain hot, caustic, liquid electrolyte.

To avoid these problems, engineers have focused on a cell in which the fuel is hydrogen gas, the oxidant is oxygen from the air, and the product is water vapor. One of the more promising hydrogen fuel cells is one in which the half-cell reactions are separated by a thin polymer sheet called a proton-exchange membrane (PEM). The PEM fuel cell operates at approximately 100°C, and the moist membrane itself is the electrolyte.

On the anode side of the membrane, a platinum catalyst causes $H_2$ molecules to dissociate into atoms. The PEM allows hydrogen protons to pass, while the electrons must travel an electrical circuit. On the cathode side of the membrane, the protons combine with oxygen from the air and the electrons from the circuit to form water.

### Making Fuel Cells Practical

Before PEM hydrogen fuel cells become practical, several issues must be resolved. PEM cells are expensive, in part because of the platinum powder that catalyzes the reaction. Safe storage and delivery of hydrogen is another key issue. The vehicle must carry enough hydrogen to power the vehicle over an acceptable range. Chemists are investigating ways to store and deliver hydrogen to fuel the cells. For example, carbon cage molecules in the form of balls or tubes can trap large quantities of hydrogen. When pressure is reduced

and the temperature is raised, these cages release the hydrogen in gaseous form.

Probably the most critical consideration is the hydrogen source. Unfortunately, much of the hydrogen gas produced commercially comes from the hydrocarbons of fossil fuels, which defeats the goal of fossil fuel conservation. Hydrogen can be produced from water by electrolysis, but this requires electrical energy that is produced by processes involving the combustion of fossil fuels. Clearly, a suitable method of hydrogen production is required. However, even with their present limitations, fuel cells are a viable energy alternative for the future.

### Investigating the Technology

1. **Thinking Critically** If electrolysis is a safe and technologically sound method to generate hydrogen gas, how might the process be made more environmentally safe and economically practical?

2. **Using Resources** Investigate the technology of carbon cage molecules, including fullerenes and nanotubes, and elaborate on their utility in hydrogen fuel cells.

Visit the Chemistry Web site at chemistrymc.com to find links about hydrogen fuel cells.

690    **Chapter 21** Electrochemistry

- A hydrogen fuel cell is only one type of fuel cell. Provide examples of fuel cells that use other fuels and ask the students to compare and contrast them.

### Investigating the Technology

1. Answers will vary, but students may suggest to establish electrolysis stations in places where electricity can be generated by alternative means such as solar power, wind power, or geothermal power.

2. Student answers should include the recent advances in the cost-effective characterization and manufacture of pure carbon nanostructures, and their use for storage of hydrogen in vehicles.

## Summary

### 21.1 Voltaic Cells

- In a voltaic cell, the oxidation and reduction half-reactions of a redox reaction are separated and ions flow through a salt-bridge conductor.

- In a voltaic cell, oxidation takes place at the anode, and reduction takes place at the cathode.

- The standard potential of a half-cell reaction is the voltage it generates when paired with a standard hydrogen electrode. Standard potentials are measured at 25°C and 1 atm pressure with a $1M$ concentration of ions in the half-cells.

- The reduction potential of a half-cell is negative if it undergoes oxidation connected to a standard hydrogen electrode. The reduction potential of a half-cell is positive if it undergoes reduction when connected to a standard hydrogen electrode.

- The standard potential of a voltaic cell is the difference between the standard reduction potentials of the half-cell reactions.

### 21.2 Types of Batteries

- Batteries are voltaic cells packaged in a compact, usable form.

- A battery can consist of a single cell or multiple cells.

- Primary batteries can be used only once, whereas secondary batteries can be recharged.

- When a battery is recharged, electrical energy supplied to the battery reverses the direction of the redox reaction that takes place when the battery is delivering current. Thus, the original reactants are restored.

- Fuel cells are batteries in which the substance oxidized is a fuel such as hydrogen.

- Iron can be protected from corrosion: by applying a coating of another metal or paint to keep out air and water, or by attaching a piece of metal (a sacrificial anode) that is oxidized more readily than iron.

### 21.3 Electrolysis

- Electrical energy can be used to bring about nonspontaneous redox reactions that produce useful products. This process is called electrolysis and takes place in an electrolytic cell.

- Metallic sodium and chlorine gas may be obtained by the electrolysis of molten sodium chloride.

- Electrolysis of strong aqueous sodium chloride solution (brine) yields hydrogen gas and hydroxide ions at the cathode while producing chlorine gas at the anode.

- Metals such as copper can be purified by making them the anode of an electrolytic cell where they are oxidized to ions, which are then reduced to pure metal at the cathode.

- Objects can be electroplated by making them the cathode of an electrolytic cell in which ions of the desired plating metal are present.

- Aluminum is produced by the electrolysis of aluminum oxide. The process uses a great amount of electrical energy.

## Key Equations and Relationships

- Potential of a voltaic cell (p. 669)   $E^0_{cell} = E^0_{reduction} - E^0_{oxidation}$

## Vocabulary

- anode (p. 665)
- battery (p. 672)
- cathode (p. 665)
- corrosion (p. 679)
- dry cell (p. 673)
- electrochemical cell (p. 665)
- electrolysis (p. 683)
- electrolytic cell (p. 683)
- fuel cell (p. 677)
- galvanizing (p. 681)
- half-cell (p. 665)
- primary battery (p. 675)
- reduction potential (p. 666)
- salt bridge (p. 664)
- secondary battery (p. 675)
- standard hydrogen electrode (p. 666)
- voltaic cell (p. 665)

chemistrymc.com/vocabulary_puzzlemaker

Study Guide   **691**

### Using the Vocabulary

To reinforce chapter vocabulary, have students write a sentence using each term. L2 ELL

### Review Strategies

- Have students work in cooperative groups to create a puzzle of scrambled words using the vocabulary from Chapter 21. When complete, the puzzle can be handed to another group to solve. The group completing the puzzle will unscramble the words and provide a definition. L2 COOP LEARN

- Have students draw and label an electrochemical cell with the appropriate terms. L2 ELL

- Problems from Appendix A or the **Supplemental Problems** booklet can be used for review. L2

VOCABULARY PuzzleMaker

For additional help with vocabulary, have students access the Vocabulary PuzzleMaker online.

chemistrymc.com/ vocabulary_puzzlemaker

Chemistry Online

---

## EXAMVIEW® PRO

### Use ExamView® Pro Testmaker CD-ROM to:

- Create **multiple versions** of tests.
- Create **modified** tests with one mouse click for struggling students.
- **Edit** existing questions and add your own questions.
- **Build** tests based on national curriculum standards.

National Science Content Standards

Pages 688–691
UCP.1, UCP.3; A.1, A.2; B.3, B.6; E.2; F.4, F.6

## Concept Mapping

**25.** 1. electrochemical cells;
2. electrodes; 3. electrolyte;
4. anode; 5. oxidation;
6. cathode; 7. reduction

## Mastering Concepts

**26.** the transfer of electrons between atoms

**27.** oxidation of Zn(s) to $Zn^{2+} + 2e^-$

**28.** to complete the electrical circuit and prevent the accumulation of excess + or − ions in one half-cell

**29.** standard reduction potentials for each half-reaction

**30.** Al is oxidized and Cu is reduced.

**31.** 25°C, 1 atm, $1M$ ion solution

**32.** The anode is the zinc shell. Oxidation of Zn atoms to $Zn^{2+}$ ions takes place.

**33.** Primary batteries are "throw away"; the reaction is not easily reversed. Secondary batteries are rechargeable; the redox reaction is reversible.

**34.** $PbO_2$ reduced; Pb(s) oxidized; $PbSO_4$ produced

**35.** In a fuel cell, the oxidation of a fuel is used to produce electricity. Batteries must be recharged or replaced. Current can be produced and sustained as long as a fuel source is present.

**36.** Galvanizing is the coating of corrosion-susceptible metals with "self-protecting" metals to prevent corrosion.

**37.** by passing a current through it in the opposite direction

**38.** Electrolysis requires outside energy to force a nonspontaneous reaction to occur.

**39.** anode

**40.** $Na^+$ ions are reduced to Na atoms.

**41.** The products of electrolysis of brine, hydrogen gas, chlorine gas, and sodium hydroxide, are important commercial products.

---

## Chemistry Online

*Go to the Chemistry Web site at*
**chemistrymc.com** *for additional*
*Chapter 21 Assessment.*

## Concept Mapping

**25.** Complete the concept map using the following terms: reduction, electrodes, electrochemical cells, anode, oxidation, cathode, electrolyte.

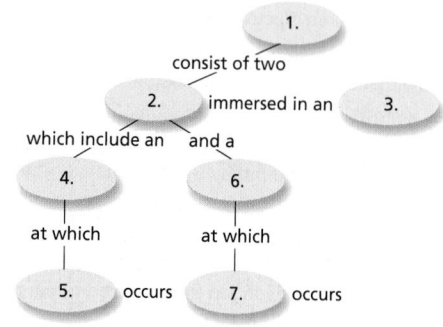

## Mastering Concepts

**26.** What feature of an oxidation–reduction reaction allows it to be used to generate an electric current? (21.1)

**27.** Describe the process that releases electrons in a zinc–copper voltaic cell. (21.1)

**28.** What is the function of a salt bridge in a voltaic cell? (21.1)

**29.** What information do you need in order to determine the standard voltage of a voltaic cell? (21.1)

**30.** In a voltaic cell represented by $Al|Al^{3+}||Cu^{2+}|Cu$, what is oxidized and what is reduced as the cell delivers current? (21.1)

**31.** Under what conditions are standard reduction potentials measured? (21.1)

**32.** What part of a zinc–carbon dry cell is the anode? Describe the reaction that takes place there. (21.2)

**33.** How do primary and secondary batteries differ? (21.2)

---

**34.** What substance is reduced in a lead–acid storage battery? What substance is oxidized? What substance, other than water, is produced in each reaction? (21.2)

**35.** List two ways that a fuel cell differs from an ordinary battery. (21.2)

**36.** What is galvanizing? How does galvanizing protect iron from corrosion? (21.2)

**37.** How can the spontaneous redox reaction of a voltaic cell be reversed? (21.3)

**38.** Why is an outside source of energy needed for electrolysis? (21.3)

**39.** Where does oxidation take place in an electrolytic cell? (21.3)

**40.** What reaction takes place at the cathode when molten sodium chloride is electrolyzed? (21.3)

**41.** Explain why the electrolysis of brine is done on a large scale at many sites around the world. (21.3)

**42.** Explain how recycling aluminum conserves energy. (21.3)

## Mastering Problems

### Voltaic Cells (21.1)

*Use data from* **Table 21-1** *in the following problems. Assume that all half-cells are under standard conditions.*

**43.** Write the standard cell notation for the following cells in which the half-cell listed is connected to the standard hydrogen electrode. An example is $Na|Na^+||H^+|H_2$.
  **a.** $Zn|Zn^{2+}$
  **b.** $Hg|Hg^{2+}$
  **c.** $Cu|Cu^{2+}$
  **d.** $Al|Al^{3+}$

**44.** Determine the voltage of the cell formed by pairing each of the following half-cells with the standard hydrogen electrode.
  **a.** $Cr|Cr^{2+}$
  **b.** $Br_2|Br^-$
  **c.** $Ga|Ga^{3+}$
  **d.** $NO_2|NO_3^-$

**45.** Determine whether each of the following redox reactions is spontaneous or nonspontaneous as written.
  **a.** $Mn^{2+} + 2Br^- \rightarrow Br_2 + Mn$
  **b.** $Fe^{2+} + Sn^{2+} \rightarrow Fe^{3+} + Sn$
  **c.** $Ni^{2+} + Mg \rightarrow Mg^{2+} + Ni$
  **d.** $Pb^{2+} + Cu^+ \rightarrow Pb + Cu^{2+}$

**chemistrymc.com/chapter_test**

---

## Resource Manager

**Chapter Assessment,** pp. 121–126
**Supplemental Problems,** Ch. 21
**ExamView® Pro CD-ROM**
**MindJogger Videoquizzes DVD/VHS**
**Solutions Manual,** Ch. 21
**Chemistry Interactive CD-ROM,**
  Ch. 21 quiz

**46.** Calculate the cell potential of voltaic cells that contain the following pairs of half-cells.

  **a.** Chromium in a solution of $Cr^{3+}$ ions; copper in a solution of $Cu^{2+}$ ions

  **b.** Zinc in a solution of $Zn^{2+}$ ions; platinum in a solution of $Pt^{2+}$ ions

  **c.** A half-cell containing both $HgCl_2$ and $Hg_2Cl_2$; lead in a solution of $Pb^{2+}$ ions

  **d.** Tin in a solution of $Sn^{2+}$ ions; iodine in a solution of $I^-$ ions

## Mixed Review ───────────

*Sharpen your problem-solving skills by answering the following.*

**47.** Why do electrons flow from one electrode to the other in a voltaic cell?

**48.** What substance is electrolyzed to produce aluminum metal?

**49.** Write the oxidation and reduction half-reactions for a silver-chromium voltaic cell. Identify the anode, cathode, and electron flow.

$$Zn(s) \rightarrow \qquad Cu^{2+}(aq) + 2e^- \rightarrow$$
$$Zn^{2+}(aq) + 2e^- \qquad Cu(s)$$

**50.** Primary cells are cells like the ordinary dry cell that cannot be recharged. Storage cells are cells like the nickel–cadmium cell or the lead-storage battery that can be recharged. Is the $Zn–Cu^{2+}$ cell shown above a primary cell or a storage cell?

**51.** Determine the voltage of the cell in which each of the following half-cells is connected to a $Ag\,|\,Ag^+$ half-cell.

  **a.** $Be^{2+}\,|Be$
  **b.** $S\,|\,S^{2-}$
  **c.** $Au^+|Au$
  **d.** $I_2\,|\,I^-$

**52.** Explain why water is necessary for the corrosion of iron.

**53.** In the electrolytic refining of copper, what factor determines which piece of copper is the anode and which is the cathode?

**54.** Explain how the oxidation of hydrogen in a fuel cell differs from the oxidation of hydrogen when it burns in air.

**55.** Lead–acid batteries and other rechargeable batteries are sometimes called *storage batteries*. Precisely what is being stored in these batteries?

**56.** Buried steel pipeline can be protected against corrosion by cathodic protection. In this process, the steel pipe is connected to a more active metal, such as magnesium, that would corrode instead of the steel. Use the diagram to answer the following questions.

  **a.** What is the cathode? What is the anode?
  **b.** Describe briefly how the magnesium metal protects the steel.

## Thinking Critically ──────────

**57. Communicating** Write two or three sentences describing the processes that take place in a voltaic cell and account for the direction of electron flow. Use the words *cathode, anode, oxidation, reduction*, and *potential difference* in your sentences.

**58. Predicting** How would standard reduction potentials be different if scientists had chosen the $Cu^{2+}–Cu$ half-cell as a standard instead of the $H^+–H_2$ half-cell? What would the potential of the hydrogen electrode be if the copper electrode were the standard? How would the relationships among the standard reduction potentials change?

**59. Applying Concepts** Suppose that you have a voltaic cell in which one half-cell is made up of a strip of tin immersed in a solution of tin(II) ions.

  **a.** How could you tell by measuring voltage whether the tin strip was acting as a cathode or an anode in the cell?
  **b.** How could you tell by simple observation whether the tin strip was acting as a cathode or an anode?

**42.** The cost to produce aluminum from raw materials is much more expensive than the cost to heat and reuse existing aluminum.

## Mastering Problems

Complete solutions to Chapter Assessment problems can be found in the **Solutions Manual**.

### Voltaic Cells (21.1)
**43. a.** $Zn|Zn^{2+} \parallel H^+|H_2$
  **b.** $H_2|H^+ \parallel Hg^{2+}|Hg$
  **c.** $H_2|H^+ \parallel Cu^{2+}|Cu$
  **d.** $Al|Al^{3+} \parallel H^+|H_2$
**44. a.** $+0.913$ V
  **b.** $+1.06$ V
  **c.** $+0.549$ V
  **d.** $-0.775$ V
**45. a.** $E^0 = -2.251$ V nonspontaneous
  **b.** $E^0 = -0.908$ V nonspontaneous
  **c.** $E^0 = +2.115$ V spontaneous
  **d.** $E^0 = -0.279$ V nonspontaneous
**46. a.** $E^0 = +1.086$ V
  **b.** $E^0 = +1.94$ V
  **c.** $E^0 = +1.046$ V
  **d.** $E^0 = +0.6730$ V

## Mixed Review

**47.** In a voltaic cell, ions in solution at the cathode accept electrons more readily than the ions at the anode. When a salt bridge and wire are in place, redox occurs spontaneously and the electrons flow from the anode to the cathode.

**48.** aluminum oxide

**49.** oxidation:
  $Cr(s) \rightarrow Cr^{3+}(aq) + 3e^-$
  reduction:
  $Ag^+(aq) + e^- \rightarrow Ag(s)$
  Electrons flow from anode (Cr) to cathode (Ag).

**50.** storage (rechargeable)
**51. a.** $+2.647$ V
  **b.** $+1.2759$ V
  **c.** $+0.892$ V
  **d.** $+0.2641$ V
**52.** Fe atoms oxidize to aqueous $Fe^{2+}$ ions. These ions are then oxidized to $Fe^{3+}$ ions, which combine with reduced $O_2$ to produce $Fe_2O_3$ (rust).
**53.** purity of copper

**54.** In a fuel cell, the oxidation of hydrogen is controlled so that most of the chemical energy is converted to electrical energy instead of heat.
**55.** chemical potential energy
**56. a.** cathode is steel; anode is Mg
  **b.** Mg is more active and therefore more susceptible to redox and therefore corrodes before steel.

## Thinking Critically

**57.** See Solutions Manual.

**58.** Values in the table would change by −0.342. Hydrogen electrode would be −0.342. Relationships would not change but voltage values would change.

**59. a.** A voltmeter indicates the flow of electrons to or from the tin strip, which shows whether it acts as a cathode or an anode.

**b.** Anode: strip decreases
Cathode: strip increases

**60.** Pressure is an indication of concentration; therefore, pressure is a concentration factor in half-cells involving gases.

**61.** The reactants and products of both half-reactions are insoluble solid substances. Their ions do not mix, and no separator is needed.

**62.** alkaline for duration; rechargeable goes dead abruptly

**63.** The density of water is 1.000 g/mL so by comparison the battery is (nearly) dead.

**64.** Ag has a greater tendency to be reduced and Al the greater tendency to be oxidized.

**65.** The car's alternator generates current to recharge the battery. The extra voltage is used to force the nonspontaneous recharge reaction.

**66.** potassium bromide and water

**67.** If the copper cracked, sites for corrosion would be exposed. No, iron is more readily oxidized than copper, so protection is diminished.

**60. Hypothesizing** The potential of a half-cell varies with concentration of reactants and products. For this reason, standard potentials are measured at $1M$ concentration. Maintaining a pressure of 1 atm is especially important in half-cells that involve gases as reactants or products. Suggest a reason that gas pressure is especially critical in these cells.

**61. Analyze and Conclude** Zinc–carbon, alkaline, mercury, lithium, and NiCad batteries all contain a separator between the anode and cathode that allows exchange of ions but keeps the anode and cathode reactants from mixing. No such separator is present (or needed) in a lead–acid battery.

Separator

Study the structures of this battery carefully and suggest a reason why no separator is required.

**62. Interpreting Graphs** Various commercial batteries were tested to determine how each would perform when operating a motorized toy. Use the graph below to determine which battery would be the best choice to operate the toy for a long period of time. Which battery goes dead abruptly?

**63. Hypothesizing** The density of a sample of electrolyte from a lead–acid battery is measured and found to be 1.09 g/mL. Do you think this density indicates a fully charged battery, partially discharged battery, or a "dead" battery? Give a reason for your choice.

**64. Drawing a Conclusion** The black tarnish that appears on silver is silver sulfide ($Ag_2S$). A way to get rid of silver tarnish is to place the silver object into a pan lined with wrinkled aluminum foil and water in which some salt or baking soda has been dissolved. As the silver sits in contact with the aluminum foil, the black tarnish disappears where the object is immersed in the solution. Using what you have learned about electrochemistry, propose an explanation for this observation.

**65. Thinking Critically** Lead–acid storage batteries produce current with a voltage of about 12 volts. If you have a voltmeter in your car, you see that the meter reads about 14 V while the car is running normally. Suggest an explanation for this higher voltage reading.

**66. Applying Concepts** During electrolysis, an electrolytic cell gives off bromine vapor and hydrogen gas. After electrolysis, the cell is found to contain a concentrated solution of potassium hydroxide. What was the composition of the cell before electrolysis began?

**67. Hypothesizing** Instead of galvanizing iron, it can be plated with copper to protect it. What would happen when the copper coating became broken or cracked? Would the copper continue to protect the iron as zinc does? Explain fully.

## Writing in Chemistry

**68.** Research the commercial process of electroplating silver in the costume jewelry industry. Write a summary of your findings, including a diagram.

**69.** Several years ago, the supporting structure of the Statue of Liberty became so corroded that it had to be replaced entirely. Find out what the structure was and why it corroded so badly. Write a report that discusses the chemical processes involved and include a timeline of the statue, starting before 1886 in France.

## Cumulative Review

*Refresh your understanding of previous chapters by answering the following.*

**70.** If the volume of a sample of chlorine gas is 8.2 L at 1.2 atm and 306 K, what volume will the gas occupy at STP? (Chapter 14)

**71.** According to the collision model of chemical reactions, how is it possible that two molecules may collide but not react? (Chapter 17)

*Use these questions and the test-taking tip to prepare for your standardized test.*

**1.** A salt bridge is essential to a voltaic cell for all of the following reasons EXCEPT

  **a.** it allows ions to move from the solution of one cell to the other.
  **b.** it causes electric current to flow between the two electrodes of a cell.
  **c.** it relieves the buildup of positive charge on the anode side of the cell.
  **d.** it allows electrons to move from the solution of one cell to the other.

**Using Tables** Use the table to answer questions 2–5.

| Selected Standard Reduction Potentials at 25°C, 1 atm, and 1M Ion Concentration | |
|---|---|
| **Half-Reaction** | **$E^0$ (V)** |
| $Mg^{2+} + 2e^- \rightarrow Mg$ | −2.372 |
| $Al^{3+} + 3e^- \rightarrow Al$ | −1.662 |
| $Pb^{2+} + 2e^- \rightarrow Pb$ | −0.1262 |
| $Ag^+ + e^- \rightarrow Ag$ | 0.7996 |
| $Hg^{2+} + 2e^- \rightarrow Hg$ | 0.851 |

**2.** Which of the metal ions is most easily reduced?

  **a.** $Mg^{2+}$
  **b.** $Hg^{2+}$
  **c.** $Ag^+$
  **d.** $Al^{3+}$

**3.** On the basis of the standard reduction potentials shown above, which of the following standard cell notations below correctly represents its voltaic cell?

  **a.** $Ag \mid Ag^+ \parallel Al^{3+} \mid Al$
  **b.** $Mg \mid Mg^{2+} \parallel H^+ \mid H_2$
  **c.** $H_2 \mid H^+ \parallel Pb^{2+} \mid Pb$
  **d.** $Pb \mid Pb^{2+} \parallel Al^{3+} \mid Al$

**4.** A voltaic cell consists of a magnesium bar dipping into a $1M$ $Mg^{2+}$ solution and a silver bar dipping into a $1M$ $Ag^+$ solution. What is the standard potential of this cell?

  **a.** 1.572 V
  **b.** 3.172 V
  **c.** 0.773 V
  **d.** 3.971 V

**5.** Assuming standard conditions, which of the following cells will produce a potential of 2.513 V?

  **a.** $Al \mid Al^{3+} \parallel Hg^{2+} \mid Hg$
  **b.** $H_2 \mid H^+ \parallel Hg^{2+} \mid Hg$
  **c.** $Mg \mid Mg^{2+} \parallel Al^{3+} \mid Al$
  **d.** $Pb \mid Pb^{2+} \parallel Ag^+ \mid Ag$

**6.** Which of the following statements is NOT true of batteries?

  **a.** Batteries are compact forms of voltaic cells.
  **b.** Secondary batteries also are known as storage batteries.
  **c.** Batteries can consist only of a single cell.
  **d.** The redox reaction in a rechargeable battery is reversible.

**7.** The corrosion, or rusting, of iron is an example of a naturally occurring voltaic cell. To prevent corrosion, sacrificial anodes are sometimes attached to rust-susceptible iron. Sacrificial anodes must

  **a.** be more likely to be reduced than iron.
  **b.** have a higher reduction potential than iron.
  **c.** be more porous and abraded than iron.
  **d.** lose electrons more easily than iron.

**8.** A strip of metal X is immersed in a $1M$ solution of $X^+$ ions. When this half-cell is connected to a standard hydrogen electrode, a voltmeter reads a positive reduction potential. Which of the following is true of the X electrode?

  **a.** It accepts electrons more readily than $H^+$ ions.
  **b.** It is undergoing oxidation.
  **c.** It is adding positive $X^+$ ions to its solution.
  **d.** It acts as the anode in the cell.

**9.** To electroplate an iron fork with silver, which of the following is true?

  **a.** The silver electrode must have more mass than the fork.
  **b.** The iron fork must act as the anode in the cell.
  **c.** Electrical current must be applied to the iron fork.
  **d.** Iron ions must be present in the cell solution.

---

**TEST-TAKING TIP**

**Your Mistakes Can Teach You** The mistakes you make before the test are helpful because they show you the areas in which you need more work. When calculating the standard potential of an electrochemical cell, remember that coefficients do not change the standard reduction potentials of the half-reactions.

---

## Cumulative Review

**70.** $\dfrac{P_1V_1}{T_1} = \dfrac{P_2V_2}{T_2}$

$V_2 = \dfrac{P_1V_1T_2}{T_1P_2} =$

$\dfrac{(1.2 \text{ atm})(8.2 \text{ L})(273 \text{ K})}{(306 \text{ K})(1.0 \text{ atm})} = 8.8 \text{ L}$

**71.** The molecules may not collide with the correct orientation, or the collision may lack the energy required to form the activated complex.

## Standardized Test Practice

| | |
|---|---|
| **1.** d | **6.** c |
| **2.** b | **7.** d |
| **3.** b | **8.** a |
| **4.** b | **9.** c |
| **5.** a | |

National Science Content Standards

Pages 694–695
UCP.1, UCP.3; B.3, B.6; E.2

# Resource Manager

| Section | Objectives | Activities/Features |
|---------|-----------|---------------------|
| **Section 22.1**<br>**Alkanes**<br>1 session<br>1 block | 1. **Describe** the structures of alkanes.<br>2. **Name** an alkane by examining its structure.<br>3. **Draw** the structure of an alkane given its name. | **Discovery Lab:** Viscosity of Motor Oil, p. 697<br>**Biology Connection,** p. 701<br>**Careers Using Chemistry:** Alternative Fuel Technician, p. 702<br>**ChemLab:** Analyzing Hydrocarbon Burner Gases, pp. 728–729 |
| **Section 22.2**<br>**Cyclic Alkanes and Alkane Properties**<br>1 session<br>½ block | 4. **Name** a cyclic alkane by examining its structure.<br>5. **Draw** tthe structure of a cyclic alkane given its name.<br>6. **Describe** the properties of alkanes.<br>7. **Distinguish** between saturated and unsaturated hydrocarbons. | |
| **Section 22.3**<br>**Alkenes and Alkynes**<br>1½ sessions<br>1 block | 8. **Compare** the properties of alkenes and alkynes with those of alkanes.<br>9. **Describe** the molecular structures of alkenes and alkynes.<br>10. **Name** an alkene or alkyne by examining its structure.<br>11. **Draw** the structure of an alkene or alkyne by analyzing its name. | **MiniLab:** Synthesis and Reactivity of Ethyne, p. 715 |
| **Section 22.4**<br>**Isomers**<br>1½ sessions<br>1 block | 12. **Distinguish** between the two main categories of isomers, structural isomers and stereoisomers.<br>13. **Differentiate** between *cis-* and *trans-* geometric isomers.<br>14. **Recognize** different structural isomers given a structural formula.<br>15. **Describe** the structural variation in molecules that results in optical isomers. | **Problem-Solving Lab:** Identifying Structural, Geometric, and Optical Isomers, p. 720 |
| **Section 22.5**<br>**Aromatic Hydrocarbons and Petroleum**<br>2 sessions<br>1 block | 16. **Compare** and **contrast** the properties of aromatic and aliphatic hydrocarbons.<br>17. **Explain** what a carcinogen is and list some examples.<br>18. **Describe** the processes used to separate petroleum into fractions and to balance each fraction's output with market demands.<br>19. **Identify** the fractions into which petroleum can be separated. | **Earth Science Connection,** p. 726<br>**Everyday Chemistry:** Unlimited Alternative Energy, p. 730 |

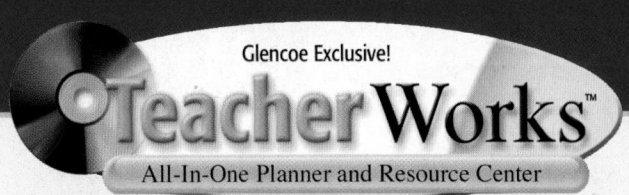

| National Science Content Standards | State/Local Standards | Reproducible Masters | Transparencies |
|---|---|---|---|
| UCP.2, UCP.5; A.1, A.2; B.1, B.2; E.1; F.3, F.6; G.1, G.2, G.3 | | **Study Guide for Content Mastery,** p. 127 **L2** <br> **ChemLab and MiniLab Worksheets,** pp. 86–88 **L2** <br> **Challenge Problems,** p. 22 **L3** | **Section Focus Transparency 81** **L1** **ELL** <br> **Math Skills Transparency 34** **L2** **ELL** |
| UCP.2, UCP.5; A.1; B.2, B.4, B.6 | | **Study Guide for Content Mastery,** p. 128 **L2** <br> **Laboratory Manual,** pp. 169–172 **L2** | **Section Focus Transparency 82** **L1** **ELL** <br> **Math Skills Transparencies 35, 36** **L2** **ELL** |
| UCP.2, UCP.5; A.1; B.2, B.3 | | **Study Guide for Content Mastery,** p. 129 **L2** <br> **ChemLab and MiniLab Worksheets,** p. 85 **L2** <br> **Challenge Problems,** p. 22 **L3** <br> **Laboratory Manual,** pp. 173–176 **L2** | **Section Focus Transparency 83** **L1** **ELL** |
| UCP.2, UCP.5; B.2, B.4, B.6; E.2; F.1; G.2, G.3 | | **Study Guide for Content Mastery,** p. 130 **L2** | **Section Focus Transparency 84** **L1** **ELL** <br> **Teaching Transparency 66, 67** **L2** **ELL** |
| UCP.2, UCP.5; A.1, A.2; B.2, B.4, B.6; E.2; F.1, F.3, F.4, F.5, F.6; G.2, G.3 | | **Study Guide for Content Mastery,** pp. 131–132 **L2** | **Section Focus Transparency 85** **L1** **ELL** |

# Resource Manager

## Materials List

**ChemLab** (pages 728–729)
barometer, thermometer, 1-L plastic soda bottle with cap, burner tubing, pneumatic trough, 100-mL graduated cylinder, balance, paper towels, water

**Discovery Lab** (page 697)
wide-mouth jars with lids (3), lead weights (3 identical), small metal objects such as screws, nuts, washers (6 identical), long forceps, 10W-30 motor oil, 20W-50 motor oil, stopwatch, paper towels

**MiniLab** (page 715)
150-mL beaker, stirring rod, liquid dishwashing detergent, calcium carbide($CaC_2$), forceps, wood splints, matches, ruler, rubber band, phenolphthalein solution, distilled water, water

**Demonstration** (pages 702–703)
400-mL beaker, 150-mL beaker, 25 mL liquid detergent, 5 mL glycerin, 5 g sucrose, rubber tubing (1 m), small funnel, meterstick, candle, matches, newspaper, masking tape, water

## Preparation of Solutions

For a review of solution preparation, see page 46T of the Teacher Guide.

Quantities are for a class of 30 students.

**MiniLab** (page 715)
**Phenolphthalein solution** Dissolve 0.1 g phenolphthalein powder in 70 mL 95% ethanol. Make up to 100 mL final volume with distilled water.

**Demonstration** (pages 702–703)
**Soap-bubble solution** Add 25 mL liquid detergent and 5 mL glycerin to 160 mL water. Dissolve 5 g sucrose in 60 mL water and gently mix with the detergent-glycerin solution.

## Assessment Resources

**Chapter Assessment,** pp. 127–132
**MindJogger Videoquizzes** DVD/VHS
**Alternate Assessment in the Science Classroom**
**ExamView® Pro CD-ROM**
**Solutions Manual,** Chapter 22
**Supplemental Problems,** Chapter 22
**Performance Assessment in the Science Classroom**
**Chemistry Interactive CD-ROM,** Chapter 22 quiz

## Additional Resources

**Spanish Resources** ELL
**Guided Reading Audio Program,** Chapter 22 ELL
**Cooperative Learning in the Science Classroom**
**Lab and Safety Skills in the Science Classroom**
**Lesson Plans**
**Block Scheduling Lesson Plans**
**Chemistrymc.com**

## Glencoe Technology

The following multimedia for this chapter are available from Glencoe.

**VIDEOTAPE/DVD**
MindJogger Videoquizzes,
Chapter 22

**CD-ROM**
**Chemistry: Matter and Change**
*Modeling Hydrocarbons,* Demonstration
*Combustion of Methane,* Demonstration
*Properties of Ethyne,* Demonstation
*Isomers,* Animation
*Polarimetry,* Experiment
*Petroleum Refinery,* Video

**CD-ROM**
**ExamView® Pro**
**Testmaker**

**CD-ROM**
**Interactive Chalkboard**

**CD-ROM**
**TeacherWorks™**

## Multiple Learning Styles

Look for the following icons for strategies that emphasize different learning modalities.

**Kinesthetic**
Building a Model, pp. 697, 718; Differentiated Instruction, pp. 707, 713; Reteach, p. 716; Extension, p. 716

**Visual-Spatial**
Visual Learning, p. 701; Differentiated Instruction, pp. 701, 717; Reinforcement, p. 702; Check for Understanding, p. 721; Reteach, p. 721

**Interpersonal**
Differentiated Instruction, pp. 698, 711

**Intrapersonal**
Extension, p. 701; Chemistry Journal, p. 704; Differentiated Instruction, p. 719

**Linguistic**
Portfolio, pp. 699, 720; Chemistry Journal, pp. 700, 708, 714, 720, 726; Using Science Terms, p. 704; Enrichment, p. 711

## Key to Teaching Strategies

**L1** Level 1 activities should be appropriate for students with learning difficulties.

**L2** Level 2 activities should be within the ability range of all students.

**L3** Level 3 activities are designed for above-average students.

**ELL** ELL activities should be within the ability range of English Language Learners.

**COOP LEARN** Cooperative Learning activities are designed for small group work.

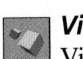 **P** These strategies represent student products that can be placed into a best-work portfolio.

These strategies are useful in a block scheduling format.

## Assessment Planner

**Portfolio Assessment**
Assessment, TWE, pp. 715, 723
Portfolio, TWE, pp. 699, 712, 720, 731
MiniLab, TWE, p. 715

**Performance Assessment**
Assessment, TWE, pp. 700, 716
ChemLab, SE, pp. 728–729
MiniLab, SE, p. 715
Discovery Lab, SE, p. 697
Problem-Solving Lab, TWE, p. 720

**Knowledge Assessment**
Assessment, TWE, pp. 700, 705, 709, 718, 719, 724, 727
Demonstration, TWE, p. 703
Section Assessment, SE, pp. 705, 710, 716, 721, 727
Chapter Assessment, SE, pp. 732–735

**Skill Assessment**
Assessment, TWE, pp. 710, 713, 721, 725
ChemLab, TWE, p. 729

## Tying to Previous Knowledge

Have students review the following concepts before studying this chapter.

Chapter 7: structure of a carbon atom

Chapter 9: covalent bonding and molecular structure

Chapter 13: changes of state—boiling and melting

## Using the Photo

Ask students what types of products they think are made from petroleum piped from Alaska. Answers may include fuels such as gasoline and kerosene, lubricating oil and grease, plastics, pharmaceuticals, synthetic textiles, paint and other finishes, and many other organic materials.

## PowerPoint® Presentations

This CD-ROM is an editable Microsoft® PowerPoint® presentation that includes:
• Section presentations
• Section checks
• Image bank
• Links to Chemistry Online
• All transparencies
• Animations
• Audio

# Hydrocarbons

### What You'll Learn

▶ You will compare the structures and properties of alkanes, alkenes, and alkynes.

▶ You will recognize and compare the properties of structural isomers and stereoisomers.

▶ You will describe how useful hydrocarbons are obtained from natural sources.

### Why It's Important

Fuels, medicines, synthetic textiles, plastics, and dyes are just a few examples of hydrocabon-derived organic chemicals we use every day.

Visit the Chemistry Web site at chemistrymc.com to find links about hydrocarbons.

Oil pipelines transport petroleum that remains a vital resource for the manufacture of fuels, plastics, solvents, pharmaceuticals, and other important carbon compounds.

**696** Chapter 22

## DISCOVERY LAB

### Purpose
Students will compare the viscosities of motor oil and water as well as the viscosities of two weights of motor oil.

### Safety and Disposal
Immediately clean up any oil spilled on the floor. Save all materials for later use.

### Teaching Strategies
• The farther the balls sink, the more accurate the comparison will be. Accordingly, you may want to use taller containers such as graduated cylinders, bud vases, or tall olive jars—and fill them to a greater depth.
• Timing the fall of a smooth, spherical weight through a column of liquid is one of the standard ways to measure the viscosity of liquids.

### Viscosity of Motor Oil

The molecules of motor oil have long chains of carbon atoms. Oil's viscosity, a measure of resistance to flow, is related to the oil's weight numbers. How do two weights of oil differ in viscosity?

**Safety Precautions**

**Procedure**

1. Add a 50-mm depth of water to the first jar, the same depth of 10W-30 motor oil to the second jar, and an equal depth of 20W-50 oil to the third jar.

2. Drop a lead weight from just above the surface of the liquid in the first jar. Time the weight as it sinks to the bottom. Repeat the process twice with two other small metal objects.

3. Repeat step 2 with the jars of oil.

4. Use forceps to remove the weights. Dry them on paper towels. Save the oil for reuse.

**Materials**

wide-mouth jars and lids (3)
lead weights, BB size (9)
screws, nuts, and washers
long forceps
10W-30 and 20W-50 motor
 oil
stopwatch
paper towels

**Analysis**

What do your results tell you about the relationship between viscosity and the weight numbers of motor oil? Which oil is more likely to be used in heavy machinery that requires a high-viscosity oil?

---

# Alkanes

### Objectives

- **Describe** the structures of alkanes.
- **Name** an alkane by examining its structure.
- **Draw** the structure of an alkane given its name.

### Vocabulary

organic compound
hydrocarbon
alkane
homologous series
parent chain
substituent group

The Alaskan pipeline shown in the photo on the opposite page was built to carry crude oil from the oil fields in the frozen north to an ice-free southern Alaskan seaport. Crude oil, also called petroleum, is a complex mixture of carbon compounds produced by heat and pressure acting on the remains of once-living organisms buried deep beneath Earth's surface.

## Organic Chemistry

Chemists of the early nineteenth century knew that living things produce an immense variety of carbon compounds. Chemists referred to these compounds as "organic" compounds because they were produced by living organisms.

Once Dalton's atomic theory was accepted in the early nineteenth century, chemists began to understand that compounds, including those made by living organisms, consisted of arrangements of atoms bonded together in certain combinations. With this knowledge, they were able to go to their laboratories and synthesize many new and useful substances—but not the organic compounds made by living things. One of the main reasons for their failure was that chemists, like most other scientists of the time, accepted an idea called *vitalism*. According to vitalism, organisms possess a mysterious

22.1 Alkanes **697**

---

### Focus Transparency

Before presenting the lesson, display **Section Focus Transparency 81** on the overhead projector. Have students answer the accompanying questions using **Section Focus Transparency Master 81.** L1 ELL

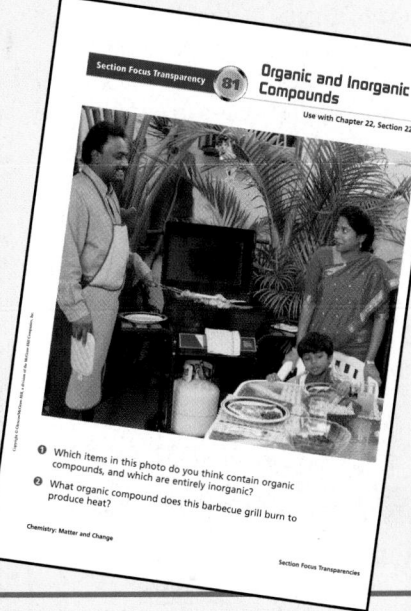

### Chapter Themes

The following themes from the National Science Education Standards are covered in this chapter. Refer to page 4T of the Teacher Guide for an explanation of the correlations.
Systems, order, and organization (UCP.1)
Evidence, models, and explanation (UCP.2)
Form and function (UCP.5)

---

### Expected Results

See the data table.

| Sample Data for a 50 mm Depth | | | |
|---|---|---|---|
| Material | Sink times | | |
| | Trial 1 | Trial 2 | Trial 3 |
| Water | 0.12 s | 0.20 s | 0.16 s |
| 10W-30 oil | 9.77 s | 9.69 s | 9.85 s |
| 20W-50 oil | 25.23 s | 27.46 s | 25.99 s |

### Analysis

Oils with higher weight numbers have greater viscosities. Although students know little about hydrocarbons at this time, they may intuit that a longer chain results in a greater viscosity. 20W-50 oil is more likely to be used in heavy machinery.

**National Science Content Standards**

Pages 696–697
UCP.2, UCP.5; A.1; B.2; E.1; F.3; G.2, G.3

**Figure 22-1**

Carbon is a nonmetal element located in group 4A of the periodic table. Elements in this group have four valence electrons. Carbon usually shares its four valence electrons to form four covalent bonds.

**Figure 22-2**

Methane ($CH_4$) consists of one carbon atom bonded to four hydrogen atoms in a tetrahedral arrangement. Here are four ways to represent a methane molecule. Refer to **Table C-1** in Appendix C for a key to atom color convention.

"vital force" that enables them to assemble carbon compounds, and such compounds could never be produced in the laboratory.

**Disproving vitalism** Friedrich Wöhler (1800–1882) was a German chemist who questioned the idea of vitalism. While working in Berlin in 1828, he carried out a reaction that he thought would produce the compound ammonium cyanate ($NH_4OCN$). To his surprise, the product of the reaction turned out to be urea ($NH_2CONH_2$), a compound that had the same empirical formula as ammonium cyanate. Previously, urea was known only as a waste product found in the urine of humans and other animals. Wöhler wrote to the Swedish chemist Berzelius that he had "made urea without the kidney of an animal, either man or dog."

Although Wöhler's experiment did not immediately disprove vitalism, it started a chain of similar experiments by other European chemists. Eventually, the idea that the synthesis of organic compounds required a vital force was discredited. Today the term **organic compound** is applied to all carbon-containing compounds with the primary exceptions of carbon oxides, carbides, and carbonates, which are considered inorganic. An entire branch of chemistry, called organic chemistry, is devoted to the study of carbon compounds.

Why is an entire field of study focused on compounds containing carbon? To answer this question, recall that carbon is in the group 4A elements of the periodic table, as shown in **Figure 22-1**. With its electron configuration of $1s^2 2s^2 2p^2$, carbon nearly always shares its electrons, forming four covalent bonds. In organic compounds, carbon atoms are found bonded to hydrogen atoms or atoms of other elements that are near carbon in the periodic table—especially nitrogen, oxygen, sulfur, phosphorus, and the halogens.

Most importantly, carbon atoms also bond to other carbon atoms and can form chains from two to thousands of carbon atoms in length. Also, because carbon forms four bonds, it can form complex, branched-chain structures, ring structures, and even cagelike structures. With all of these bonding possibilities, millions of different organic compounds are known, and chemists are synthesizing more every day.

## Hydrocarbons

The simplest organic compounds are the **hydrocarbons**, which contain only the elements carbon and hydrogen. How many different compounds do you think it is possible to make from two elements? You might guess one, or maybe a few more, say 10 or 12. Actually, thousands of hydrocarbons are known, each containing only the elements carbon and hydrogen.

As you know, carbon forms four bonds. Hydrogen, having only one valence electron, forms only one covalent bond by sharing this electron with another atom. Therefore, the simplest hydrocarbon molecule consists of a carbon atom bonded to four hydrogen atoms, $CH_4$. This substance is called methane and is an excellent fuel and the main component of natural gas.

### Models of Methane

$CH_4$

Denotes a single covalent bond

Molecular formula          Structural formula          Ball-and-stick model          Space-filling model

---

In chemistry, covalent bonds in which two electrons are shared are represented by a single straight line, denoting a single covalent bond. **Figure 22-2** shows four different ways to represent a methane molecule.

**A review of models** Chemists represent organic molecules in a variety of ways. Most often, they use the type of model that best shows the information they want to highlight. As you see in **Figure 22-2** on the previous page, molecular formulas give no information about the geometry of the molecule. A structural formula shows the general arrangement of atoms in the molecule but not the exact geometry. Space-filling models give a more realistic picture of what a molecule would look like if you could see it, but ball-and-stick models demonstrate the geometry of the molecule more clearly. Keep in mind, however, that the atoms are not at the ends of sticks but are held closely together by electron-sharing bonds.

## Straight-Chain Alkanes

Methane is the smallest member of a series of hydrocarbons known as alkanes. **Alkanes** are hydrocarbons that have only single bonds between atoms. The next member of the series consists of two carbon atoms bonded together with a single bond and six hydrogen atoms sharing the remaining valence electrons of the carbon atoms. This molecule is called ethane ($C_2H_6$) and is shown in **Figure 22-3**.

The third member of the alkane series, propane, has three carbon atoms and eight hydrogen atoms, giving it the molecular formula $C_3H_8$. The next member, butane, has four carbon atoms in a continuous chain and the formula $C_4H_{10}$. Compare the structures of ethane, propane, and butane in **Figure 22-3**.

Most propane and butane come from petroleum. Propane, known also as LP (liquified propane) gas, is sold as a fuel for cooking and heating. Another use of propane is illustrated in **Figure 22-4** on page 700. Butane is used as fuel in small lighters and in some torches. It is also used in the manufacture of synthetic rubber and gasoline. Carry out the **CHEMLAB** at the end of the chapter to determine which alkanes are found in your lab's gas supply.

**Figure 22-3**

Ethane makes up about nine percent of natural gas. Because the bonds around carbon are arranged in a tetrahedral fashion, propane and butane have a zig-zag geometry.

Ethane $C_2H_6$

Propane $C_3H_8$

Butane $C_4H_{10}$

22.1 Alkanes **699**

## Portfolio

### What's that odor?

*Linguistic* Explain that small alkane gases such as methane and propane are odorless. Ask students to find out the names and structures of compounds added to such alkane gases to give them the characteristic odor that serves to warn us that gas is leaking. Have the students record this information in their portfolios.

L2    P

**Figure 22-4**

This taxi in Bangkok, Thailand is one of many cars, trucks, and buses that have been modified to burn propane. Burning propane benefits the environment because it produces less air pollution than does gasoline.

By now you have noticed that names of alkanes end in -*ane*. Also, alkanes with five or more carbons in a chain have names that use a prefix derived from the Greek or Latin word for the number of carbons in each chain. For example, *pent*ane has five carbons just as a *pent*agon has five sides, and *oct*ane has eight carbons just as an *oct*opus has eight tentacles. Because methane, ethane, propane, and butane were named before alkane structures were known, their names do not have numerical prefixes. **Table 22-1** shows the names and structures of the first ten alkanes. Notice the underlined prefix representing the number of carbon atoms in the molecule.

**Table 22-1**

| First Ten of the Alkane Series | | | | |
|---|---|---|---|---|
| **Name** | **Molecular formula** | **Condensed structural formula** | **Melting point (°C)** | **Boiling point (°C)** |
| Methane | $CH_4$ | $CH_4$ | −182 | −162 |
| Ethane | $C_2H_6$ | $CH_3CH_3$ | −183 | −89 |
| Propane | $C_3H_8$ | $CH_3CH_2CH_3$ | −188 | −42 |
| Butane | $C_4H_{10}$ | $CH_3CH_2CH_2CH_3$ | −138 | −0.5 |
| Pentane | $C_5H_{12}$ | $CH_3CH_2CH_2CH_2CH_3$ | −130 | 36 |
| Hexane | $C_6H_{14}$ | $CH_3CH_2CH_2CH_2CH_2CH_3$ | −95 | 69 |
| Heptane | $C_7H_{16}$ | $CH_3CH_2CH_2CH_2CH_2CH_2CH_3$ | −91 | 98 |
| Octane | $C_8H_{18}$ | $CH_3CH_2CH_2CH_2CH_2CH_2CH_2CH_3$ | −57 | 126 |
| Nonane | $C_9H_{20}$ | $CH_3(CH_2)_7CH_3$ | −54 | 151 |
| Decane | $C_{10}H_{22}$ | $CH_3(CH_2)_8CH_3$ | −29 | 174 |

In **Table 22-1**, you can see that the structural formulas are written in a different way from those in **Figure 22-3.** These formulas, called condensed structural formulas, save space by not showing how the hydrogen atoms branch off the carbon atoms. Condensed formulas can be written in several ways. In **Table 22-1**, the lines between carbon atoms have been eliminated to save space.

Looking at the alkane series in **Table 22-1,** you can see that $—CH_2—$ is a repeating unit in the chain of carbon atoms. Note, for example, in the diagram below that pentane has one more $—CH_2—$ unit than butane.

Butane ($C_4H_{10}$)          Pentane ($C_5H_{12}$)

You can further condense structural formulas by writing the $—CH_2—$ unit in parentheses followed by a subscript to show the number of units, as is done with nonane and decane.

**CHEMISTRY JOURNAL**

## Alkane Names

*Linguistic* Point out to students that although the names for alkanes with five or more carbons have prefixes that were derived from Greek or Latin for the number of carbons, smaller alkanes were named using different sources. Ask students to research the origins of the prefixes used for alkanes that have from one to four carbons in a chain. They should include the information they find in their chemistry journals. **L2**

A series of compounds that differ from one another by a repeating unit is called a **homologous series**. A homologous series has a fixed numerical relationship among the numbers of atoms. For alkanes, the relationship between the numbers of carbon and hydrogen atoms can be expressed as $C_nH_{2n+2}$, where $n$ is equal to the number of carbon atoms in the alkane. Given the number of carbon atoms in an alkane, you can write the molecular formula for any alkane. For example, heptane has seven carbons so its formula is $C_7H_{2(7)+2}$, or $C_7H_{16}$. What is the molecular formula for a 13-carbon alkane?

## Branched-Chain Alkanes

The alkanes you have studied so far are called straight-chain alkanes because the carbon atoms are bonded to each other in a single line. Now look at the two structures in the following diagram. If you count the carbon and hydrogen atoms, you will discover that both structures have the same molecular formula, $C_4H_{10}$. Do these structures represent the same substance?

Butane
Molecular formula: $C_4H_{10}$

Isobutane
Molecular formula: $C_4H_{10}$

If you think that the structures represent two different substances, you are right. The structure on the left represents butane, and the structure on the right represents a branched-chain alkane, known as isobutane, a substance whose chemical and physical properties are different from those of butane. As you see, carbon atoms can bond to one, two, three, or even four other carbon atoms. This property makes possible a variety of branched-chain alkanes. How do you name isobutane using IUPAC rules?

## Naming Branched-Chain Alkanes

You've seen that both a straight-chain and a branched-chain alkane can have the same molecular formula. This fact illustrates a basic principle of organic chemistry: the order and arrangement of atoms in an organic molecule determine its identity. Therefore, the name of an organic compound also must describe the molecular structure of the compound accurately.

For the purpose of naming, branched-chain alkanes are viewed as consisting of a straight chain of carbon atoms with other carbon atoms or groups of carbon atoms branching off the straight chain. The longest continuous chain of carbon atoms is called the **parent chain**. All side branches are called **substituent groups** because they appear to substitute for a hydrogen atom in the straight chain.

22.1 Alkanes    **701**

## Biology
### CONNECTION

By the middle of the 19th century, inorganic chemistry and physics were regarded as rigorous experimental sciences. However, the biological sciences were held back in part by the prevailing belief in vitalism—the idea that the processes and materials of living things could not be explained by the same laws and theories that applied to physics and chemistry. Vitalism was dealt its final blow in 1897, when Eduard Buchner, a German chemist, showed that extracts of yeast could carry out fermentation of sugar when no living cells were present.

### In-Text Question

**Page 701** What is the molecular formula for a 13-carbon alkane? $C_nH_{2n+2}$, therefore $C_{13}H_{28}$

### Extension

*Intrapersonal* Ask students to find out the source of the energy used to heat their homes and record that information in their chemistry journals. If they burn a fuel, they should determine and record the composition of that fuel. If they use electricity, ask them to do further research to find out what type of fuel, if any, is burned to produce that electricity. Ask students to draw the structures of the major components of the fuels used. **L2**

### Visual Learning

*Visual-Spatial* Consider using the art of straight-chain and branched-chain hydrocarbons on this page to introduce the concept of structural isomers. To do so, challenge students to draw structures or make models of all possible molecules having the formula $C_5H_{12}$. Caution them that each carbon atom must have four single covalent bonds linking it to other atoms. They should discover three possible structures, which are pictured on page 717.

## GLENCOE
### TECHNOLOGY

CD-ROM
**Chemistry: Matter and Change**
Demonstration: *Combustion of Methane*

## DIFFERENTIATED INSTRUCTION

### Learning Disabled

*Visual-Spatial* Some students will find learning the meaning of the general formula of alkanes ($C_nH_{2n+2}$) easier if they use it to make models of alkane structures. Assign each student an alkane. Ask them to use the general formula to predict how many carbon atoms and hydrogen atoms they will need to make a model of that alkane. Then, ask them to make the model and test their predictions. **L2 ELL**

**Visual-Spatial** Ask students if there is an alkane having the name 2-ethylbutane. Before revealing the answer, have students draw a molecule of that name and identify the longest carbon chain. No. Following IUPAC rules, this is the name for a structure that has a 2-carbon chain attached at the second carbon of a 4-carbon chain. However, the longest continuous chain contains five carbon atoms. Ask students to give the correct name for the compound. 3-methylpentane. **L2**

## In-Text Question

**Page 702** What relationship exists between these groups and the alkanes in Table 22-1? The groups lack a terminal hydrogen atom at the place where they bond to other chains.

## CAREERS USING CHEMISTRY

**Career Path** A career as an alternative fuels technician would include high school courses in automotive technology, chemistry, math, and physics.
**Career Issue** Have students investigate the need to reduce our dependence on petroleum for fuels.

### For More Information
For more information about careers in formulating and testing alternative fuels, students can contact
National Alternative Fuels
Training Consortium
1460 Earl Core Road
Morgantown, WV 26505

---

### Alternative Fuel Technician

*Are you interested in improving the quality of the air you breathe and reducing our dependence on petroleum resources? Do you like to work with cars? Then consider a career as an alternative fuels technician.*

Alternative fuels are being developed and used today to replace fossil fuels such as oil. As an alternative fuels technician, you may work in research developing new vehicles. Or, you may educate consumers and service and maintain their environmentally friendly vehicles.

---

Each alkane-based substituent group branching from the parent chain is named for the straight-chain alkane having the same number of carbon atoms as the substituent. The ending *-ane* is replaced with the letters *-yl,* as shown in the following diagram.

Methane          Methyl group

An alkane-based substituent group is called an alkyl group. Several common alkyl groups are shown in **Table 22-2**. What relationship exists between these groups and the alkanes in **Table 22-1**?

**The naming process** To name organic structures, chemists follow systematic rules approved by the International Union of Pure and Applied Chemistry (IUPAC). Here are the rules for naming branched-chain alkanes.

1. *Count the number of carbon atoms in the longest continuous chain.* Use the name of the straight-chain alkane with that number of carbons as the name of the parent chain of the structure.

2. *Number each carbon in the parent chain.* Locate the end carbon closest to a substituent group. Label that carbon position one. This step gives all the substituent groups the lowest position numbers possible.

3. *Name each alkyl group substituent.* The names of these groups are placed before the name of the parent chain.

**Table 22-2**

| Common Alkyl Groups | | |
|---|---|---|
| **Name** | **Condensed structural formula** | **Structural formula** |
| Methyl | $CH_3-$ | |
| Ethyl | $CH_3CH_2-$ | |
| Propyl | $CH_3CH_2CH_2-$ | |
| Isopropyl | $CH_3CHCH_3$ | |
| Butyl | $CH_3CH_2CH_2CH_2-$ | |

---

## Demonstration

### Combustion of Methane

#### Purpose
Students will observe the combustion of methane.

#### Materials
400-mL beaker; 150-mL beaker; liquid detergent (25 mL); glycerin (5 mL); sucrose (5 g); rubber tubing (1-m length); small funnel; meterstick; candle; matches; newspaper; masking tape

#### Safety Precautions
**Disposal**
Solution may be poured down the drain.

#### Procedure
Prepare a soap-bubble solution by adding 160 mL $H_2O$, 25 mL liquid detergent, and 5 mL glycerin to the 400-mL beaker. In a separate beaker, dissolve 5 g sucrose in 60 mL $H_2O$. Gently mix the two solutions in the 400-mL beaker. See page 696C for preparation of solution. Connect one end of rubber tubing to a gas outlet and the other end to a small funnel. Invert the funnel into the soap mixture, then lift the funnel from the solution. Turn on the gas briefly to make a bubble. Darken the room. Dislodge bubbles by turning the funnel sideways and gently shaking. As each bubble rises

**4.** *If the same alkyl group occurs more than once as a branch on the parent structure, use a prefix (di-, tri-, tetra-, etc.) before its name to indicate how many times it appears.* Then use the number of the carbon to which each is attached to indicate its position.

**5.** *Whenever different alkyl groups are attached to the same parent structure, place their names in alphabetical order.* Do not consider the prefixes (di-, tri-, etc.) when determining alphabetical order.

**6.** *Write the entire name using hyphens to separate numbers from words and commas to separate numbers.* No space is added between the substituent name and the name of the parent chain.

Now, try to name the branched-chain structure, isobutane.

A      CH₃     B    CH₃     C   ₁CH₃    D   ₁CH₃
$$\underset{1\quad 2\quad 3}{CH_3CHCH_3}\qquad \underset{3\quad 2\quad 1}{CH_3CHCH_3}\qquad \underset{2\quad 3}{CH_3CHCH_3}\qquad \underset{3\quad 2}{CH_3CHCH_3}$$

**1.** The longest chain in the structures above contains three carbons. This is true if you start on the left (A), right (B), or carbon in the branch (C, D), as you can see in the accompanying diagram. Therefore, the name of the parent chain will be *propane*.

**2.** No matter where the numbering starts in this molecule, the alkyl group is at position 2. So, the four options are equivalent.

**3.** The alkyl group here is a methyl group because it has only one carbon.

**4.** No prefix is needed because only one alkyl group is present.

**5.** Alphabetical order does not need to be considered because only one group is present.

After applying the rules, you can write the IUPAC name *2-methylpropane* for isobutane. See **Figure 22-5.** Note that the name of the alkyl group is added in front of the name of the parent chain with no space between them. A hyphen separates the number from the word.

                    Substituent group: methyl
                    group at position 2
        CH₃
        |
   CH₃CHCH₃ ◄— 3-Carbon parent
               chain: propane
   2-Methylpropane

Because structural formulas can be written with chains oriented in various ways, you need to be careful in finding the longest continuous carbon chain. The following examples are written as skeletal formulas. A skeletal formula shows only the carbon atoms of an organic molecule in order to emphasize the chain arrangement. Hydrogen atoms are not shown in these skeletal formulas. Study the correct numbering of carbon atoms in the following examples. Note that numbering either carbon chain starting on the left-most carbon would disobey rule 1 on the previous page.

**Figure 22-5**

Many of today's automobile and truck air conditioners can use hydrocarbon refrigerant mixtures containing 2-methylpropane that are environmentally safe.

**National Science Content Standards**

**Pages 702–703**
UCP.2, UCP.5; A.1; B.2; F.6

### Identifying Misconceptions

Students may think that the line of carbon atoms written horizontally in a structural formula is always the chain to use in naming the substance.

**Uncover the Misconception**
Draw the following alkane on the chalkboard: a 6-carbon chain written horizontally with a 3-carbon propyl group branching vertically off the second carbon. Ask students to write the name of this alkane.

**Demonstrate the Concept**
Without revealing the correct IUPAC name of the compound, ask how many students named the compound 2-propylhexane and how many named it something else. Have a student who named the compound incorrectly explain his or her method for arriving at that name. Ask a student who has written the correct name, 4-methyloctane, to number the chain correctly on the board.

**Assess New Knowledge**
Write carbon-chain structures for other branched alkanes and have students find the correct numbering and write the names of the alkanes. Then, ask them to draw both skeletal and full structural formulas of compounds for which you provide names. **L2**
**ELL**

---

(natural gas) or sinks (propane gas), ignite it with a burning candle taped to the end of a meterstick. It is best to have an assistant hold the meterstick with the attached candle above or below the funnel before you shake bubbles free. **CAUTION:** *Fire hazard. Do not do this demonstration near flammable materials. Place newspapers on the floor to catch wax dripping from the candle.*

**Results**
There will be a flare-up as each bubble

bursts. The entrapped gas burns with a luminous yellow flame.

**Analysis**
**1.** The combustion you observed is a chemical reaction between what two reactants? oxygen and methane or propane
**2.** What did the combustion reaction produce? carbon dioxide, perhaps carbon monoxide, light, heat, water vapor, soot

**3.** Was the combustion reaction exothermic or endothermic? exothermic

### ✓ Assessment

**Knowledge** Have students write the balanced equation for the combustion reaction. $CH_4 + 2O_2 \rightarrow CO_2 + 2H_2O$ or $C_3H_8 + 5O_2 \rightarrow 3CO_2 + 4H_2O$

## Using Science Terms

**Linguistic** Have students write statements explaining the meaning of the terms homologous series and substituent group.

**L1** **ELL**

# 3 Assess

## Check for Understanding

Ask students to draw structures and give IUPAC names for all the alkanes with the formula $C_5H_{12}$.

They are pentane, 2-methylbutane, and 2,2-dimethylpropane.

## Reteach

Refer students to Table 22-1. Ask them to make a general statement about the relationship between number of carbons in a straight-chain alkane and melting and boiling points of those compounds.

Both melting and boiling points increase as chain length increases.

## Extension

Ask interested students to learn the names of the straight-chain alkanes that contain between 11 and 20 carbon atoms per molecule.

This ball-and-stick model of the molecule in Example Problem 22-1 shows how the molecule looks in three dimensions.

---

**EXAMPLE PROBLEM 22-1**

### Naming Branched-Chain Alkanes

Name the following alkane.

$$CH_3$$
$$|$$
$$CH_2$$
$$|$$
$$CH_3CH_2CH_2CHCHCHCH_2CH_3$$
$$|\quad\quad|$$
$$CH_3\quad CH_3$$

**1. Analyze the Problem**

You are given a structure. To determine the name of the parent chain and the names and locations of branches, follow the IUPAC rules.

**2. Solve for the Unknown**

a. Count carefully to find the longest chain. In this case, it is easy. The longest chain has eight carbon atoms, so the parent name is *octane*.

b. Number the chain in both directions. Numbering from the left puts the alkyl groups at positions 4, 5, and 6. Numbering from the right puts alkyl groups at positions 3, 4, and 5. Therefore, 3, 4, and 5 are the lowest position numbers and will be used in the name.

$$CH_3\qquad\qquad\qquad CH_3$$
$$|\qquad\qquad\qquad\quad |$$
$$CH_2\qquad\qquad\qquad CH_2$$
$$1\ 2\ 3\ 4\ |\ 6\ 7\ 8\qquad 8\ 7\ 6\ 5\ |\ 3\ 2\ 1$$
$$CH_3CH_2CH_2CHCHCHCH_2CH_3 \quad CH_3CH_2CH_2CHCHCHCH_2CH_3$$
$$|\ 5\ |\qquad\qquad\qquad |\ 4\ |$$
$$CH_3\ CH_3\qquad\qquad\quad CH_3\ CH_3$$

c. Identify and name the alkyl groups branching from the parent chain. There are one-carbon *methyl* groups at positions 3 and 5, and a two-carbon *ethyl* group at position 4.

$$\qquad\qquad\lceil CH_3$$
$$Ethyl\ \big\{\ |$$
$$\qquad\qquad\lfloor CH_2$$
$$8\ 7\ 6\ 5\ |\ 3\ 2\ 1$$
$$CH_3CH_2CH_2CHCHCHCH_2CH_3$$
$$|\ 4\ |$$
$$CH_3\ CH_3$$
$$Methyl\ Methyl$$

d. Look for and count the alkyl groups that occur more than once. Determine the prefix to use to show the number of times each group appears. In this example, the prefix *di*- will be added to the name *methyl* because two methyl groups are present. No prefix is needed for the one ethyl group. Then show the position of each group with the appropriate number.

$$\qquad\qquad\qquad\lceil CH_3$$
$$One\ ethyl\ group:\ no\ prefix\ \big\{\ |\qquad Position\ and$$
$$\qquad\qquad\qquad\lfloor CH_2\qquad\ name:\ 4\text{-}ethyl$$
$$5\ |\ 3$$
$$CH_3CH_2CH_2CHCHCHCH_2CH_3\ \ Parent\ chain:\ octane$$
$$|\ 4\ |$$
$$CH_3\ CH_3$$
$$Two\ methyl\ groups:\ use\ dimethyl$$
$$Position\ and\ name:\ 3,5\text{-}dimethyl$$

---

## CHEMISTRY JOURNAL

### Canine Arson Detectors

**Intrapersonal** Specially trained K-9 sniffer dogs are usually better able to find accelerants on a fire scene than humans with electronic detection devices. Hydrocarbon detectors are sensitive to gasoline components in the parts-per-million (ppm) range. Dogs, though, can pinpoint traces that escape electronic detection, often as little as 0.01 microliter of 50% evaporated gasoline. Ask students to research an actual court case in which the "testimony" of dogs was used to attempt to prove that arson was committed. **L2**

---

**f.** Place the names of the alkyl branches in alphabetical order, *ignoring the prefixes*. Alphabetical order puts the name <u>e</u>thyl before di<u>m</u>ethyl.

**g.** Write the name of the structure using hyphens and commas as needed. The name should be written as *4-ethyl-3,5-dimethyloctane.*

**3.** **Evaluate the Answer**

The longest continuous carbon chain has been found and numbered correctly. All branches have been designated with correct prefixes and alkyl-group names. Alphabetical order and punctuation are correct.

### PRACTICE PROBLEMS

**1.** Use IUPAC rules to name the following structures.

a.
CH₃   CH₃
|      |
CH₃CHCH₂CHCH₂CH₃

c.
CH₃  CH₃
|     |
CH₃CCH₂CHCH₃
|
CH₃

b.
CH₃
|
CH₂      CH₃  CH₃
|         |    |
CH₃CHCH₂CH₂CHCH₂CHCH₃

**2.** Draw the structures of the following branched-chain alkanes.

a. 2,3-dimethyl-5-propyldecane

b. 3,4,5-triethyloctane

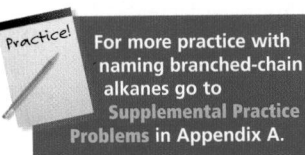

For more practice with naming branched-chain alkanes go to **Supplemental Practice Problems** in Appendix A.

---

## Section 22.1 Assessment

**3.** Use IUPAC rules to name the following structures.

a.
CH₃
|
CH₃CHCH₂CH₂CH₃

b.
CH₃
|
CH₃CCH₃
|
CH₃

**4.** Write a condensed structural formula for each of the following.

a. 3,4-diethylheptane

b. 4-isopropyl-3-methyldecane

**5.** Name two types of carbon-containing compounds that are considered inorganic rather than organic.

**6.** Write correct molecular formulas for pentadecane, a 15-carbon alkane, and icosane, a 20-carbon alkane.

**7.** Why is the name 3-*butylpentane* incorrect? Based on this name, write the structural formula for the compound. What is the correct IUPAC name for 3-butylpentane?

**8.** **Thinking Critically** Hexane is called a straight-chain alkane. Yet, a molecule of hexane has a zig-zag rather than a linear geometry. Explain this apparent paradox. Explain what characteristic of carbon atoms causes the zig-zag geometry of straight-chain alkanes.

**9.** **Graphing** Use data from **Table 22-1** to graph boiling point versus the number of carbon atoms in the alkane chain for the first ten alkanes. Use the graph to predict boiling points for straight-chain alkanes with 11 and 12 carbon atoms. For more help, refer to *Drawing and Using Line Graphs* in the **Math Handbook** on pages 903–907 of this textbook.

---

## Section 22.1 Assessment

See the Solutions Manual for graphics to questions 4, 7, and 9.

**3. a.** 2-methylpentane
    **b.** 2,2-dimethylpropane
**4. a.** Parent chain has seven carbon atoms, with ethyl groups on carbons 3 and 4.
    **b.** Parent chain has 10 carbon atoms, with a methyl group on carbon 3 and an isopropyl group on carbon 4.

**5.** carbon oxides, carbides, and carbonates
**6.** pentadecane, C₁₅H₃₂; icosane, C₂₀H₄₂
**7.** The longest continuous carbon chain contains seven carbon atoms, not five carbon atoms. Parent chain has seven carbon atoms with an ethyl group on carbon 3. 3-ethylheptane
**8.** Normal alkanes such as n-hexane are called straight-chain alkanes because

---

### Practice PROBLEMS

Have students refer to Appendix D for complete solutions to Practice Problems.

**1. a.** 2,4-dimethylhexane
   **b.** 2,4,7-trimethylnonane
   **c.** 2,2,4-trimethylpentane
**2.** See the Solutions Manual for structures.
   **a.** Parent chain has 10 carbon atoms, with methyl groups on carbons 2 and 3 and a propyl group on carbon 5.
   **b.** Parent chain has eight carbon atoms, with ethyl groups on carbons 3, 4, and 5.

---

 **Assessment**

**Knowledge** Hectane is the IUPAC name for the straight-chain alkane that contains 100 carbon atoms. Give the students that information and then ask them the following questions.

**1.** What is the molecular formula of hectane? C₁₀₀H₂₀₂
**2.** Based on the trends shown in Table 22-1, what do you predict will be the physical state of hectane at room temperature and one atmosphere pressure? solid
L2

---

of the way their molecules usually are drawn on paper. However, their molecules have zig-zag geometries because carbon atoms form single bonds at tetrahedral angles.

**9.** Students should predict the boiling points for alkanes with 11 and 12 carbons to be about 195 to 197 and 214 to 217°C, respectively. Actual boiling points are 196°C and 216°C.

**705**

# 1 Focus

Section Focus Transparency **82** Properties of Methane
Use with Chapter 22, Section 22.2

❶ This photo shows a close-up view of the bottom of a swamp. What clues suggest that the swamp is producing methane?

❷ On the basis of the photo, what can you conclude about the physical properties of methane?

Chemistry: Matter and Change

Section Focus Transparencies

# 2 Teach
## Enrichment

Have interested students research the sizes of cyclic alkane structures most commonly found in organic compounds and why. Cyclopentane and cyclohexane are the most common ring sizes found, because in those structures the carbon atoms form bonds that are less strained than are those in smaller or larger rings. Carbon atoms with single bonds form the strongest bonds possible when the bonds are located at angles of about 109.5° apart, as they are in methane. **L3**

---

# Cyclic Alkanes and Alkane Properties

## Objectives

- **Name** a cyclic alkane by examining its structure.
- **Draw** the structure of a cyclic alkane given its name.
- **Describe** the properties of alkanes.
- **Distinguish** between saturated and unsaturated hydrocarbons.

## Vocabulary

cyclic hydrocarbon
cycloalkane
saturated hydrocarbon
unsaturated hydrocarbon

One of the reasons that such a variety of organic compounds exists is that carbon atoms can form ring structures. An organic compound that contains a hydrocarbon ring is called a **cyclic hydrocarbon**.

## Cycloalkanes

To indicate that a hydrocarbon has a ring structure, the prefix *cyclo-* is used with the hydrocarbon name. Thus cyclic hydrocarbons that contain single bonds only are called **cycloalkanes.** Cycloalkanes can have rings with three, four, five, six, or even more carbon atoms. Cyclopropane, the smallest cycloalkane, is a gas that was used for many years as an anesthetic for surgery. However, it is no longer used because it is highly flammable. The name for the six-carbon cycloalkane is cyclohexane. Obtained from petroleum, cyclohexane is used in paint and varnish removers and for extracting essential oils to make perfume. Note that cyclohexane ($C_6H_{12}$) has two fewer hydrogen atoms than straight-chain hexane ($C_6H_{14}$) because a valence electron from each of two carbon atoms is now forming a carbon-carbon bond rather than a carbon-hydrogen bond.

As you can see in **Figure 22-6**, cyclic hydrocarbons such as cyclohexane are represented by condensed, skeletal, and line structures. Line structures show only the carbon-carbon bonds with carbon atoms understood to be at each vertex of the structure. Hydrogen atoms are assumed to occupy the remaining bonding positions unless substituents are present.

**Naming substituted cycloalkanes** Like other alkanes, cycloalkanes can have substituent groups. Substituted cycloalkanes are named by following the same IUPAC rules used for straight-chain alkanes, but with a few modifications. With cycloalkanes, there is no need to find the longest chain because the ring is always considered to be the parent chain. Because a cyclic structure has no ends, numbering is started on the carbon that is bonded to the substituent group. When there are two or more substituents, the carbons are numbered around the ring in a way that gives the lowest possible set of numbers for the substituents. If only one group is attached to the ring, no number is necessary. The following Example Problem will show you how a cycloalkane is named.

**Figure 22-6**

Cyclohexane can be represented in several ways. Chemists most often draw line structures for cyclic hydrocarbons because the molecules have distinct shapes that are easily identifiable.

Condensed structural formula

Skeletal structure

Line structure

---

## Internet Address Book

Note Internet addresses that you find useful in the space below for quick reference.

## EXAMPLE PROBLEM 22-2

### Naming Cycloalkanes
Name the cycloalkane shown.

Stains and varnishes used to refinish wood often use cyclohexane as a solvent.

**1. Analyze the Problem**

You are given a structure. To determine the parent cyclic structure and the location of branches, follow the IUPAC rules.

**2. Solve for the Unknown**

a. Count the carbons in the ring and use the name of the parent cyclic hydrocarbon. In this case, the ring has six carbons, so the parent name is *cyclohexane*.

b. Number the ring, starting from one of the $CH_3-$ branches. Find the numbering that gives the lowest possible set of numbers for the branches. Here are two ways of numbering the ring.

A

B

1,3,4-Trimethylcyclohexane     1,2,4-Trimethylcyclohexane

Numbering from the carbon atom at the bottom of the ring puts the $CH_3-$ groups at positions 1, 3, and 4 in structure A. Numbering from the carbon at the top of the ring gives the position numbers 1, 2, and 4. All other numbering schemes place the $CH_3-$ groups at higher position numbers. Thus, 1, 2, and 4 are the lowest possible position numbers and will be used in the name.

c. Name the substituents. All three are the same—one-carbon methyl groups.

d. Add the prefix to show the number of groups present. Three methyl groups are present, so the prefix *tri-* will be added to the name *methyl* to make *trimethyl*.

e. Alphabetical order can be ignored because only one type of group is present.

g. Put the name together using the name of the parent cycloalkane. Use commas to separate numbers and hyphens between numbers and words. Write the name as *1,2,4-trimethylcyclohexane*.

**3. Evaluate the Answer**

The parent ring structure is numbered to give the branches the lowest possible set of numbers. The prefix *tri-* indicates that three methyl groups are present. No alphabetization is necessary because all branches are methyl groups.

## Reinforcement

Point out that there are six different ways to number the ring. Starting at the top, the position numbers of the substituents can be 1,2,4 or 1,4,6. Starting at the right, the numbers can be 1,2,5 or 1,3,6. Starting at the bottom, the numbers can be 1,3,4 or 1,4,5.

### Resource Manager

**Section Focus Transparency 82 and Master** L1 ELL
**Study Guide for Content Mastery,** p. 128 L2
**Solving Problems: A Chemistry Handbook,** Section 22.2 L2
**Math Skills Transparency 35, 36 and Masters** L2 ELL
**Lab Manual,** pp. 169–172 L2

---

## DIFFERENTIATED INSTRUCTION

### Gifted

*Kinesthetic* Ask interested students to build a model of a highly branched alkane with the formula $C_{18}H_{38}$ and then name the model using IUPAC rules. L3

**National Science Content Standards**

**Pages 706–707**
UCP.2, UCP.5; A.1; B.2

Have students refer to Appendix D for complete solutions to Practice Problems.

**10. a.** methylcyclopentane

**b.** 2-ethyl-1,4-dimethylcyclohexane

**c.** 1,3-diethylcyclobutane

**11.** See the Solutions Manual for structures.

**a.** Parent chain is a five-carbon ring, with an ethyl group on carbon 1 and a propyl group on carbon 3.

**b.** Parent chain is a six-carbon ring, with methyl groups on carbons 1,2,2, and 4 (four methyl groups total).

---

**Practice!** For more practice with naming cycloalkanes go to Supplemental Practice Problems in Appendix A.

---

**10.** Use IUPAC rules to name the following structures.

**a.**

**b.**

**c.**

**11.** Draw the structures of the following cycloalkanes.

**a.** 1-ethyl-3-propylcyclopentane

**b.** 1,2,2,4-tetramethylcyclohexane

## Properties of Alkanes

You have learned that the structure of a molecule affects its properties. For example, ammonia ($NH_3$) can accept a proton from an acid to become an ammonium ion ($NH_4^+$) because the nitrogen atom has an unshared pair of electrons. As another example, the O—H bonds in a water molecule are polar, and because the H—O—H molecule has a bent geometry, the molecule itself is polar. Thus water molecules are attracted to each other and can form hydrogen bonds with each other. As a result, the boiling and melting points of water are much higher than those of other substances having similar molecular mass and size.

What properties would you predict for alkanes? All of the bonds in these hydrocarbons are between either a carbon atom and a hydrogen atom or two carbon atoms. Are these bonds polar? Remember, a bond between two atoms is polar only if the atoms differ by at least 0.5 in their Pauling electronegativity values. Carbon's electronegativity value is 2.55, and hydrogen's is 2.20, so a C—H bond has a difference of only 0.35. Thus, it is not polar. A bond between two identical atoms such as carbon can never be polar because the difference in their electronegativity values is zero. Because all of the bonds in alkanes are nonpolar, alkane molecules are nonpolar.

**Physical properties of alkanes** What types of physical properties do nonpolar compounds have? A comparison of two molecular substances—one

**Table 22-3**

| Comparing Physical Properties of Water and Methane | | |
|---|---|---|
| Substance and formula | Water ($H_2O$) | Methane ($CH_4$) |
| Model | | |
| Molecular mass | 18 amu | 16 amu |
| State at room temperature | liquid | gas |
| Boiling point | 100°C | −162°C |
| Melting point | 0°C | −182°C |

---

**CHEMISTRY JOURNAL**

## Oil and Water

*Linguistic* Ask students to write a paragraph in which they predict what will happen when they mix a small amount of gasoline or other alkane mixture and water together. Students should then describe what happens when they actually try it. They should include these paragraphs in their chemistry journals. **L2**

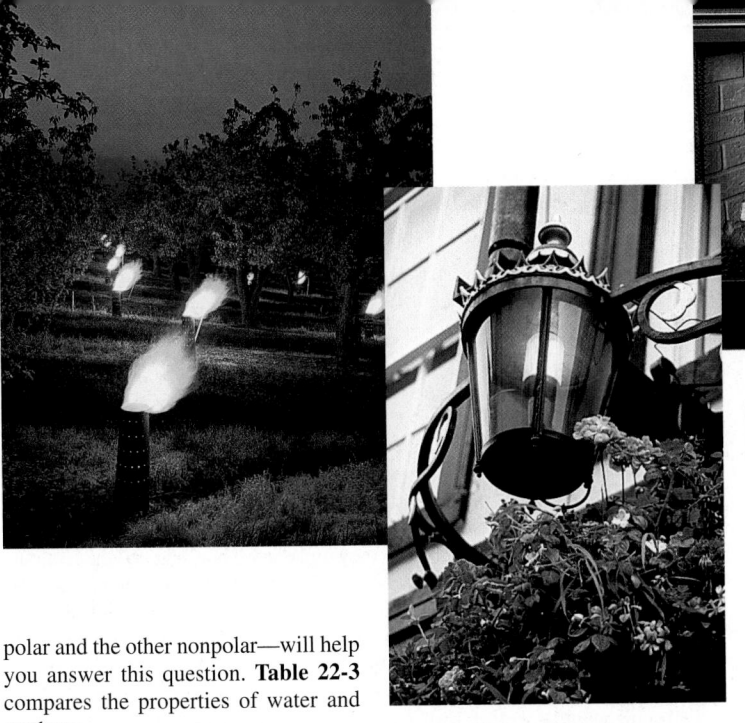

**Figure 22-7**

Alkane hydrocarbons are often used as fuels to provide heat and, sometimes, light. The smudge pots shown on the left produce heat that helps prevent cold-weather damage to citrus crops. The gas lantern gives off light, and the gas-log fireplace provides both heat and light.

polar and the other nonpolar—will help you answer this question. **Table 22-3** compares the properties of water and methane.

Note that the molecular mass of methane (16 amu) is close to the molecular mass of water (18 amu). Also, water and methane molecules are similar in size. However, when you compare the melting and boiling points of methane to those of water, you can see evidence that the molecules differ in some significant way. These temperatures differ greatly because methane molecules have little intermolecular attraction compared to water molecules. This difference in attraction can be explained by the fact that methane molecules are nonpolar and do not form hydrogen bonds with each other, whereas water molecules are polar and freely form hydrogen bonds. What straight-chain alkane in **Table 22-1** has a boiling point nearest that of water?

The difference in polarity and hydrogen bonding also explains the immiscibility of alkanes and other hydrocarbons with water. If you try to dissolve alkanes, such as lubricating oils, in water, the two liquids separate almost immediately into two phases. This separation happens because the attractive forces between alkane molecules are stronger than the attractive forces between the alkane and water molecules. Therefore, alkanes are more soluble in solvents composed of nonpolar molecules like themselves than in water, a polar solvent. This is another example of the rule of thumb that "like dissolves like."

**Chemical properties of alkanes** The main chemical property of alkanes is their low reactivity. Recall that many chemical reactions occur when a reactant with a full electrical charge, such as an ion, or with a partial charge, such as a polar molecule, is attracted to another reactant with the opposite charge. Molecules such as alkanes, in which atoms are connected by nonpolar bonds, have no charge. As a result, they have little attraction for ions or polar molecules. The low reactivity of alkanes also can be attributed to the relatively strong C—C and C—H bonds. The low reactivity of alkanes limits their uses. As you can see from **Figure 22-7,** alkanes are commonly used as fuels because they readily undergo combustion in oxygen.

22.2 Cyclic Alkanes and Alkane Properties    **709**

**Visual Learning**

**Figure 22-7** Ask students to examine the pictures in the figure and determine what types of energy interconversions are taking place in the photographs. The chemical potential energy in alkanes is converted to thermal energy, light energy, and the chemical potential energy of water and carbon dioxide as combustion takes place.

**In-Text Question**

**Page 709** What straight-chain alkane in Table 22-1 has a boiling point nearest that of water? Heptane has a boiling point nearest that of water.

**Assessment**

**Knowledge** Ask students to label the following bonds as polar or nonpolar: C–C nonpolar; C–O polar; C–H nonpolar; O–H polar; N–H polar. **L2**

**DIFFERENTIATED INSTRUCTION**

**Learning Disabled**

Some students will gain a better understanding of the terms *saturated* and *unsaturated* as they apply to hydrocarbons if you use a simple analogy. Compare the unsaturation of a dry paper towel that can still pick up lots of water to an alkene or alkyne that can potentially absorb more hydrogen by forming additional C–H bonds at the expense of double or triple bonds. In other words, the compound has fewer hydrogen atoms than its carbons can hold. Then compare the saturation of a paper towel with water after a spill has been cleaned up to an alkane that already has all of the hydrogen atoms its carbons can hold. **L1** **ELL**

**National Science Content Standards**
**Pages 708–709**
UCP.2, UCP.5; B.2, B.4, B.6

# 3 Assess

## Check for Understanding

Ask students to explain why cyclopropane is the smallest possible alkane. **A cyclic structure cannot be formed from one or two carbon atoms. Three or more carbons must be present.**

## Reteach

Have students relate the low melting points and low boiling points of alkanes to their molecular structures. **Alkane molecules are nonpolar and do not form hydrogen bonds with each other. Therefore, their intermolecular attractions are relatively weak.**

## Extension

Ask students to research the structures, discovery, and potential uses for fullerenes, the best-known example of which is buckminsterfullerene, or "bucky balls." Ask students to include their findings in their portfolios. **L2** **P** 🔲

## Assessment

**Skill** Ask students to write the molecular formulas for each of the following cyclic alkanes: cyclopropane, $C_3H_6$; cyclobutane, $C_4H_8$; cyclopentane, $C_5H_{10}$; cyclohexane, $C_6H_{12}$ **L2**

---

## Multiple Carbon-Carbon Bonds

Carbon atoms can bond to each other not only by single covalent bonds but also by double and triple covalent bonds. In a double bond, atoms share two pairs of electrons; in a triple bond, they share three pairs of electrons. The following diagram shows Lewis structures and structural formulas for single, double, and triple covalent bonds.

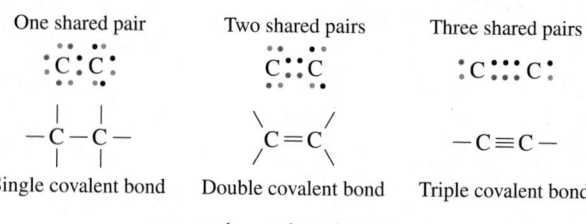

| One shared pair | Two shared pairs | Three shared pairs |
|---|---|---|
| Single covalent bond | Double covalent bond | Triple covalent bond |

• and •= carbon electrons
∘ = electron from another atom

In the nineteenth century, before they understood bonding and the structure of organic substances, chemists experimented with hydrocarbons obtained from heating animal fats and plant oils. They classified these hydrocarbons according to a chemical test in which they mixed each hydrocarbon with bromine and then measured how much reacted with the hydrocarbon. Some hydrocarbons would react with a little bromine, some would react with more, and some would not react at all. Chemists called the hydrocarbons that reacted with bromine unsaturated hydrocarbons in the same sense that an unsaturated aqueous solution can dissolve more solute. Hydrocarbons that did not react with bromine were said to be saturated.

Modern chemists can explain the results of the chemists of 170 years ago. Hydrocarbons that reacted with bromine had double or triple covalent bonds. Those that took up no bromine had only single covalent bonds. Today, a **saturated hydrocarbon** is defined as a hydrocarbon having only single bonds—in other words, an alkane. An **unsaturated hydrocarbon** is a hydrocarbon that has at least one double or triple bond between carbon atoms. You will learn more about unsaturated hydrocarbons in Section 22.3.

**Try at Home** **LAB**

See page 962 in Appendix E for
**Comparing Water and a Hydrocarbon**

---

## Section 22.2 Assessment

**12.** Use IUPAC rules to name the following structures.

**a.**

CH₃     CH₃
      
CH₃          CH₂CH₃

**b.**

CH₂CH₂CH₃

CH₂CH₂CH₃

**13.** Write a condensed structural formula for each of the following.

  **a.** 1-ethyl-4-methylcyclohexane
  **b.** 1,2-dimethylcyclopropane

**14.** Describe the main structural characteristics of alkane molecules. Give two examples of how these characteristics determine the physical properties of alkanes.

**15.** What structural characteristic distinguishes saturated from unsaturated hydrocarbons?

**16.** **Thinking Critically** Some shortening is described as "hydrogenated vegetable oil." This means that the oils reacted with hydrogen in the presence of a catalyst. Make a hypothesis to explain why hydrogen reacted with the oils.

**17.** **Modeling** Construct ball-and-stick molecular models of the following cyclic alkanes.

  **a.** isopropylcyclobutane
  **b.** 1,2,4-trimethylcyclopentane

chemistrymc.com/self_check_quiz

---

## Section 22.2 Assessment

See the Solutions Manual for question 13 and 17 structures.

**12. a.** 1-ethyl-2,4,5-trimethylcyclohexane
  **b.** 1,2-dipropylcyclopentane

**13. a.** Parent chain is a six-carbon ring, with an ethyl group on carbon 1 and a methyl group on carbon 4.

**710**

**b.** Parent chain is a three-carbon ring with methyl groups on carbons 1 and 2.

**14.** Alkanes are chain or ring hydrocarbons containing only single carbon-carbon covalent bonds. The C-C and C-H bonds are nonpolar, making alkanes insoluble in water, a polar solvent. The bonds are also strong

and stable, making alkanes relatively unreactive.

**15.** Saturated hydrocarbons have only single C-C bonds, whereas unsaturated hydrocarbons contain double or triple C-C bonds.

**16.** Student hypotheses may suggest that the original oils are unsaturated because their molecules

# Alkenes and Alkynes

You now know that alkanes are saturated hydrocarbons because they contain only single covalent bonds between carbon atoms, and that unsaturated hydrocarbons have at least one double or triple bond between carbon atoms.

## Alkenes

Unsaturated hydrocarbons that contain one or more double covalent bonds between carbon atoms in a chain are called **alkenes**. Because an alkene must have a double bond between carbon atoms, there is no 1-carbon alkene. The simplest alkene has two carbon atoms double-bonded to each other. The remaining four electrons—two from each carbon atom—are shared with four hydrogen atoms to give the molecule ethene ($C_2H_4$).

Alkenes with only one double bond constitute a homologous series. If you study the molecular formulas for the substances shown in **Table 22-4**, you will see that each has twice as many hydrogen atoms as carbon atoms. The general formula for the series is $C_nH_{2n}$. Each alkene has two fewer hydrogen atoms than the corresponding alkane because two electrons now form the second covalent bond and are no longer available for bonding to hydrogen atoms. What are the molecular formulas for 6-carbon and 9-carbon alkenes?

### Objectives

- **Compare** the properties of alkenes and alkynes with those of alkanes.

- **Describe** the molecular structures of alkenes and alkynes.

- **Name** an alkene or alkyne by examining its structure.

- **Draw** the structure of an alkene or alkyne by analyzing its name.

### Vocabulary

alkene
alkyne

**Table 22-4**

| Examples of Alkenes | | | | | |
|---|---|---|---|---|---|
| Name | Molecular formula | Structural formula | Condensed structural formula | Melting point (°C) | Boiling point (°C) |
| Ethene | $C_2H_4$ | | $CH_2 = CH_2$ | −169 | −104 |
| Propene | $C_3H_6$ | | $CH_3CH = CH_2$ | −185 | −48 |
| 1-Butene | $C_4H_8$ | | $CH_2 = CHCH_2CH_3$ | −185 | −6 |
| 2-Butene | $C_4H_8$ | | $CH_3CH = CHCH_3$ | −106 | 0.8 |

22.3 Alkenes and Alkynes **711**

## 1 Focus

### Focus Transparency

Before presenting the lesson, display **Section Focus Transparency 83** on the overhead projector. Have students answer the accompanying questions using **Section Focus Transparency Master 83.** **L1** **ELL**

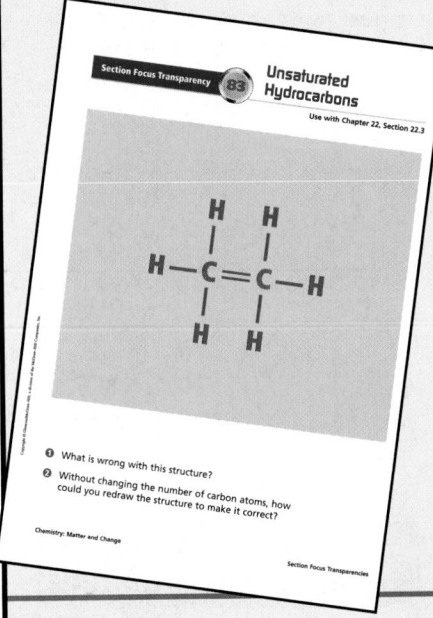

## 2 Teach

### Enrichment

*Linguistic* Ask students to research the origins of the terms originally used to describe hydrocarbon types. Alkanes are sometimes still called paraffins, while alkenes are still occasionally referred to as olefins. Ask them to record their findings in their chemistry journals. **L2**

### In-Text Question

**Page 711** What are the molecular formulas for 6-carbon and 9-carbon alkenes? $C_6H_{12}$ and $C_9H_{18}$

### DIFFERENTIATED INSTRUCTION

#### Gifted

*Interpersonal* Ask groups of interested students to design chemical tests that will distinguish alkanes from alkenes and alkynes. Have them research and compare the reactivities of saturated and unsaturated hydrocarbons. If the necessary supplies are available, encourage students to try their tests to see how well they work. **L3**

contain double or triple bonds. The molecules therefore "take up" hydrogen to form saturated chains.

**17. a.** Model's parent chain is a four-carbon ring with an isopropyl group on any carbon.

**b.** Model's parent chain is a five-carbon ring with methyl groups on carbons 1,2, and 4.

**National Science Content Standards**

**Pages 710–711**
UCP.2, UCP.5; B.2, B.4, B.6

Place two or three pieces of very ripe fruit in a bag next to a small beaker containing 20 mL of dilute aqueous iodine solution (dilute tincture of iodine or an even stronger stock solution with a light brown-yellow color that you can see through), and cover both with a larger beaker. Seal the bottom of the larger beaker to the countertop with tape. As a control, place another setup without fruit next to the first. Ask students to observe the color of the iodine solutions each day for a few days and to explain what has happened. The ethene produced by the ripening fruit is an unsaturated hydrocarbon. It reacts with iodine to form colorless alkyl halide products, so the color of the iodine solution next to the fruit lightens while the control solution remains the same color.

## Resource Manager

**Section Focus Transparency 83 and Master** L1 ELL
**Study Guide for Content Mastery,** p. 129 L2
**Solving Problems: A Chemistry Handbook,** Section 22.3 L2
**Lab Manual,** pp. 173–176 L2

**Naming alkenes** Alkenes are named in much the same way as alkanes. Their names are formed by changing the *-ane* ending of the corresponding alkane to *-ene*. An alkane with two carbons is named eth*ane*, and an alkene with two carbons is named eth*ene*. Likewise, a three-carbon alkene is named propene. Ethene and propene have older, common names *ethylene* and *propylene*, respectively.

To name alkenes with four or more carbons in the chain, it is necessary to specify the location of the double bond. You do this by numbering the carbons in the parent chain starting at the end of the chain that will give the first carbon in the double bond the lowest number. Then you use only that number in the name.

$$\overset{1}{C}=\overset{2}{C}-\overset{3}{C}-\overset{4}{C} \qquad \overset{1}{C}-\overset{2}{C}=\overset{3}{C}-\overset{4}{C} \qquad \cancel{\overset{1}{C}-\overset{2}{C}-\overset{3}{C}-\overset{4}{C}} \qquad \overset{4}{C}-\overset{3}{C}-\overset{2}{C}=\overset{1}{C}$$

1-Butene          2-Butene          3-Butene          1-Butene

Note that the third structure is not "3-butene" because it is identical to the first structure, 1-butene. It is important to recognize that 1-butene and 2-butene are two different substances, each with its own properties.

Cyclic alkenes are named in much the same way as cyclic alkanes; however, carbon number 1 must be one of the carbons connected by the double bond. Note the numbering in the compound shown below, 1,3-dimethylcyclopentene.

**Naming branched-chain alkenes** When naming branched-chain alkenes, follow the IUPAC rules for naming branched-chain alkanes—with two differences. First, in alkenes the parent chain is always the longest chain that contains the double bond, whether it is the longest chain of carbon atoms or not. Second, the position of the double bond, not the branches, determines how the chain is numbered. Note that there are two 4-carbon chains in the molecule shown below, but only the one with the double bond is used as a basis for naming. This branched-chain alkene is 2-methylbutene.

$$\overset{1}{CH_2}=\overset{2}{C}-\overset{3}{CH_2}-\overset{4}{CH_3} \quad (\text{with } CH_3 \text{ branch on C2})$$

Some unsaturated hydrocarbons contain more than one double (or triple) bond. The number of double bonds in such molecules is shown by using a prefix (*di-, tri-, tetra-*, etc.) before the suffix *-ene*. The positions of the bonds are numbered in a way that gives the lowest set of numbers. Which numbering system would you use in the following example?

$$\overset{1}{C}-\overset{2}{C}-\overset{3}{C}=\overset{4}{C}-\overset{5}{C}=\overset{6}{C}-\overset{7}{C} \quad \text{or} \quad \overset{7}{C}-\overset{6}{C}-\overset{5}{C}=\overset{4}{C}-\overset{3}{C}=\overset{2}{C}-\overset{1}{C}$$

Because the molecule has a seven-carbon chain, you use the prefix *hepta-*. Because it has two double bonds, you use the prefix *di-* before *-ene*, giving the name *heptadiene*. Adding the numbers 2 and 4 to designate the positions of the double bonds, you arrive at the name *2,4-heptadiene*.

## Portfolio

### Molecular Formulas of Hydrocarbons

Have students write the following questions in their portfolios and answer them as soon as they have learned enough from their study of Section 22.3 to do so.

1. How does the molecular formula of an alkane differ from that of an alkene with the same number of carbons? The alkane contains two more hydrogens ($C_nH_{2n+2}$) than the alkene ($C_nH_{2n}$).

2. How does the molecular formula of an alkane differ from that of an alkyne with the same number of carbons? The alkane contains four more hydrogens ($C_nH_{2n+2}$) than the alkyne ($C_nH_{2n-2}$). L2 P

**Naming Branched-Chain Alkenes**

Name the alkene shown.

$$CH_3CH=CHCHCH_2CHCH_3$$
$$\qquad\quad | \qquad\;\; |$$
$$\qquad\quad CH_3 \quad CH_3$$

**1.** **Analyze the Problem**

You are given a branched-chain alkene that contains one double bond and two alkyl groups. Follow the IUPAC rules to name the organic compound.

**2.** **Solve for the Unknown**

**a.** The longest continuous carbon chain that includes the double bond contains seven carbons. The 7-carbon alkane is heptane, but the name is changed to hept*ene* because a double bond is present.

$$CH_3CH=CHCHCH_2CHCH_3$$   *Heptene* parent chain
$$\qquad\quad | \qquad\;\; |$$
$$\qquad\quad CH_3 \quad CH_3$$

**b.** Number the chain to give the lowest number to the double bond.

$$\overset{1}{C}H_3\overset{2}{C}H=\overset{3}{C}H\overset{4}{C}H\overset{5}{C}H_2\overset{6}{C}H\overset{7}{C}H_3$$   *2-Heptene* parent chain
$$\qquad\qquad\;\; | \qquad\quad |$$
$$\qquad\qquad CH_3 \quad\; CH_3$$

**c.** Name each substituent.

$$\overset{1}{C}H_3\overset{2}{C}H=\overset{3}{C}H\overset{4}{C}H\overset{5}{C}H_2\overset{6}{C}H\overset{7}{C}H_3$$   *2-Heptene* parent chain
$$\qquad\qquad\;\; | \qquad\quad |$$
$$\qquad\qquad CH_3 \quad\; CH_3$$
$$\qquad\qquad\;\uparrow \qquad\quad\uparrow$$

Two methyl groups

**d.** Determine how many of each substituent is present, and assign the correct prefix to represent that number. Then, include the position numbers to get the complete prefix.

$$\overset{1}{C}H_3\overset{2}{C}H=\overset{3}{C}H\overset{4}{C}H\overset{5}{C}H_2\overset{6}{C}H\overset{7}{C}H_3$$   *2-Heptene* parent chain
$$\qquad\qquad\;\; | \qquad\quad |$$
$$\qquad\qquad CH_3 \quad\; CH_3$$

Two methyl groups at positions 4 and 6
Prefix is *4,6-dimethyl*

**e.** The names of substituents do not have to be alphabetized because they are the same.

**f.** Apply the complete prefix to the name of the parent alkene chain. Use commas to separate numbers and hyphens between numbers and words. Write the name *4,6-dimethyl-2-heptene.*

**3.** **Evaluate the Answer**

The longest carbon chain includes the double bond, and the position of the double bond has the lowest possible number. Correct prefixes and alkyl-group names designate the branches.

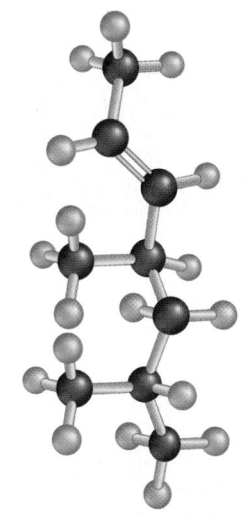

This is a ball-and-stick model of the structure in Example Problem 22-3.

## Using Science Terms

Have students write statements explaining the meaning of the terms *alkene* and *alkyne.*

## Concept Development

Be sure students realize that the general formulas for alkenes and alkynes apply to those with only one unsaturated bond. They also do not apply to cyclic alkenes and alkynes.

### ✓ Assessment

**Skill** Have students determine what additional information is needed to solve the following problem.

Alkenes can be converted into alkanes using a chemical reaction called hydrogenation in which hydrogen gas is bubbled through a solution of an alkene in the presence of a catalyst. How many moles of hydrogen gas must be added to one mole of an alkene with more than one double bond to convert it completely to an alkane? The additional information needed is the number of double bonds present in the alkene. Each double bond requires one mole of hydrogen gas per mole of alkene for the conversion. **L2**

---

### **DIFFERENTIATED INSTRUCTION**

#### Learning Disabled

**Kinesthetic** Some students will be able to understand the differences between alkanes, alkenes, and alkynes better if they can compare them using models. Ask students to make models of ethane, ethene, and ethyne. Then, ask them to list similarities and differences that are apparent from the models alone. They should also discover that the two carbon atoms in ethene cannot easily rotate with respect to each other, while those in ethane can. The carbons cannot rotate in ethyne either, but this characteristic is relatively unimportant in alkynes. **L1** **ELL**

**National Science Content Standards**
Pages 712–713
UCP.2, UCP.5; A.1; B.2

## In-Text Question

**Page 714** What are the molecular formulas for 5-carbon and 8-carbon alkynes? $C_5H_8$ and $C_8H_{14}$

## Content Background

### Preparation of Acetylene

Ethyne, or acetylene, was first described by the French chemist P. E. M. Berthelot in 1862, and it was first prepared on a large scale in the 1890s. First, limestone ($CaCO_3$) is heated to make quicklime, which is mostly calcium oxide (CaO).

$CaCO_3 \rightarrow CaO + CO_2$

The calcium oxide is then heated in a furnace with carbon in the form of coke, a material obtained by heating coal in the absence of oxygen. A by-product is carbon monoxide.

$CaO + 3C \rightarrow CaC_2 + CO$

The calcium carbide then reacts with water to form acetylene.

$CaC_2 + 2H_2O \rightarrow C_2H_2 + Ca(OH)_2$

Today, much acetylene is produced by the partial oxidation of methane.

$6CH_4 + O_2 \rightarrow 2C_2H_2 + 2CO + 10H_2$

## GLENCOE TECHNOLOGY

**CD-ROM**
**Chemistry: Matter and Change**
Demonstration: *Properties of Ethyne*

**714**

---

**Practice!** For more practice with naming alkenes go to **Supplemental Practice Problems** in Appendix A.

**Figure 22-8**

In large-scale operations, tomatoes are harvested when they are mostly green. The fruit is ripened by exposing it to ethene gas during shipment to markets.

---

## PRACTICE PROBLEMS

**18.** Use IUPAC rules to name the following structures.

  **a.** $CH_3CH=CHCHCH_3$
           $\quad\quad\quad\quad\quad\quad |$
           $\quad\quad\quad\quad\quad\quad CH_3$

  **b.**
$$
\begin{array}{l}
\quad\quad\quad CH_3 \\
\quad\quad\quad | \\
\quad\quad\quad CH_2 \quad\quad\quad\quad CH_3 \\
\quad\quad\quad | \quad\quad\quad\quad\quad\quad\quad | \\
CH_3CHCH_2CH=CHCCH_3 \\
\quad\quad\quad\quad\quad\quad\quad\quad\quad\quad\quad | \\
\quad\quad\quad\quad\quad\quad\quad\quad\quad\quad\quad CH_3
\end{array}
$$

**19.** Draw the structure of 1,3-pentadiene.

---

**Properties and uses of alkenes** Like alkanes, alkenes are nonpolar and therefore have low solubility in water as well as relatively low melting and boiling points. However, alkenes are more reactive than alkanes because the second covalent bond increases the electron density between two carbon atoms, providing a good site for chemical reactivity. Reactants that attract electrons can pull the electrons away from the double bond.

Several alkenes occur naturally in living organisms. For example, ethene (ethylene) is produced naturally by plants as a hormone. It causes fruit to ripen, and plays a part in causing leaves to fall from deciduous trees in preparation for winter. The tomatoes shown in **Figure 22-8** and other grocery store fruit can be ripened artificially by introducing ethene. Ethene also is the starting material for the synthesis of the plastic polyethylene, which is used to manufacture many products, including plastic bags and milk jugs. Natural rubber is another polymerized alkene. Other alkenes are responsible for the scents of lemons, limes, and pine trees.

## Alkynes

Unsaturated hydrocarbons that contain one or more triple bonds between carbon atoms in a chain are called **alkynes**. Triple bonds involve the sharing of three pairs of electrons. The simplest and most commonly used alkyne is ethyne ($C_2H_2$), which is widely known by its common name *acetylene*. Study the models of ethyne in the following diagram.

$$H-C\equiv C-H$$

Models of ethyne (acetylene)

**Naming alkynes** Straight-chain alkynes and branched-chain alkynes are named in the same way as alkenes. The only difference is that the name of the parent chain ends in *-yne* rather than *-ene*. Study the examples in **Table 22-5**. Alkynes with one triple covalent bond form a homologous series with the general formula $C_nH_{2n-2}$. What are the molecular formulas for 5-carbon and 8-carbon alkynes?

---

## CHEMISTRY JOURNAL

### A Natural Alkyne

**Linguistic** While alkenes occur quite often in nature, alkynes are much harder to find. One naturally occurring alkyne is the compound dynemycin A, a complex polycyclic structure with two carbon-carbon triple bonds. It has been tested as a potential anticancer agent. Ask students to research the structure and natural source of dynemycin A and record their findings in their chemistry journals. **L3**

**Table 22-5**

| | | | Examples of Alkynes | | |
|---|---|---|---|---|---|
| Name | Molecular formula | Structural formula | Condensed structural formula | Melting point (°C) | Boiling point (°C) |
| Ethyne | $C_2H_2$ | H—C≡C—H | CH≡CH | −81 | Sublimes at −85°C |
| Propyne | $C_3H_4$ | H—C≡C—C—H (with H atoms above, below, and right on carbon) | $CH_3C≡CH$ | −103 | −23 |
| 1-Butyne | $C_4H_6$ | H—C≡C—C—C—H (with H atoms on the two right carbons) | $CH≡CCH_2CH_3$ | −126 | 8 |
| 2-Butyne | $C_4H_6$ | H—C—C≡C—C—H (with H atoms on the two outer carbons) | $CH_3C≡CCH_3$ | −32 | 27 |

The reactivities of alkynes make them useful starting materials in many synthesis reactions. In the **miniLAB** below, you will generate ethyne and investigate some of its properties.

# miniLAB

## Synthesis and Reactivity of Ethyne

**Observing and Inferring** Ethyne, often called *acetylene*, is used as a fuel in welding torches. In this lab, you will generate ethyne from the reaction of calcium carbide with water.

**Materials** 150-mL beaker, stirring rod, liquid dishwashing detergent, calcium carbide, forceps, wood splints, matches, ruler about 40 cm long, rubber band, phenolphthalein solution

**Procedure**

1. Use a rubber band to attach a wood splint to one end of the ruler so that about 10 cm of the splint extends beyond the stick.
2. Place 120 mL water in the beaker and add 5 mL dishwashing detergent. Mix thoroughly.
3. Use forceps to pick up a pea-sized lump of calcium carbide ($CaC_2$). Do not touch the $CaC_2$ with your fingers. **CAUTION:** *If $CaC_2$ dust touches your skin, wash it away immediately with a lot of water.* Place the lump of $CaC_2$ in the beaker of detergent solution.

4. Use a match to light the splint while holding the ruler at the opposite end. Immediately bring the burning splint to the bubbles that have formed from the reaction in the beaker. Extinguish the splint after observing the reaction.
5. Use the stirring rod to dislodge a few large bubbles of ethyne and determine whether they float upward or sink in air.
6. Rinse the beaker thoroughly, then add 25 mL distilled water and a drop of phenolphthalein solution. Use forceps to place a small piece of $CaC_2$ in the solution. Observe the results.

**Analysis**

1. Describe your observations in steps 3 and 4. Could ethyne be used as a fuel?
2. Based on your observations in step 5, what can you infer about the density of ethyne compared to the density of air?
3. The reaction of calcium carbide with water yields two products. One is ethyne gas ($C_2H_2$). From your observation in step 6, suggest what the other product is, and write a balanced chemical equation for the reaction.

## Resource Manager

**ChemLab and MiniLab Worksheets,** p. 85 **L2**
**Challenge Problems,** p. 22 **L3**

students should realize that a base is produced. Given that the cation present is $Ca^{2+}$, they may infer that the insoluble material is $Ca(OH)_2$.
$$CaC_2 + 2H_2O → C_2H_2 + Ca(OH)_2$$

### ✔ Assessment

**Portfolio** Have students research why calcium carbide is sometimes called miners' lamp. Have them describe their findings in their portfolios. **L2** **P**

# miniLAB

**Purpose**
Students will synthesize ethyne and observe a few of its properties.

**Process Skills**
Observing and inferring, communicating, applying concepts

**Safety Precautions**
Caution students not to lean over the beaker when lighting the bubbles. Long hair should be tied back. The somewhat caustic $Ca(OH)_2$ produced when $CaC_2$ reacts with moisture is the main reason for avoiding skin and eye contact.

**Disposal**
Flush the soapy reaction solution down the drain with plenty of water. Allow any $CaC_2$ that has become moist to react completely with water before flushing the solution.

**Teaching Strategies**
- Dowels or long, fireplace matches can be used rather than rulers. Be sure students extinguish the splints before they burn the ruler.
- The bubbles will be relatively pure ethyne, so they should not burn explosively when ignited as they would if they contained an air-ethyne mixture.
- See page 696C for preparation of solutions.

**Expected Results**
When ignited, the ethyne should pop and burn in an yellow-orange ball that rises from the beaker. Soot may be deposited on the sides of the beaker as a result of incomplete combustion. Ethyne, having a molar mass of 26 g/mol, is slightly less dense than air, which has an average molar mass of about 29. Bubbles may float upward slowly but should demonstrate nearly neutral buoyancy. The phenolphthalein should turn pink as $Ca(OH)_2$ is formed.

**Analysis**
1. Bubbles form and rise to the surface as the $CaC_2$ reacts. The bubbles ignite, producing heat, light, and soot. Ethyne is a fuel because it burns.
2. Density is slightly less than air.
3. From the color change,

## 3 Assess

### Check for Understanding

Quiz students to see if they can name straight-chain and branched alkenes using models.

### Reteach

*Kinesthetic* Let students work in groups to build models of branched alkenes. Ask groups to name their model and then exchange models with another group to try to name that model as well. **L2** **ELL** **COOP LEARN**

### Extension

*Kinesthetic* Have students construct models of ethene and describe the geometry and shape of the molecule. They should establish that it is a flat molecule. Next, have them add methyl groups to both ends of the molecule to produce a molecule of 2-butene. Students should again describe the geometry. Some will discover that two different conformations exist. **L2** **ELL**

### ✓ Assessment

**Performance** Ask students to design and set up an apparatus they can use to collect and measure the volume of ethene gas produced by ripening fruit. Student designs will vary. However, it is easiest to collect and measure the volume of a gas by water displacement. In one method, the fruit could be placed in a zipper-type plastic bag. Just before closing the zipper completely, all possible gas is squeezed out of the bag. The bag is then submerged in water and the amount of water displaced is measured. After a significant amount of gas has collected in the bag, the procedure is repeated and the difference in water displacements will be approximately the volume of gas collected. The gas, however, may not be entirely ethene. Use the Performance Task Assessment List for Invention in **PASC**, p. 45. **L2**

**716**

**Figure 22-9**

**ⓐ** An alkyne you may already be familiar with is ethyne, commonly called acetylene, used to produce an extremely hot flame needed for welding metals.
**ⓑ** Early automobiles burned acetylene in their headlamps to light the road ahead. Drivers had to get out to light the headlights with a match.

**Properties of alkynes** Alkynes have physical and chemical properties similar to those of the alkenes. Many of the reactions alkenes undergo, alkynes undergo as well. However, alkynes generally are more reactive than alkenes because the triple bond of alkynes has even greater electron density than the double bond of alkenes. This cluster of electrons is effective at inducing dipoles in nearby molecules, causing them to become unevenly charged and thus reactive.

Ethyne is a by-product of oil refining and also is made in industrial quantities by the reaction of calcium carbide, $CaC_2$, with water. You learned about the production of ethyne by this method when you did the **miniLAB** on the previous page. When supplied with enough oxygen, ethyne burns with an intensely hot flame that can reach temperatures as high as 3000°C. Acetylene torches are commonly used in welding, as you see in **Figure 22-9**. Because the triple bond makes alkynes reactive, ethyne is used as a starting material in the manufacture of plastics and other organic chemicals used in industry.

## Section 22.3 Assessment

**20.** In what major way do the chemical properties of alkenes and alkynes differ from those of alkanes? What is responsible for this difference?

**21.** Name the structures shown using IUPAC rules.

a.
$$CH \equiv CCH_2$$
with $CH_3$ group above the right carbon

b.
$$CH_3CHCH = CHCH_2CH_3$$
with $CH_2CH_3$ group above

c.
$$CH_3C = CHCH = CH_2$$
with $CH_3$ group above

d.

$$C = C$$
with $CH_3$, $CH_3$ above and $CH_3$, $CH_3$ below

**22. Thinking Critically** Speculate on how the boiling and freezing points of alkynes compare with those of alkanes with the same number of carbon atoms. Explain your reasoning, then look up data to see if it supports your idea.

**23. Making Predictions** A carbon atom in an alkane is bonded to four other atoms. In an alkene, a carbon in a double bond is bonded to three other atoms, and in an alkyne, a carbon in a triple bond is bonded to two other atoms. What geometric arrangement would you predict for the bonds surrounding the carbon atom in each of these cases? (Hint:) VSEPR theory can be used to predict shape.

**716** Chapter 22 Hydrocarbons

chemistrymc.com/self_check_quiz

## Section 22.3 Assessment

**20.** Alkenes and alkynes are much more reactive than alkanes. This is because they have regions of concentrated electron density that attract reactants of opposite charge.

**21. a.** 1-butyne
**b.** 5-methyl-3-heptene
**c.** 4-methyl-1,3-pentadiene
**d.** 2,3-dimethyl-2-butene

**22.** Because alkynes are slightly more polar, they generally have higher melting and boiling points than alkanes. Data support this hypothesis.

**23.** VSEPR theory predicts the following geometric bond arrangements. alkane: tetrahedral shape; alkene: trigonal planar shape; alkyne: linear shape

Study the structural formulas in the following diagram. How many different organic compounds are represented by these structures?

$$C-C-\underset{\underset{}{\overset{\overset{C}{|}}{C}}}{C}-C \qquad C-\underset{\underset{}{\overset{\overset{C}{|}}{C}}}{C}-C-C \qquad C-C-\underset{\underset{}{\overset{}{\underset{C}{|}}}{C}}{C}-C \qquad \underset{\underset{C}{\underset{|}{\overset{\overset{C}{|}}{C}}}}{C}-C$$

If you said that all of these structures represent the same compound, you are correct. The diagram simply shows four ways of drawing a structural formula for 2-methylbutane. As you can see, the structural formula for a given hydrocarbon can be written in several ways. Before you continue reading, make sure that you understand why these structural formulas are all alike. You'll soon learn, however, that three distinctly different alkanes have the molecular formula $C_5H_{12}$.

## Structural Isomers

Now, examine the models of three alkanes in **Figure 22-10** to determine how they are similar and how they differ.

All three have five carbon atoms and 12 hydrogen atoms, so they have the molecular formula $C_5H_{12}$. However, as you can see, these models represent three different arrangements of atoms, pentane, 2-methylbutane, and 2,2-dimethylpropane. These three compounds are isomers. **Isomers** are two or more compounds that have the same molecular formula but different molecular structures. Note that cyclopentane and pentane are not isomers because cyclopentane's molecular formula is $C_5H_{10}$.

There are two main classes of isomers. **Figure 22-10** shows compounds that are examples of structural isomers. The atoms of **structural isomers** are bonded in different orders. The members of a group of structural isomers have different chemical and physical properties despite having the same formula. This observation supports one of the main principles of chemistry: The structure of a substance determines its properties. How does the trend in boiling points of $C_5H_{12}$ isomers relate to their molecular structures?

As the number of carbons in a hydrocarbon increases, the number of possible structural isomers increases. For example, nine alkanes having the molecular formula $C_7H_{16}$ exist. $C_{20}H_{42}$ has 316 319 structural isomers.

### Objectives

- **Distinguish** between the two main categories of isomers, structural isomers and stereoisomers.
- **Differentiate** between *cis-* and *trans-* geometric isomers.
- **Recognize** different structural isomers given a structural formula.
- **Describe** the structural variation in molecules that results in optical isomers.

### Vocabulary

isomer
structural isomer
stereoisomer
geometric isomer
chirality
asymmetric carbon
optical isomer
polarized light
optical rotation

### Figure 22-10

There are three different compounds that have the molecular formula $C_5H_{12}$. They are structural isomers. Note how their boiling points differ. Draw structural formulas for these three isomers.

Pentane
bp = 36°C

2-Methylbutane
bp = 28°C

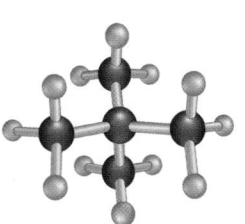

2,2-Dimethylpropane
bp = 9°C

22.4 Isomers    **717**

## 1 Focus

### Focus Transparency

Before presenting the lesson, display **Section Focus Transparency 84** on the overhead projector. Have students answer the accompanying questions using **Section Focus Transparency Master 84**. **L1** **ELL**

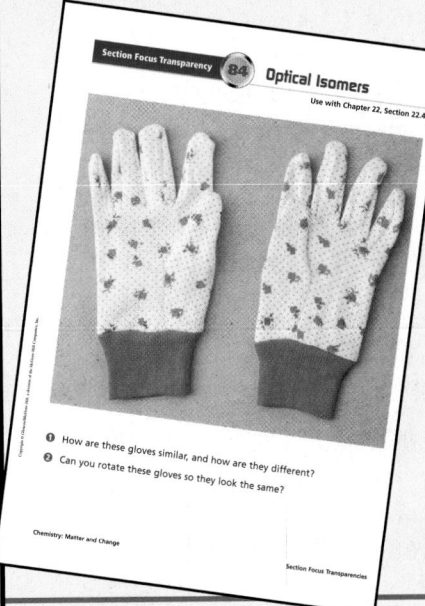

Section Focus Transparency 84  Optical Isomers
Use with Chapter 22, Section 22.4

❶ How are these gloves similar, and how are they different?
❷ Can you rotate these gloves so they look the same?

Chemistry: Matter and Change

Section Focus Transparencies

## 2 Teach

### In-Text Question

**Page 717**  How does the trend in boiling points of $C_5H_{12}$ isomers relate to their molecular structures? Students may conclude that boiling point increases as the molecule becomes less branched and more linear.

### Figure Caption Question

**Figure 22-10**  Draw structural formulas for these three isomers. See the Solutions Manual for structures.

### National Science Content Standards

Pages 716–717
UCP.2, UCP.5; B.2, B.3

### DIFFERENTIATED INSTRUCTION

**Gifted**

*Visual-Spatial*  Ask capable students to draw all the structural isomers of the hydrocarbon with the formula $C_7H_{16}$. There are nine structural isomers: heptane, 2-methylhexane, 3-methylhexane, 2,3-dimethylpentane, 2,4-dimethylpentane, 2,2-dimethylpentane, 3,3-dimethylpentane, 3-ethylpentane, and 2,2,3-trimethylbutane. **L3**

**Figure 22-11** How do you think this difference in ability to rotate would affect atoms or groups of atoms bonded to single-bonded and double-bonded carbon atoms? Groups or atoms attached to singly-bonded carbon atoms are not fixed in space—they rotate along with the carbon atoms. Groups or atoms attached to doubly-bonded carbon atoms are fixed in space with respect to each other because the double bond prevents the carbon atoms from rotating.

## Building a Model

 **Kinesthetic** Ask each group of 2 to 3 students to build models of *cis*- and *trans*-2-butene. Collect all the models and use them to demonstrate how the difference in ability for molecules to pack closely together affects their properties.
**L2** **ELL**

## ✓ Assessment

**Knowledge** Ask students to distinguish between the terms isotopes and isomers. Isotopes are elements with the same atomic number but different mass numbers; isomers are compounds with the same molecular formula but different structures.
**L2** **ELL**

## GLENCOE TECHNOLOGY

**CD-ROM**
**Chemistry: Matter and Change**
Animation: *Isomers*

---

**Figure 22-11**

The single-bonded carbons in ethane are free to rotate about the bond. The double-bonded carbons in ethene resist being rotated. How do you think this difference in ability to rotate would affect atoms or groups of atoms bonded to single-bonded and double-bonded carbon atoms?

Single covalent bond    Double covalent bond

Carbons free to rotate    Carbons fixed in position
No rotation possible

Ethane    Ethene

## Stereoisomers

The second class of isomers involves a more subtle difference in bonding. **Stereoisomers** are isomers in which all atoms are bonded in the same order but are arranged differently in space. There are two types of stereoisomers. One type occurs in alkenes, which contain double bonds. Two carbon atoms with a single bond between them can rotate freely in relationship to each other. However, when a second covalent bond is present, the carbons can no longer rotate; they are locked in place, as shown in **Figure 22-11**.

To understand the consequences of this inability to rotate, compare the two possible structures of 2-butene shown in **Figure 22-12**. The arrangement in which the two methyl groups are on the same side of the molecule is indicated by the prefix *cis*-. The arrangement in which the two methyl groups are on opposite sides of the molecule is indicated by the prefix *trans*-. These terms derive from Latin: *cis* means *on the same side*, and *trans* means *across from*. Because the double-bonded carbons cannot rotate, the *cis*- form cannot easily change into the *trans*- form.

Isomers resulting from different arrangements of groups around a double bond are called **geometric isomers**. Note how the difference in geometry affects the isomers' physical properties such as melting point and boiling point. Geometric isomers differ in some chemical properties as well. If the compound is biologically active, such as a drug, the *cis*- and *trans*- isomers usually have greatly different effects. You may have read about the possible health concerns associated with *trans*- fatty acids in the diet. The *cis*- forms of the same acids seem not to be as harmful.

**Figure 22-12**

These isomers of 2-butene differ in the arrangement in space of the two methyl groups at the ends. The double-bonded carbon atoms cannot rotate with respect to each other, so the methyl groups must be in one of these two arrangements.

*cis*-2-Butene ($C_4H_8$)
mp = −139°C
bp = 3.7°C

*trans*-2-Butene ($C_4H_8$)
mp = −106°C
bp = 0.8°C

---

## Internet Address Book

**Chemistry Online**    Note Internet addresses that you find useful in the space below for quick reference.

_____

_____

_____

_____

_____

## Chirality

In 1848, the young French chemist Louis Pasteur (1822–1895) reported his discovery that crystals of the organic compound tartaric acid, which is a by-product of the fermentation of grape juice to make wine, existed in two shapes that were not the same, but were mirror images of each other. Because a person's hands are like mirror images, as shown in **Figure 22-13a**, the crystals were called the right-handed and left-handed forms. The two forms of tartaric acid had the same chemical properties, melting point, density, and solubility in water, but only the left-handed form was produced by fermentation. In addition, bacteria were able to multiply when they were fed the left-handed form as a nutrient, but could not use the right-handed form.

Pasteur concluded that the two crystalline forms of tartaric acid exist because the tartaric acid molecules themselves exist in two arrangements, as shown in **Figure 22-13b**. Today, these two forms are called D-tartaric acid and L-tartaric acid. The letters D and L stand for the Latin prefixes *dextro-*, which means *to the right*, and *levo-*, which means *to the left*. Since Pasteur's time, chemists have discovered thousands of compounds that exist in right and left forms. This property is called **chirality**, a word derived from the Latin prefix *chiro-* for hand. Many of the substances found in living organisms, such as the amino acids that make up proteins, have this property. In general, living organisms make use of only one chiral form of a substance because only this form fits the active site of an enzyme.

## Optical Isomers

In the 1860s, chemists realized that chirality occurs whenever a compound contains an asymmetric carbon. An **asymmetric carbon** is a carbon atom that has four different atoms or groups of atoms attached to it. The four groups always can be arranged in two different ways. Suppose that groups W, X, Y, and Z are attached to the same carbon atom in the two arrangements shown on the next page. Note that the structures differ in that groups X and Y have

### Figure 22-13

**a** Molecules of D-tartaric acid and L-tartaric acid are related to each other in the same way that your right hand and left hand are related. A mirror image of your right hand appears the same as your left hand.

**b** These models represent the two forms of tartaric acid that Pasteur studied. If the model of D-tartaric acid (right) is reflected in a mirror, its image is a model of L-tartaric acid.

**b**  L-Tartaric acid     D-Tartaric acid

**719**

## problem-solving LAB

**Purpose**
Students will use what they've learned in this section to identify types of isomers.

**Process Skills**
Interpreting scientific illustrations, applying concepts, formulating models

**Teaching Strategies**
• Students will study halogen substituted organic substances in the next chapter. They were used here to provide simpler examples than would be possible with hydrocarbons alone.
• Students who have trouble distinguishing among these structures should build physical models, following the illustrations very carefully.

**Thinking Critically**
In structure 1, the hydrogen atoms attached to the doubly-bonded carbons are in the *trans* orientation; however, they are in the *cis* orientation in structure 2. Therefore, the compounds are geometric isomers.

The compounds represented by structures 1 and 3 are optical isomers.

In structure 1, a fluorine atom is bonded to the first carbon; in structure 4, the fluorine atom is bonded to the second carbon. Therefore, the compounds are structural isomers.

### ✔ Assessment

**Performance** Have students make and compare ball-and-stick models of *cis*-2- pentene and *trans*-2-pentene. Use the Performance Task List for Model in **PASC**, p. 51. **L2**

---

**In-Text Question**

**Page 721** What do you think happens to polarized light when it passes through a 50:50 mixture of the D-form and L-form of a chiral substance? Students should infer that the plane of the polarized light does not rotate because the two effects cancel.

---

been exchanged. You cannot rotate the two arrangements in any way that will make them identical to each other.

Now suppose that you build models of these two structures. Is there any way you could turn one structure so that it looks the same as the other? (Whether letters appear forward or backward does not matter.) You would discover that there is no way to accomplish the task without removing X and Y from the carbon atom and switching their positions. So, the molecules are different even though they look very much alike.

Isomers that result from different arrangements of four different groups about the same carbon atom represent another class of stereoisomers called **optical isomers**. Optical isomers have the same physical and chemical properties except in chemical reactions where chirality is important, such as enzyme-catalyzed reactions in biological systems. Human cells, for example, incorporate only L-amino acids into proteins. Only the L-form of ascorbic acid is active as Vitamin C. The chirality of a drug molecule can greatly affect its activity. For example, only the L-form of the drug methyldopa is effective in reducing high blood pressure.

Now try your hand at distinguishing among types of isomers in the **problem-solving LAB**.

**Optical rotation** Mirror-image isomers are called optical isomers because they affect light passing through them. Recall that light is a form of electromagnetic radiation—transverse waves that can travel through empty space. Normally, the light waves in a beam from the sun or a lightbulb move in all possible planes, as shown in **Figure 22-14**. However, light can be filtered or reflected in such a way that the resulting waves all lie in the same plane. This type of light is called **polarized light**.

## problem-solving LAB

### Identifying Structural, Geometric, and Optical Isomers

**Interpreting Scientific Illustrations**
Identifying isomers requires skill in visualizing a molecule in three dimensions. Building models of molecules helps clarify their geometry.

**Analysis**
**Structure 1** represents an organic molecule.
**Structures 2, 3,** and **4** represent three different isomers of the first molecule. Study each of these three structures to determine how they are related to **Structure 1**.

**Thinking Critically**
Write a sentence for each isomer describing how

it differs from **Structure 1.** Which kind of isomer does each structure represent?

Structure 1          Structure 2

Structure 3          Structure 4

---

### ✔ Portfolio

**Stereochemistry and Odor Recognition**

*Linguistic* Ask interested students to research the importance of molecular shape, particularly that caused by differences in stereochemistry, on human olfactory sensation. They should write a report on this topic to include in their portfolios. **L2** **P**

### CHEMISTRY JOURNAL

**Louis Pasteur**

*Linguistic* Have students investigate Louis Pasteur's many fields of investigation and write a brief synopsis of his work in their chemistry journals. **L2**

Light source

Polarizing filter

Sample cell

Angle of optical rotation

L-Alanine

Sample cell

D-Alanine

When polarized light passes through a solution containing an optical isomer, the plane of polarization is rotated to the right (clockwise, when looking toward the light source) by a D-isomer or to the left (counterclockwise) by an L-isomer. Rotation to the left is illustrated in the upper part of **Figure 22-14**. This effect is called **optical rotation**. What do you think happens to polarized light when it passes through a 50:50 mixture of the D-form and L-form of a chiral substance?

**Figure 22-14**

Polarized light can be produced by passing ordinary light through a filter that transmits light waves that lie in only one plane. Here, the filtered light waves are in a vertical plane before they pass through the sample cells.

## Section 22.4 Assessment

24. Explain the difference between structural isomers and stereoisomers.

25. Draw all of the structural isomers possible for the alkane with a molecular formula of $C_6H_{14}$. Show only the carbon chains.

26. Decide whether the carbon chains shown in each of the following pairs represent the same compound or pairs of isomers.

a. C—C—C—C        C—C—C—C
           |                          |
           C                          C

b.     C   C                          C
       |   |                          |
   C—C—C—C          C—C—C—C
       |                          |
       C                          C

c.         C                          C
           |                          |
   C—C—C—C—C     C—C—C—C—C—C—C
           |   |                  |
           C   C—C                C

d.
            CH₃          CH₃  CH₃
                              
    CH₃

27. Draw the structures of *cis*-3-hexene and *trans*-3-hexene.

28. **Thinking Critically** A certain reaction yields 80% *trans*-2-pentene and 20% *cis*-2-pentene. Draw the structures of these two geometric isomers, and develop a hypothesis to explain why the isomers form in the proportions cited.

29. **Formulating Models** Starting with a single carbon atom, draw two different optical isomers by attaching the following atoms or groups to the carbon: —H, —CH₃, —CH₂CH₃, —CH₂CH₂CH₃

chemistrymc.com/self_check_quiz

22.4 Isomers    **721**

**Visual-Spatial** Draw structures of the following pairs of molecules on the chalkboard; ask students to determine whether or not they each represent a pair of isomers and, if they do, what kind of isomers they are.

**a.** pentane and 2-methylbutane
    yes; structural isomers
**b.** *cis-* and *trans*-2-butene
    yes; geometric isomers
**c.** butane and cyclobutane
    no
**d.** cyclobutane and 1-butene
    yes; structural isomers

## Reteach

**Visual-Spatial** Ask students to draw and name an example of each of the following.
**a.** a pair of structural isomers
**b.** a pair of geometric isomers
**c.** a pair of optical isomers

### ✔ Assessment

**Skill** Give each group of two or three students a model of a simple chiral compound and ask them to build a model that represents the optical isomer of the compound they were given. **L2**
**ELL**

National Science Content Standards

Pages 720–721
UCP.2, UCP.5; B.2, B.6; E.2; F.1

## Section 22.4 Assessment

See the Solutions Manual for all structures in questions 25, 27, 28, and 29.

**24.** Structural isomers differ from each other in the order in which their atoms are bonded to each other, whereas stereoisomers have their atoms bonded in the same order but they are arranged differently in space.

**25.** Answers will include 5 structural isomers: hexane, 2-methylpentane, 3-methylpentane, 2,3-dimethylbutane, and 2,2-dimethylbutane.

**26. a.** same compound    **c.** isomers
       **b.** isomers    **d.** isomers

**27.** In *cis*-3-hexene, the hydrogen atoms attached to the doubly-bonded carbons are on the same side of the carbon chain. In the *trans* form, the hydrogen atoms are on opposite sides of the carbon chain.

**28.** More of the *trans* isomer forms because its structure allows the bulky methyl and ethyl groups to be farther apart than in the *cis* structure.

**29.** Structures should show the listed groups attached to a single carbon atom. They should differ in that two of the attached groups should be reversed in space.

# Aromatic Hydrocarbons and Petroleum

### Focus Transparency

Before presenting the lesson, display **Section Focus Transparency 85** on the overhead projector. Have students answer the accompanying questions using **Section Focus Transparency Master 85.** L1 ELL

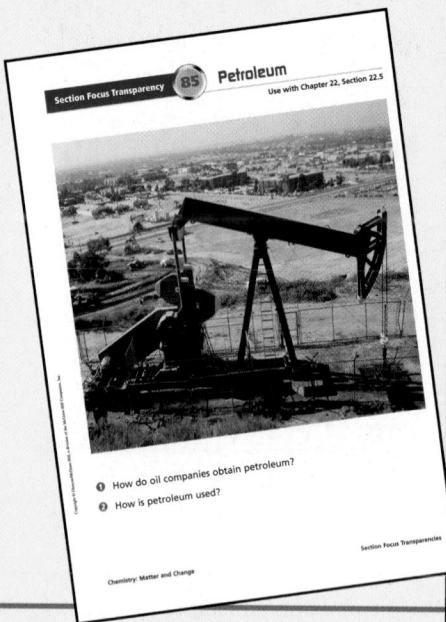

## 2 Teach

### In-Text Question

**Page 722** How does the molecular formula of this structure compare with that of benzene? Their molecular formulas are identical, $C_6H_6$.

## Objectives

• **Compare** and **contrast** the properties of aromatic and aliphatic hydrocarbons.

• **Explain** what a carcinogen is and list some examples.

• **Describe** the processes used to separate petroleum into fractions and to balance each fraction's output with market demands.

• **Identify** the fractions into which petroleum can be separated.

## Vocabulary

aromatic compound
aliphatic compound
fractional distillation
cracking

By the middle of the nineteenth century, chemists had a basic understanding of the structures of hydrocarbons with single, double, and triple covalent bonds. However, a fourth class of hydrocarbon compounds remained a mystery. The simplest example of this class of hydrocarbon is benzene, which the English physicist Michael Faraday (1791–1867) had first isolated in 1825 from the gases given off when either whale oil or coal was heated.

## The Structure of Benzene

Although chemists had determined that benzene's molecular formula was $C_6H_6$, it was hard for them to determine what sort of hydrocarbon structure would give such a formula. After all, the formula of the saturated hydrocarbon with six carbon atoms, hexane, was $C_6H_{14}$. Because the benzene molecule had so few hydrogen atoms, chemists reasoned that it must be unsaturated; that is, it must have several double or triple bonds, or a combination of both. They proposed many different structures, including this one suggested in 1860.

$$CH_2=C=CH-CH=C=CH_2$$

Although this structure has a molecular formula of $C_6H_6$, such a hydrocarbon should be unstable and extremely reactive because of its many double bonds. However, benzene was fairly unreactive and, when it did react, it was not in the ways that alkenes and alkynes usually react. For that reason, chemists reasoned that structures such as the one shown above must be incorrect.

**Kekulé's dream** In 1865, the German chemist Friedrich August Kekulé (1829–1896) proposed a different kind of structure for benzene—a hexagon of carbon atoms with alternating single and double bonds. How does the molecular formula of this structure compare with that of benzene?

Kekulé claimed that benzene's structure came to him in a dream while he dozed in front of a fireplace in Ghent, Belgium. He said that he had dreamed of the Ouroboros, an ancient Egyptian emblem of a snake devouring its own tail, and that had made him think of a ring-shaped structure. The flat, hexagonal structure Kekulé proposed explained some of the properties of benzene, but it still could not explain benzene's lack of reactivity.

**A modern model of benzene** Since the time of Kekulé's proposal, research has confirmed that benzene's molecular structure is indeed hexagonal. However, an explanation of benzene's unreactivity had to wait until the 1930s when Linus Pauling proposed the theory of hybrid orbitals. When applied to benzene, this theory predicts that the pairs of electrons that form the second bond of each

---

## DIFFERENTIATED INSTRUCTION

### Learning Disabled

Students may understand the delocalization of electrons that takes place in benzene better if they model it themselves. Ask six students to form a human ring in which they first model 1,3,5-cyclohexatriene (Kekulé's original model of benzene) and then benzene. Remind students that each carbon (each person) has four valence electrons, and that two of the four are involved in bonds (sigma bonds) with adjacent carbon atoms. Another electron is in a bond (also a sigma bond) with a hydrogen atom. This leaves one electron per carbon atom. In the first model, three pairs of adjacent students each raise both arms and hold two tennis balls together, representing the electrons in three stationary bonds (pi bonds). In the second model, all six students pass the six tennis balls continuously around the ring. L1 ELL of benzene's double bonds are not localized between only two specific carbon atoms as they are in alkenes. Instead, the electron pairs are delocalized, which means they are shared among all six carbons in the ring. **Figure 22-15** shows that this delocalization makes the benzene molecule chemically stable because electrons shared by six carbon nuclei are harder to pull away than electrons held by only two nuclei. The six hydrogen atoms are usually not shown, but you should remember that they are there. In this representation, the circle in the middle of the hexagon symbolizes the cloud formed by the three pairs of electrons.

**Figure 22-15**

Benzene's bonding electrons spread evenly in a double-donut shape around the ring instead of remaining near individual atoms.

## Aromatic Compounds

Organic compounds that contain benzene rings as part of their structure are called **aromatic compounds**. The term *aromatic* was originally used because many of the benzene-related compounds known in the nineteenth century were found in pleasant-smelling oils that came from spices, fruits, and other plant parts. Hydrocarbons such as the alkanes, alkenes, and alkynes are called **aliphatic compounds** to distinguish them from aromatic compounds. The term *aliphatic* comes from the Greek word for fat, which is *aleiphatos*. Early chemists obtained aliphatic compounds by heating animal fats.

Structures of some aromatic compounds are shown in **Figure 22-16**. Note that naphthalene has a structure that looks like two benzene rings arranged side by side. Naphthalene is an example of a *fused ring system*, in which an organic compound has two or more cyclic structures with a common side. As in benzene, electrons in naphthalene are shared around all ten carbon atoms making up the double ring. Anthracene is another example of a fused ring system; it appears to be formed from three benzene rings.

**Figure 22-16**

Shown here are a few of the many aromatic organic compounds that have practical uses. The common names of these compounds are used more frequently than their formal names.

**ⓐ Naphthalene** is used in chemical manufacturing and in some kinds of moth repellent.

**ⓑ *p*-Xylene** is a starting material for the manufacture of polyester fabrics.

*p*-Xylene
(1,4-dimethylbenzene)

Anthracene

**ⓒ Anthracene** is important in the manufacture of richly colored dyes and pigments.

22.5 Aromatic Hydrocarbons and Petroleum     **723**

Show students structures or models of the following aromatic compounds that contain a benzene ring with one or more alkyl group substituents and ask them to name the structures. Review how to name substituted cycloalkanes first if a lot of time has passed since those were presented.

1. methylbenzene (toluene)
2. 1,2-dimethylbenzene (*o*-xylene)
3. 1,3-dimethylbenzne (*m*-xylene)
4. 1,4-dimethylbenzene (*p*-xylene)

Ask students to draw structures or make models of the following compounds.

1. ethylbenzene
2. isopropylbenzene
3. 1,4-diethylbenzene

## Applying Chemistry

There are three different isomers of dimethyl-benzene, and they are referred to as *o*-, *m*-, and *p*-xylene. The ortho, or *o*-xylene, has a formal name of 1,2-dimethylbenzene; the meta, or *m*-xylene, has a formal name of 1,3-dimethylbenzene; and the para, or *p*-xylene, has a formal name of 1,4-dimethylbenzene. Xylene is used as a solvent in the paint, printing, rubber, glue, and leather industries; it is used as a degreaser and cleaning agent; it is a constituent of motor and aviation fuels; and it is used in the manufacture of some perfumes and insect repellents. Its health effects include eye damage, depression of the central nervous system, and impaired kidney and liver function.

## ✓ Assessment

**Knowledge** Ask students to list uses for each of the following aromatic compounds.

**a.** *p*-xylene   polyester synthesis
**b.** naphthalene   moth repellents
**c.** anthracene   dye and pigment
                      synthesis

**National Science Content Standards**

**Pages 724–725**
UCP.2, UCP.5; B.2, B.6; F.1, F.3, F.5

**Figure 22-17**

**a** This is the structure of ben-zopyrene, produced when coal is burned for heat. It caused can-cer in British chimney sweeps.
**b** Signs like this one warn consumers of the carcinogens in gasoline.

**a**

Benzopyrene

**b**

**Substituted aromatic compounds** Like other hydrocarbons, aromatic compounds may have different groups attached to their carbon atoms. For example, methylbenzene, also known as toluene, consists of a methyl group attached to a benzene ring in place of one hydrogen atom. Whenever you see something attached to an aromatic ring system, remember that the hydrogen atom is no longer there.

Substituted benzene compounds are named in the same way cyclic al-kanes are. For example, ethylbenzene has a 2-carbon ethyl group attached, and 1,4-dimethylbenzene, also known as *para*-xylene, has methyl groups attached at positions 1 and 4.

Methylbenzene
(toluene)

Ethylbenzene

1,4-Dimethylbenzene
(*para*-xylene)

Just as with substituted cycloalkanes, substituted benzene rings are num-bered in a way that gives the lowest possible numbers for the substituents. In the following structure, numbering the ring as shown gives the numbers 1, 2, and 4 for the substituent positions. Because *ethyl* is lower in the alphabet than *methyl*, it is written first in the name 2-ethyl-1,4-dimethylbenzene.

2-Ethyl-1,4-dimethylbenzene

**Carcinogens** Many aromatic compounds, particularly benzene, toluene, and xylene, were once commonly used as industrial and laboratory solvents. However, tests have shown that the use of such compounds should be lim-ited because they may affect the health of people who are exposed to them regularly. Health risks linked to aromatic compounds include respiratory ail-ments, liver problems, and damage to the nervous system. Beyond these haz-ards, some aromatic compounds are carcinogens, which are substances that can cause cancer.

The first known carcinogen was an aromatic substance discovered around the turn of the twentieth century in chimney soot. Chimney sweeps in Great Britain were known to have abnor-mally high rates of cancer of the scrotum, and the cause was found to be the aromatic compound ben-zopyrene, shown in **Figure 22-17a**. This compound is a by-product of the burning of complex mixtures of organic substances, such as wood and coal. Some aromatic compounds found in gasoline are also known to be carcinogenic, as you can tell from warning labels on gasoline pumps, **Figure 22-17b**.

---

## Internet Address Book

Note Internet addresses that you find useful in the space below for quick reference.

_____

_____

_____

_____

# Natural Sources of Hydrocarbons

Today, benzene and other aromatic and aliphatic hydrocarbons are obtained from fossil fuels, which formed over millions of years from the remains of living things. The main source of these compounds is petroleum, a complex mixture of alkanes, some aromatic hydrocarbons, and organic compounds containing sulfur or nitrogen atoms.

Petroleum formed from the remains of microorganisms that lived in Earth's oceans millions of years ago. Over time, the remains formed thick layers of mudlike deposits on the ocean bottom. Heat from Earth's interior and the tremendous pressure of overlying sediments transformed this mud into oil-rich shale and natural gas. In certain kinds of geological formations, the petroleum ran out of the shale and collected in pools deep in Earth's crust. Natural gas, which formed at the same time and in the same way as petroleum, is usually found with petroleum deposits. Natural gas is composed primarily of methane, but it also has small amounts of alkanes having two to five carbon atoms.

**Fractional distillation** Petroleum is a complex mixture containing more than a thousand different compounds. For this reason, raw petroleum, sometimes called crude oil, has little practical use. Petroleum is much more useful to humans when it is separated into simpler components, called fractions. Separation is carried out by boiling the petroleum and collecting the fractions as they condense at different temperatures. This process is called **fractional distillation** or sometimes just *fractionation*. Fractional distillation of petroleum is done in a fractionating tower similar to the one shown in **Figure 22-18**.

The temperature inside the fractionating tower is controlled so that it remains near 400°C at the bottom where the petroleum is boiling and gradually decreases moving toward the top. The condensation temperatures (boiling points) of alkanes generally decrease as molecular mass decreases. Therefore, as the vapors travel up through the column, hydrocarbons with more carbon atoms condense closer to the bottom of the tower and are drawn off. Hydrocarbons with fewer carbon atoms remain in the vapor phase until they reach regions of cooler temperatures farther up the column. By tapping

**Figure 22-18**

This diagram of a fractionating tower shows that fractions with lower boiling points, such as gasoline and gaseous products, are drawn off in the cooler regions near the top of the tower. Oils and greases, having much higher boiling points, stay near the bottom of the tower and are drawn off there.

22.5 Aromatic Hydrocarbons and Petroleum **725**

---

## CULTURAL DIVERSITY

### Distillation of Perfumes in Ancient India

The knowledge of chemistry has been applied since ancient times in the distillation of perfumes and ointments in the Indus Valley region of Pakistan, India, and Afghanistan. Some etymology research suggests that the word *scent* is possibly derived from the Sanskrit term *sugandha*, which literally means "good or aromatic paste." Perfumes produced by distillation included sandalwood oil, musk tamarind, costus, macir, and camphor. These aromatic perfumes were sprinkled on kings during coronation ceremonies, and fragrant ointments based on sandalwood were applied during ceremonial bathing. Even today during some festivals like *Diwali*, the Hindu festival of lights symbolizing the victory of righteousness and the lifting of spiritual darkness, aromatic slurries and pastes that are prepared out of a powder called *sugandhi* play an important part in rituals.

Table 22-6

## 3 Assess

### Check for Understanding

Ask students to list the features that distinguish aromatic from unsaturated aliphatic organic compounds. Aromatic compounds are cyclic hydrocarbons that are more stable and less reactive than unsaturated aliphatic compounds because the unsaturation of aromatic compounds involves a set of delocalized electrons instead of discrete double bonds.

### Reteach

Draw Kekulé's structure of benzene and the modern model next to each other on the chalkboard. Ask students which structure is a better representation of the actual structure of benzene and why it is better. The modern model is a better model because it represents delocalized electrons that are shared among all six carbons in the ring. This model can be used to explain benzene's unusual stability better than the Kekulé structure.

## Earth Science
### CONNECTION

Throughout human history, people have collected petroleum to burn in lamps to provide light. They found petroleum seeping from cracks in rocks in certain locations. In fact, the word petroleum literally means "rock oil" and is derived from the Latin words for rock (*petra*) and oil (*oleum*). In the 19th century, as the U.S. entered the machine age and its population increased, the demand for petroleum to produce kerosene for lighting and as a machine lubricant also increased. Because there was no reliable petroleum supply, Edwin Drake drilled the first oil well in the United States near Titusville, Pennsylvania in 1859. The oil industry flourished for a time, but when Edison introduced the electric light in 1882, investors feared that the industry was doomed. However, the invention of the automobile in the 1890s soon revived the industry on a massive scale.

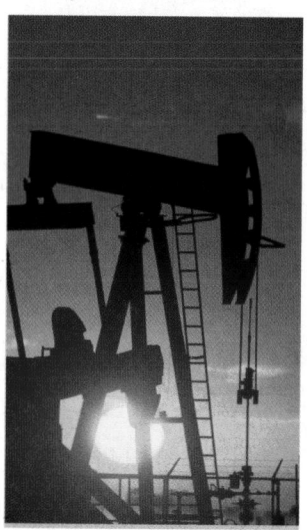

**Table 22-6**

| Petroleum Components Separated by Fractional Distillation | | | |
|---|---|---|---|
| Fraction | Sizes of hydrocarbons | Boiling range (°C) | Common uses |
| Gases | $CH_4$ to $C_4H_{10}$ | Below 40 | Fuel gas, raw material for plastics manufacture |
| Gasoline | $C_5H_{12}$ to $C_{12}H_{26}$ | 40–100 | Fuel, solvents |
| Kerosene | $C_{12}H_{26}$ to $C_{16}H_{34}$ | 105–275 | Home heating, jet fuel, diesel fuel |
| Heating oil | $C_{15}H_{32}$ to $C_{18}H_{38}$ | 240–300 | Industrial heating |
| Lubricating oil | $C_{17}H_{36}$ and up | Above 300 | Lubricants |
| Residue | $C_{20}H_{42}$ and up | Above 350 | Tar, asphalt, paraffin |

into the column at various heights, plant operators can collect the kinds of hydrocarbons they want.

Each group of components removed from the fractionating tower is called a fraction. **Table 22-6** is a list of the names given to the typical fractions separated from petroleum along with their boiling points, hydrocarbon size ranges, and common uses. Unfortunately, fractional distillation of petroleum does not yield these fractions in the same proportions that they are needed. For example, distillation seldom yields enough gasoline, yet it yields more of the heavier oils than the market demands.

Many years ago, petroleum chemists and engineers developed a process to help match the supply with the demand. This process in which heavier fractions are converted to gasoline by breaking their large molecules into smaller molecules is called **cracking**. Cracking is done in the absence of oxygen and in the presence of a catalyst. In addition to breaking heavier hydrocarbons into molecules of the size range needed for gasoline, cracking also produces starting materials for the synthesis of many different organic products.

### Rating Gasolines

None of the petroleum fractions are pure substances. As you can see in **Table 22-6**, gasoline is not a pure substance but rather a mixture of hydrocarbons. Most alkane molecules in gasoline have 5 to 12 carbon atoms. However, the gasoline you put into your car today is different from the gasoline your great-grandparents put in their Model T in 1920. The gasoline fraction that is distilled from petroleum is modified by adjusting its composition and adding substances in order to improve its performance in today's automobile engines and to reduce pollution from car exhaust.

It is critical that the gasoline-air mixture in the cylinder of an automobile engine ignite at exactly the right instant and burn evenly. If it ignites too early or too late, much energy is wasted, fuel efficiency drops, and engines wear out prematurely. Most straight-chain hydrocarbons burn unevenly and tend to ignite from heat and pressure before the piston is in the proper position and the spark plug fires. This early ignition causes a rattling or pinging noise called *knocking*. Branched-chain alkanes, as well as alkenes and cyclic alkanes burn more evenly than alkanes with straight chains. Even burning helps prevent engine knocking.

**National Science Content Standards**

Pages 726–729
UCP.2, UCP.5; A.1, A.2; B.2, B.6; E.2; F.3, F.6

## CHEMISTRY JOURNAL

### Oil Refining

*Linguistic* Ask students to locate the oil refinery nearest their home. They should call, write, or e-mail the refinery to get information about what products are produced at the company and how many barrels of crude oil the company refines per month. They should include a synopsis of their findings in their chemistry journals. **L2**

### Variety in Gasoline

Ask students to record in their chemistry journals the price of the least expensive unleaded gasoline at the same gas station for two weeks. Also ask them to record any information they find printed on the gas pump about that gasoline's composition. They should record its octane number and whether it contains any oxygenated additives. **L2**

**Figure 22-19**

Gas stations provide a range of choices in octane ratings. Many cars manufactured today require mid-grade gasoline. However, cars with high-compression engines may need fuel with a higher octane rating.

**Octane ratings** In the late 1920s, an octane rating system for gasoline was established, resulting in the octane ratings posted on gasoline pumps like those shown in **Figure 22-19**. Mid-grade gasoline today has a rating of about 89, whereas premium gasolines have higher ratings of up to about 97. Several factors determine which octane rating a car needs, including how much the piston compresses the air-fuel mixture and the altitude at which the car is driven.

What do these ratings mean? You may be surprised to learn that they have almost nothing to do with the 8-carbon, straight-chain alkane called octane. They were first established by assigning a rating of zero to heptane, which was known to cause severe knocking, and a rating of 100 to 2,2,4-trimethylpentane, the compound that had the best anti-knock properties when tests were first performed. The compound 2,2,4-trimethylpentane was commonly called isooctane and erroneously called "octane" by technicians who tested gasoline.

$$\begin{array}{c} \quad\quad\;\; C \\ \quad\quad\;\; | \\ C - C - C - C - C \\ \quad\;\; | \quad\quad\;\; | \\ \quad\;\; C \quad\quad\;\; C \end{array}$$  2,2,4-Trimethylpentane (isooctane, erroneously called "octane")

A gasoline with a rating of 90 performs about the same as a mixture of 90% isooctane and 10% heptane. Today, compounds can be added to gasoline to produce octane ratings greater than 100.

## Section 22.5 Assessment

**30.** What properties of benzene made chemists think it was not an alkene with several double bonds?

**31.** What feature accounts for the difference between aromatic and aliphatic hydrocarbons? Why should people avoid contact with aromatic hydrocarbons?

**32.** Explain how the physical properties of hydrocarbons make fractional distillation possible.

**33.** What is the purpose of cracking hydrocarbons?

**34.** **Thinking Critically** In addition to adjusting octane rating, refiners also vary the volatility of gasoline, mainly by adding (or not adding) butane, $C_4H_{10}$. Where and when do you think refiners produce gasoline of higher volatility?

**35.** **Interpreting Data** Look at the data in **Table 22-6**. What property of hydrocarbon molecules seems to correlate to the viscosity of a particular fraction when it is cooled to room temperature?

## Section 22.5 Assessment

**30.** Benzene is much less reactive than alkenes with multiple double bonds, which usually are very unstable.

**31.** Aromatic hydrocarbons are cyclic, planar molecules with high stability and low reactivity. Many aromatic hydrocarbons are carcinogenic.

**32.** Distillation works when hydrocarbons with higher boiling points condense low in the column. Those with lower boiling points condense farther up, where the temperature is lower.

**33.** Cracking is done to convert large, heavy hydrocarbons in petroleum fractions into smaller, more useful substances.

**34.** Refiners produce more volatile gasoline by adding more butane (bp = 0.5°C) during the winter months in regions that become cold. Also, fuel must be made less volatile when it is to be used at higher altitudes, where air pressure is reduced.

**35.** The length of the carbon chains in hydrocarbons shows a correlation with their viscosities. Longer chains result in greater viscosity.

**727**

## Preparation

**Time Allotment**
One laboratory period

**Process Skills**
Acquiring and analyzing information, applying concepts, measuring, using numbers, analyze and conclude

**Safety Precautions**
Be certain that students do not leave gas valves open after they have finished collecting the gas. With care, the amount of gas that escapes into room air will be minimal. Both natural gas and propane are odorized, so any substantial leakage should easily be noticed. Spillage of water is likely to occur, so caution students to clean up water on the floor or any desktop spills that are likely to run onto the floor.

**Disposal**
Plastic soda bottles can be reused. When students empty pneumatic troughs, caution them to hold the open end of the gas inlet above the water level. Otherwise, water will run out onto the floor.

**Alternative Materials**
- If you do not have pneumatic troughs, you can use plastic dish-pans, buckets, sinks or any other container of similar size.
- Any size plastic bottles, including 2-L bottles, will work, but larger ones should give better data. Be sure, however, that your balances can accommodate the large plastic bottles and can weigh to the nearest 0.01 g.

## Pre-Lab

**3.** methane ($CH_4$), 16.04 g/mol; ethane ($C_2H_6$), 30.07; propane ($C_3H_8$), 44.10

**4.** $PV = nRT$

$$n = \frac{PV}{RT}$$

**5. a.** The experimental molar mass will be larger.
**b.** The experimental molar mass will be smaller.

---

# Analyzing Hydrocarbon Burner Gases

The fuel that makes a Bunsen burner work is a mixture of alkane hydrocarbons. One type of fuel is natural gas, whose primary component is methane ($CH_4$). The other type is called LP gas and consists primarily of propane ($C_3H_8$). In this experiment, you will use the ideal gas equation to help identify the main component of your classroom fuel supply.

**Problem**
What type of alkane gas is used in the burner fuel supplied to your laboratory?

**Objectives**
- **Measure** a volume of gas by water displacement.
- **Measure** the temperature, pressure, and mass at which the volume of the gas was measured.
- **Calculate** the molar mass of the burner gas using the ideal gas equation.

**Materials**
barometer
thermometer
1-L or 2-L plastic soda bottle with cap
burner tubing
pneumatic trough
100-mL graduated cylinder
balance (0.01g)
paper towels

## Safety Precautions

- Always wear safety goggles and an apron in the lab.
- Be certain that there are no open flames in the lab.

### Pre-Lab

1. Read the entire **CHEMLAB**.
2. Prepare all written materials that you will take into the laboratory. Include safety precautions, procedure notes, and a data table.
3. Use the formulas of methane, ethane, and propane to calculate the compounds' molar masses.
4. Given $R$ and gas pressure, volume, and temperature, show how you will rearrange the ideal gas equation to solve for moles of gas.
5. Suppose that your burner gas contains a small amount of ethane ($C_2H_6$). How will the presence of this compound affect your calculated molar mass if the burner gas is predominantly:
   **a.** methane
   **b.** propane
6. Prepare your data table.

| Mass and Volume Data | |
|---|---|
| Mass of bottle + air (g) | |
| Mass of air (g) | |
| Mass of "empty" bottle (g) | |
| Mass of bottle + collected burner gas (g) | |
| Mass of collected burner gas (g) | |
| Barometric pressure (atm) | |
| Temperature (°C) | |
| Temperature (K) | |
| Volume of gas collected (L) | |

### Procedure

1. Connect the burner tubing from the gas supply to the inlet of the pneumatic trough. Fill the trough with tap water. Open the gas valve slightly and let a little gas bubble through the tank in order to flush all of the air out of the tubing.

| Sample Mass and Volume Data | |
|---|---|
| Mass of bottle + air (g) | 30.49 g |
| Mass of air (g) | 0.82 g |
| Mass of "empty" bottle (g) | 29.67 g |
| Mass of bottle + collected burner gas (g) | 30.30 g |
| Mass of collected burner gas (g) | 0.63 g |
| Barometric pressure (atm) | 1.01 atm |
| Temperature (°C) | 24°C |
| Temperature (K) | 297 K |
| Volume of gas collected (L) | 0.630 L |

## Procedure

- It is inevitable that some water will remain on the sides of the bottle. Have students "flick" the bottle with a finger to get as much water as possible to run out. Capping the bottle while the gas is still turned on will minimize the entry of water as the bottle is closed.

2. Measure the mass of the dry plastic soda bottle and cap. Record the mass in the data table (bottle + air). Record both the barometric pressure and the air temperature.

3. Fill the bottle to overflowing with tap water and screw on the cap. If some air bubbles remain, tap the bottle gently on the desktop until all air has risen to the top. Take off the cap, add more water, and recap the bottle.

4. Place the thermometer in the trough. Invert the capped bottle into the pneumatic trough and remove the cap while keeping the mouth of the bottle underwater. Hold the mouth of the bottle directly over the inlet opening of the trough.

5. Slowly open the gas valve and bubble gas into the inverted bottle until all of the water has been displaced. Close the gas valve immediately. Record the temperature of the water.

6. While the bottle is still inverted, screw on the cap. Remove the bottle from the water. Thoroughly dry the outside of the bottle.

7. Measure the mass of the bottle containing the burner gas and record the mass in the data table (bottle + burner gas).

8. Place the bottle in a fume hood and remove the cap. Compress the bottle several times to expel most of the gas. Refill the bottle to overflowing with water and determine the volume of the bottle by pouring the water into a graduated cylinder. Record the volume of the bottle.

## Cleanup and Disposal

1. Be certain that all gas valves are closed firmly and dump water out of pneumatic troughs.

2. Clean up water spills and dispose of materials as directed by your teacher.

3. Return all lab equipment to its proper place.

## Analyze and Conclude

1. **Acquiring Information** Use the volume of the bottle and look up the density of air to compute the mass of the air the bottle contains. Use gas laws to compute the density of air at the temperature and pressure of your laboratory. The density of air at 1 atm and 20°C is 1.205 g/L.

2. **Using Numbers** Calculate the mass of the empty bottle by subtracting the mass of air from the mass of the bottle and air combined.

3. **Using Numbers** Determine the mass of the collected gas by subtracting the mass of the empty bottle from the mass of the bottle and gas.

4. **Interpreting Data** Use the volume of gas, water temperature, and barometric pressure along with the ideal gas law to calculate the number of moles of gas collected.

5. **Using Numbers** Use the mass of gas and the number of moles to calculate the molar mass of the gas.

6. **Drawing a Conclusion** How does your experimental molar mass compare with the molar masses of methane, ethane, and propane? Suggest which of these gases are in the burner gas in your laboratory.

7. **Error Analysis** If your experimental molar mass does not agree with that of any one of the three possible gases, suggest possible sources of error in the experiment. What factor other than error could produce such a result?

## Real-World Chemistry

1. Substances called *odorants* are mixed with natural gas before it is distributed to homes, businesses, and institutions. Why must an odorant be used, and what substances are used as odorants?

2. At 1 atm and 20°C, the densities of methane and propane are 0.65 g/L and 1.83 g/L, respectively. Would either gas tend to settle in a low area such as the basement of a home? Explain.

CHEMLAB **729**

## Expected Results

Natural gas in the U.S. averages about 85% methane, 9% ethane, 3% propane, and 3% composed of nitrogen, butane, and helium.

## Analyze and Conclude

1. *mass of air = density × volume*
See sample data table.

2. See sample data table.

3. See sample data table.

4. At 25°C, approximately 3% of the volume of the bottle will be occupied by water vapor because the gas was collected over water. However, the molar mass of water is near that of methane, the component most likely to be present in the gas supply. Therefore, the presence of water vapor may be ignored in an experiment of this precision. Students substitute values into the ideal gas equation and solve for *n*.

Before they calculate, consider having students estimate the value of *n* based on the known volume of the bottle and Avogadro's principle.

5. Students should carry out the following calculation.
*molar mass =*
$$\frac{measured\ mass\ of\ gas}{calculated\ number\ of\ moles}$$

6. Results will depend on the composition of the gas.

7. Possibilities include excess water trapped in the bottle, incorrect or poor measurement techniques, or math error. A gas mixture would yield a molar mass that does not exactly equal the molar mass of any of the components.

## Real-World Chemistry

1. Odorants are added to warn people of the presence of gas. They are typically $H_2S$ and mercaptans (thiols and thioethers), such as ethyl mercaptan, methyl mercaptan, dimethyl sulfide, and methylethyl sulfide.

### Resource Manager

ChemLab and MiniLab Worksheets, pp. 86–88 **L2**

2. Yes. Propane would because it is more dense than air.

### ✓ Assessment

**Skill** Ask students to imagine that the gas they measured was different (propane, if they found methane, and vice versa). Have them create a table of data they might have obtained under those circumstances. **L2**

# Everyday Chemistry

## Purpose

Students gain an understanding of the need to reduce fossil fuel consumption as well as forms of an alternative energy.

## Background

Active and passive solar energy technologies are generally used for heating and cooling. Solar electric technologies such as photovoltaic cells convert sunlight into electricity. One of the least expensive and most environmentally friendly methods of providing for our energy needs is the design of homes and office buildings to capture solar energy through passive solar features.

Other forms of alternative energy include geothermal energy—the use of heat from Earth's interior—and wind energy.

## Teaching Strategies

• Ask students what alternative energy sources are familiar to them. Ask them to debate the pros and cons of each source.

• Explain to students that rooftop solar panels that heat water for household use are examples of active solar energy. Point out that south facing windows are simple passive solar features.

## Testing Your Knowledge

**1.** Students should find that a solar furnace has a field of curved mirrors driven by computers to track the Sun during the day. The mirrors focus sunlight on a central heat-collection point located on a high tower. The heat is utilized to raise the temperature high enough to melt metals and to make steam for producing electricity. It is an active solar energy technique.

# Unlimited Alternative Energy

Fossil fuels are the primary source of energy to run our cars, heat our homes, and produce electricity. Decaying plants and animals millions of years ago produced coal, oil, and natural gas. These sources of energy are finite and need to be conserved.

### The Costs of Fossil Fuels

Each time we pay an electricity bill or purchase gasoline, we pay for fossil fuels. The labor to mine coal or drill for oil, the labor and materials to build and operate power plants, and the transportation of coal and oil to these plants are just part of the costs of using fossil fuels. There also are indirect costs such as health problems caused by pollution, environmental problems such as acid rain, and the protection of foreign sources of oil. There is an alternative source of energy readily available for use in your everyday life—solar energy.

### What is solar energy?

The sun has always been an energy source. Plants use sunlight to make food through a process called photosynthesis. Animals use energy from the Sun by eating plants. Throughout history, humans have used the heat from sunlight directly to cook food and heat water and homes. When you hang laundry outside to dry, you use solar energy to do work. Plants grow in greenhouses during winter months due to warmth from the Sun. Although the Sun radiates prodigious amounts of energy each day, it will continue to dispense solar energy for approximately five billion years.

By the late 1800s, the use of solar water heaters was common in sunny parts of the United States. When large deposits of oil and natural gas were discovered, these systems were replaced with heaters using cheaper fossil fuels.

### Passive Solar Energy

Many different active solar techniques can be used to convert sunlight into useful forms of energy. Add-on devices such as photovoltaic cells that convert sunlight into electricity and rooftop solar panels that use sunlight to heat water use mechanical means to distribute solar energy. "Low-technology" passive solar techniques provide clean, inexpensive energy. Passive solar techniques make use of the building's components and design.

Each time you open the curtains to let in the Sun's rays for warmth or light, you are using passive solar energy. Every building can meet some of its heating requirements with passive solar energy. The use of triple-pane windows, heavily insulated walls and ceilings, and materials with high heat capacity such as adobe walls and clay tile floors increase energy storage. Passive solar techniques also can be used to reduce use of electricity for air conditioning. Vegetation planted for shade, light colors that reflect sunlight, and careful attention to placement of windows for good airflow will keep a home cooler in summer.

The use of sunlight to replace electric lighting in a building is called daylighting. Daylighting can be useful in the home, and large office buildings that demand large amounts of lighting during the day benefit from large windows, skylights, and atria.

### Testing Your Knowledge

**1. Acquiring Information** Investigate and describe how a solar furnace works. Is it an active or passive use of solar energy? Explain your answer.

**2. Hypothesizing** Geothermal energy, wind energy, and solar energy are forms of alternative energy. Which form might be feasible in your state? Explain.

**2.** Student choices will vary according to the climatic conditions in their state. Geothermal and wind energy depend on specific conditions found in only a few places. Some form of solar energy can be used in most locations.

## Summary

### 22.1 Alkanes

- Organic compounds contain the element carbon, which is able to bond with other carbon atoms to form straight chains and branched chains.
- Hydrocarbons are organic substances composed of only the elements carbon and hydrogen.
- Alkanes contain only single bonds between carbon atoms.
- Alkanes and other organic compounds are best represented by structural formulas and can be named using systematic rules determined by the International Union of Pure and Applied Chemistry (IUPAC).

### 22.2 Cyclic Alkanes and Alkane Propeties

- Alkanes that contain hydrocarbon rings are called cyclic alkanes.
- Alkanes are nonpolar compounds that have low reactivity and lower melting and boiling points than polar molecules of similar size and mass.

### 22.3 Alkenes and Alkynes

- Alkenes and alkynes are hydrocarbons that contain at least one double or triple bond, respectively.
- Alkenes and alkynes are nonpolar compounds with greater reactivity than alkanes but with other properties similar to those of the alkanes.
- Alkenes and alkynes, whether straight-chain, branched-chain, or cyclic, can be named using the systematic rules determined by IUPAC.

### 22.4 Isomers

- Isomers are two or more compounds with the same molecular formula but different molecular structures.

- Structural isomers differ in the order in which atoms are bonded to each other. A straight-chain hydrocarbon and a branched-chain hydrocarbon with the same molecular formula are structural isomers.
- Stereoisomers have all atoms bonded in the same order but arranged differently in space.
- Geometric isomers, a category of stereoisomers, result from different arrangements of groups about carbon atoms that are double bonded to each other.
- Optical isomers, another class of stereoisomers, result from the two possible arrangements of four different atoms or groups of atoms bonded to the same carbon atom. The two isomers are chiral because they are mirror images of each other.

### 22.5 Aromatic Hydrocarbons and Petroleum

- Aromatic hydrocarbons contain benzene rings as part of their molecular structures. Nonaromatic hydrocarbons are called aliphatic hydrocarbons.
- Aromatic hydrocarbons tend to be less reactive than alkenes or alkynes because they have no double bonds. Instead, electrons are shared evenly over the entire benzene ring.
- Some aromatic compounds, such as naphthalene, contain two or more benzene rings fused together.
- Some aromatic compounds are carcinogenic, which means they can cause cancer.
- The major sources of hydrocarbons are petroleum and natural gas.
- Petroleum can be separated into components of different boiling ranges by the process of fractional distillation.

## Using the Vocabulary

To reinforce chapter vocabulary, have students write a sentence using each term. L2 ELL

## Review Strategies

- Have students summarize the similarities and differences between alkanes, alkenes, and alkynes. L2
- Have students make a list of the names and structures of common hydrocarbons. L2
- Problems from Appendix A or the **Supplemental Problems** booklet can be used for review. L2

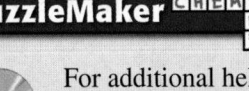

For additional help with vocabulary, have students access the Vocabulary PuzzleMaker online.

chemistrymc.com/ vocabulary_puzzlemaker

## Vocabulary

- aliphatic compound (p. 723)
- alkane (p. 699)
- alkene (p. 711)
- alkyne (p. 714)
- aromatic compound (p. 723)
- asymmetric carbon (p. 719)
- chirality (p. 719)
- cracking (p. 726)
- cyclic hydrocarbon (p. 706)

- cycloalkane (p. 706)
- fractional distillation (p. 725)
- geometric isomer (p. 718)
- homologous series (p. 701)
- hydrocarbon (p. 698)
- isomer (p. 717)
- optical isomer (p. 720)
- optical rotation (p. 721)
- organic compound (p. 698)

- parent chain (p. 701)
- polarized light (p. 720)
- saturated hydrocarbon (p. 710)
- stereoisomer (p. 718)
- structural isomer (p. 717)
- substituent group (p. 701)
- unsaturated hydrocarbon (p. 710)

## EXAMVIEW® PRO

### Use ExamView® Pro Testmaker CD-ROM to:

- Create **multiple versions** of tests.
- Create **modified** tests with one mouse click for struggling students.
- **Edit** existing questions and add your own questions.
- **Build** tests based on national curriculum standards.

National Science Content Standards

**Pages 730–731**
UCP.2, UCP.5; A.1; B.2, B.4, B.6; F.3, F.4, F.6

## Concept Mapping

**36.**
1. structural isomers
2. stereoisomers
3. geometric isomers
4. optical isomers

## Mastering Concepts

**37.** Organic compounds contain the element carbon.

**38.** Carbon is able to form four strong covalent bonds, including bonds with other carbon atoms.

**39.** It is a series of compounds that differ from each other by a repeating unit and have a fixed numerical relationship among the numbers of atoms.

**40.** See the Solutions Manual for structures.
   **a.** $CH_3CH_3$
   **b.** $CH_3CH_2CH_2CH_3$
   **c.** $CH_3CH_2CH_2CH_2CH_2CH_3$

**41.** **a.** $CH_3CH_3$
   **b.** $CH_3(CH_2)_2CH_3$
   **c.** $CH_3(CH_2)_4CH_3$

**42.** See the Solutions Manual for structures.
   **a.** methyl ($-CH_3$); **b.** butyl ($-(CH_2)_3CH_3$); **c.** octyl ($-(CH_2)_7CH_3$)

**43.** A cycloalkane contains a ring of carbon atoms.

**44.** Saturated hydrocarbons contain all single carbon-carbon bonds. Unsaturated hydrocarbons contain one or more double or triple carbon-carbon bonds.

**45.** Stronger attractions between molecules make it harder to separate them. Such substances generally have higher boiling and freezing points.

**46.** Alkanes contain only single bonds between carbon atoms, alkenes contain a double bond between two carbon atoms, and alkynes contain a triple bond between two carbon atoms.

## Chemistry Online

*Go to the Chemistry Web site at* chemistrymc.com *for additional Chapter 22 Assessment.*

## Concept Mapping

**36.** Complete the following concept map that shows how the following isomer types are related: stereoisomers, structural isomers, optical isomers, all isomers, geometric isomers.

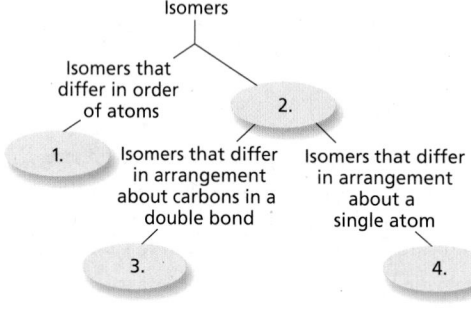

## Mastering Concepts

**37.** Why did Wohler's discovery lead to the development of the field of organic chemistry? (22.1)

**38.** What is the main characteristic of an organic compound? (22.1)

**39.** What characteristic of carbon accounts for the huge variety of organic compounds? (22.1)

**40.** Describe the characteristics of a homologous series of hydrocarbons. (22.1)

**41.** Draw the structural formula of each of the following. (22.1)
   **a.** ethane      **b.** butane      **c.** hexane

**42.** Write the condensed structural formulas for the alkanes in the previous question. (22.1)

**43.** Write the name and draw the structure of the alkyl group that corresponds to each of the following alkanes. (22.1)
   **a.** methane      **b.** butane      **c.** octane

**44.** How does the structure of a cycloalkane differ from that of a straight-chain or branched-chain alkane? (22.2)

**45.** Explain the difference between saturated hydrocarbons and unsaturated hydrocarbons. (22.2)

**46.** Explain how intermolecular attractions generally affect substances' boiling and freezing points.

**47.** Explain how alkenes differ from alkanes. How do alkynes differ from both alkenes and alkanes? (22.3)

**48.** The names of hydrocarbons are based on the name of the parent chain. Explain how the determination of the parent chain when naming alkenes differs from the same determination when naming alkanes. (22.3)

**49.** Name the most common alkyne. How is this substance used? (22.3)

**50.** How are two isomers alike and how are they different? (22.4)

**51.** Describe the difference between *cis*- and *trans*- isomers in terms of geometrical arrangement. (22.4)

**52.** What characteristics does a chiral substance have? (22.4)

**53.** How does polarized light differ from ordinary light, such as light from the Sun? (22.4)

**54.** How do optical isomers affect polarized light? (22.4)

**55.** What structural characteristic do all aromatic hydrocarbons share? (22.5)

**56.** Draw the structural formula of 1,2-dimethylbenzene. (22.5)

**57.** What are carcinogens? (22.5)

**58.** What does fractional distillation of petroleum accomplish? (22.5)

**59.** What physical property determines the height at which hydrocarbons condense in a fractionation tower? (22.5)

**60.** What is the cracking process and why is it necessary in petroleum processing? (22.5)

## Mastering Problems
### Alkanes (22.1)

**61.** Name the compound represented by each of the following structural formulas.
   **a.** $CH_3CH_2CH_2CH_2CH_3$
   **b.** $CH_3CH_2CHCH_2CH_3$
       $\quad\quad\quad\quad CH_3$

**47.** When naming alkanes, the parent chain is the longest continuous carbon chain. When naming alkenes, the parent chain is the longest continuous

## Resource Manager

**Chapter Assessment,** pp. 127–132
**Supplemental Problems,** Ch. 22
**ExamView® Pro CD-ROM**
**MindJogger Videoquizzes DVD/VHS**
**Solutions Manual,** Ch. 22
**Chemistry Interactive CD-ROM,**
   Ch. 22 quiz

**62.** Draw full structural formulas for the following compounds.

   **a.** heptane        **c.** 2,3-dimethylpentane
   **b.** 2-methylhexane    **d.** 2,2-dimethylpropane

## Cyclic Alkanes and Alkane Properties (22.2)

**63.** Draw condensed structural formulas for the following compounds. Use line structures for rings.

   **a.** 1,2-dimethylcyclopropane
   **b.** 1,1-diethyl-2-methylcyclopentane

**64.** Name the compound represented by each of the following structural formulas.

  **a.**  **c.** $CH_2CH_2CH_3$

  **b.**  **d.**

## Alkenes and Alkynes (22.3)

**65.** Name the compound represented by each of the following condensed structural formulas.

  **a.** $CH_3$ 
$C = CHCH_3$
$CH_3$

  **c.** (ring with $CH_3$)

  **b.** $CH_3CH_2$
$C = CH_2$
$CH_3CH_2$

  **d.** (ring with $CH_3$)

**66.** Draw condensed structural formulas for the following compounds. Use line structures for rings.

   **a.** 1,4-diethylcyclohexene
   **b.** 2,4-dimethyl-1-octene
   **c.** 2,2-dimethyl-3-hexyne

**67.** Name the compound represented by each of the following condensed structural formulas.

  **a.** $CH_3$    $CH_2CH_2CH_3$
$C = C$
$CH_3CH_2$    $CH_2CH_3$

**b.** (cyclohexene ring with $CH_2CH_3$, $CH_3$, $CH_3$)

## Isomers (22.4)

**68.** Identify the pair of structural isomers in the following group of condensed structural formulas.

  **a.** $CH_3$
$CH_3CCH_2CH_2CH_3$
$CH_3$

  **c.** $CH_3$
$CH_3CHCHCH_2CH_3$
$CH_3$

  **b.** $CH_3$
$CH_3CHCH_2CH$
$CH_3$   $CH_3$

  **d.** $CH_3CHCH_2CHCH_3$
$CH_3$    $CH_3$

**69.** Identify the pair of geometric isomers among the following structures. Explain your selections. Explain how the third structure is related to the other two.

  **a.** $CH_3$    $CH_3$
$C = C$
$CH_3$    $CH_2CH_2CH_3$

  **b.** $CH_3$    $CH_3$
$C = C$
$CH_3CH_2$    $CH_2CH_3$

  **c.** $CH_3$    $CH_2CH_3$
$C = C$
$CH_3CH_2$    $CH_2$

**70.** Three of the following structures are exactly alike, but the fourth represents an optical isomer of the other three. Identify the optical isomer and explain how you made your choice.

  **a.** T
$S — C — R$
Q

  **c.** R
$S — C — Q$
T

  **b.** T
$Q — C — S$
R

  **d.** R
$Q — C — S$
T

**71.** Draw condensed structural formulas for four different structural isomers with the molecular formula $C_4H_8$.

**72.** Draw and label the *cis-* and *trans-* isomers of the molecule represented by the following condensed formula.

   $CH_3CH = CHCH_2CH_3$

---

carbon chain that includes the carbons linked by a double bond.

**48.** Ethyne, or acetylene, is used as a fuel in welding torches.

**49.** Isomers have the same molecular formula but different structures. They may have very different chemical and physical properties.

**50.** *Cis* isomers have the largest groups on the carbons in the double bond on the same side of the bond; in *trans* isomers they are on opposite sides.

**51.** A chiral substance has both right- and left-handed forms.

**52.** The waves of polarized light all vibrate in one plane; in ordinary light, they vibrate in all possible planes.

**53.** They rotate polarized light.

**54.** They contain one or more benzene rings.

**55.** The structure is benzene with methyl groups on any two adjacent carbons. See the Solutions Manual.

**56.** Carcinogens are substances that can cause cancer.

**57.** It separates petroleum into its different components.

**58.** the compounds' boiling points

**59.** Cracking involves using heat and a catalyst in the absence of oxygen to convert heavier fractions of petroleum into smaller fractions, such as gasoline and starting materials for the synthesis of a variety of products. Cracking is necessary to increase the yield of medium-sized hydrocarbons useful in gasoline.

---

## Mastering Problems

Complete solutions to Chapter Assessment problems can be found in the **Solutions Manual.**

### Alkanes (22.1)
#### Level 1
  **60. a.** pentane
     **b.** 3-methylpentane

  **c.** 2,5-dimethylhexane
  **d.** 2,3-dimethylbutane

#### Level 2
  **61.** See the Solutions Manual for structures.

### Cyclic Alkanes and Alkane Properties (22.2)
#### Level 1
  **62.** See the Solutions Manual for structures.

National Science Content Standards

Pages 732–733
UCP.2, UCP.5; A.1; B.2

## Level 2

**63. a.** 1,2,4-trimethylcyclo-hexane
   **b.** 1-ethyl-3-methyl-cyclopentane
   **c.** 1-methyl-3-propyl-cyclobutane
   **d.** 6-ethyl-1,2,3-trimethyl-cyclooctane

## Alkenes and Alkynes (22.3)

### Level 1

**64. a.** 2-methyl-2-butene
   **b.** 2-ethyl-1-butene
   **c.** 1-methylcyclopentene
   **d.** 3-methylcyclobutene

### Level 2

**65.** See the Solutions Manual for structures.
**66. a.** 4-ethyl-3-methyl-3-heptene
   **b.** 6-ethyl-1,3-dimethyl-cyclohexene

## Isomers (22.4)

### Level 1

**67.** Student answers may include any two structures except b and d, which are identical.
**68.** b and c are geometric isomers. They represent a *cis/trans* pair of isomers. a is a structural isomer of both b and c.

### Level 2

**69.** a is an optical isomer of b, c, and d. a is not superim-posable with b, c, or d.
**70.** Student answers should show condensed structural formulas for cyclobutane, 1-butene, 2-butene, and 2-methylpropene. See the Solutions Manual.
**71.** The two hydrogen atoms bonded to the doubly-bonded carbons are on the same side of the carbon chain for the *cis* isomer and on opposite sides of the carbon chain for the *trans* isomer. See the Solutions Manual.

**734**

## Aromatic Hydrocarbons and Petroleum (22.5)

**73.** Name the compound represented by each of the following structural formulas.

**a.**    **b.**

## Mixed Review ────────

*Sharpen your problem-solving skills by answering the following.*

**74.** Do the following structural formulas represent the same molecule? Explain your answer.

**75.** How many hydrogen atoms are in an alkane molecule with nine carbon atoms? How many are in an alkene with nine carbon atoms and one double bond?

**76.** Determine whether or not each of the following structures represents the correct numbering. If the numbering is incorrect, redraw the structure with the correct numbering.

**a.**    **c.**

**b.** $CH_3CH_2C \equiv CCH_3$   **d.**

**77.** Why do chemists use structural formulas for organic compounds rather than molecular formulas such as $C_5H_{12}$?

**78.** The general formula for alkanes is $C_nH_{2n+2}$. Determine the general formula for cycloalkanes.

**79.** Why are unsaturated hydrocarbons more useful than saturated hydrocarbons as starting materials in chemical manufacturing?

**80.** Is cyclopentane an isomer of pentane? Explain your answer.

## Thinking Critically ────────

**81. Thinking Critically** Determine which two of the following names cannot be correct and draw the structures of the molecules.
   **a.** 2-ethyl-2-butene
   **b.** 1,4-dimethylcyclohexene
   **c.** 1,5-dimethylbenzene

**82. Drawing a Conclusion** The sugar glucose is sometimes called *dextrose* because a solution of glucose is known to be dextrorotatory. Analyze the word *dextrorotatory*, and suggest what the word means.

**83. Interpreting Scientific Illustrations** Draw Kekulé's structure of benzene and explain why it does not truly represent the actual structure.

**84. Recognizing Cause and Effect** Explain why alkanes such as hexane and cyclohexane are effective at dissolving grease, whereas water is not.

**85. Hypothesizing** Do you think that, on average, structural isomers or stereoisomers will have a larger difference in their physical properties? Explain your reasoning. Research this question by comparing physical properties of pairs of isomers as given in the *CRC Handbook of Chemistry and Physics* or *The Merck Index* to see if your hypothesis is correct.

## Writing in Chemistry ────────

**86.** For many years, a principal antiknock ingredient in gasoline was the compound tetraethyllead. Do research to learn about the structure of this compound, the history of its development and use, and why its use was discontinued in the United States. Find out if it is still used as a gasoline additive elsewhere in the world.

## Cumulative Review ────────

*Refresh your understanding of previous chapters by answering the following.*

**87.** What element has the following ground-state electron configuration: $[Ar]4s^23d^6$? (Chapter 5)

**88.** What is the charge of an ion formed from the following families? (Chapter 7)
   **a.** alkali metals
   **b.** alkaline earth metals
   **c.** halogens

**89.** Write the chemical equations for the complete combustion of ethane, ethene, and ethyne into carbon dioxide and water. (Chapter 10)

---

## Aromatic Hydrocarbons and Petroleum (22.5)

### Level 1

**72. a.** methylbenzene (toluene)
   **b.** anthracene

## Mixed Review

**73.** No. They are structural isomers.
**74.** 20 hydrogen atoms; 18 hydrogen atoms

**75. a.** Yes
   **b.** No, it should be numbered from the opposite end.
   **c.** No. The ring should be numbered clockwise starting with the carbon shown as number 2.
   **d.** Yes
**76.** Molecular formulas cannot differentiate between isomers.
**77.** $C_nH_{2n}$

*Use these questions and test-taking tip to prepare for your standardized test.*

**1.** What is the condensed structural formula of heptane?

**a.** $(CH_3)_2(CH_2)_5$    **c.** $CH_3(CH_2)_5CH_3$
**b.** $CH_3(CH_2)_6$    **d.** $CH_3CH_3(CH_2)_5$

**2.**

What is the name of the compound whose skeletal formula is shown above?

**a.** 2,2,3-trimethyl-3-ethylpentane
**b.** 3-ethyl-3,4,4-trimethylpentane
**c.** 2-butyl-2-ethylbutane
**d.** 3-ethyl-2,2,3-trimethylpentane

**3.** All of the following are structural isomers of $CH_2 = CHCH_2CH = CHCH_3$ EXCEPT ____.

**a.** $CH_2 = CHCH_2CH_2CH = CH_2$
**b.** $CH_3CH = CHCH_2CH = CH_2$
**c.** $CH_3CH = CHCH = CHCH_3$
**d.** $CH_2 = C = CHCH_2CH_2CH_3$

**Interpreting Tables** Use the table to answer questions 4–6.

### Data for Various Hydrocarbons

| Name | Number of C atoms | Number of H atoms | Melting point (°C) | Boiling point (°C) |
|------|------|------|------|------|
| Heptane | 7 | 16 | −90.6 | 98.5 |
| 1-Heptene | 7 | 14 | −119.7 | 93.6 |
| 1-Heptyne | 7 | 12 | −81 | 99.7 |
| Octane | 8 | 18 | −56.8 | 125.6 |
| 1-Octene | 8 | 16 | −101.7 | 121.2 |
| 1-Octyne | 8 | 14 | −79.3 | 126.3 |

**4.** Based on the information in the table, what type of hydrocarbon becomes a gas at the lowest temperature?

**a.** alkane    **c.** alkyne
**b.** alkene    **d.** aromatic

**5.** If *n* is the number of carbon atoms in the hydrocarbon, what is the general formula for an alkyne with one triple bond?

**a.** $C_nH_{n+2}$    **c.** $C_nH_{2n}$
**b.** $C_nH_{2n+2}$    **d.** $C_nH_{2n-2}$

**6.** It can be predicted from the table that nonane will have a melting point that is

**a.** greater than that of octane.
**b.** less than that of heptane.
**c.** greater than that of decane.
**d.** less than that of hexane.

**7.** Which compound below is 1,2-dimethylcyclohexane?

**8.** Alanine, like all amino acids, exists in two forms:

Almost all of the amino acids found in living organisms are in the L-form. What are L-Alanine and D-Alanine?

**a.** structural isomers    **c.** optical isomers
**b.** geometric isomers    **d.** stereoisotopes

**78.** Unsaturated hydrocarbons are much more reactive.
**79.** No. Cyclopentane ($C_5H_{10}$) and pentane ($C_5H_{12}$) have different molecular formulas.

## Thinking Critically

**80.** See the Solutions Manual for structures.
a and c are incorrect.
a is correctly named 3-methyl-2-pentene, and c is correctly named 1,2-dimethylbenzene.
**81.** The prefix *dextro-* means "to the right," and the suffix *rotatory* means "rotates." Therefore, the natural form of glucose is chiral and rotates the plane of polarized light to the right.
**82.** See the Solutions Manual for the structure, which shows localized electrons in the double bonds rather than delocalized electrons.
**83.** Grease and alkanes are both nonpolar. Water is polar. Like dissolves like.
**84.** Structural isomers may have vastly different physical properties because they have completely different arrangements of the carbon skeleton. Stereoisomers (geometric and optical isomers) have the same carbon skeleton but different orientations in space. Geometric isomers have different properties; optical isomers differ only in the direction of rotation of polarized light and in chemical reactions that distinguish between isomers.

## Cumulative Review

**86.** iron
**87.** **a.** 1+ **b.** 2+ **c.** 1−
**88.** ethane: $2C_2H_6 + 7O_2 \rightarrow 4CO_2 + 6H_2O$;
ethene: $C_2H_4 + 3O_2 \rightarrow 2CO_2 + 2H_2O$;
ethyne: $2C_2H_2 + 5O_2 \rightarrow 4CO_2 + 2H_2O$

## Standardized Test Practice

**1.** c   **3.** b   **5.** d   **7.** b
**2.** d   **4.** b   **6.** a   **8.** c

**National Science Content Standards**

Pages 734–735
UCP.2, UCP.5; A.1; B.2; G.3

# Resource Manager

| Section | Objectives | Activities/Features |
|---|---|---|
| **Section 23.1**<br>**Functional Groups**<br>1 session<br>½ block | 1. **Describe** a functional group and give examples.<br>2. **Name** and **draw** alkyl and aryl halide structures.<br>3. **Discuss** the chemical and physical properties of organic halides.<br>4. **Describe** how substitution reactions form alkyl and aryl halides. | **Discovery Lab:** Making Slime, p. 737<br>**Astronomy Connection,** p. 739 |
| **Section 23.2**<br>**Alcohols, Ethers, and Amines**<br>1½ sessions<br>1 block | 5. **Identify** the functional groups that characterize alcohols, ethers, and amines.<br>6. **Draw** the structures of alcohols, ethers, and amines.<br>7. **Discuss** the properties and uses of alcohols, ethers, and amines. | **ChemLab:** Properties of Alcohols, pp. 766–767 |
| **Section 23.3**<br>**Carbonyl Compounds**<br>1½ sessions<br>1 block | 8. **Draw** and **identify** the structures of carbonyl compounds including aldehydes, ketones, carboxylic acids, esters, and amides.<br>9. **Discuss** the properties and uses of compounds containing the carbonyl group. | **MiniLab:** Making an Ester, p. 751 |
| **Section 23.4**<br>**Other Reactions of Organic Compounds**<br>1½ sessions<br>1 block | 10. **Classify** an organic reaction into one of five categories: substitution, addition, elimination, oxidation-reduction, or condensation.<br>11. **Use** structural formulas to write equations for reactions of organic compounds.<br>12. **Predict** the products of common types of organic reactions. | **Problem-Solving Lab:** Categorizing Organic Compounds, p. 757 |
| **Section 23.5**<br>**Polymers**<br>2½ sessions<br>1½ blocks | 13. **Describe** the relationship between a polymer and the monomers from which it forms.<br>14. **Classify** polymerization reactions as addition or condensation.<br>15. **Predict** polymer properties based on their molecular structures and the presence of functional groups. | **Chemistry and Technology:** Carbon: Stronger Than Steel?, p. 768 |

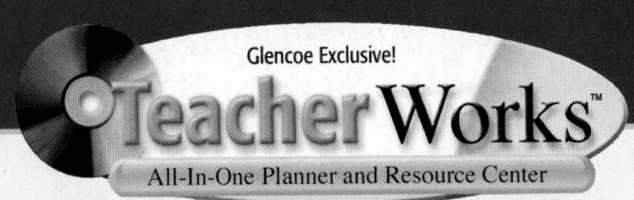

Glencoe Exclusive!
**TeacherWorks™**
All-In-One Planner and Resource Center

| National Science Content Standards | State/Local Standards | Reproducible Masters | Transparencies |
|---|---|---|---|
| UCP.1, UCP.2, UCP.5; A.1; B.2, B.3; E.2; F.4, F.6 | | **Study Guide for Content Mastery,** p. 133 L2 | **Section Focus** Transparency 86 L1 ELL **Teaching** Transparency 68 L2 ELL **Math Skills** Transparency 37 L2 ELL |
| UCP.1, UCP.2, UCP.5; B.2, B.3; E.2; G.3 | | **Study Guide for Content Mastery,** pp. 134–135 L2 **ChemLab and MiniLab Worksheets,** pp. 90–92 L2 | **Section Focus** Transparency 87 L1 ELL **Teaching** Transparency 69 L2 ELL |
| UCP.1, UCP.2, UCP.5; A.1; B.2, B.3; E.2 | | **Study Guide for Content Mastery,** p. 136 L2 **Challenge Problems,** p. 23 L3 | **Section Focus** Transparency 88 L1 ELL **Teaching** Transparency 70 L2 ELL |
| UCP.1, UCP.2, UCP.5; B.2, B.3; E.2 | | **Study Guide for Content Mastery,** p. 137 L2 **ChemLab and MiniLab Worksheets,** p. 89 L2 **Laboratory Manual,** pp. 177–180 L2 | **Section Focus** Transparency 89 L1 ELL **Teaching** Transparency 71 L2 ELL |
| UCP.1, UCP.2, UCP.5; A.1; B.2, B.3, B.4; E.1, E.2; F.6 | | **Study Guide for Content Mastery,** p. 138 L2 **Laboratory Manual,** pp. 181–184 L2 | **Section Focus** Transparency 90 L1 ELL **Teaching** Transparency 72 L2 ELL **Math Skills** Transparency 38 L2 ELL |

**Key to National Science Content Standards:** UCP = Unifying Concepts and Processes, A = Science as Inquiry, B = Physical Science, C = Life Science, D = Earth and Space Sciences, E = Science and Technology, F = Science in Personal and Social Perspectives, G = History and Nature of Science

Refer to pages 4T–5T of the Teacher Guide for an explanation of the National Science Content Standards correlations.

# Resource Manager

## Materials List

**ChemLab** (pages 766–767)
stopwatch, thermometer, facial tissues, cloth towel, Beral pipettes (5), methanol, ethanol 95%, 2-propanol 99%, small rubber band or twist tie, cardboard, water

**Discovery Lab** (page 737)
4% sodium tetraborate (borax) solution, 4% polyvinyl alcohol solution, plastic cup, stirring rod

**MiniLab** (page 751)
salicylic acid, methanol, 10-mL graduated cylinder, Beral pipette, 250-mL beaker, concentrated sulfuric acid, petri dish, cotton ball, small test tube, balance, weighing paper, hot plate, test-tube holder, distilled water

**Demonstration** (pages 762–763)
spring-type clothespins (10), 1 box of paper clips

## Preparation of Solutions

For a review of solution preparation, see page 46T of the Teacher Guide.

Quantities are for a class of 30 students.

**Discovery Lab (page 737)**
   **4% polyvinyl alcohol solution** Slowly sprinkle 40 g polyvinyl alcohol powder into 900 mL water with constant stirring. Heat the mixture on a hot plate to 80°C while continuing to stir. Add a few drops of food coloring. Do not overheat the solution. Cool and store in a stoppered bottle.
   **4% sodium tetraborate (borax) solution** Dissolve 12 g sodium tetraborate decahydrate $(Na_2B_4O_7 \cdot 10H_2O)$ in 300 mL of warm water.

## Assessment Resources

**Chapter Assessment,** pp. 133–138
**MindJogger Videoquizzes DVD/VHS**
**Alternate Assessment in the Science Classroom**
**ExamView® Pro CD-ROM**
**Solutions Manual,** Chapter 23
**Supplemental Problems,** Chapter 23
**Performance Assessment in the Science Classroom**
**Chemistry Interactive CD-ROM,** Chapter 23 quiz

## Additional Resources

**Spanish Resources** ELL
**Guided Reading Audio Program,** Chapter 23 ELL
**Cooperative Learning in the Science Classroom**
**Lab and Safety Skills in the Science Classroom**
**Lesson Plans**
**Block Scheduling Lesson Plans**
**Chemistrymc.com**

## Glencoe Technology

The following multimedia for this chapter are available from Glencoe.

**VIDEOTAPE/DVD**
MindJogger Videoquizzes,
Chapter 23

**CD-ROM**
**Chemistry: Matter and Change**
*Functional Groups,* Experiment
*Natural and Synthetic Polymers,* Video

**CD-ROM**
**ExamView® Pro**
  **Testmaker**

**CD-ROM**
**Interactive Chalkboard**

**CD-ROM**
**TeacherWorks™**

## Multiple Learning Styles

Look for the following icons for strategies that emphasize different learning modalities.

***Kinesthetic***
Differentiated Instruction, pp. 749, 761

***Visual-Spatial***
Portfolio, pp. 738, 761; Differentiated Instruction,
p. 739; Check for Understanding, p. 742; Reteach,
pp. 742, 746; Extension, p. 746; Reinforcement, p. 747

***Interpersonal***
Differentiated Instruction, pp. 741, 750;
Enrichment, p. 749

***Intrapersonal***
Differentiated Instruction, pp. 744, 754, 758;
Chemistry Journal, p. 747; Extension, p. 759

***Linguistic***
Chemistry Journal, pp. 740, 743, 756, 764;
Using Science Terms, p. 748; Reinforcement, p. 748;
Check for Understanding, p. 759; Enrichment, p. 762

## Key to Teaching Strategies

**L1** Level 1 activities should be appropriate for students with
learning difficulties.

**L2** Level 2 activities should be within the ability range of
all students.

**L3** Level 3 activities are designed for above-average students.

**ELL** ELL activities should be within the ability range of
English Language Learners.

**COOP LEARN** Cooperative Learning activities are designed
for small group work.

**P** These strategies represent student products that can be
placed into a best-work portfolio.

These strategies are useful in a block scheduling format.

## ✔ Assessment Planner

**Portfolio Assessment**
Assessment, TWE, pp. 740,
  745
Portfolio, TWE, pp. 738,
  761, 769

**Performance Assessment**
Assessment, TWE, pp. 746,
  751, 753, 763, 765
ChemLab, SE, pp. 766–767
MiniLab, SE, TWE, p. 751
Discovery Lab, SE, p. 737
Problem-Solving Lab, TWE,
  p. 757

**Knowledge Assessment**
Assessment, TWE, pp. 738,
  740, 749, 754, 756, 760
Demonstration, TWE, p. 763
Section Assessment, SE,
  pp. 742, 746, 753, 760, 765
Chapter Assessment, SE,
  pp. 770–773

**Skill Assessment**
Assessment, TWE, p. 742
ChemLab, TWE, p. 767

## Tying to Previous Knowledge

Have students review the following concepts before studying this chapter.
Chapter 7: chemistry of carbon
Chapter 10: combustion reactions
Chapter 13: interparticle forces
Chapter 22: hydrocarbons, isomers

## Using the Photo

Have students examine the photograph showing synthetic polymer threads of many colors. Ask them if they can identify the base material from which most polymers such as these are manufactured.
Most synthetic polymers are made from petroleum.

## Chapter Themes

The following themes from the National Science Education Standards are covered in this chapter. Refer to page 4T of the Teacher Guide for an explanation of the correlations.
Systems, order, and organization (UCP.1)
Evidence, models, and explanation (UCP.2)
Form and Function (UCP.5)

## INTERACTIVE CHALKBOARD with Image Bank

**PowerPoint® Presentations**
This CD-ROM is an editable Microsoft® PowerPoint® presentation that includes:
• Section presentations
• Section checks
• Image bank
• Links to Chemistry Online
• All transparencies
• Animations
• Audio

# Substituted Hydrocarbons and Their Reactions

### What You'll Learn

▶ You will recognize the names and structures of several important organic functional groups.
▶ You will classify reactions of organic substances as substitution, addition, elimination, oxidation-reduction, or condensation and predict products of these reactions.
▶ You will relate the structures of synthetic polymers to their properties.

### Why It's Important

Whether you are removing a sandwich from plastic wrap, taking an aspirin, or shooting baskets, you're using organic materials made of substituted hydrocarbons. These compounds are in turn made of molecules whose atoms include carbon, hydrogen, and other elements.

## Chemistry Online

Visit the Chemistry Web site at **chemistrymc.com** to find links about substituted hydrocarbons and their reactions.

The spooled threads shown in the photo are made from large organic molecules called polymers.

**736** Chapter 23

## DISCOVERY LAB

### Purpose
Students will observe the effect of cross-linking on polymer chains.

### Safety and Disposal
Students should wear aprons and safety goggles. They should wear plastic gloves when pouring the borax solution and wash their hands after the experiment. Contents of the paper or plastic cup can be placed in a waste container.

### Teaching Strategies
• Prepare 20 mL of 4% polyvinyl alcohol for each student. To prepare solution sufficient for 50 students, slowly add, with stirring, 40 g of 98 to100% hydrolyzed polyvinyl alcohol to 900 mL tap water. Heat this suspension to 80°C while continuing to stir. Add a few drops of food coloring. Do not overheat the solution. Cool and store the solution in a stoppered

## DISCOVERY LAB

### Making Slime

In addition to carbon and hydrogen, most organic substances contain other elements that give the substances unique properties. In this lab, you will work with an organic substance consisting of long carbon chains to which many –OH groups are bonded. How will the properties of this substance change when these groups react to form bonds called crosslinks between the chains?

### Safety Precautions

 Do not allow solutions or product to contact eyes or exposed skin.

**Materials**
4% sodium tetraborate (borax) solution
4% polyvinyl alcohol solution
disposable plastic cup
stirring rod

### Procedure

1. Pour 20 mL of 4% polyvinyl alcohol solution into a small disposable plastic cup. Note the viscosity of the solution as you stir it.

2. While stirring, add 6 mL of 4% sodium tetraborate solution to the polyvinyl alcohol solution. Continue to stir until there is no further change in the consistency of the product.

3. Use your gloved hand to scoop the material out of the cup. Knead the polymer into a ball.

### Analysis

What physical property of the product differs markedly from those of the reactants?

---

## Section 23.1

# Functional Groups

### Objectives

- **Describe** a functional group and give examples.

- **Name** and **draw** alkyl and aryl halide structures.

- **Discuss** the chemical and physical properties of organic halides.

- **Describe** how substitution reactions form alkyl and aryl halides.

### Vocabulary

functional group
halocarbon
alkyl halide
aryl halide
substitution reaction
halogenation

All of the spools shown on the opposite page hold thread manufactured from large organic molecules called polymers. By weaving these polymer threads into fabrics, they can serve many different purposes. Most of the organic molecules used to make these polymers contain atoms of other elements in addition to carbon and hydrogen. The presence of these other elements gives fabric such strength that it can be used to make a bulletproof vest or such resistance to creasing that it never has to be ironed.

## Functional Groups

You learned in Chapter 22 that thousands of different hydrocarbons exist because carbon atoms can link together to form straight and branched chains, rings of many sizes, and molecules with single, double, and triple bonds. In hydrocarbons, carbon atoms are linked only to other carbon atoms or hydrogen atoms. But carbon atoms also can form strong covalent bonds with other elements, the most common of which are oxygen, nitrogen, fluorine, chlorine, bromine, iodine, sulfur, and phosphorus.

Atoms of these elements occur in organic substances as parts of functional groups. A **functional group** in an organic molecule is an atom or group of atoms that always reacts in a certain way. The addition of a functional group

23.1 Functional Groups **737**

---

## Section 23.1

# 1 Focus

### Focus Transparency

Before presenting the lesson, display **Section Focus Transparency 86** on the overhead projector. Have students answer the accompanying questions using **Section Focus Transparency Master 86.** **L1** **ELL**

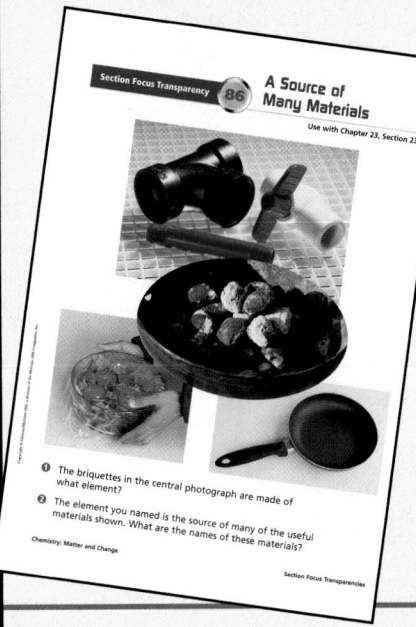

Section Focus Transparency 86

A Source of Many Materials

Use with Chapter 23, Section 23.1

❶ The briquettes in the central photograph are made of what element?

❷ The element you named is the source of many of the useful materials shown. What are the names of these materials?

Chemistry: Matter and Change

Section Focus Transparencies

---

## Resource Manager

**Section Focus Transparency 86 and Master** **L1** **ELL**
**Study Guide for Content Mastery,** p. 133 **L2**
**Solving Problems: A Chemistry Handbook,** Section 23.1 **L2**
**Math Skills Transparency 37 and Master** **L2** **ELL**

---

### National Science Content Standards

**Pages 736–737**
UCP.1, UCP.2, UCP.5; A.1; B.2, B.3; F.6

---

bottle. See page 736C for preparation of solutions.

- To prepare cross-linker (borax) solution sufficient for 50 students, dissolve 12 g of sodium tetraborate in 300 mL of warm tap water.

- To avoid the wrath of administrators and fellow teachers, be sure students do not take their product out of the science classroom.

### Expected Results

The liquid turns to a solid. It will flow when draped over a student's hand, forming long strands. The strand will break if you pull it quickly.

### Analysis

Polyvinyl alcohol is soluble in water; most hydrocarbons are not. The viscosity of the liquid increases until it becomes a solid.

Perform the Beilstein flame test for students. Explain that the procedure can be a useful qualitative test for alkyl halides. **CAUTION:** *Perform the test in a fume hood or a well-ventilated room. Wear safety goggles, an apron, and a flame-proof glove or mitt.* Dip the tip of a cool, clean, copper wire into a small sample of ethylene dichloride (1,2-dichloroethane). Place the tip of the wire in a Bunsen-burner flame. A blue or green flame demonstrates the presence of chlorine, bromine, or iodine in the compound. Advise students that chlorine-containing compounds react with copper to produce a green flame, bromine-containing compounds yield a blue-green flame, and iodine-containing compounds yield a blue flame.

## ✓ Assessment

**Knowledge** Show students ball-and-stick models of a number of alkyl halides and ask them to name the compounds. Be sure to include at least one structure with each of the halogens commonly found in organic compounds: fluorine, chlorine, bromine, and iodine. Also ask students to recall all the information they can about the properties and characteristics of halogens. Halogens form anions with a 1− charge, have seven valence electrons, react with alkali metals and alkaline earth metals to form salts, and occur naturally in the diatomic form. **L2**

## In-Text Question

**Page 738** Examine the caffeine structure in Figure 23-1 and identify the molecule's functional groups. carbonyl and amino groups

Caffeine

**Figure 23-1**

Many organic compounds contain atoms of elements in addition to carbon and hydrogen. For example, caffeine, a compound found in many beverages, contains both oxygen and nitrogen atoms. Refer to **Table C-1** in Appendix C for a key to atom color conventions.

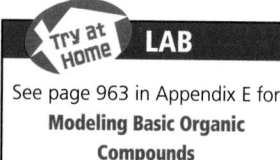

**Try at Home** **LAB**

See page 963 in Appendix E for **Modeling Basic Organic Compounds**

to a hydrocarbon structure always produces a substance with physical and chemical properties that differ from those of the parent hydrocarbon. Organic compounds containing several important functional groups are shown in **Table 23-1.** The symbols R and R' represent any carbon chains or rings bonded to the functional group. And * represents a hydrogen atom, carbon chain, or carbon ring.

**Table 23-1**

| Organic Compounds and Their Functional Groups | | |
|---|---|---|
| **Compound type** | **General formula** | **Functional group** |
| Halocarbon | R—X (X = F, Cl, Br, I) | Halogen |
| Alcohol | R—OH | Hydroxyl |
| Ether | R—O—R' | Ether |
| Amine | R—NH$_2$ | Amino |
| Aldehyde | $\overset{\displaystyle O}{\overset{\|}{*-C-H}}$ | Carbonyl |
| Ketone | $\overset{\displaystyle O}{\overset{\|}{R-C-R'}}$ | Carbonyl |
| Carboxylic acid | $\overset{\displaystyle O}{\overset{\|}{*-C-OH}}$ | Carboxyl |
| Ester | $\overset{\displaystyle O}{\overset{\|}{*-C-O-R}}$ | Ester |
| Amide | $\overset{\displaystyle O \quad H}{\overset{\|}{*-C-N-R}}$ | Amido |

Keep in mind that double and triple bonds between two carbon atoms are considered functional groups even though only carbon and hydrogen atoms are involved. By learning the properties associated with a given functional group, you can predict the properties of organic compounds for which you know the structure, even if you have never studied them. Examine the caffeine structure shown in **Figure 23-1** and identify the molecule's functional groups.

## Organic Compounds Containing Halogens

The simplest functional groups can be thought of as substituent groups attached to a hydrocarbon. The elements in group 7A of the periodic table—fluorine, chlorine, bromine, and iodine—are the halogens. Any organic compound that contains a halogen substituent is called a **halocarbon.** If you replace any of the hydrogen atoms in an alkane with a halogen atom, you form an alkyl halide. An **alkyl halide** is an organic compound containing a halogen atom covalently bonded to an aliphatic carbon atom. The first four

## ✓ Portfolio

### Functional Groups

**Visual-Spatial** Give students a worksheet showing the structures of several large organic molecules that contain a variety of functional groups. Explain that in this chapter they will learn to recognize and name most of these groups. Ask them to circle any groups that they know are not present in alkanes. Have students place the worksheets in their portfolios and supply the names of the compounds as they encounter them in their studies. **L2** **P**

halogens—fluorine, chlorine, bromine, and iodine—are found in many organic compounds. For example, chloromethane is the alkyl halide formed when a chlorine atom replaces one of methane's four carbon atoms.

Chloromethane

An **aryl halide** is an organic compound containing a halogen atom bonded to a benzene ring or other aromatic group. The structural formula for an aryl halide is created by first drawing the aromatic structure and then replacing its hydrogen atoms with the halogen atoms specified.

Chlorobenzene

## Naming Halocarbons

Organic molecules containing functional groups are given IUPAC names based on their main-chain alkane structures. For the alkyl halides, a prefix indicates which halogen is present. The prefixes are formed by changing the *–ine* at the end of each halogen name to *–o*. Thus, the prefix for fluorine is *fluoro-*, chlorine is *chloro-*, bromine is *bromo-*, and iodine is *iodo-*.

Fluoroethane

1, 2-Difluoropropane

If more than one kind of halogen atom is present in the same molecule, the atoms are listed alphabetically in the name. The chain also must be numbered in a way that gives the lowest position number to the substituent that comes first in the alphabet. Note how the following alkyl halide is named.

1-Bromo-3-chloro-2-fluorobutane

Note that the benzene ring in an aryl halide is numbered to give each substituent the lowest position number possible.

Fluorobenzene

1-Bromo-3,5-diiodobenzene

## Astronomy
### CONNECTION

**N**aphthalene, anthracene, and similar hydrocarbons are termed polycyclic aromatic hydrocarbons (PAHs) because they are composed of multiple aromatic rings. PAHs have been found in meteorites and identified in the material surrounding dying stars. Scientists have mixed PAHs with water ice in a vacuum at –260°C to simulate the conditions found in interstellar clouds. To simulate radiation emitted by nearby stars, they shined ultraviolet light on the mixture. About ten percent of the PAHs were converted to alcohols, ketones, and esters—molecules that can be used to form compounds that are important in biological systems.

## Visual Learning

**Table 23-2** Have students examine Table 23-2 on page 740 and compare the boiling point and density of pentane with those of the five-carbon compounds that have functional groups in place of one of pentane's hydrogen atoms. Pentane has a boiling point of 36°C and a density of 0.626 g/mL. Based on the information in this table, substituting a functional group for a hydrogen atom in pentane results in a higher boiling point and a higher density. Boiling point values for the substituted molecules range from 62.8°C to 155°C; densities range from 0.791 g/mL to 1.516 g/mL.

## GLENCOE TECHNOLOGY

**CD-ROM**
**Chemistry: Matter and Change**
Experiment: *Functional Groups*

---

## DIFFERENTIATED INSTRUCTION

### Gifted

*Visual-Spatial* Ask interested students to draw all the structural isomers of the halocarbon with the formula $C_4H_8Br_2$. There are nine different structures with that formula: 1,1-dibromobutane, 2,2-dibromobutane, 1,2-dibromobutane,  1,3-dibromobutane, 1,4-dibromobutane, 2,3-dibromobutane, 1,1-dibromo-2-methylpropane, 1,2-dibromo-2-methylpropane, and 1,3-dibromo-2-methylpropane.

**L3**

**National Science Content Standards**

**Pages 738–739**
UCP.1, UCP.2, UCP.5; B.2; E.2

740

## Practice PROBLEMS

Have students refer to Appendix D for complete solutions to Practice Problems.

**1.** 2,3-difluorobutane

**2.** 1-bromo-5-chloropentane

**3.** 1,3-dibromo-2-chlorobenzene

## ✓ Assessment

**Portfolio** Ask students to begin a chart in which they list the name, structure, properties, and uses for each organic functional group studied. They should add each group as it is encountered in their studies and put the completed list in their portfolios. **L2 P**

## ✓ Assessment

**Knowledge** Have each student write a question on the material in this section that involves naming alkyl halides. Have students exchange questions and quiz each other. **L2**

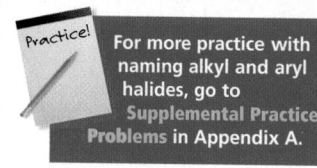

Practice! For more practice with naming alkyl and aryl halides, go to **Supplemental Practice Problems** in Appendix A.

### PRACTICE PROBLEMS

Name the alkyl or aryl halide whose structure is shown.

**1.**
```
    H  F  F  H
    |  |  |  |
H — C— C— C— C— H
    |  |  |  |
    H  H  H  H
```

**2.**
```
   Cl  H  H  H  Br
    |  |  |  |  |
H — C— C— C— C— C— H
    |  |  |  |  |
    H  H  H  H  H
```

**3.**
(benzene ring with Br, Cl, Br substituents)

## Properties and Uses of Halocarbons

It is easiest to talk about properties of organic compounds containing functional groups by comparing those compounds with alkanes, whose properties were discussed in Chapter 22. **Table 23-2** lists some of the physical properties of certain alkanes and alkyl halides.

**Table 23-2**

| A Comparison of Alkyl Halides with Their Parent Alkanes | | | |
|---|---|---|---|
| Structure | Name | Boiling point (°C) | Density (g/mL) in liquid state |
| $CH_4$ | methane | −162 | 0.423 at −162°C (boiling point) |
| $CH_3Cl$ | chloromethane | −24 | 0.911 at 25°C (under pressure) |
| $CH_3CH_2CH_2CH_2CH_3$ | pentane | 36 | 0.626 |
| $CH_3CH_2CH_2CH_2CH_2F$ | 1-fluoropentane | 62.8 | 0.791 |
| $CH_3CH_2CH_2CH_2CH_2Cl$ | 1-chloropentane | 108 *Increases* | 0.882 *Increases* |
| $CH_3CH_2CH_2CH_2CH_2Br$ | 1-bromopentane | 130 | 1.218 |
| $CH_3CH_2CH_2CH_2CH_2I$ | 1-iodopentane | 155 | 1.516 |

Note that each alkyl chloride has a higher boiling point and a higher density than the alkane with the same number of carbon atoms. Note also that the boiling points and densities increase as the halogen changes from fluorine to chlorine, bromine, and iodine. This trend occurs primarily because the halogens from fluorine to iodine have increasing numbers of electrons that lie farther from the halogen nucleus. These electrons shift position easily and, as a result, the halogen-substituted hydrocarbons have an increasing tendency to form temporary dipoles. Because the dipoles attract each other, the energy needed to separate the molecules also increases. Thus, the boiling points of halogen-substituted alkanes increase as the size of the halogen atom increases.

Alkyl halides are used as solvents and cleaning agents because they readily dissolve nonpolar molecules such as greases. Teflon (polytetrafluoroethene) is a plastic made from gaseous tetrafluoroethylene. Another plastic

**740** Chapter 23 Substituted Hydrocarbons and Their Reactions

## CHEMISTRY JOURNAL

### Chlorofluorocarbons

**Linguistic** Have students research and write a report about how some countries have banned or phased out the use of chlorofluorocarbons (CFCs) due to their suspected involvement in breaking down Earth's protective ozone layer.

**L2**

## Resource Manager

**Teaching Transparency 68 and Master**
**L2 ELL**

Teflon

The chain $-\underset{\underset{F}{\mid}}{\overset{\overset{F}{\mid}}{C}}-$ units extend for hundreds of carbon atoms

commonly called *vinyl* is polyvinyl chloride (PVC). It can be manufactured soft or hard, as thin sheets or molded into objects. Organic halides are seldom found in nature, although human thyroid hormones are organic iodides. One example of an organic halide is shown in **Figure 23-2.**

Alkyl halides are widely used as refrigerants. Until the late 1980s, alkyl halides called chlorofluorocarbons (CFCs) were widely used in refrigerators and air-conditioning systems. Because of their potential to damage Earth's ozone layer, CFCs have been replaced by HFCs, hydrofluorocarbons, which contain only hydrogen and fluorine atoms bonded to carbon. One of the more common HFCs is 1,1,2-trifluoroethane, also called R134a.

Halogen atoms bonded to carbon atoms are much more reactive than the hydrogen atoms they replace. For this reason, alkyl halides are often used as starting materials in the chemical industry.

**Figure 23-2**

Teflon increases a carpet's resistance to staining and makes it easier to clean.

1,1,2–Trifluoroethane
HFC R134a

## Substitution Reactions

Where does the immense variety of organic compounds come from? Amazingly enough, the ultimate source of nearly all synthetic organic compounds is petroleum. Petroleum is a fossil fuel that consists almost entirely of hydrocarbons, especially alkanes. How can alkanes be converted into compounds as different as alkyl halides, alcohols, and amines?

One way is to introduce a functional group through substitution. A **substitution reaction** is one in which one atom or a group of atoms in a molecule is replaced by another atom or group of atoms. With alkanes, hydrogen atoms may be replaced by atoms of halogens, typically chlorine or bromine, in a process called **halogenation**. One example of a halogenation reaction is the substitution of a chlorine atom for one of ethane's hydrogen atoms.

$$H-\underset{\underset{H}{\mid}}{\overset{\overset{H}{\mid}}{C}}-\underset{\underset{H}{\mid}}{\overset{\overset{H}{\mid}}{C}}-H + Cl_2 \rightarrow H-\underset{\underset{H}{\mid}}{\overset{\overset{H}{\mid}}{C}}-\underset{\underset{H}{\mid}}{\overset{\overset{H}{\mid}}{C}}-Cl + HCl$$

Ethane                Chloroethane

A substitution reaction

23.1 Functional Groups    **741**

## Applying Chemistry

**TECH PREP**

Synthetic dyes were not made until the 1800s, so people in earlier ages had to be content using a limited number of natural hues to put some color in their lives. Natural purple dyes were especially hard to find, so for almost 3000 years, the dye called "royal purple" or "Tyrian purple" was one of the most precious substances on Earth. By law, Tyrian purple could be used only for coloring robes and other clothing for the Roman emperors, tabernacle curtains, and priests' vestments. Its only known source was a Mediterranean sea snail, and 1200 snails had to be harvested to obtain one gram of dye. Overharvesting almost led to extinction of the snails, and the dye's production ceased by the fifteenth century. Today, we have numerous synthetic purple dyes that have replaced Tyrian purple.

**DIFFERENTIATED INSTRUCTION**

### Learning Disabled

*Interpersonal* Some students will find naming organic compounds that contain functional groups easier using a step-by-step approach. They should first name the compound as if no functional group were present, being sure to name the parent chain and all alkane branches correctly. Next, they should name each functional group and determine its position number. Finally, they should put all the information together to complete the compound's name. **L1** **ELL**

**National Science Content Standards**

Pages 740–741
UCP.1, UCP.2, UCP.5; B.2, B.3; E.2; F.4

# 3 Assess

## Check for Understanding

## Reteach

**Visual-Spatial** Illustrate the previous point by drawing the structural formula for chloroethane on the chalkboard and asking students to name it. Point out that chlorine's position on the carbon chain need not be designated.

## Extension

Have students compare the physical states of chloroethane and 1-chloropropane at room temperature and one atmosphere pressure.
Chloroethane is a gas and 1-chloropropane is a liquid. **L2**

## Assessment

**Skill** Ask students to draw structural formulas for the following alkyl halides: 2-bromobutane; 1,3-difluoropentane; iodocyclohexane; chlorobenzene; 1,3-dibromobenzene; 1-bromo-3-chloro-2-fluorooctane. **L2**

**Figure 23-3**

Moth balls are used in some closets to protect woolens from damage. 1,4-Dichlorobenzene (*p*-dichlorobenzene) is the active ingredient in some brands of moth balls.

---

Equations for organic reactions are sometimes shown in generic form. The following equation represents the halogenation of alkanes written in generic form.

$$R-CH_3 + X_2 \rightarrow R-CH_2X + HX$$

In this reaction, X can be fluorine, chlorine, or bromine, but not iodine. Iodine does not react well with alkanes. A common use of a halogented hydrocarbon is shown in **Figure 23-3.**

Once an alkane has been halogenated, the resulting alkyl halide can undergo other kinds of substitution reactions in which the halogen atom is replaced by another atom or group of atoms. For example, reacting an alkyl halide with an aqueous alkali results in the replacement of the halogen atom by an −OH group, forming an alcohol.

$$CH_3CH_2Cl + OH^- \rightarrow CH_3CH_2OH + Cl^-$$
Chloroethane              Ethanol

In generic form, the reaction is as follows.

$$R-X + OH^- \rightarrow R-OH + X^-$$
Alkyl halide              Alcohol

Reacting an alkyl halide with ammonia ($NH_3$) replaces the halogen atom with an amino group ($-NH_2$), forming an alkyl amine, as shown in the following equation.

$$R-X + NH_3 \rightarrow R-NH_2 + HX$$
Alkyl halide              Amine

You will learn more about reactions and properties of amines in the next section.

## Section 23.1 Assessment

**4.** Draw structures for the following molecules.
  **a.** 2-chlorobutane
  **b.** 1,3-difluorohexane
  **c.** 1,1,1-trichloroethane
  **d.** 4-bromo-1-chlorobenzene

**5.** Name the functional group present in each of the following structures. Name the type of organic compound each substance represents.
  **a.** $CH_3CH_2CH_2OH$     **c.** $CH_3CH_2NH_2$
  **b.** $CH_3CH_2F$     **d.**

$$CH_3\overset{\overset{\displaystyle O}{\|}}{C}-OH$$

**6.** How would you expect the boiling points of propane and 1-chloropropane to compare? Explain your answer.

**7. Thinking Critically** Examine the pair of structures shown below and decide whether it represents a pair of optical isomers. Explain your answer.

**8. Applying Concepts** Place the following substances in order of increasing boiling point. Do not look up boiling points, but use what you learned in this section to suggest the correct order.
2-chloropentane    1-bromohexane    butane
2-iodopentane    3-methylpentane

---

## Section 23.1 Assessment

**4.** See the Solutions Manual for structures.
**5. a.** hydroxyl group; alcohol
  **b.** fluoro group; alkyl halide
  **c.** amino group; amine
  **d.** carboxyl group; carboxylic acid
**6.** The boiling point of 1-chloropropane should be higher than that of propane. 1-chloropropane molecules should form

more temporary dipoles than propane molecules.
**7.** They are optical isomers. They are not superimposable; however, their structures have chiral carbons and are mirror images of each other.
**8.** butane, 3-methylpentane, 2-chloropentane, 2-iodopentane, 1-bromohexane

# Section 23.2 — Alcohols, Ethers, and Amines

In Section 23.1, you learned that hydrogen atoms bonded to carbon atoms in hydrocarbons can be replaced by halogen atoms. Many other kinds of atoms or groups of atoms also can bond to carbon in the place of hydrogen atoms. In addition to structural variations, replacement of hydrogen by other elements is a reason that such a wide variety of organic compounds is possible.

## Alcohols

Many organic compounds contain oxygen atoms bonded to carbon atoms. Because an oxygen atom has six valence electrons, it commonly forms two covalent bonds to gain a stable octet. An oxygen atom can form a double bond with a carbon atom, replacing two hydrogen atoms, or it can form one single bond with a carbon atom and another single bond with another atom, such as hydrogen. An oxygen-hydrogen group covalently bonded to a carbon atom is called a **hydroxyl group** ($-OH$). An organic compound in which a hydroxyl group replaces a hydrogen atom of a hydrocarbon is called an **alcohol**. The general formula for an alcohol is ROH. The following diagram illustrates the relationship of the simplest alkane, methane, to the simplest alcohol, methanol.

Methane (CH₄) — Alkane

Methanol (CH₃OH) — Alcohol

Ethanol, a two-carbon alcohol, and carbon dioxide are produced by yeasts when they ferment sugars, such as those in grapes and bread dough. Ethanol is found in alcoholic beverages and medicinal products. Because it is an effective antiseptic, ethanol may be used to swab skin before an injection is given, as shown in **Figure 23-4.** It also is a gasoline additive and an important starting material for the synthesis of more complex organic compounds.

Models of an ethanol molecule and a water molecule are shown in the following diagram.

Ethanol          Water

As you compare the models, you can see that the covalent bonds from oxygen are at approximately the same angle as they are in water. Therefore, the hydroxyl groups of alcohol molecules are moderately polar, as with water, and are able to form hydrogen bonds with the hydroxyl groups of other alcohol molecules. As a result, alcohols have much higher boiling points than

## Objectives

- **Identify** the functional groups that characterize alcohols, ethers, and amines.

- **Draw** the structures of alcohols, ethers, and amines.

- **Discuss** the properties and uses of alcohols, ethers, and amines.

## Vocabulary

hydroxyl group
alcohol
denatured alcohol
ether
amine

**Figure 23-4**

Ethanol is an effective antiseptic used to sterilize skin before an injection. It also is found in antiseptic hand cleaners.

---

## Section 23.2

## 1 Focus

### Focus Transparency

Before presenting the lesson, display **Section Focus Transparency 87** on the overhead projector. Have students answer the accompanying questions using **Section Focus Transparency Master 87.** L1 ELL

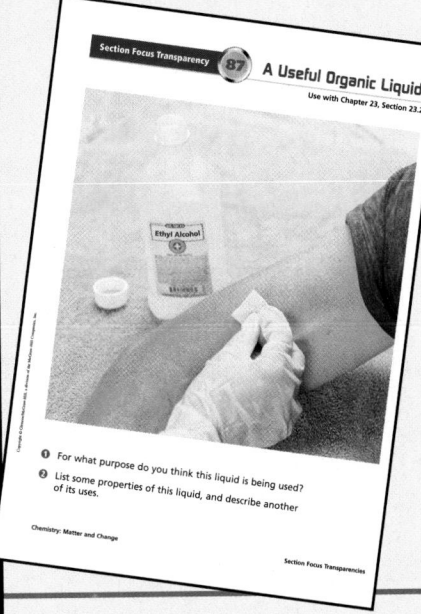

**Section Focus Transparency 87**
**A Useful Organic Liquid**
Use with Chapter 23, Section 23.2

❶ For what purpose do you think this liquid is being used?
❷ List some properties of this liquid, and describe another of its uses.

Chemistry: Matter and Change

Section Focus Transparencies

## 2 Teach

### Quick Demo

Thoroughly soak a one-dollar bill in methanol. Ask students if they think you're willing to throw away perfectly good money to demonstrate the volatility and flammability of an organic compound. Hold the bill with tongs. Then, use a hand-held lighter to ignite the methanol. The methanol will burn off before the paper bill catches fire. Ask students to explain what happened. Methanol burns at a temperature much lower than that required to ignite the paper.

---

### CHEMISTRY JOURNAL

#### Thalidomide

*Linguistic* Ask students to research the history and write a report about the medicine thalidomide, including information about the importance of the difference in biological properties of its two optical isomers. Thalidomide is a sedative that was prescribed to many pregnant women in Europe in the 1950s and early 1960s, until it was realized that it caused birth defects that included malformed arms and legs. Only one of its optical isomers causes the birth defect. Fortunately, it was never approved as a sedative in the United States. Recently, thalidomide has been approved for use in the U. S. as a treatment for leprosy; however, it cannot be prescribed for pregnant women. L2

## In-Text Question

**Page 744** Explain why the names 3-butanol and 4-butanol cannot represent real substances. The names are incorrect. 3-butanol is correctly named 2-butanol, and 4-butanol is correctly named 1-butanol.

## Figure Caption Question

**Figure 23-5** Draw the structures of two other alcohols that have the same molecular formula as 2-butanol, $C_4H_{10}O$. See the Solutions Manual. Structures should show two of the following compounds: 1-butanol; 2-methyl-1-propanol; 2-methyl-2-propanol.

## Enrichment

Have students recall the relationship between the strengths of interparticle forces and viscosities of liquids that they learned about in Chapter 13. Ask them to apply their knowledge to predict the relative viscosities of the following alcohols: ethanediol (also known as ethylene glycol); ethanol; 1,2,3-propanetriol (also know as glycerol). The order of viscosity from lowest to highest is: ethanol, ethanediol, and 1,2,3-propanetriol. The presence of more hydroxyl groups leads to more interparticle forces and higher viscosity. Chain length is also a factor. In general, a three-carbon chain has a higher viscosity than a two-carbon chain. **L2**

## CHEMLAB

ChemLab 23, located at the end of the chapter, can be used at this point in the lesson.

## Concept Development

Explain to students that an alkane with an $NH_2$ functional group bonded to a carbon atom can be named by using the suffix *-amine* or by designating the attached $NH_2$ group *amino-*. Point out, for example, that $CH_3CH_2CH_2CH_2NH_2$ may be properly named either 1-butylamine or 1-aminobutane.

**744**

2-Butanol

**Figure 23-5**

Because it evaporates more slowly than smaller alcohol molecules, 2-butanol is used as a solvent in some stains and varnishes. Draw the structures of two other alcohols that have the same molecular formula as 2-butanol, $C_4H_{10}O$.

**Figure 23-6**

Glycerol is a liquid often used in automobile antifreeze and airplane deicing fluid.

1,2,3-Propanetriol
(glycerol)

---

hydrocarbons of similar shape and size. Also, because of polarity and hydrogen bonding, ethanol is completely miscible with water. In fact, once they are mixed, it is difficult to separate water and ethanol completely. Distillation is used to remove ethanol from water, but even after that process is complete, about 5% water remains in the ethanol-water mixture.

On the shelves of drugstores you can find bottles of ethanol labeled denatured alcohol. **Denatured alcohol** is ethanol to which small amounts of noxious materials such as aviation gasoline or other organic solvents have been added. Ethanol is denatured in order to make it unfit to drink. Because of their polar hydroxyl groups, alcohols make good solvents for other polar organic substances. For example, methanol, the smallest alcohol, is a common industrial solvent found in some paint strippers, and 2-butanol is found in some stains and varnishes, as shown in **Figure 23-5**. Perform the **CHEMLAB** at the end of this chapter to learn about some other properties of small-chain alcohols.

Note that the names of alcohols are based on alkane names, like the names of alkyl halides. For example, $CH_4$ is methane and $CH_3OH$ is methanol; $CH_3CH_3$ is ethane and $CH_3CH_2OH$ is ethanol. When naming a simple alcohol based on an alkane carbon chain, the IUPAC rules call for naming the parent carbon chain or ring first and then changing the *–e* at the end of the name to *–ol* to indicate the presence of a hydroxyl group. In alcohols of three or more carbon atoms, the hydroxyl group can be at two or more positions. To indicate the position, a prefix consisting of a number followed by a dash is added. For example, examine the names and structures of two isomers of butanol shown below. Explain why the names *3-butanol* and *4-butanol* cannot represent real substances.

1-Butanol
bp = 99.5°C

2-Butanol
bp = 115°C

Now look at the following structural formula. What is the name of this compound?

You are correct if you said *cyclohexanol*. The compound's ring structure contains six carbons with only single bonds so you know that the parent hydrocarbon is cyclohexane. Because an –OH group is bonded to a carbon, it is an alcohol and the name will end in *–ol*. No number is necessary because all carbons in the ring are equivalent. Cyclohexanol is a poisonous compound used as a solvent for certain plastics and in the manufacture of insecticides.

A carbon chain also can have more than one hydroxyl group. To name these compounds, prefixes such as *di-*, *tri-*, and *tetra-* are used before the *–ol* to indicate the number of hydroxyl groups present. The full alkane name, including *–ane*, is used before the prefix as in the following example. 1,2,3-propanetriol, commonly called glycerol, is another alcohol containing more than one hydroxyl group, **Figure 23-6**.

744    Chapter 23 Substituted Hydrocarbons and Their Reactions

---

### DIFFERENTIATED INSTRUCTION

**Gifted**

**Intrapersonal** Ask interested students to research the structure of isopropanol, or "rubbing alcohol," find out which industrial synthesis process is used to make it, and report their findings to the class. **L3**

### Resource Manager

**Section Focus Transparency 87 and Master L1 ELL**

**Study Guide for Content Mastery,** pp. 134–135 **L2**

**Solving Problems: A Chemistry Handbook,** Section 23.2 **L2**

**Teaching Transparency 69 and Master L2 ELL**

# Ethers

Ethers are another group of organic compounds in which oxygen is bonded to carbon. An **ether** is an organic compound containing an oxygen atom bonded to two carbon atoms. Ethers have the general formula ROR'. The simplest ether is one in which oxygen is bonded to two methyl groups. Note the relationship between methanol and methyl ether in the following diagram.

Methanol
bp = 65°C

Methyl ether
bp = –25°C

Because ethers have no hydrogen atoms bonded to the oxygen atom, their molecules cannot form hydrogen bonds with each other. Therefore, ethers generally are more volatile and have much lower boiling points than alcohols of similar size and mass. Ethers are much less soluble in water than alcohols because they have no hydrogen to donate to a hydrogen bond. However, the oxygen atom can act as a receptor for the hydrogen atoms of water molecules.

The term *ether* was first used in chemistry as a name for ethyl ether, the volatile, highly flammable substance that was commonly used as an anesthetic in surgery from 1842 into the twentieth century, **Figure 23-7.** As time passed, the term *ether* was applied to other organic substances having two hydrocarbon chains attached to the same oxygen atom.

$$H-\underset{\underset{H}{|}}{\overset{\overset{H}{|}}{C}}-\underset{\underset{H}{|}}{\overset{\overset{H}{|}}{C}}-O-\underset{\underset{H}{|}}{\overset{\overset{H}{|}}{C}}-\underset{\underset{H}{|}}{\overset{\overset{H}{|}}{C}}-H$$

Ethyl ether

Name ethers that have two identical alkyl chains bonded to oxygen by first naming the alkyl group and then adding the word *ether.* Here are the names and structures of two of these symmetrical ethers.

$CH_3CH_2CH_2-O-CH_2CH_2CH_3$
Propyl ether

Cyclohexyl ether

If the two alkyl groups are different, they are listed in alphabetical order and then followed by the word ether. Such ethers are asymmetrical, or uneven, in appearance.

$CH_3CH_2-O-CH_2CH_2CH_2CH_3$
Butylethyl ether

$CH_3CH_2-O-CH_3$
Ethylmethyl ether

## Amines

Another class of organic compounds contains nitrogen. **Amines** contain nitrogen atoms bonded to carbon atoms in aliphatic chains or aromatic rings and have the general formula $RNH_2$.

23.2 Alcohols, Ethers, and Amines    **745**

## Figure 23-7

An apparatus similar to the one held by the man on the left was used to administer ether to patients in the 1840s. Dr. Crawford W. Long of Georgia discovered the anesthetic properties of ethyl ether in 1842.

## Internet Address Book

 Note Internet addresses that you find useful in the space below for quick reference.

# 3 Assess

## Check for Understanding

Ask students why propanol is not a correct name for a three-carbon alcohol. **The name does not specify the location of the hydroxyl group on the three-carbon parent chain. The compound may be either 1-propanol or 2-propanol.**

## Reteach

 *Visual-Spatial* Show students the structures of 2-propanol, propylamine (1-amino-propane), and ethylmethyl ether without the names. Have them identify the functional group present in each and give the IUPAC name for each compound. Then, ask them to determine the relationship between 2-propanol and ethylmethyl ether. **They are structural isomers.** L2

## Extension

*Visual-Spatial* Have students research and make a poster showing the names, structures, and characteristics of various alkaloids, naturally occurring amine compounds made by plants. Common alkaloids include caffeine and nicotine. L2 ELL

## ✔ Assessment

**Performance** Ask students to design and set up an apparatus that can be used to compare the viscosities of ethanol, ethylene glycol (1,2-ethanediol), and glycerol (1,2,3-propanetriol). Use the Performance Task Assessment List for Designing an Experiment in **PASC,** p. 23. L2

Aniline

Cyclohexylamine

Ethylamine

**Figure 23-8**

**a** Aniline is an important industrial substance, especially in the production of dyes with deep shades of color. **b** Cyclohexylamine and ethylamine are important in the manufacture of pesticides, plastics, pharmaceuticals, and the rubber used to make the tires for this race car.

When naming amines, the $-NH_2$ (amino) group is indicated by the suffix *-amine*. When necessary, the position of the amino group is designated by a number. If more than one amino group is present, the prefixes *di-, tri-, tetra-,* and so on are used to indicate the number of groups.

$$CH_2CH_2CH_2$$
$$|\quad\quad|$$
$$NH_2\quad NH_2$$

1,3-Propanediamine

$$NH_2\quad\quad NH_2$$
$$|\quad\quad\quad|$$
$$CH\ CH_2CH_2CH$$
$$|\quad\quad\quad\quad|$$
$$NH_2\quad\quad NH_2$$

1,1,4,4-Butanetetraamine

Examples of amines used in industry are shown in **Figure 23-8.** All volatile amines have odors that humans find offensive, and amines are responsible for many of the odors characteristic of dead, decaying organisms.

## Section 23.2 Assessment

**9.** Draw structures for the following alcohols:
  **a.** 1-propanol
  **b.** 2-propanol
  **c.** 2-methyl-2-butanol
  **d.** 1,3-cyclopentanediol

**10.** Draw structures for the following molecules:
  **a.** propyl ether     **c.** 1,2-propanediamine
  **b.** ethylpropyl ether     **d.** cyclobutylamine

**11.** Identify the functional group present in each of the following structures. Name the substance represented by each structure.

  **a.** 
$$NH_2$$
$$|$$
$$CH_3CHCH_3$$

  **b.** 
OH attached to cyclohexane ring

  **c.** $CH_3-O-CH_2CH_2CH_3$

**12. Thinking Critically** Which of the following compounds would you expect to be more soluble in water? Explain your reasoning.

$$CH_3-O-CH_3$$

$$OH$$
$$|$$
$$CH_3CH_2$$

**13. Applying Concepts** Alcohols and amines are used as starting materials in reactions that produce useful substances such as pharmaceuticals, plastics, and synthetic fibers, as well as other industrial chemicals. What properties of these compounds make them more useful than hydrocarbons for this purpose?

## Section 23.2 Assessment

**9.** See the Solutions Manual.
  **a.** $CH_3CH_2CH_2OH$
  **b.** $CH_3CH(OH)CH_3$
  **c.** $CH_3C(CH_3)(OH)CH_2CH_3$
  **d.** 

OH

**10. a.** $CH_3-CH_2-CH_2-O-CH_2-CH_2-CH_3$
  **b.** $CH_3-CH_2-O-CH_2-CH_2-CH_3$
  **c.** 
$$NH_2\quad NH_2$$
$$|\quad\quad|$$
$$CH_2-CH-CH_3$$
  **d.** 
$$NH_2$$
cyclobutyl ring

**11. a.** $-NH_2$ represents the amino

functional group; isopropyl-amine, 2-propylamine, or 2-aminopropane.
  **b.** $-OH$ represents the hydroxyl functional group; cyclohexanol.
  **c.** $-O-$ represents an oxygen atom in a carbon chain; methylpropyl ether.

You have now learned that in the organic compounds known as alcohols and ethers, oxygen is bonded to two different atoms. In other kinds of organic compounds, an oxygen atom is double-bonded to a carbon atom.

## Organic Compounds Containing the Carbonyl Group

The arrangement in which an oxygen atom is double-bonded to a carbon atom is called a **carbonyl group**. This group, which can be represented as shown below, is the functional group in organic compounds known as aldehydes and ketones.

**Aldehydes** An **aldehyde** is an organic compound in which a carbonyl group located at the end of a carbon chain is bonded to a carbon atom on one side and a hydrogen atom on the other. Aldehydes have the general formula *CHO, where * represents an alkyl group or a hydrogen atom.

O
‖
H—C—H
Methanal (formaldehyde)

Aldehydes are formally named by changing the final –e of the name of the alkane with the same number of carbon atoms to the suffix –al. Thus, the formal name of the compound represented above is methanal, based on the one-carbon alkane methane. Methanal is commonly called formaldehyde. A water solution of formaldehyde was used in the past to preserve biological specimens. However, formaldehyde's use has been restricted in recent years because evidence shows it may cause cancer. Industrially, large quantities of formaldehyde are reacted with urea to manufacture a type of grease-resistant, hard plastic used to make buttons, appliance and automotive parts, and electrical outlets, as well as the glue that holds the layers of plywood together.

Note the relationship between the structures and names of ethane and ethanal in the following diagram.

H H            H O
| |            | ‖
H—C—C—H     H—C—C—H
| |            |
H H            H
Ethane         Ethanal
               (acetaldehyde)

### Objectives

- **Draw** and **identify** the structures of carbonyl compounds including aldehydes, ketones, carboxylic acids, esters, and amides.

- **Discuss** the properties and uses of compounds containing the carbonyl group.

### Vocabulary

carbonyl group
aldehyde
ketone
carboxylic acid
carboxyl group
ester
amide
condensation reaction

## 1 Focus

### Focus Transparency

Before presenting the lesson, display **Section Focus Transparency 88** on the overhead projector. Have students answer the accompanying questions using **Section Focus Transparency Master 88.** L1 ELL

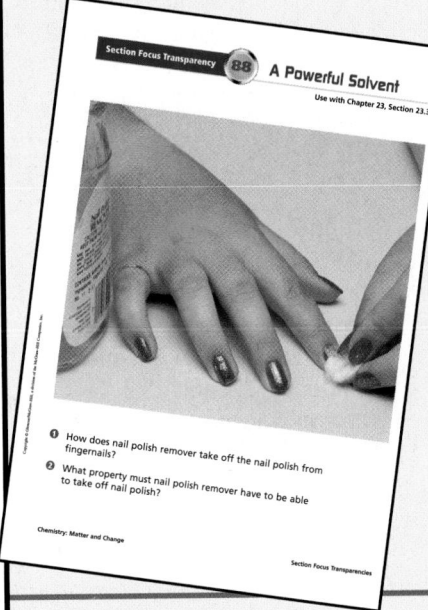

Section Focus Transparency 88  A Powerful Solvent
Use with Chapter 23, Section 23.3

❶ How does nail polish remover take off the nail polish from fingernails?

❷ What property must nail polish remover have to be able to take off nail polish?

Chemistry: Matter and Change                    Section Focus Transparencies

## 2 Teach

### Reinforcement

*Visual-Spatial* Have students draw from memory the functional groups found in alcohols, amines, and ethers. Then, have students differentiate these types of compounds from aldehydes, ketones, carboxylic acids, esters, and amides as they encounter them in the section. L2

### CHEMISTRY JOURNAL

#### Formaldehyde

*Intrapersonal* The single carbon aldehyde with the IUPAC name *methanal* is much more commonly known as formaldehyde. Have students research the uses of formaldehyde and the health problems found to be associated with exposure to this chemical. Ask students to include the results of their research in their journals. L2 P 📦

12. Ethanol (on the right) is more soluble than methyl ether. Because of their molecules' greater polarities, alcohols are usually more water-soluble than ethers.

13. Alcohols and amines are more polar than hydrocarbons, which makes them more likely to provide reactive sites for reagents.

National Science Content Standards

Pages 744–747
UCP.1, UCP.2, UCP.5; B.2, B.3; E.2; G.3

Ethanal also has the common name *acetaldehyde.* Scientists often use the common names of organic compounds because they are so familiar to chemists. Because the carbonyl group in an aldehyde always occurs at the end of a carbon chain, no numbers are used in the name unless branches or additional functional groups are present.

Many aldehydes have characteristic odors and flavors. **Figure 23-9** shows examples of naturally occurring aldehydes.

**Figure 23-9**

**a** Benzaldehyde and salicy-laldehyde are two components of the flavor of almonds. **b** The aroma and flavor of cinnamon are produced largely by cin-namaldehyde. Cinnamon is the ground bark of a tropical tree.

Benzaldehyde      Salicylaldehyde      Cinnamaldehyde

An aldehyde molecule contains a polar, reactive structure. However, like ethers, aldehyde molecules cannot form hydrogen bonds among themselves because the molecules have no hydrogen atoms bonded to an oxygen atom. Therefore, aldehydes have lower boiling points than alcohols with the same number of carbon atoms. Water molecules can form hydrogen bonds with the oxygen atom of aldehydes, so aldehydes are more soluble in water than alkanes but not as soluble as alcohols or amines.

**Ketones**  A carbonyl group also can be located within a carbon chain rather than at the end. A **ketone** is an organic compound in which the carbon of the carbonyl group is bonded to two other carbon atoms. Ketones have the general formula

$$R - \overset{\overset{\displaystyle O}{\|}}{C} - R' \qquad - \overset{|}{C} - \overset{\overset{\displaystyle O}{\|}}{C} - \overset{|}{C} -$$

The carbon atoms on either side of the carbonyl group are bonded to other atoms. The simplest ketone has only hydrogen atoms bonded to the side carbons, as shown in the following diagram. The common name of this ketone is acetone.

$$H - \overset{\overset{\displaystyle H}{|}}{C} - \overset{\overset{\displaystyle O}{\|}}{C} - \overset{\overset{\displaystyle H}{|}}{C} - H$$

2-Propanone (acetone)

748    **Chapter 23** Substituted Hydrocarbons and Their Reactions

## Internet Address Book

**Chemistry Online**  Note Internet addresses that you find useful in the space below for quick reference.

_____

_____

_____

_____

_____

**Figure 23-10**

**ⓐ** The solvent 2-propanone (acetone) is used in fingernail polish; it can dissolve and remove the polish as well.
**ⓑ** Although the solvent 2-butanone is not familiar to most people, it is a popular solvent in industries that put coatings on other materials.

**ⓐ**

H     O     H
|     ‖     |
H — C — C — C — H
|           |
H           H

**2-Propanone
(acetone)**

**ⓑ**

H     O     H     H
|     ‖     |     |
H — C — C — C — C — H
|           |     |
H           H     H

**2-Butanone
(methyethyl ketone)**

Ketones are formally named by changing the *-e* at the end of the alkane name to *-one,* and including a number before the name to indicate the position of the ketone group. In the previous example, the alkane name propane is changed to propan*one.* The carbonyl group can be located only in the center, but the prefix *2-* is usually added to the name for clarity. **Figure 23-10** shows representative ketones and their uses.

Ketones and aldehydes share many chemical and physical properties because their structures are so similar. Ketones are polar molecules and are less reactive than aldehydes. For this reason, ketones are popular solvents for other moderately polar substances, including waxes, plastics, paints, lacquers, varnishes, and glues. Like aldehydes, ketone molecules cannot form hydrogen bonds with each other but can form hydrogen bonds with water molecules. Therefore, ketones are somewhat soluble in water. Acetone is completely miscible with water.

## Carboxylic Acids

A **carboxylic acid** is an organic compound that has a carboxyl group. A **carboxyl group** consists of a carbonyl group bonded to a hydroxyl group. Thus, carboxylic acids have the general formula

O
‖
— C — OH

The following diagram shows the structure of a carboxylic acid familiar to you—acetic acid, the acid found in vinegar.

H     O
|     ‖
H — C — C — OH
|
H

**Ethanoic acid
(acetic acid)**

Although many carboxylic acids have common names, the formal name is formed by changing the *-ane* of the parent alkane to *-anoic acid.* Thus, the formal name of acetic acid is ethanoic acid.

23.3 Carbonyl Compounds    **749**

### Enrichment

👥 *Interpersonal* Have interested students browse several aisles in a supermarket and note the foods that contain palm oil, stearic acid, and benzoic acid. Have them also research the possible positive and negative effects of consuming these compounds. Have these students share their findings with the class. **L1**

### ✔ Assessment

**Knowledge** Ask students to match the formulas $C_7H_{14}O_2$ and $C_7H_6O_2$ with the names benzoic acid and heptanoic acid. $C_7H_6O_2$ is benzoic acid; $C_7H_{14}O_2$ is heptanoic acid. **L2**

**DIFFERENTIATED INSTRUCTION**

### Learning Disabled

*Kinesthetic* Some students will better understand differences between functional groups if they build models of compounds containing them. Ask these students to build models of butanal, 2-butanone, and butanoic acid. They should carefully examine each structure, noting similarities and differences. **L1**
**ELL** 📦

**Formic acid**

**Figure 23-11**

Formic acid is the simplest carboxylic acid. Stinging ants produce formic acid as a defense mechanism.

A carboxyl group is usually represented in condensed form by writing −COOH. For example, ethanoic acid can be written as $CH_3COOH$. The simplest carboxylic acid consists of a carboxyl group bonded to a single hydrogen atom, HCOOH. Its formal name is methanoic acid, but it is more commonly known as formic acid. See **Figure 23-11.**

Carboxylic acids are polar and reactive. Those that dissolve in water ionize weakly to produce hydronium ions and the anion of the acid in equilibrium with water and the un-ionized acid. The ionization of ethanoic acid is an example.

$$CH_3COOH(aq) + H_2O(l) \rightleftharpoons CH_3COO^-(aq) + H_3O^+(aq)$$

Ethanoic acid           Ethanoate ion

(acetic acid)           (acetate ion)

Carboxylic acids can ionize in water solution because the two oxygen atoms are highly electronegative and attract electrons away from the hydrogen atom in the −OH group. As a result, the hydrogen proton can transfer to another atom that has a pair of electrons not involved in bonding, such as the oxygen atom of a water molecule. Because they ionize in water, soluble carboxylic acids turn blue litmus paper red and have a sour taste.

Some important carboxylic acids, such as oxalic acid and adipic acid, have two or more carboxyl groups. An acid with two carboxyl groups is called a dicarboxylic acid. Others have additional functional groups such as hydroxyl groups, as shown in **Figure 23-12.** Typically, these acids are more soluble in water and often more acidic than acids with only a carboxyl group.

## Organic Compounds Derived From Carboxylic Acids

Several classes of organic compounds have structures in which the hydrogen or the hydroxyl group of a carboxylic acid is replaced by a different atom or group of atoms. The two most common classes are esters and amides.

**Esters** An **ester** is any organic compound with a carboxyl group in which the hydrogen of the hydroxyl group has been replaced by an alkyl group, producing the following arrangement

**Figure 23-12**

Lactic acid produces the tangy taste of buttermilk. It also accumulates in the muscles during heavy exercise.

OH
|
$CH_3 - C - COOH$
|
H

**Lactic acid**

Carboxyl group         Ester group

The name of an ester is formed by writing the name of the alkyl group followed by the name of the acid with the *–ic acid* ending replaced by *-ate*, as illustrated by the example shown below. Note how the name *propyl ethanoate*

Ethanoate group     Propyl group

$$CH_3 - \overset{O}{\overset{\|}{C}} - O - CH_2CH_2CH_3$$

Ester group

**Propyl ethanoate**
**(propyl acetate)**

$$CH_3(CH_2)_3C-O-CH_2(CH_2)_3CH_3$$

Pentyl pentanoate

$$CH_3CH_2CH_2C-O-CH_2CH_3$$

Ethyl butanoate

$$CH_3C-O-CH_2CH_2CH(CH_3)CH_3$$

3-Methylbutyl acetate

**Figure 23-13**

Esters are responsible for the flavors and aromas of many fruits. Pentyl pentanoate smells like ripe apples. Ethyl butanoate has the aroma of pineapples, and 3-methylbutyl acetate smells like bananas although it imparts a pear flavor to foods. Most natural aromas and flavors are mixtures of esters, aldehydes, and alcohols.

results from the structural formula. The name shown in parentheses is based on the name *acetic acid,* the common name for ethanoic acid.

Esters are polar molecules and many are volatile and sweet-smelling. Many kinds of esters are found in the natural fragrances and flavors of flowers and fruits. Natural flavors such as apple or banana result from mixtures of many different organic molecules, including esters. See **Figure 23-13.** But some of these flavors can be imitated by a single ester structure. Consequently, esters are manufactured for use as flavors in many foods and beverages and as fragrances in candles, perfumes, and other scented items. You will prepare an ester in the following **miniLAB.**

## miniLAB

### Making an Ester

**Observing and Inferring** Flowers and fruits have pleasant odors partly because they contain substances called esters. Companies make blends of synthetic esters to mimic the flavors and fragrances of esters found in nature. In this experiment, you will make an ester that has a familiar smell.

**Materials** salicylic acid, methanol, distilled water, 10-mL graduated cylinder, Beral pipette, 250-mL beaker, concentrated sulfuric acid, top or bottom of a petri dish, cotton ball, small test tube, balance, weighing paper, hot plate, test-tube holder

**Procedure**

1. Prepare a hot-water bath by pouring 150 mL of tap water into a 250-mL beaker. Place the beaker on a hot plate set at medium.

2. Place 1.5 g of salicylic acid in a small test tube and add 3 mL of distilled water. Then add 3 mL of methanol and 3 drops of concentrated sulfuric acid to the test tube. CAUTION: *Sulfuric acid is corrosive. Handle with care.*

3. When the water is hot but not boiling, place the test tube in the bath for 5 minutes.

4. Place the cotton ball in the petri dish half. Pour the contents of the test tube onto the cotton ball. Record your observation of the odor of the product.

### Analysis

1. The ester you produced has the common name oil of wintergreen. Write a chemical equation using names and structural formulas for the reaction that produced the ester.

2. What are the advantages and disadvantages of using synthetic esters in consumer products as compared to using natural esters?

3. Name some products that you think could contain the ester you made in this experiment.

23.3 Carbonyl Compounds **751**

### Resource Manager

**ChemLab and MiniLab Worksheets,**
  p. 89 **L2**
**Challenge Problems,** p. 23 **L3**

**Amides** An **amide** is an organic compound in which the −OH group of a carboxylic acid is replaced by a nitrogen atom bonded to other atoms. The general structure of an amide is shown below.

Carboxyl group

Amide group

Amides are named by writing the name of the alkane with the same number of carbon atoms, and then replacing the final −e with −amide. Thus, the amide shown below is called ethanamide, but it also may be named acetamide from the common name, acetic acid.

Ethanamide (acetamide)

The amide functional group is found repeated many times in natural proteins and some synthetic materials. For example, you may have used a nonaspirin pain reliever containing acetaminophen. In the acetaminophen structure shown below, you can see that the amide (−NH−) group connects a carbonyl group and an aromatic group.

$$CH_3 - C \overset{O}{\underset{\underset{H}{N}}{\|}} \underset{}{\longrightarrow} OH$$

## Condensation Reactions

Many laboratory syntheses and industrial processes involve the reaction of two organic reactants to form a larger organic product, such as the aspirin shown in **Figure 23-14**. This type of reaction is known as a condensation reaction.

**Figure 23-14**

To synthesize aspirin, two organic molecules are combined in a condensation reaction to form a larger molecule.

Salicylic acid     Acetic acid     Acetylsalicylic acid    Water
(aspirin)

---

## CULTURAL DIVERSITY

### Early Aspirin

While the German chemist Felix Hoffmann is given credit for producing the modern synthetic form of aspirin in the late 1800s, numerous ancient cultures, including Native Americans, discovered aspirin's pharmacological ancestor long before Hoffmann's time. Its past reaches to at least the fifth century B.C., when the Greek physician Hippocrates used a bitter powder he extracted from willow bark to ease aches and pains and reduce fever. The substance in the bark with medicinal properties is salicin, an organic compound very similar to the modern form of aspirin. 🔲

**National Science Content Standards**

**Pages 752–753**
UCP.1, UCP.2, UCP.5; B.2, B.3

Ethanoic acid          3–Methylbutanol          3–Methylbutyl ethanoate

In a **condensation reaction,** two smaller organic molecules combine to form a more complex molecule, accompanied by the loss of a small molecule such as water. Typically, the molecule lost is formed from one particle from each of the reactant molecules. In essence, a condensation reaction is an elimination reaction in which a bond is formed between two atoms not previously bonded to each other.

The most common condensation reactions involve the combining of carboxylic acids with other organic molecules. A common way to synthesize an ester is by a condensation reaction between a carboxylic acid and an alcohol. Such a reaction can be represented by the general equation

$$RCOOH + R'OH \rightarrow RCOOR' + H_2O$$

For example, the reaction represented by the ball-and-stick models in **Figure 23-15** produces an ester that is a part of artificial banana flavoring.

**Figure 23-15**

When ethanoic acid and 3-methylbutanol undergo a condensation reaction, the ester 3-methylbutyl ethanoate is formed. The water molecule eliminated is made up of the $-OH$ group from the acid and the $H-$ from the alcohol.

## Section 23.3 Assessment

**14.** Draw the structure for a carbonyl group.

**15.** Classify each of the following structures as one of the types of organic substances you have studied in this section.

a.
$$\underset{\displaystyle CH_3CH_2CH_2CH}{\overset{\displaystyle O}{\|}}$$

b.
$$\underset{\displaystyle CH_3CH_2CCH_3}{\overset{\displaystyle O}{\|}}$$

c.
$$\underset{\displaystyle CH_3CH_2CH_2C-OH}{\overset{\displaystyle O}{\|}}$$

d.
$$\underset{\displaystyle CH_3CH_2-O-C-CH_3}{\overset{\displaystyle O}{\|}}$$

e.
$$\underset{\displaystyle CH_3CH_2CH_2C-NH_2}{\overset{\displaystyle O}{\|}}$$

f.

**16.** What are the products of a condensation reaction between a carboxylic acid and an alcohol?

**17.** What features of the substances discussed in this section make many of them useful solvents? Explain how these features affect the properties of the molecules.

**18. Thinking Critically** Suggest a reason for the observation that water-soluble organic compounds with carboxyl groups exhibit acidic properties in solutions, whereas similar compounds with aldehyde structures do not.

**19. Formulating Models** You learned that the molecular formulas for alkanes follow the pattern $C_nH_{2n+2}$. Derive a general formula to represent an aldehyde, a ketone, and a carboxylic acid. Could you examine a molecular formula for one of these three types of compounds and determine which type the formula represents? Explain.

chemistrymc.com/self_check_quiz

23.3 Carbonyl Compounds    **753**

## Section 23.3 Assessment

**14.** $-\overset{|}{C}=O$
**15. a.** aldehyde
    **b.** ketone
    **c.** carboxylic acid
    **d.** ester
    **e.** amide
    **f.** ketone
**16.** The products are an ester and water.

**17.** Generally, a useful solvent must exist as a liquid in the temperature range where it will be used, dissolve the solute substances, and evaporate readily so that it can be removed when desired. Therefore, most solvent molecules have fairly low molecular masses, which give the solvents low boiling points.

## 3 Assess
### Check for Understanding

Ask students to give the names and structures of five compounds, one compound representing each of the following categories: an aldehyde; a ketone; a carboxylic acid; an ester; an amide. **L2**

### Reteach

Have students list all categories of carbonyl compounds discussed in the section. Ask them to describe some of the properties of and uses for each type of compound. **L2**

### Extension

Show students the structure of a large, complex, organic biomolecule, such as cholesterol or ATP. Ask them to circle and name all the functional groups present in the structure. **L2**

### ✓ Assessment

**Performance** Have students work in small groups to build ball-and-stick models of an alkyl halide, an alcohol, an aldehyde, a ketone, a carboxylic acid, an ester, and an amide. Use the models to give a practical quiz in which all the students must name the compound represented by each model. Use the Performance Task Assessment List for Model in **PASC,** p. 51. **L2** **ELL**

**18.** The carboxyl group can readily ionize, donating an $H^+$ ion. However, the hydrogen atom bonded to an aldehyde's carbonyl group does not readily ionize.

**19.** Aldehyde: $C_nH_{2n}O$; ketone: $C_nH_{2n}O$; carboxylic acid: $C_nH_{2n}O_2$. No. A molecular formula can be used to distinguish between a carboxylic acid and an aldehyde or ketone, but not between an aldehyde and a ketone because both have the same general formula.

**753**

# 1 Focus

Before presenting the lesson, display **Section Focus Transparency 89** on the overhead projector. Have students answer the accompanying questions using **Section Focus Transparency Master 89**. **L1** **ELL**

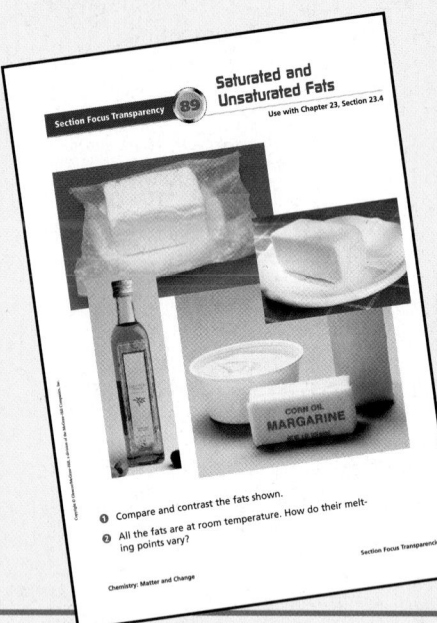

Section Focus Transparency 89

Saturated and Unsaturated Fats
Use with Chapter 23, Section 23.4

CORN OIL MARGARINE

❶ Compare and contrast the fats shown.
❷ All the fats are at room temperature. How do their melting points vary?

Chemistry: Matter and Change

Section Focus Transparencies

# 2 Teach

**Knowledge** Ask students to distinguish between the terms *addition* and *elimination*. **L1** **ELL**

## Resource Manager

Section Focus Transparency 89 and Master **L1** **ELL**
Study Guide for Content Mastery, p. 137 **L2**
Solving Problems: A Chemistry Handbook, Section 23.4 **L2**
Teaching Transparency 71 and Master **L2** **ELL**
Lab Manual, pp. 177–180 **L2**

---

# Other Reactions of Organic Compounds

## Objectives

- **Classify** an organic reaction into one of five categories: substitution, addition, elimination, oxidation-reduction, or condensation.

- **Use** structural formulas to write equations for reactions of organic compounds.

- **Predict** the products of common types of organic reactions.

## Vocabulary

elimination reaction
dehydrogenation reaction
dehydration reaction
addition reaction
hydration reaction
hydrogenation reaction

**Figure 23-16**

Through organic chemical reactions, the aliphatic and aromatic substances in petroleum are changed into compounds used to manufacture many important products, some of which are shown here.

Organic chemists have discovered thousands of reactions by which organic compounds can be changed into different organic compounds. By using combinations of these reactions, chemical industries convert simple molecules from petroleum and natural gas into the large, complex organic molecules found in many useful products—from lifesaving drugs to the plastic case of a telephone. See **Figure 23-16.**

## Reactions of Organic Substances

It is important to understand why organic reactions differ from inorganic reactions. For any chemical reaction to occur, existing bonds must be broken and new bonds formed. As you have learned, the bonds in organic substances are covalent. Because covalent bonds are fairly strong, this rearrangement of bonds causes many reactions of organic compounds to be slow and require a continuous input of energy to keep molecules moving rapidly and colliding. Sometimes catalysts must be used to speed up organic reactions that could otherwise take days, months, or even longer to yield usable amounts of product. Often, bonds can break and re-form in several different positions. Consequently, nearly all organic reactions result in a mixture of products. The unwanted products must then be separated from the expected product, a process that often requires much time and manipulation.

## Classifying Organic Reactions

You've already learned about substitution and condensation reactions in Sections 23.1 and 23.3. Two other important types of organic reactions are elimination and addition.

**Elimination reactions**  One way to change an alkane into a chemically reactive substance is to form a second covalent bond between two carbon atoms, producing an alkene. The main industrial source of alkenes is the cracking of petroleum. The process of cracking, shown in **Figure 23-17,** breaks large alkanes into smaller alkanes, alkenes, and aromatic compounds. Why do you suppose the term *cracking* was applied to this process?

The formation of alkenes from alkanes is an **elimination reaction,** a reaction in which a combination of atoms is removed from two adjacent carbon atoms forming an additional bond between the carbon atoms. The atoms that are eliminated usually form stable molecules, such as $H_2O$, HCl, or $H_2$. Ethene, an important starting material in the chemical industry, is produced by the elimination of two hydrogen atoms from ethane. A reaction that eliminates two hydrogen atoms is called a **dehydrogenation reaction.** Note that the two hydrogen atoms form a molecule of hydrogen gas.

$$H-\overset{\overset{\displaystyle H}{|}}{\underset{\underset{\displaystyle H}{|}}{C}}-\overset{\overset{\displaystyle H}{|}}{\underset{\underset{\displaystyle H}{|}}{C}}-H \rightarrow \overset{H}{\underset{H}{}}C=C\overset{H}{\underset{H}{}} + H_2$$

Ethane          Ethene

An elimination reaction (dehydrogenation)

## DIFFERENTIATED INSTRUCTION

### Gifted

 *Intrapersonal* Ask interested students to research the actual steps used in the synthesis of a large organic compound, such as the anti-cancer drug taxol. As they progress through the section, ask them to label some of the steps as substitutions, eliminations, additions, condensations, or redox reactions. **L3**

Catalytic cracking unit

**Quick Demo**

Choose one of the carboxylic acid-alcohol pairs listed below under the heading "Alcohol, Acid, Flavor." Mix together in a test tube 1 mL of each component and two drops of concentrated sulfuric acid. Place the test tube in a hot water bath for ten minutes. While you're waiting for the reaction to take place, ask students to use what they have learned in the previous section to predict what type of reaction will occur. a condensation reaction in which two molecules combine to form an ester. Ask them how they might be able to tell when the reaction is complete. The odor will change as the reaction progresses. Due to its lower density, the ester formed may produce a visible layer on top of the original mixture. Let students examine the product and carefully waft its vapors toward their noses to try to identify its scent.

**Alcohol, Acid, Flavor**
n-amyl alcohol, butyric acid, apricot; n-amyl alcohol, salicylic acid, pineapple; n-amyl alcohol, acetic acid, banana; octanol, acetic acid, fruity; methanol, salicylic acid, wintergreen; methanol, 2-naphthol, perfume; ethanol, butyric acid, apple; ethanol, acetic acid, fruity

Alkyl halides can undergo elimination reactions to produce an alkene and a hydrogen halide, as shown here.

$$R-CH_2-CH_2-X \rightarrow R-CH=CH_2 + HX$$

| Alkyl halide | Alkene | Hydrogen halide |

**Figure 23-17**

The process of catalytic cracking breaks long-chain alkanes into smaller alkanes and alkenes that are more valuable to industry.

Likewise, alcohols also can undergo elimination reactions by losing a hydrogen atom and a hydroxyl group to form water. An elimination reaction in which the atoms removed form water is called a **dehydration reaction.** In the following dehydration reaction, the alcohol is broken down into an alkene and water.

| Alcohol | Alkene | Water |

The generic form of this dehydration reaction can be written as follows.

$$R-CH_2-CH_2-OH \rightarrow R-CH=CH_2 + H_2O$$

**Addition reactions** Another type of organic reaction appears to be an elimination reaction in reverse. An **addition reaction** results when other atoms bond to each of two atoms bonded by double or triple covalent bonds. Addition reactions typically involve double-bonded carbon atoms in alkenes or triple-bonded carbon atoms in alkynes. Addition reactions occur because double and triple bonds have a rich concentration of electrons. Therefore, molecules and ions that attract electrons tend to form bonds that use some of the electrons from the multiple bonds. The most

23.4 Other Reactions of Organic Compounds **755**

**Internet Address Book**

Chemistry Online

Note Internet addresses that you find useful in the space below for quick reference.

National Science Content Standards

Pages 754–755
UCP.1, UCP.2, UCP.5; B.2, B.3

## In-Text Question

**Page 756** This reaction is the reverse of one of the reactions you studied earlier in the section. Which one? dehydrogenation

**Figure 23-18**

These examples are common addition reactions that can be carried out with alkenes. Many other addition reactions are possible.

Addition Reactions with Alkenes

common addition reactions are those in which $H_2O$, $H_2$, HX, or $X_2$ add to an alkene as shown in **Figure 23-18.**

A **hydration reaction** is an addition reaction in which a hydrogen atom and a hydroxyl group from a water molecule add to a double or triple bond. As shown in the following generic example, a hydration reaction is the opposite of a dehydration reaction.

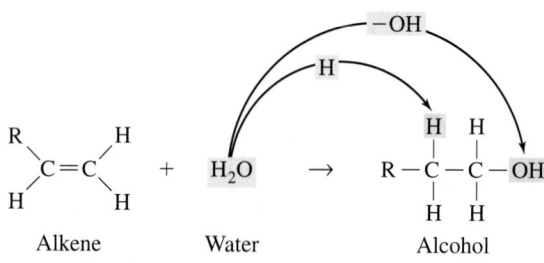

A reaction that involves the addition of hydrogen to atoms in a double or triple bond is called a **hydrogenation reaction.** This reaction is the reverse of one of the reactions you studied earlier in this section. Which one? One molecule of $H_2$ reacts to fully hydrogenate each double bond in a molecule. When $H_2$ adds to the double bond of an alkene, the alkene is converted to an alkane.

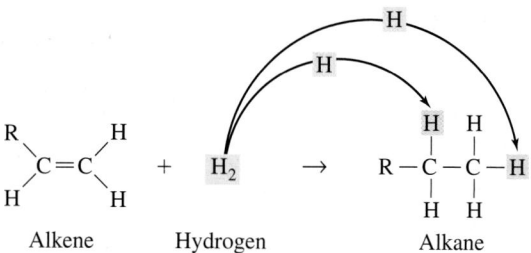

## CHEMISTRY JOURNAL

### Hydrogenated Fats

**Linguistic** Have students cruise grocery-store aisles and record at least ten products that contain hydrogenated or partially hydrogenated fats or oils. Have them look up the molecular and structural formulas for one or more of the fats or oils and record their findings in their chemistry journals. **L2**

Catalysts are usually needed in the hydrogenation of alkenes because the reaction's activation energy is too large without them. Catalysts such as powdered platinum or palladium provide a surface that adsorbs the reactants and makes their electrons more available to bond to other atoms.

Hydrogenation reactions are commonly used to convert the liquid unsaturated fats found in oils from plants such as soybean, corn, and peanuts into saturated fats that are solid at room temperature. These hydrogenated fats are then used to make margarine and solid shortening. You will learn more about the composition of fats in Chapter 24.

Alkynes also may also be hydrogenated to produce alkenes or alkanes. Two molecules of $H_2$ must be added to each triple bond in order to convert an alkyne to an alkane, as shown in the following equations.

First $H_2$ molecule added

$$R-C\equiv C-H + H_2 \quad \rightarrow \quad R-CH=CH_2$$

Alkyne                    Alkene

Second $H_2$ molecule added

$$R-CH=CH_2 + H_2 \quad \rightarrow \quad R-CH_2-CH_3$$

Alkene                    Alkane

The addition of hydrogen halides to alkenes obtained from petroleum or natural gas is an addition reaction useful to industry for the production of alkyl halides.

$$R-CH=CH-R' + HX \quad \rightarrow \quad R-CHX-CH_2-R'$$

Alkene                    Alkyl halide

As you learned earlier, R' is used to represent a second alkyl group. Chemists use the symbols R', R'', R''', and so on to represent different alkyl groups in organic molecules.

Do the **problem-solving LAB** below to learn how functional groups give organic compounds characteristic properties that may be used to identify a compound's general type.

## problem-solving LAB

### Categorizing Organic Compounds

**Analyze and Conclude** Functional groups give organic compounds distinct properties that may be used to identify the type of compound present. Suppose you examined the properties of several compounds and made the following observations.

**Analysis**

**Compound 1** is a liquid that has a pungent odor. It is miscible with water, and the solution is a weak electrolyte.

**Compound 2** is a crystalline solid with a melting point of 112°C and almost no odor. It is soluble in water, and chemical analysis shows that it contains nitrogen in addition to carbon, hydrogen and oxygen.

**Compound 3** is a liquid that has a strong aroma resembling apricots. When spilled on a wood tabletop, it damages the finish.

**Compound 4** is an oily-looking liquid with a disagreeable odor similar to a combination of ammonia and dead fish. It is soluble in water.

**Thinking Critically**

Use what you have learned about the properties of organic compounds with functional groups to suggest the category to which each compound belongs.

**Purpose**
Students will categorize organic compounds based on their properties.

**Process Skills**
Thinking critically, classifying, analyzing and concluding

**Teaching Strategies**
- You may want to let students use handbooks and access the Internet in their search for information. If so, have them visit the Chemistry Web site at science.glencoe.com.
- You may decide to assign the Problem-Solving Lab as homework.

**Thinking Critically**
Compound 1 is likely a carboxylic acid. Compound 2 is likely an amide. Compound 3 is likely an ester. Compound 4 is likely an amine.

### Assessment
**Performance** Have students draw the general structural formulas for carboxylic acids, amides, esters, and amines. Use the Performance Task Assessment List for Scientific Drawing in **PASC**, p. 55. **L2** **ELL**

758

## Reinforcement

Have students write the chemical equation for the combustion of methane to gaseous carbon dioxide and liquid water. $CH_4(g) + 2O_2(g) \rightarrow CO_2(g) + 2H_2O(l)$ Reinforce students' understanding of oxidation and reduction by having them determine the oxidation states of all elements and reactants and products. $CH_4$: C is −4, H is +1, $O_2$: O is 0; $CO_2$: C is +4, O is −2, $H_2O$: H is +1, O is −2 Then, ask students to identify the element oxidized and the element reduced. Carbon is oxidized. Oxygen is reduced. Emphasize that although both oxidation and reduction are involved in the reaction, it is called an oxidation reaction because an element in methane, the organic compound, is oxidized. **L2**

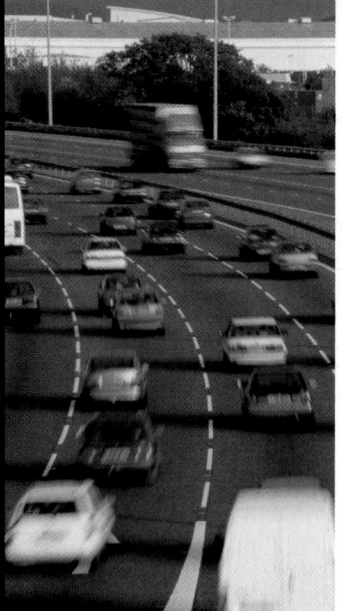

**Figure 23-19**

The oxidation of hydrocarbons provides the energy to run most of the vehicles on this crowded freeway.

**Oxidation-reduction reactions** Many organic compounds can be converted to other compounds by oxidation and reduction reactions. For example, suppose that you wish to convert methane, the main constituent of natural gas, to methanol, a common industrial solvent and raw material for making formaldehyde and methyl esters. The conversion of methane to methanol may be represented by the following equation, in which [O] represents oxygen from an agent such as copper(II) oxide, potassium dichromate, or sulfuric acid.

$$\underset{\overset{|}{H}}{\overset{\overset{\displaystyle H}{|}}{H-C-H}} + [O] \rightarrow \underset{\overset{|}{H}}{\overset{\overset{\displaystyle H}{|}}{H-C-O-H}}$$

What happens to methane in this reaction? Before answering, it might be helpful to review the definitions of oxidation and reduction. Oxidation is the loss of electrons, and a substance is oxidized when it gains oxygen or loses hydrogen. Reduction is the gain of electrons, and a substance is reduced when it loses oxygen or gains hydrogen. Thus, methane is oxidized as it gains oxygen and is converted to methanol. Of course, every redox reaction involves both an oxidation and a reduction; however, organic redox reactions are described based on the change in the organic compound.

Oxidizing the methanol produced in the previous reaction is the first step in the sequence of reactions described by the following equations. For clarity, oxidizing agents are omitted.

$$\underset{\overset{|}{H}}{\overset{\overset{\displaystyle H}{|}}{H-C-OH}} \xrightarrow[\text{(loss of hydrogen)}]{\text{oxidation}} \overset{\overset{\displaystyle O}{\|}}{H-C-H} \xrightarrow[\text{(gain of oxygen)}]{\text{oxidation}} \overset{\overset{\displaystyle O}{\|}}{H-C-OH} \xrightarrow[\text{(loss of hydrogen)}]{\text{oxidation}} O=C=O$$

Methanol  (methyl alcohol)    Methanal  (formaldehyde)    Methanoic acid  (formic acid)    Carbon dioxide

Preparing an aldehyde by this method is not always a simple task because the oxidation may continue, forming the carboxylic acid. However, not all alcohols can be oxidized to aldehydes and, subsequently, carboxylic acids. To understand why, compare the oxidations of 1-propanol and 2-propanol shown in the following equations.

$$\underset{\overset{|}{H}}{\overset{\overset{\displaystyle OH}{|}}{H-C-CH_2-CH_3}} + [O] \rightarrow \overset{\overset{\displaystyle O}{\|}}{H-C-CH_2-CH_3}$$

1-Propanol                          Propanal

$$\underset{\overset{|}{H}}{\overset{\overset{\displaystyle OH}{|}}{CH_3-C-CH_3}} + [O] \rightarrow \overset{\overset{\displaystyle O}{\|}}{CH_3-C-CH_3}$$

2-Propanol                          2-Propanone

**758**    **Chapter 23** Substituted Hydrocarbons and Their Reactions

---

### DIFFERENTIATED INSTRUCTION

#### Gifted

*Intrapersonal* Have capable students write the chemical equations for the oxidations of 1-butanol and 2-butanol. Have them use the style on this page, in which [O] represents oxygen from an oxidizing agent. **L3**

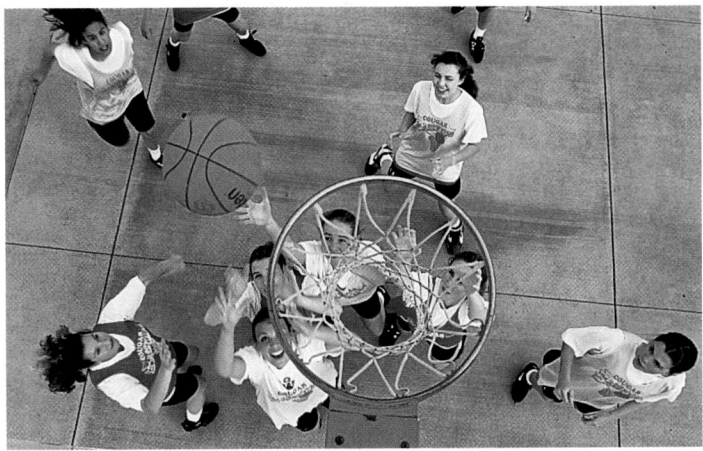

**Figure 23-20**

Organic oxidation-reduction reactions provide the energy that these students need to live and play active sports such as basketball.

Note that oxidizing 2-propanol yields a ketone, not an aldehyde. Unlike aldehydes, ketones resist further oxidation to carboxylic acids. Thus, while the propanal formed by oxidizing 1-propanol easily oxidizes to form propanoic acid, the 2-propanone formed by oxidizing 2-propanol does not react to form a carboxylic acid.

How important are organic oxidations and reductions? You've seen that oxidation and reduction reactions can change one functional group into another. That ability enables chemists to use organic redox reactions, in conjunction with the substitution and addition reactions you learned about earlier in the chapter, to synthesize a tremendous variety of useful products. On a personal note, living systems—including you—depend on the energy released by oxidation reactions. Of course, some of the most dramatic oxidation-reduction reactions are combustion reactions. All organic compounds that contain carbon and hydrogen burn in excess oxygen to produce carbon dioxide and water. For example, the highly exothermic combustion of ethane is described by the following thermochemical equation.

$$2C_2H_6(g) + 7O_2(g) \rightarrow 4CO_2(g) + 6H_2O(l) \qquad \triangle H = -3120 \text{ kJ}$$

As you learned in Chapter 10, much of the world relies on the combustion of hydrocarbons as a primary source of energy. Our reliance on the energy from organic oxidation reactions is illustrated in **Figures 23-19** and **23-20.**

## Predicting Products of Organic Reactions

The generic equations representing the different types of organic reactions you have learned—substitution, elimination, addition, oxidation-reduction, and condensation—can be used to predict the products of other organic reactions of the same types. For example, suppose you were asked to predict the product of an elimination reaction in which 1-butanol is a reactant. You know that a common elimination reaction involving an alcohol is a dehydration reaction.

The generic equation for the dehydration of an alcohol is

$$R-CH_2-CH_2-OH \rightarrow R-CH=CH_2 + H_2O$$

To determine the actual product, first draw the structure of 1-butanol. Then use the generic equation as a model to see how 1-butanol would react.

23.4 Other Reactions of Organic Compounds    **759**

From the generic reaction, you can see that only the carbon bonded to the —OH and the carbon next to it react. Finally, draw the structure of the likely products as shown in the following equation. Your result should be the following equation.

$$CH_3—CH_2—CH_2—CH_2—OH \rightarrow CH_3—CH_2—CH=CH_2 + H_2O$$
1-Butanol                          1-Butene

As another example, suppose that you wish to predict the product of the reaction between cyclopentene and hydrogen bromide. Recall that the generic equation for an addition reaction between an alkene and an alkyl halide is as follows.

$$R—CH=CH—R' + HX \rightarrow R—CHX—CH_2—R'$$

First, draw the structure for cyclopentene, the organic reactant, and add the formula for hydrogen bromide, the other reactant. From the generic equation, you can see that a hydrogen atom and a halide atom add across the double bond to form an alkyl halide. Finally, draw the formula for the likely product. If you are correct, you have written the following equation.

           ⬠        + HBr $\rightarrow$        ⬠—Br

Cyclopentene    Hydrogen bromide    Bromocyclopentane

## Section 23.4 Assessment

20. Classify each of the following reactions as either substitution, elimination, addition, or condensation.

  **a.** $CH_3CH=CHCH_2CH_3 + H_2 \rightarrow$
                         $CH_3CH_2—CH_2CH_2CH_3$

  **b.** $CH_3CH_2CH_2CHCH_3 \rightarrow$
                   |
                  OH

      $CH_3CH_2CH=CHCH_3 + H_2O$

21. Identify the type of organic reaction that would best accomplish each of the following conversions.
  **a.** alkyl halide $\rightarrow$ alkene
  **b.** alkene $\rightarrow$ alcohol
  **c.** alcohol + carboxylic acid $\rightarrow$ ester

22. Complete each of the following equations by writing the condensed structural formula for the product that is most likely to form.
  **a.** $CH_3CH=CHCH_2CH_3 + H_2 \rightarrow$
  **b.** $CH_3CH_2CHCH_2CH_3 + OH^- \rightarrow$
                 |
                 Cl

  **c.** $CH_3CH_2C\equiv CCH_3 + 2H_2 \rightarrow$
  **d.**                Dehydration
      $CH_3CH_2CHCH_2CH_3$   $\rightarrow$
                  |
                  OH

23. **Thinking Critically** Explain why the hydration reaction involving 1-butene may yield two distinct products whereas the hydration of 2-butene yields but one product.

24. **Comparing and Contrasting** Explain the difference between an elimination reaction and a condensation reaction. Which type is best represented by the following equation?

      $HO—CH_2CH_2CH_2CH_2—OH \rightarrow$

      ⬠(O) + $H_2O$

## Section 23.4 Assessment

**20. a.** addition
   **b.** elimination
**21. a.** elimination
   **b.** addition
   **c.** condensation
**22. a.** $CH_3CH_2CH_2CH_2CH_3$
   **b.** $CH_3CH_2CH(OH)CH_2CH_3$

**760**

  **c.** $CH_3CH_2CH_2CH_2CH_3$
  **d.** $CH_3CH=CHCH_2CH_3$
**23.** Hydrating 1-butene may yield 1-butanol and/or 2-butanol because hydroxyl groups may bond to carbons 1 and/or 2 of the 4-carbon chain. Hydrating 2-butene, however, yields only 2-butanol

because the hydroxyl group must be on carbon 2.
**24.** Elimination reaction: one organic molecule loses atoms or groups of atoms to form smaller molecules. Condensation reaction: two organic molecules combine to form a larger one. elimination

Think how different your life would be without plastic sandwich bags, plastic foam cups, nylon and polyester fabrics, vinyl siding on buildings, foam cushions, and a variety of other synthetic materials. Synthetic materials do not exist in nature; they are produced by the chemical industry.

## The Age of Polymers

The structural formulas shown in **Figure 23-21** represent extremely long molecules having groups of atoms that repeat in a regular pattern. These molecules are examples of synthetic polymers. **Polymers** are large molecules consisting of many repeating structural units. The letter $n$ represents the number of structural units in the polymer chain. Because polymer $n$ values vary widely, molecular masses of polymers range from less than 10 000 amu to more than 1 000 000 amu. A typical Teflon chain has about 400 units, giving it a molecular mass of around 40 000 amu.

Before the development of synthetic polymers, people were limited to using natural substances such as stone, wood, metals, wool, and cotton. By the turn of the twentieth century, a few chemically treated natural polymers such as rubber and the first plastic, celluloid, had become available. Celluloid is made by treating cellulose from cotton or wood fiber with nitric acid.

The first synthetic polymer was Bakelite, synthesized in 1909. Bakelite is still used today in stove-top appliances because of its resistance to heat. Since 1909, hundreds of other synthetic polymers have been developed. In the future, people may refer to this time as the Age of Polymers.

### Objectives

- **Describe** the relationship between a polymer and the monomers from which it forms.
- **Classify** polymerization reactions as addition or condensation.
- **Predict** polymer properties based on their molecular structures and the presence of functional groups.

### Vocabulary

polymer
monomer
polymerization reaction
addition polymerization
condensation
   polymerization
plastic
thermoplastic
thermosetting

(a) Polyvinyl chloride

(b) Polystyrene

**Figure 23-21**

(a) The polymer polyvinyl chloride is commonly called "vinyl." It is used to make flexible, waterproof objects. (b) Polystyrene plastic is inexpensive and easy to mold into parts for model cars and airplanes.

23.5 Polymers    **761**

## 1 Focus

### Focus Transparency

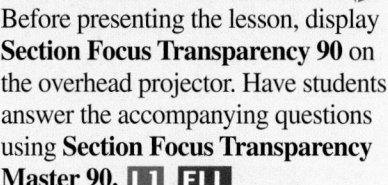

Before presenting the lesson, display **Section Focus Transparency 90** on the overhead projector. Have students answer the accompanying questions using **Section Focus Transparency Master 90.** L1 ELL

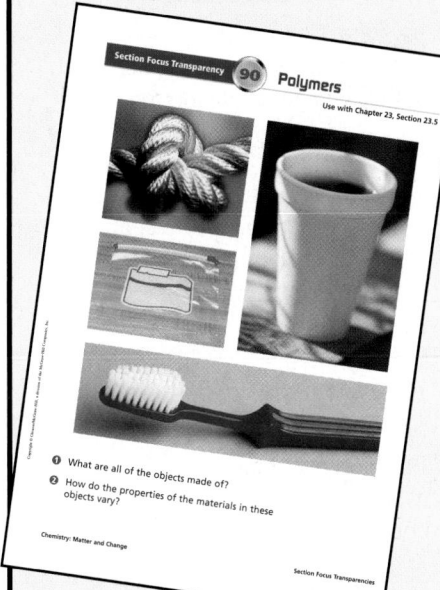

Section Focus Transparency  90  **Polymers**
Use with Chapter 23, Section 23.5

❶ What are all of the objects made of?
❷ How do the properties of the materials in these objects vary?

Chemistry: Matter and Change

Section Focus Transparencies

## 2 Teach

### Quick Demo

In a well-ventilated room, demonstrate polymer formation using one or more of the following products readily available in stores: a polyurethane foam, such as a can of insulating foam; a two-component foam used in constructing landscape items for a train set; Silly String; a two-component system for making a clear polymer used in flower arrangements. Ask students to carefully observe the different appearances of the monomers and the final polymer. Monomers are usually liquids or gases, while polymers are more solid than the monomers from which they're formed.

---

### DIFFERENTIATED INSTRUCTION

#### Learning Disabled

*Kinesthetic* Some students will better understand the relationship between polymers and monomers if they can make models of monomers, join them together as a polymer, and then take them apart again. Ask students to model the process of polymerization using paper clips, safety pins, or beads that snap together. L1 ELL

### ✔ Portfolio

#### Wrapping It Up

*Visual-Spatial* Ask students to find background information about the industrial process used to make plastic wrap. They should include a synopsis of their findings and make a poster showing a flow chart of the process. L2 ELL
P

# Reactions Used to Make Polymers

Polymers are relatively easy to manufacture. They usually can be synthesized in one step in which the major reactant is a substance consisting of small, simple organic molecules called monomers. A **monomer** is a molecule from which a polymer is made.

When a polymer is made, monomers bond together one after another in a rapid series of steps. A catalyst usually is required for the reaction to take place at a reasonable pace. With some polymers, such as Dacron and nylon, two or more kinds of monomers bond to each other in an alternating sequence. A reaction in which monomer units are bonded together to form a polymer is called a **polymerization reaction**. The repeating group of atoms formed by the bonding of the monomers is called the structural unit of the polymer. The structural unit of a polymer made from two different monomers has the components of both monomers.

Unbreakable children's toys are often made of polyethylene, which is synthesized by polymerizing ethene under pressure. Two monomers react to form polyethylene terephthalate (PET), a versatile plastic that is used to make bottles and recording tape. When made into fiber, it is called Dacron. Polyethylene and PET, examples of polymers made by two types of reactions, are shown in **Table 23-3.**

**Addition polymerization** In **addition polymerization,** all of the atoms present in the monomers are retained in the polymer product. When the monomer is ethene, an addition polymerization results in the polymer polyethylene, as shown in **Table 23-3.** Unsaturated bonds are broken in addition polymerization just as they are in addition reactions. The difference is that

**Table 23-3**

| Monomers and Polymers | | |
| --- | --- | --- |
| **Monomer(s)** | **Structural unit of polymer** | **Application** |
| Ethene (ethylene) | Polyethylene |  |
| 1,2-Ethanediol (ethylene glycol) | Polyethylene terephthalate (Dacron in fiber form) (Mylar in film form) | |
| Terephthalic acid | | |

## Demonstration

### Polymers and Monomers

#### Purpose
To help students see the relationship between a polymer and a monomer

#### Materials
Spring-type clothespins (10), paper clips (1 box)

#### Safety Precautions
**Disposal** Reuse the materials for another demonstration.

#### Procedure
Clip one clothespin onto the leg of another one and continue this process to form a polymer chain. Each clothespin represents a monomer. You also can use paper clips to represent the monomers and form a polymer

the molecule added is a second molecule of the same substance, ethene. Note that the addition polymers in **Table 23-4** are similar in structure to polyethylene. That is, the molecular structure of each is equivalent to polyethylene in which other atoms or groups of atoms are attached to the chain in place of hydrogen atoms. All of these polymers are made by addition polymerization.

**Table 23-4**

| Common Polymers | | |
|---|---|---|
| **Polymer** | **Uses** | **Structural unit** |
| Polyethylene (PE) | Plastic bags and wrap, food containers, children's toys, bottles | See **Table 23-3.** |
| Polyvinyl chloride (PVC) | Plastic pipes, meat wrap, upholstery, rainwear, house siding, garden hose | See **Figure 23-21.** |
| Polyacrylonitrile (Orlon) | Fabrics for clothing and upholstery, carpet | $\left[ CH_2 - \underset{\underset{C \equiv N}{\vert}}{CH} \right]_n$ |
| Polyvinylidene chloride (Saran) | Food wrap, fabrics | $\left[ CH_2 - \underset{\underset{Cl}{\vert}}{\overset{\overset{Cl}{\vert}}{C}} \right]_n$ |
| Polytetrafluoro-ethylene (Teflon, PTFE) | Nonstick coatings, bearings, lubricants | $\left[ \underset{\underset{F}{\vert}}{\overset{\overset{F}{\vert}}{C}} - \underset{\underset{F}{\vert}}{\overset{\overset{F}{\vert}}{C}} \right]_n$ |
| Polymethyl methacrylate (Lucite, Plexiglass) | "Nonbreakable" windows, inexpensive lenses, art objects | $\left[ CH_2 - \underset{\underset{CH_3}{\vert}}{\overset{\overset{\overset{O}{\parallel}}{C - OCH_3}}{C}} \right]_n$ |
| Polypropylene (PP) | Beverage containers, rope, netting, kitchen appliances | $\left[ CH_2 - \underset{\underset{CH_3}{\vert}}{CH} \right]_n$ |
| Polystyrene styrene plastic | Foam packing and insulation, plant pots, disposable food containers, model kits | See **Figure 23-21.** |
| Polyethylene terephthalate (PET, Dacron, Mylar) | Soft drink bottles, tire cord, clothing, recording tape, replacements for blood vessels | See **Table 23-3.** |
| Nylon | Upholstery, clothing, carpet, fishing line, small gears, bearings | See **Figure 23-22.** |
| Polyurethane | Foam furniture cushions, waterproof coatings, parts of shoes | $\left[ \overset{\overset{O}{\parallel}}{C} - NH - CH_2 - CH_2 - NH - \overset{\overset{O}{\parallel}}{C} - O - CH_2 - CH_2 - O \right]_n$ |

23.5 Polymers **763**

chain by linking them together. You may wish to amaze students in the following way: make a paper-clip chain before the class period and place it in a small box; as students watch, add loose, individual paper clips to the box. Cover the box and shake it to simulate the reaction. Uncover the box and pull out the previously connected clips.

**Results**
The monomers link together to form a long-chain polymer.

**Analysis**
1. What is the generic name of the small molecules that link together?
   Monomers
2. If a polymer is made from ethylene monomers, what is the polymer called?
   Polyethylene

Polyurethane foam is used as housing insulation and packaging material. One set of monomers used to make such a polymer is a polyalcohol ($HO-R-OH$) and a polyisocyanate ($O=CN-R-NC=O$). Amines or metal salts are used as catalysts in the industrial processes that produce this polymer. The polymer contains carbamate or urethane groups, which have the general structure $-O-R-O-C(=O)-NH-R'-NH-C(=O)-$. Producing the polymer in the presence of a fluorocarbon foaming agent causes the foamy quality. The presence of mutiple functional groups in the monomers results in a high level of cross-linking in the product, forming a rigid foam.

# 3 Assess

## Check for Understanding

Ask students to draw the structures of the monomers needed to make all the addition polymers listed in Table 23-4. PE: $CH_2=CH_2$; PVC: $CH_2=CHCl$; Orlon: $CH_2=CHCN$; Saran: $CH_2=CCl_2$; PTFE: $CF_2=CF_2$; Lucite, Plexiglas: $CH_2=C(CH_3)(CO_2CH_3)$; PP: $CH_3CH=CH_2$; PS: $CH_2=CHC_6H_5$. **L2**

## Reteach

Have students draw the structures of polymers they have not yet studied, given the monomers. Monomers you might use include: methylcyano-acrylate ($CH_2=C(CN)(CO_2CH_3)$), used to make instant glues; vinyl alcohol ($CH_2=CHOH$), used to make polyvinyl alcohol, a starting material for making water-soluble plastic packaging; chlorotrifluoro-ethylene ($CFCl=CF_2$), used to make the Kel-F polymer. **L2**

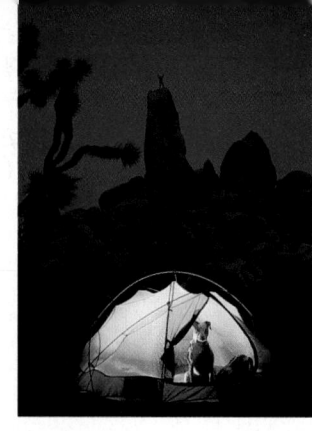

**Condensation polymerization** **Condensation polymerization** takes place when monomers containing at least two functional groups combine with the loss of a small by-product, usually water. Nylon and Kevlar are made this way. Nylon was first synthesized in 1931 and soon became popular because it is strong and can be drawn into thin strands resembling silk. Nylon-6,6 is the name of one type of nylon that is synthesized from two different six-carbon monomers. One monomer is a chain with the end carbon atoms being part of carboxyl groups. The other monomer is a chain having amino groups at both ends. These monomers undergo a condensation polymerization that forms amide groups linking the subunits of the polymer, as shown by the tinted –NH– group in **Figure 23-22**. Note that one water molecule is released for every new amide bond formed.

$$n\text{HOOC}-(CH_2)_4-\text{COOH} + n\text{H}_2\text{N}-(CH_2)_6-\text{NH}_2 \rightarrow \left[\begin{array}{c} O \\ \parallel \\ C \end{array}-(CH_2)_4-\begin{array}{c} O \\ \parallel \\ C \end{array}-NH-(CH_2)_6-NH\right]_n + n\text{H}_2\text{O}$$

Adipic acid      1,6–Diamino hexane      Nylon – 6,6

**Figure 23-22**

Adipic acid and 1,6-diamino-hexane are the monomers that polymerize by condensation to form nylon-6,6. You are probably familiar with nylon fabrics, such as those used to make tents, but nylon can be molded into solid objects too.

# Materials Made from Polymers: Uses and Recycling

Why do we use so many different polymers today? One reason is that they are easy to synthesize. Another reason is that the starting materials used to make them are inexpensive. Still another, more important, reason is that polymers have a wide range of properties. Some polymers can be drawn into fine fibers that are softer than silk, while others are as strong as steel. Polymers don't rust like steel does, and many are more durable than natural materials such as wood. Objects made from lumber that is actually plastic, such as those shown in **Figure 23-23,** may be familiar to you.

**Properties of polymers** Another reason that polymers are in such great demand is that it is easy to mold them into different shapes or to draw them into thin fibers. It is not easy to do this with metals and other natural materials because either they must be heated to high temperatures, do not melt at all, or are too weak to be used to form small, thin items. A **plastic** is a polymer that can be heated and molded while relatively soft.

As with all substances, polymers have properties that result directly from their molecular structure. For example, polyethylene is a long-chain alkane. Thus, it has a waxy feel, does not dissolve in water, is nonreactive, and is a poor electrical conductor. These properties make it ideal for use in food and beverage containers and as an insulator on electrical wire and TV cable.

Polymers fall into two different categories based on their melting characteristics. A **thermoplastic** polymer is one that can be melted and molded repeatedly into shapes that are retained when it is cooled. Polyethylene and nylon are examples of thermoplastic polymers. A **thermosetting** polymer is one that can be molded when it is first prepared, but when cool cannot be remelted. This property is explained by the fact that thermosetting polymers begin to form networks of bonds in many directions when they are synthesized. By the time they have cooled, thermosetting polymers have become, in essence, a single large molecule. Bakelite is an example of a thermosetting polymer. Instead of melting, Bakelite decomposes or burns when overheated.

**Figure 23-23**

Plastic lumber is made from recycled plastic, especially soft drink bottles and polyethylene waste.

## CHEMISTRY JOURNAL

### Serendipity

**Linguistic** Apparently, many important discoveries in polymer science have been made serendipitously, which means "finding something good accidentally." Have students research how either Teflon or nylon was discovered and decide what essential steps actually led to these lucky findings. They should write page-long essays summarizing their findings in their chemistry journals. **L2**

**Recycling polymers** The starting materials for the synthesis of most polymers are derived from fossil fuels. As the supply of fossil fuels is depleted, recycling plastics will become more important. Thermosetting polymers are more difficult to recycle than thermoplastic polymers because only thermoplastic materials can be melted and remolded repeatedly.

Currently, only about 1% of the plastic waste we produce in the United States is recycled. This figure contrasts with the 20% of paper waste and 30% of aluminum waste that are recycled. This low rate of plastics recycling is due in part to the large variety of different plastics found in products. The plastics must be sorted according to polymer composition. This task is time-consuming and expensive. The plastics industry and the government have tried to improve the process by providing standardized codes that indicate the composition of each plastic product. See **Figure 23-24.**

**Figure 23-24**

These codes tell recyclers what kind of plastic an object is made of.

## Section 23.5 Assessment

**25.** Draw the structure for the polymer that could be produced from each of the following monomers by the method stated.

**a.** Addition

$$CH = CH$$
$$\quad | \qquad |$$
$$\quad Cl \quad\ Cl$$

**b.** Condensation

$$NH_2 - CH_2CH_2 - \overset{\displaystyle O}{\overset{\displaystyle \|}{C}} - OH$$

**26.** Label each of the following polymerization reactions as addition or condensation. Write the formulas of the secondary product of the condensation reaction.

**a.**

$$HO - \overset{H}{\underset{H}{\overset{|}{C}}} - \overset{H}{\underset{H}{\overset{|}{C}}} - OH \ + \ HO - \overset{O}{\overset{\|}{C}} - \bigcirc - \overset{O}{\overset{\|}{C}} - OH \rightarrow$$

$$\left[ \overset{O}{\overset{\|}{C}} - \bigcirc - \overset{O}{\overset{\|}{C}} - O - \overset{H}{\underset{H}{\overset{|}{C}}} - \overset{H}{\underset{H}{\overset{|}{C}}} - O - \right]_n$$

**b.**

$$CH_2 = CH \rightarrow \left[ CH_2 - CH \right]_n$$
$$\qquad\ | \qquad\qquad\qquad\qquad |$$
$$\quad\ C \equiv N \qquad\qquad\qquad C \equiv N$$

**27.** Compare the properties of thermosetting and thermoplastic polymers.

**28. Thinking Critically** A chemical process called crosslinking forms covalent bonds between separate polymer chains. How do you think a polymer's properties will change as the number of crosslinks increases? What effect might additional crosslinking have on a thermoplastic polymer?

**29. Predicting** Predict the physical properties of the polymer that is made from the following monomer. Mention solubility in water, electrical conductivity, texture, and chemical reactivity. Do you think it will be thermoplastic or thermosetting? Give reasons for your predictions.

$$CH_2 = CH$$
$$\qquad\quad |$$
$$\qquad\quad CH_3$$

chemistrymc.com/self_check_quiz

## Section 23.5 Assessment

**25. a.**
$$\left[ CH - CH \right]_n$$
$$\quad\ | \qquad\ |$$
$$\quad\ Cl \qquad Cl$$

**b.**
$$\left[ CH_2 - CH_2 - \overset{O}{\overset{\|}{C}} - NH \right]_n$$

**26. a.** condensation; $H_2O$
**b.** addition

**27.** Thermosetting polymers can be molded when first prepared, but cannot be remelted when cooled. Thermoplastic polymers can be melted and molded repeatedly into shapes that are retained when the polymer is cooled.

**28.** Generally, as the number of cross-links increases, the polymer becomes more

rigid and has a higher melting temperature range. Additional cross-linking can make a thermoplastic polymer become thermosetting if melting cannot easily disrupt the cross-links.

**29.** The polymer will have a waxy feel, low water solubility, low electrical conductivity, and low reactivity. It will be thermoplastic. It is a long-chain alkane similar to polyethylene.

## Preparation

### Time Allotment
One laboratory period

### Process Skills
Acquiring and analyzing information, collecting and interpreting data, drawing a conclusion, measuring, observing and inferring, predicting, sequencing.

### Safety Precautions
Alcohols are flammable. Advise students to keep them away from open flames.

### Alternative Materials
• Bathroom tissue can be used in place of facial tissue. However, do not use recycled paper products.
• You may want to use another longer carbon chain alcohol, depending on what you have in your stockroom.

### Pre-Lab

3. $CH_3OH$, $CH_3CH_2OH$, and $CH_3CH(OH)CH_3$. Because they are alcohols, all structures contain the hydroxyl group. Parent chains are different, and the hydroxyl group is on the middle carbon in 2-propanol.

4. hydrogen bonding; 2-propanol likely has the greatest intermolecular forces.

| Evaporation Data | | | |
|---|---|---|---|
| Substance | Starting temp (°C) | Temp after 1 minute (°C) | ΔT (°C) |
| Water | 21 | 19 | 2 |
| Methanol | 22 | 8 | 14 |
| Ethanol | 22 | 13 | 9 |
| 2-Propanol | 21 | 16 | 5 |
| Other alcohol | | | |

# Properties of Alcohols

**A**lcohols are organic compounds that contain the −OH functional group. In this experiment, you will determine the strength of intermolecular forces of alcohols by determining how fast various alcohols evaporate. The evaporation of a liquid is an endothermic process, absorbing energy from the surroundings. This means that the temperature will decrease as evaporation occurs.

### Problem
How do intermolecular forces differ in three alcohols?

### Objectives
• **Measure** the rate of evaporation for water and several alcohols.
• **Infer** the relative strength of intermolecular forces of alcohols from rate of evaporation data.

### Materials
thermometer
stopwatch
facial tissue
cloth towel
Beral pipettes (5)
methanol
ethanol (95%)

2-propanol (99%)
wire twist tie or small rubber band
piece of cardboard for use as a fan

### Safety Precautions

• **Always wear safety goggles and a lab apron.**
• **The alcohols are flammable. Keep them away from open flames.**

### Pre-Lab

1. Read the entire **CHEMLAB.**

2. Prepare all written materials that you will take into the laboratory. Be sure to include safety precautions, procedure notes, and a data table.

3. Draw structural formulas for the three alcohols you will use in this activity. Describe how the structures of these compounds are alike and how they are different.

4. What types of forces exist between these kinds of molecules? Suggest which alcohol may have the greatest intermolecular forces.

| Evaporation Data | | | |
|---|---|---|---|
| Substance | Starting temp (°C) | Temp after one minute (°C) | ΔT (°C) |
| Water | | | |
| Methanol | | | |
| Ethanol | | | |
| 2-Propanol | | | |
| Other alcohol | | | |

### Procedure

1. Cut out five 2-cm by 6-cm strips of tissue.

2. Place a thermometer on a folded towel lying on a flat table so that the bulb of the thermometer extends over the edge of the table. Make sure the thermometer cannot roll off the table.

3. Wrap a strip of tissue around the bulb of the thermometer. Secure the tissue with a wire twist tie placed above the bulb of the thermometer.

4. Choose one person to control the stopwatch and read the temperature on the thermometer. A second person will put a small amount of the liquid to be tested into a Beral pipette.

5. When both people are ready, squeeze enough liquid onto the tissue to completely saturate it. At the same time, the other person starts the stopwatch, reads the temperature, and records it in the data table.

6. Fan the tissue-covered thermometer bulb with a piece of cardboard or other stiff paper. After one minute, read and record the final temperature in the data table. Remove the tissue and wipe the bulb dry.

## Procedure
• Place small marked beakers of the substances out for students.
• If time permits, students can repeat the trials to check their accuracy.

## Expected Results
See the data table.

## Analyze and Conclude

1. In order of decreasing temperature change, the liquids are methanol, ethanol, 2-propanol, and water.

2. Because evaporation is endothermic, heat is transferred from the tissue paper to the liquid as it evaporates.

3. The greater the heat transfer during evaporation, the greater the temperature change.

**7.** Repeat steps 3 through 6, for each of the three alcohols: methanol, ethanol, and 2-propanol. If your teacher has another alcohol, use it also.

## Cleanup and Disposal

**1.** Place tissues in the trash. Pipettes can be reused.

## Analyze and Conclude

**1. Communicating** Formulate a statement that summarizes your data, relating temperature change to the substances tested. Do not draw any conclusions yet.

**2. Acquiring and Analyzing Information** Explain why the temperatures changed during the experiment.

**3. Observing and Inferring** What can you conclude about the relationship between heat transfer and the differences in the temperature changes you observed?

**4. Drawing Conclusions** Assume that the three alcohols have approximately the same molar enthalpy of vaporization. What can you say about the relative rates of evaporation of the three alcohols?

**5. Drawing Conclusions** Consider your answer to question 4. What can you conclude about the relative strength of intermolecular forces existing in the three alcohols?

**6. Predicting** Suppose you also tested the alcohol 1-pentanol in this experiment. Where among the alcohols tested would you predict 1-pentanol to rank in rate of evaporation from fastest to slowest? Describe the temperature change you would expect to observe. Explain your reasoning.

**7. Thinking Critically** Molar enthalpies of vaporization for the three alcohols are given in the table below. Note that they are not the same.

| Molar Enthalpies of Vaporization | |
|---|---|
| **Substance** | **Enthalpy of vaporization at 25°C (kJ/mol)** |
| **Methanol** | 37.4 |
| **Ethanol** | 42.3 |
| **2-Propanol** | 45.4 |

In what way, if any, does this data change your conclusion about intermolecular forces?

**8. Observing and Inferring** Make a general statement comparing the molecular size of an alcohol in terms of the number of carbons in the carbon chain to the rate of evaporation of that alcohol.

**9.** **Error Analysis** Suggest a way to make this experiment more quantitative and controlled.

## Real-World Chemistry

**1.** How can this experiment help explain why small-chain alcohols have a warning label indicating that they are flammable?

**2.** Would you expect to see such a warning label on a bottle of 1-decanol? Explain.

**3.** A mixture of 70% 2-propanol (isopropanol) and 30% water is sold as rubbing alcohol, which may be used to help reduce a fever. Explain how this process works.

**4.** Why do you suppose that 2-propanol is a component in some products used to soothe sunburned skin?

**4.** Methanol may have the highest relative rate of evaporation, then ethanol, then 2-propanol.

**5.** Intermolecular attractions increase as the length of the carbon chain increases.

**6.** 1-pentanol would likely rank between 2-propanol and water in the list. $\Delta T$ would probably be 3°C or 4°C. As the longest-chain alcohol, 1-pentanol should evaporate more slowly than 2-propanol but faster than water.

**7.** The data reinforce the conclusion that intermolecular forces increase as the length of the carbon chain in the alcohol increases. The heat of vaporization is a measure of the strength of these forces. The data also support the conclusion about the relative rates of evaporation.

**8.** The rate of evaporation appears to decrease as the number of carbon atoms increases.

**9.** Care could be taken to make sure the pieces of tissue are the same size, air movement is equal, and exactly the same amount of each alcohol is used.

## Real-World Chemistry

**1.** Because small-chain alcohols evaporate quickly, they produce much vapor. Alcohol in the vapor phase is very reactive, and therefore very flammable.

**2.** No. Because it is a long-chain alcohol, 1-decanol likely has a low volatility.

**3.** Both compounds have relatively high enthalpies of vaporization. Therefore, the skin of a feverish person must lose an appreciable amount of heat to the liquids as they evaporate, cooling the skin.

**4.** The endothermic evaporation of 2-propanol helps cool the sunburned skin.

### Resource Manager

**ChemLab and MiniLab Worksheets,** pp. 90–92 L2

### ✓ Assessment

**Skill** Have students make a graph of rate of evaporation versus length of carbon chain. L2

# CHEMISTRY and
## Technology

## Purpose

Students will learn how carbon fibers are manufactured and used.

## Background

Unlike most metals, carbon fibers are chemically inert and can withstand temperatures that would melt most metals. As a result, the automotive industry is researching the possible production of engine parts from carbon fibers.

## Teaching Strategies

- Based on the fact that carbon-fiber composites are strong, yet light in weight, have students brainstorm additional uses for carbon fibers in the automotive and chemical industries. Possible student answers may include using carbon-fiber composites to build vehicles having large surface areas. Solar cells to provide electrical energy to power the vehicles could be mounted on these areas. Carbon fibers resist corrosion by most chemicals, so they may be used in pumps and valves by the chemical industry.
- Ask students to look around their homes or a sporting goods store, determine which items contain carbon fibers, and share their findings with the class. Have students speculate as to what properties of carbon fibers make them especially useful in those items.

## Investigating the Technology

1. Prosthetic limbs made of carbon fibers would weigh less than those made of metals, would be less likely to corrode, and would be less prone to denting.

**National Science Content Standards**

Pages 768–769
UCP.1, UCP.2, UCP.5; B.2, B.3; E.1, E.2; F.6

# CHEMISTRY and
## Technology

## Carbon: Stronger than Steel?

If you play golf or tennis, fish or ride a bicycle, chances are good that you have used carbon-fiber technology. In the 1960s, the aerospace industry began searching for structural materials that were as strong as metals but were light in weight because making space vehicles lighter meant that larger satellites or more experimental equipment could be lifted into space with the same amount of fuel. At about the same time, the petroleum industry showed that it could make fibers that were nearly pure carbon. Carbon fibers are stronger than steel when pulled at the ends, but they break when bent sharply. Engineers solved this problem by making a mat with carbon fibers oriented in all directions. Embedding the mat in a plastic matrix produced sheets of extremely strong but lightweight material. Such a material—a mixture of two or more materials that produces a combination stronger than the materials alone—is called a composite material.

### From Spacecraft to Sports

Carbon fibers are expensive to make, but their cost has decreased steadily. In the 1980s, a few expensive consumer items were produced, beginning with golf clubs having carbon-fiber-reinforced shafts. Then came tennis rackets, fishing rods, skis, and snowboards. Today, bicycles with frames made of carbon fiber are becoming increasingly popular. These frames are about 40% lighter than similar frames made of metal tubing. With lighter frames, riders use less energy to go the same distance. In the aircraft industry, less weight means fuel savings, so more and more parts such as seat frames and structural panels are being manufactured from carbon fiber.

### Making Carbon Fibers

Carbon fibers are polymers composed of long chains of carbon atoms in aromatic rings. Each carbon fiber is composed of narrow sheets that are extremely long. How do you polymerize carbon atoms?

Manufacturers first produce fibers of a synthetic polymer called polyacrylonitrile, or PAN. PAN fibers are heated intensely in an oxygen-free atmosphere, driving off all hydrogen, oxygen, and nitrogen atoms. After this process, the fiber consists of only carbon atoms with strong, stable bonds that give carbon fibers their great strength.

### The Future of Carbon Fibers

Other possible applications of carbon-fiber composites include prosthetic limbs, musical instruments, sports helmets and other protective gear, lightweight building materials, and reinforcing beams used to repair aging bridges. Because carbon fibers conduct electricity, scientists and engineers are working to find ways to incorporate electronic circuits into structural materials.

### Investigating the Technology

1. **Using Resources** What advantages might carbon fiber have over metals in artificial limbs?

**Chemistry Online**

Visit the Chemistry Web site at **chemistrymc.com** to find links about carbon fiber composites.

## Summary

### 23.1 Functional Groups

- Carbon forms bonds with atoms other than C and H, especially O, N, S, P, F, Cl, Br, and I.

- An atom or group of atoms that always react in a certain way in an organic molecule is referred to as a functional group.

- An alkyl halide is an organic compound that has one or more halogen atoms (F, Cl, Br, or I) bonded to a carbon atom.

### 23.2 Alcohols, Ethers, and Amines

- An alcohol is an organic compound that has an –OH group bonded to a carbon atom.

- Because they readily form hydrogen bonds, alcohols have higher boiling points and higher water solubilities than other organic compounds.

- Alcohols are used as solvents and as starting materials in synthesis reactions, medicinal products, and the food and beverage industries.

- An amine is an organic compound that contains a nitrogen atom bonded to one or more carbon atoms.

- An ether is an organic compound having the R—O—R' structure.

### 23.3 Carbonyl Compounds

- Carbonyl compounds are organic compounds that contain the C=O group.

- Five important classes of organic compounds containing carbonyl compounds are aldehydes, ketones, carboxylic acids, esters, and amides.

### 23.4 Other Reactions of Organic Compounds

- Most reactions of organic compounds can be classified into one of five categories: substitution; elimination; addition; oxidation-reduction; condensation.

- Knowing the types of organic compounds reacting may enable you to predict the reaction products.

### 23.5 Polymers

- Polymers are large molecules formed by combining smaller molecules called monomers.

- Polymers are synthesized through addition or condensation reactions.

- The functional groups present in polymers can be used to predict polymer properties.

## Vocabulary

- addition polymerization (p. 762)
- addition reaction (p. 755)
- alcohol (p. 743)
- aldehyde (p. 747)
- alkyl halide (p. 738)
- amide (p. 752)
- amine (p. 745)
- aryl halide (p. 739)
- condensation polymerization (p. 764)
- condensation reaction (p. 753)
- carbonyl group (p. 747)
- carboxylic acid (p. 749)
- carboxyl group (p. 749)
- dehydration reaction (p. 755)
- dehydrogenation reaction (p. 754)
- denatured alcohol (p. 744)
- elimination reaction (p. 754)
- ester (p. 750)
- ether (p. 745)
- functional group (p. 737)
- halocarbon (p. 738)
- halogenation (p. 741)
- hydration reaction (p. 756)
- hydrogenation reaction (p. 756)
- hydroxyl group (p. 743)
- ketone (p. 748)
- monomer (p. 762)
- plastic (p. 764)
- polymer (p. 761)
- polymerization reaction (p. 762)
- substitution reaction (p. 741)
- thermoplastic (p. 764)
- thermosetting (p. 764)

## Using the Vocabulary

To reinforce chapter vocabulary, have students write a sentence using each term. **L2** **ELL**

## Review Strategies

- Have students summarize the names and structures of alkyl halides, alcohols, amines, ethers, aldehydes, ketones, carboxylic acids, esters, and amides. **L2**
- Have students make a list of the properties and uses of alkyl halides, alcohols, amines, ethers, aldehydes, ketones, carboxylic acids, esters, and amides. **L2**
- Have students write chemical equations for representative organic reactions involving substitution, halogenation, condensation, elimination, dehydrogenation, dehydration, addition, hydration, hydrogenation, oxidation-reduction, addition polymerization, and condensation polymerization.
- Have students practice drawing the structure of a polymer given its monomer and vice versa. **L2**
- Problems from Appendix A can be used for review. **L2**

For additional help with vocabulary, have students access the Vocabulary PuzzleMaker online.

chemistrymc.com/ vocabulary_puzzlemaker

## EXAMVIEW® PRO

### Use ExamView® Pro Testmaker CD-ROM to:

- Create **multiple versions** of tests.
- Create **modified** tests with one mouse click for struggling students.
- **Edit** existing questions and add your own questions.
- **Build** tests based on national curriculum standards.

## Concept Mapping

**30.** 1. substitution; 2. condensation; 3. dehydration or elimination

## Mastering Concepts

**31.** A functional group is an atom or group of atoms in an organic molecule that always reacts in a certain way.

**32.** Alkyl halides have a halogen atom present on an aliphatic chain or ring of carbons, while aryl halides have a halogen atom directly bonded to a carbon on a benzene molecule or other aromatic ring.

**33.** bromine

**34. a.** 1-aminopentane
**b.** 1-aminoheptane
**c.** 2-aminopentane
**d.** 1-aminodecane

**35.** Ethanol is denatured by the addition of small amounts of toxic substances, which make it unsafe to drink.

**36. a.** ethanol **b.** methanol **c.** ethylene glycol or propylene glycol **d.** ethyl ether **e.** aniline

**37.** Alcohols are always polar due to the asymmetrical distribution of charge around the oxygen in the –OH group. Polarity of an ether depends on its overall geometry. Alcohols are generally more soluble than corresponding ethers in water, which is a polar solvent.

**38.** Because O-H bonds are more polar than N-H bonds, the hydrogen bonds that form between two ethanol molecules are stronger than those that form between two

---

# CHAPTER 23 ASSESSMENT

## Chemistry Online

Go to the Chemistry Web site at chemistrymc.com *for additional Chapter 23 Assessment.*

## Concept Mapping

**30.** Identify the types of reactions used to convert alcohols into alkyl halides, esters, and alkenes.

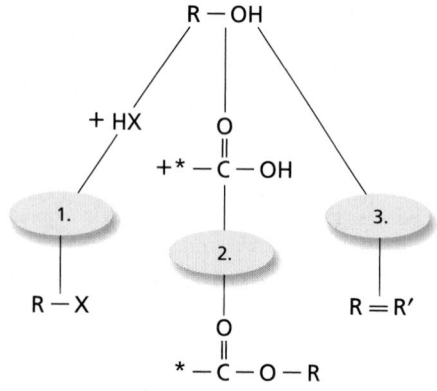

## Mastering Concepts

**31.** What is a functional group? (23.1)

**32.** Describe and compare the structures of alkyl halides and aryl halides. (23.1)

**33.** What reactant would you use to convert methane to bromomethane? (23.1)

**34.** Name the amines represented by the condensed formulas below. (23.2)

**a.** $CH_3(CH_2)_3CH_2NH_2$
**b.** $CH_3(CH_2)_5CH_2NH_2$
**c.** $CH_3(CH_2)_2CH(NH_2)CH_3$
**d.** $CH_3(CH_2)_8CH_2NH_2$

**35.** How is ethanol denatured? (23.2)

**36.** Name one alcohol, amine, or ether that is used for each of the following purposes. (23.2)

**a.** antiseptic
**b.** solvent in paint strippers
**c.** antifreeze
**d.** anesthetic
**e.** dye production

---

**37.** Explain why an alcohol molecule will always have a higher solubility in water than an ether molecule having an identical molecular mass. (23.2)

**38.** Explain why ethanol has a much higher boiling point than aminoethane even though their molecular masses are nearly equal. (23.2)

**39.** Draw the general structure for each of the following classes of organic compounds. (23.3)

**a.** aldehyde    **d.** ester
**b.** ketone    **e.** amide
**c.** carboxylic acid

**40.** Name an aldehyde, ketone, carboxylic acid, ester, or amide used for each of the following purposes. (23.3)

**a.** preserving biological specimens
**b.** solvent in fingernail polish
**c.** acid in vinegar
**d.** flavoring in foods and beverages

**41.** What type of reaction is used to produce aspirin from salicylic acid and acetic acid? (23.3)

**42.** What is the starting material for making most synthetic organic compounds? (23.4)

**43.** Explain the importance of classifying reactions. (23.4)

**44.** List the type of organic reaction needed to carry out each of the following transformations. (23.4)

**a.** alkene → alkane
**b.** alkyl halide → alcohol
**c.** alkyl halide → alkene
**d.** amine + carboxylic acid → amide
**e.** alcohol → alkyl halide
**f.** alkene → alcohol

**45.** Explain the difference between addition polymerization and condensation polymerization. (23.5)

**46.** Which type of polymer is easier to recycle, thermosetting or thermoplastic? Explain your answer. (23.5)

## Mastering Problems

### Functional Groups (23.1)

**47.** Draw structures for these alkyl and aryl halides.

**a.** chlorobenzene
**b.** 1-bromo-4-chlorohexane
**c.** 1,2-difluoro-3-iodocyclohexane
**d.** 1, 3-dibromobenzene
**e.** 1,1,2,2-tetrafluoroethane

chemistrymc.com/chapter_test

---

aminoethane molecules. Stronger intermolecular forces result in higher boiling points.

**39.** See the Solutions Manual for structures.

## Resource Manager

**Chapter Assessment,** pp. 133–138 **L2**
**Supplemental Problems,** Ch. 23
**ExamView® Pro CD-ROM**
**MindJogger Videoquizzes DVD/VHS**
**Solutions Manual,** Ch. 23
**Chemistry Interactive CD-ROM,**
   Ch. 23 quiz

**48.** For 1-bromo-2-chloropropane:

   **a.** Draw the structure.
   **b.** Does the compound have optical isomers?
   **c.** If the compound has optical isomers, identify the chiral carbon atom.

**49.** Name one structural isomer created by changing the position of one or more halogen atoms in each alkyl halide.

   **a.** 2-chloropentane
   **b.** 1,1-difluropropane
   **c.** 1,3-dibromocyclopentane
   **d.** 1-bromo-2-chloroethane

### Alcohols, Ethers, and Amines (23.2)

**50.** Name one ether that is a structural isomer of each alcohol.

   **a.** 1-butanol    **b.** 2-hexanol

**51.** Draw structures for the following alcohol, amine, and ether molecules.

   **a.** 1,2-butanediol
   **b.** 5-aminohexane
   **c.** isopropyl ether
   **d.** 2-methyl-1-butanol
   **e.** butyl pentyl ether
   **f.** cyclobutyl methyl ether
   **g.** 1,3-diaminobutane
   **h.** cyclopentanol

### Carbonyl Compounds (23.3)

**52.** Draw structures for each of the following carbonyl compounds.

   **a.** 2,2-dichloro-3-pentanone
   **b.** 4-methylpentanal
   **c.** isopropyl hexanoate
   **d.** octanoamide
   **e.** 3-fluoro-2-methylbutanoic acid
   **f.** cyclopentanal
   **g.** hexyl methanoate

**53.** Name each of the following carbonyl compounds.

   **a.**

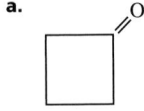

   **b.**

$$CH_3 - CH_2 - CH_2 - \overset{\overset{\displaystyle O}{\|}}{C} - H$$

**c.**

$$CH_3 + CH_2 +_4 \overset{\overset{\displaystyle O}{\|}}{C} - OH$$

**d.**

$$CH_3 + CH_2 +_4 \overset{\overset{\displaystyle O}{\|}}{C} - NH_2$$

### Other Reactions of Organic Compounds (23.4)

**54.** Classify each of the following organic reactions as substitution, addition, elimination, oxidation-reduction or condensation.

   **a.** 2-butene + hydrogen → butane
   **b.** propane + fluorine → 2-fluoropropane + hydrogen fluoride
   **c.** 2-propanol → propene + water
   **d.** cyclobutene + water → cyclobutanol

**55.** Use structural formulas to write equations for the following reactions.

   **a.** the substitution reaction between 2-chloropropane and water yielding 2-propanol and hydrogen chloride
   **b.** the addition reaction between 3-hexene and chlorine yielding 3,4-dichlorohexane

**56.** What type of reaction converts an alcohol into each of the following types of compounds?

   **a.** ester    **c.** alkene
   **b.** alkyl halide    **d.** aldehyde

**57.** Use structural formulas to write the equation for the condensation reaction between ethanol and propanoic acid.

### Polymers (23.5)

**58.** What monomers react to make each polymer?

   **a.** polyethylene    **c.** Teflon
   **b.** Dacron    **d.** Nylon 6,6

**59.** Name the polymers made from the following monomers.

   **a.** $CF_2 = CF_2$    **b.** $CH_2 = CCl_2$

**60.** Choose the polymer of each pair that you expect to have the higher water solubility.

   **a.** $\left[ CH_2 - CH_2 \right]_n$  $\left[ CH_2 - \underset{\underset{\displaystyle OH}{|}}{CH} \right]_n$

   **b.** $\left[ \underset{\underset{\displaystyle CH_3}{|}}{CH} - CH_2 \right]_n$  $\left[ CH_2 - \underset{\underset{\displaystyle C = O}{|}}{\overset{\overset{\displaystyle OH}{|}}{C}} - CH_2 \right]_n$

           I              II

**40. a.** formaldehyde
   **b.** acetone **c.** acetic acid
   **d.** ethyl butanoate, 2-methylbutylacetate, pentyl pentanoate, or other ester
**41.** condensation
**42.** fossil fuels such as petroleum
**43.** Because chemical reactions are so numerous, classifying them helps students and chemists better understand them, remember them, and predict the products of new reactions.
**44. a.** addition **b.** substitution **c.** elimination **d.** condensation **e.** substitution **f.** addition and hydration
**45.** In addition polymerization, all the atoms in the monomers are retained in the polymer product. In condensation polymerization, monomers with at least two functional groups form the polymer, losing a small by-product such as water.
**46.** Thermoplastic polymers are easier to recycle because products made from them can be re-melted and molded repeatedly.

### Mastering Problems

Complete solutions to Chapter Assessment Problems can be found in the **Solutions Manual.**

### Functional Groups (23.1)
**Level 1**
**47.** See the Solutions Manual for structures.
**48.** See the Solutions Manual.
   **a.** $CH_2(Br)CH(Cl)CH_3$
   **b.** yes; one carbon is attached to four different atoms or groups.
   **c.** The middle carbon is chiral.

**b.** 1,2-difluoropropane; 1,3-difluoropropane; 2,2-difluoropropane
**c.** 1,2- or 1,1-dibromocyclopentane
**d.** 1-bromo-1-chloroethane

### Alcohols, Ethers, and Amines (23.2)
**Level 1**
  **50. a.** ethyl ether; methyl propyl ether
      **b.** propyl ether; isopropyl ether; butyl ethyl ether; methyl pentyl ether

**Level 2**
**51.** See the Solutions Manual for structures.

### Carbonyl Compounds (23.3)
**Level 1**
**52.** See the Solutions Manual for structures.

**Level 2**
**49.** Answers may include:
   **a.** 1-chloropentane; 3-chloropentane

## Level 2
**53. a.** cyclobutanone
**b.** butanal
**c.** hexanoic acid
**d.** hexanoamide

## Other Reactions of Organic Compounds(23.4)
### Level 1
**54. a.** addition **b.** substitution
**c.** elimination **d.** addition
**55. a.** $CH_3CHClCH_3 + H_2O \rightarrow$
$CH_3CH(OH)CH_3 + HCl$
**b.** $CH_3CH_2CH=CHCH_2CH_3$
$+ Cl_2 \rightarrow CH_3CH_2CH(Cl)$
$CH(Cl)CH_2CH_3$

### Level 2
**56. a.** condensation
**b.** substitution
**c.** elimination
**d.** oxidation
**57.** See the Solutions Manual for equation.

## Polymers (23.5)
### Level 1
**58. a.** ethylene **b.** ethylene glycol and terephthalic acid **c.** tetrafluoroethylene **d.** adipic acid and 1,6-diaminohexane
**59. a.** Teflon **b.** Saran

### Level 2
**60. a.** II **b.** II
**61. a.** condensation polymerization
**b.** addition polymerization
**c.** condensation polymerization
**d.** addition polymerization

---

**61.** Examine the structures of the following polymers in **Table 23-4.** Decide whether each is made by addition or condensation polymerization.

**a.** nylon **c.** polyurethane
**b.** polyacrylonitrile **d.** polypropylene

## Mixed Review

*Sharpen your problem-solving skills by answering the following.*

**62.** Which halogen is found in hormones made by a normal human thyroid gland?

**63.** Describe the properties of carboxylic acids.

**64.** List two uses of esters.

**65.** Draw structures of the following compounds. (23.3)

**a.** butanone **d.** heptanoamide
**b.** propanal **e.** ethyl pentanoate
**c.** hexanoic acid **f.** benzoic acid

**66.** Name the type of organic compound formed by each of the following reactions.

**a.** elimination from an alcohol
**b.** addition of hydrogen chloride to an alkene
**c.** addition of water to an alkene
**d.** substitution of a hydroxyl group for a halogen atom

**67.** List two uses for each of the following polymers.

**a.** polypropylene **c.** polytetrafluoroethylene
**b.** polyurethane **d.** polyvinyl chloride

**68.** Draw structures of and supply names for the organic compounds produced by reacting ethene with each of the following substances.
**a.** water **b.** hydrogen
**c.** hydrogen chloride **d.** fluorine

## Thinking Critically

**69. Intrepreting Scientifc Illustrations** List all the functional groups present in each of the following complex organic molecules.

Levadopa

Progesterone

---

**70. Thinking Critically** Ethanoic acid (acetic acid) is very soluble in water. However, naturally occurring long-chain carboxylic acids such as palmitic acid $(CH_3(CH_2)_{14}COOH)$ are insoluble in water. Explain.

**71. Communicating** Write structural formulas for all structural isomers of molecules having the following formulas. Name each isomer.

**a.** $C_3H_8O$ **b.** $C_2H_4Cl_2$ **c.** $C_3H_6$

**72. Recognizing Cause and Effect** Arrange the following compounds in order of increasing boiling point.

butanol, butane, 1-aminobutane, ethyl ether

**73. Intrepreting Scientifc Illustrations** Human cells require vitamin C to properly synthesize materials that make up connective tissue such as that found in ligaments. List the functional groups present in the Vitamin C molecule.

Vitamin C

## Writing in Chemistry

**74.** While living organisms have made polymers like cotton, silk, wool, and latex rubber for thousands of years, the first laboratory synthesis of a polymer occurred only in the late 1800s. Imagine that you live in the 1880s, before society entered what some chemists refer to as the "Age of Polymers." Write a short story describing how your life would differ from its present form because of the absence of synthetic polymers.

## Cumulative Review

*Refresh your understanding of previous chapters by answering the following.*

**75.** Why do the following characteristics apply to transition metals? (Chapter 7)

**a.** Ions vary in charge.
**b.** Many of their solids are colored.
**c.** Many are hard solids.

**76.** What is a rate-determining step? (Chapter 17)

**77.** According to Le Châtelier's principle, how would increasing the volume of the reaction vessel affect the equilibrium $2SO_2(g) + O_2(g) \rightleftarrows 2SO_3(g)$? (Chapter 18)

## Mixed Review
**62.** iodine
**63.** Carboxylic acids are weakly acidic, taste sour, and consist of polar molecules.
**64.** Esters are used as flavorings in foods and beverages and as fragrances in candles and perfumes.
**65.** See the Solutions Manual for structures.

**66. a.** alkene **c.** alcohol
**b.** alkyl halide **d.** alcohol
**67.** See Table 23-4 for answers.
**68.** See the Solutions Manual for structures.
**a.** $CH_3CH_2OH$, ethanol
**b.** $CH_3CH_3$, ethane
**c.** $CH_3CH_2Cl$, chloroethane
**d.** $CH_2(F)CH_2F$, 1,2-difluoroethane

National Science Content Standards
Pages 772–773
UCP.1, UCP.2, UCP.5; B.2, B.3; E.2

*Use these questions and the test-taking tip to prepare for your standardized test.*

**1.** What is the compound pictured below?

$$CH_3CH_2CH_2-\overset{\overset{\displaystyle O}{\|}}{C}-H$$

a. an aldehyde   c. a ketone
b. an ether       d. an alcohol

**2.** What is the name of the compound shown?

$$F-\overset{\overset{\displaystyle H}{|}}{\underset{\underset{\displaystyle H}{|}}{C}}-\overset{\overset{\displaystyle H}{|}}{\underset{\underset{\displaystyle Cl}{|}}{C}}-\overset{\overset{\displaystyle Br}{|}}{\underset{\underset{\displaystyle H}{|}}{C}}-\overset{\overset{\displaystyle H}{|}}{\underset{\underset{\displaystyle Br}{|}}{C}}-\overset{\overset{\displaystyle H}{|}}{\underset{\underset{\displaystyle H}{|}}{C}}-H$$

a. 2-chloro-3,4-dibromo-1-fluoropentane
b. 4-chloro-2,3-dibromo-5-fluoropentane
c. 3,4-dibromo-2-chloro-1-fluoropentane
d. 2,3-dibromo-4-chloro-5-fluoropentane

**3.** What are the products of this reaction?

$$CH_3CH_2CH_2Br + NH_3 \rightarrow ?$$

a. $CH_3CH_2CH_2NH_2Br$ and $H_2$
b. $CH_3CH_2CH_2NH_3$ and $Br_2$
c. $CH_3CH_2CH_2NH_2$ and $HBr$
d. $CH_3CH_2CH_3$ and $NH_2Br$

**4.** What type of compound does this molecule represent?

$$H_2N-\overset{\overset{\displaystyle O}{\|}}{C}-\overset{\overset{\displaystyle H}{|}}{\underset{\underset{\displaystyle H}{|}}{C}}-\overset{\overset{\displaystyle H}{|}}{\underset{\underset{\displaystyle H}{|}}{C}}-\overset{\overset{\displaystyle H}{|}}{C}-H$$

a. an amine   c. an ester
b. an amide    d. an ether

**5.** What kind of reaction is this?

$$H-\overset{\overset{\displaystyle H}{|}}{\underset{\underset{\displaystyle NH_2}{|}}{C}}-\overset{\overset{\displaystyle O}{\|}}{C}-OH + H_3C-\overset{\overset{\displaystyle H}{|}}{\underset{\underset{\displaystyle NH_2}{|}}{C}}-\overset{\overset{\displaystyle O}{\|}}{C}-OH \rightarrow$$

$$H-\overset{\overset{\displaystyle H}{|}}{\underset{\underset{\displaystyle NH_2}{|}}{C}}-\overset{\overset{\displaystyle O}{\|}}{C}-\overset{\overset{\displaystyle }{}}{\underset{\underset{\displaystyle H}{|}}{N}}-\overset{\overset{\displaystyle CH_3}{|}}{\underset{\underset{\displaystyle H}{|}}{C}}-\overset{\overset{\displaystyle O}{\|}}{C}-OH + H_2O$$

a. substitution   c. addition
b. condensation   d. elimination

chemistrymc.com/standardized_test

**Interpreting Tables** Use the table to answer the following questions.

| Acid Ionization Constants for Selected Carboxylic Acids | | | |
|---|---|---|---|
| **Common name** | **Formula** | **Hydrogen ionized** | **$K_a$** |
| Succinic acid | $C_2H_4(COOH)_2$ | 1st | $6.92 \times 10^{-5}$ |
| | | 2nd | $2.45 \times 10^{-6}$ |
| Oxaloacetic acid | $C_2H_2O(COOH)_2$ | 1st | $6.03 \times 10^{-3}$ |
| | | 2nd | $1.29 \times 10^{-4}$ |
| Acrylic acid | $C_3H_4O_2$ | 1st | $5.62 \times 10^{-5}$ |
| Malic acid | $C_4H_6O_5$ | 1st | $3.98 \times 10^{-4}$ |
| | | 2nd | $7.76 \times 10^{-6}$ |

**6.** Oxaloacetic acid has a higher $K_a$ than succinic acid because it probably possesses

a. fewer carboxyl groups.
b. a less polar structure.
c. additional functional groups that make it more soluble in water.
d. fewer hydrogen atoms that can transfer to the oxygen atom in $H_2O$.

**7.** Which of the indicated hydrogen atoms will malic acid lose when it ionizes completely?

$$
\begin{array}{c}
2 \\
\downarrow \\
O \quad H \quad H \leftarrow 4 \\
\| \quad | \quad | \\
1 \rightarrow HO-C-C-C-C-OH \leftarrow 5 \\
\quad | \quad | \quad \| \\
\quad OH \ H \quad O \\
\quad \uparrow \\
\quad 3
\end{array}
$$

a. 1 and 5       c. 2, 3, and 4
b. 1, 3, and 5   d. 2 and 4

---

### TEST-TAKING TIP

**Use As Much Time As You Can** You will not get extra points for finishing early. Work slowly and carefully on any test and make sure you don't make careless errors because you are hurrying to finish.

---

## Thinking Critically

**69. a.** carboxyl, amino, hydroxyl (2)
   **b.** carbonyl (2), C=C

**70.** Ethanoic acid is soluble in water because its molecules are relatively small, form hydrogen bonds with water when unionized, and form ion-dipole attractions when ionized. Carboxylic acid molecules with much longer carbon chains are mostly nonpolar. These nonpolar molecules do not form strong bonds with water molecules, even though their carboxylic acid groups have a slight tendency to interact with water molecules.

**71.** Students should provide molecular structures for the following compounds. See the Solutions Manual for structures.
   **a.** 1-propanol, 2-propanol, ethyl methyl ether
   **b.** 1,1-dichloroethane and 1,2-dichloroethane
   **c.** propene and cyclo-propane

**72.** butane, ethyl ether, 1-aminobutane, butanol

**73.** hydroxyl (4), C=C, carbonyl, ether

## Cumulative Review

**75. a.** Transition metals can lose $ns^2$ outer electrons forming 2+ ions. They also can lose inner d electrons and form ions of 3+ or higher.
   **b.** Electrons in d orbitals can absorb visible light of specific wavelengths as the atom moves to an excited state.
   **c.** Hardness is a property determined by the number of unpaired d electrons: the more unpaired d electrons, the harder the solid.

**76.** The rate-determining step is the slowest of the elementary reactions that make up a complex reaction.

**77.** The equilibrium would shift to the left.

## Standardized Test Practice

**1.** a   **3.** c   **5.** b   **7.** a
**2.** d   **4.** b   **6.** c

# Resource Manager

| Section | Objectives | Activities/Features |
|---|---|---|
| **Section 24.1**<br>**Proteins**<br>1 session<br>1/2 block | **1. Describe** the structures of amino acids and proteins.<br>**2. Explain** the roles of proteins in cells. | **Discovery Lab:** Testing for Simple Sugars, p. 775 |
| **Section 24.2**<br>**Carbohydrates**<br>1 session<br>1/2 block | **3. Describe** the structures of monosaccharides, disaccharides, and polysaccharides.<br>**4. Explain** the functions of carbohydrates in living things. | |
| **Section 24.3**<br>**Lipids**<br>1 session<br>1/2 block | **5. Describe** the structures of fatty acids, triglycerides, phospholipids, and steroids.<br>**6. Explain** the functions of lipids in living organisms.<br>**7. Identify** some reactions that fatty acids undergo.<br>**8. Relate** the structure and function of cell membranes. | **Biology Connection,** p. 785<br>**MiniLab:** A Saponification Reaction, p. 786 |
| **Section 24.4**<br>**Nucleic Acids**<br>1 session<br>1/2 block | **9. Identify** the structural components of nucleic acids.<br>**10. Relate** the function of DNA to its structure.<br>**11. Describe** the structure and function of RNA. | **Problem-Solving Lab:** How does DNA replicate? p. 790 |
| **Section 24.5**<br>**Metabolism**<br>2 sessions<br>1 block | **12. Distinguish** between anabolism and catabolism.<br>**13. Describe** the role of ATP in metabolism.<br>**14. Compare** and **contrast** the processes of photosynthesis, cellular respiration, and fermentation. | **Careers Using Chemistry:** Personal Trainer, p. 794<br>**ChemLab CBL:** Alcoholic Fermentation in Yeast, pp. 796–797<br>**Everyday Chemistry:** Sense of Smell, p. 798 |

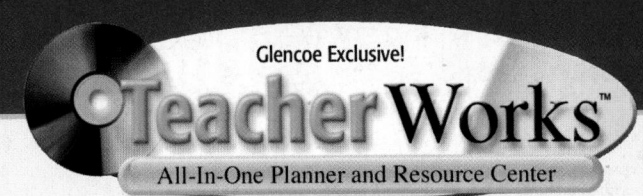

| National Science Content Standards | State/Local Standards | Reproducible Masters | Transparencies |
|---|---|---|---|
| UCP.2; A.1; B.2, B.3; F.1; G.1 | | **Study Guide for Content Mastery,** pp. 139–140 **L2** **Laboratory Manual,** pp. 185–188 **L2** | **Section Focus Transparency 91** **L1** **ELL** **Teaching Transparencies 73, 74** **L2** **ELL** **Math Skills Transparency 39** **L2** **ELL** |
| UCP.2; B.2; F.1 | | **Study Guide for Content Mastery,** p. 141 **L2** **Laboratory Manual,** pp. 189–192 **L2** | **Section Focus Transparency 92** **L1** **ELL** **Teaching Transparency 74** **L2** **ELL** |
| UCP.2; A.1; B.2, B.3, B.6 | | **Study Guide for Content Mastery,** p. 142 **L2** **ChemLab and MiniLab Worksheets,** p. 93 **L2** | **Section Focus Transparency 93** **L1** **ELL** **Teaching Transparency 74** **L2** **ELL** |
| UCP.2; A.2; B.2, B.3; E.2; G.1, G.3 | | **Study Guide for Content Mastery,** p. 143 **L2** **Challenge Problems,** p. 24 **L3** | **Section Focus Transparency 94** **L1** **ELL** **Math Skills Transparency 40** **L2** **ELL** |
| UCP.2; A.1, A.2; B.2, B.3, B.6; E.2; F.1, F.3 | | **Study Guide for Content Mastery,** p. 144 **L2** **ChemLab and MiniLab Worksheets,** pp. 94–96 **L2** | **Section Focus Transparency 95** **L1** **ELL** **Teaching Transparency 75** **L2** **ELL** |

**Key to National Science Content Standards:** UCP = Unifying Concepts and Processes, A = Science as Inquiry, B = Physical Science, C = Life Science, D = Earth and Space Sciences, E = Science and Technology, F = Science in Personal and Social Perspectives, G = History and Nature of Science

Refer to pages 4T–5T of the Teacher Guide for an explanation of the National Science Content Standards correlations.

# Resource Manager

## Materials List

**ChemLab** (pages 796–797)
600-mL beaker, stirring rod, thermometer, basting bulb, yeast suspension, vegetable oil, utility clamp, 10-mL graduated cylinder, pipette, ring stand, 5% sucrose solution, test tube, #5 rubber-stopper assembly, CBL system, graphing calculator, vernier pressure sensor, link cable, CBL-DIN cable

**Discovery Lab** (page 775)
400-mL beaker, hot plate, 10-mL graduated cylinder, boiling chip, 10% glucose solution, test tube, tongs, Benedict's solution, stirring rod, 10% starch solution, honey, 10% gelatin solution

**MiniLab** (page 786)
solid vegetable shortening (25 g), 250-mL beaker, 600-mL beaker, 6.0$M$ NaOH (5 mL), ethanol (12 mL), saturated NaCl solution (25 mL), stirring rod, hot plate, tongs, 25-mL graduated cylinder, evaporating dish, cheesecloth (20 cm $\times$ 20 cm), funnel

**Demonstration** (pages 776–777)
peanuts, test tube and holder, red litmus paper, lead acetate and cobalt chloride papers, Bunsen burner

## Preparation of Solutions

**ChemLab** (pages 796–797)
  **Yeast suspension** Add 7 g active dry yeast to 200 mL water and stir until suspended.
  **5% sucrose solution** Dissolve 5 g sucrose in 95 mL water.

**Discovery Lab** (page 775)
  **10% starch solution** Suspend 20 g starch in 50 mL distilled water. While stirring, slowly pour the suspension into 150 mL boiling distilled water. Cool before use.
  **10% gelatin solution** Soften 20 g gelatin in 50 mL distilled water. Add 100 mL boiling distilled water to dissolve. Make up to 200 mL final volume with distilled water.
  **Benedict's solution** Dissolve 86.5 g sodium citrate and 100 g sodium carbonate decahydrate ($Na_2CO_3 \cdot 10H_2O$) in 400 mL distilled water, heating if necessary. Dissolve 8.65 g copper(II) sulfate pentahydrate ($CuSO_4 \cdot 5H_2O$) in 50 mL distilled water. Pour the copper(II) sulfate solution, with constant stirring, into the first solution. Make up to 500 mL final volume with distilled water. Shelf life: indefinite

**MiniLab** (page 786)
  **6.0$M$ NaOH** Dissolve 48 g NaOH in 125 mL water, then dilute to 200 mL final volume. CAUTION: Solution will become very hot.
  **Saturated NaCl solution** Slowly add 450 g NaCl to 1 L of water while stirring constantly. Some NaCl will not dissolve. Decant or filter if desired.

## Assessment Resources

**Chapter Assessment,** pp. 139–144
**MindJogger Videoquizzes** DVD/VHS
**Alternate Assessment in the Science Classroom**
**ExamView® Pro CD-ROM**
**Solutions Manual,** Chapter 24
**Supplemental Problems,** Chapter 24
**Performance Assessment in the Science Classroom**
**Chemistry Interactive CD-ROM,** Chapter 24 quiz

## Additional Resources

**Spanish Resources** ELL
**Guided Reading Audio Program,** Chapter 24 ELL
**Cooperative Learning in the Science Classroom**
**Lab and Safety Skills in the Science Classroom**
**Lesson Plans**
**Block Scheduling Lesson Plans**
**Chemistrymc.com**

## Glencoe Technology

The following multimedia for this chapter are available from Glencoe.

**VIDEOTAPE/DVD**
MindJogger Videoquizzes,
Chapter 24

**CD-ROM**
**Chemistry: Matter and Change**
*Lock and Key Enzyme Reaction*, Animation
*Speed Up the Reaction*, Experiment
*Manufacturing Soap*, Video
*Making Soap*, Demonstration

**CD-ROM**
**ExamView® Pro**
   **Testmaker**

**CD-ROM**
**Interactive Chalkboard**

**CD-ROM**
**TeacherWorks™**

## Multiple Learning Styles

Look for the following icons for strategies that emphasize different learning modalities.

**Kinesthetic**
Building a Model, pp. 779, 785; Differentiated Instruction, p. 779; Check for Understanding, pp. 779, 787; Reteach, p. 787; Chemistry Journal, p. 794

**Visual-Spatial**
Quick Demo, p. 776; Reteach, p. 780; Differentiated Instruction, pp. 781, 785; Check for Understanding, pp. 783, 791; Portfolio, p. 788; Reinforcement, p. 789

**Interpersonal**
Enrichment, p. 777; Reteach, p. 783

**Intrapersonal**
Portfolio, p. 778; Chemistry Journal, pp. 784, 789

**Linguistic**
Using Science Terms, p. 778; Chemistry Journal, pp. 779, 781; Differentiated Instruction, p. 792

**Logical-Mathematical**
Math in Chemistry, p. 776; Differentiated Instruction, p. 789

## Key to Teaching Strategies

**L1** Level 1 activities should be appropriate for students with learning difficulties.

**L2** Level 2 activities should be within the ability range of all students.

**L3** Level 3 activities are designed for above-average students.

**ELL** ELL activities should be within the ability range of English Language Learners.

**COOP LEARN** Cooperative Learning activities are designed for small group work.

**P** These strategies represent student products that can be placed into a best-work portfolio.

 These strategies are useful in a block scheduling format.

## Assessment Planner

**Portfolio Assessment**
Portfolio, TWE, pp. 778, 788, 799
Assessment, TWE, p. 791

**Performance Assessment**
Demonstration, TWE, p. 777
Assessment, TWE, p. 783
MiniLab, TWE, p. 786
Problem-Solving Lab, TWE, p. 790
ChemLab, TWE, p. 797
ChemLab, SE, pp. 796–797
MiniLab, SE, p. 786
Discovery Lab, SE, p. 775

**Knowledge Assessment**
Assessment, TWE, pp. 779, 780, 787, 793
Section Assessment, SE, pp. 780, 783, 787, 791, 795
Chapter Assessment, SE, pp. 800–803

**Skill Assessment**
Assessment, TWE, pp. 782, 789, 795

## Tying to Previous Knowledge

Have students review the following concepts before studying this chapter.
Chapter 13: hydrogen bonds
Chapter 22: isomers
Chapter 23: functional groups, polymers

## Using the Photo

Ask students what kind of substance they think spider webs are made of and whether this substance is strong or weak. Spider webs are made of protein. These polymers form very strong threads similar to others, such as cotton and nylon, with which students may be more familiar.

## Chapter Themes

The following themes from the National Science Education Standards are covered in this chapter. Refer to page 4T of the Teacher Guide for an explanation of the correlations.
Systems, order, and organization (UCP.1)
Evolution and equilibrium (UCP.4)
Form and function (UCP.5)

## PowerPoint® Presentations

This CD-ROM is an editable Microsoft® PowerPoint® presentation that includes:
- Section presentations
- Section checks
- Image bank
- Links to Chemistry Online
- All transparencies
- Animations
- Audio

# The Chemistry of Life

### What You'll Learn

▶ You will learn the functions of the four major classes of biological molecules: proteins, carbohydrates, lipids, and nucleic acids.
▶ You will identify the building blocks that form the major biological molecules.
▶ You will compare and contrast the metabolic processes of cellular respiration, photosynthesis, and fermentation.

### Why It's Important

The large biological molecules in your body are essential to the organization and operation of its millions of cells. The structure of these molecules is directly related to their function, and how they function affects your health and survival.

Visit the Chemistry Web site at chemistrymc.com to find links about the chemistry of life.

The silk that makes up this spider's web is, gram for gram, stronger than steel, yet it is lightweight and stretchable. Spider silk is made of protein, a biological molecule.

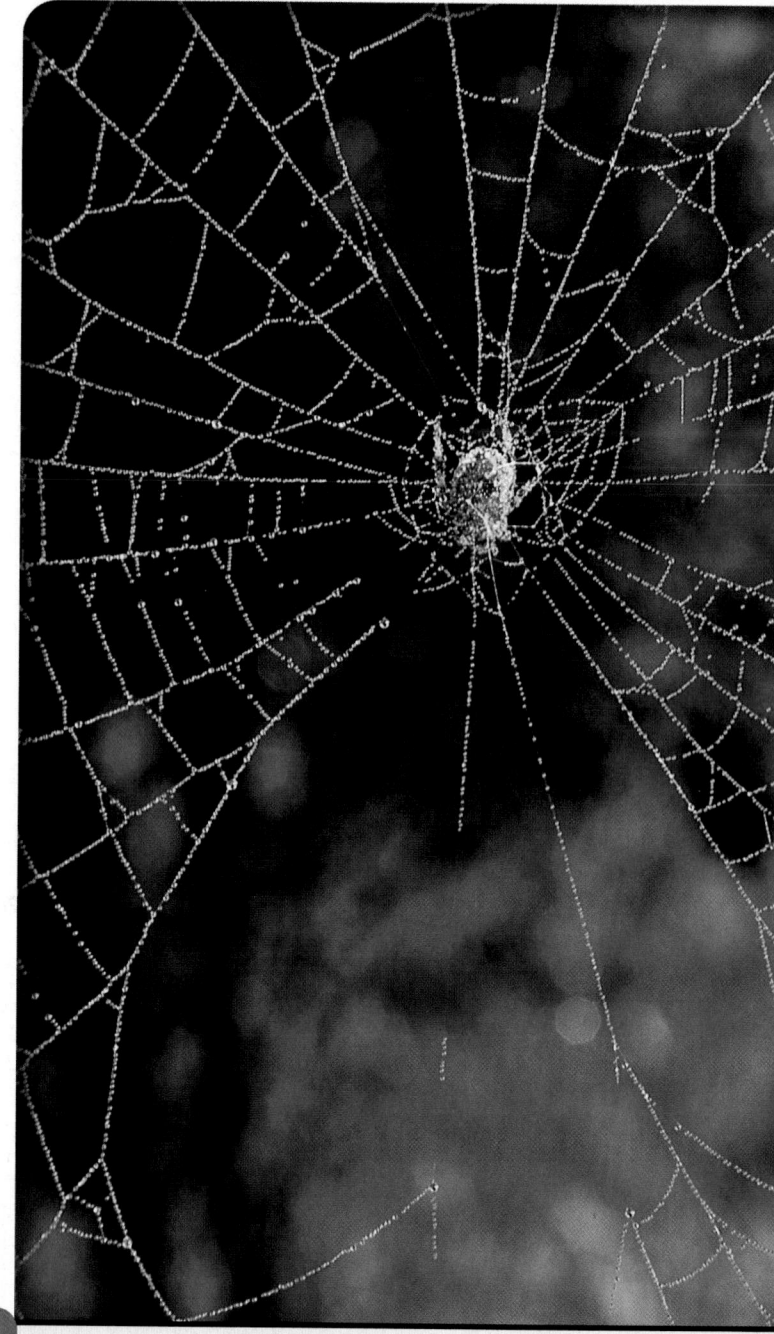

## DISCOVERY LAB

### Purpose
Students will test different foods for the presence of a simple sugar.

### Safety and Disposal
Be sure to remind students to wear aprons and goggles.
Contents of the test tube can be flushed down the sink drain with water.

### Teaching Strategies
- Use this investigation to make students aware of a possible career choice as a food scientist. Show them several detailed labels that are present on today's food containers. Food scientists provide this information to inform consumers. Discuss with students why knowledge of biochemistry is useful in

## Testing for Simple Sugars

**Y**our body constantly uses energy. Many different food sources can supply that energy, which is stored in the bonds of molecules called simple sugars. What foods contain simple sugars?

### Safety Precautions

### Procedure

1. Fill a 400-mL beaker one-third full of water. Place this water bath on a hot plate and begin to heat it to boiling.

2. Place 5.0 mL 10% glucose solution in a test tube.

3. Add 3.0 mL Benedict's solution to the test tube. Mix the two solutions using a stirring rod. Add a boiling chip to the test tube.

4. Using tongs, place the test tube in the boiling water bath and heat for five minutes.

5. Record a color change from blue to yellow or orange as a positive test for a simple sugar.

6. Repeat the procedure using food samples such as a 10% starch solution, a 10% gelatin (protein) suspension, or a few drops of honey suspended in water.

### Analysis

Was a color change observed? Which foods tested positive for the presence of a simple sugar?

### Materials

400-mL beaker
hot plate
10-mL graduated cylinder
boiling chip
10% glucose solution
test tube
tongs
Benedict's solution
stirring rod
other food solutions such as
  10% starch or honey

---

## Section 24.1 — Proteins

### Objectives

- **Describe** the structures of amino acids and proteins.
- **Explain** the roles of proteins in cells.

### Vocabulary

protein
amino acid
peptide bond
peptide
denaturation
enzyme
substrate
active site

An amazing variety of chemical reactions take place in living organisms. At the forefront of coordinating the numerous and intricate reactions of life are the large molecules called proteins, whose name comes from the Greek root word *protos*, meaning first.

### Protein Structure

You have learned that polymers are large molecules made of many repeating building blocks called monomers. **Proteins** are organic polymers made of amino acids linked together in a specific way. But proteins are not just large, randomly arranged chains of amino acids. To function properly, each protein must be folded into a specific three-dimensional structure. The spider silk shown on the opposite page would not be the incredibly strong yet lightweight protein that it is if it were not constructed in its specific way. You will learn in this section how proteins are made from their amino-acid building blocks and how different types of proteins function.

24.1 Proteins **775**

---

### Focus Transparency

Before presenting the lesson, display **Section Focus Transparency 91** on the overhead projector. Have students answer the accompanying questions using **Section Focus Transparency Master 91.** L1 ELL

Section Focus Transparency **91** Protein Polymers
Use with Chapter 24, Section 24.1

Nylon thread

Feather

Cocoon

❶ What are the characteristics of the nylon thread?
❷ How does the nylon differ from the polymers that make up the cocoon and the feather?

Chemistry: Matter and Change

Section Focus Transparencies

---

### Resource Manager

**Study Guide for Content Mastery,** pp. 139–140 L2
**Solving Problems: A Chemistry Handbook,** Section 24.1 L2
**Section Focus Transparency 91 and Master** L1 ELL

---

making informed choices about the foods they consume.
- To make up all solutions, see page 774C.

### Expected Results

The glucose solution and the honey cause the blue Benedict's solution to turn yellow. This is a positive test for a monosaccharide or simple sugar.

### Analysis

A color change from blue to yellow was observed in the test tubes containing glucose and honey. The glucose solution served as a positive control. There was no color change in the test tubes containing starch and gelatin.

---

National Science Content Standards

Pages 774–775
UCP.1, UCP.5; A.1; B.2

## In-Text Question

**Page 776** What is the abbreviation for glycine? Gly

## Math in Chemistry

*Logical-Mathematical* The number of possible peptides formed from a fixed number of amino acids can be found by using the formula $20^n$, where $n$ represents the number of amino acids in the peptide. Students may understand this formula better if it is explained that for each position in a random peptide, there is a 1/20 chance of any given amino acid being located there. For two positions, the chance of any two amino acids being present is $1/20 \times 1/20 = 1/400$, so there will be one out of 400 possible dipeptides with the given sequence of the two amino acids. The ratio 1/400 is the inverse of $20^2$, which also means that there are 400 possible dipeptides. **L3**

## Visual Learning

**Figure 24-1** Help students identify the properties of the various side chains in the amino acids shown in the figure.

**National Science Content Standards**

**Pages 776–777**
UCP.1, UCP.5; B.2, B.3

**Figure 24-1**

A large variety of side chains can be found on amino acids. Some of them are shown on these representative amino acids and are highlighted in green.

**Figure 24-2**

The amino group of one amino acid bonds to the carboxyl group of another amino acid to form a dipeptide. The organic functional group formed is an amide linkage and is called a peptide bond.

**Amino acids** As you saw in Chapter 23, many different functional groups are found in organic compounds. **Amino acids**, as their name implies, are organic molecules that have both an amino group and an acidic carboxyl group. The general structure of an amino acid is shown below.

Each amino acid has a central carbon atom around which are arranged four groups: an amino group ($-NH_2$), a carboxyl group ($-COOH$), a hydrogen atom, and a variable side chain, $R$. The side chains range from a single hydrogen atom to a complex double-ring structure. Examine the different side chains of the amino acids shown in **Figure 24-1**. Identify the nonpolar alkanes, polar hydroxyl groups, acidic and basic groups such as carboxyl and amino groups, aromatic rings, and sulfur-containing groups. This wide range of side chains gives the different amino acids a large variety of chemical and physical properties and is an important reason why proteins can carry out so many different functions.

Twenty different amino acids are commonly found in the proteins of living things. The name of each amino acid and its three-letter abbreviation are listed in **Table 24-1**. What is the abbreviation for glycine?

**The peptide bond** The amino and carboxyl groups provide convenient bonding sites for linking amino acids together. Since an amino acid is both an amine and a carboxylic acid, two amino acids can combine to form an

**776** Chapter 24 The Chemistry of Life

## Demonstration

### What's in a protein?

#### Purpose

To perform a destructive distillation of a protein

#### Materials

A few peanuts; Pyrex test tube and holder; red litmus paper; lead acetate test paper; cobalt chloride test paper; Bunsen burner

### Safety Precautions

**Disposal** All products can be thrown in the trash.

#### Procedure

Place a few peanuts in a Pyrex test tube and heat strongly. **CAUTION:** *Do this in a hood or in a room with good ventilation.* Place a piece of moist red litmus paper over the mouth of the tube while heating to test for ammonia. (Be sure to slant the tube in the amide, releasing water in the process. This reaction is a condensation reaction. As **Figure 24-2** shows, the amino group of one amino acid reacts with the carboxyl group of another amino acid to form an amide functional group. Where do the H and OH that form water come from?

The amide bond that joins two amino acids is referred to by biochemists as a **peptide bond**.

$$
\begin{array}{c}
\quad\ \ \overset{\displaystyle H}{|} \\
-C-N- \quad \text{Peptide bond} \\
\overset{\displaystyle \|}{O}
\end{array}
$$

A molecule that consists of two amino acids bound together by a peptide bond is called a dipeptide. **Figure 24-3a** shows the structure of a dipeptide that is formed from the amino acids glycine (Gly) and phenylalanine (Phe). **Figure 24-3b** shows a different dipeptide, also formed by linking together glycine and phenylalanine. Is Gly-Phe the same compound as Phe-Gly? No, they're different. Examine these two dipeptides to see that the order in which amino acids are linked in a dipeptide is important.

Each end of the two-amino-acid unit in a dipeptide still has a free group—one end has a free amino group and the other end has a free carboxyl group. Each of those groups can be linked to the opposite end of yet another amino acid, forming more peptide bonds. A chain of two or more amino acids linked together by peptide bonds is called a **peptide**. Living cells always build peptides by adding amino acids to the carboxyl end of a growing chain.

**Polypeptides** As peptide chains increase in length, other ways of referring to them become necessary. A chain of ten or more amino acids joined by peptide bonds is referred to as a polypeptide. When a chain reaches a length of about 50 amino acids, it's called a protein.

Because there are only 20 different amino acids that form proteins, it might seem reasonable to think that only a limited number of different protein structures are possible. But a protein can have from 50 to a thousand or more amino acids, arranged in any possible sequence. To calculate the number of possible sequences these amino acids can have, you need to consider that each position on the chain can have any of 20 possible amino acids. For a peptide that contains $n$ amino acids, there are $20^n$ possible sequences of the amino acids. So a dipeptide, with only two amino acids, can have $20^2$, or 400, different possible amino acid sequences. Even the smallest protein containing only 50 amino acids has $20^{50}$, or more than $1 \times 10^{65}$, possible arrangements of amino acids! It is estimated that human cells make between 80 000 and 100 000 different proteins. You can see that this is only a very small fraction of the total number of proteins possible.

**Table 24-1**

| The 20 Amino Acids | |
|---|---|
| **Amino acid** | **Abbreviation** |
| Alanine | Ala |
| Arginine | Arg |
| Asparagine | Asn |
| Aspartic acid | Asp |
| Cysteine | Cys |
| Glutamic acid | Glu |
| Glutamine | Gln |
| Glycine | Gly |
| Histidine | His |
| Isoleucine | Ile |
| Leucine | Leu |
| Lysine | Lys |
| Methionine | Met |
| Phenylalanine | Phe |
| Proline | Pro |
| Serine | Ser |
| Threonine | Thr |
| Tryptophan | Trp |
| Tyrosine | Tyr |
| Valine | Val |

Glycylphenylalanine (Gly-Phe)

Phenylalanylglycine (Phe-Gly)

**Figure 24-3**

**a** Glycine and phenylalanine can be combined in this configuration.
**b** Glycine and phenylalanine can also be combined in this configuration. Why are these two structures different substances?

24.1 Proteins **777**

flame and point opening away from people.) In a similar way, use lead acetate paper to test for hydrogen sulfide. Use cobalt chloride test paper to indicate the presence of water.

**Results**

The protein will blacken when heated, indicating carbon. The ammonia will turn the red litmus to blue. The lead acetate paper turns black for a positive test for $H_2S$. The cobalt chloride test paper indicates that

water is present by changing color.

**Analysis**

1. What does the darkening of the protein indicate is in a protein? carbon
2. What other elements are shown to be present by the test papers? sulfur, hydrogen, oxygen, and nitrogen.

Pleated sheet

Helix

**Figure 24-4**

The folding of polypeptide chains into both helices (left) and sheets (right) involves amino acids that are fairly close together in the chain being held in position by hydrogen bonds. Other interactions among the various side chains are not shown here but play an important role in determining the three-dimensional shape of a polypeptide.

**Three-dimensional protein structure** Long chains of amino acids start to fold into unique three-dimensional shapes even before they are fully synthesized, as intermolecular attractions form among the amino acids. Some areas of a polypeptide may twirl into helices, shaped like the coils on a telephone cord. Other areas may bend back and forth again and again into a sheet structure, like the folds of an accordion. A polypeptide chain may also turn back on itself and change direction. A given protein may have several helices, sheets, and turns, or none at all. **Figure 24-4** shows the folding patterns of a typical helix and a sheet. The overall three-dimensional shape of many proteins is globular, or shaped like an irregular sphere. Other proteins have a long fibrous shape. The three-dimensional shape is determined by the interactions among the amino acids.

Changes in temperature, ionic strength, pH, and other factors can act to disrupt these interactions, resulting in the unfolding and uncoiling of a protein. **Denaturation** is the process in which a protein's natural three-dimensional structure is disrupted. Cooking often denatures the proteins in foods. When an egg is hard-boiled, the protein-rich egg white solidifies due to the denaturation of its protein. Because proteins function properly only when folded, denatured proteins generally are inactive.

## The Many Functions of Proteins

Proteins play many roles in living cells. They are involved in catalyzing reactions, transporting substances, regulating cellular processes, forming structures, digesting foods, recycling wastes, and even serving as an energy source when other sources are scarce. See the **Everyday Chemistry** feature at the end of this chapter to learn how proteins play a role in the sense of smell.

**Enzymes** In most organisms, the largest number of different proteins function as enzymes, catalyzing the many reactions that go on in living cells. An **enzyme** is a biological catalyst. Recall that a catalyst speeds up a chemical reaction without being consumed in the reaction. A catalyst usually lowers the activation energy of a reaction by stabilizing the transition state.

How do enzymes function? The term **substrate** is used to refer to a reactant in an enzyme-catalyzed reaction. Substrates bind to specific sites on enzyme molecules, usually pockets or crevices. The pocket to which the substrates bind is called the **active site** of the enzyme. After the substrates bind to the active site, the active site changes shape slightly to fit more tightly around the substrates. This recognition process is called induced fit. In the diagram in **Figure 24-5**, you'll see that the shapes of the substrates must fit

Substrates → Enzyme-substrate complex → Product

Active site

Enzyme → Enzyme unchanged

**Figure 24-5**

Substrates are brought close together as they fit into the uniquely shaped active site of an enzyme. The enzyme then changes shape as it "molds itself" to the substrates, forming an enzyme-substrate complex. Bonds are broken and new bonds form to produce the product in the reaction.

that of the active site, in the same way that puzzle pieces or a lock and key fit together. A molecule only slightly different in shape from an enzyme's normal substrate doesn't bind as well to the active site or undergo the catalyzed reaction.

The structure that forms when substrates are bound to an enzyme is called an enzyme-substrate complex. The large size of enzyme molecules allows them to form multiple bonds with their substrates, and the large variety of amino acid side chains in the enzyme allows a number of different intermolecular forces to form. These intermolecular forces lower the activation energy needed for the reaction in which bonds are broken and the substrates are converted to product.

An example of an enzyme you may have used is papain, found in papayas, pineapple, and other plant sources. This enzyme catalyzes a reaction that breaks down protein molecules into free amino acids. Papain is the active ingredient in many meat tenderizers. When you sprinkle the dried form of papain on moist meat, you activate the papain so that it breaks down the tough protein fibers in the meat, making the meat more tender.

**Transport proteins** Some proteins are involved in transporting smaller molecules throughout the body. The protein hemoglobin, modeled in **Figure 24-6**, carries oxygen in the blood, from your lungs to the rest of your body. Other proteins combine with biological molecules called lipids to transport them from one part of your body to another through the bloodstream. You will learn about lipids later in this chapter.

**Figure 24-6**

ⓐ Hemoglobin is a globular protein with four polypeptide chains. The red structure in each chain is heme, an organic group containing an iron ion to which oxygen binds.
ⓑ The pink skin of this pig is due to the hemoglobin in its blood.

Heme

ⓐ

ⓑ

24.1 Proteins **779**

---

## Building a Model

**Kinesthetic** Ask students to use pipe cleaners or other materials to build a model of hemoglobin using the structure shown in Figure 24-6. Tell students to indicate clearly the location of the heme groups. Heme contains iron, to which oxygen binds.

## ✓ Assessment

**Knowledge** Ask students why the hormone insulin must be injected rather than swallowed. Insulin is a protein whose three-dimensional structure must remain intact to function properly. If insulin were swallowed, enzymes in the digestive system would break down the molecule into free amino acids. **L2**

## 3 Assess

### Check for Understanding

**Kinesthetic** Place 5 mL of a freshly made 2% lactose solution in each of two test tubes labeled "lactase" and "control." Add a ground-up tablet of lactase enzyme to the tube labeled "lactase." Mix each tube gently and let them sit in a beaker of warm water for 2 to 4 minutes. Have a pair of students test each tube for the presence of glucose using Benedict's reagent or glucose test strips. Ask students to explain what happened in each tube. The lactase enzyme broke down the lactose into glucose and galactose, which tested positive for simple sugars. The control tube gave a negative result because no enzyme was present. **L2**

---

**DIFFERENTIATED INSTRUCTION**

### Learning Disabled/Visually Impaired

**Kinesthetic** To better understand the concept of polymer formation, have students use paper clips to represent amino acid monomers that they can form into protein polymers. **L1 ELL**

**CHEMISTRY JOURNAL**

### Enzymes

**Linguistic** Have students research an enzyme and write a journal report describing the enzyme's substrates, function, and uses. **L2**

**National Science Content Standards**

**Pages 778–779**
UCP.1, UCP.5; B.2, B.3

**Reteach**

**Visual-Spatial** Use a dropper to place a few drops of 3% hydrogen peroxide on some of the following: cut pieces of fruits or vegetables, uncut pieces of fruits or vegetables, wood, rock, paper. Ask students to explain the results. **Disposal:** Wash hydrogen peroxide off materials with tap water. Bubbles should form on all sites where hydrogen peroxide was placed on cut living material; few or no bubbles should form on uncut living material or non-living material. Damaged cells release an enzyme that catalyzes the breakdown of hydrogen peroxide. The bubbles are oxygen gas produced in this reaction.

$$H_2O_2 \rightarrow H_2O + O_2 \quad \boxed{L2} \; \boxed{ELL}$$

## Extension

Ask students to find out which household products contain enzymes. Ask students to share their findings with the class. $\boxed{L2}$

## ✔ Assessment

**Knowledge** Ask each student to write a question on the material in this section. Have students exchange questions and quiz each other. $\boxed{L2}$

**Figure 24-7**

Collagen is a fibrous protein that consists of three helical polypeptides (right) that are coiled around one another to form the strong fibers of connective tissue (left). The large ropelike structures in the photo are bundles of collagen fibers, held together by cross-linkage. Collagen is an extremely large protein. Each of the three strands is about 1000 amino acids long.

**Structural proteins** The sole function of some proteins is to form structures vital to organisms. These molecules are known as structural proteins. The most abundant structural protein in most animals is collagen, which is part of skin, ligaments, tendons, and bones. **Figure 24-7** shows the structure of collagen. Other structural proteins make up hair, fur, wool, hooves, fingernails, cocoons, and feathers.

**Hormones** Hormones are messenger molecules that carry signals from one part of the body to another. Some hormones are proteins. Insulin, a familiar example, is a small (51 amino acids) protein hormone made by cells in the pancreas. When insulin is released into the bloodstream, it signals body cells that blood sugar is abundant and should be stored. A lack of insulin results in diabetes, a disease in which there is too much sugar in the bloodstream. Another protein hormone, chorionic gonadotropin, is synthesized by a developing embryo. Release of this hormone causes the development of a placenta that nourishes the embryo.

Because modern technology has made possible the laboratory synthesis of proteins, some protein hormones are being synthetically produced for use as medicines. Insulin, thyroid hormones, and growth hormones are some examples. Both natural and synthetic proteins are used in a variety of products—from meat tenderizer to cleaning solutions to health and beauty aids.

## Section 24.1 Assessment

1. Compare the structures of amino acids, dipeptides, polypeptides, and proteins. Which has the largest molecular mass? The smallest?

2. Draw the structure of the dipeptide Gly-Ser, circling the peptide bond.

3. List four functions that different proteins have in living organisms.

4. **Thinking Critically** How do the properties of proteins make them such useful catalysts? How do they differ from other catalysts you have studied?

5. **Applying Concepts** Identify an amino acid from **Figure 24-1** that can be classified into each of the categories in the following pairs.
   a. nonpolar versus polar
   b. aromatic versus aliphatic
   c. acidic versus basic

chemistrymc.com/self_check_quiz

## Section 24.1 Assessment

1. Amino acids are single-unit organic molecules that bond to each other. Two amino acids form a dipeptide, more than ten form a polypeptide, and more than 50 form a protein. From smallest to largest: amino acid, dipeptide, polypeptide, protein.

2. The structure should show the COOH of glycine and the NH₂ of serine contributing to the peptide bond. See the Solutions Manual for structure.

3. Proteins function as enzymes, in transporting small molecules, in forming structures, and as hormones.

4. Proteins are useful catalysts because of their large size and large number

and variety of functional groups on the amino acid side chains. Most inorganic catalysts are much smaller molecules.

5. a. nonpolar: Gly, Val, Phe
      polar: Ser, Cys, Gln, Lys, Glu
   b. aromatic: Phe
      aliphatic: all others
   c. acidic: Glu; basic: Lys

Analyzing the term *carbohydrate* offers a hint about the structure of this group of molecules. Early observations that these compounds have the general chemical formula $C_n(H_2O)_n$ and appear to be hydrates of carbon led to their being called carbohydrates. Although it is now known that there are no full water molecules attached to carbohydrates, the name has stayed.

## Kinds of Carbohydrates

Why do marathon runners eat large quantities of pasta before a big race? Pasta, as well as milk, fruit, bread, and potatoes, is rich in carbohydrates. The main function of carbohydrates in living organisms is as a source of energy, both immediate and stored. **Carbohydrates** are compounds that contain multiple hydroxyl groups (— OH) as well as a carbonyl functional group (C=O). These molecules range in size from single monomers to polymers made of hundreds or thousands of monomer units.

**Monosaccharides** The simplest carbohydrates, often called simple sugars, are **monosaccharides**. The most common monosaccharides have either five or six carbon atoms. They have a carbonyl group on one carbon and hydroxyl groups on most of the other carbons. The presence of a carbonyl group makes these compounds either aldehydes or ketones, depending upon the location of the carbonyl group. Multiple polar groups make monosaccharides water soluble and give them high melting points.

Glucose is a six-carbon sugar that has an aldehyde structure. Glucose is present in high concentration in blood because it serves as the major source of immediate energy in the body. For this reason, glucose is often called blood sugar. Closely related to glucose is galactose, which differs only in how a hydrogen and a hydroxyl group are oriented in space around one of the six carbon atoms. As you recall from Chapter 22, this relationship makes glucose and galactose stereoisomers; that is, their atoms are arranged differently in space. Fructose, also known as fruit sugar because it is the major carbohydrate in most fruits, is a six-carbon monosaccharide that has a ketone structure. Fructose is a structural isomer of glucose.

When monosaccharides are in aqueous solution, they exist in both open-chain and cyclic structures. The cyclic structures are more stable and are the predominant form of monosaccharides at equilibrium. Note in **Figure 24-8** that the carbonyl groups are present only in the open-chain structures. In the cyclic structures, they are converted to hydroxyl groups.

### Objectives

- **Describe** the structures of monosaccharides, disaccharides, and polysaccharides.

- **Explain** the functions of carbohydrates in living things.

### Vocabulary

carbohydrate
monosaccharide
disaccharide
polysaccharide

**Figure 24-8**

Glucose, galactose, and fructose are monosaccharides. In aqueous solutions, they exist in an equilibrium between their open-chain and cyclic forms, which are interconverted rapidly.

Cyclic form    Open-chain form
**Glucose**

Cyclic form    Open-chain form
**Galactose**

Cyclic form    Open-chain form
**Fructose**

24.2 Carbohydrates    **781**

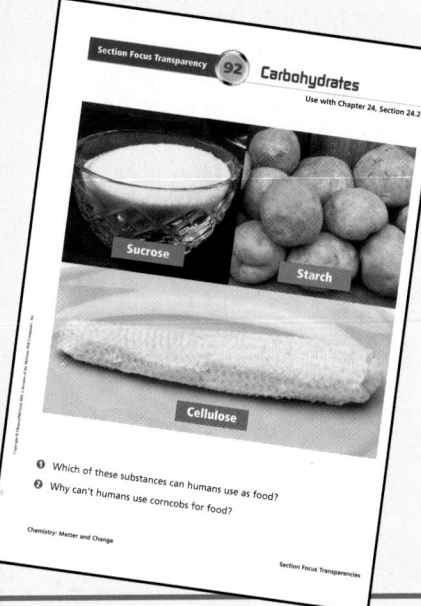
### DIFFERENTIATED INSTRUCTION

#### Gifted

*Visual-Spatial* Ask students to draw the structural formula for glucose, make a ball-and-stick model of glucose, and determine its IUPAC name. 2,3,4,5,6-pentahydroxyhexanal L3

### CHEMISTRY JOURNAL

#### Low-Carbohydrate Diets

*Linguistic* Ask students to find information about low-carbohydrate diets in the media. Ask them to research and then write a short report about the safety of that type of diet. L2

Glucose + Fructose → Sucrose + $H_2O$

## In-Text Question

**Page 782** Where does the water that is produced in this reaction come from? The OH group comes from one monosaccharide and the H comes from an OH group of a second monosaccharide.

## Quick Demo

Show students a number of materials, including cotton balls, paper, potato pieces, wood, apple pieces, laundry spray starch, bread, crackers, and metal. Ask students to predict which items will give a positive result to a test for starch. The potato, laundry spray starch, bread, and crackers all contain starch. Ask a student volunteer to use a dropper to place 1 or 2 drops of iodine solution on each material. Ask the class to interpret the results. Materials that contain starch will turn a blue-purple color due to the formation of a starch-iodine complex. Materials that contain cellulose (cotton, paper, and wood) turn brown when a similar complex forms.

## ✔ Assessment

**Skill** Have students determine how many moles of glucose are produced by the hydrolysis of $1.03 \times 10^3$ g of sucrose. 3 mol glucose

**Figure 24-9**

When glucose and fructose bond together, the disaccharide sucrose is formed. Note that water also is a product of this condensation reaction. Remember that each ring structure is made of carbon atoms, which are not shown for simplicity.

**Try at Home LAB**
See page 963 in Appendix E for
**Modeling Sugars**

**Disaccharides** Like amino acids, monosaccharides can be linked together by a condensation reaction in which water is released. When two monosaccharides bond together, a **disaccharide** is formed. See **Figure 24-9**. The new bond formed is an ether functional group (C — O — C). Where does the water that is produced in this reaction come from?

One common disaccharide is sucrose, which is also known as table sugar because sucrose is used mainly as a sweetener. Sucrose is formed by linking glucose and fructose. Another common disaccharide is lactose, the most important carbohydrate in milk. It often is called milk sugar. Lactose is formed when glucose and galactose bond together. Some foods that contain common disaccharides are shown in **Figure 24-10a**.

Disaccharides are too large to be absorbed into the bloodstream from the human digestive system, so they must first be broken down into monosaccharides. This is accomplished by a number of enzymes in the digestive system, one of which is sucrase in the small intestine. Sucrase breaks down sucrose into glucose and fructose. Another enzyme, called lactase, breaks down lactose into glucose and galactose. Some people do not have an active form of the enzyme lactase. Unless they ingest lactase enzyme along with foods that contain milk, they experience gas, bloating, and much discomfort as lactose accumulates in their digestive systems. These people are said to be lactose intolerant.

**Polysaccharides** You may have seen large carbohydrate polymers referred to as complex carbohydrates in nutritional references. Another name for a complex carbohydrate is **polysaccharide**, which is a polymer of simple sugars that contains 12 or more monomer units. The same type of bond that joins two monosaccharides in a disaccharide links them together in a polysaccharide. Pasta is a good source of polysaccharides. The pasta shown in **Figure 24-10b** contains large amounts of starch, a polysaccharide from plants.

**Figure 24-10**

**a** When you have a snack of milk and cookies, you are ingesting the disaccharides lactose and sucrose.
**b** Pasta is rich in the polysaccharide starch.

## CULTURAL DIVERSITY

### What's the source of your energy?

Complex carbohydrates are the main dietary source of energy for most people. In the United States, most Americans get their polysaccharides from wheat grain because it is commonly found in breads, pasta, and cereal. Around the world, different cultures use different grains for reasons that include taste, economics, and environmental conditions, such as amount of rainfall and soil type. In Asia, rice provides most complex carbohydrate calories. In Mexico and South America, corn is the complex carbohydrate most often eaten.

**Glycogen**

Glucose subunit

Glucose subunit

**Cellulose**

Glucose subunit

Crosslink bond

**Starch**

Glucose subunit

**Figure 24-11**

The starch in potatoes, the cellulose in lettuce leaves, and the glycogen in meat are all polymers of glucose. Cellulose has a linear, unbranched structure that resembles a chain-link fence. Starch molecules can be either branched or unbranched, and glycogen is highly branched.

Three important polysaccharides are starch, cellulose, and glycogen. All are composed solely of glucose monomers, as **Figure 24-11** illustrates. However, that's their only similarity, as all three have different properties and functions. Plants make both starch and cellulose. Starch is a soft, water-soluble molecule used to store energy, whereas cellulose is a water-insoluble polymer that forms rigid plant cell walls such as those found in wood. Glycogen is the animal counterpart of starch. It is made by animals to store energy, mostly in the liver and muscles.

How can these three polymers all be made solely of glucose monomers yet have such different properties? The answer lies in the way the bonds that link the monomers together are oriented in space. Because of this difference in bond shape, humans can digest starch but not cellulose. Digestive enzymes can't fit cellulose into their active sites due to the specific lock-and-key fit needed for enzyme action. As a result, the cellulose in the fruits, vegetables, and grains that we eat is labeled "dietary fiber" because it passes through the digestive system largely unchanged.

## Section 24.2 Assessment

**6.** Compare the structures of monosaccharides, disaccharides, and polysaccharides. Which has the largest molecular mass? The smallest?

**7.** What is the main function of carbohydrates in living organisms?

**8.** Compare and contrast the structures of starch and cellulose. How do the structural differences affect our ability to digest these two polysaccharides?

**9. Thinking Critically** If a carbohydrate has $2^n$ possible isomers, where $n$ is equal to the number of carbon atoms in the carbohydrate structure that are

chiral (meaning a carbon atom with four different groups bonded to it), calculate the number of possible isomers for each of the following monosaccharides. Use **Figure 24-8** to help you.

**a.** galactose
**b.** glucose
**c.** fructose

**10. Interpreting Scientific Illustrations** Draw the structure of the disaccharide sucrose, circling the ether functional group that bonds the monomer sugars together.

chemistrymc.com/self_check_quiz

24.2 Carbohydrates    **783**

*Visual-Spatial* Draw the structures of several different carbohydrates on the board. Use examples that students are probably not familiar with. Ask the students to label each structure as a mono-, di-, or polysaccharide. Have a student who has labeled each correctly explain to the others what information he or she used when answering. Students will have used molecular size, formula, or similarity to a more familiar example of each type to come up with their answers. **L2**

## Reteach

*Interpersonal* Have students work in groups to make ball-and-stick models of two cyclic monosaccharides. Ask them to join the two monosaccharides to make a disaccharide. Ask them what molecule is released when the structures are joined. water Now ask the groups to break down their disaccharides into the monosaccharides. Ask them what molecule is needed in addition to the disaccharide to complete the monosaccharides. They will need to add water to hydrolyze the disaccharide into two monosaccharides. **L2** **ELL** **COOP LEARN**

**Performance** Have students use a modeling kit or gumdrops and toothpicks to make models of glucose in both cyclic and open-chain structures. Use the Performance Task Assessment List for Model in **PASC**, p. 51. **L2** **ELL**

---

## Section 24.2 Assessment

**6.** Monosaccharides are molecules that contain multiple hydroxyl groups and an aldehyde or ketone group. Disaccharides are two monosaccharides joined by an ether bond. Polysaccharides are many monosaccharides joined by ether bonds. The order from smallest to largest is monosaccharide, disaccharide, polysaccharide.

**7.** Carbohydrates are the major immediate energy source in organisms and serve as a storage form of energy.

**8.** Both starch and cellulose contain only glucose monomers. They differ in how the bonds that hold glucose together are oriented in space. Because of this shape difference, our digestive enzymes cannot break

down cellulose.

**9. a.** $2^4 = 16$ isomers
**b.** $2^4 = 16$ isomers
**c.** $2^3 = 8$ isomers

**10.** Structure should resemble that of sucrose in Figure 24-9. The oxygen atom in the center should be circled. See the Solutions Manual.

# 1 Focus

Before presenting the lesson, display **Section Focus Transparency 93** on the overhead projector. Have students answer the accompanying questions using **Section Focus Transparency Master 93.** **L1** **ELL**

Section Focus Transparency **93** Lipids
Use with Chapter 24, Section 24.3

Vegetable oil

Vegetable shortening

❶ What do the two substances have in common? How do they differ?

❷ How does hydrogenation affect the melting point of vegetable oil?

Chemistry: Matter and Change

# 2 Teach

## Figure Caption Question

**Figure 24-12** How is the structure of the molecule affected by the presence of a double bond? The molecule is bent at the double bond.

## In-Text Question

**Page 784** What makes oleic acid unsaturated? the presence of a double bond

**National Science Content Standards**

**Pages 784–785**
UCP.1, UCP.5; B.2, B.3, B.6

---

## Section 24.3 Lipids

### Objectives

- **Describe** the structures of fatty acids, triglycerides, phospholipids, and steroids.
- **Explain** the functions of lipids in living organisms.
- **Identify** some reactions that fatty acids undergo.
- **Relate** the structure and function of cell membranes.

### Vocabulary

lipid
fatty acid
triglyceride
saponification
phospholipid
wax
steroid

The wax that you use to polish your car, the fat that drips out of your burger, and the vitamin D that fortifies the milk you drank for lunch—what do these diverse compounds have in common? They are all lipids.

### What is a lipid?

A **lipid** is a large, nonpolar, biological molecule. Because lipids are nonpolar, they are insoluble in water. Lipids have two major functions in living organisms. They store energy efficiently, and they make up most of the structure of cell membranes. Unlike proteins and carbohydrates, lipids are not polymers with repeated monomer subunits.

**Fatty acids** Although lipids are not polymers, many lipids have a major building block in common. This building block is the **fatty acid**, a long-chain carboxylic acid. Most naturally occurring fatty acids contain between 12 and 24 carbon atoms. Their structure can be represented by the formula

$$CH_3(CH_2)_nCOOH$$

Most fatty acids have an even number of carbon atoms, which is a result of their being constructed two carbons at a time in enzymatic reactions.

Fatty acids can be grouped into two main categories depending on the presence or absence of double bonds between carbon atoms. Fatty acids that contain no double bonds are referred to as saturated. Those that have one or more double bonds are called unsaturated. **Figure 24-12** shows the structures of two common fatty acids. Stearic acid is an 18-carbon saturated fatty acid; oleic acid is an 18-carbon unsaturated fatty acid. What makes oleic acid unsaturated?

### Stearic acid

### Oleic acid

**Figure 24-12**

Two fatty acids abundant in our diets are the 18-carbon saturated stearic acid and the 18-carbon unsaturated oleic acid. How is the structure of the molecule affected by the presence of a double bond? Refer to **Table C-1** in Appendix C for a key to atom color conventions.

**784** Chapter 24 The Chemistry of Life

---

## CHEMISTRY JOURNAL

### Dietary Lipids

*Intrapersonal* Ask students to keep a one-week record in their journals of how many grams of fat they consume each day. They should do research to find the recommended amount of fat for someone their age and size to determine if they are reaching or exceeding that recommended amount. Ask students to rank their favorite foods according to fat content and to make suggestions about how to modify their diets if they are eating too much or too little fat. **L2**

$$\begin{array}{c}
\text{CH}_2\text{OH} \\
| \\
\text{CHOH} \\
| \\
\text{CH}_2\text{OH}
\end{array}
+
\begin{array}{c}
\overset{\text{O}}{\overset{\|}{\text{HO C}}}(\text{CH}_2)_{14}\text{CH}_3 \\
\overset{\text{O}}{\overset{\|}{\text{HO C}}}(\text{CH}_2)_{16}\text{CH}_3 \\
\overset{\text{O}}{\overset{\|}{\text{HO C}}}(\text{CH}_2)_{18}\text{CH}_3
\end{array}
\rightarrow
\begin{array}{c}
\text{CH}_2-\text{O}-\overset{\text{O}}{\overset{\|}{\text{C}}}-(\text{CH}_2)_{14}-\text{CH}_3 \\
| \\
\text{CH}-\text{O}-\overset{\text{O}}{\overset{\|}{\text{C}}}-(\text{CH}_2)_{16}-\text{CH}_3 \\
| \\
\text{CH}_2-\text{O}-\overset{\text{O}}{\overset{\|}{\text{C}}}-(\text{CH}_2)_{18}-\text{CH}_3
\end{array}
+ 3\,\text{H}_2\text{O}$$

Glycerol    3 Fatty acids        A triglyceride      Water

An unsaturated fatty acid can become saturated if it reacts with hydrogen. As you learned in Chapter 23, hydrogenation is an addition reaction in which hydrogen gas reacts with carbon atoms that are linked by multiple bonds. Each unsaturated carbon atom can pick up one hydrogen atom to become saturated. For example, oleic acid can be hydrogenated to form stearic acid.

The double bonds in naturally occurring fatty acids are almost all in the *cis* geometric isomer form. Recall from Chapter 22 that the *cis* isomer has identical groups oriented on the same side of the molecule around a double bond. Because of the *cis* orientation, unsaturated fatty acids have a kink, or bend, in their structure that prevents them from packing together. They don't form as many intermolecular attractions as saturated fatty acid molecules. As a result, unsaturated fatty acids have lower melting points.

**Triglycerides** Although fatty acids are abundant in living organisms, they are rarely found alone. They most often are found bonded to glycerol, a molecule with three carbons each containing a hydroxyl group. When three fatty acids are bonded to a glycerol backbone through ester bonds, a **triglyceride** is formed. The formation of a triglyceride is shown in **Figure 24-13**.

Triglycerides can be either solids or liquids at room temperature. If liquid, they are usually called oils. If solid at room temperature, they're called fats. Most mixtures of triglycerides from plant sources, such as corn, olive, and peanut oils, are liquids because the triglycerides contain unsaturated fatty acids that have fairly low melting points. Animal fats, such as butter, contain a larger proportion of saturated fatty acids. They have higher melting points and usually are solids at room temperature.

Fatty acids are stored in fat cells of your body as triglycerides. When energy is abundant, fat cells store the excess energy in the fatty acids of triglycerides. When energy is scarce, the cells break down the triglycerides, forming free fatty acids and glycerol. Further breakdown of the fatty acids releases the energy used to form them. Although enzymes break down triglycerides in living cells, the reaction can be duplicated outside of cells by using a strong base such as sodium hydroxide. This reaction—the hydrolysis of a triglyceride using an aqueous solution of a strong base to form carboxylate salts and glycerol—is **saponification**, shown below.

$$\begin{array}{c}
\text{CH}_2-\text{O}-\overset{\text{O}}{\overset{\|}{\text{C}}}-(\text{CH}_2)_{14}\text{CH}_3 \\
| \\
\text{CH}-\text{O}-\overset{\text{O}}{\overset{\|}{\text{C}}}-(\text{CH}_2)_{14}\text{CH}_3 \\
| \\
\text{CH}_2-\text{O}-\overset{\text{O}}{\overset{\|}{\text{C}}}-(\text{CH}_2)_{14}\text{CH}_3
\end{array}
+ 3\text{NaOH} \rightarrow
\begin{array}{c}
\text{CH}_2\text{OH} \\
| \\
\text{CHOH} \\
| \\
\text{CH}_2\text{OH}
\end{array}
+ 3\text{CH}_3(\text{CH}_2)_{14}-\overset{\text{O}}{\overset{\|}{\text{C}}}-\text{O}^-\text{Na}^+$$

Triglyceride      A base    Glycerol      A soap

**Figure 24-13**

Ester bonds in a triglyceride are formed when the hydroxyl groups of glycerol combine with the carboxyl groups of the fatty acids.

## Biology
### CONNECTION

The venom of poisonous snakes contains a class of enzymes known as phospholipases. These enzymes catalyze the breakdown of phospholipids, triglycerides in which one fatty acid has been replaced by a phosphate group. The venom of the eastern diamondback rattlesnake contains a phospholipase that hydrolyzes the ester bond at the middle carbon of phospholipids. If the larger of the two breakdown products of this reaction gets into the bloodstream, it dissolves the membranes of red blood cells, causing them to rupture. A bite from the eastern diamondback can lead to death if not treated immediately.

## Building a Model

**Kinesthetic** Students often are confused when they read that fatty acids are nonpolar because the condensed structure is usually shown as $CH_3(CH_2)_n COOH$. In that structure, the carboxyl group is prominent, making the molecule appear polar. Ask students to build a ball-and-stick model of stearic acid so they can see for themselves that most of the molecule's volume is occupied by nonpolar $CH_2$ groups.
**L2** **ELL**

## Quick Demo

Ask students to predict the relative densities of corn syrup, 70% rubbing alcohol, vegetable oil, and water. Density order, from highest to lowest, is corn syrup, water, vegetable oil, rubbing alcohol. Ask a volunteer to test the predictions using a graduated cylinder and the four substances (three with different food colors added). Instruct the volunteer to pour one substance into the cylinder and then add each of the others VERY slowly. Ask students to determine the actual order of densities by observing the positions of each substance in the density gradient. **Disposal:** Dilute with soap and water and flush down drain.

## Applying Chemistry

**TECH PREP** While people tend to associate foaming in soaps and detergents with cleaning power, foaming cleansers are not necessarily more effective in removing dirt. Chemists in the detergent industry formulate foaming soaps and detergents mainly to increase product marketability because that is what consumers expect. Foaming actually can be undesirable. Too much foam formed in washing machines can cause the machine to overflow. Foaming can also denature enzymes that are added to some cleaning agents to promote dirt removal.

---

**DIFFERENTIATED INSTRUCTION**

### Learning Disabled

**Visual-Spatial** Use a simple analogy to help students understand the concept that a small number of building blocks can be used to make very large and different structures. Show students pictures of two very different buildings, both made of bricks. Ask what the building blocks are for the two buildings, and then ask how the structures can be so different when the building blocks are the same. **L1** **ELL**

## miniLAB

**Purpose**
Students will produce a small bar of soap by performing a saponification reaction.

**Process Skills**
Classifying, comparing and contrasting

**Safety Precautions**
Remind students that they are not to use the lye soap on their skin.

**Disposal**
The contents of the beaker can be flushed down the sink drain after removing the solid soap. Soap can be discarded in the trash after being washed with water.

**Teaching Strategies**
• Students can prepare their own saturated salt solution by adding 50 g of rock salt to 25 mL of water. This should be done during step 3 while the soap is being heated.
• A pea-sized piece of crayon can be added to the soap while heating to give it color.

**Expected Results**
The small bar of soap can be molded into an evaporating dish.

**Analysis**
1. ester bonds
2. a soap
3. One end of the soap molecule is a nonpolar hydrocarbon that attracts the soil. The other end of the soap molecule contains the sodium ion and is ionic. This end is attracted to polar water molecules. The dirt-laden soap is flushed away with the water.
4. triglyceride plus sodium hydroxide yields glycerol plus soap

### ✓ Assessment

**Performance** Have students do research and write a short paragraph explaining the similarities and differences between soaps and detergents. Use the Performance Task Assessment List for Writing in Science in **PASC**, page 87.

---

**Figure 24-14**

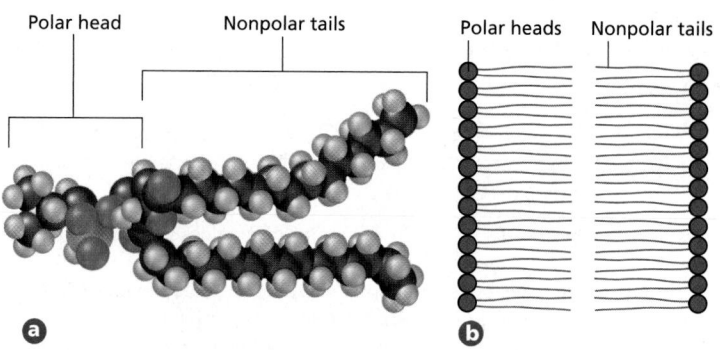

ⓐ A phospholipid has a polar head and two nonpolar tails.
ⓑ The membranes of living cells are formed by a double layer of lipids called a bilayer. The polar heads face out of both sides of the bilayer, where they are in contact with the watery environment inside and outside the cell. The nonpolar tails point into the center of the bilayer.

Polar head    Nonpolar tails    Polar heads    Nonpolar tails

ⓐ    ⓑ

Saponification is used to make soaps, which usually are the sodium salts of fatty acids. A soap has both a polar end and a nonpolar end. Soaps can be used to clean nonpolar dirt and oil with water because the nonpolar dirt and oil bond to the nonpolar end of the soap molecules, and the polar end of the soap molecules is soluble in water. Thus, the dirt-laden soap molecules can be rinsed away with the water. You can make soap by doing the **miniLAB** on this page.

**Phospholipids** Another important type of triglyceride, phospholipids, are found in greatest abundance in cellular membranes. A **phospholipid** is a triglyceride in which one of the fatty acids is replaced by a polar phosphate group. As you can see in **Figure 24-14a**, the polar part of the molecule forms

## miniLAB

### A Saponification Reaction

**Applying Concepts** The reaction between a triglyceride and a strong base such as sodium hydroxide is called saponification. In this reaction, the ester bonds in the triglyceride are hydrolyzed by the base. The sodium salts of the fatty acids, called soaps, precipitate out, and glycerol is left in solution.

**Materials** solid vegetable shortening, 250-mL beaker, 600-mL beaker, 6.0*M* NaOH, ethanol, saturated NaCl solution, stirring rod, hot plate, tongs, 25-mL graduated cylinder, evaporating dish, cheesecloth (20 cm × 20 cm), funnel

**Procedure**

1. Place a 250-mL beaker on the hot plate. Add 25 g solid vegetable shortening to the beaker. Turn the hot plate on at a medium setting.
2. As the vegetable shortening melts, slowly add 12 mL ethanol and then 5 mL 6.0*M* NaOH to the beaker. **CAUTION:** *Ethanol is flammable. NaOH causes skin burns. Wear gloves.*

3. Heat the mixture, stirring occasionally, for about 15 minutes, but do not allow it to boil.
4. When the mixture begins to thicken, use tongs to remove the beaker from the heat. Allow the beaker to cool for five minutes, then place it in a cold water bath in the 600-mL beaker.
5. Add 25 mL saturated NaCl solution to the mixture in the beaker. The soap is not very soluble and will appear as small clumps.
6. Collect the solid soap clumps by filtering them through a cheesecloth-lined funnel.
7. Using gloved hands, press the soap into an evaporating dish. Allow the soap to air dry for one or two days.
8. Remove your gloves and wash your hands.

**Analysis**
1. What type of bonds present in the triglycerides are broken during the saponification reaction?
2. What is the common name for the sodium salt of a fatty acid?
3. How does soap remove dirt from a surface?
4. Write a word equation for the saponification reaction in this lab.

**786    Chapter 24** The Chemistry of Life

---

### Resource Manager

**Study Guide for Content Mastery,** p. 142 **L2**
**Solving Problems: A Chemistry Handbook,** Section 24.3 **L2**
**ChemLab and MiniLab Worksheets,** p. 93 **L2**
**Section Focus Transparency 93 and Master** **L1** **ELL**

### *GLENCOE* TECHNOLOGY

**CD-ROM**
**Chemistry: Matter and Change**
Video: *Manufacturing Soap*
Demonstration: *Making Soap*

a "head," and the nonpolar fatty acids look like tails. How are the polar and nonpolar parts of a phospholipid arranged in the membranes of cells? A typical cell membrane has two layers of phospholipids, which are arranged with their nonpolar tails pointing inward and their polar heads pointing outward. See **Figure 24-14b.** This arrangement is called a lipid bilayer. Because the lipid bilayer structure acts as a barrier, the cell is able to regulate the materials that enter and leave through the membrane.

**Waxes** Another type of lipid, waxes, also contain fatty acids. A **wax** is a lipid that is formed by combining a fatty acid with a long-chain alcohol. The general structure of these soft, solid fats with low melting points is shown below, with $x$ and $y$ representing variable numbers of $CH_2$ groups.

$$CH_3(CH_2)_x - \overset{\overset{O}{\|}}{C} - O - (CH_2)_y CH_3$$

Both plants and animals make waxes. Plant leaves are often coated with wax, which prevents water loss. Notice in **Figure 24-15** how raindrops "bead up" on the leaves of a plant, indicating the presence of the waxy layer. The honeycomb of bees also is made of a wax, commonly called beeswax. Combining the 16-carbon fatty acid palmitic acid and a 30-carbon alcohol chain makes a common form of beeswax. Candles are sometimes made of beeswax because it burns slowly and evenly.

**Steroids** Not all lipids contain fatty acid chains. **Steroids** are lipids that have multiple cyclic rings in their structures. All steroids are built from the basic four-ring steroid structure shown below.

Some hormones, such as many sex hormones, are steroids that function to regulate metabolic processes. Cholesterol, another steroid, is an important structural component of cell membranes. Vitamin D also contains the four-ring steroid structure and plays a role in the formation of bones.

**Figure 24-15**

Plants produce wax that coats their leaves (top). The wax protects the leaves from drying out. The honeycomb of a beehive is constructed from beeswax (bottom).

---

**Section 24.3 Assessment**

**11.** Write the equation for the complete hydrogenation of the polyunsaturated fatty acid linoleic acid,
$CH_3(CH_2)_4CH=CHCH_2CH=CH(CH_2)_7COOH$.

**12.** List an important function of each of these types of lipids.
   **a.** triglycerides    **c.** waxes
   **b.** phospholipids    **d.** steroids

**13.** Compare and contrast the structures of a steroid, a phospholipid, a wax, and a triglyceride.

**14. Thinking Critically** What possible solvent can be used to extract lipids from cell membranes?

**15. Interpreting Scientific Illustrations** Draw the general structure of a phospholipid. Label the polar and nonpolar portions of the structure.

---

# 1 Focus

## Focus Transparency

Before presenting the lesson, display **Section Focus Transparency 94** on the overhead projector. Have students answer the accompanying questions using **Section Focus Transparency Master 94.** L1 ELL

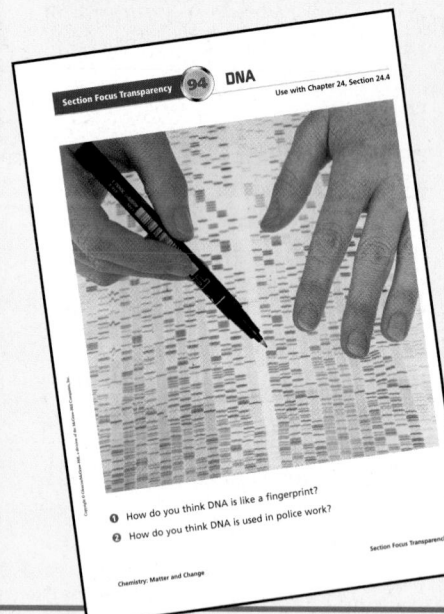

# 2 Teach

## Using Science Terms

Have students write statements explaining the meanings of the words *nucleic acid* and *nucleotide*. L1 ELL

## In-Text Questions

**Page 789** What forms the zipper's teeth? the nitrogen bases

**Page 789** How might such molecular modeling be done today? by computer graphics

## National Science Content Standards

**Pages 786–789**
UCP.1, UCP.5; A.1, A.2; B.2, B.3; G.1, G.3

**788**

---

## Objectives

- **Identify** the structural components of nucleic acids.
- **Relate** the function of DNA to its structure.
- **Describe** the structure and function of RNA.

## Vocabulary

nucleic acid
nucleotide

Nucleic acids are the fourth class of biological molecules that you will study. They are the information-storage molecules of the cell. This group of nitrogen-containing molecules got its name from the cellular location in which the molecules are primarily found—the nucleus. It is from this control center of cells that nucleic acids carry out their major functions.

## Structure of Nucleic Acids

A **nucleic acid** is a nitrogen-containing biological polymer that is involved in the storage and transmission of genetic information. The monomer that makes up a nucleic acid is called a **nucleotide**. Each nucleotide has three parts: an inorganic phosphate group, a five-carbon monosaccharide sugar, and a nitrogen-containing structure called a nitrogen base. Examine each part of **Figure 24-16a**. Although the phosphate group is the same in all nucleotides, the sugar and the nitrogen base vary.

In a nucleic acid, the sugar of one nucleotide is bonded to the phosphate of another nucleotide, as shown in **Figure 24-16b**. Thus, the nucleotides are strung together in a chain, or strand, containing alternating sugar and phosphate groups. Each sugar is also bonded to a nitrogen base that sticks out from the chain. The nitrogen bases on adjoining nucleotide units are stacked one above the other in a slightly askew position, much like the steps in a staircase. You can see this orientation in **Figure 24-16c**. Intermolecular forces hold each nitrogen base close to the nitrogen bases above and below it.

## DNA: The Double Helix

You've probably heard of DNA (deoxyribonucleic acid), one of the two kinds of nucleic acids found in living cells. DNA contains the master plans for building all the proteins in an organism's body.

**Figure 24-16**

Nucleotides are the monomers from which nucleic acid polymers are formed.

**a** Each nucleotide contains a nitrogen-containing base, a five-carbon sugar, and a phosphate group.

**b** Nucleic acids are linear chains of alternating sugars and phosphates. Attached to every sugar is a nitrogen base, which is oriented roughly perpendicular to the linear chain.

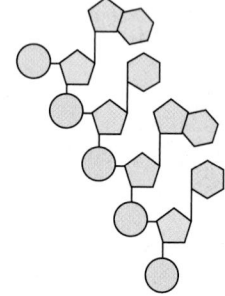

**c** Nucleotides are offset and thus resemble a staircase.

**788** Chapter 24 The Chemistry of Life

---

### Portfolio

## 3-D DNA

*Visual-Spatial* Ask students to make a 3-D model or a drawing of the DNA double helix and place it in their portfolios. L2 ELL P

### Resource Manager

**Study Guide for Content Mastery,** p. 143 L2
**Solving Problems: A Chemistry Handbook,** Section 24.4 L2
**Section Focus Transparency 94 and Master** L1 ELL

**The structure of DNA** The structure of DNA consists of two long chains of nucleotides wound together to form a spiral structure. Each nucleotide in DNA contains a phosphate group, the five-carbon sugar deoxyribose, and a nitrogen base. The alternating sugar and phosphate groups in each chain make up the outside, or backbone, of the spiral structure. The nitrogen bases are on the inside. Because the spiral structure is composed of two chains, it is known as a double helix. You can see from **Figure 24-17** that the DNA molecule is similar to a zipper in which the two ends have been twisted in opposite directions. The two sugar-phosphate backbones form the outsides of the zipper. What forms the zipper's teeth?

DNA contains four different nitrogen bases: adenine (A), thymine (T), cytosine (C), and guanine (G). As **Figure 24-18** shows, both adenine and guanine contain a double ring. Thymine and cytosine are single-ring structures. Looking back at **Figure 24-17**, you can see that each nitrogen base on one strand of the helix is oriented next to a nitrogen base on the opposite strand, in the same way that the teeth of a zipper are oriented. The side-by-side base pairs are close enough so that hydrogen bonds form between them. Because each nitrogen base has a unique arrangement of organic functional groups that can form hydrogen bonds, the nitrogen bases always pair in a specific way so that the optimum number of hydrogen bonds form. As **Figure 24-18** shows, guanine always binds to cytosine, and adenine always binds to thymine. The G—C and A—T pairs are called complementary base pairs.

It is because of complementary base pairing that the amount of adenine in a molecule of DNA always equals the amount of thymine, and the amount of cytosine always equals the amount of guanine. In 1953, James Watson and Francis Crick used this observation to make one of the greatest scientific discoveries of the twentieth century when they determined the double-helix structure of DNA. They accomplished this feat without actually carrying out many laboratory experiments themselves. Instead, they analyzed and synthesized the work of numerous scientists who had carefully carried out studies on DNA. The X-ray diffraction patterns of DNA fibers taken by Maurice Wilkins and Rosalind Franklin were of special importance because they clearly showed the dimensions of the DNA molecule and the molecule's helical structure. Watson and Crick used these results and molecular modeling techniques to build their DNA structure with balls and sticks. This discovery illustrates the importance of being able to visualize molecules in order to uncover patterns in bonding arrangements. How might such molecular modeling be done today?

**The function of DNA** Watson and Crick used their model to predict how DNA's chemical structure enables it to carry out its function. DNA stores the genetic information of a cell in the cell's nucleus. Before the cell divides, the DNA is copied so that the new generation of cells gets the same

**Figure 24-17**

The structure of DNA is a double helix that resembles a twisted zipper.

**Figure 24-18**

In DNA, base pairing exists between a double-ringed base and a single-ringed base. Adenine and thymine always pair, forming two hydrogen bonds between them. Guanine and cytosine always form three hydrogen bonds when they pair.

Thymine   Adenine

Cytosine   Guanine

24.4 Nucleic Acids   **789**

# problem-solving LAB

## Purpose

Students will model the replication of a small portion of a DNA molecule.

## Process Skills

Sequencing, observing and inferring, interpreting scientific illustrations, applying concepts, hypothesizing

## Background

When DNA replicates, more than a dozen enzymes complete the process of unzipping the strands, base-pairing a new set of nucleotides, and linking them all together. In bacteria, replication takes place at a rate of about 500 nucleotides per second; in higher organisms, the rate is one-tenth as fast.

## Teaching Strategies

- Either explain or have students research why the complementary base pairs of the DNA molecule are thymine-adenine and cytosine-guanine. These combinations of a purine and a pyrimidine produce a uniform helical diameter. T and A have two hydrogen bonding sites; C and G have three.
- Have students draw a two-dimensional sequence of the hydrogen bonding that occurs between T-A and C-G and the covalent bonding that connects adjacent sugars to phosphates.

## Thinking Critically

1. The base sequence of the new strand is complementary to the sequence of the original strand to which it is bonded.
2. All new DNA molecules will have one red strand and one blue strand. This shows that replication is semiconservative; each molecule has one original strand and one new strand.
3. If the sequence were copied incorrectly, the error would be passed on to the RNA, which would then be used to direct the production of a defective protein with an incorrect amino acid. If this error occurred in a sex cell and if the defective protein were vital to life, the new individual might not live.

genetic information. Having determined that the two chains of the DNA helix are complementary, Watson and Crick realized that complementary base pairing provides a mechanism by which the genetic material of a cell is copied. The **problem-solving LAB** shows how DNA copies, or replicates, itself.

The four nitrogen bases of DNA serve as the letters of the alphabet in the information-storage language of living cells. The specific sequence of these letters represents an organism's master instructions, just as the sequence of letters in the words of this sentence convey special meaning. The sequence of bases is different in every species of organism, allowing for an enormous diversity of life forms—all from a language that uses only four letters. It is estimated that the DNA in a human cell has about three billion complementary base pairs, arranged in a sequence unique to humans.

# problem-solving LAB

## How does DNA replicate?

**Formulating Models** DNA must be copied, or replicated, before a cell can divide so that each of the two new cells that are formed by cell division has a complete set of genetic instructions. It is very important that the replicating process be accurate; the new DNA molecules must be identical to the original. Watson and Crick noticed that their model for the three-dimensional structure of DNA provided a mechanism for accurate replication.

When DNA begins to replicate, the two nucleotide strands start to unzip. An enzyme breaks the hydrogen bonds between the nitrogen bases, and the strands separate to expose the nitrogen bases. Other enzymes deliver free nucleotides from the surrounding medium to the exposed nitrogen bases, adenine hydrogen-bonding with thymine and cytosine bonding with guanine.

Thus, each strand builds a complementary strand by base pairing with free nucleotides. This process is shown in **Diagram a**. When the free nucleotides have been hydrogen-bonded into place, their sugars and phosphates bond covalently to those on adjacent nucleotides to form the new backbone. Each strand of the original DNA molecule is now bonded to a new strand.

## Analysis

**Diagram b** shows a small segment of a DNA molecule. Copy the base sequence onto a clean sheet of paper, being careful not to make copying errors. Show the steps of replication to produce two segments of the DNA.

## Thinking Critically

1. How does the base sequence of a newly synthesized strand compare with the original strand to which it is bonded?
2. If the original DNA segment is colored red and the free nucleotides are colored blue, what pattern of colors will the newly replicated DNA segments have? Will all new segments have the same color pattern? What does this pattern mean?
3. What would happen if you had made an error when copying the base sequence onto your sheet of paper? How might an organism be affected if this error had occurred during replication of its DNA?

## ✔ Assessment

**Performance** If DNA molecular models are available, have students construct a T-A, G-C chain, describe its geometry and bonding, and describe how replication would proceed. This could also be accomplished using three-dimensional computer modeling software or the Internet. Use the Performance Task Assessment List for Model in **PASC,** p. 51.

## Resource Manager

Challenge Problems, p. 24 **L3**
Math Skills Transparency 40 and
    Master **L2** **ELL**

## Thymine

## Uracil

## Deoxyribose

## Ribose

**Figure 24-19**

DNA and RNA are nucleic acids with some important differences in structure. DNA contains thymine; RNA contains uracil, which lacks a methyl group. DNA's sugar, deoxyribose, has a hydrogen in one position instead of the hydroxyl group that ribose has.

## RNA

RNA (ribonucleic acid) also is a nucleic acid. Its general structure differs from that of DNA in three important ways. As you know, DNA contains the nitrogen bases adenine, cytosine, guanine, and thymine. RNA contains adenine, cytosine, guanine, and uracil; thymine is never found in RNA. Secondly, RNA contains the sugar ribose. DNA contains the sugar deoxyribose, which has a hydrogen atom in place of a hydroxyl group at one position. Compare these different structures shown in **Figure 24-19**.

The third difference between DNA and RNA arises as a result of these structural differences. DNA is normally arranged in a double helix in which hydrogen bonding links the two chains together through their bases. RNA is usually single stranded, with no such hydrogen bonds forming.

Whereas DNA functions to store genetic information, RNA allows cells to use the information found in DNA. You have learned that the genetic information of a cell is contained in the sequence of nitrogen bases in the DNA molecule. Cells use this base sequence to make RNA with a corresponding sequence. The RNA is then used to make proteins, each with an amino acid sequence that is determined by the order of nitrogen bases in RNA. A set of three of these nitrogen bases in RNA is called a codon. The sequences of bases in these codons are referred to as the genetic code. Because proteins are the molecular tools that actually carry out most activities in a cell, the DNA double helix is ultimately responsible for controlling the thousands of chemical reactions that take place.

---

## Section 24.4 Assessment

**16.** List the three chemical structures that make up a nucleotide.

**17.** Compare and contrast the structures and functions of DNA and RNA.

**18.** A sample of nucleic acid was determined to contain adenine, uracil, cytosine, and guanine. What type of nucleic acid is this?

**19. Thinking Critically** Analyze the structure of nucleic acids to determine what structural feature makes them acidic.

**20. Predicting** What is the genetic code? Predict what might happen to a protein if the DNA that coded for the protein contained the wrong base sequence.

chemistrymc.com/self_check_quiz

---

## 3 Assess
### Check for Understanding

**Visual-Spatial** Show pictures of DNA and RNA models. Ask students to identify which is which and explain how they arrived at their answers. Students should look for uracil and ribose in RNA, which is mostly single-stranded. They should look for thymine and deoxyribose in DNA, which is usually double-stranded.

### Reteach

Ask students to explain why, even though the DNA polymer is so stable that scientists have been able to isolate intact DNA from fossils that are millions of years old, our cells can unzip the strands of the double helix in seconds. Remind students that they should focus on the nature of interparticle forces. Each strand of the DNA polymer is held together by strong covalent ester bonds, making it very stable. The two strands of the helix are held together by the much weaker hydrogen bonds between complementary bases.

### ✔ Assessment

**Portfolio** Have students read James Watson's book, *The Double Helix,* and write reports for their portfolios. Published in 1968, the book offers insight into the scientific process and how scientists work. **L2**

**National Science Content Standards**
Pages 790–791
UCP.1, UCP.5; B.2; E.2; G.1

---

## Section 24.4 Assessment

**16.** sugar, phosphate, nitrogen base

**17.** DNA contains deoxyribose, phosphate groups, and A, C, G, and T bases. It is double-stranded and stores genetic information. RNA contains ribose, phosphate groups, and A, C, G, and U bases. It is single-stranded and functions in protein synthesis.

**18.** RNA; it contains uracil.

**19.** The phosphate groups make nucleic acids acidic.

**20.** The genetic code is the sequence of bases within codons that translates into amino acids. A protein made from DNA with the wrong base sequence may have the wrong amino acid sequence.

# 1 Focus

Before presenting the lesson, display **Section Focus Transparency 95** on the overhead projector. Have students answer the accompanying questions using **Section Focus Transparency Master 95.** L1 ELL

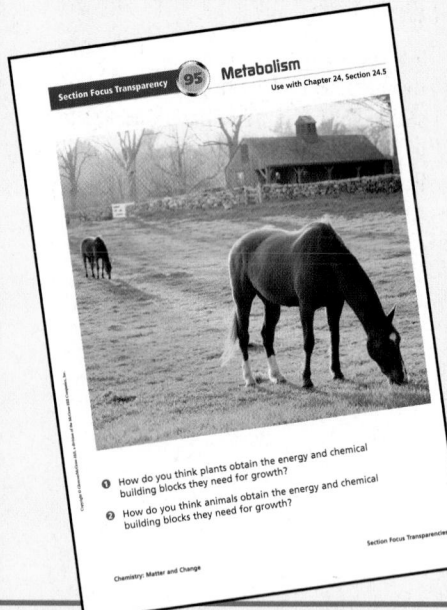

# 2 Teach
## Content Background

**Organic Compounds** In the 1800s, all compounds were placed into one of two categories. If they were produced by a living organism, they were called *organic;* if they were found in minerals, they were called *inorganic.* It was believed that organic substances could not be synthesized because they possessed a vital force that came from living things. That thinking changed after Friedrich Wohler synthesized urea from two inorganic salts. Today, organic molecules as complex as vitamin B$_{12}$ have been made in the laboratory.

---

## Objectives

- **Distinguish** between anabolism and catabolism.
- **Describe** the role of ATP in metabolism.
- **Compare** and **contrast** the processes of photosynthesis, cellular respiration, and fermentation.

## Vocabulary

metabolism
catabolism
anabolism
ATP
photosynthesis
cellular respiration
fermentation

**Figure 24-20**

A large number of different metabolic reactions take place in living cells. Some involve breaking down nutrients to extract energy; these are catabolic processes. Others involve using energy to build large biological molecules; these reactions are anabolic processes.

You've now studied the four major kinds of biological molecules and learned that they all are present in the food you eat. What happens to these molecules after they enter your body?

## Anabolism and Catabolism

Many thousands of chemical reactions take place in the cells of a living organism. The set of reactions carried out by an organism is its **metabolism**. Why are so many reactions involved in metabolism? Living organisms must accomplish two major functions in order to survive. They have to extract energy from nutrients in forms that they can use immediately as well as store for future use. In addition, they have to use nutrients to make building blocks for synthesizing all of the molecules needed to carry out their life functions. These processes are summarized in **Figure 24-20**.

The term **catabolism** refers to the metabolic reactions that break down complex biological molecules such as proteins, polysaccharides, triglycerides, and nucleic acids for the purposes of forming smaller building blocks and extracting energy. After you eat a meal of spaghetti and meatballs, your body immediately begins to break down the starch polymer in the spaghetti into glucose. The glucose is then broken down into smaller molecules in a series of energy-releasing catabolic reactions. Meanwhile, the protein polymers in the meatballs are catabolized into amino acids.

The term **anabolism** refers to the metabolic reactions that use energy and small building blocks to synthesize the complex molecules needed by an organism. After your body has extracted the energy from the starch in pasta, it uses that energy and the amino-acid building blocks produced from the meat proteins to synthesize the specific proteins that allow your muscles to contract, catalyze metabolic reactions, and carry out many other functions in your body.

**Figure 24-20** shows the relationship between catabolism and anabolism. The simple building-block molecules that are listed on the right side of the diagram are used to build the complex molecules that are listed on the left side of the diagram. As the arrow moves from right to left, anabolic reactions

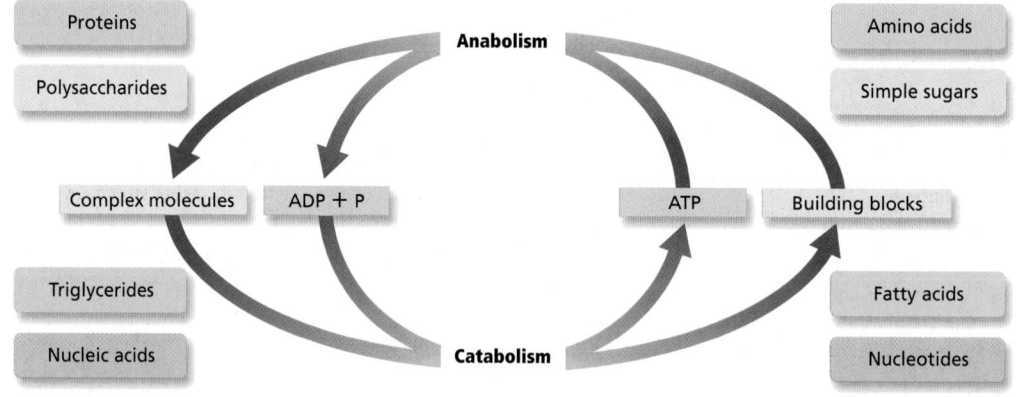

---

**DIFFERENTIATED INSTRUCTION**

### English Language Learners

*Linguistic* Have students write statements explaining the meanings of the words *anabolism* and *catabolism.* Have the students then write a short paragraph in which they incorporate both words correctly. L1 ELL

---

**Resource Manager**

**Study Guide for Content Mastery,** p. 144 L2
**Solving Problems: A Chemistry Handbook,** Section 24.5 L2
**Section Focus Transparency 95 and Master** L1 ELL

Adenine

Ribose

Triphosphate

ATP

**Figure 24-21**

ATP is a nucleotide that contains an adenine nitrogen base, a ribose sugar, and three phosphate groups. When the final phosphate group is removed from ATP, as modeled by the red dotted line, ADP is formed and energy is released.

take place. As the lower arrow moves from left to right, catabolic processes take place and the complex molecules are broken down into their smaller building blocks.

**ATP** Catabolism and anabolism are linked by common building blocks that catabolic reactions produce and anabolic reactions use. A common form of potential chemical energy also links the two processes. **ATP** (adenosine triphosphate) is a nucleotide that functions as the universal energy-storage molecule in living cells. During catabolic reactions, cells harness the chemical energy of foods and store it in the bonds of ATP. When these bonds are broken, the chemical energy is released and used by cells to drive anabolic reactions that might not otherwise occur. Most cellular reactions have an efficiency of only about 40 percent at best; the remaining 60 percent of the energy in food is lost as heat, which is used to keep your body warm.

The structure of ATP is shown in **Figure 24-21**. During catabolic reactions, cells produce ATP by adding an inorganic phosphate group to the nucleotide adenosine diphosphate (ADP) in an endothermic reaction. One mole of ATP stores approximately 30.5 kJ of energy under normal cellular conditions. During anabolism, the reverse reaction occurs. ATP is broken down to form ADP and inorganic phosphate in an exothermic reaction. Approximately 30.5 kJ of energy is released from each mole of ATP.

## Photosynthesis

What is the source of the energy that fuels metabolism? For most living things, certain wavelengths of sunlight provide all of this energy. Some bacteria and the cells of all plants and algae, including the brown algae shown in **Figure 24-22**, are able to capture light energy and convert some of it to chemical energy. Animals can't capture light energy, so they get energy by eating plants or by eating other animals that eat plants. The process that converts energy from sunlight to chemical energy in the bonds of carbohydrates is called **photosynthesis**. During the complex process of photosynthesis, carbon dioxide and water provide the carbon, hydrogen, and oxygen atoms that make up carbohydrates and oxygen gas, which also is formed. The following net reaction takes place during photosynthesis.

$$6CO_2 + 6H_2O + \text{light energy} \rightarrow C_6H_{12}O_6 + 6O_2$$

Carbon dioxide    Water    Glucose    Oxygen

Photosynthesis results in the reduction of the carbon atoms in carbon dioxide as glucose is formed. During this redox process, oxygen atoms in water are oxidized to oxygen gas.

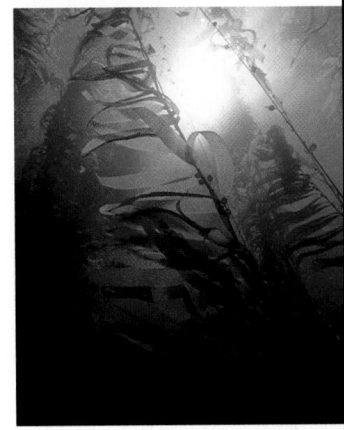

**Figure 24-22**

These giant seaweeds, called kelps, must grow close to the ocean's surface where light is available for photosynthesis. They cannot grow in the dark depths where sunlight does not penetrate the seawater.

24.5 Metabolism    **793**

## Visual Learning

**Figure 24-21** Ask students to examine the structure of ATP and compare and contrast its structure with that of the nucleotide in Figure 24-16a. Make sure students understand that the adenine rings in ATP contain four nitrogen atoms and the ribose ring contains an oxygen atom. These atoms have been deleted in this shorthand representation of ATP. Both ATP and the nucleotide contain a sugar, phosphate, and nitrogen base. ATP has three phosphates, its sugar is always ribose, and its nitrogen base is always adenine. Nucleotides can have ribose or deoxyribose, any of the five bases, and only one phosphate.

### ✓ Assessment

**Knowledge** Give students the equation for photosynthesis and ask them to convert it into the equation for cellular respiration. The answer is simply the reverse of the equation for photosynthesis.

## Quick Demo

Add 3*M* NaOH by the drop to a solution of the acid-base indicator thymol blue just until a blue color appears. Ask each student to pour 5 mL of this solution into a test tube and use a clean long straw to blow into the solution until a color change takes place. Ask them first to predict what will happen to the solution. **Disposal:** Flush down drain with plenty of water. Students should explain that the carbon dioxide they exhale forms carbonic acid in an aqueous solution. When they have acidified the solution enough, it turns from blue to clear. **L2**

## Internet Address Book

Note Internet addresses that you find useful in the space below for quick reference.

**National Science Content Standards**

**Pages 792–793**
UCP.1, UCP.5; B.2, B.3, B.6; F.3

**Figure 24-23**
These runners will need large amounts of energy if they are to complete the race. This energy is stored in the bonds of ATP in their cells.

## Cellular Respiration

Most organisms need oxygen to live. Oxygen that is produced during photosynthesis is used by living things during **cellular respiration**, the process in which glucose is broken down to form carbon dioxide, water, and large amounts of energy. Cellular respiration is the major energy-producing process in living organisms. **Figure 24-23** shows one use of energy in the body. This energy is stored in the bonds of ATP, and a maximum of 38 moles of ATP are produced for every mole of glucose that is catabolized. Cellular respiration is a redox process; the carbon atoms in glucose are oxidized while oxygen atoms in oxygen gas are reduced to the oxygen in water. The net reaction that takes place during cellular respiration is

$$C_6H_{12}O_6 + 6O_2 \rightarrow 6CO_2 + 6H_2O + energy$$
Glucose  Oxygen  Carbon  Water
dioxide

Note that the net equation for cellular respiration is the reverse of the net equation for photosynthesis. You will learn in Chapter 26 how these two processes complement each other in nature.

## Fermentation

During cellular respiration, glucose is completely oxidized, and oxygen gas is required to act as the oxidizing agent. Can cells extract energy from glucose in the absence of oxygen? Yes, but not nearly as efficiently. Without oxygen, only a fraction of the chemical energy of glucose can be released. Whereas cellular respiration produces 38 moles of ATP for every mole of glucose catabolized in the presence of oxygen, only two moles of ATP are produced per mole of glucose that is catabolized in the absence of oxygen. This provides enough energy for oxygen-deprived cells so that they don't die. The process in which glucose is broken down in the absence of oxygen is known as **fermentation**. There are two common kinds of fermentation. In one, ethanol and carbon dioxide are produced. In the other, lactic acid is produced.

**Alcoholic fermentation** Yeast and some bacteria can ferment glucose to produce the alcohol ethanol.

$$C_6H_{12}O_6 \rightarrow 2CH_3CH_2OH + 2CO_2 + energy$$
Glucose    Ethanol    Carbon
dioxide

**Figure 24-24**

Bread dough is heavy before yeast cells begin to ferment the carbohydrates (left). After fermentation has produced carbon dioxide, the dough becomes lighter and fluffier as it rises (right).

This reaction, called alcoholic fermentation, is important to certain segments of the food industry, as you can see in **Figure 24-24**. Alcoholic fermentation is needed to make bread dough rise, form tofu from soybeans, and produce the ethanol in alcoholic beverages. Another use of the ethanol that is produced by yeast is as an additive to gasoline, called gasohol. You can observe yeast cells fermenting sugar in the **CHEMLAB** at the end of this chapter.

**Lactic acid fermentation** Have you ever gotten muscle fatigue while running a race? During strenuous activity, muscle cells often use oxygen faster than it can be supplied by the blood. When the supply of oxygen is depleted, cellular respiration stops. Although animal cells can't undergo alcoholic fermentation, they can produce lactic acid and a small amount of energy from glucose through lactic acid fermentation.

$$C_6H_{12}O_6 \rightarrow 2CH_3CH(OH)COOH + energy$$
$$\text{Glucose} \qquad \text{Lactic acid}$$

The lactic acid that is produced is moved from the muscles through the blood to the liver. There, it is converted back into glucose that can be used in catabolic processes to yield more energy once oxygen becomes available. However, if lactic acid builds up in muscle cells at a faster rate than the blood can remove it, muscle fatigue results. Buildup of lactic acid is what causes a burning pain in the muscle during strenuous exercise.

**Topic: Forensic Anthropology**
To learn more about forensic anthropology, visit the Chemistry Web site at **chemistrymc.com**

**Activity:** Research forensic anthropology and explain at least four ways that knowledge of the chemistry of life helps scientists learn about what ancient ice men and animals did on their last days alive.

## CHEMLAB

ChemLab 24, located at the end of the chapter, can be used at this point in the lesson.

### Reteach

Ask students why cells use a universal energy currency such as ATP rather than just using chemical energy directly from food molecules. Remind students that most cellular processes depend on the catalytic activity of enzymes. Students should explain that having a universal energy currency allows many different enzymes to use the energy stored in ATP without requiring them to have active sites designed to bind to all the different types of fuel molecules (such as proteins, carbohydrates, and lipids).

### Extension

Have students research the role of chlorophyll in photosynthesis and summarize their findings in a short report. **L3**

### ✓ Assessment

**Skill** Have students make a table summarizing cellular respiration, alcoholic fermentation, and lactic acid fermentation. The table should include reactants, products, and moles of ATP produced. **L2**

## Section 24.5 Assessment

**21.** Compare and contrast the processes of anabolism and catabolism.

**22.** Explain the role ATP plays in the metabolism of living organisms.

**23.** Decide whether each of the following processes is anabolic or catabolic.

  **a.** photosynthesis

  **b.** cellular respiration

  **c.** fermentation

**24. Thinking Critically** Why is it necessary to use sealed casks when making wine?

**25. Calculating** How many moles of ATP would a yeast cell produce if six moles of glucose were oxidized completely in the presence of oxygen? How many moles of ATP would the yeast cell produce from six moles of glucose if the cell were deprived of oxygen? For more help, refer to *Arithmetic Operations* in the **Math Handbook** on page 887 of this textbook.

## Section 24.5 Assessment

**21.** Anabolism includes the metabolic reactions that build up large molecules from smaller nutrient building blocks, consuming energy in the process. Catabolism includes the metabolic reactions that break down nutrients, extracting energy in the process.

**22.** ATP functions as an energy currency. The potential chemical energy in food molecules is converted during metabolism to the potential energy of ATP, which organisms can use for most energy-requiring life processes.

**23. a.** anabolic
    **b.** catabolic
    **c.** catabolic

**24.** to keep oxygen out so cellular respiration does not occur

**25.** a maximum of 228 moles of ATP in the presence of oxygen; 12 moles of ATP in the absence of oxygen

## Preparation

### Time Allotment
One laboratory period

### Process Skills
Collecting data, interpreting data, communicating, comparing and contrasting, making and using graphs, predicting

### Safety Precautions
You may wish to conduct this lab behind an explosion shield because it is a closed system under pressure.

### Disposal
The yeast mixture can be flushed down the sink with lots of water.

### Preparation of Solutions
• To make the yeast suspension, add one 7-g package of yeast for every 200 mL of water.
• To make the 5% sugar solution, dissolve 5 g of sugar per 100 mL of water solution.

### Alternative Materials
• Any container must be such that the number 5 stopper from the stopper apparatus can fit into it.

### Pre-Lab

**2.** $C_6H_{12}O_6 \rightarrow 2CH_3CH_2OH + 2CO_2$ + energy

**5.** Rearranging the ideal gas law to solve for pressure, $P = (nRT)/V$. Therefore, as carbon dioxide is produced, $n$ increases, which increases $P$.

**6.** The ideal gas law clearly shows that $P$ is dependent on $T$. Therefore, if $T$ changes during the experiment, the change in pressure will be the combined result of carbon dioxide production and temperature change.

## Procedure
• The ChemBio program is part of the graphing calculator CBL kit.
• Review with students the operation of the valves on the apparatus.
• The vegetable oil is used to make the reaction mixture anaerobic. If the oil does not cover the surface of the mixture, oxygen will be

# Alcoholic Fermentation in Yeast

**Y**east cells are able to metabolize many types of sugars. In this experiment, you will observe the fermentation of sugar by baker's yeast. When yeast cells are mixed with a sucrose solution, they must first hydrolyze the sucrose to glucose and fructose. Then the glucose is broken down in the absence of oxygen to form ethanol and carbon dioxide. You can test for the production of carbon dioxide by using a CBL pressure sensor to measure an increase in pressure.

### Problem
What is the rate of alcoholic fermentation of sugar by baker's yeast?

### Objectives
• **Measure** the pressure of carbon dioxide produced by the alcoholic fermentation of sugar by yeast.
• **Calculate** the rate of production of carbon dioxide by the alcoholic fermentation of sugar by yeast.

### Materials
CBL system
graphing calculator
ChemBio program
Vernier pressure sensor
link cable
CBL-DIN cable
test tube with #5 rubber-stopper assembly
5% sucrose solution
ring stand
stirring rod
600-mL beaker
thermometer
basting bulb
hot and cold water
yeast suspension
vegetable oil
utility clamp
10-mL graduated cylinders (2)
pipette

### Safety Precautions

• Always wear safety goggles and an apron in the lab.
• Do not use the thermometer as a stirring rod.

### Pre-Lab

**1.** Reread the section of this chapter that describes alcoholic fermentation.

**2.** Write the chemical equation for the alcoholic fermentation of glucose.

**3.** Read the entire **CHEMLAB**.

**4.** Prepare all written materials that you will take into the laboratory. Be sure to include safety precautions and procedure notes.

**5.** Form a hypothesis about how the pressure inside the test tube is related to the production of carbon dioxide during the reaction. Refer to the ideal gas law in your explanation.

**6.** Why is temperature control an essential feature of the **CHEMLAB**?

### Procedure

**1.** Load the ChemBio program into your graphing calculator. Connect the CBL and calculator with the link cable. Connect the pressure sensor to the CBL with a CBL-DIN cable.

**2.** Prepare a water bath using the 600-mL beaker. The beaker should be about two-thirds full of water. The water temperature should be between 36°C and 38°C.

**3.** Set up the test tube, ring stand, and utility clamp as shown in the figure. Obtain about 3 mL yeast suspension in a 10-mL graduated cylinder, and pour it into the test tube. Obtain about 3 mL 5% sucrose solution in a 10-mL graduated cylinder. Add the sucrose solution to the yeast in the test tube. Stir to mix. Pour enough vegetable oil on top of the mixture to completely cover the surface.

available to the yeast and cellular respiration rather than fermentation will occur. The pressure will not change because the oxygen being used up during respiration will be replaced by the carbon dioxide produced.

### Expected Results
Pressure will increase in the tube as carbon dioxide gas is produced.

## Analyze and Conclude

**1.**

**4.** Place the stopper assembly into the test tube. Make sure it has an airtight fit. Leave both valves of the assembly open to the atmosphere.

**5.** While one lab partner does step 5, the other partner should do steps 6 and 7. Lower the test tube into the water bath and allow it to incubate for 10 minutes. Keep the temperature of the water bath between 36°C and 38°C by adding small amounts of hot or cold water with the basting bulb as needed.

**6.** Start the ChemBio program. Choose 1:SET UP PROBES under MAIN MENU. Choose 1 for number of probes. Choose 3:PRESSURE under SELECT PROBE. Enter 1 for Channel. Choose 1:USE STORED for CALIBRATION. Choose 1:ATM for PRESSURE UNITS.

**7.** Choose 2:COLLECT DATA under MAIN MENU. Choose 2:TIME GRAPH under DATA COLLECTION. Use time between sample seconds = 10. Use number of samples = 60. (This will give you 600 seconds or 10 minutes of data). Choose 1:USE TIME SETUP under CONTINUE? Set Ymin = 0.8, Ymax = 1.3, and Yscl = 0.1. Do not press ENTER until the test tube has finished incubating.

**8.** After the test tube has incubated for ten minutes, close the valve attached to the stopper. Make sure the valve near the pressure sensor is open to the sensor. Start measuring the gas pressure by press-

ing ENTER. Monitor the pressure reading on the CBL unit. If the pressure exceeds 1.3 atm, the stopper can pop off. Open the air valve on the pressure sensor to release this excess gas pressure.

**9.** After ten minutes, the data collection will stop. Open the air valve on the stopper. If needed, you can run a second trial by closing the air valve and choosing 2:YES to REPEAT? If you are finished, press 1:NO.

## Cleanup and Disposal

**1.** Rinse out and wash all items.

**2.** Rinse the yeast suspension/sucrose/vegetable oil mixture down the sink with large amounts of water.

**3.** Return all lab equipment to its proper place.

## Analyze and Conclude

**1. Making and Using Graphs** Choose 3:VIEW GRAPH from the MAIN MENU. Make a sketch of the graph. (You also may want to record the data table by using 4:VIEW DATA.)

**2. Interpreting Data** The rate of carbon dioxide production by the yeast can be found by calculating the slope of the graph. Return to the MAIN MENU and choose 5:FIT CURVE. Choose 1:LINEAR L1, L2. The slope will be listed under LINEAR as "A" of Y = A*X + B. Record this value.

**3. Communicating** How does your rate of carbon dioxide production compare with the rates of other members of the class?

**4. Analyzing** Why did you add vegetable oil to the test tube in step 3?

**5. Error Analysis** Suppose that the pressure does not change during a trial. What might be some possible reasons for this?

## Real-World Chemistry

**1.** Yeast is used in baking bread because the carbon dioxide bubbles make the bread rise. The other product of alcoholic fermentation is ethanol. Why can't you taste this alcohol when you eat bread?

**2.** How would the appearance of a loaf of bread be different if you used twice as much yeast as the recipe called for?

**2.** Answers will vary. The typical slope will be 0.00024 atm/s.

**3.** Answers will vary. Results should be fairly close.

**4.** The vegetable oil sealed the reaction mixture from the air, ensuring that fermentation and not cellular respiration took place in the tube.

**5.** Pressure would not change if there were a small leak in the apparatus. Also, if the vegetable oil does not cover the surface of the reaction mixture, oxygen will be used up as fast as carbon dioxide is produced as the yeast undergo cellular respiration.

## Real-World Chemistry

**1.** The ethanol evaporates as the bread is baked.

**2.** The loaf of bread would be higher and fluffier if twice the amount of yeast were used.

✓ **Assessment**

**Performance** The experiment can be repeated using a different sugar. Fructose, glucose, or undiluted fruit juice can be used. Have students compare the rates of carbon dioxide production using the different sugars. Use the Performance Task Assessment List for Carrying Out a Strategy and Collecting Data in **PASC,** p. 25.

**Resource Manager**

**ChemLab and MiniLab Worksheets,** pp. 94–96 **L2**

**National Science Content Standards**

**Pages 796–797**
UCP.1, UCP.5; A.1; B.3, B.6; E.2

## Purpose

Students will learn how the shapes of molecules play an important role in the olfactory system.

## Background

Odors are essential to the survival of most vertebrates because odors allow organisms to identify food, mates, and predators. Despite its importance, the mechanism of the olfactory system is not understood. No single theory can explain all observations about the sense of smell. The stereochemical theory of odor suggested that a molecule's shape, and not its composition, is responsible for its odor. This theory is supported by the fact that slight changes in the structure of an odorant can cause major changes in its smell. More recent research shows that odorants with similar shapes may have very different smells. To explain these contradictions, some researchers propose that odor reception depends on the vibrations and energy levels of the odorants.

## Teaching Strategies

- Have students brainstorm examples in which their sense of smell could save their lives. For example, they might detect spoiled food, smell smoke in a burning building, or smell gas leaking in the kitchen.
- To help students with the concept of receptor combinations, have them cut out several shapes in two colors to represent receptors and odorants. They should have several portions of an odorant match different receptors.
- Olfaction is linked to memory because the signal that is sent to the brain reaches the limbic system, which is responsible for emotions, behavior, and memory. Ask students to discuss specific memories they might have in response to certain odors. For example, the smell of popcorn

may always remind them of a movie theater.
- The sense of smell is tightly connected to the sense of taste. In fact, a good deal of taste is really smell. This is why foods taste bland when a person has a head cold with a stuffy nose. To test this idea, ask students to taste foods while holding their noses. Have them describe the taste of the food before and after they hold their noses.

# Everyday Chemistry

## Sense of Smell

Take a deep breath. What do you smell? Maybe it's the eraser on your pencil, some flowers outside your window, an apple pie coming out of the oven, or even stinky gym shoes on the floor. Your sense of smell, otherwise known as olfaction, tells you a lot about the world around you.

### Fitting In

How exactly do you smell odors? If you said that you smell with your nose, you are only partially correct. The nose you see when you look in the mirror doesn't actually detect odors. Its job is to pull odor molecules, known as odorants, into your nasal passages when you breathe.

The air you inhale carries odorants to a small region located high inside your nasal passage just below and between your eyes. The tissues of this region contain nerve cells that have hairlike fibers called cilia on one end. When receptors located on the cilia are stimulated by odorants, the nerve cells send messages to the brain. The brain then identifies the odors you smell.

The exact manner in which receptors detect odorants is not entirely understood. However, researchers have found evidence to suggest that it involves the shapes of both the receptors and the odorants. Receptors are usually large, globular protein molecules that are similar in shape to enzymes. Their surfaces contain small crevices. An odorant must fit into and bind with a crevice on the surface of the receptor much as a substrate molecule fits into and binds with the active site on the surface of an enzyme. Each type of receptor has a uniquely shaped crevice on its surface that binds only with an odorant of a particular shape.

### Not By Shape Alone

The process of smelling is not that simple, however. Scientists have discovered that shape is not the only property that determines whether an odorant will bind with a receptor. Odorant molecules must be able to travel through air and they must be able to dissolve in the fluids of the nasal passages. In addition, some research suggests that odor receptors can detect the energy levels of the odorants. An odorant with exactly the right energy will vibrate in such a way that it produces a response in the receptor. This may be what causes the nerve cell to send a signal to the brain.

### So Many Odors

How many odors do you think you can recognize? If your olfactory system is at its best, you can distinguish about 10 000 different odors. Does this mean that you have more than 10 000 different types of olfactory receptors? The answer is no. In fact, you have fewer than 1000 different types of olfactory receptors.

As researchers searched for an explanation of how the olfactory receptors recognize so many different odors, they found that the olfactory system uses a combination of receptors for each odor. A single odorant can be recognized by more than one receptor because different receptors respond to different parts of the same odorant molecule. Rather than responding to a signal from a single receptor for each odor, the brain interprets a combination of signals from several receptors in order to identify a particular odor. In this way, a limited number of receptors can be used to identify a large number of odors.

## Testing Your Knowledge

1. **Relating Concepts** How is the receptor-odorant relationship similar to an enzyme-substrate relationship?

2. **Applying** How might fragrance designers benefit from an understanding of how the shape of an odorant stimulates a receptor?

## Testing Your Knowledge

1. Both involve a lock-and-key relationship between two molecules.
2. Fragrance designers might be able to design odorants to bind with specific receptors. In this way, they could create fragrances that would be perceived in specific ways.

## Summary

### 24.1 Proteins

- Proteins are biological polymers made of amino acids that are linked together by peptide bonds.
- Protein chains fold into intricate three-dimensional structures.
- Many proteins function as enzymes, which are highly specific and powerful biological catalysts. Other proteins function to transport important chemical substances, or provide structure in organisms.

### 24.2 Carbohydrates

- Monosaccharides, known as simple sugars, are aldehydes or ketones that also have multiple hydroxyl groups.
- Bonding two simple sugars together forms a disaccharide such as sucrose or lactose.
- Polysaccharides such as starch, cellulose, and glycogen are polymers of simple sugars.
- Carbohydrates function in living things to provide immediate and stored energy.

### 24.3 Lipids

- Fatty acids are long-chain carboxylic acids that usually have between 12 and 24 carbon atoms.
- Saturated fatty acids have no double bonds; unsaturated fatty acids have one or more double bonds.
- Fatty acids can be linked to glycerol backbones to form triglycerides.
- The membranes of living cells have a lipid bilayer structure.
- Steroids are lipids that have a multiple-ring structure.

### 24.4 Nucleic Acids

- Nucleic acids are polymers of nucleotides, which consist of a nitrogen base, a phosphate group, and a sugar.
- DNA contains deoxyribose sugar and the nitrogen bases adenine, cytosine, guanine, and thymine.
- RNA contains ribose sugar and the nitrogen bases adenine, cytosine, guanine, and uracil.
- DNA functions to store the genetic information in living cells and transmit it from one generation of cells to the next. RNA functions in protein synthesis.

### 24.5 Metabolism

- Metabolism is the sum of the many chemical reactions that go on in living cells.
- Catabolism refers to reactions that cells undergo to extract energy and chemical building blocks from large biological molecules.
- Anabolism refers to the reactions through which cells use energy and small building blocks to build the large biological molecules needed for cell structures and for carrying out cell functions.
- During photosynthesis, cells use carbon dioxide, water, and light energy to produce carbohydrates and oxygen.
- During cellular respiration, cells break down carbohydrates in the presence of oxygen gas to produce carbon dioxide and water. Energy released is stored as chemical potential energy in the molecule ATP.
- In the absence of oxygen, cells can carry out either alcoholic or lactic acid fermentation.

## Using the Vocabulary

To reinforce chapter vocabulary, have students write a sentence using each term. **L2** **ELL**

## Review Strategies

- Have students describe the differences in structure of proteins, carbohydrates, lipids, and nucleic acids. **L2**
- Have students summarize the major functions of proteins, carbohydrates, lipids, and nucleic acids. **L2**
- Have students compare and contrast the metabolic processes of photosynthesis, cellular respiration, and fermentation. **L2**
- Problems from Appendix A or the **Supplemental Problems** booklet can be used for review. **L2**

## VOCABULARY PuzzleMaker

 For additional help with vocabulary, have students access the Vocabulary PuzzleMaker online.

chemistrymc.com/
vocabulary_puzzlemaker

## Chemistry Online

## Vocabulary

- active site (p. 778)
- amino acid (p. 776)
- anabolism (p. 792)
- ATP (p. 793)
- carbohydrate (p. 781)
- catabolism (p. 792)
- cellular respiration (p. 794)
- denaturation (p. 778)
- disaccharide (p. 782)
- enzyme (p. 778)

- fatty acid (p. 784)
- fermentation (p. 794)
- lipid (p. 784)
- metabolism (p. 792)
- monosaccharide (p. 781)
- nucleic acid (p. 788)
- nucleotide (p. 788)
- peptide (p. 777)
- peptide bond (p. 777)

- phospholipid (p. 786)
- photosynthesis (p. 793)
- polysaccharide (p. 782)
- protein (p. 775)
- saponification (p. 785)
- steroid (p. 787)
- substrate (p. 778)
- triglyceride (p. 785)
- wax (p. 787)

## EXAM*VIEW*® PRO

### Use Exam*View*® Pro Testmaker CD-ROM to:

- Create **multiple versions** of tests.
- Create **modified** tests with one mouse click for struggling students.
- **Edit** existing questions and add your own questions.
- **Build** tests based on national curriculum standards.

**National Science Content Standards**
Pages 798–799
UCP.1, UCP.5; B.2, B.3, B.6; E.2

## Concept Mapping

**26.** 1. ATP; 2. metabolism;
3. cellular respiration;
4. fermentation; 5. and
6. alcoholic, lactic acid

## Mastering Concepts

**27.** peptide; protein
**28.** hair, fingernails, toenails, tendons, ligaments, skin
**29.** An alpha helix is a coiled stretch of a protein chain. A beta sheet is a flat area where a chain folds back and forth repeatedly.
**30. a.** amide group
  **b.** hydroxyl group
  **c.** carboxyl group
  **d.** amino group
**31.** The active site and the substrates bind together. A reaction occurs between the substrates because they are held closely together and the activation energy decreases.
**32. a.** glycine
  **b.** tyrosine
  **c.** tryptophan
  **d.** phenylalanine
  **e.** glutamic acid
  **f.** histidine
**33.** phenylalanine
**34.** nonpolar: glycine, valine, phenylalanine; polar: serine, cysteine, glutamine, lysine, glutamic acid
**35.** No. Each amino acid has a different group attached to the peptide bond.
**36.** Enzymes form many bonds with the substrates, lowering the activation energy.
**37.** Tryptophan is a large, nonpolar, aromatic amino acid that is not soluble in water and has relatively high melting and boiling points. It is a building block for proteins.
**38.** Yes. The environment of a cell is aqueous, so it makes sense for cell proteins to have more polar amino acids on the outside of the

---

**Chemistry Online**

*Go to the Chemistry Web site at* chemistrymc.com *for additional Chapter 24 Assessment.*

## Concept Mapping

**26.** Complete the concept map using the following terms: lactic acid, ATP, cellular respiration, metabolism, alcoholic, fermentation.

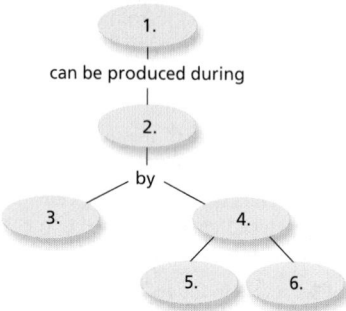

## Mastering Concepts

**27.** What should you call a chain of eight amino acids? A chain of 200 amino acids? (24.1)
**28.** Name five parts of your body that are made of structural proteins. (24.1)
**29.** Describe two common shapes found in the three-dimensional folding of proteins. (24.1)
**30.** Name the organic functional groups in the side chains of the following amino acids. (24.1)
  **a.** glutamine      **c.** glutamic acid
  **b.** serine         **d.** lysine
**31.** Explain how the active site of an enzyme functions. (24.1)
**32.** Name the amino acids represented by each of the following abbreviations. (24.1)
  **a.** Gly      **d.** Phe
  **b.** Tyr      **e.** Glu
  **c.** Trp      **f.** His
**33.** Name an amino acid that has an aromatic ring in its side chain. (24.1)
**34.** Name two nonpolar and two polar amino acids. (24.1)
**35.** Is the dipeptide lysine-valine the same compound as the dipeptide valine-lysine? Explain. (24.1)

---

**36.** How do enzymes lower the activation energy for a reaction? (24.1)
**37.** The structure shown is tryptophan. Describe some of the properties you would expect tryptophan to have, based on its structure. In what class of large molecules do you think tryptophan is a building block? (24.1)

**38.** Most proteins with a globular shape are oriented so that they have mostly nonpolar amino acids on the inside and polar amino acids located on the outer surface. Does this make sense in terms of the nature of the cellular environment? Explain. (24.1)
**39.** Classify the following carbohydrates as monosaccharides, disaccharides, or polysaccharides. (24.2)
  **a.** starch        **e.** cellulose
  **b.** glucose       **f.** glycogen
  **c.** sucrose       **g.** fructose
  **d.** ribose        **h.** lactose
**40.** Name two isomers of glucose. (24.2)
**41.** What kind of bond is formed when two monosaccharides combine to form a disaccharide? (24.2)
**42.** Give a scientific term for each of the following. (24.2)
  **a.** blood sugar    **c.** table sugar
  **b.** fruit sugar    **d.** milk sugar
**43.** Explain how the different bonding arrangements in cellulose and starch give them such different properties. (24.2)
**44.** The disaccharide maltose is formed from two glucose monomers. Draw its structure. (24.2)
**45.** Hydrolysis of cellulose, glycogen, and starch produces only one monosaccharide. Why is this so? What monosaccharide is produced? (24.2)
**46.** Digestion of disaccharides and polysaccharides cannot take place in the absence of water. Why do you think this is so? Include an equation in your answer. (24.2)
**47.** Draw the structure of the open-chain form of fructose. Circle all chiral carbons, and then calculate the number of stereoisomers with the same formula as fructose. (24.2)

chemistrymc.com/chapter_test

---

molecule and fewer polar amino acids on the inside.

## Resource Manager

Chapter Assessment, pp. 139–144
Supplemental Problems, Ch. 24
ExamView® Pro CD-ROM
MindJogger Videoquizzes DVD/VHS
Solutions Manual, Ch. 24
Chemistry Interactive CD-ROM,
  Ch. 24 quiz

**48.** Compare and contrast the structures of a triglyceride and a phospholipid. (24.3)

**49.** Predict whether a triglyceride from beef fat or a triglyceride from olive oil will have a higher melting point. Explain your reasoning. (24.3)

**50.** Explain how the structure of soaps makes them effective cleaning agents. (24.3)

**51.** Draw a portion of a lipid bilayer membrane, labeling the polar and nonpolar parts of the membrane. (24.3)

**52.** Where and in what form are fatty acids stored in the body? (24.3)

**53.** What type of lipid does not contain fatty acid chains? Why are these molecules classified as lipids? (24.3)

**54.** Draw the structure of the soap sodium palmitate (palmitate is the conjugate base of the 16-carbon saturated fatty acid, palmitic acid) and label its polar and nonpolar ends. (24.3)

**55.** What three structures make up a nucleotide? (24.4)

**56.** Name two nucleic acids found in organisms. (24.4)

**57.** Explain the roles of DNA and RNA in the production of proteins. (24.4)

**58.** Where in living cells is DNA found? (24.4)

**59.** Describe the types of bonds and attractions that link the monomers together in a DNA molecule. (24.4)

**60.** In the double helical structure of DNA, the base guanine is always bonded to cytosine and adenine is always bonded to thymine. What do you expect to be the relative proportional amounts of A, T, C, and G in a given length of DNA? (24.4)

**61.** One strand in a DNA molecule has the following base sequence. What is the base sequence of the other strand in the DNA molecule? (24.4)

C-C-G-T-G-G-A-C-A-T-T-A

**62.** Is digestion an anabolic or a catabolic process? Explain. (24.5)

**63.** Compare the net reactions for photosynthesis and cellular respiration with respect to reactants, products, and energy. (24.5)

## Mastering Problems

### Protein Structure (24.1)

**64.** How many peptide bonds are present in a peptide that has five amino acids?

**65.** How many peptides, each containing four different amino acids, can be made from Phe, Lys, Pro, and Asp? List the peptides, using the three-letter abbreviations for the amino acids.

**66.** The average molecular mass of an amino acid is 110 g/mol. Calculate the approximate number of amino acids in a protein that has a molecular mass of 36 500 g/mol.

### Calculations with Lipids (24.3)

**67.** The fatty acid palmitic acid has a density of 0.853 g/mL at 62°C. What will be the mass of a 0.886-L sample of palmitic acid at that temperature?

**68.** How many moles of hydrogen gas are required for complete hydrogenation of one mole of linolenic acid, whose structure is shown below? Write a balanced equation for the hydrogenation reaction.

$CH_3CH_2CH = CHCH_2CH = CHCH_2CH = CH(CH_2)_7COOH$
Linolenic acid

**69.** A chicken egg contains about 213 mg of cholesterol. Calculate how many moles of cholesterol this represents if the molecular mass of cholesterol is 386 amu.

**70.** Calculate the number of moles of sodium hydroxide needed in the saponification of 16 moles of a triglyceride.

### Working with DNA (24.4)

**71.** The genetic code is a triplet code, that is, a sequence of three bases in RNA codes for each amino acid in a peptide chain or protein. How many RNA bases are required to code for a protein that contains 577 amino acids?

**72.** It has been calculated that the average length of a base pair in a DNA double helix is 3.4 Å. The human genome (the complete set of all DNA in the nucleus of a human cell) contains about three billion base pairs of DNA. In centimeters, how long is the DNA in the human genome? Assume that the DNA is stretched out and not coiled around proteins as it actually is in a living cell. (1 Å = $10^{-10}$ m)

**73.** A cell of the bacterium *Escherichia coli* has about $4.2 \times 10^6$ base pairs of DNA, whereas each human cell has about $3 \times 10^9$ base pairs of DNA. What percentage of the size of the human genome does the *E. coli* DNA represent?

### Energy Calculations (24.5)

**74.** Every mole of glucose that undergoes alcoholic fermentation in yeast results in the net synthesis of two moles of ATP. How much energy in kJ is stored in two moles of ATP? Assume 100% efficiency.

**75.** How many moles of lactic acid are produced when three moles of glucose undergo fermentation in your muscle cells? Assume 100% completion of the process.

**39. a.** polysaccharide
**b.** monosaccharide
**c.** disaccharide
**d.** monosaccharide
**e.** polysaccharide
**f.** polysaccharide
**g.** monosaccharide
**h.** disaccharide
**40.** fructose and galactose
**41.** ether bond
**42. a.** glucose **c.** sucrose
**b.** fructose **d.** lactose
**43.** The monomers are linked together in different ways. Cellulose is a linear polymer of parallel chains held tightly together in bundles. Starch is a branched polymer; branching keeps the structure from forming tight bundles.
**44.** The structure should show two glucose units linked with an ether bond. See Solutions Manual.
**45.** All three polymers are made only of glucose. Upon hydrolysis, only glucose is released.
**46.** The ether bonds (COC) holding the sugars together must be broken into two COH bonds by incorporating water. This is a hydrolysis reaction. The equation is the reverse of that in Figure 24-9.
**47.** 8 isomers. See Solutions Manual.
**48.** A triglyceride is a glycerol molecule to which three fatty acids are bonded with ester bonds. A phospholipid is a glycerol molecule to which two fatty acids and a phosphate group are bonded with ester bonds.
**49.** Beef contains more saturated fats than olive oil. Saturated fatty acids pack together better than unsaturated fatty acids, so the

beef lipid will have a higher melting point than the olive lipid.

**50.** Soaps have both a nonpolar end, which dissolves nonpolar dirt and grease, and a water-soluble polar end, which allows water to wash away the soap and dirt.

**51.** Diagram should resemble Figure 24-14b. See Solutions Manual.

**52.** in fat cells as triglycerides

**53.** Steroids; they are large, nonpolar biomolecules.

**54.** $CH_3(CH_2)_{14}COO^-Na^+$; the left end is nonpolar and the charged end is polar.

**55.** sugar, phosphate, and nitrogen base

**56.** RNA and DNA

**57.** DNA holds the instructions for making proteins. These are passed to RNA, which translates the base sequence into an amino acid sequence during protein synthesis.

**58.** in the nucleus

**National Science Content Standards**

**Pages 800–801**
UCP.1, UCP.5; B.2, B.3, B.6

**59.** Covalent bonds link sugars and phosphates. Hydrogen bonds hold bases together in the center of the helix.

**60.** A = T and C = G

**61.** G-G-C-A-C-C-T-G-T-A-A-T

**62.** a catabolic process that breaks down large molecules

**63.** Photosynthesis:
$6CO_2 + 6H_2O + energy \rightarrow C_6H_{12}O_6 + 6O_2$
Cellular respiration:
$C_6H_{12}O_6 + 6O_2 \rightarrow 6CO_2 + 6H_2O + energy$

## Mastering Problems

Complete solutions to Chapter Assessment problems can be found in the **Solutions Manual.**

### Protein Structure (24.1)
**Level 1**
**64.** 4 peptide bonds

**Level 2**
**65.** 24 if each amino acid is used once
**66.** 332 amino acids

### Calculations with Lipids (24.3)
**Level 1**
**67.** 756 g
**68.** 3; $C_{18}H_{30}O_2 + 3H_2 \rightarrow C_{18}H_{36}O_2$

**Level 2**
**69.** $5.52 \times 10^{-4}$ mol cholesterol
**70.** 48 mol NaOH

### Working With DNA (24.4)
**Level 1**
**71.** 1731 RNA bases

**Level 2**
**72.** 100 cm
**73.** 0.1% of the human genome

### Energy Calculations (24.5)
**Level 1**
**74.** 61.0 kJ
**75.** 6 mol lactic acid
**76.** 214 kJ

**76.** The synthesis of one mole of the fatty acid palmitic acid from two-carbon building blocks requires seven moles of ATP. How many kJ of energy are required for the synthesis of one mole of palmitic acid?

**77.** How many grams of glucose can be oxidized completely by 2.0 L of $O_2$ gas at STP during cellular respiration?

**78.** Calculate and compare the total energy in kJ that is converted to ATP during the processes of cellular respiration and fermentation.

## Mixed Review ———————

*Sharpen your problem-solving skills by answering the following.*

**79.** Draw the carbonyl functional groups present in glucose and fructose. How are the groups similar? How are they different?

**80.** List the names of the monomers that make up proteins, complex carbohydrates, and nucleic acids.

**81.** Describe the functions of proteins, carbohydrates, lipids, and nucleic acids in living cells.

**82.** Write a balanced equation for the hydrolysis of lactose.

**83.** Write a balanced equation for photosynthesis.

**84.** Write and balance the equation for cellular respiration.

**85.** Write a balanced equation for the synthesis of sucrose from glucose and fructose.

## Thinking Critically ——————

**86.** **Using Numbers** Approximately 38 moles of ATP are formed when glucose is completely oxidized during cellular respiration. If the heat of combustion for 1 mole of glucose is $2.82 \times 10^3$ kJ/mol and each mole of ATP stores 30.5 kJ of energy, what is the efficiency of cellular respiration in terms of the percentage of available energy that is stored in the chemical bonds of ATP?

**87.** **Recognizing Cause and Effect** Some diets suggest severely restricting the intake of lipids. Why is it not a good idea to eliminate all lipids from the diet?

**88.** **Making and Using Graphs** A number of saturated fatty acids and values for some of their physical properties are listed in **Table 24-2**.

**a.** Make a graph plotting number of carbon atoms versus melting point.

**b.** Graph the number of carbon atoms versus density.

**c.** Draw conclusions about the relationships between the number of carbon atoms in a saturated fatty acid and its density and melting point values.

**d.** Predict the approximate melting point of a saturated fatty acid that has 24 carbon atoms.

Table 24-2

| Physical Properties of Saturated Fatty Acids | | | |
|---|---|---|---|
| Name | Number of carbon atoms | Melting point (°C) | Density (g/mL) (values at 60–80°C) |
| Palmitic acid | 16 | 63 | 0.853 |
| Myristic acid | 14 | 58 | 0.862 |
| Arachidic acid | 20 | 77 | 0.824 |
| Caprylic acid | 8 | 16 | 0.910 |
| Docosanoic acid | 22 | 80 | 0.822 |
| Stearic acid | 18 | 70 | 0.847 |
| Lauric acid | 12 | 44 | 0.868 |

## Writing in Chemistry ——————

**89.** Write a set of instructions that could be included in a package of contact-lens cleaning solution containing an enzyme. This enzyme catalyzes the breakdown of protein residues that adhere to the lenses. Include information about the structure and function of enzymes and the care that must be taken to avoid their denaturation during use.

**90.** Use the library or the Internet to research cholesterol. Where is this molecule used in your body? What is its function? Why is too much dietary cholesterol considered to be bad for you?

## Cumulative Review ———————

*Refresh your understanding of previous chapters by answering the following.*

**91. a.** Write the balanced equation for the synthesis of ethanol from ethene and water.
**b.** If 448 L of ethene gas reacts with excess water at STP, how many grams of ethanol will be produced? (Chapter 14)

**92.** Identify whether each of the reactants in these reactions is acting as an acid or a base. (Chapter 19)
**a.** $HBr + H_2O \rightarrow H_3O^+ + Br^-$
**b.** $NH_3 + HCOOH \rightarrow NH_4^+ + HCOO^-$
**c.** $HCO_3^- + H_2O \rightarrow CO_3^- + H_3O^+$

**93.** What is a voltaic cell? (Chapter 21)

**Level 2**
**77.** 2.7 g glucose
**78.** During cellular respiration, 1160 kJ of energy is stored in ATP. During fermentation, 61.0 kJ of energy is stored.

## Mixed Review

**79.** See Figure 24-8 and the Solutions Manual. In glucose, the C=O has an H attached and is an aldehyde. In

fructose, the C=O has other C atoms attached and is a ketone.

**80.** Protein monomers: amino acids; complex carbohydrate monomers: monosaccharides; nucleic acid monomers: nucleotides

**81.** Proteins: enzymes, structural, transport, communication and signaling; carbohydrates: energy source, structural in plants; lipids: stored form of energy,

*Use these questions and the test-taking tip to prepare for your standardized test.*

**1.** Which of the following is NOT true of carbohydrates?

  **a.** Monosaccharides in aqueous solutions interconvert continuously between an open-chain structure and a cyclic structure.

  **b.** The monosaccharides in starch are linked together by the same kind of bond that links the monosaccharides in lactose.

  **c.** All carbohydrates have the general chemical formula $C_n(H_2O)_n$.

  **d.** Cellulose, made only by plants, is easily digestible by humans.

**2.** All of the following are differences between RNA and DNA EXCEPT

  **a.** DNA contains the sugar deoxyribose, while RNA contains the sugar ribose.

  **b.** RNA contains the nitrogen base uracil, while DNA does not.

  **c.** RNA is usually single-stranded, while DNA is usually double-stranded.

  **d.** DNA contains the nitrogen base adenine, while RNA does not.

**3.** Cellular respiration produces about 38 moles of ATP for every mole of glucose consumed:

$$C_6H_{12}O_6 + 6O_2 \rightarrow 6CO_2 + 6H_2O + 38ATP$$

If each molecule of ATP can release 30.5 kJ of energy, how much energy can be obtained from a candy bar containing 130 g of glucose?

  **a.** 27.4 kJ       **c.** 1159 kJ
  **b.** 836 kJ       **d.** 3970 kJ

**4.** The sequence of bases in RNA determines the sequence of amino acids in a protein. Three bases code for a single amino acid; for example, CAG is the code for glutamine. Therefore, a strand of RNA $2.73 \times 10^4$ bases long codes for a protein that has

  **a.** $8.19 \times 10^4$ amino acids.
  **b.** $9.10 \times 10^3$ amino acids.
  **c.** $2.73 \times 10^4$ amino acids.
  **d.** $4.55 \times 10^3$ amino acids.

 chemistrymc.com/standardized_test

---

**5.** The equation for the alcoholic fermentation of glucose is shown below:

$$C_6H_{12}O_6 \rightarrow 2CH_3CH_2OH + 2CO_2 + \text{energy}$$

The ethanol content of wine is about 12%. Therefore, in every 100 g of wine there are 12.0 g of ethanol. How many grams of glucose were catabolized to produce these 12.0 g of ethanol?

  **a.** 23.4 g       **c.** 47.0 g
  **b.** 12.0 g       **d.** 27.0 g

**Analyzing Tables** Use the table below to answer the following questions.

**Note:** # of X = # of molecules of X in one DNA molecule

$$\%X = \frac{\text{\# of X}}{\text{\# of A} + \text{\# of G} + \text{\# of C} + \text{\# of T}}$$

where X is any nitrogen base

**6.** What is the %T of DNA D?

  **a.** 28.4%       **c.** 71.6%
  **b.** 78.4%       **d.** 21.6%

**7.** Every nitrogen base found in a DNA molecule is part of a nucleotide of that molecule. The A nucleotide, C nucleotide, G nucleotide, and T nucleotide have molar masses of 347.22 g/mol, 323.20 g/mol, 363.23 g/mol, and 338.21 g/mol respectively. What is the mass of one mole of DNA A?

  **a.** $2.79 \times 10^5$ g       **c.** $2.6390 \times 10^5$ g
  **b.** $2.7001 \times 10^5$ g       **d.** $2.72 \times 10^5$ g

**8.** How many molecules of adenine are in one molecule of DNA B?

  **a.** 402       **c.** 216
  **b.** 434       **d.** 175

**Nitrogen Base Data for Four Different Double-Stranded DNA Molecules**

| DNA Molecule | # of A | # of G | # of C | # of T | %A | %G | %C | %T |
|---|---|---|---|---|---|---|---|---|
| A | 165 | ? | 231 | ? | 20.8 | ? | 29.2 | ? |
| B | ? | 402 | ? | ? | ? | 32.5 | ? | ? |
| C | ? | ? | 194 | 234 | ? | ? | 22.7 | 27.3 |
| D | 266 | 203 | ? | ? | 28.4 | 21.6 | ? | ? |

---

make up cell membranes, protection, some hormones and vitamins; nucleic acids: store and transmit genetic information, function in protein synthesis

**82.** $C_{12}H_{22}O_{11} + H_2O \rightarrow C_6H_{12}O_6 + C_6H_{12}O_6$

**83.** $6CO_2 + 6H_2O + \text{energy} \rightarrow C_6H_{12}O_6 + 6O_2$

**84.** $C_6H_{12}O_6 + 6O_2 \rightarrow 6CO_2 + 6H_2O + \text{energy}$

**85.** $C_6H_{12}O_6 + C_6H_{12}O_6 \rightarrow C_{12}H_{22}O_{11} + H_2O$

## Thinking Critically

**86.** 41%

**87.** The body needs lipids for a number of functions. If the amount of lipids in the diet is severely limited, there may not be enough lipids for the body to carry out those functions.

**88. a.** The graph should plot number of carbons on the *x*-axis and melting point on the *y*-axis. It should show a fairly linear relationship, with melting point increasing as a function of the number of carbons. See the Solutions Manual.

  **b.** The graph should show a fairly linear relationship in which density decreases as the number of carbons increases.

  **c.** The more carbon atoms present, the higher the melting point and the lower the density.

  **d.** 83-86°C

---

## Cumulative Review

**91. a.** $C_2H_4(g) + H_2O(l) \rightarrow CH_3CH_2OH$
  **b.** 921 g $CH_3CH_2OH$

**92. a.** HBr is acid, $H_2O$ is base.
  **b.** HCOOH is acid, $NH_3$ is base.
  **c.** $HCO_3^-$ is acid, $H_2O$ is base.

**93.** A voltaic cell is a chemical system that proceeds spontaneously while producing an electric current.

## Standardized Test Practice

| | | |
|---|---|---|
| **1.** d | **4.** b | **7.** d |
| **2.** d | **5.** a | **8.** c |
| **3.** b | **6.** a | |

# Resource Manager

| Section | Objectives | Activities/Features |
|---------|-----------|---------------------|
| **Section 25.1**<br>**Nuclear Radiation**<br>1 session<br>½ block | 1. **List** the founding scientists in the study of radioactivity and **state** their discoveries.<br>2. **Identify** alpha, beta, and gamma radiation in terms of composition and key properties. | **Discovery Lab:** Chain Reactions, p. 805<br>**Physics Connection,** p. 808 |
| **Section 25.2**<br>**Radioactive Decay**<br>1 session<br>½ block | 3. **Explain** why certain nuclei are radioactive.<br>4. **Apply** your knowledge of radioactive decay to write balanced nuclear equations. | |
| **Section 25.3**<br>**Transmutation**<br>1 session<br>1 block | 5. **Describe** how induced transmutation is used to produce a transuranium element.<br>6. **Solve** problems involving radioactive decay rates. | **MiniLab:** Modeling Radioactive Decay, p. 819 |
| **Section 25.4**<br>**Fission and Fusion of Atomic Nuclei**<br>1 session<br>½ block | 7. **Compare** and **contrast** nuclear fission and nuclear fusion.<br>8. **Explain** the process by which nuclear reactors generate electricity. | |
| **Section 25.5**<br>**Applications and Effects of Nuclear Reactions**<br>2 sessions<br>1 block | 9. **Describe** several methods used to detect and measure radiation.<br>10. **Explain** an application of radiation used in the treatment of disease.<br>11. **Describe** some of the damaging effects of radiation on biological systems. | **Careers Using Chemistry:** Radiation Therapist, p. 828<br>**Problem-Solving Lab:** How does distance affect radiation exposure? p. 830<br>**ChemLab CBL:** Measuring Naturally Occurring Radiation, pp. 832–833<br>**Chemistry and Society:** The Realities of Radon, p. 834 |

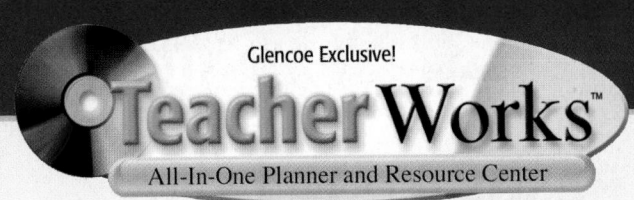

| National Science Content Standards | State/Local Standards | Reproducible Masters | Transparencies |
|---|---|---|---|
| UCP.1, UCP.3; A.1, A.2; B.1, B.3, B.6; F.5; G.1, G.2, G.3 | | **Study Guide for Content Mastery,** p. 145 **L2** | **Section Focus Transparency 96** **L1** **ELL** |
| UCP.1, UCP.3; B.1, B.4, B.6 | | **Study Guide for Content Mastery,** p. 146 **L2** **Laboratory Manual,** pp. 193–196 **L2** | **Section Focus Transparency 97** **L1** **ELL** **Math Skills Transparency 41** **L2** **ELL** |
| UCP.1, UCP.3; A.1; B.1, B.6; E.2; F.6; G.1, G.3 | | **Study Guide for Content Mastery,** p. 147 **L2** **ChemLab and MiniLab Worksheets,** pp. 97–98 **L2** **Laboratory Manual,** pp. 197–200 **L2** | **Section Focus Transparency 98** **L1** **ELL** **Teaching Transparency 76** **L2** **ELL** **Math Skills Transparency 42** **L2** **ELL** |
| UCP.1, UCP.3; B.1, B.4, B.6; E.2; F.1, F.4, F.5, F.6; G.1 | | **Study Guide for Content Mastery,** pp. 148–149 **L2** **Challenge Problems,** p. 25 **L3** | **Section Focus Transparency 99** **L1** **ELL** |
| UCP.1, UCP.3; A.1, A.2; B.1, B.6; E.1, E.2; F.1, F.5; G.1 | | **Study Guide for Content Mastery,** p. 150 **L2** **ChemLab and MiniLab Worksheets,** pp. 99–101 **L2** | **Section Focus Transparency 100** **L1** **ELL** |

**Key to National Science Content Standards:** UCP = Unifying Concepts and Processes, A = Science as Inquiry, B = Physical Science, C = Life Science, D = Earth and Space Sciences, E = Science and Technology, F = Science in Personal and Social Perspectives, G = History and Nature of Science

Refer to pages 4T–5T of the Teacher Guide for an explanation of the National Science Content Standards correlations.

# Resource Manager

## Materials List

**ChemLab** (pages 832–833)

petri dish with lid, salt substitute or pure potassium chloride (KCl), balance, CBL system, RADIATIN software program, graphing calculator, link-to-link cable, Student Radiation Monitor, CBL-P adapter, TI-Graphlink cable

**Discovery Lab** (page 805)

dominoes (28), stopwatch

**MiniLab** (page 819)

pennies (100), 5-oz. plastic cup, graph paper, graphing calculator (optional)

**Demonstration** (pages 810–811)

cloud chamber, 50 mL 95% ethanol, 500 g dry ice, tongs or thermal gloves, alpha source, high-intensity light source

## Preparation of Solutions

For a review of solution preparation, see page 46T of the Teacher Guide.

There are no solutions to be prepared for the activities in this chapter.

## Assessment Resources

**Chapter Assessment,** pp. 145–150
**MindJogger Videoquizzes DVD/VHS**
**Alternate Assessment in the Science Classroom**
**ExamView® Pro CD-ROM**
**Solutions Manual,** Chapter 25
**Supplemental Problems,** Chapter 25
**Performance Assessment in the Science Classroom**
**Chemistry Interactive CD-ROM,** Chapter 25 quiz

## Additional Resources

**Spanish Resources** ELL
**Guided Reading Audio Program,** Chapter 25 ELL
**Cooperative Learning in the Science Classroom**
**Lab and Safety Skills in the Science Classroom**
**Lesson Plans**
**Block Scheduling Lesson Plans**
**Chemistrymc.com**

## Glencoe Technology

The following multimedia for this chapter are available from Glencoe.

**VIDEOTAPE/DVD**
MindJogger Videoquizzes,
Chapter 25

**CD-ROM**
**Chemistry: Matter and Change**
*Half-Life,* Animation
*Inside a Nuclear Power Plant,* Video
*The Big Bang,* Video
*Detecting Radiation,* Demonstration
*Nuclear Medicine,* Video

**CD-ROM**
**ExamView® Pro
Testmaker**

**CD-ROM**
**Interactive Chalkboard**

**CD-ROM**
**TeacherWorks™**

## Multiple Learning Styles

Look for the following icons for strategies that emphasize different learning modalities.

***Kinesthetic***
Quick Demo, p. 807; Reteach, p. 820; Building a
Model, p. 825

***Visual-Spatial***
Differentiated Instruction, pp. 807, 812, 817;
Reteach, p. 809

***Interpersonal***
Check for Understanding, p. 809

***Intrapersonal***
Differentiated Instruction, pp. 813, 817, 824;
Chemistry Journal, pp. 815, 816

***Linguistic***
Chemistry Journal, pp. 806, 813; Portfolio, p. 822

***Logical-Mathematical***
Differentiated Instruction, p. 823; Chemistry
Journal, p. 806

## Key to Teaching Strategies

**L1** Level 1 activities should be appropriate for students with learning difficulties.

**L2** Level 2 activities should be within the ability range of all students.

**L3** Level 3 activities are designed for above-average students.

**ELL** ELL activities should be within the ability range of English Language Learners.

**COOP LEARN** Cooperative Learning activities are designed for small group work.

**P** These strategies represent student products that can be placed into a best-work portfolio.

These strategies are useful in a block scheduling format.

## ✔ Assessment Planner

**Portfolio Assessment**
Portfolio, TWE, pp. 822, 835
Assessment, TWE, p. 824

**Performance Assessment**
Assessment, TWE, pp. 813,
 826, 829, 831
Problem-Solving Lab,
 TWE, p. 830
ChemLab, TWE, p. 833
MiniLab, SE, p. 819
ChemLab, SE, pp. 832–833
Discovery Lab, SE, p. 805

**Knowledge Assessment**
Assessment, TWE, pp. 807,
 809, 812
Demonstration, TWE, p. 811
Section Assessment, SE,
 pp. 809, 814, 820, 826, 831
Chapter Assessment, SE,
 pp. 836–839

**Skill Assessment**
Assessment, TWE, pp. 812,
 814, 818, 820

## Tying to Previous Knowledge

Have students review the following concepts before studying this chapter.

Chapter 4: nuclear model of the atom, subatomic particles, isotopes, nuclear reactions, stability

## Using the Photo

Ask students if they have ever had a medical test involving nuclear technology. If students are comfortable with sharing their impressions of the test, they may do so. Most students will realize that they have had many X rays in the course of their lifetimes; a few may have experienced more extensive tests, such as a radioisotope study or a PET scan.

## PowerPoint® Presentations

This CD-ROM is an editable Microsoft® PowerPoint® presentation that includes:
- Section presentations
- Section checks
- Image bank
- Links to Chemistry Online
- All transparencies
- Animations
- Audio

**Study Guide for Content Mastery**, p. 145 **L2**
**Solving Problems: A Chemistry Handbook**, Section 25.1 **L2**
**Section Focus Transparency 96 and Master** **L1** **ELL**

---

# Nuclear Chemistry

## What You'll Learn

▶ You will trace the history of nuclear chemistry from discovery to application.
▶ You will identify types of radioactive decay and solve decay rate problems.
▶ You will describe the reactions involved in nuclear fission and fusion.
▶ You will learn about applications of nuclear reactions and the effects of radiation exposure.

## Why It's Important

From its role in shaping world politics to its applications that produce electrical power and diagnose and treat disease, nuclear chemistry has profound effects upon the world in which we live.

Visit the Chemistry Web site at **chemistrymc.com** to find links about nuclear chemistry.

Many medical diagnostic tests and treatments involve the use of radioactive substances. Here, a radioactive substance known as a radiotracer is used to illuminate the carotid artery, which runs through the neck into the skull.

**804**    Chapter 25

## DISCOVERY LAB

### Purpose

Students will model a nuclear chain reaction using dominoes. They will manipulate the arrangement of the dominoes in order to maximize the rate at which the chain reaction occurs.

### Teaching Strategies

- Suggest to students that they start with a single line of dominoes spaced relatively far apart. Have them time how long this arrangement takes to fall over.
- Encourage students to explore different factors that might affect the rate at which the dominoes fall. Factors include the type of domino used (if more than one type is available), spacing between dominoes, arrangement of dominoes into a single line or a fan-shaped pattern, etc.

## DISCOVERY LAB

### Chain Reactions

**W**hen the products of one nuclear reaction cause additional nuclear reactions to occur, the resulting chain reaction can release large amounts of energy in a short period of time. Explore escalating chain reactions by modeling them with dominoes.

### Procedure

1. Obtain a set of domino tiles.

2. Stand the individual dominoes on end and arrange them so that when the first domino falls, it causes the other dominoes to fall in series.

3. Practice using different arrangements until you determine how to cause the dominoes to fall in the least amount of time.

4. Time your domino chain reaction. Compare your time with those of your classmates.

### Analysis

What arrangement caused the dominoes to fall in the least amount of time? Do the dominoes fall at a steady rate or an escalating rate? What happens to the domino chain reaction if a tile does not contact the next tile in the sequence?

**Materials**

28 domino
 tiles (1 set)
stopwatch

# 1 Focus

### Focus Transparency

Before presenting the lesson, display **Section Focus Transparency 96** on the overhead projector. Have students answer the accompanying questions using **Section Focus Transparency Master 96.** L1 ELL

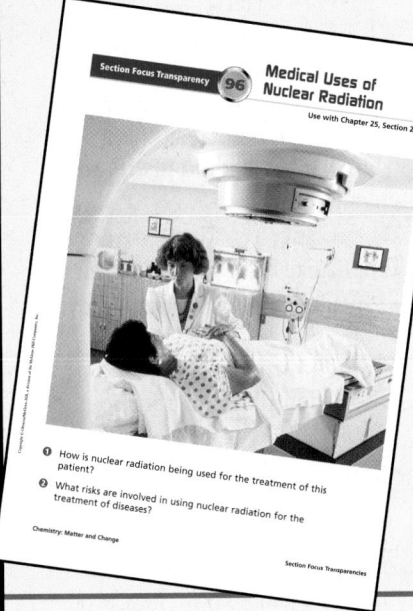

Section Focus Transparency **96** Medical Uses of Nuclear Radiation

Use with Chapter 25, Section 25.1

❶ How is nuclear radiation being used for the treatment of this patient?

❷ What risks are involved in using nuclear radiation for the treatment of diseases?

Chemistry: Matter and Change

Section Focus Transparencies

## Section 25.1

# Nuclear Radiation

## Objectives

- **List** the founding scientists in the study of radioactivity and **state** their discoveries.

- **Identify** alpha, beta, and gamma radiation in terms of composition and key properties.

## Vocabulary

radioisotope
X ray

You may recall from Chapter 4 that the nuclei of some atoms are unstable and undergo nuclear reactions. In this chapter you will study nuclear chemistry, which is concerned with the structure of atomic nuclei and the changes they undergo. An application of a nuclear reaction is shown in the photo of the human neck and skull. **Table 25-1** offers a comparison of chemical and nuclear reactions.

**Table 25-1**

| Characteristics of Chemical and Nuclear Reactions | |
|---|---|
| **Chemical reactions** | **Nuclear reactions** |
| 1. Occur when bonds are broken and formed. | 1. Occur when nuclei emit particles and/or rays. |
| 2. Atoms remain unchanged, though they may be rearranged. | 2. Atoms are often converted into atoms of another element. |
| 3. Involve only valence electrons. | 3. May involve protons, neutrons, and electrons. |
| 4. Associated with small energy changes. | 4. Associated with large energy changes. |
| 5. Reaction rate is influenced by temperature, pressure, concentration, and catalysts. | 5. Reaction rate is not normally affected by temperature, pressure, or catalysts. |

25.1 Nuclear Radiation    **805**

## Chapter Themes

The following themes from the National Science Education Standards are covered in this chapter. Refer to page 4T of the Teacher Guide for an explanation of the correlations.
Systems, order, and organization (UCP.1)
Evidence, models, and explanation (UCP.2)
Change, constancy, and measurement (UCP.3)
Evolution and equilibrium (UCP.4)

## Expected Results

Dominoes that are tightly spaced and arranged in a fan-shape (where one domino knocks two or more other dominoes over) fall at the fastest rate.

## Analysis

Results will vary as to what exact pattern falls the fastest, but in general dominoes that are tightly spaced and arranged in a

fan-shape (where one domino knocks two or more other dominoes over) fall at the fastest rate. Equally spaced dominoes in a single line fall at a constant rate.
Dominoes arranged in a fan shape fall at an escalating rate.  If the chain of dominoes is broken, the chain reaction stops.

### National Science Content Standards

Pages 804–805
UCP.1, UCP.3; A.1; B.1, B.3

## Identifying Misconceptions

Students may think that both chemical and nuclear change result in the formation of new kinds of atoms.

### Uncover the Misconception

Write the following equations on the board:

$$H_2O(l) \rightarrow H_2O(s)$$
$$2H_2(g) + O_2(g) \rightarrow 2H_2O(l)$$
$${}^2_1H(g) + {}^2_1H(g) \rightarrow {}^4_2He(g)$$
$$He(g) \rightarrow He(l)$$

Ask students which reactions represent physical change (first and fourth), chemical change (second), and nuclear change (third). They should justify their choices.

### Demonstrate the Concept

Emphasize the following points.

- Physical change: Atoms that comprise substances undergoing physical change retain their identities and chemical compositions.

- Chemical change: Atoms that comprise substances undergoing chemical change are rearranged to form new substances. The new substances have new properties, but the atoms retain their identities. Chemical change involves changes in chemical bonds.

- Nuclear change: Atoms undergoing nuclear change form new atoms with different identities and properties. Nuclear change involves changes in an atom's nucleus.

### Assess New Knowledge

Have students write out other examples of physical, chemical, and nuclear change at the board. At this point, students should be comfortable writing balanced chemical equations, but may have some difficulties writing balanced nuclear equations.

**Figure 25-1**

A sample of radioactive uranium-containing ore exposes photographic film.

**Figure 25-2**

Both Pierre and Marie Curie played important roles in founding the field of nuclear chemistry. Marie Curie went on to show that unlike chemical reactions, radioactivity is not affected by changes in physical conditions such as temperature and pressure. She is the only person in history to receive Nobel Prizes in two different sciences—physics in 1903, and chemistry in 1911.

## The Discovery of Radioactivity

In 1895, Wilhelm Roentgen (1845–1923) found that invisible rays were emitted when electrons bombarded the surface of certain materials. The emitted rays were discovered because they caused photographic plates to darken. Roentgen named these invisible high-energy emissions X rays. As is true in many fields, Roentgen's discovery of X rays created excitement within the scientific community and stimulated further research. At that time, French physicist Henri Becquerel (1852–1908) was studying minerals that emit light after being exposed to sunlight, a phenomenon called phosphorescence. Building on Roentgen's work, Becquerel wanted to determine whether phosphorescent minerals also emitted X rays. Becquerel accidentally discovered that phosphorescent uranium salts—even when not exposed to light—produced spontaneous emissions that darkened photographic plates. **Figure 25-1** shows the darkening of photographic film that is exposed to uranium-containing ore.

Marie Curie (1867–1934) and her husband Pierre (1859–1906) took Becquerel's mineral sample (called pitchblende) and isolated the components emitting the rays. They concluded that the darkening of the photographic plates was due to rays emitted specifically from the uranium atoms present in the mineral sample. Marie Curie named the process by which materials give off such rays radioactivity; the rays and particles emitted by a radioactive source are called radiation.

The work of Marie and Pierre Curie was extremely important in establishing the origin of radioactivity and the field of nuclear chemistry. In 1898, the Curies identified two new elements, polonium and radium, on the basis of their radioactivity. Henri Becquerel and the Curies shared the 1903 Nobel Prize in Physics for their work. Marie Curie also received the 1911 Nobel Prize in Chemistry for her work with polonium and radium. **Figure 25-2** shows the Curies at work in their laboratory.

## Types of Radiation

While reading about the discovery of radioactivity, several questions may have occurred to you. Which atomic nuclei are radioactive? What types of radiation do radioactive nuclei emit? It is best to start with the second question first, and explore the types of radiation emitted by radioactive sources.

---

### CHEMISTRY JOURNAL

#### Everyday Radiation

**Logical-Mathematical** Assemble a collection of household objects such as a smoke detector, pottery, a luminescent watch dial, and a shrink-wrapped object. Ask students to record in their journals what the objects have in common. **L2**

#### Serendipitous Moments

**Linguistic** Have students look up the meaning of the word *serendipity* in the dictionary and relate it to the works of such scientists as Alexander Fleming, Charles Goodyear, Louis Pasteur, and Roy Plunkett. **L2** **ELL**

As you may recall, isotopes are atoms of the same element that have different numbers of neutrons. Isotopes of atoms with unstable nuclei are called **radioisotopes**. These unstable nuclei emit radiation to attain more stable atomic configurations in a process called radioactive decay. During radioactive decay, unstable atoms lose energy by emitting one of several types of radiation. The three most common types of radiation are alpha ($\alpha$), beta ($\beta$), and gamma ($\gamma$). **Table 25-2** summarizes some of their important properties. Later in this chapter you'll learn about other types of radiation that may be emitted in a nuclear reaction.

**Try at Home** LAB

See page 964 in Appendix E for
**Modeling Radiation Penetration**

**Table 25-2**

| Properties of Alpha, Beta, and Gamma Radiation | | | |
|---|---|---|---|
| **Property** | **Alpha ($\alpha$)** | **Beta ($\beta$)** | **Gamma ($\gamma$)** |
| Composition | Alpha particles | Beta particles | High-energy electromagnetic radiation |
| Description of radiation | Helium nuclei $^4_2$He | Electrons $^0_{-1}\beta$ | photons $^0_0\gamma$ |
| Charge | 2+ | 1− | 0 |
| Mass | $6.64 \times 10^{-24}$ kg | $9.11 \times 10^{-28}$ kg | 0 |
| Approximate energy* | 5 MeV | 0.05 to 1 MeV | 1 MeV |
| Relative penetrating power | Blocked by paper | Blocked by metal foil | Not completely blocked by lead or concrete |

*(1 MeV = $1.60 \times 10^{-13}$ J)

Ernest Rutherford (1871–1937), whom you know of because of his famous gold foil experiment that helped define modern atomic structure, identified alpha, beta, and gamma radiation when studying the effects of an electric field on the emissions from a radioactive source. As you can see in **Figure 25-3**, alpha particles carry a 2+ charge and are deflected toward the negatively charged plate. Beta particles carry a 1− charge and are deflected toward the positively charged plate. In contrast, gamma rays carry no charge and are not affected by the electric field.

**Figure 25-3**

The effect of an electric field on three types of radiation is shown here. Positively charged alpha particles are deflected toward the negatively charged plate. Negatively charged beta particles are deflected toward the positively charged plate. Beta particles undergo greater deflection because they have considerably less mass than alpha particles. Gamma rays, which have no electrical charge, are not deflected.

Lead block
Slot
Positive plate +
Beta particles (1− charge) $\beta$
Gamma rays (no charge) $\gamma$
Alpha particles (2+ charge) $\alpha$
Negative plate −
Radioactive source
Zinc sulfide coated screen

25.1 Nuclear Radiation  **807**

---

### Figure 25-4

A radium-226 nucleus undergoes alpha decay to form radon-222. What is the charge on the alpha particle that is emitted?

$^{226}_{88}$Ra
Radium-226

$^{222}_{86}$Rn
Radon-222

$^{4}_{2}$He
Alpha particle

## Physics

### CONNECTION

Exposing certain foods such as strawberries to small amounts of gamma radiation allows them to last longer before spoiling. The process, called irradiation, uses decaying cobalt-60 nuclei as a source of gamma radiation. By disrupting their cell metabolism, gamma radiation destroys the microorganisms that cause food to spoil. Irradiation can also be used to slow the ripening process, extend shelf life, and allow foods to be stored for long periods of time without refrigeration. The food does not become radioactive from the process. More than 30 nations around the world have approved irradiation as a means of preserving food.

An alpha particle (α) has the same composition as a helium nucleus—two protons and two neutrons—and is therefore given the symbol $^{4}_{2}$He. The charge of an alpha particle is 2+ due to the presence of the two protons. Alpha radiation consists of a stream of alpha particles. As you can see in **Figure 25-4**, radium-226, an atom whose nucleus contains 88 protons and 138 neutrons undergoes alpha decay by emitting an alpha particle. Notice that after the decay, the resulting atom has an atomic number of 86, a mass number of 222, and is no longer radium. The newly formed radioisotope is radon-222.

In examining **Figure 25-4**, you should note that the particles involved are balanced. That is, the sum of the mass numbers (superscripts) and the sum of the atomic numbers (subscripts) on each side of the arrow are equal. Also note that when a radioactive nucleus emits an alpha particle, the product nucleus has an atomic number that is lower by two and a mass number that is lower by four. What particle is formed when polonium-210 ($^{210}_{84}$Po) undergoes alpha decay?

Because of their mass and charge, alpha particles are relatively slow-moving compared with other types of radiation. Thus, alpha particles are not very penetrating—a single sheet of paper stops alpha particles.

A beta particle is a very-fast moving electron that has been emitted from a neutron of an unstable nucleus. Beta particles are represented by the symbol $^{0}_{-1}$β. The zero superscript indicates the insignificant mass of an electron in comparison with the mass of a nucleus. The −1 subscript denotes the negative charge of the particle. Beta radiation consists of a stream of fast-moving electrons. An example of the beta decay process is the decay of iodine-131 into xenon-131 by beta-particle emission, as shown in **Figure 25-5**. Note that the mass number of the product nucleus is the same as that of the original nucleus (they are both 131), but its atomic number has increased by 1 (54 instead of 53). This change in atomic number, and thus, change in identity, occurs because the electron emitted during the beta decay has been removed from a neutron, leaving behind a proton.

$$^{1}_{0}n \rightarrow ^{1}_{1}p + ^{0}_{-1}\beta$$

As you may recall, because the number of protons in an atom determines its identity, the formation of an additional proton results in the transformation from iodine to xenon. Because beta particles are both lightweight and fast

### Figure 25-5

An iodine-131 nucleus undergoes beta decay to form xenon-131. How does beta decay affect the mass number of the decaying nucleus?

$^{131}_{53}$I
Iodine-131

$^{131}_{54}$Xe
Xenon-131

$^{0}_{-1}$β
Beta particle

---

## DIFFERENTIATED INSTRUCTION

### Learning Disabled

Students may be confused about use of the notations $^{0}_{-1}e$ and $^{0}_{-1}\beta$. Point out that if the particle is on the reactant side of a nuclear equation, it represents electron capture and the first symbol should be used. If the particle is on the product side of a nuclear equation, it represents beta decay and the second symbol should be used. **L1**

**Figure 25-6**

A heavy lead-lined vest absorbs errant radiation from a dental X-ray machine, limiting exposure to the rest of the body. Dentists use dental X rays as a diagnostic tool for determining the health of teeth and gums.

moving, they have greater penetrating power than alpha particles. A thin metal foil is required to stop beta particles.

Gamma rays are high-energy (short wavelength) electromagnetic radiation. They are denoted by the symbol $_{0}^{0}\gamma$. As you can see from the symbol, both the subscript and superscript are zero. Thus, the emission of gamma rays does not change the atomic number or mass number of a nucleus. Gamma rays almost always accompany alpha and beta radiation, as they account for most of the energy loss that occurs as a nucleus decays. For example, gamma rays accompany the alpha-decay reaction of uranium-238.

$$_{92}^{238}U \rightarrow \; _{90}^{234}Th \; + \; _{2}^{4}He \; + \; 2_{0}^{0}\gamma$$

The 2 in front of the $\gamma$ symbol indicates that two gamma rays of different frequencies are emitted. Because gamma rays have no effect on mass number or atomic number, it is customary to omit them from nuclear equations.

As you have learned, the discovery of X rays helped set off the events that led to the discovery of radioactivity. **X rays**, like gamma rays, are a form of high-energy electromagnetic radiation. Unlike gamma rays, X rays are not produced by radioactive sources. Instead, X rays are emitted from certain materials that are in an excited electron state. Both X rays and gamma rays are extremely penetrating and can be very damaging to living tissue. X rays and gamma rays are only partially blocked by lead and concrete. If your dentist has recently taken dental X rays of your teeth, you may recall wearing a heavy vest over your chest during the procedure. The vest, which can be seen in **Figure 25-6**, is lined with lead, and its purpose is to limit your body's exposure to the potentially damaging X rays.

## Section 25.1 Assessment

1. Describe the contributions of Roentgen, Becquerel, Rutherford, and the Curies to the field of nuclear chemistry.

2. What subatomic particles are involved in nuclear reactions? What subatomic particles are involved in chemical reactions?

3. Using **Table 25-2** as a guide, qualitatively compare and contrast alpha, beta, and gamma radiation in terms of composition, energy, mass, and penetrating power.

4. **Thinking Critically** An atom undergoes a reaction and attains a more stable form. How do you know if the reaction was a chemical reaction or a nuclear reaction?

5. **Converting Units** Table 25-2 gives Approximate Energy values in units of MeV. Convert each value into joules using the following conversion factor ($1 \text{ MeV} = 1.61 \times 10^{-13}$ J). For more help, refer to *Unit Conversion* in the **Math Handbook** on page 901 of this textbook.

## Section 25.1 Assessment

1. Roentgen discovered X rays; Becquerel discovered ores that fog film; the Curies discovered radioactivity; Rutherford discovered alpha, beta, and gamma radiation.

2. Protons, electrons, and neutrons may be involved in nuclear change; only electrons are involved in chemical change.

3. See Table 25-2.
4. If the new, more stable form of the atom has an identity different from the original atom, a nuclear process has occurred.
5. alpha = $8 \times 10^{-13}$ J
   beta = $8 \times 10^{-15}$ to $2 \times 10^{-13}$ J
   gamma = $2 \times 10^{-13}$ J

# 1 Focus

**Focus Transparency**

Before presenting the lesson, display **Section Focus Transparency 97** on the overhead projector. Have students answer the accompanying questions using **Section Focus Transparency Master 97.** **L1** **ELL**

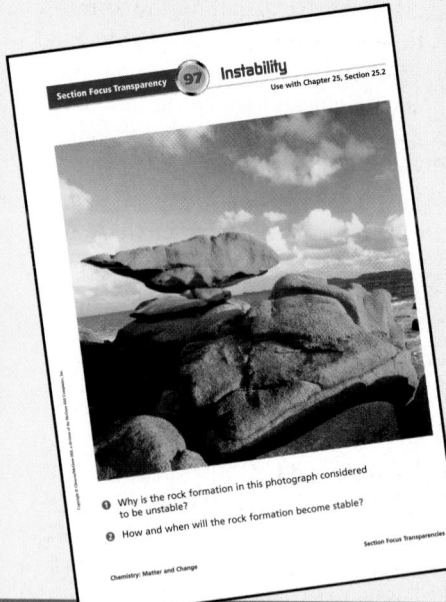

Section Focus Transparency 97 **Instability** Use with Chapter 25, Section 25.2

❶ Why is the rock formation in this photograph considered to be unstable?

❷ How and when will the rock formation become stable?

Chemistry: Matter and Change

# 2 Teach

**Resource Manager**

**Study Guide for Content Mastery,** p. 146 **L2**
**Solving Problems: A Chemistry Handbook,** Section 25.2 **L2**
**Section Focus Transparency 97 and Master** **L1** **ELL**

---

## Objectives

- **Explain** why certain nuclei are radioactive.
- **Apply** your knowledge of radioactive decay to write balanced nuclear equations.

## Vocabulary

nucleon
strong nuclear force
band of stability
positron emission
positron
electron capture
radioactive decay series

---

It may surprise you to learn that of all the known isotopes, only about 17% are stable and don't decay spontaneously. In Chapter 4 you learned that the stability of an atom is determined by the neutron-to-proton ratio of its nucleus. You may be wondering if there is a way to know what type of radioactive decay a particular radioisotope will undergo. There is, and as you'll learn in this section, it is the neutron-to-proton ratio of the nucleus that determines the type of radioactive decay that will occur.

## Nuclear Stability

Every atom has an extremely dense nucleus that contains most of the atom's mass. The nucleus contains positively charged protons and neutral neutrons, both of which are referred to as **nucleons**. You may have wondered how protons remain in the densely packed nucleus despite the strong electrostatic repulsion forces produced by the positively charged particles. The answer is that the **strong nuclear force**, a force that acts only on subatomic particles that are extremely close together, overcomes the electrostatic repulsion between protons.

The fact that the strong nuclear force acts on both protons and neutrons is important. Because neutrons are neutral, a neutron that is adjacent to a positively charged proton creates no repulsive electrostatic force. Yet these two adjacent particles are subject to the strong nuclear force that works to hold them together. Likewise, two adjacent neutrons create no attractive or repulsive electrostatic force, but they too are subject to the strong nuclear force holding them together. Thus, the presence of neutrons adds an attractive force within the nucleus. The number of neutrons in a nucleus is important because nuclear stability is related to the balance between electrostatic and strong nuclear forces.

To a certain degree, the stability of a nucleus can be correlated with its neutron-to-proton (n/p) ratio. For atoms with low atomic numbers ($< 20$), the most stable nuclei are those with neutron-to-proton ratios of 1 : 1. For example, helium ($^4_2\text{He}$) has two neutrons and two protons, and a neutron-to-proton ratio of 1 : 1. As atomic number increases, more and more neutrons are needed to produce a strong nuclear force that is sufficient to balance the electrostatic repulsion forces. Thus, the neutron-to-proton ratio for stable atoms gradually increases, reaching a maximum of approximately 1.5 : 1 for the largest atoms. An example of this is lead ($^{206}_{82}\text{Pb}$). With 124 neutrons and 82 protons, lead has a neutron-to-proton ratio of 1.51 : 1. You can see the calculation of lead's neutron-to-proton ratio in **Figure 25-7**.

**Figure 25-7**

The steps in calculating the neutron-to-proton ratio (the n/p ratio) for lead-206 are illustrated here.

$$\text{Mass number} \longrightarrow 206$$
$$\text{Atomic number} \longrightarrow 82 \quad \text{Pb}$$

Atomic number = Number of protons = 82

Mass number = Number of protons + Number of neutrons = 206

Number of neutrons = Mass number − Atomic number

Number of neutrons = 206 − 82 = 124

$$\text{Neutron-to-proton ratio} = \frac{\text{Number of neutrons}}{\text{Number of protons}}$$

$$\text{Neutron-to-proton ratio} = \frac{124}{82}$$

$$\text{Neutron-to-proton ratio} = \frac{1.51}{1}$$

---

## Demonstration

### A Cloud Chamber

**Purpose**
To observe evidence of nuclear decay

**Materials**
Cloud chamber (see procedure below); 95% ethanol (50 mL); dry ice (500 g); tongs or thermal gloves; radioactive alpha source from a supplier; high-intensity light source

**Safety Precautions**

**Disposal** Save the sources for future use.

**Procedure**
You can construct your own cloud chamber using a clear-plastic sandwich box. Use black paint to cover the outside of the bottom of the box. Wet two pieces of blotter paper with ethanol, and place them on the opposite sides of the box. **CAUTION:** *Ethanol is flammable.* Place the box on dry ice. **CAUTION:** *Dry ice can damage the skin, so use tongs or thermal gloves.* Place a packaged radioactive source in the middle of the box, and cover it with the plastic lid. After a minute, darken the room, and shine a high-intensity light beam through the box. You may need to warm the ends of the box

Examine the plot of the number of neutrons versus the number of protons for all known stable nuclei shown in **Figure 25-8**. As you can see, the slope of the plot indicates that the number of neutrons required for a stable nucleus increases as the number of protons increases. This correlates with the increase in the neutron-to-proton ratio of stable nuclei with increasing atomic number. The area on the graph within which all stable nuclei are found is known as the **band of stability**. As shown in **Figure 25-8**, $^4_2$He and $^{206}_{82}$Pb, with their very different neutron-to-proton ratios, are both positioned within the band of stability. Radioactive nuclei are found outside the band of stability—either above or below—and undergo decay in order to gain stability. After decay, the new atom is positioned more closely to, if not within, the band of stability. The band of stability ends at bismuth-209; all elements with atomic numbers greater than 83 are radioactive.

## Types of Radioactive Decay

The type of radioactive decay a particular radioisotope undergoes depends to a large degree on the underlying causes for its instability. Atoms lying above the band of stability generally have too many neutrons to be stable, whereas atoms lying below the band of stability tend to have too many protons to be stable.

**Beta decay** A radioisotope that lies above the band of stability is unstable because it has too many neutrons relative to its number of protons. For example, unstable $^{14}_6$C has a neutron-to-proton ratio of 1.33 : 1, whereas stable elements of similar mass, such as $^{12}_6$C and $^{14}_7$N, have neutron-to-proton ratios of approximately 1 : 1. It is not surprising then that $^{14}_6$C undergoes beta decay, as this type of decay decreases the number of neutrons in the nucleus.

$$^{14}_6C \rightarrow {}^{14}_7N + {}^{\ 0}_{-1}\beta$$

Note that the atomic number of the product nucleus, $^{14}_7$N, has increased by one. The nitrogen-14 atom now has a stable neutron-to-proton ratio of 1 : 1. Thus, beta emission has the effect of increasing the stability of a neutron-rich atom by lowering its neutron-to-proton ratio. The resulting atom is closer to, if not within, the band of stability.

**Alpha decay** All nuclei with more than 83 protons are radioactive and decay spontaneously. Both the number of neutrons and the number of protons must be reduced in order to make these radioisotopes stable. These very heavy nuclei often decay by emitting alpha particles. For example, polonium-210 spontaneously decays by alpha emission.

$$^{210}_{84}Po \rightarrow {}^{206}_{82}Pb + {}^4_2He$$

The atomic number of $^{210}_{84}$Po decreases by two and the mass number decreases by four as the nucleus decays into $^{206}_{82}$Pb. How does the n/p ratio change?

**The Band of Stability**

Each point on the graph represents a stable atom

$^{206}_{82}$Pb n/p ratio = 1.51

n/p ratio = 1.5

Band of stability

$^{107}_{47}$Ag n/p ratio = 1.28

n/p ratio = 1.0

$^4_2$He n/p ratio = 1.0

Number of neutrons (vertical axis)

Number of protons (horizontal axis)

**Figure 25-8**

Plotting the number of neutrons versus the number of protons for all stable nuclei produces a region called the band of stability. As you move from low atomic number nuclei to high atomic number nuclei, the neutron-to-proton ratio for stable nuclei gradually increases from 1 : 1 to 1.5 : 1.

25.2 Radioactive Decay **811**

### Quick Demo

Rub a piece of fur with a plastic or rubber wand and touch it to an electroscope. The electrons transfer from the fur to the wand and in turn to the electroscoope. Because the leaves are now similarly charged, they will repel each other. Touch the top of the electroscope to bleed off the negative charge. Next, hold a radioactive beta source with tongs near an electroscope. The negative beta particles will transfer to the foil leaves and mimic the behavior of the previous step. Ask students what this shows about the nature of the radioactive particles. Students should note that the radiation is negative. Finally, hold a radioactive alpha emitter with tongs to the electroscope. Ask students what they can infer about the nature of the emitter. The positive alpha particles remove electrons.

### In-Text Question

**Page 811** How does the n/p ratio change? The n/p ratio changes from 1.500 : 1 to 1.512 : 1.

with a light bulb to increase the saturation of the air with alcohol vapor.

### Results

Look straight down into the box to see alpha particles shooting outward from the source, leaving momentary trails of condensed alcohol vapor.

### Analysis

Ask these questions.

1. How big are the particles that caused the alcohol vapor to condense in a vapor trail? Submicroscopic, about 0.0012 picometers.

2. The alpha particles that produced the tracks are positively charged helium nuclei. How might you show that they have an electrical charge? Put a strong magnet or charged object near the cloud chamber and observe that the tracks curve.

### Assessment

**Knowledge** Ask students whether the rate of emission of the particles producing the vapor trails is constant. The rate appears constant, but it actually decreases slowly.

**Page 812** How is the neutron-to-proton ratio of the product, Kr-81, different from that of Rb-81? The n/p ratio increases from 1.19 : 1 to 1.25 : 1. Which of the decay processes listed in the table result in an increased neutron-to-proton ratio? electron capture, positron emission, alpha decay In a decrease? beta decay

✓ **Assessment**

**Skill** Ask students to calculate the neutron-to-proton ratio for $^{104}_{40}$Zr. Ask them to locate its position on the graph in Figure 25-8 and determine its stability. The n/p ratio is 1.6 : 1, which is slightly above the band of stability. This isotope undergoes beta decay.

✓ **Assessment**

**Knowledge** Instead of being powered by electricity, some exit signs are illuminated by tritium, a radioisotope of hydrogen. Ask students to list advantages and disadvantages of using tritium to light the sign. Ask students to write the correct nuclear equation for the decay. An advantage would be that the sign would continue to glow even if electricity were disrupted. A disadvantage is that over time the sign would become dimmer.

$$^3_1\text{H} \rightarrow \ ^{\ 0}_{-1}\beta + \ ^3_2\text{He}$$

**Resource Manager**

Math Skills Transparency 41 and Master, **L2** **ELL**
Lab Manual, pp. 193–196 **L2**

812

---

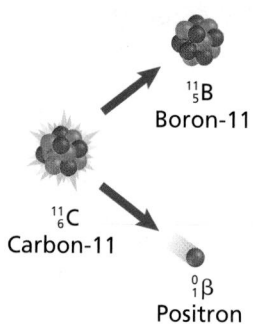

Boron-11

¹¹₆C
Carbon-11

$^{\ 0}_{1}\beta$
Positron

**Figure 25-9**

Positron emission from carbon-11 decreases the number of protons from six to five, and increases the number of neutrons from five to six.

$^{\ 0}_{-1}e$  +  $^{81}_{37}$Rb

$^{81}_{36}$Kr

X-ray photon

**Figure 25-10**

The electron capture of rubidium-81 decreases the number of protons in the nucleus while the mass number remains the same. Thus, the neutron-to-proton ratio increases from 1.19 : 1 for $^{81}_{37}$Rb to 1.25 : 1 for $^{81}_{36}$Kr.

---

**Positron emission and electron capture** For nuclei with low neutron-to-proton ratios lying below the band of stability, there are two common radioactive decay processes that occur, positron emission and electron capture. These two processes tend to increase the neutron-to-proton ratio of the neutron-poor atom. After an unstable atom undergoes electron capture or positron emission, the resulting atom is closer to, if not within, the band of stability.

**Positron emission** is a radioactive decay process that involves the emission of a positron from a nucleus. A **positron** is a particle with the same mass as an electron but opposite charge, thus it is represented by the symbol $^0_1\beta$. During positron emission, a proton in the nucleus is converted into a neutron and a positron, and then the positron is emitted.

$$^1_1\text{p} \rightarrow \ ^1_0\text{n} + \ ^0_1\beta$$

**Figure 25-9** shows the positron emission of a carbon-11 nucleus. Carbon-11 lies below the band of stability and has a low neutron-to-proton ratio of 0.8 : 1. Carbon-11 undergoes positron emission to form boron-11. Positron emission decreases the number of protons from six to five, and increases the number of neutrons from five to six. The resulting atom, $^{11}_5$B, has a neutron-to-proton ratio of 1.2 : 1, which is within the band of stability.

Electron capture is the other common radioactive decay process that decreases the number of protons in unstable nuclei lying below the band of stability. **Electron capture** occurs when the nucleus of an atom draws in a surrounding electron, usually one from the lowest energy level. This captured electron combines with a proton to form a neutron.

$$^1_1\text{p} + \ ^{\ 0}_{-1}\text{e} \rightarrow \ ^1_0\text{n}$$

The atomic number of the nucleus decreases by one as a consequence of electron capture. The formation of the neutron also results in an X-ray photon being emitted. These two characteristics of electron capture can be seen in the electron capture of rubidium-81 shown in **Figure 25-10**. The balanced nuclear equation for the reaction is shown below.

$$^{\ 0}_{-1}\text{e} + \ ^{81}_{37}\text{Rb} \rightarrow \ ^{81}_{36}\text{Kr} + \text{X-ray photon}$$

How is the neutron-to-proton ratio of the product, Kr-81, different from that of Rb-81?

The five types of radioactive decay you have read about in this chapter are summarized in **Table 25-3**. Which of the decay processes listed in the table result in an increased neutron-to-proton ratio? In a decrease?

**Table 25-3**

| Summary of Radioactive Decay Processes | | | |
|---|---|---|---|
| Type of radioactive decay | Particle emitted | Change in mass number | Change in atomic number |
| Alpha decay | $^4_2$He | Decreases by 4 | Decreases by 2 |
| Beta decay | $^{\ 0}_{-1}\beta$ | No change | Increases by 1 |
| Positron emission | $^0_1\beta$ | No change | Decreases by 1 |
| Electron capture | X-ray photon | No change | Decreases by 1 |
| Gamma emission | $^0_0\gamma$ | No change | No change |

---

**DIFFERENTIATED INSTRUCTION**

**Hearing Impaired**

*Visual-Spatial* Use two different colors of poker chips to represent neutrons and protons. Assemble different ratios of neutrons to protons and use this as a springboard for discussing stability ratios. **L2**

**CULTURAL DIVERSITY**

**Honoring Marie Curie**

In Misasa, Japan, natives hold a festival honoring radiation pioneer Marie Curie. The city also offers radon "spas" where people bask in the alpha, beta, and gamma radiation emitted from the radon. Participants consider the radon particles to be promoters of health. The atmosphere is comparable to a sauna at a health club.

## Writing and Balancing Nuclear Equations

The radioactive decay processes you have just read about are all examples of nuclear reactions. As you probably noticed, nuclear reactions are expressed by balanced nuclear equations just as chemical reactions are expressed by balanced chemical equations. However, in balanced chemical equations, numbers and kinds of atoms are conserved; in balanced nuclear equations, mass numbers and atomic numbers are conserved.

### EXAMPLE PROBLEM 25-1

**Balancing a Nuclear Equation**

Using the information provided in **Table 25-3**, write a balanced nuclear equation for the alpha decay of thorium-230 ($^{230}_{90}$Th).

**1. Analyze the Problem**

You are given that a thorium atom undergoes alpha decay and forms an unknown product. Thorium-230 is the initial reactant, while the alpha particle is one of the products of the reaction. The reaction is summarized below.

$$^{230}_{90}\text{Th} \rightarrow X + {}^{4}_{2}\text{He}$$

You must determine the unknown product of the reaction, $X$. This can be done through the conservation of atomic number and mass number. The periodic table can then be used to identify $X$.

**Known**

reactant: thorium-230 ($^{230}_{90}$Th)
decay type: alpha particle emission ($^{4}_{2}$He)

**Unknown**

reaction product $X = ?$
balanced nuclear equation = ?

**2. Solve for the Unknown**

Using each particle's mass number, make sure mass number is conserved on each side of the reaction arrow.

mass number: $230 = X + 4$

$$X = 230 - 4 = 226$$

Thus, the mass number of $X$ is 226.

Using each particle's atomic number, make sure atomic number is conserved on each side of the reaction arrow.

atomic number: $90 = X + 2$

$$X = 90 - 2 = 88$$

Thus, the atomic number of $X$ is 88. The periodic table identifies the element as radium (Ra).

Write the balanced nuclear equation.

$$^{230}_{90}\text{Th} \rightarrow {}^{226}_{88}\text{Ra} + {}^{4}_{2}\text{He}$$

**3. Evaluate the Answer**

The correct formula for an alpha particle is used. The sums of the superscripts on each side of the equation are equal. The same is true for the subscripts. Therefore, the atomic number and the mass number are conserved. The nuclear equation is balanced.

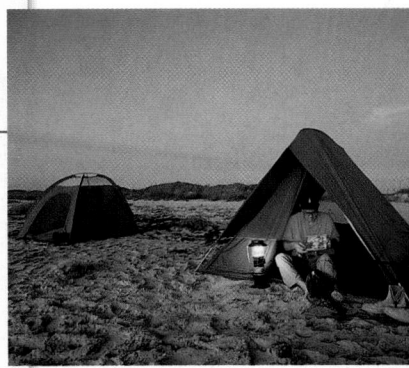

Thorium fluoride is used in the manufacture of propane lantern mantles and high-intensity searchlights.

25.2 Radioactive Decay **813**

## 3 Assess
### Check for Understanding

Ask students which member of each of the following pairs would be more stable? Why?

- $^{12}_{6}$C or $^{13}_{6}$C    $^{12}_{6}$C; n/p = 1
- $^{16}_{7}$N or $^{14}_{7}$N    $^{14}_{7}$N; n/p = 1
- Fe or Np    Fe; All elements with atomic numbers greater than 83 are radioactive.

### Reteach

Americium-241 is the radioisotope in smoke detectors. It functions by emitting alpha particles that ionize the air, thereby producing a current. If smoke interferes with this ionization, the microchip senses a cessation of current and triggers the alarm. Have students write the balanced nuclear reaction for the decay of americium-241 by alpha particle emission. Ask students if they should be concerned about radioactive americium-241 decaying in their homes.

$$^{241}_{95}\text{Am} \rightarrow {}^{4}_{2}\text{He} + {}^{237}_{93}\text{Np}$$

The decay poses no risk because alpha particles are easily blocked. Even if the alpha particles escaped their sealed chamber in the smoke detector, your skin would easily stop them.

---

### DIFFERENTIATED INSTRUCTION

**Learning Disabled**

*Intrapersonal* Students who have trouble with math might find it helpful to set up an inventory table where atomic masses and atomic numbers of reactants are tallied and compared to those of products. **L2**

### CHEMISTRY JOURNAL

**Decay Process**

*Linguistic* Have students make an entry in their journals describing the implications of having only one possible type of decay process—only alpha decay or beta decay, for instance. How would this affect the types of isotopes that could be formed? **L2**

**National Science Content Standards**
**Pages 810–813**
UCP.1, UCP.3; B.1, B.4, B.6

814

## Extension

Ask students to use the *CRC Handbook of Chemistry and Physics* to locate an element that has at least two radioisotopes that undergo two different types of decay. Have students write correct nuclear equations for each decay process.

### ✓ Assessment

**Skill** Have students draw the decay series for americium-241, which is found in smoke detectors. The radioisotope undergoes the following succession of decays: α, α, β, α, α, β, α, α, α, β, α, β. The following nuclei are formed in the decay of americium-241: Np-237, Pa-233, U-233, Th-229, Ra-225, Ac-225, Fr-221, At-217, Bi-213, Po-213, Pb-209, and Bi-209. **L2** **ELL**

### Practice PROBLEMS

Have students refer to Appendix D for complete solutions to Practice Problems.

**6.** $^{15}_{8}O \rightarrow ^{0}_{1}\beta + ^{15}_{7}N$

**7.** beta

**8.** $^{97}_{40}Zr \rightarrow ^{0}_{-1}\beta + ^{97}_{41}Nb$

**9. a.** $^{0}_{-1}e$   **b.** $^{214}_{82}Pb$   **c.** $^{226}_{88}Ra$

---

Practice! **For more practice with balancing nuclear equations, go to Supplemental Practice Problems in Appendix A.**

### PRACTICE PROBLEMS

**6.** Write a balanced nuclear equation for the reaction in which oxygen-15 undergoes positron emission.

**7.** Determine what type of decay occurs when thorium-231 undergoes radioactive decay to form protactinium-231.

**8.** Write a balanced nuclear equation for the reaction in which the transition metal zirconium-97 undergoes beta decay.

**9.** Complete the following nuclear equations.

   **a.** $^{142}_{61}Pm + ? \rightarrow ^{142}_{60}Nd$   **b.** $^{218}_{84}Po \rightarrow ^{4}_{2}He + ?$   **c.** $? \rightarrow ^{222}_{86}Rn + ^{4}_{2}He$

## Radioactive Series

A series of nuclear reactions that begins with an unstable nucleus and results in the formation of a stable nucleus is called a **radioactive decay series**. As you can see in **Figure 25-11**, uranium-238 first decays to thorium-235, which in turn decays to protactinium-234. Decay reactions continue until a stable nucleus, lead-206, is formed.

**Figure 25-11**

Uranium-238 undergoes 14 different radioactive decay processes before forming stable lead-206.

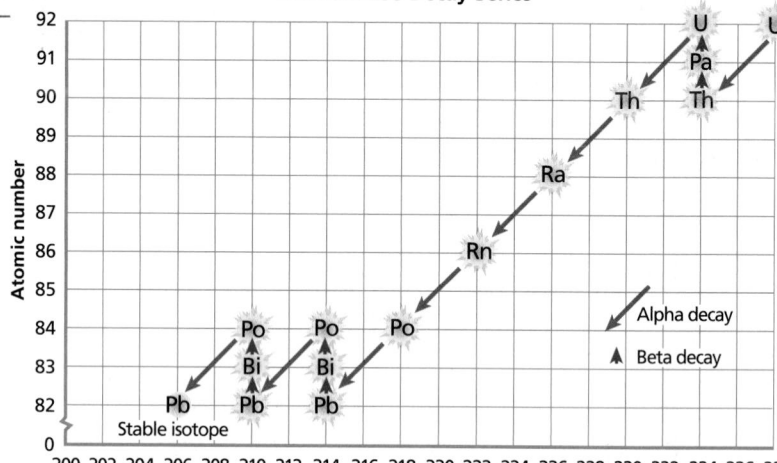

Uranium-238 Decay Series

---

### Section 25.2 Assessment

**10.** Explain how you can predict whether or not an isotope is likely to be stable if you know the number of neutrons and protons in its nucleus.

**11.** Write the nuclear equation for the alpha decay of astatine-213.

**12.** Complete and balance the following.

   **a.** $^{66}_{29}Cu \rightarrow ^{66}_{30}Zn + ?$
   **b.** $? \rightarrow ^{181}_{77}Ir + ^{4}_{2}He$

**13. Thinking Critically** A new element is synthesized in a laboratory. The element has a neutron-to-proton ratio of 1.6 : 1. Will the element be radioactive? If so, what type of radioactive decay will it most likely undergo?

**14. Communicating** Describe the forces acting on the particles within a nucleus. Explain why neutrons are the "glue" holding the nucleus together.

 chemistrymc.com/self_check_quiz

---

### Section 25.2 Assessment

**10.** Isotopes are likely to be stable if their n/p ratio is within the range of 1 : 1 to 1.5 : 1. The lightest isotopes have n/p ratios close to 1 : 1, while the heaviest isotopes have ratios close to 1.5 : 1.

**11.** $^{213}_{85}At \rightarrow ^{4}_{2}He + ^{209}_{83}Bi$

**12. a.** $^{0}_{-1}\beta$   **b.** $^{185}_{79}Au$

**13.** Yes, radioactive; beta decay

**14.** Protons are positively charged and repel each other. Neutrons do not repel each other or protons. The strong nuclear force is an attractive force that acts on both protons and neutrons in the nucleus. The greater the number of neutrons in the nucleus, the greater the strong nuclear force.

All the nuclear reactions that have been described thus far are examples of radioactive decay, where one element is converted into another element by the spontaneous emission of radiation. This conversion of an atom of one element to an atom of another element is called **transmutation**. Except for gamma emission, which does not alter an atom's atomic number, all nuclear reactions are transmutation reactions. Some unstable nuclei, such as the uranium salts used by Henri Becquerel, undergo transmutation naturally. However, transmutation may also be forced, or induced, by bombarding a stable nucleus with high-energy alpha, beta, or gamma radiation.

### Induced Transmutation

In 1919, Ernest Rutherford performed the first laboratory conversion of one element into another element. By bombarding nitrogen-14 with high-speed alpha particles, an unstable fluorine-18 occurred, and then oxygen-17 was formed. This transmutation reaction is illustrated below.

$$_2^4\text{He} + _7^{14}\text{N} \rightarrow _8^{17}\text{O} + _1^1\text{p}$$

$p^+$
Proton

$_8^{17}\text{O}$
Oxygen atom

$_2^4\text{He}$
Bombarding alpha particle

$_7^{14}\text{N}$
Target nitrogen atom

$_9^{18}\text{F}$
Unstable fluorine atom

Rutherford's experiments demonstrated that nuclear reactions can be induced, in other words, produced artificially. The process, which involves striking nuclei with high-velocity charged particles, is called **induced transmutation**. The charged particles, such as alpha particles used by Rutherford, must be moving at extremely high speeds to overcome the electrostatic repulsion between themselves and the target nucleus. Because of this, scientists have developed methods to accelerate charged particles to extreme speeds by using very strong electrostatic and magnetic fields. Particle accelerators, which are commonly called "atom smashers," are built to produce the high-speed particles needed to induce transmutation. The inside of the Fermi National Accelerator Laboratory's Tevatron is shown in **Figure 25-12**. The Tevatron is the world's highest-energy particle accelerator. The purpose of the facility, which opened in 1999, is to research high-energy nuclear reactions and particle physics. Since Rutherford's first experiments involving induced transmutation, scientists have used the technique to synthesize hundreds of new isotopes in the laboratory.

**Transuranium elements** The elements immediately following uranium in the periodic table—elements with atomic numbers 93 and greater—are known as the **transuranium elements**. All transuranium elements have been produced in the laboratory by induced transmutation and are radioactive.

### Objectives

- **Describe** how induced transmutation is used to produce a transuranium element.

- **Solve** problems involving radioactive decay rates.

### Vocabulary

transmutation
induced transmutation
transuranium element
half-life
radiochemical dating

**Figure 25-12**

The main Tevatron ring has a diameter of more than 0.8 km and a circumference of about 6.4 km. The accelerator uses conventional and superconducting magnets to accelerate particles to high speeds and high energies.

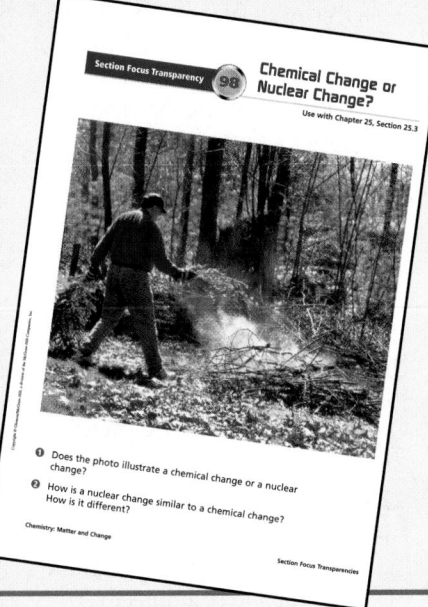

---

## CHEMISTRY JOURNAL

### Space Invaders

*Intrapersonal* Ask students to relate the studies done at particle accelerators to the following story: A visitor from another planet came to Earth and was fascinated by the abundance of different automobiles and their mechanics of operation. To research the automobile, the alien pushed them off a nearby cliff and then climbed to the bottom to study the pieces of wreckage. From this information, the alien was able to return to his home planet and begin the mass assembly of automobiles. **L2**

---

## Section 25.3

# 1 Focus

### Focus Transparency

Before presenting the lesson, display **Section Focus Transparency 98** on the overhead projector. Have students answer the accompanying questions using **Section Focus Transparency Master 98. L1 ELL**

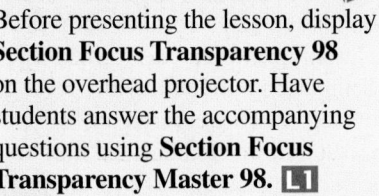

**Section Focus Transparency** **98** Chemical Change or Nuclear Change?

Use with Chapter 25, Section 25.3

❶ Does the photo illustrate a chemical change or a nuclear change?

❷ How is a nuclear change similar to a chemical change? How is it different?

*Chemistry: Matter and Change*

*Section Focus Transparencies*

# 2 Teach

## Concept Development

Students may confuse transmutation and induced transmutation. Remind students that transmutation occurs spontaneously as unstable nuclei decay, whereas induced transmutation occurs when nuclei are bombarded with other particles. It is also important to remind students that not all radioactive decay processes result in transmutation (gamma ray emission is an exception).

**National Science Content Standards**

Pages 814–815
UCP.1, UCP.3; B.1, B.6; G.1, G.3

**Seaborg** Glenn Seaborg (1913–1999), for whom element 106 is named, worked on the Manhattan Project during World War II. The Manhattan Project was responsible for creating the atomic bomb. He was a co-discoverer of plutonium, which was formed by bombarding uranium with deuterons. His research on transuranium elements led him to group the lanthanides and actinides in the lower part of the periodic table. In 1951, Seaborg received the Nobel Prize in Chemistry for his work. He served as the chairman of the Atomic Energy Commission (the forerunner of the Nuclear Regulatory Commission) from 1961 to 1971. Seaborg spent many years campaigning for peaceful uses of atomic energy and against the testing of nuclear weapons. When seaborgium was originally accepted as the official name for element 106, the name was controversial, as it was the first element named in honor of a living scientist.

## Practice PROBLEMS

Have students refer to Appendix D for complete solutions to Practice Problems.

**15.** $^{27}_{13}Al + ^{1}_{0}n \rightarrow ^{24}_{11}Na + ^{4}_{2}He$

**16.** $^{239}_{94}Pu + ^{4}_{2}He \rightarrow ^{1}_{0}n + ^{242}_{96}Cm$

## Resource Manager

**Study Guide for Content Mastery,** p. 147 **L2**

**Solving Problems: A Chemistry Handbook,** Section 25.3 **L2**

**Section Focus Transparency 98 and Master** **L1** **ELL**

First discovered in 1940, elements 93 (neptunium) and 94 (plutonium) are prepared by bombarding uranium-238 with neutrons.

$$^{238}_{92}U + ^{1}_{0}n \rightarrow ^{239}_{92}U \rightarrow ^{239}_{93}Np + ^{0}_{-1}\beta$$

$$^{239}_{93}Np \rightarrow ^{239}_{94}Pu + ^{0}_{-1}\beta$$

If you read through the names of the transuranium elements, you'll notice that many of them have been named in honor of their discoverers or the laboratories at which they were created. There are ongoing efforts throughout the world's major scientific research centers to synthesize new transuranium elements and study their properties.

## EXAMPLE PROBLEM 25-2

### Induced Transmutation Reaction Equations

Write a balanced nuclear equation for the induced transmutation of aluminum-27 into phosphorus-30 by alpha particle bombardment. A neutron is emitted from the aluminum atom in the reaction.

**1. Analyze the Problem**

You are given all of the particles involved in an induced transmutation reaction, from which you must write the balanced nuclear equation. Because the alpha particle bombards the aluminum atom, they are reactants and must appear on the reactant side of the reaction arrow. Obtain the atomic number of aluminum and phosphorus from the periodic table. Write out the nuclear reaction, being sure to include the alpha particle (reactant) and the neutron (product).

**Known**

reactants: aluminum-27 and an alpha particle
products: phosphorus-30 and a neutron

**Unknown**

nuclear equation for the reaction = ?

**2. Solve for the Unknown**

Write the formula for each participant in the reaction.
Aluminum is atomic number 13; its nuclear formula is $^{27}_{13}Al$.
Phosphorus is atomic number 15; its nuclear formula is $^{30}_{15}P$.
The formula for the alpha particle is $^{4}_{2}He$.
The formula for the neutron is $^{1}_{0}n$.
Write the balanced nuclear equation.
$$^{27}_{13}Al + ^{4}_{2}He \rightarrow ^{30}_{15}P + ^{1}_{0}n$$

**3. Evaluate the Answer**

The sums of the superscripts on each side of the equation are equal. The same is true for the subscripts. Therefore, the atomic number and the mass number are conserved. The formula for each participant in the reaction is also correct. The nuclear equation is written correctly.

## PRACTICE PROBLEMS

**15.** Write the balanced nuclear equation for the induced transmutation of aluminum-27 into sodium-24 by neutron bombardment. An alpha particle is released in the reaction.

**16.** Write the balanced nuclear equation for the alpha particle bombardment of $^{239}_{94}Pu$. One of the reaction products is a neutron.

**Practice!** For more practice with transmutation reactions, go to **Supplemental Practice Problems** in Appendix A.

## CHEMISTRY JOURNAL

### The Name Game

 **Intrapersonal** Have interested students research the politics and controversy involved in the IUPAC decision on official names for elements 104 to 110.

**L2**

## Radioactive Decay Rates

You may be wondering how it is that there are any naturally occurring radioisotopes found on Earth. After all, if radioisotopes undergo continuous radioactive decay, won't they eventually disappear? And with the exception of synthesized radioisotopes, few new radioisotopes are being formed. Furthermore, radioisotopes have been decaying for about 4.6 billion years (the span of Earth's existence). Yet naturally occurring radioisotopes are not uncommon on Earth. The explanation for this involves the differing decay rates of isotopes.

Radioactive decay rates are measured in half-lives. A **half-life** is the time required for one-half of a radioisotope's nuclei to decay into its products. For example, the half-life of the radioisotope strontium-90 is 29 years. If you had 10.0 g of strontium-90 today, 29 years from now you would have 5.0 g left. **Table 25-4** shows how this decay continues through four half-lives of strontium-90. **Figure 25-13** presents the data from the table in terms of the percent of strontium-90 remaining after each half-life.

**Table 25-4**

| The Decay of Strontium-90 | | |
|---|---|---|
| Number of half-lives | Elapsed time | Amount of strontium-90 present |
| 0 | 0 | 10.0 g |
| 1 | 29 years | $10.0 \text{ g} \times \left(\frac{1}{2}\right) = 5.00 \text{ g}$ |
| 2 | 58 years | $10.0 \text{ g} \times \left(\frac{1}{2}\right)\left(\frac{1}{2}\right) = 2.50 \text{ g}$ |
| 3 | 87 years | $10.0 \text{ g} \times \left(\frac{1}{2}\right)\left(\frac{1}{2}\right)\left(\frac{1}{2}\right) = 1.25 \text{ g}$ |
| 4 | 116 years | $10.0 \text{ g} \times \left(\frac{1}{2}\right)\left(\frac{1}{2}\right)\left(\frac{1}{2}\right)\left(\frac{1}{2}\right) = 0.625 \text{ g}$ |

The decay continues until negligible strontium-90 remains.

The data in **Table 25-4** can be summarized in a simple equation representing the decay of any radioactive element.

$$\text{Amount remaining} = (\text{Initial amount})\left(\frac{1}{2}\right)^n$$

In the equation, $n$ is equal to the number of half-lives that have passed. Note that the initial amount may be in units of mass or number of particles. A more versatile form of the equation can be written if the exponent $n$ is replaced by the equivalent quantity $t/T$, where $t$ is the elapsed time and $T$ is the duration of the half-life.

$$\text{Amount remaining} = (\text{Initial amount})\left(\frac{1}{2}\right)^{t/T}$$

Note that both $t$ and $T$ must have the same units of time. This type of expression is known as an exponential decay function. **Figure 25-13** shows the graph of a typical exponential decay function—in this case, the decay curve for strontium-90.

Each radioisotope has its own characteristic half-life. Half-lives for several representative radioisotopes are given in **Table 25-5** on the following page. As the table shows, half-lives have an incredible range of values, from millionths of a second to billions of years! To gain a greater understanding of half-life, do the **miniLAB** on page 819.

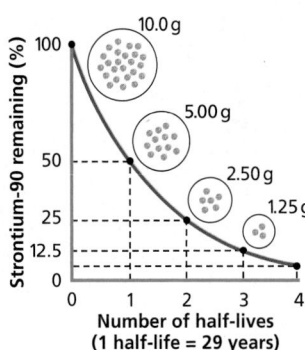

**Figure 25-13**

The graph shows the percent of a strontium-90 sample remaining over a period of four half-lives. With the passing of each half-life, half of the strontium-90 sample decays. Approximately what percent of strontium-90 remains after 1½ half-lives have passed?

### Figure Caption Question
**Figure 25-13** Approximately what percent of strontium-90 remains after $1\frac{1}{2}$ half-lives have passed?
~35%

## Quick Demo

Videotape your students as they enter your classroom and seat themselves. It would be helpful to have a timer on the video camera or arrange for a clock to be seen in the footage. Students who are seated represent decayed atoms, while those who are standing represent atoms that have not decayed. Replay the videotape and emphasize the randomness of the decay process (some students enter in groups, others individually; there are irregular time intervals between students sitting down; etc.). The half-life of the class can also be determined.

## GLENCOE TECHNOLOGY

**CD-ROM**
**Chemistry: Matter and Change**
Animation: *Half-Life*

---

## DIFFERENTIATED INSTRUCTION

### Learning Disabled

*Visual-Spatial* Demonstrate the concept of half-life by placing a number of pennies on the overhead and picking up half of them in a certain time interval. **L1** **ELL**

### Gifted

*Intrapersonal* Have students research information about the particles that result from collisions in particle accelerators. You may want to give them some key terms such as leptons, quarks, and bosons, to get them started. Have the students report to the entire class on their findings. **L3**

**National Science Content Standards**
Pages 816–819
UCP.1, UCP.3; A.1, B.1, B.6, E.2

Table 25-5

| Half-Lives of Several Radioisotopes | | |
|---|---|---|
| **Radioisotope** | **Symbol** | **Half-life** |
| Polonium-214 | $^{214}_{84}Po$ | 163.7 microseconds |
| Cobalt-60 | $^{60}_{27}Co$ | 5.272 years |
| Radon-222 | $^{222}_{86}Ra$ | 3.8 days |
| Phosphorous-32 | $^{32}_{15}P$ | 14.28 days |
| Tritium | $^{3}_{1}H$ | 12.32 years |
| Carbon-14 | $^{14}_{6}C$ | 5730 years |
| Uranium-238 | $^{238}_{92}U$ | $4.46 \times 10^9$ years |

## Extension

Have students become familiar with the *CRC Handbook of Chemistry and Physics* by looking up the Table of Isotopes and researching such questions as:
• Which element has the largest number of radioisotopes?
• Which isotope has the longest half-life? The shortest?
• Which decay has the highest associated energy?

## Applying Chemistry

People who study fine wines may need to determine the age of a particular wine. One method of doing so is to use tritium, a naturally occurring radioisotope of hydrogen. Tritium, which has two neutrons and one proton in its nucleus, constitutes a very small percentage of the hydrogen content of water. It has a half-life of 12.3 years, so it can be used for dating "young" water-containing systems. Once a wine is bottled, it no longer exchanges substances with the outer environment, and its tritium content decays at a rate dictated by its half-life. The tritium level in the environment remains relatively constant.

### Assessment

**Skill** Ask students to become oenologists (people who study wines) for a day in order to determine the authentic age of a wine that is being sold at auction. The auction house claims the wine to be 100 years old. It is found that the tritium level of the wine is 30.6% of that of environmental tritium. What is the actual age of the wine? The wine is 21 years old.

## Visual Learning

**Table 25-5** Ask students to select the best radioisotope from the table for determining the age of an artifact suspected of being 2000 years old. C-14 would be the best choice. The first five radioisotopes have half-lives that are too short, and the half-life of U-238 is too long.

Iron-59 is used to produce this image of a patient's circulatory system.

### EXAMPLE PROBLEM 25-3

**Calculating Amount of Remaining Isotope**

Iron-59 is used in medicine to diagnose blood circulation disorders. The half-life of iron-59 is 44.5 days. How much of a 2.000-mg sample will remain after 133.5 days?

**1. Analyze the Problem**

You are given a known mass of a radioisotope with a known half-life. You must first determine the number of half-lives that passed during the 133.5 day period. Then use the exponential decay equation to calculate the amount of the sample remaining.

**Known**

Initial amount = 2.000 mg
Elapsed time ($t$) = 133.5 days
Half-life ($T$) = 44.5 days

**Unknown**

Amount remaining = ? mg

**2. Solve for the Unknown**

Determine the number of half-lives passed during the 133.5 days.

$$\text{Number of half-lives } (n) = \frac{\text{Elapsed time}}{\text{Half-life}}$$

$$n = \frac{(133.5 \text{ days})}{(44.5 \text{ days/half-life})} = 3.00 \text{ half-lives}$$

Substitute the values for $n$ and initial mass into the exponential decay equation and solve.

$$\text{Amount remaining} = (\text{Initial amount})\left(\frac{1}{2}\right)^n$$

$$\text{Amount remaining} = (2.000 \text{ mg})\left(\frac{1}{2}\right)^{3.00}$$

$$\text{Amount remaining} = (2.000 \text{ mg})\left(\frac{1}{8}\right)$$

$$\text{Amount remaining} = 0.2500 \text{ mg}$$

**3. Evaluate the Answer**

Three half-lives is equivalent to $\left(\frac{1}{2}\right)\left(\frac{1}{2}\right)\left(\frac{1}{2}\right)$, or $\frac{1}{8}$. The answer (0.2500 mg) is equal to $\frac{1}{8}$ of the original mass of 2.000 mg. The answer has four significant figures because the original mass was given with four significant figures. The values of $n$ and $\frac{1}{2}$ do not affect the number of significant figures in the answer.

### GLENCOE TECHNOLOGY

**CD-ROM**
**Chemistry: Matter and Change**
Video: *Radiocarbon Dating*
Experiment: *Radiocarbon Dating*

### Resource Manager

**ChemLab and MiniLab Worksheets,** pp. 97–98 L2
**Math Skills Transparency 42 and Master** L2 ELL
**Teaching Transparency 76 and Master** L2 ELL
**Lab Manual,** pp. 197–200 L2

**17.** If gallium-68 has a half-life of 68.3 minutes, how much of a 10.0-mg sample is left after one half-life? Two half-lives? Three half-lives?

**18.** If the passing of five half-lives leaves 25.0 mg of a strontium-90 sample, how much was present in the beginning?

**19.** Using the half-life given in **Table 25-5**, how much of a 1.0-g polonium-214 sample remains after 818 microseconds?

 *Practice!* **For more practice with half-life problems, go to Supplemental Practice Problems in Appendix A.**

## Radiochemical Dating

Chemical reaction rates are greatly affected by changes in temperature, pressure, and concentration, and by the presence of a catalyst. In contrast, nuclear reaction rates remain constant regardless of such changes. In fact, the half-life of any particular radioisotope is constant. Because of this, radioisotopes can be used to determine the age of an object. The process of determining the age of an object by measuring the amount of a certain radioisotope remaining in that object is called **radiochemical dating**.

## miniLAB

### Modeling Radioactive Decay

**Formulating Models** Because of safety concerns, it is usually not possible to directly experiment with radioactive isotopes in the classroom. Thus, in this lab you will use pennies to model the half-life of a typical radioactive isotope. Each penny represents an individual atom of the radioisotope.

**Materials** 100 pennies, 5-oz. or larger plastic cup, graph paper, graphing calculator (optional)

### Procedure

1. Place the pennies in the plastic cup.

2. Place your hand over the top of the cup and shake the cup several times.

3. Pour the pennies onto a table. Remove all the pennies that are "heads-up." These pennies represent atoms of the radioisotope that have undergone radioactive decay.

4. Count the number of pennies that remain ("tails-up" pennies) and record this number in the Decay Results data table as the Number of pennies remaining for trial 1.

5. Place all of the "tails-up" pennies back in the plastic cup.

6. Repeat steps 2 through 5 for as many times as needed until no pennies remain.

| Decay Results | |
|---|---|
| Trial number | Number of pennies remaining |
| 0 | 100 |
| 1 | |
| 2 | |
| 3 | |
| 4 | |
| 5 | |
| 6 | |
| 7 | |
| 8 | |

### Analysis

1. Make a graph of Trial number versus Number of pennies remaining from the Decay Results data table. Draw a smooth curve through the plotted points.

2. How many trials did it take for 50% of the sample to decay? 75%? 90%?

3. If the time between each trial is one minute, what is the half-life of the radioisotope?

4. Suppose that instead of using pennies to model the radioisotope you use 100 dice. After each toss, any die that comes up a "6" represents a decayed atom and is removed. How would the result using the dice compare with the result obtained from using the pennies?

25.3 Transmutation **819**

Have students refer to Appendix D for complete solutions to Practice Problems.

**17.** 5.00 mg; 2.50 mg; 1.25 mg

**18.** $8.00 \times 10^2$ mg

**19.** 0.031 g

# 3 Assess

## Check for Understanding

 Have students graph on their calculators the beta decay of cesium-137 into barium-137. The half-life for this decay is 30 years. They should begin by making a table that covers 150 years (five half-lives), lists the amount of cesium-137 remaining (starting with 64 g at time 0), and lists the amount of barium-137 formed (starting with 0 g at time 0). They should graph the grams of cesium remaining (left side *y*-axis) versus time (*x*-axis), and grams of barium formed (right side *y*-axis) versus time (same *x*-axis).

## miniLAB

**Purpose**
Students will use a model to examine the concept of half-life of a radioactive isotope.

**Process Skills**
Comparing and contrasting, making and using graphs, collecting data, applying concepts, using numbers, predicting, measuring, and formulating models

**Teaching Strategies**
- Any object that has two or more distinct states, such as heads and tails, can be used in place of the pennies.

**Expected Results**
The Decay Results table should show that approximately half of the pennies decay during each trial. There will probably be no pennies remaining after 7 to 9 trials.

### Analysis

1. The graph should show an exponential decay, and in general should resemble the shape of the curve seen in Figure 25-13.

2. It took approximately one trial for 50% of the sample to decay. It took approximately two trials for 75% of the sample to decay. It took approximately four trials for 90% of the sample to decay.

3. The half-life is 1 minute.

4. Approximately one-sixth of the dice will decay with each toss. It would take approximately three tosses to get one-half of the sample to decay.

### ✔ Assessment

**Performance** Have students write a lab report that can be placed in their portfolios. Use the Performance Task Assessment List for Lab Report in **PASC**, p. 47. **L2** **P**

## Reteach

**Kinesthetic** Ask a student to stand 10 feet away from the wall. Then tell the student to halve the distance to the wall each minute by stepping toward the wall. Ask students if, in theory, their classmate will ever reach the wall. Ask them how this example differs from the decay of atoms that are not infinitely divisible. Theoretically, the student will not reach the wall—you can always take half of an amount. Because atoms are not infinitely divisible, all of a radioactive substance will decay eventually.

## Figure Caption Question

**Figure 25-14b** Could carbon-14 dating be used to determine the age of a stone disk with a leather thong which was found with the skeleton in the glacier? Carbon-14 dating could be used to determine the age of the leather thong. Stones cannot be dated using carbon-14, they are usually dated using U-238.

## Assessment

**Skill** Strontium-90 (half-life = 28 years) is produced during nuclear weapon testing. When ingested, it is assimilated into the bones of the body where it damages healthy tissue. In 1963 several countries signed a treaty banning above-ground nuclear testing. Using 1963 as time zero, when the maximum amount of Sr-90 existed in the environment (100%), ask students to calculate the amount of the radioisotope remaining after each of the first 10 half-lives. Sr-90 levels are considered safe after 10 half-lives. Ask students to explain why strontium is easily absorbed into bones. 1963 (100%); 1991 (50%); 2019 (25%); 2047 (12.5%); 2075 (6.25%); 2103 (3.13%); 2131 (1.56%); 2159 (0.781%); 2187 (0.391%); 2215 (0.195%) and 2243 (0.098%). Strontium is in the same family as calcium and is more reactive.

**Figure 25-14**

 Radiochemical dating is often used to determine the age of bones discovered at archaeological sites. Using this technique, these human bones frozen in a glacier were estimated to be from about 3000 B.C.

**b** Could carbon-14 dating be used to determine the age of a stone disk with a leather thong which was found with the skeleton in the glacier?

A type of radiochemical dating known as carbon dating is commonly used to measure the age of artifacts that were once part of a living organism, such as the human skeleton shown in **Figure 25-14**. Carbon dating, as its name implies, makes use of the radioactive decay of carbon-14. The procedure relies on the fact that unstable carbon-14 is formed by cosmic rays in the upper atmosphere at a fairly constant rate.

$$^{14}_{7}N + {}^{1}_{0}n \rightarrow {}^{14}_{6}C + {}^{1}_{1}p$$

These carbon-14 atoms become evenly spread throughout Earth's biosphere, where they mix with stable carbon-12 and carbon-13 atoms. Plants then use carbon dioxide from the environment, which contains carbon-14, to build more complex molecules through the process of photosynthesis. When animals eat plants, the carbon-14 atoms that were part of the plant become part of the animal. Because organisms are constantly taking in carbon compounds, they contain the same ratio of carbon-14 to carbon-12 and carbon-13 found in the atmosphere. However, this all changes once the organism dies. After death, organisms no longer ingest new carbon compounds, and the carbon-14 they already contain continues to decay. The carbon-14 undergoes beta decay to form nitrogen-14.

$$^{14}_{6}C \rightarrow {}^{14}_{7}N + {}^{0}_{-1}\beta$$

This beta decay reaction has a half-life of 5730 years. Because the amount of stable carbon in the dead organism remains constant while the carbon-14 continues to decay, the ratio of unstable carbon-14 to stable carbon-12 and carbon-13 decreases. By measuring this ratio and comparing it to the nearly constant ratio present in the atmosphere, the age of an object can be estimated. For example, if an object's C-14 to (C-12 + C-13) ratio is one-quarter the ratio measured in the atmosphere, the object is approximately two half-lives, or 11 460 years, old. Carbon-14 dating is limited to accurately dating objects up to approximately 24 000 years of age.

The decay process of a different radioisotope, uranium-238 to lead-206, is commonly used to date objects such as rocks. Because the half-life of uranium-238 is $4.5 \times 10^9$ years, it can be used to estimate the age of objects that are too old to be dated using carbon-14. By radiochemical dating of meteorites, the age of the solar system has been estimated at $4.6 \times 10^9$ years of age.

## Section 25.3 Assessment

**20.** Describe the process of induced transmutation. Give two examples of induced transmutation reactions that produce transuranium elements.

**21.** The initial mass of a radioisotope is 10.0 g. If the radioisotope has a half-life of 2.75 years, how much remains after four half-lives?

**22.** After 2.00 years, 1.986 g of a radioisotope remains from a sample that had an original mass of 2.000 g.

   **a.** Calculate the half-life of the radioisotope.

   **b.** How much of the radioisotope remains after 10.00 years?

**23. Thinking Critically** Compare and contrast how the half-life of a radioisotope is similar to a sporting tournament in which the losing team is eliminated.

**24. Graphing** A sample of polonium-214 originally has a mass of 1.0 g. Express the mass of polonium-214 remaining as a percent of the original sample after a period of one, two, and three half-lives. Graph the percent remaining versus the number of half-lives. Approximately how much time has elapsed when 20% of the original sample remains?

chemistrymc.com/self_check_quiz

## Section 25.3 Assessment

**20.** A target nucleus is struck with high-velocity charged particles. The new nucleus has a greater number of protons. Examples may include $^{239}_{94}Pu + {}^{4}_{2}He \rightarrow {}^{242}_{96}Cm + {}^{1}_{0}n$ and $^{238}_{92}U + {}^{1}_{0}n \rightarrow {}^{239}_{93}Np + {}^{0}_{-1}\beta$.

**21.** 0.625 g

**22. a.** 197 years    **b.** 1.931 g

**23.** In each round of the tournament, half the teams are eliminated.

**24.** The graph should resemble the shape seen in Figure 25-13. Each half-life corresponds to a 50% reduction in the amount remaining. The passing of 380 μs approximates the point at which 20% of the sample remains. See Solutions Manual.

# Fission and Fusion of Atomic Nuclei

As you know, there are major differences between chemical and nuclear reactions. One such difference is the amount of energy the reactions produce. You already know that exothermic chemical reactions can be used to generate electricity. Coal-and oil-burning power plants are common examples. The amount of energy released by chemical reactions, however, is insignificant compared with that of certain nuclear reactions. In this section you will learn about the awesome amounts of energy produced by nuclear reactions. The energy producing capability of nuclear reactions leads naturally to their best-known application—nuclear power plants.

## Nuclear Reactions and Energy

In your study of chemical reactions, you learned that mass is conserved. For most practical situations this is true—but, in the strictest sense, it is not. It has been discovered that energy and mass can be converted into each other. Mass and energy are related by Albert Einstein's most famous equation.

$$\Delta E = \Delta mc^2$$

In this equation, $\Delta E$ stands for change in energy (joules), $\Delta m$ for change in mass (kg), and $c$ for the speed of light ($3.00 \times 10^8$ m/s). This equation is of major importance for all chemical and nuclear reactions, as it means a loss or gain in mass accompanies *any* reaction that produces or consumes energy.

The binding together or breaking apart of an atom's nucleons also involves energy changes. Energy is released when an atom's nucleons bind together. The nuclear binding energy is the amount of energy needed to break one mole of nuclei into individual nucleons. The larger the binding energy per nucleon is, the more strongly the nucleons are held together, and the more stable the nucleus is. Less stable atoms have lower binding energies per nucleon. **Figure 25-15** shows the average binding energy per nucleon versus mass number for

### Objectives

- **Compare** and **contrast** nuclear fission and nuclear fusion.

- **Explain** the process by which nuclear reactors generate electricity.

### Vocabulary

mass defect
nuclear fission
critical mass
breeder reactor
nuclear fusion
thermonuclear reaction

**Binding Energy Variation**

**Figure 25-15**

The graph shows the relationship between binding energy per nucleon and mass number. The greater the binding energy, the greater the stability of the nucleus. Light nuclei can gain stability by undergoing nuclear fusion, whereas heavy nuclei can gain stability by undergoing nuclear fission.

25.4 Fission and Fusion of Atomic Nuclei **821**

---

## 1 Focus

### Focus Transparency

Before presenting the lesson, display **Section Focus Transparency 99** on the overhead projector. Have students answer the accompanying questions using **Section Focus Transparency Master 99. L1 ELL**

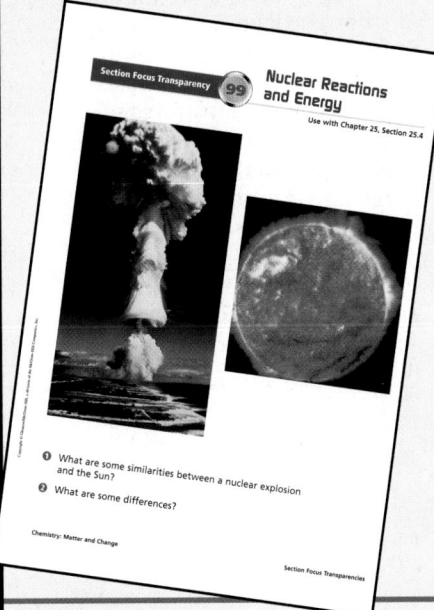

Section Focus Transparency 99

Nuclear Reactions and Energy

Use with Chapter 25, Section 25.4

❶ What are some similarities between a nuclear explosion and the Sun?
❷ What are some differences?

Chemistry: Matter and Change

Section Focus Transparencies

## 2 Teach

### Quick Demo

Hold up a simulated uranium dioxide pellet made by cutting a pencil into 3-cm sections and painting them dark gray. Explain to the students that as many as 10 million pellets may be used in one nuclear power plant per year. The pellets are loaded into long narrow steel cylinders known as fuel rods. Point out that the volume of coal needed to produce the amount of power produced by the pellets would be huge in comparison.

---

## DIFFERENTIATED INSTRUCTION

### Gifted

Present students the following data regarding the mass defect for a helium atom.

| | |
|---|---|
| 2p: (2)(1.007 276 amu) | = 2.014 552 amu |
| 2n: (2)(1.008 665 amu) | = 2.017 330 amu |
| 2e: (2)(0.000 548 6 amu) | = 0.001 097 amu |
| Total | = 4.032 979 amu |

The measured mass of helium is 4.002 60 amu, so the mass defect is 0.030 38 amu.

To calculate the binding energy related to the mass defect, the mass is converted to kg. (0.030 38 amu)(1.6605 × 10⁻²⁷ kg/amu) = 5.0446 × 10⁻²⁹ kg

Then, $E = mc^2$ is used to calculate the binding energy. $E = 4.54 \times 10^{-12}$ J. Now, have students calculate the binding energy for lithium-6, which has a measured mass of 6.015 amu. $5.2 \times 10^{-12}$ J **L3**

## Visual Learning

**Figure 25-16** Have students predict whether each of the following isotopes is a candidate for nuclear fusion or fission: lithium-6 (fusion), technetium-97 (fission), and seaborgium-260 (fission).

## Quick Demo

Divide a set of dominoes into two groups. Arrange one group in a single row so that when the lead domino falls, it causes each of the other dominoes in the line to fall sequentially. This demonstrates a chain reaction. Arrange the second group into a bowling pin pattern, where the lead domino causes two dominoes to fall, which causes three more dominoes to fall, and so on. This demonstrates an escalating chain reaction.

the elements. Note that the binding energy per nucleon reaches a maximum around a mass number of 60. This means that elements with a mass number near 60 are the most stable. You will see the importance of this relationship in the nuclear fission and fusion processes.

In typical chemical reactions, the energy produced or consumed is so small that the accompanying changes in mass are negligible. In contrast, the mass changes and associated energy changes in nuclear reactions are significant. For example, the energy released from the nuclear reaction of one kilogram of uranium is equivalent to the energy released during the chemical combustion of approximately four billion kilograms of coal!

The tremendous energy released by certain nuclear reactions is a measure of the energy required to bond the subatomic particles in nuclei together. You might be wondering where this energy comes from. The answer involves the $\Delta E = \Delta mc^2$ equation. Scientists have determined that the mass of the nucleus is always less than the sum of the masses of the individual protons and neutrons that comprise it. This difference in mass between a nucleus and its component nucleons is called the **mass defect**. Applying Einstein's $\Delta E = \Delta mc^2$ equation, you can see how the missing mass in the nucleus provides the tremendous energy required to bind the nucleus together.

## Nuclear Fission

Binding energies in **Figure 25-15** indicate that heavy nuclei would be more stable if they fragmented into several smaller nuclei. Because atoms with mass numbers around 60 are the most stable, heavy atoms (mass number greater than 60) tend to fragment into smaller atoms in order to increase their stability. The splitting of a nucleus into fragments is known as **nuclear fission**. The fission of a nucleus is accompanied by a very large release of energy.

Nuclear power plants use nuclear fission to generate power. The first nuclear fission reaction discovered involved uranium-235. As you can see in **Figure 25-16**, when a uranium-235 nucleus is struck by a neutron, it undergoes fission. Barium-141 and krypton-92 are just two of the many possible products of this fission reaction. In fact, scientists have identified more than 200 different product isotopes from the fission of a uranium-235 nucleus.

### Figure 25-16

The figure shows the nuclear fission of uranium-235. When bombarded with a neutron, uranium-235 forms unstable uranium-236, which then splits into two lighter nuclei and additional neutrons. The splitting (fission) of the nucleus is accompanied by a large release of energy.

Each fission of uranium-235 releases additional neutrons. If one fission reaction produces two neutrons, these two neutrons can cause two additional fissions. If those two fissions release four neutrons, those four neutrons could then produce four more fissions, and so on, as shown in **Figure 25-17.** This self-sustaining process in which one reaction initiates the next is called a chain reaction. As you can imagine, the number of fissions and the amount of energy released can increase extremely rapidly. The explosion from an atomic bomb is an example of an uncontrolled chain reaction.

**822**    Chapter 25  Nuclear Chemistry

## Resource Manager

**Study Guide for Content Mastery,** pp. 148–149 L2
**Solving Problems: A Chemistry Handbook,** Section 25.4 L2
**Section Focus Transparency 99 and Master** L1 ELL

## Portfolio

### The Dream and the Reality

*Linguistic* Ask students to write essays about the following topic and place them in their portfolios: In ancient times, alchemists experimented to devise a method to change base metals such as lead into gold. Is such a thing possible today? Is it probable? Why or why not? L2 P

**Figure 25-17**

This figure illustrates the on-going reactions characteristic of a nuclear fission chain reaction.

$^{1}_{0}$n (neutron)

Fission fragment

$^{235}_{92}$U nucleus

A sample of fissionable material must have sufficient mass in order for a fission chain reaction to occur. If it does not, neutrons escape from the sample before they have the opportunity to strike other nuclei and continue the chain reaction—the chain reaction never begins. A sample that is not massive enough to sustain a chain reaction is said to have subcritical mass. A sample that is massive enough to sustain a chain reaction has **critical mass**. When a critical mass is present, the neutrons released in one fission cause other fissions to occur. If much more mass than the critical mass is present, the chain reaction rapidly escalates. This can lead to a violent nuclear explosion. A sample of fissionable material with a mass greater than the critical mass is said to have supercritical mass. **Figure 25-18** shows the effect of mass on the initiation and progression of a fission reaction.

**Figure 25-18**

The amount of fissionable matter present determines whether a nuclear chain reaction can be sustained. **ⓐ** In a subcritical mass, the chain reaction stops because neutrons escape the sample before causing sufficient fissions to sustain the reaction. **ⓑ** In a supercritical mass, the chain reaction accelerates as neutrons cause more and more fissions to occur.

● neutron   ● nucleus

**ⓐ** Subcritical mass

**ⓑ** Supercritical mass

25.4 Fission and Fusion of Atomic Nuclei     **823**

---

Ask students to calculate how many cycles of a "chain letter" are needed to reach every student in their high school if they start with just one letter. Ask them to compare this process with that of an escalating nuclear chain reaction.

**Content Background**

**The Bomb** Many students may be confused about the difference between the "A-bomb" (atomic bomb) and the "H-bomb" (hydrogen bomb). The atomic bomb utilizes the principles of fission and was originally developed as part of the Manhattan project in the early 1940s. The first experimental atomic bomb detonation occurred on July 16, 1945, near Alamogordo, New Mexico. A few weeks later, atomic bombs were dropped on Hiroshima (August 6, 1945) and Nagasaki (August 9, 1945), Japan. Each bomb released energy equal to that of 20 000 tons of TNT. The dropping of the bombs hastened the end of World War II.

The hydrogen bomb has an explosive force 1000 times greater than that of the atomic bomb. In a hydrogen bomb, a fission reaction triggers a fusion reaction of hydrogen isotopes (deuterium and tritium). The United States detonated the first megaton-class hydrogen bomb (equal to 15 million tons of TNT) at Bikini Atoll in the Pacific Ocean on March 1, 1954. The hydrogen bomb has never been used in warfare.

**Extension**

Have students read *Hiroshima* by John Hersey. Hold a debate between teams of students about whether the United States should have used the atomic bomb during World War II.

**National Science Content Standards**

**Pages 820–823**
UCP.1, UCP.3; B.1, B.4, B.6; E.2 F.5, F.6

---

**DIFFERENTIATED INSTRUCTION**

**Gifted**

*Logical-Mathematical* Have students locate an electric bill from home and note the kWh (kilowatt-hours) used. Ask them to use dimensional analysis to convert kWh to kilograms of coal consumed and its equivalent in uranium-235 fuel. The *CRC Handbook of Chemistry and Physics* has conversions needed or you may give them to the students. **L2**

- 1 kWh = $3.60 \times 10^6$ J
- U-235 undergoes beta decay giving total disintegration energy of 4.68 MeV
- 1MeV = $1.61 \times 10^{-19}$ J
- Enthalpy of combustion for carbon is 393.5 kJ/mol

## Extension

Have students read the caption to Figure 25-19 and then ask them to offer reasons why some countries rely more heavily on nuclear power than the United States. Lack of geographical access to oil and coal; political agreements with oil-producing countries; and economic factors are a few reasons.

**Figure 25-19**

Worldwide, there are more than 400 operating nuclear power plants such as this one. Currently, 18 countries rely on nuclear power to supply at least 25% of their total electricity needs.

**Figure 25-20**

The exploded fourth reactor of the Chernobyl nuclear power plant is seen in this aerial view taken in April, 1986. Radiation from the reactor caused great environmental damage to the surrounding areas.

## Nuclear Reactors

You may be familiar with the sight of a nuclear power plant, such as the one shown in **Figure 25-19**. Nuclear fission produces the energy generated by nuclear reactors. This energy is primarily used to generate electricity. What fuels the energy production of the reactor? A common fuel is fissionable uranium(IV) oxide ($UO_2$) encased in corrosion-resistant fuel rods. The fuel is enriched to contain 3% uranium-235, the amount required to sustain a chain reaction. Additional rods composed of cadmium or boron control the fission process inside the reactor by absorbing neutrons released during the reaction.

Keeping the chain reaction going while preventing it from racing out of control requires precise monitoring and continual adjusting of the control rods. Much of the concern about nuclear power plants focuses on the risk of losing control of the nuclear reactor, possibly resulting in the accidental release of harmful levels of radiation. The Three Mile Island nuclear accident in the United States in 1979 and the Chernobyl nuclear accident in Ukraine in 1986, shown in **Figure 25-20**, provide powerful examples of why controlling the reactor is critical.

The fission within a nuclear reactor is started by a neutron-emitting source and is stopped by positioning the control rods to absorb virtually all of the neutrons produced in the reaction. The reactor core contains a reflector that acts to reflect neutrons back into the core where they will react with the fuel rods. A coolant, usually water, circulates through the reactor core to carry off the heat generated by the nuclear fission reaction. The hot coolant heats water that is used to power stream-driven turbines which produce electrical power.

In many ways, the design of a nuclear power plant and that of a fossil fuel burning power plant are very similar. In both cases heat from a reaction is used to generate steam. The steam is then used to drive turbines that produce electricity. In a typical fossil fuel power plant, the chemical combustion of coal, oil, or gas generates the heat, whereas in a nuclear power plant, a nuclear fission reaction generates the heat. Because of the hazardous radioactive fuels and fission products present at nuclear power plants, a dense concrete structure is usually built to enclose

Containment structure

Steam turbine (high-energy steam spins turbines and generates electricity)

Hot coolant

Steam

Control rods

Steam generator

Condenser (low-energy steam from turbines is condensed back to liquid water)

Fuel elements

Carbon moderators

Reactor

Cool coolant

Pump

Pumps

Cool water

Large body of water

Warm water

a

the reactor. The main purpose of the containment structure is to shield personnel and nearby residents from harmful radiation. The major components of a nuclear power plant are illustrated in **Figure 25-21**.

As the reactor operates, the fuel rods are gradually depleted and products from the fission reaction accumulate. Because of this, the reactor must be serviced periodically. Spent fuel rods can be reprocessed and repackaged to make new fuel rods. Some fission products, however, are extremely radioactive and cannot be used again. These products must be stored as nuclear waste. The storage of highly radioactive nuclear waste is one of the major issues surrounding the debate over the use of nuclear power. Approximately 20 half-lives are required for the radioactivity of nuclear waste materials to reach levels acceptable for biological exposure. For some types of nuclear fuels, the wastes remain substantially radioactive for thousands of years. A considerable amount of scientific research has been devoted to the disposal of radioactive wastes. How does improper disposal or storage of nuclear wastes affect the environment? Is this a short-term effect? Why?

Another issue is the limited supply of the uranium-235 used in the fuel rods. One option is to build reactors that produce new quantities of fissionable fuels. Reactors able to produce more fuel than they use are called **breeder reactors**. Although the design of breeder reactors poses many difficult technical problems, breeder reactors are in operation in several countries.

b

c

**Figure 25-21**

ⓐ The diagram illustrates the major parts of a nuclear power plant. The photos show ⓑ the submerged reactor and ⓒ the steam-driven turbines.

How does this containment structure protect the environment? What would be the effect on the environment if this structure leaked radiation?

25.4 Fission and Fusion of Atomic Nuclei    **825**

## Building a Model

🏃 *Kinesthetic* Have teams of students research the various designs of commercial nuclear reactors and build a scale model of one of them. Each team should present its model to the class and explain its operation. **L2** **ELL** **COOP LEARN**

## In-Text Questions

**Page 825** How do improper disposal or storage of nuclear wastes affect the environment? Improperly stored nuclear waste could leak from its container, polluting the environment. Is this a short-term effect? Why? No. Many damaging radioisotopes have half-lives that are hundreds and even thousands of years.

## Figure Caption Questions

**Figure 25-21** How does this containment structure protect the environment? The heavy concrete walls keep radioactive substances from escaping in the event of an accident. What would be the effect on the environment if this structure leaked radiation? The leaked radiation would damage living organisms in the environment and potentially pollute the area for hundreds of years.

# GLENCOE
## TECHNOLOGY

CD-ROM
**Chemistry: Matter and Change**
Video: *Inside a Nuclear Power Plant*
Video: *The Big Bang*

## CHEMISTRY JOURNAL

### The NIMBY Syndrome

Many strong antinuclear sentiments arise when it comes to the topic of nuclear power and storage of nuclear waste products. While many people might feel comfortable with the idea of using the energy derived from nuclear fission, they are not comfortable with the storage of radioactive waste products in their state, thus the "Not In My BackYard" syndrome. Ask students to research current radioactive waste disposal options in your state and in the nation. How would they feel living near a nuclear waste disposal site? **L2** 📦

826

## Enrichment

Have students research stellar nucleosynthesis and develop a board game based on their findings. Perhaps dice or a spinner can dictate the fate of a star (for example: supernova, red giant, white dwarf, or neutron star). **L3**

# 3 Assess

## Check for Understanding

Have the students respond to the following true-false statements. They should support their choices. This could be done individually or as a group.

1. Great amounts of energy can be liberated from small amounts of matter in nuclear reactions. True
2. The amount of U-235 in a nuclear reactor should always be kept subcritical. False
3. Nuclear power plants don't contribute to pollution. True in terms of air pollution; false if nuclear waste is considered.
4. Inserting boron or cadmium rods into the reactor core can control a fission reaction. True
5. Nuclear power plants are dangerous because they commonly release radioactive particles into the environment. False

## Reteach

Place an unlabeled diagram of a nuclear reactor on the board. Have students come up and explain the function of a particular part of the reactor beginning with the fuel rods. If they get stuck, they may "tag" another student to continue the process. **L2** **ELL**

### ✔ Assessment

**Performance** Have each student make a poster that shows and explains the sequence of events leading to the generation of steam at a nuclear power plant. Use the Performance Task Assessment List for Poster in **PASC,** p. 73.

**826**

**Figure 25-22**

The characteristic circular-shape of the tokamak reactor is clearly seen here. The reactor uses strong magnetic fields to contain the intensely hot fusion reaction and keep it from direct contact with the interior reactor walls.

## Nuclear Fusion

Recall from the binding energy diagram in **Figure 25-15** that a mass number of about 60 has the most stable atomic configuration. Thus, it is possible to bind together two or more light (mass number less than 60) and less stable nuclei to form a single more stable nucleus. The combining of atomic nuclei is called **nuclear fusion**. Nuclear fusion reactions are capable of releasing very large amounts of energy. You already have some everyday knowledge of this fact—the Sun is powered by a series of fusion reactions as hydrogen atoms fuse to form helium atoms.

$$4 {}_1^1 H \rightarrow 2 {}_{-1}^0 \beta + {}_2^4 He + energy$$

Scientists have spent several decades researching nuclear fusion. Why? One reason is that there is a tremendous abundance of lightweight isotopes, such as hydrogen, that can be used to fuel fusion reactions. Also, fusion reaction products are generally not radioactive. Unfortunately, there are major problems that have yet to be overcome on a commercially viable scale. One major problem is that fusion requires extremely high energies to initiate and sustain a reaction. The required energy, which is achieved only at extremely high temperatures, is needed to overcome the electrostatic repulsion between the nuclei in the reaction. Because of the energy requirements, fusion reactions are also known as **thermonuclear reactions**. Just how much energy is needed? The lowest temperature capable of producing a fusion reaction is 40 000 000 K! This temperature—and even higher temperatures—have been achieved using an atomic explosion to initiate the fusion process, but this approach is not practical for controlled electrical power generation.

Obviously there are many problems that must be resolved before fusion becomes a practical energy source. Another significant problem is confinement of the reaction. There are currently no materials capable of withstanding the tremendous temperatures that are required by a fusion reaction. Much of the current research centers around an apparatus called a tokamak reactor. A tokamak reactor, which you can see in **Figure 25-22**, uses strong magnetic fields to contain the fusion reaction. While significant progress has been made in the field of fusion, temperatures high enough for continuous fusion have not been sustained for long periods of time.

## Section 25.4 Assessment

**25.** Compare and contrast nuclear fission and nuclear fusion reactions in terms of the particles involved and the changes they undergo.

**26.** Describe the process that occurs during a nuclear chain reaction.

**27.** Explain how nuclear fission can be used to generate electrical power.

**28. Thinking Critically** Present an argument supporting or opposing nuclear power as your state's primary power source. Assume that the primary source of power currently is the burning of fossil fuels.

**29. Calculating** What is the energy change ($\Delta E$) associated with a change in mass ($\Delta m$) of 1.00 mg?

chemistrymc.com/self_check_quiz

## Section 25.4 Assessment

**25.** In fission, heavy nuclei break down into smaller nuclei, releasing large amounts of energy. In fusion, two or more light nuclei join together to form a more stable nucleus and release large amounts of energy.

**26.** A neutron strikes a target nucleus such as U=235, which then splits into multiple fission fragments and releases several neutrons. These neutrons collide with other nuclei, causing additional fissions and sustaining the reaction.

**27.** Fission reactions heat water and form steam. The steam spins turbines that produce electrical power.

**28.** See the Solutions Manual.

**29.** $9.00 \times 10^{10}$ kg·m$^2$/s$^2$ or J

# Applications and Effects of Nuclear Reactions

As you learned in the previous section, using nuclear fission reactions to generate electrical power is an important application of nuclear chemistry. Another very important application is in medicine, where the use of radioisotopes has made dramatic changes in the way some diseases are treated. This section explores the detection, uses, and effects of radiation.

## Detecting Radioactivity

You learned earlier that Becquerel discovered radioactivity because of the effect of radiation on photographic plates. Since this discovery, several other methods have been devised to detect radiation. The effect of radiation on photographic film is the same as the effect of visible light on the film in your camera. With some care, film can be used to provide a quantitative measure of radioactivity. A film badge is a device containing a piece of radiation-sensitive film that is used to monitor radiation exposure. People who work with radioactive substances carry film badges to monitor the extent of their exposure to radiation.

Radiation energetic enough to ionize matter with which it collides is called **ionizing radiation**. The Geiger counter is a radiation detection device that makes use of ionizing radiation in its operation. As you can see in **Figure 25-23**, a Geiger counter consists of a metal tube filled with a gas. In the center of the tube is a wire that is connected to a power supply. When ionizing radiation penetrates the end of the tube, the gas inside the tube absorbs the radiation and becomes ionized. The ionized gas contains ions and free electrons. The free electrons are attracted to the wire, causing a current to flow. A current meter that is built into the Geiger counter measures the current flow through the ionized gas. This current measurement is used to determine the amount of ionizing radiation present.

Another detection device is a scintillation counter, which uses a phosphor-coated surface to detect radiation. Scintillations are bright flashes of light

### Objectives

- **Describe** several methods used to detect and measure radiation.
- **Explain** an application of radiation used in the treatment of disease.
- **Describe** some of the damaging effects of radiation on biological systems.

### Vocabulary

ionizing radiation
radiotracer

**Figure 25-23**

The Geiger counter is used to detect and measure radiation levels. The small device is usually hand-held. Ionizing radiation produces an electric current in the Geiger counter. The current is displayed on a scaled meter, while a speaker is used to produce audible sounds.

Gas molecules are ionized by the radiation

Electrode (positively charged)

Counter and audio device

Metal tube (negatively charged)

$e^-$  $e^-$  $e^-$  $e^-$

Nonionized gas molecules

Ionizing radiation

Window

25.5 Applications and Effects of Nuclear Reactions **827**

### DIFFERENTIATED INSTRUCTION

**English Language Learners**
Have students look up the definition of ionizing radiation and use it in a sentence. Have them write an explanation of how ionizing radiation is used by a Geiger counter to detect radiation.

# 1 Focus

**Focus Transparency**

Before presenting the lesson, display **Section Focus Transparency 100** on the overhead projector. Have students answer the accompanying questions using **Section Focus Transparency Master 100.** **L1** **ELL**

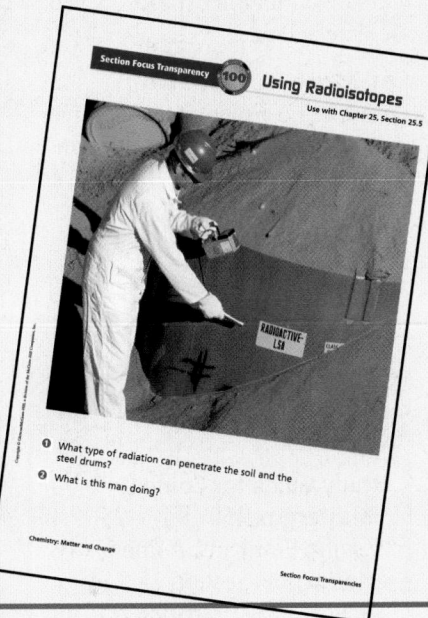

Section Focus Transparency **100** **Using Radioisotopes**
Use with Chapter 25, Section 25.5

❶ What type of radiation can penetrate the soil and the steel drums?
❷ What is this man doing?

Chemistry: Matter and Change

Section Focus Transparencies

# 2 Teach

**Quick Demo**

Check at your grocery store and obtain irradiated and nonirradiated samples of the same food. (Some produce and meats might be irradiated.) Ask employees at the store for help if needed. Place the samples in two different sealed containers in your classroom and observe them for the next several days. The irradiated sample should not spoil as quickly as the nonirradiated sample.

**National Science Content Standards**

**Pages 826–827**
UCP.1, UCP.3; B.6; E.2; F.1, F.5; G.1

**Figure 25-24**

**ⓐ** Phosphors are used to aid in the night time readability of watches.
**ⓑ** Television and computer screens are phosphor coated. An electron gun aimed at the back of the screen illuminates the phosphors.

produced when ionizing radiation excites the electrons in certain types of atoms called phosphors. The number and brightness of the scintillations are detected and recorded, giving a measure of the amount of ionizing radiation present. As shown in **Figure 25-24a**, the dials of some watches are painted with a radium-containing phosphor that causes the watch to glow in the dark. Televisions and computer monitors, such as those shown in **Figure 25-24b**, also make use of phosphor screens that produce scintillations when struck by electrons.

## Uses of Radiation

With proper safety procedures, radiation can be very useful in many scientific experiments. Neutron activation analysis is used to detect trace amounts of elements present in a sample. Computer chip manufacturers use this technique to analyze the composition of highly purified silicon wafers. In the process, the sample is bombarded with a beam of neutrons from a radioactive source, causing some of the atoms in the sample to become radioactive. The type of radiation emitted by the sample is used to determine the types and quantities of elements present. Neutron activation analysis is a very sensitive measurement technique capable of detecting quantities of less than $1 \times 10^{-9}$ g.

Radioisotopes can also be used to follow the course of an element through a chemical reaction. For example, $CO_2$ gas containing radioactive carbon-14 isotopes has been used to study glucose formation in photosynthesis.

$$6CO_2 + 6H_2O + \text{chlorophyll} \xrightarrow{\text{sunlight}} C_6H_{12}O_6 + 6O_2$$

Because the $CO_2$ containing carbon-14 is used to trace the progress of carbon through the reaction, it is referred to as a radiotracer. A **radiotracer** is a radioisotope that emits non-ionizing radiation and is used to signal the presence of an element or specific substance. The fact that all of an element's isotopes have the same chemical properties makes the use of radioisotopes possible. Thus, replacing a stable atom of an element in a reaction with one of its isotopes does not alter the reaction. Radiotracers are important in a number of areas of chemical research, particularly in analyzing the reaction mechanisms of complex, multi-step reactions.

Radiotracers also have important uses in medicine. Iodine-131, for example, is commonly used to detect diseases associated with the thyroid gland. One of the important functions of the thyroid gland is to extract iodine from the bloodstream to make the hormone thyroxine. If a thyroid problem is suspected, a doctor will give the patient a drink containing a small amount of iodine-131. The iodine-containing radioisotope is then used to monitor the functioning of the thyroid gland, as shown in **Figure 25-25**. After allowing

---

## Internet Address Book

**Chemistry Online** Note Internet addresses that you find useful in the space below for quick reference.

_____
_____
_____
_____
_____

time for the iodine to be absorbed, the amount of iodide taken up by the thyroid is measured. This is just one example of the many ways radioisotopes are useful in diagnosing disease.

Another radiation-based medical diagnostic tool is called positron emission transaxial tomography (PET). In this procedure, a radiotracer that decays by positron emission is injected into the patient's bloodstream. Positrons emitted by the radiotracer cause gamma ray emissions that are then detected by an array of sensors surrounding the patient. The type of radiotracer injected depends on what biological function the doctor wants to monitor. For example, as shown in **Figure 25-26**, a fluorine-based radiotracer is commonly used in the PET analysis of the brain's glucose metabolism. Abnormalities in how glucose is metabolized by the brain can help in the diagnosis of brain cancer, schizophrenia, epilepsy, and other brain disorders.

Radiation can pose serious health problems for humans because of the damage it causes to living cells. Healthy cells can be badly damaged or completely destroyed by radiation. However, radiation can also destroy unhealthy cells, including cancer cells. All cancers are characterized by the runaway growth of abnormal cells. This growth can produce masses of abnormal tissue, called malignant tumors. Radiation therapy is used to treat cancer by destroying the fast-growing cancer cells. In fact, cancer cells are more susceptible to destruction by radiation than healthy ones. In the process of destroying unhealthy cells, some healthy cells are also damaged. Despite this major drawback, radiation therapy has become one of the most important treatment options used in the fight against cancer.

## Biological Effects of Radiation

Although radiation has a number of medical and scientific applications, it can be very harmful. The damage produced from ionizing radiation absorbed by the body depends on several factors, such as the energy of the radiation, the type of tissue absorbing the radiation, and the distance from the source. Do the **problem-solving LAB** on the next page to see how radiation exposure is affected by distance. Gamma rays are particularly dangerous because they easily penetrate human tissue. In contrast, the skin usually stops alpha radiation, and beta radiation generally penetrates only about 1–2 cm beneath the skin.

**Figure 25-25**

Doctors analyze radiotracer produced images such as this to determine whether a patient's thyroid gland is functioning properly.

**Figure 25-26**

Shown here are images produced from a fluorine-based PET scan of a patient's brain.

**Performance** Assign a task that can be achieved or monitored through the use of nuclear technology to teams of students. Each team will represent a company that specializes in this technology. Specific roles for each group member should be outlined (chairman, graphic designer, presenter, etc.). The students will research the use of the particular technology and then sell it to the class using a visually oriented presentation. Possible topics include the use of radioisotopes in gemology and medicine, the environmental cleansing of sulfur dioxides and nitrogen oxides, airport baggage inspection, food preservation (including shrink wrapping), computer disks, and the plastics industry. Use the Performance Task Assessment List for Oral Presentation in **PASC,** p. 71. L2
**COOP LEARN**

### Extension

Invite a radiologist or radiology technician from your community hospital to discuss and show slides of the various types of nuclear technologies available for diagnosis and treatments of different medical conditions.

### GLENCOE TECHNOLOGY

CD-ROM
**Chemistry: Matter and Change**
Video: *Nuclear Medicine*

---

## CHEMISTRY JOURNAL

### Putting Risk into Perspective

On the board, list factors that increase the chance of death by one in a million: smoking 1.4 cigarettes; spending one hour in a coal mine; riding 10 miles on a bicycle; traveling 150 miles in a car; flying 1000 miles by jet; one chest X ray; living within five miles of a nuclear reactor for five years; eating 100 barbecued steaks. Ask students to comment on the following.
• Why do some risks receive more publicity than others?
• Is the concept of "zero risk" possible?
• The difference between voluntary and involuntary risk.

• Some common risks faced daily.
• Is life riskier today than it was 100 years ago?
• How does modern technology affect our perception of risk?

## problem-solving LAB

### Purpose

Students will study how distance affects exposure to sources of radiation.

### Process Skills

Recognize cause and effect, interpret and analyze data from a graph, develop predictions

### Teaching Strategies

- Discuss other point-like behavior, such as the decrease in light intensity as the distance from the light is squared. Gravitational and electrostatic forces also behave similarly.
- Relate the intensity unit $mrem/s \cdot m^2$ to sound or light intensity. It's the rate of radiation falling on a unit area.
- If the distance to a radiation source is much greater than the size of the source, the radiation level (intensity) decreases as the square of the distance (inverse square law). This is a typical behavior of point-like sources.

### Thinking Critically

1. The level at 0.2 m is one-quarter the level at 0.1 m. The level at 0.4 m is one-sixteenth the level at 0.1 m.
2. The radiation decreases with the square of the distance from the source.
3. Set up an inverse square relationship, $\frac{I_1}{d_1^2} = \frac{I_2}{d_2^2}$. Substitute values for $I_1$ and $d_1$ from the data given in the graph. Then substitute 0.69 mrem/m$^2$ for $I_2$ and solve for $d_2$. The result is $d_2 = 12$ m.

### Assessment

**Performance** Tell students that light intensity obeys the relationship used in this Problem-Solving Lab. Have students research the SI unit of light intensity and develop a set of sample problems with answers that illustrate that light obeys the inverse square law. Use the Performance Task Assessment List for Asking Questions in **PASC**, p. 19.

### Chemistry Online

**Topic: Food Irradiation**
To learn more about food irradiation, visit the Chemistry Web site at chemistrymc.com

**Activity:** Research the process of food irradiation and scientific responses to consumer concerns. Hold a class debate about its use.

High-energy ionizing radiation is dangerous because it can readily fragment and ionize molecules within biological tissue. When ionizing radiation penetrates a living biological system, the ionized atoms and molecules that are generated are unstable and highly reactive. A free radical is an atom or molecule that contains one or more unpaired electrons and is one example of the highly reactive products of ionizing radiation. In a biological system, free radicals can affect a large number of other molecules and ultimately disrupt the operation of normal cells.

Ionizing radiation damage to living systems can be classified as either somatic or genetic. Somatic damage affects only nonreproductive body tissue and therefore affects the organism only during its own lifetime. Genetic damage, on the other hand, can affect offspring because it damages reproductive tissue, which may affect the genes and chromosomes in the sperm and the eggs of the organism. Somatic damage from radiation includes burns similar to those produced by fire, and cancer caused by damage to the cell's growth mechanism. Genetic damage is more difficult to study because it may not become apparent for several generations. Many scientists presently believe that exposure to any amount of radiation poses some risk to the body.

A dose of radiation refers to the amount of radiation your body absorbs from a radioactive source. Two units, the rad and rem, are commonly used to measure radiation doses. The rad, which stands for Radiation-Absorbed Dose,

## problem-solving LAB

### How does distance affect radiation exposure?

**Interpreting Graphs** Some people, such as X-ray technicians, must work near radioactive sources. They know the importance of keeping a safe distance from the source. The graph shows the intensity of a radioactive source versus the distance from the source.

### Analysis

Note how the intensity of the radiation varies with the distance from the source. The unit of radiation intensity is millirem per second per square meter. (This is the amount of radiation striking a square meter of area each second.) Use the graph to answer the Thinking Critically questions that follow.

### Thinking Critically

1. How does the radiation exposure change as the distance doubles from 0.1 meter to 0.2 meter? As the distance quadruples from 0.1 meter to 0.4 meter?
2. State in words the mathematical relationship described in your answer to question 1.
3. The maximum radiation exposure intensity that is considered safe is 0.69 mrem/s·m². At what

**Radiation Intensity Versus Distance From Source**

distance from the source has the radiation decreased to this level? (*Hint:* Use the equation

$$\frac{I_1}{d_1^2} = \frac{I_2}{d_2^2}$$

where $I_1$ is the radiation intensity at distance $d_1$, and $I_2$ is the radiation intensity at distance $d_2$.)

**Table 25-6**

| Effects of Short-term Radiation Exposure | |
| --- | --- |
| **Dose (rem)** | **Effects on humans** |
| 0–25 | No detectable effects |
| 25–50 | Temporary decrease in white blood cell population |
| 100–200 | Nausea, substantial decrease in white blood cell population |
| 500 | 50% chance of death within 30 days of exposure |

is a measure of the amount of radiation that results in the absorption of 0.01 J of energy per kilogram of tissue. The dose in rads, however, does not account for the energy of the radiation, the type of living tissue absorbing the radiation, or the time of the exposure. To account for these factors, the dose in rads is multiplied by a numerical factor that is related to the radiation's effect on the tissue involved. The result of this multiplication is a unit called the rem. The rem, which stands for ROENTGEN EQUIVALENT FOR MAN, is named after Wilhelm Roentgen, who, as you learned in Section 25.1, discovered X rays in 1895.

So how does radiation exposure affect you? You may be surprised to learn that you are exposed to radiation on a regular basis. A variety of sources—some naturally occurring, others not—constantly bombard your body with radiation. Read the **Chemistry and Society** at the end of this chapter to learn about one of the most common sources of exposure. Your exposure to these sources results in an average annual radiation exposure of 100–300 millirems of high-energy radiation. Remembering that the SI prefix *milli-* stands for one-thousandth, this dose of radiation is equivalent to 0.10 to 0.30 rem. To help you put this in perspective, a typical dental X ray exposes you to the virtually harmless dose of 0.0005 rem. However, both short exposures to high doses of radiation and long exposures to lower doses of radiation can be harmful. As you can see from the data in **Table 25-6**, short-term radiation exposures in excess of 500 rem can be fatal. **Table 25-7** shows your annual exposure to common radiation sources. You can perform the **CHEMLAB** at the end of this chapter to examine radiation emitted by a common substance.

**Table 25-7**

| Average Annual Radiation exposure | |
| --- | --- |
| **Source** | **Average exposure (mrem/y)** |
| Cosmic Radiation | 20–50 |
| Radiation from ground | 25–170 |
| Radiation from buildings | 10–160 |
| Radiation from air | 20–260 |
| Human body (internal) | ~20 |
| Medical and dental X rays | 50–75 |
| Nuclear weapon testing | <1 |
| Air travel | 5 |
| Total average | 100–300 |

## Section 25.5 Assessment

**30.** Describe several methods used to detect and measure radiation.

**31.** Explain one way in which nuclear chemistry is used to diagnose or treat disease.

**32.** Compare and contrast somatic and genetic biological damage.

**33. Thinking Critically** Using what you know about the biological effects of radiation, explain why it is safe to use radioisotopes for the diagnosis of medical problems.

**34. Hypothesizing** The average person is exposed to 100–300 millirems of radiation per year. Airline crewmembers, however, are exposed to almost twice the average amount of radiation per year. Suggest a possible reason for their increased exposure to radiation.

chemistrymc.com/self_check_quiz

25.5 Applications and Effects of Nuclear Reactions    **831**

## Section 25.5 Assessment

**30.** Geiger counters, scintillation counters, and film badges may be described.

**31.** Explanations will vary, but might include radiotracers, PET scans, or radiation treatment to kill cancer cells.

**32.** Somatic damage affects the body cells of the organism and will have effects only on that organism in its lifetime. Genetic damage affects the DNA of the organism, and could be transferred to later generations.

**33.** Radioisotopes used in medical diagnosis have short half-lives, thereby minimizing the patient's exposure.

**34.** Airline crews experience greater exposure because they travel at altitudes where solar and cosmic radiation levels are higher.

# 3 Assess

## Check for Understanding

Ask students to compare the functioning of a Geiger counter and a smoke detector. Both systems depend on the ionization of a gas (air in a smoke detector and argon [usually] in a Geiger counter).

## Reteach

Ask students what factors determine the extent of radiation damage to an individual? Dosage, exposure time, nature of radiation, area exposed, and type of tissue are all factors to be considered.

## Extension

Radiation is more destructive to rapidly dividing cells. How can this be an advantage? because cancer cells divide rapidly How can this be a disadvantage? Healthy, non-cancerous cells could be damaged.

## CHEMLAB

ChemLab 25, located at the end of this chapter, can be used at this point in the lesson.

### Assessment

**Performance** Set up a "Jeopardy" style game with categories such as nuclear medicine, detecting radiation, nuclear power, fission or fusion. Have teams of students compete for points. Use the Performance Task Assessment List for Group Work in **PASC**, p. 97. **L2** **COOP LEARN**

**National Science Content Standards**

**Pages 830–831**
UCP.1, UCP.3; B.6; E.2; F.1, F.5

**831**

## Preparation

### Time Allotment
One laboratory period

### Process Skills
Collecting and interpreting data, making and using graphs, thinking critically, using numbers

### Preparation of Materials
• Make sure the salt substitute contains potassium chloride. Potassium chloride can also be used.

### Alternative Materials
• If you don't have CBL equipment, you may be able to use a Geiger counter, or some similar device, to measure radiation levels.

### Pre-Lab

3. Isotopes are atoms of the same element that have the same atomic number but different atomic masses due to having different numbers of neutrons. A radioactive isotope, also known as a radioisotope, is an unstable isotope that will undergo radioactive decay.

4. $^{40}_{19}K \rightarrow ^{40}_{20}Ca + ^{0}_{-1}\beta$
   parent → daughter + $^{0}_{1}\beta$

5. Potassium-40 has an n/p ratio of 21 : 19, or 1.105 : 1. Calcium-40 has an n/p ratio of 20 : 20, or 1 : 1. Calcium-40's lower n/p ratio makes it more stable.

### Radiation Level Data

| Data point | Counts/min |
|---|---|
| 1 | 21.9 |
| 2 | 17.5 |
| 3 | 17.4 |
| 4 | 19.2 |
| 5 | 19.2 |
| 6 | 43.3 |
| 7 | 76.5 |
| 8 | 79.3 |
| 9 | 93.3 |
| 10 | 67.0 |
| 11 | 65.0 |
| 12 | 54.6 |

# Measuring Naturally Occurring Radiation

**A**s you may know, some common everyday substances are radioactive. In this lab you will investigate the three naturally occurring potassium isotopes found in a common store-bought salt substitute. Two of potassium's isotopes, potassium-39 (93.1%) and potassium-41 (6.89%) are stable. However, potassium-40 (0.01%) decays by beta emission to form stable calcium-40. You will first measure the background radiation level, and then use that information to determine the radiation due to the beta decay of potassium-40. You will also measure radiation at various locations around your school.

### Problem
How can you determine if a substance contains radioactive isotopes?

### Objectives
• **Measure** background radiation and radiation emitted by a radioactive isotope.
• **Compare** the level of background radiation to the level of radiation emitted by a radioactive isotope.

### Materials
CBL system
RADIATIN software program
graphing calculator
link-to-link cable
Student Radiation Monitor

CBL-P adapter
TI-Graphlink cable
petri dish (with lid)
salt substitute or pure potassium chloride (KCl)
balance

### Safety Precautions

• Always wear safety goggles and a lab apron.

### Pre-Lab

1. Read the entire **CHEMLAB**.

2. Prepare all written materials that you will take into the laboratory. Include any necessary safety precautions, procedure notes, and a data table.

3. What is an isotope? A radioactive isotope?

4. Write the nuclear equation for the radioactive decay of potassium-40 by beta emission. Identify the "parent" and "daughter" nuclides in the decay.

5. Using nuclide-stability rules, form a hypothesis that explains why calcium-40 should be a more stable nuclide than potassium-40.

| Radiation Level Data | |
|---|---|
| **Data point** | **Counts/minute** |
| | |
| | |
| | |
| | |
| | |
| | |
| | |

### Procedure

1. Load the program RADIATIN into the graphing calculator.

2. Connect the graphing calculator to the CBL system using the link-to-link cable. Connect the CBL system to the Student Radiation Monitor using the CBL-P adapter. Turn on all devices. Set the Student Radiation Monitor on the audio setting and place it on top of an empty petri dish.

**832** Chapter 25 Nuclear Chemistry

### Procedure
• The best data are obtained if you can get the Geiger tube as close to the KCl as you can without touching the KCl. Have students mound up the KCl in the petri dish to accomplish this. KCl radiation levels run about 2 to 4 times higher than background radiation levels.

• You can reuse the KCl indefinitely. Put out a container where students can put used KCl.
• The KCl can be reused by other classes.

### Expected Results
See the data table for sample results. For the sample data, points 1 to 5 were background radiation levels and points 6 to 12 were KCl radiation levels.

3. Start the RADIATIN program. Go to MAIN MENU. Select 4:SET NO. SAMPLE. Choose 20 for the number of samples in each reading. Press ENTER.

4. Select 1:COLLECT DATA from the MAIN MENU. Select 4:TRIGGER/PROMPT from the COLLECTING MODE menu. Press ENTER to begin collecting data. After a few seconds, the calculator will ask you to enter a PROMPT. Enter 1 (because this is the first data point) and press ENTER. Choose 1:MORE DATA under TRIGGER/PROMPT.

5. Press ENTER to begin the next data point. A graph will appear. When asked to enter the next PROMPT, enter the number that appears at the top right corner of the calculator screen, and then press ENTER. Choose 1:MORE DATA under TRIGGER/PROMPT.

6. Repeat step 5 until you have at least five data points. This set of data is the background level of radiation from natural sources.

7. Use the balance to measure out 10.0 g salt substitute or pure potassium chloride (KCl). Pour the substance into the center of the petri dish so that it forms a small mound. Place the Student Radiation Monitor on top of the petri dish so that the Geiger Tube is positioned over the mound. Repeat step 5 until you have at least five data points.

8. When you are finished collecting data, choose 2:STOP AND GRAPH under TRIGGER/PROMPT. The data points (PROMPTED) are stored in L1, the counts per minute (CTS/MIN) are stored in L2. Press ENTER to view a graph of data.

## Cleanup and Disposal

1. Return the salt substitute or potassium chloride (KCl) used in the experiment to the container prepared by your instructor.

2. Disconnect the lab setup and return all equipment to its proper place.

## Analyze and Conclude

1. **Collecting Data** Record the data found in L1 and L2 (STAT, EDIT) in the Radiation Level Data table.

2. **Graphing Data** Graph the data from L1 and L2. Use the graph from the graphing calculator as a guide.

3. **Interpreting Data** What is the average background radiation level in counts/minute?

4. **Interpreting Data** What is the average radiation level in counts/minute for the potassium-40 isotope found in the salt substitute?

5. **Observing and Inferring** How can you explain the difference between the background radiation level and the radiation level of the salt substitute?

6. **Thinking Critically** Is the data for the background radiation and the radiation from the potassium-containing sample consistent or random in nature? Propose an explanation for the pattern or lack of pattern seen in the data.

7. **Error Analysis** Describe several ways to improve the experimental procedure so it yields more accurate radiation level data.

## Real-World Chemistry

1. Arrange with your teacher to plan and perform a field investigation using the experimental setup from this experiment to measure the background level radiation at various points around school or around town. Propose an explanation for your findings.

2. Using the procedure in this lab, determine if other consumer products contain radioisotopes. Report on your findings.

CHEMLAB    833

## Analyze and Conclude

1. See data table.
2. Check that student graphs accurately portray their data.
3. The average for background radiation (data points 1 to 5) is 19.0 counts/min.
4. The average for KCl radiation level (data points 6 to 12) is 68.4 counts/min.
5. Since the KCl has radiation levels higher than background radiation levels, it must contain an isotope undergoing radioactive decay.
6. A pattern of randomness may appear when collecting data for radiation levels for both background radiation and potassium-40. Radiation decay is a chance event, so levels measured over a short period of time are more likely to be random. If measured over a sufficient period of time, the data will take on a bell-shaped curve.
7. Accuracy of measuring a radiation level can be improved by collecting data over a longer period of time.

## Real-World Chemistry

1. Findings and explanations will vary. Higher radiation levels may be found near industrial sites that use radioisotopes in the manufacture of products.
2. Results will vary depending upon the consumer product tested.

### ✔ Assessment

**Performance** Have student groups repeat the experiment after placing the KCl sample inside a lead-lined film protection bag. These bags are used by travelers to protect photographic film from being damaged by airport X-ray devices. Groups should conclude about the effectiveness of the bags in blocking beta radiation. Use the Performance Task Assessment List for Carrying Out a Strategy and Collecting Data in **PASC**, p. 25.

## Resource Manager

**ChemLab and MiniLab Worksheets,** pp. 99–101  L2

## Purpose

Students will learn about the potential health risk of radon gas exposure and explore how radon enters homes and other structures.

## Background

Radon is a highly radioactive gas found in varying amounts in rock strata and soils. It is produced through the radioactive decay of the element uranium. One product of this decay is radium, which further decays to produce radon gas. The continued emission of alpha particles results in the production of polonium, lead, and bismuth. The carcinogenic effects of radon on human lung tissue have been well documented over the past 25 years. Radon exposure is believed to be a major cause of lung cancer in the United States, second only to smoking.

## Teaching Strategies

• Ask students to give examples of other environmental issues with potentially negative effects. *greenhouse effect, ozone depletion* Ask them to discuss those risks compared with the risk posed by radon.
• Have students research a variety of methods used to detect and lessen radon levels in the home.

## Investigating the Issue

1. Local levels will vary. Some communities require radon testing in homes before finalization of real estate transactions.
2. Students living in areas with high radon levels will be more likely to feel that radon testing is important and should be mandated than students who live in low-risk areas. Most students will agree that high radon levels in a home or school should be mitigated immediately.

## The Realities of Radon

In the late 1800s, doctors identified lung cancer as a prevalent cause of mine worker deaths throughout the world. It became clear that something in the air of underground mines was related to the deaths. Today scientists believe radon gas was the primary culprit. The heaviest known gas, with a density nine times greater than air, radon is naturally occurring and highly radioactive. Regardless of your location, radon, a gas you cannot see, smell, or taste, is an ever-present part of the air you breathe.

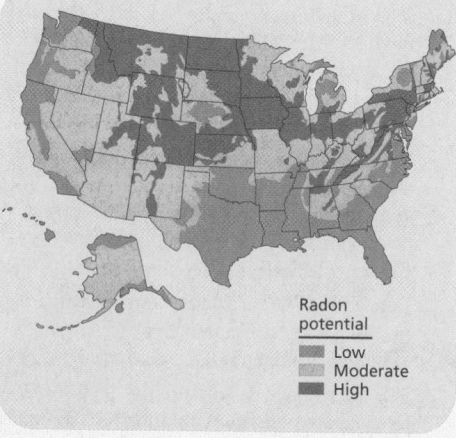

Radon potential
- Low
- Moderate
- High

### Why be concerned?

Radon is produced when uranium-238, an element present in many rock layers and soil, decays. Because buildings are built on top of soil, and sometimes constructed of stone and brick, radon gas often accumulates inside.

Radon exposure is the second leading cause of lung cancer in the United States, causing about 14 000 deaths annually. Because of the health threat posed by radon, Congress mandated the U.S. Environmental Protection Agency (EPA) make the reduction of indoor radon gas levels a national goal.

Although radon is an inert gas, its decay produces highly radioactive heavy metals. Polonium is one of the radioactive decay products. Breathing radon-containing air results in the collection of polonium in the tissues of the lungs. Inside the lungs, the polonium decays further, emitting alpha particles and gamma radiation. This radiation damages the cells of the lungs.

### How much is too much?

The average outdoor radiation level due to radon is 0.04 pCi/L (picocuries per liter of air). The maximum level considered to be safe is 4.0 pCi/L.

### What is your risk factor?

Examine the map showing the risk of radon in your area of the United States. Are you in a high-risk area? Fortunately, only 8% of U.S. homes are believed to have radon levels exceeding 4 pCi/L. Homes at highest risk include those built on uranium-rich rock and thin, dry, permeable soil. However, even buildings in high-risk areas may be safe if there are few pathways into the building, or if the building's air is regularly exchanged with the outside air. People worried about radon levels can test the quality of their air. Do-it-yourself kits are available that test for high levels of radon.

### Investigating the Issue

1. **Communicating Ideas** Research radon levels in your state, as well as any radon-related regulations governing real estate transactions. Draw a map of your state. Shade the various levels of radon. Identify your area.

2. **Debating the Issue** Knowing the radon levels in your area, should it be mandated that property inspections include radon testing prior to a sale? If radon levels above 4 pCi/L are discovered at your home or school, how should the problem be addressed?

**Chemistry** Online

Visit the Chemistry Web site at **chemistrymc.com** to find links to more information about radon exposure.

## Internet Address Book

**Chemistry** Online    Note Internet addresses that you find useful in the space below for quick reference.

_____

_____

_____

_____

_____

## Summary

### 25.1 Nuclear Radiation

- Wilhelm Roentgen discovered X rays in 1895. Henri Becquerel, Marie Curie and Pierre Curie pioneered the fields of radioactivity and nuclear chemistry.

- Radioisotopes, isotopes of atoms with unstable nuclei, emit radiation to attain more stable atomic configurations.

### 25.2 Radioactive Decay

- The strong nuclear force acts on protons and neutrons within a nucleus to hold the nucleus together.

- The neutron-to-proton (n/p) ratio of a nucleus affects its stability. Stable n/p ratios range from 1 : 1 for small atoms to 1.5 : 1 for the largest atoms.

- Atomic number and mass number are conserved in nuclear reactions and equations.

- **Table 25-3** summarizes the characteristics of the five primary types of radioactive decay.

### 25.3 Transmutation

- The conversion of an atom of one element to an atom of another by radioactive decay processes is called transmutation. Induced transmutation is the process of bombarding nuclei with high-velocity charged particles in order to create new elements.

- A half-life is the time required for half the atoms in a radioactive sample to decay. Every radioisotope has a characteristic half-life.

- Radiochemical dating is a technique for determining the age of an object by measuring the amount of certain radioisotopes remaining in the object.

### 25.4 Fission and Fusion of Atomic Nuclei

- Nuclear fission is the splitting of large nuclei into smaller more stable fragments. Fission reactions release large amounts of energy.

- In a chain reaction, one reaction induces others to occur. A sufficient mass of a fissionable material must be present for a fission chain reaction to occur.

- Nuclear reactors make use of nuclear fission reactions to generate steam. The steam is used to drive turbines that produce electrical power.

- Nuclear fusion is the process of binding smaller nuclei into a single larger and more stable nucleus. Fusion reactions release large amounts of energy, but require extremely high temperatures.

### 25.5 Applications and Effects of Nuclear Reactions

- Geiger counters, scintillation counters, and film badges are used to detect and measure radiation.

- Radiotracers, which emit non-ionizing radiation, are used to diagnose disease and to analyze complex chemical reaction mechanisms.

- Both short-term and long-term radiation exposure can cause damage to living cells.

## Key Equations and Relationships

- Exponential decay function:
$$\text{Amount remaining} = (\text{Initial amount})\left(\frac{1}{2}\right)^{n} \quad \text{or} \quad \text{Amount remaining} = (\text{Initial amount})\left(\frac{1}{2}\right)^{t/T} \quad (\text{p. 817})$$

## Vocabulary

- band of stability (p. 811)
- breeder reactor (p. 825)
- critical mass (p. 823)
- electron capture (p. 812)
- half-life (p. 817)
- induced transmutation (p. 815)
- ionizing radiation (p. 827)
- mass defect (p. 822)

- nuclear fission (p. 822)
- nuclear fusion (p. 826)
- nucleon (p. 810)
- positron (p. 812)
- positron emission (p. 812)
- radioactive decay series (p. 814)
- radiochemical dating (p. 819)
- radioisotope (p. 807)

- radiotracer (p. 828)
- thermonuclear reaction (p. 826)
- transmutation (p. 815)
- transuranium element (p. 815)
- strong nuclear force (p. 810)
- X ray (p. 809)

## Using the Vocabulary

To reinforce chapter vocabulary, have students write a sentence using each term. **L2** **ELL**

## Review Strategies

- Have students summarize the five major types of radioactive decay. **L2**

- Have students write balanced nuclear equations that show each type of nuclear decay. **L2**

- Have students describe the variable changes that can be manipulated in a radioactive decay problem. **L2**

- Problems from Appendix A or the **Supplemental Problems** booklet can be used for review. **L2**

VOCABULARY
PuzzleMaker CHEMISTRY ONLINE

For additional help with vocabulary, have students access the Vocabulary PuzzleMaker online.

chemistrymc.com/
vocabulary_puzzlemaker

Chemistry Online

EXAMVIEW® PRO

## Use ExamView® Pro Testmaker CD-ROM to:

- Create **multiple versions** of tests.
- Create **modified** tests with one mouse click for struggling students.
- **Edit** existing questions and add your own questions.
- **Build** tests based on national curriculum standards.

National Science Content Standards

Page 832–835
UCP.1, UCP.3; A.1; B.1, B.6; F.1, F.5; E.1

## Concept Mapping

**35.** 1. atoms; 2. stable; 3. unstable; 4. do not decay; 5.–9. alpha decay, beta decay, gamma emission, electron capture, positron emission

## Mastering Concepts

**36.** discovered uranium to be a source of radiation and isolated Po and Ra as elements

**37.** Nuclear reactions release more energy per mole. Nuclear reactions involve neutrons and protons, whereas chemical reactions involve electrons.

**38.** a: 2, 4, 5; b: 1; c: 3, 6

**39.** a proton or a neutron

**40.** Identical except for charge; electron has –1 charge, positron has +1 charge.

**41.** Chemical equation: all atoms are conserved, same elements are on each side of reaction arrow. Nuclear equation: mass number and atomic number are conserved, new elements form.

**42.** The strong nuclear force binds nucleons together.

**43.** In positron emission, a proton turns into a neutron: $^1_1p \rightarrow ^1_0n + ^0_1\beta$. In electron capture, a proton merges with an inner-shell electron: $^1_1p + ^0_{-1}e \rightarrow ^1_0n$.

**44.** For smaller atoms, the n/p ratio of stable isotopes is about 1 : 1. As atoms become larger, n/p ratio increases to about 1.5 : 1. Isotopes with ratios outside these values are likely to be radioactive.

**45.** Isotopes lying outside the band will spontaneously decay.

**46.** A family of decay reactions that continue until a stable, non-radioactive isotope is formed.

**Chemistry Online**

Go to the Chemistry Web site at chemistrymc.com *for additional Chapter 25 Assessment.*

## Concept Mapping

**35.** Complete the concept map using the following terms: positron emission, alpha decay, atoms, unstable, do not decay, beta decay, stable, gamma emission, and electron capture.

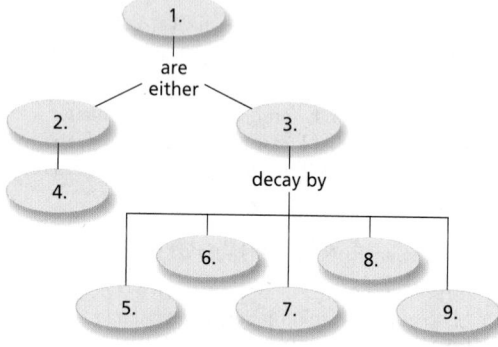

## Mastering Concepts

**36.** What did the Curies contribute to the field of radioactivity and nuclear chemistry? (25.1)

**37.** Compare and contrast chemical reactions and nuclear reactions in terms of energy changes and the particles involved. (25.1)

**38.** Match each numbered choice on the right with the correct radiation type on the left. (25.1)

    **a.** alpha     **1.** high speed electrons
    **b.** beta      **2.** 2+ charge
    **c.** gamma    **3.** no charge
                  **4.** helium nucleus
                  **5.** blocked very easily
                  **6.** electromagnetic radiation

**39.** What is a nucleon? (25. 2)

**40.** What is the difference between a positron and an electron? (25.2)

**41.** Describe the differences between a balanced nuclear equation and a balanced chemical equation. (25.2)

**42.** What is the strong nuclear force? On what particles does it act? (25.2)

**43.** Explain the difference between positron emission and electron capture. (25.2)

**44.** Explain the relationship between an atom's neutron-to-proton ratio and its stability. (25.2)

**45.** What is the significance of the band of stability? (25.2)

**46.** What is a radioactive decay series? When does the decay series end? (25.2)

**47.** What scientist performed the first induced transmutation reaction? What element was synthesized in the reaction? (25.3)

**48.** Define transmutation. Are all nuclear reactions also transmutation reactions? Explain. (25.3)

**49.** Why are some radioisotopes found in nature, while others are not? (25.3)

**50.** What are some of the characteristics of transuranium elements? (25.3)

**51.** Using the band of stability diagram shown in **Figure 25-8** would you expect $^{39}_{20}Ca$ to be radioactive? Explain. (25.3)

**52.** Carbon-14 dating makes use of a specific ratio of two different radioisotopes. Define the ratio used in carbon-14 dating. Why is this ratio constant in living organisms? (25.3)

**53.** Why is carbon-14 dating limited to objects that are approximately 24 000 years old or less? (25.3)

**54.** What is a mass defect? (25.4)

**55.** Describe some of the current limitations of fusion as a power source. (25.4)

**56.** Describe some of the problems of using fission as a power source. (25.4)

**57.** What is a chain reaction? Give an example of a nuclear chain reaction. (25.4)

**58.** How is binding energy per nucleon related to mass number? (25.4)

**59.** Explain how binding energy per nucleon is related to fission and fusion reactions. (25.4)

**60.** Discuss how the amount of a fissionable material present affects the likelihood of a chain reaction. (25.4)

**61.** Explain the purpose of control rods in a nuclear reactor. (25.4)

**62.** What is a breeder reactor? Why were breeder reactors developed? (25.4)

**63.** Why does nuclear fusion require so much heat? How is heat contained within a tokamak reactor? (25.4)

**64.** What is ionizing radiation? (25.5)

chemistrymc.com/chapter_test

**47.** Ernest Rutherford; O-17

**48.** Transmutation is the changing of an atom's nucleus such that a new element is formed. Most, but not all nuclear reactions are transmutations.

### Resource Manager

**Chapter Assessment,** pp. 145–150 **L2**
**Supplemental Problems,** Ch. 25
**ExamView® Pro CD-ROM**
**MindJogger Videoquizzes DVD/VHS**
**Solutions Manual,** Ch. 25
**Chemistry Interactive CD-ROM,**
  Ch. 25 quiz

**65.** What is the difference between somatic and genetic damage? (25.5)

**66.** What property of isotopes allows radiotracers to be useful in studying chemical reactions? (25.5)

**67.** List several applications that involve phosphors. (25.5)

## Mastering Problems
### Radioactive Decay (25.2)

**68.** Calculate the neutron-to-proton ratio for each of the following atoms.

   **a.** tin-134      **d.** nickel-63

   **b.** silver-107    **e.** carbon-14

   **c.** carbon-12    **f.** iron-61

**69.** Complete the following equations:

   **a.** $^{214}_{83}\text{Bi} \rightarrow {}^{4}_{2}\text{He} + ?$

   **b.** $^{239}_{93}\text{Np} \rightarrow {}^{239}_{94}\text{Pu} + ?$

**70.** Write a balanced nuclear equation for the alpha decay of americium-241.

**71.** Write a balanced nuclear equation for the beta decay of bromine-84.

**72.** Write a balanced nuclear equation for the beta decay of selenium-75.

### Induced Transmutation (25.3)

**73.** Write a balanced nuclear equation for the induced conversion of carbon-13 to carbon-14.

**74.** Write the balanced nuclear equation for the alpha particle bombardment of $^{253}_{99}\text{Es}$. One of the reaction products is a neutron.

**75.** Write a balanced nuclear equation for the induced transmutation of uranium-238 into californium-246 by bombardment with carbon-12.

**76.** Write the balanced nuclear equation for the alpha particle bombardment of plutonium-239. The reaction products include a hydrogen atom and two neutrons.

### Half-Life (25.3)

**77.** The half-life of tritium ($^{3}_{1}\text{H}$) is 12.3 years. If 48.0 mg of tritium is released from a nuclear power plant during the course of a mishap, what mass of the nuclide will remain after 49.2 years? After 98.4 years?

**78.** Technetium-104 has a half-life of 18.0 minutes. How much of a 165.0 g sample remains after 90.0 minutes?

**79.** Manganese-56 decays by beta emission and has a half-life of 2.6 hours. How many half-lives are there in 24 hours? How many mg of a 20.0 mg sample will remain after five half-lives?

**80.** A 20.0 g sample of thorium-234 has a half-life of 25 days. How much will remain as a percentage of the original sample after 90 days?

**81.** The half-life of polonium-218 is 3.0 minutes. If you start with 20.0 g, how long will it be before only 1.0 g remains?

**82.** A sample of an unknown radioisotope exhibits 8540 decays per second. After 350.0 minutes, the number of decays has decreased to 1250 per second. What is the half-life?

**83.** Phosphorous-32 has a half-life of 14.32 days. Write and graph an equation for the amount remaining of phosphorous-32 after $t$ days if the sample initially contains 150.0 mg of phosphorous-32.

**84.** Plot the exponential decay curve for a period of five half-lives for the decay of thorium-234 given in Problem 80. How much time has elapsed when 30% of the original sample remains?

**85.** A rock once contained 1.0 mg of uranium-238, but now contains only 0.257 mg. Given that the half-life for uranium-238 is $4.5 \times 10^9$ y, how old is the rock?

## Mixed Review

*Sharpen your problem-solving skills by answering the following.*

**86.** A sample initially contains 150.0 mg of radon-222. After 11.4 days, the sample contains 18.7 mg of radon-222. Calculate the half-life.

**87.** Write a balanced nuclear equation for the positron emission of nitrogen-13.

**88.** Describe the penetration power of alpha, beta, and gamma radiation.

**89.** Plot the exponential decay curve for a period of six half-lives using the data given for technetium-104 in Problem 78. How much time has elapsed when 60% of the original sample remains?

**90.** What information about an atom can you use to predict whether or not it will be radioactive?

**91.** A bromine-80 nucleus can decay by gamma emission, positron emission, or electron capture. What is the product nucleus in each case?

**92.** Explain how a Geiger counter measures levels of ionizing radiation present.

**93.** The half-life of plutonium-239 is 24 000 years. What fraction of nuclear waste generated today will be present in the year 3000?

**49.** Radioisotopes in nature have very long half-lives. Short-lived radioisotopes decay too quickly to exist in significant quantities.

**50.** radioactive, short half-lives, alpha emitters

**51.** Ca-39 is likely to be radioactive, since it lies just below the band of stability.

**52.** C-14 : C-12; Ratio is constant in living organisms because they assimilate new C-14 into their cells, thus replenishing C-14 lost to decay.

**53.** After 24 000 years (~5 half-lives), only about 3% of the original C-14 remains. Amounts less than this are difficult to measure.

**54.** difference between mass of the nucleons summed separately and the actual mass of the nucleus.

**55.** Answers may include generation of sufficient temperature and containing the reaction.

**56.** Answers may include safety, disposal of radioactive fuel and waste products, and the high cost of building the power plant.

**57.** A chain reaction occurs when a reaction produces one or more of the particles needed as a reactant. An example is the fission of U-235 by absorption of a neutron.

**58.** The binding energy per nucleon reaches a maximum value for mass numbers around 60 amu.

**59.** Fusion of light nuclei produces a product whose mass number is closer to

60. Fission of a heavy nucleus produces isotopes whose mass numbers are closer to 60.

**60.** In a subcritical mass, too few nuclei are present to continue the reaction. In a supercritical mass, the numerous nuclei produce an escalating reaction.

**61.** Control rods absorb neutrons from the fission reaction, allowing the rate of reaction to be controlled.

**62.** Breeder reactors produce more fissionable fuel than they use. They were developed because fissionable fuels are relatively scarce.

**63.** Extremely high temperatures are needed to fuse the positively charged nuclei together. Magnetic fields contain the hot fusion reaction.

**64.** Ionizing radiation is radiation powerful enough to strip electrons off molecules, forming ions.

**National Science Content Standards**

Pages 836–837
UCP.1, UCP.3; B.1, B.6; F.5

**65.** Genetic damage involves changing the DNA sequence in cells, thus affecting future generations. Somatic damage affects cells, but does not affect offspring.

**66.** Radiotracers have the same chemical properties as the stable isotopes of that element.

**67.** TV and computer screens, scintillation counters, "glowing" watch faces

## Mastering Problems

Complete solutions to Chapter Assessment problems can be found in the **Solutions Manual.**

### Radioactive Decay (25.2)
**Level 1**
**68. a.** 1.68   **c.** 1.0   **e.** 1.33
    **b.** 1.28   **d.** 1.25   **f.** 1.35
**69. a.** $^{210}_{81}Tl$   **b.** $^{0}_{-1}\beta$

**Level 2**
**70.** $^{241}_{95}Am \rightarrow ^{4}_{2}He + ^{237}_{93}Np$
**71.** $^{84}_{35}Br \rightarrow ^{0}_{-1}\beta + ^{84}_{36}Kr$
**72.** $^{75}_{34}Se \rightarrow ^{0}_{-1}\beta + ^{75}_{35}Br$

### Induced Transmutation (25.3)
**Level 1**
**73.** $^{13}_{6}C + ^{1}_{0}n \rightarrow ^{14}_{6}C$
**74.** $^{253}_{99}Es + ^{4}_{2}He \rightarrow ^{1}_{0}n + ^{256}_{101}Md$

**Level 2**
**75.** $^{238}_{92}U + ^{12}_{6}C \rightarrow ^{246}_{98}Cf + 4^{1}_{0}n$
**76.** $^{239}_{94}Pu + ^{4}_{2}He$
    $\rightarrow ^{1}_{1}H + 2^{1}_{0}n + ^{240}_{95}Am$

### Half-Life (25.3)
**Level 1**
**77.** 3.00 mg; 0.188 mg
**78.** 5.156 g
**79.** 9.2 half-lives; 0.625 mg
**80.** 8.25%
**81.** 13 minutes

**Level 2**
**82.** 126 minutes
**83.** Amount remaining = (150.0 mg)(1/2)$^{t/14.32\ days}$; The shape of the graph will be similar to Figure 25–13.
**84.** 6 g (30%) remains after

## Thinking Critically

**94. Making and Using Graphs** Thorium-231 decays to lead-207 in a stepwise fashion by emitting the following particles in successive steps: β, α, α, β, α, α, α, β, β, α. Plot each step of the decay series on a graph of mass number versus atomic number. Label each plotted point with the symbol of the radioisotope.

Plot the decay series from Th-230 to Pb-207

**95. Analyzing Information** Scientists often use heavy ion bombardment to produce new elements. Balance the following nuclear reactions involving heavy ion bombardments.

    **a.** $^{6}_{3}Li + ^{63}_{28}Ni \rightarrow ?$
    **b.** $^{252}_{98}Cf + ^{10}_{5}B \rightarrow ?$

**96. Applying Concepts** Chemical treatment is often used to destroy harmful chemicals. For example, bases neutralize acids. Why can't chemical treatment be applied to destroy the fission products produced in a nuclear reactor?

**97. Applying Concepts** A radioactive decay series that begins with $^{237}_{93}Np$ ends with the formation of stable $^{209}_{83}Bi$. How many alpha emissions and how many beta emissions are involved in the sequence of radioactive decays?

## Writing in Chemistry

**98.** Research and report on the lives of Marie Curie and her daughter, Irene Curie Joliot. What kind of scientific training did each receive? What was it like to be a female chemist in their time? What other discoveries did each make beyond those made in the field of nuclear chemistry?

**99.** Research and write a report on the nuclear power plant accidents that occurred at Three Mile Island in Pennsylvania and Chernobyl in the former Soviet

Union. What went wrong in each case? How much radiation escaped and entered the surrounding environment? What were the health effects of the released radiation?

**100.** Evaluate environmental issues associated with nuclear wastes. Research the Yucca Mountain nuclear waste disposal plan, the Hanford nuclear site, or a local nuclear facility. Prepare a poster or multimedia presentation on your findings.

## Cumulative Review

*Refresh your understanding of previous chapters by answering the following.*

**101.** Identify each of the following as a chemical property or a physical property. (Chapter 3)
    **a.** The element mercury has a high density.
    **b.** Solid carbon dioxide sublimes at room temperature.
    **c.** Zinc oxidizes when exposed to air.
    **d.** Sucrose is a white crystalline solid.

**102.** Why does the second period of the periodic table contain eight elements? (Chapter 6)

**103.** Draw the following molecules and show the locations of hydrogen bonds between the molecules. (Chapter 9)
    **a.** two water molecules
    **b.** two ammonia molecules
    **c.** one water molecule and one ammonia molecule

**104.** Name the process taking place in each situation described below. (Chapter 13)
    **a.** a solid air freshener cube getting smaller and smaller
    **b.** dewdrops forming on leaves in the morning
    **c.** steam rising from a hot spring
    **d.** a crust of ice forming on top of a pond

**105.** If the volume of a sample of chlorine gas is 4.5 L at 0.65 atm and 321 K, what volume will the gas occupy at STP? (Chapter 14)

**106.** The temperature of 756 g of water in a calorimeter increases from 23.2°C to 37.6°C. How much heat was given off by the reaction in the calorimeter? (Chapter 16)

**107.** Explain what a buffer is and why buffers are found in body fluids. (Chapter 19)

**108.** Explain how the structure of benzene can be used to explain its unusually high stability compared to other unsaturated cyclic hydrocarbons. (Chapter 22)

~44 days; see Solutions Manual for graph.
**85.** 8.8 × 10⁹ years

## Mixed Review
**86.** 3.80 days
**87.** $^{13}_{7}N \rightarrow ^{0}_{1}\beta + ^{13}_{6}C$
**88.** Skin easily stops alpha particles. Thin sheets of metal stop beta particles. Gamma radiation is partially blocked by lead or concrete.

**89.** 60% remains at ~0.75T; see Solutions Manual for graph.
**90.** Calculate the isotope's n/p ratio.
**91.** gamma emission: the isotope remains Br-80, but is more stable; positron emission: $^{80}_{34}Se$; electron capture: $^{80}_{34}Se$
**92.** Radiation ionizes gas molecules inside the tube, producing an electrical current. The current flow is proportional to the radiation present.

*Use these questions and the test-taking tip to prepare for your standardized test.*

**1.** All of the following are true of alpha particles EXCEPT

   **a.** they have the same composition as helium nuclei.
   **b.** they carry a charge of $2+$.
   **c.** they are more penetrating than $\beta$ particles.
   **d.** they are represented by the symbol $^4_2He$.

**2.** In the first steps of its radioactive decay series, thorium-232 decays to radium-228, which then decays to actinium-228. What are the balanced nuclear equations describing these first two decay steps?

   **a.** $^{232}_{90}Th \rightarrow ^{228}_{88}Ra + ^{0}_{-1}\beta$,
       $^{228}_{88}Ra \rightarrow ^{228}_{89}Ac + ^{0}_{1}\beta$
   **b.** $^{232}_{90}Th \rightarrow ^{228}_{88}Ra + ^{4}_{2}He$,
       $^{228}_{88}Ra \rightarrow ^{228}_{89}Ac + ^{0}_{-1}\beta$
   **c.** $^{232}_{90}Th \rightarrow ^{228}_{88}Ra + 2\,^{0}_{-1}\beta$,
       $^{228}_{88}Ra \rightarrow ^{228}_{89}Ac + ^{0}_{-1}\beta$
   **d.** $^{232}_{90}Th \rightarrow ^{228}_{88}Ra + ^{4}_{2}He$,
       $^{228}_{88}Ra + ^{0}_{-1}e \rightarrow ^{228}_{89}Ac$

**3.** In the early 1930s, van de Graaf generators were used to generate neutrons by bombarding stable beryllium atoms with deuterons ($^2_1H$), the nuclei of deuterium atoms. A neutron is released in the reaction. Which is the balanced nuclear equation describing this induced transmutation?

   **a.** $^{9}_{4}Be + ^{2}_{1}H \rightarrow ^{10}_{5}B + ^{1}_{0}n$
   **b.** $^{6}_{4}Be + ^{2}_{1}H \rightarrow ^{8}_{5}B + ^{1}_{0}n$
   **c.** $^{9}_{4}Be \rightarrow ^{10}_{5}B + ^{2}_{1}H + ^{1}_{0}n$
   **d.** $^{9}_{4}Be + ^{2}_{1}H \rightarrow ^{11}_{5}B + ^{1}_{0}n$

**4.** Geologists use the decay of potassium-40 in volcanic rocks to determine their age. Potassium-40 has a half-life of $1.26 \times 10^9$ years, so it can be used to date very old rocks. If a sample of rock $3.15 \times 10^8$ years old contains $2.73 \times 10^{-7}$ g of potassium-40 today, how much potassium-40 was originally present in the rock?

   **a.** $2.30 \times 10^{-7}$ g
   **b.** $1.71 \times 10^{-8}$ g
   **c.** $3.25 \times 10^{-7}$ g
   **d.** $4.37 \times 10^{-6}$ g

**Interpreting Graphs** Use **Figure 25-8** on page 811 to answer questions 5–7.

**5.** Why will calcium-35 will undergo positron emission?

   **a.** it lies above the line of stability
   **b.** it lies below the line of stability
   **c.** it has a high neutron-to-proton ratio
   **d.** it has an overabundance of neutrons

chemistrymc.com/standardized_test

**6.** Based on its position relative to the band of stability, $^{80}Zn$ will undergo which of the following?

   **a.** beta decay
   **b.** positron emission
   **c.** electron capture
   **d.** nuclear fusion

**7.** Based on its position relative to the band of stability, phosphorous-26 will transmute into which of the following isotopes in the first step of its radioactive decay series?

   **a.** $^{22}_{13}Al$
   **b.** $^{26}_{16}S$
   **c.** $^{26}_{17}Cl$
   **d.** $^{26}_{14}Si$

**8.** Which of the following is NOT characteristic of a sample of a fissionable element capable of sustaining a chain reaction?

   **a.** The element has a mass number $< 60$.
   **b.** The sample of the element possesses critical mass.
   **c.** The element's atoms have low binding energy per nucleon.
   **d.** The element's nuclei are more stable if split into smaller nuclei.

**9.** The immense amount of energy released by the Sun is due to which of the following reactions occuring within its core?

   **a.** nuclear fission
   **b.** gamma decay
   **c.** nuclear fusion
   **d.** alpha decay

**10.** All of the following are beneficial applications of radioactivity EXCEPT

   **a.** tracing the path of an element through a complex reaction.
   **b.** mutating genetic material using ionizing radiation.
   **c.** diagnosing brain disorders using PET scans.
   **d.** destroying cancer cells with radiation therapy.

┌─────────────────────────────────────┐
│ **TEST-TAKING TIP** │
└─────────────────────────────────────┘

**Don't Be Afraid To Ask For Help** If you're practicing for a test and you find yourself stuck, unable to understand why you got a question wrong, or unable to answer it in the first place, ask someone for help. As long as you ask for help before the test, you'll do fine!

**93.** 97%

## Thinking Critically

**94.** See Solutions Manual for detailed graph.

**95. a.** $^{6}_{3}Li + ^{63}_{28}Ni \rightarrow ^{69}_{31}Ga$
   **b.** $^{252}_{98}Cf + ^{10}_{5}B \rightarrow ^{262}_{103}Lr$

**96.** Chemical reactions do not affect nuclei, thus, the radioisotopes would continue to emit radiation.

**97.** seven alpha decays and four beta decays

## Cumulative Review

**101. a.** physical   **c.** chemical
   **b.** physical   **d.** physical

**102.** Because there are eight electrons in the 2s and 2p orbitals in the second energy level, the period contains eight elements.

**103. a.**

   **b.**

   **c.**

**104. a.** sublimation, **b.** condensation, **c.** evaporation, **d.** solidification

**105.** 2.5 L

**106.** 45.5 kJ

**107.** A buffer is a solution containing a mixture of an acid and its conjugate base that is able to resist changes in pH. Because many biochemical reactions are sensitive to changes in pH, buffers are needed in the body fluids.

**108.** The electron pairs in benzene's double bonds are shared among all six carbon atoms in the ring. Thus, the electrons cannot be pulled away as easily as electrons that are held by only two nuclei.

## Standardized Test Practice

| | | | |
|---|---|---|---|
| **1.** c | **4.** c | **7.** d | **9.** c |
| **2.** b | **5.** b | **8.** a | **10.** b |
| **3.** a | **6.** a | | |

┌─────────────────────────────────────┐
│ National Science Content Standards │
│ **Pages 838–839** │
│ UCP.1, UCP.3; B.1, B.6; E.2, F.5; G.1 │
└─────────────────────────────────────┘

# Resource Manager

| Section | Objectives | Activities/Features |
|---|---|---|
| **Section 26.1**<br>**Earth's Atmosphere**<br>$1\frac{1}{2}$ sessions<br>0 block | 1. **Describe** the structure and composition of Earth's atmosphere.<br>2. **Identify** common chemical reactions in the atmosphere.<br>3. **Analyze** how human activities affect the atmosphere. | **Discovery Lab:** Clarification of Water, p. 841<br>**Careers Using Chemistry:** Environmental Health Inspector, p. 845<br>**Earth Science Connection,** p. 847<br>**MiniLab:** Acid Rain in a Bag, p. 848 |
| **Section 26.2**<br>**Earth's Water**<br>$\frac{1}{2}$ session<br>0 block | 4. **Trace** the cycle of water in the environment.<br>5. **Identify** the chemical composition of seawater.<br>6. **Describe** methods of desalination, and **relate** the shortage of freshwater in some regions to the development of desalination techniques.<br>7. **Outline** the steps of a water-treatment process. | **Biology Connection,** p. 851<br>**ChemLab CBL:** Solar Pond, pp. 862–863 |
| **Section 26.3**<br>**Earth's Crust**<br>$\frac{1}{2}$ session<br>0 block | 8. **Identify** Earth's major regions.<br>9. **List** the major elements in Earth's crust.<br>10. **Describe** the composition of minerals. | |
| **Section 26.4**<br>**Cycles in the Environment**<br>$1\frac{1}{2}$ sessions<br>0 block | 11. **Trace** the pathways of carbon and nitrogen through the environment.<br>12. **Compare** and **contrast** the greenhouse effect and global warming. | **Problem-Solving Lab:** Global warming: fact or fiction? p. 860<br>**ChemLab CBL:** Solar Pond, pp. 862–863<br>**How It Works:** Water Softener, p. 864 |

| National Science Content Standards | State/Local Standards | Reproducible Masters | Transparencies |
|---|---|---|---|
| UCP.1, UCP.2; A.1; B.2, B.3, B.6; E.2; F.4, F.6 | | **Study Guide for Content Mastery,** pp. 151–152 L2 <br> **ChemLab and MiniLab Worksheets,** pp. 103–104 L2 | **Section Focus** Transparency 101 L1 ELL <br> **Teaching** Transparency 77 L2 ELL |
| UCP.1, UCP.2; B.2, B.4, B.6; E.2; F.1, F.3, F.4, F.6 | | **Study Guide for Content Mastery,** p. 153 L2 <br> **ChemLab and MiniLab Worksheets,** pp. 105–107 L2 <br> **Laboratory Manual,** pp. 201–204 L2 | **Section Focus** Transparency 102 L1 ELL <br> **Teaching** Transparency 78 L2 ELL <br> **Math Skills** Transparencies 43, 44 L2 ELL |
| UCP.1, UCP.2; B.2, B.4; E.2; F.3 | | **Study Guide for Content Mastery,** p. 154 L2 | **Section Focus** Transparency 103 L1 ELL |
| UCP.1, UCP.2; A.1; B.1, B.2, B.3, B.4, B.6; E.1, E.2; F.3, F.4, F.5, F.6 | | **Study Guide for Content Mastery,** pp. 155–156 L2 <br> **ChemLab and MiniLab Worksheets,** pp. 105–107 L2 <br> **Challenge Problems,** p. 26 L3 <br> **Small-Scale Laboratory Manual,** pp. 77–80 L2 <br> **Laboratory Manual,** pp. 205–208 L2 | **Section Focus** Transparency 104 L1 ELL <br> **Teaching** Transparencies 79, 80 L2 ELL |

**Key to National Science Content Standards:** UCP = Unifying Concepts and Processes, A = Science as Inquiry, B = Physical Science, C = Life Science, D = Earth and Space Sciences, E = Science and Technology, F = Science in Personal and Social Perspectives, G = History and Nature of Science

Refer to pages 4T–5T of the Teacher Guide for an explanation of the National Science Content Standards correlations.

# Resource Manager

## Materials List

### ChemLab (pages 862–863)

CBL system, graphing calculator, ChemBio program, link-to-link cable, temperature probes (2), 150-watt light bulb, socket and clamp for light bulb, black plastic frozen dinner dish, waterproof tape, table salt, water, hot plate, stirring rod, 250-mL beaker, beaker tongs, TI-Graph link (optional), ring stand and clamp, 250-mL graduated cylinder

### Discovery Lab (page 841)

soil, 600-mL beaker, 400-mL beakers (2), spoons (3), powdered lime (CaO), funnel, filter paper (2), 250-mL beaker, stirring rod, ringstand with ring

### MiniLab (page 848)

petri dish, 1 gallon zip-close plastic bag, white paper, droppers (3), 0.04% bromocresol green indicator, 0.5$M$ KNO$_2$, 1.0$M$ H$_2$SO$_4$, clock or watch

### Demonstration (pages 846–847)

wire coat hanger, wire cutters, black construction paper, 1 gallon zip-close plastic bag, 150-watt flood lamp, petri dish, food coloring, water

## Preparation of Solutions

For a review of solution preparation, see page 46T of the Teacher Guide.

Quantities are for a class of 30 students.

### MiniLab (page 848)

**0.04% bromocresol green indicator** Dissolve 0.1g of bromocresol green powder in 250 mL distilled water. Store in tightly stoppered bottle.

**0.5$M$ KNO$_2$** Dissolve 4.3 g KNO$_2$ in 75 mL distilled water. Make up to 100 mL final volume with distilled water.

**1.0$M$ H$_2$SO$_4$** Slowly add 6 mL 18$M$ sulfuric acid to 100 mL distilled water while stirring constantly. **CAUTION:** Do NOT add the water to the acid.

## Assessment Resources

**Chapter Assessment,** pp. 151–156
**MindJogger Videoquizzes DVD/VHS**
**Alternate Assessment in the Science Classroom**
**ExamView® Pro CD-ROM**
**Solutions Manual,** Chapter 26
**Supplemental Problems,** Chapter 26
**Performance Assessment in the Science Classroom**
**Chemistry Interactive CD-ROM,** Chapter 26 quiz

## Additional Resources

**Spanish Resources** ELL
**Guided Reading Audio Program,** Chapter 26 ELL
**Cooperative Learning in the Science Classroom**
**Lab and Safety Skills in the Science Classroom**
**Lesson Plans**
**Block Scheduling Lesson Plans**
**Chemistrymc.com**

## Glencoe Technology

The following multimedia for this chapter are available from Glencoe.

 **VIDEOTAPE/DVD**
MindJogger Videoquizzes,
Chapter 26

 **CD-ROM**
**Chemistry: Matter and Change**
*Ozone Reactions,* Experiment
*Desalination,* Video
*Nitrogen Fixation,* Video

 **CD-ROM**
**ExamView® Pro
Testmaker**

 **CD-ROM**
**Interactive Chalkboard**

 **CD-ROM**
**TeacherWorks™**

## Multiple Learning Styles

Look for the following icons for strategies that emphasize different learning modalities.

 **Kinesthetic**
Differentiated Instruction, pp. 845, 855; Quick Demo, p. 852

 **Visual-Spatial**
Chemistry Journal, p. 843; Portfolio, p. 850; Identifying Misconceptions, p. 851; Differentiated Instruction, p. 858; Reteach, p. 861

 **Interpersonal**
Reteach, pp. 849, 857; Chemistry Journal, p. 856

 **Intrapersonal**
Enrichment, p. 841; Extension, pp. 842, 851

 **Linguistic**
Check for Understanding, pp. 849, 861; Differentiated Instruction, p. 850; Chemistry Journal, p. 851

 **Logical-Mathematical**
Differentiated Instruction, p. 842; Portfolio, p. 859

## Key to Teaching Strategies

**L1** Level 1 activities should be appropriate for students with learning difficulties.

**L2** Level 2 activities should be within the ability range of all students.

**L3** Level 3 activities are designed for above-average students.

**ELL** ELL activities should be within the ability range of English Language Learners.

**COOP LEARN** Cooperative Learning activities are designed for small group work.

**P** These strategies represent student products that can be placed into a best-work portfolio.

 These strategies are useful in a block scheduling format.

## ✔ Assessment Planner

**Portfolio Assessment**
Assessment, TWE, pp. 845, 861
MiniLab, TWE, p. 848
Portfolio, TWE, pp. 850, 859, 865
Problem-Solving Lab, TWE, p. 860

**Performance Assessment**
Demonstration, TWE, p. 847
Assessment, TWE, p. 853
ChemLab, TWE, p. 863

MiniLab, SE, p. 848
ChemLab, SE, pp. 862–863
Discovery Lab, SE, p. 841

**Knowledge Assessment**
Assessment, TWE, p. 854
Section Assessment, SE, pp. 849, 854, 857, 861
Chapter Assessment, SE, pp. 866–869

**Skill Assessment**
Assessment, TWE, pp. 849, 856, 857

# CHAPTER 26

## Tying to Previous Knowledge

Have students review the following concepts before studying this chapter.

Chapter 3: mixtures

Chapter 10: chemical reactions, solute, solvent, aqueous solution

Chapter 14: combined gas law

Chapter 18: chemical equilibrium

Chapter 19: acids and bases, pH

## Using the Photo

Ask students to identify the components of Earth's satellite image and to estimate the percentage of each component. Students should see three basic divisions: the atmosphere, as evidenced by clouds; the blue water portions (the hydrosphere); and the land portions (the lithosphere). Students will recognize that the greatest coverage is by water (72%).

## INTERACTIVE CHALKBOARD
### with Image Bank

### PowerPoint® Presentations

This CD-ROM is an editable Microsoft® PowerPoint® presentation that includes:
- Section presentations
- Section checks
- Image bank
- Links to Chemistry Online
- All transparencies
- Animations
- Audio

# Chemistry in the Environment

## What You'll Learn

▶ You will apply the concepts you have learned to a study of the chemistry of Earth's environment.

▶ You will explore the ways in which human activities affect the chemical nature of the environment.

## Why It's Important

A knowledge of chemistry will help you develop a deeper appreciation for the environment and an increased awareness of the effect of human activities on Earth's air, land, and water.

## Chemistry Online

Visit the Chemistry Web site at **chemistrymc.com** to find links about chemistry in the environment.

This satellite photo of Earth shows some of our planet's unique features: features that allow it to sustain life.

## DISCOVERY LAB

### Purpose

Students will determine the time required for mud particles to coagulate with lime and settle out.

### Safety and Disposal

Be sure students wear aprons and goggles. The liquid can be decanted and flushed down the drain with large quantities of water. Wrap the solid in a paper towel and place it in a waste container.

### Teaching Strategies

- Discuss with students the need for clean water and the difficulty of obtaining it in many parts of the world.
- Ask students to discuss with family members ways that water can be conserved at home. Students should report these ideas to the class in writing. Prepare a written list of their ideas and distribute it to students.

## DISCOVERY LAB

### Clarification of Water

**M**unicipal water-treatment plants sometimes have to remove mud from the water after rainwater washes dirt into reservoirs. One way to do this is to use chemicals that cause the mud particles to clump together and settle to the bottom of the treatment tank, a process called sedimentation.

#### Safety Precautions

 **Lime is an irritant. It is harmful if inhaled or swallowed.**

#### Procedure

1. Place two spoonfuls of soil into a 600-mL beaker. Add water and stir until the water is muddy.

2. Divide the muddy water into two equal samples in two 400-mL beakers. Label the beakers Lime and Control.

3. Slowly sprinkle a spoonful of powdered lime (CaO) over the surface of the muddy water in the beaker labeled Lime. Do not add lime to the control beaker. Allow both beakers to remain undisturbed. Observe the beakers every five minutes until 15 minutes have elapsed. Record your observations.

4. Filter the treated water through a funnel that contains a paper filter. Collect the filtrate in a 250-mL beaker. Observe whether or not the water samples become clearer after filtration.

5. Repeat step 4 for the control, using a clean filter and beaker.

#### Analysis

How long did it take for the treated water to begin to clear? How did the addition of lime speed up the process of sedimentation? Did the paper filter help the water become clearer?

**Materials**

soil
600-mL beaker
400-mL beakers (2)
spoons (3)
powdered lime (CaO)
funnel
filter paper (2)
250-mL beakers (2)
ring stand with ring
stirring rod

---

## Section 26.1 — Earth's Atmosphere

### Objectives

- **Describe** the structure and composition of Earth's atmosphere.
- **Identify** common chemical reactions in the atmosphere.
- **Analyze** how human activities affect the atmosphere.

### Vocabulary

atmosphere
troposphere
stratosphere

To the best of our knowledge, Earth is the only planet capable of supporting life as we know it. One glance at the photo on the opposite page helps explain why. See those wispy clouds? They are part of a protective envelope, the **atmosphere**, that blankets Earth and plays a key role in maintaining life.

### A Balanced Atmosphere

Take a deep breath. You've just inhaled part of Earth's atmosphere. The atmosphere extends from Earth's surface to hundreds of kilometers into space. A largely gaseous zone, the atmosphere contains the air we breathe, the clouds overhead, and the all-important substances that protect Earth and its inhabitants from the Sun's most powerful radiation. Chemical reactions that occur in the atmosphere help maintain a balance among the different atmospheric gases, but human activities, such as burning fossil fuels, can change this balance.

26.1 Earth's Atmosphere **841**

---

## 1 Focus

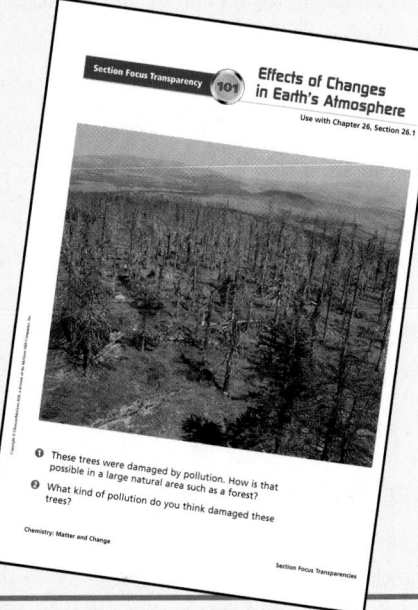

Section Focus Transparency 101

**Effects of Changes in Earth's Atmosphere**
Use with Chapter 26, Section 26.1

❶ These trees were damaged by pollution. How is that possible in a large natural area such as a forest?
❷ What kind of pollution do you think damaged these trees?

Chemistry: Matter and Change

Section Focus Transparencies

### Chapter Themes

The following themes from the National Science Education Standards are covered in this chapter. Refer to page 4T of the Teacher Guide for an explanation of the correlations.
Evidence, models, and explanation (UCP.2)
Change, constancy, and measurement (UCP.3)
Evolution and equilibrium (UCP.4)

---

### Expected Results

After three minutes, the treated water begins to clear. Throughout the 15 minute period, the treated water is clearer than the untreated sample.

### Analysis

The treated water began to clear after three minutes. The untreated water was not clear after 15 minutes. The addition of lime accelerated the process of sedimentation by causing the small mud particles to coagulate. The large clumps then settled to the bottom faster than the small particles. The paper filter helped clarify the water.

**National Science Content Standards**

Pages 840–841
UCP.1, UCP.2; A.1; E.2; F.4

## Discussion

Ask students to classify air as an element, compound, solution, or heterogeneous mixture. How would they support their classification? Air is best classified as a solution because it is two or more substances that are uniformly distributed. At this point, a review of solutes and solvents may be appropriate.

## Figure Caption Question

**Figure 26-1** Which layer of the atmosphere would you expect to have the greatest pressure? The troposphere would exert the greatest amount of pressure because it has the greatest number of molecules per unit volume.

## Extension

 *Intrapersonal* Have students research the layering effect in bodies of water and compare it to that of the atmosphere. **L2**

## Visual Learning

**Table 26-1** Have students note the very small percentages of all atmospheric gases except nitrogen, oxygen, and argon.

### Figure 26-1

Earth's atmosphere has five layers that vary in composition, temperature, altitude, and pressure. Which layer would you expect to have the greatest pressure?

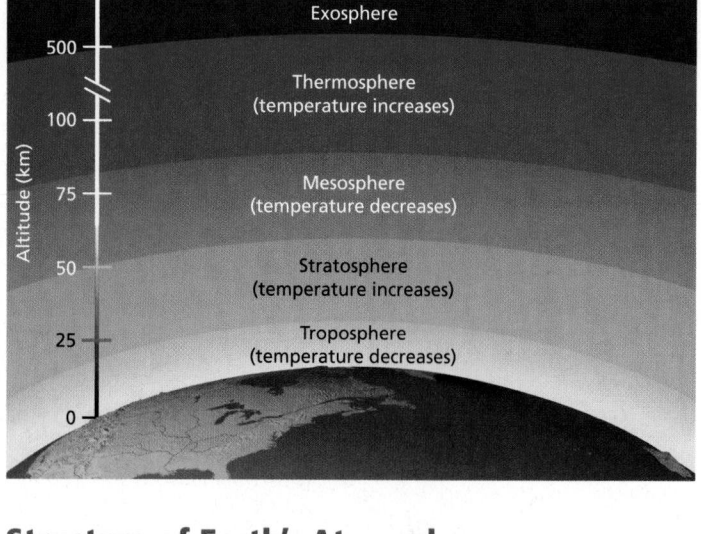

### Table 26-1

| Composition of Dry Air Near Sea Level | |
|---|---|
| **Component** | **Percent** |
| Nitrogen | 78 |
| Oxygen | 20.9 |
| Argon | 0.934 |
| Carbon dioxide | 0.033 |
| Neon | 0.00182 |
| Helium | 0.00052 |
| Methane | 0.00015 |
| Krypton | 0.00011 |
| Hydrogen | 0.00005 |
| Nitrous oxide | 0.00005 |
| Xenon | 0.000009 |

## Structure of Earth's Atmosphere

Earth's atmosphere is divided into five layers based on altitude and temperature variation. The lowest layer—the **troposphere**—extends from Earth's surface to a height of approximately 15 km, as shown in **Figure 26-1**. Temperatures in the troposphere generally decrease with increasing altitude, reaching a minimum of −58°C at 12 km. Rain, snow, wind, and other weather phenomena occur in this layer. We live our entire lives within the troposphere. Only astronauts in spacecraft go beyond its reach.

Above the troposphere, temperatures increase with altitude, reaching a maximum of nearly 2°C at about 50 km. This region of the atmosphere is called the **stratosphere**. The stratosphere contains a layer of ozone, a gas that helps shield Earth's surface from the Sun's harmful ultraviolet radiation. Ozone protects Earth by absorbing solar radiation, which raises the temperature of the stratosphere in the process. You read about the ozone layer in Chapter 1 as you began your study of chemistry.

Beyond the stratosphere lie the mesosphere and the thermosphere. Temperatures in the mesosphere decrease with altitude because there is little ozone in the air to absorb solar radiation. The thermosphere is a region of rapidly increasing temperatures. This is because the relatively few gas molecules in this region have extremely high kinetic energies. At an altitude of about 200 km, temperatures can reach 1000°C.

The outermost layer of the atmosphere is the exosphere. Extending from about 500 km outward, the exosphere marks the transition from Earth's atmosphere to outer space. There is no clear boundary between the two, however. There are simply fewer and fewer molecules of gas at increasingly higher altitudes. Eventually, there are so few molecules that, for all practical purposes, Earth's atmosphere has ended.

## Composition of Earth's Atmosphere

Just as the temperature of the atmosphere varies by altitude, so does its composition. Roughly 75% of the mass of all atmospheric gases is found in the troposphere. Nitrogen and oxygen make up the vast majority of these gases. However, there are a number of minor components. The percent composition of dry air near sea level is summarized in **Table 26-1**.

---

## DIFFERENTIATED INSTRUCTION

### Gifted

 *Logical-Mathematical* Challenge students to derive a way to measure the density of air using a balloon and the information in Table 26-1. Let them develop their own apparatus and procedure. Students can fashion a manometer from glass tubing filled with colored water instead of mercury. They attach a balloon of appropriate diameter (to get a trapped volume of air) to the manometer, then measure the height differential of the water in the manometer. They should convert their reading to a pressure in atmospheres by multiplying by 1 cm Hg/13.6 cm $H_2O$ and adding this to atmospheric pressure (in cm Hg). The average molar mass ($M$) can be determined by multiplying the molar masses of the elements listed in Table 26-1 by their percentages. Next, the ideal gas law can be rearranged into the form $d = MP/RT$. **L3** **COOP LEARN**

**Figure 26-2**

When sunlight strikes dust particles in the atmosphere, it is scattered in all directions. The blue portion of the light is scattered away from your eyes, leaving the reds, oranges, and yellows you see here.

**Quick Demo**

Cover an overhead projector with a piece of paper or cardboard that has a circle about the diameter of a 250-mL beaker cut out. Prepare approximately 150 mL of a saturated solution of sodium thiosulfate, pour it into the beaker, and place it on the overhead where the circle has been cut out. Turn on the overhead. Add a few mL of concentrated sulfuric acid. **CAUTION:** *Acid will burn skin.* As the solution becomes colloidal with precipitated sulfur, it will refract the light and simulate a sunset. **Disposal:** If too much acid is added, sulfur will precipitate out. If this happens, centrifuge it out. Wrap in paper and burn. Flush remaining decanted liquid down the drain.

In addition to gases, the troposphere contains solids in the form of dust, salts, and ice. Dust—tiny particles from Earth's surface, ash, soot, and plant pollen—enters the atmosphere when it is lifted from Earth's surface and carried by wind. The dust particles can cause sunsets to show spectacular colors, as you can see in **Figure 26-2**. Salts are picked up from ocean spray. Ice is present in the form of snowflakes and hailstones. The troposphere also contains liquids, the most common of which is water in the form of droplets found in clouds. Water is the only substance that exists as a solid, liquid, and gas in Earth's atmosphere.

Because Earth has a strong gravitational field, most gases are held relatively close to the surface of the planet. Only lighter gases such as helium and hydrogen rise to the exosphere. These light gases, consisting of molecules that have absorbed radiation from the Sun, move so rapidly that they are able to escape Earth's gravitational field. Thus, there's a small but constant seepage of gases into outer space.

## Chemistry in the Outer Atmosphere

Earth is constantly being bombarded with radiation and high-energy particles from outer space. The short-wavelength, high-energy ultraviolet (UV) radiation is the most damaging to living things. Because this radiation is capable of breaking the bonds in DNA molecules, it can cause cancer and genetic mutations. How can we exist here? Life as we know it is possible primarily because two processes, which occur in the thermosphere and the exosphere, shield us from most of this radiation.

**Photodissociation** Photodissociation is a process in which high-energy ultraviolet solar radiation is absorbed by molecules, causing their chemical bonds to break. In the upper atmosphere, the photodissociation of oxygen absorbs much of the high-energy UV radiation and produces atomic oxygen.

$$O_2(g) + \text{high-energy UV} \rightarrow 2O(g)$$

The amount of atomic oxygen in the atmosphere increases with increasing altitude. Why is this true? Because so much of the UV radiation that enters the atmosphere is absorbed in the photodissociation of oxygen, most of the oxygen above 150 km is in the form of atomic oxygen. Below this altitude, the percentage of atomic oxygen decreases, and most of the oxygen in the troposphere is in the form of $O_2$ molecules.

26.1 Earth's Atmosphere   **843**

**CHEMISTRY JOURNAL**

## Planetary Atmospheres

*Visual-Spatial* Have students research the atmospheric constituents of other planets in our solar system. The *CRC Handbook of Chemistry and Physics* is one possible reference that could be used. Students should prepare a table that shows the substances involved, the percentages of the substances, and some sort of graphic portrayal of the data (circle or bar graph). Finally, students should write a paragraph describing how the different combinations of atmospheric constituents affect the overall properties of that planet. **L2**

**National Science Content Standards**

**Pages 842–843**
UCP.1, UCP.2; B.2, B.3, B.6

**Photoionization** The second process that absorbs high-energy solar radiation is photoionization, which occurs when a molecule or atom absorbs sufficient energy to remove an electron. Molecular nitrogen and oxygen, as well as atomic oxygen, undergo photoionization in the upper atmosphere. Note that a positively charged particle is produced for every negatively charged electron in the atmosphere, so neutrality of charge is maintained.

$$N_2 + \text{high-energy UV} \rightarrow N_2^+ + e^-$$

$$O_2 + \text{high-energy UV} \rightarrow O_2^+ + e^-$$

$$O + \text{high-energy UV} \rightarrow O^+ + e^-$$

Ultraviolet radiation with the very highest energy is absorbed during photodissociation and photoionization in the upper atmosphere. Because most of this harmful radiation does not reach Earth's surface, life can exist.

## Chemistry in the Stratosphere

In addition to light gases, the upper atmosphere—more specifically, the stratosphere—contains a substance called ozone. In Chapter 1, you learned about the ozone layer and how it contributes to shielding Earth's surface from ultraviolet radiation. Now let's examine the chemical reactions that lead to the formation of ozone in the stratosphere.

**Formation of ozone** Although the UV radiation with the very highest energy has been absorbed by photoionization reactions in the outer atmosphere, much of the UV radiation that has sufficient energy to cause photodissociation still reaches the stratosphere. In the stratosphere, these ultraviolet waves are absorbed by $O_2$ molecules, which are more plentiful here than in the upper atmosphere. The $O_2$ molecules are split into two atoms of oxygen. These highly reactive atoms immediately collide with other $O_2$ molecules, forming ozone ($O_3$). The $O_3$ molecule that forms is highly unstable because its bonds contain excess energy that was gained from the UV radiation. To achieve stability, the energized $O_3$ molecule must lose this excess energy by colliding with another atom or molecule, denoted in **Figure 26-3** as molecule $X$, and transferring energy to it. Usually, $N_2$ or $O_2$ molecules are most abundant and serve as energy-absorbing molecules for the reaction.

**Figure 26-3**

Ozone molecules are formed in the stratosphere. Refer to **Table C-1** in Appendix C for a key to atom color conventions.

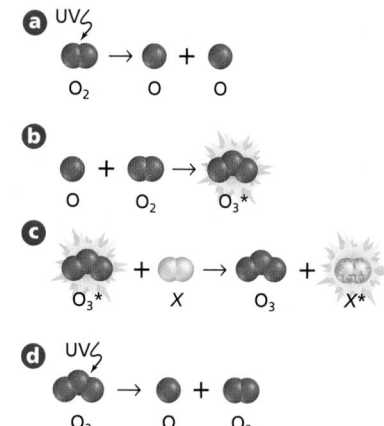

**a** An oxygen molecule forms two oxygen atoms by photodissociation.

**b** An oxygen atom combines with an oxygen molecule to form an energized ozone molecule ($O_3^*$).

**c** The energized ozone molecule collides with molecule $X$. Excess energy is transferred to $X$, producing ozone and an energized $X$ molecule ($X^*$).

**d** The oxygen molecule that forms when ozone photodissociates is available to start the ozone cycle anew.

The formation of $O_3$ and the transfer of excess energy to molecule $X$ are summarized below. Remember that $X$ is most often $N_2$ or $O_2$. An asterisk on a molecule indicates that the molecule is energized.

$$O(g) + O_2(g) \rightarrow O_3^*(g)$$
$$O_3^*(g) + X(g) \rightarrow O_3(g) + X^*(g)$$

The ozone molecule does not last long after being formed. Ozone can absorb high-energy solar radiation and photodissociate back to $O_2$ and $O$, thus starting the ozone cycle anew. If high-energy radiation were not absorbed by ozone and oxygen molecules, it would penetrate the troposphere and possibly damage or kill living things.

**Thinning of the ozone layer** As you read in earlier chapters, F. Sherwood Rowland and Mario Molina have proposed that chlorofluorocarbons (CFCs) are responsible for the thinning of the ozone layer that has been observed in the stratosphere. CFCs such as Freon-11 ($CFCl_3$) and Freon-12 ($CF_2Cl_2$), shown in **Figure 26-4**, have been used as coolants in refrigerators and air conditioners and as propellants in spray cans. They also have been used as foaming agents in the manufacture of some plastics. CFCs are highly stable molecules in the troposphere. After release, they eventually diffuse into the stratosphere, where they become unstable in the presence of the high-energy radiation found at this altitude. The CFCs absorb high-energy UV radiation, causing photodissociation in which the carbon-chlorine bonds in the molecules are broken.

$$CF_2Cl_2(g) + \text{high-energy UV} \rightarrow CF_2Cl(g) + Cl(g)$$

The atomic chlorine formed from this reaction reacts with stratospheric ozone to form chlorine monoxide (ClO) and $O_2$.

$$Cl(g) + O_3(g) \rightarrow ClO(g) + O_2(g)$$

The chlorine monoxide then combines with free oxygen atoms to regenerate free chlorine atoms and oxygen molecules.

$$ClO(g) + O(g) \rightarrow Cl(g) + O_2(g)$$

Because Cl atoms speed up the depletion of ozone and are first used and then re-formed, they function as a catalyst. The net result of these reactions is the conversion of ozone into $O_2$.

$$O_3(g) + O(g) \rightarrow 2O_2(g)$$

Each Cl atom remains in the stratosphere for about two years before it is destroyed in other reactions. During this time, it is capable of catalyzing the breakdown of about 100 000 molecules of ozone.

CFCl₃
Freon-11

CF₂Cl₂
Freon-12

 **LAB**

See page 964 in Appendix E for
**Modeling Ozone Depletion**

**Figure 26-4**

Freon-11 and Freon-12 are very stable compounds due to the strength of the C—F and C—Cl bonds. Because these bonds are so strong, Freon molecules are not easily broken down in the troposphere. In the stratosphere, however, high-energy radiation causes the bonds to break.

26.1 Earth's Atmosphere    **845**

**Figure 26-5**

Ozone distribution in the southern hemisphere was mapped by a NASA satellite from 1980 to 1994. Observe the area of lowest ozone concentration (purple) over Antarctica. How has it changed?

**Figure 26-6**

Smog reduces visibility, irritates the eyes, and damages vegetation. This smog was photographed over New York City.

An estimated several million tons of CFCs have diffused into the stratosphere. A significant change in the loss of ozone was first observed in the mid-1980s, when researchers began tracking an annual thinning of the ozone layer over the South Pole during certain months of the year. **Figure 26-5** shows satellite photos of the progressive thinning of the ozone layer over Antarctica. Scientists have recently found a similar but smaller area of thinning over the North Pole.

Because CFCs appear to play a role in the process of ozone destruction, many countries have stopped manufacturing and using these compounds. It will take many years, however, before the concentration of ozone in the stratosphere returns to its former levels. Why is this true?

## Chemistry in the Troposphere

The composition of the troposphere varies from area to area, mostly as a result of human activities. Some compounds that may be present in only minute quantities in the air above a remote rain forest area may be present in much higher quantities over a large city. If you live in a city, you may have noticed that the air occasionally appears hazy, as it does in **Figure 26-6**. The haze that you see is a form of air pollution more commonly known as smog.

**Photochemical smog** In large cities such as Los Angeles, Denver, and Mexico City, a hazy, brown blanket of smog is created when sunlight reacts with pollutants in the air. Because the smog forms with the aid of light, it is called photochemical smog. The smog-producing pollutants enter the

**Figure 26-7**

The combustion of petroleum in automobiles is a major source of smog. Sunlight acts on the exhaust gases of automobiles, factories, power plants, and homes to produce smog.

## Applying Chemistry

**TECH PREP** Since 1976, all new cars and trucks sold in the United States must be equipped with a catalytic converter, a reaction chamber attached to the exhaust system. The exhaust gases, which are produced from the combustion of fuel, consist of carbon monoxide, nitrogen oxides, and unburned hydrocarbon fragments. The gases and atmospheric oxygen pass over catalysts of finely divided platinum, palladium, or rhodium. The following reactions convert the gases to a more environmentally friendly exhaust product.

$$2NO + 2CO \rightarrow N_2 + 2CO_2$$
$$2NO + 2H_2 \rightarrow N_2 + 2H_2O$$
$$2CO + O_2 \rightarrow 2CO_2$$

troposphere when fossil fuels such as coal, natural gas, and gasoline are burned. **Figure 26-7** shows one of the major sources of smog.

The burning of fossil fuels in internal combustion engines causes nitrogen and oxygen to react, forming nitrogen oxides such as NO and $NO_2$.

$$N_2(g) + O_2(g) \rightarrow 2NO(g)$$
$$2NO(g) + O_2(g) \rightarrow 2NO_2(g)$$

The $NO_2$, in turn, photodissociates in the presence of high-energy UV that penetrates through the upper atmosphere to form atomic oxygen, which combines with $O_2$ to form ozone.

$$NO_2(g) + \text{high-energy UV} \rightarrow NO(g) + O(g)$$
$$O(g) + O_2(g) \rightarrow O_3(g)$$

In the troposphere, ozone can irritate your eyes and lungs and increase your susceptibility to asthma and pneumonia.

Photochemical smog also contains unburned hydrocarbons and carbon monoxide, both of which come from the exhaust of automobile engines. These pollutants can be reduced or eliminated from the atmosphere in a variety of ways. Cleaner running engines and catalytic converters greatly reduce NO and hydrocarbon levels. Strict federal tailpipe emission standards are encouraging automobile manufacturers to develop new cars that are powered by electricity or alternative fuels such as natural gas.

**Acid rain** Sulfur-containing compounds are normally present in small quantities in the troposphere. However, human activities have greatly increased the concentration of these compounds in the air. Sulfur dioxide ($SO_2$) is the most harmful of the sulfur-containing compounds.

Most of the sulfur dioxide in the troposphere is produced when coal and oil that contain high concentrations of sulfur are burned in power plants. The sulfur dioxide that forms is oxidized to sulfur trioxide ($SO_3$) when it combines with either $O_2$ or $O_3$ in the atmosphere. When $SO_3$ reacts with moisture in the air, sulfuric acid is formed.

$$SO_3(g) + H_2O(l) \rightarrow H_2SO_4(aq)$$

## Earth Science
### CONNECTION

**N**ot all soils and bodies of water are equally affected by acid rain. Soils that contain calcium carbonate from limestone and lakes that are surrounded by and lie on top of calcium carbonate-rich soils are protected from much of the acid rain damage. The hydrogen ion in acid rain combines with the dissolved carbonate ions from the limestone to produce hydrogen carbonate ions. The hydrogen carbonate/carbonate solution in the water and soil serves as a buffer, absorbing additional hydrogen ions from acid rain and maintaining a stable pH. Areas that contain silicate rocks and soil are affected to a greater degree by acid rain. Southern Michigan and the Adirondack Mountain region of northern New York are especially susceptible to acid rain damage because of the large percentage of silicate rocks found there.

## Quick Demo

Use a dropper bottle of dilute sulfuric acid on several mineral samples to identify those that are carbonates (make sure to include some limestone or marble in your collection). **CAUTION:** *Acid can burn skin.* Remind students that this is the reaction that occurs when acid rain damages limestone and marble structures. **Disposal:** Flush acid down the drain with water.

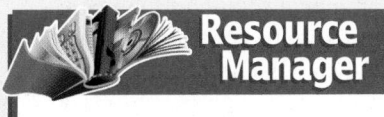

## Resource Manager

**ChemLab and MiniLab Worksheets, pp. 103–104** L2

condenses on the inside surface of the cooler top of the plastic bag. The colorless distilled water runs down the incline and collects at the bottom of the plastic bag.

### Analysis
**1.** What is a still? A still is the apparatus used in distillation.
**2.** How is distilled water different from tap water? Tap water can contain minerals and other impurities.

**3.** Will the solar still operate more efficiently if the days are sunny and warm and the nights cool? Explain. Yes, the solar energy will vaporize the water, which will condense when the air around the bag cools at night.
**4.** How could a solar still be used to aid survival in a desert or at sea? The moisture in cactus or seawater can be distilled to produce drinking water.

## Assessment
**Performance** Have students mass several cut pieces of fruit, melon, or cactus and place them in the still to extract water. Afterwards, the pieces should be massed. Students should calculate the amount of water that was distilled. Use the Performance Task Assessment List for Using Math in Science in **PASC,** p. 29.

**Page 848** What products are produced by the reaction of calcium carbonate and acid rain?
calcium sulfate, carbon dioxide, and water

**Page 849** What do you think might account for the extreme acidity of rain (in West Virginia)?
the burning of high sulfur coal in more western states, such as Ohio

## miniLAB

### Purpose
Students will simulate formation of acid rain from a point source of pollution.

### Process Skills
Observing and inferring, recognizing cause and effect

### Safety Precautions
Remind students to wear an apron and goggles. $KNO_2$ and $H_2SO_4$ are skin irritants.

### Disposal
The $NO_2$ gas that is produced is soluble in the water of the indicator solution and reacts according to the equation $2NO_2 + H_2O \rightarrow HNO_3 + HNO_2$. Contents of the dish can be flushed down the sink with water.

### Teaching Strategies
• See page 840C for preparation of all solutions.
• Before class, use an empty dropper to collect ammonia gas from the space over an aqueous ammonia solution. Bubble this gas into the bromocresol green indicator solution until it just turns blue.
• Initiate a discussion of acid rain before doing the miniLAB to assess what your students already know about the topic.

### Expected Results
Bubbles of $NO_2$ gas appear in the colorless center drop. The blue drops change to yellow as the $NO_2$ gas dissolves in the drops. The smaller drops completely change color first. The larger drops change color on the outer surface first. The drops farthest from the source change last.

**Figure 26-8**

Acid-rain damage to buildings, statues, and trees amounts to billions of dollars a year.

Acidic air pollution is created also when nitrogen oxides from car exhausts combine with atmospheric moisture to form nitric acid. In either case, when this acidic moisture falls to Earth as rain or snow, it is known as acid rain. You can model the formation of acid rain in the **miniLAB** on this page.

Acid rain increases the acidity of some types of soil, resulting in the removal of essential nutrients from the soil. The loss of nutrients adversely affects the area's vegetation, leaving trees and other plants with less resistance to disease, insects, and bad weather. Acid rain also increases the acidity of streams, rivers, and lakes, which can kill or harm aquatic life. As **Figure 26-8** shows, damage to trees and to outdoor surfaces can be extensive. The acid in precipitation reacts with $CaCO_3$, the major component of marble and limestone. What products are produced by this reaction?

## miniLAB

### Acid Rain in a Bag

**Making a Model** Acid precipitation often falls to Earth hundreds of kilometers away from where the pollutant gases enter the atmosphere because the gases diffuse through the air and are carried by the wind. In this lab, you will model the formation of acid rain to observe how the damage caused by acid varies with the distance from the source of pollution. You also will observe another factor that affects the amount of damage caused by acid rain.

**Materials** plastic petri dish bottom; 1-gallon zipper-close, plastic bag; white paper; droppers; 0.04% bromocresol green indicator; 0.5$M$ $KNO_2$; 1.0$M$ $H_2SO_4$; clock or watch

### Procedure
1. Place 25 drops of 0.04% bromocresol green indicator of varying sizes in the bottom half of a plastic petri dish so that they are about 1 cm apart. Be sure that there are both large and small drops at any given distance from the center. Leave the center of the petri dish empty.
2. Place a zipper-close plastic bag on a piece of white paper.
3. Carefully slide the petri dish containing the drops of indicator inside the plastic bag.
4. In the center of the petri dish, place one large drop of 0.5$M$ $KNO_2$. To this $KNO_2$ drop, add two drops of 1.0$M$ $H_2SO_4$. **CAUTION:** $KNO_2$ and $H_2SO_4$ are skin irritants. Carefully seal the bag. Observe whether the mixing of these two chemicals produces any bubbles of gas. This is the pollution source.
5. Observe and compare the color changes that take place in the drops of indicator of different sizes and distances from the pollution source. Record your observations every 15 seconds.
6. To clean up, carefully remove the petri dish from the bag, rinse it with water, then dry it.

### Analysis
1. As the gas reacts with water in the drops, two acids form, $2NO_2 + H_2O \rightarrow HNO_3 + HNO_2$. What are these acids?
2. Did the small or large drops change color first? Why?
3. Did the distance of the indicator drops from the pollution source have an effect on how quickly the reaction occurred? Explain.
4. State two hypotheses that will explain your observations, and incorporate the answers from questions 2 and 3 in your hypotheses.
5. Based on your hypotheses in question 4, what can you infer about the damage done to plants by acid fog as compared with acid rain?

**848** Chapter 26 Chemistry in the Environment

### Analysis
1. $HNO_3$–nitric acid, $HNO_2$–nitrous acid
2. The small drops changed color first. The surface area-to-volume ratio is greater.
3. The drops that were closer to the pollution source reacted faster because diffusion of the pollution occurred over a shorter distance.
4. The gas diffuses and dissolves faster in water drops that are smaller and closer to the source.
5. Acid fog would do more damage to plants than acid rain in the same area because the surface area-to-volume ratio is greater.

### ✓ Assessment

**Portfolio** Have students suggest other gases to test. They could place a crystal of $Na_2SO_3$ in the dish and add $H_2SO_4$ to generate $SO_2$. Results can be placed in students' portfolios. **L2** **P**

Combustion chamber

Coal →
$CaCO_3$ →
Air →

$S + O_2 \rightarrow SO_2$
CaO

$CaSO_3 + SO_2 \rightarrow$

Water + CaO

$SO_2$ scrubber

Stack

$CaSO_3$ slurry

Waste slurry →

**Figure 26-9**

Follow the process as this power plant removes the sulfur from coal to reduce air pollution. Where is the sulfur found at the end of the process?

As human dependence on fossil fuels has increased, so has the acidity of rain. About 200 years ago, rain had a pH between 6 and 7.6, almost neutral. Today, it is common in many regions for rain to have a pH between 4 and 4.5, or even lower. In fact, the pH of rain in Wheeling, West Virginia, has been measured at 1.8, midway between the acidity of lemon juice and that of stomach acid. What do you think might account for this extreme acidity?

Given the damaging effects of acid rain, measures have been taken to reduce $SO_2$ emissions into the environment. High-sulfur coal may be washed before it is burned in power plants, or the $SO_2$ that is produced when coal burns may be removed during the burning process. This removal is accomplished by adding powdered limestone ($CaCO_3$) to the combustion chamber along with the coal, as shown in **Figure 26-9**. The limestone is decomposed to lime (CaO) and carbon dioxide.

$$CaCO_3(s) \rightarrow CaO(s) + CO_2(g)$$

The lime then reacts with $SO_2$ to form calcium sulfite.

$$CaO(s) + SO_2(g) \rightarrow CaSO_3(s)$$

About half of the $SO_2$ from coal is removed by adding solid limestone powder to the combustion material. The rest of the $SO_2$ must be removed by "scrubbing" the reaction gas with a shower of CaO and water. In this step, the remaining $SO_2$ is converted into solid $CaSO_3$, which precipitates as a watery slurry. Most of the sulfur is removed from the coal-burning process.

## Section 26.1 Assessment

1. Compare and contrast the major layers of the atmosphere in terms of temperature, altitude, and composition.

2. Write the equations for the chemical reactions that lead to the formation of ozone in the stratosphere.

3. What is the source of the sulfur that contributes to the formation of acid rain?

4. **Thinking Critically** Hydrogen is the most abundant element in the universe. Why is it so rare in Earth's atmosphere?

5. **Applying Concepts** Explain why the following statement is true: Ozone in the troposphere is considered a pollutant, but ozone in the stratosphere is essential for life on Earth.

chemistrymc.com/self_check_quiz

26.1 Earth's Atmosphere    **849**

## Section 26.1 Assessment

1. Information from this section can be summarized in table form. See the Solutions Manual.

2. $O_2 + $ UV light energy $\rightarrow 2O$
   $O + O_2 \rightarrow O_3*$
   $O_3* + X \rightarrow O_3 + X*$

3. The main source of sulfur is $SO_2$ from the burning of high-sulfur coal and oil in power plants.

4. Hydrogen is so rare in Earth's atmosphere because it's a very light gas that can escape from Earth's gravitational field.

5. $O_3$ in the troposphere is a pollutant because it is an irritant and can cause disease. $O_3$ in the stratosphere is essential for life because it protects Earth's inhabitants by absorbing the Sun's harmful UV radiation.

# 1 Focus

Section **26.2**

## Focus Transparency

Before presenting the lesson, display **Section Focus Transparency 102** on the overhead projector. Have students answer the accompanying questions using **Section Focus Transparency Master 102. L1 ELL**

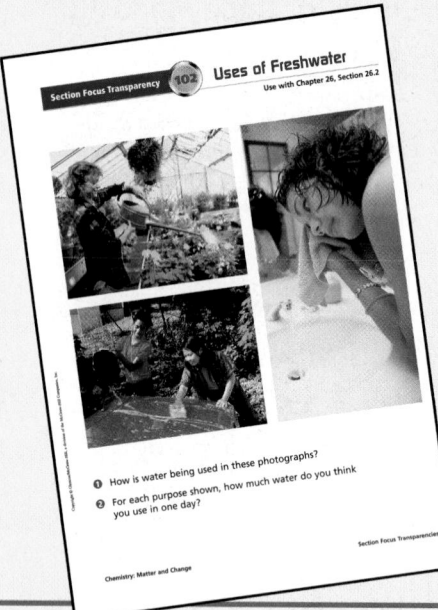

Section Focus Transparency 102

**Uses of Freshwater**
Use with Chapter 26, Section 26.2

❶ How is water being used in these photographs?

❷ For each purpose shown, how much water do you think you use in one day?

*Chemistry: Matter and Change*

Section Focus Transparencies

# 2 Teach

## Resource Manager

**Math Skills Transparency 43 and Master L2 ELL**
**Teaching Transparency 78 and Master L2 ELL**

**National Science Content Standards**

**Pages 848–851**
UCP.1, UCP.2; A.1; B.2, B.3, B.4, B.6; E.2; F.3, F.4, F.6

**850**

---

# Section 26.2 Earth's Water

## Objectives

- **Trace** the cycle of water in the environment.
- **Identify** the chemical composition of seawater.
- **Describe** methods of desalination, and **relate** the shortage of freshwater in some regions to the development of desalination techniques.
- **Outline** the steps of a water-treatment process.

## Vocabulary

hydrosphere
salinity
desalination

**Figure 26-10**

The water cycle, powered by the Sun, circulates water through the atmosphere, Earth's surface, and below its surface.

Look back at the photo of Earth in the chapter opener. The blue oceans clearly illustrate the abundance of water on Earth. Water is a rare substance on other planets. On Earth, however, water is found as a solid, liquid, and gas throughout the environment. You have read that the presence of an atmosphere is critical for the existence of living things on Earth. Because living things cannot exist without water, it, too, is essential for life.

## The Hydrosphere

Water is the most abundant substance in the human body and the most common substance on Earth, covering approximately 72% of the surface of this planet. All the water found in and on Earth's surface and in the atmosphere is collectively referred to as the **hydrosphere**. More than 97% of this surface water is located in the oceans. Another 2.1% is frozen in glaciers and polar ice caps. That leaves a meager 0.6% available as liquid freshwater.

## The Water Cycle

Both seawater and freshwater move through Earth's atmosphere, its surface, and below its surface in a process known as the water cycle. You may also see the water cycle referred to as the hydrologic cycle. In this cycle, water continually moves through the environment by the processes of evaporation, condensation, and precipitation. The Sun provides the energy for these processes. Follow **Figure 26-10** as you read about the water cycle.

Solar radiation causes liquid water to evaporate into a gaseous state. The resulting water vapor rises in the atmosphere and cools. As it cools, the water vapor again becomes a liquid when it condenses on dust particles in the air, forming clouds. Clouds are made of millions of tiny water droplets that collide with each other to form larger drops. When the drops grow so large that they can no longer stay suspended in the clouds, they fall to Earth in the form of precipitation—rain, snow, sleet, or hail.

Condensation

Precipitation

Evaporation

Runoff

Ground water

---

## Portfolio

### Drinking with the Dinos

*Visual-Spatial* Ask students to do a creative assignment that follows the path of a single water molecule that was ingested by a dinosaur 150 000 000 years ago to the water fountain outside your classroom today. The assignment should incorporate the water cycle and may take the form of a written paper, a diagram, or a cartoon. **L2 ELL P**

---

## DIFFERENTIATED INSTRUCTION

### English Language Learners

*Linguistic* Make sure students understand the meaning of *evaporation, condensation,* and *precipitation*. Have them use the terms in sentences or write descriptions of the processes. They can also write a story about a water droplet undergoing these processes. **L1 ELL**

Most of the falling precipitation soaks into the ground and becomes part of groundwater, the underground water that collects in small spaces between soil and rock particles. If the soil becomes saturated with water, the excess water flows along Earth's surface and into lakes and streams. This is called runoff.

Look again at **Figure 26-10**. As you can see, water cycles through the atmosphere, on Earth's surface, and under the surface. Can atmospheric processes affect the hydrosphere? The answer is most definitely yes. Processes that take place in the atmosphere, such as the formation of acid rain, can have a direct impact on the hydrosphere. The interrelatedness of the components of the environment is an important concept to keep in mind as you explore Earth's water, beginning with the vast and mighty seas.

## Earth's Oceans

If you've ever swallowed a gulp of seawater, you know that it tastes quite different from tap water. Seawater contains dissolved salts, which give the water a salty taste. Where do the salts come from? Rivers and groundwater dissolve elements such as calcium, magnesium, and sodium from rocks and minerals. Flowing rivers then transport these elements to the oceans. Erupting volcanoes add sulfur and chlorine to the oceans as well.

**Salinity** is a measure of the mass of salts dissolved in seawater. It is usually measured in grams of salt per kilogram of seawater. The average salinity of ocean water is about 35 g per kg, so ocean water contains about 3.5% dissolved salts. Most of these salts dissociate in water and are present in the form of ions. **Table 26-2** lists the ions in seawater. Note that chlorine and sodium are the most abundant ions in seawater. Although Earth's oceans are vast, the proportions and quantities of dissolved salts are nearly constant in all areas. Indeed, they have stayed almost the same for hundreds of millions of years. Why is this so? As rivers, volcanoes, and atmospheric processes add new substances to seawater, elements are removed from the oceans by biological processes and sedimentation. Thus, the oceans are considered to be in a steady state with respect to salinity.

**Desalination** In some areas of the world, such as the Middle East, freshwater is scarce. Can the people in these areas drink the much more abundant ocean water? Because seawater has a high salinity, it can't be consumed by living organisms. If humans are to use ocean water for drinking and for irrigation of crops, the salts must first be removed. The removal of salts from seawater to make it usable by living things is called **desalination**.

Dissolved salts can be removed from seawater by distillation, a simple process in which the seawater is boiled to evaporate the volatile water. Pure water vapor is collected and condensed, leaving the nonvolatile salts behind. This process is quite energy intensive and is not practical for a large-scale operation. It is rarely used commercially.

You learned in Chapter 15 that osmosis is the flow of solvent molecules through a semipermeable membrane from a region of higher solvent concentration to a region of lower solvent concentration. If a high-enough pressure is applied to the system, osmosis can be reversed; that is, the solvent can be forced to flow from low to high concentrations of solvent. This process is called reverse osmosis. In a modern desalination plant, seawater is forced under pressure into cylinders containing hollow, semipermeable fibers. A cylinder holds more than three million fibers, each of which has the diameter of a human hair. The water molecules pass inward through the walls of the fibers, and the salts are held back. Desalinated water flows through the inside of the fibers and is collected.

Table 26-2

| Ionic Composition of Seawater | |
| --- | --- |
| **Dissolved ion** | **Percent in seawater** |
| Chloride (Cl⁻) | 55.04 |
| Sodium (Na⁺) | 30.61 |
| Sulfate (SO₄²⁻) | 7.68 |
| Magnesium (Mg²⁺) | 3.69 |
| Calcium (Ca²⁺) | 1.16 |
| Potassium (K⁺) | 1.10 |
| Hydrogen carbonate (HCO₃⁻) | 0.41 |
| Bromide (Br⁻) | 0.19 |
| All others | 0.12 |

## Biology
### CONNECTION

What happens if you drink seawater? The ions in the water enter your blood from the digestive tract. Your kidneys can't remove the ions fast enough, so the ion concentration remains high in the blood. Water moves out of your cells by osmosis, causing dehydration. The cells shrivel and begin to malfunction. Meanwhile, your body begins to swell as the volume of blood and the fluid surrounding cells increases due to the additional water. Dehydration causes the thirst center of your brain to signal your kidneys to stop making urine, so the ions aren't removed from your body.

*Intrapersonal* Interested students can do research to learn about and report on desalination plants in the United States. North Carolina has several small distillation plants, and Florida and California have plants of varying methods of operation. **L2**

## Identifying Misconceptions

Students may believe that seawater is safe to drink.

**Uncover the Misconception** Ask students to pretend they are lost at sea, with no freshwater available to them. Have them predict the physiological effects if they drink the surrounding seawater.

**Demonstrate the Concept**
*Visual-Spatial* Place a leaf of *Elodea* (an aquarium plant available from aquatic suppliers) or a thin section of onion bulb on a microscope slide with a drop of distilled water and cover it with a coverslip. Place the slide under a microscope (if possible, attached to a projecting device). Have students draw the cells they see. Introduce a drop of 3.5% saltwater solution to one side of the coverslip and draw it under the coverslip by blotting the opposite side with a paper towel. (The cells will shrink.) Have students draw their observations and give possible explanations for the observed phenomenon. Ask them if their predictions were confirmed.

**Assess New Knowledge** Students should be able to see the effects of placing a cell in a surrounding medium that has a higher concentration of dissolved salts. Have them demonstrate their understanding of the concept by drawing a diagram of a cell placed in a medium of lower salt concentration. (The cell swells.) **L2 ELL**

## CHEMISTRY JOURNAL

### Oil and Water

*Linguistic* Ask students to write a journal entry explaining how obtaining and purifying water is similar/different from obtaining and purifying crude oil. Which is a more valuable commodity? Does one's geographic location dictate this? **L2**

## Resource Manager

**Study Guide for Content Mastery,** p. 153 **L2**
**Solving Problems: A Chemistry Handbook,** Section 26.2 **L2**
**Section Focus Transparency 102 and Master L1 ELL**

**Kinesthetic** Set out some dropper bottles of water and samples of rocks that include granite, quartz, marble, and sandstone. Ask students to identify which of the rocks would be considered aquifer rock (these are rocks that hold and release groundwater rather like a sponge). **L1** **ELL** 📦

## Visual Learning

**Figure 26-12** Using this figure as a starting point, have groups of students choose an industrial or farming process and diagram the stages where water enters into the process. For example, for a can of frozen lemonade concentrate to reach the consumer, approximately 110 L of water will be used. Some of the indirect uses of water include watering the lemon trees, washing the lemons, rinsing the aluminum portions of the can, making the labeling papers and inks, refrigeration used in transit and in the store, and all the water consumed by individuals involved in these processes. **L2** 📦

## GLENCOE
### TECHNOLOGY

💿 **CD-ROM**
**Chemistry: Matter and Change**
Video: *Desalination*

**Figure 26-11**

ⓐ This room in a desalination plant houses thousands of cylinders.

ⓑ Each cylinder contains millions of tiny fibers across which reverse osmosis takes place. Maintaining the high pressure necessary for this process makes it very energy intensive.

**Figure 26-11** shows how seawater can be desalinated under pressure by reverse osmosis. The largest desalination plant in the world is located in Jubail, Saudi Arabia, where it produces 50% of the country's drinking water by the reverse osmosis of seawater from the Persian Gulf. Smaller desalination plants are in operation in Israel, California, and Florida.

## Earth's Freshwater

How much water do you use in a day? The answer may surprise you. An average person needs to drink about 1.5 L per day for survival. But this is only a small fraction of the total amount of water used for daily activities. In the United States, about 7 L of water per person per day is used for cooking and drinking; about 120 L for bathing, laundering, and housecleaning; 80 L for flushing toilets; and 80 L for watering yards. Massive quantities of water are also used in agriculture and industry to produce food and other products. **Figure 26-12** shows the major consumers of water in the United States by daily percentage.

Recall that only 0.6% of the hydrosphere is made up of liquid freshwater. Almost all of this freshwater is found as groundwater and other underground sources. Very small amounts (0.01%) come also from surface water such as

**Figure 26-12**

Industry and farming use most of the freshwater in the United States. Residential use accounts for about 12%.

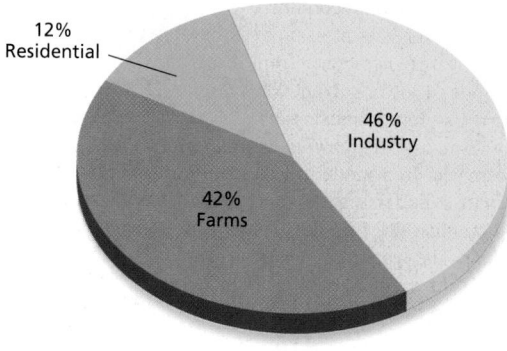

12% Residential

46% Industry

42% Farms

---

## CULTURAL DIVERSITY

### Colliding Cultures

The Cree and Inuit peoples have resided in the lands of northern Quebec, Canada, for more than 5000 years. In 1971, nimischiiuskataau, or "the fire that shakes the land," came to the territory. This is how the Cree describe the advent of electricity through the efforts of

Hydro-Quebec, the government utility company. The initial stage, called the La Grande Complex, flooded 6000 square miles by diverting and damming six waterways into larger bodies of water to increase the flow for electric output. The cost for the initial phase has been $16.3

billion (U.S.). The flooded areas contained prime caribou hunting and fishing grounds for the Cree, who believe that hunting fulfills not only a physical but a spiritual hunger. An additional problem caused by the flooding of vegetation is the presence of the neurotoxin

**Figure 26-13**

Algae often experience a population explosion when fertilizer is carried into lakes and ponds. When the algae die and decay, oxygen in the pond is depleted, and fish may die as a result.

lakes and rivers, and the atmosphere provides a tiny amount (0.001%) as water vapor. Freshwater, essential for life on Earth, is our most precious resource. Unfortunately, human activities can affect the quality of freshwater.

## Human Impact on the Hydrosphere

A freshwater stream may look sparkling and clean, but it's probably not safe for drinking. Many rivers and lakes in the United States are polluted. Bacteria and viruses enter water supplies through contamination by sewage and industrial wastes. Wastes from landfills and mines leak into groundwater reservoirs. Pesticides, herbicides, and fertilizers are picked up by rainwater and carried into streams. Streams flow into rivers, and rivers empty into oceans. In addition, coastal cities pump waste directly into the oceans. For this reason, much of the oceans' pollution is found along the coasts of continents.

A major cause of freshwater pollution, however, is caused by legal, everyday activities. Water is polluted when we flush toilets, wash hands, brush teeth, and water lawns. The main culprits are nitrogen and phosphorus—two elements found in household detergents, soaps, and fertilizers. Nitrogen and phosphorus are difficult to remove from sewage and wastewater. They contribute to water pollution by causing certain algae and bacteria to reproduce rapidly in the water. The result is an algal bloom, shown in **Figure 26-13**. When the algae die, they decompose, a process that consumes oxygen. The result is the depletion of oxygen in the water. Without sufficient oxygen, fish and other aquatic organisms cannot survive.

## Municipal Water and Sewage Treatment

As you have learned, the water that most people use for their daily activities comes from lakes, rivers, reservoirs, and underground sources. Because it has been exposed to a variety of contaminants, it must be purified at a water treatment plant before it can be used.

The treatment of water in municipal treatment plants usually involves five steps: coarse filtration, sedimentation, sand filtration, aeration, and sterilization. The water is first passed through a screen to remove large solids. It then enters large settling tanks where sand and other medium-sized particles settle out. Often, CaO (powdered lime) and $Al_2(SO_4)_3$ (alum) are added to coagulate small particles and bacteria. These clumps of particles settle out of solution during a sedimentation step, as you saw in the **DISCOVERY LAB**. After settling, the water is filtered through a bed of sand. The filtered water is then sprayed into the air in a process called aeration. During aeration, oxygen combines with many of the harmful dissolved organic substances in the water, oxidizing them to harmless compounds.

### Chemistry Online

**Topic: Wastes**
To learn more about wastes, visit the Chemistry Web site at chemistrymc.com

**Activity:** Imagine you are part of a team building a self-contained space station. List different biological and industrial wastes the society will produce. Suggest strategies and technologies to cope with those wastes.

### Assessment

**Performance** After doing appropriate research, have teams of students debate this issue: Water is a free resource and should be available to all people without volume limit or cost. Use the Performance Task Assessment List for Investigating an Issue Controversy in **PASC,** p. 65. **L2** **COOP LEARN**

### Quick Demo

Give a visual demonstration of the scarcity of available freshwater by filling a 1000-mL graduated cylinder with blue colored water and then pouring off 6 mL into a beaker to represent the available freshwater found in rivers, lakes, and groundwater.

### Resource Manager

Lab Manual, pp. 201–204 **L2**
Math Skills Transparency 44 and Master **L2** **ELL**

**National Science Content Standards**
**Pages 852–853**
UCP.1, UCP.2; B.2, B.4; F.3

methylmercury in the fish. The Cree won a 1973 injunction to stop the La Grande project, but the ruling was overturned by the Court of Appeal, citing that "the Cree lacked exclusive rights to the territory inasmuch as Charles II of England had granted exclusive rights to the Hudson's Bay Company in 1670."

Ultimately, the James Bay and Northern Quebec Agreement was signed in 1975 by the government, the Cree, and the Inuit to compensate the people with a $225 million package and rights to continue hunting and trapping on their lands. An additional two phases are planned for contiguous areas that will

contain more than 30 major dams and 500 separate dikes. The La Grande project has changed how power is delivered to the towns and cities in Quebec. In the early 1970s, nearly all homes were heated with oil or gas. A decade later, 63% of homes received electricity through hydropower.

# 3 Assess

## Check for Understanding

The solubility of NaCl is relatively constant, ranging from 35.7 g/100 g of water at 0°C to 39.12 g/100 g of water at 100°C. Ask students how this relatively flat solubility curve is important to the stability of the marine ecosystem. Because the solubility of NaCl fluctuates little due to temperature, organisms don't have to drastically adjust their physiology to compensate for seasonal changes in salt concentration.

## Reteach

Have students list the possible methods of desalination and briefly discuss the potential of using them in real-world applications. **L2**

## ✓ Assessment

**Knowledge** Have students support or reject the following statements. If a statement is wrong, it should be corrected.

- An adult human could survive for more than a month without water. (F; perhaps a week)
- 50% of Earth's surface is covered by water. (F; 72%)
- The largest amount of available freshwater is found in groundwater, rivers, and lakes. (T)
- Residential consumption accounts for the greatest use of freshwater. (F; industry consumes 46%)
- Distillation is the most cost-effective way of obtaining freshwater from saltwater. (F; reverse osmosis)
- Heavy metal ions, such as cadmium and lead, are removed during sewage treatment. (T)

**Figure 26-14**

Most public water systems use these steps to treat water for human consumption.

The final step in water treatment, sterilization, is accomplished by treating the water with substances that kill bacteria. The most commonly used substance is liquefied chlorine gas. Chlorine reacts with water to form hypochlorous acid (HClO), which destroys any remaining microorganisms in the water.

$$Cl_2(aq) + H_2O(l) \rightarrow HClO(aq) + H^+(aq) + Cl^-(aq)$$

**Figure 26-14** summarizes the flow of water through a water treatment plant.

In addition to water treatment plants, cities and towns also have sewage treatment plants to maintain clean water supplies. The steps involved in sewage treatment are similar to those used to treat water. The incoming sewage is filtered to remove debris and larger suspended solids. Then, as in conventional water treatment, the sewage is passed into large settling tanks where suspended solids settle out. During aeration, the sewage water comes into contact with large amounts of air, and the increased oxygen levels promote the rapid growth of bacteria needed to biodegrade the wastes. After treatment, about 90% of solids and dissolved biodegradable wastes have been removed.

A final treatment removes many inorganic pollutants, such as the toxic heavy metals $Cd^{2+}$ and $Pb^{2+}$. This treatment is usually expensive, but an increasing percentage of wastewater treatment facilities are taking this extra step to ensure that toxic substances do not enter water supplies. Before release into the environment, the processed water is treated with $Cl_2$ to kill any remaining bacteria.

## Section 26.2 Assessment

6. Use the water cycle to explain how the hydrosphere and atmosphere are interrelated.

7. Sequence the five steps involved in municipal water treatment.

8. Explain why much of the water that comes out of your faucet is "recycled" water.

9. **Thinking Critically** Why does desalination by reverse osmosis require the use of high pressure?

10. **Making and Using Graphs** Use the data in **Table 26-2, Ionic Composition of Seawater,** to make a bar graph showing the percentages of the most abundant ions in seawater.

---

## Section 26.2 Assessment

6. As water vapor rises in the atmosphere, it condenses and falls back to Earth (returns to the hydrosphere) in the form of precipitation.

7. coarse filtration, sedimentation, sand filtration, aeration, sterilization

8. Water coming out of the faucet can be considered "recycled" because it has been passed through the environment in the water cycle.

9. Reverse osmosis requires high pressure to force the solvent (water) through the semipermeable membrane from regions of low solvent concentration to regions of high solvent concentration (against the direction in which it tends to flow).

10. Graphs should represent data. Chloride and sodium ions are most abundant. See the Solutions Manual.

Earth is a large, dynamic planet that has existed, according to best estimates, for approximately 4.6 billion years. When Earth was newly formed, it was a huge molten mass. As this mass cooled, it differentiated into regions of varying composition and density. These regions, or layers, include a dense central core, a thick mantle, and a thin crust. The core is further divided into a small, solid inner core and a larger, liquid outer core. **Figure 26-15** shows Earth's layers.

Gravity caused more-dense elements to sink beneath less-dense elements in molten Earth. Hence, the core is composed mostly of iron and small amounts of nickel. In contrast to the dense core, the less-dense outer region at first consisted mostly of rock as oxygen combined with silicon, aluminum, magnesium, and small amounts of iron. This lighter outer region later separated into the mantle and the crust as Earth cooled further. Many light elements such as hydrogen escaped Earth's gravitational force and are now found mostly in space.

Earth's crust makes up about one percent of Earth's mass. Oceanic crust lies beneath Earth's oceans. Continental crust is the part of the crust beneath landmasses.

## The Lithosphere

You have already studied the liquid outer part of Earth—the hydrosphere—and the gaseous atmosphere. Each of these parts has a distinct composition and environmental chemistry, as you have learned.

The solid crust and the upper mantle make up the region called the **lithosphere**. Oxygen is the most abundant element in the lithosphere. Unlike the hydrosphere and the atmosphere, the lithosphere contains a large variety of other elements, including deposits of alkali, alkaline earth, and transition metal elements. **Table 26-3** lists the most abundant elements in the continental crust portion of the lithosphere. With the exception of gold, platinum, and a few other rare metals that are found free in nature, most metallic elements occur as compounds in minerals. A mineral is a solid, inorganic compound found in nature. Minerals have distinct crystalline structures and chemical compositions. Most are combinations of metals and nonmetals.

### Objectives

- **Identify** Earth's major regions.
- **List** the major elements in Earth's crust.
- **Describe** the composition of minerals.

### Vocabulary

lithosphere

**Table 26-3**

| Abundance of Elements in the Continental Crust | |
|---|---|
| **Element** | **Percent by mass** |
| Oxygen | 45.2 |
| Silicon | 27.2 |
| Aluminum | 8.2 |
| Iron | 5.8 |
| Calcium | 5.1 |
| Magnesium | 2.8 |
| Sodium | 2.3 |
| Potassium | 1.7 |
| Other elements (Ti, H, Mn, Cu, Pb, Zn, Sn, etc.) | 1.7 |

Crust (5–40 km)
2.8 g/cm³

Mantle (2900 km)
3.3–5.5 g/cm³

Outer core
(2300 km)
10–12 g/cm³

Inner core
(1200 km)
12–13 g/cm³

**Figure 26-15**

Earth's layers include a small inner core and large outer core of high density, a thick mantle of medium density, and a very thin crust of low density.

26.3 Earth's Crust **855**

## 1 Focus

### Focus Transparency

Before presenting the lesson, display **Section Focus Transparency 103** on the overhead projector. Have students answer the accompanying questions using **Section Focus Transparency Master 103.** L1 ELL

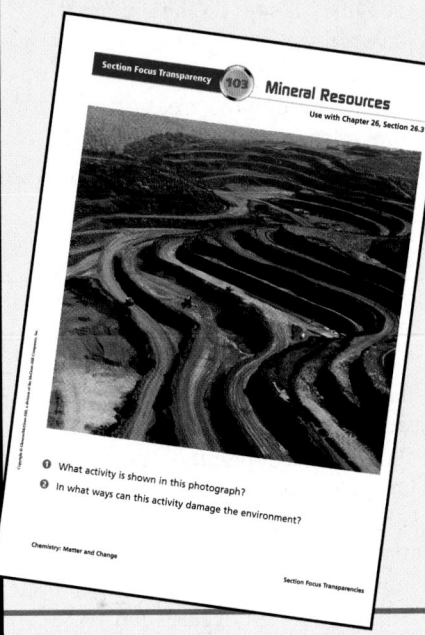

Section Focus Transparency 103 · Mineral Resources
Use with Chapter 26, Section 26.3

❶ What activity is shown in this photograph?
❷ In what ways can this activity damage the environment?

Chemistry: Matter and Change

Section Focus Transparencies

## 2 Teach

### Quick Demo

Set up a display of as many minerals as possible. Have students observe them and make a table that includes headings for common name, chemical formula, and general appearance. L2 ELL

### Resource Manager

**Study Guide for Content Mastery,** p. 154 L2
**Solving Problems: A Chemistry Handbook,** Section 26.3 L2
**Section Focus Transparency 103 and Master** L1 ELL

### DIFFERENTIATED INSTRUCTION

#### Hearing Impaired

*Kinesthetic* Have students research the tests that are often done in mineralogy and gemology, such as the Mohs scale of hardness, specific gravity, cleavage, color, streak test, and flame test. Next, provide a mineral unknown to the students and have them identify it based on their test results. L2 ELL

National Science Content Standards

**Pages 854–855**
UCP.1, UCP.2; B.2, B.3, B.4; F.3, F.6

## Using Science Terms

The terms *mineral* and *ore* are often used interchangeably. A mineral is any naturally occurring, homogeneous substance of definite chemical composition and uniform crystalline structure, color, and hardness. An ore is a mineral that can be mined at a reasonable profit.

### Assessment

**Skill** Assign a mineral (different from those displayed in the Quick Demo on the previous page) for each student to research. The focus of the research should include geographic areas of mineral abundance, method of isolating the desired substance, importers of the mineral, and market price of the mineral. When the information is presented to the class, a push pin or dot sticker should be placed on a world map where the mineral is most frequently mined. Once the presentations are complete, the class should make a graph of mineral abundance and answer the following questions. Where are the majority of mineral resources located? Is there a relationship between mineral wealth and economic power? What would happen if a mineral-poor country (such as Japan) were cut off from obtaining minerals? **L2**

### Concept Development

Although bauxite is classified here as a mineral, it is actually a rock containing a mixture of various aluminum oxides and hydroxides.

**National Science Content Standards**

**Pages 856–857**
UCP.1, UCP.2; B.2; E.2; F.3

**Table 26-4**

| Some Common Oxide, Sulfide, and Carbonate Minerals | | |
|---|---|---|
| **Oxides** | **Sulfides** | **Carbonates** |
| $SnO_2$ (cassiterite) | $CuFeS_2$ (chalcopyrite) | $MgCO_3$ (magnesite) |
| $TiO_2$ (rutile) | $PbS$ (galena) | $CaCO_3$ (calcite) |
| $Al_2O_3$ (bauxite) | $HgS$ (cinnabar) | $SrCO_3$ (strontianite) |
| $Fe_3O_4$ (magnetite) | $FeS_2$ (pyrite) | $BaCO_3$ (witherite) |
| $FeCr_2O_4$ (chromite) | $ZnS$ (sphalerite) | |
| $FeTiO_3$ (ilmenite) | | |
| $MnO_2$ (pyrolusite) | | |
| $Fe_2O_3$ (hematite) | | |

Many industrially important metals are found in the form of oxides, sulfides, or carbonates. Recall that oxides are compounds of metals combined with oxygen, sulfides are compounds of metals combined with sulfur, and carbonates are compounds of metals combined with both carbon and oxygen. **Table 26-4** lists some oxide, sulfide, and carbonate minerals and their common names. The oxides are formed largely from transition metals on the left side of the periodic table because these elements have lower electronegativities and tend to lose bonding electrons when they combine with the oxide ion. The elements on the right side of the table and in some of the other groups have higher electronegativities and tend to form bonds with sulfur that are more covalent in character. The alkaline earth metals (2A) are usually found as carbonates in the marble and limestone of mountain ranges. Thus, periodic properties govern the state of combination in which elements are found in nature. **Figure 26-16** shows the major mineral sources for most of the elements. Magnesium and calcium carbonates cause water to become hard. The **How It Works** feature at the end of the chapter shows how hard water can be softened.

**Figure 26-16**

This periodic table shows the mineral sources for most elements.

### CHEMISTRY JOURNAL

#### Mine: Your Own Business

*Interpersonal* Propose to students that they are in the business of mining iron ores, extracting the iron, and then selling it for profit. Beginning with Table 26-4, student groups should research which of the six listed iron ores is most profitable based on percent composition. They may extend their research to other iron ores, such as siderite.

After choosing the iron ore with the highest composition of iron, they should develop a poster presentation that shows a creative company name, logo, stoichiometry of the isolating process (roasting, electrometallurgy, hydrometallurgy), and a cost analysis. **L2 COOP LEARN**

**a** Mercury is extracted from cinnabar and used in instruments that measure blood pressure and temperature.

**b** Bauxite is the major ore of aluminum, a metal with many uses.

**c** Galena is a major ore of lead. The material that holds a stained glass window together contains lead.

**d** Iron can be extracted from many ores, including hematite. Because iron is so strong, it is used as the framework for large buildings.

**Figure 26-17**

Metals are extracted from their ores and used for many purposes.

The metals in a mineral cannot always be extracted from the mineral in an economically feasible way. Sometimes, the concentration of the mineral in the surrounding rock is too low for the mineral to be mined at a reasonable cost. The cost of energy needed to mine, extract, or purify the metal also may be too high. If the metal can be extracted and purified from a mineral at a reasonable profit, the mineral is called an ore. Several ores and the metals extracted from them are shown in **Figure 26-17**.

## Section 26.3 Assessment

**11.** Name and describe Earth's major regions.

**12.** Why does the composition of Earth's crust differ so greatly from that of its core?

**13.** What is a mineral? List some common minerals that exist as metallic oxides, as carbonates, and as sulfides.

**14.** **Thinking Critically** Nitrogen makes up 0.002% of Earth's lithosphere but 78% of the atmosphere. How can you explain this difference?

**15.** **Applying Concepts** What is an ore? Under what conditions would a mineral not be an ore?

chemistrymc.com/self_check_quiz

26.3 Earth's Crust    **857**

## Section 26.3 Assessment

**11.** Core—central region, very dense; Mantle—thick layer of rock made of compounds containing oxygen with elements such as silicon, aluminum, magnesium, and small amounts of iron; Crust—thin outer layer, including lithosphere (solid), hydrosphere (liquid), and atmosphere (gaseous) layers.

**12.** Gravity caused the more dense elements (e.g., iron) to sink to the central core and allowed the lighter elements to rise to the crust.

**13.** Minerals are crystalline compounds of a metal and nonmetal. See Table 26–4 for examples.

**14.** Nitrogen is very light, so it is held less tightly by Earth's gravitational field and rises into the atmosphere.

**15.** A mineral would not be an ore if its metal could not be profitably extracted or purified.

**857**

# 1 Focus

**Section 26.4**

## Focus Transparency

Before presenting the lesson, display **Section Focus Transparency 104** on the overhead projector. Have students answer the accompanying questions using **Section Focus Tranparency Master 104.** L1 ELL

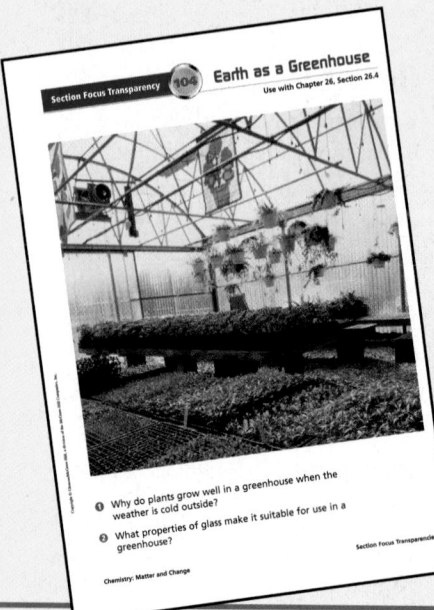

# Cycles in the Environment

## Objectives

- **Trace** the pathways of carbon and nitrogen through the environment.
- **Compare** and **contrast** the greenhouse effect and global warming.

## Vocabulary

greenhouse effect
global warming
nitrogen fixation

Did you know that the atoms of carbon, nitrogen, and other elements in your body are far older than you? In fact, they've been around since before life began on Earth. The amount of matter on Earth never changes. As a result, it must be recycled constantly. You learned about the water cycle earlier in the chapter. A number of elements cycle through the environment in similar, distinct pathways.

## The Carbon Cycle

Carbon dioxide ($CO_2$) constitutes only about 0.03% of Earth's atmosphere. However, it plays a vital role in maintaining life on Earth. There is a fine balance in nature between the processes that produce carbon dioxide and those that consume it. You have learned that green plants, algae, and some bacteria remove carbon dioxide from the atmosphere during photosynthesis. Do you recall what products are formed during this process? Photosynthesis produces carbon-containing carbohydrates, which animals ingest when they eat plants and other animals. Both plants and animals convert the carbohydrates to $CO_2$, which is released into the atmosphere as a waste product of cellular respiration. Once in the atmosphere, the $CO_2$ can be used again by plants.

**Figure 26-18** shows the carbon cycle. Carbon dioxide in the atmosphere is in equilibrium with an enormous quantity that is dissolved in oceans, lakes, and streams. Some of this dissolved $CO_2$ was once in the form of calcium carbonate ($CaCO_3$), the main component of the shells of ancient marine animals. The shells were eventually converted into limestone, which represents a large store of carbon on Earth. When the limestone was exposed to the atmosphere by receding seas, it weathered under the action of rain and surface water, producing carbon dioxide. Some of this $CO_2$ was released into the atmosphere. This process continues today.

**Figure 26-18**

Carbon cycles in and out of the environment through many pathways.

# 2 Teach

## Quick Demo

Using long straws, bubble your breath through a saturated solution of limewater [$Ca(OH)_2$]. **CAUTION:** *Avoid getting $Ca(OH)_2$ on skin.* Students will see that the solution becomes milky, that is, a white precipitate forms. Ask students to write the equation for the reaction. $Ca(OH)_2 + CO_2 \rightarrow CaCO_3 + H_2O$ If you continue to bubble your breath into the solution, the liquid will clear again due to the formation of calcium hydrogen carbonate, which is soluble. $CO_2 + CaCO_3 + H_2O \rightarrow Ca(HCO_3)_2$

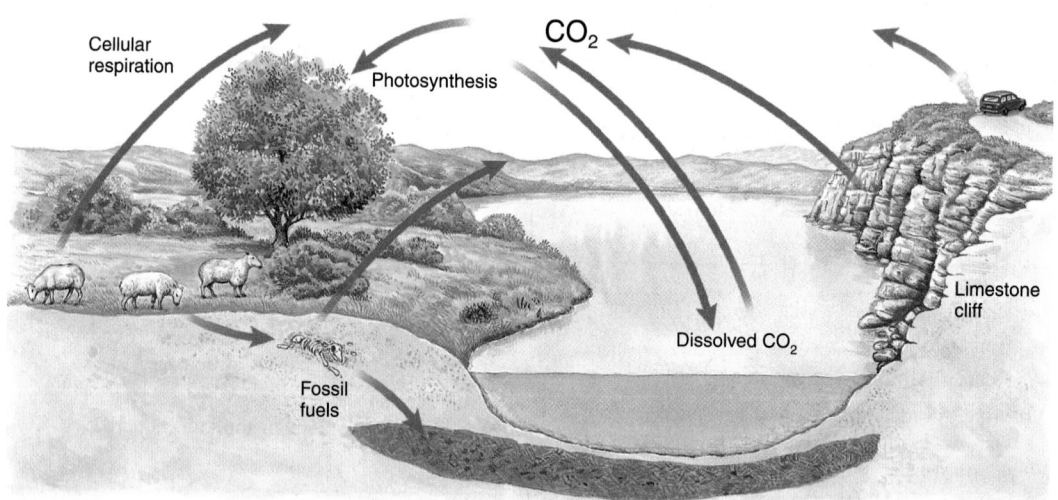

Cellular respiration

$CO_2$

Photosynthesis

Limestone cliff

Dissolved $CO_2$

Fossil fuels

## DIFFERENTIATED INSTRUCTION

### Learning Disabled

*Visual-Spatial* Break the environmental cycles into smaller sections by preparing overlays for the overhead projector and focusing on one atom (carbon in the carbon cycle) or molecule (nitrogen in the nitrogen cycle) at a time. L1 ELL

## Resource Manager

**Study Guide for Content Mastery,** pp. 155–156 L2

**Solving Problems: A Chemistry Handbook,** Section 26.4 L2

**Section Focus Transparency 104 and Master** L1 ELL

**Challenge Problems,** p. 26 L3

**Teaching Transparencies 79, 80 and Masters** L2 ELL

Reflected heat lost to outer space

Reflected heat absorbed by atmosphere

Light from the Sun

Earth's atmosphere

**Figure 26-19**

About 25% of the sunlight that strikes Earth's atmosphere is reflected back into space. Most of the remaining 75% is absorbed by atmospheric gases and Earth in the form of heat.

Carbon dioxide also enters the atmosphere when plants and animals decompose. Recall from Chapter 22 that the remains of ancient plants and animals were converted under pressure to fossil fuels. When fossil fuels are burned, the carbon is converted to $CO_2$. As you'll learn, the burning of fossil fuels and other human activities may be disrupting the balance of the carbon cycle.

**Upsetting the balance** To understand the effect of human activities on the carbon cycle, it is first necessary to explore a phenomenon known as the greenhouse effect. The **greenhouse effect** is the natural warming of Earth's surface that occurs when certain gases in the atmosphere absorb some of the solar energy that is converted to heat and reflected from Earth's surface. As **Figure 26-19** shows, the process works much like a greenhouse. Sunlight reaches Earth and is converted to heat, but the heat can't easily escape through the "greenhouse gases" to travel back into space. Instead, the heat is absorbed by molecules of greenhouse gases and transferred to the atmosphere, where it warms Earth's surface. Without the greenhouse effect, the surface of our planet would be too cold to sustain life as we know it.

Carbon dioxide is a major greenhouse gas. Most $CO_2$ occurs naturally. But, when we burn fossil fuels, huge quantities of $CO_2$—more than 5 billion metric tons a year—are added to the atmosphere. Moreover, the amount of $CO_2$ that is removed from the atmosphere by photosynthesis is being reduced by the continued destruction of vast forested areas, particularly rain forests. As a result of these activities, the level of atmospheric $CO_2$ has been increasing slowly over the past 200 years. **Diagram a** in the **problem-solving LAB** on the next page shows that the rate of increase is accelerating.

Increases in greenhouse gases such as $CO_2$ lead to corresponding increases in the greenhouse effect. Some scientists have predicted that these increases will cause global temperatures to rise, a condition known as **global warming**.

Scientists don't agree on the causes or the consequences of global warming, but they do know that average global temperatures are increasing slightly—about 0.5°C over the past 100 years. At present levels of fossil-fuel consumption, some scientists predict that global temperatures could increase by as much as 0.3°C each decade during the twenty-first century. Although this may seem like a small amount, it may result in the largest increase in global temperatures since the end of the last ice age.

26.4 Cycles in the Environment **859**

---

## Quick Demo

Place a few drops of an acid-base indicator, such as bromothymol blue, into a flask of distilled water with a sprig of *Elodea*, a water plant. Repeat with a second flask. Bubble your breath into both of the flasks and ask students why the change in color occurs. The carbon dioxide forms carbonic acid. Next, place one of the flasks on a windowsill or under a bright light and the other under a box or in a drawer. Ask students to predict what will happen to each system and to draw a diagram that shows what happens to the carbon dioxide. The *Elodea* plant in light will utilize the $CO_2$ in photosynthesis, and the indicator will return to its neutral color.

## CHEMLAB

ChemLab 26, located at the end of the chapter, can be used at this point in the lesson.

## Resource Manager

Small-Scale Laboratory Manual, pp. 77–80 **L2**

Lab Manual, pp. 205–208 **L2**

National Science Content Standards

Pages 858–859

UCP.1, UCP.2; B.2, B.6; F.3, F.5, F.6

---

## Portfolio

### You and the Greenhouse

*Logical-Mathematical* Burning a 100-watt light bulb in a porch light for eight hours per night for 365 days a year will use a total of 292 kWh (kilowatt hours) per year. Each kilowatt of electricity requires the burning of 0.77 kg of coal and produces 1.1 kg of the greenhouse gas carbon dioxide. Because the porch light uses 292 kWh per year, this equates to 225 kg of coal burned and 321 kg of carbon dioxide emitted per year. Challenge students to find an appliance (furnace, car, toaster, hair dryer) in their home and note the number of hours the appliance is used per day. Next, they should check the bottom of the appliance or the owner's manual to find out how much energy is used and convert this using dimensional analysis (the *CRC Handbook of Chemistry and Physics* has conversion factors) to quantities of fuel consumed and carbon dioxide produced. Students should substitute or try to reduce the use of that appliance and calculate the difference in $CO_2$ emissions. **L3** **P**

**859**

## Purpose 🔲

Students will examine and relate graphs of various environmental factors to global warming.

## Process Skills

Drawing conclusions, recognizing cause and effect, interpreting and analyzing data, making predictions

## Background

The topic of global warming has been a contentious issue for many scientists because its consequences could profoundly change our reliance upon fossil fuels. Scientists are in a wait-and-see posture as more data are collected and better climate models are developed.

## Teaching Strategies

- Explain how Earth's greenhouse gases trap the sun's radiant energy. Gases, such as water and carbon dioxide, absorb infrared light and re-emit it, thus preventing it from easily escaping into space.
- Discuss how the interactions of many variables make it difficult to measure the effect of one variable and relate it to weather prediction.

## Thinking Critically

1. Before this century, there was a general cooling of Earth's surface. This trend predicted an average temperature change for the year 2000 of about −0.15°C to −0.20°C.

2. The most recent atmospheric data suggest no noticeable change in temperature, unlike the surface data that indicate a definite increase. This anomaly could be caused by heat generated by urbanization, not enough data taken on land, too small a land-area sample, and the filtering effects of clouds.

3. There appears to be a link between the concentration of carbon dioxide and Earth's surface temperature. To determine how serious this problem is will require more data. Since it takes decades for carbon

**860**

---

While scientists continue to study and debate the issue of global warming, most concede that it has the potential to change Earth's climate and that tampering with the climate could be dangerous. Thus, a drastic reduction in the use of fossil fuels is considered by many to be essential to slow and eventually stop global warming. For this reason, alternative energy resources such as solar power are now important areas of scientific research. You can learn about one type of alternative energy source—solar ponds—by doing the **CHEMLAB** at the end of the chapter.

## The Nitrogen Cycle

Nitrogen is an essential component of many substances that make up living organisms. It is a key element in protein molecules, nucleic acids, and ATP. Like other elements, the supply of nitrogen on Earth is fixed. It must be recycled, as shown in **Figure 26-20**. Follow the diagram as you read about the nitrogen cycle.

Although nitrogen makes up 78% of Earth's atmosphere, most living things can't use nitrogen in its gaseous state. It must be fixed, or converted to a useful form, by a process called **nitrogen fixation**.

## Global warming: fact or fiction?

**Drawing Conclusions** Environmental issues affecting the entire planet usually involve so many variables that it is often difficult to pinpoint a primary source of the problem. Conflicting data from many experiments often divide the views of those in the scientific community. The effect of carbon dioxide emissions on global warming has been a particularly controversial issue because efforts to reduce carbon dioxide emissions may require humans to make dramatic changes in their lifestyles and could exact enormous demands on the world economy.

### Analysis

Each graph shows an indicator that is being used to monitor global warming. **Diagram a** shows the atmospheric $CO_2$ concentration for the past millennium. **Diagram b** shows the average temperature

change of Earth's surface during the past millennium. **Diagram c** shows the average temperature change of Earth's atmosphere since 1978.

### Thinking Critically

1. Before the twenty-first century, what was the trend (the dotted line in **diagram b**) for Earth's average surface temperature? What does this trend predict for the average surface temperature in the year 2000?

2. What do the atmospheric temperature data suggest? How does this compare to the surface data? What could cause this discrepancy?

3. In comparing these three graphs, how strong is the relationship between global warming and the concentration of carbon dioxide in the atmosphere? Is there a reason for concern? What other environmental influences would you consider to help answer this question?

**860**    Chapter 26 Chemistry in the Environment

---

dioxide levels to change, whatever damage is done will be around for some time. Changes in ocean levels, glaciers, coral reefs, and peat bogs are important indicators of global warming.

✓ **Assessment**

**Portfolio** Have students model how the temperature inside their car is affected by various factors. Ask them to supply two variables that could be adjusted to offset each other, thus obscuring the effect of each. **L2**  **P**

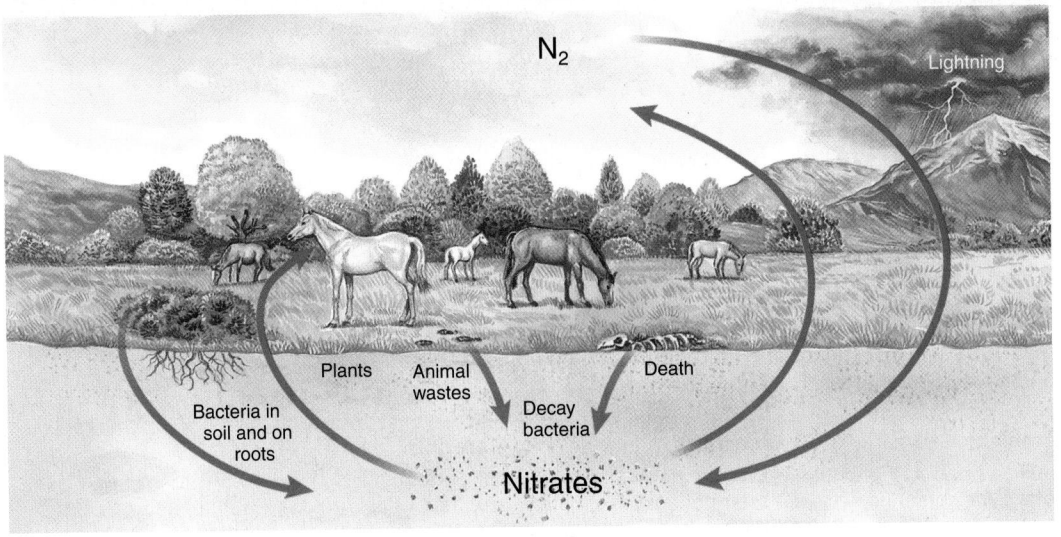

N₂

Lightning

Plants    Animal
         wastes

Death

Bacteria in
soil and on
roots

Decay
bacteria

Nitrates

Two primary routes for nitrogen fixation exist in nature. In the atmosphere, lightning combines $N_2$ and $O_2$ to form NO.

$$N_2(g) + O_2(g) \rightarrow 2NO(g)$$

Once NO is formed, it is oxidized to $NO_2$.

$$2NO(g) + O_2(g) \rightarrow 2NO_2(g)$$

In the atmosphere, rain converts $NO_2$ to $HNO_3$, which then falls to Earth as aqueous $NO_3^-$.

$$2NO_2(g) + H_2O(l) \rightarrow HNO_2(aq) + HNO_3(aq)$$

Nitrogen fixation is also accomplished by nitrogen-fixing bacteria, which live in the soil and on the roots of certain legumes such as peas, beans, peanuts, and alfalfa. In this process, $N_2$ is first reduced to $NH_3$ and $NH_4^+$, then oxidized to $NO_3^-$.

Plants absorb nitrate ions through their roots and use them to synthesize complex nitrogen compounds. Because animals can't synthesize these complex molecules, they must get them by eating plants or other animals. Nitrogen compounds that are unused by the animals' bodies are excreted as waste. Soil microorganisms convert this waste to $N_2$ and nitrogen is recycled back into the environment.

## Section 26.4 Assessment

**16.** Diagram and label the important parts of the carbon cycle.

**17.** Describe the two primary routes of nitrogen fixation.

**18.** What two cellular processes are important parts of the carbon cycle?

**19. Thinking Critically** Levels of $CO_2$, a major greenhouse gas, fluctuate on a seasonal basis. Recalling how carbon is cycled through the environment, explain the seasonal fluctuations of $CO_2$.

**20. Applying Concepts** How might the greenhouse effect lead to global warming?

**Linguistic** Ask students to write about the parallel roles that the various trophic levels (producers, primary consumers, secondary consumers, decomposers) have in each of the cycles. **L2**

**Reteach**

**Visual-Spatial** Develop a series of overheads of cycles that have missing steps in them. Call on students to complete and explain the missing steps. **L1** **ELL**

**Assessment**

**Portfolio** Have each student write two questions covering the material in this section and then exchange questions with another student. The student who writes the question should validate the answer. Questions can be placed in students' portfolios. **L2** **P**

## GLENCOE
### TECHNOLOGY

**CD-ROM**
**Chemistry: Matter and Change**
Video: *Nitrogen Fixation*

**National Science Content Standards**

**Pages 860–863**
UCP.1, UCP.2; A.1; B.3, B.6; E.1; F.6

---

## Section 26.4 Assessment

**16.** Student diagrams should resemble Figure 26-18.

**17.** Lightning-initiated reaction with oxygen in the atmosphere
$N_2 + O_2 + \text{lightning} \rightarrow 2NO$
$2NO + O_2 \rightarrow 2NO_2$
$2NO_2 + H_2O \rightarrow HNO_2 + HNO_3$
Nitrogen-fixing bacteria reduce $N_2$ to $NH_3$ and $NH_4^+$ and then oxidize it to $NO_3^-$.

**18.** photosynthesis and cellular respiration

**19.** Seasonal fluctuations in the level of $CO_2$ in the atmosphere are the result of decreased photosynthesis by plants and increased burning of fossil fuels in winter.

**20.** The greenhouse effect could lead to global warming if increases in the levels of greenhouse gases in the atmosphere increase the amount of solar energy absorbed.

**861**

## Preparation

### Time Allotment
Two laboratory periods, one to prepare the saturated salt solution and one to conduct the experiment.

### Process Skills
Applying concepts, collecting and interpreting data, comparing and contrasting, formulating models

### Safety Precautions
Students should use care around the hot plate and light bulb.

### Disposal
Remind students to wash the temperature probes thoroughly after contact with the concentrated salt solution to prevent corrosion.

### Alternative Materials
The plastic dish used to gather the sample data came from a frozen dinner. It is black, made from PETE plastic, and has a somewhat oval design. It makes a good model of a solar pond because it has a large surface area but is only about 3 to 4 cm deep. You may want to ask students or staff members to collect the dishes for you. Different dinners have different size containers, so you may have to adjust the volume of liquid used in the experiment.

### Pre-Lab

**3.** Heat will not penetrate the water in the upper layer, but light energy will reach the bottom.

**4.** No; the warm salt water will not rise to the surface because it is denser than the tap water.

**5.** The saltwater layer will have the higher final temperature because there are no convection currents to bring the warm water to the surface to be cooled.

### Procedure

• This experiment can be done without the CBL probes by using ordinary thermometers.
• The run time for each experiment

# Solar Pond

If you made a list of popular types of alternative energy sources, solar energy probably would be near the top. Of course, the energy we use from all sources ultimately originates from the Sun. It would seem that solar energy would be the easiest to use. The problem is how to store solar energy when the Sun is not shining. In this experiment, you will investigate one method that could be used to trap and store solar energy.

### Problem
Build a small-scale model of a solar pond and test how it traps and stores solar energy.

### Objectives
• **Construct** a small-scale solar pond using simple materials.
• **Collect** temperature data as the solar pond model heats and cools.
• **Hypothesize** as to why a solar pond is able to trap and store energy.

### Materials
CBL System
graphing calculator
ChemBio program
link-to-link cable
temperature probes (2)
150-watt light bulb
socket and clamp for bulb
black plastic frozen-dinner dish

waterproof tape
table salt
hot plate
stirring rod
250-mL beaker
beaker tongs
TI-Graph Link (optional)
ring stand and clamp
250-mL graduated cylinder

### Safety Precautions

• The light bulb will become hot when it is turned on.
• Do not touch the hot plate while it is on.

### Pre-Lab

1. Read the entire **CHEMLAB.**
2. Prepare all written materials that you will take into the laboratory. Include safety precautions and procedure notes.
3. Water is transparent to visible light but opaque to infrared radiation. How do you think these properties will affect your solar pond model?
4. If you used only tap water in your model, convection currents would bring warmer, less dense water from the bottom to the surface. Do you think this will happen with your solar pond model? Explain your answer.
5. Predict which of the two layers of the model will have the higher final temperature. Explain your prediction.

### Procedure

1. Prepare a saturated table salt (NaCl) solution by heating 100 mL of tap water in a beaker on a hot plate. When the water is boiling, slowly add enough table salt to saturate the solution while stirring with a stirring rod. Remove the beaker from the hot plate with beaker tongs and allow the solution to cool slowly overnight.
2. The next day, prepare the solar pond model. Place the black plastic dish on the lab bench where you want to run the experiment. Use a small piece of waterproof tape to attach one of the temperature probes to the bottom of the black plastic dish. Plug this probe into Channel 1 of the CBL System. Slowly pour the 100 mL of saturated salt solution into the dish.
3. Carefully add about 100 mL of tap water on top of the saturated salt-water layer in the dish. Use care not to mix the two layers. Suspend the end of the second temperature probe in the tap-water layer and plug it into Channel 2 of the CBL System.

can be longer than 30 minutes if more lab time is available. The sample data had a run time of 40 minutes.
• A discussion about convection currents will aid students' analyses of their results.
• Students can add food coloring to the salt-water layer to confirm that convection does not occur.

### Expected Results
Students will find that the saturated salt-solution layer retains the heat better than the tap-water layer.

4. Connect the graphing calculator to the CBL System using the link cable. Turn on both units. Run the ChemBio program. Choose 1:SET UP PROBES from MAIN MENU. Choose 2 probes. Under SELECT PROBE, choose 1:TEMPERATURE. Enter 1 for Channel. This is for the probe at the bottom of the salt water. Under SELECT PROBE, choose 1: TEMPERATURE. Enter 2 for Channel. This is for the probe in the tap-water layer.

5. Under MAIN MENU, choose 2: COLLECT DATA. Choose 2: TIME GRAPH. For time between samples in seconds, choose 30. For number of samples, choose 60. This will allow the experiment to run for 30 minutes. Set the calculator to use this time setup. Input the following: Ymin = 0, Ymax = 30, Yscl = 1. Do not start collecting data yet.

6. Position the 150-watt light bulb about 15 to 20 cm over the top of the solar pond model. Turn on the light. Press ENTER on the calculator to begin collecting data. After about 6 to 8 minutes, turn off the light bulb and move it away from the solar pond model. Do not disturb the experiment until the calculator is finished with its 30 minute run.

## Cleanup and Disposal

Rinse the salt solution off the temperature probes.

## Analyze and Conclude

1.  **Graphing Data** Make a copy of the graph from the graphing calculator. If you have TI-Graph Link and a computer, do a screen print.

2. **Interpreting Graphs** Describe the shape of each curve in the graph of time versus temperature before and after the light bulb was turned off. Explain the significance of the difference.

3. **Comparing and Contrasting** Which layer of your solar pond model did the best job of trapping and storing heat?

4. **Applying Concepts** Why does the graph of time versus temperature decrease more rapidly near the surface when the light bulb is turned off?

5. **Forming a Hypothesis** Make a hypothesis to explain what is happening in your model.

6. **Designing an Experiment** How would you test your hypothesis?

7. **Error Analysis** How might your results have been different if you had used a white dish by mistake instead of a black dish? Explain.

## Real-World Chemistry

1. Water in a lake rises to the surface when heated and sinks to the bottom when cooled in a process called convection. Compare and contrast the density of the water as it rises with the density of the water as it sinks.

2. The El Paso Solar Pond was the first in the world to successfully use solar pond technology to store and supply heat for industrial processes. It was built with three main layers: a top layer that contains little salt, a middle layer with a salt content that increases with depth, and a very salty bottom layer that stores the heat. Which layer has the greatest density? The least density? Why doesn't the storage layer in the El Paso Solar Pond cool by convection?

**Resource Manager**

**ChemLab and MiniLab Worksheets,** pp. 105–107 L2

## Analyze and Conclude

1.

Solar Pond Model graph — Temperature (°C) vs Time(s), showing Top Water Layer and Bottom Salt Layer curves.

2. Water layer–the curve climbs rapidly until the bulb is turned off, when it falls rapidly. Salt layer–curve climbs steadily. When the bulb is turned off, the curve levels off. This indicates that heat is retained.

3. The salt-water layer traps and stores heat better.

4. Contact with the cooler air causes rapid cooling. Evaporation of the warm water causes the water to lose heat.

5. Convection currents do not occur because salt water is denser than tap water. Thus, the warm salt water does not rise to the surface to be cooled.

6. Repeat the experiment using colored salt water. The color will not mix with the water layer if there is no convection.

7. The bottom layer will not warm up as rapidly because the white dish will not absorb as much heat as the black dish.

## Real-World Chemistry

1. The density of the water decreases as it rises and increases as it sinks.

2. The density of the layers decreases from bottom to top. The storage layer doesn't cool by convection because its density is greater than that of the layers above it.

# How It Works

## How It Works

## Purpose

Students will learn how an ion exchange water softener works.

## Background

The water softener contains a material called an ion exchange resin, made from polystyrene pellets or beads, which are then treated with sulfuric acid followed by sodium hydroxide. The sulfuric acid treatment causes the surface of the material to acquire a negative charge and the sodium hydroxide treatment places positively charged sodium ions on the surface.

## Visual Learning

Students may question how the doubly charged hardness ions can be replaced by the singly charged sodium ions during the recharge cycle. Logically, the double charge should be more tightly bound to the resin. The sodium ions displace the hardness ions because they are present in such large numbers that the equilibrium is shifted in their favor. The effectiveness of the recharge is dependent on the salt concentration of the brine. Brine of a higher concentration gives more softening capacity before a recharge is needed at the expense of increased salt usage.

## Teaching Strategies

- Students should be made aware of the fact that a water softener does not remove all of the hardness ions from the water. It removes large numbers of the offending ions, but the process is concentration dependent. If the hardness ion concentration is small, then the displacement reaction does not proceed because it has reached equilibrium.
- Ask students what effect hard water has on hot water heaters and hot water pipes. Water heaters and pipes can become clogged with a material called scale, a mixture of calcium and/or

## How It Works
### Water Softener

Water that contains substantial amounts of dissolved calcium and magnesium salts is called hard water. Water acquires these salts when it passes through soil and rocks that contain calcium and magnesium carbonates. While these salts are not toxic, they react with soaps and detergents to form an insoluble scum on sinks, bathtubs, and showers. When clothes are washed in hard water, some of the insoluble material adheres to the clothes and alters the way they feel. A device called a water softener can solve the hard-water problem by removing the excess calcium and magnesium ions.

1. Hard water flows over an ion exchange column containing pellets coated with sodium ions.

2. Because sodium is more reactive than calcium, sodium and calcium ions exchange places.

Ion exchange resin

3. Softened water containing sodium salts flows to faucets.

Softening process

6. Calcium ions and brine solution flow to the sewer.

5. Sodium ions attach to the resin, and the resin releases trapped calcium ions.

4. When the sodium ions on the resin are used up, they are replaced by flowing a brine solution through the ion exchange resin.

Recharge process

### Thinking Critically

1. **Predicting**  Would you expect a water softener to be effective in removing materials such as sugar, alcohol, grease, and oil? Explain your answer.

2. **Using Resources**  Find information about water softening processes that use ions other than sodium ions. Report your findings to the class.

magnesium carbonates similar to limestone. Scale is less soluble in hot water than in cold and so it slowly coats the surfaces of the hot water supply plumbing.

## Thinking Critically

1. Since these substances do not form ions, the water softener would not affect them. (The oil and grease can actually

damage a water softener because they may adhere to the resin, reducing its effectiveness and clogging the spaces between the resin pellets.)

2. Almost all development in this area centers on finding a way to use hydrogen ions in the exchange process. This would eliminate the possible health problems associated with excess sodium ions in the diet.

## Summary

### 26.1 Earth's Atmosphere

- Earth's atmosphere is divided into the troposphere, stratosphere, mesosphere, thermosphere, and exosphere. The layers vary according to altitude and temperature.

- Nitrogen and oxygen make up the majority of the atmospheric gases.

- Photodissociation and photoionization are important processes that absorb high-energy ultraviolet radiation in the upper atmosphere.

- The ozone layer in the stratosphere forms a protective barrier against harmful high-energy ultraviolet radiation. Levels of ozone have been depleted by chemical reactions with CFCs in the upper atmosphere above the North and South Poles.

- Photochemical smog is a major pollutant in many urban centers and is formed from chemicals that are produced principally by internal combustion engines.

- Emissions of $SO_2$ from the burning of fossil fuels have led to the production of acid rain.

### 26.2 Earth's Water

- Water is continuously recycled in the environment by the processes of evaporation, condensation, and precipitation.

- Earth has massive oceans that contain large quantities of dissolved salts. Salinity is a measure of the mass of these dissolved salts.

- Salinity is expressed as grams of salt per kilogram of seawater.

- Reverse osmosis can be used to desalinate ocean water and make it fit for human use.

- Freshwater is a precious natural resource. Municipal water supplies must be treated to ensure that they are safe to use. Sewage treatment plants process water that has been used so that it can be returned safely to the environment.

### 26.3 Earth's Crust

- Earth is divided into a core, mantle, and crust. The core is further divided into an inner and outer core. The crust is where living things reside. The crust can be divided further into the solid lithosphere, liquid hydrosphere, and gaseous atmosphere.

- The lithosphere contains a large number of elements. Most of these occur as minerals.

- Minerals are solid, inorganic compounds found in nature. They have distinct crystalline structures and chemical compositions. Minerals of various elements are found in the lithosphere mainly as oxides, carbonates, and sulfides.

- An ore is a substance, commonly a mineral, from which the metal it contains can be extracted and purified at a reasonable profit.

### 26.4 Cycles in the Environment

- Carbon dioxide, one of the principal components in the carbon cycle, is taken up by plants during photosynthesis and given off by plants and animals as a product of cellular respiration.

- The $CO_2$ in the atmosphere is a major cause of the greenhouse effect. Increases in greenhouse gases may cause global warming. Scientists do not agree on the causes or consequences of global warming.

- Nitrogen gas is converted into biologically useful nitrates by nitrogen fixation. Nitrogen is returned to the atmosphere by a cycle in the environment.

## Vocabulary

- atmosphere (p. 841)
- desalination (p. 851)
- global warming (p. 859)
- greenhouse effect (p. 859)
- hydrosphere (p. 850)
- lithosphere (p. 855)
- nitrogen fixation (p. 860)
- salinity (p. 851)
- stratosphere (p. 842)
- troposphere (p. 842)

## Using the Vocabulary

To reinforce chapter vocabulary, have students write a sentence using each term. **L2** **ELL**

## Review Strategies

- Have students list the major divisions of the atmosphere and name the common gases and pollutants associated with each layer. **L2**

- Have students summarize the water cycle and the impact of human activities on the quality and quantity of freshwater. **L2**

- Have students list the major components of the lithosphere and the composition of each layer. **L2**

- Have students relate the commonalities of the carbon and nitrogen cycles. **L2**

For additional help with vocabulary, have students access the Vocabulary PuzzleMaker online.

chemistrymc.com/ vocabulary_puzzlemaker

## EXAMVIEW® PRO

### Use ExamView® Pro Testmaker CD-ROM to:

- Create **multiple versions** of tests.
- Create **modified** tests with one mouse click for struggling students.
- **Edit** existing questions and add your own questions.
- **Build** tests based on national curriculum standards.

**National Science Content Standards**

Pages 864–865
UCP.1, UCP.2; B.2, B.3, B.4, B.6; E.1; F.3, F.4, F.5, F.6

## Concept Mapping

**21.** 1. bacteria; 2–3. soil, roots of legumes; 4. lightning; 5. nitrogen gas; 6. nitrogen oxides; 7. nitrogen fixation

## Mastering Concepts

**22.** a molecule of three oxygen atoms, which is formed in the stratosphere

**23.** It forms when sunlight reacts with pollutants in the air.

**24.** high-energy UV radiation

**25.** variations in altitude and temperature

**26.** Cl promotes the destruction of $O_3$ without being consumed in the process.

**27.** washing high-sulfur coal before it's burned and removing the $SO_2$ produced in the burning process before it's released into the atmosphere

**28.** the Sun

**29.** $Na^+$ and $Cl^-$

**30.** Substances are continuously added to seawater by rivers, volcanoes, and atmospheric processes and continuously removed by biological processes and sedimentation.

**31.** The semipermeable membrane allows the water but not the salt to pass through.

**32.** oxygen, silicon, aluminum, and iron

**33.** Whether a metal exists in nature as an oxide, sulfide, or carbonate is determined by its electronegativity, which reflects the element's position in the periodic table.

**34.** photosynthesis

**35.** the natural warming of Earth's surface when certain gases in the atmosphere absorb solar energy that has been reflected from Earth's surface

**36.** by lightning-initiated reactions with oxygen and nitrogen in the atmosphere and by nitrogen-fixing bacteria in the soil and on plant roots

## Chemistry Online

*Go to the Chemistry Web site at* **chemistrymc.com** *for additional Chapter 26 Assessment.*

## Concept Mapping

**21.** Complete the concept map using the following terms: roots of legumes, nitrogen oxides, soil, bacteria, nitrogen fixation, nitrogen gas, lightning.

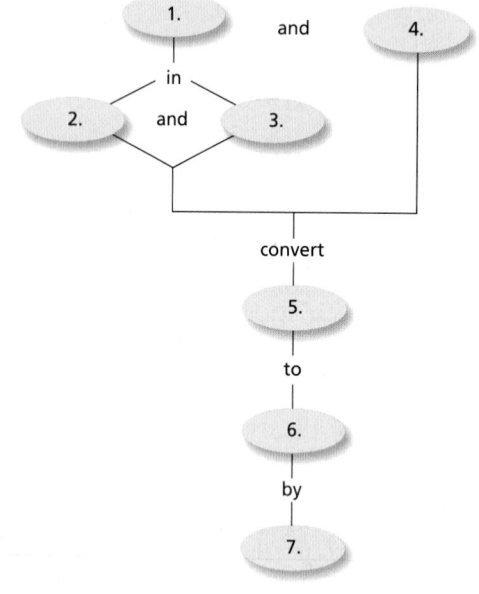

## Mastering Concepts

**22.** What is ozone? (26.1)

**23.** Why is smog more correctly termed photochemical smog? (26.1)

**24.** What kind of radiation causes molecules to be ionized in the upper atmosphere? (26.1)

**25.** What is the basis for the division of the atmosphere into layers? (26.1)

**26.** How do chlorine atoms act as a catalyst for ozone decomposition? (26.1)

**27.** What steps can be taken to reduce sulfur dioxide emissions into the environment? (26.1)

**28.** What provides the energy for the water cycle? (26.2)

**29.** What are the two most abundant ions in seawater? (26.2)

**30.** Why does the chemical composition of the oceans remain constant over time? (26.2)

**31.** What is the function of a semipermeable membrane in reverse-osmosis desalination? (26.2)

**32.** What are the four most abundant elements in the lithosphere? (26.3)

**33.** How does the position of a metal in the periodic table determine whether the element exists in nature as an oxide, a carbonate, or a sulfide? (26.3)

**34.** During what process is $CO_2$ from the troposphere converted into carbohydrates? (26.4)

**35.** What is the greenhouse effect? (26.4)

**36.** In what two ways is nitrogen fixed? (26.4)

## Mastering Problems
### Calculations About the Atmosphere (26.1)

**37.** How many liters of nitrogen are there in a 25.3-liter sample of air?

**38.** Identify the layer of the atmosphere that is represented by the following graph of temperature versus altitude.

**39.** Assuming a temperature of 20.0°C and an atmo-

spheric pressure of 729 mm Hg, calculate the number of particles of carbon dioxide gas in one cubic meter of dry air.

### Calculations About the Hydrosphere (26.2)

**40.** Water must have a salt concentration less than 500 ppm by mass to be fit for human use. Assuming that the salt is all NaCl, what is the molarity of this concentration?

**41.** Construct a circle graph to illustrate the amount of water used for various purposes by an average person each day.

**42.** What is the molarity of NaCl in a saltwater solution with a salinity of 6 g/kg? Assume that the only salt in the solution is NaCl and that the solution has a density of 1.0 g/mL.

chemistrymc.com/chapter_test

### Resource Manager

**Chapter Assessment,** pp. 151–156
**Supplemental Problems,** Ch. 26
**ExamView® Pro CD-ROM**
**MindJogger Videoquizzes DVD/VHS**
**Solutions Manual,** Ch. 26
**Chemistry Interactive CD-ROM,** Ch. 26 quiz

## Calculations About the Lithosphere (26.3)

**43.** **Table 26-5** shows the mass percent of iron in the universe, in Earth as a whole, and in various layers of Earth. Explain the differences in terms of the process that caused formation of Earth.

**Table 26-5**

| Abundance of Iron in Various Locations | |
| --- | --- |
| **Location** | **Percent by mass** |
| Whole universe | 0.19 |
| Whole Earth | 34.6 |
| Atmosphere, Lithosphere, Hydrosphere | 4.7 |
| Mantle | 13.3 |
| Core | 88.6 |

**44.** Earth's crust is 0.87% hydrogen by mass. The lithosphere is only 0.15% hydrogen. Account for this difference.

**45.** What is the mass percent of iron in each of the following iron minerals: $FeS_2$, $Fe_2O_3$, $Fe_3O_4$? If the iron can be extracted with equal ease from all three minerals, which would you use as a source of iron?

## Calculations About Natural Cycles (26.4)

**46.** About 30 million tons of $HNO_3$ are produced each year when lightning fixes nitrogen in the atmosphere. What is the mass percent of nitrogen in $HNO_3$? How much nitrogen does 30 million tons of $HNO_3$ contain?

**47.** If a plant consumes 50 g carbon dioxide in the process of photosynthesis during a given time period, how many liters of oxygen would it produce at 1 atm and 25°C? The balanced equation for photosynthesis is
$$6CO_2 + 6H_2O \rightarrow C_6H_{12}O_6 + 6O_2$$

## Mixed Review

*Sharpen your problem-solving skills by answering the following.*

**48.** Why must living organisms rely on nitrogen fixation for their source of nitrogen?

**49.** What is the major cause of the greenhouse effect?

**50.** What is the purpose of adding CaO and $Al_2(SO_4)_3$ in municipal water treatment?

**51.** Write balanced equations for the destruction of ozone by CFCs.

**52.** Why does nitrogen cause freshwater pollution?

**53.** In what form do plants use nitrogen? In what biological molecules is nitrogen found?

**54.** Write balanced equations showing the formation of acid rain.

**55.** Using balanced equations, compare photoionization and photodissociation of an oxygen molecule in the upper atmosphere.

**56.** What two elements would you expect to be most abundant in Earth's hydrosphere? Why?

## Thinking Critically

**57.** **Recognizing Cause and Effect** Environmental chemistry has a number of cause-and-effect relationships. Describe these relationships in **a)** the formation of acid rain, **b)** ozone depletion.

**58.** **Interpreting Data** Why are photodissociation and photoionization reactions more common in the upper atmosphere than in the lower atmosphere?

**59.** **Applying Concepts** Why do oxygen atoms exist for a longer period of time in the upper atmosphere than in the stratosphere?

## Writing in Chemistry

**60.** Write a short story tracing the path that a carbon atom in a carbon dioxide molecule might follow. Assume that the $CO_2$ molecule is in the troposphere.

**61.** Prepare an instruction sheet for a portable, reverse-osmosis desalination apparatus that can be used for camping. Research and include information on how efficient the apparatus is, how much pressure must be used, and how much drinking water can be produced in a given amount of time.

**62.** Metallurgy is the study of extracting and purifying metals from their ores. Conduct research to learn how iron is extracted from its ores, how it is purified, and how steel is made. Make a poster showing the steps in these processes, and include a short summary of each step and the chemical equations involved.

## Mastering Problems

Complete solutions to Chapter Assessment problems can be found in the **Solutions Manual.**

### Calculations about the Atmosphere (26.1)
**Level 1**
**37.** 19.7 L of $N_2$
**38.** the stratosphere

**Level 2**
**39.** $7.92 \times 10^{21}$ particles of $CO_2$

### Calculations about the Hydrosphere (26.2)
**Level 1**
**40.** 0.009*M* NaCl
**41.**

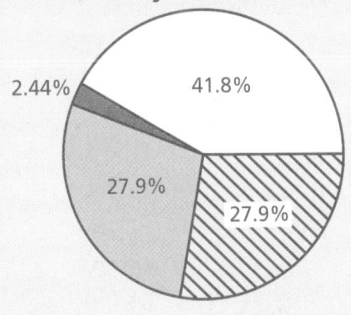

**Daily Water Use**

2.44%   41.8%
27.9%   27.9%

■ cooking and drinking      ■ toilet flushing
□ bathing, laundry, and housecleaning      ▨ yardwork

**Level 2**
**42.** 0.1*M*

### Calculations about the Lithosphere (26.3)
**Level 1**
**43.** Earth formed by the gradual cooling of a large molten mass. As it cooled, the heavy element iron was drawn to the central core by gravity, whereas lighter elements rose to the mantle and crust. As a result, iron makes up the largest mass

**National Science Content Standards**

**Pages 866–867**
UCP.1, UCP.2; B.2, B.3, B.6; E.2; F.3, F.4, F.5, F.6

percentage of Earth's core, less of the mantle, and still less of the crust. Iron makes up an even smaller mass percentage of the entire universe because the vast majority of the matter in the universe consists of lighter elements such as hydrogen and helium.

**44.** Most of the hydrogen in Earth's crust exists in the form of water in the hydrosphere, rather than as compounds with other elements in the lithosphere.

**Level 2**
**45.** $FeS_2$: 46.55%; $Fe_2O_3$: 69.94%; $Fe_3O_4$: 72.36% $Fe_3O_4$ should be used.

## Calculations about Natural Cycles (26.4)

### Level 1
**46.** mass % N = 22.23% N
mass N = $7 \times 10^6$ tons N

### Level 2
**47.** 30 L $O_2$

## Mixed Review

**48.** They cannot use nitrogen gas.

**49.** The greenhouse effect is caused by the absorption of solar energy by certain gases in the atmosphere.

**50.** CaO and $Al_2(SO_4)_3$ help coagulate small particles and bacteria so that they settle out of the water.

**51.** See Solutions Manual and equations on page 845.

**52.** Nitrogen oxides from car exhaust combine with atmospheric moisture to form nitric acid, which falls to Earth as acid rain, thereby increasing the acidity of freshwater. Nitrogen from fertilizers and detergents cause algal blooms, which deplete oxygen in water.

**53.** Plants use nitrogen in the form of nitrates. Nitrogen is found in proteins, nucleic acids, and ATP.

**54.** See page 847 and Solutions Manual.

**55.** See pages 843–844 and Solutions Manual.

**56.** Hydrogen and oxygen because the hydrosphere includes all water ($H_2O$) on Earth's surface.

## Thinking Critically

**57. a.** Cause: Burning of high-sulfur coal and oil and fossil fuels. Effect: Formation of acid rain.
**b.** Cause: Use of CFCs as coolants and propel-lants. Effect: Ozone depletion.

**58.** There is more high-energy UV radiation that causes

## Cumulative Review

*Refresh your understanding of previous chapters by answering the following.*

**63.** Why is it necessary to perform repeated experiments in order to support a hypothesis? (Chapter 1)

**64.** A 49.01-g sample of lead displaces 4.5 mL of water. What is the density of lead? (Chapter 2)

**65.** Are the following physical or chemical changes? (Chapter 3)
**a.** water boils
**b.** charcoal burns
**c.** sugar dissolves in tea
**d.** potassium reacts with water
**e.** an ice cube melts

**66.** The isotope of carbon that is used to date artifacts contains six protons and eight neutrons. What is the atomic number of this isotope? How many electrons does it have? What is its mass number? (Chapter 4)

**67.** **Table 26-6** shows abundance of the two isotopes of silver found in nature. The more abundant isotope has an atomic mass of a little less than 107, but the average atomic mass of silver on the periodic table is about 107.9. Explain why it is higher. (Chapter 5)

**Table 26-6**

| Abundance of Silver | |
|---|---|
| **Isotope** | **Abundance** |
| Ag-107 | 51.8% |
| Ag-109 | 48.2% |

**68.** For each of the following elements, tell how many electrons are in each energy level and write the electron dot structure. (Chapter 6)
**a.** Ar       **d.** Al
**b.** Mg       **e.** F
**c.** N        **f.** S

**69.** Use the periodic table to separate these 12 elements into six pairs of elements having similar properties. (Chapter 7)

Ca, K, Ga, P, Si, Rb, B, Sr, Sn, Cl, Bi, Br

**70.** Write the formula for the binary ionic compound that forms from each pair of elements. (Chapter 8)
**a.** manganese(III) and iodine
**b.** calcium and oxygen
**c.** aluminum and fluorine
**d.** potassium and sulfur

**e.** zinc and bromine
**f.** lead(IV) and oxygen

**71.** Name the following molecular compounds. (Chapter 9)
**a.** NO
**b.** IBr
**c.** $N_2O_4$
**d.** CO
**e.** $SiO_2$
**f.** $ClF_3$

**72.** Classify each of the following reactions. (Chapter 10)
**a.** $N_2O_4(g) \rightarrow 2NO_2(g)$
**b.** $2Fe(s) + O_2(g) \rightarrow 2FeO(s)$
**c.** $2Al(s) + 3Cl_2(g) \rightarrow 2AlCl_3(s)$
**d.** $BaCl_2(aq) + Na_2SO_4(aq) \rightarrow BaSO_4(s) + 2NaCl(aq)$
**e.** $Mg(s) + CuSO_4(aq) \rightarrow Cu(s) + MgSO_4(aq)$

**73.** Calculate the total number of ions in 10.8 g of magnesium bromide. (Chapter 11)

**74.** Calculate the mass of AgCl formed when 85.6 g of silver sulfide ($Ag_2S$) react with excess hydrochloric acid (HCl). (Chapter 12)

**75.** Why will water in a flask begin to boil at room temperature as air is pumped out of the flask? (Chapter 13)

**76.** How many moles are contained in a 2.44-L sample of gas at 25.0°C and 202 kPa? (Chapter 14)

**77.** How would you prepare 5.0 L of a 1.5*M* solution of glucose ($C_6H_{12}O_6$)? (Chapter 15)

**78.** Compare the energy of the reactants and the products for a reaction in which $\Delta H$ is negative. Is the reaction endothermic or exothermic? (Chapter 16)

**79.** Identify the following hydrocarbons as alkane, alkene, or alkyne. (Chapter 22)
**a.** 1-hexyne
**b.** 3-methyldecane
**c.** propene
**d.** *cis*-2-butene

**80.** Water is released in a reaction in which two different functional groups condense to form an ester. What two functional groups take part in this reaction? (Chapter 23)

**81.** Name the two functional groups in an amino acid that become linked when a peptide bond is formed. (Chapter 24)

**82.** What element is formed if magnesium-24 is bombarded with a neutron and then ejects a proton? Write the balanced nuclear equation. (Chapter 25)

photodissociation and photoioniza-tion in the upper atmosphere.

**59.** In the upper atmosphere, there are fewer other gas particles for the oxygen atoms to collide and react with.

## Cumulative Review

**63.** Experiments must be repeated to be sure that they yield similar results each time.

**64.** 11 g/mL

**65. a.** physical       **d.** chemical
**b.** chemical       **e.** physical
**c.** physical

**66.** The atomic number is six; it has six electrons; its mass number is 14.

**67.** The value 107.9 represents the weighted average of both isotopes present with their abundances taken into account.

# STANDARDIZED TEST PRACTICE
## CHAPTER 26

*Use these questions and the test-taking tip to prepare for your standardized test.*

**1.** Photodissociation, photoionization, and photochemical smog are all caused by the reaction of atmospheric gases with high energy

  **a.** infrared radiation.    **c.** cosmic rays.
  **b.** ultraviolet radiation.    **d.** microwaves.

**2.** What is the most abundant gas in Earth's atmosphere?

  **a.** $O_2$      **c.** $CO_2$
  **b.** $N_2$      **d.** $H_2$

**3.** When high-sulfur coal is burned, the following series of reactions occurs to produce acid rain:

$$S(s) + O_2(g) \rightarrow SO_2(g)$$
$$3SO_2(g) + O_3(g) \rightarrow 3SO_3(g)$$
$$SO_3(g) + H_2O(l) \rightarrow H_2SO_4(aq)$$

A coal is classified as high-sulfur by the United States Department of Energy if it contains more than 763 g of sulfur per unit. A unit is defined as the amount of coal needed to produce $1.0 \times 10^6$ British thermal units (BTUs) of heat. If a unit of coal containing 768 g of sulfur is burned, how much sulfuric acid ($H_2SO_4$) will be produced?

  **a.** $2.35 \times 10^3$ g    **c.** $7.06 \times 10^3$ g
  **b.** $4.08 \times 10^3$ g    **d.** $7.53 \times 10^4$ g

**Interpreting Graphs**   Use the graph to answer questions 4–6.

**4.** The nitrogen cycle occurs in the oceans as well as in the soil. Nitrates ($NO_3^-$) at the surface of the ocean are almost completely used up by living organisms. As these organisms die, they sink. As they sink, the nitrogen compounds inside their bodies are oxidized back to $NO_3^-$. In very deep waters, ocean currents mix the

water and decrease $NO_3^-$ concentration. These processes explain why the graph shows $NO_3^-$ concentration

  **a.** continuously decreasing with depth.
  **b.** continuously increasing with depth.
  **c.** decreasing and then increasing with depth.
  **d.** increasing and then decreasing with depth.

**5.** Nitrate concentration reaches a maximum at approximately what depth?

  **a.** 5500 m    **c.** 3000 m
  **b.** 500 m    **d.** 1500 m

**6.** At a depth of 4000 m, about how many grams of $NO_3^-$ are found in each liter of seawater?

  **a.** $1.6 \times 10^{-3}$ g    **c.** $3.5 \times 10^{-7}$ g
  **b.** $2.2 \times 10^{-3}$ g    **d.** $2.0 \times 10^3$ g

**7.** In the water cycle, evaporation must be balanced by which processes?

  **a.** condensation and sublimation
  **b.** ionization and precipitation
  **c.** precipitation and condensation
  **d.** dissolution and precipitation

**8.** Because the denser elements sank to the center of Earth as the new planet cooled, all of the following elements are relatively rare in Earth's crust EXCEPT

  **a.** aluminum.    **c.** platinum.
  **b.** gold.    **d.** lead.

**9.** Why do the proportions and amounts of dissolved salts in the oceans remain almost constant?

  **a.** the sources from which the ocean receives its salts have constant compositions
  **b.** the rates at which salts are added to and taken from the oceans balance each other
  **c.** none of the dissolved salts are ever removed from the seawater
  **d.** living organisms have no use for any of the salts dissolved in seawater

---

### TEST-TAKING TIP

**If It Looks Too Good To Be True** Beware of answer choices in multiple-choice questions that seem ready-made and obvious. Remember that only one answer choice for each question is correct. The rest are made up by the test-makers to distract you. This means that they may look very appealing. Check each answer choice carefully before finally selecting it.

---

 **chemistrymc.com/standardized_test**

Standardized Test Practice   **869**

---

**68.**   **a.** 2,8,8 :Är:  **d.** 2,8,3 .Äl·
      **b.** 2,8,2 Mg·  **e.** 2,7 :F̈:
      **c.** 2,5 .N̈:    **f.** 2,8,6 ·S̈:

**69.** Ca and Sr, K and Rb, Ga and B, P and Bi, Si and Sn, Cl and Br

**70.**   **a.** $MnI_3$  **d.** $K_2S$
      **b.** CaO    **e.** $ZnBr_2$
      **c.** $AlF_3$   **f.** $PbO_2$

**71.**   **a.** nitrogen monoxide
      **b.** iodine monobromide
      **c.** dinitrogen tetroxide
      **d.** carbon monoxide
      **e.** silicon dioxide
      **f.** chlorine trifluoride

**72.**   **a.** decomposition
      **b.** synthesis
      **c.** synthesis
      **d.** double replacement
      **e.** single replacement

**73.** $1.06 \times 10^{23}$ ions

**74.** 99.0 g AgCl

**75.** Decreasing the air pressure decreases the boiling point because boiling occurs when the vapor pressure equals the pressure exerted on the liquid's surface.

**76.** 0.199 mol

**77.** Dissolve 1350 g glucose in water to a final volume of 5 L of solution.

**78.** The energy of the products is less than the energy of the reactants. The reaction is exothermic.

**79.**   **a.** alkyne  **c.** alkene
      **b.** alkane  **d.** alkene

**80.** a hydroxyl group and a carboxyl group

**81.** an amino group and a carboxyl group

**82.** Sodium-23 is formed.
$$^{24}_{12}Mg + ^{1}_{0}n \rightarrow ^{23}_{11}Na + ^{1}_{1}p$$

---

## Standardized Test Practice

| | |
|---|---|
| **1.** b | **6.** b |
| **2.** b | **7.** c |
| **3.** a | **8.** a |
| **4.** d | **9.** b |
| **5.** d | |

---

National Science Content Standards
Pages 868–869
UCP.1, UCP.2; B.1, B.2, B.3, B.6

# Appendices

Complete solutions to
Supplemental Practice Problems
can be found in the **Solutions
Manual.**

## Chapter 2

### Section 2-1

**1.** The density of a substance is 4.8 g/mL. What is the volume of a sample that is 19.2 g?

**2.** A 2.00-mL sample of substance A has a density of 18.4 g/mL and a 5.00-mL sample of substance B has a density of 35.5 g/mL. Do you have an equal mass of substances A and B?

### Section 2-2

**3.** Express the following quantities in scientific notation.
   **a.** 5 453 000 m
   **b.** 300.8 kg
   **c.** 0.005 36 ng
   **d.** 0.012 032 5 km
   **e.** 34 800 s
   **f.** 332 080 000 cm
   **g.** 0.000 238 3 ms
   **h.** 0.3048 mL

**4.** Solve the following problems. Express your answers in scientific notation.
   **a.** $3 \times 10^2$ m + $5 \times 10^2$ m
   **b.** $8 \times 10^{-5}$ m + $4 \times 10^{-5}$ m
   **c.** $6.0 \times 10^5$ m + $2.38 \times 10^6$ m
   **d.** $2.3 \times 10^{-3}$ L + $5.78 \times 10^{-2}$ L
   **e.** $2.56 \times 10^2$ g − $1.48 \times 10^2$ g
   **f.** $5.34 \times 10^{-3}$ L − $3.98 \times 10^{-3}$ L
   **g.** $7.623 \times 10^5$ nm − $8.32 \times 10^4$ nm
   **h.** $9.052 \times 10^{-2}$ s − $3.61 \times 10^{-3}$ s

**5.** Solve the following problems. Express your answers in scientific notation.
   **a.** $(8 \times 10^3$ m$) \times (1 \times 10^5$ m$)$
   **b.** $(4 \times 10^2$ m$) \times (2 \times 10^4$ m$)$
   **c.** $(5 \times 10^{-3}$ m$) \times (3 \times 10^4$ m$)$
   **d.** $(3 \times 10^{-4}$ m$) \times (3 \times 10^{-2}$ m$)$
   **e.** $(8 \times 10^4$ g$) \div (4 \times 10^3$ mL$)$
   **f.** $(6 \times 10^{-3}$ g$) \div (2 \times 10^{-1}$ mL$)$
   **g.** $(1.8 \times 10^{-2}$ g$) \div (9 \times 10^{-5}$ mL$)$
   **h.** $(4 \times 10^{-4}$ g$) \div (1 \times 10^3$ mL$)$

**6.** Convert the following as indicated.
   **a.** 96 kg to g
   **b.** 155 mg to g
   **c.** 15 cg to kg
   **d.** 584 $\mu$s to s
   **e.** 188 dL to L
   **f.** 3600 m to km
   **g.** 24 g to pg
   **h.** 85 cm to nm

**7.** How many minutes are there in 5 days?

**8.** A car is traveling at 118 km/h. What is its speed in Mm/h?

### Section 2-3

**9.** Three measurements of 34.5 m, 38.4 m, and 35.3 m are taken. If the accepted value of the measurement is 36.7 m, what is the percent error for each measurement?

**10.** Three measurements of 12.3 mL, 12.5 mL, and 13.1 mL are taken. The accepted value for each measurement is 12.8 mL. Calculate the percent error for each measurement.

## Chapter 2
### Section 2.1
**1.** 4.0 mL
**2.** No, mass A does not equal mass B.

### Section 2.2
**3.** **a.** $5.453 \times 10^6$ m
   **b.** $3.008 \times 10^2$ kg
   **c.** $5.36 \times 10^{-3}$ ng
   **d.** $1.203\ 25 \times 10^{-2}$ km
   **e.** $3.48 \times 10^4$ s
   **f.** $3.3208 \times 10^8$ cm
   **g.** $2.383 \times 10^{-4}$ ms
   **h.** $3.048 \times 10^{-1}$ mL

**4.** **a.** $8 \times 10^2$ m
   **b.** $1.2 \times 10^{-4}$ m
   **c.** $2.98 \times 10^6$ m
   **d.** $6.01 \times 10^{-2}$ L
   **e.** $1.08 \times 10^2$ g
   **f.** $1.36 \times 10^{-3}$ L
   **g.** $6.791 \times 10^5$ nm
   **h.** $8.691 \times 10^{-2}$ s

**5.** **a.** $8 \times 10^8$ m²
   **b.** $8 \times 10^6$ m²
   **c.** $1.5 \times 10^2$ m²
   **d.** $9 \times 10^{-6}$ m²
   **e.** $2 \times 10^1$ g/mL
   **f.** $3 \times 10^{-2}$ g/mL
   **g.** $2 \times 10^2$ g/mL
   **h.** $4 \times 10^{-7}$ g/mL

**6.** **a.** $9.6 \times 10^4$ g
   **b.** $1.55 \times 10^{-1}$ g
   **c.** $1.5 \times 10^{-4}$ kg
   **d.** $5.84 \times 10^{-4}$ s
   **e.** $1.88 \times 10^1$ L
   **f.** 3.6 km
   **g.** $2.4 \times 10^{13}$ pg
   **h.** $8.5 \times 10^8$ nm
**7.** 7200 minutes
**8.** 0.118 Mm/h

### Section 2.3
**9.** 5.99%, 4.63%, 3.81%
**10.** 3.91%, 2.34%, 2.34%

**11. a.** 6
  **b.** 2
  **c.** 3
  **d.** 8
  **e.** 4
  **f.** 3
  **g.** 4
  **h.** 3
**12. a.** 0.003 09 km
  **b.** 3.08 g
  **c.** 5810 mL
  **d.** 34.7 mg
**13. a.** $5.832 \times 10^{-3}$ g
  **b.** $3.868\ 08 \times 10^{5}$ ns
  **c.** $5.800 \times 10^{-4}$ km
  **d.** $2.086 \times 10^{3}$ L
**14. a.** 103.8 m
  **b.** 0.167 kg
  **c.** 705 mL
  **d.** 8.00 mg
  **e.** 2.223 km
  **f.** 21.8 s
  **g.** 462.9 dm
  **h.** $4.7 \times 10^{2}$ m
**15. a.** 410 cm$^2$
  **b.** 0.021 mm$^2$
  **c.** 604 km$^2$
  **d.** 2.94 g/mL
  **e.** 1.426 g/mL
  **f.** 15.3 g/mL

## Chapter 3
### Section 3.2
  **1.** 0.2 kg oxygen
  **2.** 3.1 g hydrochloric acid

### Section 3.3
  **3.** 6.25 g sulfur
  **4.** No. Compound I contains 62.6% tin and 37.4% chlorine, and compound II contains 45.6% tin and 54.4% chlorine.

## Chapter 4
### Section 4.3
  **1. a.** 31; 31
  **b.** 14; 14
  **c.** 55; 55
  **d.** 20; 20
  **e.** 42; 42
  **f.** 22; 22
  **2. a.** 37
  **b.** 72
  **c.** 1
  **d.** 85

**11.** Determine the number of significant figures in each measurement.
  **a.** 340 438 g
  **b.** 87 000 ms
  **c.** 4080 kg
  **d.** 961 083 110 m
  **e.** 1.040 s
  **f.** 0.0483 m
  **g.** 0.2080 mL
  **h.** 0.000 048 1 g

**12.** Write the following in three significant figures.
  **a.** 0.003 085 0 km
  **b.** 3.0823 g
  **c.** 5808 mL
  **d.** 34.654 mg

**13.** Write the answers in scientific notation.
  **a.** 0.005 832g
  **b.** 386 808 ns
  **c.** 0.000 580 0 km
  **d.** 2086 L

**14.** Use rounding rules when you complete the following.
  **a.** 34.3 m + 35.8 m + 33.7 m
  **b.** 0.056 kg + 0.0783 kg + 0.0323 kg
  **c.** 309.1 mL + 158.02 mL + 238.1 mL
  **d.** 1.03 mg + 2.58 mg + 4.385 mg
  **e.** 8.376 km − 6.153 km
  **f.** 34.24 s −12.4 s
  **g.** 804.9 dm − 342.0 dm
  **h.** $6.38 \times 10^{2}$ m − $1.57 \times 10^{2}$ m

**15.** Complete the following calculations. Round off the answers to the correct number of significant figures.
  **a.** 34.3 cm × 12 cm
  **b.** 0.054 mm × 0.3804 mm
  **c.** 45.1 km × 13.4 km
  **d.** 45.5g ÷ 15.5 mL
  **e.** 35.43 g ÷ 24.84 mL
  **f.** 0.0482 g ÷ 0.003 146 mL

### Chapter 3

**Section 3-2**

**1.** A 3.5-kg iron shovel is left outside through the winter. The shovel, now orange with rust, is rediscovered in the spring. Its mass is 3.7 kg. How much oxygen combined with the iron?

**2.** When 5.0 g of tin reacts with hydrochloric acid, the mass of the products, tin chloride and hydrogen, totals 8.1 g. How many grams of hydrochloric acid were used?

**Section 3-3**

**3.** A compound is analyzed and found to be 50.0% sulfur and 50.0% oxygen. If the total amount of the sulfur oxide compound is 12.5 g, how many grams of sulfur are there?

**4.** Two unknown compounds are analyzed. Compound I contain 5.63 g of tin and 3.37 g of chlorine, while compound II contains 2.5 g of tin and 2.98 g of chlorine. Are the compounds the same?

### Chapter 4

**Section 4-3**

**1.** How many protons and electrons are in each of the following atoms?
  **a.** gallium
  **b.** silicon
  **c.** cesium
  **d.** calcium
  **e.** molybdenum
  **f.** titanium

**2.** What is the atomic number of each of the following elements?
  **a.** an atom that contains 37 electrons
  **b.** an atom that contains 72 protons

c. an atom that contains 1 electron
d. an atom that contains 85 protons

3. Use the periodic table to write the name and the symbol for each element identified in question 2.

4. An isotope of copper contains 29 electrons, 29 protons, and 36 neutrons. What is the mass number of this isotope?

5. An isotope of uranium contains 92 electrons and 144 neutrons. What is the mass number of this isotope?

6. Use the periodic table to write the symbols for each of the following elements. Then, determine the number of electrons, protons, and neutrons each contains.
   a. yttrium-88          d. bromine-79
   b. arsenic-75          e. gold-197
   c. xenon-129           f. helium-4

7. An element has two naturally occurring isotopes: $^{14}X$ and $^{15}X$. $^{14}X$ has a mass of 14.003 07 amu and a relative abundance of 99.63%. $^{15}X$ has a mass of 15.000 11 amu and a relative abundance of 0.37%. Identify the unknown element.

8. Silver has two naturally occurring isotopes. Ag-107 has an abundance of 51.82% and a mass of 106.9 amu. Ag-109 has a relative abundance of 48.18% and a mass of 108.9 amu. Calculate the atomic mass of silver.

### Chapter 5

**Section 5-1**

1. What is the frequency of an electromagnetic wave that has a wavelength of $4.55 \times 10^{-3}$ m? $1.00 \times 10^{-12}$ m?

2. Calculate the wavelength of an electromagnetic wave with a frequency of $8.68 \times 10^{16}$ Hz; $5.0 \times 10^{14}$ Hz; $1.00 \times 10^6$ Hz.

3. What is the energy of a quantum of visible light having a frequency of $5.45 \times 10^{14}$ s$^{-1}$?

4. An X ray has a frequency of $1.28 \times 10^{18}$ s$^{-1}$. What is the energy of a quantum of the X ray?

**Section 5-3**

5. Write the ground-state electron configuration for the following.
   a. nickel          c. boron
   b. cesium          d. krypton

6. What element has the following ground-state electron configuration [He]2s$^2$? [Xe]6s$^2$4f$^{14}$5d$^{10}$6p$^1$?

7. Which element in period 4 has four electrons in its electron-dot structure?

8. Which element in period 2 has six electrons in its electron-dot structure?

9. Draw the electron-dot structure for each element in question 5.

---

3. a. rubidium; Rb
   b. hafnium; Hf
   c. hydrogen; H
   d. astatine; At
4. 65
5. 236
6. a. Y; 39 electrons, 39 protons, 49 neutrons
   b. As; 33 electrons, 33 protons, 42 neutrons
   c. Xe; 54 electrons, 54 protons, 75 neutrons
   d. Br; 35 electrons, 35 protons, 44 neutrons
   e. Au; 79 electrons, 79 protons, 118 neutrons
   f. He; 2 electrons, 2 protons, 2 neutrons
7. nitrogen
8. 107.87 amu

### Chapter 5
**Section 5.1**
1. $6.59 \times 10^{10}$ Hz; $3.00 \times 10^{20}$ Hz
2. $3.46 \times 10^{-9}$ m; $6.0 \times 10^{-7}$ m; $3.00 \times 10^2$ m
3. $3.61 \times 10^{-19}$ J
4. $8.48 \times 10^{-16}$ J

**Section 5.3**
5. a. 1s$^2$2s$^2$2p$^6$3s$^2$3p$^6$4s$^2$3d$^8$ or [Ar]4s$^2$3d$^8$
   b. 1s$^2$2s$^2$2p$^6$3s$^2$3p$^6$4s$^2$3d$^{10}$4p$^6$5s$^2$4d$^{10}$5p$^6$6s$^1$ or [Xe]6s$^1$
   c. 1s$^2$2s$^2$2p$^1$ or [He]2s$^2$2p$^1$
   d. 1s$^2$2s$^2$2p$^6$3s$^2$3p$^6$4s$^2$3d$^{10}$4p$^6$ or [Kr]
6. beryllium; thallium
7. germanium
8. oxygen
9. a. Ni·
   b. Cs·
   c. ·B·
   d. :Kr:

# Chapter 6

## Section 6.2

1. **a.** 3A, 2, p
   **b.** 7B, 5, d
   **c.** 7B, 6, d
2. **a.** helium: $1s^2$ or [He]
   **b.** zirconium: $1s^22s^22p^63s^2$
   $3p^64s^23d^{10}4p^65s^24d^2$ or
   [Kr] $5s^24d^2$
   **c.** lead: $1s^22s^22p^63s^23p^64s^2$
   $3d^{10}4p^65s^24d^{10}5p^66s^24f^{14}$
   $5d^{10}6p^2$ or [Xe] $6s^24f^{14}$
   $5d^{10}6p^2$
   **d.** francium: $1s^22s^22p^63s^2$
   $3p^64s^23d^{10}4p^65s^24d^{10}5p^6$
   $6s^24f^{14}5d^{10}6p^67s^1$ or [Rn]
   $7s^1$

## Section 6.3

3. **a.** magnesium, calcium,
   and strontium
   **b.** fluorine, oxygen,
   and lithium
   **c.** fluorine, calcium,
   and cesium
   **d.** chlorine, selenium,
   and tellurium
   **e.** beryllium, krypton,
   and iodine

# Chapter 8

## Section 8.2

1. Zinc has two valence electrons. Chlorine has seven
   valence electrons. One zinc
   atom will lose two electrons forming a 2+ ion.
   Two chlorine atoms will
   each gain one electron
   forming two 1− ions. The
   oppositely charged ions
   will attract and form the
   ionic compound $ZnCl_2$. The
   two positive charges
   balance the two negative
   charges.
2. Barium has two valence
   electrons. Nitrogen has five
   valence electrons. Three
   barium atoms will each
   lose two electrons forming
   2+ ions. Two nitrogen
   atoms will each gain three
   electrons forming 3− ions.
   The oppositely charged
   ions will attract and form
   the ionic compound $Ba_3N_2$.
   The six positive charges
   balance the six negative
   charges.

---

### Chapter 6

**Section 6-2**

1. Identify the group, period, and block of an atom with the following electron configuration.
   **a.** $[He]2s^22p^1$    **b.** $[Kr]5s^24d^5$    **c.** $[Xe]6s^25f^{14}6d^5$

2. Write the electron configuration for the element fitting each of the following descriptions.
   **a.** The noble gas in the first period.
   **b.** The group 4B element in the fifth period.
   **c.** The group 4A element in the sixth period.
   **d.** The group 1A element in the seventh period.

**Section 6-3**

3. Using the periodic table and not **Figure 6-11,** rank each main group element in order of increasing size.
   **a.** calcium, magnesium, and strontium
   **b.** oxygen, lithium, and fluorine
   **c.** fluorine, cesium, and calcium
   **d.** selenium, chlorine, tellurium
   **e.** iodine, krypton, and beryllium

### Chapter 8

**Section 8-2**

1. Explain the formation of an ionic compound from zinc and chlorine.

2. Explain the formation of an ionic compound from barium and nitrogen.

**Section 8-3**

3. Write the chemical formula of an ionic compound composed of the following ions.
   **a.** calcium and arsenide
   **b.** iron(III) and chloride
   **c.** magnesium and sulfide
   **d.** barium and iodide
   **e.** gallium and phosphide

4. Determine the formula for ionic compounds composed of the following ions.
   **a.** copper(II) and acetate
   **b.** ammonium and phosphate
   **c.** calcium and hydroxide
   **d.** gold(III) and cyanide

5. Name the following compounds.
   **a.** $Co(OH)_2$    **d.** $K_2Cr_2O_7$
   **b.** $Ca(ClO_3)_2$    **e.** $SrI_2$
   **c.** $Na_3PO_4$    **f.** $HgF_2$

### Chapter 9

**Section 9-1**

1. Draw the Lewis structure for the following molecules.
   **a.** $CCl_2H_2$    **c.** $PCl_3$
   **b.** HF    **d.** $CH_4$

**Section 9-2**

2. Name the following binary compounds.
   **a.** $S_4N_2$    **d.** NO
   **b.** $OCl_2$    **e.** $SiO_2$
   **c.** $SF_6$    **f.** $IF_7$

---

## Section 8.3

3. **a.** $Ca_3As_2$    **c.** MgS    **e.** GaP
   **b.** $FeCl_3$    **d.** $BaI_2$
4. **a.** $Cu(C_2H_3O_2)_2$    **c.** $Ca(OH)_2$
   **b.** $(NH_4)_3PO_4$    **d.** $Au(CN)_3$
5. **a.** cobalt(II) hydroxide
   **b.** calcium chlorate
   **c.** sodium phosphate
   **d.** potassium dichromate
   **e.** strontium iodide
   **f.** mercury(II) fluoride

# Chapter 9

## Section 9.1

1. **a.** 

   **b.** $H-\ddot{\underset{\displaystyle\cdot\cdot}{F}}:$

**3.** Name the following acids: $H_3PO_4$, HBr, $HNO_3$.

**Section 9-3**   **4.** Draw the Lewis structure for each of the following.
   **a.** CO                    **d.** $OCl_2$
   **b.** $CH_2O$               **e.** $SiO_2$
   **c.** $N_2O$                **f.** $AlBr_3$

**5.** Draw the Lewis resonance structure for $CO_3{}^{2-}$.

**6.** Draw the Lewis resonance structure for $CH_3CO_2{}^-$.

**7.** Draw the Lewis structure for NO and $IF_4{}^-$.

**Section 9-4**   **8.** Determine the molecular geometry, bond angles, and hybrid of each molecule in question 4.

**Section 9-5**   **9.** Determine whether each of the following molecules is polar or nonpolar.
   **a.** $CH_2O$               **c.** $SiH_4$
   **b.** $BF_3$                **d.** $H_2S$

---

## Chapter 10

**Section 10-1** Write skeleton equations for the following reactions.
   **1.** Solid barium and oxygen gas react to produce solid barium oxide.
   **2.** Solid iron and aqueous hydrogen sulfate react to produce aqueous iron(III) sulfate and gaseous hydrogen.

Write balanced chemical equations for the following reactions.
   **3.** Liquid bromine reacts with solid phosphorus ($P_4$) to produce solid diphosphorus pentabromide.
   **4.** Aqueous lead(II) nitrate reacts with aqueous potassium iodide to produce solid lead(II) iodide and aqueous potassium nitrate.
   **5.** Solid carbon reacts with gaseous fluorine to produce gaseous carbon tetrafluoride.
   **6.** Aqueous carbonic acid reacts to produce liquid water and gaseous carbon dioxide.
   **7.** Gaseous hydrogen chloride reacts with gaseous ammonia to produce solid ammonium chloride.
   **8.** Solid copper(II) sulfide reacts with aqueous nitric acid to produce aqueous copper(II) sulfate, liquid water, and nitrogen dioxide gas.

**Section 10-2** Classify each of the following reactions in as many classes as possible.
   **9.** $2Mo(s) + 3O_2(g) \rightarrow 2MoO_3(s)$
   **10.** $N_2H_4(l) + 3O_2(g) \rightarrow 2NO_2(g) + 2H_2O(l)$

Write balanced chemical equations for the following decomposition reactions.
   **11.** Aqueous hydrogen chlorite decomposes to produce water and gaseous chlorine(III) oxide.
   **12.** Calcium carbonate(s) decomposes to produce calcium oxide(s) and carbon dioxide(g).

Use the activity series to predict whether each of the following single-replacement reactions will occur:
   **13.** $Al(s) + FeCl_3(aq) \rightarrow AlCl_3(aq) + Fe(s)$
   **14.** $Br_2(l) + 2LiI(aq) \rightarrow 2LiBr(aq) + I_2(aq)$
   **15.** $Cu(s) + MgSO_4(aq) \rightarrow Mg(s) + CuSO_4(aq)$

**Practice Problems**

**c.** (Lewis structure of $Cl{-}P{-}Cl$ with $Cl$ below)

**d.** (Lewis structure of $H{-}C{-}H$ with H above and below)

## Section 9.2

**2. a.** tetrasulfur dinitride
   **b.** oxygen dichloride
   **c.** sulfur hexafluoride
   **d.** nitrogen monoxide
   **e.** silicon dioxide
   **f.** iodine heptafluoride
**3.** phosphoric acid; hydrobromic acid; nitric acid

## Section 9.3

**4. a.** :C≡O:
   **b.** (Lewis structure H—C=O with H above)
   **c.** :N=O=N:
   **d.** (Lewis structure Cl—O with Cl below)
   **e.** :O=Si=O:
   **f.** (Lewis structure Br—Al—Br with Br above)

**5.** (resonance structures of $CO_3{}^{2-}$, three forms, each $2-$)

**6.** (resonance structures of $CH_3CO_2{}^-$, two forms, each $-$)

**7.** (Lewis structures of N=O and $IF_4$ with $-$ charge)

---

## Section 9.4

**8. a.** CO: linear, 180°, sp
   **b.** $CH_2O$: trigonal planar, 120°, $sp^2$
   **c.** $N_2O$: linear, 180°, sp
   **d.** $OCl_2$: bent, 104.5°, $sp^3$
   **e.** $SiO_2$: linear, 180°, sp
   **f.** $AlBr_3$: trigonal planar, 120°, $sp^2$

## Section 9.5

**9. a.** polar     **c.** nonpolar
   **b.** nonpolar  **d.** polar

## Chapter 10

### Section 10.1

   **1.** $Ba(s) + O_2(g) \rightarrow BaO(s)$
   **2.** $Fe(s) + H_2SO_4(aq) \rightarrow$ $Fe_2(SO_4)_3(aq) + H_2(g)$
   **3.** $5Br_2(l) + P_4(s) \rightarrow 2P_2Br_5(s)$
   **4.** $Pb(NO_3)_2(aq) + 2KI(aq) \rightarrow PbI_2(s) +$ $2KNO_3(aq)$

**National Science Content Standards**

**Pages 874–875**
UCP.1, UCP.2, UCP.3, UCP.5; B.1, B.2, B.3

**5.** $C(s) + 2F_2(g) \rightarrow CF_4(g)$

**6.** $H_2CO_3(aq) \rightarrow H_2O(l) + CO_2(g)$

**7.** $HCl(g) + NH_3(g) \rightarrow NH_4Cl(s)$

**8.** $CuS(s) + 8HNO_3(aq) \rightarrow CuSO_4(aq) + 4H_2O(l) + 8NO_2(g)$

## Section 10.2

**9.** synthesis; combustion

**10.** combustion

**11.** $2HClO_2(aq) \rightarrow H_2O(l) + Cl_2O_3(g)$

**12.** $CaCO_3(s) \rightarrow CaO(s) + CO_2(g)$

**13.** yes

**14.** yes

**15.** no

**16.** $2Bi(NO_3)_3(aq) + 3Na_2S(aq) \rightarrow Bi_2S_3(s) + 6NaNO_3(aq)$

**17.** $MgCl_2(aq) + K_2CO_3(aq) \rightarrow MgCO_3(s) + 2KCl(aq)$

## Section 10.3

**18.** $Ba^{2+}(aq) + 2F^-(aq) \rightarrow BaF_2(s)$

**19.** $2Cu^+(aq) + S^{2-}(aq) \rightarrow Cu_2S(s)$

**20.** $H^+(aq) + OH^-(aq) \rightarrow H_2O(l)$

**21.** $H^+(aq) + OH^-(aq) \rightarrow H_2O(l)$

**22.** $2H^+(aq) + CO_3^{2-} \rightarrow CO_2(g) + H_2O(l)$

**23.** $H^+(aq) + CN^-(aq) \rightarrow HCN(g)$

# Chapter 11

## Section 11.1

**1.** $2.26 \times 10^{24}$ atoms Fe

**2.** $7.53 \times 10^{24}$ formula units $CaCO_3$

**3.** 2.09 mol $CaCl_2$

**4.** 76.2 mol Ag

## Section 11.2

**5.** 1.47 g S

**6.** 0.143 g Fe

**7.** $2.52 \times 10^3$ g Ne

**8.** 1.49 mol Ti

**9.** 45.9 mol Pb

**10.** 0.0254 mol As

**11.** $1.19 \times 10^{21}$ atoms Na

**12.** $2.46 \times 10^{25}$ atoms Ga

**13.** 741 g Se

**14.** $4.32 \times 10^{-2}$ g Li

## Section 11.3

**15.** 0.0500 mol K; 0.0250 mol Cr; 0.100 mol O

**National Science Content Standards**

**Pages 876–877**
UCP.1, UCP.3; B.2, B.3

---

Write chemical equations for the following chemical reactions:

**16.** Bismuth(III) nitrate(aq) reacts with sodium sulfide(aq) yielding bismuth(III) sulfide(s) plus sodium nitrate(aq).

**17.** Magnesium chloride(aq) reacts with potassium carbonate(aq) yielding magnesium carbonate(s) plus potassium chloride(aq).

**Section 10-3** Write net ionic equations for the following reactions.

**18.** Aqueous solutions of barium chloride and sodium fluoride are mixed to form a precipitate of barium fluoride.

**19.** Aqueous solutions of copper(I) nitrate and potassium sulfide are mixed to form insoluble copper(I) sulfide.

**20.** Hydrobromic acid reacts with aqueous lithium hydroxide

**21.** Perchloric acid reacts with aqueous rubidium hydroxide

**22.** Nitric acid reacts with aqueous sodium carbonate.

**23.** Hydrochloric acid reacts with aqueous lithium cyanide.

### Chapter 11

**Section 11-1**  **1.** Determine the number of atoms in 3.75 mol Fe.

**2.** Calculate the number of formula units in 12.5 mol $CaCO_3$.

**3.** How many moles of $CaCl_2$ contains $1.26 \times 10^{24}$ formula units $CaCl_2$?

**4.** How many moles of Ag contains $4.59 \times 10^{25}$ atoms Ag?

**Section 11-2**  **5.** Determine the mass in grams of 0.0458 moles of sulfur.

**6.** Calculate the mass in grams of $2.56 \times 10^{-3}$ moles of iron.

**7.** Determine the mass in grams of 125 mol of neon.

**8.** How many moles of titanium are contained in 71.4 g?

**9.** How many moles of lead are equivalent to $9.51 \times 10^3$ g Pb?

**10.** Determine the number of moles of arsenic in 1.90 g As.

**11.** Determine the number of atoms in $4.56 \times 10^{-2}$ g of sodium.

**12.** How many atoms of gallium are in $2.85 \times 10^3$ g of gallium?

**13.** Determine the mass in grams of $5.65 \times 10^{24}$ atoms Se.

**14.** What is the mass in grams of $3.75 \times 10^{21}$ atoms Li?

**Section 11-3**  **15.** How many moles of each element is in 0.0250 mol $K_2CrO_4$.

**16.** How many moles of ammonium ions are in 4.50 mol $(NH_4)_2CO_3$?

**17.** Determine the molar mass of silver nitrate.

**18.** Calculate the molar mass of acetic acid ($CH_3COOH$).

**19.** Determine the mass of 8.57 mol of sodium dichromate ($Na_2Cr_2O_7$).

**20.** Calculate the mass of 42.5 mol of potassium cyanide.

**21.** Determine the number of moles present in 456 g $Cu(NO_3)_2$.

**22.** Calculate the number of moles in 5.67 g potassium hydroxide.

**23.** Calculate the number of each atom in 40.0 g of methanol ($CH_3OH$).

**16.** 9.00 mol $NH_4^+$

**17.** 169.88 g/mol $AgNO_3$

**18.** 60.05 g/mol $CH_3COOH$

**19.** 2250 g $Na_2Cr_2O_7$

**20.** 2770 g KCN

**21.** 2.43 mol $Cu(NO_3)_2$

**22.** 0.101 mol KOH

**23.** $7.53 \times 10^{23}$ atoms C, $3.01 \times 10^{24}$ atoms H, $7.53 \times 10^{23}$ atoms O

**24.** What mass of sodium hydroxide contains $4.58 \times 10^{23}$ formula units?

**Section 11-4** **25.** What is the percent by mass of each element in sucrose ($C_{12}H_{22}O_{11}$)?

**26.** Which of the following compounds has a greater percent by mass of chromium, $K_2CrO_4$ or $K_2Cr_2O_7$?

**27.** Analysis of a compound indicates the percent composition 42.07% Na, 18.89% P, and 39.04% O. Determine its empirical formula.

**28.** A colorless liquid was found to contain 39.12% C, 8.76% H, and 52.12% O. Determine the empirical formula of the substance.

**29.** Analysis of a compound used in cosmetics reveals the compound contains 26.76% C, 2.21% H, 71.17% O and has a molar mass of 90.04 g/mol. Determine the molecular formula for this substance.

**30.** Eucalyptus leaves are the food source for panda bears. Eucalyptol is an oil found in these leaves. Analysis of eucalyptol indicates it has a molar mass of 154 g/mol and contains 77.87% C, 11.76% H, and 10.37% O. Determine the molecular formula of eucalyptol.

**31.** Beryl is a hard mineral which occurs in a variety of colors. A 50.0-g sample of beryl contains 2.52 g Be, 5.01 g Al, 15.68 g Si, and 26.79g O. Determine its empirical formula.

**32.** Analysis of a 15.0-g sample of a compound used to leach gold from low grade ores is 7.03 g Na, 3.68 g C, and 4.29 g N. Determine the empirical formula for this substance.

**Section 11-5** **33.** Analysis of a hydrate of iron(III) chloride revealed that in a 10.00-g sample of the hydrate, 6.00 g is anhydrous iron(III) chloride and 4.00 g is water. Determine the formula and name of the hydrate.

**34.** When 25.00 g of a hydrate of nickel(II) chloride was heated, 11.37 g of water were released. Determine the name and formula of the hydrate.

<hr>

**Chapter 12**

**Section 12-1** Interpret the following balanced chemical equation in terms of particles, moles, and mass.
  **1.** $Mg + 2HCl \rightarrow MgCl_2 + H_2$
  **2.** $2Al + 3CuSO_4 \rightarrow Al_2(SO_4)_3 + 3Cu$

**3.** Write and balance the equation for the decomposition of aluminum carbonate. Determine the possible mole ratios.

**4.** Write and balance the equation for the formation of magnesium hydroxide and hydrogen from magnesium and water. Determine the possible mole ratios.

**Section 12-2** **5.** Some antacid tablets contain aluminum hydroxide. The aluminum hydroxide reacts with stomach acid according to the equation: $Al(OH)_3 + 3HCl \rightarrow AlCl_3 + 3H_2O$. Determine the moles of acid neutralized if a tablet contains 0.200 mol $Al(OH)_3$.

**6.** Chromium reacts with oxygen according to the equation: $4Cr + 3O_2 \rightarrow 2Cr_2O_3$. Determine the moles of chromium(III) oxide produced when 4.58 moles of chromium is allowed to react.

Supplemental Practice Problems     **877**

**24.** 32.7 g NaOH

**Section 11.4**
**25.** 42.103% C, 6.480% H, 51.417% O
**26.** $K_2Cr_2O_7$
**27.** $Na_3PO_4$
**28.** $C_3H_8O_3$
**29.** $C_2H_2O_4$
**30.** $C_{10}H_{18}O$
**31.** $Be_3Al_2Si_6O_{18}$
**32.** NaCN

**Section 11.5**
**33.** $FeCl_3 \cdot 6H_2O$, iron(III) chloride hexahydrate
**34.** $NiCl_2 \cdot 6H_2O$, nickel(II) chloride hexahydrate

**Chapter 12**

**Section 12.1**
**1.** 1 atom Mg + 2 molecules HCl → 1 formula unit $MgCl_2$ + 1 molecule $H_2$
1 mole Mg + 2 moles HCl → 1 mole $MgCl_2$ + 1 mole $H_2$
24.31 g Mg + 72.92 g HCl → 95.21 g $MgCl_2$ + 2.02 g $H_2$

**2.** 2 atoms Al + 3 formula units $CuSO_4$ → 1 formula unit $Al_2(SO_4)_3$ + 3 atoms Cu
2 moles Al + 3 moles $CuSO_4$ → 1 mole $Al_2(SO_4)_3$ + 3 moles Cu
53.96 g Al + 478.86 g $CuSO_4$ → 342.17 g $Al_2(SO_4)_3$ + 190.65 g Cu

**3.** $Al_2(CO_3)_3(s) \rightarrow Al_2O_3(s) + 3CO_2(g)$

$$\frac{1 \text{ mol } Al_2(CO_3)_3}{1 \text{ mol } Al_2O_3} \quad \frac{1 \text{ mol } Al_2(CO_3)_3}{3 \text{ mol } CO_2}$$

$$\frac{1 \text{ mol } Al_2O_3}{1 \text{ mol } Al_2(CO_3)_3} \quad \frac{1 \text{ mol } Al_2O_3}{3 \text{ mol } CO_2}$$

$$\frac{3 \text{ mol } CO_2}{1 \text{ mol } Al_2(CO_3)_3} \quad \frac{3 \text{ mol } CO_2}{1 \text{ mol } Al_2O_3}$$

**Practice Problems**

**4.** $Mg(s) + 2H_2O(l) \rightarrow Mg(OH)_2(s) + H_2(g)$

$$\frac{1 \text{ mol Mg}}{2 \text{ mol } H_2O} \quad \frac{1 \text{ mol Mg}}{1 \text{ mol } Mg(OH)_2} \quad \frac{1 \text{ mol Mg}}{1 \text{ mol } H_2}$$

$$\frac{2 \text{ mol } H_2O}{1 \text{ mol Mg}} \quad \frac{2 \text{ mol } H_2O}{1 \text{ mol } Mg(OH)_2} \quad \frac{2 \text{ mol } H_2O}{1 \text{ mol } H_2}$$

$$\frac{1 \text{ mol } Mg(OH)_2}{1 \text{ mol Mg}} \quad \frac{1 \text{ mol } Mg(OH)_2}{2 \text{ mol } H_2O} \quad \frac{1 \text{ mol } Mg(OH)_2}{1 \text{ mol } H_2}$$

$$\frac{1 \text{ mol } H_2}{1 \text{ mol Mg}} \quad \frac{1 \text{ mol } H_2}{2 \text{ mol } H_2O} \quad \frac{1 \text{ mol } H_2}{1 \text{ mol } Mg(OH)_2}$$

**Section 12.2**

**5.** 0.600 mol HCl
**6.** 2.29 mol $Cr_2O_3$

**7.** 924 g $CO_2$

**8.** 314 g $H_2SO_4$

**9.** 1.31 g $CO_2$

**10.** 195.7 g aspirin

## Section 12.3

**11.** Benzene is the limiting reactant; 4.2 g $Cl_2$ is in excess; 64.8 g chlorobenzene produced

**12.** HCl is the limiting reactant; 2.99 g Ni is in excess; 4.44 g $NiCl_2$ produced

## Section 12.4

**13.** $Sn + 2I_2 \rightarrow SnI_4$: theoretical yield is 26.4 g $SnI_4$; 94.7% yield

**14.** theoretical yield is 41.4 g $NaAu(CN)_2$; percent yield is 93.7%

## Chapter 13

### Section 13.1

**1.** 1.32:1

**2.** 58 g/ mol

### Section 13.2

**3.** 1469 mm Hg

**7.** Space vehicles use solid lithium hydroxide to remove exhaled carbon dioxide according to the equation: $2LiOH + CO_2 \rightarrow Li_2CO_3 + H_2O$. Determine the mass of carbon dioxide removed if the space vehicle carries 42.0 mol LiOH.

**8.** Some of the sulfur dioxide released into the atmosphere is converted to sulfuric acid according to the equation $2SO_2 + 2H_2O + O_2 \rightarrow 2H_2SO_4$. Determine the mass of sulfuric acid formed from 3.20 moles of sulfur dioxide.

**9.** How many grams of carbon dioxide are produced when 2.50 g of sodium hydrogen carbonate react with excess citric acid according to the equation: $3NaHCO_3 + H_3C_6H_5O_7 \rightarrow Na_3C_6H_5O_7 + 3CO_2 + 3H_2O$.

**10.** Aspirin ($C_9H_8O_4$) is produced when salicylic acid ($C_7H_6O_3$) reacts with acetic anhydride ($C_4H_6O_3$) according to the equation: $C_7H_6O_3 + C_4H_6O_3 \rightarrow C_9H_8O_4 + HC_2H_3O_2$. Determine the mass of aspirin produced when 150.0 g of salicylic acid reacts with an excess of acetic anhydride.

**Section 12-3** **11.** Chlorine reacts with benzene to produce chlorobenzene and hydrogen chloride, $Cl_2 + C_6H_6 \rightarrow C_6H_5Cl + HCl$. Determine the limiting reactant if 45.0 g of benzene reacts with 45.0 g of chlorine, the mass of the excess reactant after the reaction is complete, and the mass of chlorobenzene produced.

**12.** Nickel reacts with hydrochloric acid to produce nickel(II) chloride and hydrogen according to the equation $Ni + 2HCl \rightarrow NiCl_2 + H_2$. If 5.00 g Ni and 2.50 g HCl react, determine the limiting reactant, the mass of the excess reactant after the reaction is complete, and the mass of nickel(II) chloride produced.

**Section 12-4** **13.** Tin(IV) iodide is prepared by reacting tin with iodine. Write the balanced chemical equation for the reaction. Determine the theoretical yield if a 5.00-g sample of tin reacts in an excess of iodine. Determine the percent yield, if 25.0 g $SnI_4$ was actually recovered.

**14.** Gold is extracted from gold bearing rock by adding sodium cyanide in the presence of oxygen and water, according to the reaction, $4\ Au\ (s) + 8\ NaCN\ (aq) + O_2\ (g) + 2H_2O(l) \rightarrow 4\ NaAu(CN)_2$ (aq) $+ NaOH\ (aq)$. Determine the theoretical yield of $NaAu(CN)_2$ if 1000.0 g of gold bearing rock is used which contains 3.00% gold by mass. Determine the percent yield of $NaAu(CN)_2$ if 38.790 g $NaAu(CN)_2$ is recovered.

### Chapter 13

**Section 13-1** **1.** Calculate the ratio of effusion rates for methane ($CH_4$) and nitrogen.

**2.** Calculate the molar mass of butane. Butane's rate of diffusion is 3.8 times slower than that of helium.

**Section 13-2** **3.** What is the total pressure in a canister that contains oxygen gas at a partial pressure of 804 mm Hg, nitrogen at a partial pressure of 220 mm Hg, and hydrogen at a partial pressure of 445 mm Hg?

4. Calculate the partial pressure of neon in a flask that has a total pressure of 1.87 atm. The flask contains krypton at a partial pressure of 0.77 atm and helium at a partial pressure of 0.62 atm.

## Chapter 14

**Section 14-1**

1. The pressure of air in a 2.25-L container is 1.20 atm. What is the new pressure if the sample is transferred to a 6.50-L container? Temperature is constant.

2. The volume of a sample of hydrogen gas at 0.997 atm is 5.00 L. What will be the new volume if the pressure is decreased to 0.977 atm? Temperature is constant.

3. A gas at 55.0°C occupies a volume of 3.60 L. What volume will it occupy at 30.0°C? Pressure is constant.

4. The volume of a gas is 0.668 L at 66.8°C. At what Celsius temperature will the gas have a volume of 0.942 L, assuming the pressure remains constant?

5. The pressure in a bicycle tire is 1.34 atm at 33.0°C. At what temperature will the pressure inside the tire be 1.60 atm? Volume is constant.

6. If a sample of oxygen gas has a pressure of 810 torr at 298 K, what will be its pressure if its temperature is raised to 330 K?

7. Air in a tightly sealed bottle has a pressure of 0.978 atm at 25.5°C. What will its pressure be if the temperature is raised to 46.0°C?

**Section 14-2**

8. Hydrogen gas at a temperature of 22.0°C that is confined in a 5.00-L cylinder exerts a pressure of 4.20 atm. If the gas is released into a 10.0-L reaction vessel at a temperature of 33.6°C, what will be the pressure inside the reaction vessel?

9. A sample of neon gas at a pressure of 1.08 atm fills a flask with a volume of 250 mL at a temperature of 24.0°C. If the gas is transferred to another flask at 37.2°C at a pressure of 2.25 atm, what is the volume of the new flask?

10. What volume of beaker contains exactly $2.23 \times 10^{-2}$ mol of nitrogen gas at STP?

11. How many moles of air are in a 6.06-L tire at STP?

12. How many moles of oxygen are in a 5.5-L canister at STP?

13. What mass of helium is in a 2.00-L balloon at STP?

14. What volume will 2.3 kg of nitrogen gas occupy at STP?

**Section 14-3**

15. Calculate the number of moles of gas that occupy a 3.45-L container at a pressure of 150 kPa and a temperature of 45.6°C.

16. What is the pressure in torr that a 0.44-g sample of carbon dioxide gas will exert at a temperature of 46.2°C when it occupies a volume of 5.00 L?

17. What is the molar mass of a gas that has a density of 1.02 g/L at 0.990 atm pressure and 37°C?

4. 0.48 atm

## Chapter 14
### Section 14.1
1. 0.415 atm
2. 5.10 L
3. 3.33 L
4. 206°C
5. 92°C
6. $9.0 \times 10^2$ torr
7. 1.04 atm

### Section 14.2
8. 2.19 atm
9. 130 mL
10. 0.500 L
11. 0.271 mol
12. 0.25 mol
13. 0.357 g He
14. $1.8 \times 10^3$ L $N_2$

### Section 14.3
15. 0.20 mol
16. $4.0 \times 10^1$ torr
17. 26 g/mol

Practice Problems

Supplemental Practice Problems    **879**

**Practice Problems**

**18.** Calculate the grams of oxygen gas present in a 2.50-L sample kept at 1.66 atm pressure and a temperature of 10.0°C.

**19.** What volume of oxygen gas is needed to completely combust 0.202 L of butane ($C_4H_{10}$) gas?

**20.** Determine the volume of methane ($CH_4$) gas needed to react completely with 0.660 L of $O_2$ gas to form methanol ($CH_3OH$).

**Section 14-4 21.** Calculate the mass of hydrogen peroxide needed to obtain 0.460 L of oxygen gas at STP. $2H_2O_2(aq) \rightarrow 2H_2O(l) + O_2(g)$

**22.** When potassium chlorate is heated in the presence of a catalyst such as manganese dioxide, it decomposes to form solid potassium chloride and oxygen gas: $2KClO_3(s) \rightarrow 2KCl(s) + 3O_2(g)$. How many liters of oxygen will be produced at STP if 1.25 kg of potassium chlorate decomposes completely?

### Chapter 15

**Section 15-1 1.** Calculate the mass of gas dissolved at 150.0 kPa, if 0.35 g of the gas dissolves in 2.0 L of water at 30.0 kPa.

**2.** At which depth, 33 ft. or 133 ft, will a scuba diver have more nitrogen dissolved in the bloodstream?

**Section 15-2 3.** What is the percent by mass of a sample of ocean water that is found to contain 1.36 grams of magnesium ions per 1000 g?

**4.** What is the percent by mass of iced tea containing 0.75 g of aspartame in 250 g of water?

**5.** A bottle of hydrogen peroxide is labeled 3%. If you pour out 50 mL of hydrogen peroxide solution, what volume is actually hydrogen peroxide?

**6.** If 50 mL of pure acetone is mixed with 450 mL of water, what is the percent volume?

**7.** Calculate the molarity of 1270 g $K_3PO_4$ in 4.0 L aqueous solution.

**8.** What is the molarity of 90.0 g $NH_4Cl$ in 2.25 L aqueous solution?

**9.** Which is more concentrated, 25 g NaCl dissolved in 500 mL of water or a 10% solution of NaCl (percent by mass)?

**10.** Calculate the mass of NaOH required to prepare a 0.343$M$ solution dissolved in 2500 mL of water?

**11.** Calculate the volume required to dissolve 11.2 g $CuSO_4$ to prepare a 0.140$M$ solution.

**12.** How would you prepare 500 mL of a solution that has a new concentration of 4.5$M$ if the stock solution is 11.6$M$?

**13.** Caustic soda is 19.1$M$ NaOH and is diluted for household use. What is the household concentration if 10 mL of the concentrated solution is diluted to 400 mL?

**14.** What is the molality of a solution containing 63.0 g $HNO_3$ in 0.500 kg of water?

**15.** What is the molality of an acetic acid solution containing 0.500 mole of $HC_2H_3O_2$ in 0.800 kg of water?

**16.** What mass of ethanol ($C_2H_5OH$) will be required to prepare a 2.00$m$ solution in 8.00 kg of water?

**17.** Determine the mole fraction of nitrogen in a gas mixture containing 0.215 mol $N_2$, 0.345 mol $O_2$, 0.023 mol $CO_2$, and 0.014 mol $SO_2$. What is the mole fraction of $N_2$?

**18.** A necklace contains 4.85 g of gold, 1.25 g of silver, and 2.40 g of copper. What is the mole fraction of each metal?

**Section 15-3** **19.** Calculate the freezing point and boiling point of a solution containing 6.42 g of sucrose ($C_{12}H_{22}O_{11}$) in 100.0 g of water.

**20.** Calculate the freezing point and boiling point of a solution containing 23.7 g copper(II) sulfate in 250.0 g of water.

**21.** Calculate the freezing point and boiling point of a solution containing 0.15 mol of the molecular compound naphthalene in 175 g of benzene ($C_6H_6$).

## Chapter 16

**Section 16-1** **1.** What is the equivalent in joules of 126 Calories?

**2.** Convert 455 kilojoules to kilocalories.

**3.** How much heat is required to warm 122 g of water by 23.0°C?

**4.** The temperature of 55.6 grams of a material decreases by 14.8°C when it loses 3080 J of heat. What is its specific heat?

**5.** What is the specific heat of a metal if the temperature of a 12.5-g sample increases from 19.5°C to 33.6°C when it absorbs 37.7 J of heat?

**Section 16-2** **6.** A 75.0-g sample of a metal is placed in boiling water until its temperature is 100.0°C. A calorimeter contains 100.00 g of water at a temperature of 24.4°C. The metal sample is removed from the boiling water and immediately placed in water in the calorimeter. The final temperature of the metal and water in the calorimeter is 34.9°C. Assuming that the calorimeter provides perfect insulation, what is the specific heat of the metal?

**Section 16-3** **7.** Use **Table 16-6** to determine how much heat is released when 1.00 mole of gaseous methanol condenses to a liquid.

**8.** Use **Table 16-6** to determine how much heat must be supplied to melt 4.60 grams of ethanol.

**Section 16-4** **9.** Calculate $\Delta H_{rxn}$ for the reaction $2C(s) + 2H_2(g) \rightarrow C_2H_4(g)$ given the following thermochemical equations:
$2CO_2(g) + 2H_2O(l) \rightarrow C_2H_4(g) + 3O_2(g)$ $\Delta H = 1411$ kJ
$C(s) + O_2(g) \rightarrow CO_2(g)$ $\Delta H = -393.5$ kJ
$2H_2(g) + O_2(g) \rightarrow 2H_2O(l)$ $\Delta H = -572$ kJ

**Practice Problems**

**15.** 0.625$m$
**16.** 737 g ethanol
**17.** 0.360
**18.** 0.332 Au, 0.157 Ag, 0.511 Cu

### Section 15.3
**19.** $T_f = -0.350°C$
    $T_b = 100.096°C$
**20.** $T_f = -2.20°C$
    $T_b = 100.606°C$
**21.** $T_f = 1.1°C$
    $T_b = 82.3°C$

## Chapter 16
### Section 16.1
**1.** $5.27 \times 10^5$ J
**2.** 109 Cal
**3.** $1.17 \times 10^4$ J
**4.** 3.74 J/(g·°C)

### Section 16.2
**5.** 0.214 J/(g·°C)
**6.** 0.900 J/(g·°C)

### Section 16.3
**7.** 35.2 kJ
**8.** 0.494 kJ

### Section 16.4
**9.** $\Delta H = 52$ kJ

National Science Content Standards

Pages 880–881
UCP.1, UCP.3, UCP.4; B.2, B.3, B.4, B.5, B.6

**10.** Calculate $\Delta H_{rxn}$ for the reaction $HCl(g) + NH_3(g) \rightarrow NH_4Cl(s)$ given the following thermochemical equations:
$H_2(g) + Cl_2(g) \rightarrow 2HCl(g)$ $\Delta H = -184$ kJ
$N_2(g) + 3H_2(g) \rightarrow 2NH_3(g)$ $\Delta H = -92$ kJ
$N_2(g) + 4H_2(g) + Cl_2(g) \rightarrow 2NH_4Cl(s)$ $\Delta H = -628$ kJ

Use standard enthalpies of formation from **Table 16-7** and **Appendix C** to calculate $\Delta H°_{rxn}$ for each of the following reactions.
**11.** $2HF(g) \rightarrow H_2(g) + F_2(g)$
**12.** $2H_2S(g) + 3O_2(g) \rightarrow 2H_2O(l) + 2SO_2(g)$

**Section 16-5** Predict the sign of $\Delta S_{system}$ for each reaction or process.
**13.** $FeS(s) \rightarrow Fe^{2+}(aq) + S^{2-}(aq)$
**14.** $SO_2(g) + H_2O(l) \rightarrow H_2SO_3(aq)$

Determine if each of the following processes or reactions is spontaneous or nonspontaneous.
**15.** $\Delta H_{system} = 15.6$ kJ, T = 415 K, $\Delta S_{system} = 45$ J/K
**16.** $\Delta H_{system} = 35.6$ kJ, T = 415 K, $\Delta S_{system} = 45$ J/K

### Chapter 17

**Section 17-1**   **1.** In the reaction A $\rightarrow$ 2B, suppose that [A] changes from 1.20 mol/L at time = 0 to 0.60 mol/L at time = 3.00 min and that [B] = 0.00 mol/L at time = 0.
**a.** What is the average rate at which A is consumed in mol/(L·min)?
**b.** What is the average rate at which B is produced in mol/(L·min)?

**Section 17-3**   **2.** What are the overall reaction orders in practice problems 16-18 on page 545?

**3.** If halving [A] in the reaction A $\rightarrow$ B causes the initial rate to decrease to one fourth its original value, what is the probable rate law for the reaction?

**4.** Use the data below and the method of initial rates to determine the rate law for the reaction $2NO(g) + O_2(g) \rightarrow 2NO_2(g)$

| Formation of NO₂ Data | | | |
|---|---|---|---|
| Trial | Initial [NO] (*M*) | Initial [O₂] (*M*) | Initial rate (mol/(L s)) |
| 1 | 0.030 | 0.020 | 0.0041 |
| 2 | 0.060 | 0.020 | 0.0164 |
| 3 | 0.030 | 0.040 | 0.0082 |

**Section 17-4**   **5.** The rate law for the reaction in which one mole of cyclobutane $(C_4H_8)$ decomposes to two moles of ethylene $(C_2H_4)$ at 1273 K is Rate = (87 s⁻¹)[C₄H₈]. What is the instantaneous rate of this reaction when
**a.** $[C_4H_8] = 0.0100$ mol/L?
**b.** $[C_4H_8] = 0.200$ mol/L?

## Chapter 18

### Section 18-1  Write equilibrium constant expressions for the following equilibria.

**1.** $N_2(g) + O_2(g) \rightleftharpoons 2NO$

**2.** $3O_2(g) \rightleftharpoons 2O_3(g)$

**3.** $P_4(g) + 6H_2(g) \rightleftharpoons 4PH_3(g)$

**4.** $CCl_4(g) + HF(g) \rightleftharpoons CFCl_2(g) + HCl(g)$

Write equilibrium constant expressions for the following equilibria.

**5.** $NH_4Cl(s) \rightleftharpoons NH_3(g) + HCl(g)$

**6.** $SO_3(g) + H_2O(l) \rightleftharpoons H_2SO_4(l)$

Calculate $K_{eq}$ for the following equilibria.

**7.** $H_2(g) + I_2(g) \rightleftharpoons 2HI(g)$
$[H_2] = 0.0109$, $[I_2] = 0.00290$, $[HI] = 0.0460$

**8.** $I_2(s) \rightleftharpoons I_2(g)$
$[I_2(g)] = 0.0665$

### Section 18-3

**9.** At a certain temperature, $K_{eq} = 0.0211$ for the equilibrium
$PCl_5(g) \rightleftharpoons PCl_3(g) + Cl_2(g)$.
  **a.** What is $[Cl_2]$ in an equilibrium mixture containing 0.865 mol/L $PCl_5$ and 0.135 mol/L $PCl_3$?
  **b.** What is $[PCl_5]$ in an equilibrium mixture containing 0.100 mol/L $PCl_3$ and 0.200 mol/L $Cl_2$?

**10.** Use the $K_{sp}$ value for zinc carbonate given in **Table 18-3** to calculate its molar solubility at 298 K.

**11.** Use the $K_{sp}$ value for iron(II) hydroxide given in **Table 18-3** to calculate its molar solubility at 298 K.

**12.** Use the $K_{sp}$ value for silver carbonate given in **Table 18-3** to calculate $[Ag^+]$ in a saturated solution at 298 K.

**13.** Use the $K_{sp}$ value for calcium phosphate given in **Table 18-3** to calculate $[Ca^{2+}]$ in a saturated solution at 298 K.

**14.** Does a precipitate form when equal volumes of $0.0040M$ $MgCl_2$ and $0.0020M$ $K_2CO_3$ are mixed? If so, identify the precipitate.

**15.** Does a precipitate form when equal volumes of $1.2 \times 10^{-4}M$ $AlCl_3$ and $2.0 \times 10^{-3}M$ NaOH are mixed? If so, identify the precipitate.

## Chapter 19

### Section 19-1

**1.** Write the balanced formula equation for the reaction between zinc and nitric acid.

**2.** Write the balanced formula equation for the reaction between magnesium carbonate and sulfuric acid.

**3.** Identify the base in the reaction
$H_2O(l) + CH_3NH_2(aq) \rightarrow OH^-(aq) + CH_3NH_3^+(aq)$

**4.** Identify the conjugate base described in the reaction in practice problems 1 and 2.

**5.** Write the steps in the complete ionization of hydrosulfuric acid.

**6.** Write the steps in the complete ionization of carbonic acid.

**Practice Problems**

## Chapter 18

### Section 18.1

**1.** $K_{eq} = \dfrac{[NO]^2}{[N_2][O_2]}$

**2.** $K_{eq} = \dfrac{[O_3]^2}{[O_2]^3}$

**3.** $K_{eq} = \dfrac{[PH_3]^4}{[P_4][H_2]^6}$

**4.** $K_{eq} = \dfrac{[CFCl_2][HCl]}{[CCl_4][HF]}$

**5.** $K_{eq} = [NH_3][HCl]$

**6.** $K_{eq} = \dfrac{1}{[SO_3]}$

**7.** $K_{eq} = 66.9$

**8.** $K_{eq} = 0.0665$

### Section 18.3

**9. a.** $0.135M$
   **b.** $0.948M$

**10.** $1.2 \times 10^{-5}M$

**11.** $8.9 \times 10^{-14}M$

**12.** $2.6 \times 10^{-4}M$

**13.** $3.4 \times 10^{-7}M$

**14.** No precipitate forms.

**15.** Yes; $Al(OH)_3$

## Chapter 19

### Section 19.1

**1.** $Zn(s) + 2HNO_3(aq) \rightarrow$
$Zn(NO_3)_2(aq) + H_2(g)$

**2.** $MgCO_3(s) + H_2SO_4(aq) \rightarrow$
$MgSO_4(aq) + H_2O(l) +$
$CO_2(g)$

**3.** The base is $CH_3NH_2$.

**4.** $OH^-$

**5.** $H_2S(aq) + H_2O(l) \rightleftharpoons$
$H_3O^+(aq) + HS^-(aq)$
$HS^-(aq) + H_2O(l) \rightleftharpoons$
$H_3O^+(aq) + S^{2-}(aq)$

**6.** $H_2CO_3(aq) + H_2O(l) \rightleftharpoons$
$H_3O^+(aq) + HCO_3^-(aq)$
$HCO_3^-(aq) + H_2O(l) \rightleftharpoons$
$H_3O^+(aq) + CO_3^{2-}(aq)$

**National Science Content Standards**

**Pages 882–883**
UCP.1, UCP.3, UCP.4; B.2, B.3, B.5, B.6

## Section 19.2

7. $K_a = \dfrac{[H^+][COOH^-]}{[HCOOH]}$

8. $K_a = \dfrac{[H^+][CO_3{}^{2-}]}{[HCO_3{}^-]}$

9. $K_b = \dfrac{[NH_4{}^+][OH^-]}{[NH_3]}$

10. $K_b = \dfrac{[C_6H_5NH_3{}^+][OH^-]}{[C_6H_5NH_2]}$

## Section 19.3

11. acidic
12. acidic
13. 3.35
14. pH = 11.94; pOH = 2.06
15. pH = 5.57; pOH = 8.43
16. $1.2 \times 10^{-3}M$
17. $3.6 \times 10^{-1}M$
18. 3.17
19. 9.53
20. $K_a = 2.2 \times 10^{-9}$
21. $K_a = 1.4 \times 10^{-5}$

## Section 19.4

22. $2HI(aq) + Be(OH)_2(aq) \rightarrow$ $BeI_2(aq) + 2H_2O(l)$
23. $HClO_4(aq) + LiOH(aq) \rightarrow$ $LiClO_4(aq) + H_2O(l)$
24. 0.1845$M$
25. 2.439$M$
26. $HCO_3{}^-(aq) + H_2O(l) \rightarrow$ $CO_3{}^{2-}(aq) + OH^-(aq)$; basic
27. No reaction; neutral

## Chapter 20
## Section 20.1

1. P is oxidized, Cl is reduced
   $Cl_2$ is the oxidizing agent
   P is the reducing agent
2. C is oxidized, H is reduced
   $H_2O$ is the oxidizing agent
   C is the reducing agent

**Section 19-2**  **7.** Write the acid ionization equation and ionization constant expression for formic acid (HCOOH).

**8.** Write the acid ionization equation and ionization constant expression for the hydrogen carbonate ion ($HCO^{3-}$).

**9.** Write the base ionization constant expression for ammonia.

**10.** Write the base ionization expression for aniline ($C_6H_5NH_2$).

**Section 19-3**  **11.** Is a solution in which $[H^+] = 1.0 \times 10^{-5}M$ acidic, basic, or neutral?

**12.** Is a solution in which $[OH^-] = 1.0 \times 10^{-11}M$ acidic, basic, or neutral?

**13.** What is the pH of a solution in which $[H^+] = 4.5 \times 10^{-4}M$?

**14.** Calculate the pH and pOH of a solution in which $[OH^-] = 8.8 \times 10^{-3}M$.

**15.** Calculate the pH and pOH of a solution in which $[H^+] = 2.7 \times 10^{-6}M$.

**16.** What is $[H^+]$ in a solution having a pH of 2.92?

**17.** What is $[OH^-]$ in a solution having a pH of 13.56?

**18.** What is the pH of a 0.000 67$M$ $H_2SO_4$ solution?

**19.** What is the pH of a 0.000 034$M$ NaOH solution?

**20.** The pH of a 0.200$M$ HBrO solution is 4.67. What is the acid's $K_a$?

**21.** The pH of a 0.030$M$ $C_2H_5COOH$ solution is 3.20. What is the acid's $K_a$?

**Section 19-4**  **22.** Write the formula equation for the reaction between hydroiodic acid and beryllium hydroxide.

**23.** Write the formula equation for the reaction between perchloric acid and lithium hydroxide.

**24.** In a titration, 15.73 mL of 0.2346$M$ HI solution neutralizes 20.00 mL of a LiOH solution. What is the molarity of the LiOH?

**25.** What is the molarity of a caustic soda (NaOH) solution if 35.00 mL of solution is neutralized by 68.30 mL of 1.250$M$ HCl?

**26.** Write the chemical equation for the hydrolysis reaction that occurs when sodium hydrogen carbonate is dissolved in water. Is the resulting solution acidic, basic, or neutral?

**27.** Write the chemical equation for any hydrolysis reaction that occurs when cesium chloride is dissolved in water. Is the resulting solution acidic, basic, or neutral?

### Chapter 20

**Section 20-1** Identify the following information for each problem. What element is oxidized? Reduced? What is the oxidizing agent? Reducing agent?
   **1.** $2P + 3Cl_2 \rightarrow 2PCl_3$
   **2.** $C + H_2O \rightarrow CO + H_2$

**3.** Determine the oxidation number for each element in the following compounds.
  **a.** $Na_2SeO_3$
  **b.** $HAuCl_4$
  **c.** $H_3BO_3$

**4.** Determine the oxidation number for the following compounds or ions.
  **a.** $P_4O_8$
  **b.** $Na_2O_2$ (hint: this is like $H_2O_2$)
  **c.** $AsO_4^{-3}$

**Section 20-2**  **5.** How many electrons will be lost or gained in each of the following half-reactions? Identify whether it is an oxidation or reduction.
  **a.** $Cr \rightarrow Cr^{3+}$
  **b.** $O_2 \rightarrow O^{2-}$
  **c.** $Fe^{+2} \rightarrow Fe^{3+}$

**6.** Balance the following reaction by the oxidation number method: $MnO_4^- + CH_3OH \rightarrow MnO_2 + HCHO$ (acidic). (Hint: assign the oxidation of hydrogen and oxygen as usual and solve for the oxidation number of carbon.)

**7.** Balance the following reaction by the oxidation number method: $Zn + HNO_3 \rightarrow ZnO + NO_2 + NH_3$

**8.** Use the oxidation number method to balance these net ionic equations:
  **a.** $SeO_3^{2-} + I^- \rightarrow Se + I_2$ (acidic solution)
  **b.** $NiO_2 + S_2O_3^{2-} \rightarrow Ni(OH)_2 + SO_3^{2-}$ (acidic solution)

**Section 20-3** Use the half-reaction method to balance the following redox equations.
  **9.** $Zn(s) + HCl(aq) \rightarrow ZnCl_2(aq) + H_2(g)$
  **10.** $MnO_4^-(aq) + H_2SO_3(aq) \rightarrow Mn^{2+}(aq) + HSO_4^-(aq) + H_2O(l)$ (acidic solution)
  **11.** $NO_2(aq) + OH^-(aq) \rightarrow NO_2^-(aq) + NO_3^-(aq) + H_2O(l)$ (basic solution)
  **12.** $HS^-(aq) + IO_3^-(aq) \rightarrow I^-(aq) + S(s) + H_2O(l)$ (acidic solution)

## Chapter 21

**Section 21-1**  **1.** Calculate the cell potential for each of the following.
  **a.** $Co^{2+}(aq) + Al(s) \rightarrow Co(s) + Al^{3+}(aq)$
  **b.** $Hg^{2+}(aq) + Cu(s) \rightarrow Cu^{2+}(aq) + Hg(s)$
  **c.** $Zn(s) + Br_2(l) \rightarrow Br^{1-}(aq) + Zn^{2+}(aq)$

**2.** Calculate the cell potential to determine whether the reaction will occur spontaneously or not spontaneously. For each reaction that is not spontaneous, correct the reactants or products so that a reaction would occur spontaneously.
  **a.** $Ni^{2+}(aq) + Al(s) \rightarrow Ni(s) + Al^{3+}(aq)$
  **b.** $Ag^+(aq) + H_2(g) \rightarrow Ag(s) + H^+(aq)$
  **c.** $Fe^{2+}(aq) + Cu(s) \rightarrow Fe(s) + Cu^{2+}(aq)$

**Practice Problems**

**3. a.** $+1, +4, -2$
   **b.** $+1, +3, -1$
   **c.** $+1, +3, -2$
**4. a.** $+4, -2$
   **b.** $+1, -1$
   **c.** $+5, -2$
**5. a.** loss of 3 electrons, oxidation
   **b.** gain 2 electrons, reduction
   **c.** loss 1 electron, oxidation

### Section 20.2
  **6.** $2MnO_4^- + 3CH_3OH + 2H^+ \rightarrow 2MnO_2 + 3HCHO + 4H_2O$
  **7.** $5Zn + 3HNO_3 \rightarrow 5ZnO + 2NO_2 + NH_3$
  **8. a.** $SeO_3^{2-} + 4I^- + 6H^+ \rightarrow Se + 2I_2 + 3H_2O$
   **b.** $2NiO_2 + S_2O_3^{2-} + 3H_2O \rightarrow 2Ni(OH)_2 + 2SO_3^{2-} + 2H^+$

### Section 20.3
  **9.** $Zn(s) + 2HCl(aq) \rightarrow ZnCl_2(aq) + H_2(g)$
  **10.** $2MnO_4^-(aq) + H^+(aq) + 5H_2SO_3(aq) \rightarrow 2Mn^{2+}(aq) + 5HSO_4^-(aq) + 3H_2O(l)$
  **11.** $2NO_2(aq) + 2OH^-(aq) \rightarrow NO_2^-(aq) + NO_3^-(aq) + H_2O(l)$
  **12.** $3HS^-(aq) + IO_3^-(aq) + 3H^+ \rightarrow I^-(aq) + 3S(s) + 3H_2O(l)$

## Chapter 21
### Section 21.1
  **1. a.** $+1.38$ V
   **b.** $+0.509$ V
   **c.** $+1.82$ V
  **2. a.** $+1.41$ V; spontaneous
   **b.** $+0.7996$ V; spontaneous
   **c.** $-0.789$ V; nonspontaneous; $Cu^{2+}(aq) + Fe(s) \rightarrow Fe^{2+}(aq) + Cu(s)$

Supplemental Practice Problems    **885**

# Chapter 22

## Section 22.1

1. a.

$CH_3CCH_2CHCHCH_2CH_2CH_3$ with $CH_3$, $CH_3$ groups and $CH_3$ group

b.

## Section 22.2

2. a.

b.

## Section 22.3

3. a. $H_2C=CHCH_2C=CHCH_3$

b. $H_3CC=CCH_3$ with $CH_3$ groups

c.

$H_2C=CHCH_2CHCH_2CH_2CH_3$ with $C_3H_7$

d.

# Chapter 23

## Section 23.1

1. a. $CH_3CH_2Cl$

b. $CH_3Cl$

c. $CH_3CH_2CH_2CH_2CH_2F$

d.

e. $CH_2CHCH_2$ with $Br$ $Br$ $Cl$

---

**Practice Problems**

### Chapter 22

**Section 22-1** **1.** Draw the structure of the following branched alkanes.
  **a.** 2,2,4-trimethylheptane
  **b.** 4-isopropyl-2-methylnonane

**Section 22-2** **2.** Draw the structure of each of the following cycloalkanes.
  **a.** 1-ethyl-2-methylcyclobutane
  **b.** 1,3-dibutylcyclohexane

**Section 22-3** **3.** Draw the structure of each of the following alkenes.
  **a.** 1,4-hexadiene
  **b.** 2,3-dimethyl-2-butene
  **c.** 4-propyl-1-octene
  **d.** 2,3-diethylcyclohexene

### Chapter 23

**Section 23-1** **1.** Draw the structures of the following alkyl halides.
  **a.** chloroethane          **d.** 1,3-dibromocyclohexane
  **b.** chloromethane        **e.** 1,2-dibromo-3-chloropropane
  **c.** 1-fluoropentane

### Chapter 25

**Section 25-2** **1.** Write balanced equations for each of the following decay processes.
  **a.** Alpha emission of $^{244}_{96}Cm$
  **b.** Positron emission of $^{70}_{33}As$
  **c.** Beta emission of $^{210}_{83}Bi$
  **d.** Electron capture by $^{116}_{51}Sb$

**2.** $^{47}_{20}Ca \rightarrow {}^{0}_{-1}\beta + ?$

**3.** $^{240}_{95}Am + ? \rightarrow {}^{243}_{97}Bk + {}^{1}_{0}n$

**Section 25-3** **4.** How much time has passed if 1/8 of an original sample of radon-222 is left? Use **Table 25-5** for half-life information.

**5.** If a basement air sample contains 3.64 $\mu$g of radon-222, how much radon will remain after 19 days?

**6.** Cobalt-60, with a half-life of 5 years, is used in cancer radiation treatments. If a hospital purchases a supply of 30.0 g, how much would be left after 15 years?

---

# Chapter 25

## Section 25.2

1. a. $^{244}_{96}Cm \rightarrow {}^{240}_{94}Pu + {}^{4}_{2}He$

b. $^{70}_{33}As \rightarrow {}^{70}_{32}Ge + {}^{0}_{1}\beta$

c. $^{210}_{83}Bi \rightarrow {}^{210}_{84}Po + {}^{0}_{-1}\beta$

d. $^{116}_{51}Sb + {}^{0}_{-1}e \rightarrow {}^{116}_{50}Sn$

2. $^{47}_{20}Ca \rightarrow {}^{0}_{-1}\beta + {}^{47}_{21}Sc$

3. $^{240}_{95}Am + {}^{4}_{2}He \rightarrow {}^{243}_{97}Bk + {}^{1}_{0}n$

## Section 25.3

4. 11.4 days

5. 0.114 $\mu$g

6. 3.75 g

*Mathematics is a language used in science to express and solve problems. Use this handbook to review basic math skills and to reinforce some math skills presented in the chapters in more depth.*

## Arithmetic Operations

Calculations you perform during your study of chemistry require arithmetic operations, such as addition, subtraction, multiplication, and division, using numbers. Numbers can be positive or negative, as you can see in **Figure 1.** Examine the number line below. Numbers that are positive are greater than zero. A plus sign ($+$) or no sign at all indicates a positive number. Numbers that are less than zero are negative. A minus sign ($-$) indicates a negative number. Zero (the origin) is neither positive nor negative.

## 1. Addition and subtraction

Addition is an arithmetic operation. As you can see in **Table 1,** the result of addition is called a sum. When the signs of the numbers you are adding are alike, add the numbers and keep the same sign. Use the number line below to solve for the sum $5 + 2$ in which both numbers are positive. To represent the first number, draw an arrow that starts at the origin. The arrow that represents the second number starts at the arrowhead of the first arrow. The sum is at the head of the second arrow. In this case, the sum equals the positive number seven.

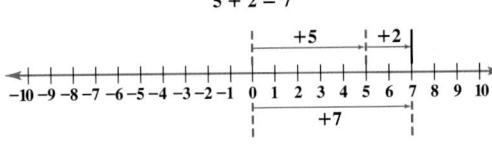

The process of adding two negative numbers is similar to adding two positive numbers. The negative sign indicates that you must move in the direction opposite to the direction that you moved to add two positive numbers. Use the number line below to verify that the sum below equals $-7$. Notice that the sign of the resulting number when you add two negative numbers is always negative.

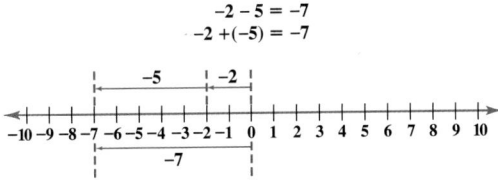

### Figure 1

Water freezes at 32°F and 0°C. What temperature scale do you think was used on this sign? Explain.

### Table 1

| Arithmetic Operations | | |
|---|---|---|
| **Operation** | **Sign** | **Result** |
| Addition | $+$ | Sum |
| Subtraction | $-$ | Difference |
| Multiplication | $\times$ | Product |
| Division | $\div$ | Quotient |

Math Handbook    **887**

## Figure Caption Question

**Figure 1** What temperature scale do you think was used on this sign? Explain. Student answers will vary but may include that the United States generally uses Fahrenheit or that $-42$ on the Celsius scale would be too cold.

National Science Content Standards

**Pages 886–887**
UCP.1, UCP.2, UCP.3, UCP.4; A.1; B.1, B.2

**APPENDIX B   Math Handbook**

**Figure 2**

The total mass of the eggs and the bowl is the sum of their individual masses. How would you determine the total mass of the eggs?

Math Handbook

When adding a negative number to a positive number, the sign of the resulting number will be the same as the larger number.

Suppose you must find the mass of the dozen eggs in **Figure 2.** You would measure the mass of the bowl alone. Then, subtract it from the mass of the eggs and the bowl. The result of this subtraction is called the difference. To find the difference between numbers, change the sign of the number being subtracted and follow the rules for addition. Use a number line to verify that the sign of the resulting number always will be the same as the larger number.

$$4 - 5 = 4 + (-5) = -1$$
$$4 - (-5) = 4 + 5 = 9$$
$$-4 - (-5) = -4 + 5 = 1$$
$$-4 - (+5) = -4 - 5 = -9$$

## 2. Multiplication

The result of multiplication is called a product. The operation "three times three" can be expressed by $3 \times 3$, $(3)(3)$, or $3 \cdot 3$. Multiplication is simply repeated addition. For example, $3 \times 3 = 3 + 3 + 3 = 9$.

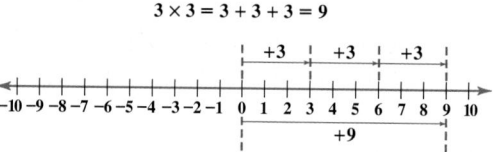

Use a number line to show that a negative number multiplied by a positive number yields a negative number.

$$(3)(-3) = -9$$
$$(-3) + (-3) + (-3) = -9$$

Math Handbook

What happens when a negative number is multiplied by a negative number? The product is always positive.

$$(-4)(-5) = 20$$

## 3. Division

Division is an arithmetic operation whose result is called a quotient. A quotient is expressed by ÷ or as a ratio. The quotient of numbers that have the same sign is always positive.

$$\frac{32}{8} = 4 \text{ and } \frac{-32}{-4} = 8$$

A negative number divided by a positive number, or a positive number divided by a negative number always yields a negative number.

$$\frac{35}{-7} = -5 \text{ and } \frac{-48}{8} = -6$$

### PRACTICE PROBLEMS

**1.** Perform the following operations.

a. $8 + 5 - 6$
b. $-4 - 9$
c. $6 \times 8$
d. $56 \div 7$
e. $0 - 12$
f. $-6 \times 5$
g. $-14 + 9$
h. $-44 \div 2$
i. $(-16)(-4)$
j. $(-32) \div (-8)$

## Scientific Notation

Scientists must use extremely small and extremely large numbers to describe the objects in **Figure 3**. The mass of the proton at the center of a hydrogen atom is 0.000 000 000 000 000 000 000 000 001 673 kg. The length of the AIDS virus is about 0.000 000 11 m. The temperature at the center of the Sun reaches 15 000 000 K. Such small and large numbers are difficult to read and hard to work with in calculations. Scientists have adopted a method of writing exponential numbers called scientific notation. It is easier than writing numerous zeros when numbers are very large or small. It also is easier to compare the relative size of numbers when they are written in scientific notation.

**Figure 3**

Scientific notation provides a convenient way to express data with extremely large or small numbers. Express the mass of a proton **a**, the length of the AIDS virus **b**, and the temperature of the Sun **c** in scientific notation.

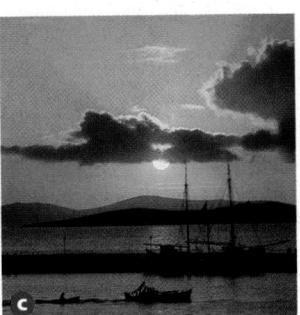

### Practice PROBLEMS

Complete solutions to Appendix B Math Handbook Practice Problems can be found in the **Solutions Manual.**

**1. a.** 7
 **b.** −13
 **c.** 48
 **d.** 8
 **e.** −12
 **f.** −30
 **g.** −5
 **h.** −22
 **i.** 64
 **j.** 4

## Figure Caption Questions

**Figure 3** Express the mass of a proton **a**, the length of the AIDS virus **b**, and the temperature of the Sun **c** in scientific notation.
 **a.** Proton: $1.673 \times 10^{-27}$ kg
 **b.** AIDS virus: $1.1 \times 10^{-7}$ m
 **c.** Sun: $1.5 \times 10^{7}$ K

Math Handbook

**National Science Content Standards**

**Pages 888–889**
UCP.3; A.1

**Figure 4b** Estimate the length of this nanoguitar in microns. about 10 microns

A number written in scientific notation has two parts.

$$N \times 10^n$$

The first part ($N$) is a number in which only one digit is placed to the left of the decimal point and all remaining digits to the right of the decimal point. The second part is an exponent of ten ($10^n$) by which the decimal portion is multiplied. For example, the number $2.53 \times 10^6$ is written in scientific notation.

$$2.53 \times 10^6$$

Number between one and ten   Exponent of ten

The decimal portion is 2.53 and the exponent is $10^6$.

### Positive exponents

A positive exponent of ten ($n$) tells how many times a number must be multiplied by ten to give the long form of the number.

$$2.53 \times 10^6 = 2.53 \times 10 \times 10 \times 10 \times 10 \times 10 \times 10 = 2\ 530\ 000$$

You also can think of the positive exponent of ten as the number of places you move the decimal to the left until only one nonzero digit is to the left of the decimal point.

$$2\ 530\ 000.$$

The decimal point moves six places to the left.

To convert the number 567.98 to scientific notation, first write the number as an exponential number by multiplying by $10^0$.

$$567.98 \times 10^0$$

(Remember that multiplying any number by $10^0$ is the same as multiplying the number by 1.) Move the decimal point to the left until there is only one digit to the left of the decimal. At the same time, increase the exponent by the same number as the number of places the decimal is moved.

$$5\ 67.98 \times 10^{0+2}$$

The decimal point moves two places to the left.

Thus, 567.98 written in scientific notation is $5.6798 \times 10^2$.

### Negative exponents

Measurements also can have negative exponents. See **Figure 4.** A negative exponent of ten tells how many times a number must be divided by ten to give the long form of the number.

$$6.43 \times 10^{-4} = \frac{6.43}{10 \times 10 \times 10 \times 10} = 0.000643$$

2 micron

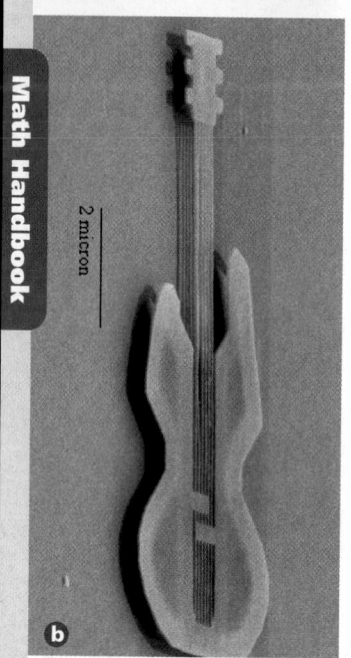

**Figure 4**

(a) Because of their short wavelengths ($10^{-8}$ m to $10^{-13}$ m), X rays can pass through some objects. (b) A micron is $10^{-6}$ meter. Estimate the length of this nanoguitar in microns.

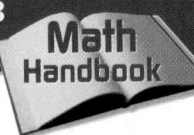

A negative exponent of ten is the number of places you move the decimal to the right until it is just past the first nonzero digit.

When converting a number that requires the decimal to be moved to the right, the exponent is decreased by the appropriate number. For example, the expression of 0.0098 in scientific notation is as follows:

$$0.\,0098 \times 10^0 \qquad \text{The decimal point}$$
$$0\,\underbrace{0098} \times 10^{0-3} \qquad \text{moves}$$
$$\qquad\qquad\qquad\qquad \text{three places}$$
$$9.8 \times 10^{-3} \qquad \text{to the right.}$$

Thus, 0.0098 written in scientific notation is $9.8 \times 10^{-3}$.

## Operations with scientific notation

The arithmetic operations performed with ordinary numbers can be done with numbers written in scientific notation. But, the exponential portion of the numbers also must be considered.

### 1. Addition and subtraction

Before numbers in scientific notation can be added or subtracted, the exponents must be equal. Remember that the decimal is moved to the left to increase the exponent and to the right to decrease the exponent.

$$(3.4 \times 10^2) + (4.57 \times 10^3) = (0.34 \times 10^3) + (4.57 \times 10^3)$$
$$= (0.34 + 4.57) \times 10^3$$
$$= 4.91 \times 10^3$$

### 2. Multiplication

When numbers in scientific notation are multiplied, only the decimal portion is multiplied. The exponents are added.

$$(2.00 \times 10^3)(4.00 \times 10^4) = (2.00)(4.00) \times 10^{3+4}$$
$$= 8.00 \times 10^7$$

### 3. Division

When numbers in scientific notation are divided, again, only the decimal portion is divided, while the exponents are subtracted as follows:

$$\frac{9.60 \times 10^7}{1.60 \times 10^4} = \frac{9.60}{1.60} \times 10^{7-4} = 6.00 \times 10^3$$

---

**PRACTICE** PROBLEMS

**2.** Express the following numbers in scientific notation.

**a.** 5800

**b.** 453 000

**c.** 67 929

**d.** 0.000 587 7

**e.** 0.0036

**f.** 0.000 087 5

*Continued on next page*

**Figure 5**

As blood passes through the body's tissues, red blood cells deliver oxygen and remove wastes. There are approximately 270 million hemoglobin molecules in one red blood cell.

**Math Handbook**

**Practice** PROBLEMS

Complete solutions to Appendix B Math Handbook Practice Problems can be found in the **Solutions Manual.**

**2. a.** $5.8 \times 10^3$

 **b.** $4.53 \times 10^5$

 **c.** $6.7929 \times 10^4$

 **d.** $5.877 \times 10^{-4}$

 **e.** $3.6 \times 10^{-3}$

 **f.** $8.75 \times 10^{-5}$

National Science Content Standards

Pages 890–891
UCP.3; A.1

## Practice PROBLEMS

Complete solutions to Appendix B Math Handbook Practice Problems can be found in the **Solutions Manual.**

**3. a.** $3.5 \times 10^7$
   **b.** $2.0 \times 10^9$
   **c.** $3.7 \times 10^{12}$
   **d.** $5.6 \times 10^{-8}$
**4. a.** $2.4 \times 10^{-9}$
   **b.** $2.7$
   **c.** $3.0 \times 10^{-4}$
   **d.** $6.0 \times 10^{14}$
   **e.** $1.0 \times 10^{16}$
   **f.** $3.1$
**5.** $6.75 \times 10^{18}$ hemoglobin molecules

## Figure Caption Question

**Figure 6c** Use your calculator to determine the cube root of 16. 2.52

## In-Text Question

**Page 892** What is the square root of 9, shown in **Figure 6b**? 3

**Math Handbook**

**3.** Perform the following operations.

  **a.** $(5.0 \times 10^6) + (3.0 \times 10^7)$
  **b.** $(1.8 \times 10^9) + (2.5 \times 10^8)$
  **c.** $(3.8 \times 10^{12}) - (1.9 \times 10^{11})$
  **d.** $(6.0 \times 10^{-8}) - (4.0 \times 10^{-9})$

**4.** Perform the following operations.

  **a.** $(6.0 \times 10^{-4}) \times (4.0 \times 10^{-6})$
  **b.** $(4.5 \times 10^9) \times (7.0 \times 10^{-10})$
  **c.** $\dfrac{4.5 \times 10^{-8}}{1.5 \times 10^{-4}}$
  **d.** $\dfrac{9.6 \times 10^8}{1.6 \times 10^{-6}}$
  **e.** $\dfrac{(2.5 \times 10^6)(7.0 \times 10^4)}{1.8 \times 10^{-5}}$
  **f.** $\dfrac{(6.2 \times 10^{12})(5.8 \times 10^{-7})}{1.2 \times 10^6}$

**5.** See **Figure 5.** If you contain an average of 25 billion red blood cells, how many hemoglobin molecules are in your body?

## Square and Cube Roots

A square root is one of two identical factors of a number. As you can see in **Figure 6a,** the number four is the product of two identical factors—two. Thus, the square root of four is two. The symbol $\sqrt{\ }$, called a radical sign, is used to indicate a square root. Most scientific calculators have a square root key labeled $\boxed{\sqrt{\ }}$.

$$\sqrt{4} = \sqrt{2 \times 2} = 2$$

This equation is read "the square root of four equals two." What is the square root of 9, shown in **Figure 6b?**

There may be more than two identical factors of a number. You know that $2 \times 4 = 8$. Are there any other factors of the number 8? It is the product of $2 \times 2 \times 2$. A cube root is one of three identical factors of a number. Thus, what is the cube root of 8? It is 2. A cube root also is indicated by a radical.

$$\sqrt[3]{8} = \sqrt[3]{2 \times 2 \times 2} = 2$$

Check your calculator handbook for more information on finding roots.

**Figure 6**

**a** The number four can be expressed as two groups of two. The identical factors are two. **b** The number nine can be expressed as three groups of three. Thus, three is the square root of nine. **c** Four is the square root of 16. Use your calculator to determine the cube root of 16.

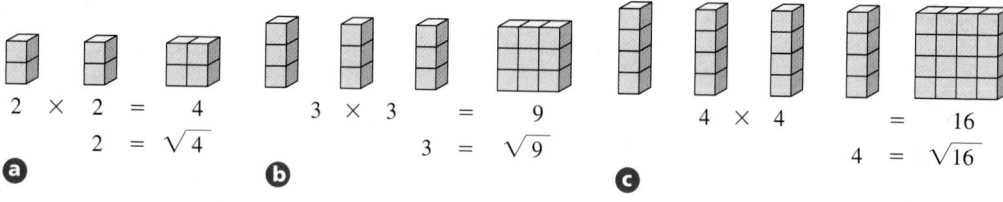

$$2 \times 2 = 4$$
$$2 = \sqrt{4}$$
**a**

$$3 \times 3 = 9$$
$$3 = \sqrt{9}$$
**b**

$$4 \times 4 = 16$$
$$4 = \sqrt{16}$$
**c**

**Figure Caption Question**
**Figure 7** Why is the bottom ruler less precise? There is greater distance between the markings on the bottom ruler that will cause greater variation in the estimated digit.

**Figure 7**

The estimated digit must be read between the millimeter markings on the top ruler. Why is the bottom ruler less precise?

## Significant Figures

Much work in science involves taking measurements. Measurements that you take in the laboratory should show both accuracy and precision. Accuracy reflects how close your measurement comes to the real value. Precision describes the degree of exactness of your measurement. Which ruler in **Figure 7** would give you the most precise length? The top ruler with the millimeter markings would allow your measurements to come closer to the actual length of the pencil. The measurement would be more precise.

Measuring tools are never perfect, nor are the people doing the measuring. Therefore, whenever you measure a physical quantity, there will always be uncertainty in the measurement. The number of significant figures in the measurement indicates the uncertainty of the measuring tool.

The number of significant figures in a measured quantity is all of the certain digits plus the first uncertain digit. For example, the pencil in **Figure 8** has a length that falls between 27.6 and 27.7 cm. You can read the ruler to the nearest millimeter (27.6 cm), but after that you must estimate the next digit in the measurement. If you estimate that the next digit is 5, you would report the measured length of the pencil as 27.65 cm. Your measurement has four significant figures. The first three are certain and the last is uncertain. The ruler used to measure the pencil has precision to the nearest tenth of a millimeter.

### How many significant figures?

When a measurement is provided, the following series of rules will help you to determine how many significant figures there are in that measurement.

**1.** *All nonzero figures are significant.*

**2.** *When a zero falls between nonzero digits, the zero is also significant.*

**3.** *When a zero falls after the decimal point and after a significant figure, that zero is significant.*

**4.** *When a zero is used merely to indicate the position of the decimal, it is not significant.*

**5.** *All counting numbers and exact numbers are treated as if they have an infinite number of significant figures.*

**Figure 8**

If you determine that the length of this pencil is 27.65 cm, that measurement has four significant figures.

Math Handbook

Math Handbook 893

**National Science Content Standards**
**Pages 892–893**
UCP.3; A.1, A.2; C.5

Examine each of the following measurements. Use the rules on the previous page to check that all of them have three significant figures.

245 K    18.0 L    308 km    0.006 23 g    186 000 m

Suppose you must do a calculation using the measurement 200 L. You cannot be certain which zero was estimated. To indicate the significance of digits, especially zeros, write measurements in scientific notation. In scientific notation, all digits in the decimal portion are significant. Which of the following measurements is most precise?

200 L has unknown significant figures.
$2 \times 10^2$ L has one significant figure.
$2.0 \times 10^2$ L has two significant figures.
$2.00 \times 10^2$ L has three significant figures.

The greater the number of digits in a measurement expressed in scientific notation, the more precise the measurement is. In this example, $2.00 \times 10^2$ L is the most precise data.

## EXAMPLE PROBLEM 1

How many significant digits are in the measurement 0.00302 g? 5.620 m? $9.80 \times 10^2$ m/s²?

0.003 02 g

Not significant          Significant
(Rule 4)                 (Rules 1 and 2)

The measurement 0.00302 g has three significant figures.

60 min
Unlimited significant figures
(Rule 5)

5.620 m
Significant
(Rules 1 and 3)

The measurement 5.620 m has four significant figures.

$9.80 \times 10^2$ m/s²
Significant
(Rules 1 and 3)

The measurement $9.80 \times 10^2$ m/s² has three significant figures.

Math
Handbook

## PRACTICE PROBLEMS

6. Determine the number of significant figures in each measurement:

a. 35 g

b. 3.57 m

c. 3.507 km

d. 0.035 kg

e. 0.246 L

f. 0.004 m³

g. 24.068 kPa

h. 268 K

i. 20.040 80 g

j. 20 dozen

k. 730 000 kg

l. 6.751 g

m. 0.157 kg

n. 28.0 mL

o. 2500 m

p. 0.070 mol

q. 30.07 nm

r. 0.106 cm

s. 0.0076 g

t. 0.0230 cm³

u. 26.509 cm

v. 54.52 cm³

w. 2.40 × 10⁶ kg

x. 4.07 × 10¹⁶ m

### Rounding

Arithmetic operations that involve measurements are done the same way as operations involving any other numbers. But, the results must correctly indicate the uncertainty in the calculated quantities. Perform all of the calculations and then round the result to the least number of significant figures. To round a number, use the following rules.

1. *When the leftmost digit to be dropped is less than 5, that digit and any digits that follow are dropped. Then the last digit in the rounded number remains unchanged.* For example, when rounding the number 8.7645 to 3 significant figures, the leftmost digit to be dropped is 4. Therefore, the rounded number is 8.76.

2. *When the leftmost digit to be dropped is greater than 5, that digit and any digits that follow are dropped, and the last digit in the rounded number is increased by one.* For example, when rounding the number 8.7676 to 3 significant figures, the leftmost digit to be dropped is 7. Therefore, the rounded number is 8.77.

3. *When the leftmost digit to be dropped is 5 followed by a nonzero number, that digit and any digits that follow are dropped. The last digit in the rounded number increases by one.* For example, 8.7519 rounded to 2 significant figures equals 8.8.

4. *If the digit to the right of the last significant figure is equal to 5 and 5 is not followed by a nonzero digit, look at the last significant figure. If it is odd, increase it by one; if even, do not round up.* For example, 92.350 rounded to 3 significant figures equals 92.4 and 92.25 equals 92.2.

### Calculations with significant figures

Look at the glassware in **Figure 9.** Would you expect to measure a more precise volume with the beaker or the graduated cylinder? When you perform any calculation using measured quantities such as volume, it is important to

**Figure 9**

Compare the markings on the graduated cylinder ⓐ to the markings on the beaker ⓑ. Which piece of glassware will yield more precise measurements?

Math Handbook    **895**

Math Handbook

### Figure Caption Question

**Figure 9** Which piece of glassware will yield more precise measurements? Measurements made with the graduated cylinder will be more precise.

**National Science Content Standards**

Pages 894–895
UCP.3; A.1, A.2

remember that the result never can be more precise than the least precise measurement. That is, your answer cannot have more significant figures than the least precise measurement. Be sure to perform all calculations before dropping any insignificant digits.

The following rules determine how to use significant figures in calculations that involve measurements.

1. *To add or subtract measurements, first perform the mathematical operation, then round off the result to the least precise value.* There should be the same number of digits to the right of the decimal as the measurement with the least number of decimal digits.

2. *To multiply or divide measurements, first perform the calculation, then round the answer to the same number of significant figures as the measurement with the least number of significant figures.* The answer should contain no more significant figures than the fewest number of significant figures in any of the measurements in the calculation.

**Table 2**

| Gas Pressures in Air | |
| --- | --- |
| | Pressure (kPa) |
| Nitrogen gas | 79.10 |
| Carbon dioxide gas | 0.040 |
| Trace gases | 0.94 |
| Total gases | 101.3 |

### EXAMPLE PROBLEM 2

Air contains oxygen ($O_2$), nitrogen ($N_2$), carbon dioxide ($CO_2$), and trace amounts of other gases. Use the known pressures in **Table 2** to calculate the partial pressure of oxygen.

To add or subtract measurements, first perform the operation, then round off the result to correspond to the least precise value involved.

$$P_{O_2} = P_{total} - (P_{N_2} + P_{CO_2} + P_{trace})$$
$$P_{O_2} = 101.3 \text{ kPa} - (79.10 \text{ kPa} + 0.040 \text{ kPa} + 0.94 \text{ kPa})$$
$$P_{O_2} = 101.3 \text{ kPa} - 80.080 \text{ kPa}$$
$$P_{O_2} = 21.220 \text{ kPa}$$

The total pressure ($P_{total}$) was measured to the tenths place. It is the least precise measurement. Therefore, the result should be rounded to the nearest tenth of a kilopascal. The leftmost dropped digit (1) is less than five, so the last two digits can be dropped.

The pressure of oxygen is $P_{O_2} = 21.2 \text{ kPa}$.

A small, hand-held pressure gauge can be used to monitor tire pressure.

### EXAMPLE PROBLEM 3

The reading on a tire-pressure gauge is 35 psi. What is the equivalent pressure in kilopascals?

$$P = 35 \text{ psi} \times \frac{101.3 \text{ kPa}}{14.7 \text{ psi}}$$
$$P = 241.1904762 \text{ kPa}$$

There are two significant figures in the measurement, 35 psi. Thus, the answer can have only two significant figures. Do not round up the last digit to be kept because the leftmost dropped digit (1) is less than five.

The equivalent pressure is $P = 240 \text{ kPa} = 2.4 \times 10^2 \text{ kPa}$.

**Math Handbook**

Math Handbook

Complete solutions to Appendix B Math Handbook Practice Problems can be found in the **Solutions Manual.**

**7. a.** 2.75 g
**b.** 8.6 m
**c.** 14 g
**d.** 186.50 m
**e.** $6.349 \times 10^5$ g
**f.** $3.6 \times 10^5$ g
**8. a.** 10.6 m
**b.** 54 m
**c.** $4.72 \times 10^{-4}$ g
**d.** $5.83 \times 10^{12}$ m
**e.** $3.5 \times 10^{31}$ m$^2$
**f.** $1.9 \times 10^{-1}$
**g.** $3.6 \times 10^{12}$ m

## PRACTICE PROBLEMS

**7.** Round off the following measurements to the number of significant figures indicated in parentheses.

**a.** 2.7518 g (3)
**b.** 8.6439 m (2)
**c.** 13.841 g (2)
**d.** 186.499 m (5)
**e.** 634 892.34 g (4)
**f.** 355 500 g (2)

**8.** Perform the following operations.

**a.** (2.475 m) + (3.5 m) + (4.65 m)
**b.** (3.45 m) + (3.658 m) + (47 m)
**c.** $(5.36 \times 10^{-4}$ g$) - (6.381 \times 10^{-5}$ g$)$
**d.** $(6.46 \times 10^{12}$ m$) - (6.32 \times 10^{11}$ m$)$
**e.** $(6.6 \times 10^{12}$ m$) \times (5.34 \times 10^{18}$ m$)$
**f.** $\dfrac{5.634 \times 10^{11} \text{ m}}{3.0 \times 10^{12} \text{ m}}$
**g.** $\dfrac{(4.765 \times 10^{11} \text{ m})(5.3 \times 10^{-4} \text{ m})}{7.0 \times 10^{-5} \text{ m}}$

## Solving Algebraic Equations

When you are given a problem to solve, it often can be written as an algebraic equation. You can use letters to represent measurements or unspecified numbers in the problem. The laws of chemistry are often written in the form of algebraic equations. For example, the ideal gas law relates pressure, volume, amount, and temperature of the gases the pilot in **Figure 10** breathes. The ideal gas law is written

$$PV = nRT$$

where the variables are pressure ($P$), volume ($V$), number of moles ($n$), and temperature ($T$). $R$ is a constant. This is a typical algebraic equation that can be manipulated to solve for any of the individual variables.

**Figure 10**

Pilots must rely on additional oxygen supplies at high altitudes to prevent hypoxia–a condition in which the tissues of the body become oxygen deprived.

Math Handbook **897**

When you solve algebraic equations, any operation that you perform on one side of the equal sign must be performed on the other side of the equation. Suppose you are asked to use the ideal gas law to find the pressure of the gas ($P$) in the bottle in **Figure 11.** To solve for, or isolate, $P$ requires you to divide the left-hand side of the equation by $V$. This operation must be performed on the right-hand side of the equation as well.

$$PV = nRT$$

$$\frac{PV}{V} = \frac{nRT}{V}$$

The $V$'s on the left-hand side of the equation cancel each other out.

$$\frac{PV}{V} = \frac{nRT}{V}$$

$$P \times \frac{V}{V} = \frac{nRT}{V}$$

$$P \times 1 = \frac{nRT}{V}$$

$$P = \frac{nRT}{V}$$

The ideal gas law equation is now written in terms of pressure. That is, $P$ has been isolated.

## Order of operations

When isolating a variable in an equation, it is important to remember that arithmetic operations have an order of operations that must be followed. See **Figure 12.** Operations in parentheses (or brackets) take precedence over multiplication and division, which in turn take precedence over addition and subtraction. For example, in the equation

$$a + b \times c$$

variable $b$ must be multiplied first by variable $c$. Then, the resulting product is added to variable $a$. If the equation is written

$$(a + b) \times c$$

the operation in parentheses or brackets must be done first. In the equation above, variable $a$ is added to variable $b$ before the sum is multiplied by variable $c$.

**Figure 11**

This beverage is bottled under pressure in order to keep carbon dioxide gas in the beverage solution.

Math Handbook

To see the difference order of operations makes, try replacing $a$ with 2, $b$ with 3, and $c$ with 4.

$$a + (b \times c) = 2 + (3 \times 4) = 14$$
$$(a + b) \times c = (2 + 3) \times 4 = 20$$

To solve algebraic equations, you also must remember the distributive property. To remove parentheses to solve a problem, any number outside the parentheses is "distributed" across the parentheses as follows:

$$6(x + 2y) = 6x + 12y$$

## EXAMPLE PROBLEM 4

The temperature on a cold day was 25°F. What was the temperature on the Celsius scale?

Begin with the equation for the conversion from the Celsius to Fahrenheit temperature. Celsius temperature is the unknown variable.

$$°F = \frac{9}{5}°C + 32$$

Rearrange the equation to isolate °C. Begin by subtracting 32 from both sides.

$$°F - 32 = \frac{9}{5}°C + 32 - 32$$

$$°F - 32 = \frac{9}{5}°C$$

Then, multiply both sides by 5.

$$5 \times (°F - 32) = 5 \times \frac{9}{5}°C$$

$$5 \times (°F - 32) = 9°C$$

Finally, divide both sides by 9.

$$\frac{5 \times (°F - 32)}{9} = \frac{9°C}{9}$$

$$°C = \frac{5}{9}(°F - 32)$$

Substitute in the known Fahrenheit temperature.

$$°C = \frac{5}{9}(°F - 32)$$

$$= \frac{5}{9}(25 - 32)$$

$$= -3.9°C$$

The Celsius temperature is -3.9°C.

## PRACTICE PROBLEMS

Isolate the indicated variable in each equation.

**9.** $PV = nRT$ for $R$

**10.** $3 = 4(x + y)$ for $y$

**11.** $z = x(4 + 2y)$ for $y$

**12.** $\frac{2}{x} = 3 + y$ for $x$

**13.** $\frac{2x + 1}{3} = 6$ for $x$

**Figure 12**

When faced with an equation that contains more than one operation, use this flow chart to determine the order in which to perform your calculations.

### Order of Operations

Examine all arithmetic operations.

Do all operations inside parentheses or brackets.

Do all multiplication and division from left to right.

Perform addition and subtraction from left to right.

---

**Practice PROBLEMS**

Complete solutions to Appendix B Math Handbook Practice Problems can be found in the **Solutions Manual.**

**9.** $R = \frac{PV}{nT}$

**10.** $y = \frac{3}{4} - x$

**11.** $y = \frac{1}{2}\left(\frac{z}{x} - 4\right)$

**12.** $x = \frac{2}{(3 + y)}$

**13.** $x = 8.5$

**National Science Content Standards**

**Pages 898–899**
UCP.1, UCP.2, UCP.3; A.1

**Practice** PROBLEMS

Complete solutions to Appendix B Math Handbook Practice Problems can be found in the **Solutions Manual.**

**14.** No; units are not the same on both sides of the equation.

**15.** No; units are not the same on both sides of the equation.

**16.** No; units are not the same on both sides of the equation.

**17.** Yes; units are the same on both sides of the equation.

## Dimensional Analysis

The dimensions of a measurement refer to the type of units attached to a quantity. For example, length is a dimensional quantity that can be measured in meters, centimeters, and kilometers. Dimensional analysis is the process of solving algebraic equations for units as well as numbers. It is a way of checking to ensure that you have used the correct equation, and that you have correctly applied the rules of algebra when solving the equation. It also can help you to choose and set up the correct equation, as you will see on the next page when you learn how to do unit conversions. It is good practice to make dimensional analysis a habit by always stating the units as well as the numerical values whenever substituting values into an equation.

Math Handbook

### EXAMPLE PROBLEM 5

The density ($D$) of aluminum is 2700 kg/m³. Determine the mass ($m$) of a piece of aluminum of volume ($V$) 0.20 m³.

The equation for density is

$$D = \frac{m}{V}$$

Multiply both sides of the equation by $V$ and isolate $m$.

$$DV = \frac{mV}{V}$$

$$DV = \frac{V}{V} \times m$$

$$m = DV$$

Substitute the known values for $D$ and $V$.

$$m = DV = (2700 \text{ kg/m}^3)(0.20 \text{ m}^3) = 540 \text{ kg}$$

Notice that the unit m³ cancels out, leaving mass in kg, a unit of mass.

Aluminum is a metal that is useful from the kitchen to the sculpture garden.

### PRACTICE PROBLEMS

**Determine whether the following equations are dimensionally correct. Explain.**

**14.** $v = s \times t$   where $v = 24$ m/s, $s = 12$ m and $t = 2$ s.

**15.** $R = \frac{nT}{PV}$ where $R$ is in L·atm/mol·K, $n$ is in mol, $T$ is in K, $P$ is in atm, and $V$ is in L.

**16.** $t = \frac{v}{s}$ where $t$ is in seconds, $v$ is in m/s and $s$ is in m.

**17.** $s = \frac{at^2}{2}$ where $s$ is in m, $a$ is in m/s², and $t$ is in s.

# Unit Conversion

Recall from Chapter 2 that the universal unit system used by scientists is called Le Système Internationale d'Unités or SI. It is a metric system based on seven base units—meter, second, kilogram, kelvin, mole, ampere, and candela—from which all other units are derived. The size of a unit in a metric system is indicated by a prefix related to the difference between that unit and the base unit. For example, the base unit for length in the metric system is the meter. One tenth of a meter is a decimeter where the prefix *deci-* means one tenth. And, one thousand meters is a kilometer. The prefix *kilo-* means one thousand.

You can use the information in **Table 3** to express a measured quantity in different units. For example, how is 65 meters expressed in centimeters? **Table 3** indicates one centimeter and one-hundredth meter are equivalent, that is, $1 \text{ cm} = 10^{-2} \text{ m}$. This information can be used to form a conversion factor. A conversion factor is a ratio equal to one that relates two units. You can make the following conversion factors from the relationship between meters and centimeters. Be sure when you set up a conversion factor that the measurement in the numerator (the top of the ratio) is equivalent to the denominator (the bottom of the ratio).

$$1 = \frac{1 \text{ cm}}{10^{-2} \text{ m}} \text{ and } 1 = \frac{10^{-2} \text{ m}}{1 \text{ cm}}$$

Recall that the value of a quantity does not change when it is multiplied by one. To convert 65 m to centimeters, multiply by a conversion factor.

$$65 \text{ m} \times \frac{1 \text{ cm}}{10^{-2} \text{ m}} = 65 \times 10^2 \text{ cm} = 6.5 \times 10^3 \text{ cm}$$

Note the conversion factor is set up so that the unit meters cancels and the answer is in centimeters as required. When setting up a unit conversion, use dimensional analysis to check that the units cancel to give an answer in the desired units. And, always check your answer to be certain the units make sense.

**Table 3**

| Common SI Prefixes | | | | | |
|---|---|---|---|---|---|
| Prefix | Symbol | Exponential notation | Prefix | Symbol | Exponential notation |
| Peta | P | $10^{15}$ | Deci | d | $10^{-1}$ |
| Tera | T | $10^{12}$ | Centi | c | $10^{-2}$ |
| Giga | G | $10^{9}$ | Milli | m | $10^{-3}$ |
| Mega | M | $10^{6}$ | Micro | $\mu$ | $10^{-6}$ |
| Kilo | k | $10^{3}$ | Nano | n | $10^{-9}$ |
| Hecto | h | $10^{2}$ | Pico | p | $10^{-12}$ |
| Deka | da | $10^{1}$ | Femto | f | $10^{-15}$ |

Math Handbook **901**

National Science Content Standards

Pages 900–901
UCP.2, UCP.3; A.1; B.2, B.4

## Example Problem Question

**Example Problem 6** How many significant figures are in this measurement (54.94 g)? four

---

### Practice PROBLEMS

Complete solutions to Appendix B Math Handbook Practice Problems can be found in the **Solutions Manual.**

**18. a.** $4 \times 10^2$ cm
   **b.** $5.00 \times 10^{-1}$ m
   **c.** 150 mm
   **d.** 0.567 g
   **e.** $4.6 \times 10^6$ mm
   **f.** 83 kg
   **g.** $7.3 \times 10^2$ L
   **h.** $8.4 \times 10^7$ km
   **i.** $3.8 \times 10^{10}$ mm$^2$
   **j.** $6.9 \times 10^8$ m$^2$
   **k.** $6.3 \times 10^{18}$ cm$^3$
   **l.** $9.4 \times 10^6$ m$^3$

---

You make unit conversions everyday when you determine how many quarters are needed to make a dollar or how many feet are in a yard. One unit that is often used in calculations in chemistry is the mole. Chapter 11 shows you equivalent relationships among mole, grams, and the number of representative particles (atoms, molecules, formula units, or ions). For example, one mole of a substance contains $6.02 \times 10^{23}$ representative particles. Try the next example to see how this information can be used in a conversion factor to determine the number of atoms in a sample of manganese.

**Math Handbook**

How many significant figures are in this measurement?

### EXAMPLE PROBLEM 6

One mole of manganese (Mn) in the photo has a mass of 54.94 g. How many atoms are in two moles of manganese?

You are given the mass of one mole of manganese. In order to convert to the number of atoms, you must set up a conversion factor relating the number of moles and the number of atoms.

$$\frac{1 \text{ mole}}{6.02 \times 10^{23} \text{ atoms}} \quad \text{and} \quad \frac{6.02 \times 10^{23} \text{ atoms}}{1 \text{ mole}}$$

Choose the conversion factor that cancels units of moles and gives an answer in number of atoms.

$$2.0 \text{ mole} \times \frac{6.02 \times 10^{23} \text{ atoms}}{1 \text{ mole}} = 12.04 \times 10^{23} \text{ atoms}$$
$$= 1.2 \times 10^{24} \text{ atoms}$$

The answer is expressed in the desired units (number of atoms). It is expressed in two significant figures because the number of moles (2.0) has the least number of significant figures.

### PRACTICE PROBLEMS

**18.** Convert the following measurements as indicated.

   **a.** 4 m = _____cm
   **b.** 50.0 cm = _____m
   **c.** 15 cm = _____mm
   **d.** 567 mg = _____g
   **e.** $4.6 \times 10^3$ m = _____mm
   **f.** $8.3 \times 10^4$ g = _____kg
   **g.** $7.3 \times 10^5$ mL = _____L
   **h.** $8.4 \times 10^{10}$ m = _____km
   **i.** $3.8 \times 10^4$ m$^2$ = _____mm$^2$
   **j.** $6.9 \times 10^{12}$ cm$^2$ = _____m$^2$
   **k.** $6.3 \times 10^{21}$ mm$^3$ = _____cm$^3$
   **l.** $9.4 \times 10^{12}$ cm$^3$ = _____m$^3$

**Graph of Line with Point A**

y axis

Dependent variable

A (x,y)

x axis

Origin  0
0        Independent variable

**a**

**b**

## Drawing Line Graphs

Scientists, such as the one in **Figure 13a,** as well as you and your classmates, use graphing to analyze data gathered in experiments. Graphs provide a way to visualize data in order to determine the mathematical relationship between the variables in your experiment. Most often you use line graphs.

Line graphs are drawn by plotting variables along two axes. See **Figure 13b.** Plot the independent variable on the x-axis (horizontal axis), also called the abscissa. The independent variable is the quantity controlled by the person doing the experiment. Plot the dependent variable on the y-axis (vertical axis), also called the ordinate. The dependent variable is the variable that depends on the independent variable. Label the axes with the variables being plotted and the units attached to those variables.

### Determining a scale

An important part of graphing is the selection of a scale. Scales should be easy to plot and easy to read. First, examine the data to determine the highest and lowest values. Assign each division on the axis (the square on the graph paper) with an equal value so that all data can be plotted along the axis. Scales divided into multiples of 1, 2, 5, or 10, or decimal values, often are the most convenient. It is not necessary to start at zero on a scale, nor is it necessary to plot both variables to the same scale. Scales must, however, be labeled clearly with the appropriate numbers and units.

### Plotting data

The values of the independent and dependent variables form ordered pairs of numbers, called the x-coordinate and the y-coordinate (x,y), that correspond to points on the graph. The first number in an ordered pair always corresponds to the x-axis; the second number always corresponds to the y-axis. The ordered pair (0,0) always is the origin. Sometimes the points are named by using a letter. In **Figure 13b,** point A corresponds to the point (x,y).

**Figure 13**

**a** Once experimental data has been collected, it must be analyzed to determine the relationships between the measured variables.
**b** Any graph of your data should include labeled x- and y-axes, a suitable scale, and a title.

Math Handbook

Math Handbook    **903**

## In-Text Questions

**Page 904** Which direction is positive on the *y*-axis? The positive direction is up. Negative? The negative direction is down.

# APPENDIX B   Math Handbook

**Figure 14**

**a** To plot a point on a graph, place a dot at the location for each ordered pair (*x,y*) determined by your data. In this example, the dot marks the ordered pair (40 mL, 40 g).
**b** Generally, the line or curve that you draw will not include all of your experimental data points.

Density of Water

Experimental Data

After the scales are chosen, plot the data. To graph or plot an ordered pair means to place a dot at the point that corresponds to the values in the ordered pair. The *x*-coordinate indicates how many units to move right (if the number is positive) or left (if the number is negative). The *y*-coordinate indicates how many units to move up or down. Which direction is positive on the *y*-axis? Negative? Locate each pair of *x*- and *y*-coordinates by placing a dot as shown in **Figure 14a.** Sometimes, a pair of rulers, one extending from the *x*-axis and the other from the *y*-axis, can ensure that data is plotted correctly.

## Drawing a curve

Once the data is plotted, a straight line or a curve is drawn. It is not necessary to make it go through every point plotted, or even any of the points, as shown in **Figure 14b.** Graphing of experimental data is an averaging process. If the points do not fall along a line, the best-fit line or most probable smooth curve through the points should be drawn. When drawing the curve, do not assume it will go through the origin (0,0).

## Naming a graph

Last but not least, give each graph a title that describes what is being graphed. The title should be placed at the top of the page, or in a box on a clear area of the graph. It should not cross the data curve.

Once the data from an experiment has been collected and plotted, the graph must be interpreted. Much can be learned about the relationship between the independent and dependent variables by examining the shape and slope of the curve.

## Using Line Graphs

The curve on a graph gives a great deal of information about the relationship between the variables. Four common types of curves are shown in **Figure 15.** Each type of curve corresponds to a mathematical relationship between the independent and dependent variables.

Math Handbook

Math Handbook

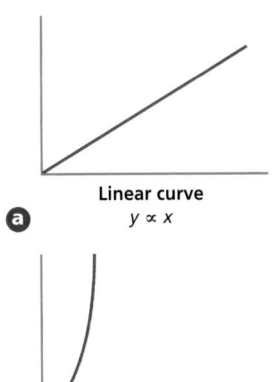

**a** Linear curve
$y \propto x$

**b** Inverse curve
$y \propto \frac{1}{x}$

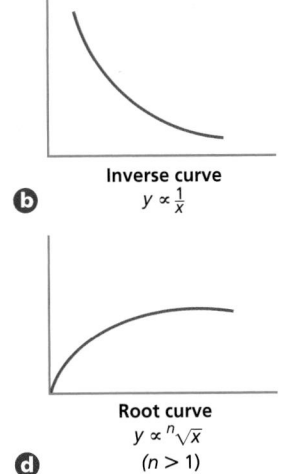

**c** Exponential curve
$y \propto x^n$
$(n > 1)$

**d** Root curve
$y \propto \sqrt[n]{x}$
$(n > 1)$

**Figure 15**

The shape of the curve formed by a plot of experimental data indicates how the variables are related.

Math Handbook

## Direct and inverse relationships

In your study of chemistry, the most common curves are the linear, representing the direct relationship ($y \propto x$), and the inverse, representing the inverse relationship ($y \propto 1/x$), where $x$ represents the independent variable and $y$ represents the dependent variable. In a direct relationship, $y$ increases in value as $x$ increases in value or $y$ decreases when $x$ decreases. In an inverse relationship, $y$ decreases in value as $x$ increases in value.

An example of a typical direct relationship is the increase in volume of a gas with increasing temperature. When the gases inside a hot air balloon are heated, the balloon gets larger. As the balloon cools, its size decreases. However, a plot of the decrease in pressure as the volume of a gas increases yields a typical inverse curve.

You also may encounter exponential and root curves in your study of chemistry. See **Figure 15c** and **d.** What types of relationships between the independent and dependent variables do the curves describe? How do the curves differ from **a** and **b**? An exponential curve describes a relationship in which one variable is expressed by an exponent. And, a root curve describes a relationship in which one variable is expressed by a root. What type of relationship is described by the curve in **Figure 16**?

## The linear graph

The linear graph is useful in analyzing data because a linear relationship can be translated easily into equation form using the equation for a straight line

$$y = mx + b$$

where $y$ stands for the dependent variable, $m$ is the slope of the line, $x$ stands for the independent variable, and $b$ is the $y$-intercept, the point where the curve crosses the $y$-axis.

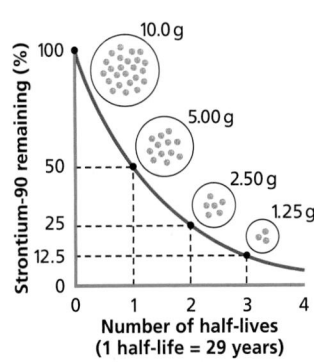

**Figure 16**

Half-life is the amount of time it takes for half of a sample of a radioactive isotope to decay (Chapters 4 and 25). Notice that as the number of half-lives increases, the amount of sample decreases.

Math Handbook    **905**

## In-Text Questions

**Page 905** See **Figure 15c** and **d.** What types of relationships between the independent and dependent variables do the curves describe? How do the curves differ from **a** and **b**? **Figure 15c** describes an exponential curve. *y* is proportional to *x*ⁿ. **Figure 15d** describes a root curve. *y* is proportional to the *n*th root of *x*.

**Page 905** What type of relationship is described by the curve in **Figure 16?** an inverse relationship

National Science Content Standards

Pages 904–905
UCP.1, UCP.2, UCP.3; A.1

## Figure Caption Question

**Figure 17** What would an almost flat line indicate? An almost flat line indicates little change in the dependent variable when the independent variable changes.

**Density of Water**

**Figure 17**

A steep slope indicates that the dependent variable changes rapidly with a change in the independent variable. What would an almost flat line indicate?

The slope of a linear graph is the steepness of the line. Slope is defined as the ratio of the vertical change (the rise) to the horizontal change (the run) as you move from one point to the next along the line. See **Figure 17.** To calculate slope, choose any two points on the line, $(x_1, y_1)$ and $(x_2, y_2)$. The two points need not be actual data points, but both must fall somewhere on the straight line. Once two points have been selected, calculate slope $m$ using the equation

$$m = \frac{\text{rise}}{\text{run}} = \frac{\Delta y}{\Delta x} = \frac{y_2 - y_1}{x_2 - x_1}, \text{ where } x_1 \neq x_2$$

where the symbol $\Delta$ stands for change, $x_1$ and $y_1$ are the coordinates or values of the first point, and $x_2$ and $y_2$ are the coordinates of the second point.

Choose any two points along the graph of mass vs. volume in **Figure 18** and calculate its slope.

$$m = \frac{135 \text{ g} - 54 \text{ g}}{50.0 \text{ cm}^3 - 20.0 \text{ cm}^3} = 2.7 \text{ g/cm}^3$$

Note that the units for the slope are the units for density. Plotting a graph of mass versus volume is one way of determining the density of a substance.

Apply the general equation for a straight line to the graph in **Figure 18.**

$$y = mx + b$$
$$mass = (2.7 \text{ g/cm}^3)(volume) + 0$$
$$mass = (2.7 \text{ g/cm}^3)(volume)$$

This equation verifies the direct relationship between mass and volume. For any increase in volume, the mass also increases.

### Interpolation and extrapolation

Graphs also serve functions other than determining the relationship between variables. They permit interpolation, the prediction of values of the independent and dependent variables. For example, you can see in the table in **Figure 18** that the mass of 40.0 cm³ of aluminum was not measured. But, you can interpolate from the graph that the mass would be 108 g.

Graphs also permit extrapolation, which is the determination of points beyond the measured points. To extrapolate, draw a broken line to extend the

### Density of Aluminum

| Data | |
|---|---|
| Volume (mL) | Mass (g) |
| 20.0 | 54.0 |
| 30.0 | 81.0 |
| 50.0 | 135.0 |

**Figure 18**

Interpolation and extrapolation will help you determine the values of points you did not plot.

**Practice** PROBLEMS

Complete solutions and graphs to Appendix B Math Handbook Practice Problems can be found in the **Solutions Manual.**

**19. Table 4** Graph is a downward curve with a negative slope that indicates an inverse relationship between pressure and volume.

**Table 5** Graph is a straight line with positive slope that indicates a direct relationship between pressure and temperature.

curve to the desired point. In **Figure 18,** you can determine that the mass at 10.0 cm³ equals 27 g. One caution regarding extrapolation—some straight-line curves do not remain straight indefinitely. So, extrapolation should only be done where there is a reasonable likelihood that the curve doesn't change.

## PRACTICE PROBLEMS

**19.** Plot the data in each table. Explain whether the graphs represent direct or inverse relationships.

**Table 4**

| Effect of Pressure on Gas | |
|---|---|
| Pressure (mm Hg) | Volume (mL) |
| 3040 | 5.0 |
| 1520 | 10.0 |
| 1013 | 15.0 |
| 760 | 20.0 |

**Table 5**

| Effect of Pressure on Gas | |
|---|---|
| Pressure (mm Hg) | Temperature (K) |
| 3040 | 1092 |
| 1520 | 546 |
| 1013 | 410 |
| 760 | 273 |

## Ratios, Fractions, and Percents

When you analyze data, you may be asked to compare measured quantities. Or, you may be asked to determine the relative amounts of elements in a compound. Suppose, for example, you are asked to compare the molar masses of the diatomic gases, hydrogen ($H_2$) and oxygen ($O_2$). The molar mass of hydrogen gas equals 2.00 g/mol; the molar mass of oxygen equals 32.00 g/mol. The relationship between molar masses can be expressed in three ways: a ratio, a fraction, or a percent.

Math Handbook **907**

Math Handbook

**Figure 19**

**a** The mass of one lime would be one-twelfth the mass of one dozen limes. **b** In a crystal of table salt (sodium chloride), each sodium ion is surrounded by chloride ions, yet the ratio of sodium ions to chloride ions is one:one. The formula for sodium chloride is NaCl.

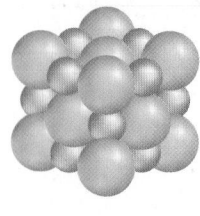

**a**

**b**

Math Handbook

## Ratios

You make comparisons using ratios in your daily life. For example, if the mass of a dozen limes is shown in **Figure 19a,** how does it compare to the mass of one lime? The mass of one dozen limes is twelve times larger than the mass of one lime. In chemistry, the chemical formula for a compound compares the elements that make up that compound. See **Figure 19b.** A ratio is a comparison of two numbers by division. One way it can be expressed is with a colon (:). The comparison between the molar masses of oxygen and hydrogen can be expressed as follows.

$$\text{molar mass } (H_2) : \text{molar mass } (O_2)$$
$$2.00 \text{ g/mol} : 32.00 \text{ g/mol}$$
$$2.00 : 32.00$$
$$1 : 16$$

Notice that the ratio 1:16 is the smallest integer (whole number) ratio. It is obtained by dividing both numbers in the ratio by the smaller number, and then rounding the larger number to remove the digits after the decimal. The ratio of the molar masses is one to sixteen. In other words, the ratio indicates that the molar mass of diatomic hydrogen gas is sixteen times smaller than the molar mass of diatomic oxygen gas.

## Fractions

Ratios are often expressed as fractions in simplest form. A fraction is a quotient of two numbers. To express the comparison of the molar masses as a fraction, place the molar mass of hydrogen over the molar mass of oxygen as follows:

$$\frac{\text{molar mass } H_2}{\text{molar mass } O_2} = \frac{2.00 \text{ g/mol}}{32.00 \text{ g/mol}} = \frac{2.00}{32.00} = \frac{1}{16}$$

In this case, the simplified fraction is calculated by dividing both the numerator (top of the fraction) and the denominator (bottom of the fraction) by 2.00. This fraction yields the same information as the ratio. That is, diatomic hydrogen gas has one-sixteenth the mass of diatomic oxygen gas.

## Percents

A percent is a ratio that compares a number to 100. The symbol for percent is %. You also are used to working with percents in your daily life. The number of correct answers on an exam may be expressed as a percent. If you answered 90 out of 100 questions correctly, you would receive a grade of 90%. Signs like the one in **Figure 20** indicate a reduction in price. If the item's regular price is $100, how many dollars would you save? Sixty-five percent means 65 of every 100, so you would save $65. How much would you save if the sign said 75% off?

The comparison between molar mass of hydrogen gas and the molar mass of oxygen gas described on the previous page also can be expressed as a percent by taking the fraction, converting it to decimal form, and multiplying by 100 as follows:

$$\frac{\text{molar mass } H_2}{\text{molar mass } O_2} \times 100 = \frac{2.00 \text{ g/mol}}{32.00 \text{ g/mol}} \times 100 = 0.0625 \times 100 = 6.25\%$$

Thus, diatomic hydrogen gas has 6.25% of the mass of diatomic oxygen gas.

## Operations Involving Fractions

Fractions are subject to the same type of operations as other numbers. Remember that the number on the top of a fraction is the numerator and the number on the bottom is the denominator. See **Figure 21.**

### 1. Addition and subtraction

Before two fractions can be added or subtracted, they must have a common denominator. Common denominators are found by finding the least common multiple of the two denominators. Finding the least common multiple often is as easy as multiplying the two denominators together. For example, the least common multiple of the denominators of the fractions 1/2 and 1/3 is $2 \times 3$ or 6.

$$\frac{1}{2} + \frac{1}{3} = \left(\frac{3}{3} \times \frac{1}{2}\right) + \left(\frac{2}{2} \times \frac{1}{3}\right) = \frac{3}{6} + \frac{2}{6} = \frac{5}{6}$$

Sometimes, one of the denominators will divide into the other, which makes the larger of the two denominators the least common multiple. For example, the fractions 1/2 and 1/6 have 6 as the least common multiple denominator.

$$\frac{1}{2} + \frac{1}{6} = \left(\frac{3}{3} \times \frac{1}{2}\right) + \frac{1}{6} = \frac{3}{6} + \frac{1}{6} = \frac{4}{6}$$

In still other situations, both denominators will divide into a number that is not the product of the two. For example, the fractions 1/4 and 1/6 have the number 12 as their least common multiple denominator, rather than 24, the product of the two denominators. This can be deduced as follows:

$$\frac{1}{6} + \frac{1}{4} = \left(\frac{4}{4} \times \frac{1}{6}\right) + \left(\frac{6}{6} \times \frac{1}{4}\right) = \frac{4}{24} + \frac{6}{24} = \frac{2}{12} + \frac{3}{12} = \frac{5}{12}$$

Because both fractions can be simplified by dividing numerator and denominator by 2, the least common multiple must be 12.

**Figure 20**

Would the savings be large at this sale? How would you determine the sale price?

$$\text{Quotient} = \frac{9 \times 10^8}{3 \times 10^{-4}} \begin{matrix} \text{Dividend} \\ \text{(numerator)} \\ \text{Divisor} \\ \text{(denominator)} \end{matrix}$$

**Figure 21**

When two numbers are divided, the one on top is the numerator and the one on the bottom is the denominator. The result is called the quotient. When you perform calculations with fractions, the quotient may be expressed as a fraction or a decimal.

Math Handbook **909**

Practice PROBLEMS

Complete solutions to Appendix B Math Handbook Practice Problems can be found in the **Solutions Manual.**

**20. a.** $1\frac{5}{12}$

**b.** $1\frac{1}{10}$

**c.** $\frac{1}{12}$

**d.** $\frac{1}{24}$

**e.** $\frac{1}{4}$

**f.** $\frac{6}{35}$

**g.** $2\frac{1}{2}$

**h.** $1\frac{5}{27}$

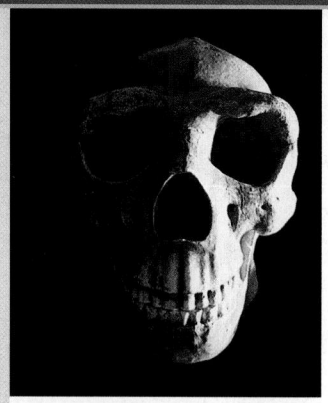

**Figure 22**

Carbon-dating of this skull is based on the radioactive decay of carbon-14 atoms which is measured in half-lives.

Math Handbook

**Table 4**

| Comparison Between Exponents and Logs | |
|---|---|
| **Exponent** | **Logarithm** |
| $10^0 = 1$ | $\log 1 = 0$ |
| $10^1 = 10$ | $\log 10 = 1$ |
| $10^2 = 100$ | $\log 100 = 2$ |
| $10^{-1} = 0.1$ | $\log 0.1 = -1$ |
| $10^{-2} = 0.01$ | $\log 0.01 = -2$ |

### 2. Multiplication and division

When multiplying fractions, the numerators and denominators are multiplied together as follows:

$$\frac{1}{2} \times \frac{2}{3} = \frac{1 \times 2}{2 \times 3} = \frac{2}{6} = \frac{1}{3}$$

Note the final answer is simplified by dividing the numerator and denominator by two.

When dividing fractions, the divisor is inverted and multiplied by the dividend as follows:

$$\frac{2}{3} \div \frac{1}{2} = \frac{2}{3} \times \frac{2}{1} = \frac{2 \times 2}{3 \times 1} = \frac{4}{3}$$

**PRACTICE** PROBLEMS

**20.** Perform the indicated operation:

**a.** $\frac{2}{3} + \frac{3}{4}$       **e.** $\frac{1}{3} \times \frac{3}{4}$

**b.** $\frac{4}{5} + \frac{3}{10}$       **f.** $\frac{3}{5} \times \frac{2}{7}$

**c.** $\frac{1}{4} - \frac{1}{6}$       **g.** $\frac{5}{8} \div \frac{1}{4}$

**d.** $\frac{7}{8} - \frac{5}{6}$       **h.** $\frac{4}{9} \div \frac{3}{8}$

### Logarithms and Antilogarithms

When you perform calculations, such as using half-life of carbon to determine the age of the skull in **Figure 22** or the pH of the products in **Figure 23,** you may need to use the log or antilog function on your calculator. A logarithm (log) is the power or exponent to which a number, called a base, must be raised in order to obtain a given positive number. This textbook uses common logarithms based on a base of 10. Therefore, the common log of any number is the power to which ten is raised to equal that number. Examine **Table 4.** Note the log of each number is the power of ten for the exponent of that number. For example, the common log of 100 is two and the common log of 0.01 is $-2$.

$$\log 10^2 = 2$$
$$\log 10^{-2} = -2$$

A common log can be written in the following general form.

If $10^n = y$, then $\log y = n$.

In each example in **Table 4,** the log can be determined by inspection. How do you express the common log of $5.34 \times 10^5$? Because logarithms are exponents, they have the same properties as exponents. See **Table 5.**

$$\log 5.34 \times 10^5 = \log 5.34 + \log 10^5$$

Math Handbook

Most scientific calculators have a button labeled $\boxed{\log}$ and, in most cases, the number is simply entered and the log button is pushed to display the log of the number. Note that there is the same number of digits after the decimal in the log as there are significant figures in the original number entered.

$$\log 5.34 \times 10^5 = \log 5.34 + \log 10^5 = 0.728 + 5 = 5.728$$

Suppose the pH of the aqueous ammonia in **Figure 23** is 9.54 and you are asked to find the concentration of the hydrogen ions in that solution. By definition, $pH = -\log [H^+]$. Compare this to the general equation for the common log.

Equation for pH: $\qquad pH = -\log [H^+]$
General equation: $\qquad y = \log 10^n$

To solve the equation for $[H^+]$, you must follow the reverse process and calculate the antilogarithm (antilog) of $-9.54$ to find $[H^+]$.

Antilogs are the reverse of logs. To find the antilog, use a scientific calculator to input the value of the log. Then, use the inverse function and press the log button.

If $n = $ antilog $y$, then $y = 10^n$.
Thus, $[H^+] = $ antilog$(-9.54) = 10^{-9.54} = 10^{0.46\,+(-10)}$
$$= 10^{0.46} \times 10^{-10}$$
$$= 2.9 \times 10^{-10} M$$

Check the instruction manual for your calculator. The exact procedure to calculate logs and antilogs may vary.

**Table 5**

| Properties of Exponents | |
|---|---|
| **Exponential Notation** | **Logarithm** |
| $10^A \times 10^B = 10^{A+B}$ | $\log (A \times B) = \log A + \log B$ |
| $10^A \div 10^B = 10^{A-B}$ | $\log (A \div B) = \log A - \log B$ |
| $A^B$ | $(\log A) \times B$ |

**Figure 23**

Ammonia is a base. That means, its hydrogen ion concentration is less than $10^{-7}M$.

## PRACTICE PROBLEMS

**21.** Find the log of each of the following numbers:

  **a.** 367        **c.** $X^n$
  **b.** 4078      **d.** $\left(\frac{1}{2}\right)^{t/T}$

**22.** Find the antilog of each of the following logs:

  **a.** 4.663      **c.** 0.371
  **b.** 2.367      **d.** $-1.588$

**Practice** PROBLEMS

Complete solutions to Appendix B Math Handbook Practice Problems can be found in the **Solutions Manual.**

**21. a.** 2.565
   **b.** 3.6104
   **c.** $(\log x) \times n$
   **d.** $-0.3 \left(\frac{t}{T}\right)$
**22. a.** $4.60 \times 10^4$
   **b.** $2.33 \times 10^2$
   **c.** 2.35
   **d.** $2.58 \times 10^{-2}$

Math Handbook   **911**

National Science Content Standards
Pages 910–911
UCP.1, UCP.2; A.1; B.2

# APPENDIX C Tables

## Table C-1

| Color Key | | |
|---|---|---|
| Carbon | Bromine | Sodium/Other metals |
| Hydrogen | Iodine | Gold |
| Oxygen | Sulfur | Copper |
| Nitrogen | Phosphorus | Electron |
| Chlorine | Silicon | Proton |
| Fluorine | Helium | Neutron |

## Table C-2

### Symbols and Abbreviations

| | | | | | |
|---|---|---|---|---|---|
| $\alpha$ | = rays from radioactive materials, helium nuclei | $E$ | = energy, electromotive force | min | = minute (*time*) |
| $\beta$ | = rays from radioactive materials, electrons | $F$ | = force | N | = newton (*force*) |
| | | $G$ | = free energy | $N_A$ | = Avogadro's number |
| $\gamma$ | = rays from radioactive materials, high-energy quanta | g | = gram (*mass*) | $n$ | = number of moles |
| | | Gy | = gray (*radiation*) | $P$ | = pressure, power |
| | | $H$ | = enthalpy | Pa | = pascal (*pressure*) |
| $\Delta$ | = change in | Hz | = hertz (*frequency*) | $q$ | = heat |
| $\lambda$ | = wavelength | $h$ | = Planck's constant | $R$ | = ideal gas constant |
| $\nu$ | = frequency | h | = hour (*time*) | $S$ | = entropy |
| A | = ampere (*electric current*) | J | = joule (*energy*) | s | = second (*time*) |
| amu | = atomic mass unit | K | = kelvin (*temperature*) | Sv | = sievert (*absorbed radiation*) |
| Bq | = becquerel (*nuclear disintegration*) | $K_a$ | = ionization constant (*acid*) | $T$ | = temperature |
| | | $K_b$ | = ionization constant (*base*) | $V$ | = volume |
| °C | = Celsius degree (*temperature*) | $K_{eq}$ | = equilibrium constant | V | = volt (*electric potential*) |
| C | = coulomb (*quantity of electricity*) | $K_{sp}$ | = solubility product constant | $v$ | = velocity |
| c | = speed of light | kg | = kilogram (*mass*) | W | = watt (*power*) |
| cd | = candela (*luminous intensity*) | $M$ | = molarity | $w$ | = work |
| c | = specific heat | $m$ | = mass, molality | $X$ | = mole fraction |
| $D$ | = density | m | = meter (*length*) | | |
| | | mol | = mole (*amount*) | | |

## Table C-3

| SI Prefixes | | |
|---|---|---|
| **Prefix** | **Symbol** | **Scientific notation** |
| femto | f | $10^{-15}$ |
| pico | p | $10^{-12}$ |
| nano | n | $10^{-9}$ |
| micro | $\mu$ | $10^{-6}$ |
| milli | m | $10^{-3}$ |
| centi | c | $10^{-2}$ |
| deci | d | $10^{-1}$ |
| deka | da | $10^{1}$ |
| hecto | h | $10^{2}$ |
| kilo | k | $10^{3}$ |
| mega | M | $10^{6}$ |
| giga | G | $10^{9}$ |
| tera | T | $10^{12}$ |
| peta | P | $10^{15}$ |

## Table C-4

| The Greek Alphabet | | | | | |
|---|---|---|---|---|---|
| Alpha | A | $\alpha$ | Nu | N | $\nu$ |
| Beta | B | $\beta$ | Xi | $\Xi$ | $\xi$ |
| Gamma | $\Gamma$ | $\gamma$ | Omicron | O | $o$ |
| Delta | $\Delta$ | $\delta$ | Pi | $\Pi$ | $\pi$ |
| Epsilon | E | $\epsilon$ | Rho | P | $\rho$ |
| Zeta | Z | $\zeta$ | Sigma | $\Sigma$ | $\sigma$ |
| Eta | H | $\eta$ | Tau | T | $\tau$ |
| Theta | $\Theta$ | $\theta$ | Upsilon | $\Upsilon$ | $\upsilon$ |
| Iota | I | $\iota$ | Phi | $\Phi$ | $\phi$ |
| Kappa | K | $\kappa$ | Chi | X | $\chi$ |
| Lambda | $\Lambda$ | $\lambda$ | Psi | $\Psi$ | $\psi$ |
| Mu | M | $\mu$ | Omega | $\Omega$ | $\omega$ |

## Table C-5

| Physical Constants | | |
|---|---|---|
| **Quantity** | **Symbol** | **Value** |
| Atomic mass unit | amu | $1.6605 \times 10^{-27}$ kg |
| Avogadro's number | $N$ | $6.022 \times 10^{23}$ particles/mole |
| Ideal gas constant | $R$ | 8.31 L·kPa/mol·K<br>0.0821 L·atm/mol·K<br>62.4 mm Hg·L/mol<br>62.4 torr·L/mol |
| Mass of an electron | $m_e$ | $9.109 \times 10$<br>$5.48586 \times$ |
| Mass of a neutron | $m_n$ | 1.6749<br>1 |
| Mass of a proton | $m_p$ | 1.67<br>1.00 |
| Molar volume of ideal gas at STP | $V$ | 22.4 |
| Normal boiling point of water | $T_b$ | 373.1<br>100.0° |
| Normal freezing point of water | $T_f$ | 273.15 K<br>0.00°C |
| Planck's constant | $h$ | $6.626\ 076 \times 10^{-34}$ |
| Speed of light in a vacuum | $c$ | $2.997\ 925 \times 10^8$ m |

Table C-6

## Properties of Elements

| Element | Symbol | Atomic Number | Atomic Mass* (amu) | Melting Point (°C) | Boiling Point (°C) | Density (g/cm³) (gases measured at STP) | Atomic Radius (pm) | First Ionization Energy (kJ/mol) | Standard Reduction Potential (V) (for elements from or to oxidation state indicated) | Enthalpy of Fusion (kJ/mol) | Specific Heat (J/g·°C) | Enthalpy of Vaporization (kJ/mol) | Abundance in Earth's Crust (%) | Major Oxidation States |
|---|---|---|---|---|---|---|---|---|---|---|---|---|---|---|
| Actinium | Ac | 89 | [227] | 1050 | 3300 | 10.07 | 203 | 499 | (3+) −2.13 | 14.3 | 0.120 | 293 | trace | 3+ |
| Aluminum | Al | 13 | 26.981539 | 660.37 | 2517.6 | 2.699 | 143 | 577.5 | (3+) −1.67 | 10.71 | 0.9025 | 290.8 | 8.1 | 3+ |
| Americium | Am | 95 | [243] | 1176 | 2607 | 13.67 | 183 | 579 | (3+) −2.07 | 10 | — | 238.5 | — | 2+, 3+, 4+ |
| Antimony | Sb | 51 | 121.760 | 630.7 | 1587 | 6.697 | 161 | 834 | (3+) +0.15 | 19.5 | 0.2072 | 193 | $2 \times 10^{-5}$ | 3+, 5+ |
| Argon | Ar | 18 | 39.948 | −189.37 | −185.86 | 0.001784 | 98 | 1521 | — | 1.18 | 0.52033 | 6.52 | $4 \times 10^{-6}$ | — |
| Arsenic | As | 33 | 74.92159 | 816 (2840 kPa) | 615 (sublimes) | 5.778 | 121 | 947 | (3+) +0.24 | 27.7 | 0.3289 | (sublimes) | $1.9 \times 10^{-4}$ | 3+, 5+ |
| Astatine | At | 85 | [210] | 300 | 350 | — | — | 916 | (1−) +0.2 | 23.8 | — | 90.3 | trace | 1−, 5+ |
| Barium | Ba | 56 | 137.327 | 726.9 | 1845 | 3.62 | 222 | 502.9 | (2+) −2.92 | 8.012 | 0.2044 | 140 | 0.039 | 2+ |
| Berkelium | Bk | 97 | [247] | 986 | — | 14.78 | 170 | 601 | (3+) −2.01 | — | — | — | — | 3+, 4+ |
| Beryllium | Be | 4 | 9.012182 | 1287 | 2468 | 1.848 | 112 | 899.5 | (2+) −1.97 | 7.895 | 1.824 | 297.6 | $2 \times 10^{-4}$ | 2+ |
| Bismuth | Bi | 83 | 208.98037 | 271.4 | 1564 | 9.78 | 151 | 703 | (3+) +0.317 | 10.9 | 0.1221 | 179 | $8 \times 10^{-7}$ | 3+, 5+ |
| Bohrium | Bh | 107 | [264] | — | — | — | — | — | — | — | — | — | — | — |
| Boron | B | 5 | 10.811 | 2080 | 3927 | 2.46 | 85 | 800.6 | (3+) −0.89 | 50.2 | 1.026 | 504.5 | $9 \times 10^{-4}$ | 3+ |
| Bromine | Br | 35 | 79.904 | −7.25 | 59.35 | 3.1028 | 119 | 1139.9 | (1−) +1.065 | 10.571 | 0.47362 | 29.56 | $2.5 \times 10^{-4}$ | 1−, 1+, 3+, 5+ |
| Cadmium | Cd | 48 | 112.411 | 320.8 | 770 | 8.65 | 151 | 867.7 | (2+) −0.4025 | 6.19 | 0.2311 | 100 | $1.6 \times 10^{-5}$ | 2+ |
| Calcium | Ca | 20 | 40.078 | 841.5 | 1484 | 1.55 | 197 | 589.8 | (2+) −2.84 | 8.54 | 0.6315 | 155 | 4.66 | 2+ |
| Californium | Cf | 98 | [251] | 900 | — | — | 186 | 608 | (3+) −2 | — | — | — | — | 3+, 4+ |
| Carbon | C | 6 | 12.011 | 3620 | 4200 | 2.266 | 77 | 1086.5 | (4−) +0.132 | 104.6 | 0.7099 | 711 | 0.018 | 4−, 2+, 4+ |
| Cerium | Ce | 58 | 140.115 | 804 | 3470 | 6.773 | 181.8 | 541 | (3+) −2.34 | 5.2 | 0.1923 | 313 | 0.007 | 3+, 4+ |
| Cesium | Cs | 55 | 132.90543 | 28.4 | 674.8 | 1.9 | 262 | 375.7 | (1+) −2.923 | 2.087 | 0.2421 | 67 | $2.6 \times 10^{-4}$ | 1+ |
| Chlorine | Cl | 17 | 35.4527 | −101 | −34 | 0.003214 | 91 | 1255.5 | (1−) +1.3583 | 6.41 | 0.47820 | 20.41 | 0.013 | 1−, 1+, 3+, 5+ |
| Chromium | Cr | 24 | 51.9961 | 1907 | 2679 | 7.2 | 128 | 652.8 | (3+) −0.74 | 20.5 | 0.4491 | 339 | 0.01 | 2+, 3+, 6+ |
| Cobalt | Co | 27 | 58.9332 | 1495 | 2912 | 8.9 | 125 | 758.8 | (2+) −0.277 | 16.192 | 0.4210 | 382 | 0.0028 | 2+, 3+ |
| Copper | Cu | 29 | 63.546 | 1085 | 2570 | 8.92 | 128 | 745.5 | (2+) +0.34 | 13.38 | 0.38452 | 304 | 0.0058 | 1+, 2+ |
| Curium | Cm | 96 | [247] | 1340 | 3540 | 13.51 | 174 | 581 | (3+) −2.06 | — | — | — | — | 3+, 4+ |
| Darmstadtium | Ds | 110 | [281] | — | — | — | — | — | — | — | — | — | — | — |
| Dubnium | Db | 105 | [262] | — | — | — | — | — | — | — | — | — | — | — |
| Dysprosium | Dy | 66 | 162.5 | 1407 | 2600 | 8.536 | 178.1 | 572 | (3+) −2.29 | 10.4 | 0.1733 | 250 | $6 \times 10^{-4}$ | 2+, 3+ |
| Einsteinium | Es | 99 | [252] | 860 | — | — | 186 | 619 | (3+) −2 | — | — | — | — | 3+ |
| Erbium | Er | 68 | 167.26 | 1497 | 2900 | 9.045 | 176.1 | 589 | (3+) −2.32 | 17.2 | 0.1681 | 293 | $3.5 \times 10^{-4}$ | 3+ |
| Europium | Eu | 63 | 151.965 | 826 | 1596 | 5.245 | 208.4 | 547 | (3+) −1.99 | 10.5 | 0.1820 | 176 | $2.1 \times 10^{-3}$ | 2+, 3+ |
| Fermium | Fm | 100 | [257] | 1527 | — | — | — | 627 | (3+) −1.96 | — | — | — | — | 2+, 3+ |
| Fluorine | F | 9 | 18.9984032 | −219.7 | −188.2 | 0.001696 | 69 | 1681 | (1−) +2.87 | 0.51 | 0.8238 | 6.54 | 0.0544 | 1− |
| Francium | Fr | 87 | [223] | 27 | 650 | — | 280 | 393 | — | 2 | — | 63.6 | trace | 1+ |
| Gadolinium | Gd | 64 | 157.25 | 1312 | 3000 | 7.886 | 180.4 | 592 | (3+) −2.29 | 15.5 | 0.2355 | 311.7 | $6.3 \times 10^{-4}$ | 3+ |
| Gallium | Ga | 31 | 69.723 | 29.77 | 2203 | 5.904 | 134 | 578.8 | (3+) −0.529 | 5.59 | 0.3709 | 256 | 0.0018 | 1+, 3+ |
| Germanium | Ge | 32 | 72.64 | 945 | 2850 | 5.323 | 123 | 761.2 | (4+) +0.124 | 31.8 | 0.3215 | 334.3 | $1.5 \times 10^{-4}$ | 2+, 4+ |

* [ ] indicates mass of longest-lived isotope.

## Table C-6

### Properties of Elements (continued)

| Element | Symbol | Atomic Number | Atomic Mass* (amu) | Melting Point (°C) | Boiling Point (°C) | Density (g/cm³) (gases measured at STP) | Atomic Radius (pm) | First Ionization Energy (kJ/mol) | Standard Reduction Potential (V) (for elements from or to oxidation state indicated) | Enthalpy of Fusion (kJ/mol) | Specific Heat (J/g·°C) | Enthalpy of Vaporization (kJ/mol) | Abundance in Earth's Crust (%) | Major Oxidation States |
|---|---|---|---|---|---|---|---|---|---|---|---|---|---|---|
| Gold | Au | 79 | 196.96654 | 1064 | 2856 | 19.32 | 144 | 889.9 | (3+) +1.52 | 12.4 | 0.12905 | 324.4 | $3 \times 10^{-7}$ | 1+, 3+ |
| Hafnium | Hf | 72 | 178.49 | 2227 | 4603 | 13.28 | 159 | 654.4 | (4+) −1.56 | 29.288 | 0.1442 | 661 | $3 \times 10^{-4}$ | 4+ |
| Hassium | Hs | 108* | [277] | — | — | — | — | — | — | — | — | — | — | — |
| Helium | He | 2 | 4.002602 | −269.7 (2536 kPa) | −268.93 | 0.00017847 | 31 | 2372 | — | 0.02 | 5.1931 | 0.084 | — | — |
| Holmium | Ho | 67 | 164.9032 | 1461 | 2600 | 8.78 | 176.2 | 581 | (3+) −2.33 | 17.1 | 0.1646 | 251 | $1.5 \times 10^{-4}$ | 3+ |
| Hydrogen | H | 1 | 1.00794 | −259.19 | −252.76 | 0.0000899 | 37 | 1312 | (1+) 0.0000 | 0.117 | 14.298 | 0.904 | — | 1−, 1+ |
| Indium | In | 49 | 114.818 | 156.61 | 2080 | 7.29 | 167 | 558.2 | (3+) −0.3382 | 3.26 | 0.2407 | 231.8 | $2 \times 10^{-5}$ | 1+, 3+ |
| Iodine | I | 53 | 126.90447 | 113.6 | 184.5 | 4.93 | 138 | 1008.4 | (1−) +0.5355 | 15.517 | 0.21448 | 41.95 | $4.6 \times 10^{-5}$ | 1−, 1+, 5+, 7+ |
| Iridium | Ir | 77 | 192.22 | 2447 | 4550 | 22.65 | 135.5 | 880 | (4+) +0.926 | 26.4 | 0.1306 | 563.6 | $1 \times 10^{-7}$ | 3+, 4+, 5+ |
| Iron | Fe | 26 | 55.845 | 1536 | 2860 | 7.874 | 126 | 759.4 | (3+) −0.4 | 13.807 | 0.4494 | 350 | 5.8 | 2+, 3+ |
| Krypton | Kr | 36 | 83.80 | −157.2 | −153.35 | 0.0037493 | 112 | 1351 | — | 1.64 | 0.2480 | 9.03 | — | — |
| Lanthanum | La | 57 | 138.9055 | 920 | 3420 | 6.17 | 187 | 538 | (3+) −2.37 | 8.5 | 0.1952 | 402 | 0.0035 | 3+ |
| Lawrencium | Lr | 103 | [262] | — | — | — | — | — | (3+) −2.06 | — | — | — | — | 3+ |
| Lead | Pb | 82 | 207.2 | 327 | 1746 | 11.342 | 146 | 715.6 | (2+) −0.1251 | 4.77 | 0.1276 | 178 | 0.0013 | 2+, 4+ |
| Lithium | Li | 3 | 6.941 | 180.5 | 1347 | 0.534 | 156 | 520.2 | (1+) −3.045 | 3 | 3.569 | 148 | 0.002 | 1+ |
| Lutetium | Lu | 71 | 174.967 | 1652 | 3327 | 9.84 | 173.8 | 524 | (3+) −2.3 | 11.9 | 0.1535 | 414 | $8 \times 10^{-5}$ | 3+ |
| Magnesium | Mg | 12 | 24.305 | 650 | 1105 | 1.738 | 160 | 737.8 | (2+) −2.356 | 8.477 | 1.024 | 127.4 | 2.76 | 2+ |
| Manganese | Mn | 25 | 54.93805 | 1246 | 2061 | 7.43 | 127 | 717.5 | (2+) −1.18 | 12.058 | 0.4791 | 219.7 | 0.1 | 2+, 3+, 4+, 6+, 7+ |
| Meitnerium | Mt | 109 | [268] | — | — | — | — | — | — | — | — | — | — | — |
| Mendelevium | Md | 101 | [258] | — | — | — | — | 635 | — | — | — | — | — | 2+, 3+ |
| Mercury | Hg | 80 | 200.59 | −38.9 | 357 | 13.534 | 151 | 1007 | (2+) +0.8535 | 2.2953 | 0.13950 | 59.1 | $2 \times 10^{-6}$ | 1+, 2+ |
| Molybdenum | Mo | 42 | 95.94 | 2623 | 4679 | 10.28 | 139 | 685 | (6+) 0.114 | 36 | 0.2508 | 590 | $1.2 \times 10^{-4}$ | 4+, 5+, 6+ |
| Neodymium | Nd | 60 | 144.24 | 1024 | 3111 | 7.003 | 181.4 | 530 | (3+) −2.32 | 7.13 | 0.1903 | 283.7 | 0.004 | 2+, 3+ |
| Neon | Ne | 10 | 20.1797 | −248.61 | −246.05 | 0.0008999 | 71 | 2081 | — | 0.34 | 1.0301 | 1.77 | — | — |
| Neptunium | Np | 93 | [237] | 640 | 3900 | 20.45 | 155 | 597 | (5+) −0.91 | 9.46 | 0.4442 | 336 | — | 2+, 3+, 4+, 5+, 6+ |
| Nickel | Ni | 28 | 58.6934 | 1455 | 2883 | 8.908 | 124 | 736.7 | (2+) −0.257 | 17.15 | 0.4442 | 375 | 0.0075 | 2+, 3+, 4+ |
| Niobium | Nb | 41 | 92.90638 | 2477 | 4858 | 8.57 | 146 | 664.1 | (5+) −0.65 | 26.9 | 0.2648 | 690 | 0.002 | 4+, 5+ |
| Nitrogen | N | 7 | 14.0067 | −210 | −195.8 | 0.0012409 | 75 | 1402 | (3−) −0.092 | 0.72 | 1.0397 | 5.58 | 0.002 | 3−, 2−, 1−, 1+, 2+, 3+, 4+, 5+ |
| Nobelium | No | 102 | [259] | — | — | — | — | 642 | (2+) −2.5 | — | — | — | — | 2+, 3+ |
| Osmium | Os | 76 | 190.23 | 3045 | 5025 | 22.57 | 135 | 840 | (4+) +0.687 | 31.7 | 0.130 | 627.6 | $2 \times 10^{-7}$ | 4+, 6+, 8+ |
| Oxygen | O | 8 | 15.9994 | −218.8 | −183 | 0.001429 | 60 | 1313.9 | (2−) 1.229 | 0.44 | 0.91738 | 6.82 | 45.5 | 2−, 1− |
| Palladium | Pd | 46 | 106.42 | 1552 | 2940 | 11.99 | 137 | 805 | (2+) 0.915 | 17.6 | 0.2441 | 362 | $3 \times 10^{-7}$ | 2+, 4+ |
| Phosphorus | P | 15 | 30.973762 | 44.2 | 280.5 | 1.823 | 109 | 1012 | (3−) −0.063 | 0.659 | 0.76968 | 49.8 | 0.11 | 3−, 3+, 5+ |
| Platinum | Pt | 78 | 195.078 | 1769 | 3824 | 21.41 | 138.5 | 868 | (4+) +1.15 | 19.7 | 0.1326 | 510.4 | $1 \times 10^{-6}$ | 2+, 4+ |
| Plutonium | Pu | 94 | [244] | 640 | 3230 | 19.86 | 162 | 585 | (4+) −1.25 | 2.8 | 0.138 | 343.5 | — | 3+, 4+, 5+, 6+ |
| Polonium | Po | 84 | [209] | 254 | 962 | 9.4 | 164 | 813 | (4+) +0.73 | 3.81 | 0.125 | 103 | — | 2−, 2+, 4+, 6+ |
| Potassium | K | 19 | 39.0983 | 63.2 | 766.4 | 0.862 | 231 | 418.8 | (1+) −2.925 | 2.334 | 0.7566 | 76.9 | 1.84 | 1+ |
| Praseodymium | Pr | 59 | 140.90765 | 935 | 3520 | 6.782 | 182.4 | 522 | (3+) −2.35 | 11.3 | 0.1930 | 332.6 | $9.1 \times 10^{-4}$ | 3+, 4+ |
| Promethium | Pm | 61 | [145] | 1042 | 3000 | 7.2 | 183.4 | 536 | (3+) −2.29 | 8.17 | — | 293 | — | 3+ |

\* [ ] indicates mass of longest-lived isotope.

## Table C-6

### Properties of Elements (continued)

| Element | Symbol | Atomic Number | Atomic Mass* (amu) | Melting Point (°C) | Boiling Point (°C) | Density (g/cm³) (gases measured at STP) | Atomic Radius (pm) | First Ionization Energy (kJ/mol) | Standard Reduction Potential (V) (for elements from or to oxidation state indicated) | Enthalpy of Fusion (kJ/mol) | Specific Heat (J/g·°C) | Enthalpy of Vaporization (kJ/mol) | Abundance in Earth's Crust (%) | Major Oxidation States |
|---|---|---|---|---|---|---|---|---|---|---|---|---|---|---|
| Protactinium | Pa | 91 | 231.03588 | 1552 | 4227 | 15.37 | 163 | 568 | (5+)−1.19 | 14.6 | — | 481 | trace | 3+, 4+, 5+ |
| Radium | Ra | 88 | [226] | 700 | 1630 | 5 | 228 | 509.1 | (2+)−2.916 | 8.36 | — | 136.8 | — | 2+ |
| Radon | Rn | 86 | [222] | −71 | −62 | 0.00973 | 140 | 1037 | — | 16.4 | — | 16.4 | — | — |
| Rhenium | Re | 75 | 186.207 | 3180 | 5650 | 21.232 | 137 | 760 | (7+)+0.34 | 33.4 | 0.1368 | 707 | $1 \times 10^{-7}$ | 3+, 4+, 6+, 7+ |
| Rhodium | Rh | 45 | 102.9055 | 1960 | 3727 | 12.39 | 134 | 720 | (3+)+0.76 | 21.6 | 0.2427 | 494 | $1 \times 10^{-7}$ | 3+, 4+, 5+ |
| Rubidium | Rb | 37 | 85.4678 | 39.5 | 697 | 1.532 | 248 | 403 | (1+)−2.925 | 2.19 | 0.36344 | 69.2 | 0.0078 | 1+ |
| Ruthenium | Ru | 44 | 101.07 | 2310 | 4119 | 12.41 | 134 | 711 | (4+)+0.68 | 25.5 | 0.2381 | 567.8 | — | 2+, 3+, 4+, 5+ |
| Rutherfordium | Rf | 104 | [261] | — | — | — | — | — | — | — | — | — | — | |
| Samarium | Sm | 62 | 150.36 | 1072 | 1800 | 7.536 | 180.4 | 542 | (3+)−2.3 | 8.9 | 0.1965 | 191 | $7 \times 10^{-4}$ | 2+, 3+ |
| Scandium | Sc | 21 | 44.95591 | 1539 | 2831 | 3 | 162 | 631 | (3+)−2.03 | 15.77 | 0.5677 | 304.8 | 0.0022 | 3+ |
| Seaborgium | Sg | 106 | [266] | — | — | — | — | — | — | — | — | — | — | |
| Selenium | Se | 34 | 78.96 | 221 | 685 | 4.79 | 117 | 940.7 | (2−)−0.924 | 5.43 | 0.3212 | 26.3 | $5 \times 10^{-6}$ | 2−, 2+, 4+, 6+ |
| Silicon | Si | 14 | 28.0855 | 1411 | 3231 | 2.336 | 118 | 786.5 | (4−)−0.143 | 50.2 | 0.7121 | 359 | 27.2 | 2+, 4+ |
| Silver | Ag | 47 | 107.8682 | 961 | 2195 | 10.49 | 144 | 730.8 | (1+)+0.7991 | 11.65 | 0.23502 | 255 | $8 \times 10^{-6}$ | 1+ |
| Sodium | Na | 11 | 22.989768 | 97.83 | 897.4 | 0.968 | 186 | 495.9 | (1+)−2.714 | 2.602 | 1.228 | 97.4 | 2.27 | 1+ |
| Strontium | Sr | 38 | 87.62 | 776.9 | 1382 | 2.6 | 215 | 549.5 | (2+)−2.89 | 7.4308 | 0.301 | 137 | 0.0384 | 2+ |
| Sulfur | S | 16 | 32.065 | 115.2 | 444.7 | 2.08 | 103 | 999.6 | (2−)−0.45 | 1.7272 | 0.7060 | 9.62 | 0.03 | 2−, 4+, 6+ |
| Tantalum | Ta | 73 | 180.9479 | 3017 | 5458 | 16.65 | 146 | 760.8 | (5+)−0.81 | 36.57 | 0.1402 | 737 | $2 \times 10^{-4}$ | 4+, 5+ |
| Technetium | Tc | 43 | [98] | 2157 | 4265 | 11.5 | 136 | 702 | (6+)+0.83 | 23.0 | — | 577 | — | 2+, 4+, 6+, 7+ |
| Tellurium | Te | 52 | 127.60 | 450 | 990 | 6.25 | 138 | 869 | (2−)−1.14 | 17.4 | 0.2016 | 50.6 | $2 \times 10^{-7}$ | 2−, 2+, 4+, 6+ |
| Terbium | Tb | 65 | 158.92534 | 1356 | 3230 | 8.272 | 177.3 | 564 | (3+)−2.31 | 10.3 | 0.1819 | 293 | $1 \times 10^{-5}$ | 3+, 4+ |
| Thallium | Tl | 81 | 204.3833 | 303.5 | 1457 | 11.85 | 170 | 589.1 | (1+)−0.3363 | 4.27 | 0.1288 | 162 | $7 \times 10^{-5}$ | 1+, 3+ |
| Thorium | Th | 90 | 232.0381 | 1750 | 4787 | 11.78 | 179 | 587 | (4+)−1.83 | 16.11 | 0.1177 | 543.9 | $8.1 \times 10^{-4}$ | 4+ |
| Thulium | Tm | 69 | 168.93421 | 1545 | 1950 | 9.318 | 175.9 | 596 | (3+)−2.32 | 18.4 | 0.1600 | 213 | $5 \times 10^{-5}$ | 2+, 3+ |
| Tin | Sn | 50 | 118.710 | 232 | 2623 | 7.265 | 141 | 708.4 | (4+)+0.151 | 7.07 | 0.2274 | 296 | $2.1 \times 10^{-4}$ | 2+, 4+ |
| Titanium | Ti | 22 | 47.867 | 1666 | 3358 | 4.5 | 147 | 658.1 | (4+)−0.86 | 14.146 | 0.5226 | 425 | 0.63 | 2+, 3+, 4+ |
| Tungsten | W | 74 | 183.84 | 3422 | 5555 | 19.3 | 139 | 770.4 | (6+)−0.09 | 35.4 | 0.1320 | 806 | $1.2 \times 10^{-4}$ | 4+, 5+, 6+ |
| Ununbium | Uub | 112 | [285] | — | — | — | — | — | — | — | — | — | — | |
| Ununquadium | Uuq | 114 | [289] | — | — | — | — | — | — | — | — | — | — | |
| Unununium | Uuu | 111 | [272] | — | — | — | — | — | — | — | — | — | — | |
| Uranium | U | 92 | 238.0289 | 1130 | 4131 | 19.05 | 156 | 597 | (6+)−0.83 | 12.6 | 0.11618 | 423 | $2.3 \times 10^{-4}$ | 3+, 4+, 5+, 6+ |
| Vanadium | V | 23 | 50.9415 | 1917 | 3417 | 6.11 | 134 | 650.3 | (4+)−0.54 | 22.84 | 0.4886 | 459.7 | 0.0136 | 2+, 3+, 4+, 5+ |
| Xenon | Xe | 54 | 131.293 | −111.8 | −108.09 | 0.0058971 | 218 | 1170 | — | 2.29 | 0.15832 | 12.64 | — | 2+, 4+ |
| Ytterbium | Yb | 70 | 173.04 | 824 | 1196 | 6.973 | 193.3 | 603 | (3+)−2.22 | 7.66 | 0.1545 | 155 | $3.4 \times 10^{-4}$ | 2+, 3+ |
| Yttrium | Y | 39 | 88.90585 | 1530 | 3264 | 4.5 | 180 | 600 | (3+)−2.37 | 17.15 | 0.2984 | 393 | 0.0035 | 3+ |
| Zinc | Zn | 30 | 65.39 | 419.6 | 907 | 7.14 | 134 | 906.4 | (2+)−0.7626 | 7.322 | 0.3884 | 115 | 0.0076 | 2+ |
| Zirconium | Zr | 40 | 91.224 | 1852 | 4400 | 6.51 | 160 | 640 | (4+)−1.7 | 20.92 | 0.2780 | 590.5 | 0.0162 | 4+ |

\* [ ] indicates mass of longest-lived isotope.

## Table C-7

| Electron Configurations of Elements | | | | | | | | | | | | | | | | | | | |
|---|---|---|---|---|---|---|---|---|---|---|---|---|---|---|---|---|---|---|---|
| **Elements** | **1s** | **2s** | **2p** | **3s** | **3p** | **3d** | **4s** | **4p** | **4d** | **4f** | **5s** | **5p** | **5d** | **5f** | **6s** | **6p** | **6d** | **6f** | **7s** |
| 1 Hydrogen | 1 | | | | | | | | | | | | | | | | | | |
| 2 Helium | 2 | | | | | | | | | | | | | | | | | | |
| 3 Lithium | 2 | 1 | | | | | | | | | | | | | | | | | |
| 4 Beryllium | 2 | 2 | | | | | | | | | | | | | | | | | |
| 5 Boron | 2 | 2 | 1 | | | | | | | | | | | | | | | | |
| 6 Carbon | 2 | 2 | 2 | | | | | | | | | | | | | | | | |
| 7 Nitrogen | 2 | 2 | 3 | | | | | | | | | | | | | | | | |
| 8 Oxygen | 2 | 2 | 4 | | | | | | | | | | | | | | | | |
| 9 Fluorine | 2 | 2 | 5 | | | | | | | | | | | | | | | | |
| 10 Neon | 2 | 2 | 6 | | | | | | | | | | | | | | | | |
| 11 Sodium | 2 | 2 | 6 | 1 | | | | | | | | | | | | | | | |
| 12 Magnesium | 2 | 2 | 6 | 2 | | | | | | | | | | | | | | | |
| 13 Aluminum | 2 | 2 | 6 | 2 | 1 | | | | | | | | | | | | | | |
| 14 Silicon | 2 | 2 | 6 | 2 | 2 | | | | | | | | | | | | | | |
| 15 Phosphorus | 2 | 2 | 6 | 2 | 3 | | | | | | | | | | | | | | |
| 16 Sulfur | 2 | 2 | 6 | 2 | 4 | | | | | | | | | | | | | | |
| 17 Chlorine | 2 | 2 | 6 | 2 | 5 | | | | | | | | | | | | | | |
| 18 Argon | 2 | 2 | 6 | 2 | 6 | | | | | | | | | | | | | | |
| 19 Potassium | 2 | 2 | 6 | 2 | 6 | | 1 | | | | | | | | | | | | |
| 20 Calcium | 2 | 2 | 6 | 2 | 6 | | 2 | | | | | | | | | | | | |
| 21 Scandium | 2 | 2 | 6 | 2 | 6 | 1 | 2 | | | | | | | | | | | | |
| 22 Titanium | 2 | 2 | 6 | 2 | 6 | 2 | 2 | | | | | | | | | | | | |
| 23 Vanadium | 2 | 2 | 6 | 2 | 6 | 3 | 2 | | | | | | | | | | | | |
| 24 Chromium | 2 | 2 | 6 | 2 | 6 | 5 | 1 | | | | | | | | | | | | |
| 25 Manganese | 2 | 2 | 6 | 2 | 6 | 5 | 2 | | | | | | | | | | | | |
| 26 Iron | 2 | 2 | 6 | 2 | 6 | 6 | 2 | | | | | | | | | | | | |
| 27 Cobalt | 2 | 2 | 6 | 2 | 6 | 7 | 2 | | | | | | | | | | | | |
| 28 Nickel | 2 | 2 | 6 | 2 | 6 | 8 | 2 | | | | | | | | | | | | |
| 29 Copper | 2 | 2 | 6 | 2 | 6 | 10 | 1 | | | | | | | | | | | | |
| 30 Zinc | 2 | 2 | 6 | 2 | 6 | 10 | 2 | | | | | | | | | | | | |
| 31 Gallium | 2 | 2 | 6 | 2 | 6 | 10 | 2 | 1 | | | | | | | | | | | |
| 32 Germanium | 2 | 2 | 6 | 2 | 6 | 10 | 2 | 2 | | | | | | | | | | | |
| 33 Arsenic | 2 | 2 | 6 | 2 | 6 | 10 | 2 | 3 | | | | | | | | | | | |
| 34 Selenium | 2 | 2 | 6 | 2 | 6 | 10 | 2 | 4 | | | | | | | | | | | |
| 35 Bromine | 2 | 2 | 6 | 2 | 6 | 10 | 2 | 5 | | | | | | | | | | | |
| 36 Krypton | 2 | 2 | 6 | 2 | 6 | 10 | 2 | 6 | | | | | | | | | | | |
| 37 Rubidium | 2 | 2 | 6 | 2 | 6 | 10 | 2 | 6 | | | 1 | | | | | | | | |
| 38 Strontium | 2 | 2 | 6 | 2 | 6 | 10 | 2 | 6 | | | 2 | | | | | | | | |
| 39 Yttrium | 2 | 2 | 6 | 2 | 6 | 10 | 2 | 6 | 1 | | 2 | | | | | | | | |
| 40 Zirconium | 2 | 2 | 6 | 2 | 6 | 10 | 2 | 6 | 2 | | 2 | | | | | | | | |
| 41 Niobium | 2 | 2 | 6 | 2 | 6 | 10 | 2 | 6 | 4 | | 1 | | | | | | | | |
| 42 Molybdenum | 2 | 2 | 6 | 2 | 6 | 10 | 2 | 6 | 5 | | 1 | | | | | | | | |
| 43 Technetium | 2 | 2 | 6 | 2 | 6 | 10 | 2 | 6 | 5 | | 2 | | | | | | | | |
| 44 Ruthenium | 2 | 2 | 6 | 2 | 6 | 10 | 2 | 6 | 7 | | 1 | | | | | | | | |
| 45 Rhodium | 2 | 2 | 6 | 2 | 6 | 10 | 2 | 6 | 8 | | 1 | | | | | | | | |
| 46 Palladium | 2 | 2 | 6 | 2 | 6 | 10 | 2 | 6 | 10 | | | | | | | | | | |
| 47 Silver | 2 | 2 | 6 | 2 | 6 | 10 | 2 | 6 | 10 | | 1 | | | | | | | | |
| 48 Cadmium | 2 | 2 | 6 | 2 | 6 | 10 | 2 | 6 | 10 | | 2 | | | | | | | | |
| 49 Indium | 2 | 2 | 6 | 2 | 6 | 10 | 2 | 6 | 10 | | 2 | 1 | | | | | | | |
| 50 Tin | 2 | 2 | 6 | 2 | 6 | 10 | 2 | 6 | 10 | | 2 | 2 | | | | | | | |
| 51 Antimony | 2 | 2 | 6 | 2 | 6 | 10 | 2 | 6 | 10 | | 2 | 3 | | | | | | | |
| 52 Tellurium | 2 | 2 | 6 | 2 | 6 | 10 | 2 | 6 | 10 | | 2 | 4 | | | | | | | |
| 53 Iodine | 2 | 2 | 6 | 2 | 6 | 10 | 2 | 6 | 10 | | 2 | 5 | | | | | | | |
| 54 Xenon | 2 | 2 | 6 | 2 | 6 | 10 | 2 | 6 | 10 | | 2 | 6 | | | | | | | |

## Table C-7

| | | | | | | | | | | | Sublevels | | | | | | | | | | |
|---|---|---|---|---|---|---|---|---|---|---|---|---|---|---|---|---|---|---|---|---|---|
| | **Elements** | **1s** | **2s** | **2p** | **3s** | **3p** | **3d** | **4s** | **4p** | **4d** | **4f** | **5s** | **5p** | **5d** | **5f** | **6s** | **6p** | **6d** | **6f** | **7s** | **7p** |
| 55 | Cesium | 2 | 2 | 6 | 2 | 6 | 10 | 2 | 6 | 10 | | 2 | 6 | | | 1 | | | | | |
| 56 | Barium | 2 | 2 | 6 | 2 | 6 | 10 | 2 | 6 | 10 | | 2 | 6 | | | 2 | | | | | |
| 57 | Lanthanum | 2 | 2 | 6 | 2 | 6 | 10 | 2 | 6 | 10 | | 2 | 6 | 1 | | 2 | | | | | |
| 58 | Cerium | 2 | 2 | 6 | 2 | 6 | 10 | 2 | 6 | 10 | 2 | 2 | 6 | | | 2 | | | | | |
| 59 | Praseodymium | 2 | 2 | 6 | 2 | 6 | 10 | 2 | 6 | 10 | 3 | 2 | 6 | | | 2 | | | | | |
| 60 | Neodymium | 2 | 2 | 6 | 2 | 6 | 10 | 2 | 6 | 10 | 4 | 2 | 6 | | | 2 | | | | | |
| 61 | Promethium | 2 | 2 | 6 | 2 | 6 | 10 | 2 | 6 | 10 | 5 | 2 | 6 | | | 2 | | | | | |
| 62 | Samarium | 2 | 2 | 6 | 2 | 6 | 10 | 2 | 6 | 10 | 6 | 2 | 6 | | | 2 | | | | | |
| 63 | Europium | 2 | 2 | 6 | 2 | 6 | 10 | 2 | 6 | 10 | 7 | 2 | 6 | | | 2 | | | | | |
| 64 | Gadolinium | 2 | 2 | 6 | 2 | 6 | 10 | 2 | 6 | 10 | 7 | 2 | 6 | 1 | | 2 | | | | | |
| 65 | Terbium | 2 | 2 | 6 | 2 | 6 | 10 | 2 | 6 | 10 | 9 | 2 | 6 | | | 2 | | | | | |
| 66 | Dysprosium | 2 | 2 | 6 | 2 | 6 | 10 | 2 | 6 | 10 | 10 | 2 | 6 | | | 2 | | | | | |
| 67 | Holmium | 2 | 2 | 6 | 2 | 6 | 10 | 2 | 6 | 10 | 11 | 2 | 6 | | | 2 | | | | | |
| 68 | Erbium | 2 | 2 | 6 | 2 | 6 | 10 | 2 | 6 | 10 | 12 | 2 | 6 | | | 2 | | | | | |
| 69 | Thulium | 2 | 2 | 6 | 2 | 6 | 10 | 2 | 6 | 10 | 13 | 2 | 6 | | | 2 | | | | | |
| 70 | Ytterbium | 2 | 2 | 6 | 2 | 6 | 10 | 2 | 6 | 10 | 14 | 2 | 6 | | | 2 | | | | | |
| 71 | Lutetium | 2 | 2 | 6 | 2 | 6 | 10 | 2 | 6 | 10 | 14 | 2 | 6 | 1 | | 2 | | | | | |
| 72 | Hafnium | 2 | 2 | 6 | 2 | 6 | 10 | 2 | 6 | 10 | 14 | 2 | 6 | 2 | | 2 | | | | | |
| 73 | Tantalum | 2 | 2 | 6 | 2 | 6 | 10 | 2 | 6 | 10 | 14 | 2 | 6 | 3 | | 2 | | | | | |
| 74 | Tungsten | 2 | 2 | 6 | 2 | 6 | 10 | 2 | 6 | 10 | 14 | 2 | 6 | 4 | | 2 | | | | | |
| 75 | Rhenium | 2 | 2 | 6 | 2 | 6 | 10 | 2 | 6 | 10 | 14 | 2 | 6 | 5 | | 2 | | | | | |
| 76 | Osmium | 2 | 2 | 6 | 2 | 6 | 10 | 2 | 6 | 10 | 14 | 2 | 6 | 6 | | 2 | | | | | |
| 77 | Iridium | 2 | 2 | 6 | 2 | 6 | 10 | 2 | 6 | 10 | 14 | 2 | 6 | 7 | | 2 | | | | | |
| 78 | Platinum | 2 | 2 | 6 | 2 | 6 | 10 | 2 | 6 | 10 | 14 | 2 | 6 | 9 | | 1 | | | | | |
| 79 | Gold | 2 | 2 | 6 | 2 | 6 | 10 | 2 | 6 | 10 | 14 | 2 | 6 | 10 | | 1 | | | | | |
| 80 | Mercury | 2 | 2 | 6 | 2 | 6 | 10 | 2 | 6 | 10 | 14 | 2 | 6 | 10 | | 2 | | | | | |
| 81 | Thallium | 2 | 2 | 6 | 2 | 6 | 10 | 2 | 6 | 10 | 14 | 2 | 6 | 10 | | 2 | 1 | | | | |
| 82 | Lead | 2 | 2 | 6 | 2 | 6 | 10 | 2 | 6 | 10 | 14 | 2 | 6 | 10 | | 2 | 2 | | | | |
| 83 | Bismuth | 2 | 2 | 6 | 2 | 6 | 10 | 2 | 6 | 10 | 14 | 2 | 6 | 10 | | 2 | 3 | | | | |
| 84 | Polonium | 2 | 2 | 6 | 2 | 6 | 10 | 2 | 6 | 10 | 14 | 2 | 6 | 10 | | 2 | 4 | | | | |
| 85 | Astatine | 2 | 2 | 6 | 2 | 6 | 10 | 2 | 6 | 10 | 14 | 2 | 6 | 10 | | 2 | 5 | | | | |
| 86 | Radon | 2 | 2 | 6 | 2 | 6 | 10 | 2 | 6 | 10 | 14 | 2 | 6 | 10 | | 2 | 6 | | | | |
| 87 | Francium | 2 | 2 | 6 | 2 | 6 | 10 | 2 | 6 | 10 | 14 | 2 | 6 | 10 | | 2 | 6 | | | 1 | |
| 88 | Radium | 2 | 2 | 6 | 2 | 6 | 10 | 2 | 6 | 10 | 14 | 2 | 6 | 10 | | 2 | 6 | | | 2 | |
| 89 | Actinium | 2 | 2 | 8 | 2 | 6 | 10 | 2 | 6 | 10 | 14 | 2 | 6 | 10 | | 2 | 6 | 1 | | 2 | |
| 90 | Thorium | 2 | 2 | 6 | 2 | 6 | 10 | 2 | 6 | 10 | 14 | 2 | 6 | 10 | | 2 | 6 | 2 | | 2 | |
| 91 | Protactinium | 2 | 2 | 6 | 2 | 6 | 10 | 2 | 6 | 10 | 14 | 2 | 6 | 10 | 2 | 2 | 6 | 1 | | 2 | |
| 92 | Uranium | 2 | 2 | 6 | 2 | 6 | 10 | 2 | 6 | 10 | 14 | 2 | 6 | 10 | 3 | 2 | 6 | 1 | | 2 | |
| 93 | Neptunium | 2 | 2 | 6 | 2 | 6 | 10 | 2 | 6 | 10 | 14 | 2 | 6 | 10 | 4 | 2 | 6 | 1 | | 2 | |
| 94 | Plutonium | 2 | 2 | 6 | 2 | 6 | 10 | 2 | 6 | 10 | 14 | 2 | 6 | 10 | 6 | 2 | 6 | | | 2 | |
| 95 | Americium | 2 | 2 | 6 | 2 | 6 | 10 | 2 | 6 | 10 | 14 | 2 | 6 | 10 | 7 | 2 | 6 | | | 2 | |
| 96 | Curium | 2 | 2 | 6 | 2 | 6 | 10 | 2 | 6 | 10 | 14 | 2 | 6 | 10 | 7 | 2 | 6 | 1 | | 2 | |
| 97 | Berkelium | 2 | 2 | 6 | 2 | 6 | 10 | 2 | 6 | 10 | 14 | 2 | 6 | 10 | 9 | 2 | 6 | | | 2 | |
| 98 | Californium | 2 | 2 | 6 | 2 | 6 | 10 | 2 | 6 | 10 | 14 | 2 | 6 | 10 | 10 | 2 | 6 | | | 2 | |
| 99 | Einsteinium | 2 | 2 | 6 | 2 | 6 | 10 | 2 | 6 | 10 | 14 | 2 | 6 | 10 | 11 | 2 | 6 | | | 2 | |
| 100 | Fermium | 2 | 2 | 6 | 2 | 6 | 10 | 2 | 6 | 10 | 14 | 2 | 6 | 10 | 12 | 2 | 6 | | | 2 | |
| 101 | Mendelevium | 2 | 2 | 6 | 2 | 6 | 10 | 2 | 6 | 10 | 14 | 2 | 6 | 10 | 13 | 2 | 6 | | | 2 | |
| 102 | Nobelium | 2 | 2 | 6 | 2 | 6 | 10 | 2 | 6 | 10 | 14 | 2 | 6 | 10 | 14 | 2 | 6 | | | 2 | |
| 103 | Lawrencium | 2 | 2 | 6 | 2 | 6 | 10 | 2 | 6 | 10 | 14 | 2 | 6 | 10 | 14 | 2 | 6 | 1 | | 2 | |
| 104 | Rutherfordium | 2 | 2 | 6 | 2 | 6 | 10 | 2 | 6 | 10 | 14 | 2 | 6 | 10 | 14 | 2 | 6 | 2 | | 2? | |
| 105 | Dubnium | 2 | 2 | 6 | 2 | 6 | 10 | 2 | 6 | 10 | 14 | 2 | 6 | 10 | 14 | 2 | 6 | 3 | | 2? | |
| 106 | Seaborgium | 2 | 2 | 6 | 2 | 6 | 10 | 2 | 6 | 10 | 14 | 2 | 6 | 10 | 14 | 2 | 6 | 4 | | 2? | |
| 107 | Bohrium | 2 | 2 | 6 | 2 | 6 | 10 | 2 | 6 | 10 | 14 | 2 | 6 | 10 | 14 | 2 | 6 | 5 | | 2? | |
| 108 | Hassium | 2 | 2 | 6 | 2 | 6 | 10 | 2 | 6 | 10 | 14 | 2 | 6 | 10 | 14 | 2 | 6 | 6 | | 2? | |
| 109 | Meitnerium | 2 | 2 | 6 | 2 | 6 | 10 | 2 | 6 | 10 | 14 | 2 | 6 | 10 | 14 | 2 | 6 | 7 | | 2? | |
| 110 | Darmstadtium | 2 | 2 | 6 | 2 | 6 | 10 | 2 | 6 | 10 | 14 | 2 | 6 | 10 | 14 | 2 | 6 | 8 | | 2? | |
| 111 | Unununium | 2 | 2 | 6 | 2 | 6 | 10 | 2 | 6 | 10 | 14 | 2 | 6 | 10 | 14 | 2 | 6 | 9 | | 2? | |
| 112 | Unumbium | 2 | 2 | 6 | 2 | 6 | 10 | 2 | 6 | 10 | 14 | 2 | 6 | 10 | 14 | 2 | 6 | 10 | | 2? | |
| 114 | Ununquadium | 2 | 2 | 6 | 2 | 6 | 10 | 2 | 6 | 10 | 14 | 2 | 6 | 10 | 14 | 2 | 6 | 10 | | 2? | 2? |

## Table C-8

| Names and Charges of Polyatomic Ions | | | |
|---|---|---|---|
| **1−** | **2−** | **3−** | **4−** |
| Acetate, $CH_3COO^-$ | Carbonate, $CO_3^{2-}$ | Arsenate, $AsO_4^{3-}$ | Hexacyanoferrate(II), $Fe(CN)_6^{4-}$ |
| Amide, $NH_2^-$ | Chromate, $CrO_4^{2-}$ | Arsenite, $AsO_3^{3-}$ | Orthosilicate, $SiO_4^{4-}$ |
| Astatate, $AtO_3^-$ | Dichromate, $Cr_2O_7^{2-}$ | Borate, $BO_3^{3-}$ | Diphosphate, $P_2O_7^{4-}$ |
| Azide, $N_3^-$ | Hexachloroplatinate, $PtCl_6^{2-}$ | Citrate, $C_6H_5O_7^{3-}$ | |
| Benzoate, $C_6H_5COO^-$ | Hexafluorosilicate, $SiF_6^{2-}$ | Hexacyanoferrate(III), $Fe(CN)_6^{3-}$ | |
| Bismuthate, $BiO_3^-$ | Molybdate, $MoO_4^{2-}$ | Phosphate, $PO_4^{3-}$ | |
| Bromate, $BrO_3^-$ | Oxalate, $C_2O_4^{2-}$ | Phosphite, $PO_3^{3-}$ | |
| Chlorate, $ClO_3^-$ | Peroxide, $O_2^{2-}$ | | |
| Chlorite, $ClO_2^-$ | Peroxydisulfate, $S_2O_8^{2-}$ | **1+** | **2+** |
| Cyanide, $CN^-$ | Ruthenate, $RuO_4^{2-}$ | Ammonium, $NH_4^+$ | Mercury(I), $Hg_2^{2+}$ |
| Formate, $HCOO^-$ | Selenate, $SeO_4^{2-}$ | Neptunyl(V), $NpO_2^+$ | Neptunyl(VI), $NpO_2^{2+}$ |
| Hydroxide, $OH^-$ | Selenite, $SeO_3^{2-}$ | Plutonyl(V), $PuO_2^+$ | Plutonyl(VI), $PuO_2^{2+}$ |
| Hypobromite, $BrO^-$ | Silicate, $SiO_3^{2-}$ | Uranyl(V), $UO_2^+$ | Uranyl(VI), $UO_2^{2+}$ |
| Hypochlorite, $ClO^-$ | Sulfate, $SO_4^{2-}$ | Vanadyl(V), $VO_2^+$ | Vanadyl(IV), $VO^{2+}$ |
| Hypophosphite, $H_2PO_2^-$ | Sulfite, $SO_3^{2-}$ | | |
| Iodate, $IO_3^-$ | Tartrate, $C_4H_4O_6^{2-}$ | | |
| Nitrate, $NO_3^-$ | Tellurate, $TeO_4^{2-}$ | | |
| Nitrite, $NO_2^-$ | Tellurite, $TeO_3^{2-}$ | | |
| Perbromate, $BrO_4^-$ | Tetraborate, $B_4O_7^{2-}$ | | |
| Perchlorate, $ClO_4^-$ | Thiosulfate, $S_2O_3^{2-}$ | | |
| Periodate, $IO_4^-$ | Tungstate, $WO_4^{2-}$ | | |
| Permanganate, $MnO_4^-$ | | | |
| Perrhenate, $ReO_4^-$ | | | |
| Thiocyanate, $SCN^-$ | | | |
| Vanadate, $VO_3^-$ | | | |

## Table C-9

| Ionization Constants | | | | | |
|---|---|---|---|---|---|
| **Substance** | **Ionization Constant** | **Substance** | **Ionization Constant** | **Substance** | **Ionization Constant** |
| $HCOOH$ | $1.77 \times 10^{-4}$ | $HBO_3^{-2}$ | $1.58 \times 10^{-14}$ | $HS^-$ | $1.00 \times 10^{-19}$ |
| $CH_3COOH$ | $1.75 \times 10^{-5}$ | $H_2CO_3$ | $4.5 \times 10^{-7}$ | $HSO_4^-$ | $1.02 \times 10^{-2}$ |
| $CH_2ClCOOH$ | $1.36 \times 10^{-3}$ | $HCO_3^-$ | $4.68 \times 10^{-11}$ | $H_2SO_3$ | $1.29 \times 10^{-2}$ |
| $CHCl_2COOH$ | $4.47 \times 10^{-2}$ | $HCN$ | $6.17 \times 10^{-10}$ | $HSO_3^-$ | $6.17 \times 10^{-8}$ |
| $CCl_3COOH$ | $3.02 \times 10^{-1}$ | $HF$ | $6.3 \times 10^{-4}$ | $HSeO_4^-$ | $2.19 \times 10^{-2}$ |
| $HOOCCOOH$ | $5.36 \times 10^{-2}$ | $HNO_2$ | $5.62 \times 10^{-4}$ | $H_2SeO_3$ | $2.29 \times 10^{-3}$ |
| $HOOCCOO^-$ | $1.55 \times 10^{-4}$ | $H_3PO_4$ | $7.08 \times 10^{-3}$ | $HSeO_3^-$ | $4.79 \times 10^{-9}$ |
| $CH_3CH_2COOH$ | $1.34 \times 10^{-5}$ | $H_2PO_4^-$ | $6.31 \times 10^{-8}$ | $HBrO$ | $2.51 \times 10^{-9}$ |
| $C_6H_5COOH$ | $6.25 \times 10^{-5}$ | $HPO_4^{2-}$ | $4.17 \times 10^{-13}$ | $HClO$ | $2.9 \times 10^{-8}$ |
| $H_3AsO_4$ | $6.03 \times 10^{-3}$ | $H_3PO_3$ | $5.01 \times 10^{-2}$ | $HIO$ | $3.16 \times 10^{-11}$ |
| $H_2AsO_4^-$ | $1.05 \times 10^{-7}$ | $H_2PO_3^-$ | $2.00 \times 10^{-7}$ | $NH_3$ | $5.62 \times 10^{-10}$ |
| $H_3BO_3$ | $5.75 \times 10^{-10}$ | $H_3PO_2$ | $5.89 \times 10^{-2}$ | $H_2NNH_2$ | $7.94 \times 10^{-9}$ |
| $H_2BO_3^-$ | $1.82 \times 10^{-13}$ | $H_2S$ | $9.1 \times 10^{-8}$ | $H_2NOH$ | $1.15 \times 10^{-6}$ |

## Table C-10

### Solubility Guidelines

A substance is considered soluble if more than three grams of the substance dissolves in 100 mL of water. The more common rules are listed below.

1. All common salts of the group 1A elements and ammonium ions are soluble.
2. All common acetates and nitrates are soluble.
3. All binary compounds of group 7A elements (other than F) with metals are soluble except those of silver, mercury(I), and lead.
4. All sulfates are soluble except those of barium, strontium, lead, calcium, silver, and mercury(I).
5. Except for those in Rule 1, carbonates, hydroxides, oxides, sulfides, and phosphates are insoluble.

### Solubility of Compounds in Water

|  | Acetate | Bromide | Carbonate | Chlorate | Chloride | Chromate | Hydroxide | Iodide | Nitrate | Oxide | Perchlorate | Phosphate | Sulfate | Sulfide |
|---|---|---|---|---|---|---|---|---|---|---|---|---|---|---|
| Aluminum | S | S | — | S | S | — | I | S | S | I | S | I | S | D |
| Ammonium | S | S | S | S | S | S | S | S | S | — | S | S | S | S |
| Barium | S | S | P | S | S | I | S | S | S | S | S | I | I | D |
| Calcium | S | S | P | S | S | S | S | S | S | P | S | P | P | P |
| Copper (II) | S | S | — | S | S | — | I | — | S | I | S | I | S | I |
| Hydrogen | S | S | — | S | S | — | — | S | S | S | S | S | S | S |
| Iron(II) | — | S | P | S | S | — | I | S | S | I | S | I | S | I |
| Iron(III) | — | S | — | S | S | I | I | S | S | I | S | P | P | D |
| Lead(II) | S | S | — | S | S | I | P | P | S | P | S | I | P | I |
| Lithium | S | S | S | S | S | ? | S | S | S | S | S | P | S | S |
| Magnesium | S | S | P | S | S | S | I | S | S | I | S | P | S | D |
| Manganese(II) | S | S | P | S | S | — | I | S | S | I | S | P | S | I |
| Mercury(I) | P | I | I | S | I | P | — | I | S | I | S | I | P | I |
| Mercury(II) | S | S | — | S | S | P | I | P | S | P | S | I | D | I |
| Potassium | S | S | S | S | S | S | S | S | S | S | S | S | S | S |
| Silver | P | I | I | S | I | P | — | I | S | P | S | I | P | I |
| Sodium | S | S | S | S | S | S | S | S | S | D | S | S | S | S |
| Strontium | S | S | P | S | S | P | S | S | S | S | S | I | P | S |
| Tin(II) | D | S | — | S | S | I |  | S | D | I | S | I | S | I |
| Tin(IV) | S | S | — | — | S | S | I | D | — | I | S | — | S | I |
| Zinc | S | S | P | S | S | P | P | S | S | P | S | I | S | I |

S – soluble          P – partially soluble          I – insoluble          D – decomposes

## Table C-11

| Substance | $c$ | Substance | $c$ | Substance | $c$ |
|---|---|---|---|---|---|
| $AlF_3$ | 0.8948 | $Fe_3C$ | 0.5898 | $NaVO_3$ | 1.540 |
| $BaTiO_3$ | 0.79418 | $FeWO_4$ | 0.37735 | $Ni(CO)_4$ | 1.198 |
| $BeO$ | 1.020 | $HI$ | 0.22795 | $PbI_2$ | 0.1678 |
| $CaC_2$ | 0.9785 | $K_2CO_3$ | 0.82797 | $SF_6$ | 0.6660 |
| $CaSO_4$ | 0.7320 | $MgCO_3$ | 0.8957 | $SiC$ | 0.6699 |
| $CCl_4$ | 0.85651 | $Mg(OH)_2$ | 1.321 | $SiO_2$ | 0.7395 |
| $CH_3OH$ | 2.55 | $MgSO_4$ | 0.8015 | $SrCl_2$ | 0.4769 |
| $CH_2OHCH_2OH$ | 2.413 | $MnS$ | 0.5742 | $Tb_2O_3$ | 0.3168 |
| $CH_3CH_2OH$ | 2.4194 | $Na_2CO_3$ | 1.0595 | $TiCl_4$ | 0.76535 |
| $CdO$ | 0.3382 | $NaF$ | 1.116 | $Y_2O_3$ | 0.45397 |
| $CuSO_4 \cdot 5H_2O$ | 1.12 | | | | |

**Specific Heat Values (J/g·K)**

## Table C-12

**Molal Freezing Point Depression and Boiling Point Elevation Constants**

| Substance | $K_{fp}$ (C°kg/mol) | Freezing Point (°C) | $K_{bp}$ (C°kg/mol) | Boiling Point (°C) |
|---|---|---|---|---|
| Acetic acid | 3.90 | 16.66 | 3.22 | 117.90 |
| Benzene | 5.12 | 5.533 | 2.53 | 80.100 |
| Camphor | 37.7 | 178.75 | 5.611 | 207.42 |
| Cyclohexane | 20.0 | 6.54 | 2.75 | 80.725 |
| Cyclohexanol | 39.3 | 25.15 | -- | -- |
| Nitrobenzene | 6.852 | 5.76 | 5.24 | 210.8 |
| Phenol | 7.40 | 40.90 | 3.60 | 181.839 |
| Water | 1.86 | 0.000 | 0.512 | 100.000 |

## Table C-13

**Heat of Formation Values**

$\Delta H_f^\circ$ (kJ/mol)   (concentration of aqueous solutions is 1$M$)

| Substance | $\Delta H_f^\circ$ | Substance | $\Delta H_f^\circ$ | Substance | $\Delta H_f^\circ$ | Substance | $\Delta H_f^\circ$ | Substance | $\Delta H_f^\circ$ |
|---|---|---|---|---|---|---|---|---|---|
| $Ag(s)$ | 0 | $CsCl(s)$ | −443.04 | $H_3PO_4(aq)$ | −1279.0 | | | $NaBr(s)$ | −361.062 |
| $AgCl(s)$ | −127.068 | $Cs_2SO_4(s)$ | −1443.02 | $H_2S(g)$ | −20.63 | | | $NaCl(s)$ | −411.153 |
| $AgCN(s)$ | 146.0 | $CuI(s)$ | −67.8 | $H_2SO_3(aq)$ | −608.81 | | | $NaHCO_3(s)$ | −950.8 |
| $Al_2O_3$ | −1675.7 | $CuS(s)$ | −53.1 | $H_2SO_4(aq)$ | −814.0 | | | $NaNO_3(aq)$ | −447.48 |
| $BaCl_2(aq)$ | −871.95 | $Cu_2S(s)$ | −79.5 | $HgCl_2(s)$ | −224. 3 | | | $NaOH(s)$ | −425.609 |
| $BaSO_4$ | −1473.2 | $CuSO_4(s)$ | −771.36 | $Hg_2Cl_2(s)$ | −265.22 | | | $Na_2CO_3(s)$ | −1130.7 |
| $BeO(s)$ | −609.6 | $F_2(g)$ | 0 | $Hg_2SO_4(s)$ | −743.12 | | | $Na_2S(aq)$ | −447.3 |
| $BiCl_3(s)$ | −379.1 | $FeCl_3(s)$ | −399.49 | $I_2(s)$ | 0 | | | $Na_2SO_4(s)$ | −1387.08 |
| $Bi_2S_3(s)$ | −143.1 | $FeO(s)$ | −272.0 | $K(s)$ | 0 | | | $NH_4Cl(s)$ | −314.4 |
| $Br_2$ | 0 | $FeS(s)$ | −100.0 | $KBr(s)$ | −393.798 | | | $O_2(g)$ | 0 |
| $CCl_4(l)$ | −128.2 | $Fe_2O_3(s)$ | −824.2 | $KMnO_4(s)$ | −837.2 | | | $P_4O_6(s)$ | −1640.1 |
| $CH_4(g)$ | −74.81 | $Fe_3O_4(s)$ | −1118.4 | $KOH$ | −424.764 | | | $P_4O_{10}(s)$ | −2984.0 |
| $C_2H_2(g)$ | 226.73 | $H(g)$ | 217.965 | $LiBr(s)$ | −351.213 | | | $PbBr_2(s)$ | −278.7 |
| $C_2H_4(g)$ | 52.26 | $H_2(g)$ | 0 | $LiOH(s)$ | −484.93 | | | $PbCl_2(s)$ | −359.41 |
| $C_2H_6(g)$ | −84.68 | $HBr(g)$ | −36.40 | $Mn(s)$ | 0 | | | $SF_6(g)$ | −1220.5 |
| $CO(g)$ | −110.525 | $HCl(g)$ | −92.307 | $MnCl_2(aq)$ | −555.05 | | | $SO_2(g)$ | −296.830 |
| $CO_2(g)$ | −393.509 | $HCl(aq)$ | −167.159 | $Mn(NO_3)_2(aq)$ | −635.5 | | | $SO_3(g)$ | −454.51 |
| $CS_2(l)$ | 89.70 | $HCN(aq)$ | 108.9 | $MnO_2(s)$ | −520.03 | | | $SrO(s)$ | −592.0 |
| $Ca(s)$ | 0 | $HCHO$ | −108.57 | $MnS(s)$ | −214.2 | | | $TiO_3(s)$ | −939.7 |
| $CaCO_3(s)$ | −1206.9 | $HCOOH(l)$ | −424.72 | $N_2(g)$ | 0 | | | $TlI(s)$ | −123.5 |
| $CaO(s)$ | −635.1 | $HF(g)$ | −271.1 | $NH_3(g)$ | −46.11 | | | $UCl_4(s)$ | −1019.2 |
| $Ca(OH)_2(s)$ | −986.09 | $HI(g)$ | 26.48 | $NH_4Br(s)$ | −270.83 | | | $UCl_5(s)$ | −1059 |
| $Cl_2(g)$ | 0 | $H_2O(l)$ | −285.830 | $NO(g)$ | 90.25 | | | $Zn(s)$ | 0 |
| $Co_3O_4(s)$ | −891 | $H_2O(g)$ | −241.818 | $NO_2(g)$ | 33.18 | | | $ZnCl_2(aq)$ | −488.19 |
| $CoO(s)$ | −237.94 | $H_2O_2(l)$ | −187.8 | $N_2O(g)$ | 82.05 | | | $ZnO(s)$ | −348.28 |
| $Cr_2O_3(s)$ | −1139.7 | $H_3PO_4(l)$ | −595.4 | $Na(s)$ | 0 | | | $ZnSO_4(aq)$ | −1063.15 |

## Chapter 1

No practice problems

## Chapter 2

**1.** density = $\dfrac{\text{mass}}{\text{volume}}$

volume = 41 mL − 20 mL = 21 mL

density = $\dfrac{147 \text{ g}}{21 \text{ mL}}$ = 7.0 g/mL

**2.** volume = $\dfrac{\text{mass}}{\text{density}}$

volume = $\dfrac{20 \text{ g}}{4 \text{ g/mL}}$ = 5 mL

**3.** density = $\dfrac{\text{mass}}{\text{volume}}$

density = $\dfrac{20 \text{ g}}{5 \text{ cm}^3}$ = 4 g/cm$^3$

The density of pure aluminum is 2.7 g/cm$^3$, so the cube cannot be made of aluminum.

**12. a.** $7 \times 10^2$ m
 **b.** $3.8 \times 10^4$ m
 **c.** $4.5 \times 10^6$ m
 **d.** $6.85 \times 10^{11}$ m
 **e.** $5.4 \times 10^{-3}$ kg
 **f.** $6.87 \times 10^{-6}$ kg
 **g.** $7.6 \times 10^{-8}$ kg
 **h.** $8 \times 10^{-10}$ kg

**13. a.** $3.6 \times 10^5$ s
 **b.** $5.4 \times 10^{-5}$ s
 **c.** $5.06 \times 10^3$ s
 **d.** $8.9 \times 10^{10}$ s

**14. a.** $7 \times 10^{-5}$ m
 **b.** $3 \times 10^8$ m
 **c.** $2 \times 10^2$ m
 **d.** $5 \times 10^{-12}$ m
 **e.** $1.26 \times 10^4$ kg + $0.25 \times 10^4$ kg = $1.51 \times 10^4$ kg
 **f.** $7.06 \times 10^{-3}$ kg + $0.12 \times 10^{-3}$ kg
 = $7.18 \times 10^{-3}$ kg
 **g.** $4.39 \times 10^5$ kg − $0.28 \times 10^5$ kg = $4.11 \times 10^5$ kg
 **h.** $5.36 \times 10^{-1}$ kg − $0.740 \times 10^{-1}$ kg
 = $4.62 \times 10^{-1}$ kg

**15. a.** $4 \times 10^{10}$ cm$^2$
 **b.** $6 \times 10^{-2}$ cm$^2$
 **c.** $9 \times 10^{-1}$ cm$^2$
 **d.** $5 \times 10^2$ cm$^2$

**16. a.** $3 \times 10^1$ g/cm$^3$
 **b.** $2 \times 10^3$ g/cm$^3$
 **c.** $3 \times 10^6$ g/cm$^3$
 **d.** $2 \times 10^{-1}$ g/cm$^3$

**17. a.** $360 \text{ s} \times \dfrac{1000 \text{ ms}}{1 \text{ s}}$ = 360 000 ms
 **b.** $4800 \text{ g} \times \dfrac{1 \text{ kg}}{1000 \text{ g}}$ = 4.8 kg
 **c.** $5600 \text{ dm} \times \dfrac{1 \text{ m}}{10 \text{ dm}}$ = 560 m
 **d.** $72 \text{ g} \times \dfrac{1000 \text{ mg}}{1 \text{ g}}$ = 72 000 mg

**18. a.** $245 \text{ ms} \times \dfrac{1 \text{ s}}{1000 \text{ ms}}$ = 0.245 s
 **b.** $5 \text{ m} \times \dfrac{100 \text{ cm}}{1 \text{ m}}$ = 500 cm
 **c.** $6800 \text{ cm} \times \dfrac{1 \text{ m}}{100 \text{ cm}}$ = 68 m
 **d.** $25 \text{ kg} \times \dfrac{1 \text{ Mg}}{1000 \text{ kg}}$ = 0.025 Mg

**19.** $24 \text{ h} \times \dfrac{60 \text{ min}}{1 \text{ h}} \times \dfrac{60 \text{ s}}{1 \text{ min}}$ = 86 400 s

**20.** $\dfrac{19.3 \text{ g}}{1 \text{ mL}} \times \dfrac{10 \text{ dg}}{1 \text{ g}} \times \dfrac{1000 \text{ mL}}{1 \text{ L}}$ = 193 000 dg/L

**21.** $\dfrac{90.0 \text{ km}}{1 \text{ h}} \times \dfrac{0.62 \text{ mi}}{1 \text{ km}} \times \dfrac{1 \text{ h}}{60 \text{ min}}$ = 0.930 mi/min

**29.** $\dfrac{0.19}{1.59} \times 100$ = 11.9%

$\dfrac{0.09}{1.59} \times 100$ = 5.66%

$\dfrac{0.14}{1.59} \times 100$ = 8.80%

**30.** $\dfrac{0.11}{1.59} \times 100$ = 6.92%

$\dfrac{0.10}{1.59} \times 100$ = 6.29%

$\dfrac{0.12}{1.59} \times 100$ = 7.55%

**31. a.** 4
 **b.** 7
 **c.** 5
 **d.** 3

**32. a.** 5
 **b.** 3
 **c.** 5
 **d.** 2

**33. a.** 84 790 kg
 **b.** 38.54 g
 **c.** 256.8 cm
 **d.** 4.936 m

**34. a.** $5.482 \times 10^{-4}$ g
**b.** $1.368 \times 10^5$ kg
**c.** $3.087 \times 10^8$ mm
**d.** 2.014 mL

**35. a.** 142.9 cm
**b.** 768 kg
**c.** 0.1119 mg

**36. a.** 12.12 cm
**b.** 2.10 cm
**c.** $2.7 \times 10^3$ cm

**37. a.** 78 $m^2$
**b.** 12 $m^2$
**c.** 2.5 $m^2$
**d.** 81.1 $m^2$

**38. a.** 2.0 m/s
**b.** 3.00 m/s
**c.** 2.00 m/s
**d.** 2.9 m/s

## Chapter 3

**6.** $mass_{reactants} = mass_{products}$

$mass_{reactants} = mass_{water\ electrolyzed}$

$mass_{products} = mass_{hydrogen} + mass_{oxygen}$

$mass_{water\ electrolyzed} = mass_{hydrogen} + mass_{oxygen}$

$mass_{water\ electrolyzed} = 10.0\ g + 79.4\ g = 89.4\ g$

**7.** $mass_{reactants} = mass_{products}$

$mass_{sodium} + mass_{chlorine} = mass_{sodium\ chloride}$

$mass_{sodium} = 15.6\ g$

$mass_{sodium\ chloride} = 39.7\ g$

Substituting and solving for $mass_{chlorine}$ yields,
$15.6\ g + mass_{chlorine} = 39.7\ g$

$mass_{chlorine} = 39.7\ g - 15.6\ g = 24.1\ g$ used in the reaction.

Because the sodium reacts with excess chlorine, all of the sodium is used in the reaction; that is, 15.6 g of sodium are used in the reaction.

**8.** The reactants are aluminum and bromine. The product is aluminum bromide. The mass of bromine used in the reaction equals the initial mass minus the mass remaining after the reaction is complete. Thus,

$mass_{bromine}$ reacted $= 100.0\ g - 8.5\ g = 91.5\ g$

Because no aluminum remains after the reaction, you know that all of the aluminum is used in the reaction. Thus,
$mass_{aluminum} =$ initial mass of aluminum $= 10.3\ g$

To determine the mass of aluminum bromide formed, use conservation of mass.

$mass_{products} = mass_{reactants}$

$mass_{aluminum\ bromide} = mass_{aluminum} + mass_{bromine}$

$mass_{aluminum\ bromide} = 10.3\ g + 91.5\ g = 101.8\ g$

**9.** Magnesium and oxygen are the reactants. Magnesium oxide is the product.

$mass_{reactants} = mass_{products}$

$mass_{magnesium} + mass_{oxygen} = mass_{magnesium\ oxide}$

$mass_{magnesium} = 10.0\ g$

$mass_{magnesium\ oxide} = 16.6\ g$

Substituting and solving for $mass_{oxygen}$ yields,
$10.0\ g + mass_{oxygen} = 16.6\ g$

$mass_{oxygen} = 16.6\ g - 10.0\ g = 6.6\ g$

Solutions

**20.** $\text{percent by mass}_{\text{hydrogen}} = \dfrac{\text{mass}_{\text{hydrogen}}}{\text{mass}_{\text{compound}}} \times 100$

$\text{percent by mass}_{\text{hydrogen}} = \dfrac{12.4\ g}{78.0\ g} \times 100 = 15.9\%$

**21.** $\text{mass}_{\text{compound}} = 1.0\ g + 19.0\ g = 20.0\ g$

$\text{percent by mass}_{\text{hydrogen}} = \dfrac{\text{mass}_{\text{hydrogen}}}{\text{mass}_{\text{compound}}} \times 100$

$\text{percent by mass}_{\text{hydrogen}} = \dfrac{1.0\ g}{20.0\ g} \times 100 = 5.0\%$

**22.** $\text{mass}_{xy} = 3.50\ g + 10.5\ g = 14.0\ g$

$\text{percent by mass}_{x} = \dfrac{\text{mass}_{x}}{\text{mass}_{xy}} \times 100$

$\text{percent by mass}_{x} = \dfrac{3.50\ g}{14.0\ g} \times 100 = 25.0\%$

$\text{percent by mass}_{y} = \dfrac{\text{mass}_{y}}{\text{mass}_{xy}} \times 100$

$\text{percent by mass}_{y} = \dfrac{10.5\ g}{14.0\ g} \times 100 = 75.0\%$

**23.** Compound I

$\text{mass}_{\text{compound}} = 15.0\ g + 120.0\ g = 135.0\ g$

$\text{percent by mass}_{\text{hydrogen}} = \dfrac{\text{mass}_{\text{hydrogen}}}{\text{mass}_{\text{compound}}} \times 100$

$\text{percent by mass}_{\text{hydrogen}} = \dfrac{15.0\ g}{135.0\ g} \times 100 = 11.1\%$

Compound II

$\text{mass}_{\text{compound}} = 2.0\ g + 32.0\ g = 34.0\ g$

$\text{percent by mass}_{\text{hydrogen}} = \dfrac{\text{mass}_{\text{hydrogen}}}{\text{mass}_{\text{compound}}} \times 100$

$\text{percent by mass}_{\text{hydrogen}} = \dfrac{2.0\ g}{34.0\ g} \times 100 = 5.8\%$

The composition by percent by mass is not the same for the two compounds. Therefore, they must be different compounds.

**24.** No, you cannot be sure. The fact that two compounds have the same percent by mass of a single element does not guarantee that the composition of the two compounds is the same.

## Chapter 4

**11.**

| Element | Protons | Electrons |
|---|---|---|
| **a.** boron | 5 | 5 |
| **b.** radon | 86 | 86 |
| **c.** platinum | 78 | 78 |
| **d.** magnesium | 12 | 12 |

**12.** dysprosium

**13.** silicon

**14.**

| | Protons and electrons | Neutrons | Isotope | Symbol |
|---|---|---|---|---|
| **b.** | 20 | 26 | calcium-46 | $^{46}_{20}\text{Ca}$ |
| **c.** | 8 | 9 | oxygen-17 | $^{17}_{8}\text{O}$ |
| **d.** | 26 | 31 | iron-57 | $^{57}_{26}\text{Fe}$ |
| **e.** | 30 | 34 | zinc-64 | $^{64}_{30}\text{Zn}$ |
| **f.** | 80 | 124 | mercury-204 | $^{204}_{80}\text{Hg}$ |

**15.** For $^{10}\text{B}$: mass contribution = (10.013 amu)(0.198) = 1.98 amu

For $^{11}\text{B}$: mass contribution = (11.009 amu)(0.802) = 8.83 amu

Atomic mass of B = 1.98 amu + 8.83 amu = 10.81 amu

**16.** Helium-4 is more abundant in nature because the atomic mass of naturally occurring helium is closer to the mass of helium-4 (approximately 4 amu) than to the mass of helium-3 (approximately 3 amu).

**17.** For $^{24}\text{Mg}$: mass contribution = (23.985 amu)(0.7899) = 18.95 amu

For $^{25}\text{Mg}$: mass contribution = (24.986 amu)(0.1000) = 2.498 amu

For $^{26}\text{Mg}$: mass contribution = (25.982 amu)(0.1101) = 2.861 amu

Atomic mass of Mg = 18.95 amu + 2.498 amu + 2.861 amu = 24.31 amu

## Chapter 5

**1.** $c = \lambda\nu$

$3.00 \times 10^8$ m/s $= (4.90 \times 10^{-7}$ m$)\nu$

$\nu = \dfrac{3.00 \times 10^8 \text{ m/s}}{4.90 \times 10^{-7} \text{ m}} = 6.12 \times 10^{14}$ s$^{-1}$

**2.** $c = \lambda\nu$

$3.00 \times 10^8$ m/s $= (1.15 \times 10^{-10}$ m$)\nu$

$\nu = \dfrac{3.00 \times 10^8 \text{ m/s}}{1.15 \times 10^{-10} \text{ m}} = 2.61 \times 10^{18}$ s$^{-1}$

**3.** The speed of all electromagnetic waves is $3.00 \times 10^8$ m/s.

**4.** $c = \lambda\nu$

$94.7$ MHz $= 9.47 \times 10^7$ Hz

$3.00 \times 10^8$ m/s $= \lambda(9.47 \times 10^7$ Hz$)$

$\lambda = \dfrac{3.00 \times 10^8 \text{ m/s}}{9.47 \times 10^7 \text{ s}^{-1}} = 3.17$ m

**5. a.** $E_{photon} = h\nu =$
$(6.626 \times 10^{-34}$ J·s$)(6.32 \times 10^{20}$ s$^{-1})$
$E_{photon} = 4.19 \times 10^{-13}$ J

**b.** $E_{photon} = h\nu =$
$(6.626 \times 10^{-34}$ J·s$)(9.50 \times 10^{13}$ s$^{-1})$
$E_{photon} = 6.29 \times 10^{-20}$ J

**c.** $E_{photon} = h\nu =$
$(6.626 \times 10^{-34}$ J·s$)(1.05 \times 10^{16}$ s$^{-1})$
$E_{photon} = 6.96 \times 10^{-18}$ J

**6. a.** gamma ray or X ray
**b.** infrared
**c.** ultraviolet

**18. a.** bromine (35 electrons): $[Ar]4s^2 3d^{10}4p^5$
**b.** strontium (38 electrons): $[Kr]5s^2$
**c.** antimony (51 electrons): $[Kr]5s^2 4d^{10}5p^3$
**d.** rhenium (75 electrons): $[Xe]6s^2 4f^{14}5d^5$
**e.** terbium (65 electrons): $[Xe]6s^2 4f^9$
**f.** titanium (22 electrons): $[Ar]4s^2 3d^2$

**19.** Sulfur (16 electrons) has the electron configuration $[Ne]3s^2 3p^4$. Therefore, 6 electrons are in orbitals related to the third energy level of the sulfur atom.

**20.** Chlorine (17 electrons) has the electron configuration $[Ne]3s^2 3p^5$, or $1s^2 2s^2 2p^6 3s^2 3p^5$. Therefore, 11 electrons occupy p orbitals in a chlorine atom.

**21.** indium (In)

**22.** barium (Ba)

**23. a.** $\cdot$Mg$\cdot$
**b.** :$\overset{\cdot\cdot}{\underset{\cdot\cdot}{S}}$:
**c.** $\cdot\overset{\cdot\cdot}{\underset{\cdot\cdot}{Br}}$:
**d.** Rb$\cdot$
**e.** $\cdot\overset{\cdot}{Tl}\cdot$
**f.** :$\overset{\cdot\cdot}{\underset{\cdot\cdot}{Xe}}$:

## Chapter 6

**7.**

| | Electron configuration | Group | Period | Block |
|---|---|---|---|---|
| **a.** | $[Ne]3s^2$ | 2A | 3 | s-block |
| **b.** | $[He]2s^2$ | 2A | 2 | s-block |
| **c.** | $[Kr]5s^2 4d^{10}5p^5$ | 7A | 5 | p-block |

**8. a.** $[Ar]4s^2$
**b.** $[Xe]$
**c.** $[Ar]\,4s^2 3d^{10}$
**d.** $[He]2s^2 2p^4$

**9. a.** Sc, Y, La, Ac
**b.** N, P, As, Sb, Bi
**c.** Ne, Ar, Kr, Xe, Rn

**16.** Largest: Na
Smallest: S

**17.** Largest: Xe
Smallest: He

**18.** No. If all you know is that the atomic number of one element is 20 greater than that of the other, then you will be unable to determine the specific groups and periods that the elements are in. Without this information, you cannot apply the periodic trends in atomic size to determine which element has the larger radius.

## Chapter 7

No Practice Problems

Solutions

## Chapter 8

**7.** $3 \text{ Na ions}\left(\dfrac{1+}{\text{Na ion}}\right) + 1 \text{ N ion}\left(\dfrac{3-}{\text{N ion}}\right) =$

$3(1+) + 1(3-) = 0$

The overall charge on one formula unit of $Na_3N$ is zero.

**8.** $2 \text{ Li ions}\left(\dfrac{1+}{\text{Li ion}}\right) + 1 \text{ O ion}\left(\dfrac{2-}{\text{O ion}}\right) =$

$2(1+) + 1(2-) = 0$

The overall charge on one formula unit of $Li_2O$ is zero.

**9.** $1 \text{ Sr ion}\left(\dfrac{2+}{\text{Sr ion}}\right) + 2 \text{ F ions}\left(\dfrac{1-}{\text{F ion}}\right) =$

$1(2+) + 2(1-) = 0$

The overall charge on one formula unit of $SrF_2$ is zero.

**10.** $2 \text{ Al ions}\left(\dfrac{3+}{\text{Al ion}}\right) + 3 \text{ S ions}\left(\dfrac{2-}{\text{S ion}}\right) =$

$2(3+) + 3(2-) = 0$

The overall charge on one formula unit of $Al_2S_3$ is zero.

**11.** $3 \text{ Cs ions}\left(\dfrac{1+}{\text{Cs ion}}\right) + 1 \text{ P ion}\left(\dfrac{3-}{\text{P ion}}\right) =$

$3(1+) + 1(3-) = 0$

The overall charge on one formula unit of $Cs_3P$ is zero.

**19.** KI

**20.** $MgCl_2$

**21.** $AlBr_3$

**22.** $Cs_3N$

**23.** BaS

**24.** $NaNO_3$

**25.** $Ca(ClO_3)_2$

**26.** $Al_2(CO_3)_3$

**27.** $K_2CrO_4$

**28.** $MgCO_3$

**29.** sodium bromide

**30.** calcium chloride

**31.** potassium hydroxide

**32.** copper(II) nitrate

**33.** silver chromate

## Chapter 9

**1.**

**2.**

**3.**

**4.**

**5.**

**13.** carbon tetrachloride

**14.** diarsenic trioxide

**15.** carbon monoxide

**16.** sulfur dioxide

**17.** nitrogen trifluoride

**18.** hydroiodic acid

**19.** chloric acid

**20.** chlorous acid

**21.** sulfuric acid

**22.** hydrosulfuric acid

**30.**

**31.**

**32.**

**33.**

**34.**

**35.**

**36.**

**37.**

**38.**

$$\left[ :\ddot{O}\!-\!\overset{..}{N}\!=\!\ddot{O}: \right]^{1-} \longleftrightarrow \left[ :\ddot{O}\!=\!\overset{..}{N}\!-\!\ddot{O}: \right]^{1-}$$

**39.**

F₆S structure with S central bonded to six F atoms

**40.**

PCl₅ structure with P central bonded to five Cl atoms

**41.**

ClF₃ structure

| Mole-cule | Geometry | | Bond angle | Hybridi-zation |
|---|---|---|---|---|
| **49.** BF₃ | BF₃ structure | Trigonal planar | 120° | sp² |
| **50.** NH₄⁺ | NH₄⁺ structure (with 1+ charge) | Tetrahedral | 109° | sp³ |
| **51.** OCl₂ | Cl–O–Cl structure | Bent | 104.5° | sp³ |
| **52.** BeF₂ | :F̈–Be–F̈: | Linear | 180° | sp |
| **53.** CF₄ | CF₄ structure | Tetrahedral | 109° | sp³ |

**60.** $SCl_2$ is polar because the molecule is asymmetric (bent).

Cl–S–Cl bent structure

**61.** $H_2S$ is polar because the molecule is asymmetric (bent).

H–S–H bent structure

**62.** $CF_4$ is nonpolar because the molecule is symmetric (tetrahedral).

CF₄ structure

**63.** $CS_2$ is nonpolar because the molecule is symmetric (linear).

$:\!\ddot{S}\!=\!C\!=\!\ddot{S}\!:$

## Chapter 10

**1.** $H_2(g) + Br_2(g) \rightarrow HBr(g)$

**2.** $CO(g) + O_2(g) \rightarrow CO_2(g)$

**3.** $KClO_3(s) \rightarrow KCl(s) + O_2(g)$

**4.** $FeCl_3(aq) + 3NaOH(aq) \rightarrow Fe(OH)_3(s) + 3NaCl(aq)$

**5.** $CS_2(l) + 3O_2(g) \rightarrow CO_2(g) + 2SO_2(g)$

**6.** $Zn(s) + H_2SO_4(aq) \rightarrow H_2(g) + ZnSO_4(aq)$

**14.** $2Al(s) + 3S(s) \rightarrow Al_2S_3(s)$     synthesis

**15.** $H_2O(l) + N_2O_5(g) \rightarrow 2HNO_3(aq)$     synthesis

**16.** $4NO_2(g) + O_2(g) \rightarrow 2N_2O_5(g)$     synthesis and combustion

**17.** $2C_2H_6(g) + 7O_2(g) \rightarrow 4CO_2(g) + 6H_2O(g)$
combustion

**18.** $2Al_2O_3(s) \rightarrow 4Al(s) + 3O_2(g)$

**19.** $Ni(OH)_2(s) \rightarrow NiO(s) + H_2O(l)$

**20.** $2NaHCO_3(s) \rightarrow Na_2CO_3(aq) + CO_2(g) + H_2O(l)$

**21.** Yes. K is above Zn in the metal activity series.
$2K(s) + ZnCl_2(aq) \rightarrow Zn(s) + 2KCl(aq)$

**22.** No. Cl is below F in the halogen activity series.

**23.** No. Fe is below Na in the metal activity series.

**24.** $LiI(aq) + AgNO_3(aq) \rightarrow AgI(s) + LiNO_3(aq)$

**25.** $BaCl_2(aq) + K_2CO_3(aq) \rightarrow BaCO_3(s) + 2KCl(aq)$

**26.** $Na_2C_2O_4(aq) + Pb(NO_3)_2(aq) \rightarrow$
$PbC_2O_4(s) + 2NaNO_3(aq)$

**33.** chemical equation:
$KI(aq) + AgNO_3(aq) \rightarrow KNO_3(aq) + AgI(s)$

complete ionic equation:
$\cancel{K^+}(aq) + I^-(aq) + Ag^+(aq) + \cancel{NO_3^-}(aq) \rightarrow$
$\cancel{K^+}(aq) + \cancel{NO_3^-}(aq) + AgI(s)$

net ionic equation: $I^-(aq) + Ag^+(aq) \rightarrow AgI(s)$

**34.** chemical equation: $2(NH_4)_3PO_4(aq) + 3Na_2SO_4(aq)$
$\rightarrow 3(NH_4)_2SO_4(aq) + 2Na_3PO_4(aq)$

complete ionic equation: $6\cancel{NH_4^+}(aq) + 2\cancel{PO_4^{3-}}(aq)$
$+ 6\cancel{Na^+}(aq) + 3\cancel{SO_4^{2-}}(aq) \rightarrow 6\cancel{NH_4^+}(aq) +$
$3\cancel{SO_4^{2-}}(aq) + 6\cancel{Na^+}(aq) + 2\cancel{PO_4^{3-}}(aq)$

No reaction occurs; therefore, there is no net ionic equation.

**35.** chemical equation:
$AlCl_3(aq) + 3NaOH(aq) \rightarrow Al(OH)_3(s) + 3NaCl(aq)$

complete ionic equation:
$Al^{3+}(aq) + 3\cancel{Cl^-}(aq) + 3\cancel{Na^+}(aq) + 3OH^-(aq) \rightarrow$
$Al(OH)_3(s) + 3\cancel{Na^+}(aq) + 3\cancel{Cl^-}(aq)$

net ionic equation:
$Al^{3+}(aq) + 3OH^-(aq) \rightarrow Al(OH)_3(s)$

Solutions

**36.** chemical equation:
$Li_2SO_4(aq) + Ca(NO_3)_2(aq) \rightarrow 2LiNO_3(aq) + CaSO_4(s)$

complete ionic equation:
$2\cancel{Li^+}(aq) + SO_4^{2-}(aq) + Ca^{2+}(aq) + 2\cancel{NO_3^-}(aq) \rightarrow$
$2\cancel{Li^+}(aq) + 2\cancel{NO_3^-}(aq) + CaSO_4(s)$

net ionic equation:
$SO_4^{2-}(aq) + Ca^{2+}(aq) \rightarrow CaSO_4(s)$

**37.** chemical equation: $5Na_2CO_3(aq) + 2MnCl_5(aq) \rightarrow$
$10NaCl(aq) + Mn_2(CO_3)_5(s)$

complete ionic equation:
$10\cancel{Na^+}(aq) + 5CO_3^{2-}(aq) + 2Mn^{5+}(aq) + 10\cancel{Cl^-}(aq)$
$\rightarrow 10\cancel{Na^+}(aq) + 10\cancel{Cl^-}(aq) + Mn_2(CO_3)_5(s)$

net ionic equation:
$5CO_3^{2-}(aq) + 2Mn^{5+}(aq) \rightarrow Mn_2(CO_3)_5(s)$

**38.** chemical equation:
$H_2SO_4(aq) + 2KOH(aq) \rightarrow 2H_2O(l) + K_2SO_4(aq)$

complete ionic equation:
$2H^+(aq) + \cancel{SO_4^{2-}}(aq) + 2\cancel{K^+}(aq) + 2OH^-(aq) \rightarrow$
$2H_2O(l) + 2\cancel{K^+}(aq) + \cancel{SO_4^{2-}}(aq)$

net ionic equation:
$2H^+(aq) + 2OH^-(aq) \rightarrow 2H_2O(l)$
or $H^+(aq) + OH^-(aq) \rightarrow H_2O(l)$

**39.** chemical equation:
$2HCl(aq) + Ca(OH)_2(aq) \rightarrow 2H_2O(l) + CaCl_2(aq)$

complete ionic equation:
$2H^+(aq) + 2\cancel{Cl^-}(aq) + \cancel{Ca^{2+}}(aq) + 2OH^-(aq) \rightarrow$
$2H_2O(l) + \cancel{Ca^{2+}}(aq) + 2\cancel{Cl^-}(aq)$

net ionic equation: $H^+(aq) + OH^-(aq) \rightarrow H_2O(l)$

**40.** chemical equation:
$HNO_3(aq) + NH_4OH(aq) \rightarrow H_2O(l) + NH_4NO_3(aq)$

complete ionic equation:
$H^+(aq) + \cancel{NO_3^-}(aq) + \cancel{NH_4^+}(aq) + OH^-(aq) \rightarrow$
$H_2O(l) + \cancel{NH_4^+}(aq) + \cancel{NO_3^-}(aq)$

net ionic equation: $H^+(aq) + OH^-(aq) \rightarrow H_2O(l)$

**41.** chemical equation:
$H_2S(aq) + Ca(OH)_2(aq) \rightarrow 2H_2O(l) + CaS(aq)$

complete ionic equation:
$2H^+(aq) + \cancel{S^{2-}}(aq) + \cancel{Ca^{2+}}(aq) + 2OH^-(aq) \rightarrow$
$2H_2O(l) + \cancel{Ca^{2+}}(aq) + \cancel{S^{2-}}(aq)$

net ionic equation: $H^+(aq) + OH^-(aq) \rightarrow H_2O(l)$

**42.** chemical equation: $2H_3PO_4(aq) + 3Mg(OH)_2(aq) \rightarrow$
$6H_2O(l) + Mg_3(PO_4)_2(aq)$

complete ionic equation:
$6H^+(aq) + 2PO_4^{3-}(aq) + 3Mg^{2+}(aq) + 6OH^-(aq) \rightarrow$
$6H_2O(l) + 3Mg^{2+}(aq) + 2PO_4^{3-}(aq)$

net ionic equation: $H^+(aq) + OH^-(aq) \rightarrow H_2O(l)$

**43.** chemical equation: $2HClO_4(aq) + K_2CO_3(aq) \rightarrow$
$H_2O(l) + CO_2(g) + 2KClO_4(aq)$

complete ionic equation:
$2H^+(aq) + 2\cancel{ClO_4^-}(aq) + 2\cancel{K^+}(aq) + CO_3^{2-}(aq) \rightarrow$
$H_2O(l) + CO_2(g) + 2\cancel{K^+}(aq) + 2\cancel{ClO_4^-}(aq)$

net ionic equation:
$2H^+(aq) + CO_3^{2-}(aq) \rightarrow H_2O(l) + CO_2(g)$

**44.** chemical equation:
$H_2SO_4(aq) + 2NaCN(aq) \rightarrow 2HCN(g) + Na_2SO_4(aq)$

complete ionic equation:
$2H^+(aq) + \cancel{SO_4^{2-}}(aq) + 2\cancel{Na^+}(aq) + 2CN^-(aq) \rightarrow$
$2HCN(g) + 2\cancel{Na^+}(aq) + \cancel{SO_4^{2-}}(aq)$

net ionic equation:
$2H^+(aq) + 2CN^-(aq) \rightarrow 2HCN(g)$
or $H^+(aq) + CN^-(aq) \rightarrow HCN(g)$

**45.** chemical equation: $2HBr(aq) + (NH_4)_2CO_3(aq) \rightarrow$
$H_2O(l) + CO_2(g) + 2NH_4Br(aq)$

complete ionic equation:
$2H^+(aq) + 2\cancel{Br^-}(aq) + 2\cancel{NH_4^+}(aq) + CO_3^{2-}(aq) \rightarrow$
$H_2O(l) + CO_2(g) + 2\cancel{NH_4^+}(aq) + 2\cancel{Br^-}(aq)$

net ionic equation:
$2H^+(aq) + CO_3^{2-}(aq) \rightarrow H_2O(l) + CO_2(g)$

**46.** chemical equation:
$2HNO_3(aq) + KRbS(aq) \rightarrow H_2S(g) + KRb(NO_3)_2(aq)$

complete ionic equation: $2H^+(aq) + 2\cancel{NO_3^-}(aq) +$
$\cancel{K^+}(aq) + \cancel{Rb^+}(aq) + S^{2-}(aq) \rightarrow H_2S(g) + \cancel{K^+}(aq) +$
$\cancel{Rb^+}(aq) + 2\cancel{NO_3^-}(aq)$

net ionic equation: $2H^+(aq) + S^{2-}(aq) \rightarrow H_2S(g)$

## Chapter 11

**1.** $2.50 \text{ mol } Zn \times \dfrac{6.02 \times 10^{23} \text{ atoms}}{1 \text{ mol}}$

$= 1.51 \times 10^{24}$ atoms of Zn

**2.** $3.25 \text{ mol } AgNO_3 \times \dfrac{6.02 \times 10^{23} \text{ formula units}}{1 \text{ mol}}$

$= 1.96 \times 10^{24}$ formula units of $AgNO_3$

**3.** $11.5 \text{ mol } H_2O \times \dfrac{6.02 \times 10^{23} \text{ molecules}}{1 \text{ mol}}$

$= 6.92 \times 10^{24}$ molecules of $H_2O$

**4. a.** $5.75 \times 10^{24} \text{ atoms Al} \times \dfrac{1 \text{ mol}}{6.02 \times 10^{23} \text{ atoms}}$

$= 9.55$ mol Al

**b.** $3.75 \times 10^{24} \text{ molecules } CO_2 \times$

$\dfrac{1 \text{ mol}}{6.02 \times 10^{23} \text{ molecules}} = 6.23$ mol $CO_2$

**c.** $3.58 \times 10^{23} \text{ formula units } ZnCl_2 \times$

$\dfrac{1 \text{ mol}}{6.02 \times 10^{23} \text{ formula units}} = 0.595$ mol $ZnCl_2$

**d.** $2.50 \times 10^{20} \text{ atoms Fe} \times \dfrac{1 \text{ mol}}{6.02 \times 10^{23} \text{ atoms}}$

$= 4.15 \times 10^{-4}$ mol Fe

**11. a.** $3.57 \text{ mol Al} \times \dfrac{26.98 \text{ g Al}}{1 \text{ mol Al}} = 96.3$ g Al

**b.** $42.6 \text{ mol Si} \times \dfrac{28.09 \text{ g Si}}{1 \text{ mol Si}} = 1.20 \times 10^3$ g Si

**c.** $3.45 \text{ mol Co} \times \dfrac{58.93 \text{ g Co}}{1 \text{ mol Co}} = 203$ g Co

**d.** $2.45 \text{ mol Zn} \times \dfrac{65.38 \text{ g Zn}}{1 \text{ mol Zn}} = 1.60 \times 10^2$ g Zn

**12. a.** $25.5 \text{ g Ag} \times \dfrac{1 \text{ mol Ag}}{107.9 \text{ g Ag}} = 0.236$ mol Ag

**b.** $300.0 \text{ g S} \times \dfrac{1 \text{ mol S}}{32.07 \text{ g S}} = 9.355$ mol S

**c.** $125 \text{ g Zn} \times \dfrac{1 \text{ mol Zn}}{65.38 \text{ g Zn}} = 1.91$ mol Zn

**d.** $1.00 \text{ kg Fe} \times \dfrac{1000 \text{ g Fe}}{1 \text{ kg Fe}} \times \dfrac{1 \text{ mol Fe}}{55.85 \text{ g Fe}}$

$= 17.9$ mol Fe

**13. a.** $55.2 \text{ g Li} \times \dfrac{1 \text{ mol Li}}{6.941 \text{ g Li}} \times \dfrac{6.02 \times 10^{23} \text{ atoms}}{1 \text{ mol}}$

$= 4.79 \times 10^{24}$ atoms Li

**b.** $0.230 \text{ g Pb} \times \dfrac{1 \text{ mol Pb}}{207.2 \text{ g Pb}} \times \dfrac{6.02 \times 10^{23} \text{ atoms}}{1 \text{ mol}}$

$= 6.68 \times 10^{20}$ atoms Pb

**c.** $11.5 \text{ g Hg} \times \dfrac{1 \text{ mol Hg}}{200.6 \text{ g Hg}} \times \dfrac{6.02 \times 10^{23} \text{ atoms}}{1 \text{ mol}}$

$= 3.45 \times 10^{22}$ atoms Hg

**d.** $45.6 \text{ g Si} \times \dfrac{1 \text{ mol Si}}{28.09 \text{ g Si}} \times \dfrac{6.02 \times 10^{23} \text{ atoms}}{1 \text{ mol}}$

$= 9.77 \times 10^{23}$ atoms Si

**e.** $0.120 \text{ kg Ti} \times \dfrac{1000 \text{ g Ti}}{1 \text{ kg Ti}} \times \dfrac{1 \text{ mol Ti}}{47.88 \text{ g Ti}} \times$

$\dfrac{6.02 \times 10^{23} \text{ atoms}}{1 \text{ mol}} = 1.51 \times 10^{24}$ atoms Ti

**14. a.** $6.02 \times 10^{24} \text{ atoms Bi} \times \dfrac{1 \text{ mol}}{6.02 \times 10^{23} \text{ atoms}} \times$

$\dfrac{209.0 \text{ g Bi}}{1 \text{ mol Bi}} = 2.09 \times 10^3$ g Bi

**b.** $1.00 \times 10^{24} \text{ atoms Mn} \times \dfrac{1 \text{ mol}}{6.02 \times 10^{23} \text{ atoms}} \times$

$\dfrac{54.94 \text{ g Mn}}{1 \text{ mol Mn}} = 91.3$ g Mn

**c.** $3.40 \times 10^{22} \text{ atoms He} \times \dfrac{1 \text{ mol}}{6.02 \times 10^{23} \text{ atoms}} \times$

$\dfrac{4.003 \text{ g He}}{1 \text{ mol He}} = 0.226$ g He

**d.** $1.50 \times 10^{15} \text{ atoms N} \times \dfrac{1 \text{ mol}}{6.02 \times 10^{23} \text{ atoms}} \times$

$\dfrac{14.01 \text{ g N}}{1 \text{ mol N}} = 3.49 \times 10^{-8}$ g N

**e.** $1.50 \times 10^{15} \text{ atoms U} \times \dfrac{1 \text{ mol}}{6.02 \times 10^{23} \text{ atoms}} \times$

$\dfrac{238.0 \text{ g U}}{1 \text{ mol U}} = 5.93 \times 10^{-7}$ g U

**20.** $2.50 \text{ mol } ZnCl_2 \times \dfrac{2 \text{ mol } Cl^-}{1 \text{ mol } ZnCl_2} = 5.00 \text{ mol } Cl^-$

**21.** $1.25 \text{ mol } C_6H_{12}O_6 \times \dfrac{6 \text{ mol C}}{1 \text{ mol } C_6H_{12}O_6} = 7.50$ mol C

$1.25 \text{ mol } C_6H_{12}O_6 \times \dfrac{12 \text{ mol H}}{1 \text{ mol } C_6H_{12}O_6} = 15.0$ mol H

$1.25 \text{ mol } C_6H_{12}O_6 \times \dfrac{6 \text{ mol O}}{1 \text{ mol } C_6H_{12}O_6} = 7.50$ mol O

**22.** $3.00 \text{ mol } Fe_2(SO_4)_3 \times \dfrac{3 \text{ mol } SO_4{}^{2-}}{1 \text{ mol } Fe_2(SO_4)_3}$

$= 9.00 \text{ mol } SO_4{}^{2-}$

**23.** $5.00 \text{ mol } P_2O_5 \times \dfrac{5 \text{ mol O}}{1 \text{ mol } P_2O_5} = 25.0$ mol O

**24.** $11.5 \text{ mol } H_2O \times \dfrac{2 \text{ mol H}}{1 \text{ mol } H_2O} = 23.0$ mol H

Solutions

**25.** NaOH

$1 \text{ mol Na} \times \dfrac{22.99 \text{ g Na}}{1 \text{ mol Na}} = 22.99 \text{ g}$

$1 \text{ mol O} \times \dfrac{16.00 \text{ g O}}{1 \text{ mol O}} = 16.00 \text{ g}$

$1 \text{ mol H} \times \dfrac{1.008 \text{ g H}}{1 \text{ mol H}} = \underline{1.008 \text{ g}}$

molar mass NaOH  $= 40.00 \text{ g/mol}$

$CaCl_2$

$1 \text{ mol Ca} \times \dfrac{40.08 \text{ g Ca}}{1 \text{ mol Ca}} = 40.08 \text{ g}$

$2 \text{ mol Cl} \times \dfrac{35.45 \text{ g Cl}}{1 \text{ mol Cl}} = \underline{70.90 \text{ g}}$

molar mass $CaCl_2$  $= 110.98 \text{ g/mol}$

$KC_2H_3O_2$

$1 \text{ mol K} \times \dfrac{39.10 \text{ g K}}{1 \text{ mol K}} = 39.10 \text{ g}$

$2 \text{ mol C} \times \dfrac{12.01 \text{ g C}}{1 \text{ mol C}} = 24.02 \text{ g}$

$3 \text{ mol H} \times \dfrac{1.008 \text{ g H}}{1 \text{ mol H}} = 3.024 \text{ g}$

$2 \text{ mol O} \times \dfrac{16.00 \text{ g O}}{1 \text{ mol O}} = \underline{32.00 \text{ g}}$

molar mass $KC_2H_3O_2$ $= 98.14 \text{ g/mol}$

$Sr(NO_3)_2$

$1 \text{ mol Sr} \times \dfrac{87.62 \text{ g Sr}}{1 \text{ mol Sr}} = 87.62 \text{ g}$

$2 \text{ mol N} \times \dfrac{14.01 \text{ g N}}{1 \text{ mol N}} = 28.02 \text{ g}$

$6 \text{ mol O} \times \dfrac{16.00 \text{ g O}}{1 \text{ mol O}} = \underline{96.00 \text{ g}}$

molar mass $Sr(NO_3)_2$  $= 211.64 \text{ g/mol}$

$(NH_4)_3PO_4$

$3 \text{ mol N} \times \dfrac{14.01 \text{ g N}}{1 \text{ mol N}} = 42.03 \text{ g}$

$12 \text{ mol H} \times \dfrac{1.008 \text{ g H}}{1 \text{ mol H}} = 12.096 \text{ g}$

$1 \text{ mol P} \times \dfrac{30.97 \text{ g P}}{1 \text{ mol P}} = 30.97 \text{ g}$

$4 \text{ mol O} \times \dfrac{16.00 \text{ g O}}{1 \text{ mol O}} = \underline{64.00 \text{ g}}$

molar mass $(NH_4)_3PO_4$ $= 149.10 \text{ g/mol}$

**26.** $C_2H_5OH$

$2 \text{ mol C} \times \dfrac{12.01 \text{ g C}}{1 \text{ mol C}} = 24.02 \text{ g}$

$6 \text{ mol H} \times \dfrac{1.008 \text{ g H}}{1 \text{ mol H}} = 6.048 \text{ g}$

$1 \text{ mol O} \times \dfrac{16.00 \text{ g O}}{\text{mol O}} = \underline{16.00 \text{ g}}$

molar mass $C_2H_5OH$  $= 46.07 \text{ g/mol}$

$C_{12}H_{22}O_{11}$

$12 \text{ mol C} \times \dfrac{12.01 \text{ g C}}{1 \text{ mol C}} = 144.12 \text{ g}$

$22 \text{ mol H} \times \dfrac{1.008 \text{ g H}}{1 \text{ mol H}} = 22.176 \text{ g}$

$11 \text{ mol O} \times \dfrac{16.00 \text{ g O}}{1 \text{ mol O}} = \underline{176.00 \text{ g}}$

molar mass $C_{12}H_{22}O_{11}$  $= 342.30 \text{ g/mol}$

HCN

$1 \text{ mol H} \times \dfrac{1.008 \text{ g H}}{1 \text{ mol H}} = 1.008 \text{ g}$

$1 \text{ mol C} \times \dfrac{12.01 \text{ g C}}{1 \text{ mol C}} = 12.01 \text{ g}$

$1 \text{ mol N} \times \dfrac{14.01 \text{ g N}}{1 \text{ mol N}} = \underline{14.01 \text{ g}}$

molar mass HCN  $= 27.03 \text{ g/mol}$

$CCl_4$

$1 \text{ mol C} \times \dfrac{12.01 \text{ g C}}{1 \text{ mol C}} = 12.01 \text{ g}$

$4 \text{ mol Cl} \times \dfrac{35.45 \text{ g Cl}}{1 \text{ mol Cl}} = \underline{141.80 \text{ g}}$

molar mass $CCl_4$  $= 153.81 \text{ g/mol}$

$H_2O$

$2 \text{ mol H} \times \dfrac{1.008 \text{ g H}}{1 \text{ mol H}} = 2.016 \text{ g}$

$1 \text{ mol O} \times \dfrac{16.00 \text{ g O}}{1 \text{ mol O}} = \underline{16.00 \text{ g}}$

molar mass $H_2O$  $= 18.02 \text{ g/mol}$

**27.** Step 1: Find the molar mass of $H_2SO_4$.

$2 \text{ mol H} \times \dfrac{1.008 \text{ g H}}{1 \text{ mol H}} = 2.016 \text{ g}$

$1 \text{ mol S} \times \dfrac{32.07 \text{ g S}}{1 \text{ mol S}} = 32.07 \text{ g}$

$4 \text{ mol O} \times \dfrac{16.00 \text{ g O}}{1 \text{ mol O}} = \underline{64.00 \text{ g}}$

molar mass $H_2SO_4$  $= 98.09 \text{ g/mol}$

Step 2: Make mole → mass conversion.

$3.25 \text{ mol } H_2SO_4 \times \dfrac{98.09 \text{ g } H_2SO_4}{1 \text{ mol } H_2SO_4} = 319 \text{ g } H_2SO_4$

**28.** Step 1: Find the molar mass of $ZnCl_2$.

$1 \text{ mol Zn} \times \dfrac{65.38 \text{ g Zn}}{1 \text{ mol Zn}} = 65.38 \text{ g}$

$2 \text{ mol Cl} \times \dfrac{35.45 \text{ g Cl}}{1 \text{ mol Cl}} = \underline{70.90 \text{ g}}$

molar mass $ZnCl_2$    $= 136.28 \text{ g/mol}$

Step 2: Make mole → mass conversion.

$4.35 \times 10^{-2} \text{ mol ZnCl}_2 \times \dfrac{136.28 \text{ g ZnCl}_2}{1 \text{ mol ZnCl}_2}$

$= 5.93 \text{ g ZnCl}_2$

**29.** Step 1: Find the molar mass of $KMnO_4$.

$1 \text{ mol K} \times \dfrac{39.10 \text{ g K}}{1 \text{ mol K}} = 39.10 \text{ g}$

$1 \text{ mol Mn} \times \dfrac{54.94 \text{ g Mn}}{1 \text{ mol Mn}} = 54.94 \text{ g}$

$4 \text{ mol O} \times \dfrac{16.00 \text{ g O}}{1 \text{ mol O}} = \underline{64.00 \text{ g}}$

molar mass $KMnO_4$    $= 158.04 \text{ g/mol}$

Step 2: Make mole → mass conversion.

$2.55 \text{ mol KMnO}_4 \times \dfrac{158.04 \text{ g KMnO}_4}{1 \text{ mol KMnO}_4}$

$= 403 \text{ g KMnO}_4$

**30. a.** Step 1: Find the molar mass of $AgNO_3$.

$1 \text{ mol Ag} \times \dfrac{107.9 \text{ g Ag}}{1 \text{ mol Ag}} = 107.9 \text{ g}$

$1 \text{ mol N} \times \dfrac{14.01 \text{ g N}}{1 \text{ mol N}} = 14.01 \text{ g}$

$3 \text{ mol O} \times \dfrac{16.00 \text{ g O}}{1 \text{ mol O}} = \underline{48.00 \text{ g}}$

molar mass $AgNO_3$    $= 169.9 \text{ g/mol}$

Step 2: Make mass → mole conversion.

$22.6 \text{ g AgNO}_3 \times \dfrac{1 \text{ mol AgNO}_3}{169.9 \text{ g AgNO}_3}$

$= 0.133 \text{ mol AgNO}_3$

**b.** Step 1: Find molar mass of $ZnSO_4$.

$1 \text{ mol Zn} \times \dfrac{65.39 \text{ g Zn}}{1 \text{ mol Zn}} = 65.39 \text{ g}$

$1 \text{ mol S} \times \dfrac{32.07 \text{ g S}}{1 \text{ mol S}} = 32.07 \text{ g}$

$4 \text{ mol O} \times \dfrac{16.00 \text{ g O}}{1 \text{ mol O}} = \underline{64.00 \text{ g}}$

molar mass $ZnSO_4$    $= 161.46 \text{ g/mol}$

Step 2: Make mass → mole conversion.

$6.50 \text{ g ZnSO}_4 \times \dfrac{1 \text{ mol ZnSO}_4}{161.46 \text{ g ZnSO}_4}$

$= 0.0403 \text{ mol ZnSO}_4$

**c.** Step 1: Find the molar mass of HCl.

$1 \text{ mol H} \times \dfrac{1.008 \text{ g H}}{1 \text{ mol H}} = 1.008 \text{ g}$

$1 \text{ mol Cl} \times \dfrac{35.45 \text{ g Cl}}{1 \text{ mol Cl}} = \underline{35.45 \text{ g}}$

molar mass HCl    $= 36.46 \text{ g/mol}$

Step 2: Make mass → mole conversion.

$35.0 \text{ g HCl} \times \dfrac{1 \text{ mol HCl}}{36.46 \text{ g HCl}} = 0.960 \text{ mol HCl}$

**d.** Step 1: Find the molar mass of $Fe_2O_3$.

$2 \text{ mol Fe} \times \dfrac{55.85 \text{ g Fe}}{1 \text{ mol Fe}} = 111.70 \text{ g}$

$3 \text{ mol O} \times \dfrac{16.00 \text{ g O}}{1 \text{ mol O}} = \underline{48.00 \text{ g}}$

molar mass $Fe_2O_3$    $= 159.70 \text{ g/mol}$

Step 2: Make mass → mole conversion.

$25.0 \text{ g Fe}_2O_3 \times \dfrac{1 \text{ mol Fe}_2O_3}{159.70 \text{ g Fe}_2O_3}$

$= 0.157 \text{ mol Fe}_2O_3$

**e.** Step 1: Find the molar mass of $PbCl_4$.

$1 \text{ mol Pb} \times \dfrac{207.2 \text{ g Pb}}{1 \text{ mol Pb}} = 207.2 \text{ g}$

$4 \text{ mol Cl} \times \dfrac{35.45 \text{ g Cl}}{1 \text{ mol Cl}} = \underline{141.80 \text{ g}}$

molar mass $PbCl_4$    $= 349.0 \text{ g/mol}$

Step 2: Make mass → mole conversion.

$254 \text{ g PbCl}_4 \times \dfrac{1 \text{ mol PbCl}_4}{349.0 \text{ g PbCl}_4} = 0.728 \text{ mol PbCl}_4$

**31.** Step 1: Find the molar mass of $Ag_2CrO_4$.

$2 \text{ mol Ag} \times \dfrac{107.9 \text{ g Ag}}{1 \text{ mol Ag}} = 215.8 \text{ g}$

$1 \text{ mol Cr} \times \dfrac{52.00 \text{ g Cr}}{1 \text{ mol Cr}} = 52.00 \text{ g}$

$4 \text{ mol O} \times \dfrac{16.00 \text{ g O}}{1 \text{ mol O}} = \underline{64.00 \text{ g}}$

molar mass $Ag_2CrO_4$    $= 331.8 \text{ g/mol}$

Step 2: Make mass → mole conversion.

$25.8 \text{ g Ag}_2CrO_4 \times \dfrac{1 \text{ mol Ag}_2CrO_4}{331.8 \text{ g Ag}_2CrO_4}$

$= 0.0778 \text{ mol Ag}_2CrO_4$

Step 3: Make mole → formula unit conversion.

$0.0778 \text{ mol Ag}_2CrO_4 \times \dfrac{6.02 \times 10^{23} \text{ formula units}}{1 \text{ mol}}$

$= 4.68 \times 10^{22} \text{ formula units Ag}_2CrO_4$

**a.** $4.68 \times 10^{22} \text{ formula units Ag}_2CrO_4 \times$

$\dfrac{2 \text{ Ag}^+ \text{ ions}}{1 \text{ formula unit Ag}_2CrO_4} = 9.36 \times 10^{22} \text{ Ag}^+ \text{ ions}$

**b.** $4.68 \times 10^{22} \text{ formula units Ag}_2CrO_4 \times$

$\dfrac{1 \text{ CrO}_4^{2-} \text{ ion}}{1 \text{ formula unit Ag}_2CrO_4}$

$= 4.68 \times 10^{22} \text{ CrO}_4^{2-} \text{ ions}$

**c.** $\dfrac{331.8 \text{ g Ag}_2CrO_4}{1 \text{ mol Ag}_2CrO_4} \times \dfrac{1 \text{ mol}}{6.02 \times 10^{23} \text{ formula units}}$

$= 5.51 \times 10^{-22} \text{ g Ag}_2CrO_4/\text{formula unit}$

Solutions

**32.** Step 1: Find the number of moles of NaCl.

$4.59 \times 10^{24}$ formula units NaCl $\times$

$$\dfrac{1 \text{ mol}}{6.02 \times 10^{23} \text{ formula units}} = 7.62 \text{ mol NaCl}$$

Step 2: Find the molar mass of NaCl.

$1 \text{ mol Na} \times \dfrac{22.99 \text{ g Na}}{1 \text{ mol Na}} = 22.99 \text{ g}$

$1 \text{ mol Cl} \times \dfrac{35.45 \text{ g Cl}}{1 \text{ mol Cl}} = \underline{35.45 \text{ g}}$

molar mass NaCl        $= 58.44 \text{ g/mol}$

Step 3: Make mole → mass conversion.

$7.62 \text{ mol NaCl} \times \dfrac{58.44 \text{ g NaCl}}{1 \text{ mol NaCl}} = 445 \text{ g NaCl}$

**33.** Step 1: Find molar mass of $C_2H_5OH$.

$2 \text{ mol C} \times \dfrac{12.01 \text{ g C}}{1 \text{ mol C}} = 24.02 \text{ g}$

$6 \text{ mol H} \times \dfrac{1.008 \text{ g H}}{1 \text{ mol H}} = 6.048 \text{ g}$

$1 \text{ mol O} \times \dfrac{16.00 \text{ g O}}{1 \text{ mol O}} = \underline{16.00 \text{ g}}$

molar mass $C_2H_5OH = 46.07 \text{ g/mol}$

Step 2: Make mass → mole conversion.

$45.6 \text{ g } C_2H_5OH \times 1 \dfrac{\text{mol } C_2H_5OH}{46.07 \text{ g } C_2H_5OH}$

$= 0.990 \text{ mol } C_2H_5OH$

Step 3: Make mole → molecule conversion.

$0.990 \text{ mol } C_2H_5OH \times \dfrac{6.02 \times 10^{23} \text{ molecules}}{1 \text{ mol}}$

$= 5.96 \times 10^{23} \text{ molecules } C_2H_5OH$

**a.** $5.96 \times 10^{23}$ molecules $C_2H_5OH \times$

$\dfrac{2 \text{ C atoms}}{1 \text{ molecule } C_2H_5OH} = 1.19 \times 10^{24} \text{ C atoms}$

**b.** $5.96 \times 10^{23}$ molecules $C_2H_5OH \times$

$\dfrac{6 \text{ H atoms}}{1 \text{ molecule } C_2H_5OH} = 3.58 \times 10^{24} \text{ H atoms}$

**c.** $5.96 \times 10^{23}$ molecules $C_2H_5OH \times$

$\dfrac{1 \text{ O atom}}{1 \text{ molecule } C_2H_5OH} = 5.96 \times 10^{23} \text{ O atoms}$

**34.** Step 1: Find the molar mass of $Na_2SO_3$.

$2 \text{ mol Na} \times \dfrac{22.99 \text{ g Na}}{1 \text{ mol Na}} = 45.98 \text{ g}$

$1 \text{ mol S} \times \dfrac{32.07 \text{ g S}}{1 \text{ mol S}} = 32.07 \text{ g}$

$3 \text{ mol O} \times \dfrac{16.00 \text{ g O}}{1 \text{ mol O}} = \underline{48.00 \text{ g}}$

molar mass $Na_2SO_3$        $= 126.04 \text{ g/mol}$

Step 2: Make mass → mole conversion.

$2.25 \text{ g } Na_2SO_3 \times \dfrac{1 \text{ mol } Na_2SO_3}{126.04 \text{ g } Na_2SO_3}$

$= 0.0179 \text{ mol } Na_2SO_3$

Step 3: Make mole → formula unit conversion.

$0.0179 \text{ mol } Na_2SO_3 \times \dfrac{6.02 \times 10^{23} \text{ formula units}}{1 \text{ mol}}$

$= 1.08 \times 10^{22} \text{ formula units } Na_2SO_3$

**a.** $1.08 \times 10^{22}$ formula units $Na_2SO_3 \times$

$\dfrac{2 \text{ Na}^+ \text{ ions}}{1 \text{ formula unit } Na_2SO_3} = 2.16 \times 10^{22} \text{ Na}^+ \text{ ions}$

**b.** $1.08 \times 10^{22}$ formula units $Na_2SO_3 \times$

$\dfrac{1 \text{ SO}_3{}^{2-} \text{ ions}}{1 \text{ formula unit } Na_2SO_3} = 1.08 \times 10^{22} \text{ SO}_3{}^{2-} \text{ ions}$

**c.** $\dfrac{126.08 \text{ g } Na_2SO_3}{1 \text{ mol } Na_2SO_3} \times \dfrac{1 \text{ mol}}{6.02 \times 10^{23} \text{ formula units}}$

$= 2.09 \times 10^{-22} \text{ g } Na_2SO_3 \text{/formula unit}$

**35.** Step 1: Find the molar mass of $CO_2$.

$1 \text{ mol C} \times \dfrac{12.01 \text{ g C}}{1 \text{ mol C}} = 12.01 \text{ g}$

$2 \text{ mol O} \times \dfrac{16.00 \text{ g O}}{1 \text{ mol O}} = \underline{32.00 \text{ g}}$

molar mass $CO_2$        $= 44.01 \text{ g/mol}$

Step 2: Make mass → mole conversion.

$52.0 \text{ g } CO_2 \times \dfrac{1 \text{ mol } CO_2}{44.01 \text{ g } CO_2} = 1.18 \text{ mol } CO_2$

Step 3: Make mole → molecule conversion.

$1.18 \text{ mol } CO_2 \times \dfrac{6.02 \times 10^{23} \text{ molecules}}{1 \text{ mol}}$

$= 7.11 \times 10^{23} \text{ molecules } CO_2$

**a.** $7.11 \times 10^{23}$ molecules $CO_2 \times \dfrac{1 \text{ C atom}}{1 \text{ molecule } CO_2}$

$= 7.11 \times 10^{23} \text{ C atoms}$

**b.** $7.11 \times 10^{23}$ molecules $CO_2 \times \dfrac{2 \text{ O atoms}}{1 \text{ molecule } CO_2}$

$= 1.42 \times 10^{24} \text{ O atoms}$

**c.** $\dfrac{44.01 \text{ g } CO_2}{1 \text{ mol } CO_2} \times \dfrac{1 \text{ mol}}{6.02 \times 10^{23} \text{ molecules}}$

$= 7.31 \times 10^{-23} \text{ g } CO_2 \text{/molecule}$

**42.** Steps 1 and 2: Assume 1 mole; calculate molar mass of $CaCl_2$.

$1 \text{ mol Ca} \times \dfrac{40.08 \text{ g Ca}}{1 \text{ mol Ca}} = 40.08 \text{ g}$

$2 \text{ mol Cl} \times \dfrac{35.45 \text{ g Cl}}{1 \text{ mol Cl}} = \underline{70.90 \text{ g}}$

molar mass $CaCl_2$        $= 110.98 \text{ g/mol}$

Solutions

Step 3: Determine percent by mass of each element.

$$\text{percent Ca} = \frac{40.08 \text{ g Ca}}{110.98 \text{ g CaCl}_2} \times 100 = 36.11\% \text{ Ca}$$

$$\text{percent Cl} = \frac{70.90 \text{ g Cl}}{110.98 \text{ g CaCl}_2} \times 100 = 63.89\% \text{ Cl}$$

**43.** Steps 1 and 2: Assume 1 mole; calculate molar mass of $Na_2SO_4$.

$$2 \text{ mol Na} \times \frac{22.99 \text{ g Na}}{1 \text{ mol Na}} = 45.98 \text{ g}$$

$$1 \text{ mol S} \times \frac{32.06 \text{ g S}}{1 \text{ mol S}} = 32.07 \text{ g}$$

$$4 \text{ mol O} \times \frac{16.00 \text{ g O}}{1 \text{ mol O}} = \underline{64.00 \text{ g}}$$

molar mass $Na_2SO_4$ = 142.05 g/mol

Step 3: Determine percent by mass of each element.

$$\text{percent Na} = \frac{45.98 \text{ g Na}}{142.05 \text{ g Na}_2SO_4} \times 100 = 32.37\% \text{ Na}$$

$$\text{percent S} = \frac{32.07 \text{ g S}}{142.05 \text{ g Na}_2SO_4} \times 100 = 22.58\% \text{ S}$$

$$\text{percent O} = \frac{64.00 \text{ g O}}{142.05 \text{ g Na}_2SO_4} \times 100 = 45.05\% \text{ O}$$

**44.** Steps 1 and 2: Assume 1 mole; calculate molar mass of $H_2SO_3$.

$$2 \text{ mol H} \times \frac{1.008 \text{ g H}}{1 \text{ mol H}} = 2.016 \text{ g}$$

$$1 \text{ mol S} \times \frac{32.06 \text{ g S}}{1 \text{ mol S}} = 32.06 \text{ g}$$

$$3 \text{ mol O} \times \frac{16.00 \text{ g O}}{1 \text{ mol O}} = \underline{48.00 \text{ g}}$$

molar mass $H_2SO_3$ = 82.08 g/mol

Step 3: Determine percent by mass of S.

$$\text{percent S} = \frac{32.06 \text{ g S}}{82.08 \text{ g H}_2SO_3} \times 100 = 39.06\% \text{ S}$$

Repeat steps 1 and 2 for $H_2S_2O_8$. Assume 1 mole; calculate molar mass of $H_2S_2O_8$.

$$2 \text{ mol H} \times \frac{1.008 \text{ g H}}{1 \text{ mol H}} = 2.016 \text{ g}$$

$$2 \text{ mol S} \times \frac{32.06 \text{ g S}}{1 \text{ mol S}} = 64.12 \text{ g}$$

$$8 \text{ mol O} \times \frac{16.00 \text{ g O}}{1 \text{ mol O}} = \underline{128.00 \text{ g}}$$

molar mass $H_2S_2O_8$ = 194.14 g/mol

Step 3: Determine percent by mass of S.

$$\text{percent S} = \frac{64.12 \text{ g S}}{194.14 \text{ g H}_2S_2O_8} \times 100 = 33.03\% \text{ S}$$

$H_2SO_3$ has a larger percent by mass of S.

**45.** Steps 1 and 2: Assume 1 mole; calculate molar mass of $H_3PO_4$.

$$3 \text{ mol H} \times \frac{1.008 \text{ g H}}{1 \text{ mol H}} = 3.024 \text{ g}$$

$$1 \text{ mol P} \times \frac{30.97 \text{ g P}}{1 \text{ mol P}} = 30.97 \text{ g}$$

$$4 \text{ mol O} \times \frac{16.00 \text{ g O}}{1 \text{ mol O}} = 64.00 \text{ g}$$

molar mass $H_3PO_4$ = 97.99 g/mol

Step 3: Determine percent by mass of each element.

$$\text{percent H} = \frac{3.024 \text{ g H}}{97.99 \text{ g H}_3PO_4} \times 100 = 3.08\% \text{ H}$$

$$\text{percent P} = \frac{30.97 \text{ g P}}{97.99 \text{ g H}_3PO_4} \times 100 = 31.61\% \text{ P}$$

$$\text{percent O} = \frac{64.00 \text{ g O}}{97.99 \text{ g H}_3PO_4} \times 100 = 65.31\% \text{ O}$$

**46.** Step 1: Assume 100 g sample; calculate moles of each element.

$$36.84 \text{ g N} \times \frac{1 \text{ mol N}}{14.01 \text{ g N}} = 2.630 \text{ mol N}$$

$$63.16 \text{ g O} \times \frac{1 \text{ mol O}}{16.00 \text{ g O}} = 3.948 \text{ mol O}$$

Step 2: Calculate mole ratios.

$$\frac{2.630 \text{ mol N}}{2.630 \text{ mol N}} = \frac{1.000 \text{ mol N}}{1.000 \text{ mol N}} = \frac{1 \text{ mol N}}{1 \text{ mol N}}$$

$$\frac{3.948 \text{ mol O}}{2.630 \text{ mol N}} = \frac{1.500 \text{ mol O}}{1.000 \text{ mol N}} = \frac{1.5 \text{ mol O}}{1 \text{ mol N}}$$

The simplest ratio is 1 mol N: 1.5 mol O.

Step 3: Convert decimal fraction to whole number.

In this case, multiply by 2, because $1.5 \times 2 = 3$. Therefore, the empirical formula is $N_2O_3$.

Solutions

**47.** Step 1: Assume 100 g sample; calculate moles of each element

$$35.98 \cancel{g\,Al} \times \frac{1 \text{ mol Al}}{26.98 \cancel{g\,Al}} = 1.334 \text{ mol Al}$$

$$64.02 \cancel{g\,S} \times \frac{1 \text{ mol S}}{32.06 \cancel{g\,S}} = 1.996 \text{ mol S}$$

Step 2: Calculate mole ratios.

$$\frac{1.334 \text{ mol Al}}{1.334 \text{ mol Al}} = \frac{1.000 \text{ mol Al}}{1.000 \text{ mol Al}} = \frac{1 \text{ mol Al}}{1 \text{ mol Al}}$$

$$\frac{1.996 \text{ mol S}}{1.334 \text{ mol Al}} = \frac{1.500 \text{ mol S}}{1.000 \text{ mol Al}} = \frac{1.5 \text{ mol S}}{1 \text{ mol Al}}$$

The simplest ratio is 1 mol Al: 1.5 mol S.

Step 3: Convert decimal fraction to whole number.

In this case, multiply by 2, because 1.5 × 2 = 3. Therefore, the empirical formula is $Al_2S_3$.

**48.** Step 1: Assume 100 g sample; calculate moles of each element.

$$81.82 \cancel{g\,C} \times \frac{1 \text{ mol C}}{12.01 \cancel{g\,C}} = 6.813 \text{ mol C}$$

$$18.18 \cancel{g\,H} \times \frac{1 \text{ mol H}}{1.008 \cancel{g\,H}} = 18.04 \text{ mol H}$$

Step 2: Calculate mole ratios.

$$\frac{6.813 \text{ mol C}}{6.813 \text{ mol C}} = \frac{1.000 \text{ mol C}}{1.000 \text{ mol C}} = \frac{1 \text{ mol C}}{1 \text{ mol C}}$$

$$\frac{18.04 \text{ mol H}}{6.813 \text{ mol C}} = \frac{2.649 \text{ mol H}}{1.000 \text{ mol C}} = \frac{2.65 \text{ mol H}}{1 \text{ mol C}}$$

The simplest ratio is 1 mol: 2.65 mol H.

Step 3: Convert decimal fraction to whole number.

In this case, multiply by 3, because 2.65 × 3 = 7.95 ≈ 8. Therefore, the empirical formula is $C_3H_8$.

**49.** Step 1: Assume 100 g sample; calculate moles of each element.

$$60.00 \cancel{g\,C} \times \frac{1 \text{ mol C}}{12.01 \cancel{g\,C}} = 5.00 \text{ mol C}$$

$$4.44 \cancel{g\,H} \times \frac{1 \text{ mol H}}{1.008 \cancel{g\,H}} = 4.40 \text{ mol H}$$

$$35.56 \cancel{g\,O} \times \frac{1 \text{ mol O}}{16.00 \cancel{g\,O}} = 2.22 \text{ mol O}$$

Step 2: Calculate mole ratios.

$$\frac{5.00 \text{ mol C}}{2.22 \text{ mol O}} = \frac{2.25 \text{ mol C}}{1.00 \text{ mol O}} = \frac{2.25 \text{ mol C}}{1 \text{ mol O}}$$

$$\frac{4.40 \text{ mol H}}{2.22 \text{ mol O}} = \frac{1.98 \text{ mol H}}{1.00 \text{ mol O}} = \frac{2 \text{ mol H}}{1 \text{ mol O}}$$

$$\frac{2.22 \text{ mol O}}{2.22 \text{ mol O}} = \frac{1.00 \text{ mol O}}{1.00 \text{ mol O}} = \frac{1 \text{ mol O}}{1 \text{ mol O}}$$

The simplest ratio is 2.25 mol C: 2 mol H: 1 mol O.

Step 3: Convert decimal fraction to whole number.

In this case, multiply by 4, because 2.25 × 4 = 9. Therefore, the empirical formula is $C_9H_8O_4$.

**50.** Step 1: Assume 100 g sample; calculate moles of each element.

$$10.89 \cancel{g\,Mg} \times \frac{1 \text{ mol Mg}}{24.31 \cancel{g\,Mg}} = 0.4480 \text{ mol Mg}$$

$$31.77 \cancel{g\,Cl} \times \frac{1 \text{ mol Cl}}{35.45 \cancel{g\,Cl}} = 0.8962 \text{ mol Cl}$$

$$57.34 \cancel{g\,O} \times \frac{1 \text{ mol O}}{16.00 \cancel{g\,O}} = 3.584 \text{ mol O}$$

Step 2: Calculate mole ratios.

$$\frac{0.4480 \text{ mol Mg}}{0.4480 \text{ mol Mg}} = \frac{1.000 \text{ mol Mg}}{1.000 \text{ mol Mg}} = \frac{1 \text{ mol Mg}}{1 \text{ mol Mg}}$$

$$\frac{0.8962 \text{ mol Cl}}{0.4480 \text{ mol Mg}} = \frac{2.000 \text{ mol Cl}}{1.000 \text{ mol Mg}} = \frac{2 \text{ mol Cl}}{1 \text{ mol Mg}}$$

$$\frac{3.584 \text{ mol O}}{0.4480 \text{ mol Mg}} = \frac{7.999 \text{ mol O}}{1.000 \text{ mol Mg}} = \frac{8 \text{ mol O}}{1 \text{ mol Mg}}$$

The empirical formula is $MgCl_2O_8$.

The simplest ratio is 1 mol Mg: 2 mol Cl: 8 mol O.

**51.** Step 1: Assume 100 g sample; calculate moles of each element

$$65.45 \cancel{g\,C} \times \frac{1 \text{ mol C}}{12.01 \cancel{g\,C}} = 5.450 \text{ mol C}$$

$$5.45 \cancel{g\,H} \times \frac{1 \text{ mol H}}{1.008 \cancel{g\,H}} = 5.41 \text{ mol H}$$

$$29.09 \cancel{g\,O} \times \frac{1 \text{ mol O}}{16.00 \cancel{g\,O}} = 1.818 \text{ mol O}$$

Step 2: Calculate mole ratios

$$\frac{5.450 \text{ mol C}}{1.818 \text{ mol O}} = \frac{3.000 \text{ mol C}}{1.000 \text{ mol O}} = \frac{3 \text{ mol C}}{1 \text{ mol O}}$$

$$\frac{5.41 \text{ mol H}}{1.818 \text{ mol O}} = \frac{2.97 \text{ mol H}}{1.00 \text{ mol O}} = \frac{3 \text{ mol H}}{1 \text{ mol O}}$$

$$\frac{1.818 \text{ mol O}}{1.818 \text{ mol O}} = \frac{1.000 \text{ mol O}}{1.000 \text{ mol O}} = \frac{1 \text{ mol O}}{1 \text{ mol O}}$$

The simplest ratio is 1 mol:2.65 mol H.

Therefore, the empirical formula is $C_3H_3O$.

Step 3: Calculate the molar mass of the empirical formula.

$$3 \cancel{\text{mol C}} \times \frac{12.01 \text{ g C}}{1 \cancel{\text{mol C}}} = 36.03 \text{ g}$$

$$3 \cancel{\text{mol H}} \times \frac{1.008 \text{ g H}}{1 \cancel{\text{mol H}}} = 3.024 \text{ g}$$

$$1 \cancel{\text{mol O}} \times \frac{16.00 \text{ g O}}{1 \cancel{\text{mol O}}} = \underline{16.00 \text{ g}}$$

   molar mass $C_3H_3O$ = 55.05 g/mol

Step 4: Determine whole number multiplier.

$$\frac{110.0 \text{ g/mol}}{55.05 \text{ g/mol}} = 1.998, \text{ or } 2$$

The molecular formula is $C_6H_6O_2$.

Solutions

**52.** Step 1: Assume 100 g sample; calculate moles of each element.

$$49.98 \text{ g C} \times \frac{1 \text{ mol C}}{12.01 \text{ g C}} = 4.162 \text{ mol C}$$

$$10.47 \text{ g H} \times \frac{1 \text{ mol H}}{1.008 \text{ g H}} = 10.39 \text{ mol H}$$

Step 2: Calculate mole ratios.

$$\frac{4.162 \text{ mol C}}{4.162 \text{ mol C}} = \frac{1.000 \text{ mol C}}{1.000 \text{ mol C}} = \frac{1 \text{ mol C}}{1 \text{ mol C}}$$

$$\frac{10.39 \text{ mol H}}{4.162 \text{ mol C}} = \frac{2.50 \text{ mol H}}{1.000 \text{ mol C}} = \frac{2.5 \text{ mol H}}{1 \text{ mol C}}$$

The simplest ratio is 1 mol C: 2.5 mol H.

Because 2.5 × 2 = 5, the empirical formula is $C_2H_5$.

Step 3: Calculate the molar mass of the empirical formula.

$$2 \text{ mol C} \times \frac{12.01 \text{ g C}}{1 \text{ mol C}} = 24.02 \text{ g}$$

$$5 \text{ mol H} \times \frac{1.008 \text{ g H}}{1 \text{ mol H}} = \underline{5.040 \text{ g}}$$

molar mass $C_2H_5$ = 29.06 g/mol

Step 4: Determine whole number multiplier.

$$\frac{58.12 \text{ g/mol}}{29.06 \text{ g/mol}} = 2.000$$

The molecular formula is $C_4H_{10}$.

**53.** Step 1: Assume 100 g sample; calculate moles of each element.

$$46.68 \text{ g N} \times \frac{1 \text{ mol N}}{14.01 \text{ g N}} = 3.332 \text{ mol N}$$

$$53.32 \text{ g O} \times \frac{1 \text{ mol O}}{16.00 \text{ g O}} = 3.333 \text{ mol O}$$

Step 2: Calculate mole ratios.

$$\frac{3.332 \text{ mol N}}{3.332 \text{ mol N}} = \frac{1.000 \text{ mol N}}{1.000 \text{ mol N}} = \frac{1 \text{ mol N}}{1 \text{ mol N}}$$

$$\frac{3.333 \text{ mol O}}{3.332 \text{ mol N}} = \frac{1.000 \text{ mol O}}{1.000 \text{ mol N}} = \frac{1 \text{ mol O}}{1 \text{ mol N}}$$

The simplest ratio is 1 mol N: 1 mol O.

The empirical formula is NO.

Step 3: Calculate the molar mass of the empirical formula.

$$1 \text{ mol N} \times \frac{14.01 \text{ g N}}{1 \text{ mol N}} = 14.01 \text{ g}$$

$$1 \text{ mol O} \times \frac{16.00 \text{ g O}}{1 \text{ mol O}} = \underline{16.00 \text{ g}}$$

molar mass NO = 30.01 g /mol

Step 4: Determine whole number multiplier.

$$\frac{60.01 \text{ g/mol}}{30.01 \text{ g/mol}} = 2.000$$

The molecular formula is $N_2O_2$.

**54.** Step 1: Calculate moles of each element.

$$19.55 \text{ g K} \times \frac{1 \text{ mol K}}{39.10 \text{ g K}} = 0.5000 \text{ mol K}$$

$$4.00 \text{ g O} \times \frac{1 \text{ mol O}}{16.00 \text{ g O}} = 0.250 \text{ mol O}$$

Step 2: Calculate mole ratios.

$$\frac{0.5000 \text{ mol K}}{0.250 \text{ mol O}} = \frac{2.00 \text{ mol K}}{1.00 \text{ mol O}} = \frac{2 \text{ mol K}}{1 \text{ mol O}}$$

$$\frac{0.250 \text{ mol O}}{0.250 \text{ mol O}} = \frac{1.00 \text{ mol O}}{1.00 \text{ mol O}} = \frac{1 \text{ mol O}}{1 \text{ mol O}}$$

The simplest ratio is 2 mol K: 1 mol O.

The empirical formula is $K_2O$.

**55.** Step 1: Calculate moles of each element

$$174.86 \text{ g Fe} \times \frac{1 \text{ mol Fe}}{55.85 \text{ g Fe}} = 3.131 \text{ mol Fe}$$

$$75.14 \text{ g O} \times \frac{1 \text{ mol O}}{16.00 \text{ g O}} = 4.696 \text{ mol O}$$

Step 2: Calculate mole ratios.

$$\frac{3.131 \text{ mol Fe}}{3.131 \text{ mol Fe}} = \frac{1.000 \text{ mol Fe}}{1.000 \text{ mol Fe}} = \frac{1 \text{ mol Fe}}{1 \text{ mol Fe}}$$

$$\frac{4.696 \text{ mol O}}{3.131 \text{ mol Fe}} = \frac{1.500 \text{ mol O}}{1.000 \text{ mol Fe}} = \frac{1.5 \text{ mol O}}{1 \text{ mol Fe}}$$

The simplest ratio is 1 mol Fe: 1.5 mol O.

Because 1.5 × 2 = 3, the empirical formula is $Fe_2O_3$.

**56.** Step 1: Calculate moles of each element.

$$17.900 \text{ g C} \times \frac{1 \text{ mol C}}{12.01 \text{ g C}} = 1.490 \text{ mol C}$$

$$1.680 \text{ g H} \times \frac{1 \text{ mol H}}{1.008 \text{ g H}} = 1.667 \text{ mol H}$$

$$4.225 \text{ g O} \times \frac{1 \text{ mol O}}{16.00 \text{ g O}} = 0.2641 \text{ mol O}$$

$$1.228 \text{ g N} \times \frac{1 \text{ mol N}}{14.01 \text{ g N}} = 0.08765 \text{ mol N}$$

Step 2: Calculate mole ratios.

$$\frac{0.08765 \text{ mol N}}{0.08765 \text{ mol N}} = \frac{1.000 \text{ mol N}}{1.000 \text{ mol N}} = \frac{1 \text{ mol N}}{1 \text{ mol N}}$$

$$\frac{1.490 \text{ mol C}}{0.08765 \text{ mol N}} = \frac{17.00 \text{ mol C}}{1.000 \text{ mol N}} = \frac{17 \text{ mol C}}{1 \text{ mol N}}$$

$$\frac{1.667 \text{ mol H}}{0.08765 \text{ mol N}} = \frac{19.02 \text{ mol H}}{1.000 \text{ mol N}} = \frac{19 \text{ mol H}}{1 \text{ mol N}}$$

$$\frac{0.2641 \text{ mol O}}{0.08765 \text{ mol N}} = \frac{3.013 \text{ mol O}}{1.000 \text{ mol N}} = \frac{3 \text{ mol O}}{1 \text{ mol N}}$$

The simplest ratio is 17 mol C: 19 mol H: 3 mol O: 1 mol N.

The empirical formula is $C_{17}H_{19}O_3N$.

Solutions

**57.** Step 1: Calculate moles of each element.

$$0.545 \text{ g Al} \times \frac{1 \text{ mol Al}}{26.98 \text{ g Al}} = 0.0202 \text{ mol Al}$$

$$0.485 \text{ g O} \times \frac{1 \text{ mol O}}{16.00 \text{ g O}} = 0.0303 \text{ mol O}$$

Step 2: Calculate mole ratios.

$$\frac{0.0202 \text{ mol Al}}{0.0202 \text{ mol Al}} = \frac{1.00 \text{ mol Al}}{1.00 \text{ mol Al}} = \frac{1 \text{ mol Al}}{1 \text{ mol Al}}$$

$$\frac{0.0303 \text{ mol O}}{0.0202 \text{ mol Al}} = \frac{1.50 \text{ mol O}}{1.00 \text{ mol Al}} = \frac{1.5 \text{ mol O}}{1 \text{ mol Al}}$$

The simplest ratio is 1 mol Al: 1.5 mol O.

Because $1.5 \times 2 = 3$, the empirical formula is $Al_2O_3$.

**63.** Step 1: Assume 100 g sample; calculate moles of each component.

$$48.8 \text{ g MgSO}_4 \times \frac{1 \text{ mol MgSO}_4}{120.38 \text{ g MgSO}_4}$$
$$= 0.405 \text{ mol MgSO}_4$$

$$51.2 \text{ g H}_2\text{O} \times \frac{1 \text{ mol H}_2\text{O}}{18.02 \text{ g H}_2\text{O}} = 2.84 \text{ mol H}_2\text{O}$$

Step 2: Calculate mole ratios.

$$\frac{0.405 \text{ mol MgSO}_4}{0.405 \text{ mol MgSO}_4} = \frac{1.00 \text{ mol MgSO}_4}{1.00 \text{ mol MgSO}_4}$$
$$= \frac{1 \text{ mol MgSO}_4}{1 \text{ mol MgSO}_4}$$

$$\frac{2.84 \text{ mol H}_2\text{O}}{0.405 \text{ mol MgSO}_4} = \frac{7.01 \text{ mol H}_2\text{O}}{1.00 \text{ mol MgSO}_4}$$
$$= \frac{7 \text{ mol H}_2\text{O}}{1 \text{ mol MgSO}_4}$$

The formula of the hydrate is $MgSO_4\cdot7H_2O$. Its name is magnesium sulfate heptahydrate.

**64.** Step 1: Calculate the mass of water driven off.

mass of hydrated compound − mass of anhydrous compound remaining
= 11.75 g $CoCl_2\cdot xH_2O$ − 9.25 g $CoCl_2$
= 2.50 g $H_2O$

Step 2: Calculate moles of each component.

$$9.25 \text{ g CoCl}_2 \times \frac{1 \text{ mol CoCl}_2}{129.83 \text{ g CoCl}_2} = 0.0712 \text{ mol CoCl}_2$$

$$2.50 \text{ g H}_2\text{O} \times \frac{1 \text{ mol H}_2\text{O}}{18.02 \text{ g H}_2\text{O}} = 0.139 \text{ mol H}_2\text{O}$$

Step 2: Calculate mole ratios.

$$\frac{0.0712 \text{ mol CoCl}_2}{0.0712 \text{ mol CoCl}_2} = \frac{1.00 \text{ mol CoCl}_2}{1.00 \text{ mol CoCl}_2} = \frac{1 \text{ mol CoCl}_2}{1 \text{ mol CoCl}_2}$$

$$\frac{0.139 \text{ mol H}_2\text{O}}{0.0712 \text{ mol CoCl}_2} = \frac{1.95 \text{ mol H}_2\text{O}}{1.00 \text{ mol CoCl}_2} = \frac{2 \text{ mol H}_2\text{O}}{1 \text{ mol CoCl}_2}$$

The formula of the hydrate is $CoCl_2\cdot2H_2O$. Its name is cobalt(II) chloride dihydrate.

# Chapter 12

**1. a.** 1 molecule $N_2$ + 3 molecules $H_2 \rightarrow$ 2 molecules $NH_3$

1 mole $N_2$ + 3 moles $H_2 \rightarrow$ 2 moles $NH_3$

28.02 g $N_2$ + 6.06 g $H_2 \rightarrow$ 34.08 g $NH_3$

**b.** 1 molecule HCl + 1 formula unit KOH $\rightarrow$ 1 formula unit KCl + 1 molecule $H_2O$

1 mole HCl + 1 mole KOH $\rightarrow$ 1 mole KCl + 1 mole $H_2O$

36.46 g HCl + 56.11 g KOH $\rightarrow$ 74.55 g KCl + 18.02 g $H_2O$

**c.** 4 atoms Zn + 10 molecules $HNO_3 \rightarrow$ 4 formula units $Zn(NO_3)_2$ + 1 molecule $N_2O$ + 5 molecules $H_2O$

4 moles Zn + 10 moles $HNO_3 \rightarrow$ 4 moles $Zn(NO_3)_2$ + 1 mole $N_2O$ + 5 moles $H_2O$

261.56 g Zn + 630.2 g $HNO_3 \rightarrow$ 757.56 g $Zn(NO_3)_2$ + 44.02 g $N_2O$ + 90.10 g $H_2O$

**d.** 2 atoms Mg + 1 molecule $O_2 \rightarrow$ 2 formula units MgO

2 moles Mg + 1 mole $O_2 \rightarrow$ 2 moles MgO

48.62 g Mg + 32.00 g $O_2 \rightarrow$ 80.62 g MgO

**e.** 2 atoms Na + 2 molecules $H_2O \rightarrow$ 2 formula units NaOH + 1 molecule $H_2$

2 moles Na + 2 moles $H_2O \rightarrow$ 2 moles NaOH + 1 mole $H_2$

45.98 g Na + 36.04 g $H_2O \rightarrow$ 80.00 g NaOH + 2.02 g $H_2$

**2. a.**

$$\frac{4 \text{ mol Al}}{3 \text{ mol O}_2} \qquad \frac{3 \text{ mol O}_2}{2 \text{ mol Al}_2\text{O}_3} \qquad \frac{2 \text{ mol Al}_2\text{O}_3}{4 \text{ mol Al}}$$

$$\frac{3 \text{ mol O}_2}{4 \text{ mol Al}} \qquad \frac{2 \text{ mol Al}_2\text{O}_3}{3 \text{ mol O}_2} \qquad \frac{4 \text{ mol Al}}{2 \text{ mol Al}_2\text{O}_3}$$

**b.**

$$\frac{3 \text{ mol Fe}}{4 \text{ mol H}_2\text{O}} \qquad \frac{3 \text{ mol Fe}}{4 \text{ mol H}_2} \qquad \frac{3 \text{ mol Fe}}{1 \text{ mol Fe}_3\text{O}_4}$$

$$\frac{4 \text{ mol H}_2\text{O}}{3 \text{ mol Fe}} \qquad \frac{4 \text{ mol H}_2}{3 \text{ mol Fe}} \qquad \frac{1 \text{ mol Fe}_3\text{O}_4}{3 \text{ mol Fe}}$$

$$\frac{1 \text{ mol Fe}_3\text{O}_4}{4 \text{ mol H}_2} \qquad \frac{1 \text{ mol Fe}_3\text{O}_4}{4 \text{ mol H}_2\text{O}} \qquad \frac{4 \text{ mol H}_2\text{O}}{4 \text{ mol H}_2}$$

$$\frac{4 \text{ mol H}_2}{1 \text{ mol Fe}_3\text{O}_4} \qquad \frac{4 \text{ mol H}_2\text{O}}{1 \text{ mol Fe}_3\text{O}_4} \qquad \frac{4 \text{ mol H}_2}{4 \text{ mol H}_2\text{O}}$$

**c.**

$$\frac{2 \text{ mol HgO}}{2 \text{ mol Hg}} \qquad \frac{1 \text{ mol O}_2}{2 \text{ mol Hg}} \qquad \frac{1 \text{ mol O}_2}{2 \text{ mol HgO}}$$

$$\frac{2 \text{ mol Hg}}{2 \text{ mol HgO}} \qquad \frac{2 \text{ mol Hg}}{1 \text{ mol O}_2} \qquad \frac{2 \text{ mol HgO}}{1 \text{ mol O}_2}$$

**3. a.** $ZnO(s) + 2HCl(aq) \rightarrow ZnCl_2(aq) + H_2O(l)$

| | | |
|---|---|---|
| $\dfrac{1 \text{ mol ZnO}}{2 \text{ mol HCl}}$ | $\dfrac{1 \text{ mol ZnO}}{1 \text{ mol ZnCl}_2}$ | $\dfrac{1 \text{ mol ZnO}}{1 \text{ mol H}_2\text{O}}$ |
| $\dfrac{2 \text{ mol HCl}}{1 \text{ mol ZnO}}$ | $\dfrac{2 \text{ mol HCl}}{1 \text{ mol ZnCl}_2}$ | $\dfrac{2 \text{ mol HCl}}{1 \text{ mol H}_2\text{O}}$ |
| $\dfrac{1 \text{ mol ZnCl}_2}{1 \text{ mol ZnO}}$ | $\dfrac{1 \text{ mol ZnCl}_2}{2 \text{ mol HCl}}$ | $\dfrac{1 \text{ mol ZnCl}_2}{1 \text{ mol H}_2\text{O}}$ |
| $\dfrac{1 \text{ mol H}_2\text{O}}{1 \text{ mol ZnO}}$ | $\dfrac{1 \text{ mol H}_2\text{O}}{2 \text{ mol HCl}}$ | $\dfrac{1 \text{ mol H}_2\text{O}}{1 \text{ mol ZnCl}_2}$ |

**b.** $2C_4H_{10}(g) + 13O_2(g) \rightarrow 8CO_2(g) + 10H_2O(l)$

| | | |
|---|---|---|
| $\dfrac{2 \text{ mol C}_4\text{H}_{10}}{13 \text{ mol O}_2}$ | $\dfrac{2 \text{ mol C}_4\text{H}_{10}}{8 \text{ mol CO}_2}$ | $\dfrac{2 \text{ mol C}_4\text{H}_{10}}{10 \text{ mol H}_2\text{O}}$ |
| $\dfrac{13 \text{ mol O}_2}{2 \text{ mol C}_4\text{H}_{10}}$ | $\dfrac{8 \text{ mol CO}_2}{2 \text{ mol C}_4\text{H}_{10}}$ | $\dfrac{10 \text{ mol H}_2\text{O}}{2 \text{ mol C}_4\text{H}_{10}}$ |
| $\dfrac{10 \text{ mol H}_2\text{O}}{13 \text{ mol O}_2}$ | $\dfrac{10 \text{ mol H}_2\text{O}}{8 \text{ mol CO}_2}$ | $\dfrac{8 \text{ mol CO}_2}{13 \text{ mol O}_2}$ |
| $\dfrac{13 \text{ mol O}_2}{10 \text{ mol H}_2\text{O}}$ | $\dfrac{8 \text{ mol CO}_2}{10 \text{ mol H}_2\text{O}}$ | $\dfrac{13 \text{ mol O}_2}{8 \text{ mol CO}_2}$ |

**9.** $2SO_2(g) + O_2(g) + 2H_2O(l) \rightarrow 2H_2SO_4(aq)$

$12.5 \text{ mol SO}_2 \times \dfrac{2 \text{ mol H}_2\text{SO}_4}{2 \text{ mol SO}_2}$
$= 12.5 \text{ mol H}_2\text{SO}_4 \text{ produced}$

$12.5 \text{ mol SO}_2 \times \dfrac{1 \text{ mol O}_2}{2 \text{ mol SO}_2} = 6.25 \text{ mol O}_2 \text{ needed}$

**10. a.** $2CH_4(g) + S_8(s) \rightarrow 2CS_2(l) + 4H_2S(g)$

**b.** $1.50 \text{ mol S}_8 \times \dfrac{2 \text{ mol CS}_2}{1 \text{ mol S}_8} = 3.00 \text{ mol CS}_2$

**c.** $1.50 \text{ mol S}_8 \times \dfrac{4 \text{ mol H}_2\text{S}}{1 \text{ mol S}_8} = 6.00 \text{ mol H}_2\text{S}$

**11.** $TiO_2(s) + C(s) + 2Cl_2(g) \rightarrow TiCl_4(s) + CO_2(g)$

Step 1: Make mole → mole conversion.
$1.25 \text{ mol TiO}_2 \times \dfrac{2 \text{ mol Cl}_2}{1 \text{ mol TiO}_2} = 2.50 \text{ mol Cl}_2$

Step 2: Make mole → mass conversion.
$2.50 \text{ mol Cl}_2 \times \dfrac{70.9 \text{ g Cl}_2}{1 \text{ mol Cl}_2} = 177 \text{ g Cl}_2$

**12.** Step 1: Balance the chemical equation.

$2NaCl(s) \rightarrow 2Na(s) + Cl_2(g)$

Step 2: Make mole → mole conversion.
$2.50 \text{ mol NaCl} \times \dfrac{1 \text{ mol Cl}_2}{2 \text{ mol NaCl}} = 1.25 \text{ mol Cl}_2$

Step 3: Make mole → mass conversion.
$1.25 \text{ mol Cl}_2 \times \dfrac{70.9 \text{ g Cl}_2}{1 \text{ mol Cl}_2} = 88.6 \text{ g Cl}_2$

**13.** $2NaN_3(s) \rightarrow 2Na(s) + 3N_2(g)$

Step 1: Make mass → mole conversion.

$100.0 \text{ g NaN}_3 \times \dfrac{1 \text{ mol NaN}_3}{65.02 \text{ g NaN}_3} = 1.538 \text{ mol NaN}_3$

Step 2: Make mole → mole conversion.

$1.538 \text{ mol NaN}_3 \times \dfrac{3 \text{ mol N}_2}{2 \text{ mol NaN}_3} = 2.307 \text{ mol N}_2$

Step 3: Make mole → mass conversion.

$2.307 \text{ mol N}_2 \times \dfrac{28.02 \text{ g N}_2}{1 \text{ mol N}_2} = 64.64 \text{ g N}_2$

**14.** Step 1: Balance the chemical equation.

$2SO_2(g) + O_2(g) + 2H_2O(l) \rightarrow 2H_2SO_4(aq)$

Step 2: Make mass → mole conversion.

$2.50 \text{ g SO}_2 \times \dfrac{1 \text{ mol SO}_2}{64.07 \text{ g SO}_2} = 0.0390 \text{ mol SO}_2$

Step 3: Make mole → mole conversion.

$0.0390 \text{ mol SO}_2 \times \dfrac{2 \text{ mol H}_2\text{SO}_4}{2 \text{ mol SO}_2} =$
$0.0390 \text{ mol H}_2\text{SO}_4$

Step 4: Make mole → mass conversion.

$0.0390 \text{ mol H}_2\text{SO}_4 \times \dfrac{98.09 \text{ g H}_2\text{SO}_4}{1 \text{ mol H}_2\text{SO}_4}$
$= 3.83 \text{ g H}_2\text{SO}_4$

**20.** $6Na(s) + Fe_2O_3(s) \rightarrow 3Na_2O(s) + 2Fe(s)$

Step 1: Make mass → mole conversion.
$100.0 \text{ g Na} \times \dfrac{1 \text{ mol Na}}{22.99 \text{ g Na}} = 4.350 \text{ mol Na}$

$100.0 \text{ g Fe}_2\text{O}_3 \times \dfrac{1 \text{ mol Fe}_2\text{O}_3}{159.7 \text{ g Fe}_2\text{O}_3}$
$= 0.6261 \text{ mol Fe}_2\text{O}_3$

Step 2: Make mole ratio comparison.
$\dfrac{0.6261 \text{ mol Fe}_2\text{O}_3}{4.350 \text{ mol Na}} \quad \text{compared to} \quad \dfrac{1 \text{ mol Fe}_2\text{O}_3}{6 \text{ mol Na}}$

$0.1439 \qquad \text{compared to} \quad 0.1667$

**a.** The actual ratio is less than the needed ratio, so iron(III) oxide is the limiting reactant.

**b.** Sodium is the excess reactant.

**c.** Step 1: Make mole → mole conversion.
$0.6261 \text{ mol Fe}_2\text{O}_3 \times \dfrac{2 \text{ mol Fe}}{1 \text{ mol Fe}_2\text{O}_3} = 1.252 \text{ mol Fe}$

Step 2: Make mole → mass conversion.

$1.252 \text{ mol Fe} \times \dfrac{55.85 \text{ g Fe}}{1 \text{ mol Fe}} = 69.92 \text{ g Fe}$

**d.** Step 1: Make mole → mole conversion.

$0.6261 \text{ mol Fe}_2\text{O}_3 \times \dfrac{6 \text{ mol Na}}{1 \text{ mol Fe}_2\text{O}_3}$

$= 3.757 \text{ mol Na needed}$

Step 2: Make mole → mass conversion.

$$3.757 \text{ mol Na} \times \frac{22.99 \text{ g Na}}{1 \text{ mol Na}} = 86.36 \text{ g Na needed}$$

100.0 g Na given − 86.36 g Na needed
= 13.6 g Na in excess

**21.** Step 1: Write the balanced chemical equation.

$$6CO_2(g) + 6H_2O(l) \rightarrow C_6H_{12}O_6(aq) + 6O_2(g)$$

Step 2: Make mass → mole conversion.

$$88.0 \text{ g CO}_2 \times \frac{1 \text{ mol CO2}}{44.01 \text{ g CO}_2} = 2.00 \text{ mol CO}_2$$

$$64.0 \text{ g H}_2O \times \frac{1 \text{ mol H}_2O}{18.02 \text{ g H}_2O} = 3.55 \text{ mol H}_2O$$

Step 3: Make mole ratio comparison.

$$\frac{2.00 \text{ mol CO}_2}{3.55 \text{ mol H}_2O} \quad \text{compared to} \quad \frac{6 \text{ mol CO}_2}{6 \text{ mol H}_2O}$$

0.563         compared to        1.00

**a.** The actual ratio is less than the needed ratio, so carbon dioxide is the limiting reactant.

**b.** Water is the excess reactant.

Step 1: Make mole → mole conversion.

$$2.00 \text{ mol CO}_2 \times \frac{6 \text{ mol H}_2O}{6 \text{ mol CO}_2} = 2.00 \text{ mol H}_2O$$

Step 2: Make mole → mass conversion.

$$2.00 \text{ mol H}_2O \times \frac{18.02 \text{ g H}_2O}{1 \text{ mol H}_2O}$$
$$= 36.0 \text{ g H}_2O \text{ needed}$$

64.0 g $H_2O$ given − 36.0 g $H_2O$ needed
= 28.0 g $H_2O$ in excess

**c.** Step 1: Make mole → mole conversion.

$$2.00 \text{ mol CO}_2 \times \frac{1 \text{ mol C}_6H_{12}O_6}{6 \text{ mol CO}_2}$$
$$= 0.333 \text{ mol C}_6H_{12}O_6$$

Step 2: Make mole → mass conversion.

$$0.333 \text{ mol C}_6H_{12}O_6 \times \frac{180.2 \text{ g C}_6H_{12}O_6}{1 \text{ mol C}_6H_{12}O_6}$$
$$= 60.0 \text{ g C}_6H_{12}O_6$$

**27.** $Al(OH)_3(s) + 3HCl(aq) \rightarrow AlCl_3(aq) + 3H_2O(l)$

Step 1: Make mass → mole conversion.

$$14.0 \text{ g Al(OH)}_3 \times \frac{1 \text{ mol Al(OH)}_3}{78.0 \text{ g Al(OH)}_3}$$
$$= 0.179 \text{ mol Al(OH)}_3$$

Step 2: Make mole → mole conversion.

$$0.179 \text{ mol Al(OH)}_3 \times \frac{1 \text{ mol AlCl}_3}{1 \text{ mol Al(OH)}_3}$$
$$= 0.179 \text{ mol AlCl}_3$$

Step 3: Make mole → mass conversion.

$$0.179 \text{ mol AlCl}_3 \times \frac{133.3 \text{ g AlCl}_3}{1 \text{ mol AlCl}_3} = 23.9 \text{ g AlCl}_3$$

23.9 g of $AlCl_3$ is the theoretical yield.

$$\% \text{ yield} = \frac{22.0 \text{ g AlCl}_3}{23.9 \text{ g AlCl}_3} \times 100 = 92.1\% \text{ yield of AlCl}_3$$

**28.** Step 1: Write the balanced chemical equation.

$$Cu(s) + 2AgNO_3(aq) \rightarrow 2Ag(s) + Cu(NO_3)_2(aq)$$

Step 2: Make mass → mole conversion.

$$20.0 \text{ g Cu} \times \frac{1 \text{ mol Cu}}{63.55 \text{ g Cu}} = 0.315 \text{ mol Cu}$$

Step 3: Make mole → mole conversion.

$$0.315 \text{ mol Cu} \times \frac{2 \text{ mol Ag}}{1 \text{ mol Cu}} = 0.630 \text{ mol Ag}$$

Step 4: Make mole → mass conversion.

$$0.630 \text{ mol Ag} \times \frac{107.9 \text{ g Ag}}{1 \text{ mol Ag}} = 68.0 \text{ g Ag}$$

68.0 g of Ag is the theoretical yield.

$$\% \text{ yield} = \frac{60.0 \text{ g Ag}}{68.0 \text{ g Ag}} \times 100 = 88.2\% \text{ yield of Ag}$$

**29.** Step 1: Write the balanced chemical equation.

$$Zn(s) + I_2(s) \rightarrow ZnI_2(s)$$

Step 2: Make mass → mole conversion.

$$125.0 \text{ g Zn} \times \frac{1 \text{ mol Zn}}{65.38 \text{ g Zn}} = 1.912 \text{ mol Zn}$$

Step 3: Make mole → mole conversion.

$$1.912 \text{ mol Zn} \times \frac{1 \text{ mol ZnI}_2}{1 \text{ mol Zn}} = 1.912 \text{ mol ZnI}_2$$

Step 4: Make mole → mass conversion.

$$1.912 \text{ mol ZnI}_2 \times \frac{319.2 \text{ g ZnI}_2}{1 \text{ mol ZnI}_2} = 610.3 \text{ g ZnI}_2$$

610.3 g of $ZnI_2$ is the theoretical yield.

$$\% \text{ yield} = \frac{515.6 \text{ g ZnI}_2}{610.3 \text{ g ZnI}_2} \times 100$$
$$= 84.48\% \text{ yield of ZnI}_2$$

## Chapter 13

**1.** $\dfrac{\text{Rate}_{\text{nitrogen}}}{\text{Rate}_{\text{neon}}} = \sqrt{\dfrac{20.2 \text{ g/mol}}{28.0 \text{ g/mol}}} = \sqrt{0.721} = 0.849$

**2.** $\dfrac{\text{Rate}_{\text{carbon monoxide}}}{\text{Rate}_{\text{carbon dioxide}}} = \sqrt{\dfrac{44.0 \text{ g/mol}}{28.0 \text{ g/mol}}}$

$= \sqrt{1.57}$

$= 1.25$

**3.** Rearrange Graham's law to solve for Rate$_A$.

$\text{Rate}_A = \text{Rate}_B \times \sqrt{\dfrac{\text{molar mass}_B}{\text{molar mass}_A}}$

$\text{Rate}_B = 3.6 \text{ mol/min}$

$\dfrac{\text{molar mass}_B}{\text{molar mass}_A} = 0.5$

$\text{Rate}_A = 3.6 \text{ mol/min} \times \sqrt{0.5}$

$= 3.6 \text{ mol/min} \times 0.71$

$= 2.5 \text{ mol/min}$

**4.** $P_{\text{hydrogen}} = P_{\text{total}} - P_{\text{helium}}$

$= 600 \text{ mm Hg} - 439 \text{ mm Hg}$

$= 161 \text{ mm Hg}$

**5.** $P_{\text{total}} = 5.00 \text{ kPa} + 4.56 \text{ kPa} + 3.02 \text{ kPa} + 1.20 \text{ kPa}$

$= 13.78 \text{ kPa}$

**6.** $P_{\text{carbon dioxide}} = 30.4 \text{ kPa} - (16.5 \text{ kPa} + 3.7 \text{ kPa})$

$= 30.4 \text{ kPa} - 20.2 \text{ kPa} = 10.2 \text{ kPa}$

## Chapter 14

**1.** $V_2 = \dfrac{V_1 P_1}{P_2} = \dfrac{(300.0 \text{ mL})(99.0 \text{ kPa})}{188 \text{ kPa}} = 158 \text{ mL}$

**2.** $P_2 = \dfrac{V_1 P_1}{V_2} = \dfrac{(1.00 \text{ L})(0.988 \text{ atm})}{2.00 \text{ L}} = 0.494 \text{ atm}$

**3.** $V_2 = \dfrac{V_1 P_1}{P_2} = \dfrac{(145.7 \text{ mL})(1.08 \text{ atm})}{1.43 \text{ atm}}$

$= 1.10 \times 10^2 \text{ mL}$

**4.** $P_2 = \dfrac{V_1 P_1}{V_2} = \dfrac{(4.00 \text{ L})(0.980 \text{ atm})}{0.0500 \text{ L}} = 78.4 \text{ atm}$

**5.** $29.2 \text{ kPa} \times \dfrac{1 \text{ atm}}{101.3 \text{ kPa}} = 0.288 \text{ atm}$

$V_2 = \dfrac{V_1 P_1}{P_2} = \dfrac{(0.220 \text{ L})(0.860 \text{ atm})}{0.288 \text{ atm}} = 0.657 \text{ L}$

**6.** $T_1 = 89°C + 273 = 362 \text{ K}$

$T_2 = \dfrac{T_1 V_2}{V_1} = \dfrac{(362 \text{ K})(1.12 \text{ L})}{0.67 \text{ L}} = 605 \text{ K}$

$605 - 273 = 330°C$

**7.** $T_1 = 80.0°C + 273 = 353 \text{ K}$

$T_2 = 30.0°C + 273 = 303 \text{ K}$

$V_2 = \dfrac{V_1 T_2}{T_1} = \dfrac{(3.00 \text{ L})(303 \text{ K})}{353 \text{ K}} = 2.58 \text{ L}$

**8.** $T_1 = 25°C + 273 = 298 \text{ K}$

$T_2 = 0.00°C + 273 = 273 \text{ K}$

$V_2 = \dfrac{V_1 T_2}{T_1} = \dfrac{(0.620 \text{ L})(273 \text{ K})}{298 \text{ K}} = 0.57 \text{ L}$

**9.** $T_1 = 30.0°C + 273 = 303 \text{ K}$

$T_2 = \dfrac{T_1 P_2}{P_1} = \dfrac{(303 \text{ K})(201 \text{ kPa})}{125 \text{ kPa}} = 487 \text{ K}$

$487 \text{ K} - 273 = 214°C$

**10.** $T_1 = 25.0°C + 273 = 298 \text{ K}$

$T_2 = 37.0°C + 273 = 310 \text{ K}$

$P_2 = \dfrac{P_1 T_2}{T_1} = \dfrac{(1.88 \text{ atm})(310 \text{ K})}{298 \text{ K}} = 1.96 \text{ atm}$

**11.** $T_2 = 36.5°C + 273 = 309.5 \text{ K}$

$T_1 = \dfrac{T_2 P_1}{P_2} = \dfrac{(309.5 \text{ K})(1.12 \text{ atm})}{2.56 \text{ atm}} = 135 \text{ K}$

$135 \text{ K} - 273 = -138°C$

**12.** $T_1 = 0.00°C + 273 = 273 \text{ K}$

$T_2 = \dfrac{T_1 P_2}{P_1} = \dfrac{(273 \text{ K})(28.4 \text{ kPa})}{30.7 \text{ kPa}} = 252.5 \text{ K}$

$252.5 \text{ K} - 273 = -20.5°C = -21°C$

The temperature must be lowered by 21°C.

**13.** $T_1 = 22.0°C + 273 = 295 \text{ K}$

$T_2 = 44.6°C + 273 = 318 \text{ K}$

$P_2 = \dfrac{P_1 T_2}{T_1} = \dfrac{(660 \text{ torr})(318 \text{ K})}{295 \text{ K}} = 711 \text{ torr}$

$711 \text{ torr} - 660 \text{ torr} = 51 \text{ torr more}$

**19.** $T_1 = 36°C + 273 = 309$ K

$T_2 = 28°C + 273 = 301$ K

$V_2 = \dfrac{P_1 T_2 V_1}{P_2 T_1} = \dfrac{(0.998 \text{ atm})(301 \text{ K})(2.1 \text{ L})}{(0.900 \text{ atm})(309 \text{ K})} = 2.3$ L

**20.** $T_1 = 0.00°C + 273 = 273$ K

$T_2 = 30.00°C + 273 = 303$ K

$P_2 = \dfrac{V_1 T_2 P_1}{V_2 T_1} = \dfrac{(30.0 \text{ mL})(303 \text{ K})(1.00 \text{ atm})}{(20.0 \text{ mL})(273 \text{ K})}$

$= 1.66$ atm

**21.** $T_1 = 22.0°C + 273 = 295$ K

$T_2 = 100.0°C + 273 = 373$ K

$V_1 = \dfrac{V_2 T_1 P_2}{T_2 P_1} = \dfrac{(0.224 \text{ mL})(295 \text{ K})(1.23 \text{ atm})}{(373 \text{ K})(1.02 \text{ atm})}$

$= 0.214$ mL

**22.** $T_1 = 5.0°C + 273 = 278$ K

$T_2 = 2.09°C + 273 = 275$ K

$V_2 = \dfrac{P_1 T_2 V_1}{P_2 T_1} = \dfrac{(1.30 \text{ atm})(275 \text{ K})(46.0 \text{ mL})}{(1.52 \text{ atm})(278 \text{ K})}$

$= 39$ mL

**23.** $P_1 = \dfrac{V_2 T_1 P_2}{V_1 T_2} = \dfrac{(0.644 \text{ L})(298 \text{ K})(32.6 \text{ kPa})}{(0.766 \text{ L})(303 \text{ K})} =$

$= 27.0$ kPa

**24.** $2.4 \text{ mol} \times \dfrac{22.4 \text{ L}}{\text{mol}} = 54$ L

**25.** $0.0459 \text{ mol} \times \dfrac{22.4 \text{ L}}{\text{mol}} = 1.03$ L

**26.** $1.02 \text{ mol} \times \dfrac{22.4 \text{ L}}{\text{mol}} = 22.8$ L

**27.** $2.00 \text{ L} \times \dfrac{1 \text{ mol}}{22.4 \text{ L}} = 0.0893$ mol

**28.** Set up problem as a ratio.

$\dfrac{? \text{ mol He}}{0.865 \text{ L}} = \dfrac{0.0226 \text{ mol He}}{0.460 \text{ L}}$

Solve for mol He.

$? \text{ mol He} = \dfrac{0.0226 \text{ mol He}}{0.460 \text{ L}} \times 0.865 \text{ L}$

$= 0.0425$ mol He

**29.** $1.0 \text{ L} \times \dfrac{1 \text{ mol}}{22.4 \text{ L}} = 0.045$ mol

$0.045 \text{ mol} \times \dfrac{44.0 \text{ g}}{\text{mol}} = 2.0$ g

**30.** $0.00922 \text{ g} \times \dfrac{1 \text{ mol}}{2.016 \text{ g}} = 0.00457$ mol

$0.00457 \text{ mol} \times \dfrac{22.4 \text{ L}}{\text{mol}} = 0.102$ L or 102 mL

**31.** $0.416 \text{ g} \times \dfrac{1 \text{ mol}}{83.8 \text{ g}} = 0.00496$ mol

$0.00496 \text{ mol} \times \dfrac{22.4 \text{ L}}{\text{mol}} = 0.111$ L

**32.** $0.860 \text{ g} - 0.205 \text{ g} = 0.655$ g He remaining

Set up problem as a ratio.

$\dfrac{V}{0.655 \text{ g}} = \dfrac{19.2 \text{ L}}{0.860 \text{ g}}$

Solve for $V$.

$V = \dfrac{(19.2 \text{ L})(0.655 \text{ g})}{0.860 \text{ g}} = 14.6$ L

**33.** $4.5 \text{ kg} \times \dfrac{1000 \text{ g}}{1 \text{ kg}} \times \dfrac{1 \text{ mol}}{28.0 \text{ g}} \times \dfrac{22.4 \text{ L}}{1 \text{ mol}} = 3.6 \times 10^3$ L

**41.** $n = \dfrac{PV}{RT} = \dfrac{(3.81 \text{ atm})(0.44 \text{ L})}{\left(0.0821 \frac{\text{L} \cdot \text{atm}}{\text{mol} \cdot \text{K}}\right)(298 \text{ K})}$

$= 6.9 \times 10^{-3}$ mol

**42.** $143 \text{ kPa} \times \dfrac{1.00 \text{ atm}}{101.3 \text{ kPa}} = 1.41$ atm

$T = \dfrac{PV}{nR} = \dfrac{(1.41 \text{ atm})(1.00 \text{ L})}{(2.49 \text{ mol})\left(0.0821 \frac{\text{L} \cdot \text{atm}}{\text{mol} \cdot \text{K}}\right)} = 6.90$ K

$6.90 \text{ K} - 273 = -266°C$

**43.** $V = \dfrac{nRT}{P} = \dfrac{(0.323 \text{ mol})\left(0.0821 \frac{\text{L} \cdot \text{atm}}{\text{mol} \cdot \text{K}}\right)(265 \text{ K})}{0.900 \text{ atm}}$

$= 7.81$ L

**44.** $T = 20.0°C + 273 = 293$ K

$P = \dfrac{nRT}{V} = \dfrac{(0.108 \text{ mol})\left(0.0821 \frac{\text{L} \cdot \text{atm}}{\text{mol} \cdot \text{K}}\right)(293 \text{ K})}{0.505 \text{ L}}$

$= 5.14$ atm

**45.** $T = \dfrac{PV}{nR} = \dfrac{(0.988 \text{ atm})(1.20 \text{ L})}{(0.0470 \text{ mol})\left(0.0821 \frac{\text{L} \cdot \text{atm}}{\text{mol} \cdot \text{K}}\right)} = 307$ K

**46.** $117 \text{ kPa} \times \dfrac{1.00 \text{ atm}}{101.3 \text{ kPa}} = 1.15$ atm

$T = 35.1°C + 273 = 308$ K

$m = \dfrac{PMV}{RT} = \dfrac{(1.15 \text{ atm})(70.0 \text{ g/mol})(2.00 \text{ L})}{\left(0.0821 \frac{\text{L} \cdot \text{atm}}{\text{mol} \cdot \text{K}}\right)(308 \text{ K})}$

$= 6.39$ g

**47.** $T = 22.0°C + 273 = 295$ K

$m = \dfrac{MPV}{RT} = \dfrac{(28.0 \text{ g/mol})(1.00 \text{ atm})(0.600 \text{ L})}{\left(0.0821 \frac{\text{L} \cdot \text{atm}}{\text{mol} \cdot \text{K}}\right)(295 \text{ K})}$

$= 0.694$ g

Solutions

**48.** $D = \dfrac{PM}{RT} = \dfrac{(1.00\text{ atm})(44.0\text{ g/mol})}{\left(0.0821\dfrac{\text{L·atm}}{\text{mol·K}}\right)(273\text{ K})} = 1.96$ g/L

**49.** $T = 25.0°C + 273 = 298$ K

$M = \dfrac{DRT}{P} = \dfrac{(1.09\text{ g/L})\left(0.0821\dfrac{\text{L·atm}}{\text{mol·K}}\right)(298\text{ K})}{1.02\text{ atm}}$

$= 26.1$ g/mol

**50.** $D = \dfrac{MP}{RT} = \dfrac{(39.9\text{ g/mol})(1.00\text{ atm})}{\left(0.0821\dfrac{\text{L·atm}}{\text{mol·K}}\right)(273\text{ K})} = 1.78$ g/L

**56.** $S(s) + O_2(g) \rightarrow SO_2(g)$

3.5 L $SO_2 \times \dfrac{1\text{ volume }O_2}{1\text{ volume }SO_2} = 3.5$ L $O_2$

**57.** $2H_2(g) + O_2(g) \rightarrow 2H_2O(g)$

5.00 L $O_2 \times \dfrac{2\text{ volumes }H_2}{1\text{ volume }O_2} = 10.0$ L $H_2$

**58.** $C_3H_8(g) + 5O_2(g) \rightarrow 3CO_2(g) + 4H_2O(g)$

34.0 L $O_2 \times \dfrac{1\text{ volume }C_3H_8}{5\text{ volumes }O_2} = 6.80$ L $C_3H_8$

**59.** $CH_4(g) + 2O_2(g) \rightarrow CO_2(g) + 2H_2O(g)$

2.36 L $CH_4 \times \dfrac{2\text{ volumes }O_2}{1\text{ volume }CH_4} = 4.72$ L $O_2$

**60.** 0.100 L $N_2O \times \dfrac{1\text{ mol}}{22.4\text{ L}} = 0.00446$ mol $N_2O$

0.00446 mol $N_2O \times \dfrac{1\text{ mol }NH_4NO_3}{1\text{ mol }N_2O}$

$= 0.00446$ mol $NH_4NO_3$

0.00446 mol $NH_4NO_3 \times 80.0$ g/mol

$= 0.357$ g $NH_4NO_3$

**61.** 2.38 kg $\times \dfrac{1000\text{ g}}{\text{kg}} \times \dfrac{1\text{ mol }CaCO_3}{100.0\text{ g}} \times$

$\dfrac{1\text{ mol }CO_2}{1\text{ mol }CaCO_3} \times \dfrac{22.4\text{ L}}{1\text{ mol}} = 533$ L $CO_2$

**62.** $CH_4(g) + 2O_2(g) \rightarrow CO_2(g) + 2H_2O(g)$

$n = \dfrac{PV}{RT} = \dfrac{(1.00\text{ atm})(10.5\text{ L})}{\left(0.0821\dfrac{\text{L·atm}}{\text{mol·K}}\right)(473\text{ K})}$

$= 0.271$ mol $CH_4$

0.271 mol $CH_4 \times \dfrac{2\text{ mol }H_2O}{1\text{ mol }CH_4} = 0.541$ mol $H_2O$

**63.** 52.0 g Fe $\times \dfrac{1\text{ mol Fe}}{55.85\text{ g Fe}} \times \dfrac{3\text{ mol }O_2}{4\text{ mol Fe}} \times \dfrac{22.4\text{ L}}{1\text{ mol}}$

$= 15.6$ L $O_2$

**64.** $2K(s) + Cl_2(g) \rightarrow 2KCl(s)$

0.204 g K $\times \dfrac{1\text{ mol K}}{39.1\text{ g K}} \times \dfrac{1\text{ mol }Cl_2}{2\text{ mol K}} \times \dfrac{22.4\text{ L}}{1\text{ mol}}$

$= 0.0584$ L $Cl_2$

## Chapter 15

**1.** $S_1 = \dfrac{0.55\ g}{1.0\ L} = 0.55\ g/L$

$S_2 = P_2 \times \dfrac{S_1}{P_1} = 110.0\ \text{kPa} \times \dfrac{0.55\ g/L}{20.0\ \text{kPa}} = 3.0\ g/L$

**2.** $S_2 = \dfrac{1.5\ g}{1.0\ L} = 1.5\ g/L$

$P_2 = \dfrac{S_2}{S_1} \times P_1 = \dfrac{1.5\ g/L}{0.66\ g/L} \times 10.0\ atm = 23\ atm$

**8.** 600 mL $H_2O$ × 1.0 g/mL = 600 g $H_2O$

$\dfrac{20\ g\ NaHCO_3}{600\ g\ H_2O + 20\ g\ Na\ HCO_3} \times 100 = 3\%$

**9.** $3.62\% = 100 \times \dfrac{\text{mass NaOCl}}{1500.0\ g}$

mass NaOCl = 54.3 g

**10.** 1500.0 g − 54.3 g = 1445.7 g solvent

**11.** $\dfrac{35\ mL}{115\ mL + 35\ mL} \times 100 = 23\%$

**12.** $30.0\% = 100 \times \dfrac{\text{volume ethanol}}{\text{volume solution}}$

volume ethanol = 0.300 × (volume solution) = 0.300 × 100.0 mL

volume ethanol = 30.0 mL

volume water = 100.0 mL − 30.0 mL = 70.0 mL

**13.** $\dfrac{24\ mL}{24\ mL + 1100\ mL} \times 100 = 2.1\%$

**14.** mol $C_6H_{12}O_6 = 40.0\ g \times \dfrac{1\ mol}{180.16\ g} = 0.222\ mol$

molarity $= \dfrac{\text{mol } C_6H_{12}O_6}{1.5\ L\ \text{solution}} = \dfrac{0.222\ mol}{1.5\ L} = 0.148M$

**15.** mol NaOCl $= 9.5\ g \times \dfrac{1\ mol}{74.44\ g} = 0.128\ mol$

molarity $= \dfrac{\text{mol NaOCl}}{1.00\ L\ \text{solution}} = \dfrac{0.128\ mol}{1.00\ L} = 0.128M$

**16.** mol KBr $= 1.55\ g \times \dfrac{1\ mol}{119.0\ g} = 0.0130\ mol\ KBr$

molarity $= \dfrac{\text{mol KBr}}{1.60\ L\ \text{solution}} = \dfrac{0.0130\ mol}{01.60\ L}$

$= 8.13 \times 10^{-3}M$

**17.** mol $CaCl_2 = (0.10M)(1.0\ L) = (0.10\ mol/L)(1.0\ L)$

$= 0.10\ mol\ CaCl_2$

mass $CaCl_2 = 0.10\ \text{mol}\ CaCl_2 \times \dfrac{110.98\ g}{1\ \text{mol}}$

$= 11\ g\ CaCl_2$

**18.** mol NaOH $= (2M)(1\ L) = (2\ mol/L)(1\ L) = 2\ mol$

mass NaOH $= 2\ \text{mol NaOH} \times \dfrac{40.00\ g}{1\ \text{mol}}$

$= 80\ g\ NaOH$

**19.** mol $CaCl_2 = 500.0\ mL \times \dfrac{1\ L}{1000\ mL} \times 0.20M$

$= 500.0\ \text{mL} \times \dfrac{1\ L}{1000\ \text{mL}} \times \dfrac{0.20\ mol}{1\ L}$

$= 0.10\ mol$

mass $CaCl_2 = 0.10\ \text{mol}\ CaCl_2 \times \dfrac{110.98\ g}{1\ \text{mol}}$

$= 11\ g\ CaCl_2$

**20.** mol NaOH $= 250\ mL \times \dfrac{1\ L}{1000\ mL} \times 3.0M$

$= 250\ \text{mL} \times \dfrac{1\ L}{1000\ \text{mL}} \times \dfrac{3.0\ mol}{1\ L}$

$= 0.75\ mol$

mass NaOH $= 0.75\ mol\ NaOH \times \dfrac{40.00\ g}{1\ mol}$

$= 3.0 \times 10^1\ g\ NaOH$

**21.** $(3.00M)V_1 = (1.25M)(0.300\ L)$

$V_1 = \dfrac{(1.25M)(0.300\ L)}{3.00M} = 0.125\ L = 125\ mL$

**22.** $(5.0M)V_1 = (0.25M)(100.0\ mL)$

$V_1 = \dfrac{(0.25M)(100.0\ mL)}{5.0M} = 5.0\ mL$

**23.** $(3.5M)(20.0\ mL) = M_2(100.0\ mL)$

$M_2 = \dfrac{(3.5M)(20.0\ mL)}{100.0\ mL} = 0.70M$

**24.** mol $Na_2SO_4 = 10.0\ g\ Na_2SO_4 \times \dfrac{1\ mol}{142.04\ g}$

$= 0.0704\ mol\ Na_2SO_4$

molality $= \dfrac{0.0704\ mol\ Na_2SO_4}{1000.0\ g\ H_2O} = 0.0704m$

**25.** mol $C_{10}H_8 = 30.0\ g\ C_{10}H_8 \times \dfrac{1\ mol}{128.16\ g}$

$= 0.234\ mol\ C_{10}H_8$

molality $= \dfrac{0.234\ mol\ C_{10}H_8}{500.0\ g\ \text{toluene}} \times \dfrac{1000.0\ g\ \text{toluene}}{1.0000\ kg\ \text{toluene}}$

$= 0.468m$

**26.** $22.8\% = \dfrac{\text{mass NaOH}}{\text{mass NaOH + mass } H_2O} \times 100$

Assume 100.0 g sample.

Then, mass NaOH = 22.8 g and mass $H_2O$ = 100.0 g − (mass NaOH) = 77.2 g

mol NaOH $= 22.8\ g \times \dfrac{1\ mol}{40.00\ g} = 0.570\ mol\ NaOH$

mol $H_2O = 77.2\ g \times \dfrac{1\ mol}{18.02\ g} = 4.28\ mol\ H_2O$

mol fraction NaOH $= \dfrac{\text{mol NaOH}}{\text{mol NaOH + mol } H_2O}$

$= \dfrac{0.570\ mol\ NaOH}{0.570\ mol\ NaOH + 4.28\ mol\ H_2O} = \dfrac{0.570}{4.85}$

$= 0.118$

The mole fraction of NaOH is 0.118.

Solutions

**27.** $0.21 = \dfrac{\text{mol NaCl}}{\text{mol NaCl} + \text{mol H}_2\text{O}}$

$0.21(\text{mol NaCl}) + 0.21(\text{mol H}_2\text{O}) = \text{mol NaCl}$

$0.79(\text{mol NaCl}) = 0.21(\text{mol H}_2\text{O})$

$\text{mol H}_2\text{O} = 100.0 \text{ mL} \times \dfrac{1.0 \text{ g}}{1 \text{ mL}} \times \dfrac{1 \text{ mol}}{18.016 \text{ g}}$

$= 5.55 \text{ mol H}_2\text{O}$

Therefore, $\text{mol NaCl} = \dfrac{0.21 \times 5.55 \text{ mol}}{0.79}$

$= 1.48 \text{ mol}$

$\text{mass NaCl} = 1.48 \text{ mol} \times 58.44 \text{ g/mol} = 86.5 \text{ g}$

The mass of dissolved NaCl is 86.5 g.

**33.** $\Delta T_b = 0.512°\text{C}/m \times 0.625m = 0.320°\text{C}$
$T_b = 100°\text{C} + 0.320°\text{C} = 100.320°\text{C}$
$\Delta T_f = 1.86°\text{C}/m \times 0.625m = 1.16°\text{C}$
$T_f = 0.0°\text{C} - 1.16°\text{C} = -1.16°\text{C}$

**34.** $\Delta T_b = 1.22°\text{C}/m \times 0.40m = 0.49°\text{C}$
$T_b = 78.5°\text{C} + 0.49°\text{C} = 79.0°\text{C}$
$\Delta T_f = 1.99°\text{C}/m \times 0.40m = 0.80°\text{C}$
$T_f = -114.1°\text{C} - 0.80°\text{C} = -114.9°\text{C}$

**35.** $1.12°\text{C} = 0.512°\text{C}/m \times m$
$m = 2.19m$

**36.** $0.500 \text{ mol}/1 \text{ kg} = 0.500m$
$\Delta T_b = 2.53°\text{C}/m \times 0.500m = 1.26°\text{C}$

# Chapter 16

**1.** 142 Calories = 142 kcal

$142 \text{ kcal} \times \dfrac{1000 \text{ cal}}{1 \text{ kcal}} = 142\ 000 \text{ cal}$

**2.** $86.5 \text{ kJ} \times \dfrac{1 \text{ kcal}}{4.184 \text{ kJ}} = 20.7 \text{ kcal}$

**3.** $256 \text{ J} \times \dfrac{1 \text{ cal}}{4.184 \text{ J}} \times \dfrac{1 \text{ kcal}}{1000 \text{ cal}} = 6.12 \times 10^{-2} \text{ kcal}$

**4.** $q = c \times m \times \Delta T$
$q = 2.44 \text{ J/(g·°C)} \times 34.4 \text{ g} \times 53.8°\text{C} = 4.52 \times 10^3 \text{ J}$

**5.** $q = c \times m \times \Delta T$
$276 \text{ J} = 0.129 \text{ J/(g·°C)} \times 4.50 \text{ g} \times \Delta T$
$\Delta T = 475°\text{C}$

$\Delta T = T_f - T_i$
Because the gold gains heat, let $\Delta T = +475°\text{C}$
$475 °\text{C} = T_f - 25.0°\text{C}$
$T_f = 5.00 \times 10^{2}°\text{C}$

**6.** $q = c \times m \times \Delta T$
$5696 \text{ J} = c \times 155 \text{ g} \times 15.0°\text{C}$
$c = 2.45 \text{ J/(g · °C)}$
The specific heat is very close to the value for ethanol.

**12.** $q = c \times m \times \Delta T$
$9750 \text{ J} = 4.184 \text{ J/(g·°C)} \times 335 \text{ g} \times \Delta T$
$\Delta T = 6.96°\text{C}$

Because the water lost heat, let $\Delta T = -6.96°\text{C}$
$\Delta T = -6.96°\text{C} = T_f - 65.5°\text{C}$
$T_f = 58.5°\text{C}$

**13.** $q = c \times m \times \Delta T$

$5650 \text{ J} = 4.184 \text{ J/(g·°C)} \times m \times 26.6°\text{C}$

$m = 50.8 \text{ g}$

**20.** $25.7 \text{ g CH}_3\text{OH} \times \dfrac{1 \text{ mol CH}_3\text{OH}}{32.04 \text{ g CH}_3\text{OH}} \times \dfrac{3.22 \text{ kJ}}{1 \text{ mol CH}_3\text{OH}}$
$= 2.58 \text{ kJ}$

**21.** $275 \text{ g NH}_3 \times \dfrac{1 \text{ mol NH}_3}{17.03 \text{ g NH}_3} \times \dfrac{23.3 \text{ kJ}}{1 \text{ mol NH}_3} = 376 \text{ kJ}$

**22.** $12\ 880 \text{ kJ} = m \times \dfrac{1 \text{ mol CH}_4}{16.04 \text{ g CH}_4} \times \dfrac{891 \text{ kJ}}{1 \text{ mol CH}_4}$

$m = 12\ 880 \text{ kJ} \times \dfrac{16.04 \text{ g CH}_4}{1 \text{ mol CH}_4} \times \dfrac{1 \text{ mol CH}_4}{891 \text{ kJ}}$

$m = 232 \text{ g CH}_4$

**28.** Add the first equation to the second equation reversed.

| | |
|---|---|
| $2\text{CO(g)} + \text{O}_2\text{(g)} \rightarrow 2\text{CO}_2\text{(g)}$ | $\Delta H = -566.0 \text{ kJ}$ |
| $2\text{NO(g)} \rightarrow \text{N}_2\text{(g)} + \text{O}_2\text{(g)}$ | $\Delta H = -180.6 \text{ kJ}$ |

$2\text{CO(g)} + 2\text{NO(g)} \rightarrow 2\text{CO}_2\text{(g)} + \text{N2(g)}$   $\Delta H = -746.6 \text{ kJ}$

**29.** Add the first equation to the second equation reversed and tripled.

$4Al(s) + 3O_2(g) \rightarrow 2Al_2O_3(s)$      $\Delta H = -3352$ kJ
$3MnO_2(s) \rightarrow 3Mn(s) + 3O_2(g)$      $\Delta H = +1563$ kJ

$4Al(s) + 3MnO_2(s) \rightarrow 2Al_2O_3(s) + 3Mn(s) \, \Delta H = -1789$ kJ

**30. a.** One mole of $O_2(g)$ in the first equation cancels the $O_2(g)$ in the second equation.

$2[\frac{1}{2} N_2(g) + O_2(g) \rightarrow NO_2(g)]$
$2[NO(g) \rightarrow \frac{1}{2} O_2(g) + \frac{1}{2} N_2(g)]$

$2NO(g) + O_2(g) \rightarrow 2NO_2(g)$

**b.** $H_2(g) + S(s) + 2O_2(g) \rightarrow H_2SO_4(l)$
$SO_3(g) \rightarrow S(s) + \frac{3}{2}O_2(g)$
$H_2O(l) \rightarrow H_2(g) + \frac{1}{2}O_2(g)$

$SO_3(g) + H_2O(l) \rightarrow H_2SO_4(l)$

**31. a.** $\Delta H^{\circ}_{rxn} = \Sigma \Delta H_f^{\circ} (\text{products}) - \Sigma \Delta H_f^{\circ} (\text{reactants})$
$\Delta H^{\circ}_{rxn} = (-635.1 \text{ kJ} - 393.509 \text{ kJ}) - (-1206.9 \text{ kJ})$
$= 178.3$ kJ

**b.** $\Delta H^{\circ}_{rxn} = (-128.2 \text{ kJ}) - (-74.81 \text{ kJ}) = -53.4$ kJ

**c.** $\Delta H^{\circ}_{rxn} = 2(33.18 \text{ kJ}) - (0 \text{ kJ}) = 66.36$ kJ

**d.** $\Delta H^{\circ}_{rxn} = 2(-285.830 \text{ kJ}) - 2(-187.8 \text{ kJ}) =$
$-196.1$ kJ

**e.** $\Delta H^{\circ}_{rxn} = [4(33.18 \text{ kJ}) + 6(-285.830 \text{ kJ})] -$
$4(-46.11) \text{ kJ} = -1397.82$ kJ

**38. a.** $\Delta S_{system}$ is negative because the system's entropy decreases.

**b.** $\Delta S_{system}$ is negative because the system's entropy decreases.

**c.** $\Delta S_{system}$ is positive because the system's entropy increases.

**d.** $\Delta S_{system}$ is negative because the system's entropy decreases.

**39. a.** $\Delta G_{system} = \Delta H_{system} - T\Delta S_{system}$
$\Delta G_{system} = -75\,900 \text{ J} - (273 \text{ K})(138 \text{ J/K})$
$\Delta G_{system} = -75\,900 \text{ J} - 37\,700 \text{ J} = -113\,600$ J
spontaneous reaction

**b.** $\Delta G_{system} = \Delta H_{system} - T\Delta S_{system}$
$\Delta G_{system} = -27\,600 \text{ J} - (535 \text{ K})(-55.2 \text{ J/K})$
$\Delta G_{system} = -27\,600 \text{ J} + 29\,500 \text{ J} = 1900$ J
nonspontaneous reaction

**c.** $\Delta G_{system} = \Delta H_{system} - T\Delta S_{system}$
$\Delta G_{system} = 365\,000 \text{ J} - (388 \text{ K})(-55.2 \text{ J/K})$
$\Delta G_{system} = 365\,000 \text{ J} + 21\,400 \text{ J} = 386\,000$ J
nonspontaneous reaction

## Chapter 17

**1.** Average reaction rate $=$

$- \dfrac{[H_2] \text{ at time } t_2 - [H_2] \text{ at time } t_1}{t_2 - t_1} = - \dfrac{\Delta [H_2]}{\Delta t}$

Average reaction rate $= - \dfrac{0.020M - 0.030M}{4.00 \text{ s} - 0.00 \text{ s}}$

$= - \dfrac{-0.010M}{4.00 \text{ s}} = 0.0025$ mol/(L·s)

**2.** Average reaction rate $=$

$- \dfrac{[Cl_2] \text{ at time } t_2 - [Cl_2] \text{ at time } t_1}{t_2 - t_1} = - \dfrac{\Delta [Cl_2]}{\Delta t}$

Average reaction rate $= - \dfrac{0.040M - 0.050M}{4.00 \text{ s} - 0.00 \text{ s}}$

$= - \dfrac{-0.010M}{4.00 \text{ s}} = 0.0025$ mol/(L·s)

**3.** Average reaction rate $=$

$\dfrac{[HCl] \text{ at time } t_2 - [HCl] \text{ at time } t_1}{t_2 - t_1} = \dfrac{\Delta [HCl]}{\Delta t}$

Average reaction rate $= \dfrac{0.020M - 0.000M}{4.00 \text{ s} - 0.00 \text{ s}}$

$= \dfrac{0.020M}{4.00 \text{ s}} = 0.0050$ mol/(L·s)

**16.** Rate $= k[A]^3$

**17.** Examining trials 1 and 2, doubling [A] has no effect on the rate; therefore, the reaction is zero order in A. Examining trials 2 and 3, doubling [B] doubles the rate; therefore, the reaction is first order in B. Rate $= k[A]^0[B] = k[B]$

**18.** Examining trials 1 and 2, doubling $[CH_3CHO]$ increases the rate by a factor of four. Examining trials 2 and 3, doubling $[CH_3CHO]$ again increases the rate by a factor of four. Therefore, the reaction is second order in $CH_3CHO$.
Rate $= k[CH_3CHO]^2$

**24.** $[NO] = 0.00500M$
$[H_2] = 0.00200M$
$k = 2.90 \times 10^2$ L²/(mol²·s)

Rate $= k \, [NO]^2[H_2]$
$= [2.90 \times 10^2 \text{ L}^2/(\text{mol}^2 \cdot \text{s})](0.00500M)^2$
$(0.00200M)$
$= [2.90 \times 10^2 \, \cancel{L^2}/(\cancel{\text{mol}^2} \cdot \text{s})](0.00500 \, \cancel{\text{mol}}/\cancel{L})^2$
$(0.00200 \text{ mol/L})$
$= 1.45 \times 10^{-5}$ mol/(L·s)

**25.** $[NO] = 0.0100M$

$[H_2] = 0.00125M$

$k = 2.90 \times 10^2$ L$^2$/(mol$^2$·s)

Rate $= k\ [NO]^2[H_2]$

$= [2.90 \times 10^2$ L$^2$/(mol$^2$·s)] $(0.0100M)^2(0.00125M)$

$= [2.90 \times 10^2$ L̶$^2$/(mol̶$^2$·s)] $(0.0100$ mol̶/L̶$)^2$
$(0.00125$ mol/L$)$

$= 3.63 \times 10^{-5}$ mol/(L·s)

**26.** $[NO] = 0.00446M$

$[H_2] = 0.00282M$

$k = 2.90 \times 10^2$ L$^2$/(mol$^2$·s)

Rate $= k\ [NO]^2[H_2]$

$= [2.90 \times 10^2$ L$^2$/(mol$^2$·s)]$(0.00446M)^2(0.00282M)$

$= [2.90 \times 10^2$ L̶$^2$/(mol̶$^2$·s)]$(0.00446$ mol̶/L̶$)^2$
$(0.00282$ mol/L$)$

Rate $= 1.63 \times 10^{-5}$ mol/(L·s)

## Chapter 18

**1. a.** $K_{eq} = \dfrac{[NO_2]^2}{[N_2O_4]}$

**b.** $K_{eq} = \dfrac{[CH_4][H_2O]}{[CO][H_2]^3}$

**c.** $K_{eq} = \dfrac{[H_2]^2[S_2]}{[H_2S]^2}$

**2. a.** $K_{eq} = [C_{10}H_8(g)]$

**b.** $K_{eq} = [CO_2(g)]$

**c.** $K_{eq} = [H_2O(g)]$

**d.** $K_{eq} = \dfrac{[H_2(g)][CO(g)]}{[H_2O(g)]}$

**e.** $K_{eq} = \dfrac{[CO_2(g)]}{[CO(g)]}$

**3.** $K_{eq} = \dfrac{[NO_2]^2}{[N_2O_4]} = \dfrac{(0.0627)^2}{(0.0185)} = 0.213$

**4.** $K_{eq} = \dfrac{[CH_4][O_2H]}{[CO][H_2]^3} = \dfrac{(0.0387)(0.0387)}{(0.0613)(0.1839)^3} = 3.93$

**16. a.** $K_{eq} = \dfrac{[CH_3OH]}{[CO][H_2]^2}$

$10.5 = \dfrac{(1.32)}{[CO](0.933)^2}$

$[CO] = 0.144M$

**b.** $K_{eq} = \dfrac{[CH_3OH]}{[CO][H_2]^2}$

$10.5 = \dfrac{(0.325)}{(1.09)[H_2]^2}$

$[H_2] = 0.169M$

**c.** $K_{eq} = \dfrac{[CH_3OH]}{[CO][H_2]^2}$

$10.5 = \dfrac{[CH_3OH]}{(3.85)(0.0661)^2}$

$[CH_3OH] = 0.177M$

**17. a.**   $PbCrO_4(s) \rightleftharpoons Pb^{2+}(aq) + CrO_4{}^{2-}(aq)$
   $s$ mol/L dissolves     $s$ mol/L     $s$ mol/L

$K_{sp} = [Pb^{2+}][CrO_4{}^{2-}]$

$2.3 \times 10^{-13} = (s)(s) = s^2$

$s = \sqrt{2.3 \times 10^{-13}} = 4.8 \times 10^{-7}M$

**b.**   $AgCl(s) \rightleftharpoons Ag^+(aq) + Cl^-(aq)$
   $s$ mol/L dissolves     $s$ mol/L     $s$ mol/L

$K_{sp} = [Ag^+][Cl^-]$

$1.8 \times 10^{-10} = (s)(s) = s^2$

$s = \sqrt{1.8 \times 10^{-10}} = 1.3 \times 10^{-5}M$

**c.**   $CaCO_3(s) \rightleftharpoons Ca^{2+}(aq) + CO_3{}^{2-}(aq)$
   $s$ mol/L dissolves     $s$ mol/L     $s$ mol/L

$K_{sp} = [Ca^{2+}][CO_3{}^{2-}]$

$3.4 \times 10^{-9} = (s)(s) = s^2$

$s = \sqrt{3.4 \times 10^{-9}} = 5.8 \times 10^{-5}M$

**d.**   $CaSO_4(s) \rightleftharpoons Ca^{2+}(aq) + SO_4{}^{2-}(aq)$
   $s$ mol/L dissolves     $s$ mol/L     $s$ mol/L

$K_{sp} = [Ca^{2+}][SO_4{}^{2-}]$

$4.9 \times 10^{-5} = (s)(s) = s^2$

$s = \sqrt{4.9 \times 10^{-5}} = 7.0 \times 10^{-3}M$

**18. a.**   $AgBr(s) \rightleftharpoons Ag^+(aq) + Br^-(aq)$
   $s$ mol/L dissolves     $s$ mol/L     $s$ mol/L

$K_{sp} = [Ag^+][Br^-]$

$5.4 \times 10^{-13} = (s)(s) = s^2$

$s = \sqrt{5.4 \times 10^{-13}} = 7.3 \times 10^{-7}M = [Ag^+]$

**b.**   $CaF_2(s) \rightleftharpoons Ca^{2+}(aq) + 2F^-(aq)$
   $s$ mol/L dissolves     $s$ mol/L     $2s$ mol/L

$[CaF_2] = \dfrac{1}{2}[F^-]$

$K_{sp} = [Ca^{2+}][F^-]^2$

$3.5 \times 10^{-11} = (s)(2s)^2 = 4s^3$

$s = \sqrt[3]{\dfrac{3.5 \times 10^{-11}}{4}} = 2.1 \times 10^{-4}M$

$\dfrac{1}{2}[F^-] = 2.1 \times 10^{-4}M$

$[F^-] = 4.2 \times 10^{-4}M$

Solutions

**c.**  $Ag_2CrO_4(s) \rightleftharpoons 2Ag^+(aq) + CrO_4^{2-}(aq)$
 $s$ mol/L dissolves    $2s$ mol/L    $s$ mol/L

$$[Ag_2CrO_4] = \frac{1}{2}[Ag^+]$$

$$K_{sp} = [Ag^+]^2[CrO_4^{2-}]$$

$$1.1 \times 10^{-12} = (2s)^2(s) = 4s^3$$

$$s = \sqrt[3]{\frac{1.1 \times 10^{-12}}{4}} = 6.5 \times 10^{-5} M$$

$$\frac{1}{2}[Ag^+] = 6.5 \times 10^{-5} M$$

$$[Ag^+] = 1.3 \times 10^{-4} M$$

**d.**  $PbI_2(s) \rightleftharpoons Pb^{2+}(aq) + 2I^-(aq)$
 $s$ mol/L dissolves    $s$ mol/L    $2s$ mol/L

$$K_{sp} = [Pb^{2+}][I^-]^2$$

$$9.8 \times 10^{-9} = (s)(2s)^2 = 4s^3$$

$$s = \sqrt[3]{\frac{9.8 \times 10^{-9}}{4}} = 1.3 \times 10^{-3} M$$

**19. a.** $PbF_2(s) \rightleftharpoons Pb^{2+}(aq) + 2F^-(aq)$

$Q_{sp} = [Pb^{2+}][F^-]^2 = (0.050M)(0.015M)^2$

$= 1.12 \times 10^{-5}$

$K_{sp} = 3.3 \times 10^{-8}$

$Q_{sp} > K_{sp}$ so a precipitate will form.

**b.** $Ag_2SO_4(s) \rightleftharpoons 2Ag^+(aq) + SO_4^{2-}(aq)$

$Q_{sp} = [Ag^+]^2[SO_4^{2-}] = (0.0050M)^2(0.125M)$

$= 3.1 \times 10^{-6}$

$K_{sp} = 1.2 \times 10^{-5}$

$Q_{sp} < K_{sp}$ so no precipitate will form.

**c.** $Mg(OH)_2(s) \rightleftharpoons Mg^{2+}(aq) + 2OH^-(aq)$

$Q_{sp} = [Mg^{2+}][OH^-]^2 = (0.10M)(0.00125M)^2$

$= 1.56 \times 10^{-7}$

$K_{sp} = 5.6 \times 10^{-12}$

$Q_{sp} > K_{sp}$ so a precipitate will form.

## Chapter 19

**1. a.** $Mg(s) + 2HNO_3(aq) \rightarrow Mg(NO_3)_2(aq) + H_2(g)$
**b.** $2Al(s) + 3H_2SO_4(aq) \rightarrow Al_2(SO_4)_3(aq) + 3H_2(g)$
**c.** $CaCO_3(s) + 2HBr(aq) \rightarrow CaBr_2(aq) + H_2O(l) + CO_2(g)$
**d.** $KHCO_3(s) + HCl(aq) \rightarrow KCl(aq) + H_2O(l) + CO_2(g)$

**2.**

| | Acid | Conjugate base | Base | Conjugate acid |
|---|---|---|---|---|
| **a.** | $NH_4^+$ | $NH_3$ | $OH^-$ | $H_2O$ |
| **b.** | $HBr$ | $Br^-$ | $H_2O$ | $H_3O^+$ |
| **c.** | $H_2O$ | $OH^-$ | $CO_3^{2-}$ | $HCO_3^-$ |
| **d.** | $HSO_4^-$ | $SO_4^{2-}$ | $H_2O$ | $H_3O^+$ |

**3. a.** $H_2Se(aq) + H_2O(l) \rightleftharpoons H_3O^+(aq) + HSe^-(aq)$
$HSe^-(aq) + H_2O(l) \rightleftharpoons H_3O^+(aq) + Se^{2-}(aq)$

**b.** $H_3AsO_4(aq) + H_2O(l) \rightleftharpoons H_3O^+(aq) + H_2AsO_4^-(aq)$

$H_2AsO_4^-(aq) + H_2O(l) \rightleftharpoons H_3O^+(aq) + HAsO_4^{2-}(aq)$

$HAsO_4^{2-}(aq) + H_2O(l) \rightleftharpoons H_3O^+(aq) + AsO_4^{3-}(aq)$

**c.** $H_2SO_3(aq) + H_2O(l) \rightleftharpoons H_3O^+(aq) + HSO_3^-(aq)$
$HSO_3^-(aq) + H_2O(l) \rightleftharpoons H_3O^+(aq) + SO_3^{2-}(aq)$

**10. a.** $HClO_2(aq) + H_2O(l) \rightleftharpoons H_3O^+(aq) + ClO_2^-(aq)$
$$K_a = \frac{[H_3O^+][ClO_2^-]}{[HClO_2]}$$

**b.** $HNO_2(aq) + H_2O(l) \rightleftharpoons H_3O^+(aq) + NO_2^-(aq)$
$$K_a = \frac{[H_3O^+][NO_2^-]}{[HNO_2]}$$

**c.** $HIO(aq) + H_2O(l) \rightleftharpoons H_3O^+(aq) + IO^-(aq)$
$$K_a = \frac{[H_3O^+][IO^-]}{[HIO]}$$

**11. a.** $C_6H_{13}NH_2(aq) + H_2O(l) \rightleftharpoons C_6H_{13}NH_3^+(aq) + OH^-(aq)$
$$K_b = \frac{[C_6H_{13}NH_3^+][OH^-]}{[C_6H_{13}NH_2]}$$

**b.** $C_3H_7NH_2(aq) + H_2O(l) \rightleftharpoons C_3H_7NH_3+(aq) + OH^-(aq)$
$$K_b = \frac{[C_3H_7NH_3^+][OH^-]}{[C_3H_7NH_2]}$$

**c.** $CO_3^{2-}(aq) + H_2O(l) \rightleftharpoons HCO_3^-(aq) + OH^-(aq)$
$$K_b = \frac{[HCO_3^-][OH^-]}{[CO_3^{2-}]}$$

**d.** $HSO_3^-(aq) + H_2O(l) \rightleftharpoons H_2SO_3(aq) + OH^-(aq)$

$$K_b = \frac{[H_2SO_3^-][OH^-]}{[HSO_3^-]}$$

**18. a.** $[H^+] = 1.0 \times 10^{-13}M$

$K_w = [H^+][OH^-]$

$1.0 \times 10^{-14} = (1.0 \times 10^{-13})[OH^-]$

$\dfrac{1.0 \times 10^{-14}}{1.0 \times 10^{-13}} = \dfrac{(1.0 \times 10^{-13})[OH^-]}{1.0 \times 10^{-13}}$

$[OH^-] = 1.0 \times 10^{-1}M$

$[OH^-] > [H^+]$, so the solution is basic.

**b.** $[OH^-] = 1.0 \times 10^{-7}M$

$K_w = [H^+][OH^-]$

$1.0 \times 10^{-14} = [H^+](1.0 \times 10^{-7})$

$\dfrac{1.0 \times 10^{-14}}{1.0 \times 10^{-7}} = \dfrac{[H^+](1.0 \times 10^{-7})}{1.0 \times 10^{-7}}$

$[H^+] = 1.0 \times 10^{-7}M$

$[OH^-] = [H^+]$, so the solution is neutral.

**c.** $[OH^-] = 1.0 \times 10^{-3}M$

$K_w = [H+][OH^-]$

$1.0 \times 10^{-14} = [H^+](1.0 \times 10^{-3})$

$\dfrac{1.0 \times 10^{-14}}{1.0 \times 10^{-3}} = \dfrac{[H^+](1.0 \times 10^{-3})}{1.0 \times 10^{-3}}$

$[H^+] = 1.0 \times 10^{-11}M$

$[OH^-] > [H^+]$, so the solution is basic.

**19. a.** $pH = -\log(1.0 \times 10^{-2}) = -(-2.00) = 2.00$

**b.** $pH = -\log(3.0 \times 10^{-6}) = -(-5.52) = 5.52$

**c.** $K_w = [H^+][OH^-] = [H^+](8.2 \times 10^{-6})$

$[H^+] = \dfrac{1.0 \times 10^{-14}}{8.2 \times 10^{-6}} = 1.2 \times 10^{-9}$

$pH = -\log(1.2 \times 10^{-9}) = -(-8.92) = 8.92$

**20. a.** $pOH = -\log(1.0 \times 10^{-6}) = -(-6.00) = 6.00$
$pH = 14.00 - pOH = 14.00 - 6.00 = 8.00$

**b.** $pOH = -\log(6.5 \times 10^{-4}) = -(-3.19) = 3.19$
$pH = 14.00 - pOH = 14.00 - 3.19 = 10.81$

**c.** $pH = -\log(3.6 \times 10^{-9}) = -(-8.44) = 8.44$
$pOH = 14.00 - pH = 14.00 - 8.44 = 5.56$

**d.** $pH = -\log(0.025) = -(-1.60) = 1.60$
$pOH = 14.00 - pH = 14.00 - 1.60 = 12.40$

**21. a.** $[H^+] = \text{antilog}\ (-2.37) = 4.3 \times 10^{-3}M$
$pOH = 14.00 - pH = 14.00 - 2.37 = 11.63$
$[OH^-] = \text{antilog}\ (-11.63) = 2.3 \times 10^{-12}M$

**b.** $[H^+] = \text{antilog}\ (-11.05) = 8.9 \times 10^{-12}M$
$pOH = 14.00 - pH = 14.00 - 11.05 = 2.95$
$[OH^-] = \text{antilog}\ (-2.95) = 1.1 \times 10^{-3}M$

**c.** $[H^+] = \text{antilog}\ (-6.50) = 3.2 \times 10^{-7}M$
$pOH = 14.00 - pH = 14.00 - 6.50 = 7.50$

$[OH^-] = \text{antilog}\ (-7.50) = 3.2 \times 10^{-8}M$

**22. a.** $[H^+] = [HI] \times \dfrac{1\ \text{mol}\ H^+}{1\ \text{mol}\ HI} = 1.0M$

$pH = -\log(1.0) = 0.00$

**b.** $[H^+] = [HNO_3] \times \dfrac{1\ \text{mol}\ H^+}{1\ \text{mol}\ HNO_3} = 0.050M$

$pH = -\log(0.050) = 1.30$

**c.** $[OH^-] = [KOH] \times \dfrac{1\ \text{mol}\ OH^-}{1\ \text{mol}\ KOH} = 1.0M$

$pOH = -\log(1.0) = 0.00$

$pH = 14.00 - 0.00 = 14.00$

**d.** $[OH^-] = [Mg(OH)_2] \times \dfrac{2\ \text{mol}\ OH^-}{1\ \text{mol}\ Mg(OH)_2}$

$= 4.8 \times 10^{-5}M$

$pOH = -\log(4.8 \times 10^{-5}) = 4.32$

$pH = 14.00 - 4.32 = 9.68$

**23. a.** $K_a = \dfrac{[H^+][H_2AsO_4]}{[H_3AsO_4]}$

$[H^+] = \text{antilog}\ (-1.50) = 3.2 \times 10^{-2}M$

$[H_3AsO_4] = [H^+] = 3.2 \times 10^{-2}M$

$[H_3AsO_4] = 0.220M - 3.2 \times 10^{-2}M = 0.188M$

$K_a = \dfrac{(3.2 \times 10^{-2})(3.2 \times 10^{-2})}{0.188}$

$= 5.4 \times 10^{-3}$

**b.** $K_a = \dfrac{[H^+][ClO_2^-]}{[HClO_2]}$

$[H^+] = \text{antilog}\ (-1.80) = 1.6 \times 10^{-2}M$

$[ClO_2] = [H^+] = 1.6 \times 10^{-2}M$

$[HClO_2] = 0.0.0400M - 1.6 \times 10^{-2}M$
$= 0.024M$

$K_a = \dfrac{(1.6 \times 10^{-2})(1.6 \times 10^{-2})}{0.024}$

$= 1.1 \times 10^{-2}$

**29. a.** $HNO_3(aq) + CsOH(aq) \rightarrow CsNO_3(aq) + H_2O(l)$
**b.** $2HBr(aq) + Ca(OH)_2(aq) \rightarrow CaBr_2(aq) + 2H_2O(l)$
**c.** $H_2SO_4(aq) + 2KOH(aq) \rightarrow K_2SO_4(aq) + 2H_2O(l)$
**d.** $CH_3COOH(aq) + NH_4OH(aq) \rightarrow$
$CH_3COONH_4(aq) + H_2O(l)$

Solutions

**30.** $26.4 \text{ mL HBr} \times \dfrac{1 \text{ L}}{1000 \text{ mL}} \times \dfrac{0.250 \text{ mol HBr}}{1 \text{ L HBr}}$

$= 6.60 \times 10^{-3} \text{ mol HBr}$

$6.60 \times 10^{-3} \text{ mol HBr} \times \dfrac{1 \text{ mol CsOH}}{1 \text{ mol HBr}}$

$= 6.60 \times 10^{-3} \text{ mol CsOH}$

$M_{\text{CsOH}} = \dfrac{6.60 \times 10^{-3} \text{ mol CsOH}}{0.0300 \text{ L CsOH}} = 0.220M$

**31.** $43.33 \text{ mL KOH} \times \dfrac{1 \text{ L}}{1000 \text{ mL}} \times \dfrac{0.1000 \text{ mol KOH}}{1 \text{ L KOH}}$

$= 4.333 \times 10^{-3} \text{ mol KOH}$

$4.333 \times 10^{-3} \text{ mol KOH} \times \dfrac{1 \text{ mol HNO}_3}{1 \text{ mol KOH}}$

$= 4.333 \times 10^{-3} \text{ mol HNO}_3$

$M_{\text{HNO}_3} = \dfrac{4.333 \times 10^{-3} \text{ mol HNO}_3}{0.02000 \text{ L HNO}_3} = 0.2167M$

**32.** $49.90 \text{ mL HCl} \times \dfrac{1 \text{ L}}{1000 \text{ mL}} \times \dfrac{0.5900 \text{ mol HCl}}{1 \text{ L HCl}}$

$= 2.944 \times 10^{-2} \text{ mol HCl}$

$2.944 \times 10^{-2} \text{ mol HCl} \times \dfrac{1 \text{ mol NH}_3}{1 \text{ mol HCl}}$

$= 2.944 \times 10^{-2} \text{ mol NH}_3$

$M_{\text{NH3}} = \dfrac{2.944 \times 10^{-2} \text{ mol NH}_3}{0.02500 \text{ L NH}_3} = 1.178M$

**33. a.** $\text{NH}_4^+(aq) + \text{H}_2\text{O}(l) \rightleftharpoons \text{NH}_3(aq) + \text{H}_3\text{O}^+(aq)$
The solution is acidic.

**b.** $\text{CH}_3\text{COO}^-(aq) + \text{H}_2\text{O}(l) \rightleftharpoons$
$\text{CH}_3\text{COOH}(aq) + \text{OH}^-(aq)$
The solution is basic.

**c.** $\text{SO}_4^{2-}(aq) + \text{H}_2\text{O}(l) \rightleftharpoons \text{HSO}_4^-(aq) + \text{OH}^-(aq)$
The solution is neutral.

**d.** $\text{CO}_3^{2-}(aq) + \text{H}_2\text{O}(l) \rightleftharpoons \text{HCO}_3^-(aq) + \text{OH}^-(aq)$
The solution is basic.

## Chapter 20

**1. a.** reduction
**b.** oxidation
**c.** oxidation
**d.** reduction

**2. a.** oxidized: bromide ion
reduced: chlorine
**b.** oxidized: cerium
reduced: copper(II) ion
**c.** oxidized: zinc
reduced: oxygen

**3. a.** oxidizing agent: iodine
reducing agent: magnesium
**b.** oxidizing agent: hydrogen ion
reducing agent: sodium
**c.** oxidizing agent: chlorine
reducing agent: hydrogen sulfide

**4. a.** $+7$
**b.** $+5$
**c.** $+3$

**5. a.** $-3$
**b.** $+5$
**c.** $+6$

**12.**

$$3(+2)$$

$$\overset{+1\ -1}{\text{HCl}} + \overset{+1\ +5\ -2}{\text{HNO}_3} \rightarrow \overset{+1\ -2\ +1}{\text{HOCl}} + \overset{+2\ -2}{\text{NO}} + \overset{+1\ -2}{\text{H}_2\text{O}}$$

$$2(-3)$$

$3\text{HCl} + 2\text{HNO}_3 \rightarrow 3\text{HOCl} + 2\text{NO} + \text{H}_2\text{O}$

**13.**

$$2(+3)$$

$$\overset{+4\ -1}{\text{SnCl}_4} + \overset{0}{\text{Fe}} \rightarrow \overset{+2\ -1}{\text{SnCl}_2} + \overset{+3\ -1}{\text{FeCl}_3}$$

$$3(-2)$$

$3\text{SnCl}_4 + 2\text{Fe} \rightarrow 3\text{SnCl}_2 + 2\text{FeCl}_3$

**14.**

$$4(+3)(2)$$

$$\overset{-3\ +1}{\text{NH}_3(g)} + \overset{+4\ -2}{\text{NO}_2(g)} \rightarrow \overset{0}{\text{N}_2(g)} + \overset{+1\ -2}{\text{H}_2\text{O}(l)}$$

$$3(-4)(2)$$

$8\text{NH}_3(g) + 6\text{NO}_2(g) \rightarrow 7\text{N}_2(g) + 12\text{H}_2\text{O}(l)$

**15.**

$$3(+2)$$

$$\overset{+1\ -2}{\text{H}_2\text{S}(g)} + \overset{+5\ -2}{\text{NO}_3^-(aq)} \rightarrow \overset{0}{\text{S}(s)} + \overset{+2\ -2}{\text{NO}(g)}$$

$$2(-3)$$

$2\text{H}^+(aq) + 3\text{H}_2\text{S}(g) + 2\text{NO}_3^-(aq) \rightarrow$
$3\text{S}(s) + 2\text{NO}(g) + 4\text{H}_2\text{O}(l)$

**16.**

$$3(+1)(2)$$

$$\overset{+6\;-2}{Cr_2O_7{}^{2-}}(aq) + 2\overset{-1}{I^-}(aq) \rightarrow \overset{+3}{Cr^{3+}}(aq) + \overset{0}{I_2}(s)$$

$$-3(2)$$

$$14H^+(aq) + Cr_2O_7{}^{2-}(aq) + 6I^-(aq) \rightarrow$$
$$2Cr^{3+}(aq) + 3I_2(s) + 7H_2O(l)$$

**17.**

$$3(+1)(2)$$

$$2\overset{-1}{I^-} + \overset{+7\;-2}{MnO_4} \rightarrow \overset{0}{I_2} + \overset{+4\;-2}{MnO_2}$$

$$(-3)(2)$$

$$6I^-(aq) + 2MnO_4{}^-(aq) + 4H_2O(l) \rightarrow$$
$$3I_2(s) + 2MnO_2(s) + 8OH^-(aq)$$

**24.** $2I^-(aq) \rightarrow I_2(s) + 2e^-$ (oxidation)

$$14H^+(aq) + 6e^- + Cr_2O7_2{}^-(aq) \rightarrow$$
$$2Cr_3{}^+(aq) + 7H_2O(l) \text{ (reduction)}$$

Multiply oxidation half-reaction by 3 and add to reduction half-reaction

$$14H^+(aq) + 6e^- + Cr_2O_7{}^{2-}(aq) + 6I^-(aq) \rightarrow$$
$$3I_2(s) + 2Cr^{3+}(aq) + 7H_2O(l) + 6e^-$$

$$14H^+(aq) + Cr_2O_7{}^{2-}(aq) + 6I^-(aq) \rightarrow$$
$$3I_2(s) + 2Cr^{3+}(aq) + 7H_2O(l)$$

**25.** $Mn^{2+}(aq) + 4H_2O(l) \rightarrow$
$MnO_4{}^-(aq) + 5e^- + 8H^+(aq)$ (oxidation)

$$BiO_3{}^-(aq) + 3e^- + 6H^+(aq) \rightarrow$$
$$Bi^{2+}(aq) + 3H_2O(l) \text{ (reduction)}$$

Multiply oxidation half-reaction. Multiply reduction half-reaction by 5 and add to oxidation half-reaction.

$$3Mn^{2+}(aq) + 12H_2O(l) + 5BiO_3{}^-(aq) + 15e^- +$$
$$30H^+(aq) \rightarrow 3MnO_4{}^-(aq) + 15e^- + 24H^+(aq) +$$
$$5Bi^{2+}(aq) + 15H_2O(l)$$

$$3Mn^{2+}(aq) + 5BiO_3{}^-(aq) + 6H^+(aq) \rightarrow$$
$$3MnO_4{}^-(aq) + 5Bi^{2+}(aq) + 3H_2O(l)$$

**26.** $6OH^-(aq) + N_2O(g) \rightarrow 2NO_2{}^-(aq) + 4e^- + 3H_2O(l)$
(oxidation)

$$ClO^-(aq) + 2e^- + H_2O(l) \rightarrow Cl^-(aq) + 2OH^-(aq)$$
(reduction)

Multiply reduction half-reaction by 2 and add to oxidation half-reaction.

$$6OH^-(aq) + N_2O(g) + 2ClO^-(aq) + 4e^- + 2H_2O(l)$$
$$\rightarrow 2NO_2{}^-(aq) + 4e^- + 3H_2O(l) + 2Cl^-(aq) +$$
$$4OH^-(aq)$$

$$N_2O(g) + 2ClO^-(aq) + 2OH^-(aq) \rightarrow 2NO_2{}^-(aq) +$$
$$2Cl^-(aq) + H_2O(l)$$

## Chapter 21

**1.** $Pt^{2+}(aq) + Sn(s) \rightarrow Pt(s) + Sn^{2+}(aq)$
$E^0_{cell} = 1.18 \text{ V} - (-0.1375 \text{ V})$
$E^0_{cell} = 1.32 \text{ V}$
$Sn|Sn^{2+}||Pt^{2+}|Pt$

**2.** $3Co^{2+}(aq) + 2Cr(s) \rightarrow 3Co(s) + 2Cr^{3+}(aq)$
$E^0_{cell} = (-0.28 \text{ V}) - (-0.744 \text{ V})$
$E^0_{cell} = 0.46 \text{ V}$
$Cr|Cr^{3+}||Co^{2+}|Co$

**3.** $Hg^{2+}(aq) + Cr(s) \rightarrow Hg(l) + Cr^{2+}(aq)$
$E^0_{cell} = 0.851 \text{ V} - (-0.913 \text{ V})$
$E^0_{cell} = 1.764 \text{ V}$
$Cr|Cr^{2+}||Hg^{2+}|Hg$

**4.** $E^0_{cell} = (0.521 \text{ V}) - (-0.1375 \text{ V})$
$E^0_{cell} = 0.659 \text{ V}$
$E^0_{cell} > 0$  spontaneous

**5.** $E^0_{cell} = (-0.1262 \text{ V}) - (-2.372 \text{ V})$
$E^0_{cell} = 2.246 \text{ V}$
$E^0_{cell} > 0$  spontaneous

**6.** $E^0_{cell} = (0.920 \text{ V}) - (1.507 \text{ V})$
$E^0_{cell} = -0.587 \text{ V}$
$E^0_{cell} < 0$  not spontaneous

**7.** $E^0_{cell} = (-0.28 \text{ V}) - 2.010 \text{ V}$
$E^0_{cell} = -2.29 \text{ V}$
$E^0_{cell} < 0$  not spontaneous

Solutions

# Chapter 22

**1. a.**  2,4-dimethylhexane
  **b.** 2,4,7-trimethylnonane
  **c.** 2,2,4-trimethylpentane

**2. a.**

$$CH_3CHCHCH_2CH(CH_2)_4CH_3$$

with $CH_3$ and $C_3H_7$ substituents above, and $CH_3$ below

**b.**

$$CH_3CH_2CHCHCHCH_2CH_2CH_3$$

with $C_2H_5$ and $C_2H_5$ substituents above, and $C_2H_5$ below

**10. a.**  methylcyclopentane
  **b.** 2-ethyl-1,4-dimethylcyclohexane
  **c.** 1,3-diethylcyclobutane

**11. a.**

cyclopentane with $C_2H_5$ and $C_3H_7$ substituents

**b.**

cyclohexane with $CH_3$, $CH_3$, $CH_3$, $CH_3$ substituents

**18. a.**  4-methyl-2-pentene
  **b.** 2,2,6-trimethyl-3-octene

**19.**

$$CH_2{=}CHC{=}CHCH_3$$

# Chapter 23

**1.** 2,3-difluorobutane

**2.** 1-bromo-5-chloropentane

**3.** 1,3-dibromo-2-chlorobenzene

# Chapter 24

No practice problems

## Chapter 25

**6.** $^{15}_{8}O \rightarrow ^{0}_{1}\beta + ^{15}_{7}N$

**7.** $^{231}_{90}Th \rightarrow ^{231}_{91}Pa + ^{0}_{-1}\beta$, beta decay

**8.** $^{97}_{40}Zr \rightarrow ^{0}_{-1}\beta + ^{97}_{41}Nb$

**9. a.** $^{142}_{61}Pm + ^{0}_{-1}e \rightarrow ^{142}_{60}Nd$
   **b.** $^{218}_{84}Po \rightarrow ^{4}_{2}He + ^{214}_{82}Pb$
   **c.** $^{226}_{88}Ra \rightarrow ^{222}_{86}Rn + ^{4}_{2}He$

**15.** $^{27}_{13}Al + ^{1}_{0}n \rightarrow ^{24}_{11}Na + ^{4}_{2}He$

**16.** $^{239}_{94}Pu + ^{4}_{2}He \rightarrow ^{242}_{96}Cm + ^{1}_{0}n$

**17.** amount remaining $= (10.0 \text{ mg})\left(\frac{1}{2}\right)^{n}$

For $n = 1$, amount remaining $= (10.0 \text{ mg})\left(\frac{1}{2}\right)^{1}$
$= 5.00$ mg

For $n = 2$, amount remaining $= (10.0 \text{ mg})\left(\frac{1}{2}\right)^{2}$
$= 2.50$ mg

For $n = 3$, amount remaining $= (10.0 \text{ mg})\left(\frac{1}{2}\right)^{3}$
$= 1.25$ mg

**18.** amount remaining $= 25.0$ mg
$= (\text{initial amount})\left(\frac{1}{2}\right)^{5}$
initial amount $= (25.0 \text{ mg})(2)^{5} = 8.00 \times 10^{2}$ mg

**19.** half-life $= 163.7 \ \mu s$

$n = (818 \ \mu s) \times \dfrac{1 \text{ half-life}}{163.7 \ \mu s} = 5.00$ half-lives

amount remaining $= (1.0 \text{ g})\left(\frac{1}{2}\right)^{5.00} = 0.031$ g

## Chapter 26

No practice problems

**Lab 1**

## Materials

- Horoscopes can be found in many magazines and newspapers.
- Students can white out zodiac signs and birth dates with liquid correction fluid, but caution them to be thorough to prevent cheating.

## Safety Precautions

- Caution students against interviewing strangers.
- Caution students against calling astrologers using high-priced phone numbers.

## Teaching Strategies

- Challenge students to establish experimental controls that prevent cheating.
- Students also can collect horoscopes from several sources to compare the predictions of specific signs from the different sources to search for contradictions.

## Conclude and Apply

1. Answers will vary but should be about 8 percent.
2. 8.3%
3. Answers will vary but may include test subjects being familiar with the horoscope, test subjects being tipped off by other test subjects, or test subjects seeing the code list.
4. Students should find that all tightly controlled experiments to test astrology have concluded that its predictive ability is no better than chance.

 **From your Kitchen, Junk Drawer, or Yard**

## 1 Testing Predictions

**Real-World Question** How can predictions be tested scientifically?

### Possible Materials

- horoscope from previous week
- scissors
- transparent tape
- white paper
- liquid correction fluid

### Procedure

1. Obtain a horoscope from last week and cut out the predictions for each sign. Do not cut out the zodiac signs or birth dates accompanying each prediction.
2. As you cut out a horoscope prediction, write the correct zodiac sign on the back of each prediction.
3. Develop a code for the predictions to allow you to identify them. For example, X11 could refer to the Leo prediction. Maintain a list of your codes during the experiment.
4. Scramble your predictions and tape them to a sheet of white paper. Write each prediction's code above it.
5. Ask 10 people to read all the predictions and ask each person to choose the one that best matched his or her life events from the previous week.

### Conclude and Apply

1. Calculate the percentage of people who chose the correct sign.
2. Calculate the chances of a person randomly choosing his or her correct sign.
3. Identify the experimental error in your experiment.
4. Research other strictly controlled experiments that have tested the reliability of horoscopes or astrology and write a summary of your findings.

## 2 SI Measurement Around the Home

**Real-World Question** What are the SI measurements of common items or dimensions in your home?

### Possible Materials

- measuring cup with SI units
- bathroom scale
- meterstick or metric tape measure
- metric ruler
- several empty cans or bottles

### Procedure

1. Use a bathroom scale to weigh yourself, your science textbook, and a gallon of milk. Divide your measurements by 2.2 to calculate the mass of each object in kilograms.
2. Collect several empty containers such as bottles and cans. Use a measuring cup with SI units to measure the volume of each container. Accurately measure each container to the nearest milliliter.
3. Use a meterstick to measure the length, width, and height of your room. Accurately measure each dimension to the nearest millimeter and estimate each length to the nearest tenth of a millimeter.

### Conclude and Apply

1. Convert your metric mass measurements from kilograms to grams.
2. Identify the number of significant figures for each of your volume measurements.
3. Calculate the area of your room in square meters.
4. Infer why you cannot comment on the accuracy or the precision of your answers.

**Try at Home Labs**

 **Lab 2**

## Materials:

- Most kitchen measuring cups have both American units and SI units.

## Safety Precautions

- Caution students not to stand on a chair or table when measuring the heights of their rooms. If the height cannot be reached with a meterstick, a small stepladder should be used with a person holding the ladder for safety.

**Teaching Strategy** Extend this lab by having students calculate the volume of their rooms using the formula V=lwh. Explain that they might have to add or subtract certain room parts if their rooms are not perfect cubes.

## Conclude and Apply

1. Answers will vary. Kilograms are converted to grams by moving the decimal point to the right three places.
2. Answers will vary, but students should include all known numbers and one estimated number in their calculations.
3. Answers will vary, but answers are derived using the formula A=lw.
4. Since none of the measurements have a known value, students cannot compare their values with an accepted value. A discussion on precision would require several measurements for each value.

## 3 Comparing Frozen Liquids

**Real-World Question** How do different kitchen liquids react when placed in a freezer?

**Possible Materials**
- five identical, narrow-necked plastic bottles or photographic film canisters
- large cutting board or cookie sheet
- water
- orange juice
- vinegar
- soft drink
- cooking oil
- freezer

**Procedure**
1. Obtain permission to use the freezer before beginning this activity.
2. Fill one of the clean, plastic containers with water. The water should come to the top brim of the container.
3. Fill the other four containers in the same way with the other four liquids.
4. Place the cutting board or cookie sheet in a freezer so that it is level and place the four containers on the board.
5. Leave the containers in the freezer overnight and observe the effect of the freezer's temperature on each liquid the following day.

**Conclude and Apply**
1. Describe the effect of the colder temperature on each liquid.
2. Infer why the water behaved as it did.
3. Infer why some liquids froze but others did not.

## 4 Comparing Atom Sizes

**Real-World Question** How do the sizes of different atoms and subatomic particles compare?

**Possible Materials**
- metric ruler
- meterstick
- white sheet of paper
- fine tipped black marker
- masking tape or transparent tape
- three plastic milk containers

**Procedure**
1. Using a black marker, draw a 0.1-mm-wide dot on one end of a white sheet of paper. This dot represents the diameter of an electron.
2. Measure a distance of 10 cm from the dot and draw a second dot. The distance between the two dots represents the diameter of a proton or a neutron.
3. Securely tape the paper to the top of a plastic milk container.
4. Measure a distance of 6.2 m from the plastic milk container and place a second plastic milk container. This distance represents the diameter of the smallest atom, a helium atom.
5. Measure a distance of 59.6 m from the first plastic milk container and place a third plastic milk container. This distance represents the diameter of the largest atom, a cesium atom.

**Conclude and Apply**
1. Research the length of a picometer.
2. Calculate the scale you used for this activity if the diameter of a proton equals one picometer.
3. Compare the size of an electron with a proton.
4. Considering the comparative sizes of protons and neutrons with the sizes of atoms, infer what makes up most of an atom.

**Materials**
- Have students use a home freezer at a normal temperature.

**Safety Precautions**
- Do not use glass bottles.
- Caution students not to eat or drink anything involved in the lab.

**Teaching Strategy** Students can extend this experiment by filling containers of different sizes and shapes with water and observing the different patterns formed by the expanding ice in each container.

**Conclude and Apply**
1. The water in the bottle will be frozen solid. Rivulets of ice will form down the sides of the bottle, and a small pool of ice will form on the plate. The vinegar, soft drink, and orange juice will be frozen but slightly slushy. The cooking oil and rubbing alcohol will remain in a liquid state. Only the volume of the ice will change significantly.
2. Water expands when it changes into a solid state instead of contracting like most substances.
3. Each liquid has a different freezing point. The temperature in the freezer is above the freezing points of cooking oil and rubbing alcohol.

**Try at Home Labs**

### Try at Home — Lab 4

**Materials**
- To complete this lab, students will require a large space such as a grass lawn or playing field.
- Students can use brightly colored tennis balls instead of cones.

**Safety Precautions**
- Caution students to handle the metersticks with care.
- Students should not complete this lab near roads, parking lots, or other high-traffic areas.

**Teaching Strategies**
- On windy days, be certain students tape the white sheet of paper securely to the plastic milk carton.
- Extend this lab by having students research why the element helium and not hydrogen has the smallest atoms.

**Conclude and Apply**
1. $1 \times 10^{(-12)}$ m
2. 10 cm: 1 pm
3. A proton has a diameter that is 1,000 times greater than an electron.
4. empty space filled by orbiting electrons

**Try at Home   Lab 5**

## Materials

- Students can also observe the light emanating from a light bulb, but the dark and light bands will not be seen as clearly.

## Safety Precautions

- Caution students to set the candle on a flat surface where it will not tip over.

## Teaching Strategies

- If you use this lab in the classroom, consider conducting it inside an equipment closet in total darkness.
- Encourage students to hold the pencil at various lengths away from their eyes. When held close to the eyes, many dark and light bands will appear, but when the pencils are held farther away from the eyes, the bands will be longer and fewer.

## Conclude and Apply

1. Alternating dark and light bands will appear in the slit between the pencils.
2. Visible light energy travels in waves. When light waves strike the pencils, they bend slightly as they come through the slit causing the waves to alternately reinforce and cancel each other. Reinforced waves will appear as bright bands and canceled light waves will appear as dark bands.

## 5   Observing Light's Wave Nature

**Real-World Question** How can you observe light traveling in waves?

**Possible Materials**

- two pencils
- two pens
- transparent tape
- candle
- candle holder
- matches

### Procedure

1. Obtain permission before beginning this activity.
2. Tape two pencils together lengthwise so that only a 1-mm space separates them.
3. Place a candle in a candleholder. Go into a dark room, light the candle, and set it on a flat surface.
4. Hold the pencils about 25 cm from your eyes and look at the candle light through the slit between the pencils. Slowly squeeze the pencils together and apart and observe what the light coming through the slit looks like.
5. Experiment with viewing the candle light through the slits at different distances from your eyes.

### Conclude and Apply

1. Describe the appearance of the light when you viewed it through the slit between the pencils.
2. Infer why the light appeared as it did.

## 6   Turning Up the Heat

**Real-World Question** What type of metal would be best for making cooking pots?

**Possible Materials**

- stove top or hotplate
- pan
- water
- 30-cm length of iron wire
- 30-cm length of copper wire
- 30-cm length of aluminum wire
- kitchen knife
- butter
- three small paperclips
- thermometer
- stopwatch or watch with second hand

### Procedure

1. Obtain permission to use the stove or hot-plate.
2. Create a data table to record your data.
3. Fill a pan with water. Cut three peanut-sized dabs of butter and insert a wire into each dab. Be certain each dab of butter is equal in size.
4. Insert a small paper clip into each dab of butter so that the clip hangs downward.
5. Place the wires in the water so that the paperclips are all hanging over the edge of the pot in the same direction.
6. Slowly heat the water on a stovetop or hot-plate bringing it to boil.
7. Record the temperature at which the butter melts and the paperclip falls from each wire. Record the amount of time it takes for each paperclip to fall.

### Conclude and Apply

1. Research and define the term "rate of conductivity."
2. Compare the rate of conductivity for the three elements.
3. Infer the relationship between the times you recorded and the rates of conductivity of the elements.
4. Infer which metal would be best suited for making cooking pots.

**Try at Home   Lab 6**

## Materials

- Students can also use a candle and heat pad to heat up the metal wires.
- Students can cut a coat hanger to obtain iron wire. Aluminum and copper wire are available for sale at a hardware store.

- The butter should be refrigerated before the lab.

## Safety Precautions

- Caution students not to eat anything involved in the lab.

## Teaching Strategies

- In class, students can use balances to make certain all the dabs of butter are equal in size.
- Extend this lab by having students

compare the conductivity rates of alloys such as steel and bronze with the conductivity rates of the elemental metals they tested.

## Conclude and Apply

1. The rate of conductivity is how quickly a substance will allow heat to pass through it.
2. Copper has the greater rate of conductivity followed by aluminum and iron. The rate of conductivity

of copper is only slightly higher than aluminum.
3. The time it takes for the butter to melt is inversely proportional to the metal's rate of conductivity.
4. Answers may vary. Copper conducts heat slightly better than aluminum, but aluminum is cheaper and more abundant than copper.

# 7  Amazing Aluminum

**Real-World Question** What properties of aluminum make it a common kitchen element?

**Possible Materials**
- aluminum foil (several sheets)
- iron nail
- glass
- water
- frying pan
- kitchen knife
- butter
- tablespoon
- oven mitt or hot pad
- hammer
- metric ruler
- stove top or hotplate
- plate

**Procedure**
1. Obtain permission to use the stove or hotplate before beginning this activity.
2. Roll up a piece of aluminum foil into a tight ball and drop it into a glass of water. Carefully drop an iron nail into the water. After a week, observe and compare any changes in the two metals.

3. Place a 10-cm × 10-cm square of aluminum foil in a frying pan, place the pan on a stove-top burner or hotplate, and turn the burner to a high setting. Drop a tablespoon of butter on the foil.  Observe the butter for five minutes. Use an oven mitt to take the aluminum foil out of the pan and place it on a plate. After one minute, quickly touch the foil to test how hot it is.
4. On a workbench or other hard surface, hammer a 2-cm × 2-cm space on the edge of a sheet of wrinkled aluminum foil. Compare how easy it is to rip the hammered foil with a section of foil that was not hammered.

**Conclude and Apply**
1. Compare the appearance of the iron nail and aluminum foil after each was submerged in water for a week. What do you observe?
2. Infer why the hammered aluminum foil tore easier than the foil that was hammered.
3. Infer what properties make aluminum a desirable element for aluminum foil, pots, and pans.

# 8  Comparing Sport Drink Electrolytes

**Real-World Question** Which sport drink has the greatest amounts of electrolytes?

**Possible Materials**
- several bottles of different brand name sport drinks
- graph paper
- color pencils
- metric ruler

**Procedure**
1. Research the three major electrolytes needed for good health.
2. Create a data table to record the amount of electrolytes found in several brand name sport drinks.

3. Obtain several bottles of different sport drink brands and read the nutrition facts chart on the back of each bottle.
4. Compare the amounts of the three major electrolytes found in each sport drink brand and record the amounts in your data table. Be certain you compare electrolyte amounts for equal volumes.

**Conclude and Apply**
1. Create a circle graph or bar graph comparing the amounts of electrolytes found in the sport drinks you compared.
2. Compare the amounts of electrolytes found in the major brands of sport drinks.
3. Infer why a sport drink should not have sodium.

Glossary    **955**

---

**Try at Home    Lab 7**

**Materials**
- Students can also hammer the foil on a thick cutting board.

**Safety Precautions**
- Students should exercise care when handling hot materials and using a heat source.
- Students should not hammer aluminum foil on kitchen counters or other breakable surfaces.
- Have students use caution when hammering the foil.

**Teaching Strategies**
- Have students research the abundance of aluminum compared to other metals with similar properties, such as silver and gold. Aluminum is the most abundant metal in Earth's crust, making it an inexpensive material.
- Have students research the benefits of recycling aluminum compared to extracting the metal from the ground.

**Conclude and Apply**
1. The aluminum will be free of corrosion, but the nail will have started to rust.
2. Aluminum is highly malleable, making it easier to hammer into a thinner sheet.
3. Aluminum is lightweight, malleable, conducts heat well, and resists corrosion.

amount with the potassium amounts found in the sport drinks. The average banana has 450 mg of potassium.

**Conclude and Apply**
1. Students should draw separate circle graphs for each electrolyte, but different-colored bars can be used to compare the different electrolytes on a bar graph.
2. Answers may vary. Different brands of sport drinks will vary in potassium levels (for a 355-mL sample) from 24–584 mg, sodium levels from 12–282 mg, and magnesium levels from 0–210 mg.
3. Excess sodium is a health risk, and many foods consumed by Americans already are high in sodium.

---

**Try at Home    Lab 8**

**Materials**
- Encourage students to trade empty bottles of their favorite sport drinks to collect nutrition facts charts without purchasing extra drinks.

**Safety Precautions**
- Caution students that excess sodium causes high blood pressure and cardiovascular disease. A normal diet is sufficient for a person's sodium needs.

**Teaching Strategies**
- Have students research whether or not they need to drink a sport drink given their current levels of

physical activity. Intense physical activity of more than an hour requires the body to replenish its electrolyte supply. Water is sufficient after activities of less than one hour in duration.
- The most important electrolyte to replace after intense physical activity is potassium. Have students research the amount of potassium found in a banana and compare the

## Lab 9

### Materials
- Any type of kitchen oil can be used for the lab.

### Teaching Strategies
- Students also can place a polystyrene cup in a shallow dish of acetone to watch it melt.
- To observe the speed of the chemical reaction, students can drop a handful of peanuts into the acetone so that they stack up above the liquid.
- Dispose of the acetone by diluting it with water to ten times its volume and slowly pour it down the drain.
- The residue of the polystyrene can be reclaimed, washed, and dried.

### Conclude and Apply
1. The polystyrene peanuts will not react with the water, cooking oil, or rubbing alcohol, but they will dissolve and disappear in the acetone.
2. The water, cooking oil, and rubbing alcohol will not break the covalent bonds holding the polystyrene polymer together, but the acetone does break the bonds that hold the molecules together.

## 9   Breaking Covalent Bonds

**Real-World Question** What liquids will break the covalent bonds of polystyrene?

**Possible Materials**
- polystyrene packing peanuts or polystyrene cups
- 500-mL container
- acetone or nail polish remover
- shallow dish
- rubbing alcohol
- water
- cooking oil
- measuring cup

**Procedure**
1. Pour 200 mL of water into a 500-mL container.
2. Drop a polystyrene packing peanut into the water and observe how the polystyrene and water react.
3. Thoroughly wash out the glass and repeat steps 1 and 2 using cooking oil, rubbing alcohol, and acetone or nail polish remover.
4. Drop several packing peanuts into any of the liquids that cause a chemical reaction with the polystyrene peanuts and observe what happens to them.

**Conclude and Apply**
1. Describe the reaction between the polystyrene peanuts and each of the four liquids.
2. Infer why the polystyrene reacted as it did with each of the liquids.

## 10   Preventing a Chemical Reaction

**Real-World Question** How can the chemical reaction that turns apples brown be prevented?

**Possible Materials**
- seven identical glasses
- measuring cup
- bottled water (large bottle)
- apple
- 100-mg vitamin C tablets
- wax paper
- rolling pin
- paper towels
- kitchen knife
- masking tape
- permanent black marker

**Procedure**
1. Measure and pour 200 mL of water into each of the glasses.
2. Label glass #1 *no vitamin C*, glass #2 *100 mg*, glass #3 *200 mg*, glass #4 *500 mg*, glass #5 *1 000 mg*, glass #6 *2 000 mg*, and glass #7 *3 000 mg*.
3. Place a 100-mg vitamin C tablet between two sheets of wax paper and use a rolling pin to grind the tablet into powder.
4. Place the powder into glass #2 and stir the mixture vigorously.
5. Repeat steps 3 and 4 for glasses 3, 4, 5, 6, and 7 using the appropriate masses of vitamin C.
6. Cut seven equal-sized wedges of apple and immediately place an apple wedge into each glass. Cut wedges large enough to float with the skin facing upward in the mixture.
7. After 5 minutes, lay the wedges on paper towels in front of the beakers in which they were soaking. Observe the apples every 5 minutes for 45 minutes.

**Conclude and Apply**
1. Describe the results of your experiment.
2. Research why apple tissues turn brown in the presence of air.
3. Infer why vitamin C prevents apples from turning brown.

### Materials
- Brand-name vitamin C tablets will dissolve quicker than generic-brand vitamin C.

### Safety Precautions
- Caution students not to eat or drink anything involved in the lab.

**Teaching Strategy** Extend this lab by having students design an experiment to test different dilutions of orange juice.

### Conclude and Apply
1. Times may vary, but after 5 minutes, apples 1, 2, and 3 will turn light brown, and the other apple wedges will remain white. After 10 minutes, apple 4 will start to brown; after 15 minutes, apple 5 will start browning, and after 45 minutes all the apple wedges will start to brown.
2. When exposed to air, apple tissues undergo a chemical reaction called oxidation that turns the tissues brown.
3. Vitamin C is an antioxidant that prevents the chemical reaction from occurring.

## 11  Calculating Carbon Percentages

**Real-World Question** What percentages of common household substances are made of the element carbon?

**Possible Materials** 🪧 🧪 🔬

- nail polish remover
- vitamin C tablet
- barbeque charcoal
- mothballs
- table sugar
- chemical handbook

**Procedure**

1. Research the chemical formulas for the following common household items: nail polish remover (acetone), vitamin C (ascorbic acid), barbeque charcoal, mothballs (naphthalene), and table sugar (sucrose).

2. Calculate the percent composition of the element carbon in the molecules of each substance. Use the formula method outlined in the textbook to calculate your answers.

**Conclude and Apply**

1. List the percentage of carbon that makes up the molecules of each substance.

2. Calculate the mass of carbon in a 200-g sample of table sugar.

## 12  Baking Soda Stoichiometry

**Real-World Question** How many moles of baking soda will react with 1 mL of vinegar?

**Possible Materials** 🔬 👓 🖐

- vinegar
- sodium bicarbonate (baking soda)
- large bowl
- measuring cup with SI units
- spoon
- kitchen scale

**Procedure**

1. Measure 100 mL of vinegar and pour it into a bowl.

2. Measure 10 g of sodium bicarbonate.

3. Gradually add sodium bicarbonate to the vinegar and observe the reaction that occurs.

4. Continue adding small amounts of the baking soda to the vinegar until there is no longer a reaction.

5. Calculate the mass of sodium bicarbonate that reacted with the 100 mL of vinegar.

**Conclude and Apply**

1. Research the chemical formula of sodium bicarbonate (baking soda) and calculate the mass of one mole of the substance.

2. Describe the reaction that occurs when sodium bicarbonate and vinegar are mixed.

3. Calculate the number of moles of sodium bicarbonate that will completely react with 100 mL of vinegar.

Try at Home Labs

**Materials**

- Students do not need the actual substances to complete this lab, but having them will help them match a chemical formula with a specific substance.

**Safety Precautions**

- Caution students to never eat anything involved in the lab.

**Teaching Strategies**

- The formulas for the substances are: nail polish remover (acetone): $CH_3COCH_3$; vitamin C (ascorbic acid): $C_6H_8O_6$; barbeque charcoal: C; mothballs (naphthalene): $C_{10}H_8$; table salt: NaCl, and table sugar (sucrose): $C_{12}H_{22}O_{11}$.

- Extend this lab by having students calculate the percentage of the element carbon in the atmosphere. The major atmospheric gas with carbon is carbon dioxide, which comprises 0.033% of the atmosphere.

**Conclude and Apply**

1. Nail polish remover: 62.1%; vitamin C: 40.9%; barbeque charcoal: 100%; mothballs: 93.8%; table salt: 0%, and table sugar: 42.1%.

2. 84.2 g

**Materials**

- Explain to students that the vinegar sold in grocery stores has been reduced to 5 percent acidity with water.

**Safety Precautions**

- Caution students to never eat or drink anything involved in the lab.

**Teaching Strategies**

- Extend this lab by having students research the chemical equation that takes place between vinegar and baking soda.

- If students use kitchen scales at home, explain that 1 ounce equals 28 grams.

**Conclude and Apply**

1. $NaHCO_3$/84 grams

2. The liquid fizzes producing white bubbles.

3. Answers may vary but approximately 0.003 moles of sodium bicarbonate will react with vinegar.

**Lab 13**

## Materials

- Students can substitute different liquids that are available to them, but caution students against using opaque liquids that will obscure their view of the marble.
- Students can also compare the viscosities of different brands of shampoo.

## Safety Precautions

- Caution students not to eat or drink anything involved in the lab.

## Teaching Strategies

- Review with students the formula $v=d/t$ for calculating speed.
- Encourage students to conduct several test trials by dropping the marble in the water to practice starting and stopping the stopwatch.

## Conclude and Apply

1. Answers may vary. The water and apple juice will have low viscosities, and the honey, maple syrup, and corn syrup will have high viscosities.
2. Answers will vary but may include coordinating the start time with the initial drop of the marble, having the marble hit the side of the glass, and using marbles of different masses.
3. Marble speed and liquid viscosity are inversely proportional.

# 13   Viscosity Race

**Real-World Question** How do the viscosity of different kitchen liquids compare?

**Possible Materials**

- stopwatch or watch with second hand
- five identical, tall, clear glasses
- five marbles (identical size)
- water
- maple syrup
- corn syrup
- apple juice
- honey
- measuring cup
- metric ruler

## Procedure

1. Fill five identical glasses with equal volumes of the five different liquids.
2. Measure the height of each liquid to the nearest millimeter.
3. Create a data table to record the distance (liquid height), time, and speed for each marble traveling through each liquid.
4. Hold a marble just above the water, drop it so that it falls through the water in the center of the glass, and time how long it takes for the marble to reach the bottom of the glass. You may want to have a friend or family member help with this part.
5. Repeat step 4 for the other four liquids.
6. Record your measurements in your data table and calculate the speed of the marble through each liquid.

## Conclude and Apply

1. List the liquids you tested in order of increasing viscosity.
2. Identify possible experimental errors in your experiment.
3. Infer the relationship between marble speed and liquid viscosity.

# 14   Under Pressure

**Real-World Question** Why does the compression of gases affect the density of an object filled with air?

**Possible Materials**

- 2-L clear, plastic bottle with cap (with label removed)
- water
- small dropper (with glass cylinder if possible)

## Procedure

1. Perform this activity at the kitchen sink.
2. Remove the label from a 2-L soda bottle and fill the bottle with water to the brim.
3. Carefully place a small dropper into the bottle without spilling any water so that the dropper floats at the top of the bottle.
4. Replace any water that was lost in the bottle.
5. Screw the bottle cap on tightly and squeeze the sides of the bottle.

## Conclude and Apply

1. Describe what you observed when you squeezed the sides of the bottle.
2. Identify the law demonstrated by this lab.
3. Infer why the dropper behaved the way it did.

**Try at Home Labs**

**Lab 14**

## Safety Precautions

- Caution students not to eat anything involved in the lab.
- Caution students not to squeeze the bottle too hard so that the cap pops off the bottle.

## Teaching Strategies

- For the best results, have students insert the glass portion of the dropper as far as they can into the rubber bulb of the stopper. Students can first experiment with making their droppers float in a glass or bowl of water.
- The bottle must be completely filled for the lab to work properly.

## Conclude and Apply

1. The dropper sank to the bottom of the bottle.
2. Boyle's Law
3. The dropper initially floated because it was less dense than water. The air trapped inside the cylinder of the dropper greatly lowered its density. When the sides of the bottle were squeezed, water was forced up into the cylinder, and according to Boyle's Law, as the pressure on the air increases, its volume decreases. The pressure compressed the air in the dropper's cylinder into a smaller space increasing the density of the dropper. Once enough water entered the cylinder to increase the dropper's density to a value greater than 1 g/mL, the dropper sank.

## 15  Identifying Colloids

**Real-World Question** Which household mixtures are solutions and which are colloids?

**Possible Materials**

- four clear glasses
- flashlight (narrow beam)
- dropper
- spoon
- stirring rod
- iron nail
- bottled water (2 L)
- milk
- cornstarch
- salt

**Procedure**

1. Fill the first glass with bottled water and place an iron nail in the water. Allow the nail to sit in the water overnight.

2. Fill the other three glasses with bottled water.

3. Add a drop of milk to the second glass and stir it vigorously so that the mixture appears clear.

4. Add a small amount of salt to the third glass and an equal amount of cornstarch to the fourth glass. Stir the mixtures until both appear clear.

5. Darken the room and shine the light beam from a flashlight into each mixture. Be certain not to position the beam so that it reflects into your eyes.

**Conclude and Apply**

1. Describe the results of your experiment.

2. Identify which mixtures are solutions and which are colloids.

## 16  Observing Entropy

**Real-World Question** How quickly do common household liquids enter into a state of entropy?

**Possible Materials**

- seven identical, clear-glass containers
- stopwatch or watch with second hand
- water
- corn syrup
- rubbing alcohol
- clear soft drink
- vinegar
- cooking oil
- milk
- food coloring
- measuring cup with SI units

**Procedure**

1. Fill identical glass containers with equal volumes of seven different liquids: water, corn syrup, rubbing alcohol, clear soft drink, vinegar, cooking oil, and milk. Label each container.

2. Create a data table to record your observations and measurements about how quickly food dye will spread throughout each liquid to reach a state of total entropy between the two substances.

3. Place one drop of food coloring into the first container while a friend or family member simultaneously starts a stopwatch.

4. Observe how the food coloring behaves in each liquid. Time how quickly the coloring and each liquid reach total entropy.

5. Record your data in your data table.

6. Repeat with the remaining liquids.

**Conclude and Apply**

1. List the liquids in order of decreasing rates of entropy. List the liquid that reached a total state of entropy most quickly first and so on.

2. Infer the relationship between the rate at which a liquid and the dye achieved a state of total entropy and the time measurement from your data table.

3. Infer why the entropy rates for the different liquids varied.

**Try at Home Labs**

Glossary   **959**

---

## Materials

- Students should use brand-name bottled water that has little hardness.
- Students can use a laser beam instead of a narrow beam flashlight if they have parental supervision. Encourage students to experiment with other mixtures of common kitchen liquids to determine which mixtures form solutions and which form colloids.

## Safety Precautions

- Caution students not to eat or drink anything involved in the lab.
- Caution students not to flash the laser beam into someone else's eyes.
- Caution students not to move the laser beam back and forth in the liquid to avoid the light reflecting into their own eyes.

## Teaching Strategies

- Have students shine a laser beam through tap water and observe the effect. A beam of light will be visible in hard tap water (above 150 ppm hardness). Make soft water hard by adding a sufficient amount of $0.1 M CaC_{12}$ to it.
- Consider having students warm water in a microwave or over a hot plate to better dissolve the salt.

## Conclude and Apply

1. Students should observe a beam of light in glasses 1, 2, and 4, but the glass with water and dissolved salt should show no beam of light.

2. The salt and water is a solution. The other three mixtures are colloids.

of the alcohol and on the top of the soft drink for some time. The cooking oil will not reach a state of entropy, but the corn syrup will after several days.

2. They are directly proportional. The longer the time, the slower the rate of complete entropy.

3. Answers will vary. Oils are immiscible with water, and since food colorings are water and coloring, the food coloring will not dissolve in the oil. Highly viscous liquids such as milk will have slower rates for achieving entropy. Dissolved substances such as carbon dioxide in soft drinks also will slow entropy rates.

---

## Materials

- Students also can compare the entropy rates for whole milk, 2% milk, skim milk, and heavy cream.
- Blue or green food coloring shows up best for this lab.

## Safety Precautions

- Caution students not to drink anything involved in the lab.

## Teaching Strategies

- Water, vinegar, and rubbing alcohol will reach a state of entropy quickly (within 10-15 minutes) depending on their volumes. Milk and soda take considerably more time (25–30 minutes).

- Review several key concepts with students such as liquid density, viscosity, and miscible and immiscible liquids.
- Caution students not to bump the table of liquids.

## Conclude and Apply

1. water, vinegar, rubbing alcohol, clear soft drink, and milk; Due to density differences, a layer of coloring will remain on the bottom

**959**

# APPENDIX E

## Materials

- Students should cook the eggs in containers made of the same material to eliminate the variable of different conductivity rates for different metals.
- Students should use a hotplate or stove-top burner that is large enough for the entire cooking surface of the medium-sized frying pan to fit on.

## Safety Precautions

- Caution students not to eat anything involved in the lab.

**Teaching Strategy** Review with students that the area of a circle is calculated by using the formula $A = \pi r_{\_}$.

## Conclude and Apply

1. Controls include equal-sized eggs, proportionately equal volumes of cooking oil, equal temperature of the stovetop burner, and the use of the same timing device.
2. Answers will vary but may include slight differences in egg size, slight setting differences of the burner, differences in heat distribution on the burner, and differences with the breaking of the yolks.
3. Students will observe the egg cooking much faster on the larger surfaces of the medium and small pans, and they will observe the egg cooking considerably slower in the measuring cup.
4. They are directly proportional. Larger surface areas will speed up the chemical reaction and cook eggs more quickly. A greater surface area allows more egg molecules to come in contact with the heated surface.

## 17 Surface Area and Cooking Eggs

**Real-World Question** How does the amount of surface area affect the chemical reaction of an egg cooking?

**Possible Materials**

- small stainless steel frying pan
- medium stainless steel frying pan
- 1/2-cup stainless steel measuring cup
- two medium eggs (equal size)
- cooking oil
- spatula
- measuring cup
- stove top or hotplate
- oven mitt or pot holder
- metric ruler
- stopwatch or watch with second hand

### Procedure

1. Obtain permission to use the stove.
2. Calculate the area of the cooking surface for each of the three different containers.
3. Using a ratio of 1 mL of cooking oil for every 10 cm$^2$ of cooking surface, measure the appropriate volume of cooking oil for the medium frying pan and pour the oil into the pan.
4. Turn a stove top burner on medium heat and wait 5 minutes.
5. Crack an egg and empty its contents into the center of the frying pan. Use a spatula to break open the yolk of the egg.
6. Measure the amount of time it takes for the egg to cook completely.
7. Turn off the burner and wait 5 minutes.
8. Repeat steps 2–6 using the small frying pan.

### Conclude and Apply

1. Identify the variables and controls of your experiment.
2. Identify possible procedural errors that might have occurred in your experiment.
3. Describe the results of your experiment.
4. Infer the relationship between the cooking surface area and the speed of the chemical reaction happening to the egg. Explain why this relationship exists.

## 18 Cornstarch Solubility

**Real-World Question** How does heat affect the solubility equilibrium of a water and cornstarch mixture?

**Possible Materials**

- cornstarch
- water
- pan
- oven mitt or hot pad
- tablespoon
- kitchen scale
- stove top or hotplate

### Procedure

1. Obtain permission to use the stove or hotplate.
2. Measure 300 mL of water and pour the water into a pan.
3. Measure 2-3 tablespoons of cornstarch and empty the cornstarch into the pan of water.
4. Stir the cornstarch and water vigorously and observe the reaction that occurs.
5. Place the pan on a heat source and raise the temperature of the mixture until the water starts to boil. Observe what occurs.

### Conclude and Apply

1. Describe what occurred when you initially added the cornstarch to the water.
2. Describe what occurred when you raised the temperature of the mixture to the boiling point.
3. Infer the effect of heat on the solubility equilibrium of water and cornstarch.

Try at Home Labs

## Teaching Strategies

- Have students raise the temperature of the solution to a boil over medium heat to better observe the chemical reaction.
- Have students research what substance is formed during the chemical reaction that happens when a water and cornstarch mixture is heated. At 177°C, starch is turned into a substance called dextrine. Adding more energy will convert dextrine into sugar.

## Conclude and Apply

1. No reaction will occur, and the cornstarch will not completely dissolve in the water.
2. The cornstarch and water will become a thick, clear liquid.
3. Heat increases the solubility of a cornstarch-water mixture, shifting the solubility equilibrium to the right of the equation.

## 19  Testing for Ammonia

**Real-World Question** What substances elevate ammonia levels in natural waterways?

**Possible Materials**

- four glass jars with lids (spaghetti jars work well)
- measuring cup
- raw chicken (6 ounces)
- water
- ammonia test kit
- scale
- kitchen knife
- masking tape
- black marker

### Procedure

1. Use a kitchen scale to measure 28-g (1-ounce), 56-g (2-ounce), and 84-g (3-ounce) pieces of raw chicken.

2. Fill jars with 500 mL of water.

3. Do not put any chicken into the first jar. Place 28 g (1 ounce) of raw chicken into the second jar, 56 g (2 ounces) into the third jar, and 84 g (3 ounces) in the fourth jar.

4. Label your jars.

5. Create a data table to record your data.

6. Measure the amount of ammonia in each water sample every day for five days. Also observe the clarity of each sample.

### Conclude and Apply

1. Identify possible procedural errors in your experiment.

2. Summarize your results.

3. Infer the common causes for elevated ammonia levels in natural waterways.

## 20  Kitchen Oxidation

**Real-World Question** How do the oxidation rates of a nail in various kitchen liquids compare?

**Possible Materials**

- seven identical glasses or beakers
- water
- vinegar
- dark soft drink
- orange juice
- milk
- cooking oil
- rubbing alcohol
- seven iron nails
- measuring cup
- large tweezers
- masking tape
- black marker

### Procedure

1. Create a data table to record your observations about the oxidation rates of a nail in the seven liquids.

2. Use masking tape and a marker to label the liquids in your seven glasses.

3. Pour 200 mL of water, vinegar, dark soft drink, orange juice, milk, cooking oil, and rubbing alcohol into seven separate glasses.

4. Carefully place an iron nail into each container.

5. Observe the nail and the liquid in each container every day for a week. Record all your observations in your data table.

### Conclude and Apply

1. Summarize your observations about the oxidation rates of a nail in the seven different liquids.

2. Infer why the oxidation reactions in water and cooking oil were different.

Try at Home Labs

---

### Materials

- Inexpensive ammonia test kits may be purchased at pet stores.

### Safety Precautions

- Caution students to never eat or drink anything during involved in the lab.

### Teaching Strategies

- Extend this lab by having students collect and test water samples from local streams, rivers, ponds, and lakes.
- Inform students that ammonia is measured in the unit "parts per million" (ppm). A mere 0.5 ppm of ammonia can be harmful to aquatic life.

### Conclude and Apply

1. Answers will vary, but may include scale inaccuracies, residue left in the jar that was not cleaned out, and accuracy limitations of the ammonia test kits.

2. Answers will vary, but the second and third jars should show at least trace ammonia levels on day one and increasingly elevated levels over the next four days. The fourth jar should have elevated ammonia levels of 1-3 ppm the first day and maximum levels over 7 ppm by day two.

3. Answers may vary. Dead or decaying matter from natural causes and waste and animal parts from livestock farms are common sources of ammonia.

---

### Materials

- Students should use large nails that are easily seen in the liquids.
- Large tweezers are useful for lifting a nail out of an opaque liquid such as milk for observations.

### Safety Precautions

- Caution students not to drink anything involved in the lab.
- Set up the containers in a place where they will not be disturbed or knocked over.

### Teaching Strategies

- Have students research the false claim that dark soft drinks will dissolve a nail in one day and ask them to compare this claim with the results of their experiment.
- Have students design an experiment to prevent or slow the oxidation reaction between the nail and water. Students can coat nails with different types of oil or experiment with adding substances to the water that would prevent the reaction.

### Conclude and Apply

1. Answers may vary, but the nail in the water will begin to rust within 24 hours. The nails in the orange juice and vinegar may show slight signs of oxidation after one week. The nails in the oil, milk, soft drink, and vinegar will show no signs of oxidation.

2. Water is an ionic compound that readily causes a redox reaction, but cooking oil is a covalent compound that does not readily enter into a redox reaction.

## Materials

- Students can purchase galvanized rods at hardware stores.
- Students can firmly hold the rod on a worktable if a vise is not available.

## Safety Precautions

- Caution students to be certain the rod is secured tightly in the vise.

## Teaching Strategies

- Extend this lab by having students experiment with rods made of different galvanizing materials.
- This lab also works well as a class demonstration.

## Conclude and Apply

1. Answers may vary, but zinc is the most common galvanizing material.
2. Answers will vary, but students should observe little or no rust in the cuts still protected by the galvanizing metal. Rust will form in the cuts that penetrate deeper than the galvanizing metal.
3. The galvanizing metal oxidizes in air to form a metal oxide coating that protects the inner iron core from rust.

---

# 21  Old Pennies

**Real-World Question** How can you make an old penny look like new?

### Possible Materials

- 15 dull, dirty pennies
- vinegar
- table salt
- measuring cup with SI units
- teaspoon
- shallow bowl (not metal, plastic, or polystyrene
- steel nail
- sandpaper
- paper towels

### Procedure

1. Measure one teaspoon of salt into 60 mL of vinegar in the bowl. Stir until the salt dissolves.
2. Drop the pennies into the salt solution. Stir and observe.
3. After 5 minutes, remove one penny from the bowl. Rinse it in running water. Place it on the paper towel to dry.
4. Clean the nail with sandpaper. Place it into the salt solution with the pennies. Do not let the nail touch the pennies. What do you observe?
5. After 24–48 hours, remove the nail from the solution. Rinse and observe.

### Conclude and Apply

1. Compare and contrast the pennies before and after they were placed in the salt solution. Why did the pennies look dirty? How did the salt solution clean the pennies?
2. Compare and contrast the nail before and after it was placed in the salt solution. Infer what is on the nail.
3. What oxidation-reduction reaction do you think occurred?

---

# 22  Comparing Water and a Hydrocarbon

**Real-World Question** How do the properties of water and a hydrocarbon compare?

### Possible Materials

- water
- food coloring
- vegetable oil
- measuring cup
- three glasses
- stopwatch or watch with second hand
- two marbles
- stirring rod
- spoon
- kitchen scale
- metric ruler

### Procedure

1. Create a data table for comparing the physical properties of water and cooking oil.
2. Compare the color, feel, and odor of each liquid.
3. Measure the masses of equal volumes of each liquid and calculate the density of water and cooking oil.  Mix the water and oil together and observe the behavior of the liquids.
4. Pour 100 mL of water into a glass and 100 mL of cooking oil into a second glass. Measure the time it takes for a marble to pass through each liquid and compare the viscosities of the liquids.
5. Squeeze a drop of food coloring into each glass and observe the behavior of the coloring in the two liquids.

### Conclude and Apply

1. Summarize your comparisons of water and the cooking oil.
2. Infer why the food coloring behaved the way it did in each liquid.
3. Infer why water and oil are immiscible.

Try at Home Labs

---

## Materials

- Students can use a variety of different types of oil, but the odor, density, and viscosity of other oils will vary slightly.

## Safety Precautions

- Caution students never to eat anything involved in the lab.

**962**

## Teaching Strategies

- Students can measure the height of each liquid in its graduated cylinder and calculate the velocity of the falling marble through each liquid using the formula $v=d/t$.

- See the sample data chart below.

### Physical Properties Comparison

|  | Texture | Color | Odor | Viscosity | Density |
|---|---|---|---|---|---|
| Water | None | Clear | None | Low | 1.0 g/mL |
| Cooking oil | Slimy | Yellow | Slight | Moderate | 0.89 g/mL |

## Conclude and Apply

1. Water has no color, no real texture, and no odor, but cooking oil is yellow, has a slimy feel, and has a slight odor. Water is more dense than oil, but the oil has a greater viscosity.
2. Food coloring is primarily made of water; it is miscible with water but immiscible with oil.
3. Water molecules have a slight charge (polar), but oil molecules are made of carbon and hydrogen chains and have no charge (nonpolar).

## 23   Modeling Basic Organic Compounds

**Real-World Question** What do the molecules of different organic compounds and their functional groups look like?

**Possible Materials**

- toothpicks
- gumdrops (clear, yellow, green, red, orange, blue, and purple in color)
- marshmallows

**Procedure**

1. Study the basic types of organic compounds in Table 23-1 on page 738 in the textbook.
2. Use the gumdrops, marshmallows, and toothpicks to create molecule models of the general formula for each of the nine basic types of organic compounds. Use marshmallows to represent R groups (carbon chains or rings). Use the green gumdrops to represent fluorine atoms, yellow for chlorine atoms, red for bromine atoms, blue for oxygen atoms, orange for hydrogen atoms, and purple for nitrogen atoms. Clear gumdrops will represent carbon atoms. Use orange gumdrops (hydrogen atoms) in place of the asterisks.
3. Be certain to construct three different halo-carbon models.

**Conclude and Apply**

1. Explain how you represented single and double bonds in your models.
2. Explain the effect of a functional group on a carbon chain or ring.

## 24   Modeling Sugars

**Real-World Question** What do sugar molecules look like?

**Possible Materials**

- gumdrops (three different colors)
- toothpicks

**Procedure**

1. Using blue gumdrops to represent oxygen atoms, red gumdrops to represent hydrogen atoms, and green gumdrops to represent carbon atoms, construct a model of a glucose molecule from the diagram on page 781. Use toothpicks to represent the bonds between the atoms.
2. Use gumdrops and toothpicks to construct a model of a fructose molecule from the diagram on page 781.
3. Use gumdrops and toothpicks to construct a model of a sucrose molecule from the diagram on page 782.

**Conclude and Apply**

1. Research common foods containing monosaccrides such as glucose and fructose.
2. Research common foods containing the disaccride sucrose.
3. Infer why it is preferable for an athlete to eat an orange before a game instead of a candy bar.

**Try at Home Labs**

---

### Try at Home — Lab 23

**Materials**

- Students can replace the gumballs with clay balls or other spherically shaped soft candies.

**Safety Precautions**

- Caution students to use care when inserting the toothpicks into the gumballs.

**Teaching Strategies**

- Have students compare their models with the models constructed by their classmates.
- Choose a set of models to display in your room along with labels for the models. Stringing the models from the ceiling will help students visualize the organic compounds as you teach the chapter.

**Conclude and Apply**

1. One toothpick joining two polystyrene balls can represent a single bond and two toothpicks a double bond.
2. A functional group changes the chemical and physical properties of the substance.

---

### Try at Home — Lab 24

**Materials**

- Students can replace the gumdrops with painted polystyrene balls.

**Safety Precautions**

- Caution students never to eat anything involved in the lab.

**Teaching Strategies**

- Suspend the best student models from the ceiling of your classroom to serve as a reference while you teach this chapter.
- Be certain students use two toothpicks to represent double bonds.
- Extend this lab by asking students to construct models of galactose and lactose.

**Conclude and Apply**

1. Answers will vary but fruits and vegetables are common foods containing monosaccharides.
2. Answers will vary, but many processed foods such as pastries, soda, candy, and cereals have added sucrose.
3. The monosaccharide found in an orange is readily available for the body to use and can be quickly turned into energy. The disaccharide sucrose found in a candy bar is a more complex sugar that must first be broken down into simpler sugars before the body can convert it into energy.

## Lab 25

### Materials

- Students should use pencils that are slightly dull so that they will puncture the paper but not the foil.
- If possible, borrow a lead apron used by dentists or X-ray technicians to show your class.

### Safety Precautions

- Caution students to carefully poke the pencil at the paper and foil. Students should not try to puncture the paper near their partners' hands.

### Teaching Strategies

- Try this lab yourself first so that you can instruct students on the proper pencil to choose to model beta radiation.
- Show students a cement block or three bricks stacked on top of each other. Explain to them that a thick sheet of lead or thick concrete the thickness of the bricks is needed to completely block gamma radiation.

### Conclude and Apply

1. The cotton swab modeled alpha radiation, which is blocked by a sheet of paper. The dull pencil modeled beta radiation, which is blocked by a foil sheet.
2. Answers will vary but may include a drill bit drilled through a layer of lead or a chisel hammered through a cement block.
3. Exposure at low levels (<10 rad ) increases cancer risks; bone marrow cancer or illness is common with moderate doses (10-500 rad), and extreme doses over 500 rad frequently are fatal.

## 25  Modeling Radiation Penetration

**Real-World Question** How can you model the penetration power of different forms of radiation?

**Possible Materials**

- cotton swab
- dull pencil
- sheet of tissue paper
- aluminum foil

**Procedure**

1. Have a friend or family member hold up a sheet of tissue paper by the edges so that the flat side of the paper is facing you.
2. Carefully use a cotton swab to try to puncture a hole in the center of the tissue paper without ripping the sheet in half or pulling it out of the hands of your friend or family member. Next, try using a dull pencil to puncture a hole in the center of the paper.
3. Fold a sheet of aluminum foil in half. The foil sheet should be about the size of a sheet of paper. Have a friend or family member hold up the foil sheet by the edges so that the flat side of the foil is facing you.
4. Using the dull pencil, carefully try to puncture a hole in the center of the foil without ripping the sheet in half or pulling it out of the hands of your friend or family member.

**Conclude and Apply**

1. Infer what type of radiation the cotton swab and dull pencil modeled.
2. Infer how you could model the penetration power of gamma radiation.
3. Research the human health effects of gamma radiation exposure.

## 26  Modeling Ozone Depletion

**Real-World Question** What does the destruction of an ozone molecule look like?

**Possible Materials**

- toothpicks
- gumdrops (green, yellow, red, and purple)
- three white sheets of paper
- black marker

**Procedure**

1. Draw a black arrow on each of the sheets of white paper. Arrange the arrows (facing right) one above the other on a flat surface.
2. On page 845, study the three equations that describe the photodissociation of a CFC molecule, destruction of an ozone molecule, and the regeneration of a free chlorine atom.
3. Create models of all the atoms and molecules involved in these three reactions using green gumdrops to represent carbon atoms, yellow gumdrops to represent fluorine atoms, red gumdrops to represent chlorine atoms, and purple gumdrops to represent oxygen atoms.
4. Arrange your models to represent the three reactions involved in ozone depletion.

**Conclude and Apply**

1. Infer from your models why small amounts of CFCs can deplete large volumes of ozone gas.
2. Infer why the replacement of CFCs with HFCs helps protects the ozone layer.

Try at Home Labs

## Lab 26

### Materials

- Students can replace the gumdrops with clay balls.

### Teaching Strategies

- Extend this lab by having students research and create a model of an HFC molecule.

- Have students research why ozone depletion is greatest above the Antarctic. Polar stratospheric clouds, which are long clouds made of ice particles, form over polar regions during cold winter months creating a large surface area where free chlorine atoms collect. During the spring, the sun finally rises flooding the clouds with UV energy and causing the chlorine atoms to rapidly deplete ozone molecules.

### Conclude and Apply

1. The chlorine atoms that destroy ozone molecules are constantly freed to destroy more ozone when chlorine monoxide combines with free oxygen.
2. In the presence of high ultraviolet energy, chlorine atoms are easily knocked free from CFC molecules, but HFC molecules are more stable and will not disassociate when subjected to high levels of UV radiation.

# Glossary/Glosario

## A

accuracy (p. 36) Refers to how close a measured value is to an accepted value.

acid-base indicator (p. 619) A chemical dye whose color is affected by acidic and basic solutions.

acid ionization constant (p. 605) The value of the equilibrium constant expression for the ionization of a weak acid.

actinide series (p. 197) In the periodic table, the f-block elements from period 7 that follow the element actinium.

activated complex (p. 532) A short-lived, unstable arrangement of atoms that may break apart and re-form the reactants or may form products; also sometimes referred to as the transition state.

activation energy (p. 533) The minimum amount of energy required by reacting particles in order to form the activated complex and lead to a reaction.

active site (p. 778) The pocket or crevice to which a substrate binds in an enzyme-catalyzed reaction.

actual yield (p. 370) The amount of product actually produced when a chemical reaction is carried out in an experiment.

addition polymerization (p. 762) Occurs when all the atoms present in the monomers are retained in the polymer product.

addition reaction (p. 755) An organic reaction that occurs when other atoms bond to each of two atoms bonded by double or triple covalent bonds.

alcohol (p. 743) An organic compound in which a hydroxyl group replaces a hydrogen atom of a hydrocarbon; is used in medicinal products, foods, and beverages, and as a solvent and starting material in synthesis reactions.

aldehyde (p. 747) An organic compound containing the structure in which a carbonyl group at the end of a carbon chain is bonded to a carbon atom on one side and a hydrogen atom on the other side.

aliphatic compounds (p. 723) Nonaromatic hydrocarbons, such as the alkanes, alkenes, and alkynes.

alkali metals (p. 155) Group 1A elements, except for hydrogen, that are on the left side of the modern periodic table.

alkaline earth metals (p. 155) Group 2A elements in the modern periodic table.

alkane (p. 699) A saturated hydrocarbon, such as methane ($CH_4$), with only single, nonpolar bonds between atoms.

alkene (p. 711) An unsaturated hydrocarbon, such as ethene ($C_2H_4$), with one or more double covalent bonds between carbon atoms in a chain.

alkyl halide (p. 738) An organic compound that contains one or more halogen atoms (F, Cl, Br, or I) covalently bonded to an aliphatic carbon atom.

alkyne (p. 714) An unsaturated hydrocarbon, such as ethyne ($C_2H_2$), with one or more triple bonds between carbon atoms in a chain.

allotropes (p. 188) Forms of an element with different structures and properties when they are in the same state—solid, liquid, or gas.

alloy (p. 230) A mixture of elements that has metallic properties; most commonly forms when the elements are either similar in size (substitutional alloy) or the atoms of one element are much smaller than the atoms of the other (interstitial alloy).

accuracy/exactitud (pág. 36) Se refiere a la cercanía con que se encuentra un valor medido de un valor aceptado.

acid-base indicator/indicador ácido-base (pág. 619) Tinta química cuyo color es afectado por soluciones ácidas y básicas.

acid ionization constant/constante ácida de ionización (pág. 605) Valor de la expresión de la constante de equilibrio para la ionización de un ácido débil.

actinide series/serie de actínidos (pág. 197) En la tabla periódica, los elementos del bloque F del período 7 que van después del elemento actinio.

activated complex/complejo activado (pág. 532) Un arreglo efímero e inestable de átomos que pueden romper y reagrupar reactantes o puede formar productos; a veces también se le llama estado de transición.

activation energy/energía de activación (pág. 533) La cantidad mínima de energía requerida por partículas reaccionantes, para formar el complejo activado y conducir a una reacción.

active site/sitio activo (pág. 778) Abolsamiento o ranura a la que se une un sustrato en una reacción catalizada por enzimas.

actual yield/rendimiento real (pág. 370) Cantidad del producto realmente generado cuando se lleva a cabo una reacción química en un experimento.

addition polymerization/polimerización de adición (pág. 762) Ocurre cuando todos los átomos presentes en los monómeros son retenidos en el producto polimérico.

addition reaction/reacción de adición (pág. 755) Reacción orgánica que ocurre cuando otros átomos se unen a cada uno de los dos átomos unidos por enlaces covalentes dobles o triples.

alcohol/alcohol (pág. 743) Compuesto orgánico en que un grupo hidroxilo reemplaza un átomo de hidrógeno de un hidrocarburo; se utiliza en medicinas, alimentos y bebidas y como disolvente como material inicial en reacciones de síntesis.

aldehyde/aldehido (pág. 747) Compuesto orgánico en el cual un grupo carbonilo al final de una cadena de carbono está unido a un átomo de carbono por un lado y a un átomo de hidrógeno por el otro.

aliphatic compounds/compuestos alifáticos (pág. 723) Hidrocarburos no aromáticos, como los alcanos, los alquenos y los alquinos.

alkali metals/metales alcalinos (pág. 155) Elementos del Grupo 1A, exceptuando el hidrógeno, que se ubican en el lado izquierdo de la tabla periódica moderna.

alkaline earth metals/metales alcalinotérreos (pág. 155) Elementos del Grupo 2A en la tabla periódica moderna.

alkane/alcano (pág. 699) Hidrocarburo saturado, como el metano ($CH_4$), con sólo enlaces sencillos y no polares entre los átomos.

alkene/alqueno (pág. 711) Un hidrocarburo insaturado, como el etileno ($C_2H_4$), con uno o más enlaces dobles entre átomos de carbono de una cadena.

alkyl halide/alquilhaluro (pág. 738) Compuesto orgánico que contiene uno o más átomos de halógeno (F, Cl, Br o I) unidos covalentemente a un átomo de carbono alifático.

alkyne/alquino (pág. 714) Hidrocarburo insaturado, como el acetileno ($C_2H_2$), con uno o más enlaces triples entre átomos de carbono en una cadena.

allotropes/alótropos (pág. 188) ) Formas de un elemento con estructuras y propiedades diferentes cuando están en el mismo estado: sólido, líquido o gaseoso.

alloy/aleación (pág. 230) Mezcla de elementos que posee propiedades metálicas; la mayoría se forma comúnmente cuando los elementos son semejantes de tamaño (aleación de sustitución) o cuando los átomos de un elemento son mucho más pequeños que los átomos del otro (aleación intersticial).

**alpha particle** (p. 106) A particle with two protons and two neutrons, with a 2+ charge; is equivalent to a helium-4 nucleus, can be represented as α, and is emitted during radioactive decay.

**alpha radiation** (p. 106) Radiation that is made up of alpha particles; is deflected toward a negatively charged plate when radiation from a radioactive source is directed between two electrically charged plates.

**amide** (p. 752) An organic compound in which the —OH group of a carboxylic acid is replaced by a nitrogen atom bonded to other atoms.

**amines** (p. 745) Organic compounds that contain nitrogen atoms bonded to carbon atoms in aliphatic chains or aromatic rings and have the general formula $RNH_2$.

**amino acid** (p. 776) An organic molecule that has both an amino group (—NH2) and a carboxyl group (—COOH).

**amorphous solid** (p. 403) A solid in which particles are not arranged in a regular, repeating pattern that often is formed when molten material cools too quickly to form crystals.

**amphoteric** (p. 599) Describes water and other substances that can act as both acids and bases.

**amplitude** (p. 119) The height of a wave from the origin to a crest, or from the origin to a trough.

**anabolism** (p. 792) Refers to the metabolic reactions through which cells use energy and small building blocks to build large, complex molecules needed to carry out cell functions and for cell structures.

**anion** (p. 214) An ion that has a negative charge; forms when valence electrons are added to the outer energy level, giving the ion a stable electron configuration.

**anode** (p. 665) In an electrochemical cell, the electrode where oxidation takes place.

**applied research** (p. 14) A type of scientific investigation that is undertaken to solve a specific problem.

**aqueous solution** (p. 292) A solution in which the solvent is water.

**aromatic compounds** (p. 723) Organic compounds that contain one or more benzene rings as part of their molecular structure.

**Arrhenius model** (p. 597) A model of acids and bases; states that an acid is a substance that contains hydrogen and ionizes to produce hydrogen ions in aqueous solution and a base is a substance that contains a hydroxide group and dissociates to produce a hydroxide ion in aqueous solution.

**aryl halide** (p. 739) An organic compound that contains a halogen atom bonded to a benzene ring or another aromatic group.

**asymmetric carbon** (p. 719) A carbon atom that has four different atoms or groups of atoms attached to it; occurs in chiral compounds.

**atmosphere** (p. 390) The unit that is often used to report air pressure; (p. 841) the protective, largely gaseous envelope around Earth, hundreds of kilometers thick, that is divided into the troposphere, stratosphere, mesosphere, thermosphere, and exosphere.

**atom** (p. 90) The smallest particle of an element that retains all the properties of that element; is electrically neutral, spherically shaped, and composed of electrons, protons, and neutrons.

**atomic emission spectrum** (p. 125) A set of frequencies of electromagnetic waves given off by atoms of an element; consists of a series of fine lines of individual colors.

**alpha particle/partícula alfa** (pág. 106) Partícula con dos protones y dos neutrones, con una carga de 2+ que equivale a un núcleo de helio 4; se puede representar como α y se emite durante la descomposición radiactiva.

**alpha radiation/radiación alfa** (pág. 106) Radiación compuesta de partículas alfa; es desviada hacia una placa cargada negativamente cuando la radiación proveniente de una fuente radiactiva se dirige entre dos placas cargadas eléctricamente.

**amide/amida** (pág. 752) Compuesto orgánico en que el grupo —OH de un ácido carboxílico es reemplazado por un átomo de nitrógeno unido con otros átomos.

**amines/aminas** (pág. 745) Compuestos orgánicos que contienen átomos de nitrógeno unidos a átomos de carbono en cadenas de alifáticas o anillos aromáticos y su fórmula general es $RNH_2$.

**amino acid/aminoácido** (pág. 776) Molécula orgánica que tiene un grupo amino (—NH2) y un grupo carboxilo (—COOH).

**amorphous solid/sólido amorfo** (pág. 403) Sólido en el cuál las partículas no están ordenadas en un patrón regular repetitivo; a menudo se forma cuando el material fundido se enfría demasiado rápido para formar cristales.

**amphoteric/anfotérico** (pág. 599) Término que describe al agua y a otras sustancias que pueden actuar como ácidos y como bases.

**amplitude/amplitud** (pág. 119) Altura de una onda desde el origen hasta una cresta o desde el origen hasta un seno.

**anabolism/anabolismo** (pág. 792) Se refiere a las reacciones metabólicas a través de las cuales las células usan energía y bloques constitutivos pequeños para construir moléculas grandes y complejas que son necesarias para llevar a cabo las funciones celulares y para construir estructuras celulares.

**anion/anión** (pág. 214) Ion que tiene una carga negativa; se forma cuando los electrones de valencia se incorporan al nivel de energía externo, dando el ion una configuración electrónica estable.

**anode/ánodo** (pág. 665) En una celda electroquímica, el electrodo donde se lleva a cabo la oxidación.

**applied research/investigación aplicada** (pág. 14) Tipo de investigación científica que se lleva a cabo para resolver un problema concreto.

**aqueous solution/solución acuosa** (pág. 292) Solución en la que el disolvente es agua.

**aromatic compounds/compuestos aromáticos** (pág. 723) Compuestos orgánicos que contienen uno o más anillos de benceno como parte de su estructura molecular.

**Arrhenius model/modelo de Arrhenius** (pág. 597) Modelo de ácidos y bases; establece que un ácido es una sustancia que contiene hidrógeno y se ioniza para producir iones hidrógeno en solución acuosa y una base es una sustancia que contiene un grupo hidróxido y se disocia para producir un ion hidróxido en solución acuosa.

**aryl halide/haluro de arilo** (pág. 739) Compuesto orgánico que contiene un átomo de halógeno unido a un anillo de benceno u otro grupo aromático.

**asymmetric carbon/carbono asimétrico** (pág. 719) Átomo de carbono que tiene cuatro átomos o grupos de átomos diferentes unidos a él; se encuentra en compuestos quirales.

**atmosphere/atmósfera** (pág. 390) Unidad que se emplea a menudo para indicar la presión del aire; (pág. 841) la gran cubierta gaseosa protectora que rodea a la Tierra de centenares de kilómetros de ancho y que se divide en troposfera, estratosfera, mesosfera, termosfera y exosfera.

**atom/átomo** (pág. 90) La partícula más pequeña de un elemento que retiene todas las propiedades de ese elemento; es eléctricamente neutro, de forma esférica y compuesto de electrones, protones y neutrones.

**atomic emission spectrum/espectro de emisión atómica** (pág. 125) Conjunto de frecuencias de ondas electromagnéticas emitida por los átomos de un elemento; consta de una serie de líneas finas de colores individuales.

**atomic mass** (p. 102) The weighted average mass of the isotopes of that element.

**atomic mass unit (amu)** (p. 102) One-twelfth the mass of a carbon-12 atom.

**atomic number** (p. 98) The number of protons in an atom.

**atomic orbital** (p. 132) A three-dimensional region around the nucleus of an atom that describes an electron's probable location.

**ATP** (p. 792) Adenosine triphosphate—a nucleotide that functions as the universal energy-storage molecule in living cells.

**aufbau principle** (p. 135) States that each electron occupies the lowest energy orbital available.

**Avogadro's number** (p. 310) The number 6.022 1367 × $10^{23}$, which is the number of representative particles in a mole, and can be rounded to three significant digits: 6.02 × $10^{23}$.

**Avogadro's principle** (p. 430) States that equal volumes of gases at the same temperature and pressure contain equal numbers of particles.

**atomic mass/masa atómica** (pág. 102) La masa promedio ponderada de los isótopos de ese elemento.

**atomic mass unit (amu)/unidad de masa atómica(uma)** (pág. 102) ) Un doceavo de la masa de un átomo de carbono 12.

**atomic number/número atómico** (pág. 98) El número de protones en un átomo.

**atomic orbital/orbital atómico** (pág. 132) Región tridimensional alrededor del núcleo de un átomo que describe la ubicación probable del electrón.

**ATP/ATP** (pág. 792) Trifosfato de adenosina, un nucleótido que funciona como la molécula universal de almacenamiento de energía en las células vivas.

**aufbau principle/principio de Aufbau** (pág. 135) Establece que cada electrón ocupa el orbital de energía más bajo disponible.

**Avogadro's number/número de Avogadro** (pág. 310) El número 6.022 × $10^{23}$, que es el número de partículas representativas en un mol, el cual se puede redondear a tres dígitos significativos: 6.02 × $10^{23}$.

**Avogadro's principle/principio de Avogadro** (pág. 430) Establece que volúmenes iguales de gases a la misma temperatura y presión contienen igual número de partículas.

# B

**band of stability** (p. 811) The region on a graph within which all stable nuclei are found when plotting the number of neutrons versus the number of protons for all stable nuclei.

**barometer** (p. 389) An instrument that is used to measure atmospheric pressure.

**base ionization constant** (p. 606) The value of the equilibrium constant expression for the ionization of a base.

**base unit** (p. 26) A defined unit in a system of measurement that is based on an object or event in the physical world and is independent of other units.

**battery** (p. 672) One or more electrochemical cells in a single package that generates electrical current.

**beta particle** (p. 107) A high-speed electron with a 1− charge that is emitted during radioactive decay.

**beta radiation** (p. 107) Radiation that is made up of beta particles; is deflected toward a positively charged plate when radiation from a radioactive source is directed between two electrically charged plates.

**boiling point** (p. 406) The temperature at which a liquid's vapor pressure is equal to the external or atmospheric pressure.

**boiling point elevation** (p. 472) The temperature difference between a solution's boiling point and a pure solvent's boiling point.

**Boyle's law** (p. 421) States that the volume of a given amount of gas held at a constant temperature varies inversely with the pressure.

**breeder reactor** (p. 825) A nuclear reactor that is able to produce more fuel than it uses.

**Brønsted-Lowry model** (p. 598) A model of acids and bases in which an acid is a hydrogen-ion donor and a base is a hydrogen-ion acceptor.

**Brownian motion** (p. 478) The jerky, random, rapid movements of colloid particles that results from collisions of particles of the dispersion medium with the dispersed particles.

**buffer** (p. 623) A solution that resists changes in pH when limited amounts of acid or base are added.

**band of stability/banda de la estabilidad** (pág. 811) Región de la gráfica dentro de la cual se encuentran todos los núcleos estables cuando se grafica el número de neutrones contra el número de protones para todos los núcleos estables.

**barometer/barómetro** (pág. 389) Instrumento que se utiliza para medir la presión atmosférica.

**base ionization constant/constante de ionización base** (pág. 606) El valor de la expresión de la constante de equilibrio para la ionización de una base.

**base unit/unidad base** (pág. 26) Unidad definida en un sistema de la medida que se basa en un objeto o el acontecimiento en el mundo físico y es independiente de otras unidades.

**battery/batería** (pág. 672) Una o más celdas electroquímicas en un solo paquete que genera corriente eléctrica.

**beta particle/partícula de beta** (pág. 107) Electrón de alta velocidad con una carga 1− que se emite durante la desintegración radiactiva.

**beta radiation/radiación beta** (pág. 107) Radiación compuesta de partículas beta; es desviada hacia un placa positivamente cargada cuando la radiación de una fuente radiactiva es dirigida entre dos placas cargadas eléctricamente.

**boiling point/punto de ebullición** (pág. 406) Temperatura a la cual la presión de vapor de un líquido es igual a la presión externa o atmosférica.

**boiling point elevation/elevación del punto de ebullición** (pág. 472) Diferencia de temperatura entre el punto de ebullición de una solución y el de un disolvente puro.

**Boyle's law/Ley de Boyle** (pág. 421) Establece que el volumen de una cantidad dada de gas a temperatura constante, varía inversamente con la presión.

**breeder reactor/reactor regenerador** (pág. 825) Reactor nuclear que es capaz de producir más combustible de lo que utiliza.

**Brønsted-Lowry model/modelo de Brønsted-Lowry** (pág. 598) Modelo de ácidos y bases en que un ácido es un donador de ion hidrógeno y una base es un aceptor de ion hidrógeno.

**Brownian motion/movimiento browniano** (pág. 478) Movimientos erráticos, aleatorios y rápidos de las partículas coloidales que resultan de choques de partículas del medio de dispersión con las partículas dispersadas.

**buffer/amortiguador** (pág. 623) Solución que resiste los cambios de pH cuando se agregan cantidades moderadas del ácido o la base.

**buffer capacity** (p. 623) The amount of acid or base a buffer solution can absorb without a significant change in pH.

**buffer capacity/capacidad amortiguadora** (pág. 623) Cantidad de ácido o base que una solución amortiguadora puede absorber sin un cambio significativo en el pH.

## C

**calorie** (p. 491) The amount of heat required to raise the temperature of one gram of pure water by one degree Celsius.

**calorimeter** (p. 496) An insulated device that is used to measure the amount of heat released or absorbed during a physical or chemical process.

**carbohydrates** (p. 781) Compounds that contain multiple hydroxyl groups, plus an aldehyde or a ketone functional group, and function in living things to provide immediate and stored energy.

**carbonyl group** (p. 747) Arrangement in which an oxygen atom is double-bonded to a carbon atom.

**carboxyl group** (p. 749) Consists of a carbonyl group bonded to a hydroxyl group.

**carboxylic acid** (p. 749) An organic compound that contains a carboxyl group and is polar and reactive.

**catabolism** (p. 792) Refers to metabolic reactions that cells undergo to extract energy and chemical building blocks from large, complex biological molecules such as proteins, carbohydrates, lipids, and nucleic acids.

**catalyst** (p. 539) A substance that increases the rate of a chemical reaction by lowering activation energies but is not itself consumed in the reaction.

**cathode** (p. 665) In an electrochemical cell, the electrode where reduction takes place.

**cathode ray** (p. 92) A ray of radiation that originates from the cathode and travels to the anode of a cathode ray tube.

**cation** (p. 212) An ion that has a positive charge; forms when valence electrons are removed, giving the ion a stable electron configuration.

**cellular respiration** (p. 794) The process in which glucose is broken down in the presence of oxygen gas to produce carbon dioxide, water, and large amounts of energy.

**Charles's law** (p. 424) States that the volume of a given mass of gas is directly proportional to its kelvin temperature at constant pressure.

**chemical bond** (p. 211) The force that holds two atoms together; may form by the attraction of a positive ion for a negative ion or by the attraction of a positive nucleus for negative electrons.

**chemical change** (p. 62) A process involving one or more substances changing into new substances; also called a chemical reaction.

**chemical equation** (p. 280) A statement using chemical formulas to describe the identities and relative amounts of the reactants and products involved in the chemical reaction.

**chemical equilibrium** (p. 561) The state in which forward and reverse reactions balance each other because they occur at equal rates.

**chemical potential energy** (p. 490) The energy stored in a substance because of its composition; is released or absorbed as heat during chemical reactions or processes.

**chemical property** (p. 57) The ability or inability of a substance to combine with or change into one or more new substances.

**calorie/caloría** (pág. 491) Cantidad de calor que se requiere para elevar, por un grado centígrado la temperatura de un gramo de agua pura.

**calorimeter/calorímetro** (pág. 496) Dispositivo aislado que se utiliza para medir la cantidad de calor liberado o absorbido durante un proceso físico o químico.

**carbohydrates/carbohidratos** (pág. 781) Compuestos que contienen múltiples grupos hidroxilo, más un grupo funcional aldehido o cetona y cuya función en los seres vivos es proporcionar energía inmediata y almacenada.

**carbonyl group/grupo carbonilo** (pág. 747) Arreglo en el cual un átomo de oxígeno está unido por un doble enlace a un átomo de carbono.

**carboxyl group/grupo carboxilo** (pág. 749) Consiste en un grupo de carbonilo unido a un grupo hidroxilo.

**carboxylic acid/ácido carboxílico** (pág. 749) Compuesto orgánico que contiene un grupo carboxilo y el cual es polar y reactivo.

**catabolism/catabolismo** (pág. 792) Se refiere a reacciones metabólicas que sufren las células para extraer energía y componentes químicos de moléculas biológicas, complejas y grandes tales como proteínas, carbohidratos, lípidos y ácidos nucleicos.

**catalyst/catalizador** (pág. 539) Sustancia que aumenta la velocidad de reacción química disminuyendo las energías de activación pero él mismo no es consumido durante la reacción.

**cathode/cátodo** (pág. 665) En una celda de electroquímica, el electrodo donde se lleva a cabo la reducción.

**cathode ray/rayo catódico** (pág. 92) Rayo de radiación que se origina en el cátodo y viaja al ánodo de un tubo de rayos catódicos.

**cation/catión** (pág. 212) Ion que tiene una carga positiva; se forma cuando se descartan los electrones de valencia, dándole al ion una configuración electrónica estable.

**cellular respiration/respiración celular** (pág. 794) El proceso en cual la glucosa se rompe en presencia de oxígeno para producir dióxido de carbono, agua y grandes cantidades de energía.

**Charles's law/Ley de Charles** (pág. 424) Establece que el volumen de una masa dada de gas es directamente proporcional a su temperatura Kelvin a presión constante.

**chemical bond/enlace químico** (pág. 211) La fuerza que mantiene juntos a dos átomos; puede formarse por la atracción de un ion positivo por un ion negativo o por la atracción de un núcleo positivo hacia los electrones negativos.

**chemical change/cambio químico** (pág. 62) Proceso que involucra una o más sustancias que se transforman en sustancias nuevas; también llamado reacción química.

**chemical equation/ecuación química** (pág. 280) Expresión que utiliza fórmulas químicas para describir las identidades y cantidades relativas de los reactantes y productos presentes en la reacción química.

**chemical equilibrium/equilibrio químico** (pág. 561) El estado en que las reacciones directa e inversa se equilibran mutuamente debido a que ocurren a velocidades iguales.

**chemical potential energy/energía potencial química** (pág. 490) La energía almacenada en una sustancia debido a su composición; se libera o se absorbe como calor durante reacciones o procesos químicos.

**chemical property/propiedad química** (pág. 57) La capacidad o incapacidad de una sustancia para combinarse o transformarse en uno o más sustancias nuevas.

**chemical reaction** (p. 277) The process by which the atoms of one or more substances are rearranged to form different substances; occurrence can be indicated by changes in temperature, color, odor, and physical state.

**chemistry** (p. 7) The study of matter and the changes that it undergoes.

**chirality** (p. 719) A property of a compound to exist in both left ($l-$) and right ($d-$) forms; occurs whenever a compound contains an asymmetric carbon.

**chromatography** (p. 69) A technique that is used to separate the components of a mixture based on the tendency of each component to travel or be drawn across the surface of another material.

**coefficient** (p. 280) In a chemical equation, the number written in front of a reactant or product; tells the smallest number of particles of the substance involved in the reaction.

**colligative property** (p. 471) A physical property of a solution that depends on the number, but not the identity, of the dissolved solute particles; example properties include vapor pressure lowering, boiling point elevation, osmotic pressure, and freezing point depression.

**collision theory** (p. 532) States that atoms, ions, and molecules must collide in order to react.

**colloids** (p. 477) Heterogeneous mixtures containing particles larger than solution particles but smaller than suspension particles that are categorized according to the phases of their dispersed particles and dispersing mediums.

**combined gas law** (p. 428) A single law combining Boyle's, Charles's, and Gay-Lussac's laws that states the relationship among pressure, volume, and temperature of a fixed amount of gas.

**combustion reaction** (p. 285) A chemical reaction that occurs when a substance reacts with oxygen, releasing energy in the form of heat and light.

**common ion** (p. 584) An ion that is common to two or more ionic compounds.

**common ion effect** (p. 584) The lowering of the solubility of a substance by the presence of a common ion.

**complete ionic equation** (p. 293) An ionic equation that shows all the particles in a solution as they realistically exist.

**complex reaction** (p. 548) A chemical reaction that consists of two or more elementary steps.

**compound** (p. 71) A chemical combination of two or more different elements; can be broken down into simpler substances by chemical means and has properties different from those of its component elements.

**concentration** (p. 462) A quantitative measure of the amount of solute in a given amount of solvent or solution.

**conclusion** (p. 12) A judgment based on the information obtained.

**condensation** (p. 407) The energy-releasing process by which a gas or vapor becomes a liquid.

**condensation polymerization** (p. 764) Occurs when monomers having at least two functional groups combine with the loss of a small by-product, usually water.

**condensation reaction** (p. 753) Occurs when two smaller organic molecules combine to form a more complex molecule, accompanied by the loss of a small molecule such as water.

**chemical reaction/reacción química** (pág. 277) El proceso por el cual los átomos de una o más sustancias se reordenan para formar sustancias diferentes; su ocurrencia puede identificarse por cambios en temperatura, color, olor y producción de un gas.

**chemistry/química** (pág. 7) El estudio de la materia y los cambios que experimenta.

**chirality/quiralidad** (pág. 719) Propiedad de un compuesto para existir en ambas formas: izquierda ($i-$) y derecha ($d-$); ocurre siempre que un compuesto contiene un carbono asimétrico.

**chromatography/cromatografía** (pág. 69) Técnica usada para separar los componentes de una mezcla basada en la tendencia de cada componente para moverse o ser absorbido a través de la superficie de otra materia.

**coefficient/coeficiente** (pág. 280) En una ecuación química, el número escrito delante de un reactante o producto; indica el número más pequeño de partículas de la sustancia involucrada en la reacción.

**colligative property/propiedad coligativa** (pág. 471) Propiedad física de una solución que depende del número, pero no de la identidad, de las partículas solubles disueltas; ejemplos de propiedades incluyen disminución de la presión de vapor, elevación del punto de ebullición, la presión osmótica y la depresión del punto de congelación.

**collision theory/teoría de colisión** (pág. 532) Establece que los átomos, iones y moléculas deben chocar para reaccionar.

**colloids/coloides** (pág. 477) Mezclas heterogéneas que contienen partículas más grandes que las partículas de una solución pero más pequeñas que las partículas de una suspensión; se clasifican según las fases de sus partículas dispersadas y los medios dispersantes.

**combined gas law/ley combinada de los gases** (pág. 428) Una sola ley que combina las leyes de Boyle, Charles y de Gay-Lussac, que indica la relación entre la presión, el volumen y la temperatura de una cantidad fija de gas.

**combustion reaction/reacción de combustión** (pág. 285) Reacción química que ocurre cuando una sustancia reacciona con oxígeno, liberando energía en forma de calor y luz.

**common ion/ion común** (pág. 584) Un ion que es común a dos o más compuestos iónicos.

**common ion effect/efecto de ion común** (pág. 584) Disminución de la solubilidad de una sustancia por la presencia de un ion común.

**complete ionic equation/ecuación iónica completa** (pág. 293) Una ecuación iónica que muestra como existen en realidad todas las partículas en una solución.

**complex reaction/reacción compleja** (pág. 548) Reacción química que consiste en dos o más pasos elementales.

**compound/compuesto** (pág. 71) Combinación química de dos o más elementos diferentes; puede separarse en sustancias más sencillas por medios químicos y exhibe propiedades diferentes de aquellas de sus elementos constituyentes.

**concentration/concentración** (pág. 462) Medida cuantitativa de la cantidad de soluto en una cantidad dada de disolvente o solución.

**conclusion/conclusión** (pág. 12) ) Juicio basado en la información obtenida.

**condensation/condensación** (pág. 407) El proceso de liberación de energía mediante el cual un gas o vapor se convierte en un líquido.

**condensation polymerization/polimerización de condensación** (pág. 764) Ocurre cuando se combinan monómeros que tienen por lo menos dos grupos funcionales, con la pérdida de un producto secundario pequeño, generalmente agua.

**condensation reaction/reacción de condensación** (pág. 753) Ocurre cuando dos moléculas orgánicas más pequeñas se combinan para formar una molécula más compleja, lo cual va acompañado de la pérdida de una molécula pequeña como el agua.

**conjugate acid** (p. 598) The species produced when a base accepts a hydrogen ion from an acid.

**conjugate acid-base pair** (p. 598) Consists of two substances related to each other by the donating and accepting of a single hydrogen ion.

**conjugate base** (p. 598) The species produced when an acid donates a hydrogen ion to a base.

**control** (p. 12) In an experiment, the standard that is used for comparison.

**conversion factor** (p. 34) A ratio of equivalent values used to express the same quantity in different units; is always equal to 1 and changes the units of a quantity without changing its value.

**coordinate covalent bond** (p. 257) Forms when one atom donates a pair of electrons to be shared with an atom or ion that needs two electrons to become stable.

**corrosion** (p. 679) The loss of metal that results from an oxidation-reduction reaction of the metal with substances in the environment.

**covalent bond** (p. 242) A chemical bond that results from the sharing of valence electrons.

**cracking** (p. 726) The process by which heavier fractions of petroleum are converted to gasoline by breaking their large molecules into smaller molecules.

**critical mass** (p. 823) The minimum mass of a sample of fissionable material necessary to sustain a nuclear chain reaction.

**crystalline solid** (p. 400) A solid whose atoms, ions, or molecules are arranged in an orderly, geometric, three-dimensional structure; can be classified by shape and by composition.

**crystallization** (p. 69) A separation technique that produces pure solid particles of a substance from a solution that contains the dissolved substance.

**cyclic hydrocarbon** (p. 706) An organic compound that contains a hydrocarbon ring.

**cycloalkane** (p. 706) A saturated hydrocarbon that can have rings with three, four, five, six, or more carbon atoms.

**conjugate acid/ácido conjugado** (pág. 598) Especie producida cuando una base acepta un ion hidrógeno de un ácido.

**conjugate acid-base pair/par ácido-base conjugado** (pág. 598) Consiste en dos sustancias relacionadas una con otra por la donación y aceptación de un solo ion hidrógeno.

**conjugate base/base conjugada** (pág. 598) Especie producida cuando un ácido dona un ion hidrógeno a una base.

**control/control** (pág. 12) Estándar de comparación en un experimento.

**conversion factor/factor de conversión** (pág. 34) Proporción de valores equivalentes utilizados para expresar la misma cantidad en unidades diferentes; siempre es igual a 1 y cambia las unidades de una cantidad sin cambiar su valor.

**coordinate covalent bond/enlace covalente coordinado** (pág. 257) Se forma cuando un átomo dona un par de electrones para ser compartidos con un átomo o ion que requiere dos electrones para volverse estable.

**corrosion/corrosión** (pág. 679) Pérdida de metal que resulta de una reacción de óxido-reducción del metal con sustancias en el ambiente.

**covalent bond/enlace covalente** (pág. 242) Enlace químico que resulta al compartir electrones de valencia.

**cracking/cracking** (pág. 726) El proceso por el cual las fracciones más pesadas de petróleo se convierten en gasolina, rompiendo sus moléculas grandes en moléculas más pequeñas.

**critical mass/masa crítica** (pág. 823) La masa mínima de una muestra de material fisionable necesario para sostener una reacción nuclear en cadena.

**crystalline solid/sólido cristalino** (pág. 400) Sólido cuyos átomos, iones o moléculas se arreglan en una estructura tridimensional, ordenada y geométrica; puede clasificarse por forma y por composición.

**crystallization/cristalización** (pág. 69) Técnica de separación que produce partículas sólidas puras de una sustancia a partir de una solución que contiene la sustancia disuelta.

**cyclic hydrocarbon/hidrocarburo cíclico** (pág. 706) Compuesto orgánico que contiene un hidrocarburo aromático (con un anillo).

**cycloalkane/cicloalcano** (pág. 706) Hidrocarburo saturado que puede tener anillos con tres, cuatro, cinco, seis o más átomos de carbono.

# D

**Dalton's atomic theory** (p. 89) A theory proposed by John Dalton in 1808, based on numerous scientific experiments, that marked the beginning of the development of modern atomic theory.

**Dalton's law of partial pressures** (p. 391) States that the total pressure of a mixture of gases is equal to the sum of the pressures of all the gases in the mixture.

**de Broglie equation** (p. 130) Predicts that all moving particles have wave characteristics and relates each particle's wavelength to its frequency, its mass, and Planck's constant.

**decomposition reaction** (p. 286) A chemical reaction that occurs when a single compound breaks down into two or more elements or new compounds.

**dehydration reaction** (p. 755) An organic elimination reaction in which the atoms removed form water.

**dehydrogenation reaction** (p. 754) Organic reaction that eliminates two hydrogen atoms, which form a hydrogen molecule.

**Dalton's atomic theory/teoría atómica de Dalton** (pág. 89) Teoría propuesta por John Dalton en 1808, basada en numerosos experimentos científicos, que marcó el principio del desarrollo de la teoría atómica moderna.

**Dalton's law of partial pressures/ley de presiones parciales de Dalton** (pág. 391) Establece que la presión total de una mezcla de gases es igual a la suma de las presiones de todos los gases en la mezcla.

**de Broglie equation/ecuación de deBroglie** (pág. 130) Predice que todas las partículas móviles tienen características de onda y relaciona la longitud de onda de cada partícula con su frecuencia, su masa y la constante de Planck.

**decomposition reaction/reacción de descomposición** (pág. 286) Reacción química que ocurre cuando un solo compuesto se divide en dos o más elementos o compuestos nuevos.

**dehydration reaction/reacción de deshidratación** (pág. 755) Una reacción de eliminación orgánica en la que los átomos eliminados forman agua.

**dehydrogenation reaction/reacción de deshidrogenación** (pág. 754) Reacción orgánica que elimina dos átomos de hidrógeno, los cuales forman una molécula de hidrógeno.

**delocalized electrons** (p. 228) The electrons involved in metallic bonding that are free to move easily from one atom to the next throughout the metal and are not attached to a particular atom.

**denaturation** (p. 778) The process in which a protein's natural, intricate three-dimensional structure is disrupted.

**denatured alcohol** (p. 744) Ethanol to which noxious substances have been added in order to make it unfit to drink.

**density** (p. 27) A ratio that compares the mass of an object to its volume.

**dependent variable** (p. 12) In an experiment, the variable whose value depends on the independent variable.

**deposition** (p. 408) The energy-releasing process by which a substance changes from a gas or vapor to a solid without first becoming a liquid.

**derived unit** (p. 27) A unit defined by a combination of base units.

**desalination** (p. 851) The removal of salts from seawater by processes such as reverse osmosis or distillation in order to make it fit for use by living things.

**diagonal relationships** (p. 180) The close relationships between elements in neighboring groups of the periodic table.

**diffusion** (p. 387) The movement of one material through another from an area of higher concentration to an area of lower concentration.

**dimensional analysis** (p. 34) A problem-solving method that focuses on the units that are used to describe matter.

**dipole–dipole forces** (p. 394) The attractions between oppositely charged regions of polar molecules.

**disaccharide** (p. 782) Forms when two monosaccharides bond together.

**dispersion forces** (p. 393) The weak forces resulting from temporary shifts in the density of electrons in electron clouds.

**distillation** (p. 69) A technique that can be used to physically separate most homogeneous mixtures based on the differences in the boiling points of the substances involved.

**double-replacement reaction** (p. 290) A chemical reaction that involves the exchange of positive ions between two compounds and produces either a precipitate, a gas, or water.

**dry cell** (p. 673) An electrochemical cell that contains a moist electrolytic paste inside a zinc shell.

**delocalized electrons/electrones deslocalizados** (pág. 228) Los electrones implicados en el enlace metálico que están libres para moverse fácilmente de un átomo al próximo a través del metal y no están relacionados con cierto átomo en particular.

**denaturation/desnaturalización** (pág. 778) Proceso en que se interrumpe la estructura tridimensional, intrincada y natural de una proteína.

**denatured alcohol/alcohol desnaturalizado** (pág. 744) Etanol al cual se le añadieron sustancias nocivas a fin de inhabilitarlo para beber.

**density/densidad** (pág. 27) Proporción que compara la masa de un objeto con su volumen.

**dependent variable/variable dependiente** (pág. 12) En un experimento, la variable cuyo valor depende de la variable independientele.

**deposition/depositación** (pág. 408) Proceso de liberación de energía por el cual una sustancia cambia de un gas o vapor a un sólido sin convertirse antes en un líquido.

**derived unit/unidad derivada** (pág. 27) Unidad definida por una combinación de unidades base.

**desalination/desalinación** (pág. 851) Eliminación de las sales del agua marina por procesos como la ósmosis inversa o la destilación para que puedan usarla los seres vivos.

**diagonal relationships/relaciones diagonales** (pág. 180) Relaciones estrechas entre elementos en grupos vecinos de la tabla periódica.

**diffusion/difusión** (pág. 387) El movimiento de un material a través de otro, de un área de mayor concentración a un área de menor concentración.

**dimensional analysis/análisis dimensional** (pág. 34) Método de resolución de problemas enfocado en las unidades que se utilizan para describir la materia.

**dipole–dipole forces/fuerzas dipolo-dipolo** (pág. 394) Las atracciones entre regiones opuestamente cargadas de moléculas polares.

**disaccharide/disacárido** (pág. 782) Se forma de la unión de dos monosacáridos.

**dispersion forces/fuerzas de dispersión** (pág. 393) Fuerzas débiles resultantes de los cambios temporales en la densidad de electrones en la nube electrónica.

**distillation/destilación** (pág. 69) Técnica que se puede emplear para separar físicamente la mayoría de las mezclas homogéneas, basándose en las diferencias en los puntos de ebullición de las sustancias implicadas.

**double-replacement reaction/reacción de doble desplazamiento** (pág. 290) Reacción química que involucra el cambio de iones positivos entre dos compuestos y produce un precipitado o un gas o agua.

**dry cell/celda seca** (pág. 673) Una celda electroquímica que contiene una pasta electrolítica húmeda dentro de un armazón de zinc.

# E

**elastic collision** (p. 386) Describes a collision in which kinetic energy may be transferred between the colliding particles but the total kinetic energy of the two particles remains the same.

**electrochemical cell** (p. 665) An apparatus that uses a redox reaction to produce electrical energy or uses electrical energy to cause a chemical reaction.

**electrolysis** (p. 683) The process that uses electrical energy to bring about a chemical reaction.

**electrolyte** (p. 218) An ionic compound whose aqueous solution conducts an electric current.

**elastic collision/choque elástico** (pág. 386) Describe una colisión en la cual energía cinética se puede transferir entre las partículas que chocan pero la energía cinética total de las dos partículas permanece igual.

**electrochemical cell/celda electroquímica** (pág. 665) Aparato que usa una reacción redox para producir energía eléctrica o utiliza energía eléctrica para causar una reacción química.

**electrolysis/electrólisis** (pág. 683) ) Proceso que emplea energía eléctrica para producir una reacción química.

**electrolyte/electrolito** (pág. 218) Compuesto iónico cuya solución acuosa conduce una corriente eléctrica.

**electrolytic cell** (p. 683) An electrochemical cell in which electrolysis occurs.

**electromagnetic radiation** (p. 118) A form of energy exhibiting wavelike behavior as it travels through space; can be described by wavelength, frequency, amplitude, and speed and includes visible light, microwaves, X rays, and radio waves.

**electromagnetic spectrum** (p. 120) Includes all forms of electromagnetic radiation, with the only differences in the types of radiation being their frequencies and wavelengths.

**electron** (p. 93) A negatively charged, fast-moving particle with an extremely small mass that is found in all forms of matter and moves through the empty space surrounding an atom's nucleus.

**electron capture** (p. 812) A radioactive decay process that occurs when an atom's nucleus draws in a surrounding electron, which combines with a proton to form a neutron, resulting in an X-ray photon being emitted.

**electron configuration** (p. 135) The arrangement of electrons in an atom, which is prescribed by three rules—the aufbau principle, the Pauli exclusion principle, and Hund's rule.

**electron-dot structure** (p. 140) Consists of an element's symbol, representing the atomic nucleus and inner-level electrons, that is surrounded by dots, representing the atom's valence electrons.

**electron sea model** (p. 228) Proposes that all metal atoms in a metallic solid contribute their valence electrons to form a "sea" of electrons, and can explain properties of metallic solids such as malleability, conduction, and ductility.

**electronegativity** (p. 168) Indicates the relative ability of an element's atoms to attract electrons in a chemical bond.

**element** (p. 70) A pure substance that cannot be broken down into simpler substances by physical or chemical means.

**elimination reaction** (p. 754) A reaction of organic compounds that occurs when a combination of atoms is removed from two adjacent carbon atoms forming an additional bond between the atoms.

**empirical formula** (p. 331) A formula that shows the smallest whole-number mole ratio of the elements of a compound, and may or may not be the same as the actual molecular formula.

**endothermic** (p. 247) A chemical reaction in which a greater amount of energy is required to break the existing bonds in the reactants than is released when the new bonds form in the product molecules.

**end point** (p. 619) The point at which the indicator that is used in a titration changes color.

**energy** (p. 489) The capacity to do work or produce heat; exists as potential energy, which is stored in an object due to its composition or position, and kinetic energy, which is the energy of motion.

**energy sublevels** (p. 133) The energy levels contained within a principal energy level.

**enthalpy** (p. 499) The heat content of a system at constant pressure.

**enthalpy (heat) of combustion** (p. 501) The enthalpy change for the complete burning of one mole of a given substance.

**enthalpy (heat) of reaction** (p. 499) The change in enthalpy for a reaction—the difference between the enthalpy of the sub-

**electrolytic cell/celda electrolítica** (pág. 683) Celda electroquímica en la cual se lleva a cabo la electrólisis.

**electromagnetic radiation/radiación electromagnética** (pág. 118) Forma de energía que exhibe un comportamiento parecido al de una onda al viajar por el espacio; puede describirse por su longitud de onda, frecuencia, amplitud y velocidad e incluye a la luz visible, las microondas, los rayos X y las ondas radiales.

**electromagnetic spectrum/espectro electromagnético** (pág. 120) Incluye toda forma de radiación electromagnética, en el cual las frecuencias y longitudes de onda son las únicas diferencias entre los tipos de radiación.

**electron/electrón** (pág. 93) Partícula móvil rápida, cargada negativamente y con una masa muy pequeña, que se encuentra en todas las formas de materia y se mueve a través del espacio vacío que rodea el núcleo de un átomo.

**electron capture/captura del electrón** (pág. 812) Proceso de desintegración radiactiva que ocurre cuando el núcleo de un átomo atrae un electrón circundante, que se combina con un protón para formar un neutrón, lo cual resulta en la emisión de un fotón de rayos X.

**electron configuration/configuración del electrón** (pág. 135) ) El arreglo de electrones en un átomo, que está establecido por tres reglas: el principio de Aufbau, el principio de la exclusión de Pauli y la regla de Hund.

**electron-dot structure/estructura punto electrón** (pág. 140) Consiste en el símbolo de un elemento, que representa el núcleo atómico y los electrones de los niveles interiores, rodeado por puntos que representan los electrones de valencia del átomo.

**electron sea model/modelo del mar de electrones** (pág. 228) Propone que todos los átomos de metal en un sólido metálico contribuyen con sus electrones de valencia para formar un "mar" de electrones y esto puede explicar propiedades de sólidos metálicos como maleabilidad, conducción y ductilidad.

**electronegativity/electronegatividad** (pág. 168) Indica la capacidad relativa de los átomos de un elemento para atraer electrones en un enlace químico.

**element/elemento** (pág. 70) Sustancia pura que no se puede separar en sustancias más sencillas por medios físicos ni químicos.

**elimination reaction/reacción de eliminación** (pág. 754) Reacción de compuestos orgánicos que ocurre cuando una combinación de átomos se elimina de dos átomos adyacentes del carbono, formando un enlace adicional entre los átomos.

**empirical formula/fórmula empírica** (pág. 331) Fórmula que muestra la proporción molar más pequeña en números enteros de los elementos de un compuesto y puede o no puede ser igual que la fórmula molecular real.

**endothermic/endotérmica** (pág. 247) Reacción química en la cual se requiere una mayor cantidad de energía para romper los enlaces existentes en los reactantes que aquella que se libera cuando se forman los enlaces nuevos en las moléculas del producto.

**end point/punto final** (pág. 619) Punto en el cual el indicador que se utiliza en la titulación cambia de color.

**energy/energía** (pág. 489) Capacidad de hacer trabajo o producir calor; existe como energía potencial, que se almacena en un objeto debido a su composición o posición y como energía cinética, que es la energía del movimiento.

**energy sublevels/subniveles de energía** (pág. 133) Los niveles de energía dentro de un nivel principal de energía.

**enthalpy/entalpía** (pág. 499) El contenido de calor en un sistema a presión constante.

**enthalpy (heat) of combustion/entalpía (calor) de combustión** (pág. 501) El cambio de entalpía para la combustión completa de un mol de una sustancia dada.

**enthalpy (heat) of reaction/entalpía (calor) de la reacción** (pág. 499) El cambio en la entalpía para una reacción, es decir, la stances that exist at the end of the reaction and the enthalpy of the substances present at the start.

**entropy** (p. 514) A measure of the disorder or randomness of the particles of a system.

**enzyme** (p. 778) A highly specific, powerful biological catalyst.

**equilibrium constant** (p. 563) $K_{eq}$, which describes the ratio of product concentrations to reactant concentrations, with each raised to the power corresponding to its coefficient in the balanced equation.

**equivalence point** (p. 618) The stoichiometric point of a titration.

**ester** (p. 750) An organic compound with a carboxyl group in which the hydrogen of the hydroxyl group is replaced by an alkyl group; may be volatile and sweet-smelling and is polar.

**ether** (p. 745) An organic compound that contains an oxygen atom bonded to two carbon atoms.

**evaporation** (p. 405) The process in which vaporization occurs only at the surface of a liquid.

**excess reactant** (p. 364) A reactant that remains after a chemical reaction stops.

**exothermic** (p. 247) A chemical reaction in which more energy is released than is required to break bonds in the initial reaction.

**experiment** (p. 11) A set of controlled observations that test the hypothesis.

**extensive property** (p. 56) A physical property, such as mass, length, and volume, that is dependent upon the amount of substance present.

diferencia entre la entalpía de las sustancias que existen al final de la reacción y la entalpía de las sustancias presentes al comienzo de la misma.

**entropy/entropía** (pág. 514) Medida del desorden o la aleatoriedad de las partículas de un sistema.

**enzyme/enzima** (pág. 778) Catalizador biológico, poderoso y sumamente específico.

**equilibrium constant/constante de equilibrio** (pág. 563) $K_{eq}$, la cual describe la proporción de concentraciones de producto a concentraciones de reactante, con cada uno elevado a la potencia correspondiente a su coeficiente en la ecuación equilibrada.

**equivalence point/punto de equivalencia** (pág. 618) Punto estequiométrico de una titulación.

**ester/éster** (pág. 750) Compuesto orgánico con un grupo carboxilo en que el hidrógeno del grupo de hidroxilo es reemplazado por un grupo alquilo; puede ser volátil y de olor dulce y es polar.

**ether/éter** (pág. 745) Compuesto orgánico que contiene un átomo de oxígeno unido a dos átomos del carbono.

**evaporation/evaporación** (pág. 405) ) Proceso en el cual la vaporización ocurre sólo en la superficie de un líquido.

**excess reactant/reactante en exceso** (pág. 364) Reactante que queda después de que se detiene una reacción química.

**exothermic/exotérmica** (pág. 247) Reacción química en que se libera más energía que aquella requerida para romper los enlaces en la reacción inicial.

**experiment/experimento** (pág. 11) Conjunto de las observaciones controladas para comprobar la hipótesis.

**extensive property/propiedad extensiva** (pág. 56) Propiedad física, como masa, longitud y volumen, dependiente de la cantidad de sustancia presente.

# F

**fatty acid** (p. 784) A long-chain carboxylic acid that usually has between 12 and 24 carbon atoms and can be saturated (no double bonds), or unsaturated (one or more double bonds).

**fermentation** (p. 794) The process in which glucose is broken down in the absence of oxygen, producing either ethanol, carbon dioxide, and energy (alcoholic fermentation) or lactic acid and energy (lactic acid fermentation).

**ferromagnetism** (p. 199) The strong attraction of a substance to a magnetic field.

**filtration** (p. 68) A technique that uses a porous barrier to separate a solid from a liquid.

**formula unit** (p. 221) The simplest ratio of ions represented in an ionic compound.

**fractional distillation** (p. 725) The process by which petroleum can be separated into simpler components, called fractions, as they condense at different temperatures.

**free energy** (p. 517) The energy that is available to do work—the difference between the change in enthalpy and the product of the entropy change and the absolute temperature.

**freezing point** (p. 408) The temperature at which a liquid is converted into a crystalline solid.

**freezing point depression** (p. 473) The difference in temperature between a solution's freezing point and the freezing point of its pure solvent.

**frequency** (p. 118) The number of waves that pass a given point per second.

**fuel cell** (p. 677) A voltaic cell in which the oxidation of a fuel, such as hydrogen gas, is used to produce electric energy.

**fatty acid/ácido graso** (pág. 784) Ácido carboxílico de cadena larga que tiene generalmente entre 12 y 24 átomos de carbono y puede ser saturado (sin enlaces dobles) o insaturado (uno ó más enlaces dobles).

**fermentation/fermentación** (pág. 794) Proceso en el que la glucosa se rompe en ausencia de oxígeno, produciendo ya sea etanol, dióxido de carbono y energía (fermentación alcohólica) o ácido láctico y energía (fermentación ácido láctica).

**ferromagnetism/ferromagnetismo** (pág. 199) Atracción fuerte de una sustancia a un campo magnético.

**filtration/filtración** (pág. 68) Técnica que utiliza una barrera porosa para separar un sólido de un líquido.

**formula unit/fórmula unitaria** (pág. 221) La proporción más sencilla de iones representados en un compuesto iónico.

**fractional distillation/destilación fraccionaria** (pág. 725) Proceso mediante el cual el petróleo se puede separar en componentes más simples, llamados fracciones, dado que se condensan a temperaturas diferentes.

**free energy/energía libre** (pág. 517) Energía disponible para hacer trabajo: la diferencia entre el cambio en la entalpía y el producto del cambio de entropía y la temperatura absoluta.

**freezing point/punto de congelación** (pág. 408) ) La temperatura a la cual un líquido se convierte en un sólido cristalino.

**freezing point depression/disminución del punto de congelación** (pág. 473) Diferencia de temperatura entre el punto de congelación de una solución y el punto de congelación de su disolvente puro.

**frequency/frecuencia** (pág. 118) Número de ondas que pasan por un punto dado en un segundo.

**fuel cell/celda de combustible** (pág. 677) Celda voltaica en la cual la oxidación de un combustible, como el gas hidrógeno, se utiliza para producir energía eléctrica.

**functional group** (p. 737) An atom or group of atoms that always react in a certain way in an organic molecule.

**functional group/grupo funcional** (pág. 737) Átomo o grupo de átomos que siempre reaccionan de cierta manera en una molécula orgánica.

# G

**galvanizing** (p. 681) The process in which an iron object is dipped into molten zinc or electroplated with zinc to make the iron more resistant to corrosion.

**gamma rays** (p. 107) High-energy radiation that has no electrical charge and no mass, is not deflected by electric or magnetic fields, usually accompanies alpha and beta radiation, and accounts for most of the energy lost during radioactive decay.

**gas** (p. 59) A form of matter that flows to conform to the shape of its container, fills the container's entire volume, and is easily compressed.

**Gay-Lussac's law** (p. 426) States that the pressure of a given mass of gas varies directly with the kelvin temperature when the volume remains constant.

**geometric isomers** (p. 718) A category of stereoisomers that results from different arrangements of groups around a double bond.

**global warming** (p. 859) The rise in global temperatures, which may be due to increases in greenhouse gases, such as $CO_2$.

**Graham's law of effusion** (p. 387) States that the rate of effusion for a gas is inversely proportional to the square root of its molar mass.

**graph** (p. 43) A visual representation of information, such as a circle graph, line graph, or bar graph, that can reveal patterns in data.

**greenhouse effect** (p. 859) The natural warming of Earth's surface due to certain atmospheric gases that absorb solar energy, which is converted to heat; prevents Earth from becoming too cold to support life.

**ground state** (p. 127) The lowest allowable energy state of an atom.

**group** (p. 154) A vertical column of elements in the periodic table; also called a family.

**galvanizing/galvanizado** (pág. 681) Proceso en que un objeto de hierro se sumerge en zinc fundido o se electroemplaca con zinc para hacer el hierro más resistente a la corrosión.

**gamma rays/rayos gamma** (pág. 107) Radiación de alta energía que no tiene ni carga eléctrica ni masa, no es desviada por campos eléctricos ni magnéticos, acompaña generalmente a la radiación alfa y beta y representan la mayor parte de la energía perdida durante la desintegración radiactiva.

**gas/gas** (pág. 59) Forma de la materia que fluye para adaptarse a la forma de su contenedor, llena el volumen entero del recipiente y se comprime fácilmente.

**Gay-Lussac's law/ley de Gay- Lussac** (pág. 426) Establece que la presión de una masa dada de gas varía directamente con la temperatura en Kelvin cuando el volumen permanece constante.

**geometric isomers/isómeros geométricos** (pág. 718) Categoría de estereoisómeros que es una consecuencia de arreglos diferentes de grupos alrededor de un enlace doble.

**global warming/calentamiento global** (pág. 859) Incremento en temperaturas globales, que puede deberse a aumentos en gases invernadero, como el $CO_2$.

**Graham's law of effusion/ley de efusión de Graham** (pág. 387) Establece que la velocidad de efusión de un gas es proporcional al inverso de la raíz cuadrada de su masa molar.

**graph/gráfica** (pág. 43) Representación visual de información, como por ejemplo, las gráficas circulares, las gráficas lineales y las gráficas de barras, que pueden revelar patrones en los datos.

**greenhouse effect/efecto de invernadero** (pág. 859) El calentamiento natural de la superficie de la Tierra debido a ciertos gases atmosféricos que absorben energía solar, que es convertida a calor; previene que la Tierra llegue a ser demasiado fría para sostener la vida.

**ground state/estado base** (pág. 127) Estado de energía más bajo admisible de un átomo.

**group/grupo** (pág. 154) Columna vertical de elementos en la tabla periódica; llamado también familia.

# H

**half-cells** (p. 665) The two parts of an electrochemical cell in which the separate oxidation and reduction reactions occur.

**half-life** (p. 817) The time required for one-half of a radioisotope's nuclei to decay into its products.

**half-reaction** (p. 651) One of two parts of a redox reaction—the oxidation half, which shows the number of electrons lost when a species is oxidized, or the reduction half, which shows the number of electrons gained when a species is reduced.

**halocarbon** (p. 738) Any organic compound containing a halogen substituent.

**halogen** (p. 158) A highly reactive group 7A element.

**halogenation** (p. 741) A process by which hydrogen atoms may be replaced by halogen atoms (typically Cl or Br).

**half-cells/celdas medias** (pág. 665) Las dos partes de una celda electroquímica en que se llevan a cabo las reacciones separadas de la oxidación y la reducción.

**half-life/media vida** (pág. 817) Tiempo requerido para que la mitad de los núcleos de un radioisótopo se desintegren en sus productos.

**half-reaction/reacción media** (pág. 651) Una de dos partes de una reacción redox: la parte de la oxidación, la cual muestra el número de electrones perdidos cuando una especie se oxida o la parte de la reducción, que muestra el número de electrones ganados cuando una especie se reduce.

**halocarbon/halocarbono** (pág. 738) Cualquier compuesto orgánico que contiene un sustituyente de halógeno.

**halogen/halógeno** (pág. 158) Elemento del grupo 7A, sumamente reactivo.

**halogenation/halogenación** (pág. 741) Proceso mediante el cual átomos de hidrógeno pueden ser reemplazados por átomos de halógeno (típicamente Cl o Br).

heat (p. 491) A form of energy that flows from a warmer object to a cooler object.

heat of solution (p. 457) The overall energy change that occurs during the solution formation process.

Heisenberg uncertainty principle (p. 131) States that it is not possible to know precisely both the velocity and the position of a particle at the same time.

Henry's law (p. 460) States that at a given temperature, the solubility of a gas in a liquid is directly proportional to the pressure of the gas above the liquid.

Hess's law (p. 506) States that if two or more thermochemical equations can be added to produce a final equation for a reaction, then the sum of the enthalpy changes for the individual reactions is the enthalpy change for the final reaction.

heterogeneous catalyst (p. 541) A catalyst that exists in a different physical state than the reaction it catalyzes.

heterogeneous equilibrium (p. 565) A state of equilibrium that occurs when the reactants and products of a reaction are present in more than one physical state.

heterogeneous mixture (p. 67) One that does not have a uniform composition and in which the individual substances remain distinct.

homogeneous catalyst (p. 541) A catalyst that exists in the same physical state as the reaction it catalyzes.

homogeneous equilibrium (p. 564) A state of equilibrium that occurs when all the reactants and products of a reaction are in the same physical state.

homogeneous mixture (p. 67) One that has a uniform composition throughout and always has a single phase; also called a solution.

homologous series (p. 701) Describes a series of compounds that differ from one another by a repeating unit.

Hund's rule (p. 136) States that single electrons with the same spin must occupy each equal-energy orbital before additional electrons with opposite spins can occupy the same orbitals.

hybridization (p. 261) The process by which the valence electrons of an atom are rearranged to form four new, identical hybrid orbitals.

hydrate (p. 338) A compound that has a specific number of water molecules bound to its atoms.

hydration reaction (p. 756) An addition reaction in which a hydrogen atom and a hydroxyl group from a water molecule add to a double or triple bond.

hydrocarbon (p. 698) Simplest organic compound composed only of the elements carbon and hydrogen.

hydrogenation reaction (p. 756) An addition reaction in which hydrogen is added to atoms in a double or triple bond; usually requires a catalyst and is often used to convert liquid unsaturated fats into saturated fats that are solid at room temperature.

hydrogen bond (p. 395) A strong dipole-dipole attraction between molecules that contain a hydrogen atom bonded to a small, highly electronegative atom with at least one lone electron pair.

hydrosphere (p. 850) All the water in and on Earth's surface, more than 97% of which is found in the oceans.

heat/calor (pág. 491) Forma de energía que fluye de un cuerpo más caliente a uno más frío.

heat of solution/calor de solución (pág. 457) El cambio global de energía que ocurre durante el proceso de formación de la solución.

Heisenberg uncertainty principle/principio de incertidumbre de Heisenberg (pág. 131) Establece que no es posible saber precisamente la velocidad y la posición de una partícula al mismo tiempo.

Henry's law/ley de Henry (pág. 460) Establece que a una temperatura dada, la solubilidad de un gas en un líquido es directamente proporcional a la presión del gas por encima del líquido.

Hess's law/ley de Hess (pág. 506) Establece que si dos o más ecuaciones termoquímicas se pueden sumar para producir una ecuación final para una reacción, entonces la suma de los cambios de entalpía para las reacciones individuales es igual al cambio de entalpía para la reacción final.

heterogeneous catalyst/catalizador heterogéneo (pág. 541) Catalizador que existe en un estado físico diferente al de la reacción que cataliza.

heterogeneous equilibrium/equilibrio heterogéneo (pág. 565) Estado de equilibrio que ocurre cuando los reactantes y los productos de una reacción están presentes en más de un estado físico.

heterogeneous mixture/mezcla heterogénea (pág. 67) Aquélla que no tiene una composición uniforme y en la que las sustancias individuales permanecen separadas.

homogeneous catalyst/catalizador homogéneo (pág. 541) Catalizador que existe en el mismo estado físico de la reacción que cataliza.

homogeneous equilibrium/equilibrio homogéneo (pág. 564) estado de equilibrio que ocurre cuando todos los reactantes y productos de una reacción están en el mismo estado físico.

homogeneous mixture/mezcla homogénea (pág. 67) Aquélla que tiene una composición uniforme a lo largo de todo su sistema y siempre tiene una sola fase; también llamada solución.

homologous series/serie homóloga (pág. 701) Describe una serie de compuestos que difieren uno del otro por una unidad repetitiva.

Hund's rule/regla de Hund (pág. 136) Establece que electrones individuales con igual rotación deben ocupar cada orbital de igual energía antes de que electrones adicionales con rotaciones opuestas puedan ocupar los mismos orbitales.

hybridization/hibridación (pág. 261) El proceso mediante el cual los electrones de valencia de un átomo se reordenan para formar cuatro orbitales híbridos nuevos e idénticos.

hydrate/hidrato (pág. 338) Compuesto que tiene un número específico de moléculas de agua asociadas a sus átomos.

hydration reaction/reacción de hidratació (pág. 756) Reacción de adición en que un átomo de hidrógeno y un grupo hidroxilo de una molécula de agua se añaden a un enlace doble o triple.

hydrocarbon/hidrocarburo (pág. 698) Compuesto orgánico más simple compuesto sólo de los elementos carbono e hidrógeno.

hydrogenation reaction/reacción de hidrogenación (pág. 756) Reacción de adición en la que hidrógeno se agrega a átomos en un enlace doble o triple; requiere generalmente un catalizador y a menudo se emplea para convertir grasas insaturadas líquidas en grasas saturadas que son sólidas a temperatura ambiente.

hydrogen bond/puente de hidrógeno (pág. 395) Fuerte atracción bipolo- bipolo entre moléculas que contienen un átomo de hidrógeno unido a un átomo pequeño, sumamente electronegativo con por lo menos un par de electrones no combinados.

hydrosphere/hidrosfera (pág. 850) Toda el agua dentro y sobre la superficie de la Tierra, más del 97% de la cual se encuentra en los océanos.

**hydroxyl group** (p. 743) An oxygen-hydrogen group covalently bonded to a carbon atom.

**hypothesis** (p. 11) A tentative, testable statement or prediction about what has been observed.

**hydroxyl group/grupo hidroxilo** (pág. 743) Un grupo hidrógeno-oxígeno unido covalentemente a un átomo de carbono.

**hypothesis/hipótesis** (pág. 11) Enunciado tentativo y sujeto a comprobación o predicción acerca de lo que se ha observado.

---

**ideal gas constant** (R) (p. 434) An experimentally determined constant whose value in the ideal gas equation depends on the units that are used for pressure.

**ideal gas law** (p. 434) Describes the physical behavior of an ideal gas in terms of the temperature, volume, and pressure, and number of moles of a gas that are present.

**immiscible** (p. 454) Describes two liquids that can be mixed together but separate shortly after you cease mixing them.

**independent variable** (p. 12) In an experiment, the variable that the experimenter plans to change.

**induced transmutation** (p. 815) The process in which nuclei are bombarded with high-velocity charged particles in order to create new elements.

**inhibitor** (p. 540) A substance that slows down the reaction rate of a chemical reaction or prevents a reaction from happening.

**inner transition metal** (p. 158) A type of group B element that is contained in the f-block of the periodic table and is characterized by a filled outermost s orbital, and filled or partially filled 4f and 5f orbitals.

**insoluble** (p. 454) Describes a substance that cannot be dissolved in a given solvent.

**instantaneous rate** (p. 546) The rate of decomposition at a specific time, calculated from the rate law, the specific rate constant, and the concentrations of all the reactants.

**intensive property** (p. 56) A physical property that remains the same no matter how much of a substance is present.

**intermediate** (p. 548) A substance produced in one elementary step of a complex reaction and consumed in a subsequent elementary step.

**ion** (p. 165) An atom or bonded group of atoms with a positive or negative charge.

**ionic bond** (p. 215) The electrostatic force that holds oppositely charged particles together in an ionic compound.

**ionization energy** (p. 167) The energy required to remove an electron from a gaseous atom; generally increases in moving from left-to-right across a period and decreases in moving down a group.

**ionizing radiation** (p. 827) Radiation that is energetic enough to ionize matter it collides with.

**ion product constant for water** (p. 608) The value of the equilibrium constant expression for the self-ionization of water.

**isomers** (p. 717) Two or more compounds that have the same molecular formula but have different molecular structures.

**isotopes** (p. 100) Atoms of the same element with the same number of protons but different numbers of neutrons.

**ideal gas constant (R)/constante de los gases ideales (R)/** (pág. 434) Constante experimentalmente determinada cuyo valor en la ecuación ideal de gas depende de las unidades que se utilizan para la presión.

**ideal gas law/ley del gas ideal** (pág. 434) Describe el comportamiento físico de un gas ideal en términos de temperatura, volumen y presión y del número de moles de un gas que están presentes.

**immiscible/inmiscible** (pág. 454) Describe dos líquidos que se pueden mezclar juntos pero que se separan poco después de que se cesa de mezclarlos.

**independent variable/variable independiente** (pág. 12) En un experimento, la variable que el experimentador piensa cambiar.

**induced transmutation/trasmutación inducida** (pág. 815) Proceso en cual núcleos se bombardean con partículas cargadas de alta velocidad para crear elementos nuevos.

**inhibitor/inhibidor** (pág. 540) Sustancia que decelera la velocidad de reacción de una reacción química o previene que ésta suceda.

**inner transition metal/metal de transición interna** (pág. 158) Tipo de elemento del grupo B que está situado en el bloque F de la tabla periódica y se caracteriza por tener el orbital más externo lleno y los orbitales 4f y 5f parcialmente llenos.

**insoluble/insoluble** (pág. 454) Describe una sustancia que no se puede disolver en un disolvente dado.

**instantaneous rate/velocidad instantánea** (pág. 546) Velocidad de descomposición a un tiempo específico, calculada a través de la ley de velocidad, la constante específica de velocidad y las concentraciones de todos los reactantes.

**intensive property/propiedad intensiva** (pág. 56) Propiedad física que permanece igual sea cual sea la cantidad de sustancia presente.

**intermediate/intermediario** (pág. 548) Sustancia producida en un paso elemental de una reacción compleja y consumida en un paso elemental subsecuente.

**ion/ion** (pág. 165) Átomo o grupo de átomos unidos con carga positiva o negativa.

**ionic bond/enlace iónico** (pág. 215)Fuerza electrostática que mantiene unidas las partículas opuestamente cargadas en un compuesto iónico.

**ionization energy/energía de ionización** (pág. 167) Energía que se requiere para quitar un electrón de un átomo gaseoso; generalmente aumenta al moverse de izquierda a derecha a través de un período y disminuye al moverse un grupo hacia abajo.

**ionizing radiation/radiación ionizante** (pág. 827) Radiación que es suficientemente energética para ionizar la materia con la que choca.

**ion product constant for water/constante del producto ion para el agua** (pág. 608) Valor de la expresión de la constante de equilibrio para la autoionización del agua.

**isomers/isómeros** (pág. 717) Dos o más compuestos que tienen la misma fórmula molecular pero poseen estructuras moleculares diferentes.

**isotopes/isótopos** (pág. 100) Átomos del mismo elemento con el mismo número de protones, pero números diferentes de neutrones.

# J

joule (p. 491) The SI unit of heat and energy.

joule/julio (pág. 491) La unidad SI del calor y la energía.

# K

kelvin (p. 30) The SI base unit of temperature.

ketone (p. 748) An organic compound in which the carbon of the carbonyl group is bonded to two other carbon atoms.

kilogram (p. 27) The SI base unit for mass; about 2.2 pounds.

kinetic-molecular theory (p. 385) Explains the properties of gases in terms of the energy, size, and motion of their particles.

kelvin/kelvin (pág. 30) La unidad base de temperatura del SI.

ketone/cetona (pág. 748) Compuesto orgánico en que el carbono del grupo carbonilo está unido a otros dos átomos de carbono.

kilogram/kilogramo (pág. 27) Unidad base del SI para la masa; aproximadamente equivale a 2.2 libras.

kinetic-molecular theory/teoría cinético-molecular (pág. 385) Explica las propiedades de gases en términos de energía, tamaño y movimiento de sus partículas.

# L

lanthanide series (p. 197) In the periodic table, the f-block elements from period 6 that follow the element lanthanum.

lattice energy (p. 219) The energy required to separate one mole of the ions of an ionic compound, which is directly related to the size of the ions bonded and is also affected by the charge of the ions.

law of chemical equilibrium (p. 563) States that at a given temperature, a chemical system may reach a state in which a particular ratio of reactant and product concentrations has a constant value.

law of conservation of energy (p. 490) States that in any chemical or physical process, energy may change from one form to another but it is neither created nor destroyed.

law of conservation of mass (p. 63) States that mass is neither created nor destroyed during a chemical reaction but is conserved.

law of definite proportions (p. 75) States that, regardless of the amount, a compound is always composed of the same elements in the same proportion by mass.

law of disorder (p. 514) States that entropy of the universe must increase as a result of a spontaneous reaction or process.

law of multiple proportions (p. 76) States that when different compounds are formed by the combination of the same elements, different masses of one element combine with the same mass of the other element in a ratio of small whole numbers.

Le Châtelier's principle (p. 569) States that if a stress is applied to a system at equilibrium, the system shifts in the direction that relieves the stress.

Lewis structure (p. 243) A model that uses electron-dot structures to show how electrons are arranged in molecules. Pairs of dots or lines represent bonding pairs.

limiting reactant (p. 364) A reactant that is totally consumed during a chemical reaction, limits the extent of the reaction, and determines the amount of product.

lanthanide series/serie de lantánidos (pág. 197) En la tabla periódica, los elementos del bloque F del período 6 que siguen después del elemento lantano.

lattice energy/energía de rejilla (pág. 219) Energía requerida para separar un mol de iones de un compuesto iónico, lo cual está directamente relacionado con el tamaño de los iones unidos y es afectado también por la carga de los iones.

law of chemical equilibrium/ley del equilibrio químico (pág. 563) Establece que a una temperatura dada, un sistema químico puede alcanzar un estado en que cierta proporción de concentraciones de reactante y producto tiene un valor constante.

law of conservation of energy/ley de la conservación de energía (pág. 490) Establece que en un proceso químico o físico, la energía puede cambiar de una forma a otra pero ni se crea ni se destruye.

law of conservation of mass/ley de la conservación de masa (pág. 63) Establece que la masa ni se crea ni se destruye durante una reacción química sino que se conserva.

law of definite proportions/ley de proporciones definidas (pág. 75) Indica que, a pesar de la cantidad, un compuesto siempre está constituido por los mismos elementos en la misma proporción másica.

law of disorder/ley del desorden (pág. 514) Indica que la entropía del universo debe aumentar como resultado de una reacción o proceso espontáneo.

law of multiple proportions/ley de proporciones múltiples (pág. 76) Establece que cuando compuestos diferentes están formados por la combinación de los mismos elementos, masas diferentes de un elemento se combinan con la misma masa del otro elemento en una proporción de números enteros pequeños.

Le Châtelier's principle/Principio de Le Châtelier (pág. 569) Establece que si se aplica un estrés a un sistema en el equilibrio, el sistema cambia en la dirección en que se disminuye el estrés.

Lewis structure/estructura de Lewis (pág. 243) Modelo que utiliza las estructuras punto electrón para mostrar como están distribuidos los electrones en las moléculas. Los pares de puntos o líneas representan pares de unión.

limiting reactant/reactante limitante (pág. 364) Reactante que se consume completamente durante una reacción química, limita el alcance de la reacción y determina la cantidad de producto.

lipids (p. 784) Large, nonpolar biological molecules that vary in structure, store energy in living organisms, and make up most of the structure of cell membranes.

liquid (p. 58) A form of matter that flows, has constant volume, and takes the shape of its container.

liter (p. 27) The metric unit for volume equal to one cubic decimeter.

lithosphere (p. 855) The solid part of Earth's crust and upper mantle, which contains a large variety of elements including oxygen, silicon, aluminum, and iron.

lipids/lípidos (pág. 784) Moléculas biológicas no polares de gran tamaño que varían en estructura, guardan energía en organismos vivos y representan la mayor parte de la estructura de membranas de célula.

liquid/líquido (pág. 58) Forma de materia que fluye, tiene volumen constante y toma la forma de su envase.

liter/litro (pág. 27) Unidad métrica para el volumen igual a un decímetro cúbico.

lithosphere/litosfera (pág. 855) La parte sólida de la corteza y el manto superior de la Tierra, que contiene una gran variedad de elementos, incluyendo oxígeno, silicio, aluminio y hierro.

## M

mass (p. 8) A measure of the amount of matter.

mass defect (p. 822) The difference in mass between a nucleus and its component nucleons.

mass number (p. 100) The number after an element's name, representing the sum of its protons and neutrons.

matter (p. 8) Anything that has mass and takes up space.

melting point (p. 405) For a crystalline solid, the temperature at which the forces holding a crystal lattice together are broken and it becomes a liquid.

metabolism (p. 792) The sum of the many chemical reactions that occur in living cells.

metal (p. 155) An element that is solid at room temperature, a good conductor of heat and electricity, and generally is shiny; most metals are ductile and malleable.

metallic bond (p. 228) The attraction of a metallic cation for delocalized electrons.

metalloid (p. 158) An element, such as silicon or germanium, that has physical and chemical properties of both metals and nonmetals.

metallurgy (p. 199) The branch of applied science that studies and designs methods for extracting metals and their compounds from ores.

meter (p. 26) The SI base unit for length.

method of initial rates (p. 544) Determines the reaction order by comparing the initial rates of a reaction carried out with varying reactant concentrations.

mineral (p. 187) An element or inorganic compound that occurs in nature as solid crystals and usually is found mixed with other materials in ores.

miscible (p. 454) Describes two liquids that are soluble in each other.

mixture (p. 66) A physical blend of two or more pure substances in any proportion in which each substance retains its individual properties; can be separated by physical means.

model (p. 13) A visual, verbal, and/or mathematical explanation of data collected from many experiments.

molality (p. 469) The ratio of the number of moles of solute dissolved in one kilogram of solvent; also known as molal concentration.

molar enthalpy (heat) of fusion (p. 502) The amount of heat required to melt one mole of a solid substance.

molar enthalpy (heat) of vaporization (p. 502) The amount of heat required to evaporate one mole of a liquid.

mass/masa (pág. 8) Medida de la cantidad de materia.

mass defect/defecto másico (pág. 822) La diferencia de masa entre un núcleo y sus nucleones componentes.

mass number/número de masa (pág. 100) El número después del nombre de un elemento, la cual representa la suma de sus protones y neutrones.

matter/materia (pág. 8) Cualquier cosa que tiene masa y ocupa espacio.

melting point/punto de fusión (pág. 405) Para un sólido cristalino, la temperatura en que se rompen las fuerzas que mantienen la matriz cristalina estable y éste se convierte en un líquido.

metabolism/matabolismo (pág. 792) La suma de las numerosas reacciones químicas que ocurren en células vivas.

metal/metal (pág. 155) Elemento sólido a temperatura ambiente que es buen conductor de calor y electricidad y generalmente es brillante; la mayoría de los metales son dúctiles y maleables.

metallic bond/enlace metálico (pág. 228) Atracción de un catión metálico hacia electrones deslocalizados.

metalloid/metaloide (pág. 158) Elemento, como el silicio o el germanio, que tiene las propiedades físicas y químicas tanto de metales como de no metales.

metallurgy/metalurgia (pág. 199) Rama de la ciencia aplicada que estudia y diseña los métodos para extraer de menas a metales y sus compuestos.

meter/metro (pág. 26) Unidad base para longitud del SI.

method of initial rates/método de velocidades iniciales (pág. 544) Determina el orden de la reacción comparando las velocidades iniciales de una reacción llevada a cabo con diversas concentraciones de reactante.

mineral/mineral (pág. 187) Elemento o compuesto inorgánico que está presente en la naturaleza como cristales sólidos y se encuentra generalmente mezclado con otros materiales en menas.

miscible/miscible (pág. 454) Describe dos líquidos que son solubles uno en el otro.

mixture/mezcla (pág. 66) Combinación física de dos o más sustancias puras en cualquier proporción, en la cual cada sustancia retiene sus propiedades individuales; puede ser separada por medios físicos.

model/modelo (pág. 13) Explicación matemática, verbal y/o visual de datos recolectados de muchos experimentos.

molality/molalidad (pág. 469) Proporción del número de moles de soluto disueltos en un kilogramo de disolvente; también conocida como concentración molal.

molar enthalpy (heat) of fusion/entalpía (calor) molar de fusión (pág. 502) Cantidad requerida de calor para fundir un mol de una sustancia sólida.

molar enthalpy (heat) of vaporization/entalpía (calor) molar de vaporización (pág. 502) Cantidad requerida de calor para evaporar un mol de un líquido.

**molarity** (p. 464) The number of moles of solute dissolved per liter of solution; also known as molar concentration.

**molar mass** (p. 313) The mass in grams of one mole of any pure substance.

**molar volume** (p. 431) For a gas, the volume that one mole occupies at 0.00°C and 1.00 atm pressure.

**mole** (p. 310) The SI base unit used to measure the amount of a substance, abbreviated mol; one mole is the amount of a pure substance that contains $6.02 \times 10^{23}$ representative particles.

**molecular formula** (p. 333) A formula that specifies the actual number of atoms of each element in one molecule or formula unit of the substance.

**molecule** (p. 242) Forms when two or more atoms covalently bond and is lower in potential energy than its constituent atoms.

**mole fraction** (p. 470) The ratio of the number of moles of solute in solution to the total number of moles of solute and solvent.

**mole ratio** (p. 356) In a balanced equation, the ratio between the numbers of moles of any two substances.

**monatomic ion** (p. 221) An ion formed from only one atom.

**monomer** (p. 762) A molecule from which a polymer is made.

**monosaccharides** (p. 781) The simplest carbohydrates, which are aldehydes or ketones that also have multiple hydroxyl groups; also called simple sugars.

**molarity/molaridad** (pág. 464) Número de moles de soluto disueltos por litro de solución; también conocida como concentración molar.

**molar mass/masa molar** (pág. 313) Masa en gramos de un mol de cierta sustancia pura.

**molar volume/volumen molar** (pág. 431) Para un gas, el volumen que ocupa un mol a 0.00°C y 1.00 atm de presión.

**mole/mol** (pág. 310) Unidad base del SI utilizada para medir la cantidad de una sustancia, abreviada mol; un mol es la cantidad de sustancia pura que contienen $6.02 \times 10^{23}$ partículas representativas.

**molecular formula/fórmula molecular** (pág. 333) Fórmula que especifica el número real de átomos de cada elemento en una molécula o unidad de fórmula de la sustancia.

**molecule/molécula** (pág. 242) Se forma cuando dos o más átomos se unen covalentemente y la cual tiene menor energía potencial que sus átomos constituyentes.

**mole fraction/fracción mol** (pág. 470) Proporción del número de moles de soluto en solución entre el número total de moles de soluto y disolvente.

**mole ratio/proporción molar** (pág. 356) En una ecuación equilibrada, la proporción entre los números de moles de dos sustancias cualesquiera.

**monatomic ion/monómero** (pág. 221) Ion formado a partir de un sólo átomo.

**monomer/** (pág. 762) Molécula a partir de la cual se forma un polímero.

**monosaccharides/monosacáridos** (pág. 781) Los carbohidratos más simples, los cuales son aldehidos o cetonas que tienen también múltiples grupos hidroxilo; llamados también azúcares simples.

## N

**net ionic equation** (p. 293) An ionic equation that includes only the particles that participate in the reaction.

**neutralization reaction** (p. 617) A reaction in which an acid and a base react in aqueous solution to produce a salt and water.

**neutron** (p. 96) A neutral subatomic particle in an atom's nucleus that has a mass nearly equal to that of a proton.

**nitrogen fixation** (p. 860) The process that converts nitrogen gas into biologically useful nitrates.

**noble gas** (p. 158) An extremely unreactive group 8A element.

**nonmetals** (p. 158) Elements that are generally gases or dull, brittle solids that are poor conductors of heat and electricity.

**nuclear equation** (p. 106) A type of equation that shows the atomic number and mass number of the particles involved.

**nuclear fission** (p. 822) The splitting of a nucleus into smaller, more stable fragments, accompanied by a large release of energy.

**nuclear fusion** (p. 826) The process of binding smaller atomic nuclei into a single larger and more stable nucleus.

**nuclear reaction** (p. 105) A reaction that involves a change in the nucleus of an atom.

**nucleic acid** (p. 788) A nitrogen-containing biological polymer that is involved in the storage and transmission of genetic information.

**nucleons** (p. 810) The positively charged protons and neutral neutrons contained in an atom's densely packed nucleus.

**net ionic equation/ecuación iónica neta** (pág. 293) Ecuación iónica que incluye sólo las partículas que participan en la reacción.

**neutralization reaction/reacción de neutralización** (pág. 617) Reacción en que un ácido y una base reaccionan en una solución acuosa para producir una sal y agua.

**neutron/neutrón** (pág. 96) Partícula subatómica neutral en el núcleo de un átomo que tiene una masa casi igual a la de un protón.

**nitrogen fixation/fijación de nitrógeno** (pág. 860) Proceso que convierte gas nitrógeno en nitratos biológicamente útiles.

**noble gas/gas noble** (pág. 158) Elemento extremadamente poco reactivo del grupo 8A.

**nonmetals/no metales** (pág. 158) Elementos que generalmente son gases o sólidos quebradizos sin brillo y malos conductores de calor y electricidad.

**nuclear equation/ecuación nuclear** (pág. 106) Tipo de ecuación que muestra el número atómico y el número másico de las partículas involucradas.

**nuclear fission/fisión nuclear** (pág. 822) Ruptura de un núcleo en fragmentos más pequeños y más estables, acompañado de una gran liberación de energía.

**nuclear fusion/fusión nuclear** (pág. 826) El proceso de unión de núcleos atómicos más pequeños en un sólo núcleo más grande y más estable.

**nuclear reaction/reacción nuclear** (pág. 105) Reacción que implica un cambio en el núcleo de un átomo.

**nucleic acid/ácido nucleico** (pág. 788) Polímero biológico que contiene nitrógeno y que está involucrado en el almacenamiento y transmisión de información genética.

**nucleons/nucleones** (pág. 810) Protones positivamente cargados y neutrones neutros en el núcleo densamente poblado de un átomo.

**nucleotide** (p. 788) The monomer that makes up a nucleic acid; consists of a nitrogen base, an inorganic phosphate group, and a five-carbon monosaccharide sugar.

**nucleus** (p. 95) The extremely small, positively charged, dense center of an atom that contains positively charged protons, neutral neutrons, and is surrounded by empty space through which one or more negatively charged electrons move.

**nucleotide/nucleótido** (pág. 788) Monómero que constituye un ácido nucleico; consiste en una base nitrogenada, un grupo fosfato inorgánico y un azúcar monosacárido de cinco carbonos.

**nucleus/núcleo** (pág. 95) El diminuto centro de un átomo, denso y positivamente cargado, que contiene protones positivamente cargados, neutrones neutrales y está rodeado de un espacio vacío a través del cual se mueven uno o más electrones cargados negativamente.

## O

**octet rule** (p. 168) States that atoms lose, gain, or share electrons in order to acquire a full set of eight valence electrons (the stable electron configuration of a noble gas).

**optical isomers** (p. 720) A class of chiral stereoisomers that results from two possible arrangements of four different atoms or groups of atoms bonded to the same carbon atom.

**optical rotation** (p. 721) An effect that occurs when polarized light passes through a solution containing an optical isomer and the plane of polarization is rotated to the right by a $d$-isomer or to the left by an $l$-isomer.

**ore** (p. 187) A material from which a mineral can be extracted at a reasonable cost.

**organic compounds** (p. 698) All compounds that contain carbon with the primary exceptions of carbon oxides, carbides, and carbonates, all of which are considered inorganic.

**osmosis** (p. 475) The diffusion of solvent particles across a semi-permeable membrane from an area of higher solvent concentration to an area of lower solvent concentration.

**osmotic pressure** (p. 475) The additional pressure needed to reverse osmosis.

**oxidation** (p. 637) The loss of electrons from the atoms of a substance; increases an atom's oxidation number.

**oxidation number** (p. 222) The positive or negative charge of a monatomic ion.

**oxidation-number method** (p. 644) The technique that can be used to balance more difficult redox reactions, based on the fact that the number of electrons transferred from atoms must equal the number of electrons accepted by other atoms.

**oxidation-reduction reaction** (p. 636) Any chemical reaction in which electrons are transferred from one atom to another; also called a redox reaction.

**oxidizing agent** (p. 638) The substance that oxidizes another substance by accepting its electrons.

**oxyacid** (p. 250) Any acid that contains hydrogen and an oxyanion.

**oxyanion** (p. 225) A polyatomic ion composed of an element, usually a nonmetal, bonded to one or more oxygen atoms.

**octet rule/regla del octeto** (pág. 168) Establece que átomos pierden, ganan o comparten electrones para adquirir un conjunto completo de ocho electrones de valencia (la configuración electrónica estable de un gas noble).

**optical isomers/isómeros ópticos** (pág. 720) Clase de estereoisómeros quirales que resulta de dos posibles arreglos de cuatro átomos o grupos de átomos diferentes unidos al mismo átomo de carbono.

**optical rotation/rotación óptica** (pág. 721) Efecto que ocurre cuando la luz polarizada pasa a través de una solución que contiene un isómero óptico y el plano de polarización es rotado a la derecha por un isómero $d$ o a la izquierda por un isómero $l$

**ore/mena** (pág. 187) Material del cual puede extraerse un mineral a un costo razonable.

**organic compounds/compuestos orgánicos** (pág. 698) Todo compuesto que contiene carbono, con las excepciones primarias de óxidos de carbono, carburos y carbonatos, todos los cuales se consideran inorgánicos.

**osmosis/ósmosis** (pág. 475) Difusión de partículas de disolvente a través de una membrana semipermeable de un área de mayor concentración de disolvente a un área de menor concentración.

**osmotic pressure/presión osmótica** (pág. 475) Presión adicional necesaria para invertir la ósmosis.

**oxidation/oxidación** (pág. 637) Pérdida de electrones de los átomos de una sustancia; incrementa el número de oxidación de un átomo.

**oxidation number/número de oxidación** (pág. 222) La carga positiva o negativa de un ion monoatómico.

**oxidation-number method/método del número de oxidación** (pág. 644) ) Técnica que puede utilizarse para equilibrar las reacciones redox más difíciles, en base al hecho de que el número de electrones transferidos de ciertos átomos debe igualar el número de electrones aceptados por otros átomos.

**oxidation-reduction reaction/reacción de óxido-reducción** (pág. 636) Cualquier reacción química en la cual se transfieren electrones de un átomo a otro; también llamada reacción redox.

**oxidizing agent/agente oxidante** (pág. 638) Sustancia que oxida otra sustancia aceptando sus electrones.

**oxyacid/oxiácido** (pág. 250) Cualquier ácido que contiene hidrógeno y un oxianión.

**oxyanion/oxianión** (pág. 225) Ion poliatómico compuesto de un elemento, generalmente un no metal, unido a uno o a más átomos de oxígeno.

## P

**parent chain** (p. 701) The longest continuous chain of carbon atoms in a branched-chain alkane, alkene, or alkyne.

**pascal** (p. 390) The SI unit of pressure; one pascal (Pa) is equal to a force of one newton per square meter.

**parent chain/cadena principal** (pág. 701) Cadena continua más larga de átomos de carbono en un alcano, alqueno o alquino ramificado.

**pascal/pascal** (pág. 390) La unidad SI de presión; un pascal (Pa) es igual a una fuerza de un newton por metro cuadrado.

**Pauli exclusion principle** (p. 136) States that a maximum of two electrons may occupy a single atomic orbital, but only if the electrons have opposite spins.

**peptide** (p. 777) A chain of two or more amino acids linked by peptide bonds.

**peptide bond** (p. 777) The amide bond that joins two amino acids.

**percent by mass** (p. 75) A percentage determined by the ratio of the mass of each element to the total mass of the compound.

**percent composition** (p. 328) The percent by mass of each element in a compound.

**percent error** (p. 37) The ratio of an error to an accepted value.

**percent yield** (p. 370) The ratio of actual yield (from an experiment) to theoretical yield (from stoichiometric calculations) expressed as a percent.

**period** (p. 154) A horizontal row of elements in the modern periodic table.

**periodic law** (p. 153) States that when the elements are arranged by increasing atomic number, there is a periodic repetition of their chemical and physical properties.

**periodic table** (p. 70) A chart that organizes all known elements into a grid of horizontal rows (periods) and vertical columns (groups or families) arranged by increasing atomic number.

**pH** (p. 610) The negative logarithm of the hydrogen ion concentration of a solution; acidic solutions have pH values between 0 and 7, basic solutions have values between 7 and 14, and a solution with a pH of 7.0 is neutral.

**phase diagram** (p. 408) A graph of pressure versus temperature that shows which phase a substance exists in under different conditions of temperature and pressure.

**phospholipid** (p. 786) A triglyceride in which one of the fatty acids is replaced by a polar phosphate group.

**photoelectric effect** (p. 123) A phenomenon in which photoelectrons are emitted from a metal's surface when light of a certain frequency shines on the surface.

**photon** (p. 123) A particle of electromagnetic radiation with no mass that carries a quantum of energy.

**photosynthesis** (p. 793) The complex process that converts energy from sunlight to chemical energy in the bonds of carbohydrates.

**physical change** (p. 61) A type of change that alters the physical properties of a substance but does not change its composition.

**physical property** (p. 56) A characteristic of matter that can be observed or measured without changing the sample's composition—for example, density, color, taste, hardness, and melting point.

**pi bond** (p. 246) A bond that is formed when parallel orbitals overlap to share electrons.

**Planck's constant** (p. 123) $h$, which has a value of $6.626 \times 10^{-34}$ J•s, where J is the symbol for the joule.

**plastic** (p. 764) A polymer that can be heated and molded while relatively soft.

**pOH** (p. 611) The negative logarithm of the hydroxide ion concentration of a solution; a solution with a pOH above 7.0 is acidic, a solution with a pOH below 7.0 is basic, and a solution with a pOH of 7.0 is neutral.

**polar covalent** (p. 264) A type of bond that forms when electrons are not shared equally.

**polarized light** (p. 720) Light that can be filtered and reflected so that the resulting waves all lie in the same plane.

**polyatomic ion** (p. 224) An ion made up of two or more atoms bonded together that acts as a single unit with a net charge.

**Pauli exclusion principle/principio de exclusión de Pauli** (pág. 136) Establece que un máximo de dos electrones pueden ocupar un solo orbital atómico, pero sólo si los electrones tienen giros opuestos.

**peptide/péptido** (pág. 777) Cadena de dos o más aminoácidos unidos por enlaces peptídicos.

**peptide bond/enlace peptídico** (pág. 777) Enlace amida que une dos aminoácidos.

**percent by mass/por ciento masa** (pág. 75) Porcentaje determinado por la proporción de la masa de cada elemento en relación con la masa total del compuesto.

**percent composition/composición porcentual** (pág. 328) Por ciento de masa de cada elemento en un compuesto.

**percent error/porcentaje de error** (pág. 37) Proporción de un error en relación con un valor aceptado.

**percent yield/porcentaje de rendimiento** (pág. 370) Razón del rendimiento real (de un experimento) al rendimiento teórico (de cálculos estequiométricos) expresado como un por ciento.

**period/período** (pág. 154) Fila horizontal de elementos en la tabla periódica moderna.

**periodic law/ley periódica** (pág. 153) Establece que cuando los elementos se ordenan por número atómico ascendente, existe una repetición periódica de sus propiedades físicas y químicas.

**periodic table/tabla periódica** (pág. 70) Gráfica que organiza todos los elementos conocidos en una cuadrícula de filas horizontales (períodos) y columnas verticales (grupos o familias) ordenados según el aumento del número atómico.

**pH/pH** (pág. 610) El logaritmo negativo de la concentración de ion hidrógeno de una solución; las soluciones ácidas poseen valores de pH entre 0 y 7, las soluciones básicas tienen valores entre 7 y 14 y una solución con un pH de 7.0 es neutra.

**phase diagram/diagrama de fase** (pág. 408) Gráfica de presión contra temperatura que muestra en qué fase se encuentra una sustancia bajo condiciones diferentes de temperatura y presión.

**phospholipid/fosfolípido** (pág. 786) Triglicérido en el cual un grupo fosfato polar reemplaza uno de los ácidos grasos.

**photoelectric effect/efecto fotoeléctrico** (pág. 123) Fenómeno en el cual se emiten fotoelectrones de la superficie de un metal cuando brilla en la superficie luz de cierta frecuencia.

**photon/fotón** (pág. 123) Partícula de radiación electromagnética sin masa que lleva un cuanto de energía.

**photosynthesis/fotosíntesis** (pág. 793) Proceso complejo que convierte la energía de la luz solar en energía química en los enlaces de carbohidratos.

**physical change/cambio físico** (pág. 61) Tipo del cambio que altera las propiedades físicas de una sustancia pero no cambia su composición.

**physical property/propiedad física** (pág. 56) Característica de la materia que se puede observar o medir sin cambiar la composición de la muestra; por ejemplo, la densidad, el color, el sabor, la dureza y el punto de fusión.

**pi bond/enlace pi** (pág. 246) Enlace que se forma cuando losorbitales paralelos se superponen para compartir electrones.

**Planck's constant/constante de Planck** (pág. 123) $h$, que tiene un valor de $6.626 \times 10^{-34}$ J•s, donde J es el símbolo del julio.

**plastic/plástico** (pág. 764) Polímero que puede calentarse y moldearse mientras está relativamente suave.

**pOH/pOH** (pág. 611) El logaritmo negativo de la concentración de ion hidróxido de una solución; una solución con un pOH mayor que 7.0 es ácida, una solución con un pOH menor que 7.0 es básica y una solución con un pOH de 7.0 es neutra.

**polar covalent/covalente polar** (pág. 264) Tipo de enlace que se forma cuando los electrones no se comparten igualmente.

**polarized light/luz polarizada** (pág. 720) Luz que puede filtrarse y reflejarse para que todas las ondas resultantes se encuentren en el mismo plano.

**polyatomic ion/ion poliatómico** (pág. 224) Ion compuesto de dos o más átomos unidos que actúan como una sola unidad con una carga neta.

**polymerization reaction** (p. 762) A reaction in which monomer units are bonded together to form a polymer.

**polymers** (p. 761) Large molecules formed by combining many repeating structural units (monomers); are synthesized through addition or condensation reactions and include polyethylene, polyurethane, and nylon.

**polysaccharide** (p. 782) A complex carbohydrate, which is a polymer of simple sugars that contains 12 or more monomer units.

**positron** (p. 812) A particle that has the same mass as an electron but an opposite charge.

**positron emission** (p. 812) A radioactive decay process in which a proton in the nucleus is converted into a neutron and a positron and then the positron is emitted from the nucleus.

**precipitate** (p. 290) A solid produced during a chemical reaction in a solution.

**precision** (p. 36) Refers to how close a series of measurements are to one another; precise measurements show little variation over a series of trials but may not be accurate.

**pressure** (p. 388) Force applied per unit area.

**primary battery** (p. 675) A type of battery that produces electric energy by redox reactions that are not easily reversed, delivers current until the reactants are gone, and then is discarded.

**principal energy levels** (p. 133) The major energy levels of an atom.

**principal quantum numbers** (p. 132) *n*, which the quantum mechanical model assigns to indicate the relative sizes and energies of atomic orbitals.

**product** (p. 278) A substance formed during a chemical reaction.

**protein** (p. 775) An organic polymer made up of amino acids linked together by peptide bonds that can function as an enzyme, transport important chemical substances, or provide structure in organisms.

**proton** (p. 96) A subatomic particle in an atom's nucleus that has a positive charge of 1+.

**pure research** (p. 14) A type of scientific investigation that seeks to gain knowledge for the sake of knowledge itself.

**polymerization reaction/reacción de polimerización** (pág. 762) Reacción en la cual las unidades monoméricas se unen para formar un polímero.

**polymers/polímeros** (pág. 761) Moléculas grandes formadas de la combinación de muchas unidades estructurales repetidas (monómeros); se sintetizan a través de reacciones de adición o de condensación e incluyen el polietileno, el poliuretano y el nilón.

**polysaccharide/polisacárido** (pág. 782) Carbohidrato complejo, que es un polímero de azúcares simples que contiene 12 o más unidades monoméricas.

**positron/positrón** (pág. 812) ) Partícula que tiene la misma masa que un electrón pero una carga opuesta.

**positron emission/emisión del positrón** (pág. 812) ) Proceso de desintegración radiactiva en que un protón en el núcleo se convierte en un neutrón y un positrón y entonces el positrón se emite del núcleo.

**precipitate/precipitado** (pág. 290) Sólido que se produce durante una reacción química en una solución.

**precision/precisión** (pág. 36) Se refiere al grado de cercanía en que una serie de medidas están de unas de otras; las medidas precisas muestran poca variación durante una serie de pruebas, pero quizazás no sean exactas.

**pressure/presión** (pág. 388) Fuerza aplicada por unidad de área.

**primary battery/batería primaria** (pág. 675) Tipo de batería que produce energía eléctrica por reacciones redox que no son fácilmente reversibles, produce corriente hasta agotar los reactantes y entonces se desecha.

**principal energy levels/niveles de energía principal** (pág. 133) Los niveles más importantes de energía de un átomo.

**principal quantum numbers/números cuánticos principales** (pág. 132) *n*, el cual asigna el modelo mecánico-cuántico para indicar tamaños y energías relativas de orbitales atómicos.

**product/producto** (pág. 278) Sustancia formada durante una reacción química.

**protein/proteína** (pág. 775) Polímero orgánico compuesto de aminoácidos unidos por enlaces peptídicos que puede funcionar como una enzima, transportar sustancias químicas importantes o proporcionar estructura en los organismos.

**proton/protón** (pág. 96) Partícula subatómica en el núcleo de un átomo que tiene una carga positiva de 1+.

**pure research/investigación pura** (pág. 14) Tipo de investigación científica que busca obtener conocimiento en nombre del conocimiento mismo.

# Q

**qualitative data** (p. 10) Information describing color, odor, shape, or some other physical characteristic.

**quantitative data** (p. 11) Numerical information describing how much, how little, how big, how tall, how fast, etc.

**quantum** (p. 122) The minimum amount of energy that can be gained or lost by an atom.

**quantum mechanical model of the atom** (p. 131) An atomic model in which electrons are treated as waves; also called the wave mechanical model of the atom.

**qualitative data/datos cualitativos** (pág. 10) Información que describe el color, el olor, la forma o alguna otra característica física.

**quantitative data/datos cuantitativos** (pág. 11) Información numérica que describe cantidad (grande o pequeña), dimensión, altura, rapidez, etc.

**quantum/cuanto** (pág. 122) La cantidad mínima de energía que puede ganar o perder un átomo.

**quantum mechanical model of the atom/modelo mecánico cuántico del átomo** (pág. 131) Modelo atómico en el cual los electrones se tratan como si fueran ondas; también llamado modelo mecánico de ondas del átomo.

# R

**radiation** (p. 105) The rays and particles—alpha and beta particles and gamma rays—that are emitted by radioactive materials.

**radioactive decay** (p. 106) A spontaneous process in which unstable nuclei lose energy by emitting radiation.

**radioactive decay series** (p. 814) A series of nuclear reactions that starts with an unstable nucleus and results in the formation of a stable nucleus.

**radioactivity** (p. 105) The process in which some substances spontaneously emit radiation.

**radiochemical dating** (p. 819) The process that is used to determine the age of an object by measuring the amount of a certain radioisotope remaining in that object.

**radioisotopes** (p. 807) Isotopes of atoms that have unstable nuclei and emit radiation to attain more stable atomic configurations.

**radiotracer** (p. 828) An isotope that emits nonionizing radiation and is used to signal the presence of an element or specific substance; can be used to analyze complex chemical reactions mechanisms and to diagnose disease.

**rate-determining step** (p. 549) The slowest elementary step in a complex reaction; limits the instantaneous rate of the overall reaction.

**rate law** (p. 542) The mathematical relationship between the rate of a chemical reaction at a given temperature and the concentrations of reactants.

**reactant** (p. 278) The starting substance in a chemical reaction.

**reaction mechanism** (p. 548) The complete sequence of elementary steps that make up a complex reaction.

**reaction order** (p. 543) For a reactant, describes how the rate is affected by the concentration of that reactant.

**reaction rate** (p. 530) The change in concentration of a reactant or product per unit time, generally calculated and expressed in moles per liter per second.

**redox reaction** (p. 636) An oxidation-reduction reaction.

**reducing agent** (p. 638) The substance that reduces another substance by losing electrons.

**reduction** (p. 637) The gain of electrons by the atoms of a substance; decreases an atom's oxidation number.

**reduction potential** (p. 666) The tendency of an ion to gain electrons.

**representative elements** (p. 154) Groups of elements in the modern periodic table that are designated with an A (1A through 8A) and possess a wide range of chemical and physical properties.

**resonance** (p. 256) Condition that occurs when more than one valid Lewis structure exists for the same molecule.

**reversible reaction** (p. 560) A reaction that can take place in both the forward and reverse directions; leads to an equilibrium state where the forward and reverse reactions occur at equal rates and the concentrations of reactants and products remain constant.

**radiation/radiación** (pág. 105) Los rayos y partículas (partículas alfa y beta y rayos gamma) que emiten los materiales radiactivos.

**radioactive decay/desintegración radiactiva** (pág. 106) Proceso espontáneo en el cual los núcleos inestables pierden energía emitiendo radiación.

**radioactive decay series/serie de desintegración radiactiva** (pág. 814) Serie de reacciones nucleares que empieza con un núcleo inestable y tiene como resultado la formación de un núcleo fijo.

**radioactivity/radiactividad** (pág. 105) ) El proceso en que algunas sustancias emiten radiación espontáneamente.

**radiochemical dating/datación radioquímica** (pág. 819) Proceso que se utiliza para determinar la edad de un objeto midiendo la cantidad de cierto radioisótopo remanente en ese objeto.

**radioisotopes/radioisótopos** (pág. 807) Isótopos de átomos que tienen los núcleos inestables y emiten radiación para alcanzar configuraciones atómicas más estables.

**radiotracer/radiolocalizador** (pág. 828) Isótopo que emite radiación no ionizante y que se utiliza para señalar la presencia de un elemento o sustancia específica; puede usarse para analizar mecanismos de reacciones químicas complejas y para diagnosticar enfermedades.

**rate-determining step/paso de determinación de velocidad** (pág. 549) Paso elemental más lento en una reacción compleja; limita la velocidad instantánea en la reacción global.

**rate law/ley de velocidad** (pág. 542) Relación matemática entre la velocidad de una reacción química a una temperatura dada y las concentraciones de reactantes.

**reactant/reactante** (pág. 278) Sustancia inicial en una reacción química.

**reaction mechanism/mecanismo de reacción** (pág. 548) Sucesión completa de pasos elementales que componen una reacción compleja.

**reaction order/orden de reacción** (pág. 543) Para un reactante, describe cómo la velocidad se ve afectada por la concentración del reactante.

**reaction rate/velocidad de reacción** (pág. 530) Cambio en la concentración de reactante o producto por unidad de tiempo, generalmente se calcula y expresa en moles por litro por segundo.

**redox reaction/reacción redox** (pág. 636) Una reacción de óxido–reducción.

**reducing agent/agente reductor** (pág. 638) Sustancia que reduce otra sustancia perdiendo electrones.

**reduction/reducción** (pág. 637) Ganancia de electrones de átomos de una sustancia; disminuye el número de oxidación de un átomo.

**reduction potential/potencial de reducción** (pág. 666) Tendencia de un ion a ganar electrones.

**representative elements/elementos representativos** (pág. 154) Grupos de elementos en la tabla periódica moderna que se designan con una A (1A hasta 8A) y poseen una gran variedad de propiedades físicas y químicas.

**resonance/resonancia** (pág. 256) Condición que ocurre cuando existe más de una estructura válida de Lewis para la misma molécula.

**reversible reaction/reacción reversible** (pág. 560) Reacción que puede ocurrir en dirección normal e inversa; conduce a un estado de equilibrio donde las reacciones normales e inversas ocurren a velocidades iguales y las concentraciones de reactantes y productos permanecen constantes.

# S

salinity (p. 851) A measure of the mass of salts dissolved in sea-water, which is 35 g per kg, on average.

salt (p. 617) An ionic compound made up of a cation from a base and an anion from an acid.

salt bridge (p. 664) A pathway constructed to allow positive and negative ions to move from one solution to another.

salt hydrolysis (p. 621) The process in which anions of the dissociated salt accept hydrogen ions from water or the cations of the dissociated salt donate hydrogen ions to water.

saponification (p. 785) The hydrolysis of the ester bonds of a triglyceride using an aqueous solution of a strong base to form carboxylate salts and glycerol; is used to make soaps.

saturated hydrocarbon (p. 710) A hydrocarbon that contains only single bonds.

saturated solution (p. 458) Contains the maximum amount of dissolved solute for a given amount of solvent at a specific temperature and pressure.

scientific law (p. 13) Describes a relationship in nature that is supported by many experiments.

scientific method (p. 10) A systematic approach used in scientific study that typically includes observation, a hypothesis, experiments, data analysis, and a conclusion.

scientific notation (p. 31) Expresses numbers as a multiple of two factors—a number between 1 and 10, and 10 raised to a power, or exponent; makes it easier to handle extremely large or small measurements.

second (p. 26) The SI base unit for time.

secondary battery (p. 675) A rechargeable battery that depends on reversible redox reactions and powers such devices as laptop computers and cordless drills.

sigma bond (p. 245) A single covalent bond that is formed when an electron pair is shared by the direct overlap of bonding orbitals.

significant figures (p. 38) The number of all known digits reported in measurements plus one estimated digit.

single-replacement reaction (p. 287) A chemical reaction that occurs when the atoms of one element replace the atoms of another element in a compound.

solid (p. 58) A form of matter that has its own definite shape and volume, is incompressible, and expands only slightly when heated.

solubility (p. 457) The maximum amount of solute that will dissolve in a given amount of solvent at a specific temperature and pressure.

solubility product constant (p. 578) $K_{sp}$, which is an equilibrium constant for the dissolving of a sparingly soluble ionic compound in water.

soluble (p. 454) Describes a substance that can be dissolved in a given solvent.

solute (p. 292) A substance dissolved in a solution.

solution (p. 67) A uniform mixture that may contain solids, liquids, or gases; also called a homogeneous mixture.

solvation (p. 455) The process of surrounding solute particles with solvent particles to form a solution; occurs only where and when the solute and solvent particles come in contact with each other.

salinity/salinidad (pág. 851) Medida de la masa de sales disueltas en el agua de mar, que en promedio es de 35 g por kg.

salt/sal (pág. 617) Compuesto iónico constituido por un catión de una base y un anión de un ácido.

salt bridge/puente salino (pág. 664) Vía construida para permitir que los iones positivos y negativos se muevan de una solución a otra.

salt hydrolysis/hidrólisis de sal (pág. 621) Proceso en el cual los aniones de la sal disociada aceptan iones hidrógeno del agua o los cationes de la sal disociada donan iones hidrógeno al agua.

saponification/saponificación (pág. 785) Hidrólisis de los enlaces éster de un triglicérido usando una solución acuosa de una base fuerte para formar sales de carboxilato y glicerol; se usa en la elaboración de jabones.

saturated hydrocarbon/hidrocarburo saturado (pág. 710) Hidrocarburo que contiene únicamente enlaces sencillos.

saturated solution/solución saturada (pág. 458) La que contiene la cantidad máxima de soluto disuelto para una cantidad dada de disolvente a una temperatura y presión específicas.

scientific law/ley científica (pág. 13) Describe una relación en la naturaleza que es avalada por muchos experimentos.

scientific method/método científico (pág. 10) Enfoque sistemático utilizado en el estudio científico que incluye típicamente la observación, una hipótesis, los experimentos, los análisis de datos y una conclusión.

scientific notation/notación científica (pág. 31) Expresa los números como un múltiplo de dos factores: un número entre 1 y 10 y 10 elevado a una potencia o exponente; facilita el manejo de medidas extremadamente grandes o pequeñas.

second/segundo (pág. 26) La unidad base del SI para el tiempo.

secondary battery/batería secundaria (pág. 675) Batería recargable que depende de reacciones redox reversibles y provee energía a dispositivos como computadoras portátiles y taladros inalámbricos.

sigma bond/enlace sigma (pág. 245) Enlace covalente sencillo que se forma cuando un par de electrón es compartido por la superposición directa de orbitales de unión.

significant figures/cifras significativas (pág. 38) El número de dígitos conocidos reportados en medidas, más un dígito estimado.

single-replacement reaction/reacción de reemplazo simple (pág. 287) Reacción química que ocurre cuando los átomos de un elemento reemplazan los átomos de otro elemento en un compuesto.

solid/sólido (pág. 58) Forma de materia que tiene su propia forma y volumen, es incompresible y sólo se expande levemente cuando se calienta.

solubility/solubilidad (pág. 457) Cantidad máxima de soluto que se disolverá en una cantidad dada de disolvente a una temperatura y presión específicas.

solubility product constant/constante del producto de solubilidad (pág. 578) $K_{sp}$, que es una constante de equilibrio para la disolución de un compuesto iónico moderadamente soluble en agua.

soluble/soluble (pág. 454) Describe una sustancia que se puede disolver en un disolvente dado.

solute/soluto (pág. 292) Sustancia disuelta en una solución.

solution/solución (pág. 67) Mezcla uniforme que puede contener sólidos, líquidos o gases; llamada también mezcla homogénea.

solvation/solvatación (pág. 455) Proceso de rodear partículas de soluto con partículas de disolvente para formar una solución; ocurre sólo en lugares donde y cuando las partículas de soluto y disolvente entran en contacto.

**solvent** (p. 292) The substance that dissolves a solute to form a solution.

**species** (p. 650) Any kind of chemical unit involved in a process.

**specific heat** (p. 492) The amount of heat required to raise the temperature of one gram of a given substance by one degree Celsius.

**specific rate constant** (p. 542) A numerical value that relates reaction rate and concentration of reactant at a specific temperature.

**spectator ion** (p. 293) An ion that does not participate in a reaction and usually is not shown in an ionic equation.

**spontaneous process** (p. 513) A physical or chemical change that occurs without outside intervention and may require energy to be supplied to begin the process.

**standard enthalpy (heat) of formation** (p. 509) The change in enthalpy that accompanies the formation of one mole of a compound in its standard state from its constituent elements in their standard states.

**standard hydrogen electrode** (p. 666) The standard electrode against which the reduction potential of all electrodes can be measured.

**states of matter** (p. 58) The physical forms in which all matter naturally exists on Earth—most commonly as a solid, a liquid, or a gas.

**stereoisomers** (p. 718) A class of isomers whose atoms are bonded in the same order but are arranged differently in space.

**steroids** (p. 787) Lipids that have multiple cyclic rings in their structures.

**stoichiometry** (p. 354) The study of quantitative relationships between the amounts of reactants used and products formed by a chemical reaction; is based on the law of conservation of mass.

**stratosphere** (p. 842) The atmospheric layer above the troposphere and below the mesosphere; contains an ozone layer, which forms a protective layer against ultraviolet radiation, and has temperatures that increase with increasing altitude.

**strong acid** (p. 602) An acid that ionizes completely in aqueous solution.

**strong base** (p. 606) A base that dissociates entirely into metal ions and hydroxide ions in aqueous solution.

**strong nuclear force** (p. 810) A force that acts only on subatomic particles that are extremely close together and overcomes the electrostatic repulsion between protons.

**structural formula** (p. 252) A molecular model that uses symbols and bonds to show relative positions of atoms; can be predicted for many molecules by drawing the Lewis structure.

**structural isomers** (p. 717) A class of isomers whose atoms are bonded in different orders with the result that they have different chemical and physical properties despite having the same formula.

**sublimation** (p. 407) The energy-requiring process by which a solid changes directly to a gas without first becoming a liquid.

**substance** (p. 55) A form of matter that has a uniform and unchanging composition; also known as a pure substance.

**substituent groups** (p. 701) The side branches that extend from the parent chain because they appear to substitute for a hydrogen atom in the straight chain.

**solvent/disolvente** (pág. 292) Sustancia que disuelve un soluto para formar una solución.

**species/especie** (pág. 650) Cualquier clase de unidad química implicada en un proceso.

**specific heat/calor específico** (pág. 492) Cantidad de calor requerida para elevar la temperatura de un gramo de una sustancia dada en un grado centígrado.

**specific rate constant/constante de velocidad específica** (pág. 542) Valor numérico que relaciona la velocidad de reacción y la concentración de reactante a una temperatura específica.

**spectator ion/ion espectador** (pág. 293) Ion que no participa en una reacción y generalmente no se muestra en una ecuación iónica.

**spontaneous process/proceso espontáneo** (pág. 513) Cambio físico o químico que ocurre sin intervención exterior y puede requerir de un suministro de energía para empezar el proceso.

**standard enthalpy (heat) of formation/entalpía (calor) estándar de formación** (pág. 509) Cambio en la entalpía que acompaña la formación de un mol de un compuesto en su estado estándar a partir de sus elementos constituyentes en sus estados estándares.

**standard hydrogen electrode/electrodo estándar de hidrógeno** (pág. 666) Electrodo estándar contra el cual se puede medir el potencial de reducción de todos los electrodos.

**states of matter/estados de la materia** (pág. 58) Las formas físicas en que toda materia existe naturalmente en la Tierra, más comúnmente como un sólido, un líquido o un gas.

**stereoisomers/estereoisómeros** (pág. 718) Clase de isómeros cuyos átomos están unidos en el mismo orden pero se arreglan de manera diferente en el espacio.

**steroids/esteroides** (pág. 787) Lípidos que tienen múltiples anillos cíclicos en sus estructuras.

**stoichiometry/estequiometría** (pág. 354) El estudio de las relaciones cuantitativas entre las cantidades de reactantes utilizados y los productos formados por una reacción química; se basa en la ley de la conservación de masa.

**stratosphere/estratosfera** (pág. 842) Capa atmosférica encima de la troposfera y debajo de la mesosfera; contiene una capa de ozono, que forma una capa protectora contra la radiación ultravioleta y tiene temperaturas que aumentan al incrementar la altitud.

**strong acid/ácido fuerte** (pág. 602) Ácido que se ioniza completamente en solución acuosa.

**strong base/base fuerte** (pág. 606) Base que disocia enteramente en iones metálicos e iones hidróxido en solución acuosa.

**strong nuclear force/fuerza nuclear fuerte** (pág. 810) Fuerza que actúa sólo en las partículas subatómicas que están extremadamente cercanas y vence la repulsión electrostática entre protones.

**structural formula/fórmula estructural** (pág. 252) Modelo molecular que usa símbolos y enlaces para mostrar las posiciones relativas de los átomos; para muchas moléculas puede predecirse dibujando la estructura de Lewis.

**structural isomers/isómeros estructurales** (pág. 717) Clase de isómeros cuyos átomos están unidos en diferente orden y como resultado tienen propiedades químicas y físicas diferentes, a pesar de tener la misma fórmula.

**sublimation/sublimación** (pág. 407) Proceso demandante de energía por el que un sólido cambia directamente a un gas sin llegar a ser primero un líquido.

**substance/sustancia** (pág. 55) Forma de la materia que tiene una composición uniforme e inmutable; también conocida como sustancia pura.

**substituent groups/grupo sustituyente** (pág. 701) Cadenas ramificadas que se extiende a partir de la cadena principal porque aparentemente sustituyen a un átomo de hidrógeno en la cadena recta.

substitution reaction (p. 741) A reaction of organic compounds in which one atom or group of atoms in a molecule is replaced by an atom or group of atoms.

substrate (p. 778) A reactant in an enzyme-catalyzed reaction that binds to specific sites on enzyme molecules.

supersaturated solution (p. 459) Contains more dissolved solute than a saturated solution at the same temperature.

surface tension (p. 398) The energy required to increase the surface area of a liquid by a given amount; results from an uneven distribution of attractive forces.

surfactant (p. 398) A compound, such as soap, that lowers the surface tension of water by disrupting hydrogen bonds between water molecules; also called a surface active agent.

surroundings (p. 498) In thermochemistry, includes everything in the universe except the system.

suspension (p. 476) A type of heterogeneous mixture whose particles settle out over time and can be separated from the mixture by filtration.

synthesis reaction (p. 284) A chemical reaction in which two or more substances react to yield a single product.

system (p. 498) In thermochemistry, the specific part of the universe containing the reaction or process being studied.

substitution reaction/reacción de la sustitución (pág. 741) Reacción de compuestos orgánicos en la cual un átomo o grupo de átomos en una molécula son reemplazados por un átomo o grupo de átomos.

substrate/sustrato (pág. 778) Reactante en una reacción catalizada por enzimas que se une a sitios específicos en moléculas de enzima.

supersaturated solution/solución sobresaturada (pág. 459) La que contiene más soluto disuelto que una solución saturada a la misma temperatura.

surface tension/tensión superficial (pág. 398) Energía requerida para aumentar el área superficial de un líquido en una cantidad dada; se produce por una distribución desigual de fuerzas atractivas.

surfactant/surfactante (pág. 398) Compuesto, como el jabón, que disminuye la tensión superficial del agua interrumpiendo los puentes de hidrógeno entre moléculas de agua; llamado también agente activo de superficie.

surroundings/alrededores (pág. 498) En termoquímica, incluye el todo en el universo menos el sistema.

suspension/suspensión (pág. 476) Tipo de mezcla heterogénea cuyas partículas se asientan con el tiempo y pueden ser separadas de la mezcla por filtración.

synthesis reaction/reacción de la síntesis (pág. 284) Reacción química en que dos o más sustancias reaccionan para generar un solo producto.

system/sistema (pág. 498) En termoquímica, la parte específica del universo que contiene la reacción o el proceso que se está estudiado.

## T

technology (p. 17) The practical use of scientific information.

temperature (p. 386) A measure of the average kinetic energy of the particles in a sample of matter.

theoretical yield (p. 370) In a chemical reaction, the maximum amount of product that can be produced from a given amount of reactant.

theory (p. 13) An explanation supported by many experiments; is still subject to new experimental data, can be modified, and is considered successful it if can be used to make predictions that are true.

thermochemical equation (p. 501) A balanced chemical equation that includes the physical states of all the reactants and products and specifies the change in enthalpy.

thermochemistry (p. 498) The study of heat changes that accompany chemical reactions and phase changes.

thermonuclear reaction (p. 826) A nuclear fusion reaction.

thermoplastic (p. 764) A type of polymer that can be melted and molded repeatedly into shapes that are retained when it is cooled.

thermosetting (p. 764) A type of polymer that can be molded when it is first prepared but when cool cannot be remelted.

titration (p. 618) The process in which an acid-base neutralization reaction is used to determine the concentration of a solution of unknown concentration.

transition elements (p. 154) Groups of elements in the modern periodic table that are designated with a B (1B through 8B) and are further divided into transition metals and inner transition metals.

technology/tecnología (pág. 17) Uso práctico de información científica.

temperature/temperatura (pág. 386) Medida de la energía cinética promedio de las partículas en una muestra de materia.

theoretical yield/rendimiento teórico (pág. 370) En una reacción química, la cantidad máxima del producto que se puede producir a partir de una cantidad dada de reactante.

theory/teoría (pág. 13) Explicación respaldada por muchos experimentos; está todavía sujeta a datos experimentales nuevos, puede modificarse y es considerada exitosa si se puede utilizar para hacer predicciones verdaderas.

thermochemical equation/ecuación termoquímica (pág. 501) Ecuación química equilibrada que incluye los estados físicos de todos los reactantes y productos y especifica el cambio en entalpía.

thermochemistry/termoquímica (pág. 498) El estudio de los cambios caloríficos que acompañan las reacciones químicas y los cambios de fase.

thermonuclear reaction/reacción termonuclear (pág. 826) Reacción de fusión nuclear.

thermoplastic/termoplástico (pág. 764) Tipo de polímero que puede fundirse y moldearse repetidas veces en formas que se retienen cuando se enfría.

thermosetting/fraguado (pág. 764) Tipo de polímero que se puede moldear mientras se está preparando pero cuando se enfría no puede fundirse de nuevo.

titration/titulación (pág. 618) Proceso en que una reacción de neutralización ácido- base se utiliza para determinar la concentración de una solución de concentración desconocida.

transition elements/elementos de transición (pág. 154) Grupos de elementos en la tabla periódica moderna que se designan con una B (1B a 8B) y son divididos adicionalmente en metales de transición y metales de transición interna.

**transition metal** (p. 158) A type of group B element that is contained in the d-block of the periodic table and, with some exceptions, is characterized by a filled outermost s orbital of energy level $n$, and filled or partially filled d orbitals of energy level $n - 1$.

**transition state** (p. 532) Term used to describe an activated complex because the activated complex is as likely to form reactants as it is to form products.

**transmutation** (p. 815) The conversion of an atom of one element to an atom of another element.

**transuranium element** (p. 815) An element with an atomic number of 93 or greater in the periodic table that is produced in the laboratory by induced transmutation.

**triglyceride** (p. 785) Forms when three fatty acids are bonded to a glycerol backbone through ester bonds; can be either solid or liquid at room temperature.

**triple point** (p. 409) The point on a phase diagram representing the temperature and pressure at which the three phases of a substance (solid, liquid, and gas) can coexist.

**troposphere** (p. 842) The lowest layer of Earth's atmosphere where weather occurs and in which we live; has temperatures that generally decrease with increasing altitude.

**Tyndall effect** (p. 479) The scattering of light by colloidal particles.

**transition metal/metal de transición** (pág. 158) Tipo de elemento del grupo B contenido en el bloque D de la tabla periódica y que, con algunas excepciones, se caracteriza por un orbital exterior lleno con nivel de energía $n$, y orbitales llenos o parcialmente llenos con niveles de energía $n - 1$.

**transition state/estado de transición** (pág. 532) Término que se usa para describir un complejo activado dado que el complejo activado es igualmente probable que forme reactantes a que forme productos.

**transmutation/trasmutación** (pág. 815) Conversión de un átomo de un elemento a un átomo de otro elemento.

**transuranium element/elemento transuránico** (pág. 815) Un elemento en la tabla periódica con un número atómico de 93 ó mayor que es producido en el laboratorio por trasmutación inducida.

**triglyceride/triglicérido** (pág. 785) Se forma cuando tres ácidos grasos son unidos a un cadena principal de glicerol por enlaces éster; puede ser sólido o líquido a temperatura ambiente.

**triple point/punto triple** (pág. 409) El punto en un diagrama de fase que representa la temperatura y la presión en que las tres fases de una sustancia (sólido, líquido y gas) pueden coexistir.

**troposphere/troposfera** (pág. 842) La capa más baja de la atmósfera terrestre donde se presenta el clima y en la que vivimos; las temperaturas disminuyen generalmente conforme aumenta la altitud.

**Tyndall effect/efecto de Tyndall** (pág. 479) Dispersión de la luz por partículas coloidales.

# U

**unit cell** (p. 400) The smallest arrangement of connected points that can be repeated in three directions to form a crystal lattice.

**universe** (p. 498) In thermochemistry, is the system plus the surroundings.

**unsaturated hydrocarbon** (p. 710) A hydrocarbon that contains at least one double or triple bond between carbon atoms.

**unsaturated solution** (p. 458) Contains less dissolved solute for a given temperature and pressure than a saturated solution; has further capacity to hold more solute.

**unit cell/celda unitaria** (pág. 400) El arreglo más pequeño de puntos conectados que se puede repetir en tres direcciones para formar una red cristalina.

**universe/universo** (pág. 498) En termoquímica, es el sistema más los alrededores.

**unsaturated hydrocarbon/hidrocarburo insaturad** (pág. 710) Hidrocarburo que contiene por lo menos uno enlace doble o triple entre átomos de carbono.

**unsaturated solution/solución insaturada** (pág. 458) La que contiene menos soluto disuelto a una temperatura y presión dadas que una solución saturada; tiene capacidad para contener soluto adicional.

# V

**valence electrons** (p. 140) The electrons in an atom's outermost orbitals; determine the chemical properties of an element.

**vapor** (p. 59) Gaseous state of a substance that is a liquid or a solid at room temperature.

**vaporization** (p. 405) The energy-requiring process by which a liquid changes to a gas or vapor.

**vapor pressure** (p. 406) The pressure exerted by a vapor over a liquid.

**vapor pressure lowering** (p. 472) The lowering of vapor pressure of a solvent by the addition of a nonvolatile solute to the solvent.

**viscosity** (p. 397) A measure of the resistance of a liquid to flow, which is affected by the size and shape of particles, and generally increases as the temperature decreases and as intermolecular forces increase.

**valence electrons/electrones de valencia** (pág. 140) Los electrones en el orbital más externo de un átomo; determinan las propiedades químicas de un elemento.

**vapor/vapor** (pág. 59) Estado gaseoso de una sustancia que es líquida o sólida a temperatura ambiente.

**vaporization/vaporización** (pág. 405) Proceso demandante de energía por el que un líquido cambia a gas o vapor.

**vapor pressure/presión del vapor** (pág. 406) Presión ejercida por un vapor sobre un líquido.

**vapor pressure lowering/disminución de la presión del vapor** (pág. 472) Disminución de la presión de vapor de un disolvente por la adición de un soluto no volátil al disolvente.

**viscosity/viscosidad** (pág. 397) Medida de la resistencia de un líquido para fluir, que se ve afectada por el tamaño y la forma de las partículas y aumenta generalmente cuando la temperatura disminuye y cuando se incrementan las fuerzas intermoleculares.

Glossary/Glosario

voltaic cell (p. 665) A type of electrochemical cell that converts chemical energy into electrical energy.

VSEPR model (p. 259) **V**alence **S**hell **E**lectron **P**air **R**epulsion model, which is based on an arrangement that minimizes the repulsion of shared and unshared pairs of electrons around the central atom.

voltaic cell/celda voltaica (pág. 665) Tipo de la celda electroquímica que convierte energía química en energía eléctrica.

VSEPR model/modelo RPCEV (pág. 259) Modelo de **R**epulsión de los **P**ares **E**lectrónicos de la **C**apa de **V**alencia, que se basa en un arreglo que minimiza la repulsión de los pares de electrones compartidos y no compartidos alrededor del átomo central.

## W

wavelength (p. 118) The shortest distance between equivalent points on a continuous wave; is usually expressed in meters, centimeters, or nanometers.

wax (p. 787) A type of lipid that is formed by combining a fatty acid with a long-chain alcohol; is made by both plants and animals.

weak acid (p. 603) An acid that ionizes only partially in dilute aqueous solution.

weak base (p. 606) A base that ionizes only partially in dilute aqueous solution to form the conjugate acid of the base and hydroxide ion.

weight (p. 8) A measure of an amount of matter and also the effect of Earth's gravitational pull on that matter.

wavelength/longitud de onda (pág. 118) La distancia más corta entre puntos equivalentes en una onda continua; se expresa generalmente en metros, en centímetros o en nanómetros.

wax/cera (pág. 787) Tipo de lípido que se forma combinando un ácido graso con un alcohol de cadena larga; es elaborada por plantas y animales.

weak acid/ácido débil (pág. 603) Ácido que se ioniza sólo parcialmente en solución acuosa diluida.

weak base/base débil (pág. 606) Base que se ioniza sólo parcialmente en solución acuosa diluida para formar el ácido conjugado de la base y el ion hidróxido.

weight/peso (pág. 8) Medida de la cantidad de materia y también del efecto de la fuerza gravitatoria de la Tierra sobre esa materia.

## X

X ray (p. 809) A form of high-energy, penetrating electromagnetic radiation emitted from some materials that are in an excited electron state.

X ray/rayo X (pág. 809) Forma de radiación electromagnética penetrante de alta energía emitida por algunas materias en un estado electrónico excitado.

# Index

## A

Abbreviations, physics-related, 912 –

Absorption spectrum, 142–143 *lab*

Accuracy, **36**–37, 893

Acetaldehyde, 747–748

Acetic acid, 751

Acetone, evaporation of, 410–411 *lab*

Acetylene. *See* Ethyne

Acid-base indicators, **619**

Acid-base titration, **618**–621, 621 *prob.*, 626–627 *lab*

Acidic solutions, **597**

Acid ionization constant ($K_a$), **605**, 605 *prob.*, 605 *table*; calculating from pH, 615, 615–616 *prob.*

Acidosis, 625

Acid rain, 193, 847–849, 848 *lab*

Acids, acid ionization constant ($K_a$), 605, 605 *prob.*, 605 *table*, 615–616; anhydrides, 601; Arrhenius model of, 597–598; Brønsted-Lowry, 598–599; electrical conductivity and, 596, 602, 604; in household products, 595 *lab*; ions in solutions of, 596–597; monoprotic, 600; naming, 250, 250 *prob.*; neutralization reactions. *See* Neutralization reactions; oxyacids, 250, 250 *prob.*; pH of. *See* pH; polyprotic, 600, 601 *prob.*; properties of, 595–596; strength of, 602–605, 604 *lab*, 607, 614; strong, 602; titration of. *See* Acid-base titration; weak, 603

Actinide series, 158, **197**, 201

Activated complex, **532**

Activation energy ($Ea$), 533–534, 540

Active sites, **778**–779

Activities. *See* CHEMLABs; MiniLabs; Problem-Solving Labs

Activity series, 288–289

Actual yield, **370**

Additional Practice Problems, 871–886 *prob.*

Addition operations, 887–888

Addition polymerization, **762**–763

Addition reactions, **755**–757

Adenine (A), 789, 791

Adipic acid, 750

Aeration, 853, 854

Agitation, 456

Agricultural technician, 599

Agriculture, fertilizers and, 190, 191 *lab*

Air, density of, 439 *lab*

Air bags, 286, 376

Air pollution, 4, 6, 845–849, 848 *lab*; acid rain and. *See* Acid rain; global warming and, 859–860, 860 *lab*; photochemical smog and, 846–847

Air pressure, 389, 390

Airships, 180, 196, 446

Alchemy, 90

Alcoholic fermentation, 794–795, 796–797 *lab*

Alcohols, 737 *lab*, 738 *table*, **743**–744; elimination reactions involving, 755; evaporation rates of, 410–411 *lab*; layering in graduated cylinder, 25 *lab*; properties of, 766–767 *lab*

Aldehydes, 738 *table*, **747**–748

Algae, 190, 793, 853

Algal blooms, 853

Algebraic equations, 897–899, 899 *prob.*

Aliphatic compounds, **723**

Alkali metals (Group 1A), **155**, 155 *lab*, 181–182

Alkaline dry cells, 674

Alkaline earth metals (Group 2A), **155**, 183–185, 856

Alkaline solutions, 181

Alkanes, **699**–704; alkyl groups and, 702, 702 *table*; alkyl halides vs., 740–741; analyzing, 728–729 *lab*; branched-chain, 701–704, 704–705 *prob.*; chemical properties, 709; cycloalkanes, 706, 707–708 *prob.*; elimination reactions involving, 754; halogenation of, 741–742; naming, 700, 700 *table*; physical properties, 708–709; straight-chain, 699–701

Alkenes, **711**–712, 714; examples of, 711 *table*; naming, 712, 713–714 *prob.*

Alkyl groups, 702, 702 *table*

Alkyl halides, **738**–741, 740 *table*, 755

Alkynes, **714**–716; examples of, 715 *table*; hydrogenation of, 757; synthesis and reactivity of, 715 *lab*, 716

Allotropes, **188**; of carbon, 188; of oxygen, 192; of phosphorus, 190; of sulfur, 193

Alloys, 67, **230**–231; commercially important, 231 *table*; heat treatment of steel, 230 *lab*; Onion's Fusible Alloy, 211 *lab*; shape-memory, 412

Alnico, 231 *table*

Alpha decay, 808, 811–812, 812 *table*

Alpha particles, **106**, 807 *table*, 808

Alpha radiation, **106**, 107 *table*, 807, 807 *table*, 829

Alternative energy sources, 730, 860, 862–863 *lab*

Alternative fuel technician, 702

Alum, 187

Aluminum, 186, 187, 356; in Earth's lithosphere, 855 *table*; electron configuration of, 138 *table*; from electrolysis, 685–686; reactivity of, 300–301 *lab*

Aluminum bromide, 356

Aluminum oxide, 187

Aluminum sulfate, 187

American Wire Gauge (AWG) standard, 46–47 *lab*

Americium, 201

Amethyst, 234

Amides, 738 *table*, **752**, 776 *illus.*, 777

Amines, 738 *table*, **745**–746

Amino acids, **776**–777, 777 *table*

Amino group, 738 *table*, 745–746, 776

Ammonia, 190, 559; evaporation rate, 410–411 *lab*; Lewis structure, 253 *prob.*; molecular compound name, 249 *table*; polarity of, 265–266; production of, 181, 190, 588; VSEPR model of, 261 *lab*

Ammonium nitrate, 286, 302

Amorphous solids, **403**

Ampere (A), 26 *table*

Amphoteric substances, **599**

Amplitude, **119**

Anabolism, **792**–793

Analytical balance, 63–64

Analytical chemistry, 9 *table*; percent composition and, 328–329, 329 *lab*, 330–331 *prob.*

Analytical chemists, 328, 329

Anhydrides, 601

Aniline, 746 *illus.*

Anions, **214**, 219 *lab*

Anodes, 92 *illus.*, **665**

Answers, Practice Problems, 922–951

Antacids, 183, 628

Anthracene, 723, 739

Antilogarithms, 911, 911 *prob.*

Antimony, 189, 191

Antimony sulfide, 191

Applied research, **14**, 17

Aquamarines, 183 *illus.*

Aqueous solutions, **292**–299. *See also* Solutions; calculating ion concentrations, 580, 580–581 *prob.*; calculating molar solubility, 579, 579 *prob.*; common ion effect and, 584–585; heat of solution and, 457; of ionic compounds, 455; of molecular compounds, 456; nonelectrolytes in, 471; precipitation reactions, 292–293, 294 *prob.*, 295 *lab*; reactions forming gases, 296–298, 299 *prob.*; reactions forming water, 295, 296 *prob.*; reactivity of metals in, 300–301 *lab*; solubility and, 457 *table*, 457–460; solvation in, 455–457

Aragonite, 218 *illus.*

Argon, 138 *table*, 196, 842 *table*

Aristotle, 88–89

Aromatic compounds, **723**–724; benzene, 722–723; carcinogenic, 724; substituted, 724

Arrhenius model of acids and bases, **597**–598

Arsenic, 139 *illus.*, 191

Arsenic sulfide, 191

Aryl halides, **739**

Aspirin, 344, 753

Astatine, 194

Astronomy connection, composition of stars, 152; luminous intensity of stars, 26; polycyclic aromatic hydrocarbons (PAHs), 739

Asymmetric carbon, **719**–720

Atmosphere (atm), **390**, 390 *table*

Atmosphere, Earth's, 4, **841**–849; acid

# Photo Credits

# Photo Credits

Meadows; **436** (l)Larry Hamill, (r)Matt Meadows; **438** Richard Megna/Fundamental Photographs; **439** Matt Meadows; **441** Jim Sugar Photography/CORBIS; **442** Thomas Hovland from Grant Heilman; **445** Matt Meadows; **450** David & Doris Krumholz/Fundamental Photographs; **452** Jeff Lepore/Photo Researchers; **453** Matt Meadows; **454** (l)Paul Conklin/PhotoEdit, (c)Dr. Tony Brain/Science Photo Library/Photo Researchers, (r)David Young-Wolff/PhotoEdit; **456** (t)Richard Megna/Fundamental Photographs, (b)Andy Levin/Photo Researchers; **457** Kirtley-Perkins/Visuals Unlimited; **458** Matt Meadows; **459** (bl)Aaron Haupt, (br)Tony Craddock/Science Photo Library/Photo Researchers, (others)Richard Megna/Fundamental Photographs; **460** Runk/Schoenberger from Grant Heilman; **462** Mark Steinmetz; **463** Andrea Pistolesi/The Image Bank; **464** Aaron Haupt; **465** Richard T. Nowitz/CORBIS; **466 467 468** Matt Meadows; **469** Geoff Butler; **471** Stephen Frisch/Stock Boston; **476** Matt Meadows; **477** (l)Stan Skaggs/Visuals Unlimited, (c)Skip Comer, (r)Matt Meadows; **478** Clint Farlinger/Visuals Unlimited; **479** (l)Richard Hamilton Smith/CORBIS, (r)Kip & Pat Peticolas/Fundamental Photographs; **482** Dr. Gopal Murti/Science Photo Library/Photo Researchers; **488** AFP/CORBIS; **489** Matt Meadows; **490** (l)Davis Barber/PhotoEdit, (r)L.S. Stepanowicz; **491** Doug Martin; **492** Michael Pole/CORBIS; **493** Ted Rice; **494** William Stranton from Rainbow/PictureQuest; **495** NASA/Liaison Agency; **497** Matt Meadows; **498** Michael Newman/PhotoEdit; **499** Mark Burnett; **501** Lawrence Migdale/Photo Researchers; **503** Jim Strawser from Grant Heilman; **507** InterNetwork Media/Photodisc; **508** Dean Conger/CORBIS; **510** Hank de Lespinasse/The Image Bank; **511** CORBIS; **513** Steve Kaufman/Peter Arnold, Inc.; **514** Matt Meadows; **515** Mark Steinmetz; **516** Matt Meadows; **517** Bernhard Edmaier/Science Photo Library/Photo Researchers; **521** Matt Meadows; **528** NASA/Science Photo Library/Photo Researchers; **529** Matt Meadows; **530** (t)Greg Vaughn/Tom Stack & Associates, (b)Brian Bailey/Stone; **532** Mary Messenger/Stock Boston; **535 536** Richard Megna/Fundamental Photographs; **537** (l)Michael Dalton/Fundamental Photographs, (r)Richard Megna/Fundamental Photographs; **538** Matt Meadows; **539** Leonard Lessin/Peter Arnold, Inc.; **540** Art Wolfe/Stone; **541** Matt Meadows; **542 543** Stephen Frisch; **548** Ray Juno/The Stock Market; **551** Matt Meadows; **552** (l)AC Rochester Division of General Motors, (r)Aaron Haupt; **558** Grant Heilman Photography; **559** Geoff Butler; **562** Jan Halaska/Photo Researchers; **563** Robbie Jack/CORBIS; **564** Jeffrey Muir Hamilton/Stock Boston; **566** Matt Meadows; **570** Tim Courlas; **572** Matt Meadows; **574** Davis Barber/PhotoEdit; **575** Barry Runk from Grant Heilman; **577** Doug Martin; **578** CNRI/Science Photo Library/Photo Researchers; **579** Peter Essick/Aurora/PictureQuest; **580** Matt Meadows; **582** (t)Matt Meadows, (b)Hank Erdmann/Visuals Unlimited; **583** David Simson/Stock Boston/PictureQuest; **584 587** Matt Meadows; **588** PhotoDisc; **594** Ian Harwood; Ecoscene/CORBIS; **595** Geoff Butler; **596** Matt Meadows; **597** Aaron Haupt; **598** Doug Menuez/PhotoDisc; **600** Millard H. Sharp/Photo Researchers; **602** Matt Meadows; **609** Mitch Hrdlicka/PhotoDisc; **612** Geoff Butler; **613** David York/Medichrome; **614** Matt Meadows; **615** Jon Bertsch/Visuals Unlimited; **616 618 620 621** Matt Meadows; **622** Mike Buxton/CORBIS; **625** Tim David/Photo Researchers; **627** Matt Meadows; **628** (t)Mark Steinmetz, (b)PhotoDisc; **634** Thomas Eisner & D. Anashansly/Visuals Unlimited; **635** Mike & Carol Werner/Stock Boston; **636** (t) Doug Martin, (b)Bob Rogers; **637** Runk/Schoenberger from Grant Heilman; **638** Barry Runk from Grant Heilman; **639** (tl)Geoff Butler, (bl)Michael Newman/PhotoEdit, (r)David Young-Wolff/PhotoEdit; **641** Matt Meadows; **642** CORBIS; **644** Richard Megna/Fundamental Photographs; **645** Geoff Butler; **647** NASA; **651** Richard Megna/Fundamental Photographs; **652** Wolfgang Kaehler/CORBIS; **655** Matt Meadows; **656** (t to b)Dennie Cody/FPG, Dennie Cody/FPG, Richard Pasley/Stock Boston, Gunter Marx/CORBIS, Gunter Marx/CORBIS; **662** Ron Chapple/FPG; **663** Matt Meadows; **665** Bettmann/CORBIS; **674** Matt Meadows; **674** Lester V. Bergman/CORBIS; **675** Novastock/Tom Stack & Associates; **676** Aaron Haupt; **677** Michael W. Thomas/Pictor; **680** (t)Greig Cranna/Stock Boston, (c)Robert Fried/Stock Boston, (b)Visuals Unlimited; **681** Geoff Butler; **682** Marty Pardo; **684** Capital Features/The Image Works; **685** (t)Grant Heilman Photography, (b)Doug Martin; **686** (t)Charles E. Rotkin/CORBIS, (b)Stephen Frisch/Stock Boston/PictureQuest; **687** ALCOA; **690** Eric Sander/Liaison Agency; **696** Paul Souders/Liaison Agency; **697** Matt Meadows; **700** James Marshall/CORBIS; **703** Peter Menzel/Stock Boston/PictureQuest; **707** Tony Freeman/PhotoEdit; **709** (l)Peter Marbach from Grant Heilman, (c)George N. Matchneer, (r)Geoff Butler; **714** Bob Krist/CORBIS; **716** (l)Larry Hamill, (r)Archive Photos; **719** Aaron Haupt; **723** (l)Mark Steinmetz, (c)Rudi Von Briel, (r)Mark Steinmetz; **724** Bonnie Kamin/PhotoEdit; **726** Bob Daemmrich/Stock Boston/PictureQuest; **727** Myrleen Cate/PhotoEdit; **729** Matt Meadows; **730** David M. Dennis; **736** Roger Tully/Stone; **737** Matt Meadows; **741** Kevin C. Rose/The Image Bank; **742** Nancy Sheehan/PhotoEdit; **743** Steven Peters/Stone; **744** (t)Tony Freeman/PhotoEdit, (b)Jeff Greenberg/Visuals Unlimited **745** Bettmann/CORBIS; **746** (t)Doug Martin, (b) Dean Siracusa/FPG; **748** (l)B. Borrell Casals, Frank Lane Picture Agency/CORBIS, (r)Deborah Denker/Liaison Agency; **749** (l)Doug Martin, (r)Telegraph Colour Library/FPG; **750** (t)Ralph A. Clevenger/CORBIS, (b)Geoff Butler; **751** (l r)Larry Hamill, (c)Matt Meadows, **752** Charles Michael Murray/CORBIS; **754** Matt Meadows; **758** David Toase/PhotoDisc; **761** (l)Jim McGuire/Index Stock, (r)Mark Steinmetz; **762** (t)Aaron Haupt, (b)Geoff Butler; **764** (t)David Brooks/The Stock Market, (b)CORBIS; **765 767** Matt Meadows; **768** Ales Fevzer/CORBIS; **774** David Ulmer/Stock Boston; **775** Richard Megna/Fundamental Photographs; **779** Peter Cade/Stone; **780** Quest/Science Photo Library/Photo Researchers; **782** (l)Aaron Haupt, **782** (r)Jeff Smith/Fotosmith, (l)Aaron Haupt; **783** Aaron Haupt; **784** (l)PhotoDisc, (r)Digital Stock; **785** Mike Hopiak for the Cornell Laboratory of Ornithology; **787** (t)Lynn M. Stone, (b)William J. Weber; **793** Gregory Ochocki/Photo Researchers; **794** Lori Adamski Peek/Stone; **795** Aaron Haupt; **797** Matt Meadows; **798** Spencer Grant/PhotoEdit; **804** CORBIS; **806** (t)Paul Silverman/Fundamental Photographs, (b)Bettmann/CORBIS; **809** (l)Richard T. Nowitz/Photo Researchers, (r)James King-Holmes/Science Photo Library/Photo Researchers; **815** Fermi Lab/Photo Researchers; **818** Vince Michaels/Stone; **820** (t)Sygma/CORBIS, (b)Kenneth Garrett/National Geographic Image Collection; **824** (t)Wolfgang Kaehler/CORBIS, (b)Reuters/Str/Archive Photos; **825** (l)Tim Wright/CORBIS, (r)Alex Bartel/Science Photo Library/Photo Researchers; **826** U.S. DOE/Science Photo Library/Photo Researchers; **827** Michael Collier/Stock Boston; **828** (l)Klaus Guldbrandsen/Science Photo Library/Photo Researchers, (r)Aaron Haupt; **829** (t)JISAS/Lockheed/Science Photo Library/Photo Researchers, (b)Mark Harmel/Stone; **833** Matt Meadows; **840** VCG/FPG; **841** Telegraph Colour Library/FPG; **843** Edna Douthat; **846** (t)NASA, (b)EPA Documerica; **847** Telegraph Colour Library/FPG; **848** (l)Richard A. Cooke/CORBIS, (r)Ray Pfortner/Peter Arnold, Inc.; **852** Nubar Alexanian/CORBIS; **853** Tom McGuire; **855** NASA; **857** (tl)Mark A. Schneider/Photo Researchers, (tcl)John Greim/Medichrome, (tcr)George Whitely/Photo Researchers, (tr)Cobalt, (bl)Doug Martin, (bc)PhotoDisc, (br)Will & Deni McIntyre/Photo Researchers; **863** Matt Meadows; **864** Spencer Grant/Stock Boston/PictureQuest; **888** Larry B. Jennings/Photo Researchers; **888** Matt Meadows; **889** (l)NIBSC/Science Photo Library/Photo Researchers, (r)Edna Douthat; **890** (t)PhotoDisc, (b)Dustin W. Carr & Harold G. Craighead/Physics New Graphics/American Institute of Physics; **891** CNRI/Science Photo Library/Photo Researchers; **895** Matt Meadows; **896** Brian Heston; **897** George Hall/Corbis; **898** Brent Turner; **900** Phyllis Picardi/Stock Boston; **902** Matt Meadows; **903** Kenji Kerins; **908** Matt Meadows; **909** Alexander Lowry/Photo Researchers; **910** Michael Collier/Stock Boston; **911** Geoff Butler.

# PERIODIC TABLE OF THE ELEMENTS

Element ——— Hydrogen
Atomic number ——— 1
Symbol ——— H
Atomic mass ——— 1.008
State of matter

🎈 Gas
💧 Liquid
⬜ Solid
⊙ Synthetic

**1A**
**1**

+1

1 | Hydrogen
1
**H** 🎈
1.008

+2

**2A**
**2**

2 | Lithium
3
**Li** ⬜
6.941 | Beryllium
4
**Be** ⬜
9.012

3 | Sodium
11
**Na** ⬜
22.990 | Magnesium
12
**Mg** ⬜
24.305

**3B**
**3** | **4B**
**4** | **5B**
**5** | **6B**
**6** | **7B**
**7** | **8B**
**8** | **9**

4 | Potassium
19
**K** ⬜
39.098 | Calcium
20
**Ca** ⬜
40.078 | Scandium
21
**Sc** ⬜
44.956 | Titanium
22
**Ti** ⬜
47.867 | Vanadium
23
**V** ⬜
50.942 | Chromium
24
**Cr** ⬜
51.996 | Manganese
25
**Mn** ⬜
54.938 | Iron
26
**Fe** ⬜
55.845 | Cobalt
27
**Co** ⬜
58.933

5 | Rubidium
37
**Rb** ⬜
85.468 | Strontium
38
**Sr** ⬜
87.62 | Yttrium
39
**Y** ⬜
88.906 | Zirconium
40
**Zr** ⬜
91.224 | Niobium
41
**Nb** ⬜
92.906 | Molybdenum
42
**Mo** ⬜
95.94 | Technetium
43 ⊙
**Tc**
(98) | Ruthenium
44
**Ru** ⬜
101.07 | Rhodium
45
**Rh** ⬜
102.906

6 | Cesium
55
**Cs** ⬜
132.905 | Barium
56
**Ba** ⬜
137.327 | Lanthanum
57
**La** ⬜
138.906 | Hafnium
72
**Hf** ⬜
178.49 | Tantalum
73
**Ta** ⬜
180.948 | Tungsten
74
**W** ⬜
183.84 | Rhenium
75
**Re** ⬜
186.207 | Osmium
76
**Os** ⬜
190.23 | Iridium
77
**Ir** ⬜
192.217

7 | Francium
87
**Fr** ⬜
(223) | Radium
88
**Ra** ⬜
(226) | Actinium
89
**Ac** ⬜
(227) | Rutherfordium
104 ⊙
**Rf**
(261) | Dubnium
105 ⊙
**Db**
(262) | Seaborgium
106 ⊙
**Sg**
(266) | Bohrium
107 ⊙
**Bh**
(264) | Hassium
108 ⊙
**Hs**
(277) | Meitnerium
109 ⊙
**Mt**
(268)

The number in parentheses is the mass number of the longest lived isotope for that element.

**Lanthanide series**

Cerium
58
**Ce** ⬜
140.116 | Praseodymium
59
**Pr** ⬜
140.908 | Neodymium
60
**Nd** ⬜
144.24 | Promethium
61 ⊙
**Pm**
(145) | Samarium
62
**Sm** ⬜
150.36 | Europium
63
**Eu** ⬜
151.964

**Actinide series**

Thorium
90
**Th** ⬜
232.038 | Protactinium
91
**Pa** ⬜
231.036 | Uranium
92
**U** ⬜
238.029 | Neptunium
93 ⊙
**Np**
(237) | Plutonium
94 ⊙
**Pu**
(244) | Americium
95 ⊙
**Am**
(243)